Chilton's import car repair manual

second edition

General Manager	William D. Byrne
Assistant General Manager	Michael J. Hamilton
...lanaging Editor	John D. Kelly
...uction Manager	Warren Owens
...lanaging Editor	Peter J. Meyer
Senior Editor	Kerry A. Freeman
...chnical Editors	Robert J. Brown Philip A. Canal Stephen J. Davis David P. Galluccio Mitchell F. Gordon John M. McGuigan William J. Jones Eugene P. Nicolo Ronald L. Sessions N. Banks Spence Jr.
Editor	Paul J. Driscoll Jr.
...rial Production	Edna H. Jones, *Manager* Renée W. Bauchner
...OK COMPANY	Radnor, Pennsylvania

Published in Radnor by Chilton Book Company
Chilton Way, Radnor, Pa. 19089 □ 215-687-8200
ISBN: 0-8019-5872-5
Library of Congress Catalog No. 73-8430
Manufactured in the United States of America

contents

AUDI

Index

GENERAL ENGINE SPECIFICATIONS

Year and Model	Engine Cu in. Displacement	Carburetor Type	SAE Horsepower @ rpm	SAE Torque @ rpm (ft lbs)	Bore x Stroke (in.)	Compression Ratio	Normal Oil Pressure (psi)
1970-1971 Super 90	107.5 (1,760 cc)	2 bbl	100 @ 5,200	116 @ 3,000	3.21 x 3.32	10.2:1	14-85
1972 Super 90	107.5 (1,760 cc)	2 bbl	N.A.	105 @ 3,000	3.21 x 3.32	8.2:1	14-85
1970-1971 100 LS	107.5 (1,760 cc)	2 bbl	115 @ 5,500	119 @ 3,200	3.21 x 3.32	10.2:1	14-85
1972-1973 100, 100 LS, 100 GL	114.2 (1,871 cc)	2 bbl	91 @ 5,500	110 @ 3,500	3.31 x 3.32	8.2:1	14-85

TUNE-UP SPECIFICATIONS

When analyzing compression test results, look for uniformity among cylinders, rather than specific pressures.

Year and Model	Engine Cu in. Displacement	Spark Plugs Type	Spark Plugs Gap (in.)	Distributor Point Dwell (deg)	Distributor Point Gap (in.)	Ignition Timing (deg) MT	Ignition Timing (deg) AT	Intake Valve Opens (deg)	Fuel Pump Pressure (psi)	Idle Speed (rpm) MT	Idle Speed (rpm) AT	Valve Clear. (in.) ① In	Valve Clear. (in.) ① Ex
1970-1971 Super 90	107.5 (1,760 cc)	Ch N3	0.016-0.020	47-53	0.016	9A @ 950 rpm②	—	6B	3	950	—	0.006	0.012
1972 Super 90	107.5 (1,760 cc)	Ch N8Y	0.024-0.030	47-53	0.016	9A @ 950 rpm②	—	5B	3	950	—	0.008	0.016
1970-1971 100 LS	107.5 (1,760 cc)	Ch N7Y	0.023-0.029	47-53	0.016	9A @ 950 rpm③	9A @ 950 rpm③	5B	3.6	850-1000	850-1000	0.008	0.016
1972 100 100 LS	114.2 (1,871 cc)	Ch N8Y	0.024-0.030 ④	47-53	0.016	8A @ idle③	8A @ idle③	5B	3.6	850-1000	850-1000	0.008	0.016
1973 100 100 LS 100 GL	114.2 (1,871 cc)	Ch N7Y	0.036-0.039	47-53	0.016	8A @ idle⑤	8A @ idle⑤	5B	3.6	850-1000	850-1000	0.008	0.016

NOTE: % of CO at idle should be 1.0 for all 100, 100 LS, and 100 GL, 1.5 for 1970-1971 Super 90, and 1.0 for 1972 Super 90.

① Set warm
② 18B @ 2,500 with vacuum hose disconnected
③ 27B @ 2,500 with vacuum hose disconnected
④ 0.036-0.040 with capacitive discharge ignition system
⑤ 30B @ 2,750 with vacuum hose disconnected

FIRING ORDER

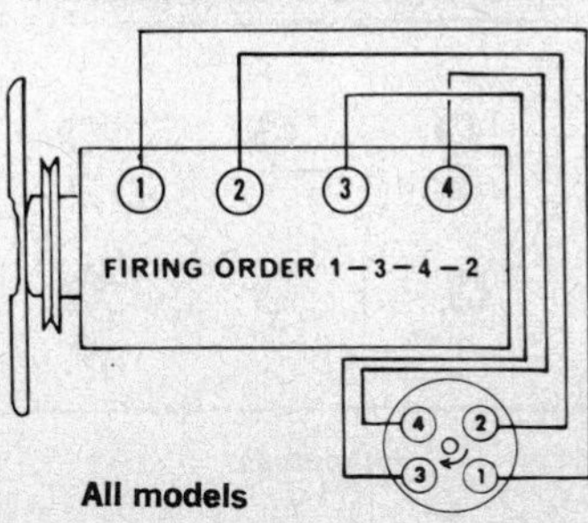

All models

CRANKSHAFT AND CONNECTING ROD SPECIFICATIONS

All measurements are given in inches.

Engine	CRANKSHAFT Main Brg. Journal Dia.	Main Brg. Oil Clearance	Shaft End-Play	Thrust on No.	CONNECTING ROD Journal Diameter	Oil Clearance	Side Clearance
All	2.3322-2.3622	0.002-0.004	0.003-0.007	3	1.8598-1.8898	0.001-0.003	0.004-0.009

PISTON AND RING SPECIFICATIONS

All measurements in inches

Engine	Piston Clearance	RING GAP Top Compression	Bottom Compression	Oil Control	RING SIDE CLEARANCE Top Compression	Bottom Compression	Oil Control
Super 90	0.001	0.012-0.018	0.010-0.020	0.010-0.016	0.003-0.005	0.002-0.003	0.001-0.002
100, 100 LS, 100 GL	0.001	0.039	0.039	0.039	0.006	0.006	0.006

NOTE: Three oversizes of pistons are available to accommodate overbores up to 0.040 in.

VALVE SPECIFICATIONS

Engine	Seat Angle (deg)	Face Angle (deg)	STEM TO GUIDE CLEARANCE (in.) Intake	Exhaust	STEM DIAMETER (in.) Intake	Exhaust
Super 90	45	45°15′	0.001	0.002	0.3507	0.3890
100, 100 LS, 100 GL	45	45°15′	0.001	0.002	0.3507	0.3499

NOTE: Valve guides are removable.

TORQUE SPECIFICATONS

All readings in ft lbs

Engine	Cylinder Head Bolts	Rod Bearing Bolts	Main Bearing Bolts	Crankshaft Pulley Bolt	Flywheel To Crankshaft Bolts	MANIFOLD Intake	Exhaust
Super 90	65	25-31	29①	130-180	65	17	17
100, 100 LS, 100 GL	65	25-31	58②	130-180	65	18	18

① 23 on bearing cap no. 5
② 24 on bearing cap no. 5

TORQUE SEQUENCE

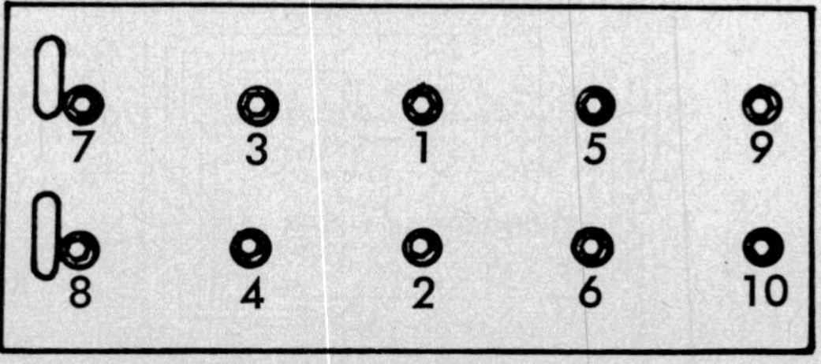

All models

CAPACITIES

Model	Engine Crankcase (qts) With Filter	Engine Crankcase (qts) Without Filter	Transaxle (pts) Manual	Transaxle (pts) Automatic	Drive Axle (pts) ①	Gasoline Tank (gals)	Cooling System (qts)
All	4.3	N.A.	4.2	12.5 fill 6.0 change	3	15	8

① Only with automatic transmission.

BRAKE SPECIFICATIONS

All measurements are given in in.

Year	Model	Master Cylinder Bore	Rear Wheel Cylinder Piston Bore	Brake Disc or Drum Diameter Front Disc	Brake Disc or Drum Diameter Rear Drum	New Pad Lining Thickness	Minimum Safe Pad Lining Thickness
1970-1972	Super 90	N.A.	0.625	11.02	7.87	0.39	0.08
1970-1972	100, 100 LS	0.813	0.625	11.02①	7.87	0.39②	0.08
1973	100, 100 LS, 100 GL	0.874	0.688	11.5	7.87	0.49	0.08③

① 11.5 on later models with automatic transmission
② 0.41 on some later versions
③ Electrical wear indicators

WHEEL ALIGNMENT

Model	Caster Range (deg)	Caster Pref Setting (deg)	Camber Range (deg)	Camber Pref Setting (deg)	Toe-out (in.)	Wheel Pivot Ratio Inner Wheel	Wheel Pivot Ratio Outer Wheel
Super 90	0°10′N-0°30′P	0°10′P	0°5′N-0°35′P	0°15′P	0.00-0.08	20	18°50′-19°30′
100, 100 LS 100 GL	0°14′N-0°26′P	0°6′P	0°9′N-0°31′P	0°11′P	0.00-0.08	20	18°30′-19°30′

N Negative
P Positive

BATTERY AND STARTER SPECIFICATIONS

Engine	Battery Ampere Hour Capacity	Battery Volts	Battery Terminal Grounded	Starter Lock Test Amps.	Starter Lock Test Volts	Starter Lock Test (Torque) (ft lbs)	Minimum Brush Length (in.)
All	45/55	12	Neg	250-300	7	N.A.	0.47

ALTERNATOR AND REGULATOR SPECIFICATIONS

Year	ALTERNATOR Part No. or Manufacturer	ALTERNATOR Output (amps.)	REGULATOR Part No. or Manufacturer	REGULATOR Volts
Early models	Bosch K1 14V 35A 20	35	Bosch AD 1/14V	13.9-14.8
Late models	Bosch K1 14V 55A 20	55	Bosch AD 1/14V	13.9-14.8

A running change to a regulator built into the alternator took place during the 1971 model year. Previous to this, the regulator was mounted on the right front wheelhousing.

WIRING DIAGRAMS

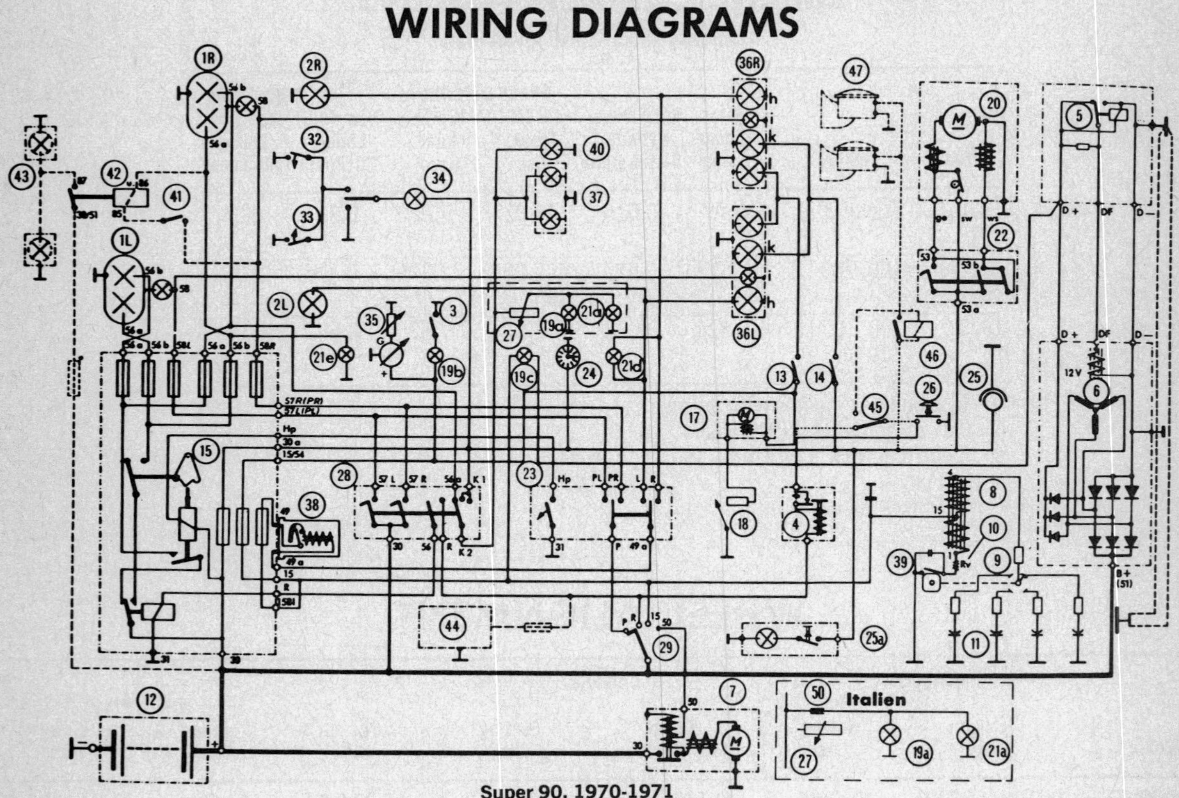

Super 90, 1970-1971

1R Headlight, right
1L Headlight, left
2R Indicator light, right
2L Indicator light, left
3. Oil pressure switch
4. Horn
5. Regulator
6. Alternator
7. Starter
8. Ignition coil
9. Distributor
10. Series resistor, ignition coil
11. Spark plugs
12. Battery 12 volt
13. Backup light switch
15. Combination relay
16. Connection, left indicator light
17. Fan motor
18. Regulating resistor, fan motor
18(a) Connector, fan motor
19. Combination instrument
(a) Instrument illumination
(b) Oil warning light
(c) Alternator warning light
20. Windshield wiper motor
21. Speedometer
(a) Instrument illumination
(d) Indicator warning light
(e) High beam warning light
22. Windshield wiper motor switch
23. Indicator—dimmer switch
24. Clock
(a) Instrument illumination
25. Cigarette lighter
25(a) Glove compartment light
26. Horn contact ring
27. Resistor, instrument illumination
28. Light switch
29. Steering—ignition lock
30. Connector, steering—ignition lock
31. Connector, tail light harness
32. Door contact, right
33. Door contact, left
34. Courtesy light
35. Tank fuel gauge
36R Tail light, right
36L Tail light, left
(h) Indicator light
(i) Tail light
(k) Brake light
(l) Backup light
37. License plate illumination
38. Indicator unit
39. Contact breaker
40. Trunk light

OPTIONAL ACCESSORIES

41. Fog lamp switch
42. Relay
43. Fog lamps
44. Radio
45. Horn changeover switch
46 Relay, two-tone horn
47. Two-tone horn

COLOR CODES

ws white
sw black
ge yellow
br brown
gr grey
gn green
rt red
li lilac
hbl light blue

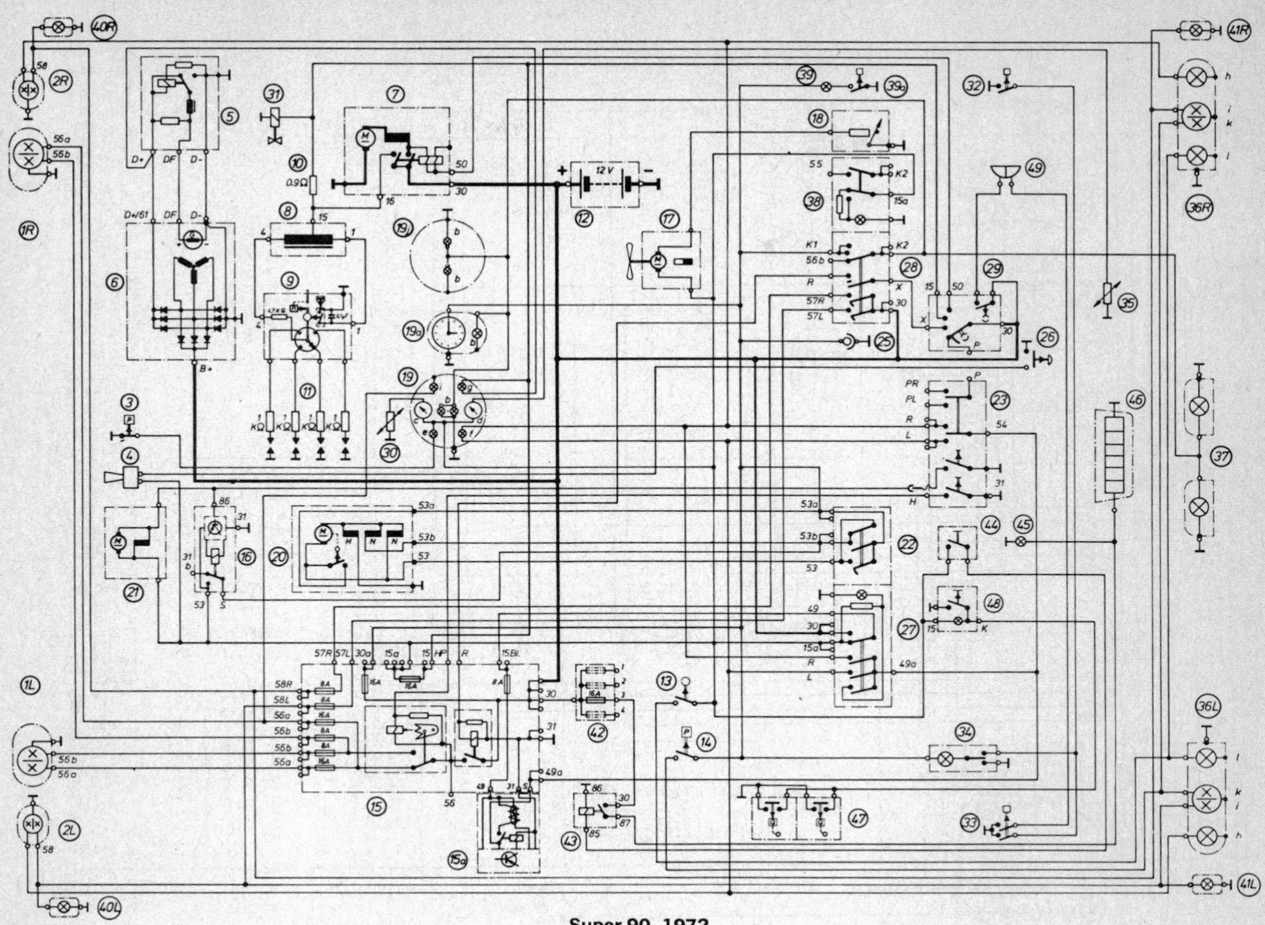

Super 90, 1972

1R Right headlight
1L Left headlight
2R Right turnsignal/parking light
2L Left turn signal/parking light
3. Oil pressure switch
4. Horn
5. Regulator
6. Alternator
7. Starter
8. Ignition coil
9. Distributor and contact breaker points
10. Resistor for item 8
11. Sparkplug
12. Battery
13. Backup light switch
14. Brake light switch
15. Combination relay
15(a) Flasher relay
16. Relay for windshield washer
17. Fan meter
18. Resistor for item 17
19. Combination gauge
19(a) Clock
19(b) Instrument illumination
19(c) Temperature gauge
19(d) Fuel guage
19(e) Oil pressure warning light
19(f) Turn signal indicator light
19(g) Alternator charge indicator light
19(h)
19(i) High beam indicator light
19(j) Odometer
20. Wipermotor
21. Washermotor
22. Wiper switch
23. Flasher/headlight dimmer/windshield washer switch
24.
25. Cigarette lighter/socket
26. Horn button
27. Emergency flasher switch
28. Light switch
29. Ignition/Steering lock
30. Engine temperature sending unit
31. Electromagnetic valve
32. Front right door contact switch
33. Front left door/contact switch
34. Interior light and switch
35. Fuel guage sending unit
36R Right tail light
36L Left tail light
36h Turn signal light
i Tail light
k Brake warning light
l Backup light
37. License plate lights
38. Auxiliary switch
39. Glove compartment light
39(a) Glove compartment light switch
40R Right front side marker light
40L Left front side marker light
41R Right rear side marker light
41L Left rear side marker light
42. Auxiliary fuse box
43. Relay for item 46
44. Relay for item 46
45. Indicator light for item 46
46. Rear window defogger
47. Dual circuit brake control system
48. Switch and control light for item 47
49. Buzzer

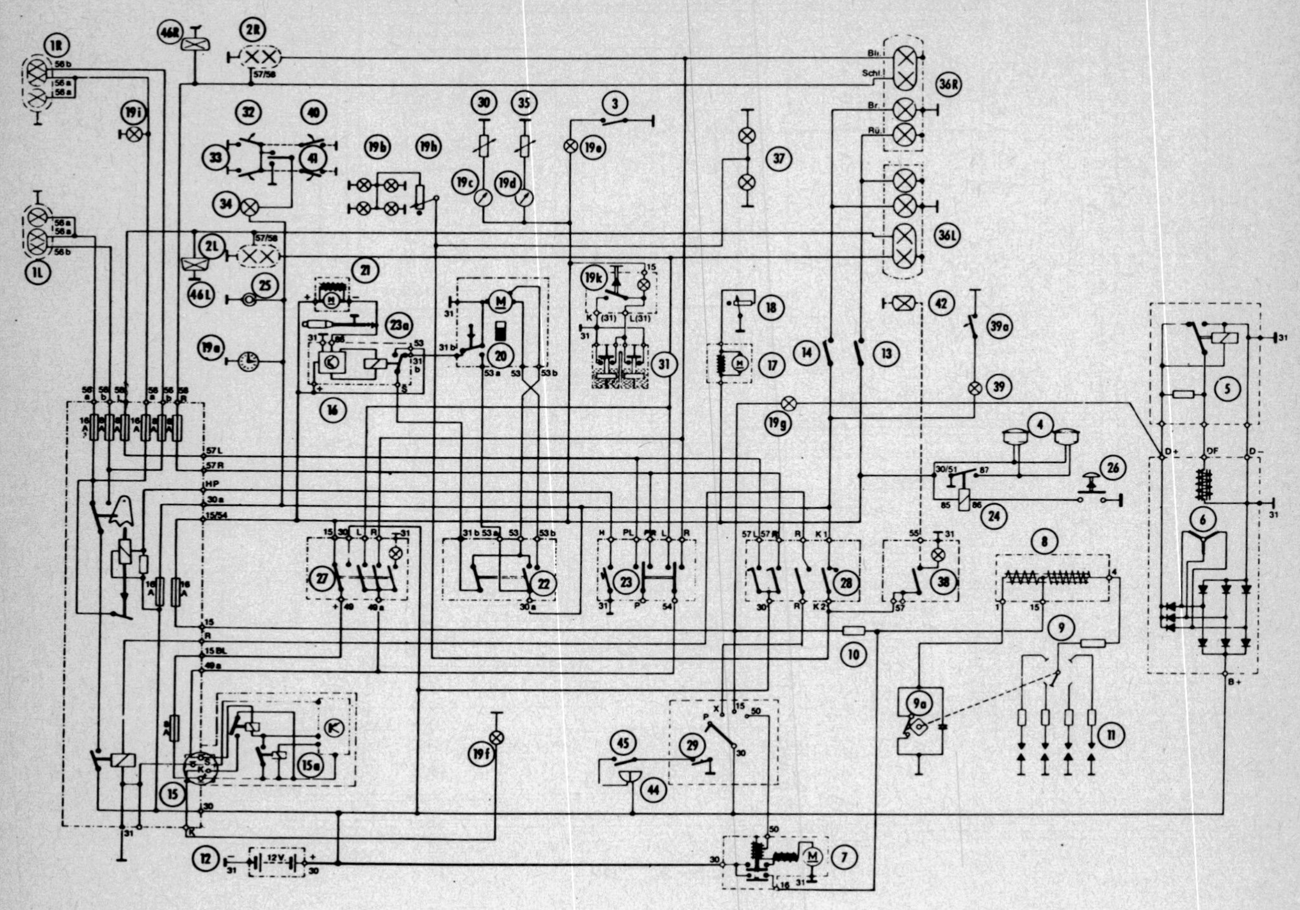

100 and 100 LS, 1970-1971

1R Headlight, right
1L Headlight, left
2R Turn signal, right
2L Turn signal, left
3. Oil pressure switch
4. Horn
5. Governor
6. Alternator
7. Starter
8. Ignition coil
9. Distributor
9(a) Contact breaker
10. Series resistor for item 8
11. Spark plugs
12. Battery
13. Backup light switch
14. Brake light switch
15. Combination relay
15(a) Flasher unit
16. Relay, windshield washer
17. Blower motor
18. Series resistor for item 17
19(a) Clock
19(b) Instrument illumination
19(c) Temperature gauge
19(d) Fuel gauge
19(e) Oil warning lamp
19(f) Turn signal warning lamp
19(g) Battery warning lamp
19(h) Regulating resistor for item 19b
19(i) High beam warning lamp
19(k) Twin-circuit brake warning lamp
20. Wiper motor
21. Washer motor
22. Wiper switch
23. Turn signal—dimmer switch
23(a) Washer impulse tracer
24. Multi-connector
24(a) Switching relay for position 4
25. Cigarette lighter
26. Horn button
27. Emergency warning light switch
28. Light switch
29. Steering-ignition lock
30. Temperature transmitter
31. Twin-circuit braking system
32. Door contact switch, front, right
33. Door contact switch, front, left
34. Interior light and switch
35. Fuel tank guage
36R Tail light, right
36L Tail light, left
37. License plate light
38. Switch, tail, fog light
39. Glove compartment light
39(a) Switch for item 39
40. Door contact switch, rear, right
41. Door contact switch, rear, left
42. Tail fog light (optional extra)
44. Audible buzzer
45. Door contact switch for item 44
46R } Side marker lights
46L }

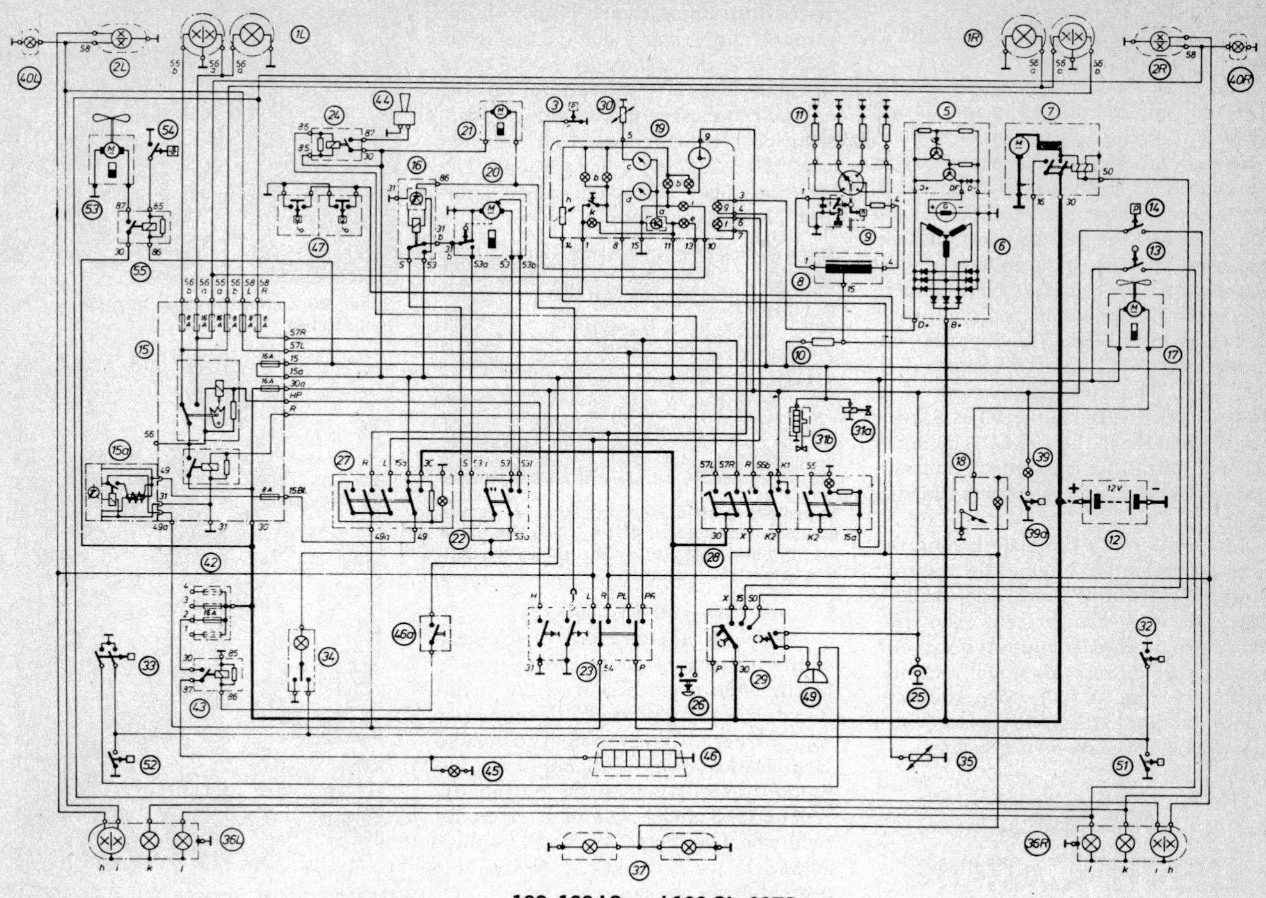

100, 100 LS, and 100 GL, 1972

1R Right headlight
1L Left headlight
2R Right turn signal/parking light
2L Left turn signal/parking light
3. Oil pressure switch
5. Regulator
6. Alternator
7. Starter
8. Ignition coil
9. Distributor with contact breaker
10. Resistor, item 8
11. Spark plugs
12. Battery
13. Backup light switch
14. Stop light switch
15. Combination relay
15(a) Flasher relay
16. Windshield washer relay
17. Fan motor for heater and fresh air
18. Resistor, item 17
19. Combination gauge
19(a) Electronic voltage compensator
19(b) Instrument illumination
19(c) Temperature gauge
19(d) Fuel gauge
19(e) Oil pressure warning light
19(f) Turn signal indicator light
19(g) Alternator charge warning light
19(h) Resistor for item 19b
19(i) High beam indicator light
19(j) Clock
19(k) Dual circuit brake warning light and control button
20. Wiper motor
21. Washer motor
22. Wiper switch
23. Turn signal and headlight dimmer switch with windshield washer button
24. Relay (horn)
25. Cigarette lighter
26. Horn button
27. Emergency flasher
28. Light switch
29. Ignition/steering lock
30. Engine temperature sending unit
31(a) Idle cut-off valve
31(b) Mixture control valve
32. Front right door contact switch
33. Front left door contact switch
34. Interior light and switch
35. Fuel gauge sending unit
36R Right rear lights
36L Left rear lights
36(h) Turn signal
36(i) Tail light
36(k) Stop light
36(l) Backup light
37. License plate lights
39. Glove compartment light
39(a) Switch, item 39
40R Right side marker
40L Left side marker
42. Fuse box
43. Relay for item 46
44. Horn signal
45. Indicator light for item 46
46. Rear window defogger
46(a) Switch for item 46
47. Dual circuit brake control system
49. Buzzer
51. Rear door contact switch, right
52. Rear door contact switch, left
53. fan motor (radiator)
54. thermal starting valve
55. Relay for item 53

INTRODUCTION

The Audi, produced by Auto Union of Germany and distributed in the United States by Porsche Audi, a division of Volkswagen of America, has been available in the United States since 1970. Three models, the Super 90, Super 90 station wagon (Variant), and the 100 LS, were initially imported using one basic engine. A 1,760 cc. slanted four-cylinder, OHV engine was used. Displacement has since been increased to 1,871 cc. The Super 90 was dropped in 1972, after an estimated 4,500 sales. The 100 was introduced in 1972, to replace the Super 90 as a lower cost alternative to the 100 LS. The top of the line 100 GL, with automatic transmission as standard equipment, was added in 1973.

The Audi uses a transaxle behind the forward mounted engine to transmit power to the front drive axle, while a dead axle is used in the rear. Also standard are inboard mounted front disc brakes, rear drum brakes, and rack and pinion steering. A four-speed transmission is standard but can be replaced with an optional three-speed automatic.

MODEL IDENTIFICATION

Super 90

100 LS, the 100 and 100 GL differ only in trim.

SERIAL NUMBER IDENTIFICATION

Vehicle

Super 90

The chassis number is on a plate on top of the instrument panel, clearly visible through the driver's side of the windshield. It is also stamped into the crossmember behind the battery, in the engine compartment. The vehicle identification plate is mounted on the right side of the engine compartment. The chassis number follows the words "Fahrgest.-Nr." on this plate.

Super 90 vehicle identification, (a) is the vehicle identification plate, (b) is the chassis number, and (c) is the emission control information sticker.

100, 100 LS, 100 GL

The chassis number is on a plate on top of the instrument panel, clearly visible through the driver's side of the windshield. It is also stamped into the upper right corner of the firewall. The vehicle identification plate is mounted on the support directly behind the engine, except on 1973 models. On these it is on the right wheel housing. The chassis number follows the words "Fahrgest.-Nr." on this plate.

100, 100 LS, 100 GL vehicle identification, (a) is the chassis number, (b) is the vehicle identification plate.

Engine

Super 90

Up to chassis numbers 6842 025 559, 6843 018 078 and 6834 000 156 the engine number is stamped on the engine block above the fuel pump. After the above chassis numbers, the engine number is located on the left side of the engine block.

An engine code number indicating the exact cylinder bore of the particular engine is stamped on the starter end of the cylinder block, just below the cylinder head.

100, 100 LS, 100 GL

The engine number is stamped on the left side of the engine block (clutch housing).

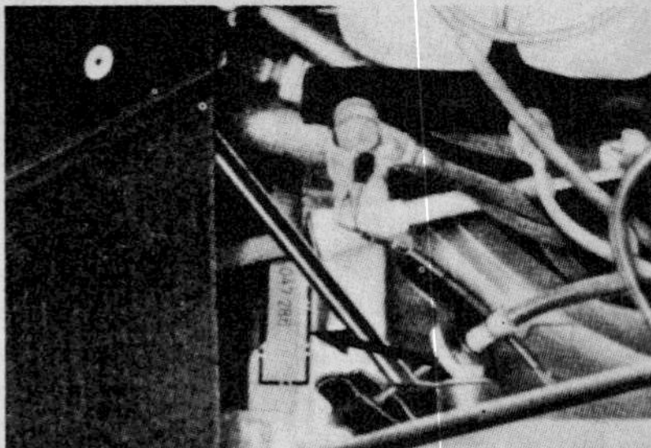

Super 90 engine number location for current models.

Engine number location for 100, 100 LS, and 100 GL.

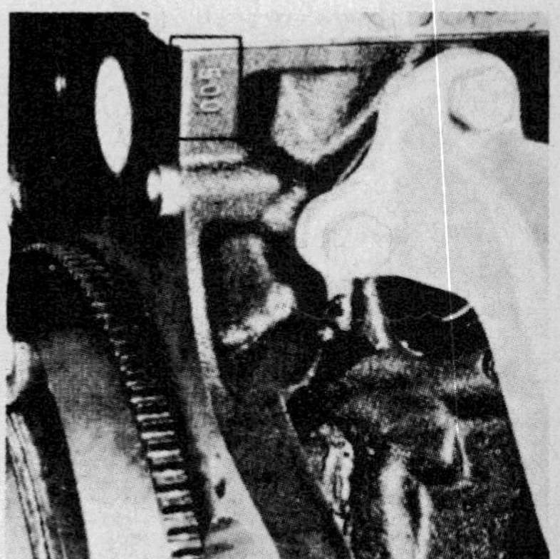

Engine code number location

In addition to the engine number, an engine code number is also stamped on the starter end of the cylinder block, just below the cylinder head. This number indicates the cylinder bore of the particular engine.

TUNE-UP PROCEDURES

The following are the specific procedures to be used in performing each tune-up step. For a more general discussion of tune-up, see the Tune-Up section at the end of this book.

The manufacturer recommends that a tune-up be carried out at specified intervals. Naturally, this interval should be shortened if the vehicle is subjected to severe usage, or if starting or running deficiences are noted. It is assumed that routine maintenance has been kept up-to-date, as this will have an effect on the results of the tune-up. All the tune-up steps should be followed, as each adjustment complements the effects of the other adjustments. If the tune-up specifications sticker on the inside of the hood disagrees with the Tune-Up Specifications Chart, the sticker figures must be followed.

Spark Plugs

1. Disconnect each spark plug wire by pulling on the rubber cap, not on the wire.
2. Wipe the wires clean with a cloth dampened in kerosine and wipe them dry. If the wires appear to be cracked, they should be replaced.
3. Blow or brush the dirt away from each of the spark plugs. Sometimes this is done by loosening the plugs and cranking the engine with the starter.
4. Remove each spark plug with a spark plug socket. Be careful that the socket is all the way down on the plug to prevent it from slipping and cracking the porcelain insulator.
5. Refer to the Troubleshooting Section at the end of this book for details on evaluating the condition of the plugs. In general, a tan or medium gray color on the business end of the plug indicates normal combustion conditions. Refer to the Tune-Up Specifications Chart for the proper spark plug type.
6. If the plugs are to be reused, file the center and side electrodes with a small, fine file. It is often suggested that plugs be tested and cleaned on a service station sandblasting machine; however, this piece of equipment is becoming rare. Check the gap between the two electrodes with a spark plug gap gauge. The round wire type is the most accurate. If the gap is not as specified, use the adjusting device on the gap gauge to bend the outside electrode to correct. Be careful not to bend the electrode too far, because excessive bending may cause it to weaken and possibly fall off into the engine. This would require cylinder head removal to reach the broken piece, and could result in cylinder wall and ring damage.
7. Clean the plug threads with a wire brush. Crank the engine with the starter to blow out any dirt particles from the cylinder head threads.
8. Screw the plugs in finger tight. Tighten them with the plug socket. If a torque wrench is available, tighten them to 22 ft lbs.
9. Reinstall the wires. If there is any doubt as to their proper locations, refer to the Firing Order Illustration.

Breaker Points and Condenser

The condenser need not be replaced each time the points are replaced, since this item is not cheap and does not often give trouble. It should be replaced, however, if the points are severely burned. After every breaker point adjustment or replacement, the ignition timing must be checked and, if necessary, adjusted. No special equipment other than a feeler gauge is required for point replacement or adjustment, although a dwell meter should be used to ensure the accuracy of the adjustment.

1. Detach the two spring clips securing the distributor cap. Remove the cap.
2. Clean the cap inside and out. Check for cracks and carbon paths. A carbon path shows up as a dark line, usually from one of the cap sockets or inside terminals to a ground. Check the condition of the button inside the center of the cap and the four inside terminals. Replace the cap if necessary.

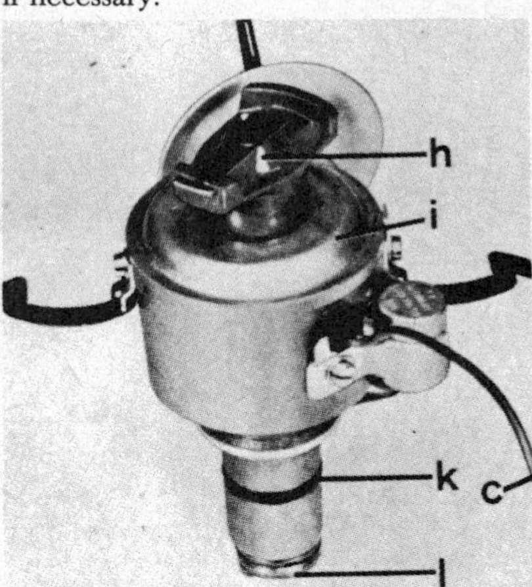

Distributor with cap removed

(c)—Lead to coil
(h)—Rotor
(i)—Dust cap
(k)—Seal
(l)—Drive connection

3. Pull the rotor up and off the shaft. Clean off the metal end if it is burned or corroded. Replace the rotor if necessary. Remove the dust cap.
4. The manufacturer states that the points must be replaced, not reconditioned. Experience also shows that it is more economical and reliable in the long run to replace the point set while the distributor is open, than to have to do this at a later (and possibly more inconvenient) time.
5. Pull off the flat plug wire terminal from the points. Remove the point set hold-down screw, being very careful not to drop it into the inside of the distributor. If this happens, the distributor will probably have to be removed to get at the screw. If the screw is lost elsewhere, it must be replaced with one that is no longer than the original to avoid interference with distributor workings. Remove the point set.
6. Remove the condenser by removing the screw and pulling the assembly out. Detach the lead from the coil. The condenser, wire, flat plug connection, and plastic sealing boot are a single assembly.
7. Install the new condenser, attaching the lead to the coil.
8. Apply a small amount of grease to the pivot side of the point set rubbing block.
9. Replace the point set and tighten the screw tightly. Replace the flat plug terminals.

Breaker point installation

(c)—Lead to coil
(g)—Vacuum line connection
(m)—Flat plug wire terminal
(n)—Raised lugs
(o)—Screwdriver slot
(p)—Hold-down screw

10. Check that the contacts meet squarely. If they do not, bend the tab supporting the fixed contact.
11. Turn the engine until a high point on the cam that opens the points contacts the rubbing block on the point arm. This is easier if the spark plugs have been removed.
12. There is a screwdriver slot and two raised lugs near the contacts. Insert a screwdriver and lever the points open or closed until they appear to be open about the correct gap.
13. Insert the correct size feeler gauge and adjust the gap with the screwdriver until you can push the gauge in and out

between the contacts with a slight drag but without moving the point arm. Another check is to try the gauges 0.001–0.002 larger and smaller than the setting size. The larger one should disturb the point arm, whereas the smaller one should not drag at all. Tighten the point set hold-down screw snugly. Recheck the gap, because it often changes when the screw is tightened.

14. After all the point adjustments are complete, pull a white business card through (between) the contacts to remove any traces of oil. Oil will cause rapid point burning.

15. Replace the dust cap.

16. Push the rotor firmly down into place. It will only go on one way. If it is not installed properly, it will probably break when the starter is operated.

17. Replace the distributor cap and install the spring clips.

18. Check the dwell. The dwell meter hookup is shown in the Troubleshooting Section. Dwell can be checked with the engine running or cranking. Decrease dwell by increasing the point gap; increase by decreasing the gap. Dwell angle is simply the number of degrees of distributor shaft rotation during which the points stay closed. Theoretically, if the point gap is correct, the dwell should also be correct or nearly so. If dwell varies more than 3 degrees from idle speed to 2,500 engine rpm, the distributor is worn.

19. Start the engine. If it won't start, check:

a. That all the spark plug wires are in place.

b. That the rotor has been installed.

c. That the wire inside the distributor is connected.

d. That the points open and close when the engine turns.

e. That the gap is correct and the hold-down screw is tight.

f. That the condenser lead to the coil is attached.

20. After the first 200 miles on a new set of points, the point gap often closes up due to initial rubbing block wear. For best performance, recheck the gap at this time.

21. Since changing the point gap affects the ignition timing setting, the timing should be checked and adjusted if necessary after each point replacement or adjustment.

Ignition Timing

A basic timing adjustment can be made in the following manner. Turn the engine until the basic ignition timing mark is aligned with the ignition timing pointer on the timing cover and the distributor rotor points toward the No. 1 cylinder mark on the rim of the distributor body. This will put No. 1 cylinder at TDC. Connect a 12 volt test lamp between the ignition coil terminal, No. 1 connected to the distributor, and a ground. Rotate the distributor clockwise until the lamp goes out. Turn the distributor counterclockwise until the lamp just lights, and tighten the clamp on the distributor at that point. The ignition timing is now approximately set. As soon as possible, check the adjustment with a timing light.

The distributor rotor (L) aligned with the No. 1 cylinder mark (M) on the rim of the distributor body. The dust cap is removed here.

Timing marks for 100, 100 LS, and 100 GL. The Super 90 has a similar arrangement with different numbers. (M) is the timing cover pointer and (K) is the ignition timing mark used at 2,500 rpm.

To check with a timing light, connect a timing light to No. 1 cylinder and connect a tachometer. Loosen the distributor clamp screw until it is just possible to turn the distributor by hand. Run the engine at idle speed and point the timing light at the pulley. Turn the distributor until the specified notch on the crankshaft pulley aligns with the pointer on the timing cover. Disconnect the vacuum hoses and check the timing at 2,500 rpm.

Adjust as necessary.

NOTE: *Timing should always be checked both at idle and at 2,500 rpm.*

Valve Lash

The valve clearance should be adjusted in firing order, with the engine at operating temperature. See the specifications for the proper clearances. Remove the air filter and rocker cover. Set the engine at TDC on No. 1 cylinder by aligning the 0°T mark on the crankshaft pulley with the timing cover pointer and aligning the distributor rotor with the No. 1 cylinder mark on the rim of the distributor body. Turn the engine in the normal direction of rotation. The valve clearance of cylinder No. 1 should be adjusted when the valves of No. 4 cylinder overlap, i.e. when both arms move in opposite directions simultaneously. When this occurs, the exhaust valve is closing and the intake opening.

Thus adjust:

A. Valve clearance of cylinder No. 3 at overlap of cylinder No. 2

B. Valve clearance of cylinder No. 4 at overlap of cylinder No. 1

C. Valve clearance of cylinder No. 2 at overlap of cylinder No. 3

When making adjustments, tighten the self-locking adjustment nut until it is just possible to remove the feeler gauge.

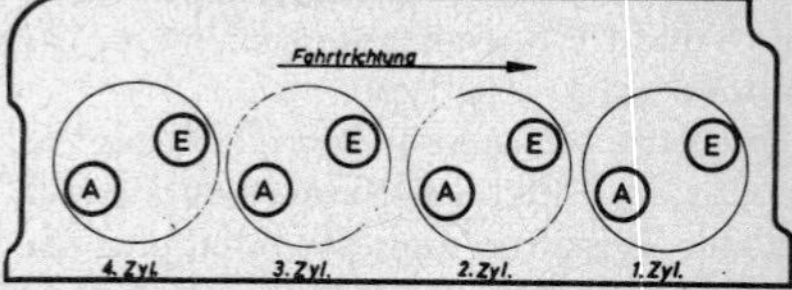

Exhaust valve location is indicated by (A) and intake valve by (E). The arrow points to the front.

Carburetor

Idle Speed and Mixture

The idle speed and mixture should be adjusted only after the engine has

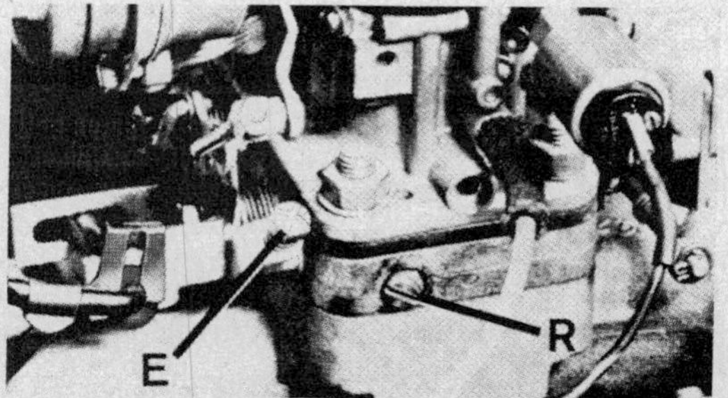

Standard carburetor adjustments. (E) is the idle speed adjusting screw and (R) is the idle mixture adjusting screw.

reached normal operating temperature. The air cleaner must be in place and the preheater hose from the exhaust manifold disconnected. The high beam headlights must be on. The ignition system must be properly adjusted before any carburetor adjustments are attempted. The only accurate way to set the idle mixture is with a CO meter. The allowable percentage of CO in the exhaust gases is shown on the engine compartment emission control sticker.

Standard Carburetors

The carburetor has only two adjusting screws: one on the throttle linkage for idle speed, and one in the carburetor body for idle mixture.

1. Set the idle speed with the idle speed adjusting screw.
2. Turn the mixture screw in until the engine just begins to slow down and to run roughly. If turning this screw has no effect, the carburetor idle passages are probably clogged.
3. Back the mixture adjusting screw out 1/8–1/4 turn. The engine should resume smooth operation.
4. Reset the idle speed if necessary.
5. Check the CO content of the exhaust gases. Reset the mixture screw if the allowable percentage is exceeded.
6. Complete the job by making a final adjustment of idle speed.

Idle Air Bypass Carburetors

The carburetor has three adjusting screws. The one on the throttle linkage controls the position of the throttle plate. This screw is sealed and is not to be adjusted. The fuel-air mixture bypasses around the throttle plate at idle. There is an idle mixture adjusting screw and an air control screw in the carburetor body.

1. Use the mixture adjusting screw to set the idle speed to specifications.
2. Tighten the air control screw all the way in gently. Back it out slightly less than a full turn.
3. Adjust the mixture adjusting screw to obtain the specified percentage of CO in the exhaust gases at idle.
4. If the idle speed is now too high, tighten the mixture adjusting screw to correct. Then tighten the air control screw to get the proper CO content.

NOTE: *It is normal for idle speed to be low on new engines. This need not be adjusted unless the condition persists after break-in.*

ENGINE ELECTRICAL

Distributor

Removal and Installation

Remove the air cleaner. Pry back the retaining clips and remove the distributor cap. Mark the relationship between the distributor body and the engine block. Disconnect the green condenser lead at the ignition coil. Detach the vacuum line, being careful not to damage the plastic tube. Remove the bolt at the retaining clamp and pull the distributor from the housing. If the distributor is difficult to remove, the rubber seal is probably sticking. Carefully pry the distributor loose with a screwdriver

Distributor installation is the reverse of removal. When installing the distributor, the projections on the shaft, at the bottom of the distributor, must engage the slots in the oil pump driveshaft. Turn the rotor until the two engage. The projections and grooves have been milled off center, making it impossible to install the distributor incorrectly. Lubricate the seal with a small amount of oil before installation. Align the marks made on removal, then tighten the clamp bolt.

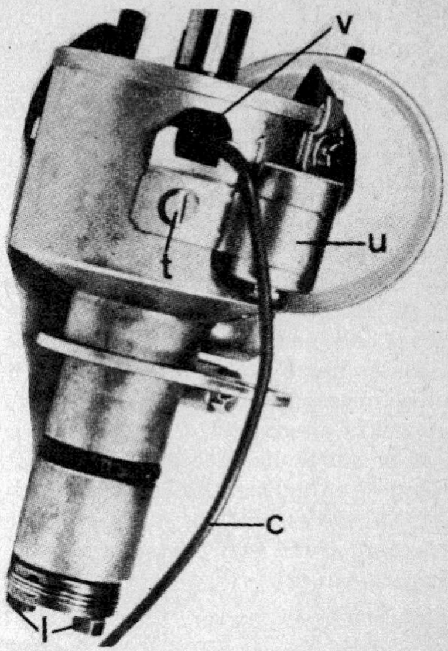

Distributor body removed from the engine. The projections (1) engage the slots in the oil pump driveshaft.

(c)—Green condenser lead
(t)—Condenser clamp screw
(u)—Condenser
(v)—Plastic boot

Alternator

Alternator Precautions

All Audi models are equipped with alternators. When performing any service to the alternator or alternator system the following precautions should be observed.

A. Leads or cables to any part of the charging circuit should be disconnected only after the engine has been switched off and has stopped running.

B. When working on the electrical system, always disconnect the lead from the negative battery terminal.

C. When performing tests with the engine running, the battery must always be connected.

D. Temporary connections should never be made to the alternator. Always make firm connections.

The alternator warning light on the instrument panel should go out when the engine reaches idle speed, or shortly after.

1. Intake manifold
2. Retarded vacuum connection
5. Advanced vacuum connection
6. Electric fuel cutoff jet

Idle air bypass carburetor adjustments. (3) is the idle mixture adjusting screw, (4) is the air control screw, and (7) is the sealed throttle plate adjusting screw.

Removal and Installation

1. Disconnect the battery ground strap.
2. Disconnect all the leads to the alternator, tagging them first. Various arrangements of plug-in or bolt-on connections have been used. On some models the wiring may be unplugged from the back of the alternator; on others, it must be unplugged at the voltage regulator on the right front wheelhousing.

NOTE: *Current models have a voltage regulator built into the alternator.*

3. Remove the belt tensioning bolt from the slotted adjusting bracket.
4. Remove the drive belt.
5. Unbolt and remove the alternator.

To install the unit:

6. Install the hinge bolts, making sure that the head of the rear bolt is to the rear of the car.
7. Install the drive belt and the belt tensioning bolt.
8. Adjust the belt tension.

9. Replace all the electrical connections, making sure that they are installed in their original locations.

10. Connect the battery ground strap.

Belt Tension Adjustment

The alternator drive belt is correctly tensioned when the longest span of belt between pulleys can be depressed about ½ in., by moderate thumb pressure. To adjust, loosen the slotted adjusting bracket bolt, under the alternator. If the alternator hinge bolts are very tight, it may be necessary to loosen them slightly to move the alternator. Move the alternator in or out by hand to get the correct tension, then tighten the adjusting bolt.

NOTE: *Be careful not to overtighten the belt, as this may damage the alternator bearings.*

(C) is the alternator belt tension adjusting bolt, as viewed from underneath.

Regulator

The voltage regulator is on the right front wheelhousing in the engine compartment. If there is none there, as on current models, it is built into the alternator.

Removal and Installation

To remove the regulator, disconnect the battery ground cable, disconnect the three-pronged plug, and unscrew the unit from the wheelhousing. Be careful to make a good ground connection on reinstallation. The manufacturer does not recommend any adjustments to the regulator.

Starter

Removal and Installation

Disconnect the battery ground lead. Remove the oil filter. **NOTE:** *When the oil filter is removed, a certain amount of oil will escape.* Disconnect both leads from the upper terminal of the solenoid. Remove the open cable shoe lead from the lower solenoid terminal. The screw need only be slightly opened to permit removal. On the Super 90, the crossbrace under the starter must be unbolted and removed. Unbolt the starter from the mounting flanges and remove it forward.

Installation is the reverse of removal. Be sure that all leads are positioned correctly and are not pinched. If necessary, replace the lower mounting bolt with the head to the front of the car. Thoroughly clean the seal and oil filter sealing surface. Lightly lubricate both surfaces and tighten the oil filter to approximately 14–18 ft lbs or about one turn by hand. Replace the oil that escaped and run the engine, checking the filter for leaks. **CAUTION:** *Some starters are equipped with an additional terminal (16) which is under full battery voltage, with a direct connection to the ignition coil. This connection bridges the ignition coil series resistor to create higher ignition voltage.*

Battery

Location

The battery in the 100, 100 LS, and 100 GL is located under the right side of the rear seat and is accessible by lifting the front edge of the rear seat. The battery in the Super 90 is located in the engine compartment. Be sure that the terminals are clean and provide an adequate connection. The terminals should be coated (lightly) periodically with petroleum jelly or grease to prevent corrosion.

Water should be added only to bring the solution level up to the bottom of the cell filler well, but not above.

ENGINE MECHANICAL

The Audi engine is a four-cylinder, four-stroke, carbureted, in-line unit. The engine is canted at an angle of 40 degrees to the left. The engine/transmission unit is mounted in the integral body and frame by engine carriers bolted to the engine block and supports on the transmission.

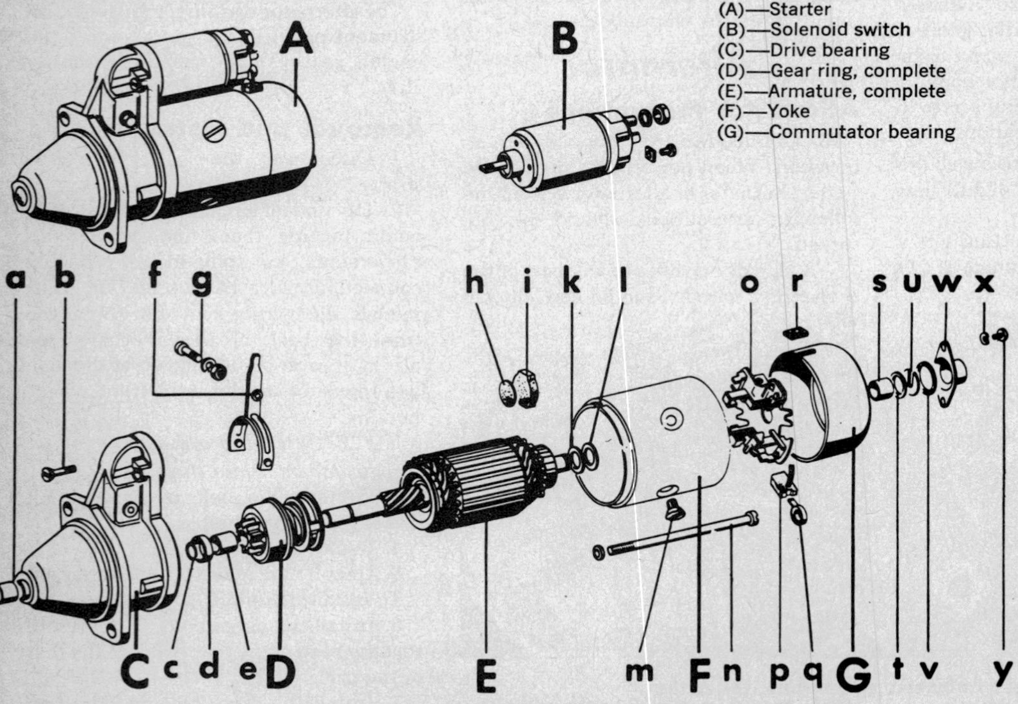

(a)—Bearing bushing and drive bearing
(b)—Countersunk screw (for Solenoid switch)
(c)—Snap-ring
(d)—Stop-ring
(e)—Bearing bushing (2 required for gear ring)
(f)—Control lever
(g)—Cylinder head screw with lock ring and hex nut (for control lever)
(h)—Plate
(i)—Rubber seal
(k)—Washer (on armature shaft)
(l)—Insulator (on armature shaft)
(m)—Countersunk screw (4 req. for Pole shoes)
(n)—Cylinder head screw (2 required for washers)
(o)—Brush holder plate
(p)—Carbon brush (4 req.)
(q)—Spring (4 req.)
(r)—Rubber sleeve, cable
(s)—Bearing bushing (in commutator bearing)
(t)—Shim (as required 0.1, 0.2, 0.3, 0.5, 0.8 mm)
(u)—Fixing washer
(v)—Rubber seal ring
(w)—End cap
(x)—Spring washer (domed)
(y)—Cylinder head screw

Exploded view of Super 90 starter

Engine Removal and Installation

The transmission and engine must be lowered from the car as a unit. The following procedure is for manual transmission cars; see Automatic Transmission Removal and Installation for details on items that must be disconnected on the automatic transmission.

1. Remove the hood (only if using a hoist to remove the engine).
2. Unbolt and remove the apron just below the front bumper.
3. Remove the negative connection from the battery. Remove the air cleaner and carburetor breather hose at the air filter. Drain the coolant. Disconnect all hoses between the radiator and engine and the heater and engine. Disconnect the fuel hose at the fuel pump and plug the end of the line. Remove the power brake unit vacuum hose at the intake manifold.
4. Disconnect the speedometer cable at the transmission, the clutch cable at the mount and the gearshift linkage at the transmission.
5. Disconnect the accelerator linkage at the carburetor, mounting point, and connecting rod, and remove the throttle shaft.
6. Separate the brake line at the body mount and plug the line to prevent loss of fluid.
7. Remove the guard plate from the right engine mount.
8. Disconnect the following electrical wiring from the engine and transmission: ignition leads, idle cut-off valve (if installed), temperature switch, four pole plug of regulator, oil pressure switch, starter connections, backup light switch and ground leads.
9. Remove the Super 90 oil filter.
10. Remove the radiator and the fan support together with the fan and stop pad.

NOTE: *This operation is only necessary if working with a frame contact hoist or in a pit where the opening in the pit is not large enough to permit lowering the engine with the fan attached. If the opening is large enough, unscrew the stop only.*

11. Remove the front exhaust pipe at the exhaust manifold and at the primary muffler.
12. Unbolt the driveshaft flange at the brake disc. Do not lose the thin insulator from between the brake disc and the flange. Turn the driveshaft flange slightly in the direction of the wheel and wire it to the upper wishbone.
13. Detach the stabilizer from the lower wishbone, left and right.
14. Position the jack or lifting apparatus and lift the weight from the engine mounts. Remove the bolts retaining the rear crossmember to the body. Remove the retaining nut at the right engine/transmission mount. Note the position of the washers and sleeve on the right engine/transmission mount.

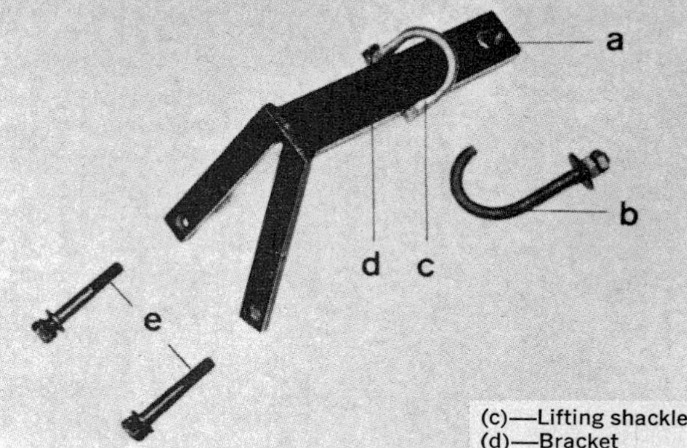

Engine lifting (or lowering) bracket. Bolt (b) goes through hole (a) and around the rear branch of the intake manifold. Bolts (e) go into the top of the transmission flange.

(g) is the fan support, (h) is the stop pad, and (i) is the stop.

When installing the engine, the same distance (X) must be maintained on both sides between the brake discs and the suspension wishbones. The maximum allowable deviation is 0.08 in.

15. Remove the retaining nut from the left engine/transmission mount, but do not move the locknut. Lower the engine/transmission unit from the car.
16. Installation procedures are the reverse of removal. The engine and transmission unit must be aligned in such a way that the same distance between brake disc and wishbone exists on each side. The distance between the pulley and front end of the side-member must also be the same on each side. After installation, bleed the brakes.

When installing the engine, the same distance (y) must be maintained between the pulley and the front of the side member on both sides. The maximum allowable deviation is 0.08 in.

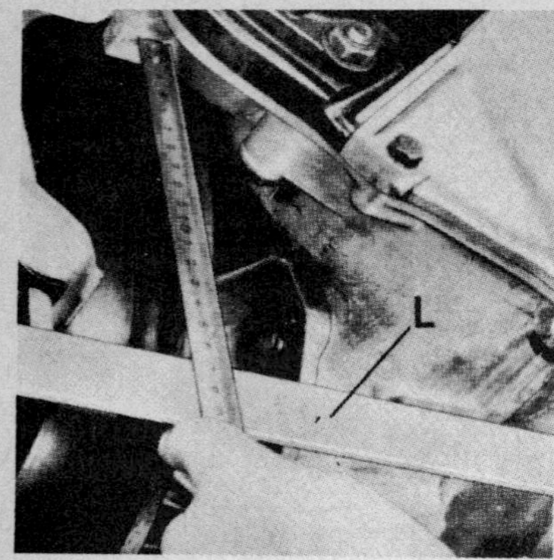

When installing the engine, the distance between the transmission casting at the point shown and a straightedge (L) must not vary more than 0.16 in. from side to side.

Cylinder Head

Removal and Installation

1. Drain the coolant from the radiator. Disconnect the spark plug wires.
2. Remove the sheet metal cover from the exhaust manifold. Remove the intake and exhaust manifolds.
3. Disconnect the hoses from the thermostat housing.
4. Remove the valve cover. Loosen the valve rocker arm adjusting nuts and remove the pushrods. Note their original locations; they must all go back in the same place.
5. Loosen the cylinder head bolts in the same order as shown for tightening. Remove the bolts. A metric allen wrench is required for the head bolts.

   NOTE: *Do not loosen the head bolts until the engine has thoroughly cooled.*
6. Remove the head. If it sticks, operate the starter to loosen it by compression or rap it upward with a soft hammer. Do not force anything between the head and block. Check the head for warpage as detailed in the Engine Rebuilding Section.
7. Reinstallation of the head is made easier by the use of guide studs installed in opposite corners of the block. These can be made by cutting the heads off two bolts of the same size as the head bolts.
8. Put the gasket in place on the block.
9. Guide the cylinder head into place.
10. Coat the head bolt threads with a graphite lubricant. Install them finger tight.
11. Tighten the bolts in the sequence shown in four stages until the proper torque is reached. The bolts should be torqued again after the first 500–1000 miles.
12. Install the pushrods in their original locations. Make a preliminary valve lash adjustment.
13. Replace the valve cover, using a new gasket. Replace the manifolds. Connect the coolant hoses and the spark plug wires.
14. Refill the cooling system.
15. Run the engine until it reaches normal operating temperature, watching for leaks. Make a final valve adjustment with the engine warm.

Overhaul

See the "Engine Rebuilding Section" for details on a valve job or cylinder head overhaul. This section should be consulted for checking the head for warpage, even if no other work is to be done on the head. If the rocker studs and pushrod guide plates have been removed, the guides must be aligned so that the pushrods will not contact them. The cylinder head must be heated to 248°F in an oven in order to install or remove the valve guides.

Intake Manifold

Removal and Installation

1. Drain the coolant.
2. Remove the air cleaner.
3. Disconnect the coolant hoses from the manifold and the automatic choke. Remove the wire from the electric choke.
4. Disconnect the vacuum hose and the lead to the idle cutoff valve. Detach the fuel line and the accelerator linkage.
5. Remove the manifold nuts and the manifold support.
6. Pull the manifold off the studs. If it sticks, rap it with a soft hammer. Do not force anything between the manifold and the cylinder head. Discard the gaskets.
7. Installation is the reverse of the removal procedure. New gaskets must be used. Tighten the nuts to the specified torque. After refilling the cooling system, start the engine and check for leaks.

Exhaust manifold gaskets. (d) is the type with the oval opening which must be installed with the notched (arrow) side down, (e) is the type with the round opening. Both types must have the beaded edge around the opening outward.

Exhaust Manifold

Removal and Installation

1. Disconnect the heated air intake hose from the manifold.
2. Unbolt the exhaust pipe from the manifold.
3. Remove the sheet metal cover.
4. Remove the manifold nuts. Pull the manifold off the studs. If it sticks, rap it with a soft hammer. Do not force anything between the manifold and the cylinder head. Discard the gaskets.
5. Installation is the reverse of the removal procedure. New gaskets must be used. If the gaskets are the type with round openings, they must be installed with the beaded side outward from the head and the notched edge down. Gaskets with oval openings must be installed with the beaded edge outward from the head. Tighten the manifold nuts to the specified torque. Torque the front exhaust pipe flange nuts to 18–22 ft lbs, in steps. A new gasket should also be used between the exhaust pipe and the manifold.

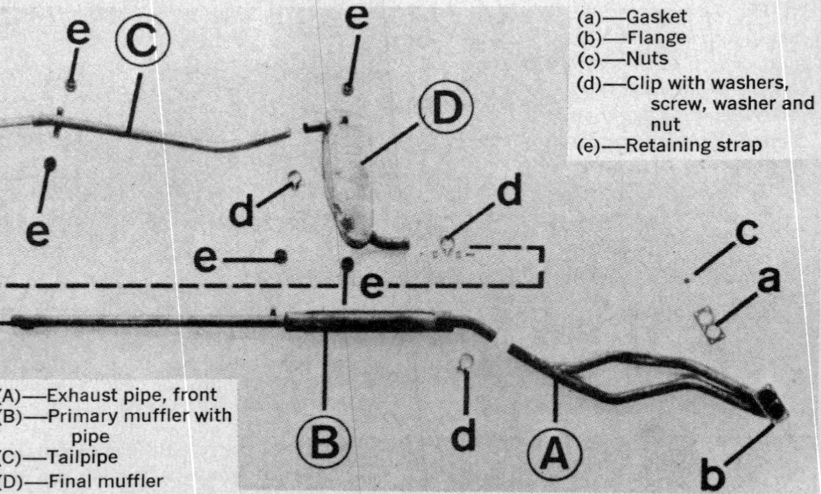

An exploded view of the complete exhaust system.

Exhaust System

Removal

Front Exhaust Pipe

Loosen the clip at the primary muffler and unbolt the flange at the exhaust manifold. Remove the front exhaust pipe.

Primary Muffler and Pipe

Loosen the clamps at the muffler inlet and outlet. Disconnect the rubber damping loop at the muffler. Remove the primary muffler and pipe.

Tailpipe

Loosen the clamp at the final muffler outlet, disconnect the retaining straps from the tailpipe and remove the tailpipe.

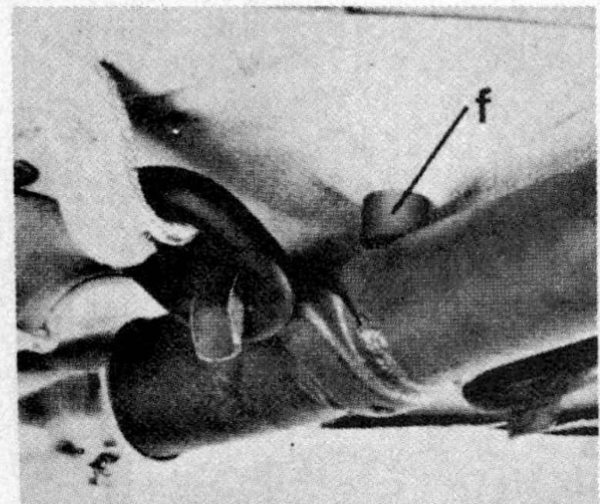

The rubber pad (f) prevents the exhaust pipe from hitting the body.

Final Muffler

Disconnect both the inlet and outlet clamps. Disconnect both straps retaining the final muffler and remove the muffler.

Installation

To install the exhaust system components, reverse the removal procedure. When installing the flange use a new gasket. Tighten the front exhaust pipe flange nuts to 18–22 ft lbs, in steps. When installing the tailpipe, be sure that the rubber pad is in position. The pad prevents the tailpipe from contacting the body. Always use new clamps.

Timing Chain Cover

Removal and Installation

1. Place the car on a lift or pit.
2. Remove the apron under the front bumper.
3. Have an assistant place the car in first gear and hold the brake on. Remove the crankshaft pulley nut. On cars with automatic transmission the nut can be removed by affixing a heavy wrench and rapping the wrench with a hammer. The nut must be unscrewed in the opposite direction of normal engine rotation.
4. Loosen the fan and alternator adjustments and remove the belts.
5. Remove the pulley, rapping it with a soft hammer if necessary. Be careful not to lose the shaft key.
6. Drain the oil.
7. Remove first the oil pan, then the timing chain cover.
8. Reverse the procedure to install, using new gaskets. Timing chain cover bolt torque is 7 ft lbs.

Timing Chain Cover Oil Seal Replacement

Current models have the lip retaining the oil seal in the cover to the inside. Thus the oil seal is pressed in from the front of the cover. Older models have the retaining lip toward the outside of the cover; the seal is pressed in from the inside of the cover. The result of this is that the oil seal may be replaced with the cover in place on the current models, while on older models the cover must be removed to replace the seal. The only way to determine which cover is installed is by inspection, after removing the crankshaft pulley. Virtually all US models use the current type. The seal can be replaced without removing the engine.

To replace either type:

1. Remove the timing chain cover on older models. Follow Steps 1–6 of the "Timing Chain Cover Removal and Installation" procedure for current models.
2. Carefully pry out the old seal with a screwdriver, being careful not to damage the housing.
3. Apply grease between the lips of the seal and apply a little oil to the outside edge.
4. On older models press in the seal from the inside of the cover. Press or drive it in with a seal installer or a suitable improvised tool, until it bottoms on the retaining lip. If there is no retaining lip, press the seal in until it is flush with the inside of the cover.
5. On current models, press or drive the seal in with the metal side out until it bottoms on the retaining lip. A good way to do this is to tighten a flat plate against the seal with the pulley retaining nut.
6. Reverse the procedure followed in Step 1 to reassemble the engine.

Timing Chain and Tensioner

Removal and Installation

1. Remove the timing chain cover.
2. Some older Super 90 engines may have a leaf spring chain tensioner. If this is the case, simply unbolt and remove it. All other engines have a hydraulic chain tensioner. Bend open the lock plate, unscrew the chain tensioner plug, insert a Phillips screwdriver and turn counterclockwise. If this is not done, the chain tensioner will fly apart as it is removed. On some models, the tensioner must be held together while it is removed. Unbolt and remove the tensioner.
3. Remove the camshaft sprocket retaining bolt. Some way to keep the sprocket from turning will have to be devised.
4. Remove the camshaft sprocket, chain, and crankshaft sprocket together, using a puller on the crankshaft sprocket. Be careful not to lose the key for the crankshaft sprocket.
5. On reinstallation, heat the crankshaft sprocket to 140°F in an oven. Do not heat it with a flame, as it will be warped. Install the shaft key and slide the

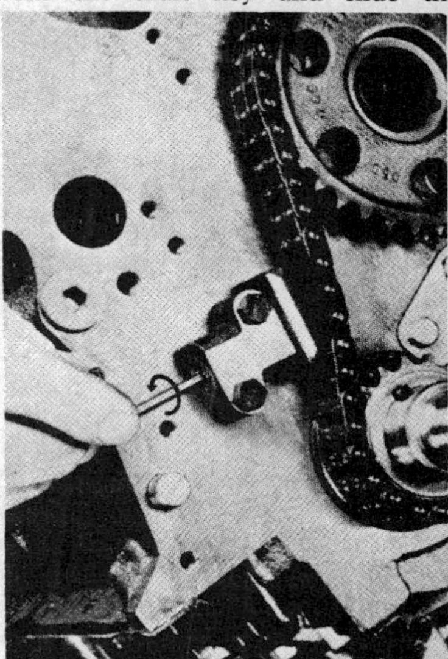

Use a Phillips screwdriver as shown to prevent the chain tensioner from coming apart when it is removed.

sprocket into place until it rests against the stop.

6. Align the mark on the distributor body rim with the rotor. Set No. 1 cylinder precisely at top dead center. Place the camshaft sprocket on the camshaft and align the sprocket punch mark with the notch in the chain guide rail.
7. Remove the camshaft sprocket, being careful not to turn the camshaft.
8. Place the timing chain over the crankshaft sprocket and place the camshaft sprocket in the chain, so that the camshaft sprocket can be installed without moving either the camshaft or the crankshaft.

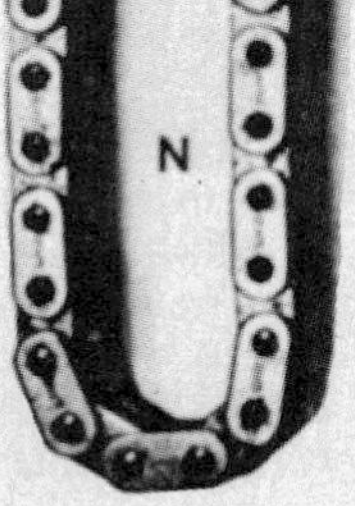

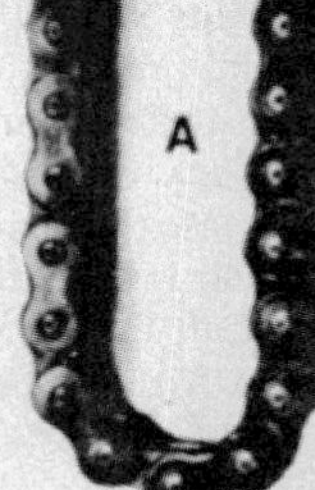

Only timing chains with straight links are to be used.

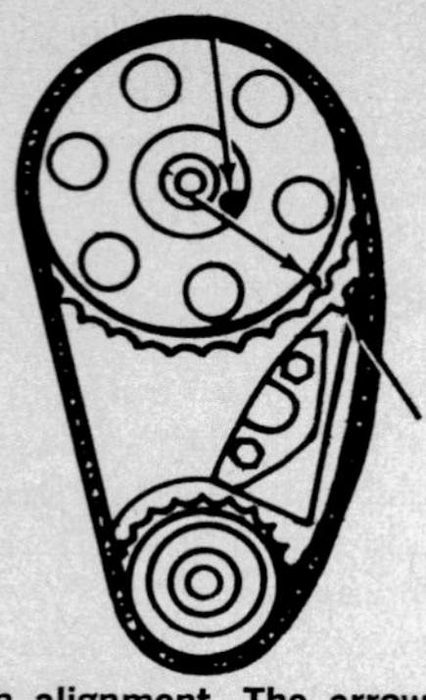

Timing chain alignment. The arrows show the camshaft sprocket punch mark, the notch in the chain guide rail, and the dowel which aligns the camshaft sprocket and camshaft.

NOTE: *The factory specifies that timing chains with indented links should not be reused. They must be replaced with a straight-link chain.*

9. Torque the camshaft sprocket bolt to 58 ft lbs.

10. The manufacturer states that the leaf spring chain tensioner used on older Super 90 engines must be replaced with the hydraulic type. However, this entails drilling a hole into the engine block oil bore with the aid of special equipment. The engine also has to be lowered in the chassis to gain access. Assemble and install the chain tensioner, torquing the bolts to 9 ft lbs. Turn the chain plunger clockwise to release it. Current production models have a self-releasing chain tensioner. Make absolutely sure that the hydraulic chain tensioner is free to move. Install the tensioner plunger and lock plate.

11. Replace the timing cover.

Camshaft

Removal and Installation

This operation requires that the engine be removed from the car and rather extensively disassembled.

1. Remove the timing chain and tensioner.
2. Remove the cylinder head.
3. Remove the tappets (valve lifters). A special tool is used by dealers to lift them out. Keep them in order so they can be replaced in their original locations.
4. Remove the distributor.
5. Remove the oil pump.
6. Unbolt and remove the camshaft locating plate.
7. Carefully guide the camshaft out of the block, being cautious not to bang the lobes into the bearings. This is a lot easier if a bolt is threaded into the front of the camshaft for use as a handle.
8. On reinstallation, oil the camshaft bearing surfaces. Insert the camshaft carefully.
9. Install the locating plate, torquing the bolts to 18 ft lbs.
10. Check the camshaft end-play in and out of the block, using a dial indicator. If it exceeds 0.004 in., install a new locating plate.
11. The rest of the reassembly procedure is the reverse of disassembly. Check the ignition timing when the job is complete.

Pistons and Connecting Rods

The connecting rods must be installed in the engine with the grooved side toward the camshaft. Both the pistons and the piston pins must be heated to 140°F in an oven in order to install the pins. Three oversizes of pistons are available to accommodate overbores up to 0.040 in.

ENGINE LUBRICATION

Oil Pan

Removal and Installation

1. Place the car on a lift or pit.
2. Remove the apron under the front bumper for better access.
3. Undo the radiator mounting bolts and press the radiator up out of the brackets.
4. Drain the oil.
5. Loosen and remove the Allen head bolts holding the pan. Tap it lightly with a soft hammer to break it loose. Remove the pan.
6. Clean the pan out thoroughly while it is off the engine.
7. Install new gaskets at either end of the oil pan. Apply a very thin coat of adhesive to them. Attach the pan rail gaskets to the block, using a slight amount of adhesive at both ends and in the middle. Put a tiny amount of adhesive at the extreme ends of the gaskets, adjacent to the rear main bearing cap and the timing cover. Stick on the small gasket segment below the starter.
8. Torque the larger pan bolts to 11 ft lbs and the rest to 6 ft lbs.
9. The rest of the installation is the reverse of removal. Fill the crankcase and run the engine, checking for leaks.

Rear Main Bearing Oil Seal Replacement

When this seal fails, the usual result is oil leakage onto the clutch. This, of course, causes clutch slippage or failure to disengage. This repair requires that the engine be removed from the car and extensively disassembled.

1. Remove the engine.
2. Remove the transmission and clutch from the engine.
3. Remove the flywheel. Some method of preventing the flywheel from turning will have to be devised.

NOTE: *Mark the relationship between the flywheel and crankshaft to preserve balance.*

4. Remove the oil pan.
5. Unbolt and remove the rear main bearing cap.
6. The circular seal may now be removed.
7. Press the new seal evenly into place with the sealing lip toward the front of the engine. This is rather difficult without special seal installing tools.
8. Torque the bearing cap to specifications.
9. The remainder of the procedure is the reverse of disassembly. Make sure to align the flywheel marks made in Step 3.

(l) is the oil pan rail gaskets, stuck to the block at (x). (n) is a small separate gasket segment and the arrows show where adhesive is to be applied over the gaskets.

The wide segment (c) on the oil pump driveshaft must face forward when installing the pump.

When installing the distributor, the rotor (r) must be aligned with the No. 1 cylinder notch (s). The vacuum unit (t) should parallel the engine block. (u) is the distributor mounting bolt.

Oil Pump

Removal and Installation

1. Remove the distributor. Remove the oil pan.
2. Disconnect the oil line from the block and the pump.
3. Unbolt the pump and pull it out of the block, being careful not to lose the bolt spacer.
4. Place No. 1 cylinder on top dead center. This can be done by turning the engine with a finger held over the No. 1 spark plug hole. When compression is felt, turn the engine to align the 0°T mark on the crankshaft pulley with the timing pointer.
5. On replacement, turn the pump until the wide segment of the pump driveshaft faces forward. Turn the shaft 15 degrees counterclockwise and slide the oil pump shaft into the gear teeth of the camshaft.
6. Install the spacer under the pump and mounting bolt and tighten the bolt finger tight.
7. Put the oil line in place. Turn the pump or add extra gaskets at either end of the oil line to prevent any strain on the line.
8. Torque the pump mounting bolt to 18 ft lbs and the oil line bolts to 7 ft lbs. Use the lock plates to hold the oil line bolts.
9. Align the distributor rotor with the No. 1 cylinder notch in the rim of the housing. Insert the distributor with the vacuum unit parallel to the engine block and pointing to the rear of the engine. When installing the distributor, wiggle the rotor back and forth to allow the shaft projections to engage the oil pump dirveshaft slots. Tighten the distributor mounting bolt.
10. Replace and fill the oil pan.
11. Start the engine and watch for oil leaks. If it won't start, check the basic ignition timing as described in Chapter 2. If it does start, check the final ignition timing with a stroboscopic timing light.

ENGINE COOLING

The radiator drain plug is at the bottom, adjacent to the lower hose. The engine drain plug is at the front, adjacent to the alternator. The Super 90 also has a drain plug at the bottom of the heater, inside the car. There is a breather plug in the upper heater hose, near the firewall. The breather plug must be used to remove air from the system, when the engine is first started after refilling.

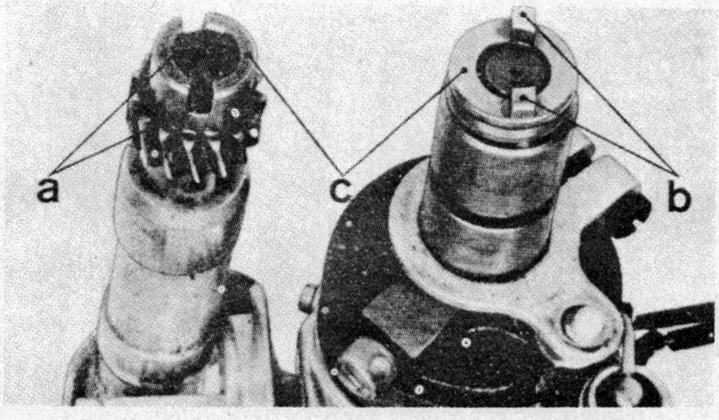

The slots (a) in the oil pump driveshaft and the projections (b) on the distributor driveshaft are offset. (c) indicates the wide segment of each shaft. Because of this construction, the shafts can mate in only one way.

Radiator drain plug; 100, 100 LS, and 100 GL shown.

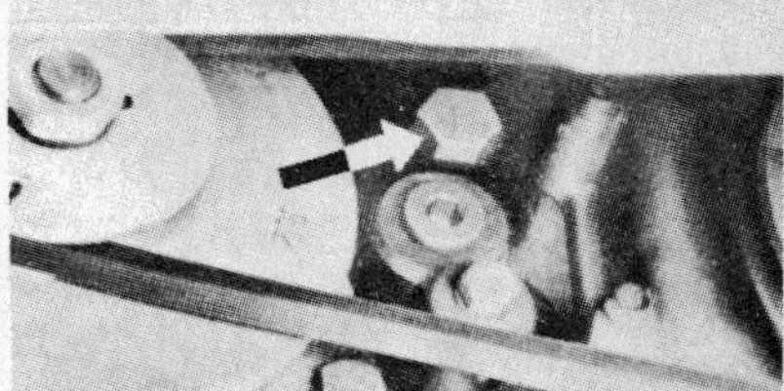

Engine block coolant drain plug

Cooling system breather plug; 100, 100 LS, and 100 GL shown.

Radiator

Removal and Installation

Super 90

1. Drain the coolant.
2. Remove the upper and lower hoses. Remove the small hose at the top.
3. Undo the mounting nuts and remove the radiator downward.
4. To install, reverse the removal procedures. Make sure that the gasket between the cowl and the radiator seals the crack completely. Be sure that the rubber fan ring is flat around the cowl.

100, 100 LS, 100 GL

1. Drain the coolant.
2. Remove the upper radiator hose.
3. Detach the mounting strut at the top of the radiator, and swing it forward.
4. Detach the lower radiator hose.
5. Unbolt the radiator mountings.
6. Lift the radiator out.
7. To install, reverse the removal procedures. Make sure that the rubber sealing strips between the radiator and radiator cowl are in place.

Water Pump

Removal and Installation

Super 90

1. Loosen the adjustment and remove the water pump drive belt.
2. Drain the coolant.
3. Remove the bolt that holds the small diameter hose to the front of the pump.
4. Detach the inlet and outlet hoses from the pump.
5. Remove the three Allen head bolts and remove the pump.
6. Reverse the procedure for installation, using new gaskets and adjusting the water pump drive belt tension. Tighten the pump mounting bolts to 18 ft lbs.

100, 100 LS, 100 GL

1. Loosen the adjustment and remove the water pump drive belt.
2. Drain the coolant.
3. Remove the alternator pivot bolt at the front.
4. Loosen the clamp and pull the lower hose off the pump.
5. Remove the thermostat housing.
6. Unbolt the fan pulley. The pulley may be prevented from turning by wedging a screwdriver between the pulley hub and one of the bolts.
7. The pulley may be carefully pried off the hub with two large screwdrivers.
8. Loosen the clamp and pull the upper hose off the pump.
9. Remove the five bolts and remove the pump.
10. Reverse the procedure for installation, using new gaskets and adjusting the alternator drive belt tension. Pump

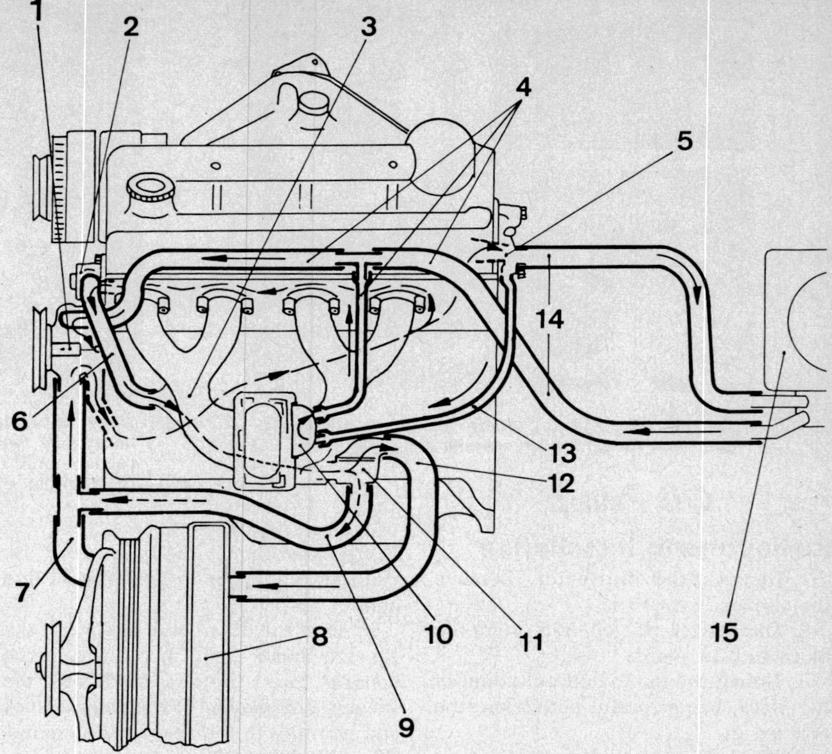

Coolant flow; 1970-1971, 100 LS shown

1. Water pump
2. Flange, front of cylinder head
3. Intake manifold
4. Return line, heater and automatic choke
5. Flange, rear of cylinder head
6. Connecting line to intake manifold
7. Radiator circuit from radiator to water pump
8. Radiator and fan (or electric fan)
9. Bypass line from intake manifold to water pump
10. Preheating, automatic choke
11. Thermostat, intake manifold
12. Radiator circuit
13. Automatic choke circuit
14. Heater circuit
15. Heat exchanger, heater

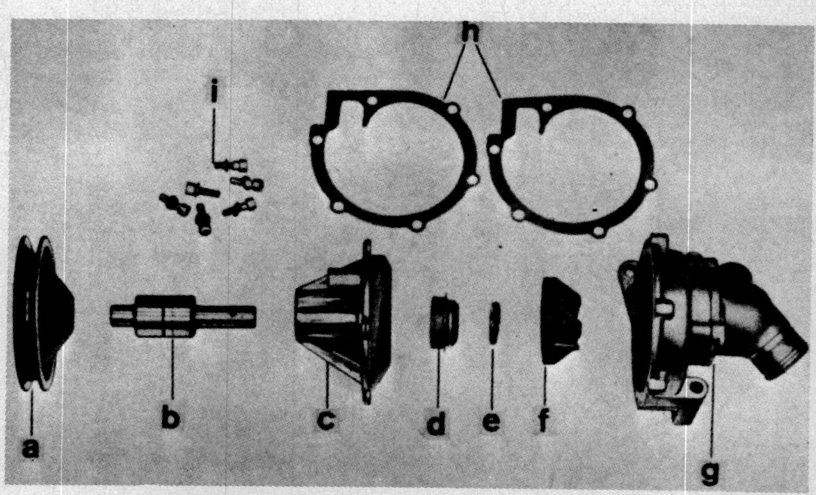

Exploded view of Super 90 water pump

(a)—Pulley
(b)—Water pump bearing with shaft
(c)—Bearing housing
(d)—Sliding seal ring
(e)—Counter ring with rubber ring
(f)—Impeller
(g)—Housing
(h)—Gaskets
(i)—Bolts

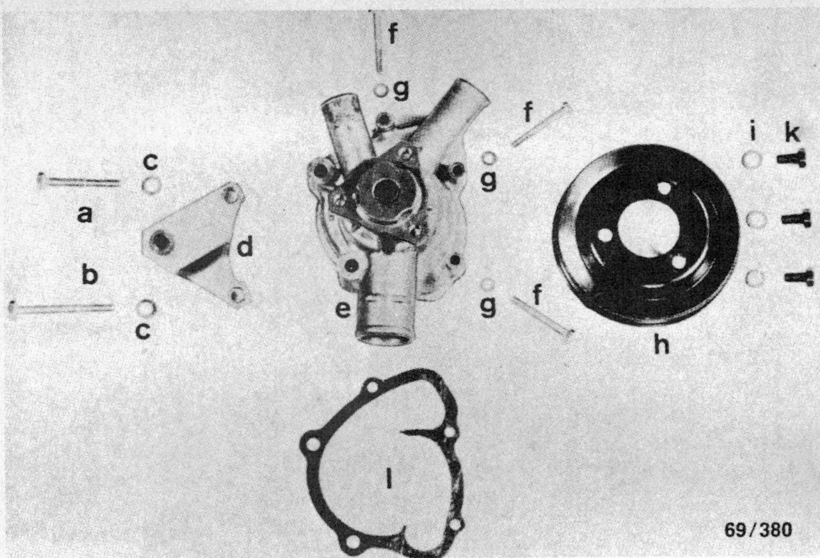

Exploded view of 100, 100 LS, and 100 GL water pump

(a)—Bolt
(b)—Bolt
(c)—Lockwasher
(d)—Mounting plate, alternator
(e)—Water pump
(f)—Bolt
(g)—Lockwasher
(h)—Pulley
(i)—Lockwasher
(k)—Bolt
(l)—Water pump gasket

mounting bolt torque is 15 ft lbs for the large bolts, and 9 ft lbs for the small ones. Thermostat housing bolt torque is 15 ft lbs. Pulley bolt torque is 7 ft lbs.

Thermostat

The thermostat normally installed is rated at 181°F (83°C). There is also available a winter thermostat rated at 189°F (87°C).

Removal and Installation

1. Drain the coolant from the radiator.
2. Remove the air cleaner on the Super 90.

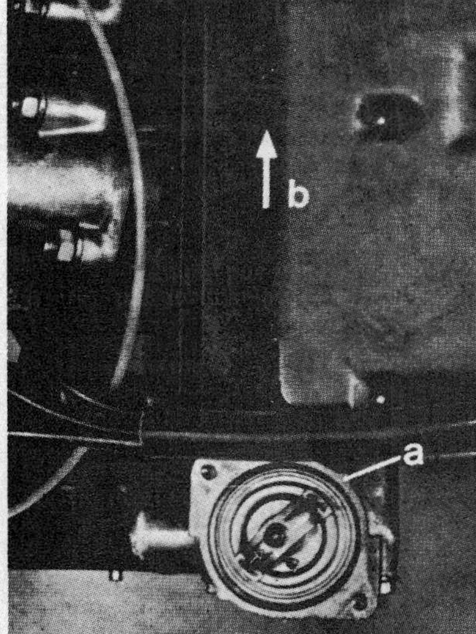

When installing the Super 90 thermostat, the bar (or arrow) should point at the projection (a). (b) points to the front.

Correct installation of the 100, 100 LS, and 100 GL thermostat

3. The thermostat is inside a cast housing on the engine, connected to the upper radiator hose. Unbolt the cover and remove the gasket and the thermostat.
4. When replacing the thermostat on the 100, 100 LS, and 100 GL, the bar on the thermostat should be facing up and running from front to rear. On the Super 90, the bar should be facing up and pointing at the projection on the housing. Some thermostats have an arrow on the bar which should also point at the projection. The housing bolts should be torqued to 7 ft lbs. Always use a new gasket.
5. Replace the Super 90 air cleaner and refill the radiator.

Radiator Fan

On the Super 90, the radiator fan is driven by the same belt that drives the water pump. On the 100, 100 LS, and 100 GL, the radiator fan is driven by a separate belt, the water pump being driven by the same belt that drives the alternator. Current models have an electric fan which requires no belt or adjustment.

Belt Tension Adjustment

1. Loosen the two bolts holding the fan housing to the fan support arm.
2. Move the fan and housing out to tighten the belt. The belt is correctly tensioned when the longest span of belt between pulleys can be depressed about ½ in. by moderate thumb pressure.
3. Tighten the bolts.

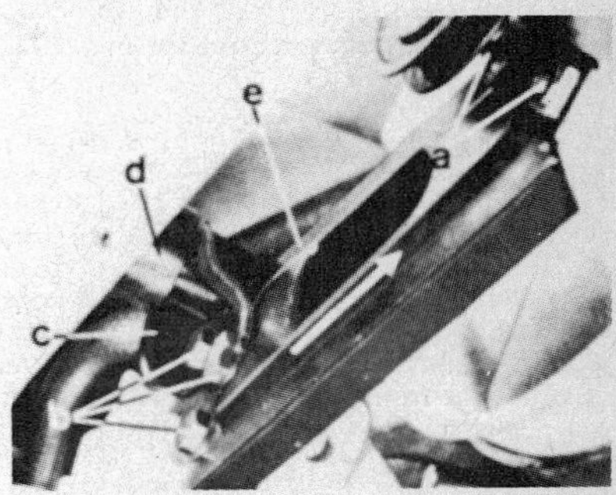

Radiator fan belt tension is adjusted with the bolts (a).

(b)—Mounting bolts
(c)—Pad
(d)—Stop
(e)—Fan support

EMISSION CONTROLS

Several emission control devices are used to control different sources of emissions. Engine crankcase emissions are controlled by routing them directly into the carburetor air cleaner or into the fuel vapor control system, which is connected to the air cleaner.

Fuel vapor emissions from the carburetor float bowl and the fuel tank are handled by the fuel vapor control system. This system has an activated carbon container in the engine compartment to store vapors until they can be drawn in through the air cleaner and burned.

The 100, 100 LS, and 100 GL use certain basic equipment to control exhaust emissions. The Super 90 uses some of this equipment. The parts of the system are: a triple port intake manifold, an air cleaner with a temperature controlled inlet beginning in 1972, a double vacuum unit distributor on 1970–1971 models, and a heating circuit to preheat the intake manifold. A single vacuum unit distributor was introduced in 1972.

The triple port intake manifold has a

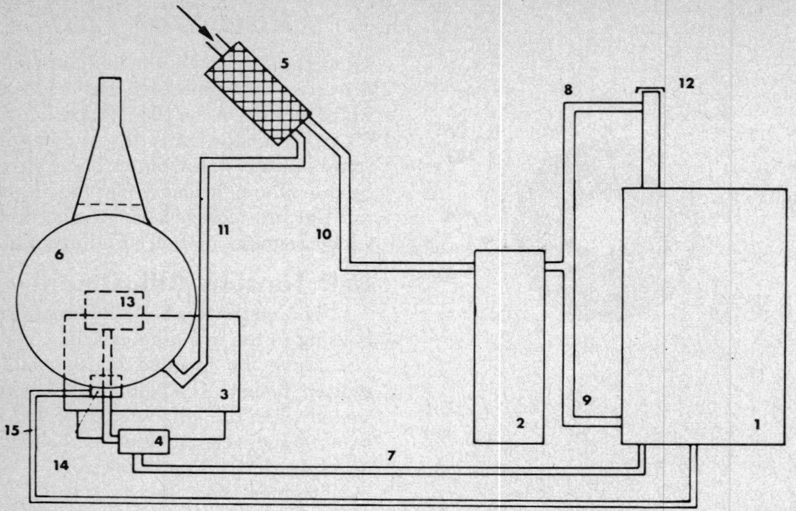

Fuel vapor emission control system, 1972-1973. Earlier versions do not have items (14) and (15).

1. Fuel tank
2. Vapor expansion container
3. Engine
4. Fuel pump
5. Activated carbon container
6. Air cleaner
7. Fuel line from tank to pump
8. Breather line from neck to expansion container
9. Breather line from tank to expansion container
10. Breather line to carbon container
11. Line from carbon
11. Line from carbon container to air cleaner
12. Non-vented tank filler cap
13. Carburetor
14. Fuel return valve
15. Line from return valve to tank

separate intake for water, used to preheat the manifold. The preheating and the conduction of the fuel/air mixture from each stage separately leads to more complete combustion and a lower level of exhaust emissions.

The distributor uses both centrifugal and vacuum advance mechanisms. When adjusting the ignition timing at idle speed on 1970–1971 models, both vacuum hoses must be disconnected. When reconnecting them, make sure that the hose from the carburetor connects to the plastic tube and the hose from the intake manifold connects to the metal tube.

1970-1971 distributor vacuum hoses. (a) is the vacuum unit, (EC) is the hose to the carburetor, and (RI) is the hose to the intake manifold.

All 1973 models are equipped with a capacitive discharge ignition system. This system eliminates the normal decline in ignition system performance between tune-ups, keeping exhaust emissions at a minimum.

NOTE: *Some tachometers, dwell meters, and oscilloscopes will not work with this system.*

1973 automatic transmission models have an exhaust gas recirculation system, while manual transmission models have a system which permits full distributor vacuum advance only in fourth gear.

For adjustments of emission levels, see "Tune-Up Procedures".

FUEL SYSTEM

Fuel Pump

Removal and Installation

Super 90

The Super 90 fuel pump is on the side of the block, beneath the intake manifold.

1. Detach the hose at the carburetor, since the other end is hard to reach.
2. Remove and plug the pump intake hose.
3. Remove the mounting bolts.
4. Remove the crankcase dipstick and reach around the radiator to pull the pump out to the rear. Be careful not to spill any fuel into the crankcase.
5. When replacing the pump, use new gaskets and rock the pump back and forth to make sure that the lever rests on the camshaft.

100, 100 LS, 100 GL

The fuel pump is on the left side of the engine block.

1. Disconnect the hoses from the pump. Plug the inlet hose.
2. Remove the mounting bolts and pull out the pump.
3. When replacing the pump, use a new insulator.

Measuring Output Pressure

A fuel pump pressure testing gauge can be connected between the fuel pump and the carburetor. With the engine running at about 2,000 rpm, the pressure should be approximately as specified in the "Tune-Up Specifications Chart".

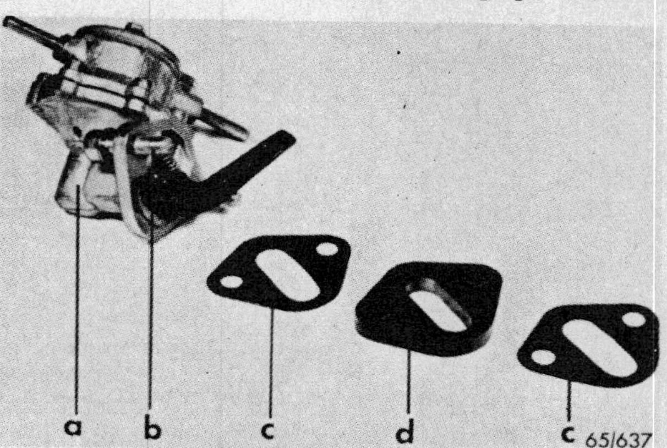

(a) is the Super 90 fuel pump, (b) is the mounting bolts, (c) is the gaskets, and (d) is the insulator.

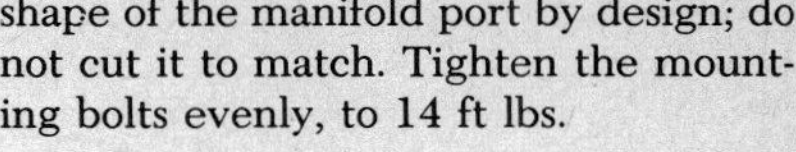

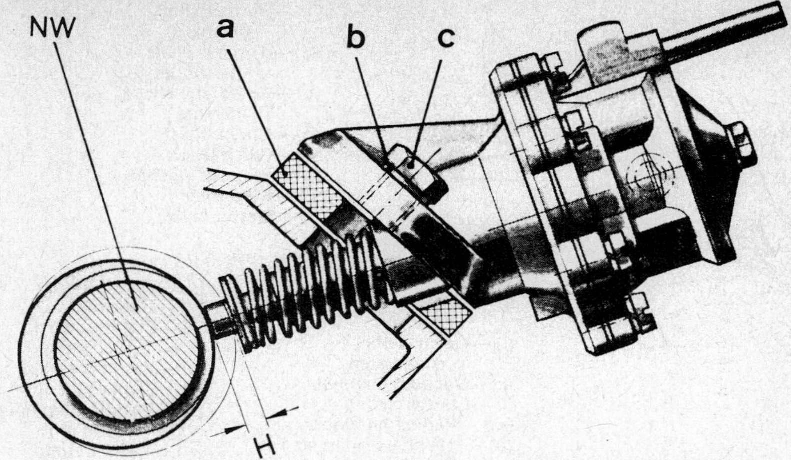

100, 100 LS, 100 GL fuel pump. (NW) is the camshaft, (a) is the insulator, (b) is the lockwasher, and (c) is the mounting bolt.

CARBURETORS

The carburetors used are:

Model	Year	Carburetor
Super 90	1970-1971	Solex 32/32 DIDTA
Super 90	1972	Solex 32/32 TDID
100 LS	1970-1971	Solex 32/32 TDID
100, 100 LS 100 GL	1972-1973	Solex 32/32 TDID

NOTE: *Solex carburetors are marked with the model number on the float bowl and on the outside of the throttle bore.*

These are all progressive two-barrel units; that is, the secondary throttle opens only on wide throttle opening. This results in good high rpm performance, as well as smooth and economical low-speed operation.

Removal and Installation

1. Remove the air cleaner.
2. Disconnect the fuel hose, being careful not to spill any fuel on hot engine parts.
3. If a choke with coolant connections is used, remove the radiator cap. Disconnect the coolant lines and fasten them up in some way to avoid losing any coolant. Disconnect the lead from the electric choke.
4. Disconnect the vacuum line and the electrical lead to the idle cutoff valve.
5. Remove the clip holding the throttle linkage at the carburetor. Detach the linkage, being careful not to lose any plastic washers or bushings.
6. Unbolt the carburetor from the manifold and remove.
7. When replacing, use a new gasket between the carburetor and manifold. The gasket does not quite match the shape of the manifold port by design; do not cut it to match. Tighten the mounting bolts evenly, to 14 ft lbs.

Overhaul

All Types

Efficient carburetion depends greatly on careful cleaning and inspection during overhaul since dirt, gum, water, or varnish in or on the carburetor parts are often responsible for poor performance.

Overhaul your carburetor in a clean, dust-free area. Carefully disassemble the carburetor, referring often to the diagrams. Keep all similar and look-alike parts segregated during disassembly and cleaning to avoid accidental interchange during assembly. Make a note of all jet sizes.

When the carburetor is disassembled, wash all parts (except diaphragms, electric choke units, pump plunger, and any other plastic, leather, fiber, or rubber parts) in clean carburetor solvent. Do not leave parts in the solvent any longer than is necessary to sufficiently loosen the deposits. Excessive cleaning may remove the special finish from the float bowl and choke valve bodies, leaving these parts unfit for service. Rinse all parts in clean solvent and blow them dry with compressed air or allow them to air dry. Wipe clean all cork, plastic, leather, and fiber parts with a clean, lint-free cloth.

Blow out all passages and jets with compressed air and be sure that there are no restrictions or blockages. Never use wire or similar tools to clean jets, fuel passages, or air bleeds. Clean all jets and valves separately to avoid accidental interchange.

Check all parts for wear or damage. If wear or damage is found, replace the defective parts. Especially check the following:

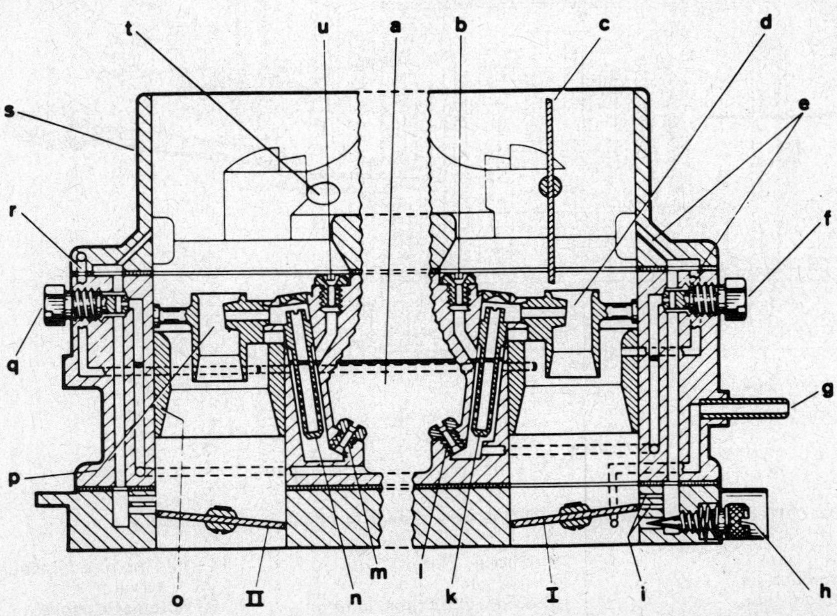

Cross-section of Solex 32/32 DIDTA carburetor

(I)—Primary Throttle
(II)—Secondary Throttle
(a)—Float chamber
(b)—Air correction jet (Primary)
(c)—Choke
(d)—Outlet arm with atomizer
(e)—Idle air bore
(f)—Idle jet (Primary)
(g)—Connection tube, ignition timing
(h)—Idle mixture regulating screw
(i)—Bypass bores
(k)—Mixture tube (Primary)
(l)—Main jet (Primary)
(m)—Main jet (Secondary)
(n)—Mixture tube (Secondary)
(o)—Venturi (Secondary)
(p)—Outlet arm with atomizer (Secondary)
(q) Idle jet (Secondary)
(r)—Bore, vacuum unit
(s)—Carburetor cover
(t)—Breathing bore
(u)—Air correction jet (Secondary)

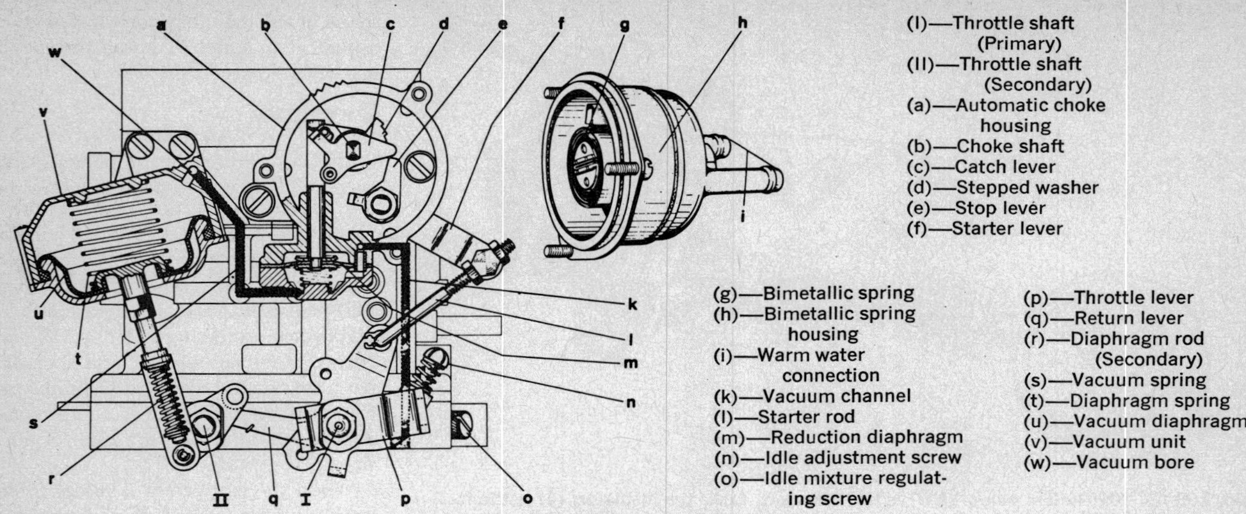

Cross-section of Solex 32/32 DIDTA carburetor

1. Check the float needle and seat for wear. If wear is found, replace the complete assembly.
2. Check the float hinge pin for wear and the float(s) for dents or distortion. Replace the float if fuel has leaked into it.
3. Check the throttle and choke shaft bores for wear or an out-of-round condition. Damage or wear to the throttle arm, shaft, or shaft bore will often require replacement of the throttle body. These parts require a close tolerance of fit; wear may allow air leakage, which could affect starting and idling.

NOTE: *Throttle shafts and bushings are not included in overhaul kits. They can be purchased separately.*

4. Inspect the idle mixture adjusting needles for burrs or grooves. Any such condition requires replacement of the needle, since you will not be able to obtain a satisfactory idle.
5. Test the accelerator pump check valves. They should pass air one way but not the other. Test for proper seating by blowing and sucking on the valve. Re-

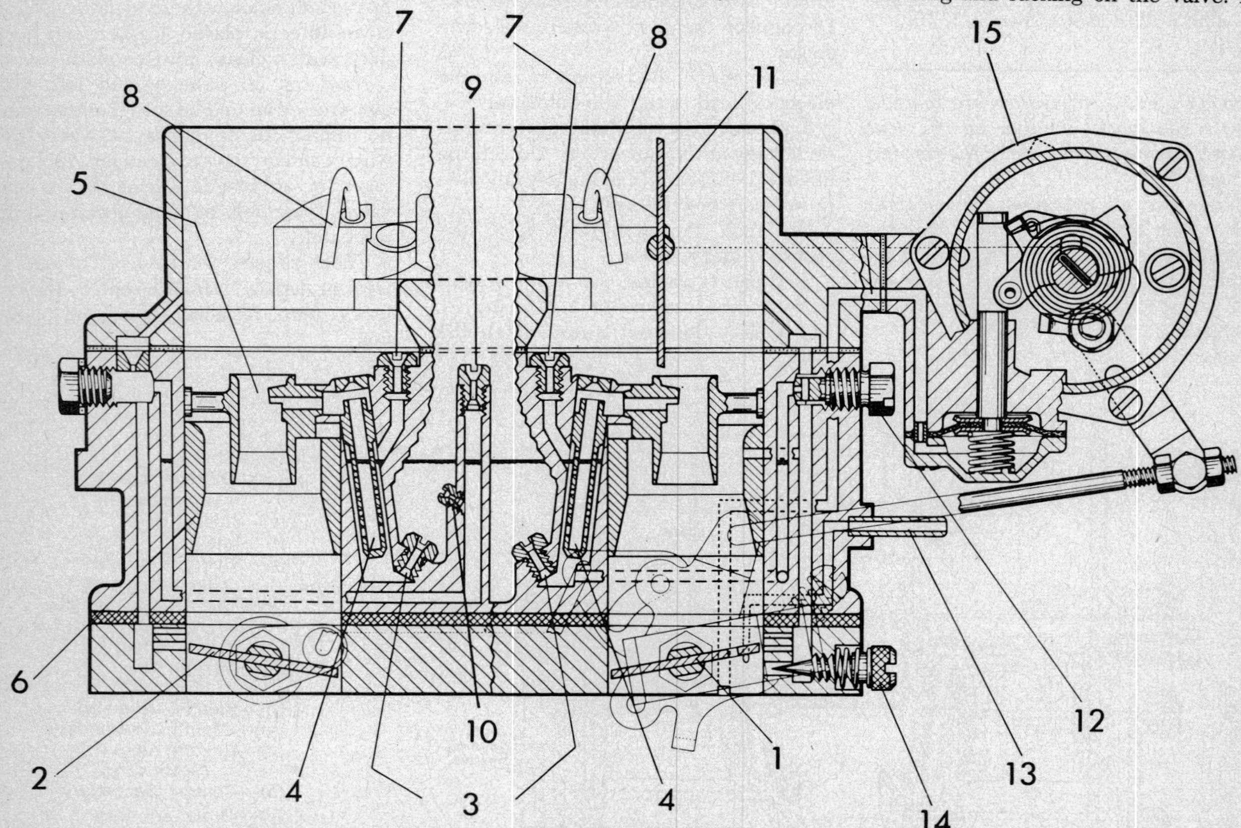

Cross-section of Solex 32/32 TDID carburetor, the 32/35 TDID is very similar but has an electric choke.

1. Primary throttle
2. Secondary throttle
3. Main jet
4. Mixture tube
5. Outlet arm with atomizer
6. Venturi
7. Air correction jet
8. Enrichment tube
9. Breather jet
10. Transfer jet
11. Choke
12. Idle jet
13. Connection tube, ignition timing
14. Idle mixture regulating screw
15. Automatic choke

place the valve if necessary. If the valve is satisfactory, wash the valve again to remove breath moisture.

6. Check the bowl cover for warped surfaces with a straightedge.

7. Closely inspect the valves and seats for wear and damage, replacing as necessary.

8. After the carburetor is assembled, check the choke valve for freedom of operation.

Carburetor overhaul kits are recommended for each overhaul. These kits contain all gaskets and new parts to replace those that deteriorate most rapidly. Failure to replace all parts supplied with the kit (especially gaskets) can result in poor performance later.

Some carburetor manufacturers supply overhaul kits of three basic types: minor repair; major repair; and gasket kits. Basically, they contain the following:

Minor Repair Kits:

All gaskets
Float needle valve
Volume control screw
All diaphragms
Spring for the pump diaphragm

Major Repair Kits:

All jets and gaskets
All diaphragms
Float needle valve
Volume control screw
Pump ball valve
Main jet carrier
Float
Complete intermediate rod
Intermediate pump lever
Complete injector tube
Some cover hold-down screws and washers

Gasket Kits:

All gaskets

After cleaning and checking all components, reassemble the carburetor, using new parts and referring to the exploded view. When reassembling, make sure that all screws and jets are tight in their seats, but do not overtighten. Tighten all screws gradually, in rotation. Do not tighten needle valves into their seats; uneven jetting will result. Always use new gaskets. Be sure to adjust the float level when reassembling.

Throttle Linkage Adjustment

Throttle linkage adjustments are not normally required. However, it is a good idea to check that the throttle valve(s) in the carburetor open all the way when the accelerator pedal is held in the wide-open throttle position. Only the primary throttle valve will open on the 32/32 DIDTA carburetor; the secondary throttle is vacuum operated. On the Super 90, there is an adjustment point on the linkage inside the car. To adjust, simply loosen the clamp bolt and vary the position of the two levers. There is also an adjustable accelerator pedal stop on the floor to prevent overtravel of the linkage.

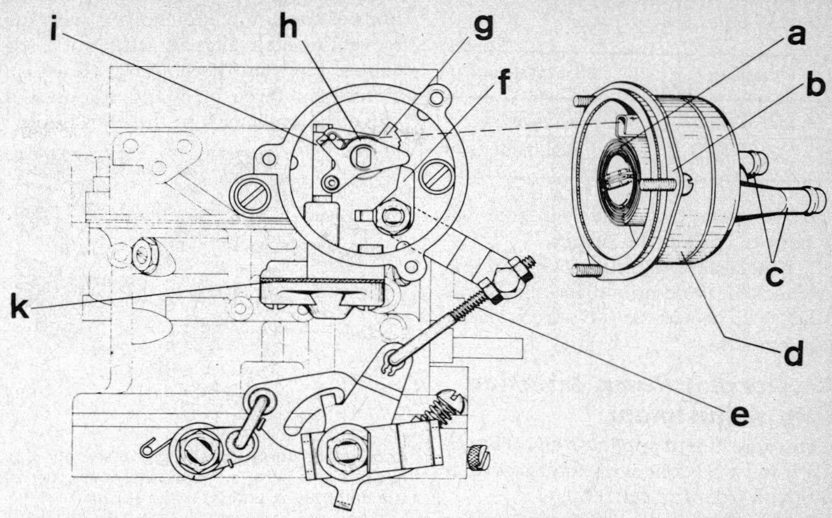

Cross-section of Solex 32/32 TDID carburetor, the 32/35 TDID is very similar but has an electric choke.

(a)—Bimetallic spring
(b)—Retaining ring
(c)—Water connection
(d)—Choke cover
(e)—Connecting rod
(f)—Stop lever
(g)—Stepped washer
(h)—Follower
(i)—Diaphragm rod
(k)—Diaphragm

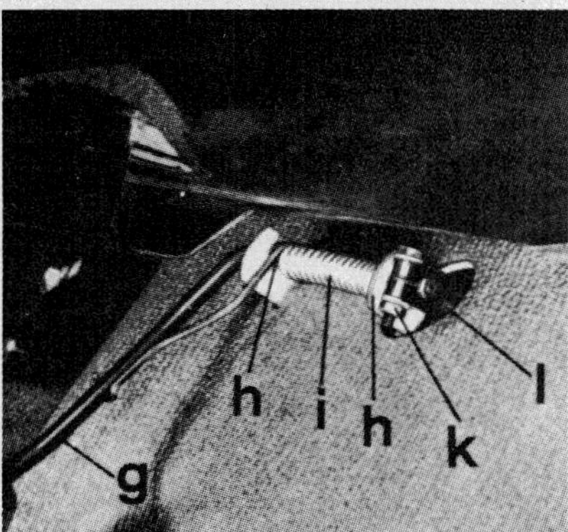

Super 90 throttle linkage, (k) is the clamp bolt.

(g)—Lever with slider behind accelerator pedal
(h)—Bushing
(i)—Spring
(h)—Bushing
(l)—Lever

Fuel Level Adjustment—32/32 DIDTA

This adjustment is made with the carburetor installed on the engine.

1. Idle the engine for one minute.

2. Stop the engine. Remove the air cleaner.

3. Detach the fuel line.

4. Remove the five carburetor cover mounting screws.

5. Plug the fuel inlet with a finger and lift off the carburetor cover and gasket. Set them to the side, leaving the linkages attached.

6. Using a sliding T-scale, measure the distance from the top of the fuel surface to the edge of the housing. It should be 0.67–0.74 in. on carburetors with finned floats (after No. 7279), and 0.63–0.71 in. on earlier models.

7. The measurement may be corrected by varying the thickness of the fiber sealing ring under the float needle valve.

Float Level Adjustment—32/32 and 32/35 TDID

This adjustment can be made with the carburetor either installed or removed.

1. If the carburetor is on the car, perform Steps 1–5 of "Fuel Level Adjustment—32/32 DIDTA."

2. Disconnect the linkage between the upper and lower parts of the carburetor.

3. Turn the carburetor cover upside down.

4. Measure the distance between the upper edge of the bead around the float and the carburetor cover flange surface.

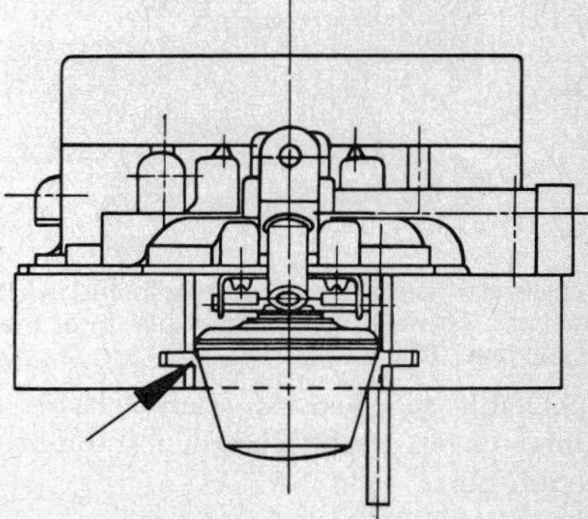

32/32 and 32/35 TDID float level measurement, the arrow points to the upper edge of the float bead.

It should be as follows:

Carburetor	Float Level (in.)
32/32 TDID	0.51-0.59
32/35 TDID	0.61-0.69

5. The metal tab of the float lever can be bent to correct the height.

6. If necessary, the fuel level can also be checked as described for the 32/32 DIDTA. It should be 0.53–0.55 in. for both models.

Accelerator Pump Injection Rate Adjustment

This adjustment applies to all carburetors. It must be done with the carburetor removed from the car.

1. Place the carburetor over a clean container. Make sure that the float bowl is full.

2. Pump the throttle linkage full stroke 10–20 times. Injection should start as soon as the linkage is moved.

3. Measure the amount of fuel pumped, with a chemist's graduated cylinder. Divide the amount in cc (ml) by the number of strokes to get the average volume per stroke. The figure should be:

Carburetor	Injection Rate (cc)
32/32 DIDTA up to No. 7279	1.3
32/32 DIDTA after No. 7279	0.9-1.1
32/32 TDID, 100 LS	1.4-1.5
32/32 TDID, Super 90	1.1-1.4
32/35 TDID	1.4-1.9

4. To increase the injection rate, place more washers between the cotter pin and the pump lever. To decrease the rate, remove washers or move the cotter pin further out.

Accelerator pump output is adjusted with washers between the cotter pin and the pump lever (b).

5. If the specified rate cannot be obtained, check the diaphragm and the injection tube.

Automatic Choke Adjustment

The standard adjustment on all versions of the automatic choke is with the movable notch aligned with the large central tooth on the housing. To adjust, loosen the three clamping screws and move the outer part of the choke unit.

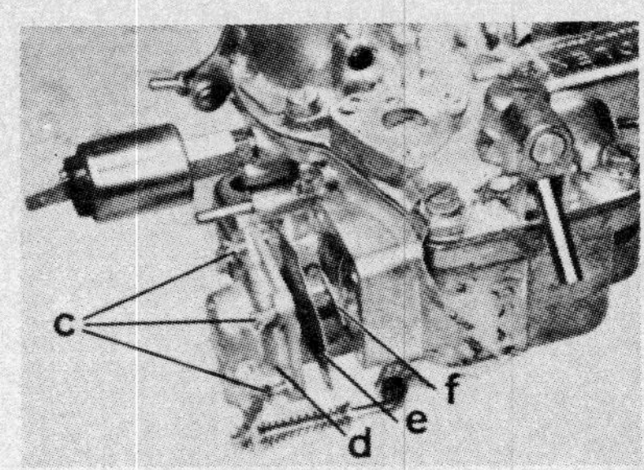

Accelerator pump diaphragm assembly, (c) is the cover screws, (d) is the cover, (e) is the diaphragm, and (f) is the spring.

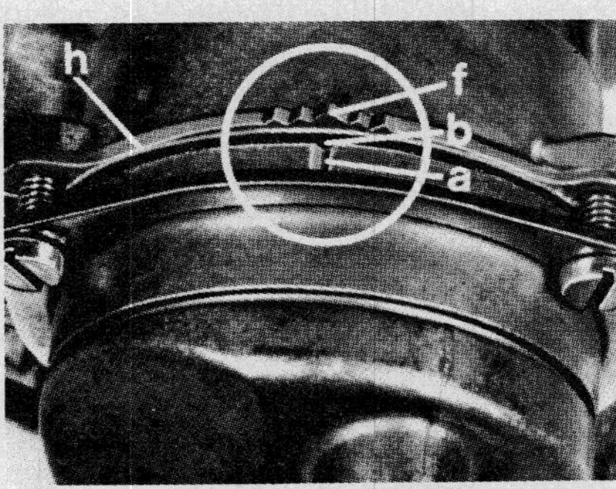

Automatic choke is correctly adjusted when (a), (b), and (f) are aligned. (h) is an insulator.

Choke Gap Adjustment

This adjustment can be made with the carburetor in place, but it is much easier with it removed. The procedure applies to all carburetors.

1. Close the choke tightly.

2. Press the diaphragm rod down against the stop.

3. Hold the follower against the stop.

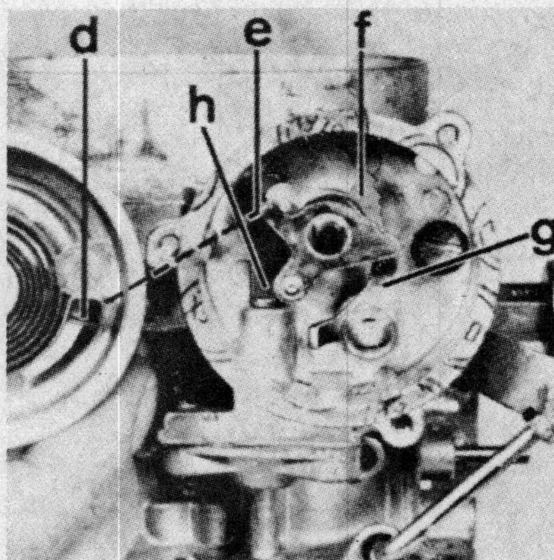

When checking choke gap, press the diaphragm rod (h) down against the stop and hold the follower (e) against the stop.

(d)—Bimetallic spring eyelet
(f)—Stepped washer
(g)—Stop lever

4. Check the gap between the upper edge of the choke valve and the housing wall with a drill. The gap should be:

Carburetor	Choke gap (in.)
32/32 DIDTA	0.087-0.095
32/32 TDID, 100 LS	0.118-0.134
32/32 TDID, Super 90	0.094-0.106
32/35 TDID	0.132-0.144

5. To correct the gap, bend the pin up or down slightly.

Bend pin (k) to adjust the choke gap

Throttle Gap Adjustment

This adjustment could possibly be made with the carburetor in place, but it is much easier with it removed.

1. Close the choke tightly. The stop lever should rest on the highest step of the stepped washer, holding the throttle open slightly.

2. Check the gap between the lower edge of the throttle valve and the housing wall with a drill. The measurement should be

Carburetor	Throttle Gap (in.)
32/32 DIDTA	0.056-0.064
32/32 TDID	0.051-0.059
32/35 TDID	0.055-0.059

3. Adjust the gap by means of the two nuts on the connecting rod.

When checking the throttle gap, the stop lever (1) should rest on the highest step of the stepped washer (m) and hold the throttle open by means of the connecting rod, (p) indicates the adjusting nuts.

Idle Speed and Mixture Adjustments

See "Tune-Up Procedures" for these adjustments. The procedure to be used depends on the type of carburetor. There are two types: standard and idle air bypass. The standard has only one adjusting screw, the idle mixture screw, on the body of the carburetor. These units are found mainly on early and non-US models. The idle air bypass carburetor is the current emission control type. It can be identified by the two adjusting screws on the body of the carburetor. These are the idle mixture and idle air control screws.

MANUAL TRANSMISSION

The transmission is combined with the differential in a transaxle.

Removal and Installation

The engine/transaxle unit must be removed from the car as explained under "Engine Removal and Installation". Then the transmission can simply be unbolted from the engine and slid back. On replacement, tighten the bolts to 54, 33, and 18 ft lbs, respectively, for the three sizes of bolts.

It is possible to remove the transaxle only from the Super 90, but this procedure is fully as difficult as removing the whole unit. It requires moving the engine and transaxle about in the chassis while supporting them with some rather elaborate lifting and supporting brackets. The front crossmember must also be removed.

Linkage Adjustment

1. Slide the seats all the way back and set the handbrake.
2. Remove the six sheetmetal screws which secure the console. Unscrew the shift knob and lift off the console.
3. The shift lever bracket has a spring-loaded ball which should engage the groove in the long shift rod when the transmission is in Neutral.

When adjusting the floorshift linkage, the spring loaded ball should engage the slot (N) in the shift rod (33) with the transmission in Neutral. If it does not, loosen bolts (8) and move the bracket.

4. To adjust, loosen the four bolts which hold the shift lever bracket to the floor and move the bracket to the front or rear. Tighten the bolts and recheck the adjustment.
5. If the long shift rod has a rubber damper apparatus in the middle, make sure that it is in good condition and not causing any unnecessary play.
6. Grease the moving parts lightly.
7. Replace the console and the shift knob.

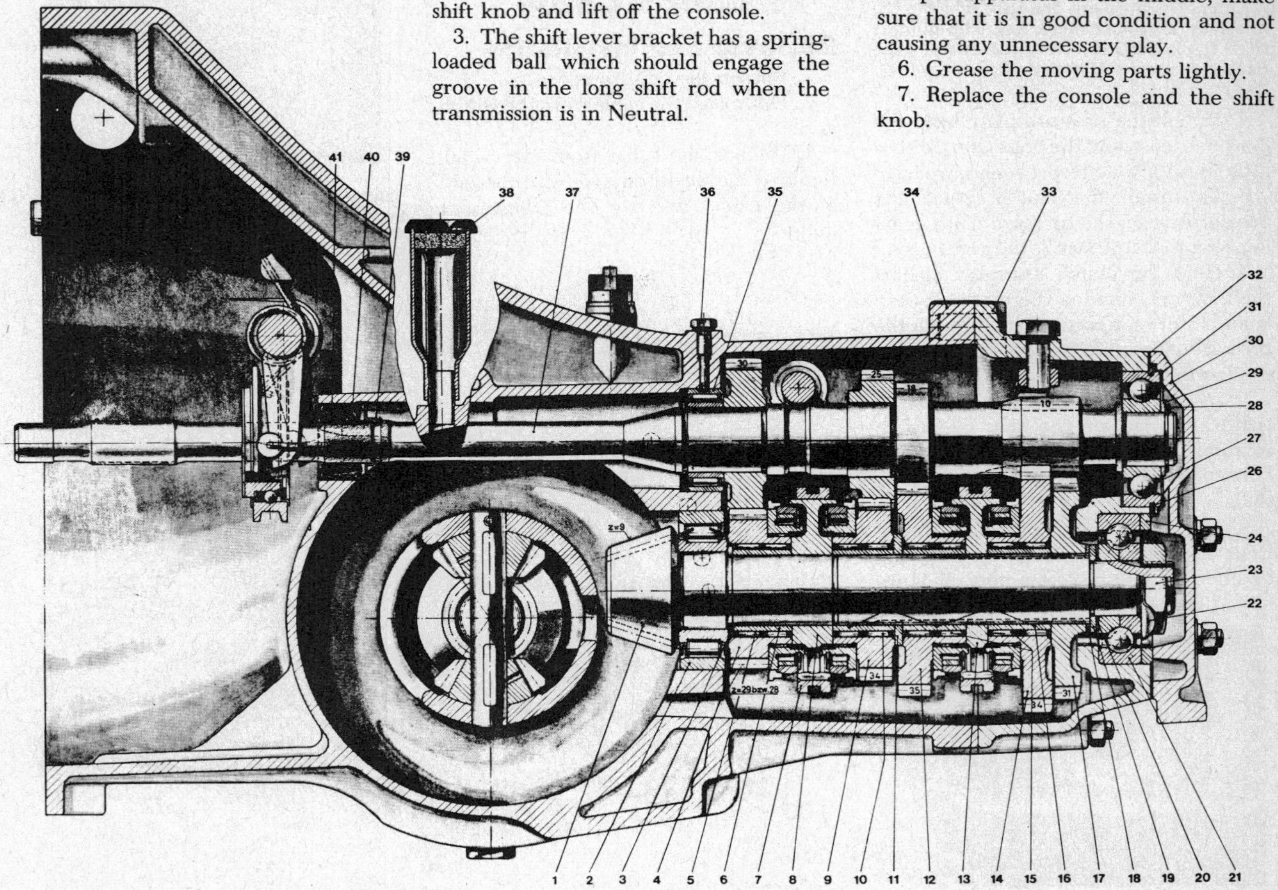

Cross-section of the manual transmission (transaxle).

1. Drive pinion
2. Roller bearing
3. Spacer
4. Sliding gear, 4th gear
5. Needle bearing
6. Needle bearing inner race
7. Operating sleeve
8. Guide sleeve
9. Sliding gear, 3rd gear
10. Needle bearing
11. Thrust washer
12. Sliding gear, 2nd gear
13. Guide sleeve
14. Sliding gear, 1st gear
15. Needle bearing
16. Needle bearing, inner race
17. Reverse gear
18. Shim
19. Shim
20. Shim
21. Four point bearing
22. Lock plate
23. Hex nut
24. Shim
25. Reverse gear ass. (not illustrated)
26. Snap-ring
27. Grooved ball bearing
28. Circlip
29. Support disc
30. End cover
31. Shim
32. Gasket, end cover
33. Transmission cover
34. Transmission case
35. Needle bearing
36. Hex head screw
37. Main shaft
38. Breather valve
39. Oil slinger
40. Shaft
41. Bushing

CLUTCH

Removal and Installation

1. Remove the engine and transaxle as a unit.
2. Separate the engine and transaxle.
3. Mark the relationship of the pressure plate to the flywheel.

Before removing the pressure plate bolts (a) mark the pressure plate (b) and the flywheel as shown at the arrow. The dummy shaft (d) is used to center the driven plate (clutch disc) on reinstallation.

4. Unbolt the pressure plate from the flywheel, loosening the bolts alternately a little bit at a time to prevent warpage.
5. To install the clutch, place the driven plate on the pressure plate, making sure that it is facing the right way.
6. Hold the clutch assembly against the flywheel, aligning the marks in Step 3, and insert a dummy shaft through the pressure plate and the driven plate into the crankshaft pilot bearing.
7. Install the pressure plate bolts finger tight. Then tighten the bolts evenly, in rotation, to avoid distortion. Torque the bolts to 24–27 ft lbs. Remove the dummy shaft.
8. The clutch release bearing in the front of the transmission housing should be checked before reassembly. It is retained by two springs.

The clutch release bearing can easily be removed by disengaging the two springs.

9. Bolt the transaxle back to the engine. Bolt torque is 54, 33, and 18 ft lbs, respectively, for the three sizes of bolts.
10. Replace the engine/transaxle unit in the car. Check the clutch adjustment.

Pedal Free-Play Adjustment

The pedal free-play is adjusted at the clutch end of the cable. Free-play is the distance that the pedal travels from the released position to the point at which clutch spring pressure can be felt. This can be measured by placing a yardstick alongside the clutch pedal. Play should be 0.6–0.8 in.

1. On the 100, 100 LS, and 100 GL, loosen the upper cable nut. Turn both nuts clockwise to reduce play, and counterclockwise to increase. After the adjustment is made, tighten the upper nut to lock the cable in place.
2. On the Super 90, turn the adjusting nut at the end of the inner cable clockwise to increase play, and counterclockwise to reduce play. Make sure that the toggle is seated in the notch on the clutch arm.
3. The total pedal travel should be at least 6.1 in. If it is not adequate, the pedal pivot can be loosened and moved up.

Clutch Cable

Removal and Installation

1. Loosen the adjustment.
2. Disengage the cable from the clutch arm.
3. Unhook the cable from the pedal. Remove the threaded eye from the end of the cable. Remove the adjustment nut(s).

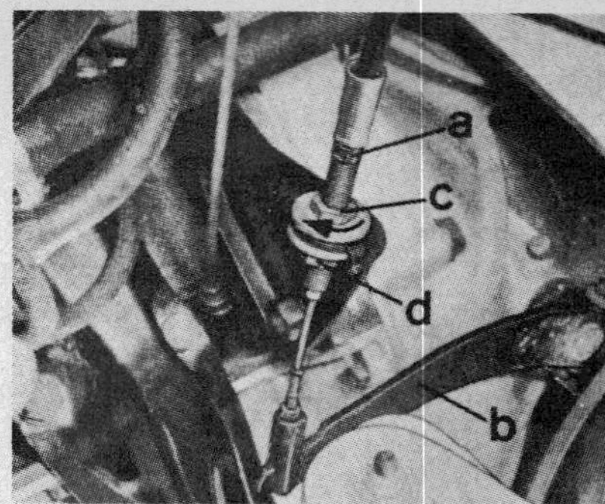

Clutch adjustment point on the 100, 100 LS, and 100 GL. (a) is the clutch cable, (b) is the clutch lever, (c) and (d) are the adjusting nuts.

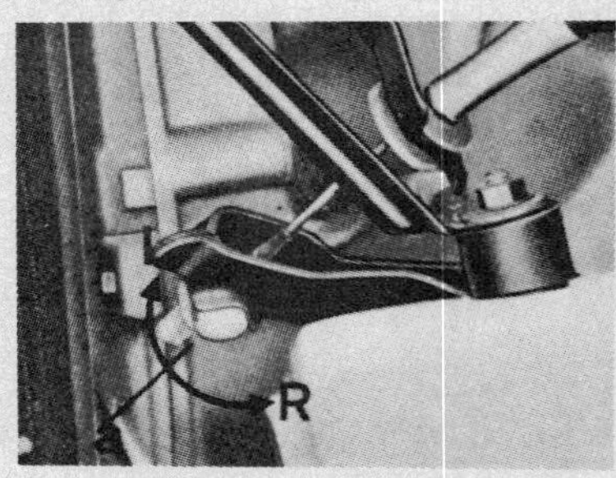

Super 90 clutch adjustment nut (a). (L) and (R) indicate left and right.

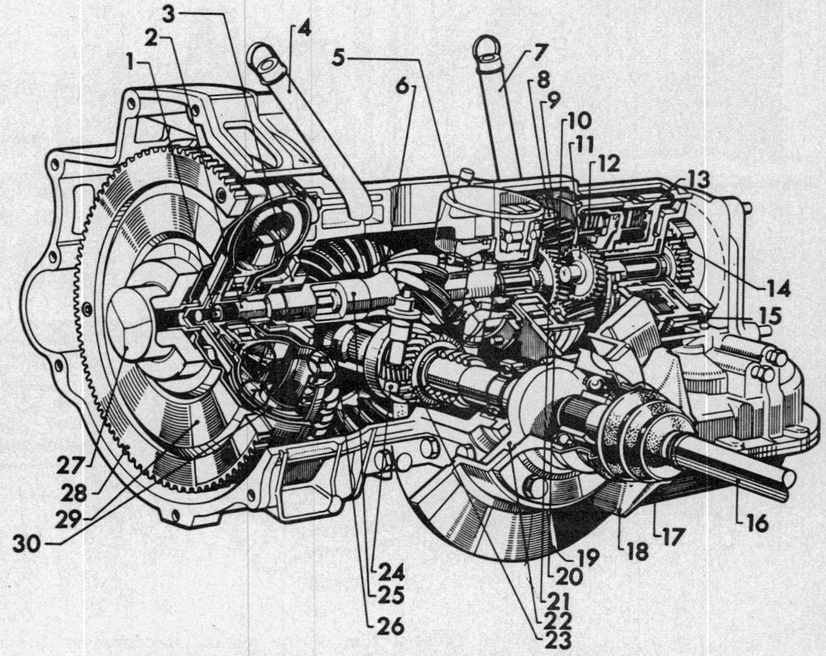

Cross-section of the automatic transmission (transaxle)

1. Pump shaft
2. Turbine shaft
3. Stator support
4. Oil filler tube, differential
5. Governor
6. Drive pinion
7. Filler tube, planetary gear
8. Annulus
9. Small planetary gear
10. Large sun gear
11. Large planetary pinion
12. Forward clutch
13. Direct and reverse clutch
14. Oil pump
15. 2nd gear brake band
16. Driveshaft
17. Oil pan
18. Brake caliper
19. Brake disc
20. Ist gear and reverse brake band
21. Planetary gear carrier
22. Stub axle
23. Impeller, governor and speedometer
24. Speedometer pinion shaft
25. Drive pinion shaft
26. Differential
27. Crankshaft, engine
28. Gear ring
29. Drive plate
29. Torkue converter
(P)—Impeller
(L)—Stator
(T)—Turbine

4. Remove the C-clip which holds the outer cable at the adjustment point. Remove all the washers and bushings, first noting their locations.

5. Pull the cable out of the firewall toward the engine compartment side.

6. Install and connect the new cable. Adjust the pedal free-play.

AUTOMATIC TRANSMISSION

The Audi automatic transmission is a hydraulically operated three-speed unit, with a torque converter.

Removal and Installation

The automatic transmission can be disconnected from the engine and removed with the engine in the car.

1. Drain the transmission. Remove the grille and front apron. The engine must be mounted to the frame in some manner or suspended on a lift or jack to prevent it from falling from the mounts when the mounts are disconnected.

2. Loosen the brake pipe lines from the brake hoses and plug the ends of the brake hoses.

3. Disconnect the accelerator linkage.

4. Remove the front exhaust pipe.

5. Remove the oil filter and starter.

6. Disconnect both driveshafts and suspend them from the upper wishbones. Disconnect the stabilizer bar at both lower wishbones.

7. Unbolt the holder for the selector cable at the transmission. Remove the selector cable from the lever at the transmission. Remove the selector cable holder.

8. Disconnect the crossmember at the engine mounting and at the support. Place a jack or support under the transmission.

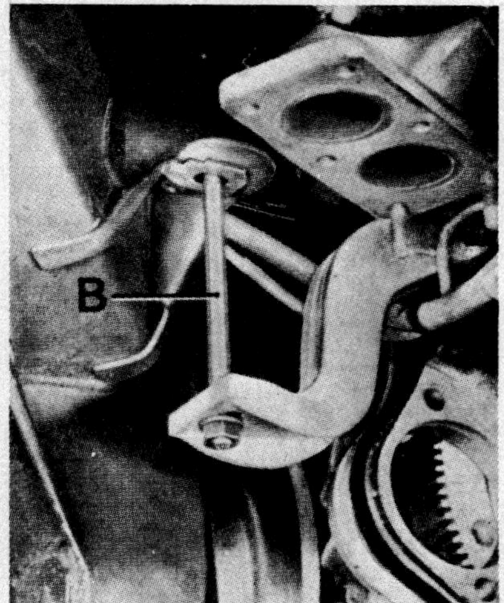

Insert bolts (B) through each engine mount to support the engine. Note that the starter has been removed for access to the torque converter bolts.

9. Remove the guard and disconnect the left and right engine mounts. Be careful not to alter the position of the left mount, which is fixed by means of locknuts.

10. Insert bolts (3/8 in. x 8 in.) through each side in place of the engine mounts. Lower the complete power plant until the unit rests on the bolts.

11. Disconnect the transmission vacuum hose at the vacuum unit or at the T adaptor.

12. Unbolt the torque converter Allen bolts by working through the hole for the starter.

13. Unbolt the engine-to-transmission connections and remove the transmission. Secure the torque converter in the transmission with a strap.

14. To install the transmission, reverse the removal procedure, noting the following: Lift the transmission and bolt it to the engine. Lift both the engine and transmission and install the selector lever holder. When installing the engine mounts, be sure that the projection engages the groove of the mount. After installing the engine and transmission assembly, check the alignment of the unit. Refer to "Engine Installation." Torque converter bolt torque is 22 ft lbs. Transmission-to-engine bolt torque is 54, 33, and 18 ft lbs, respectively, for the three bolt sizes. Refill the transmission.

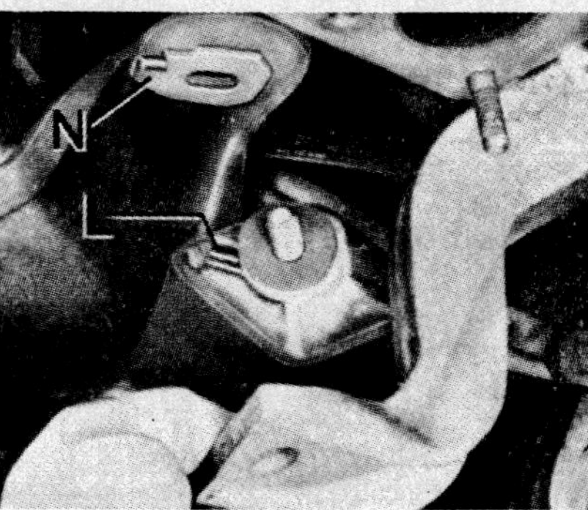

Be sure that the projection (N) engages the groove (L) of the engine mount.

Pan Removal and Installation

The automatic transmission fluid should be changed and the pan cleaned out every 18,000 miles. The interval should be shortened to 12,000 miles under severe use such as city driving or trailer towing.

To change the fluid:

1. Run the engine in Neutral for a minute or two.

2. Make sure that the vehicle is parked on level ground. Stop the engine.

3. Place a pan of at least four quarts capacity under the transmission.

4. Remove the plug from the transmission bottom pan, after wiping the area clean.

5. Remove the starter.

6. Remove and clean out the pan.

7. Replace the pan, using a new gasket. Torque the bolts to 7 ft lbs. Wait ten minutes and retorque the bolts.

8. Clean off the plug, particularly the threads, and replace it.

9. Replace the starter.

10. Pour in five pints of fluid through the dipstick filler tube. The proper transmission fluid is Dexron with the prefix letter B.

11. Start the engine and shift through all the lever positions.

12. The level should reach the tip of the dipstick. Add fluid until the level reaches this point.

13. Take a short test drive. Fill the transmission until the level is between the marks on the dipstick. Retorque the bolts.

NOTE: *If the transmission is overfilled, the excess must be drained.*

Kickdown Switch

The kickdown switch is mounted behind the accelerator pedal. With the ignition switch on, the switch should make an audible click when the pedal is pressed all the way down.

The transmission should downshift when the accelerator is depressed to the wide open throttle position at speeds between 39 and 65 mph for second gear, and 16 and 36 mph for first gear.

Neutral Safety Switch Adjustment

The neutral safety switch prevents the engine from being started with the transmission in any position other than Park or Neutral. It also activates the backup lights. The switch is at the base of the shift lever, inside the floorshift console.

To replace or adjust the switch:

1. Remove the four screws which hold the console to the floor.

2. Shift into Neutral. Remove the two screws which hold the shift position indicator plate to the console. Remove the shift knob and the console.

3. Disconnect the switch electrical leads. These are: red/black—neutral safety; black—backup lights; blue/red—backup lights. The backup light wires are at the front.

4. Remove the two switch retaining screws. Remove the switch.

5. Install the new switch so that the neutral safety switch contacts are together.

6. Install the electrical connectors. Hold the footbrake while making sure that the engine will start only in Neutral and Park. Make sure that the backup lights operate only in Reverse. If the switch does not operate properly, it may have to be moved on its slotted mounting bracket.

7. Replace the console cover.

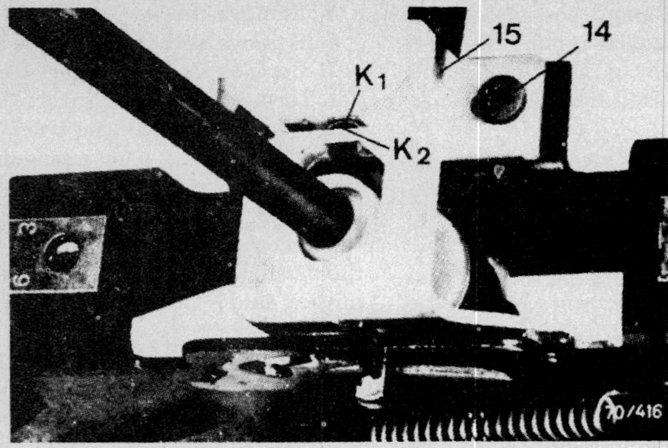

When installing the neutral safety/backup light switch (15) contacts (K1) and (K2) must be together with the shift lever in Neutral. (14) is one of the mounting screws.

Shift Linkage Adjustment

The function of this adjustment is to make sure that the transmission is fully engaged in each shift position. If this is not done, the transmission may be only partially engaged in a range position. This would result in severe damage due to clutch slippage.

1. Place the selector lever in Park.
2. Loosen the cable clamping nut at the transmission end.
3. Press the selector lever on the transmission back to the stop.

When adjusting the automatic transmission linkage, the selector lever (3) should be pushed back to the stop with the clamping nut (2) loose so that the cable (1) is free to move. 30-104 is a special tool used to push the selector lever back; it is not necessary.

4. Tighten the clamping nut.
5. Start the engine and move the selector lever toward Drive. The engine speed must decrease before the lever reaches Drive. Move the selector lever toward Reverse. The engine speed must also fall off before the lever reaches Reverse.
6. If the lever is adjusted correctly, the distance from Neutral to Drive and from Neutral to Reverse must be equal. If the distances vary, repeat the adjustment.

Vacuum Modulator Adjustment

The vacuum modulator, on the rear of the transmission, regulates the firmness and timing of shifts in relation to speed and throttle opening. A leaking modulator will result in transmission fluid being sucked into the engine through the vacuum modulator and burned. This will produce a smoky exhaust and a continually low transmission fluid level. The modulator must be adjusted any time it, or its seal, has been replaced. This adjustment is also necessary if the gearshift timing is incorrect.

1. Disconnect and plug the vacuum hose at the modulator.
2. Remove the test plug from the right side of the transmission. Connect a pressure gauge with a scale up to 150 psi.
3. Place the selector lever in Neutral and idle the engine at 1,000 rpm. Adjust the modulator until the gauge shows 48.4 psi. Stop the engine.

The two (Bs) show where the test gauge is to be connected.

4. Remove the gauge and replace the plug and vacuum line.
5. The transmission should upshift with wide open throttle from First to Second gear at 19—21 mph, and from Second to Third at 54—58 mph.

Band Adjustments

Second Gear Band

1. Loosen the locknut.
2. Tighten the adjusting screw to 87 in. lbs.
3. Loosen the adjusting screw and retighten to 44 in. lbs.
4. Turn the adjusting screw out 1¾–2 turns.
5. Tighten the locknut.

Second gear brake band adjusting screw and locknut (66) and (67). First gear brake band adjusting screw and locknut (60 and (67).

First Gear Band

1. Loosen the locknut.
2. Tighten the adjusting screw to 87 in. lbs.
3. Loosen the adjusting screw and retighten to 44 in. lbs.
4. Turn the adjusting screw out 3¼–3¾ turns.
5. Tighten the locknut.

TRANSAXLE

The transmission and differential are combined in a transaxle. On models with manual transmission, the transmission and differential share a common lubricant supply. No transaxle overhaul procedures are given here due to the extensive specialized tools, knowledge, and procedures required. The final drive ratio is 3.89:1 (3.91 with automatic). All 1973 models have a 4.11:1 ratio. With the overdrive fourth gear used, the actual final drive ratio in fourth gear is 3.63 for the Super 90 and 3.76 (3.99 in 1973) for the 100, 100 LS, and 100 GL.

Removal and Installation

The transaxle is removed from the car in unit with the engine. See "Engine Removal and Installation" for details. On the automatic, it is possible to remove the transaxle only, leaving the engine in place. See "Automatic Transmission Removal and Installation" for details.

DRIVE AXLES

Each front wheel drive axle shaft has

two Rzeppa constant velocity joints. These joints can handle lateral movement caused by suspension travel, as well as steering movements.

Driveshafts

Removal and Installation

The steering knuckles must be removed along with the shafts.

1. Support the vehicle and remove the wheels. Let the front suspension hang free.
2. Have an assistant hold the brakes. Unbolt the driveshaft from the transmission stub axle and brake disc. There should be an insulator between the driveshaft and brake disc.
3. Remove the cotter pin and the castellated nut from the steering tie-rod end. Press out the tie-rod end from the steering knuckle arm. A small puller or press is required to free the tie-rod end.
4. Remove the two steering knuckle mounting bolts.
5. Remove the steering knuckle and driveshaft assembly.

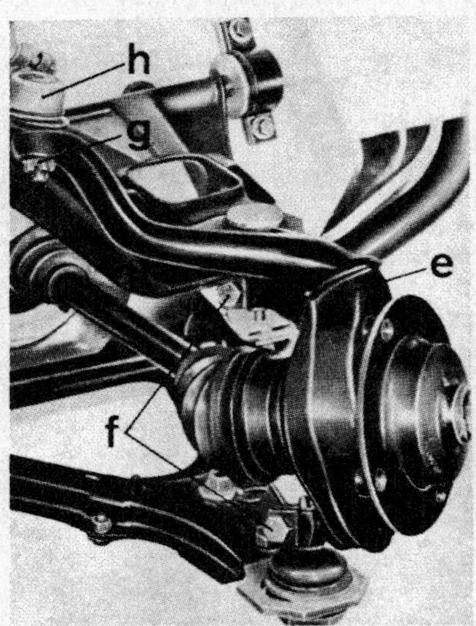

The castellated nut (g) and the cotter pin must be removed before pulling out the tie-rod end (h) from the steering knuckle (e). (f) indicates the steering knuckle mounting bolts.

6. Reverse the procedure for installation. Torques are:

Fastener	Torque (ft lbs)
Driveshaft to stub axle	77
Steering knuckle mounting bolts	34
Tie-Rod end	26

7. Check the wheel alignment.

Disassembly

This operation requires the use of a press or puller setup. It is necessary in order to replace the rubber boots.

1. Clamp the steering knuckle in a vise.
2. Remove the cotter pin. Unscrew the castellated nut and reverse it on the threads to protect them from damage.
3. Press the driveshaft from the steering knuckle. Steps 4–8 cover steering knuckle service.
4. Press out the wheel hub from the steering knuckle.
5. Remove the spacer, Nilos ring, and ball bearing inner race.
6. Drive the outer ball bearing race from the knuckle. Remove the internal snap-rings, using snap-ring pliers, and press out the second ball bearing outer race.
7. Replace the snap-rings. Press in the outer races. Fill the space between the races with high melting point wheel bearing grease.
8. Place the spacer and Nilos ring in the wheel hub. Press on the ball bearing inner race and install a new spacer bushing. Place the hub in the steering knuckle and press in the second ball bearing inner race.

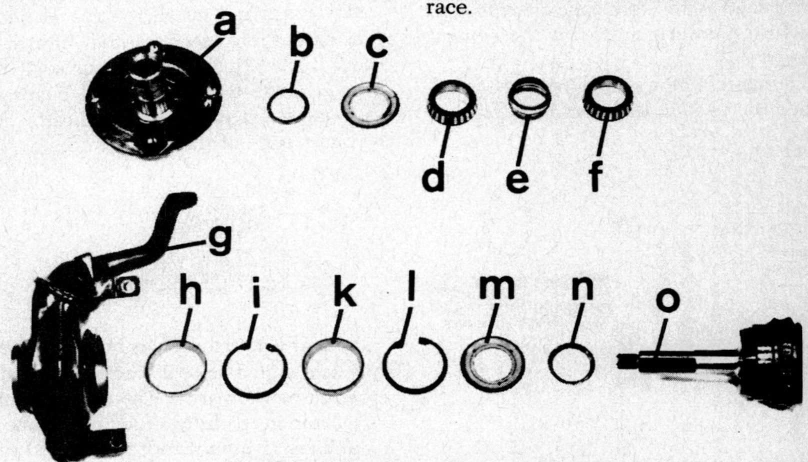

Steering knuckle and wheel hub assembly

(a)—Wheel hub
(b)—Spacer
(c)—Nilos ring
(d)—Ball bearing inner race
(e)—Spacer bushing
(f)—Ball bearing inner race
(g)—Right steering knuckle
(h)—Ball bearing outer race
(i)—Snap-ring
(k)—Outer ball bearing race
(l)—Snap-ring
(m)—Nilos ring
(n)—Spacer
(o)—Driveshaft

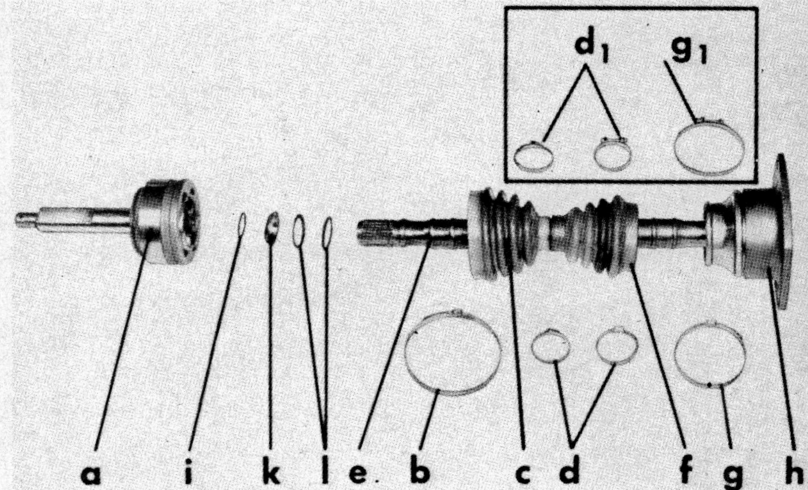

Driveshaft assembly

(a)—Outer driveshaft with Rzeppa joint
(b)—Clamp
(c)—Rubber boot
(d)—Clamps
(d_1)—Clamps
(e)—Inner driveshaft
(f)—Rubber boat
(g)—Clamp
(G_1)—Clamp
(h)—Rzeppa joint with flange
(i)—Snap-ring
(k)—Pressure ring
(l)—Disc springs

9. Remove both rubber boot clamps and slide the boots off the joints.

10. Clamp the inner driveshaft in a vise. Spread the snap-ring in the joint and have an assistant hit the outer end of the shaft with a soft hammer. A "powerful" blow is required.

11. Drive the joint housing off the inner shaft, using the soft hammer.

12. Pull off the rubber boots.

13. Clean the joint with alcohol and air dry.

14. Install new rubber boots.

15. Place two new disc springs on the inner shaft with their concave side out. Install a pressure ring with the convex side out.

16. Place a new snap-ring in the joint. Place the ends in the machined groove.

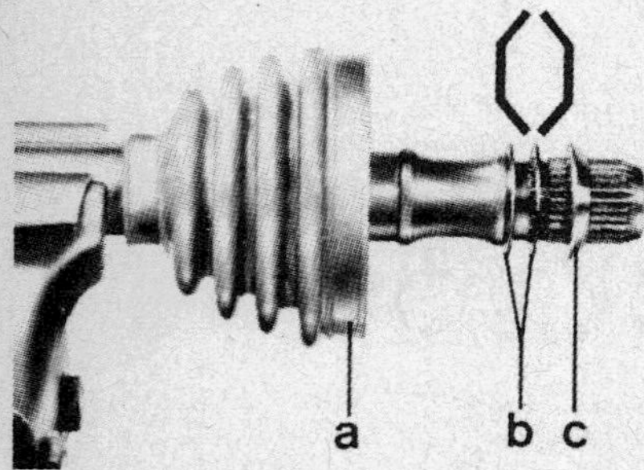

Installation of disc springs and pressure ring on inner drive shaft.
(a)—Outer rubber boot
(b)—Disc springs
(c)—Pressure ring

17. Slide the joint onto the inner shaft, so that the snap-ring begins to go into place. Drive the joint into place, hitting the outer end of the driveshaft with a soft hammer. The snap-ring should snap into place. The outer end of the shaft may also be pounded on with a wooden block.

18. Fill each joint with 60 cc of Molykote® grease or its equivalent.

19. Put the rubber boots in place. Install the boot clamps, making sure that the free ends trail in the normal direction of rotation.

20. Grease and install the spacer and Nilos ring. Press the driveshaft into the wheel hub. Adjust the hub nut so that there is 0.002–0.003 in. wheel bearing play, measured with a dial indicator at the outer edge of the wheel hub.

REAR SUSPENSION

The rear axle assembly is bolted to the body as a unit. The rear axle is attached to two suspension arms. The torsion bars are located in the fully sealed cross tube. A stabilizer (Panhard rod) is attached to the rear axle tube. In case of repairs, the rear axle may be removed with or without the cross tube.

NOTE: *A jack must never be placed under the axle tube. A jack can be placed under the cross tube safely.*

Rear Axle

Removal and Installation

Without Cross Tube

1. Depress the brake pedal approximately 1.2 in. and hold the pedal in this position to close the compensating bore in the brake master cylinder.

2. Remove both shock absorbers.

3. Raise and support the vehicle and remove the rear wheels. Support the axle tube.

4. Disconnect the handbrake cable. Push out the protective sleeve on either side of the cable. Remove the rubber boot and pull the handbrake cable out. Pull the cable down through the slot in the bracket.

5. Disconnect the brake lines.

6. Remove the handbrake cable from the suspension arms by bending open the retaining clamps.

7. Remove the transverse stabilizer bar.

8. Unbolt the right and left suspension arms.

9. Lift the rear axle from the suspension arms.

Rear suspension components

(a)—Brake drum and wheel hub
(b)—Brake assembly
(c)—Stop pad
(d)—Shock absorber
(e)—Suspension arm
(f)—Handbrake cable
(g)—Brake line
(h)—Transverse (panhard) rod
(i)—Axle tube
(k)—Stabilizer
(l)—Cross tube
(m)—Torsion bar
(n)—Mounting tube
(o)—Torsion bar
(p)—Handbrake adjustment
(r)—Stop pad
(s)—Shock absorber
(t)—Rubber bearing
(u)—Wheel cylinder
(v)—Rear axle, outer
(w)—Brake drum and wheel hub
(x)—Grease cap
(y)—Mounting bolt
(z)—Mounting bolt

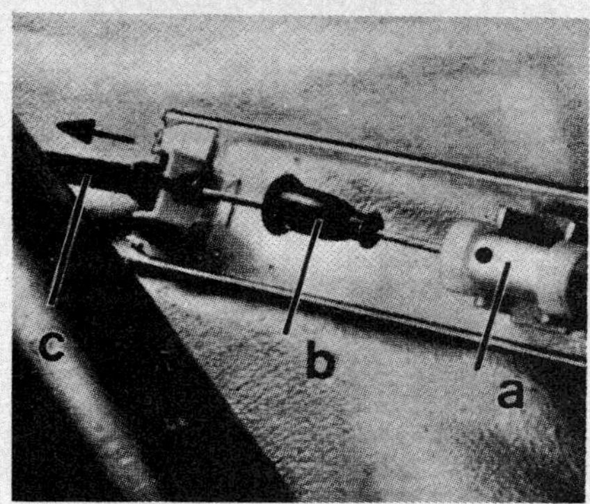

Handbrake cable attachment. The protective sleeve (a) must be pulled out and the rubber boot (b) pulled back, so that the cable (c) can be pulled out in the direction of the arrow.

10. Installation is the reverse of removal. Torques are:

Fastener	Torque (ft lbs)
Suspension arms to axle	27-34
Panhard rod to axle	27-34

With Cross Tube

It is not advisable to remove the cross tube or complete rear axle, since a special centering gauge is required for proper installation of the cross tube.

Wheel Bearings and Stub Axles

Removal and Installation

1. Depress the brake pedal approximately 1.2 in. and hold it in that position to close the master cylinder compensating bore.
2. Detach the brake lines on both sides and plug the lines.
3. Pry off the grease cap and remove the cotter pin, castellated nut, and washer. Remove the wheel and brake drum.
4. Remove the bearing inner race from the brake drum.
5. Carefully (the spring can fly out) pry out the brake shoe retaining spring. Remove the brake shoes complete with pressure rod and spring, bottom bracket first. Disconnect the handbrake cable.
6. Unbolt the rear stub axle and brake backing plate.
7. Pry out the shaft seal (which should be replaced) and remove the inner race of the roller bearing.
8. Drive the roller bearing outer race from the brake drum. Remove the snap-ring and drive the outer roller bearing race from the drum.
9. Replace the snap-ring and drive in the outer race of the outer roller bearing.
10. Press in the outer race of the inner roller bearing.
11. Lightly coat the inner race of the inner roller bearing with wheel bearing grease and push it into the outer race.
12. Drive a new shaft seal into position (the open side of the seal should face the roller bearing). Fill the space between the two roller bearings with approximately 10 oz of wheel bearing grease.
13. Coat the inner race of the outer roller bearing with grease and install the inner race.
14. Replace the stub axle and brake backing plate with the groove in the stub axle facing upward. Bolt torque is 14–15 ft lbs for 8G bolts and 22 ft lbs for 10K bolts.
15. Assemble the brake shoes, connect the handbrake cable, and insert the brake shoes on the bottom bracket first, then at the wheel cylinder. Replace the retaining spring.
16. Replace the brake drum and wheel, special washer, nut, castellated nut, and a new cotter pin. Wheel bearing play should be 0.001–0.002 in. It can be measured with a dial indicator. Fill the dust cap with approximately 10 oz of wheel bearing grease and replace it.

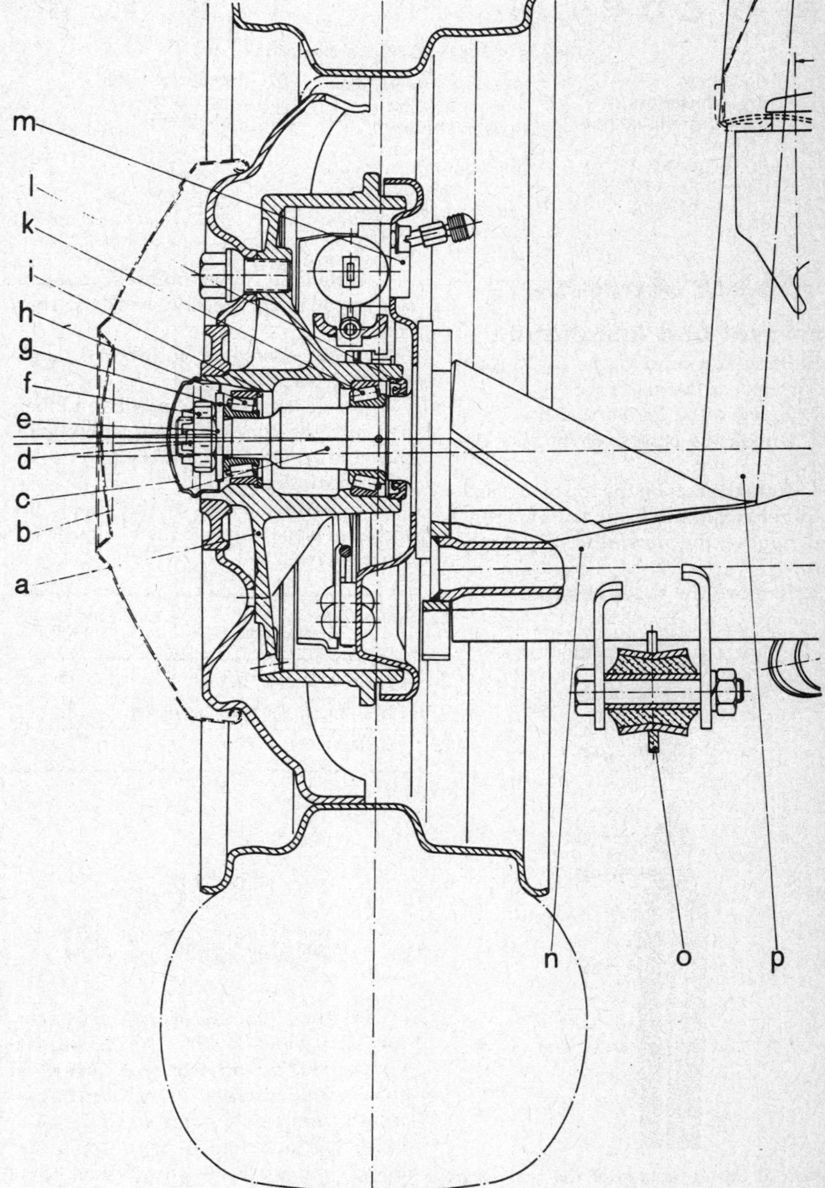

Rear wheel bearing and stub axle assembly

(a)—Brake drum
(b)—Rear stub axle
(c)—Cap
(d)—Cotter pin
(e)—Nut
(f)—Castellated nut
(g)—Washer
(h)—Roller bearing
(i)—Snap-ring
(k)—Roller bearing
(l)—Shaft seal
(m)—Brake assembly
(n)—Rear axle
(o)—Suspension arm
(p)—Shock absorber

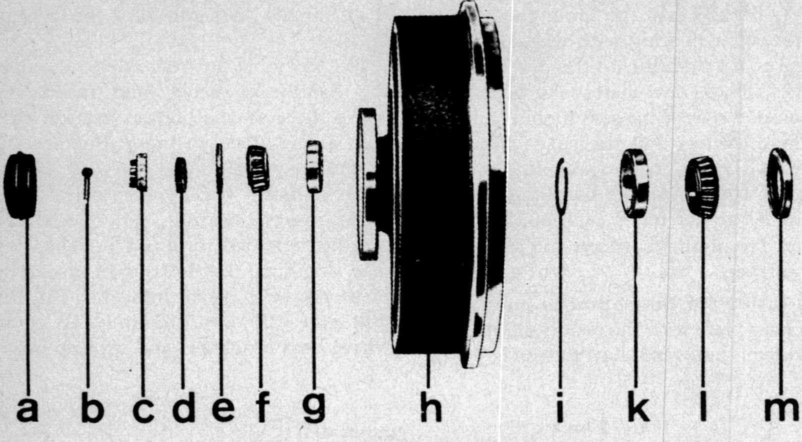

Details of Super 90 front suspension

(a)—Cap
(b)—Cotter pin
(c)—Castellated nut
(d)—Nut
(e)—Washer
(f)—Inner race roller bearing
(g)—Outer race roller bearing
(h)—Brake drum
(i)—Snap-ring
(k)—Outer race roller bearing
(l)—Inner race roller bearing
(m)—Shaft seal

Shock Absorbers

Removal and Installation

1. Raise and support the car. Support the weight of the axle tube.
2. Remove the Panhard rod.
3. Unbolt the bottom of the shock absorber.
4. Hold the flats on the top of the shock absorber rod in the trunk with a wrench and remove the nuts, disc, and rubber pad.
5. Remove the shock absorber.

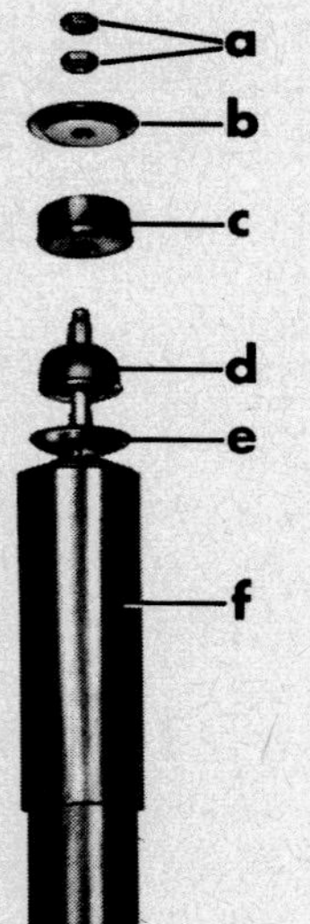

Details of the upper end of the rear shock absorbers, parts (a-c) are installed inside the trunk.

(a)—Nuts
(b)—Disc, edge up
(c)—Rubber pad, curved side up
(d)—Rubber pad, curved side up
(e)—Disc, part of shock absorber
(f)—Shock absorber

6. Install the rubber bumper, rounded side up, on top of the new shock absorber rod.
7. Install the shock absorber through the floor pan.
8. Inside the trunk, install a rubber pad with the curved side up, a disc with the edge up, and the nuts. Use the second nut to lock the first.
9. Bolt the bottom of the shock absorber in place. Replace the Panhard rod. Torques are:

Fastener	Bolt Torque (ft lbs)
Upper shock absorber nut	18
Lower shock absorber mounting	32
Panhard rod	27-34

FRONT SUSPENSION

The Super 90 front suspension uses torsion bars, while the 100, 100 LS, and 100 GL use McPherson strut type spring and shock absorber units. Otherwise the two front suspension systems are quite similar, being independent with upper and lower control arms (wishbones) and having a cross-chassis stabilizer bar connecting the two lower control arms.

NOTE: *Exercise extreme caution when working with the front suspension. Coil springs and torsion bars are under great tension and can cause severe injury if released suddenly.*

Shock Absorbers

Removal and Installation—Super 90

This operation is best performed with the vehicle resting on its wheels.

1. Unbolt the shock absorber from the lower control arm.
2. Inside the engine compartment, hold the flats on top of the shock absorber rod with a wrench. Remove the locknut and nut. Remove the disc and upper mounting pad.
3. Remove the shock absorber.
4. Install the lower mounting pad (it has deep cavities on both sides) and disc on the new shock absorber rod.
5. Install the shock absorber from underneath.
6. Inside the engine compartment, install the upper mounting pad and disc. Install the nuts, torquing the first to 30 ft lbs, and using the second to lock the first.
7. Bolt the bottom of the shock absorber in place. Torque the bolt to 34 ft lbs.

McPherson Strut

Removal and Installation—100, 100 LS, 100 GL

1. Support the vehicle and remove the wheels. Let the front suspension hang free.
2. Unbolt the strut unit from the upper control arm.
3. Inside the engine compartment, remove the three nuts which hold the top of the strut unit. Do not remove the nut and locknut in the center.
4. Pull the unit down and pull the top out through the wheel opening. It may be necessary to pull the steering knuckle down a bit for clearance.
5. It is not recommended that the strut unit be disassembled unless the necessary special tools to do this safely are available. The units should be serviced in pairs to maintain equal shock absorbing qualities and ride height. Spacers are available to correct ride height. The strut unit must be disassembled to install these. The proper ride height with standard size tires is 8.2–8.7 in., measured from the floor to the 0.32 in. diameter hole in the front bearing shell of the lower control arm inner pivot.
6. When replacing the strut unit, torque the three bolts and nuts, which hold the upper end of the strut to the body, to 13–15 ft lbs, and the lower end to 62–69 ft lbs. The torque for the shock absorber to spring retaining nut is 18–26 ft lbs.
7. Check the wheel alignment.

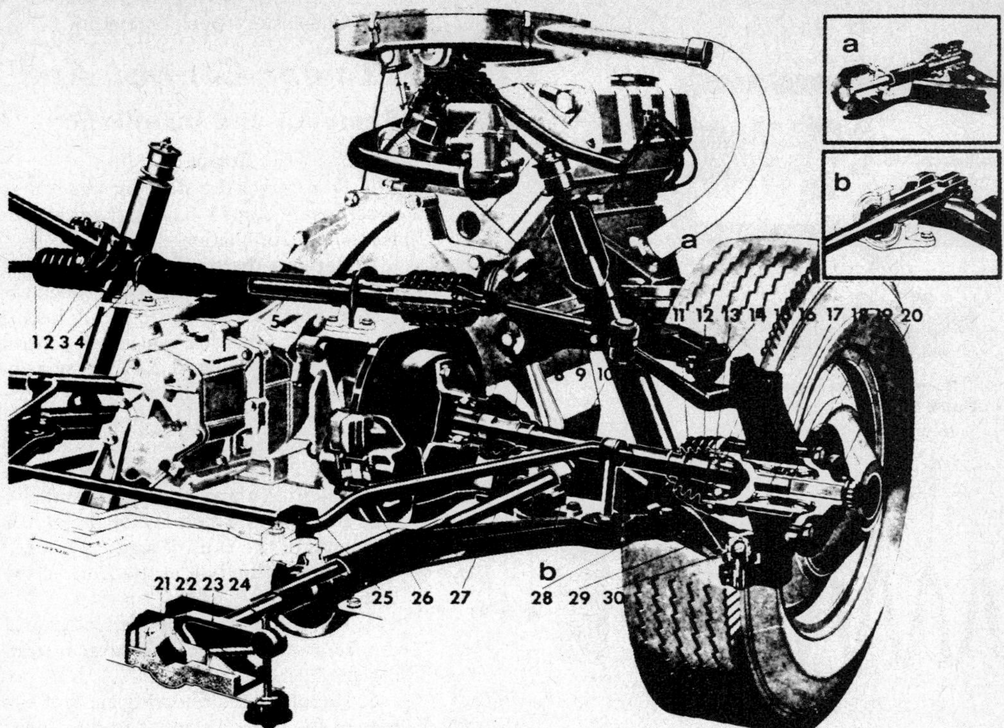

1. Steering column
2. Hardy disc
3. Steering gear
4. Bracket
5. Rack
6. Rzeppa joint, inner
7. Boot, inner
8. Tie-rod
9. Shock absorber
10. Driveshaft
11. Boot, outer
12. Rzeppa joint, outer
13. Springs
14. Wishbone joint
15. Fit ring
16. Snap-ring
17. Steering knuckle
18. Outer drive joint
19. Spacer
20. Hub
21. Pressure piece
22. Hex. head screw
23. Adjustment level
24. Strut bearing assembly
25. Rubber bearing
26. Stabilizer
27. Front spring
28. Stabilizer strut
29. Wishbone
30. Support joint assembly

(a) Wishbone bearing, upper
(b) Stabilizer strut bearing

Details of 100, 100 LS, and 100 GL front suspension

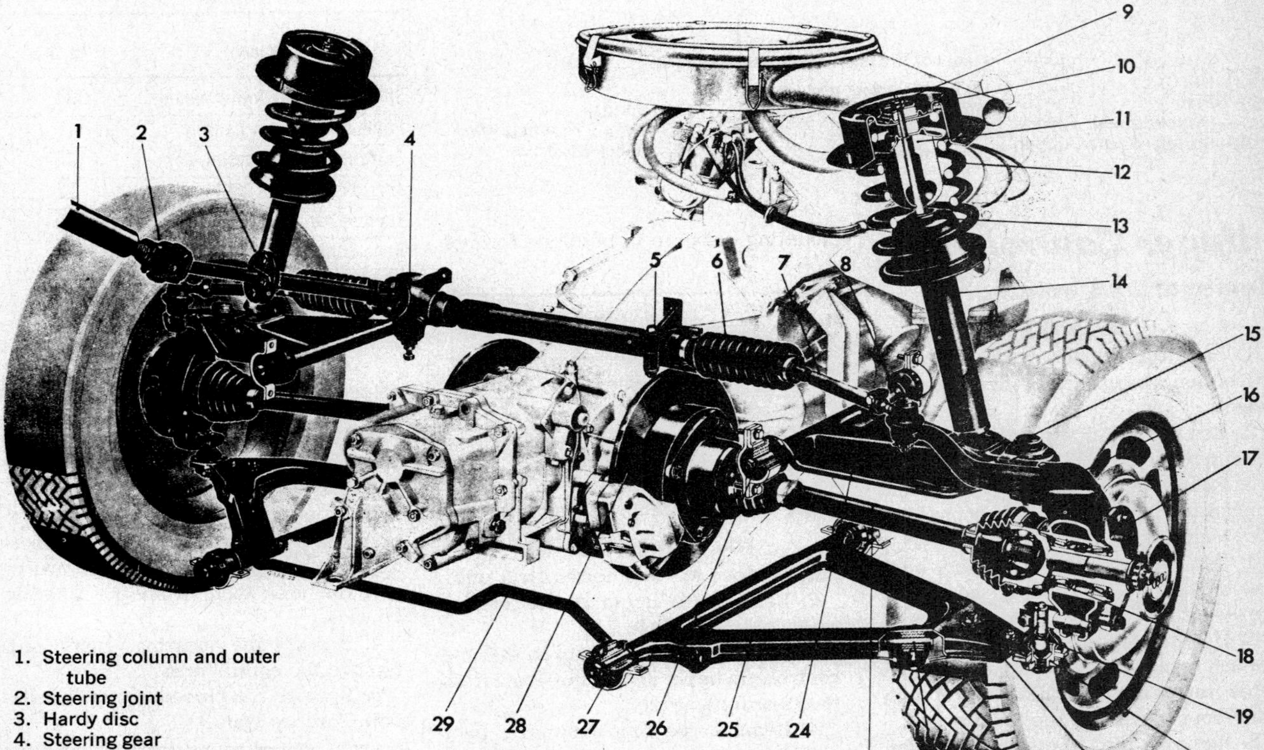

Overhead view of the Super 90 upper control arm

1. Steering column and outer tube
2. Steering joint
3. Hardy disc
4. Steering gear
5. Mount
6. Boot
7. Tie-rod
8. Front ball and socket joint
9. Spring retainer, upper
10. Rubber ring
11. Stop pad
12. Spring
13. Spring retainer, lower
14. Shock absorber
15. Support joint
16. Steering knuckle and tie-rod arm
17. Wheel hub
18. Rzeppa joint
19. Wishbone joint
20. Caster adjustment
21. Camber adjustment
22. Stabilizer bearing
23. Driveshaft
24. Wishbone, upper
25. Wishbone, lower
26. Wishbone bearing, upper
27. Wishbone bearing, lower
28. Brake disc
29. Stabilizer

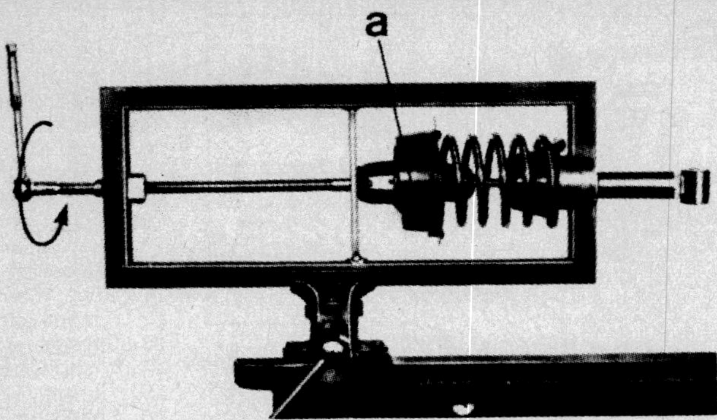

This special tool is required to dismantle the front suspension strut unit (a).

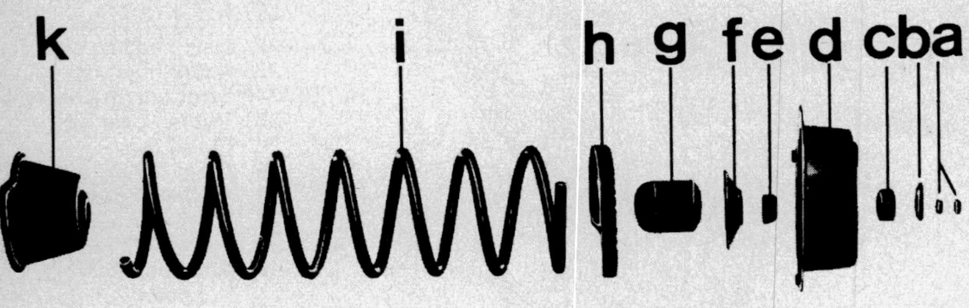

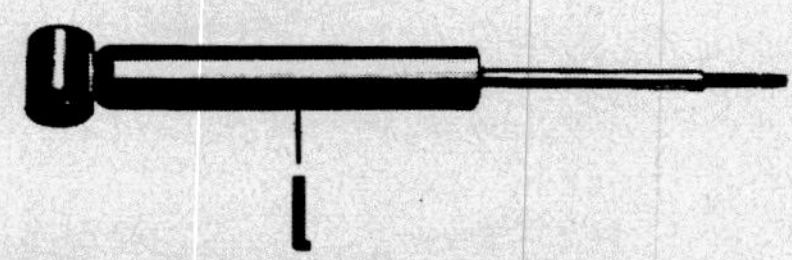

Exploded view of the front suspension strut unit

(a)—Nut
(b)—Plate
(c)—Mounting pad, upper
(d)—Spring retainer, upper
(e)—Mounting pad, lower
(f)—Plate
(g)—Stop pad
(h)—Ring
(i)—Spring
(k)—Spring retainer, lower
(l)—Shock absorber

Upper Control Arm

Removal and Installation

Super 90

1. Raise the vehicle and let the front suspension hang free. Remove the wheels.

2. Remove the upper control arm-to-steering knuckle bolt.

3. Pull the control arm up so that the control arm upper joint comes loose from the steering knuckle.

4. Remove the two nuts and bolts which hold the outer end of the control arm together.

5. Hold the long control arm inner pivot bolt in place and loosen the nut about three turns. Remove the control arm joint from the end of the control arm.

6. Remove the front crossmember. Remove the nuts from the pivot bracket bolts from inside the engine compartment.

7. Pull the pivot bracket away from the body. It is located by two pins.

8. Remove the bolts and take the control arm off around the shock absorber.

9. Reverse the procedure for installation. Make sure that the pivot bracket mounting bolts are in position. Torques are:

Fastener	Torque (ft lbs)
Steering knuckle mounting bolt	34
Pivot bracket bolts	34
Control arm inner pivot bolt nut	54

10. Check the wheel alignment.

100, 100 LS, 100 GL

1. Remove the McPherson strut unit.

2. Remove the upper control arm to steering knuckle bolt.

3. Pull the control arm up so that the control arm upper joint comes loose from the steering knuckle.

4. Remove the four mounting bolts and the control arm.

5. Reverse the procedure for installation. Torques are:

Fastener	Torque (ft lbs)
Steering knuckle mounting bolt	34
Control arm to body	14-18

6. Check the wheel alignment.

Lower Control Arm

Removal and Installation

Super 90

1. Disconnect the steering knuckle as described in Steps 1–5 of "Driveshaft Removal and Installation."

2. Remove the stabilizer bar.

3. Detach the bottom of the shock absorber. This is easier if the spring load is temporarily taken off the lower control arm by prying upward. Let the suspension hang free after this is done.

4. Loosen the bolt at the front of the torsion bar until only 4–5 threads are still engaged. This can be seen by lifting the floor covering above the crossmember.

5. Remove the bolt which holds the two parts of the control arm together.

6. Remove the bolt at the front of the torsion bar.

7. Pull the front of the control arm off the front of the torsion bar after unbolting the bearing.

8. Unbolt the rear bearing and pull the rear of the control arm off to the front.

9. Reverse the procedure for installation. Torques are:

Fastener	Torque (ft lbs)
Shock absorber lower mount	34
Front control arm bearing	18
Control arm connecting bolt	26
Torsion bar front bolt	22
Torsion bar front bolt locknut	29
Rear control arm bearing	18
Stabilizer bar ends	26

10. Check the wheel alignment.

100, 100 LS, 100 GL

1. Raise the vehicle and let the suspension hang free. Remove the wheels.

2. Remove the stabilizer bar. It may be necessary to move the exhaust pipe.

3. Support the lower control arm. Remove the lower control arm to steering knuckle bolt. Let the arm down to pull the joint loose from the steering knuckle.

4. Unbolt the bearing bolts and remove the control arm.

5. Reverse the procedure for installation. Torques are:

Fastener	Torque (ft lbs)
Stabilizer	14-18
Steering knuckle mounting bolt	34
Control arm pivot bearings, front	26-34
Control arm pivot bearings, rear	14-18

6. Check the wheel alignment.

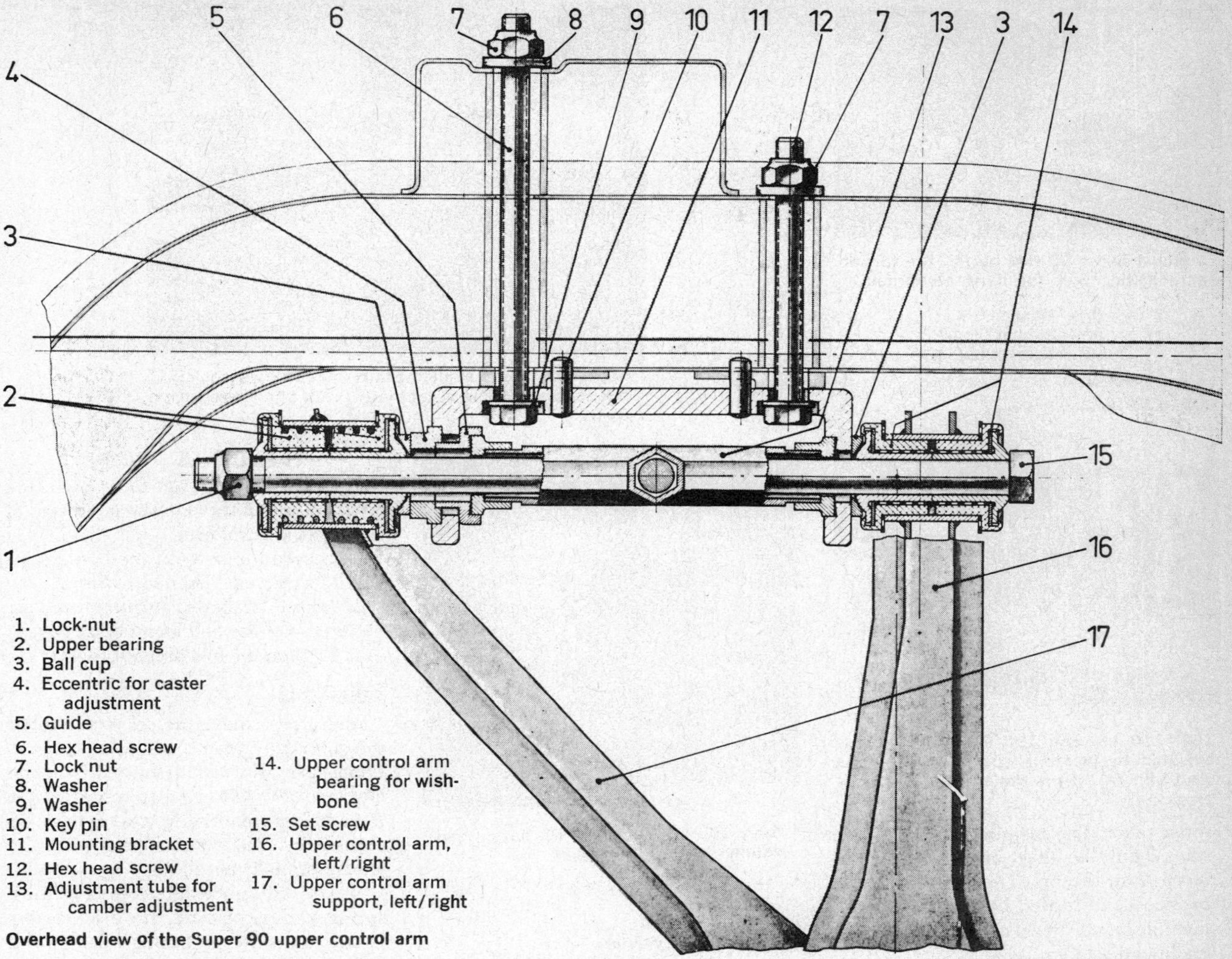

1. Lock-nut
2. Upper bearing
3. Ball cup
4. Eccentric for caster adjustment
5. Guide
6. Hex head screw
7. Lock nut
8. Washer
9. Washer
10. Key pin
11. Mounting bracket
12. Hex head screw
13. Adjustment tube for camber adjustment
14. Upper control arm bearing for wishbone
15. Set screw
16. Upper control arm, left/right
17. Upper control arm support, left/right

Overhead view of the Super 90 upper control arm

Super 90 lower control arm

(a)—Torsion bar front bolt locknut
(b)—Torsion bar front bolt
(d)—Torsion bar
(c)—Reinforcement bracket
(e)—Control arm connecting bolt
(f)—Front cover arm bearing

Adjustments

Ride Height

Super 90

Rear ride height is not readily adjustable. Front ride height is measured from the floor to the underside of the lower control arm inner bearing. With standard size tires it should be 6.9–8.3 in. for the sedan and 6.2–7.6 in. for the station wagon. The car should be bounced and settled before making the measurement. To adjust the ride height turn the rear torsion bar adjusting bolt. The measurements on both sides should be alike, or different by no more than 0.4 in.

100, 100 LS, 100 GL

The suspension strut units must be removed and be disassembled and new springs or spacers installed to adjust ride height on these models. It is not recommended that the strut unit be disassembled unless the necessary special tools to do this safely are available. The proper front ride height with standard size tires is 8.2–8.7 in., measured from the floor to the 0.32 in. diameter hole in the front bearing shell of the lower control arm

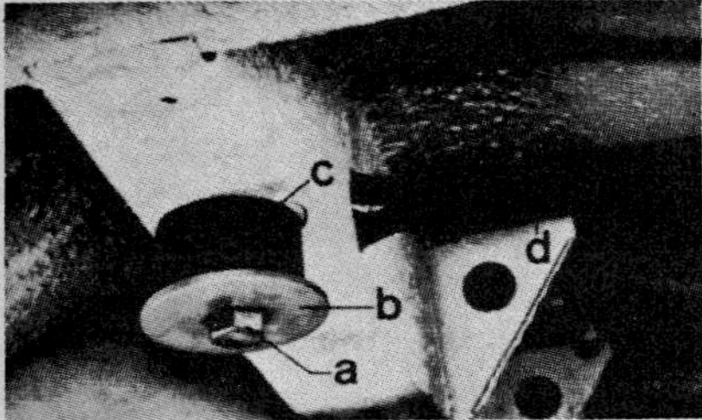

To adjust Super 90 ride height, the torsion bar adjusting bolt (a) must be turned.

(b)—Washer
(c)—Rubber block
(d)—Torsion bar

100, 100 LS, and 100 GL ride height is adjusted by inserting spacers (D) on the strut unit (A). (S) is the special strut compressor.

inner pivot. The measurements on both sides should be alike, or different by no more than 0.3 in. The car should be bounced and settled before making the measurement. Rear ride height is not readily adjustable.

Wheel Alignment

Before checking wheel alignment, tire pressures should be brought up to specifications and the front ride height checked. The car should be bounced and settled before each alignment check or adjustment. The adjustments should be made in this order: caster, camber, toe-out.

Caster

Super 90

1. Loosen the front nut on the upper control arm inner pivot bolt.
2 Using a thin wrench in front of the upper control arm mounting bracket, adjust the caster angle.
3. Leave the nut loose for the camber adjustment. Otherwise, tighten it to 54 ft lbs while holding the bolt head.

100, 100 LS, 100 GL

1. Loosen the large locknut at the bottom of the outer end of the lower control arm.
2. Turn the eccentric bolt, which passes through the locknut, to adjust caster.

Super 90 caster adjustment is made by loosening nut (b) and turning eccentric (a) with a thin wrench, SW32.

100, 100 LS, and 100 GL caster and camber adjustment points.

(a)—Camber adjustment
(b)—Nut
(c)—Bolt
(d)—Locknut
(e)—Caster adjustment

Camber

Camber is checked with the wheels straight ahead.

Super 90

1. Loosen the front nut on the upper control arm inner pivot bolt.
2. Turn the adjustment tube in the center of the upper control arm mounting bracket to adjust camber.
3. Hold the bolt head and tighten the nut to 54 ft lbs.

Super 90 camber adjustment is made by loosening nut (b) and turning the adjustment tube (a) with a wrench, SW19.

100, 100 LS, 100 GL

1. Loosen the nut (on the top) on the bolt that passes through the outer end of the lower control arm.
2. Loosen the bolt (on the bottom) inboard of the nut loosened in Step 1.
3. Adjust camber by turning the large nut on top of the bolt loosened in Step 2.
4. Tighten the bolt and nut to 32 ft lbs.

Toe-Out

Audi front wheels are set with a slight toe-out, rather than toe-in as on conventional cars. Most front-wheel drive vehicles are set with toe-out to conteract the tendency of the driving wheels to toe-in excessively. Toe-out is checked with the wheels straight ahead.

1. Toe-out can be determined by measuring and comparing the distance between the center of the tire tread, front and rear, or by measuring and comparing the distance between the inside edges of the wheel rims, front and rear. If the wheel rims are used as the basis of measurement, the car should be rolled forward slightly and a second set of measurements taken. This avoids any error induced by bent wheels. If at all possible, a toe-in gauge should be used; it will give a much more accurate measurement.
2. Toe-out is adjusted at the steering tie-rods at either end of the steering rack. Loosen the clamp. Loosen the clip for the rubber boot at the end of the rack and slide the boot back.

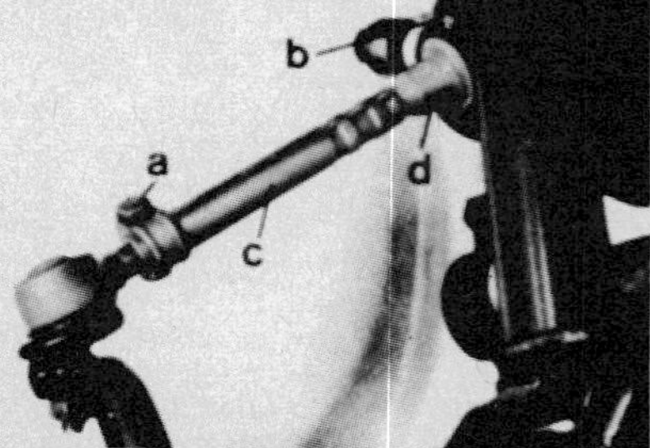

Toe-out is adjusted by loosening nut (a) on each steering tie-rod (c) and pushing back the rubber boot and clamp (b) in order to use a wrench on the flats (d).

3. Turn both rods to lengthen or shorten them an equal amount. If the tie-rods are not adjusted equally, the steering wheel will be crooked and the turning arcs of the front wheels will be changed.

4. Tighten the clamps and replace the boots.

STEERING

The steering is a rack and pinion type. The steering geometry is designed to give a variable ratio effect, giving faster steering response as the steering wheel is turned toward either right or left lock. The steering column and linkage is arranged so as to break away and telescope safely in an accident, rather than penetrating into the passenger compartment.

Steering Wheel

Removal and Installation

1. Center the wheel.

2. Pry off the wheel pad (horn button). The Super 90 has two small holes in the back of the wheel. A small screwdriver may be inserted to push the pad off.

3. Unbolt and remove the wheel. A steering wheel puller should not be necessary.

4. On installation, torque the bolt to 36 ft lbs. Do not pound on the wheel, as the collapsible column may be damaged.

Turn Signal and Headlight Dimmer Switch Replacement

1. Remove the steering wheel.

2. Disconnect the battery ground cable.

3. Remove the wire from the horn contact ring. Remove the two screws and the horn contact ring.

4. Remove the screws which hold the column casing at the top and just below the instrument panel. The Super 90 has an additional screw in the top edge of the casing. It may be necessary, for access, to remove the padding from the underside of the instrument panel.

5. Remove the casing. Be careful to note the arrangement of any springs and washers removed from the top of the column.

6. The switch may now be disconnected, unscrewed, and removed. The wires are color coded for ease of replacement.

Ignition and Steering Lock Switch

Removal and Installation

To perform this operation, proceed with Steps 1–5 of "Turn Signal and Headlight Dimmer Switch Replacement". The lock switch is clamped to the steering column with special bolts whose heads shear off on installation. These must be drilled out in order to remove the switch. When replacing the unit, make sure that the lock tang is aligned with the slot in the steering column.

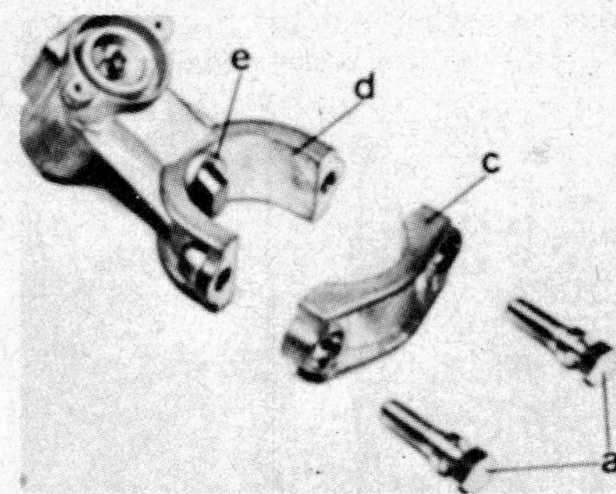

The ignition and steering lock switch is held in place by two bolts (a) whose heads shear on installation to deter theft.

(c)—Lower housing
(d)—Upper housing
(e)—Steering lock tang

Steering Gear

Removal and Installation

Super 90

1. Point the front wheels straight ahead. Loosen the bolt and open the clamp at the bottom of the steering column, inside the car.

2. Remove the four bolts and slide up the plate at the base of the steering column.

3. Bend open the lockplate and remove the coupling bolts.

4. Disconnect the ends of the steering tie-rods from the steering knuckles by removing the cotter pins and nuts and pressing out the tie-rod ends. A small puller or press is required to free the tie-rod ends.

5. Unbolt the support brackets from below.

6. Pry the brackets loose inside the engine compartment.

7. Pull the steering gear out to the left, after turning the coupling down.

8. On installation, center the steering gear and the steering wheel. Torques are:

Fastener	Torque (ft lbs)
Coupling bolts	11-15
Steering gear bracket bolts	13
Tie-rod ends	26

100, 100 LS, 100 GL

1. Point the front wheels straight ahead. Disconnect the steering column from the firewall.

2. Disconnect the steering shaft from the steering gear.

3. Disconnect the ends of the steering tie-rods from the steering knuckles by removing the cotter pins and nuts and pressing out the tie-rod ends. A small puller or press is required to free the tie-rod ends.

4. Unbolt the steering gear from the firewall. Slide the unit toward the right and pull it up and out through the engine compartment.

5. On installation, center the steering gear and the steering wheel. Torques are:

Fastener	Torque (ft lbs)
Steering gear to firewall	25
Tie-rod ends	26
Steering shaft to steering gear	18
Steering column to firewall	18

Steering Linkage

Tie-Rod Removal and Installation

1. Jack up the car and remove the wheels.

2. Disconnect the end of the steering tie-rod from the steering knuckle by removing the cotter pin and nut and pressing out the tie-rod end. A small puller or press is required to free the tie-rod end.

3. The steering gear boots can be replaced with no further disassembly at this point.

4. Loosen the clamp and slide the rubber boot as far back as possible.

5. Turn the steering all the way to the side being worked on. Do not force it against the stops.

6. Bend open the lockplate behind the knurled cylinder on the tie-rod. Unscrew the tie rod.

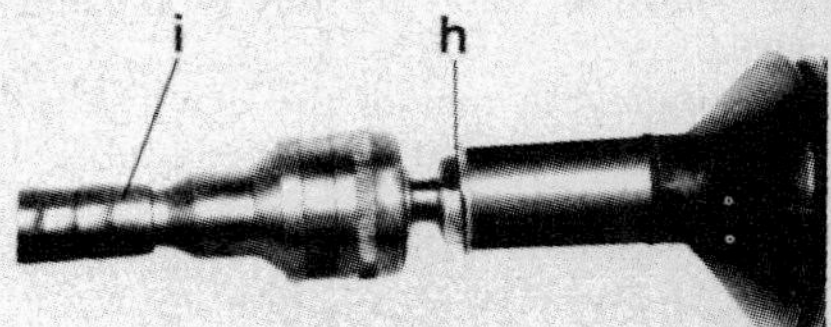

Nut (h) is loosened to remove the tie-rod (i) from the steering gear.

7. Reverse the procedure for installation. Adjust the new tie-rod to the same length as the old one. Torque the tie-rod to 51 ft lb, then set the lockplate. Tie-rod outer end torque is 26 ft lbs.

8. Check the toe-out.

BRAKE SYSTEMS

All models have dual circuit hydraulic brakes with front disc brakes and rear drum brakes. A vacuum operated power assist is standard equipment. On the 100,

100 LS, and 100 GL, some 1972, and all 1973 models have cooling air directed to the brake discs from the electric radiator fan. The fan is switched on by a thermal switch in the right brake caliper. 1973 models have a brake pad lining thickness warning light.

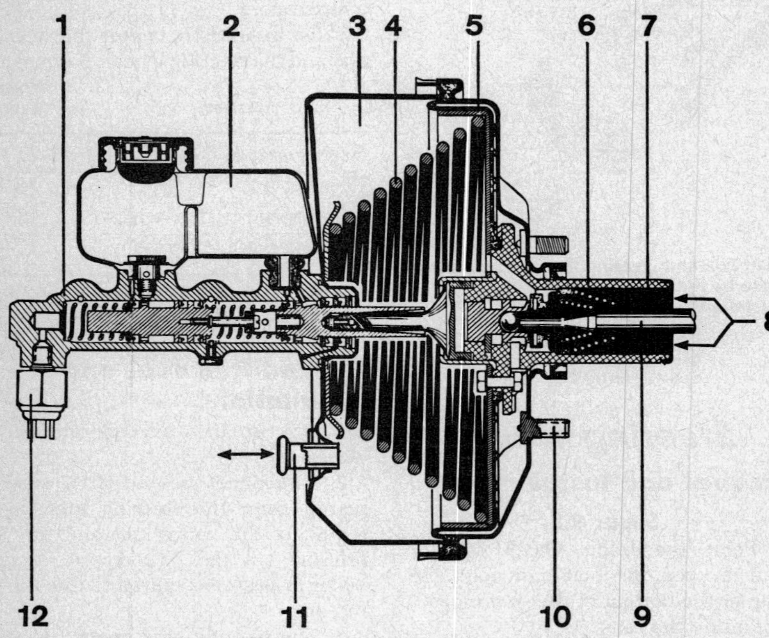

Cross-section of brake master cylinder and vacuum brake booster

1. Master cylinder
2. Brake fluid container
3. Vacuum cylinder
4. Spring
5. Diaphragm
6. Timing housing
7. Filter
8. Air intake
9. Pressure rod
10. Mounting bolts
11. Vacuum connection
12. Brake light switch

Adjustment

The front disc brakes are self-adjusting. The rear drum brakes must be adjusted periodically, or whenever free travel is one third or more of the total pedal travel.

1. Raise the rear of the car. Do not place a jack under the rear axle tube.
2. Block the front wheels and release the parking brake. Step on the brake pedal hard to center the linings.
3. Turn the front adjusting nut on the brake backing plate until the wheel can't be rotated forward by hand.

When adjusting the rear brakes, turn adjusting nuts (A) toward (a) to tighten and (b) to loosen.

4. Loosen the adjusting nut until the wheel can be turned freely without drag.
5. Repeat Steps 3 and 4 for the rear adjusting nut.
6. Repeat Steps 3, 4, and 5 for the other rear wheel.
7. Step on the brake pedal hard and make sure the wheels still rotate without drag.

HYDRAULIC SYSTEM

Master Cylinder

Removal and Installation

1. Have an assistant hold the brake pedal down about 1½ in. Disconnect the brake line nearest the firewall.
2. Hold a container under the fitting disconnected in Step 1 and have the assistant release the pedal. The contents of the reservoir will drain into the container. Discard the used fluid.
3. Disconnect the other brake line.
4. Disconnect the stoplight switch from the master cylinder.
5. Unbolt and remove the master cylinder from the power brake unit. Be careful not to lose the sealing ring between the two units.
6. Installation is the reverse of removal. Master cylinder bolt torque is 17 ft lbs. Fill and bleed the system. There should be a pedal free-play of 0.2 in. It can be adjusted on the linkage, inside the car.

Overhaul

1. Clean the outside of the master cylinder.
2. Remove the brake fluid reservoir, unscrew the brake light switch, remove the snap-ring and dismantle the unit. It will be necessary to partially unscrew the stop screw to remove the secondary piston.
3. All parts must be thoroughly cleaned in alcohol or clean brake fluid only. Dry the parts with compressed air and be sure that the compensating port is not plugged.
4. Visually inspect all components. Replace any that are suspect. Rubber boots and container plugs should always be replaced.
5. On assembly, lubricate all metal parts with clean brake fluid.
6. Preassemble and install the piston.
7. Be sure that the boots are installed correctly and are not damaged.
8. Check the pistons for ease of operation. If the pistons do not return quickly to the stop screw or disc, dismantle the master cylinder and lightly polish the cylinder surface.
9. Further assembly is the reverse of disassembly. Grease should not be applied to the pushrod, as it will swell the rubber boots.

System Bleeding

The hydraulic system must be bled whenever the pedal feels spongy, indicating that compressible air has entered the system. The system must also be bled whenever any component has been disconnected or there has been a leak.

1. Clean off the top of the master cylinder. Check that the fluid level in each reservoir is between the marks.
2. Attach a hose to the bleeder valve at the first wheel to be bled. Mechanics customarily start at the wheel farthest from the master cylinder and work closer. Pour a few inches of brake fluid into a clear container and stick the end of the tube below the surface.

   NOTE: *The tube and container of brake fluid are not absolutely necessary, but this is a very sloppy job without them.*

3. Open the bleed valve about ½ turn. Have a helper slowly depress the pedal. Close the valve just before the pedal reaches the end of its travel. Have the helper let the pedal back up.
4. Check the fluid level. If the reservoir runs dry, the procedure will have to be restarted from the beginning.
5. Repeat Step 3 until no more bubbles come out the hose.
6. Repeat the bleeding operation, Steps 3 to 5, at the other three wheels.

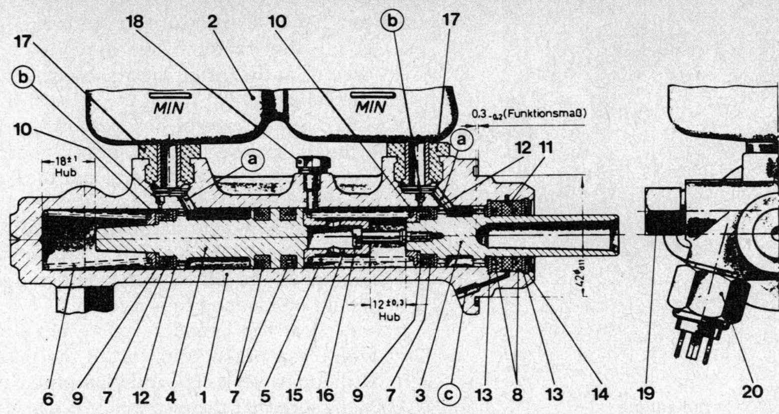

Cross-section of brake master cylinder

1. Master cylinder
2. Brake fluid container
3. Primary piston
4. Secondary piston
5. Primary spring
6. Secondary spring
7. Primary boot
8. Secondary boot
9. Support ring
10. Spring retainer
11. Intermediate ring
12. Filler disc
13. Stop disc
14. Snap-ring
15. Stop sleeve
16. Inner stop screw
17. Container plug
18. Outer stop screw
19. Pressure valve
20. Brake light switch

(a) Filling bore
(b) Compensating bore
(c) Air compensating bore

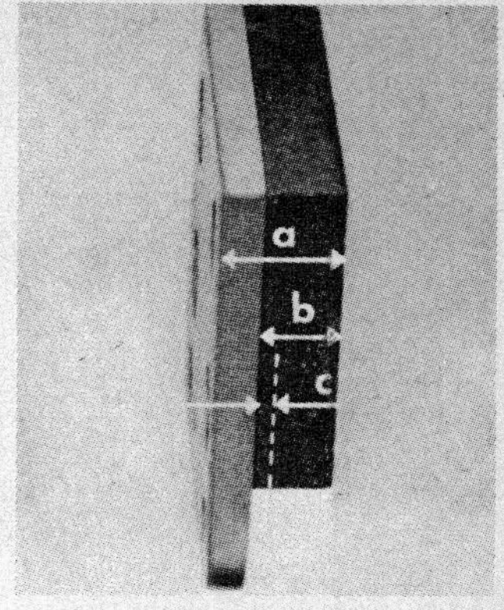

(a) is the thickness of the new pad and the backplate (b) is the thickness of the new pad, and (c) is the minimum safe pad thickness, 0.08 in.

(e) is the pad retaining pins and (f) is the cross spring.

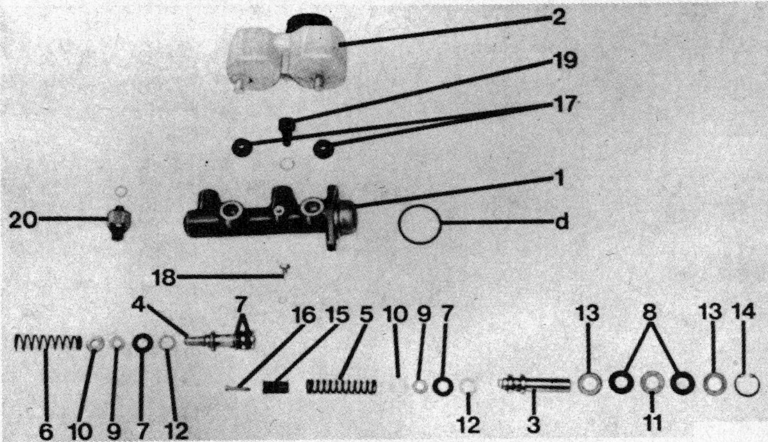

Exploded view of brake master cylinder

Some cars with automatic transmission have three bleeder screws on each front brake caliper. On these cars, the bleeding sequence should be: upper right front, upper left front, lower outer right front, lower inner right front, lower outer left front, lower inner left front, left rear, and right rear.

7. Check the master cylinder level again.

8. If repeated bleeding has no effect, there is an air leak, probably internally in the master cylinder or in one of the wheel cylinders.

FRONT DISC BRAKES

All models use the same type of two-piston front disc brakes, except for some automatic transmission models, primarily 1972, which use four-piston brakes. These four-piston units can be readily identified by the presence of three bleeder screws instead of the usual one. Procedures for the two-piston brakes may be adapted to the four-piston units.

Disc Brake Pads

Removal and Installation

Although the four front brake pads may wear unevenly, they may not be switched around to equalize wear. They must always be replaced in sets of four. Minimum permissible friction pad thickness is 0.08 in.

NOTE: *This is the factory recommendation. State inspection laws may not allow this much wear.*

1. Pull out the lock clips and remove the retaining pins. While doing this, hold the cross springs in place.

2. Remove the cross springs and pull the brake pads from the calipers. On 1973 models, disconnect the pad lining wear indicator leads.

3. To install new pads, drain off some of the brake fluid from the master cylinder, since pressing the pistons back to install pads will cause the brake fluid level to rise.

4. Press the pistons completely into the cylinder and check their alignment. They should be at an angle of 20°; if not they must be rotated. A gauge may be made up to check this.

5. Slide the pads into the caliper recess.

6. Replace the retaining spring and install the cross springs, retaining pins, and new lock clips.

7. Pump the brakes several times to position the pads.

8. Test the brakes, but do not make any panic stops. New brake pads must be "run-in" and no hard stops should be made with new pads for a distance of approximately 100 miles if possible.

Disc Brake Calipers

Removal and Installation

Super 90

The calipers are bolted to the transaxle housing.

1. To remove the right caliper, disconnect the battery and remove it.

2. Unscrew the upper caliper mounting nut.

3. Depress the brake pedal approximately 1½ in. and secure it, in order to

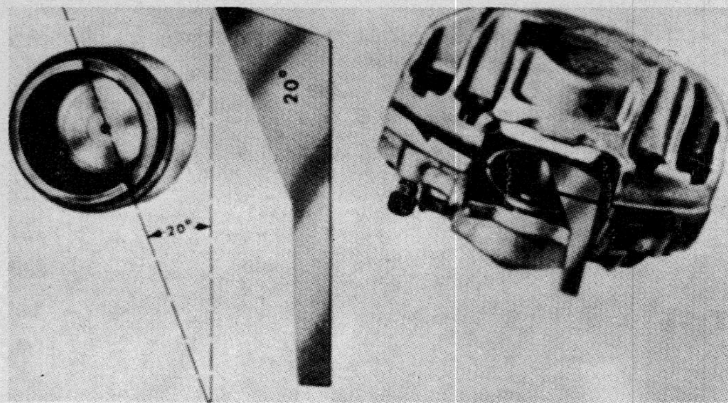

The pistons must be aligned at 20° in the caliper

block the compensating port in the master cylinder and prevent fluid from running out.

4. Disconnect the brake line.

5. Remove the lower caliper mounting nut.

6. Installation is the reverse of removal. Note the following points: The left and right calipers must not be interchanged, and should always be installed with the bleeder valve up. Install the calipers without brake pads (these can be installed later). Always use new lockwashers. Torque the mounting nuts to 69 ft lbs. Refill the master cylinder reservoir and bleed the system. Recheck the fluid level and test the brakes (with no load).

The caliper mounting nuts (a) on the 100, 100 LS, and 100 GL.

100, 100 LS, 100 GL

The caliper and brake disc can only be removed together.

1. The front exhaust pipe must be removed for access to the right side.

2. Depress the brake pedal about 1½ in. and secure it in this position to block the master cylinder compensating port and prevent fluid from running out. Remove the brake pads.

3. Disconnect the brake line at the caliper and plug the opening. On 1972 and 1973 models, disconnect the electrical lead to the right caliper.

4. Remove the caliper nuts.

5. Unbolt the driveshaft flange and slide it back and upward.

6. Remove the brake disc and caliper, noting the insulating washer between the flange and brake disc.

7. Installation is the reverse of removal. Make sure that the calipers are not interchanged. On calipers with single bleeder screws, the screw must be at the top. Torque the caliper mounting nuts to 69–76 ft lbs, and the driveshaft flange bolts to 70–78 ft lbs. Refill the master cylinder reservoir and bleed the system. Recheck the fluid level and test the brakes.

Overhaul

NOTE: *The two halves of the caliper must not be separated, nor should the connecting screws be loosened.*

1. Remove the pads.

2. Plug the brake line connection. Clean off the outside of the caliper unit, using hot water and a non-alkaline detergent.

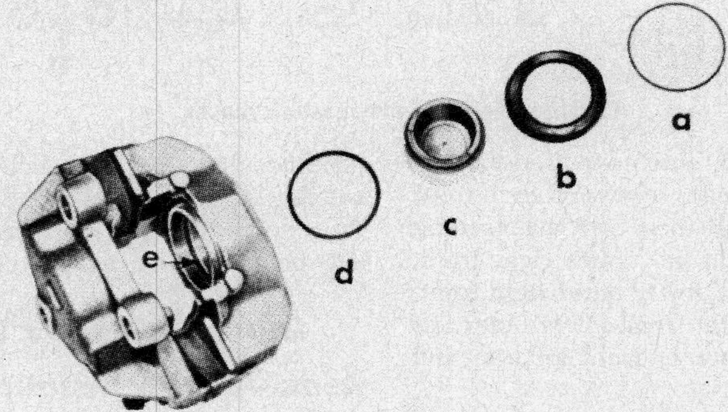

The caliper with one piston and cylinder assembly disassembled.

(a)—Clamping ring
(b)—Cap
(c)—Piston
(d)—Seal
(e)—Seal groove

3. Pry off the clamping ring from one cylinder, using a screwdriver.

4. Remove the cap from the same cylinder by hand.

5. Clamp an old pad in place on the cylinder opposite to the one being removed. Do not use a good pad; it will be ruined. Place a piece of wood across the center of the caliper to catch the piston. Apply air pressure to the brake line connection to force out the piston. Be careful, as the piston may be blown out of the caliper.

6. The seal can be removed from the cylinder groove with a plastic instrument. Be extremely careful not to damage the cylinder finish.

7. The cylinder and the piston may not be resurfaced; they must be replaced if damaged. The piston and cylinder parts should be cleaned in alcohol.

8. Coat the cylinder and piston parts with clean brake fluid. Install the piston with a new seal, cap, and clamping ring. Make sure that the piston face is installed at a 20° angle, as discussed under "Brake Pad Replacement."

9. Steps 3–8 may now be repeated for the second piston.

Brake Disc

Removal and Installation

Super 90

1. Jack up the vehicle and remove the wheel.

2. Disconnect the steering knuckle from the upper wishbone. See "Upper Control Arm Removal and Installation" for details.

3. Unbolt the driveshaft flange and move it toward the outside.

4. Remove the brake disc downward, being careful not to drop it.

5. Installation is the reverse of removal. Torque the driveshaft flange bolts to 77 ft lbs.

100, 100 LS, 100 GL

Follow the procedure for "Caliper Removal and Installation." The caliper and disc must be removed together.

Inspection

Maximum permissible disc runout is 0.-005 in. The disc may be reground but no more than 0.026 in. thickness may be

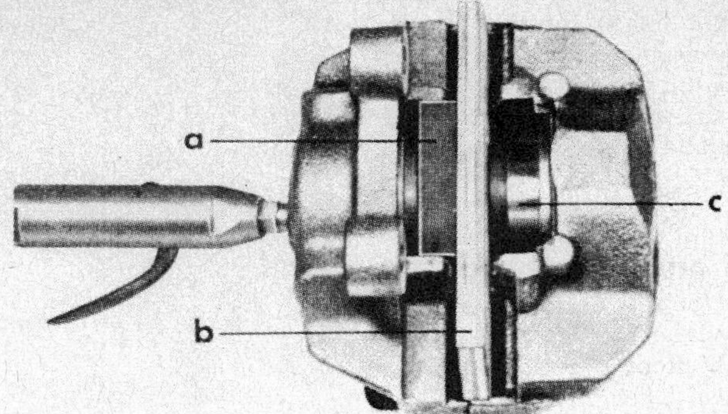

Air pressure is used to remove the piston (c) from the caliper. An old pad (a) and a piece of wood (b) are installed in the caliper.

removed from each side. Original disc thickness is 0.410 in. Maximum permissible thickness variation is 0.001 in.

Front Wheel Bearings

Removal and Installation, Adjustment

Refer to "Transaxle—Driveshaft Disassembly" for these procedures.

REAR DRUM BRAKES

Brake Drums

Removal and Installation

1. Jack up the car and remove the wheel. Do not use a jack under the rear axle tube. Release the parking brake.
2. Pry off the grease cap.
3. Remove the cotter pin and the nuts.
4. Pull off the brake drum by hand, making sure that the washer and roller bearing don't fall out. If the drum is held by the brakes, back off on the brake adjustment.
5. On reinstallation, tighten the nut to force the brake drum into place, then loosen it until there is 0.001–0.002 in. bearing play measured with a dial indicator.
6. Replace the castellated nut and install a new cotter pin.
7. Fill the grease cap with about 10 oz of wheel bearing grease.
8. Adjust the brakes if necessary.

Brake Shoes

Removal and Installation

1. Remove the brake drum.
2. Remove the big retaining spring at the bottom. Be careful it doesn't fly out.
3. Disconnect the parking brake cable and pull the shoes from the wheel cylinder.
4. Remove the shoes.
5. Reverse the procedure for installation, making sure that the front and rear shoes are not interchanged.

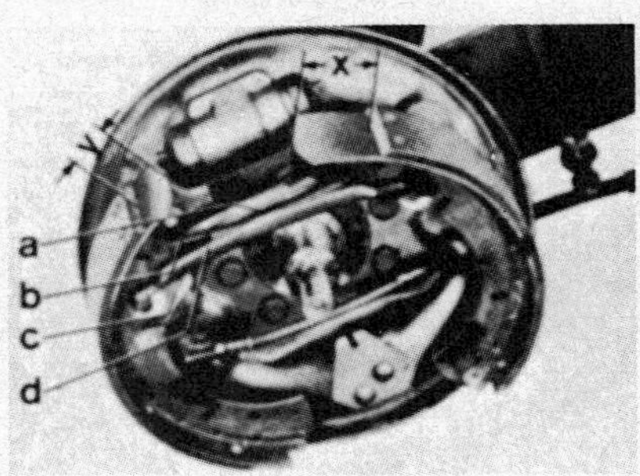

Details of the rear brakes with the bottom retaining spring removed. The measurement (x) for the front shoe is greater than (y) for the rear shoe.

(a)—Retaining clip
(b)—Spring (long end at the rear)
(c)—Handbrake lever
(d)—Pressure rod

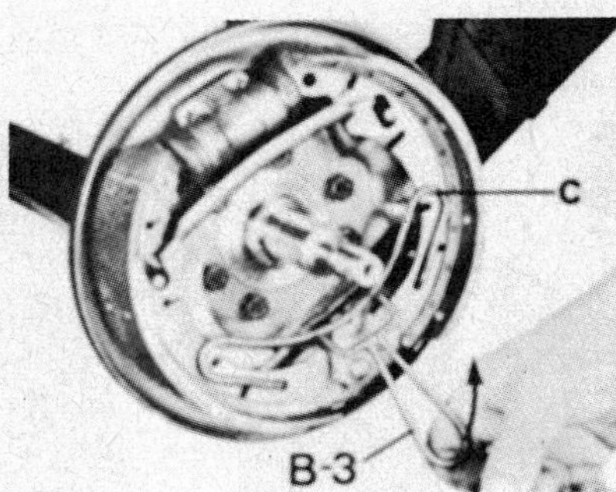

The bottom brake shoe retaining spring (c) is being replaced. Tool B-3 can be fabricated.

Wheel Cylinders

Removal and Installation

1. Remove the brake shoes.
2. Depress the brake pedal about 1½ in. to block the master cylinder compensating port and prevent leakage. Secure the pedal in this position.
3. Disconnect the brake line and plug the opening.

Wheel cylinder attachment details; (a) is the brake line fitting; (b) is the two cylinder mounting screws; (c) is the bleeder screw fitted with a cap.

4. Remove the two mounting screws from the backing plate.
5. Remove the cylinder.
6. Reverse the procedure for installation.

Overhaul

1. Clean the outside of the cylinder, using alcohol or clean brake fluid.
2. Remove the rubber boots and disassemble the cylinder.
3. Clean all parts in alcohol.
4. Air dry all parts.
5. If there are any pits or roughness inside the cylinder, it must be replaced.
6. Replace the piston if it is scratched or damaged in any way.
7. Lubricate all internal parts with clean brake fluid and reassemble the cylinder. Replace all rubber parts.

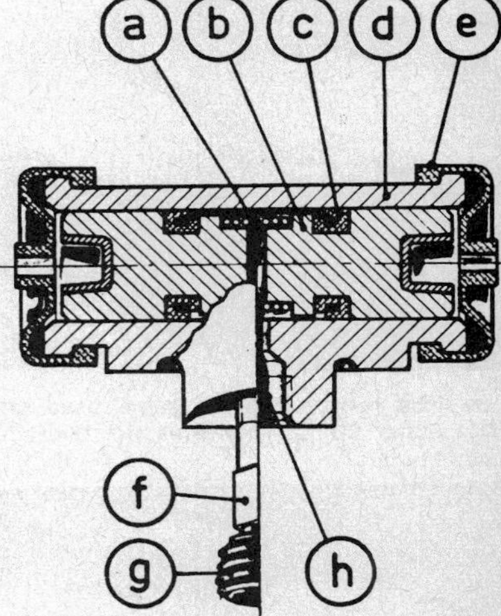

Cross-section of a rear wheel cylinder

(a)—Spring
(b)—Piston
(c)—Grooved cup
(d)—Cylinder
(e)—Cap
(f)—Bleeder valve
(g)—Dust cap
(h)—Brake line connection

8. Make sure that the cylinder slides freely. If it does not, disassemble the cylinder and polish the inside of the cylinder lightly by revolving the cylinder around

a piece of crocus cloth held by a finger. Do not polish the cylinder in a lengthwise direction. Clean the cylinder again after polishing. Air dry.

9. Replace the boots.

10. Replace the cylinder and tighten the bolts evenly. Bleed the system after it is reassembled.

Rear Wheel Bearings

Removal and Installation, Adjustment

Refer to "Rear Suspension—Wheel Bearings and Stub Axle Removal and Installation" for these procedures.

PARKING BRAKE

Adjustment

The handbrake (parking brake) must be adjusted periodically to compensate for lining wear and cable stretching. The adjuster is at the cable junction, under the center of the car.

1. Block the front wheels. Raise and support the rear of the vehicle. Do not use a jack under the rear axle tube.

2. Pull the brake up to the first or second notch and put the transmission in Neutral.

3. If the wheels will not rotate freely, loosen the adjusting nut. Some early Super 90 models may have two wing nuts for adjustment; adjust them individually for equal tension.

Two-piece rear handbrake cable used on early Super 90, (a) indicates the two adjusting nuts.

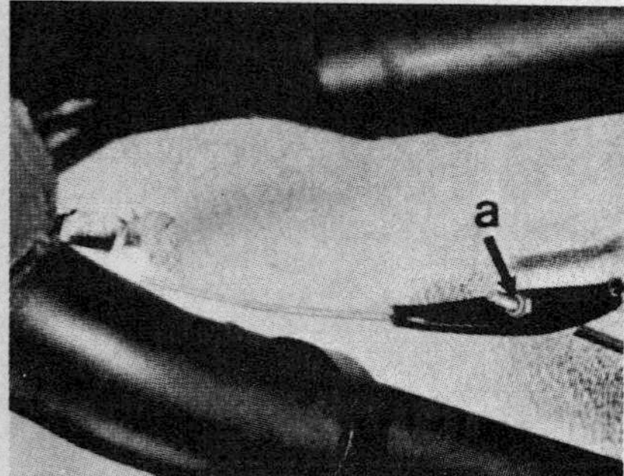

(a) indicates the adjusting point for one piece rear handbrake cables used on most models.

4. Tighten the adjusting nut until there is a slight drag on the rear wheels.

5. Pull the handle up to the third or fourth notch; the wheels should lock.

6. Check that there is no drag when the brake handle is fully released.

Cable

Removal and Installation

1. Jack up the rear of the car. Do not place a jack under the axle tube.

2. Block the front wheels and release the handbrake.

3. Remove the rear brake shoes.

4. Remove the cable adjusting nut(s) and detach the cable guides from the floorpan.

5. Replace the cable and brake shoes. Check the parking brake adjustment.

CHASSIS ELECTRICAL

Heater

Removal and Installation

To remove either the heater blower or the core, it is necessary to remove the heater unit from the car and disassemble it.

Super 90

1. Drain the radiator coolant, disconnect the battery and remove the instrument panel lower trim.

2. Drain the remaining coolant from the plug in the bottom of the heater.

3. If necessary, unscrew the blower duct at the bottom of the heater and remove.

4. Unbolt and remove the hood latch cable.

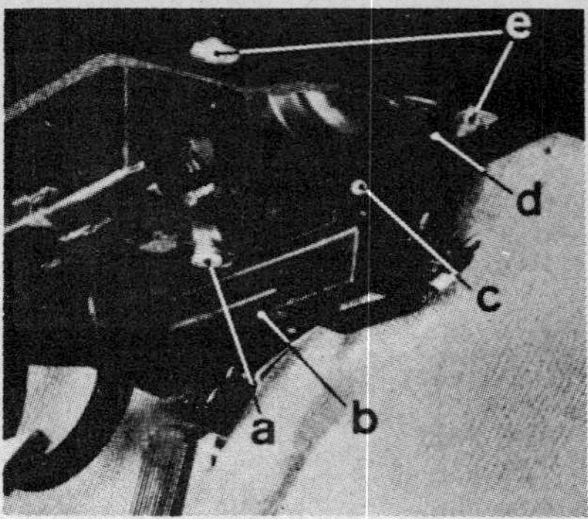

The Super 90 heater has a drain plug (a) at the bottom.

(a)—Drain plug
(b)—Blower duct
(c)—Retaining screw for b
(d)—Retaining screw for b
(e)—Self-tapping screw with washer

5. Disconnect the brown and red wires.

6. Remove the right and left defroster hoses and push them toward the engine compartment.

7. Disconnect the heater control cable from the lever, to the right of the steering column. Disconnect the cables from the lower and center heater control levers.

8. Remove the left and right water drain hoses.

9. Unbolt and remove the heater.

10. Installation is the reverse of removal. Adjust the control cables so that they allow the control levers full movement.

100, 100 LS, 100 GL

1. Drain the coolant, disconnect the battery, and remove the lower instrument panel trim and center shelf.

2. Remove the breather screw from the hose inside the engine compartment, being careful not to damage the firewall seal.

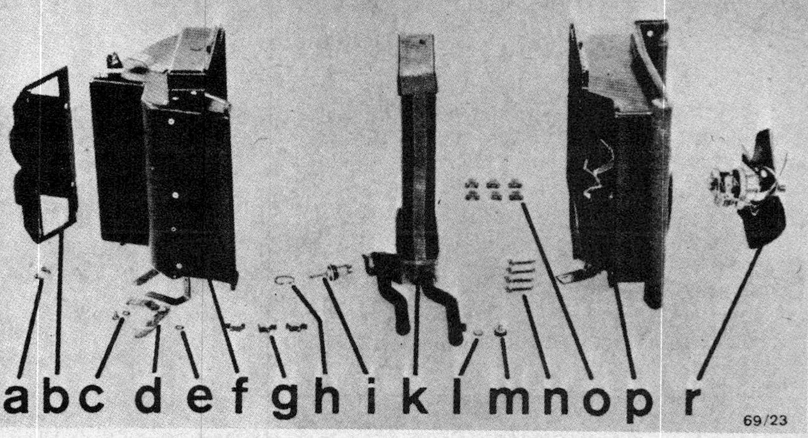

Exploded view of 100, 100 LS, and 100 GL heater

(a)—Self-tapping screw
(b)—Foot area nozzle
(c)—Hex head screw
(d)—Adjusting lever
(e)—Nut
(f)—Housing lower section
(g)—Spring clip, cable
(h)—Snap-ring
(i)—Plunger
(k)—Heater core
(l)—Seal
(m)—Breather screw
(n)—Spring, blower motor
(o)—Clip, housing halves
(p)—Housing upper section
(r)—Motor and fan

3. Detach both heater hoses.

4. Disconnect the cables that control the foot area heater flaps, the windshield flap and the heater valve.

5. Remove the plug connector from the heater controls and the lead from terminal 15 of the emergency warning light switch.

6. From the passenger compartment unbolt the heater and pull it down.

7. Installation is the reverse of removal.

8. When installing the cables, place the heater levers in the Off position. Place the leg of the spring clip in the mount and install the spring clip. The cable sleeve must protrude at least 0.2 in. beyond the spring clip.

Windshield Wiper System

Wiper Motor and Linkage Removal and Installation—Super 90

The wiper motor and the linkage can be removed from inside the engine compartment after removing the heater.

1. Disconnect the battery ground cable. Remove the wiper arm. It is mounted either with a cap nut and domed washer, or, by a spring which engages a groove.

2. Pull the windshield washer pump from the instrument panel and remove the hoses (long connection to the jets and short connection to the water supply).

3. Remove the ring nut from the instrument panel, remove the switch, and pull off the cables.

4. Remove the brown cable from the instruments.

5. Drain the coolant and remove the heater.

6. Remove the nuts from the wiper arm mounts.

7. Disconnect the hoses from the washer jets.

8. Tilt the wiper motor and linkage assembly to remove it.

9. Installation is the reverse of removal. Seal the cable hole in the firewall with a plastic sealant if necessary. Operate the wiper motor to be sure that the wipers park properly. Remove the motor crank arm and mount it properly if this does not occur.

Wiper Motor Removal and Installation—100, 100 LS, 100 GL

The motor can be removed from inside the engine compartment.

1. Disconnect the battery negative terminal.

2. Remove the right and left knee padding.

3. From the engine compartment, pull out the rubber grommet to give the wiring harness more play. Pull out the wiper switch and remove the leads.

4. Bend open the metal tabs holding the wiring harness and remove the harness which runs below the spray jets, together with the spray jet line.

5. Loosen the nut and pry off the lever for the linkage.

6. Remove the motor and harness.

7. Reverse the procedure for installation.

Wiper Linkage Removal and Installation—100, 100 LS, 100 GL

The linkage can be removed from inside the engine compartment.

1. Remove the windshield wiper arms from the studs by prying off the cap and removing the retaining nut. Remove the lower nut, washer and seal from the recess in the body.

3. Remove the mounting screws in the engine compartment and tilt the wiper base to remove.

4. Installation of the wiper linkage and the motor is done by reversing the removal procedures. The lever connected to the wiper motor should be installed at approximately 90° to the front and rear centerline of the vehicle. The wiper arm blades have different angles. The arm with the blade at the greater angle is installed on the driver's side.

Instruments

The instruments can be removed separately in the Super 90, but the entire instrument cluster must be removed in the 100, 100 LS, and 100 GL.

Fuel and Water Temperature Gauge Removal and Installation—Super 90

1. Disconnect the battery ground cable.

2. Unscrew and remove the blower duct from the bottom of the heater.

3. Remove the instrument panel bottom trim. If it is held in place by round

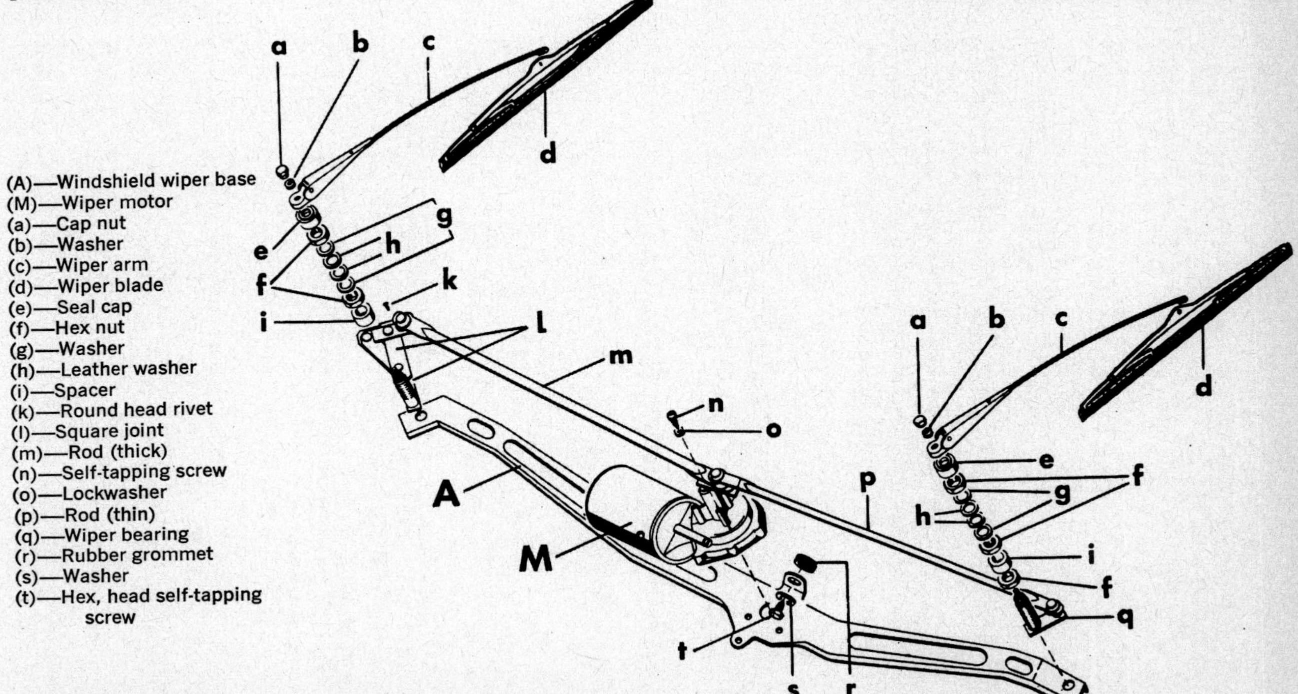

Exploded view of the Super 90 wiper linkage and motor

plastic clips, use a punch to drive the plastic pins through. The pins will be needed for installation.

4. Pull the three bulbs from the back of the housing.

5. Unscrew the knurled nuts and remove the retaining bracket.

6. Pull the instrument through the panel and detach all the connections.

7. Reverse the procedure for installation.

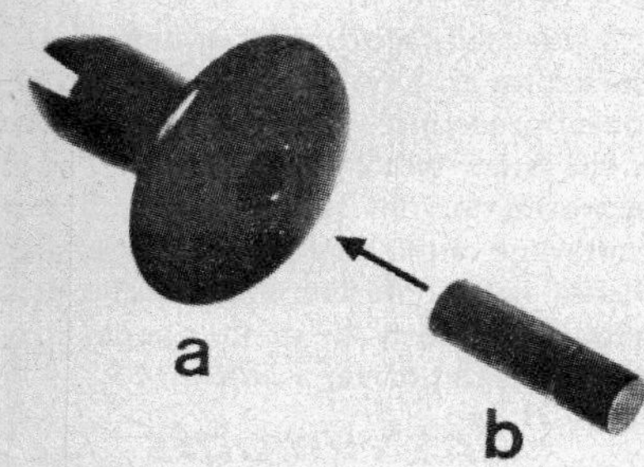

To disengage the plastic clips (a) drive the pins (b) in the direction indicated. The pins should be driven in the same direction on replacement.

Clock removal and Installation—Super 90

The clock is easier to remove if one of the large instruments is removed first.

1. Follow Steps 1–3 of "Fuel and Water Temperature Gauge Removal and Installation—Super 90."

2. Unscrew the retaining nuts and remove the retaining bracket.

3. Pull the light bulb from the side of the case.

4. Remove the clock. Detach the wire.

5. Reverse the procedure for installation.

Speedometer Removal and Installation—Super 90

1. Follow Steps 1–3 of "Fuel and Water Temperature Gauge Removal and Installation—Super 90."

2. Unscrew the cable from the back of the case.

3. Remove the nut and the retaining bracket.

4. Remove the speedometer and detach the wires.

5. Reverse the procedure for installation.

Instrument Cluster Removal and Installation—100, 100 LS, 100 GL

1. Disconnect the battery ground cable.

2. Remove the screws which hold the padding on top of the instrument panel. Remove the padding.

3. Remove the nuts at the rear of the instrument cluster and remove the cover.

4. Pull the cluster out toward the driver's seat.

5. Pull off the electrical connections and unscrew the speedometer cable.

6. Remove the instrument cluster. It may be further disassembled as necessary.

Fuse Box Location

On the Super 90, the fuse box is on the left, under the hood. It has a transparent cover. The turn signal flasher and the headlight relays are directly behind it.

On the 100, 100 LS, and 100 GL, the fuse box is near the clutch pedal on the left side of the car. The turn signal flasher, windshield washer, and headlight relays are mounted on the fuse box.

The fuse box on the 100, 100 LS, and 100 GL contains nine fuses. The windshield washer delayed action relay (a) the flasher unit (b) and the headlight relay (c) are mounted on the fuse box.

BMW

Index

INTRODUCTION

BMW is produced by Bavarian Motor Works of Munich Germany. The company was originally formed as Bavarian Aircraft Works on March 7, 1916. The plant produced the aircraft engines for early German war planes. Baron von Richthofen's Fokker D-7 tri-plane was BMW powered. BMW engines have set speed records in the air, on the water, and on the ground and BMW also produced the first jet engine.

The first vehicle to wear the BMW insignia was a motorcycle produced in 1923 which used a horizontally opposed two cylinder engine. This same design is used today.

The company began producing cars in 1928 and have continued with similar in-line 4-cylinder water cooled engine design. Current engines are the result of testing and modifying a reliable and strong powerplant.

BMW produces the 1600, 1800, 2000, 2000CS, 2002, 2002Ti, and 2002Tii with 4 cylinder engines. The 2500, 2800, 2800 CS and Bavaria use an in-line 6 cylinder engine.

BMW produces cars which are known for their power and handling ability. The 4-cylinder models have a cruising speed in excess of 100 mph while the 6 cylinder units are capable of speeds over 120 mph.

MODEL IDENTIFICATION

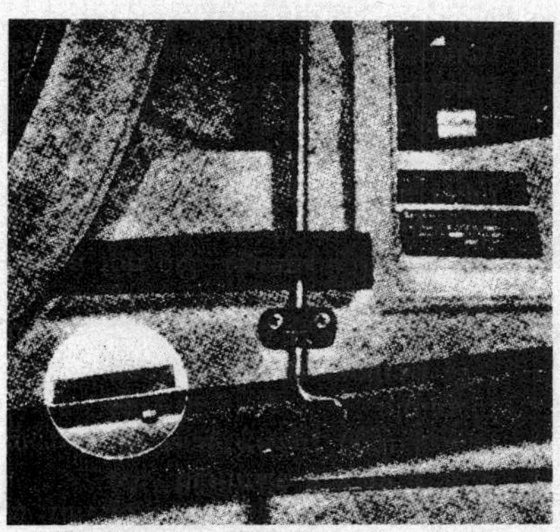

Chassis and Manufacturer number location

Model 2800

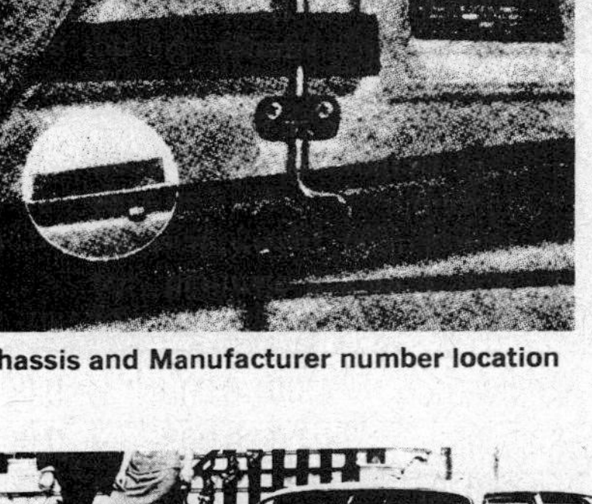

Model 2000

Model 1800

Model 2002

Model 2500

Model 1600

Model 2800CS

GENERAL ENGINE SPECIFICATIONS

Model	Engine Displacement (cu in)	Carburetor Type	Horsepower (RPM)	Torque @ RPM	Bore & Stroke (in.)	Compression Ratio
1600	95.99	Solex 38 PDSI	96 @ 5700	91.2/3000	3.307 x 2.795	8.6:1
1800	107.77	Solex 38 PDSI	102 @ 5800	105.6/3000	3.504 x 2.795	8.6:1
2000	121.44	Solex 40 PDSI	113 @ 6000	115.7/3000	3.504 x 3.150	8.5:1
2000CS	121.44	Solex 40 PDSI	135 @ 5800	122.9/3600	3.504 x 3.150	9.3:1
2002	121.44	Solex 40 PDSIT	113 @ 5800	115.7/3000	3.504 x 3.150	8.5:1
2002TI	121.44	Solex 40 PHH	135 @ 5800	123.0/3000	3.504 x 3.150	9.3:1
2002tii	121.44	Fuel Injected	147 @ 5800	130.0/3000	3.504 x 3.150	10.3:1
2500	151.22	Zenith 35/40 INAT	170 @ 6000	154.8/3700	3.14 x 2.81	9.0:1
2800	168.97	Zenith 35/40 INAT	192 @ 6000	173.6/3700	3.14 x 3.1	9.0:1
2800CS	168.97	Zenith 35/40 INAT	192 @ 6000	173.6/3700	3.14 x 3.1	9.0:1

CRANKSHAFT AND CONNECTING ROD SPECIFICATIONS

All measurements are given in inches

	CRANKSHAFT				CONNECTING ROD		
Model	Main Brg Journal Dia.	Main Brg Oil Clearance	Shaft End-Play	Thrust Washer On No. (Bearing Cap)	Journal Dia.	Oil Clearance	Side Clearance
1600	2.1654	0.0019-0.0028	0.0034-0.0069	3	2.0472 ± 0.00039	0.001-0.003	0.001
1800	2.1654	0.0019-0.0028	0.0034-0.0069	3	2.0472 ± 0.00039	0.001-0.003	0.001
2000	2.1654	0.0019-0.0028	0.0024-0.0064	3	2.0472 ± 0.00039	0.001-0.003	0.001
2000CS	2.1654	0.0019-0.0028	0.0024-0.0064	3	2.0472 ± 0.00039	0.001-0.003	0.001
2002	2.1654	0.0019-0.0028	0.0034-0.0069	3	2.0472 ± 0.00039	0.001-0.003	0.001
2002TI	2.1654	0.0019-0.0028	0.0034-0.0069	3	2.0472 ± 0.00039	0.001-0.003	0.001
2002tii	2.1654	0.0019-0.0028	0.0034-0.0069	3	2.0472 ± 0.00039	0.001-0.003	0.001
2500	2.3622	0.0011-0.0027	0.0034-0.0069	4	2.0472 + 0.0004	—	0.0013-0.0027-
2800	2.3622	0.0011-0.0027	0.0034-0.0069	4	2.0472 + 0.0004	—	0.0013-0.0027-
2800CS	2.3622	0.0011-0.0027	0.0034-0.0069	4	2.0472 + 0.0004	—	0.0013-0.0027-

— Not Available

PISTON AND RING SPECIFICATIONS

All measurements are given in inches

		RING GAP			RING SIDE CLEARANCE		
Model	Piston Clearance	Top Compression	Bottom Compression	Oil Control Top	Top Compression	Bottom Compression	Oil Control
1600	0.001	0.012-0.018	0.012-0.018	0.010-0.016	0.0006-0.001	0.0005-0.001	0.0004-0.001
1800	0.001	0.012-0.018	0.012-0.018	0.010-0.016	0.0006-0.001	0.0005-0.001	0.0004-0.001
2000	0.001	0.012-0.018	0.012-0.018	0.010-0.016	0.0020-0.004	0.0010-0.002	0.0020-0.004
2000CS	0.001	0.012-0.018	0.012-0.018	0.010-0.016	0.0020-0.004	0.0010-0.002	0.0020-0.004
2002	0.001	0.012-0.018	0.012-0.018	0.010-0.016	0.0006-0.001	0.0005-0.001	0.0004-0.001
2002TI	0.001	0.012-0.018	0.012-0.018	0.010-0.016	0.0006-0.001	0.0005-0.001	0.0004-0.001
2002tii	0.001	0.012-0.018	0.012-0.018	0.010-0.016	0.0006-0.001	0.0005-0.001	0.0004-0.001

TUNE-UP SPECIFICATIONS

Model	Engine Displacement (cut in)	Spark Plugs Type	Spark Plugs Plug Gap	Distributor Point Dwell (deg)	Distributor Point Gap	Ignition Timing (deg @ RPM)	Intake Valve Opens (Deg)	Fuel Pump Pressure (gal/hr)	Idle Speed (RPM)	Valve Clearance (Engine Cold) Intake (in.)	Valve Clearance (Engine Cold) Exhaust (in.)
1600	95.99	Bosch— W200T30 WG190T30 Beru— 200/14/3A Champ—N-9Y	0.024	61	0.016	26° @ 1500	4°BTDC① 18°BTDC②	12	800 ±100	0.006-0.008	0.006-0.008
1800	107.77	Bosch— W200T30 WG190T30 Beru— 200/14/3A Champ—N-9Y	0.024	61	0.016	26° @ 1500	4°BTDC① 18°BTDC②	12	800 ±100	0.006-0.008	0.006-0.008
2000	121.44	Bosch— W200T30 Beru— 230/14/3A	0.024	61	0.016	26° @ 1500	4°BTDC① 18°BTDC②	12	800-1000	0.006-0.008	0.006-0.008
2000CS	121.44	Bosch— W200T30 Beru— 230/14/3A	0.024	61	0.016	26° @ 1500	4°BTDC① 18°BTDC②	12	800-1000	0.006-0.008	0.006-0.008
2002	121.44	Bosch— W200T30 Beru— 200/14/3A Champ—N-8Y	0.024	59	0.016	27° @ 1500	4°BTDC① 18°BTDC②	14	800 ±100	0.006-0.008	0.006-0.008
2002TI	121.44	Bosch— W200T30 WG190T30 ①	0.024	59	0.016	24° @ 1500	4°BTDC① 18°BTDC②	14	800 ±100	0.006-0.008	0.006-0.008
2002tii	121.44	Bosch— W200T30 WG190T30 ①	0.024	59	0.016	13° @ 1500	4°BTDC① 18°BTDC②	29	900 ±50	0.006-0.008	0.006-0.008
2500	151.22	Bosch— W175T2 Beru— 175/14/3 Champ—N-11Y	0.023	35-41	0.011-0.015	22° @ 1500	6°③	23-24	900 ±50④	0.011	0.013
2800	168.97	Bosch— W175T2 Beru— 175/14/3 Champ—N-11Y	0.023	35-41	0.011-0.015	22° @ 1500	14°③	23-24	900 ±50④	0.011	0.013
2800CS	168.97	Bosch— W175T2 Beru— 175/14/3 Champ—N-11Y	0.023	35-41	0.011-0.015	22° @ 1500	14°③	23-24	900 ±50④	0.011	0.013

① With 0.02 in clearance between the cam base circle and the rocker pad.
② With 0.011 in clearance between the cam base circle and the rocker pad.
③ With 0.02 inches clearance between the cam base circle and the rocker arm bearing surface
④ Automatic transmission setting is 1000 RPM.

CAPACITIES

Model	Engine Crankcase W/Filter (US Pts)	Engine Crankcase W/O Filter (US Pts)	Manual Transmission (US Pts)	Drive Axle (Qts)	Gasoline Tank (Gals)	Cooling System (Qts)	Auto. Trans. (US pt.)
1600	9.1	8.6	232 Gearbox (4 sp) 2.1 235/5 Gearbox (5 sp) 2.94	0.95 0.95	10.1	7.4	—
1800	9.1	8.6	232 Gearbox (4 sp) 2.1 235/5 Gearbox (5 sp) 2.94	0.95 0.95	10.1	7.4	—
2000	9.1	8.6	232 Gearbox (4 sp) 2.1	1.9 pts.	14.5	7.4	—
2000CS	9.1	8.6	232 Gearbox (4 sp) 2.1	1.9 pts.	14.5	7.4	—
2002	9.1	8.6	232 Gearbox (4 sp) 2.1 235/5 Gearbox (5 sp) 2.94	0.95 0.95	10.1	7.4	—
2002TI	9.1	8.6	232 Gearbox (4 sp) 2.1 235/5 Gearbox (5 sp) 2.94	0.95 0.95	10.1	7.4	—
2002tii	9.1	8.6	232 Gearbox (4 sp) 2.1 235/5 Gearbox (5 sp) 2.94	0.95 0.95	10.1	7.4	—
2500	12.2	10.6	2.5	1.6	19.8	12.7	17.4
2800	12.2	10.6	2.5	1.6	19.8	12.7	17.4
2800CS	12.2	10.6	2.5	1.6	19.8	12.7	17.4

— Not applicable

TORQUE SPECIFICATIONS

All Readings in ft lbs

Model	Cylinder Head Bolts (3 Stage Torque Procedure)	Rod Bearing Bolts	Main Bearing Bolts	Crankshaft Pulley Bolt	Flywheel To Crankshaft
1600	25.3 to 32.6—43.4 to 47.1—47.1 to 54.2	37.6-41.2	42-46	101-108	75-83
1800	25.3 to 32.6—43.4 to 47.1—47.1 to 54.2	37.6-41.2	42-46	101-108	75-83
2000	21.7—50.6—50.6 ± 1.4	37.6-41.2	42-46	101	75-83
2000CS	21.7—50.6—50.6 ± 1.4	37.6-41.2	42-46	101	75-83
2002	25.3 to 32.6—43.4 to 47.1—47.1 to 54.2	37.6-41.2	42-46	101-108	75-83
2002TI	25.3 to 32.6—43.4 to 47.1—47.1 to 54.2	37.6-41.2	42-46	101-108	75-83
2002tii	25.3 to 32.6—43.4 to 47.1—47.1 to 54.2	37.6-41.2	42-46	101-108	75-83
2500	25—46—55	37-41	41-45	173-187① 318-332②	72-83
2800	25—46—55	37-41	41-45	173-187① 318-332②	72-83
2800CS	25—46—55	37-41	41-45	173-187① 318-332②	72-83

① With flat nut
② With collar nut

FIRING ORDER

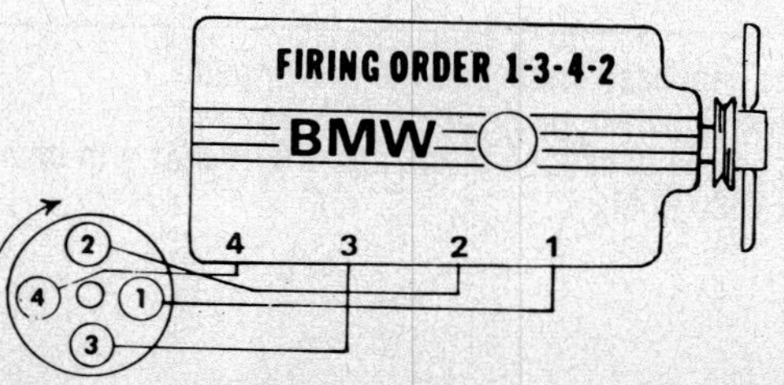

VALVE SPECIFICATIONS

Model	Angle (Deg)	Spring Pressure (Lbs. @ In)	Installed Height (in)	VALVE STEM DIAMETER Intake (in.)	Exhaust (in.)
1600	45° + 20′ − 0	154 @ 1.48	1.712	0.315-0.0157 -0.0098	0.315-0.0157 -0.0217
1800	45° + 20′ − 0	154 @ 1.48	1.712	0.315-0.0157 -0.0098	0.315-0.0157 -0.0217
2000	45°	154 @ 1.48	1.811	0.315-0.0157 -0.0098	0.315-0.0157 -0.0217
2000CS	45°	154 @ 1.12	1.811	0.315-0.0157 -0.0098	0.315-0.0157 -0.0217
2002	45° + 20′ − 0	154 @ 1.12	1.712	0.315-0.0157 -0.0098	0.315-0.0157 -0.0217
2002TI	45° + 20′ − 0	154 @ 1.12	1.712	0.315-0.0157 -0.0098	0.315-0.0157 -0.0217
2002tii	45° + 20′ − 0	154 @ 1.12	1.712	0.315-0.0157 -0.0098	0.315-0.0157 -0.0217
2500	45°	154 @ 1.12	1.48	0.315-0.0157 -0.0098	0.315-0.0157 -0.0217
2800	45°	154 @ 1.12	1.48	0.315-0.0157 -0.0098	0.315-0.0157 -0.0217
2800CS	45°	154 @ 1.12	1.48	0.315-0.0157 -0.0098	0.315-0.0157 -0.0217

BRAKE SPECIFICATIONS

All measurements are given in inches

Model	Master Cyl. Bore	CALIPER PISTON BORE Front	Rear	BRAKE DISC OR DRUM DIAMETER Front Disc	Rear Drum	New Pad Or Lining Thickness
1600	0.81	1.339	0.685	9.45	7.87	0.16
1800	0.81	1.339	0.685	9.45	7.87	0.20
2000	0.94	2.13	0.688	10.71	9.84	—
2000CS	0.94	2.13	0.688	10.71	9.84	—
2002	0.81	1.339	0.685	9.45	9.06	0.20
2002TI	0.81	1.575	0.685	10.08	9.06	0.20
202tii	0.81	1.575	0.685	10.08	9.06	0.20
2500	0.93	1.574	1.653	10.71	10.71	—
2800	0.93	1.574	1.653	10.71	10.71	—
2800CS	0.93	1.574	0.874	10.71	10.71	—

— Not Available

ALTERNATOR AND REGULATOR SPECIFICATIONS

Model	Alternator Type	Alternator Field Current (Amp)	Alternator Output (Amps)	Regulator Type	Regulator Output Amp @ RPM	Regulator Voltage at Temp.
1600	Bosch	3	35	Bosch	35 @ 2700	13-14 @ 68° F.
1800	Bosch	3	35	Bosch	35 @ 2700	13-14 @ 68° F.
2000	Bosch	—	35	Bosch	—	—
2000CS	Bosch	—	35	Bosch	—	—
2002	Bosch	3	35	Bosch	35 @ 2700	13-14 @ 68° F.
2002TI	Bosch	3	35	Bosch	35 @ 2700	13-14 @ 68° F.
2002tii	Bosch	3	35	Bosch	35 @ 2700	13-14 @ 68° F.
2500	Bosch	—	45	Bosch	—	—
2800	Bosch	—	45	Bosch	—	—
2800CS	Bosch	—	45	Bosch	—	—

— Not Available

WHEEL ALIGNMENT

Model	Camber Setting (Deg.)	Caster (Deg.)	Toe-In (in.)	Steering Axis Inclination
1600	0°30′ ± 30′	4° ± 30′	0.04 ± 0.04	—
1800	0°30′ ± 30′	4° ± 30′	0.04 ± 0.04	—
2000	0°15′ ± 30′	3° ± 30′	0.059 ± 0.059	8°40′ ± 30′
2000CS	0°15′ ± 30′	3° ± 30′	0.059 ± 0.059	8°40′ ± 30′
2002	0°30′ ± 30′	4° ± 30′	0.04 ± 0.04	—
2002TI	0°30′ ± 30′	4° ± 30′	0.04 ± 0.04	—
2002tii	0°30′ ± 30′	4° ± 30′	0.04 ± 0.04	—
2500	0° ± 30′	9°30′ ± 30′	0°10′ ± 10	6°20′ ± 30′
2800	0° ± 30′	9°30′ ± 30′	0°10′ ± 10	6°20′ ± 30′
2800CS	0° ± 30′	9°30′ ± 30′	0°10′ ± 10	6°20′ ± 30′

— Not Available

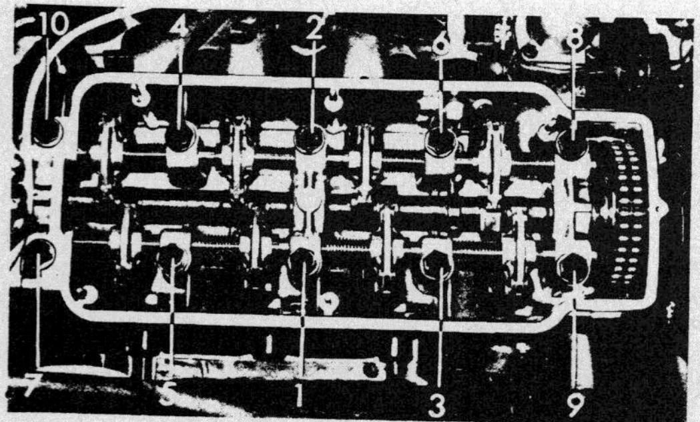

Cylinder head tightening sequence for four cylinder engines.

BATTERY AND STARTER SPECIFICATIONS

Model	Amp. Hr. Capacity	Volts	Terminal Ground	No-Load Test Amps	No-Load Test Volts	No-Load Test RPM
1600	36	12	Neg	175	9.6	2400
1800	36	12	Neg	175	9.6	2400
2000	—	—	Neg	—	—	—
2000CS	—	—	Neg	—	—	—
2002	44	12	Neg	210	9.6	1300
2002TI	44	12	Neg	210	9.6	1300
2002tii	44	12	Neg	210	9.6	1300
2500	55	12	Neg	380	—	—
2800	55	12	Neg	380	—	—
2800CS	55	12	Neg	380	—	—

— Not Available

FRONT

12	10	4	2	6	8	14
13	7	5	1	3	9	11

Cylinder head tightening sequence for BMW 2500, 2800.

WIRING DIAGRAMS

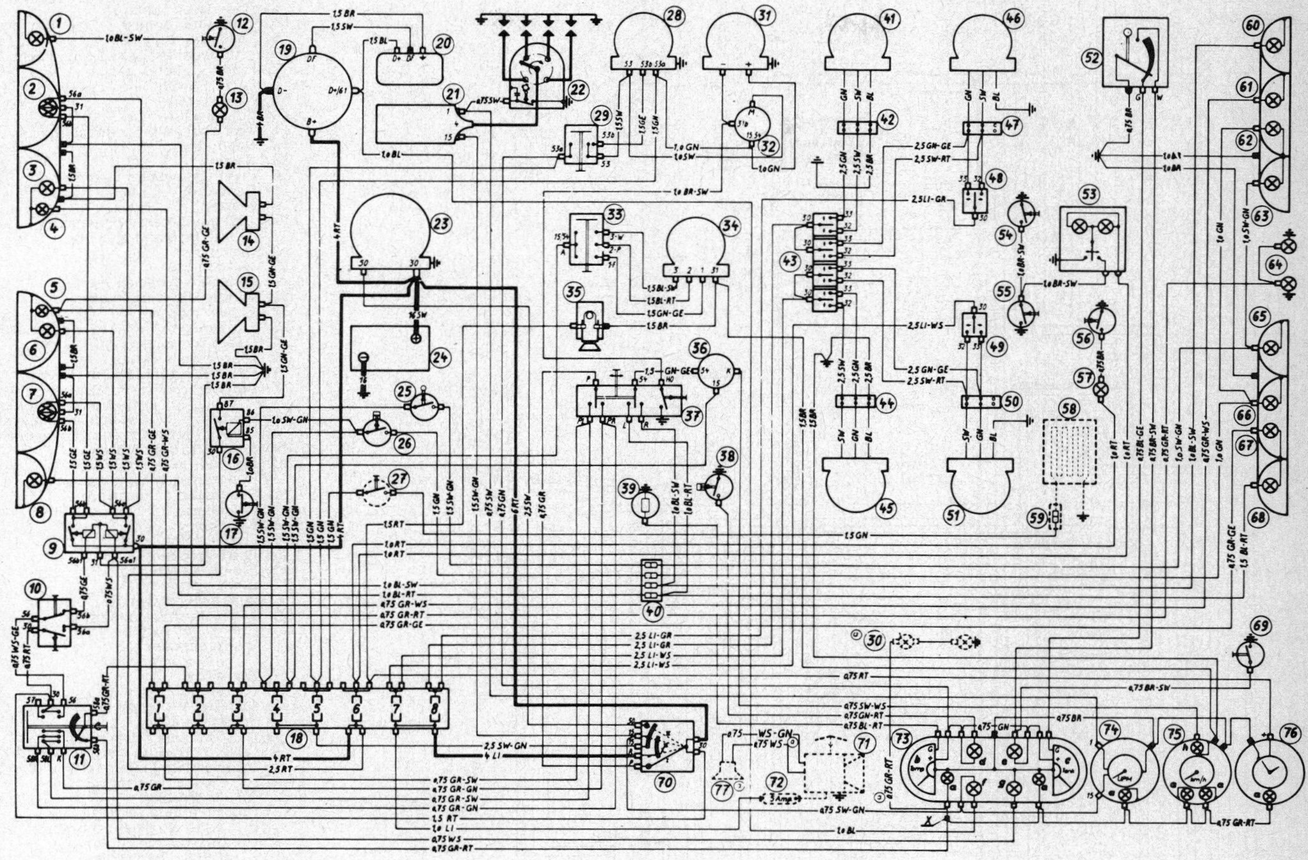

Wiring diagram 2000 CS

1. Turn indicator front RH
2. Headlight RH
3. Long-range headlight RH
4. Parking light RH
5. Parking light LH
6. Long-range headlight LH
7. Headlight LH
8. Turn indicator front LH
9. Dip relay
10. Dipswitch with headlight flasher
11. Light switch
12. Engine compartment light switch
13. Engine compartment light
14. Horn RH
15. Horn LH
16. Horn relay
17. Horn ring
18. Fuse box
19. Alternator
20. Voltage regulator
21. Coil
22. Distributor
23. Starter
24. Battery
25. Reversing light switch
26. Stop light switch
27. Heated rear window switch
28. Screenwiper motor
29. Screenwiper switch
30. Selector gate light
31. Screenwasher pump
32. Delay relay
33. Heater switch
34. Heater blower motor
35. Cigar lighter
36. Flasher unit
37. Turn indicator/parking light/ screenwasher switch
38. Oil pressure contact
39. Water temperature thermocouple
40. Plug-in connector
41. Electric window lift front RH
42. Terminal board
43. Front window lift switch
44. Terminal board
45. Electrical window lift front LH
46. Electric window lift rear RH
47. Terminal board
48. Rear RH window lift switch
49. Rear LH window lift switch
50. Terminal board
51. Electric window lift rear LH
52. Fuel gauge tank contact
53. Interior light
54. Door switch RH
55. Door switch LH
56. Luggage compartment light switch
57. Luggage compartment light
58. Heated rear window
59. Plug-in connector
60. Turn indicator rear RH
61. Rear light RH
62. Top light RH
63. Reversing light RH
64. Number plate lights
65. Reversing light LH
66. Stop light LH
67. Rear light LH
68. Turn indicator rear LH
69. Choke cable contact
70. Ignition/starter switch
71. Radio
72. Separate fuse
73. Combined instrument
74. Revolution counter
75. Speedometer
76. Clock
77. Rear loudspeaker

Instruments:

(a) Instrument lighting
(b) Cooling water thermometer
(c) Fuel gauge
(d) Oil pressure telltale
(e) Choke and fuel reverse telltale
(f) Battery charge telltale
(g) Main beam telltale
(h) Turn indicator telltale

Ignition/starter switch:

Key positions:

WIRING DIAGRAMS

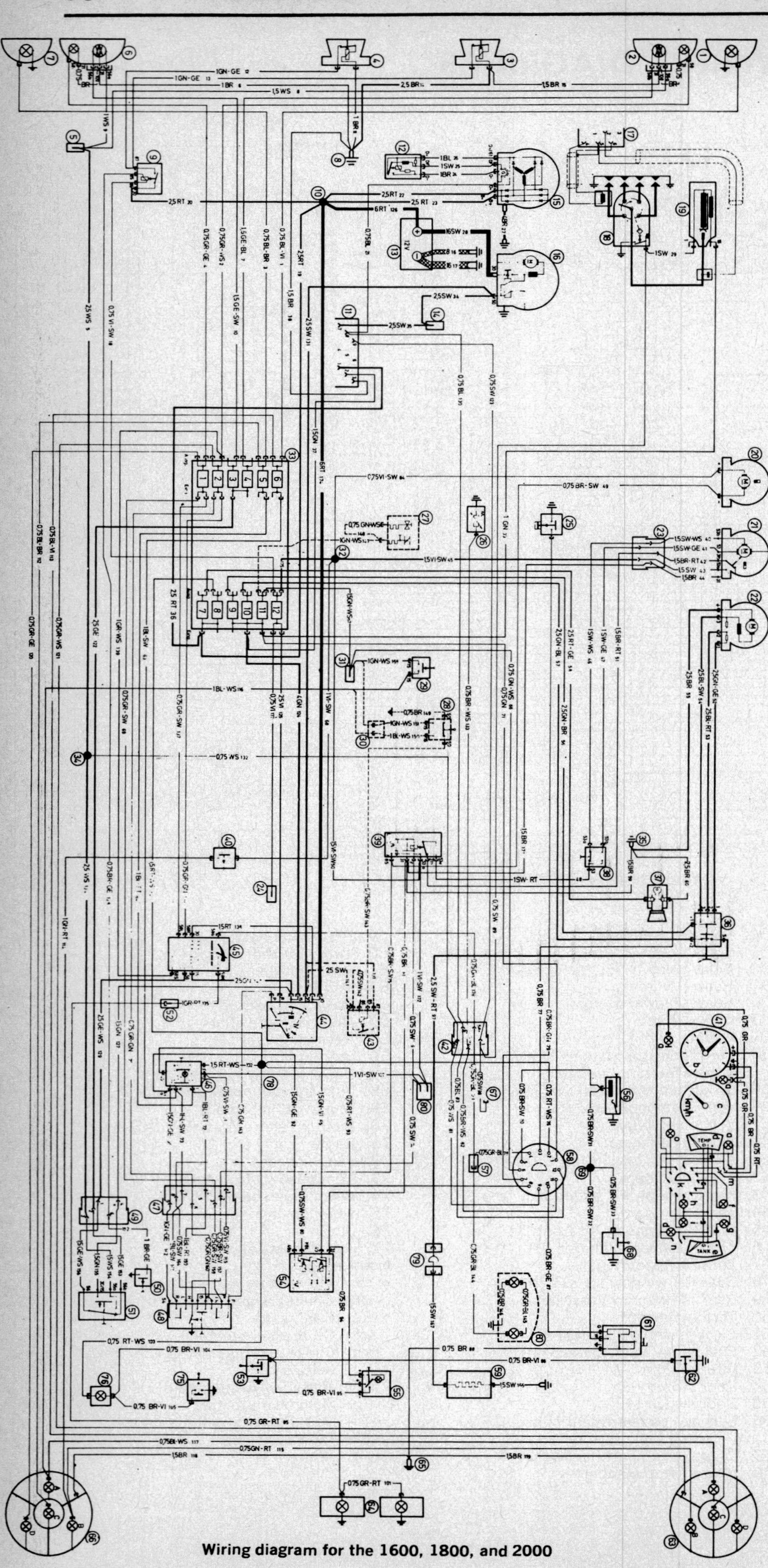

Wiring diagram for the 1600, 1800, and 2000

1. Front right-hand flasher
2. R.H. headlight with parking light
3. Right-hand fanfare
4. Left-hand fanfare
5. Fog lamp relay connection
6. L.H. headlight with parking light
7. Front left-hand flasher
8. Earth (ground)
9. Fanfare relay
10. Solder point
11. Test equipment connection
12. Regulator
13. Battery
14. Electrical system connection
15. Generator
16. Starter
17. Test equipment connection with lead and pick up
18. Distributor
19. Ignition coil
20. Windshield washer pump
21. Windshield wiper motor
22. Blower motor
23. 5 pin plug terminal to wiper motor
24. Radio connection
25. Oil pressure switch
26. Remote reading therm. trans.
27. Auto. starter carburetor (only with auto. transmission)
28. Reversing light switch with starter lock (only with auto. transmission)
29. Reversing light switch
30. 2 pin terminal (only with automatic transmission)
31. Fuel pump connection
32. Solder point
33. Fuse box
34. Solder point
35. Earth (ground)
36. Blower switch
37. Cigar lighter
38. Wiper speed switch
39. Wiper-Washer transmitter
40. Brake light switch
41. Instrument set
    - (a) Illuminated scale
    - (b) clock
    - (c) Speedometer
    - (d) Coolant temperature gauge
    - (e) Fuel gauge
    - (f) Charging lamp (red)
    - (g) Oil pressure control (orange)
    - (h) Headlight beam telltale (blue)
    - (i) Flasher control (green)
    - (k) 12 pin plug
    - (m) 3 pin plug (clock)
    - (n) 3 pin plug (rev. counter)
    - (o) Central control lamp (Choke, handbrake, petrol)
42. 5 pin plug terminal
43. Starter relay (only with automatic transmission)
44. Ignition switch
    I = Off; II = O; III = On; VI = Start
45. Light switch
46. Hazard flasher switch
47. 9 pin plug to turn indicator switch
48. Turn indicator switch
49. 6 pin plug to dip switch
50. Signal button
51. Dip switch
52. Number plate light and fog lamp connection
53. Left-hand door contact
54. Hazard flasher
55. Interior light
56. Choke
57. Selector lever connection
58. 12 pin plug to instrument cluster
59. Heater rear window
60. Selector gate light
61. Fuel gauge transmitter
62. Right-hand door contact
63. Right-hand rear light
    - (a) Reversing light
    - (b) Brake light
    - (c) Flasher
    - (d) Tail light
64. License plate lights
65. Earth (ground)
66. Left-hand rear light
    - (a) Reversing light
    - (b) Brake light
    - (c) Flasher
    - (d) Tail light
67. Revolution counter connection
68. Handbrake switch
69. Solder point
75. Rear door contact
76. L.H. light in luggage compartment
78. Solder point
79. Contact plate
80. Rear windshield wiper connection

BL = blue
BR = brown
GE = yellow
GN = green
GR = grey
RT = red
SW = black
VI = violet
WS = white

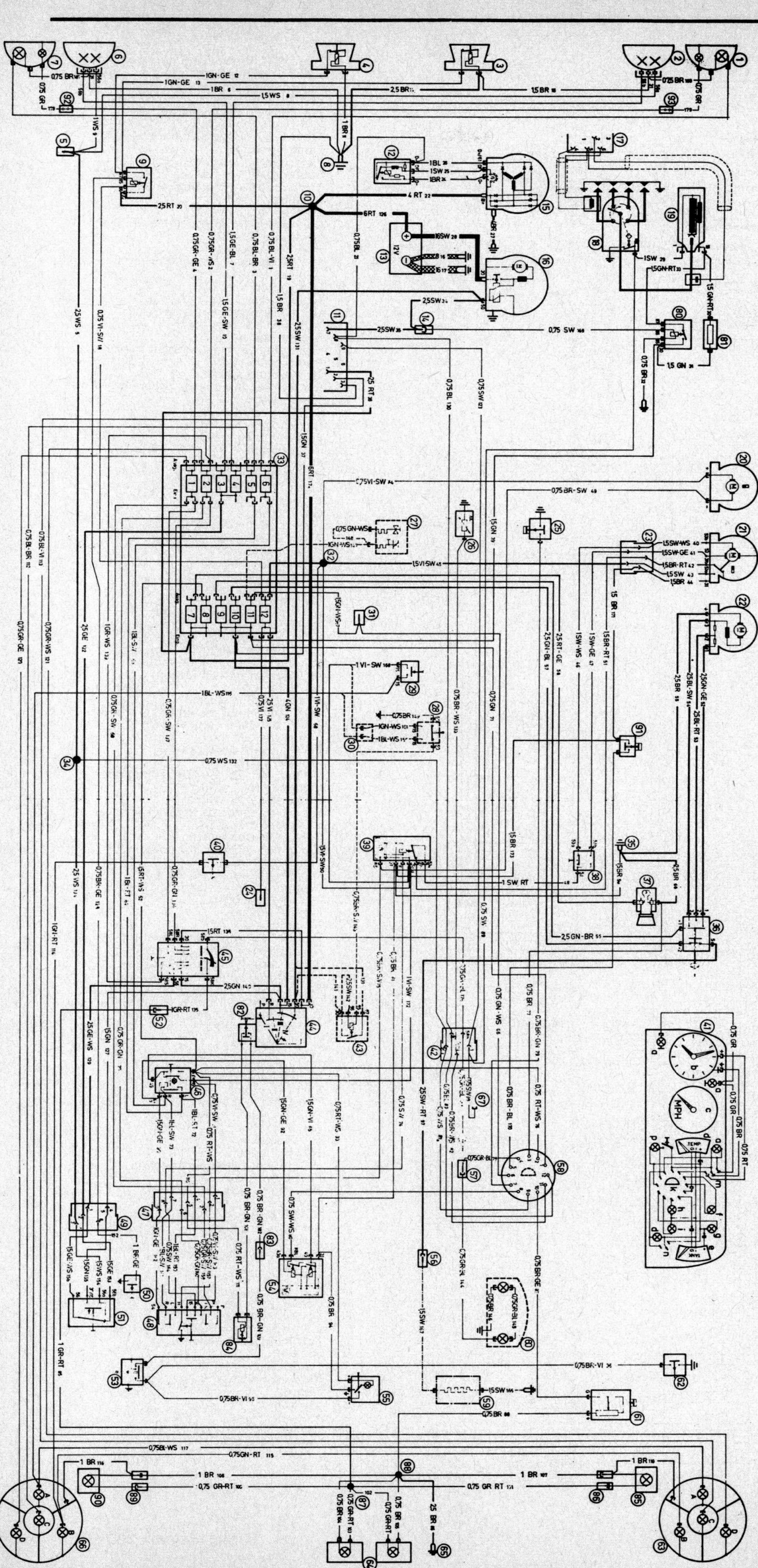

1. Front R.H. flasher with parking light
2. Right-hand headlight
3. Right-hand fanfare
4. Left-hand fanfare
5. Connection for fog lamp relay
6. Left-hand headlight
7. Front L.H. flasher with parking light
8. Earth (ground)
9. Fanfare relay
10. Solder point
11. Test equipment connection
12. Regulator
13. Battery
14. Connection for electrical system
15. Generator
16. Starter
17. Connection for test equipment with lead and pickup
18. Distributor
19. Ignition coil
20. Windshield washer pump
21. Windshield wiper motor
22. Blower motor
23. 5 pin plug terminal to wiper motor
24. Radio connection
25. Oil pressure switch
26. Remote reading therm. transmitter
27. Automatic starter carb. (only with automatic transmission)
28. Reversing light switch with starter lock (only with automatic transmission)
29. Reversing light switch
30. 2 pin plug terminal (only with automatic transmission)
31. Connection for fuel pump
32. Solder point
33. Fuse box
34. Solder point
35. Earth (ground)
36. Blower switch
37. Cigar lighter
38. Wiper speed switch
39. Wiper washer transmitter
40. Brake light switch
41. Instrument set
    - (a) Illuminated scale
    - (b) Clock
    - (c) Tachometer
    - (d) Coolant temperature gauge
    - (e) Fuel gauge
    - (f) Charging lamp (red)
    - (g) Oil pressure telltale (orange)
    - (h) High beam telltale (blue)
    - (i) Flasher control (green)
    - (k) 12 pin plug
    - (m) 3 pin plug (clock)
    - (n) 3 pin plug (rev. counter)
    - (p) Brake fluid level (red)
42. 5 pin plug
43. Starter relay (only with automatic transmission)
44. Ignition switch I = Off; II = O; III = On; IV = Start
45. Light switch
46. Hazard flasher switch
47. 9 pin plug terminal to turn indicator switch
48. Turn indicator switch
49. 6 pin plug to dip switch
50. Signal button
51. Dip switch
52. Connection for number plate light and fog lamp
53. Door double contact
54. Hazard flasher
55. Interior light
56. Connection for heater rear window
57. Selector lever light connection
58. 12 pin plug to instrument set
59. Heater rear window
60. Selector gate light
61. Fuel gauge transmitter
62. Door contact
63. Right-hand rear light
    - (a) Reversing light
    - (b) Brake light
    - (c) Flasher
    - (d) Tail light
64. Number plate light
65. Earth (ground)
66. Left-hand rear light
    - (a) Reversing light
    - (b) Brake light
    - (c) Flasher
    - (d) Tail light
67. Connection for rev. counter
80. HT ignition system relay
81. Series resistance
82. Buzzer contact
83. Connection for buzzer contact
84. Buzzer
85. R.H. side marker light
86. R.H. side light connector
87. Solder point 58 K
88. Solder point 31
89. L.H. side marker light connection
90. L.H. side marker light
91. Brake fluid level switch
92. Cable connector
93. Cable connector

BL = blue
BR = brown
GE = yellow
GN = green
GR = grey
RT = red
SW = black
VI = violet
WS = white

Wiring diagram 2002

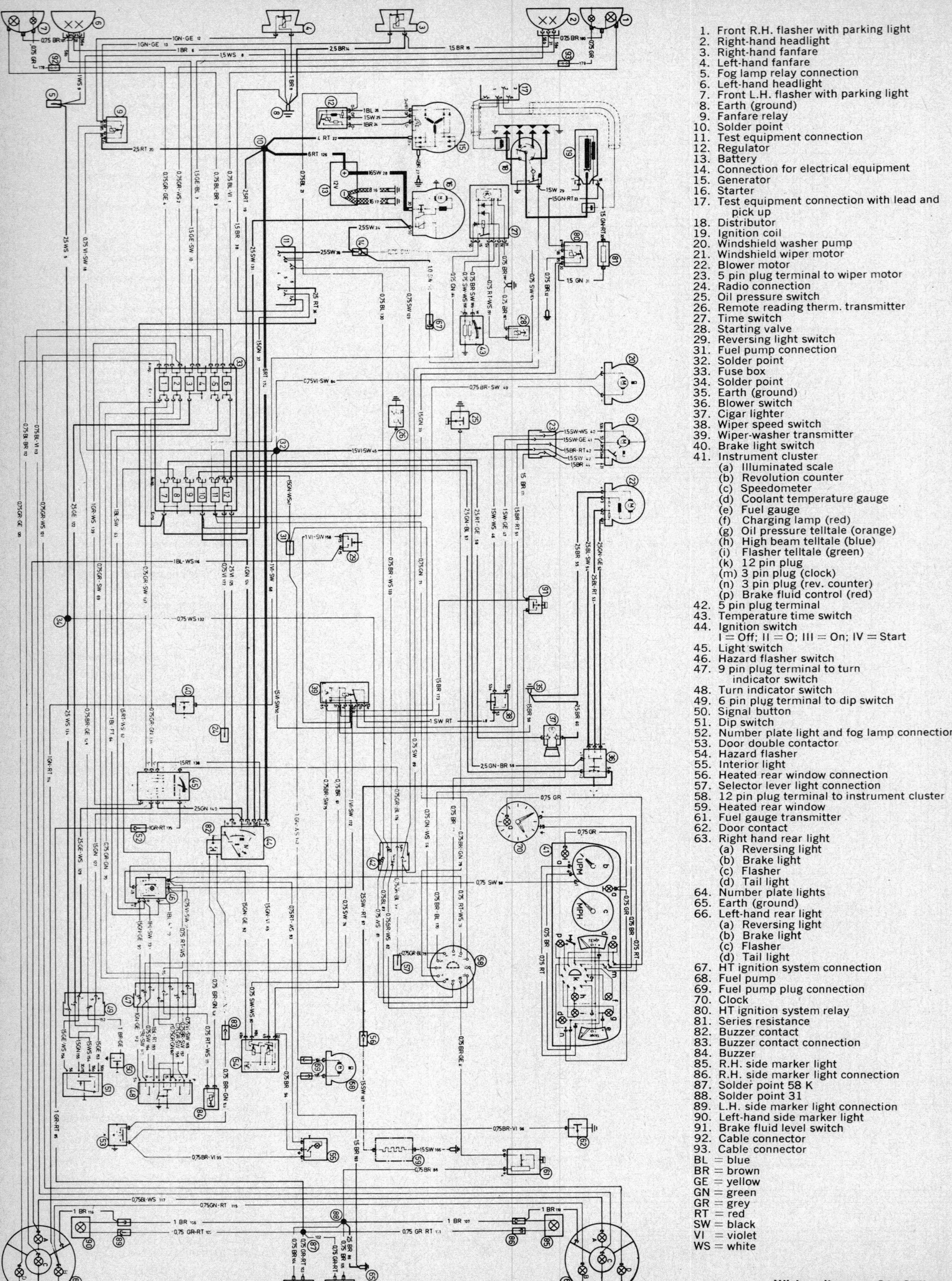

1. Front R.H. flasher with parking light
2. Right-hand headlight
3. Right-hand fanfare
4. Left-hand fanfare
5. Fog lamp relay connection
6. Left-hand headlight
7. Front L.H. flasher with parking light
8. Earth (ground)
9. Fanfare relay
10. Solder point
11. Test equipment connection
12. Regulator
13. Battery
14. Connection for electrical equipment
15. Generator
16. Starter
17. Test equipment connection with lead and pick up
18. Distributor
19. Ignition coil
20. Windshield washer pump
21. Windshield wiper motor
22. Blower motor
23. 5 pin plug terminal to wiper motor
24. Radio connection
25. Oil pressure switch
26. Remote reading therm. transmitter
27. Time switch
28. Starting valve
29. Reversing light switch
31. Fuel pump connection
32. Solder point
33. Fuse box
34. Solder point
35. Earth (ground)
36. Blower switch
37. Cigar lighter
38. Wiper speed switch
39. Wiper-washer transmitter
40. Brake light switch
41. Instrument cluster
    (a) Illuminated scale
    (b) Revolution counter
    (c) Speedometer
    (d) Coolant temperature gauge
    (e) Fuel gauge
    (f) Charging lamp (red)
    (g) Oil pressure telltale (orange)
    (h) High beam telltale (blue)
    (i) Flasher telltale (green)
    (k) 12 pin plug
    (m) 3 pin plug (clock)
    (n) 3 pin plug (rev. counter)
    (p) Brake fluid control (red)
42. 5 pin plug terminal
43. Temperature time switch
44. Ignition switch
    I = Off; II = O; III = On; IV = Start
45. Light switch
46. Hazard flasher switch
47. 9 pin plug terminal to turn indicator switch
48. Turn indicator switch
49. 6 pin plug terminal to dip switch
50. Signal button
51. Dip switch
52. Number plate light and fog lamp connection
53. Door double contactor
54. Hazard flasher
55. Interior light
56. Heated rear window connection
57. Selector lever light connection
58. 12 pin plug terminal to instrument cluster
59. Heated rear window
61. Fuel gauge transmitter
62. Door contact
63. Right hand rear light
    (a) Reversing light
    (b) Brake light
    (c) Flasher
    (d) Tail light
64. Number plate lights
65. Earth (ground)
66. Left-hand rear light
    (a) Reversing light
    (b) Brake light
    (c) Flasher
    (d) Tail light
67. HT ignition system connection
68. Fuel pump
69. Fuel pump plug connection
70. Clock
80. HT ignition system relay
81. Series resistance
82. Buzzer contact
83. Buzzer contact connection
84. Buzzer
85. R.H. side marker light
86. R.H. side marker light connection
87. Solder point 58 K
88. Solder point 31
89. L.H. side marker light connection
90. Left-hand side marker light
91. Brake fluid level switch
92. Cable connector
93. Cable connector

BL = blue
BR = brown
GE = yellow
GN = green
GR = grey
RT = red
SW = black
VI = violet
WS = white

Wiring diagram 2002Tii

SERIAL NUMBER IDENTIFICATION

The manufacturer's plate, chassis number and engine number are the means of identifying your car, and must be quoted in all correspondence with the dealer when requesting information or ordering spare parts.

Engine number location on rear left side of crankcase.

The manufacturer's plate is located at the back of the engine compartment on the right. The chassis number is also located at the back of the engine compartment next to the lock. The engine number is on the rear left hand side of the crankcase.

TUNE-UP PROCEDURES

Spark Plugs

First disconnect the spark plug wires from the plug insulators. To remove the wires, twist the end of the wire slightly to break it free of the insulator and then pull it from the top of the plug.

Remove the plug with a socket wrench and the correct socket. Examine the plugs for defective components and replace if necessary. Install the plugs by reversing the removal procedure. Remember not to overtorque the plugs.

Breaker Points and Condenser

Breaker points can be removed by removing the primary breaker connection and removing the point hold down screw.

CAUTION: *Guard against losing the screw in the distributor housing.*

To install the new points, first clean any grease from the points and then lubricate the felt insert in the distributor cam. Lubricate the cam and follower. Install the points and make the necessary connections. Replace the distributor cap and check the ignition timing.

Distributor internal components

1. Point main connection
2. Point hold down screw
3. Felt lubricator
4. Cam rubbing block

The condenser is located on the side of the distributor housing. It may be replaced by removing the hold down screw and the electrical connection. Installation is the reverse of removal. Make certain that the condenser is properly grounded.

Dwell Angle

To check engine dwell, connect a dwell meter to the negative pole of the ignition coil and the other lead to a good ground. It is important that the meter be at the proper setting (4 cyl or 6 cyl). Start the engine and read the proper scale. If the dwell is correct, stop the engine and disconnect the dwell meter. If the dwell is not correct, make adjustments to the ignition points to obtain the correct reading.

Ignition Timing

To set the ignition timing, remove and plug the vacuum hose after the engine has reached operating temperature. Using a strobe timing light, the correct timing is obtained when the center of the ball is visible at the edge of the inspection hole. If the setting is not correct, loosen the distributor and turn it until the ball is in the correct position.

Timing axcess hole

On some models it is necessary to increase the idle speed before setting the timing.

Valve Lash

Check valve lash by removing the valve cover to gain access to the rocker arm assembly. It will be necessary to rotate the engine in order to adjust the valves. Turn the engine until it is positioned at top dead center (TDC) of No. 1 cylinder. Loosen the rocker arm nut and insert the proper feeler gauge between the valve and the eccentric. Adjust the eccentric and tighten the locknut when the proper adjustment is obtained.

NOTE: *Valve clearance should never be measured between the rocker pad and the cam.*

After adjusting the No. 1 valves, continue with 3, 4, and 2 in that order.

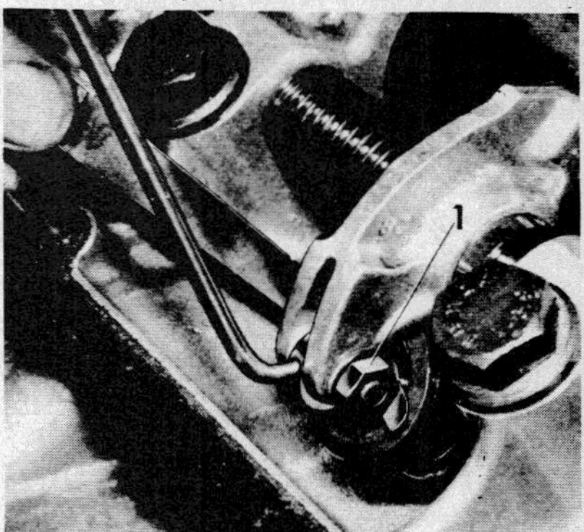

Adjusting the valve

Carburetor

(See "Fuel System" for further adjustments)

Idle Speed and Mixture

On 1600 and 2002 models, adjust the idle speed to 800 rpm by regulating the idle speed adjusting screw. Turn the idle mixture screw slowly until the engine runs erratically. Make further adjustments to the mixture screw so that the

Carburetor adjusting screws

1. Idle speed adjusting screw
2. Mixture screw

Weber carburetors adjusting screws
1. to 4. Mixture regulating screws (2002Ti)
5. Synchronizing screw
6. Idle speed adjusting screw

engine runs smoothly. Adjust the idle speed to specifications if it has changed.

On 2002Ti models, tighten the four mixture screws until they lightly contact their seats. This is done with the engine stopped. Turn each of the screws one half turn counterclockwise. Back out the synchronizing screw until it no longer contacts the throttle lever. Loosen the idle speed adjusting screw as far as possible and tighten the synchronizing screw until it just contacts the throttle lever. Tighten the idle speed adjusting screw until it just contacts the lever and then tighten it two full turns from that point.

The 2002Ti can also be adjusted with the engine running using a Uni-Syn®. To adjust, remove the air cleaner, start the engine, and adjust the idle to 1200 rpm. Adjust all four carburetors using the Uni-Syn® to balance the carburetors. Air flow is correct when the indicator on the gauge remains at zero.

Adjust carburetor no. 2 to equal carburetor no. 3 by using the synchronizing screw. Then adjust carburetor no. 1 to equal the input of carburetor no. 2 by using the connecting screw. Adjust carburetor no. 3 to equal no. 4. If the engine loses rpm during this procedure, increase the engine idle speed to keep the plugs from fouling.

After synchronizing the carburetors, set the mixture adjustments so that the engine runs smoothly. Set the idle speed to 800 rpm.

Adjusting carburetors 2 and 3
5. Synchronizing screw

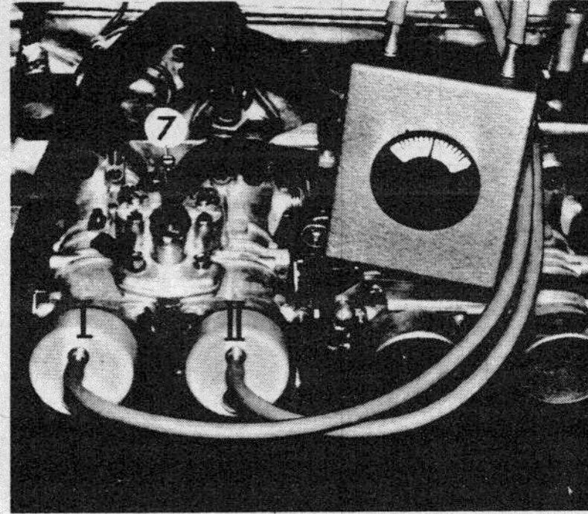

Adjusting carburetors 1 and 2

Adjusting carburetors 3 and 4
8. Connecting screw

The 2002Tii carburetor is adjusted in the following manner.

1. Run the engine until it reaches operating temperature. The air regulating cone must project at least 0.39 in.
2. Measure the distance from the fuel adjusting lever to the collar nut. It should be 0.157 in.
3. The threaded throttle pin must contact the stop screw.
4. If the above adjustments cannot be made, check the warm-up sensor (which should only be checked in the cold position). With a screwdriver, press out the air regulating cone so that retaining plate (6073) may be inserted into the air regulating cone. At this point, distance (A) must be 0.102 in.
5. If after adjusting the warm up sensor, the prescribed specifications are still not reached, the sensor must be replaced.

Adjusting the air regulating cone

Also, the thermo-element may be defective.

6. Set the idle speed to 900 rpm.

Carburetor adjustment on 2500 and 2800 models are made in the following manner.

Before adjusting the carburetor, make certain that the valve clearance, dwell angle, and ignition timing are correctly set. Warm the engine to operating temperature and remove the air cleaner. Turn the air/fuel adjustment screws until they just seat and then turn them out 1 ½–2 turns. Disconnect the linkage bar on the rear carburetor.

1. Start the engine and set the idle speed to 900 rpm. Synchronize the butterflys.
1. Using a vacuum gauge make sure that the vacuum is equal at each carburetor.
3. Adjust the engine to maximum speed by turning the two fuel/air screws.
4. Adjust the idle to 900 rpm.
5. Adjust the length of the linkage bar so that the engine speed is not changed when the bar is placed in position.
6. Install the air filter. The idle speed should drop by 100 rpm.

ENGINE ELECTRICAL

Distributor

Removal and Installation

1. To remove the distributor for overhaul or replacement, remove the cap and rotate the crankshaft to place No. 1 cylinder in firing position with the timing marks properly aligned.
2. The distributor rotor should point to the notch on the distributor housing.
3. Disconnect the vacuum line and the primary ignition wire, and remove the fastening bolts and distributor.

Rotor position for distributor removal

4. Remove the distributor mounting bolts and take out the distributor.
5. Remove the distributor flange.
6. When replacing, coat the mating surfaces of the distributor and the cylinder head with a non-hardening sealer. In-

stall the distributor with the vacuum chamber on the right when viewed facing forward. The rotor should be just about aligned with the mark on the distributor housing.

7. Set the point gap and dwell angle and adjust ignition timing.

Alternator Removal and Replacement

CAUTION: *Never disconnect any leads to the alternator when the battery is connected.*

Alternator connection location

To remove the alternator, disconnect the negative lead from the battery and pull off the multiple plug from the back of the unit. Remove the other cables from the alternator (Brown-Earth, Red-B+). On Tii models, it is necessary to remove the battery and the stabilizer. Remove the attaching bolts and remove the unit from the vehicle.

Install the unit by reversing the removal procedure. The belt tension should be adjusted so that there is 0.02–0.04 in. deflection at the center of the belt.

Belt tension adjustment

Regulator Removal and Installation

Pull off plug connection and remove the attaching screws.

There are two types of regulators: suppressed and unsuppressed. The suppressed model is used with an installed radio and is recognized by a white band. The unsuppressed has a yellow band.

Starter

Starter Service

1. Disconnect the battery ground cable from the negative terminal.
2. Remove the starter cables and the starter.

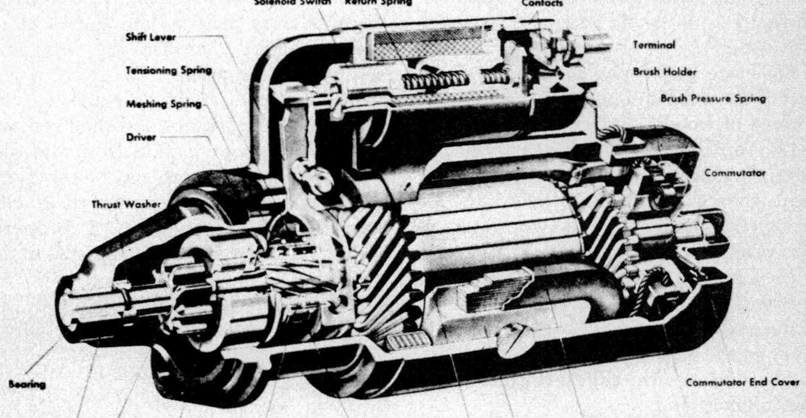

Cross-section of a starter motor

3. Remove the solenoid from the motor housing, saving the gasket.
4. Remove the support bracket and the dust cap.
5. Remove the brush holder plate and take out the brushes.
6. Remove the through-bolts and separate the commutator end-frame and field frame assemblies.
7. Remove the bolt, nut and lockwasher from the solenoid shift lever fulcrum.
8. Remove the armature and drive assembly from the shift (yoke) lever. To remove the drive assembly from the armature, place a cylinder, such as a 2 in. pipe coupling, over the end of the shaft to bear against the pinion stop retainer.
9. Tap the retainer toward the armature to uncover the snap ring. (Models with castle nut–remove the cotter pin and the left-hand thread castle nut).
10. Remove the snap ring from the groove in the shaft and slide the retainer and pinion drive assembly from the shaft.
11. Remove the spring.
12. Carefully inspect all mechanical parts for wear and damage, wash in kerosene, and blow dry with compressed air. Do not submerge the armature or roller clutches in solvent. Check the condition and tension of the brushes. Check the field coil and armature commutator with AC test lamp for short circuits to the shaft and pole pieces. The test lamp should not light.
13. Check the brush holder for shorts, inspect the armature commutator for burnt or flat spots. Coat the polished

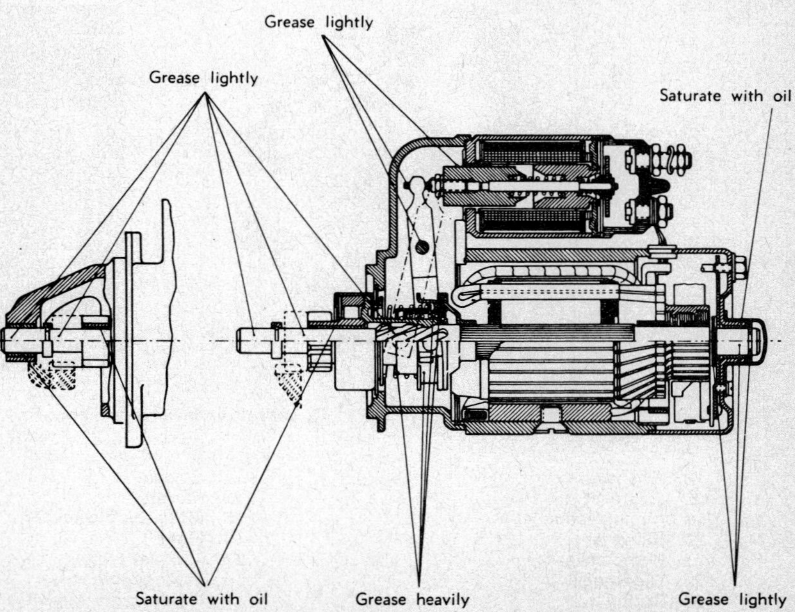

Starter lubrication points

metal surfaces, other than the commutator, with engine oil. Lubricate the illustrated points.

14. When reassembling the starter, lubricate the armature shaft with silicone grease.

15. Install the assist spring and then the drive assembly with the pinion outward.

16. Slide the pinion stop retainer down over the shaft with the recessed side out.

17. Place a new snap ring on the drive end of the shaft and hold it in place with a block of wood.

18. Tap the block with a hammer to force the snap-ring over the end of the shaft, then slide the ring down into the groove in the shaft. Pry the stop retainer into position over snap ring.

19. Lubricate the drive housing bushings with silicone grease and set the armature drive assembly with the shift lever in the housing.

20. Lubricate the shift lever linkage at the solenoid end.

21. Position the shift lever and attach the bolt, nut and lockwasher. Use care in tightening the pole shoe screws to prevent distortion of parts.

22. Position the field frame over the armature and place the washer on the commutator end of the armature assembly.

23. Install the commutator end-frame after lubricating the bushing.Install the through-bolts and tighten.

24. Connect the field leads to the motor terminal of the solenoid with the connecting nut and washer.

25. Attach the solenoid, with its gasket, to the drive housing. Connect the four brushes and install the cover band.

FUEL SYSTEM

Fuel Pump

Removal and Installation

Remove the mechanical fuel pumps by disconnecting the fuel line and block in some manner. Remove the attaching screws and the pump.

On electrical pumps, it is necessary to disconnect the battery and then remove the electrical connection from the fuel pump before the pump may be removed.

When installing the pump, make certain that the connection is properly made. The nose of the plug must fit in the groove.

Fuel pump

Carburetors

Removal and Installation

1600–2002

1. Remove the air cleaner and the choke cable.

2. Remove the carburetor clamp spring, accelerator rod and the vacuum hose.

3. Remove the carburetor attaching nuts and the carburetor.

4. To install the unit reverse the removal procedure using new flange gaskets. When attaching the choke cable sheath the sheath must not project more than .06 inches in front of the clamp. The choke lever must be placed against the stop before the clamp screw is tightened.

2002TI

1. Remove the air cleaner and the choke cable.

2. Loosen the retaining clip on the oil dip stick and remove the fuel lines.

3. Remove the carburetor linkage by pulling off the spring and loosening the support bracket. Move the accelerator rod away from the rotary shaft.

4. Remove the carburetor from the intake manifold and remove the gaskets.

To install use the following procedure.

1. Position the carburetor on the manifold.The right hand carburetor butterfly lever must be pulled back slightly. For this purpose insert a suitable tool to keep the butterfly open.

2. When inserting the torsion spring make certain it is positioned securely.

3. Position the choke cable with the sheath in the same position as the 1600 models.

4. Install the air cleaner housing.

2500–2800

1. Remove the air filter housing, fuel line and the vacuum pipe. Also disconnect the pressure bar.

2. Remove the starter cap, carburetor attaching nuts and pull off the carburetor.

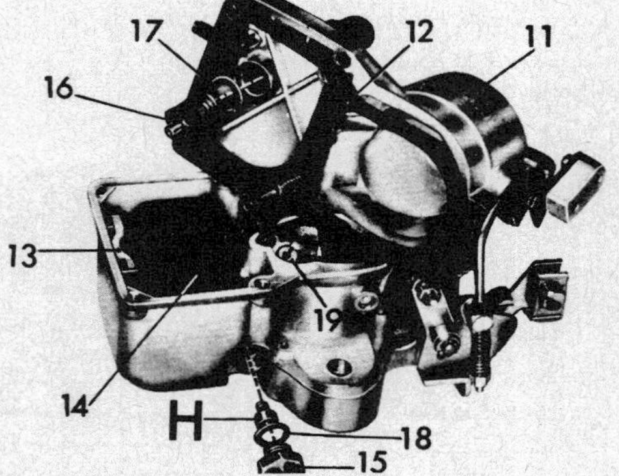

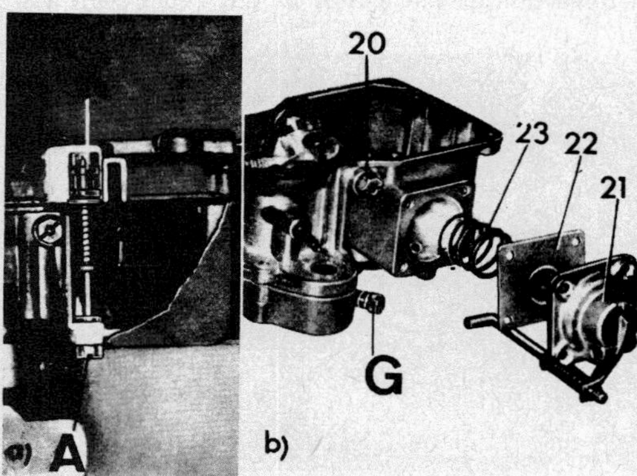

Downdraft carburetor components

18. Washer
(h)—Main jet
19. Air correction jet
20. Idling jet
21. Pump cover
22. Diaphragm
23. Spring

11. Cover
12. Gasket
13. Float spindle keeper
14. Float
15. Main jet plug
16. Float needle valve
17. Float needle valve gasket

(a)—Enrichment valve
(k)—Piston
(g)—Idle mixture adjustment screw

To install:

1. Position the carburetor on the intake manifold.

NOTE: *The carburetor mounting holes are of different sizes. The hole with the smallest diameter must face the cylinder head.*

2. When installing the cap the follower must be hooked to the bi-metal spring. The notch in the starter must be flush with the ridge on the starter body.

3. Install the fuel and vacuum lines and the air cleaner.

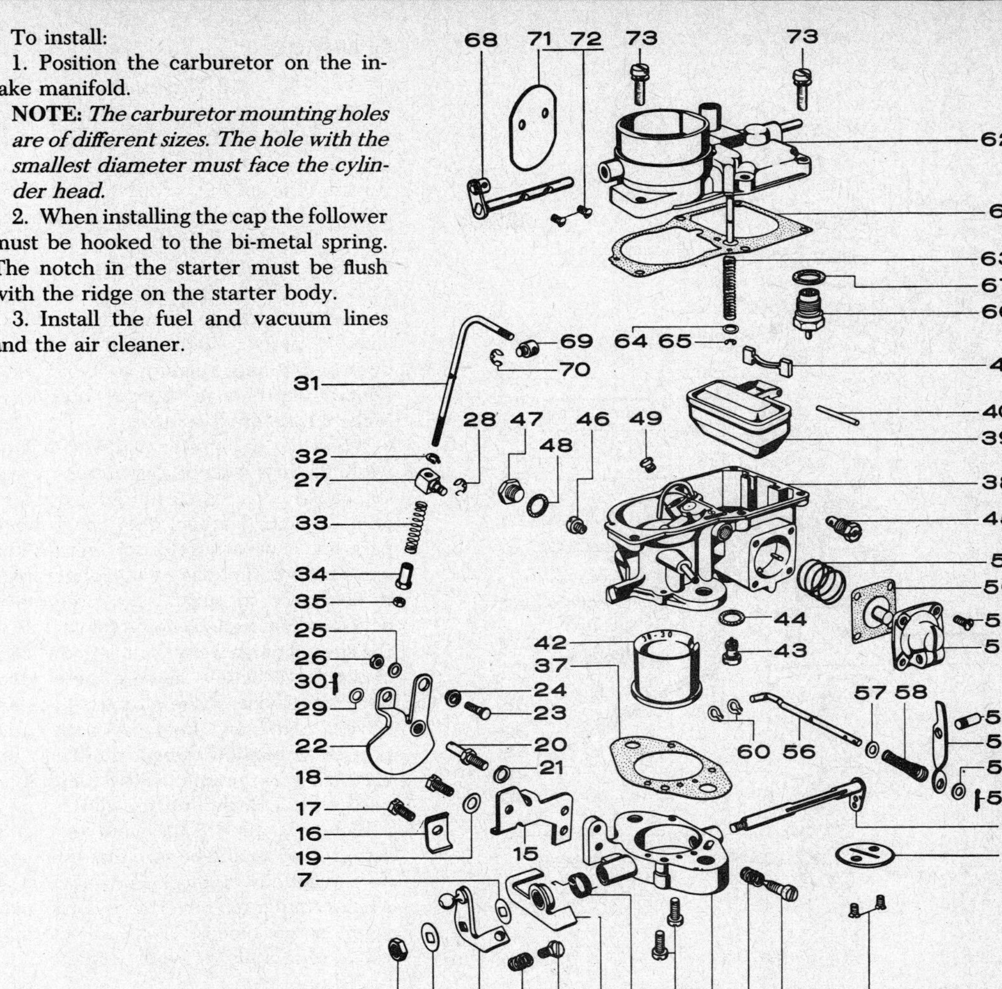

Exploded view of Solex 36 PDSI carburetor used in 1600 models

1. Throttle body
2. Throttle spindle with intermediate lever
3. Throttle butterfly
4. Fixing screw
5. Return spring
6. Intermediate lever compl.
7. Distance washer (between throttle lever and intermediate lever)
8. Throttle lever compl.
9. Tab washer
10. Throttle spindle end nut
11. Slow running adjustment screw (on throttle lever)
12. Slow running adjustment screw spring
13. Volume control screw
14. Volume control screw spring
15. Bowden cable bracket
16. Cable clamp
17. Clamping screw
18. Hexagon screw (for bowden cable bracket)
19. Spring washer (for hexagon screw)
20. Bearing pin
21. Bearing pin spring washer
22. Starter lever
23. Clamping screw
24. Bushing
25. Washer
26. Hexagon nut
27. Grip roller
28. Spring washer
29. Washer
30. Split pin
31. Starter control rod
32. Clamping ring (for starter control rod)
33. Spring (for starter control rod)
34. Shoulder nut (for starter control rod)
35. Hexagon nut (for starter control rod)
36. Throttle body fixing screw
37. Insulating gasket
38. Float chamber with pressed-in emulsion tube and injector tube
39. Float 8.5 gr.
40. Float toggle spindle
41. Holder for float toggle spindle
42. Choke tube
43. Enrichment valve
44. Enrichment valve washer
45. Pilot jet
46. Main jet
47. Main jet screw plug
48. Screw plug washer
49. Air correction jet
50. Diaphragm compl.
51. Diaphragm spring
52. Pump cover
53. Pump lever
54. Pump lever spindle
55. Fixing screw
56. Pump control rod
57. Pump control rod washer
58. Pump control rod spring
59. Pump control rod split pin
60. Pump control rod clip
61. Float chamber cover gasket
62. Float chamber cover compl. with depression actuated piston
63. Spring (for depression actuated piston)

— Cover plate

64. Washer
65. Spring washer
66. Float needle valve 2 mm with ball
67. Float needle valve washer
68. Strangler spindle compl. (with lever, grip roller)
69. Grip roller
70. Grip roller washer
71. Strangler
72. Strangler fixing screw
73. Assembly screw with spring washer

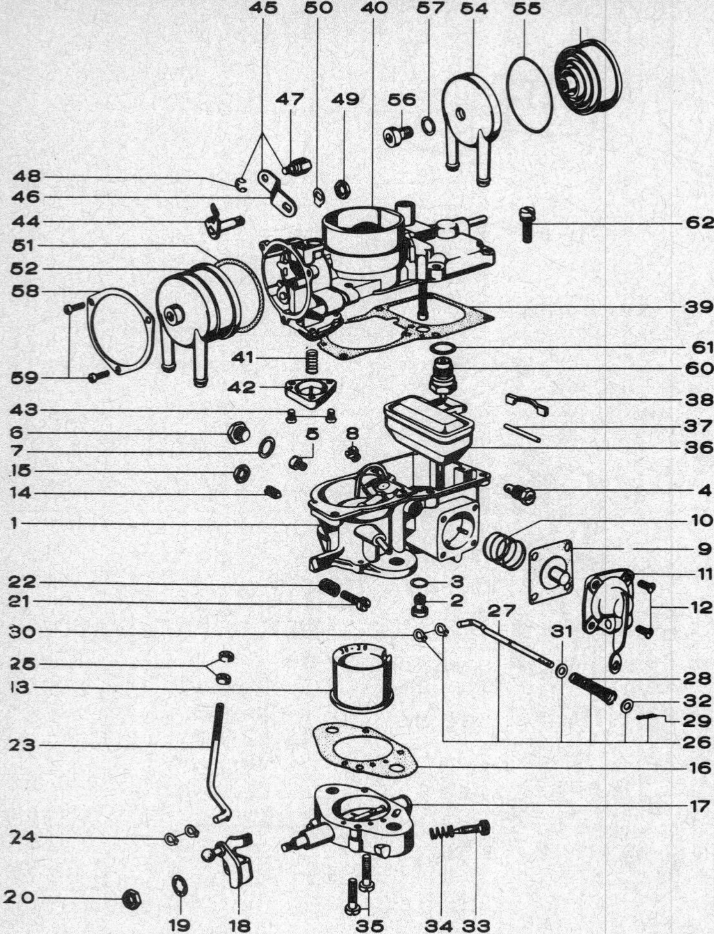

Exploded view of Solex 40 PDSIT carburetor used on 2002 and 2000 models

— Carburetor compl.
1 Body compl.
2 Enrichment valve compl.
3 Enrichment valve washer
4 Idle jet compl.
5 Main jet
6 Main jet screw plug
7 Screw plug washer
8 Air correction jet
9 Diaphragm compl.
10 Diaphragm spring
11 Pump cover compl.
12 Pump cover fixing screw
13 Choke tube
14 Choke tube fixing screw
15 Hexagon nut
16 Insulating gasket
17 Throttle body compl.
18 Throttle level compl.
19 Toothed washer (on throttle spindle)
20 Throttle spindle end nut
21 Slow running adjustment screw
22 Slow running adjustment screw spring
23 Control rod (between starter and throttle lever)
24 Control rod clip
25 Control rod nut
26 Control rod compl. (between intermediate and pump lever)
27 Control rod
28 Spring
29 Split pin
30 Clip
31 Washer
32 Washer
33 Volume control screw
34 Volume control screw spring
35 Throttle body fixing screw
36 Float compl.
37 Float toggle spindle
38 Float toggle spindle holder
39 Float chamber cover gasket
40 Float chamber cover compl.
41 Spring (for starter diaphragm)
42 Valve cover (for starter diaphragm)
43 Valve cover fixing screw
44 Spindle with abutment lever compl.
45 Strangler lever compl.
46 Strangler lever
47 Clamp roller
48 Clip
49 Hexagon nut
50 Clip
51 Insulating washer
52 Starter cover compl.
53 Starter cover compl.
54 Water connection
55 O-ring
56 Cylindrical screw (with internal hexagon)
57 Washer
58 Retaining screw
59 Fixing screw (for retaining ring)
60 Float needle valve compl.
61 Float needle valve washer
62 Assembly screw

Overhaul

All Types

Efficient carburetion depends greatly on careful cleaning and inspection during overhaul since dirt, gum, water, or varnish in or on the carburetor parts are often responsible for poor performance.

Overhaul your carburetor in a clean, dust-free area. Carefully disassemble the carburetor, referring often to the exploded views. Keep all similar and look-alike parts segregated during disassembly and cleaning to avoid accidental interchange during assembly. Make a note of all jet sizes.

When the carburetor is disassembled, wash all parts (except diaphragms, electric choke units, pump plunger, and any other plastic, leather, fiber, or rubber parts) in clean carburetor solvent. Do not leave parts in the solvent any longer than is necessary to sufficiently loosen the deposits. Excessive cleaning may remove the special finish from the float bowl and choke valve bodies, leaving these parts unfit for service. Rinse all parts in clean solvent and blow them dry with compressed air or allow them to air dry. Wipe clean all cork, plastic, leather, and fiber parts with a clean, lint-free cloth.

Blow out all passages and jets with compressed air and be sure that there are no restrictions or blockages. Never use wire or similar tools to clean jets, fuel passages, or air bleeds. Clean all jets and valves separately to avoid accidental interchange.

Check all parts for wear or damage. If wear or damage is found, replace the defective parts. Especially check the following:

1. Check the float needle and seat for wear. If wear is found, replace the complete assembly.
2. Check the float hinge pin for wear and the float(s) for dents or distortion. Replace the float if fuel has leaked into it.
3. Check the throttle and choke shaft bores for wear or an out-of-round condition. Damage or wear to the throttle arm, shaft, or shaft bore will often require replacement of the throttle body. These parts require a close tolerance of fit; wear may allow air leakage, which could affect starting and idling.

NOTE: *Throttle shafts and bushings are not included in overhaul kits. They can be purchased separately.*

4. Inspect the idle mixture adjusting needles for burrs or grooves. Any such condition requires replacement of the needle, since you will not be able to obtain a satisfactory idle.
5. Test the accelerator pump check valves. They should pass air one way but not the other. Test for proper seating by blowing and sucking on the valve. Replace the valve if necessary. If the valve

1, 1a Throttle valve
2. Pin screw
3. Screw
4. Screw
5. Joint lever
6. Return spring
7. Safety washer
8. Roller
9. Safety washer
10. Flat washer
11. Safety washer
12. Idle mixture screw
13. Pressure spring
14. Adjustment screw
15. Spring washer
16. Hex head nut
17. Flat washer
18. Throttle lever
19. Safety washer
20. Spacer
21. Choke body
22. Return spring
23. Diaphragm spring
24. Pressure spring
25. Valve cover
26. Screw
27. Seal ring
28. Hex head nut
29. Countersunk screw
30. Transfer lever
31. Transfer lever
32. Spring washer
33. Hex head nut
34. Gasket
35. Gasket
36. Star washer
37. Countersunk screw
38. Spring washer
39. Screw
40. Safety washer
41. Stop lever
42. Pressure spring
43. Stop screw
44. Hex head nut
45. Choke cover
46. Stop ring
47. Hex head nut
48. Hex head nut
49. Clamp
50. Isolation flange
51. Spring washer
52. Screw
53. Float bowl
54. Spring washer
55. Bearing bolt
56. Safety washer
57. Cheesehead screw
58. Spring washer
59. Vacuum chamber
60. Lockwasher
61. Bearing bolt
62. Operating lever
63. Cheesehead screw
64. Hex head nut
65. Expansion ring
66. Threaded pin
67. Cable holder
68. Seal ring
69. Spring washer
70. Cheesehead screw
71. Connecting rod
72. Return spring
73. Connecting rod
74. Flat washer
75. Pressure spring
76. Washer
77. Tension ring
78. Seal ring
79. Air valve
80. Bushing
81. Needle valve
82. Seal ring
83. Float
84. Shaft

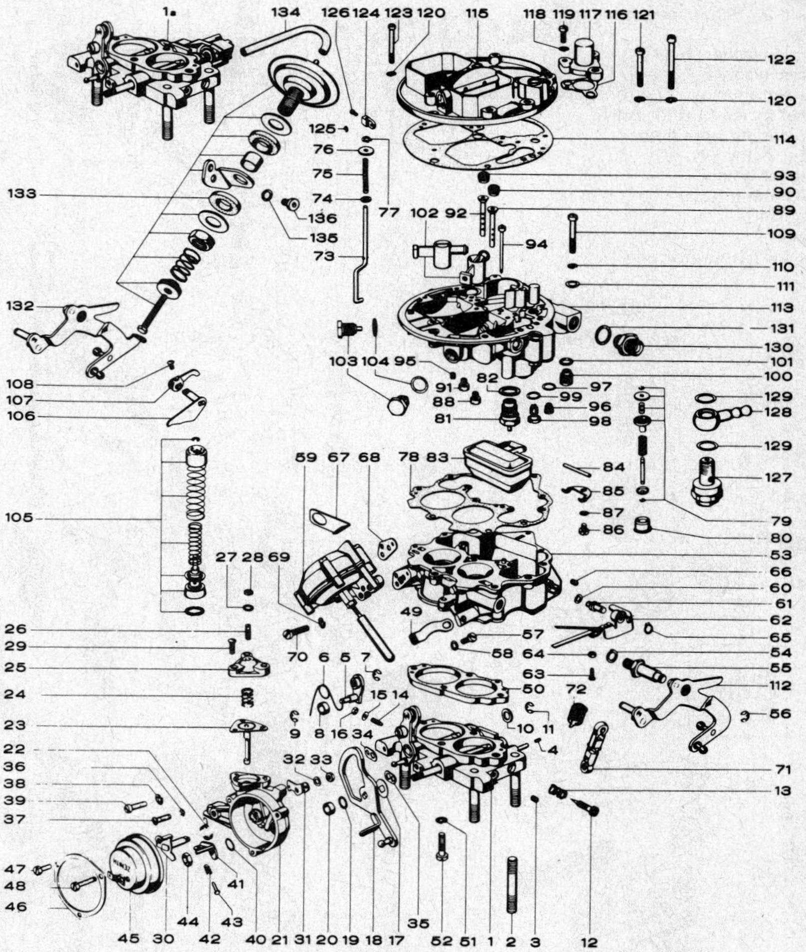

Exploded view of Zenith 35/40 INAT carburetor used in dual installation on the 2500, 2800, and 2800 CS.

85. Bracket
86. Cheesehead screw
87. Spring washer
88. Main jet
89. Mixture tube
90. Air correction jet
91. Main jet
92. Mixture tube
93. Air correction jet
94. Idle jet
95. Jet
96. Pump suction valve
97. Seal ring
98. Pump pressure valve
99. Seal ring
100. Jet
101. Seal ring
102. Sprayer
103. Pressure screw
104. Seal ring
105. Pump piston
106. Pump lever
107. Inner pump lever
108. Countersunk screw
109. Cheesehead screw
110. Lockwasher
111. Spring washer
112. Complete operating lever
113. Platin block
114. Carburetor body gasket
115. Carburetor top
116. Seal ring
117. Cover
118. Lockwasher
119. Cheesehead screw
120. Lockwasher
121. Cheesehead screw
122. Cheesehead screw
123. Cheesehead screw
124. Joint piece
125. Safety washer
126. Cheesehead screw
127. Fuel return valve
128. Ring hose piece
129. Seal ring
130. Threaded fitting
131. Seal ring
132. Operating lever
133. Vacuum regulator
134. Rubber hose
135. Lockwasher
136. Cheesehead screw

1 Jets inspection cover
2 Screw securing carburetor cover
2A Securing screw for well-bottom cover
3 Gasket for jets inspection cover
4 Normal washer
4A Normal washer
5 Carburetor cover
6 Gasket for carburetor cover
7 Emulsioning tube holder
8 Air corrector jet
9 Idling jet-holder
10 Emulsioning tube
11 Idling jet
12 Main jet
13 Plate for carburetor bowl

65 Spring for plunger
66 Pump plunger
67 Spring for idling adjustment screw
67A Throttle adjusting spring—DCOE 15
68 Idling adjustment screw
69 Throttle adjusting screw—DCOE 15
70 Screw for progression holes inspection
71 Gasket for pump jet
72 Pump jet
73 Seal
74 Screw plug
75 Intake and discharge valve
76 Starter jet
77 Float
78 Fulcrum pin
79 Ball for valve

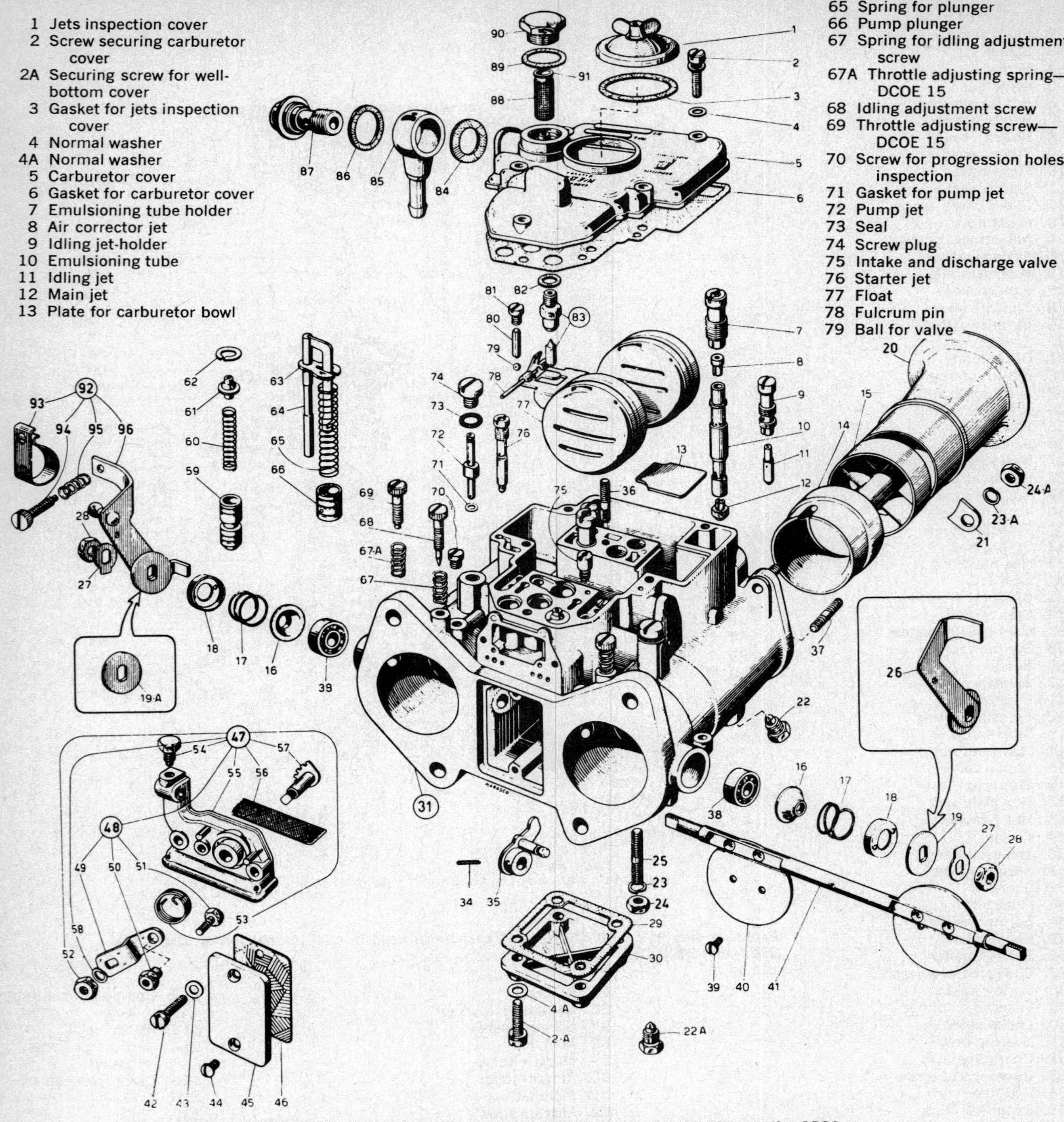

Exploded view of the Weber 45 DCOE carburetors used in dual installation on the 1800 TISA.

14 Choke
15 Auxiliary venturi
16 Dust cover
17 Spring
18 Spring retaining cover
19 Shim washer—DCOE 15
19A Shim washer—DCOE 16
20 Air intake horn
21 Retaining plate
22 Auxiliary venturi fixing screw
22A Choke fixing screw
23 Spring washer
23A Spring washer
24 Carburetor anchoring nut
24A Nut for air intake
25 Stud bolt
26 Throttle control lever DCOE 16
27 Lockwasher

28 Hexagonal nut
29 Gasket for cap
30 Cap for bottom of bowl
31 Carburetor body
34 Lever fixing pin
35 Pump control lever
36 Stud bolt
37 Stud bolt
38 Ball bearing
39 Throttle securing screw
40 Throttle valve
41 Throttle spindle
42 Starter control securing screw
43 Normal washer
44 Cap securing screw
45 Cap for pump opening
46 Gasket for cap
47 Starter control, including:

48 Starter control lever, complete with:
49 Starter lever
50 Nut for screw
51 Cable securing screw
52 Lever securing nut
53 Lever return spring
54 Sheath securing screw
55 Cover for sheath support
56 Strainer
57 Starter shaft
58 Spring washer
59 Starter valve
60 Spring for starter valve
61 Spring retainer and guide
62 Spring washer
63 Spring retaining plate
64 Pump control rod

80 Stuffing for ball
81 Retaining screw for stuffing ball
82 Gasket for needle valve
83 Needle valve
84 Gasket for union
85 Spherical union
86 Gasket for union
87 Screw plug for union
88 Strainer
89 Gasket for filter plug
90 Filter inspection plug
91 Plug for protecting strainer
92 Throttle control lever—DCOE 15, including:
93 Spring
94 Throttle adjusting screw
95 Spring
96 Throttle control lever

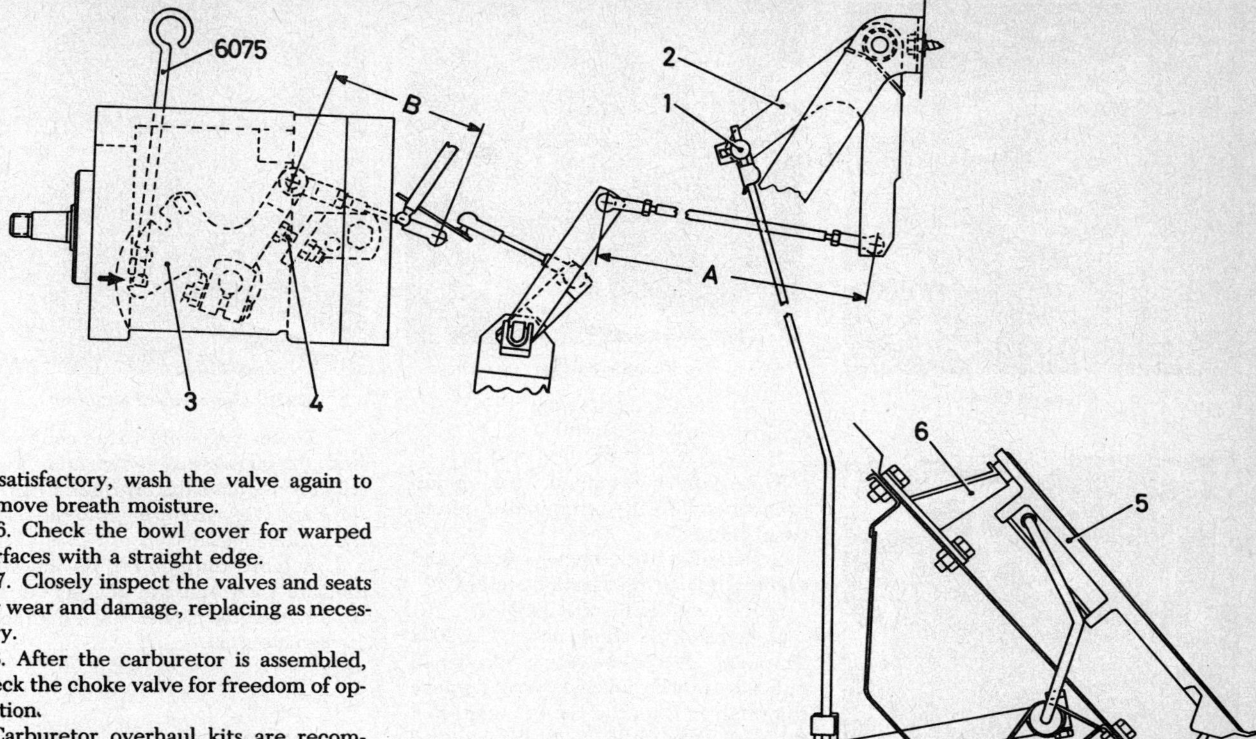

Accelerator linkage adjustment

is satisfactory, wash the valve again to remove breath moisture.

6. Check the bowl cover for warped surfaces with a straight edge.

7. Closely inspect the valves and seats for wear and damage, replacing as necessary.

8. After the carburetor is assembled, check the choke valve for freedom of operation.

Carburetor overhaul kits are recommended for each overhaul. These kits contain all gaskets and new parts to replace those that deteriorate most rapidly. Failure to replace all parts supplied with the kit (especially gaskets) can result in poor performance later.

Some carburetor manufacturers supply overhaul kits of three basic types: minor repair; major repair; and gasket kits. Basically, they contain the following:

Minor Repair Kits:
- All gaskets
  - Float needle valve
  - Volume control screw
  - All diaphragms
  - Spring for the pump diaphragm

Major Repair Kits:
- All jets and gaskets
- All diaphragms
- Float needle valve
- Volume control screw
- Pump ball valve
- Main jet carrier
- Float
- Complete intermediate rod
- Intermediate pump lever
- Complete injector tube
- Some cover hold-down screws and washers

Gasket Kits:
- All gaskets

After cleaning and checking all components, reassemble the carburetor, using new parts and referring to the exploded view. When reassembling, make sure that all screws and jets are tight in their seats, but do not overtighten, as the tips will be distorted. Tighten all screws gradually, in rotation. Do not tighten needle valves into their seats; uneven jetting will result. Always use new gaskets. Be sure to adjust the float level when reassembling.

Throttle Linkage Adjustment

Remove the joint pin (1) from the transmission lever (2). Measure the length of rods (A) and (B). (A) should be 11.378 in. and B 3.346 in.

Position the pump regulating lever with pull hook 6075 in the lower hole.

Adjust the stop screw (4) so that it just contacts the pump regulating lever.

Press the accelerator pedal (5) against the full load stop (6). Adjust the joint pin (1) so that it allows easy insertion into the slot in the transmission lever (2). Tighten the joint pin and remove the pull hook 6075.

Choke Linkage Adjustment

To adjust the linkage, remove the air filter housing to gain access to the choke cable. The choke sleeve should protrude 0.53 in. past the support. If this is not done, it would not be possible to close the choke fully. Set the cable to the lowest notch on the instrument panel, press the choke against the stop, and secure the clamp screw.

ENGINE MECHANICAL

Engine Removal and Installation

1. Remove the hood and cover the fenders. Remove the air filter and the attaching hoses.

2. Disconnect the battery ground, remove the alternator plug and remove the starter leads. On some models it will be necessary to detach the automatic choke cable at the thermo-start valve and pull the cable loom out of the retainer at the gearbox.

Air cleaner vacuum line connection

Breather tube

Negative battery connection

Automatic choke cable location

Fuel hose and vacuum line location

Throttle linkage

1. Return spring
2. Clamp spring
3. Control rod

3. Remove the radiator, fuel pump connection and the temperature sensor connection.

4. Remove the heater hose and vacuum line at the intake manifold.

5. Remove the throttle linkage.

6. Remove the choke cable. On 2002 TI models, detach the return spring and pull the throttle linkage back. Remove the retainer from the torsion shaft. Pull the shaft back until the ball is free and then pull the shaft forward.

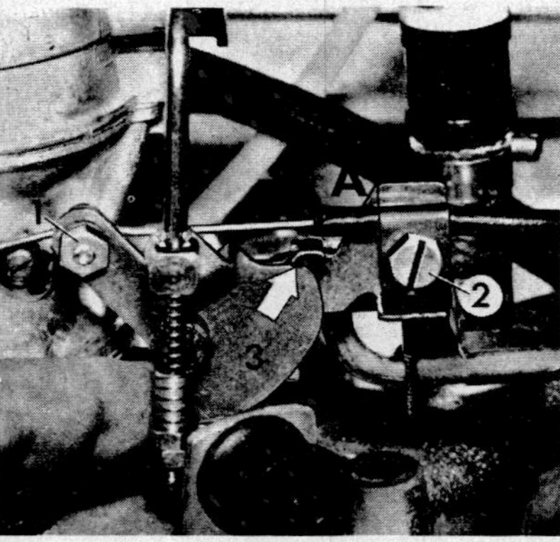

Choke cable

1. Clamp screw
2. Clamp
3. Choke lever
4. A=0.59 in.

Torsion shaft removal

1. Return spring
2. Pull rod
3. Retainer

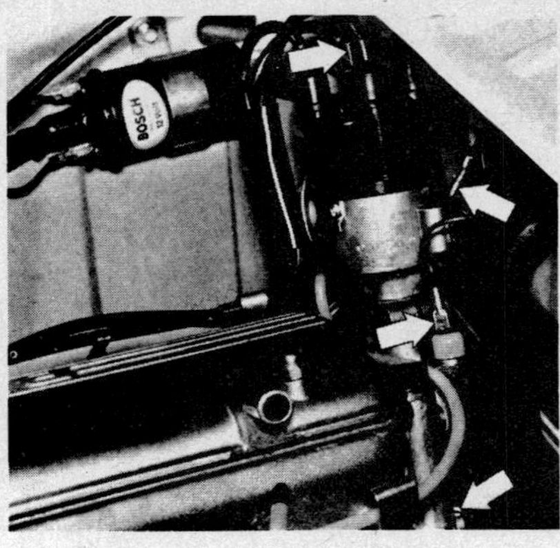
Distributor areas of attention

7. Remove the electrical connection from the oil pressure switch and the distributor. Remove the distributor cap and rotor and the water hose from the rear of the cylinder head.

8. Remove the pull rod on the intermediate shaft and the bearing support from the engine carrier. Take out the intermediate shaft.

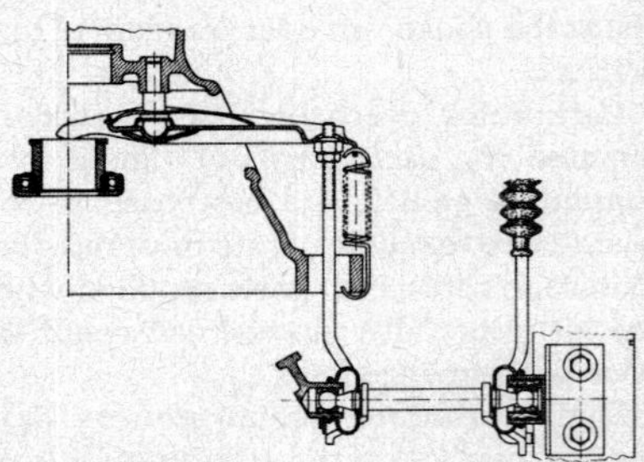
Removing the intermediate rod and the bearing support.

Removing the intermediate shaft and push rod.

NOTE: *On vehicles equipped with power steering, disconnect and secure the pump away from the working area.*

9. Check the clutch play before dismantling the clutch mechanism. If the free travel is less than 0.197 in., the clutch disc should be replaced.

10. Pull back the collar on the slave cylinder and lift out the circlip. Move the cylinder forward.

11. Loosen the left hand engine bushing.

12. Remove the selector lever by removing the retainer. Separate the lever from the rod.

13. Remove the exhaust pipe clamp and the exhaust pipe from the exhaust manifold.

Measuring the pushrod travel

1. Length A is 0.197 inches

Positioning the slave cylinder

Loosening the engine bushing

Removing the gear selection lever

Exhaust support

1. Retaining plate
2. Support bracket
3. Clamp

14. Remove the driveshaft from the transmission. Loosen the retaining screws at the center bearing

15. Attach the engine hoist. Remove the cross member and the speedometer shaft. If the transmission is equipped with a back-up light switch, detach it.

16. Loosen the right hand engine mount. Remove the windshield washer reservoir.

17. Lower the gearbox and lift the engine out toward the right side of the vehicle.

Installation is the reverse of removal. Observe the following when installing the engine:

1. The right hand engine mount stop must be set to 0.118 in.

2. The driveshaft center bearing should be preloaded forward 0.08 in.

3. When attaching the exhaust, connect the exhaust pipe to the manifold. Loosen the retaining plate and press the support against the exhaust pipe. Tighten the retaining plate to the gearbox and the support and then tighten the bracket. The tightening sequence must be done in this manner or severe noise will result.

4. Don't forget to replace the torsional retainer on the clutch slave cylinder.

5. The bearing support should be aligned at a 90° angle to the engine.

6. When securing the choke cable sleeve, the sleeve may only extend forward 0.59 in.The adjustment is obtained by placing the choke cable into the bottom notch and placing the choke lever against the stop. Tighten the clamp screw.

Cylinder Head

4-cylinder Models

Removal

1. Disconnect the following items: radiator hose from thermostat housing; vacuum hose from check valve; fuel line from fuel pump; temperature sensor from thermostat housing; throttle linkage from carburetor; choke cable from lever and sleeve from clamp; water hose from intake manifold and heater hose from cylinder head; and oil dipstick bracket.

2. Disconnect the wire plug connections on the distributor and on the oil pressure switch, and remove the distributor cap.

3. Disconnect the spark plug leads and cable from the ignition coil.

4. Detach the exhaust pipe from the manifold.

5. Remove the nuts and the cylinder head cover with its gasket. Note that when No. 1 cylinder is on TDC, the pointer will be opposite the 2nd notch in the drive pulley. The notch in the camshaft flange must coincide with the notch in the cylinder head.

Setting the engine to TDC

6. Detach the timing gear cover at the top. Loosen the chain tensioner plug and unscrew by hand.

CAUTION: *The spring is under heavy pressure. Depress the plug when loosening it.*

7. Remove the spring and plunger.

8. Bend down the lock plate tabs, remove the bolts and the camshaft sprocket. Tie up the chain, with wire, to the generator housing.

9. Remove the cylinder head bolts, cylinder head and gasket.

Installation

1. Tighten the cylinder head bolts in sequence 1–10. Tighten in three stages; 21.7 ft. lbs., 50.5 ft. lbs., and 49.2–52.0 ft. lbs. After test-running the engine and cooling to 95°F. or less, give the cylinder head bolts a final tightening to 49.2–52.0 ft. lbs. Then check and adjust valve clearance.

CAUTION: *Be sure the gasket water passage holes coincide exactly with those in the block and the head. The Ti cylinder head gasket can be used on the 1800 cc engine. But under no circumstances should the cylinder head gasket of an 1800 cc engine be used on the Ti engine.*

Cylinder Head Removal and Installation 6-cylinder Model

1. Drain the coolant from the radiator, engine block and heater bleeder, and disconnect all coolant hoses from the cylinder head.
2. Remove the carburetor fuel lines and the accelerator linkage.
3. Remove the vacuum line from the intake manifold which connects to the brake servo.
4. Remove all cooling hoses from the working area.
5. Position No. 1 cylinder at TDC. At this point the rotor should be pointing to the notch in the distributor body.
6. Remove the upper timing case cover.
7. Loosen and remove the chain tensioner piston.
8. Remove the chain sprocket after bending back the locking tabs.

NOTE: *When installing, position the chain and sprocket so that the sprocket pin is at the bottom left position. The upper hole in the sprocket must line up with the threaded hole in the head.*

9. Remove the exhaust pipe clamp and the pipes from the exhaust manifolds.
10. Loosen the cylinder head bolts and carefully remove the head.

Rocker Arm Removal and Replacement

Remove the guide plate bolts and attach rocker arm holder BMW 601 or an equivalent device, tightening the nuts down evenly. Take out the camshaft and guide plate. Remove the rocker arm holder.

Push the rocker arms (1) and thrust rings (2) far enough to one side on the rocker shaft (3) to permit removal of the circlips (4). Then drive the rocker shafts out the front.

When re-installing, align the rocker shafts immediately so that the cylinder head bolts can be fitted into their proper recesses. The thrust ring (2) should cover the circlip (4). The notch in the camshaft flange should be opposite the notch in the cylinder head. The guide plate should be thoroughly de-burred, and after assembly, the camshaft should revolve easily.

Removing the rocker shaft

Valve, Valve Guide Removal and Replacement

Remove the valves with a suitable spring compressor. Check the spring length. Always replace the oil seal rings. A damaged oil seal ring will increase oil consumption. Lay the oil seal ring in the spring washer. The valve guides can be reamed. To renew the valve guides, heat the cylinder head to about 356°F. and press the guides out into the combustion chamber. Press new guides in from the rocker shaft side.

Exhaust Manifold

The exhaust manifold is removed by releasing the sleeve for the carburetor heat, loosening the exhaust support, and removing the exhaust pipe from the manifold. Remove the manifold from the engine.

The manifold can be installed by reversing the removal procedure.

Timing Chain

Removal and Replacement (4-cyl models)

1. Remove the cylinder head and the oil pan.
2. Remove the water pump and loosen the chain cover plate.
3. Loosen the nut on the crankshaft while holding the flywheel with a screwdriver. Remove the crankshaft pulley.
4. Remove the alternator and its mounting bracket.
5. Remove the timing chain cover and the timing chain.

To install, reverse the removal procedure.

Adjustment

The chain can be adjusted by the tensioning rail which is mounted to the left side of the chain. The rail must be free and have axial play to work correctly.

Removal and Installation (6-cyl models)

1. The following procedure is performed with the gearbox cover removed at the top and bottom.
2. Move No. 1 piston to the TDC position. The rotor should be pointing to the notch in the distributor casing.
3. Loosen the locking plates and remove the sprocket wheel.

CAUTION: *Mark the direction of timing chain rotation and make sure it is maintained during reassembly.*

4. Remove the timing chain.

When assembling the unit make certain that:

1. the upper hole in the flange is flush with the lubrication pipe;
2. the timing chain is adjusted to the correct tension.

NOTE: *Timing chain replacement is normally not necessary before 30,000 miles.*

Piston and Connecting Rods

Servicing Piston and Rod Assemblies

Pistons and rods can be serviced without removing the engine from the car. To remove the pistons, remove the cylinder head and oil pan, position the piston to BDC, remove the bearing cap and push the piston and connecting rod upward.

Wrist pins can be replaced cold. They are color coded: W on the piston crown—wrist pin marked white; S on the piston crown—wrist pin marked black. Oil holes in the connecting rod for wrist pin lubrication should face forward in the direction of travel.

Connecting rod bolts are expansion bolts and must be discarded after removal. Do not reuse bolts that have been in service. Rods and bearing caps are marked in pairs for each cylinder and should not be interchanged. Number 4 is at the flywheel end.

Check the ring clearance in the piston groove and the ring end gap with the ring inserted in the cylinder bore and compare with specifications.

Each ring is marked for top and bottom. Install in the following grooves in the piston:

(top) Rectangular ring
(middle) Stepped ring
(bottom) Equal chamfer scraper ring

Only pistons and rods of the same weight classification should be used. The weight class of the piston is stamped on the crown with a + or −. An arrow stamped on the crown points forward in direction of travel. Rod class is coded by colors.

Camshaft (4-cyl models)

Removal and Installation

1. Remove the cylinder head and remove the distributor.
2. Disconnect the oil pipe and the fuel pump.
3. Set the valve adjustment to the highest possible clearance.
4. Remove the guide plate and pull out the camshaft.

Direction of the bore pin

Checking the cam axial play

To install the unit use the following procedure:

1. Install the camshaft carefully. The notch in the flange must be in alignment with the nose in the cylinder head. The bore for the set pin faces downward.
2. Check the axial play between the guide plate and the camshaft. It should be 0.0008–0.005 in.
3. Adjust the valve clearance.
4. Install new fuel pump gaskets and a new insulating flange.
5. Position the sealing rings and the oil pipe.
6. Install the distributor and adjust the ignition timing.

Removal and Installation (6-cyl models)

1. Remove the cylinder head, fuel pump, and push rod.
2. Remove the oil pipe
3. Back off the valve adjusting screws.
4. Remove the guide plate from the cylinder head and pull out the camshaft.

When installing the camshaft, the side of the oil pipe must be 6.496 in. from the middle of the oil riser hole to the end of the pipe. The distance to the opposite end of the pipe must measure 6.102 in. If these measurements are not adhered to, the camshaft could be damaged by lack of lubrication.

After the guide plate has been installed it is possible to turn the camshaft without difficulty. The tapped hole in the flange must be flush with the protrusion in the casting.

ENGINE LUBRICATION

Oil Pan

Removal and Installation (Engine Installed 4-cyl models)

1. Remove the steering stabilizer on the 2002 and 2002TI.
2. Drain the engine oil.
3. Loosen the mounting bolts and raise the engine slightly.
4. Set the No. 4 piston at top dead center and remove the sump attaching bolts. Remove the pan.

(Engine Removed)

1. Remove the pan from the engine by removing the attaching bolts.

To install use the following procedure:

1. Clean the sealing surfaces and then coat them with a thin application of sealant.
2. Place the pan in position and secure it with the attaching screws.

Removal and Installation (Engine Installed 6-cyl models)

1. Remove the lower front shield.
2. Drain the engine oil and remove the front stabilizer.
3. Loosen the alternator and remove the oil pump and one mounting screw.
4. Loosen the sump attaching bolts and the engine mounting bolts.
5. Turn the crankshaft until the No. 6 connecting rod is above the pan.
6. Lower the front of the pan, turn the rear, and remove.

Installation is the reverse of removal.

Oil Pump

Removal

1. Remove the oil pan and the chain sprocket. Open the retaining plates and remove the oil pump from its holder.

NOTE: *When removing the unit, check the O-ring in the housing and the pressure relief pipe.*

Installation

1. Adjust the timing chain tension so that it may be depressed with light pressure.

NOTE: *Some of the shim plates which are used to adjust chain tension have oil holes. Make sure they are aligned.*

2. Loosen the retaining plate on the pump and align and tighten it.

ENGINE COOLING

Radiator

Removal and Installation

Turn the heater control to HOT and allow the coolant to drain from the radiator and engine block. Remove the radiator hoses. Unscrew the radiator bolts and lift out the radiator. Install in reverse order.

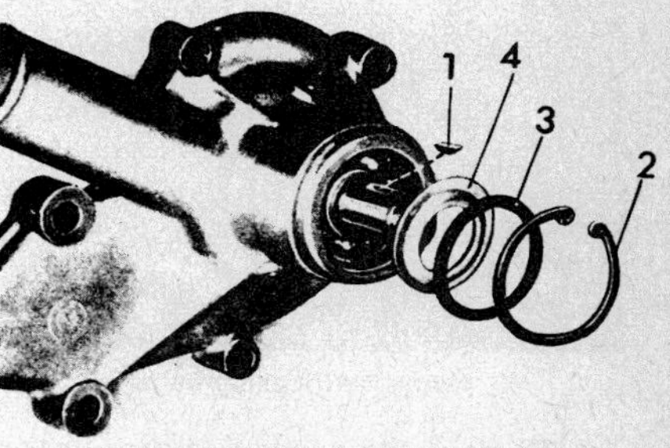

Water pump assembly

1. Water pump key
2. Snap-ring
3. Spacer
4. Seal

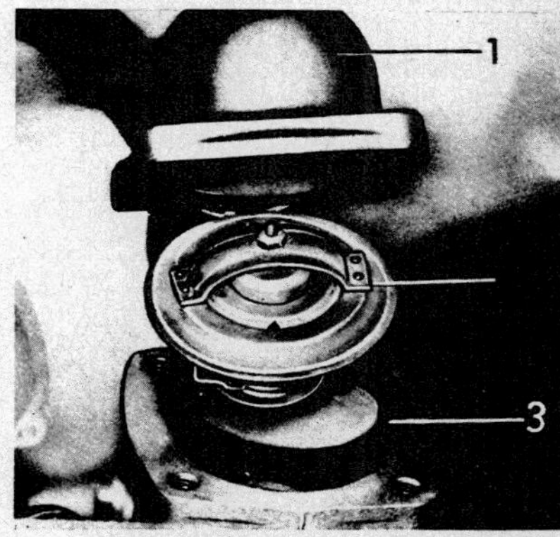

Thermostat assembly

1. Housing
2. Thermostat
3. Gasket

Water Pump

Water Pump Servicing

Remove the air filter, radiator, and fan, and pull the fan pulley from the water pump shaft. Remove the mounting screws and the water pump. Disassemble by removing the flange (on one type), snap-ring, spacer and seal. Remove the key from the shaft and press the shaft, with the bearing off the impeller. Drive the sealing ring out of the housing.

When the water pump is reassembled, there should be a clearance of 0.038–0.-047 in. (0.8–1.2 mm) between the housing and the impeller. 6-cylinder models should have a clearance of 0.038 in.

MANUAL TRANSMISSION

Removal and Installation (4-cyl models)

1. Remove the upper bolts from the transmission housing.

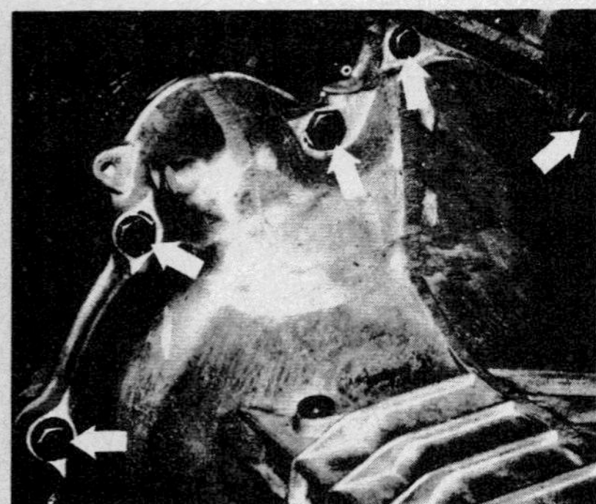

Upper bellhousing bolts

2. Remove the gaiter and the rubber ring from around the shifter and lift out the circlip.
3. Remove the exhaust bracket and the exhaust pipe from the manifold.
4. Remove the driveshaft. The flex-coupling should remain on the drive shaft.
5. Remove the center driveshaft bearing. The driveshaft can be pulled downward and away from the centering pin.

Removing the bearing pin

1. Bearing pin
2. Screw

6. Remove the bearing pin and push the gear lever upward. On models with intermediate shafts it is necessary to detach the spring, push the retainer downward, and remove the pushrod. On slave cylinder models, detach the spring, lift out the circlip, and remove the slave cylinder.
7. Remove the transmission cover plate and support the engine securely.
8. Remove the speedometer shaft and the back-up light connections. Loosen the cross member.

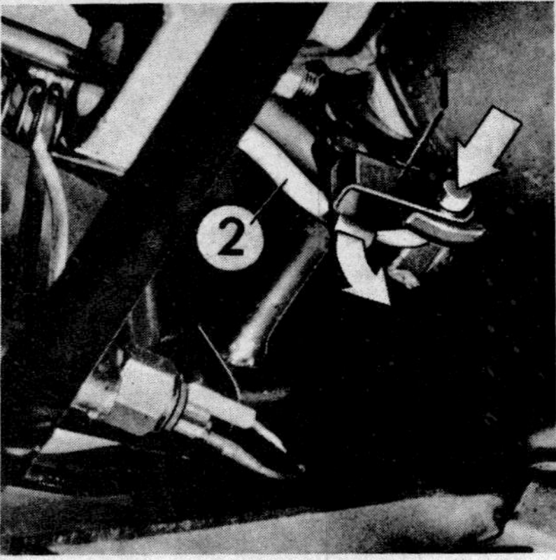

Removing the pushrod

1. Retainer
2. Push Rod

9. Turn the steering wheel to the full right position and remove the remaining attaching bolts. Remove the gearbox.

The installation procedure is the reverse of the removal.

Removal and Installation (6-cyl.) Manual Transmission

1. Remove the gear shift lever
2. Disconnect the exhaust manifold and the manifold supports.
3. Remove the drive shaft and the center bearing.
4. Remove the driveshaft from the end of the transmission.
5. Remove the speedometer drive gear and the back-up light switch.
6. Remove the transmission-to-bell-housing bolts.
7. Support the engine with a jack between the front axle supports and loosen the rubber bearing on the gearbox. Then remove the crossmember.
8. Pull the gearbox out slightly, enough to lift the retaining spring over the spherical bolt collar.
9. Remove and lower the transmission.

To assemble, reverse the removal procedure.

Overhaul (Four Speed 232)

1. Remove the bracket and the stay. Push back the sleeve and drive out the pin. Pull out the selector shaft and the joint.
2. Remove the exhaust support bracket. Position the gearbox on a level and clean area before proceeding.
3. Drain the oil. Remove the guide sleeve and lift out the circlip. Remove the shims.
4. Remove the grooved bearing and the fixing bolts on the housing. Drive the pins out of the housing.
5. Remove the grooved bearing on the layshaft. It may be necessary to heat the housing around the sealing cover to remove this bearing.

Removing the housing bearing

Removing the transmission housing

6. Remove the gearbox housing and the plug, spring, and locking pin which is threaded into the housing.
7. Position the selector rod to the Fourth gear position then turn the guide sleeve until the locating pin can be driven out properly. Then pull the selector rod forward.
8. Remove the selector shaft. It may be necessary to swing the selector bar upward.
9. Position the selector sleeve to Neutral and remove the selector fork. Check the selector fork for wear.
10. Place the selector rod into the Second gear position then turn the guide sleeve until the locating pin can be driven out.

Selector rod and pin assembly

1. Selector rod
2. Securing pin

11. Remove the selector fork. Place the second gear wheel into the neutral position. Check the selector fork for wear. Remove the plug-in bushing and the speedometer pinion.

12. Remove the rubber bumper and lift out the locking plate.

Removing the flange

13. Remove the flange nut and the flange. Also remove the support ring. To prevent the synchromesh unit of the Third gear wheel from falling off when the bearing on the output shaft is removed, a 0.079 in. metal strip must be placed between the second and third gears.

14. Remove the grooved ball bearing with a puller. This bearing is positioned in the gearbox housing cover.

15. Position the drive and output shafts to the right. Remove the jackshaft. Be careful not to loose the shims.

Moving the drive and output shafts to remove the jackshaft.

16. Pull the shift rod with the lever and the reverse gear pinion out of the gearbox. Be careful as the balls are loose.

NOTE: *When Borg-Warner synchromesh was introduced, the meshing angle of the reverse pinion and the gears was changed from 20° to 15°. The 15° mesh angle pinions and gears are identified by a groove around their outer face.*

17. Remove the input shaft with its roller cage and the selector sleeve from the output shaft.

18. Press out the output shaft. Check the sychromesh components and lift out the lock ring.

Output shaft

1. Speedometer pinion
2. Thrust washer
3. Reverse gear pinion
4. First gear pinion
5. Needle cage
6. Distance bushing
7. Selector sleeve
8. Guide sleeve
9. Second gear pinion
10. Needle cage

NOTE: *The first gear synchromesh ring is more oval then the second, third, and fourth rings. The first gear ring has a white spot on the outer surface while the others have blue spots.*

If the synchromesh rings are worn at the two ends they must be replaced. When assembled, the ring should turn freely.

19. Assemble and measure the output shaft. It should be 5.394 in. Press the speedometer pinion onto the output shaft and the grooved bearing into the gearbox housing.

20. Examine the jackshaft for broken or chipped gears. They should only be replaced in pairs. To disassemble the shaft, remove the grooved bearing and the fourth gear pinion. Lift off the circlip and remove the third gear pinion. The pinions are installed by reversing the above procedure.

21. Install the jackshaft into the housing. Place the reverse idler pin in position. The hole in the pin must face the jackshaft.

22. When replacing the reverse idler pinion, install a new bushing.

23. Remove the backup light switch and the sealing cap.

24. Press in the jackshaft after the arrestor ball is installed downward and the reverse gear selector rod has been placed into the housing with the proper shim.

25. Place the drive and output shafts into the housing.

26. Place the shim in front of the speedometer pinion and drive the grooved bearing into the housing cover.

27. Check the tooth pattern. This can be altered by adding shims in front of the grooved bearing on the jackshaft.

NOTE: *There should no play between the grooved bearing outer race and the sealing cover.*

Checking the tooth pattern and shim location

(c)—Shim

28. Push the first/second gear into the selector sleeve. Install the locking pin and arrestor ball. Position the selector rod and fork and secure the fork with the locating pin.

29. Place the third/fourth gear selector fork into the selector sleeve. Position the selector shaft. Insert the locking pin in the tapered bushing.

Third and Fourth gear selector postion

30. Install the sealing cap and the back up light switch. Position the end housing bearing and its shim.

Slip the gearbox housing over the gear assembly. Press the input shaft into the ball bearing. Position the housing onto the housing cover.

Overhaul of 5-speed transmission

The procedures for disassembly and assembly of the 5-speed transmission is similar to that of the 4-speed.

Overhaul (ZF- S-4)

1. Secure the gearbox on the working support.
2. Remove the gearshift lug from the arm.
3. If the torsion spring is defective, remove the catch plate together with the torsion spring. The long stud must face toward the torsion spring.
4. Remove the gearshift arm and the vibration damper.
5. Slide off the guide piece along with the guide flange. Use caution as shims will drop.

6. Lift out the circlip and remove the bearing and bearing pin.

7. Remove the front housing and the shift rails for third/fourth and first/second gears.

8. Remove the shift rail for reverse by pulling it to the rear.

9. Engage First gear and remove the selector fork for third and fourth gears.

10. Lift out the locking plate.

11. Remove the flange nut and the retaining spanner and pull off the drive flange.

12. Remove the outer cover, speedometer gear, and washer.

13. Using a puller, remove the bearing from the layshaft.

14. Remove the main shaft and the layshaft with the roller assembly and the synchromesh unit.

15. On the mainshaft all play is adjusted by shims.

16. Engage second gear and remove the bearing bolt for first and second gearshift forks. Remove the reverse gear fork.

17. Reverse gear can be removed by pressing the first and second gears against the notch. When assembling, the chamferred side of the gears must face toward the casing.

18. Press the drive shaft out of the ball bearing. Remove the gearshift fork for first and second gears.

19. First and reverse gears may be pressed off at this point.

20. Remove the synchromesh unit and second gear. It is necessary to remove the needle bearing.

21. Remove the circlip and press off the synchromesh unit and third gear.

NOTE: *If the gap between the synchronizing ring and the clutch body is less than 0.0157 in., the ring must be replaced. If the synchronizing rings rattle, synchronizing springs with protruding ends must be used.*

CAUTION: *If there is a rattle in the synchronizing rings, install only rings with protruding ends.*

22. Place the hooks on the spring ends in any longitudinal groove. Position the pressure elements. For first and second gear, the pressure elements are placed in the lower teeth on the synchronizing ring.

23. Place the third gear needle bearing into position and position the synchronizing ring and the synchromesh unit on the thicker side of the hub.

24. Position the second gear needle bearing, the synchronizing ring, and the synchromesh unit. Position the synchromesh unit and compensate for play by means of a retaining ring.

25. Position the needle bearing on first gear and press on reverse gear. The thicker hub must face the outside.

26. Measure the distance from the synchromesh unit hub to the polished surface of the reverse gear hub and compare it to the distance from the housing joint face (without gasket) to the ball bearing inner race. Shims are available in varying thicknesses.

27. Insert the selector fork of first and second gears onto the shift sleeve. Press the drive shaft into the ball bearing in the housing.

28. Engage second gear then press the selector fork against the stop. Insert the selector fork, install the bearing pin and position second gear into the neutral position.

29. Install the synchromesh springs and engage the pressure pieces. Position the sliding sleeves into the synchromesh position.

30. Place the roller rim on the drive shaft and insert the synchromesh ring.

31. Insert the layshaft and support.

32. After heating the bearing inner surface, press the layshaft into the housing. The bearing should project 0.196 in.

33. Fit the cover onto the housing.

34. Insert the bearing pin on the left in the direction of travel and position all shift rails. Install the front housing, vibration damper, and shift arm.

35. Shim the front bearing to zero with the circlip installed

36. Calculate and install the necessary shim for the guide flange. Install the shim and the flange.

Getrag 262 Gearbox Overhaul

1. Remove the transmission from the vehicle. Remove the console and check the bearing blocks and replace if necessary.

2. Remove the gearshift rod after removing the cylindrical pin.

3. Loosen the front lock collar and remove the three pointed flange. The safety plate should be pushed into the groove of the flange.

4. Remove the bearing cap bolts and the guide sleeve. Be careful not to loose the shims.

5. Pull out the bearing circlip and remove the grooved bearing from the output drive shaft and the mainshaft.

6. Remove the side locking bolt with its spring. Note the initial position of the locking bolt.

7. Remove the back-up light switch.

8. Remove the side bolt so that the reverse gear shift lever can be removed.

9. Pull out the tension rods. There are two for each gearshift fork.

10. Rotate the center shaft until the third and fourth gears can be removed.

CAUTION: *When removing the rod, the ball will fall out.*

11. Remove the shift rod for first and second gears observing the same caution as Step 10.

12. Remove the reverse shift rod and the gearshift forks. Note a higher shifter fork for third and fourth gear. Remove the gearshift shaft.

13. Heat the casting to approximately 80° and remove the drive shaft, output drive shaft, layshaft, and reverse gear from the casing.

14. Remove the synchronizing rings making sure to mark them for each gear. Also remove the retaining rings and shims.

15. Remove the synchromesh unit with the sliding sleeve, synchronizing ring, third gear, shim, and needle retainer ring. Also mark the synchronizing ring for each gear.

16. Remove the output driveshaft.

NOTE: *The synchronizing rings must be replaced if the gap between the synchronizing ring and the clutch element is less than 0.0315 in. With new rings the gap must be 0.0394 in.*

17. Disassemble the synchromesh unit if necessary.

18. To assemble the output, drive the layshaft and the reverse gear into the casing top. Insert the gearshift shaft and fit the shift forks. Place the stop ball into position and install the reverse shift rod.

19. Install the stop and locking bolts. Turn the gearshift shaft to the reverse gear position and install the gearshift shaft for first and second gear.

20. Install the third and fourth gear shaft and the shift forks with two tension pins in each.

21. Install the sealing caps and place the reverse gear shift lever in the straight position.

22. Install the casing and the back-up light switch. Place the grooved bearing onto the layshaft after heating. Do the same with the bearing on the driveshaft.

23. Position the drive shaft into the casing. Install the support ring and circlip. The gap between the ball bearing and the driveshaft should be 0.2757 in. and the gap between the bearing and the countershaft should be 0.1811 in.

24. After calculating the shim for the guide flange, install the guide flange.

25. Install the three-legged flange and secure.

CLUTCH

Removal and Installation

Remove the transmission and brace the flywheel so that it won't turn. Remove the pressure plate securing bolts in a diagonal pattern. Lift off the pressure plate and the clutch disc. Do not drop either of these parts as both are heavy.

The installation procedure is the reverse of removal. It is important to align the splines on the clutch disc with the center of the flywheel pilot bushing. This will make transmission alignment easier.

Free-Play Adjustment

Loosen the lock nut on the adjusting rod. Set the clutch play to 0.02 in. by turning the adjusting nut. Re-tighten the lock nut.

Clutch Master Cylinder

Removal and Installation

1. Bleed the hydraulic system to drain the line.
2. Syphon the fluid in the compensating tank up to a point just below the fill marking.
3. Remove the extra fluid line from the master cylinder. Insert a plug so that air will not enter the system.
4. Remove the pressure line from the master cylinder.
5. Remove the carpet from around the pedal mechanism and remove the push rod from the clutch pedal.
6. Loosen and remove the attaching bolts and the master cylinder.

Slave Cylinder

Removal and Replacement

1. Follow Steps 1 and 2 of "Master Cylinder Removal"
2. Remove the retaining ring and the circlip.
3. Pull the slave cylinder forward to remove it.
4. Detach the pressure line before removing the cylinder.

AUTOMATIC TRANSMISSION

Removal and Installation

1. Disconnect the battery and remove the accelerator cable from its mounting.
2. Remove the transmission filler pipe and seal the opening.
3. Remove the transmission attaching bolts which are accessible from above.
4. Drain the transmission oil. Remove the exhaust supports from the transmission and loosen the transmission mount.
5. Remove the exhaust pipe from the elbow and turn the steering wheel to the full left position.
6. Remove the drive shaft and the center bearing support.
7. Disconnect the selector rod and the speedometer drive. Also remove the cable from the starter lock switch.
8. Remove the flywheel cover plate and the torque converter-to-drive plate bolts.
9. While supporting the transmission securely, remove the cross member and the remaining transmission attaching bolts.
10. Move the transmission away from the engine and at the same time remove the torque converter.

Torque converter to drive plate bolts

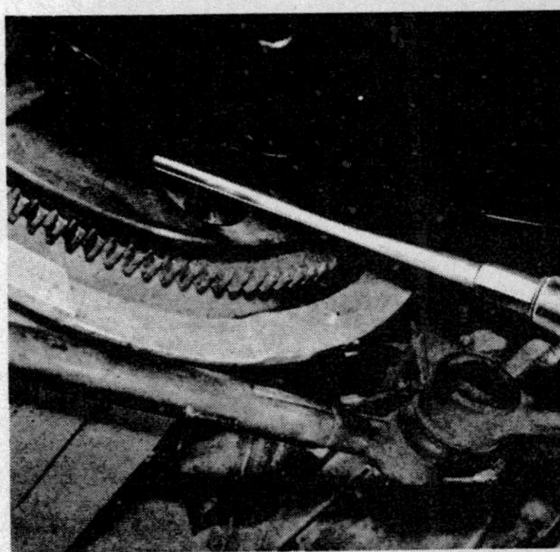

Removing the converter

The transmission may be installed by reversing the removal procedures. When installing, note that the torque converter should be positioned so that the guide journal is situated below the rim of the casing. If this cannot be accomplished, place the torque converter onto the primary pump. It may be necessary to turn the converter slightly in order to mesh.

Pan Removal and Installation

1. Drain the transmission fluid.

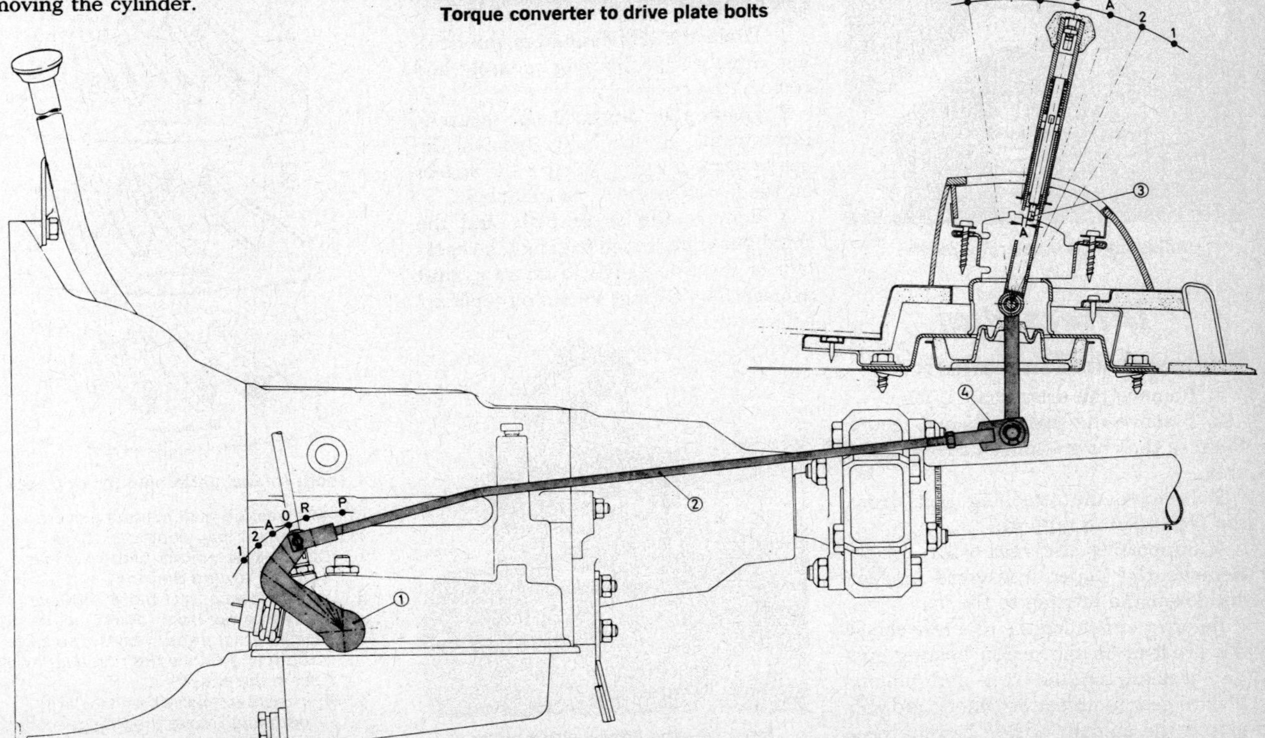

Shift linkage adjustment

2. Remove the transmission pan attaching bolts.

3. Remove the pan and scrape the old gasket from both the pan and the housing surfaces.

4. Install a new gasket and then the transmission pan. Fill the transmission to the proper level.

Shift Linkage Adjustment

1. Check the bearing bracket to make sure it is tight.

2. Place the selector lever in Neutral and remove the selector rod from the selector lever.

3. Adjust the selector rod until the stop lug touches the rear shift gate.

4. Turn the selector rod adjuster three full turns in from this position. The clearance between the stop lug and the stop must be 0.039 in.

Throttle Linkage Adjustment

1. Remove the air cleaner and the accelerator cable.

2. Position the throttle to the full throttle, kickdown position. At this position the throttle valve must be fully open and must not extend beyond the vertical position.

3. Adjust the accelerator linkage using the eyebolt.

Adjusting the accelerator cable

Differential

Removal and Installation

1. Remove the drive shaft U-joint.

2. Remove the axle shafts and secure them to the chassis—out of the working area.

3. Remove the attaching bolts from the rear housing support.

4. Supporting the rear with a jack. Remove the upper transverse bracket and lower the housing to the floor.

Before overhauling the rear axle check the pre-load on the pinion bearing and the backlash on the ring and pinion. Make a gear tooth pattern check and also record the amount of side bearing pre-

Removing the rear housing support bolts

Removing the transverse bracket

load. Take a micrometer reading of the pinion shim thickness. Record all these measurements so that they can be refered to upon assembly.

Check all internal components for possible damage before assembly.

Overhaul

1. Drain the lubricant from the housing. Support the housing securely and remove the cover plate.

2. Holding the driving flange securely, remove the center bolt. Remove the flange using a puller. Secure the spacer on the flange in the same manner.

3. Remove the cover plate and the shim. The shim is used to gauge the backlash of the axle flange to guard against damage. The O-rings should be replaced before installation.

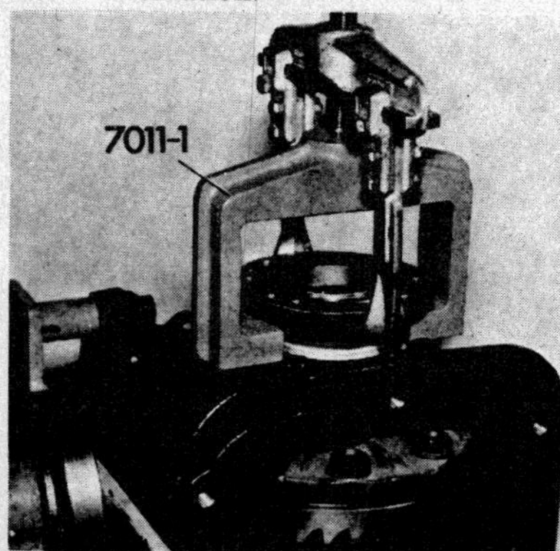

Removing the flange with a puller

4. Place the housing with the cover plate opening facing upward and brace it securely. Move the housing bearing through the end hole in the housing far enough to lift the differential housing out of the casing.

The installation procedure is the reverse of removal.

Axle flange and shim

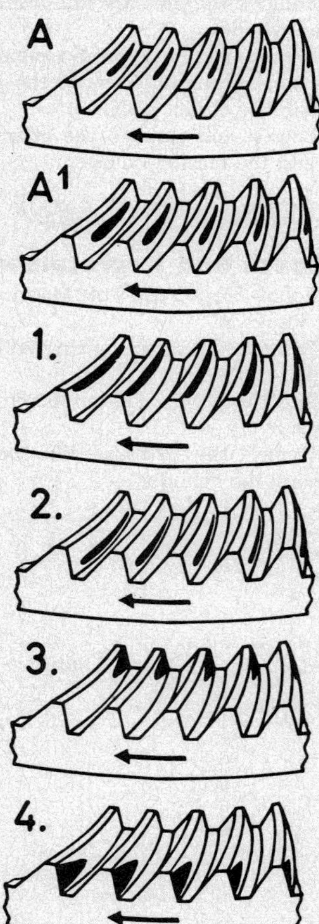

Tooth contact pattern on the ring gear

(a)—Correct no load contact pattern
(a1)—Correct load contact pattern
1. High narrow contact pattern (Move pinion toward the ring gear)
2. Low narrow contact pattern (Move pinion away from the ring gear)
3. Short contact pattern on the small tooth end (Move the ring gear away from the pinion)
4. Short contact pattern on the large tooth end (Move the ring gear toward the pinion)

O-ring location on the cover plate

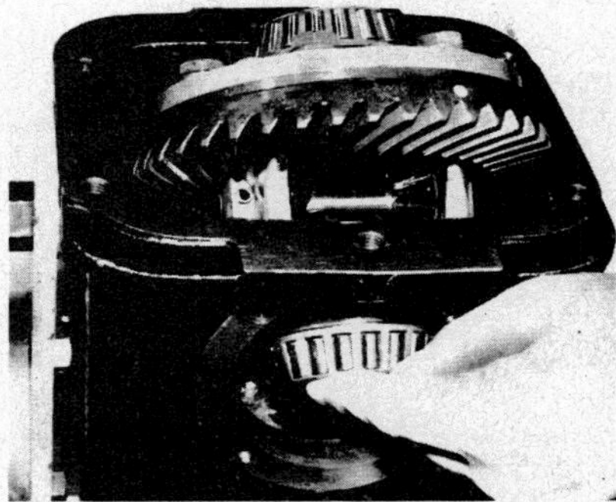

Removing the differential from the casing

Pinion Removal

1. Remove the 8 crown wheel bolts and clean them. Apply Loctite® to the crown wheel bolts before installation.

2. Tap out the pinion sleeves with a drift pin and hammer. Remove the differential pinion shaft.

3. Remove the differential pinions and the drive flange along with the rear axle shaft pinions and the cup springs (B) and shims (A).

Removing the differential pinion

(a)—Shim
(b)—Cup springs

To install the pinions, take one at a time and position them in the casing. Press the rear axle shaft pinion in the direction of the differential pinions. Install a dial indicator or similar tool. Set the gauge at zero still exerting pressure against the pinion. Push the pinion back in the other direction and read the dial.

Pressing the pinion toward the center of the housing.

Pushing the pinion back to check pinion play.

It should be 0.01 in. With one rear axle shaft pinion and two differential pinions installed, the rotating torque must not be more than 14.4 ft lbs.

The other pinion is installed in the same way. The spring cup and the shim are installed with the concave side of the cup facing the rear axle shaft pinion.

Position the drive flange in one pinion shaft and install the washer (0.394 in.) Compress the spring cups until the pinions can be screwed into the housing.

4. Installation of the housing into the axle casing can be accomplished by reversing the removal procedure.

Limited Slip Differential Overhaul

1. Remove the ring gear housing. Remember that the oil channels of the thrust washer face the housing cover.

2. Turn the housing over and the clutch assembly can be removed.

Removing the spacer ring from the clutch assembly.

Clutch assembly

1. Thrust washer
2. Spacer ring
3. Outer disc
4. Inner disc

3. From the assembly, remove the spacer ring, outer disc, and inner disc.

When assembling these units, the clearance between the discs is gauged by the molybdenum coated inner discs.

4. Remove the pressure cover and the axle shaft pinion. Lift off the differential pinions with the shaft.

5. The clutch mechanism should be reassembled after all parts are checked for defects. The discs should be positioned in the housing cover and then placed under 220 lbs of pressure. The distance between the lower part of the flange and the top of the clutch (B) must be 0.004–0.008 in. less than the housing depth A.

Clutch compression distance

Housing depth

6. Install the disc assembly in the housing. Test the system by holding one pinion and the second should rotate under 50 cmkp.

Install the housing into the casing.

TRANSMISSION AND DIFFERENTIAL SPECIFICATIONS

Model	Ratio	Capacity (US qts)	Oil Type	Ring Gear to Pinion Backlash	Pinion Rotating Torque
1600	4.11:1	0.85	SAE 90	0.003-0.005	2.30-2.34
1800	4.11:1	0.85	SAE 90	0.003-0.005	2:30-2.34
2000	4.10:1	1.37	SAE 90	0.003-0.005	1.81-1.95
2000CS	4.10:1	1.37	SAE 90	0.003-0.005	1.81-1.95
2002	3.64:1	0.85	SAE 90	0.003-0.005	2.30-2.34
2002TI	3.64:1	0.85	SAE 90	0.003-0.005	2.30-2.34
2002tii	3.45:1	0.85	SAE 90	0.003-0.005	2.30-2.34

Universal Joint

Removal and Installation

1. Remove the circlip and press out the upper needle bushing which pushes the lower bushing out.

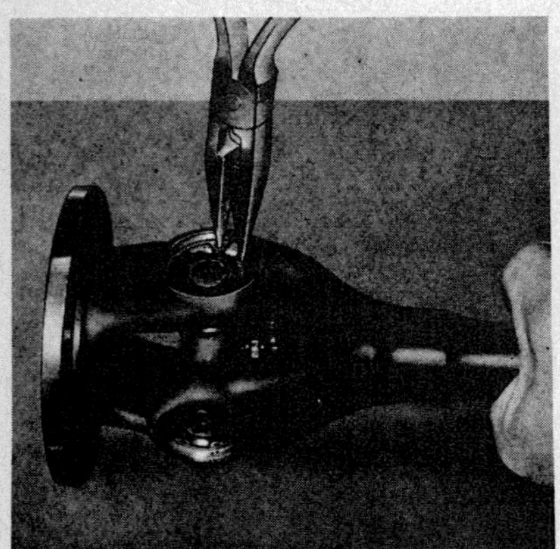

Circlip removal

2. Turn the assembly over and press out the other bushing.
3. Press the other two bushings out using the same procedure.

To install the bushings:

1. Insert one bushing into its proper location and position the universal.

NOTE: *The grease nipple must face the universal shaft yoke.*

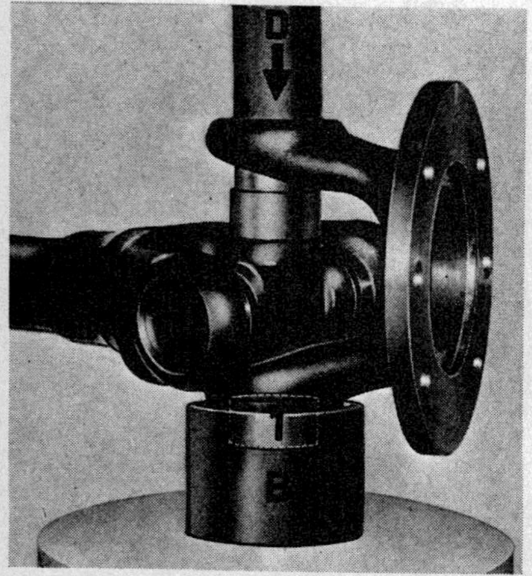

Pressing out the upper needle bushing

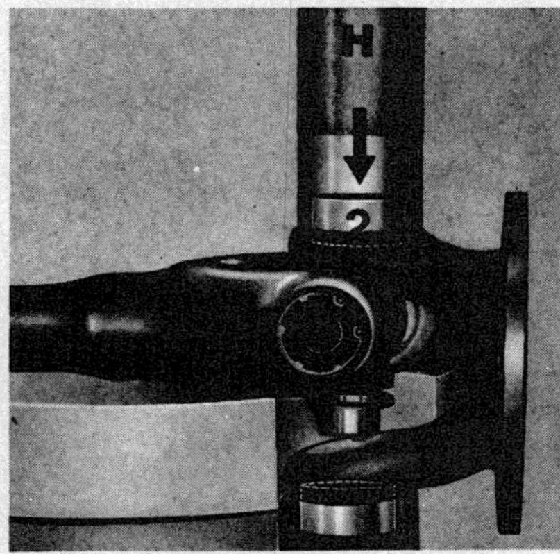

Pressing out the lower needle bushing

2. Position the opposite bushing and crush it into position using a press. Insert the retaining clips. Use the same procedure for the other two bushings.

Axle Half Shaft

Removal and Installation

1. Remove the driving flange and the output shaft and secure away from the working area.
2. Drive out the half shaft with a plastic or rubber hammer. To protect the half shaft, screw a nut onto the end of the shaft.

Reverse the procedure to install.

Removing the axle flange

Securing the output shaft

Driving out the half shaft

REAR SUSPENSION

Springs

Removal and Installation

1. Remove the shock absorber and the rear wheel.
2. Remove the stabilizer from the trailing arm and the output shaft from the halfshaft. Secure the output shaft away from the working area.
3. Lower the trailing arm with a jack and remove the coil spring.

Check the damper rings at the top and bottom spring pads before installing the springs and locate the spring ends at the top of the damper.

Removing the coil spring

Removing the lower shock mount

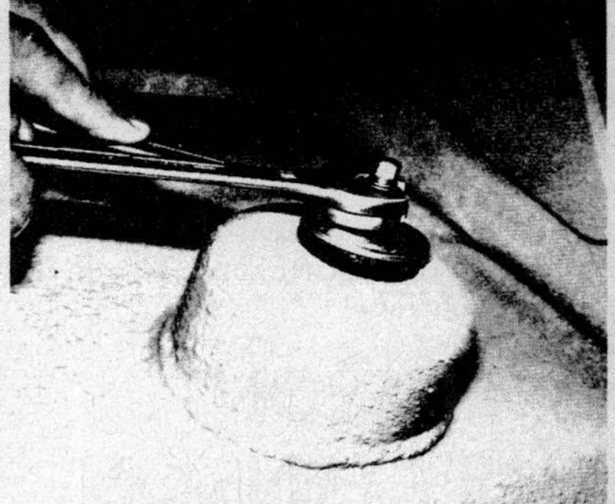
Removing the upper shock mount

Inspecting the spring pads

Shock Absorbers

Removal and Installation (4-cyl. models)

1. Jack the vehicle so that it is supported securely.
2. Place another jack under the trailing arm.
3. Remove the protective cap and remove the upper shock absorber mounting.
4. Remove the lower shock mounting screw, compress the shock, and remove it.

Shock absorbers should always be installed in pairs and should be the same brand and model. Check the shock bushings before installation. Replace them if necessary. Installation is the reverse of removal.

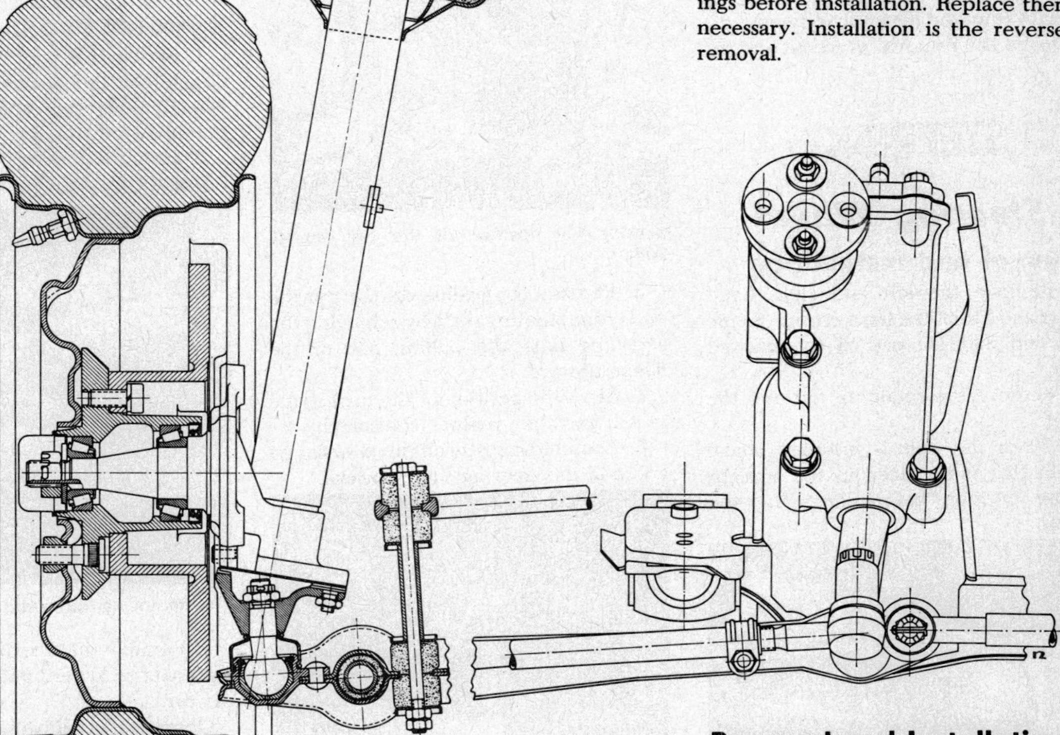
Cross section of BMW suspension

Removal and Installation (6-cyl models)

NOTE: *Replace the spring strut shock absorbers with the load on the longitudinal arms.*

1. Take the centering bushing off of the wheel arch and remove the cover

disc and the damping disc.

2. Take out the spring strut shock absorber together with the damping disc.

Assemble by reversing the removal procedure. Use a spacer tube on the knurled head bolt. It is important to fit on the damping disc so that the projecting rubber tabs face the front and rear in the direction of travel.

FRONT SUSPENSION

Springs

Removal and Installation

1. Remove the spring and shock assembly.

2. Remove the upper spring cup and remove the coil spring. Check the spring supports and the auxiliary spring and the check collar for damage.

3. When installing, the coil spring ends must fit on the stops in the lower and upper spring cups.

McPherson Strut

Removal and Installation

1. Remove the lockwire and the tie rod lever from the strut.

2. Remove the strut support bearing and withdraw the assembly downward.

Reverse the removal procedure to install.

STEERING

Steering Wheel

Removal and Installation

1. Remove the left and right hand screws and lift off the horn cover. On the 2002 and 2002Tii, pry off the padded cover.

2. Remove the retaining nut and the wheel

3. When the unit is installed, make certain that it is placed in the straight driving position before engaging the splines.

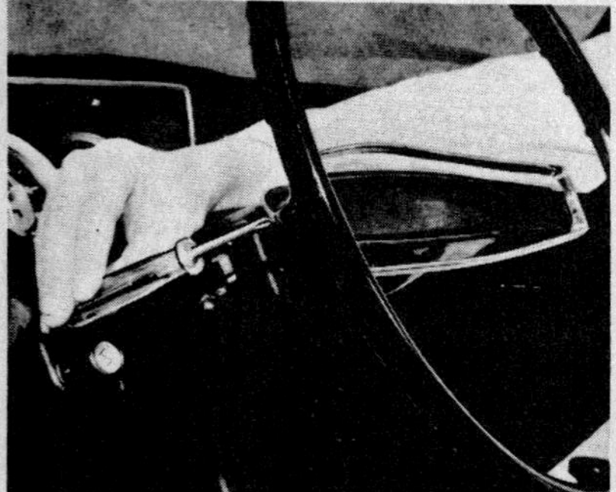

Removing the horn cover

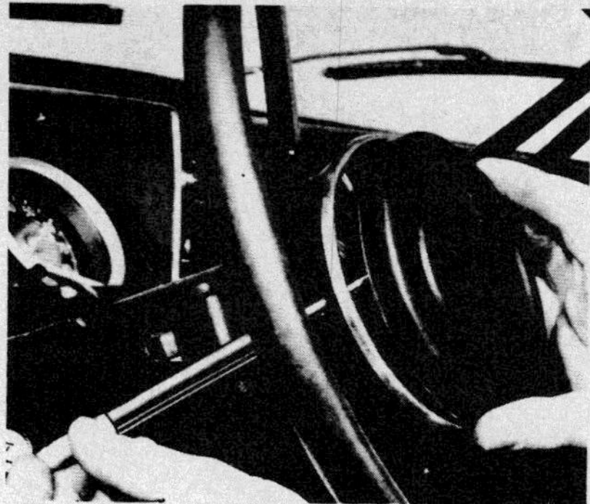

Removing the padded cover

4. The play between the dog and the reset cam of the directional signal is approximately 0.01 in.

Steering Column

Removal and Installation

1. Remove the steering wheel and loosen the under-dash mounting screws.

2. Unscrew the engine starting knob and its retaining nut. Remove the lower cowl and mark the position of the turn signal switch.

Marking the position of the turn signal switch.

3. Remove the flexible coupling at the end of the steering shaft by removing the retaining nuts and pulling half of the flange upward.

4. Mark the position of the turn signal switch and then remove the switch.

5. Loosen the screw on the joint flange and pull the steering shaft upward.

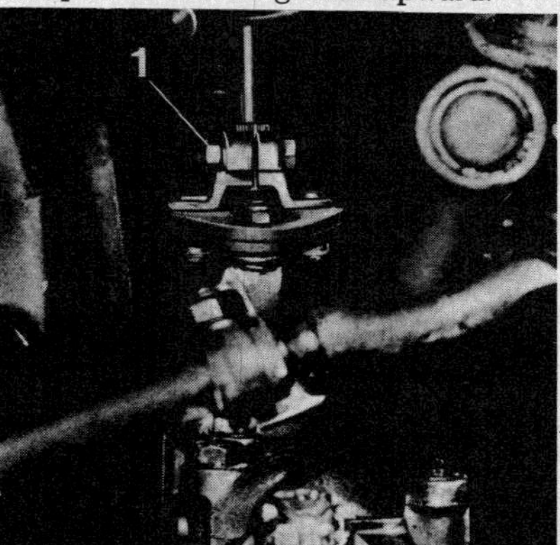

Removing the retaining nut (1)

When installing the shaft, remember that the steering shaft bearing is assembled with 0.24–0.26 in. of preload. To obtain this, press hard against the steering wheel and tighten the retaining screw at the same time. (An assistant is necessary) Other installation procedures can be accomplished by reversing the removal procedure.

Ignition Lock Switch

1. Remove the steering shaft as listed previously.

2. Disconnect the negative battery cable and remove the under-dash column casting.

3. Remove the headlight dimmer switch.

4. Loosen the outer column retaining screws.

5. Loosen the retaining screws for the steering column lock and remove the cable from the lock switch.

6. Loosen the shear bolts with a punch and then remove them. Remove the retaining screw and the lock.

When assembling the unit, make certain that the retaining screw is correctly located in the hole provided in the outer tube. Reverse the removal procedure for installation.

Steering Gear

Removal and Installation

1. Scribe the position of the flexible coupling at the steering shaft.

2. Remove the steering shaft upper bolt and push the flex coupling upward.

3. Remove the left tie rod retaining nut and then the tie rod.

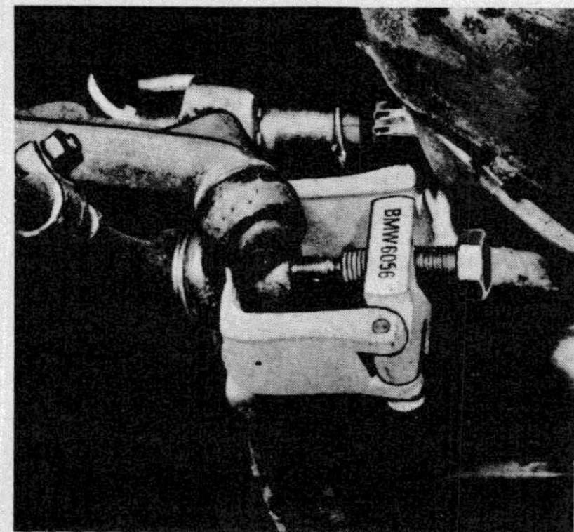

Removing the tie rod retaining nut

4. Remove the steering gear from the front axle by lowering it down and out of the car.

Observe the following when installing the steering gear.

1. Make certain that the gear is inserted cleanly into the guide sleeves.

2. To install the rod ends, turn the steering wheel and the front wheels. The marks on the steering box and the pitman shaft must be aligned.

3. Follow the column installation procedure for correct flex coupling preload.

Removal and Installation (6-cyl models)

1. Scribe aligning marks on the steering box and shaft.
2. Loosen and remove the universal joint lock screw and press the joint as far upward as possible.
3. Remove the track rod after removing the castellated nut.
4. Separate the steering box from the front axle beam and remove from beneath the car.

Steering Adjustment

This is best made using a friction coefficient gauge attached to the nut of the steering wheel. The adjustment is correct —without play—with a friction coefficient of 0.72–1.16 ft lbs.

Jack up the front of the car with both wheels free. Remove the cover cap from the steering wheel. Turn the steering wheel about one turn to the left. Attach a friction gauge to the wheel, turn the friction gauge to the right beyond the straight-ahead position. Turn the wheel back to the left if another test is required.

Adjusting the steering box

Loosen the locknut and turn the adjustment screw while checking the friction coefficient until the proper value is obtained.

BRAKE SYSTEMS

Disc brakes are on both the front and rear wheels of BMW 2500 and 2800 cars. Other BMW models have disc brakes on the front and drum brakes on the rear. Brakes are power assisted, and the master cylinder has a tandem arrangement whereby each chamber actuates either the front or rear brake cylinders. Failure of either circuit is indicated by a warning light. The twin brake fluid reservoir is located in the engine compartment.

Warning Light Test

Warning of failure of the dual brake system is provided by a 3-watt lamp. Proper functioning of the light system can be tested by turning on the ignition switch and then pressing a small button on the instrument panel. The warning lamp should light when this button is pressed and the ignition switch is on.

Servicing Master Cylinder —2002 Series

Disconnect the brake lines: left front right front and rear Remove the master cylinder.

NOTE: *When reassembling, check the rubber ring which, if defective, will prevent vacuum formation. If renewing the master cylinder, also check for proper clearance between the pushrod and piston. This should be adjusted to 0.02 in. (0.5 mm) with shims.*

Check all components and replace any that show signs of wear.

Servicing Master Cylinder —1600

NOTE: *The master cylinder has a special bottom valve with a throttle bore (1). If the throttle bore is clogged, the brakes will drag.*

Play between piston rod and piston must be 0.02 in. (0.5 mm).

Servicing Master Cylinder —1800

Check through the filling opening with a wire to ensure that the compensation bore is not clogged. If the bore is clogged, the brakes will drag. Play between the piston rod and piston must be 0.02 in. (0.5 mm).

Servicing Disc Brakes

Disc brakes are self adjusting and therefore require no manual adjustment, but the pad linings should be replaced when they are worn to a thickness of 0.7 in. (2 mm). Brake discs should also be checked for maximum runout which is 0.0039 in. (0.10 mm). If the discs should have to be refinished, minimum brake disc thickness is 0.335 in. (8.5 mm). To change pads, first remove the securing lugs, if so equipped, then drive the fastening pins from the calipers. Remove the cross spring and pull out the pads with an extractor hook.

Removing the fastening pins

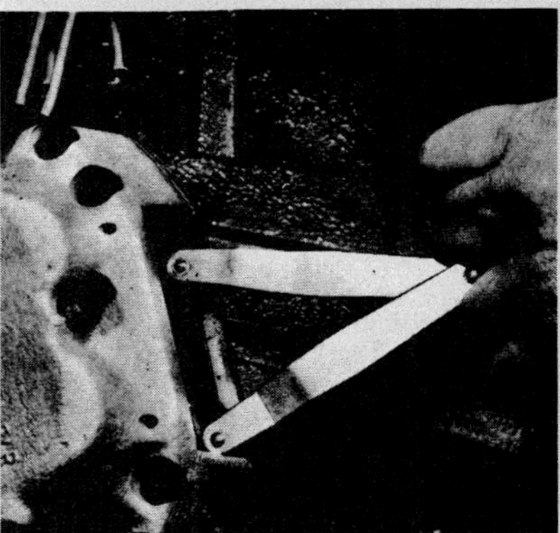

Pulling the brake pads from the calipers

When replacing the cross springs, place the cross spring with the embossed area under the upper fastening pin. Preload the opposed section: slide it beneath the fastening pin. The cross spring eliminates undesirable movement of the brake pad linings.

Return the piston to the wheel cylinder using piston pressback pliers. Do not use any other tools to avoid damage to wheel cylinder or brake disc. Check the brake fluid level in the reservoir before returning to avoid overflowing.

For caliper pistons without protective caps, make sure that the 20-degree setting line of the piston faces the brake disc inlet. Incorrect adjustment of the piston causes fluttering or squeaking of the disc brake and may prevent correct application of the brake lining to the disc. Installation of the protective cap (S) is recommended where possible. The cap can only be installed on pistons with a shoulder measuring 0.0315 in. (0.8 mm).

When removing pads that will be used again, mark them to be sure the inside and outside pads will be reassembled in their proper places. Make sure that each pair of wheels (front and rear) have pads of the same type as marked by the manufacturer.

NOTE: *Bleeding of the hydraulic system after caliper repair is made easier if the calipers are filled with fluid before being installed. Remove the bleeder connector and pour in fluid, tilting the caliper.*

Removing and Installing the Brake Disc

1. Remove the caliper assembly.
2. Loosen and remove the wheel hub.
3. Disconnect the hub from the disc by loosening the socket head screws.

To install, reverse the removal procedure. Remember to pack the wheel hub before installing.

REAR DRUM BRAKES

Removal and Installation

1. Jack the car and remove the wheel.
2. Remove the brake drum. There are no drum retainers.
3. Loosen the brake shoes. This is done by turning the left hand adjustment screw clockwise and the right hand adjusting screw counter-clockwise.
4. Remove the cotter pin and nut from the axle and, using a puller, remove the drive flange from the axle.

Removing the flange from the drive axle

5. Release the lower brake shoe spring and compress the shoes at the bottom. This will allow the top of the shoes to be removed from the wheel cylinder.

Removal of the lower brake spring

6. Remove the hand brake cable from the rear shoe.

To install, reverse the removal procedure.

Drum Brake Adjustment

Adjust the brake shoes, apply the brakes forcefully to center the shoes then, with the pedal released, turn the adjustment cams to lock the wheels. Turn the cams backward a fraction of a turn until the wheel rotates freely with no noticeable drag and with the pedal released. If any brake lines have been disconnected or the pedal operation is spongy, bleed the brake system.

Wheel Bearings

Removal and Installation

Remove the dust cap, cotter pin and bearing retaining bolt. Shake the rotor from side to side to remove the bearing.

Clean the bearing with suitable solvent and repack it. Insert the rotor, bearing, washer, and nut. Turn the rotor and at the same time tighten the nut to 7 ft lbs. This will seat the bearing properly. Then back off the nut approximately 1/3 turn. Install the dust cover.

CHASSIS ELECTRICAL

Heater Blower Removal and Installation

1. Remove the negative terminal of the battery, drain the cooling system, and move the temperature indicator to warm.
2. Remove the heater input and output water hoses. Remove the water valve with the input.
3. Remove the storage tray and the center and outer trim panels. The steering column lower casing must also be removed.
4. Remove the dash trim panel and knobs for the temperature controls.
5. The controls can be removed by loosening the attaching screws and removing the ashtray.
6. Disconnect the electrical connections and remove the heater retaining nut.
7. Remove the left hand hot air hose and turn the retaining bracket.
8. Remove the glove compartment lower panel and remove the right hand hot air hose.
9. Lift out the heater.
10. Once the heater assembly is removed the blower mechanism can be separated.

To install, reverse the removal procedure.

Radio

Installation and Removal (4-cyl models)

1. Attach the radio assembly to the right hand side panel and then to the left.
2. Connect the ground cable to the left hand mounting screw of the heater.
3. Connect the positive wire of the radio to the plug on the hazard warning flasher switch. Attach the antenna cable to the radio.

Removal is the reverse of installation.

Removal and Installation (6-cyl Models)

1. Remove the negative battery cable and the dashboard cover along with the speaker cover.
2. If the speaker is to be installed, connect the speaker leads and channel them to the floor panel of the storage space. Replace the dashboard cover.
3. Remove the floor panel of the storage space and pull the brown and violet cables into the opening.
4. Unscrew the fusebox and plug the bent back cable (violet) into the plug sleeve fuse and refasten the fusebox.
5. Assemble the receiver and install it into the compartment. Check the receiver polarity.
6. Make all electrical connections and secure the radio.

Windshield Wiper Motor

Removal and Installation

1. Remove the drive crank lever.

Removing the drive crank lever

2. Release the attaching screws and the three electrical contacts along with the ground wire.
3. Remove the motor assembly. Installation is the reverse of removal.

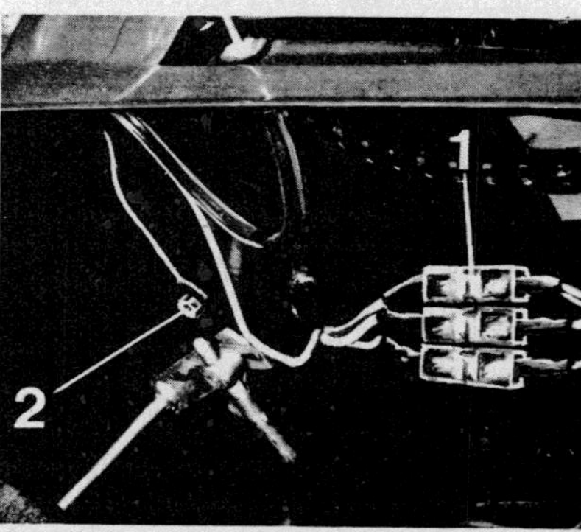

Remove the electrical contacts (1) and the ground wire (2).

Instrument Cluster

Removal and Installation

To remove the instrument cluster, disconnect the negative battery connection and the cluster retaining screws. Release the lower steering column casing. Remove the speedometer drive cable and the central and secondary electrical connections. Push the cluster out to the front.

Installation is the reverse of removal.

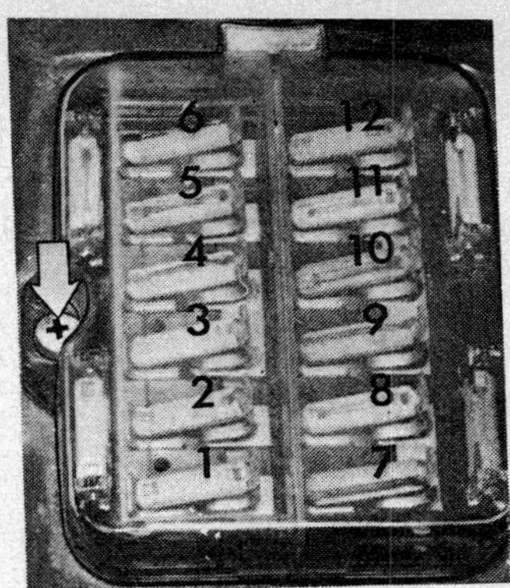

1971 and later 4-cyl.

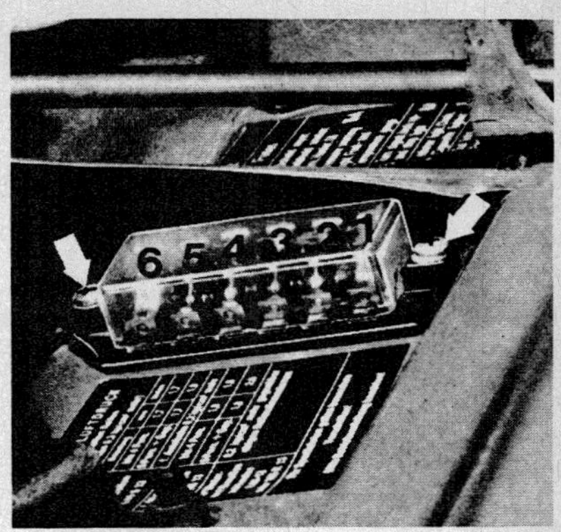

Fuse box location and the two attaching screws.

Fuse Box Location (4-cyl models)

The fuse box is located on the engine cowl and consists of ten inputs and six fuses. The following chart will list the fuses and functions.

(6-cyl Models)

The fuse box on the 6 cylinder models is located in the glove compartment at the left hand side.

FUSE CHART

Fuse	Amperage	Function
1	8	Left side parking and side marker lights
2	8	License plate and instrument panel lights
3	8	Right side parking and side marker lights
4	8	Interior light, clock, and cigar lighter
5	8	Brake, turn signal, and back-up lights
6	16	Windshield wipers and washers, fuel, engine temperature, and oil pressure gauges, tail lights, and heater fan.

CAPRI

Index

INTRODUCTION

Capri, imported by Lincoln-Mercury, is a product of Ford of Europe. The efforts of Ford of England and Ford of Germany. Capri has been available in Europe for several years; however, it has been imported to the United States only since 1970. In 1970 the car was offered with a 1600 cc engine and manual transmission. As popularity grew, the option list was extended to include a 2000 cc engine and automatic transmission in 1971. In 1972, in addition to the 1600 and 2000 cc engines, a 2600 cc V6 engine was made available. A GT package was offered with the V6.

Serial Number Identification

Engine

NOTE: *There is no engine serial number. Engine type can be determined by using the Vehicle Identification Plate.*

MODEL IDENTIFICATION

1600

1973 2600

Vehicle Identification Plate

The vehicle identification plate is located on the right-side front fender apron in the engine compartment. This plate gives details of the engine, axle, body, and transmission.

Engine Identification Chart

No. of Cyl.	Displace. (cc)	Type	Engine Model Code
4	1600	OHV	L1/L4
4	2000	OHC	NB
6	2600	OHV	UX

Vehicle identification plate—1970

A) Driver code
  1—left hand drive
B) Engine code
  L1—1600 cc
C) Transmission code
  5—manual transmission
D) Rear axle code (ratio)—
  3.89:1
E) Paint code
  B—Ermine Gold
  7—Amber Gold Metallic
  1—Blue Mint Metallic
  5—Fern Green Metallic
  6—Aquatic Jade Metallic
  H—Red
F) Trim code
  refers to color and type of material used
G) S.V.C. Reference
  signifies the date of manufacture
H) Vehicle Number—
  051—G assembled in Germany
  052—A denotes Cologne
    B denotes Genk
  053—ECJ Tudor Sedan only
  054—year and month of manufacture
  055—original number for that model

A) Body Type
  GECJ—Tudor Coupe
B) Vehicle Number
  consists of eleven symbols
  G A E C K U 78175
  1) G—assembled in Germany
  2) A—denotes Cologne
    B—denotes Genk
  3) model type (EC-Capri)
  4) year and month of manufacturer
  5) original number for that model
C) Driver code
  1—left hand drive
D) Engine code
  L4—1600 cc
  NB—2000 cc
  UX—2600 cc
E) Transmission code
  5—manual shift
  7—automatic
F) Rear Axle Code
  V—3.89:1
  Q—3.44:1
G) Paint code
  1—Sapphire Metallic
  3—Silver Fox Metallic
  6—Evergreen Metallic
  7—Tawny Metallic
  J—Sunset
  T—Yellow
  B—Ermine White
  A—Vinyl Roof Black
H) Trim code
  AE—Black
  FE—Marquis Blue
  JE—Tan
  KE—Parchment

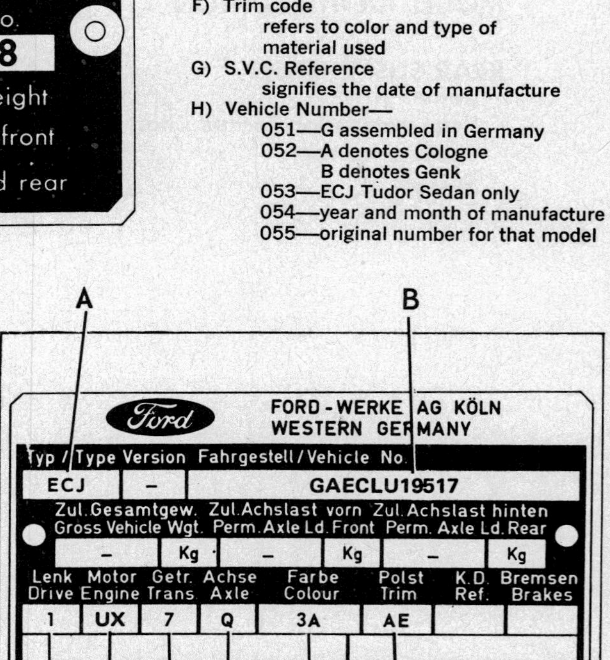

Vehicle identification plate—1971-72

GENERAL ENGINE SPECIFICATIONS

Year	Engine Displacement Cu. In. (cc)	Carburetor Type	Horsepower (@ rpm)	Torque @ rpm (ft lbs)	Bore x Stroke (in.)	Compression Ratio	Oil Pressure @ rpm (psi)
1970-71	97.6 (1600)	Motorcraft 1V	75 @ 5000	96 @ 3000	3.188 x 3.056	8.0:1	35 @ 1000
1970-72	122 (2000)	Motorcraft 2V	100 @ 5600	120 @ 3600	3.575 x 3.029	9.0:1	50 @ 1500
1972	158.6 (2600)	Motorcraft 2V	107 @ 5700	N.A.	3.545 x 2.630	8.2:1	40-55 @ 1500

TUNE-UP SPECIFICATIONS

Year	Engine Displace. (cc)	Spark Plugs Type (Autolite)	Spark Plugs Gap (in.)	Distributor Point Dwell (deg)	Distributor Point Gap (in.)	Ignition Timing (deg)▲ MT	Ignition Timing (deg)▲ AT	Intake Valve Opens (deg)	Fuel Pump Pressure (psi)	Compression Press. (psi)	Idle Speed (rpm) MT	Idle Speed (rpm) AT	Valve Clearance (in.) In	Valve Clearance (in.) Ex
1970-71	1600	AGR-22	0.025	38-42	0.024-0.026	12B② ⑨⑩	12B	17B	$3^1/_2$-$4^1/_2$	④	800/500⑤	—	0.010	0.017
1970-72	2000	BRF-42	0.034	38-42	0.024-0.026	6B①	10B ⑧	18B	$3^1/_2$-$4^1/_2$	④	750/500⑦	650/500⑦	0.008③	0.010③
1972	2600	AGR-32	0.034	37-40	0.025	12B	12B	20B	$3^1/_2$-$4^1/_2$	④	750	650	0.014⑥	0.016⑥

▲ With the vacuum lines disconnected and plugged
B Before top dead center
① At 650 rpm in Drive (AT); 750 rpm in Neutral (MT)
② At 900 rpm
③ Between the cam and follower
④ Lowest within 75 per cent of the highest
⑤ Higher speed with solenoid energized
⑥ Cold
⑦ Air conditioner on, if so equipped
⑧ California Automatic, 9°
⑨ 12 Degrees Before With 28mm Carburetor
⑩ 6 Degrees Before With 25 mm Carburetor
MT Manual Transmission
AT Automatic Transmission
— Not Applicable

FIRING ORDER

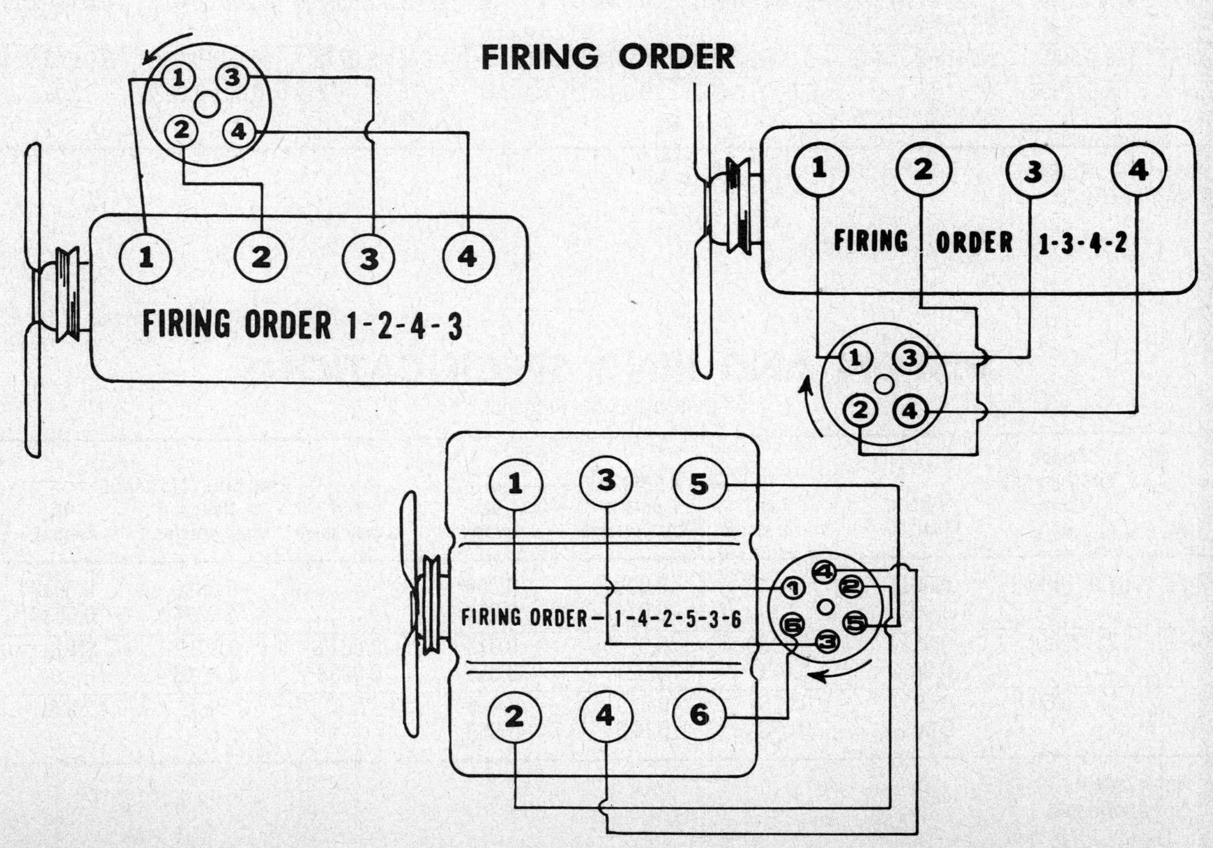

CARBURETOR SPECIFICATIONS

All specifications given in inches unless specified otherwise

Engine Model (cc)	Carburetor Number	Bore Size	JET SIZE		Air Flow (CFM)	Float Level	Fast Idle	CHOKE SYSTEM	
			Main	Secondary				Gap Setting	Pulldown Setting
1600	701W-9510EA⑩	1.34	0.049	N.A.	125	1.200	0.210⑨	Index	0.65-0.085
2000	D1RY-9510-K⑤⑪	1.26③ 1.42④	0.052	0.059	233	0.420	0.156⑨	1-Lean② Index	 0.236⑨
2600	72TF-BEA①	1.260③ 1.420④	0.062	0.070	233	0.420	0.118⑨	1-Lean① Index	0.236⑨ 0.236⑨
	72TF-BFA②	1.260③ 1.420④	0.048	0.080	233	0.420	0.156⑨	N.A.	N.A.

① Manual Transmission
② Automatic Transmission
③ Primary
④ Secondary
⑤ Manual Transmission, 1971
⑥ Automatic Transmission, 1971
⑦ Manual Transmission, 1972
⑧ Automatic Transmission, 1972
⑨ ±0.020 in.
⑩ Specifications the same for carburetor number 701-9510-EB
⑪ Specifications the same for carburetor numbers D1RY-9510-L⑥, D2RY-9510-D⑦, D2RY-9510-E⑧
N.A. Not Available

CRANKSHAFT AND CONNECTING ROD SPECIFICATIONS

All measurements are given in inches

Year	Engine Displacement (cu in.)	CRANKSHAFT				CONNECTING ROD		
		Main Brg Journal Dia	Main Brg Oil Clearance	Shaft End-Play	Thrust on No.	Journal Diameter	Oil Clearance	Side Clearance
1970-71	97.6 (1600)	2.1253-2.1257① 2.1257-2.1261②	0.0005-0.0016	0.003-0.011	3	1.9368-1.9376	0.001-0.015	0.004-0.010
1970-72	122 (2000)	2.2432-2.24440	0.0005-0.0015	0.004-0.008	3	2.0464-2.0772	0.001-0.005	0.010-0.024
1972	158.6 (2600)	2.244① 2.243②	0.0005-0.002	0.004-0.008	3	2.126① 2.125②	0.005-0.002	N.A.

① Red ② Blue
N.A. Not Available

PISTON AND RING SPECIFICATIONS

All measurements in inches

Year	Engine Displacement Cu In. (cc)	Piston Clearance	RING GAP			RING SIDE CLEARANCE		
			Top Compression	Bottom Compression	Oil Control	Top Compression	Bottom Compression	Oil Control
1970-71	97.6 (1600)	0.0016-0.0022	—	0.009-0.014	0.009-0.014	—	0.0016-0.0036	0.0018-0.0038
1970-72	122 (2000)	0.001-0.002	0.0189-0.021	0.0189-0.021	0.016-0.055	0.0019-0.0038	0.0019-0.0038	SNUG
1972	158.6 (2600)	0.001-0.003	0.015-0.023	0.015-0.023	0.015-0.055	N.A.	N.A.	N.A.

N.A. Not Available
— Not Applicable

TORQUE SPECIFICATIONS

All readings in ft lbs

Year	Engine Displacement Cu In.	Cylinder Head Bolts	Rod Bearing Bolts	Main Bearing Bolts	Crankshaft Pulley Bolt	Flywheel-to-Crankshaft Bolts	MANIFOLDS Intake	MANIFOLDS Exhaust
1970-71	97.6 (1600)	65-70	65-70	65-70	24-28	50-55	12-15	15-18
1970-72	122 (2000)	39-43	29-34	65-75	39-43	47-51	12-15	12-15
1972	158.6 (2600)	65-80	22-26	65-75	32-36	45-50	15-18	15-18

Torque Sequences

Cylinder Head

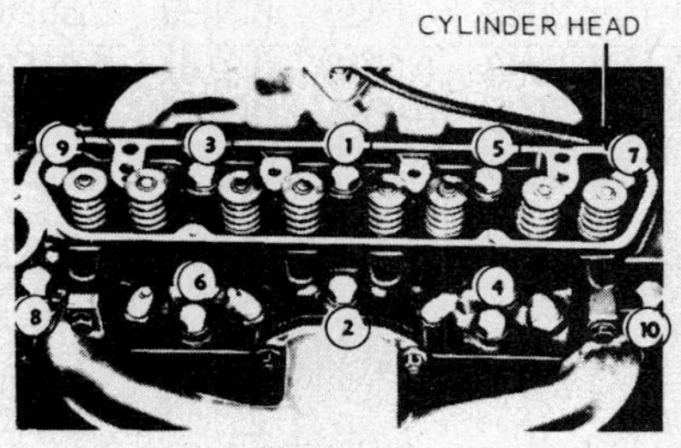

1600 cc engine

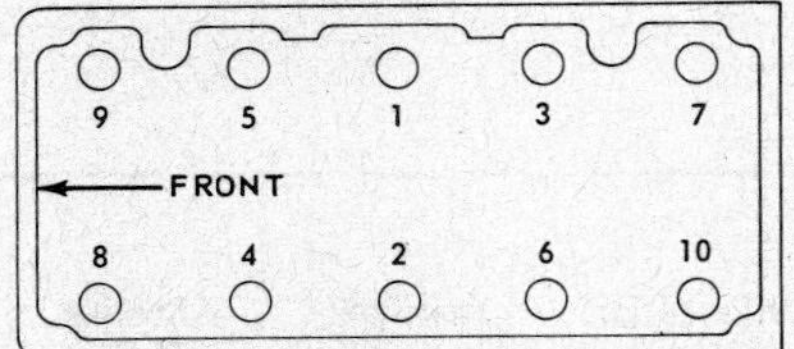

200 cc engine

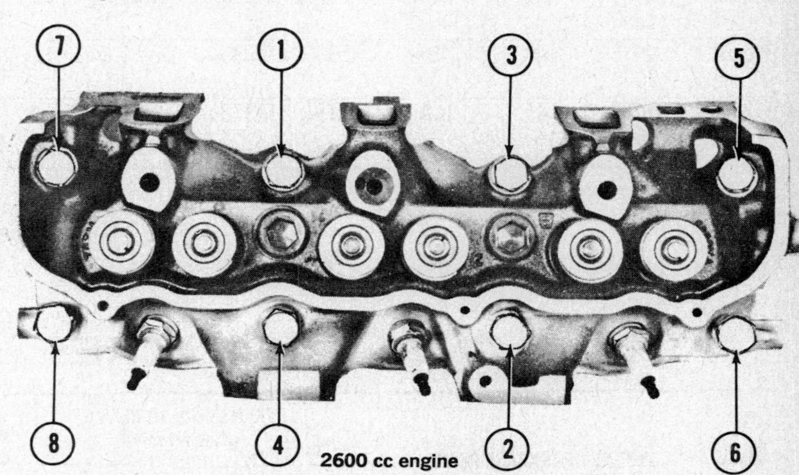

2600 cc engine

Intake Manifold

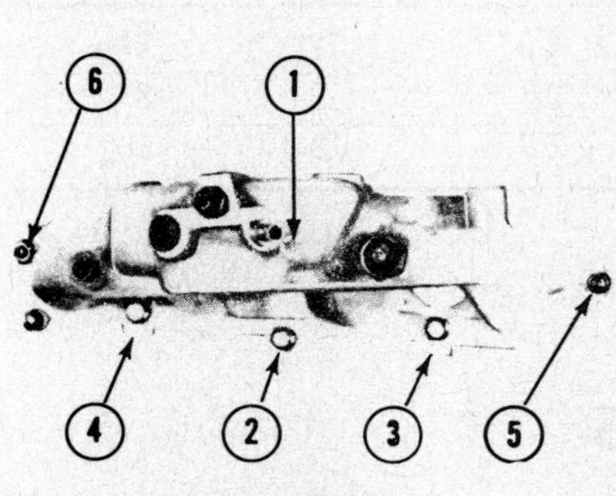

2000 cc engine

4 8 6 2

3 7 5 1

2600 cc engine

Exhaust Manifold

8 3 1 5

2 4 7

6

2000 cc engine

VALVE SPECIFICATIONS

Year	Engine Displacement Cu. In. (cc)	Seat Angle (deg)	Face Angle (deg)	LIFT Intake (in.)	LIFT Exhaust (in.)	Spring Test Pressure (lbs @ in.)	Spring Installed Height (in.)	STEM TO GUIDE CLEARANCE (in.) Intake	STEM TO GUIDE CLEARANCE (in.) Exhaust	STEM DIAMETER (in.) Intake	STEM DIAMETER (in.) Exhaust
1970-71	97.6 (1600)	44	45	0.297	0.320	44-49 @ 1.263	1.263	0.0008-0.0027	0.0017-0.0036	0.3098-0.3089	0.3105-0.3096
1970-72	122 (2000)	44	45	0.399	0.399	60-64 @ 1.417	1.417	0.0008-0.0025	0.0018-0.0035	0.3167-0.3156	0.3159-0.3149
1972	158.6 (2600)	45	N.A.	0.373	0.373	N.A.	N.A.	N.A.	N.A.	0.316	0.315

① Cold
N.A. Not Available

CAPACITIES

Model	ENGINE CRANKCASE REFILL after draining (qt) With filter	ENGINE CRANKCASE REFILL after draining (qt) Without filter	TRANSMISSION REFILL after draining (pt) Manual 4 speed	TRANSMISSION REFILL after draining (pt) Automatic (total cap.) C4	TRANSMISSION REFILL after draining (pt) Automatic (total cap.) Borg Warner	Differential (pt)	Fuel Tank (gal)	Cooling System
1600	3½	3	2.9	16	13½	2.3	12	6½
2000	5	4	2.8	16	13½	2.3	12	8
2600	5¼	4¼	2.8	16	13½	2.3	12	8¼

BRAKE SPECIFICATIONS

All measurements are given in inches

Year	Model	WHEEL CYLINDER BORE Front Disc	WHEEL CYLINDER BORE Front Drum	WHEEL CYLINDER BORE Rear	BRAKE DISC OR DRUM DIAMETER Front Disc	BRAKE DISC OR DRUM DIAMETER Front Drum	BRAKE DISC OR DRUM DIAMETER Rear	PAD AND LINING THICKNESS Front Pad	PAD AND LINING THICKNESS Rear Lining
1970-72	All models	2.125	—	0.75	9.625	—	9.0	0.50	0.188

— Not Applicable

BATTERY AND STARTER SPECIFICATIONS

Year	Engine Displacement cu in. (cc)	BATTERY			STARTERS			
		Ampere Hour Capacity	Volts	Terminal Grounded	Lock Test			Brush Spring Tension (oz)
					Amps	Volts	Torque (ft lbs)	
1970-71	97.6 (1600)	55①	12	neg	— Not Recommended —			28③ 42.3④
1970-72	122 (2000)	55① 6②	12	neg	— Not Recommended —			28③ 42.3④
1972	158.6 (2600)	66	12	neg	— Not Recommended —			28③ 42.3④

① Manual Transmission, 4 cylinder
② Automatic Transmission, 4 cylinder
③ Lucas Starter
④ Bosch Starter

ALTERNATOR AND REGULATOR SPECIFICATIONS

Year	ALTERNATOR			REGULATOR						
					Field Relay			Regulator		
	Part No. or Manufacturer	Field Current @ 12 v	Output (amps)	Part No. or Manufacturer	Air Gap (in.)	Point Gap (in.)	Volts to Close	Air Gap (in.)	Point Gap (in.)	Volts @ 75°
1970-72	17 ACR	N.A.	7.5	—	Integral With Alternator			Integral With Alternator		
1970-72	K-1	N.A.	10	—	Integral With Alternator			Integral With Alternator		

① Lucas ② Bosch

WHEEL ALIGNMENT

Year	Model	Caster	Camber	Toe-In	Turning Circle
1970-72	All Models	$+\frac{1}{2}°$-$+1\frac{1}{2}°$	$-\frac{1}{4}$-$+\frac{3}{4}$	0.0 in.-$\frac{1}{4}$ in.	31.5 ft

Wiring Diagrams

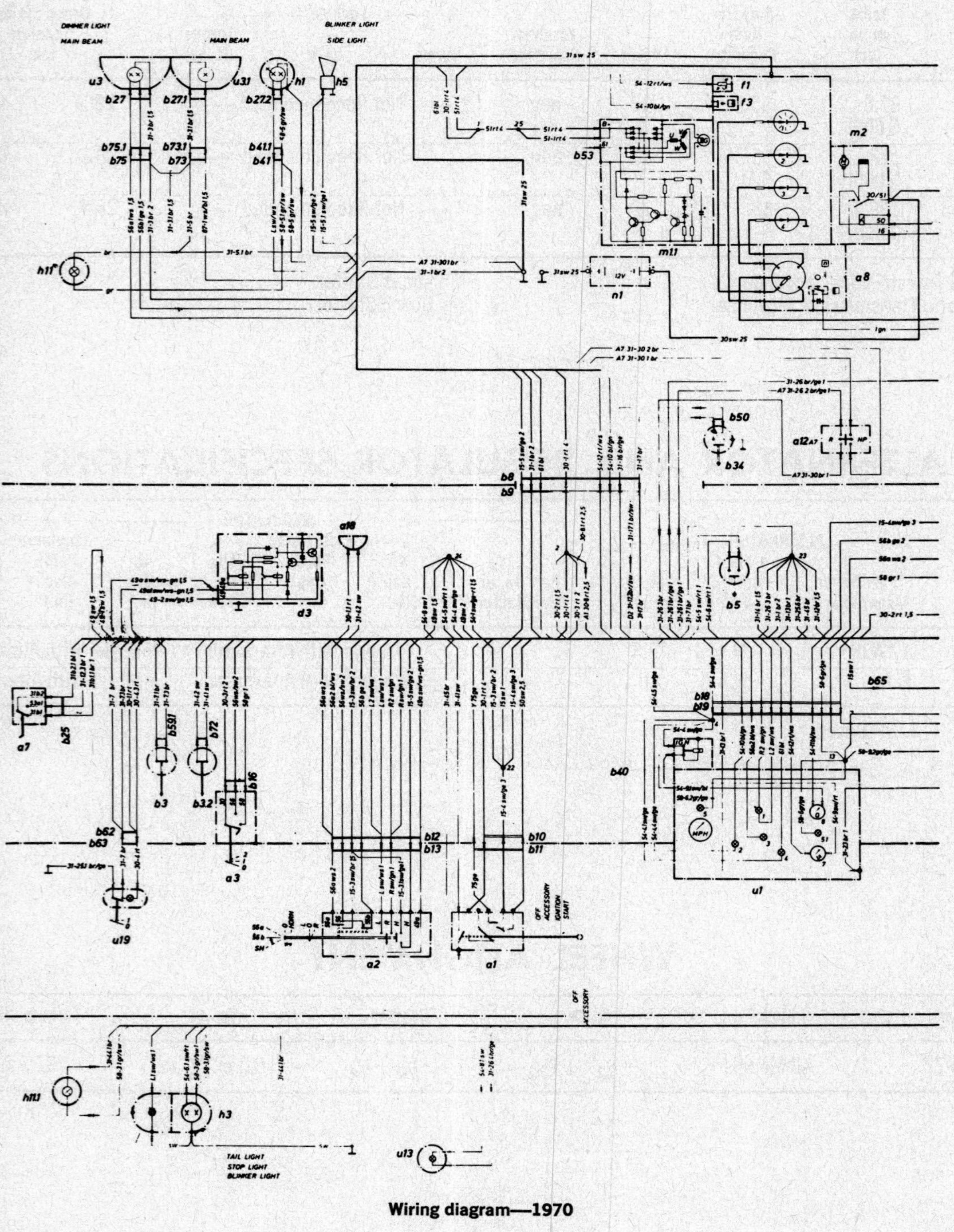

Wiring diagram—1970

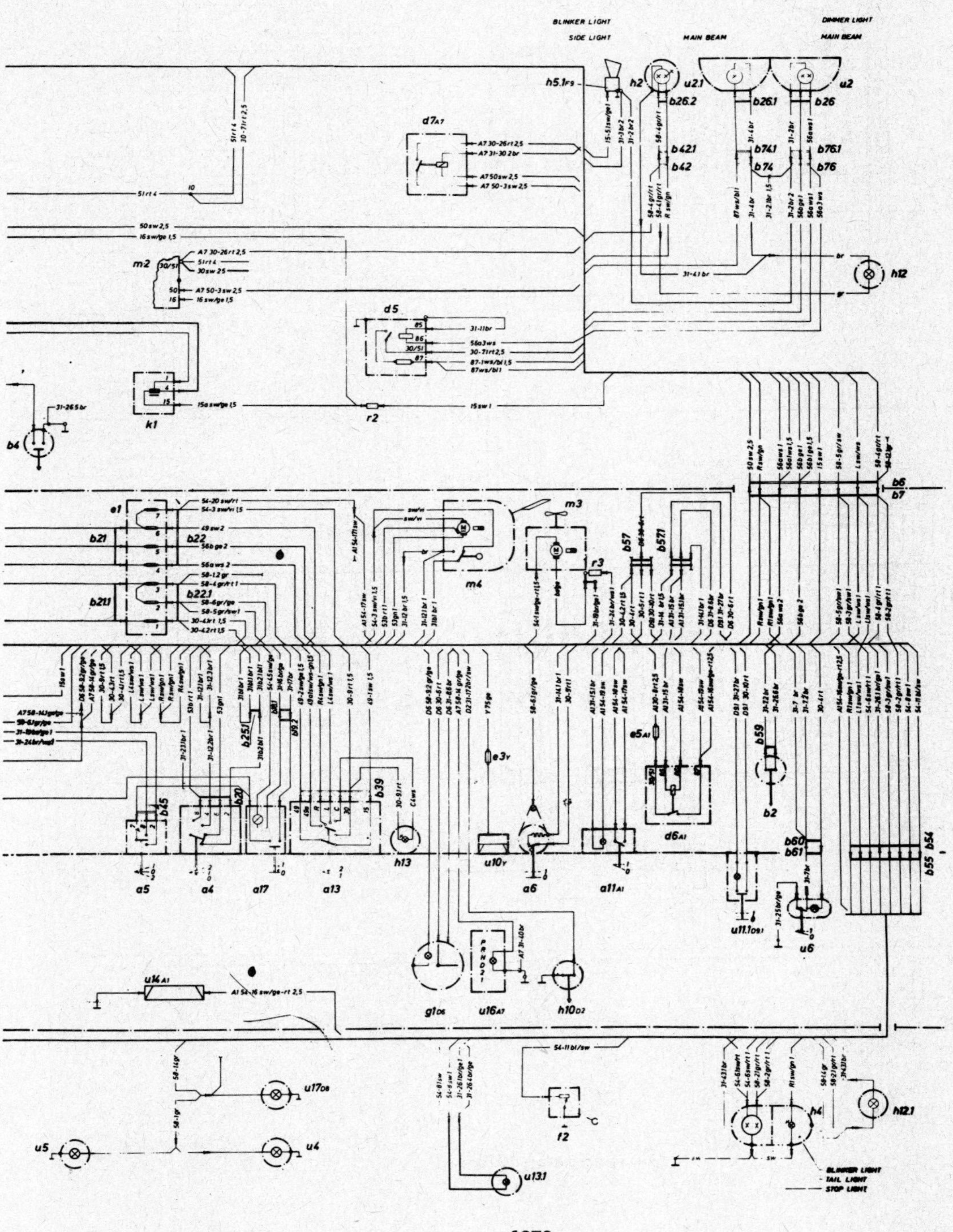
BLINKER LIGHT
SIDE LIGHT
MAIN BEAM
DIMMER LIGHT
MAIN BEAM
h5.1
h2
u2.1
u2
b26.2
b26.1
b26
d7
b42.1
b42
b74.1
b74
b76.1
b76
m2
h12
d5
k1
r2
b4
b6
b7
e1
b21
b22
b21.1
b22.1
m3
m4
r3
b57
b57.1
b25.1
b9.2
b45
b20
b39
e3
e5
b59
b2
d6
a5
a4
a17
a13
h13
u10
a6
a11
b60
b61
b54
b55
u11.1
u6
g1
u16
h10
u14
u17
u5
u4
f2
u13.1
h4
h12.1
BLINKER LIGHT
TAIL LIGHT
STOP LIGHT

1970

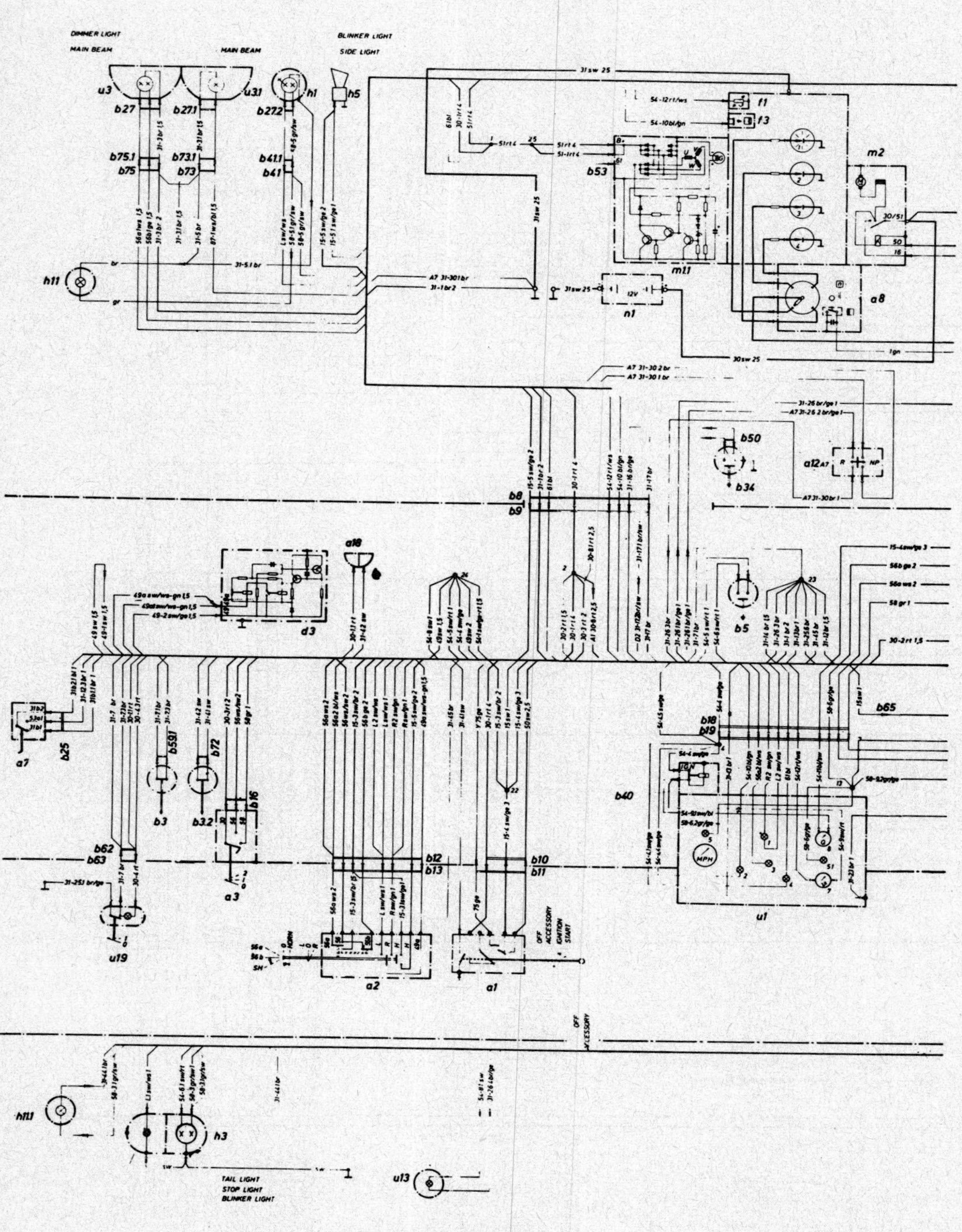

Wiring diagram—1971

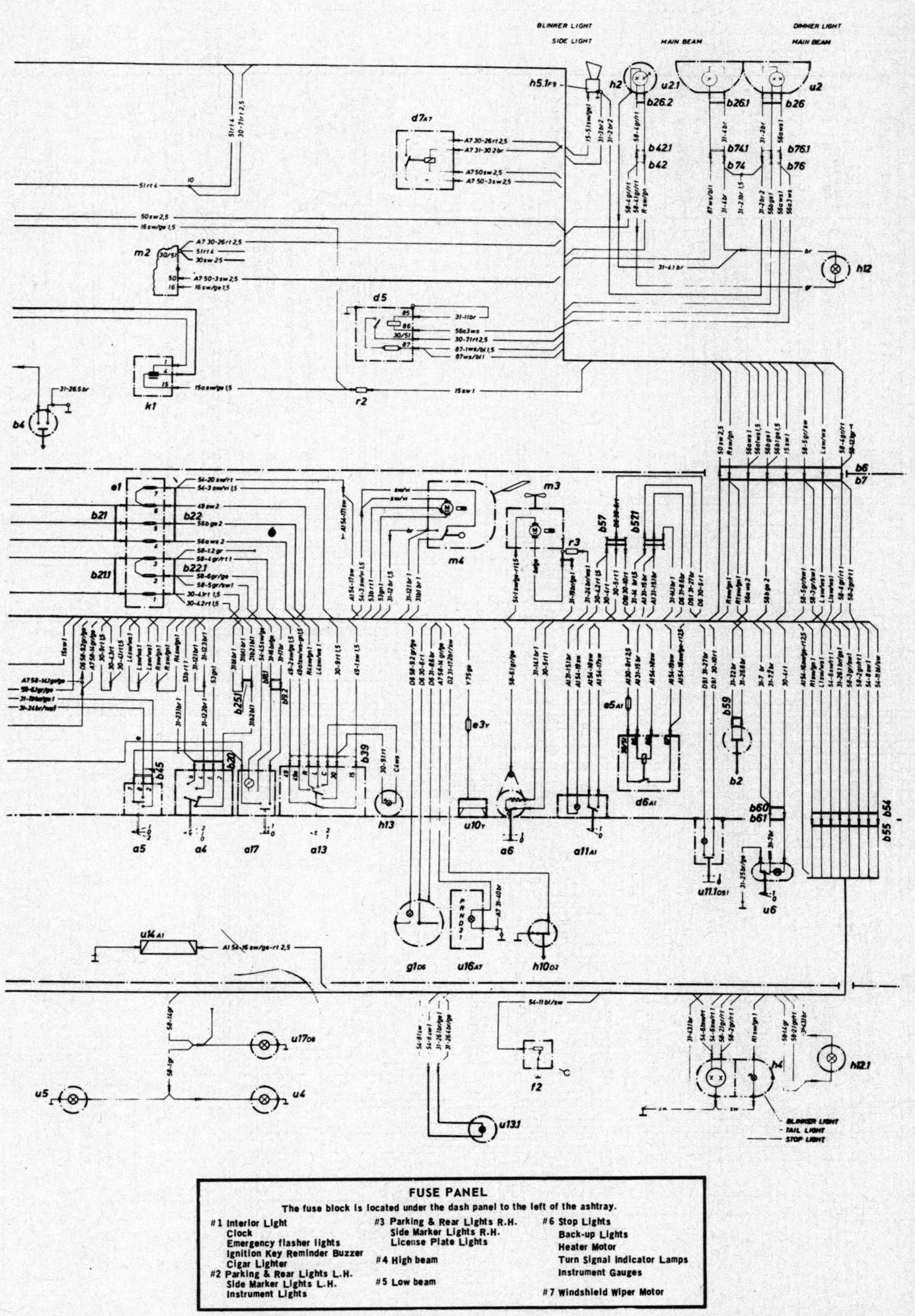

FUSE PANEL

The fuse block is located under the dash panel to the left of the ashtray.

#1 Interior Light
Clock
Emergency flasher lights
Ignition Key Reminder Buzzer
Cigar Lighter
#2 Parking & Rear Lights L.H.
Side Marker Lights L.H.
Instrument Lights
#3 Parking & Rear Lights R.H.
Side Marker Lights R.H.
License Plate Lights
#4 High beam
#5 Low beam
#6 Stop Lights
Back-up Lights
Heater Motor
Turn Signal Indicator Lamps
Instrument Gauges
#7 Windshield Wiper Motor

1971

1971 1600 cc

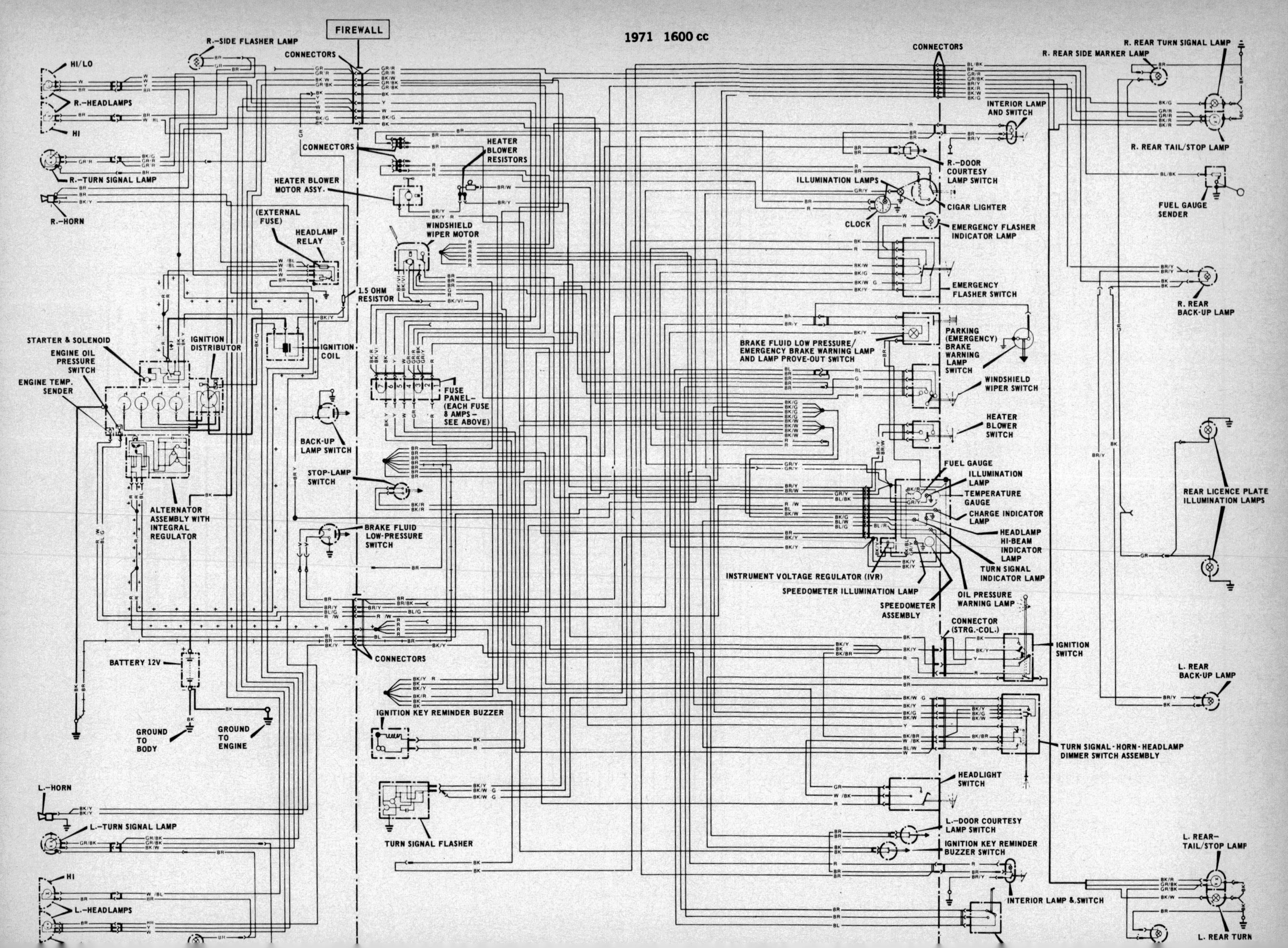

FIREWALL
R.-SIDE FLASHER LAMP
CONNECTORS
HI/LO
R.-HEADLAMPS
HI
R.-TURN SIGNAL LAMP
R.-HORN
HEATER BLOWER RESISTORS
HEATER BLOWER MOTOR ASSY.
(EXTERNAL FUSE)
HEADLAMP RELAY
WINDSHIELD WIPER MOTOR
1.5 OHM RESISTOR
IGNITION COIL
STARTER & SOLENOID
ENGINE OIL PRESSURE SWITCH
ENGINE TEMP. SENDER
IGNITION DISTRIBUTOR
FUSE PANEL- (EACH FUSE 8 AMPS - SEE ABOVE)
BACK-UP LAMP SWITCH
STOP-LAMP SWITCH
BRAKE FLUID LOW-PRESSURE SWITCH
ALTERNATOR ASSEMBLY WITH INTEGRAL REGULATOR
BATTERY 12V
GROUND TO BODY
GROUND TO ENGINE
IGNITION KEY REMINDER BUZZER
TURN SIGNAL FLASHER
L.-HORN
L.-TURN SIGNAL LAMP
L.-HEADLAMPS
R. REAR TURN SIGNAL LAMP
R. REAR SIDE MARKER LAMP
INTERIOR LAMP AND SWITCH
R. REAR TAIL/STOP LAMP
R.-DOOR COURTESY LAMP SWITCH
ILLUMINATION LAMPS
CIGAR LIGHTER
FUEL GAUGE SENDER
CLOCK
EMERGENCY FLASHER INDICATOR LAMP
EMERGENCY FLASHER SWITCH
R. REAR BACK-UP LAMP
PARKING (EMERGENCY) BRAKE WARNING LAMP SWITCH
BRAKE FLUID LOW PRESSURE/ EMERGENCY BRAKE WARNING LAMP AND LAMP PROVE-OUT SWITCH
WINDSHIELD WIPER SWITCH
HEATER BLOWER SWITCH
FUEL GAUGE
ILLUMINATION LAMP
TEMPERATURE GAUGE
CHARGE INDICATOR LAMP
HEADLAMP HI-BEAM INDICATOR LAMP
TURN SIGNAL INDICATOR LAMP
REAR LICENCE PLATE ILLUMINATION LAMPS
INSTRUMENT VOLTAGE REGULATOR (IVR)
SPEEDOMETER ILLUMINATION LAMP
OIL PRESSURE WARNING LAMP
SPEEDOMETER ASSEMBLY
CONNECTOR (STRG.-COL.)
IGNITION SWITCH
L. REAR BACK-UP LAMP
TURN SIGNAL-HORN-HEADLAMP DIMMER SWITCH ASSEMBLY
HEADLIGHT SWITCH
L.-DOOR COURTESY LAMP SWITCH
IGNITION KEY REMINDER BUZZER SWITCH
INTERIOR LAMP & SWITCH
L. REAR- TAIL/STOP LAMP
L. REAR TURN

a1—Steering/ignition lock
a2—Blinker switch
a3—Light switch
a4—Windshield wiper motor switch-two stage
a5—Heating blower switch-two stage
a6—Cigar lighter
a7—Foot operated switch windshield wiper motor
a8—Ignition distributor
a13—Blinker switch warning system
a17—Switch-control-light-two circuit brake system
a18—Buzzer
b2—Door contact interruptor RH interior light
b3—Door contact interruptor LH interior light
b3.2—Door contact interruptor buzzer
b4—Back-up light switch
b5—Stop light switch
b6—Multiple connector-dash board, R
b7—Multiple connector-dash board, R
b8—Multiple connector-dash board, L
b9—Multiple connector-dash board, L
b10—Multiple connector-steering/ignition lock
b11—Multiple connector-steering/ignition lock
b12—Multiple connector-blinker switch
b13—Multiple connector-blinker switch

b16—Multiple connector-light switch
b18—Multiple connector-instrument cluster
b18.1—Multiple connector-switch-control light-two circuit brake system
b19—Multiple connector-instrument cluster
b19.2—Multiple connector-switch-control light-two circuit brake system
b20—Multiple connector-windshield wiper motor switch
b21—Multiple connector-fuse box
b21.1—Multiple connector-fuse box
b22—Multiple connector-fuse box
b22.1—Multiple connector-fuse box
b25—Multiple connector foot operated switch windshield wiper motor
b25.1—Multiple connector wiper wash system
b26—Multiple connector main beam headlight, R
b26.1—Multiple connector remote headlight, R
b26.2—Multiple connector blinker-side light, R
b27—Multiple connector main beam headlight, L
b27.1—Multiple connector remote headlight, L

b41.1—Multiple connector blinker-side light, L
b42—Multiple connector blinker-side light, R
b42.1—Multiple connector blinker-side light, R
b45—Multiple connector heating blower switch
b50—Multiple connector warning light switch-two circuit brake system
b53—Multiple connector alternator
b54—Multiple connector-instrument panel, R
b55—Multiple connector-instrument panel, R

b57—Multiple connector
b57.1—Multiple connector

b59—Door contact switch, R
b59.1—Door contact switch, L
b60—Multiple connector-interior light, R
b61—Multiple connector-interior light, R
b62—Multiple connector-interior light, L
b63—Multiple connector-interior light, L
b65—Connector wire 15
b72—Multiple connector buzzer switch
b73—Multiple connector remote headlight, L
b73.1—Multiple connector remote headlight, L
b74—Multiple connector remote headlight, R
b74.1—Multiple connector remote headlight, R
b75—Multiple connector main beam headlight, L
b75.1—Multiple connector main beam headlight, L
b76—Multiple connector main beam headlight, R
b76.1—Multiple connector main beam headlight, R
d3—Blinker unit
d5—Relay remote headlights
e1—Fuse box

f1—Transmitter water temperature gauge
f2—Transmitter fuel gauge
f3—Oil pressure control switch
h1—Blinker-side light, L
h2—Blinker-side light, R
h3—Combined tail light, L
h4—Combined tail light, R
h5—Horn, L
h11—Side marker front, L
h11.1—Side marker back, L
h12—Side marker front, R
h12.1—Side marker back, R
h13—Warning indicator-control light

k1—Ignition coil

m1.1—Alternator
m2—Starter
m3—Heating blower motor
m4—Windshield wiper motor

n1—Battery
r2—Series resistance wire iginition
r3—Series resistor heating blower
u1—Instrument cluster
u2—Main beam headlight, R
u2.1—Remote headlight, R
u3—Main beam headlight, L
u3.1—Remote headlight, L
u4—License plate light, R
u5—License plate light, L
u6—Interior light, R

u13—Back up light, L
u13.1—Back up light, R
u19—Interior light, L

a11—Heating plate switch
d6—Working current relay heating plate
e5—Fuse heating plate
u14—Heating plate

a12—Blocking-switch automatic transmission
u16—Transmission control selector dial
d7—Working current relay automatic transmission

h10—Hand brake warning switch

g1—Clock

u17—Luggage compartment light

u11.1—Reading light

h5.1—Horn, R

e3—Fuse radio
u10—Radio

b27.2—Multiple connector blinker-side light, L
b34—Warning light switch two circuit brake system
b39—Multiple connector blinker switch warning system
b40—Voltage divider
b41—Multiple connector blinker-side light, L
30—Interior lights
Reading lights
Four way hazard flasher
Clock
Buzzer
Cigar lighter

58—Tail light, L
Side light front and back, L
Illumination-instrument cluster
Illumination-cigar lighter
Illumination-transmission control selector dial
Illumination-clock
Tail light, R
Side light front and back, R
Luggage compartment lights
License plate lights
56a—Main beam
Relay remote head lights

56b—Low beam

15—Back-up lights
Heating blower motor
Blinker system
Stop light
Voltage divider
Control light-two circuit brake system
Control light charging current
Control light oil pressure

15—Windshield wiper motor
Current circuit heating plate

Interior wiring and symbol
According to din. A. IEC.

A1—In combination with heating plate
A7—In combination with automatic gear

D2—In combination with two circuit brake system

D6—In combination with clock

D8—In combination with luggage compartment light
D9—In combination with interior light, L
D9.1—In combination with reading light

F9—In combination with horn, R

Y—In combination with radio

1971 1600 cc

TUNE-UP PROCEDURES

Spark Plugs

Before removing the spark plugs, clean the surrounding area. Grasp the plug wire by the rubber boot at the end of the wire and pull the wire from the plug. When removing wires, be careful not to confuse which wire goes on which plug. A piece of tape should be placed on the wire to identify the cylinder number. Loosen and remove each spark plug with a 13/16 in. spark plug socket. Be especially careful not to crack the porcelain insulator. If a plug is tight, use a breaker bar on the socket to remove the spark plug. Once the spark plugs are removed, be careful not to let any dirt fall into the cylinders. Examine the plugs, using the "Troubleshooting Section" for diagnosis. If you decide to reuse the spark plugs, clean them in the following manner.

1. File the center electrode flat.
2. Inspect the porcelain insulator for cracks.
3. Clean all deposits on the base of the plug with a wire brush.

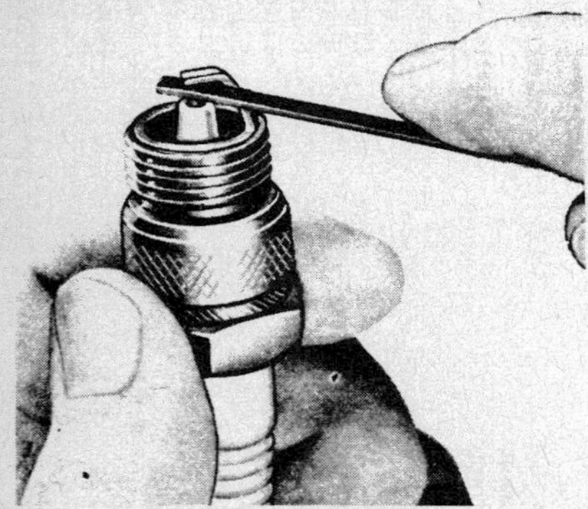

Filing down electrode

Before installing the spark plugs, adjust the plug gap according to the "Tune-Up Specifications Chart" with a wire feeler gauge. When installing new spark plugs, the gap must also be checked and set. Hand-tighten each of the plugs and then torque them to 15 ft lbs.

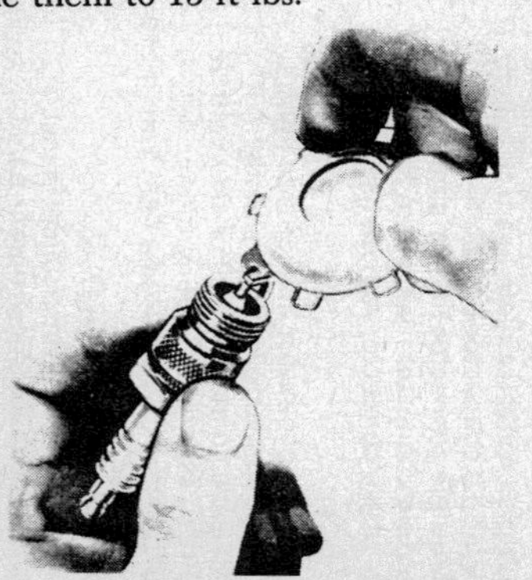

Adjusting spark plug gap

Breaker Points and Condenser

The point set and condenser should be replaced as a unit. Whenever the points are adjusted, the ignition timing should be checked since adjusting the points will change the timing.

Release the clips which secure the distributor cap. Remove the cap and the rotor. Inspect the inside of the distributor cap for cracks or excessive wear and also check the rotor for burning or excessive wear. If any of these conditions exist, those parts should be replaced.

If the breaker points are not pitted or burned, they may be cleaned rather than replaced. If you decide to clean them, proceed in the following manner.

1. Pry open the points with a screwdriver.
2. Place a point file between the contacts.
3. Release the points. (Let the points exert their own pressure; don't apply any external pressure.)
4. File the contacts.
5. Adjust the points. (See "Breaker Point Adjustment.")

Removal and Installation

When replacing the points and condenser, special care should be taken to prevent dropping any of the attaching screws into the distributor or on the ground. To remove the points and condenser follow this procedure:

1. Remove the screws which retain the points and condenser.
2. Remove the condenser and distributor wires from the points.
3. Remove the points and condenser.
4. Wipe the area clean.
5. Apply a small amount of heat-resistant white grease to the distributor cam.
6. Replace the points and condenser.
7. Replace the screws, being careful not to strip the threads.
8. Replace the condenser and distributor wires.
9. Adjust the points.

Breaker Point Adjustment

Using a socket and breaker bar, turn the bolt on the crankshaft pulley to rotate the engine until the rubbing block of the points is on a high point of the distributor cam.

> **CAUTION:** *The 2000 cc engine must only be rotated clockwise.* Insert the correct size feeler gauge between the contacts and adjust them to the proper gap. (See "Tune-Up Specifications Chart.")

Slightly loosen the attaching screws, insert a screwdriver in the notch on the breaker plate, and twist the screwdriver to open or close the points to the proper gap. The feeler gauge should have a slight drag on it at the proper gap. Retighten the attaching screws. Replace the rotor, aligning the tab inside the rotor with the notch on the distributor shaft. Replace the distributor cap and snap the retaining clips into place.

Dwell Angle

The dwell angle is the angle that the distributor cam rotates while the breaker points are closed. This is a more precise adjustment than point gap. To adjust the dwell angle, remove the distributor cap and connect a dwell meter between the primary lead and ground. Crank the engine with the key and observe the dwell angle on the meter. Refer to the

Adjusting breaker points—Autolite

"Tune-up Specifications Chart" for the proper dwell angle. If it is necessary to adjust the angle, adjust it by opening or closing the point gap as previously described. Remove the dwell meter and replace the distributor cap.

Spark Plug Wires

Wipe the spark plug wires clean and inspect them for cracks, breaks, or frayed insulation. Replace any damaged wires. If you replace any wires, make sure you replace them with the same type (resistor or non-resistor type).

Ignition Timing

On the 1600 cc engines, you must determine which model carburetor you have before you can set the ignition timing. The carburetor number is stamped on the fuel bowl opposite the accelerator pump. The 28 mm venturi carburetor bears the number 701W-9510-EA; the 25 mm venturi carburetor number is 701-9510-EB. The ignition timing for the 28 mm carburetor should be set at 12 degrees before top dead center (BTDC); the 25 mm carburetor setting should be 6 degrees BTDC.

Timing mark—1600 cc engine

Timing mark—2000 cc engine

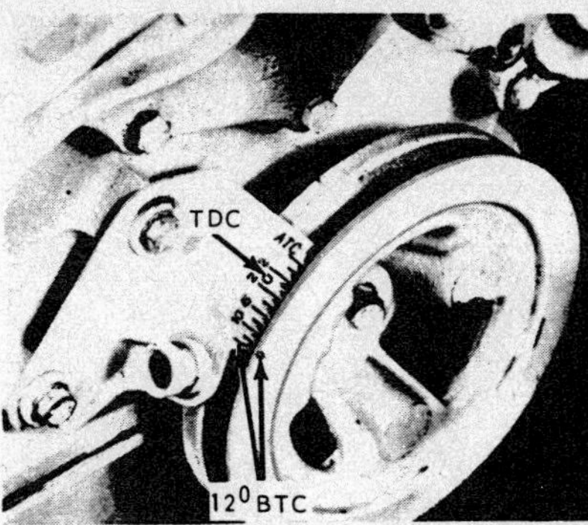

Timing mark—2600 cc engine

Set the dwell angle before setting the timing. Disconnect and plug the vacuum lines. Locate the timing mark on the pulley and the pointer on the engine block. Clean the pointer and the timing mark. Mark the correct timing position on the pulley with a piece of chalk or paint. (See the "Tune-up Specifications Chart.") Install a timing light and set the idle at 600 rpm. Adjust the ignition timing to the proper specifications by turning the distributor. (Align the pointer and the mark.) Loosen the distributor locknut at the base of the distributor. On the 1600 cc engine, turn the distributor counterclockwise to advance the spark. On the 2000 and 2600 cc engines, turn the distributor clockwise to advance timing. Make sure that the locknut is retightened and the vacuum lines are reconnected.

Valve Lash Adjustment

1600 Engine

Allow the engine to run until operating temperature is reached. Stop the engine and remove the rocker arm cover. Using a socket and a breaker bar, rotate the engine to open the valves by turning the nut on the crankshaft pulley. Turn the engine until the valves listed in the first column are fully open, then adjust the valves in the second column.

Valves Open	Valves to Adjust
1 and 6	3 and 8
2 and 4	5 and 7
3 and 8	1 and 6
5 and 7	2 and 4

Using a feeler gauge and a 7/16 in. box wrench, insert the feeler gauge between the valve stem and rocker arm, and turn the adjustment screw in or out to adjust the clearance. There should be a slight drag on the feeler gauge at the proper clearance. Refer to the "Tune-up Specifications Chart" for the proper valve lash adjustment of all engines. Clean all material from the cylinder head and rocker arm cover. Install a new gasket and install the rocker arm cover. Run the engine and check for oil leaks.

2000 cc Engine

The valves should be set when the engine is cold. If the engine has been running, allow it to cool. Remove the valve cover. Using a socket and a breaker bar, rotate the engine by turning the bolt on the crankshaft pulley clockwise. Rotate the engine until the high point of the number cam lobe is pointing straight down. Remove the rocker arm retaining springs by inserting a screwdriver under the spring at the rocker arm and snapping the spring up and off. Loosen the locknut with a ¾ in. wrench. Adjust the clearance between the cam lobe and the rocker arm by inserting the feeler gauge. Turn the adjustment screw in or out, with a 15 mm wrench, to obtain the proper clearance. Retighten the locknuts when the adjustment is complete. Repeat the procedure for the rest of the valves, adjusting each with its cam lobe pointing straight down. Adjust the valves in the following order: 6, 7, 3, 8, 2, 5, 1, 4.

Adjusting valve clearance—1600 cc engine

Adjusting valve clearance—2000 cc engine

Snap the retaining spring back into place. Install a new valve cover gasket and install the valve cover. Run the engine and check for oil leaks.

2600 cc Engine

If some component of the valve system is replaced, the valves must be set cold first. If the valves are set for a tune–up, use the hot procedure. When setting the valves of the cold engine, rotate each cylinder so that the piston is at top dead center (TDC). Remove the valve covers. Place a socket and breaker bar on the nut of the crankshaft pulley. Remove the spark plug from the cylinder where you are adjusting the valves and have an assistant place their finger in the hole. Rotate the engine until the pressure pops their finger out. Now that cylinder is at TDC. Adjust the valves as explained in the 1600 cc engine section. To adjust the valves when the engine is hot, run the engine until it reaches operating temperature. With the engine running at idle speed, insert a feeler gauge between the valve stem and rocker arm and adjust the valve. After adjusting each valve tighten the locknuts and recheck the valve clearance.

Carburetor

Idle Speed and Fuel Mixture

The 1600 cc engine uses a single-barrel downdraft carburetor with an automatic choke. The 2000 and 2600 cc engines use two-barrel carburetors. The carburetor number is stamped on the fuel bowl opposite the accelerator pump. Idle speed and ignition settings are located on the emission decal in the engine compartment. Single-barrel carburetors should be adjusted in the following manner:

1. Remove the air cleaner.
2. Connect a tachometer to the engine.
3. Allow the engine to run until it reaches operating temperature.
4. Disconnect the throttle solenoid lead from the wiring harness.
5. Disconnect the hose which runs from the carburetor to the decel valve and plug the hole.

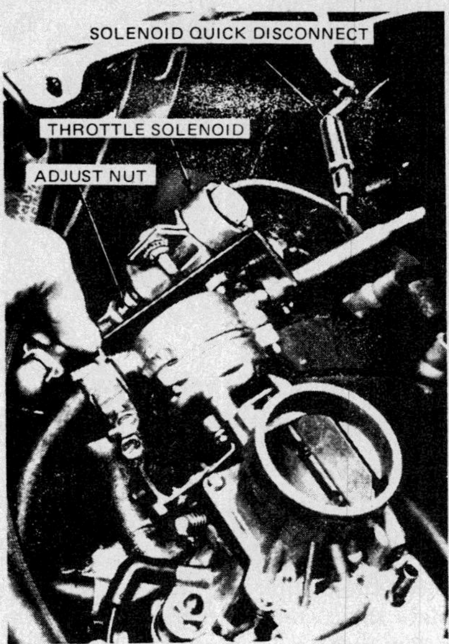

Throttle solenoid adjustment and solenoid lead disconnect.

6. Turn the headlights on high beam. Turn the curb idle adjusting screw to set the engine at the proper idle speed (See the "Tune-up Specifications Chart.") It may be necessary to use the adjusting screw on the throttle solenoid as well as the curb idle screw to achieve the proper idle.
7. Reconnect the throttle solenoid.
8. Move the throttle lever to allow the solenoid plunger to extend.
9. Turn the idle mixture screw to the right or left to obtain the smoothest idle.
10. Reconnect the decel valve hose and the air cleaner.

Use the following procedure for two-barrel carburetors:

1. Remove the air cleaner.
2. Connect a tachometer.
3. Allow the engine to run until it reaches operating temperature.
4. Check the ignition timing as in the previous section, and make sure it is set to proper specifications.
5. Disconnect the hose which runs from the carburetor to the decel valve and plug the decel valve fitting.
6. Place the car in Drive, if the car is equipped with an automatic transmission, and in neutral if it has a manual transmission.
7. Turn the headlights on the high beam and set the idle speed to the speed listed in the "Tune-Up Specifications Chart" by using the curb idle screw. This reading must be taken with the air cleaner connected.
8. Turn the idle mixture screw to the right or left to obtain the smoothest idle.

ENGINE ELECTRICAL

Distributor

Removal and Installation

The distributor is located on the right side of the 1600 cc engine, on the left side of the 2000 cc engine, and at the right rear of the 2600 cc engine.

Before removing the distributor, match mark the distributor body and engine block with chalk or paint, and mark the engine block so the two marks align. Remove the distributor cap and mark the distributor body to show the direction in which the rotor is pointing. This will ensure correct distributor installation and timing.

Remove the vacuum lines and the locknut and retainer. Do not crank the engine while the distributor is removed.

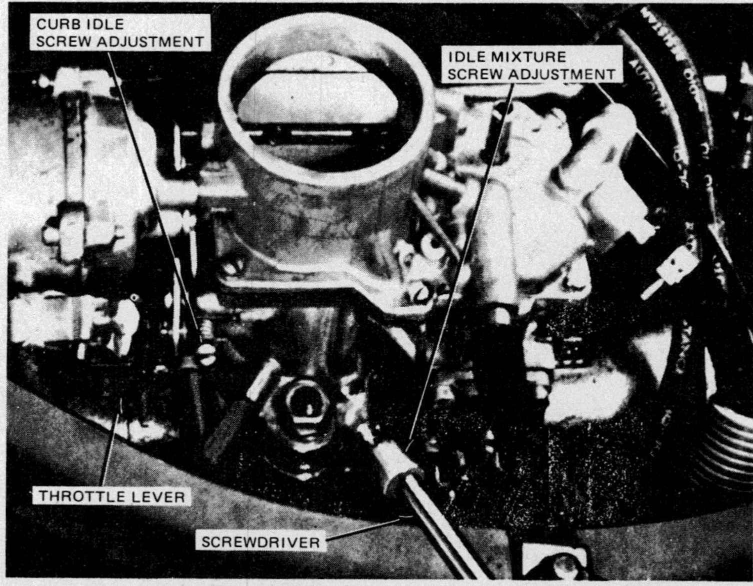

Curb idle adjustment and idle mixture screw —1600 and 2000 cc engines.

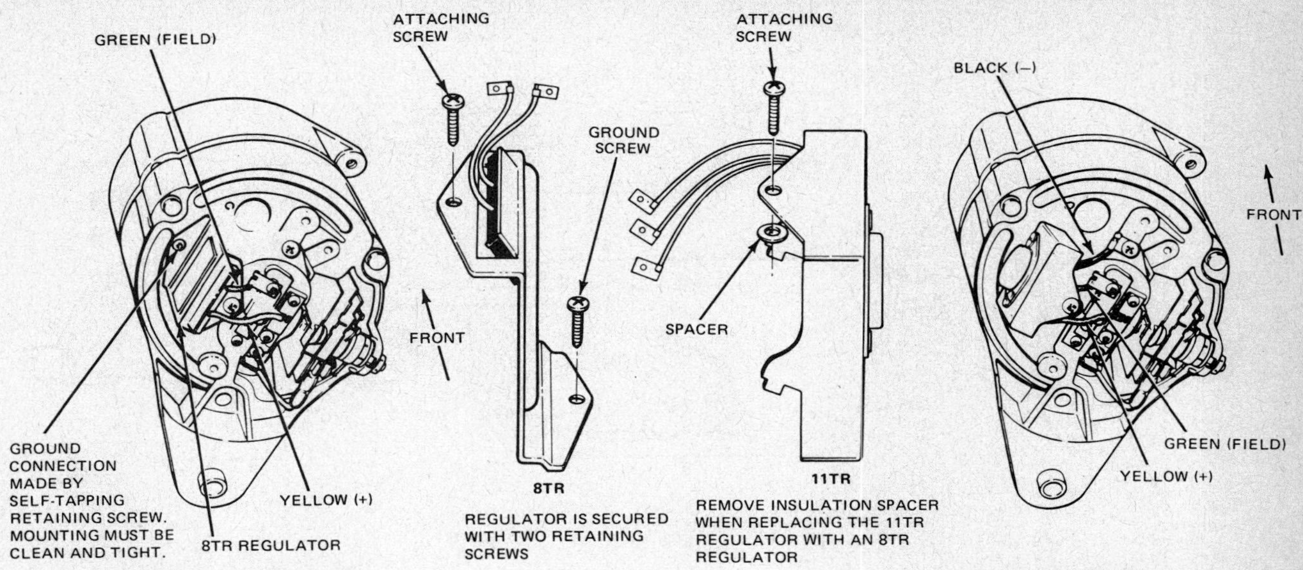

Alternator regulator connectors—two-and-three wire regulators

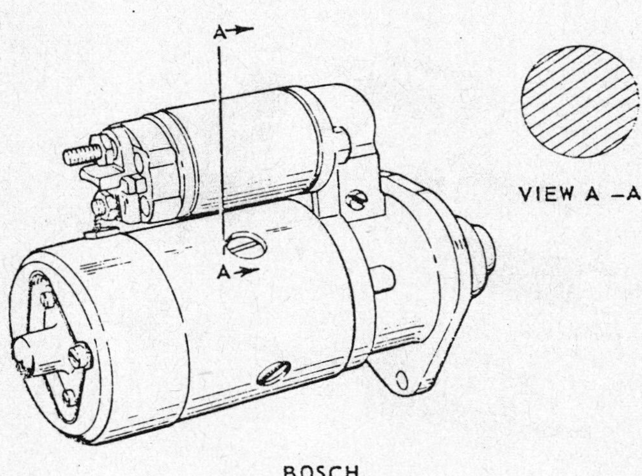

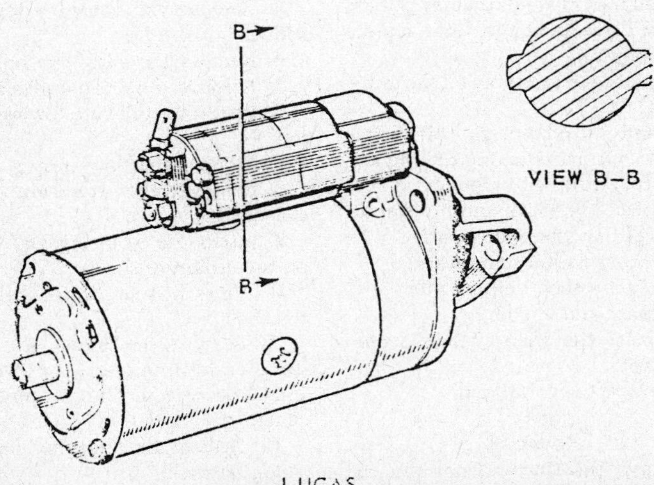

Starter motor identification

Lucas

1. Disconnect the wires from the battery.
2. Remove the wires from the starter.
3. Remove the solenoid attaching nuts, washers, and connecting strap, and then remove the solenoid.
4. Apply the parking brake and block the rear wheels. Jack the front of the car and place jackstands under it.
5. Remove the lower mounting bolts.
6. Loosen the upper mounting bolt.
7. Support the starter, remove the upper mounting bolt, and remove the starter.
8. Reverse the procedure to install the starter. (When installing the solenoid, be sure to have the correct location of the plunger extension on the fork mechanism.)

Bosch, 4 cylinder

1. Disconnect the battery ground cable.
2. Disconnect the wires at the solenoid.
3. Remove the attaching screws and then the starter.
4. Reverse the procedure to install the starter.

Bosch, 6 cylinder

1. Disconnect the battery ground cable.
2. Jack up the front of the car, block the rear wheels, and support the car with jackstands.
3. Disconnect the battery cable and the two push-on wire connectors from the solenoid.
4. Remove the mounting bolts and the starter.
5. Reverse the procedures to install the starter.

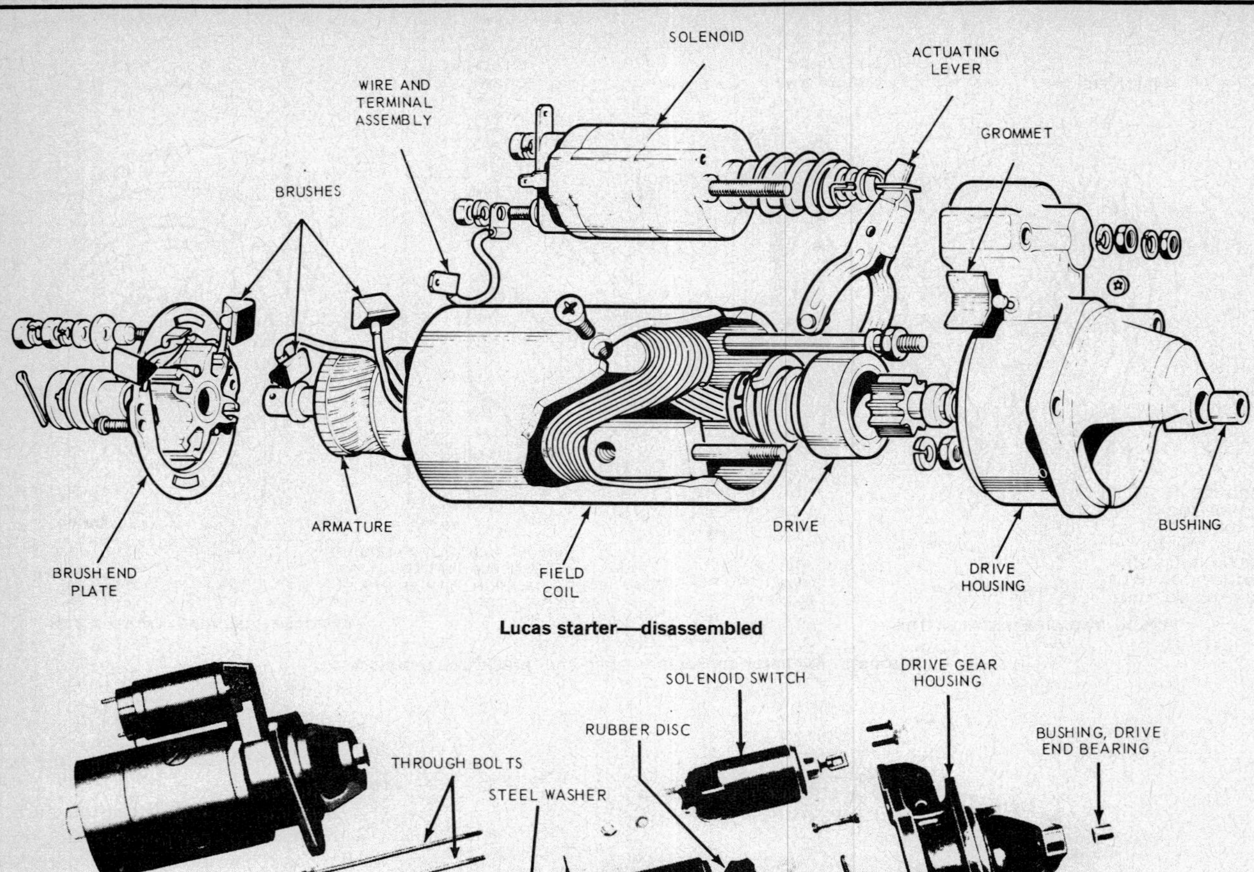

Lucas starter—disassembled

Bosch starter—disassembled

Starter Drive Replacement

Lucas

1. Remove the starter from the car.
2. Remove the end plate and housing cover from the starter.
3. Remove the cotter pin, shim washers, and thrust plate from the armature shaft.
4. Remove the bolts which secure the commutator end plate.
5. Remove the end plate with brush box molding and gasket.
6. Unscrew the two retaining nuts on the studs and remove the end drive bracket, armature, pinion gear, and drive engaging lever.
7. Place the armature in a vise and tap off the snap-ring. Remove the snap-ring and detach the starter drive.
8. Remove the spring from the starter drive after removing the retaining clip.
9. Install the ring and retainer plate to the starter drive and clutch unit, and install the snap-ring.
10. Replace the assembly on the armature shaft.
11. Install the snap-ring on the armature shaft. Pull the retaining ring up and over the snap-ring with a puller.
12. Replace the drive and bracket armature, holding them in position with the two spring washers and nuts.
13. Replace the commutator end plate, brushes and gaskets.
14. Replace the screws which secure the end plate.
15. Replace the cotter pin.

Bosch

1. Remove the starter from the engine.
2. Detach the wiring and remove the solenoid switch.
3. Remove the engaging lever guide screw.
4. Remove the end plate bolts.
5. Remove the drive end plate.
6. Press the stop-ring toward the pinion.
7. Remove the snap-ring.
8. Remove the stop-ring and the starter drive.
9. Install the stop-ring and snap-ring on the armature shaft.
10. Press the snap-ring in the groove of the shaft.
11. Press on the stop-ring.
12. Install the engaging lever on the engaging ring and install the drive end plate.
13. Attach the engaging fork to the guide screw.
14. Install the steel washer, and then the rubber washer, with the tab pointing toward the armature.

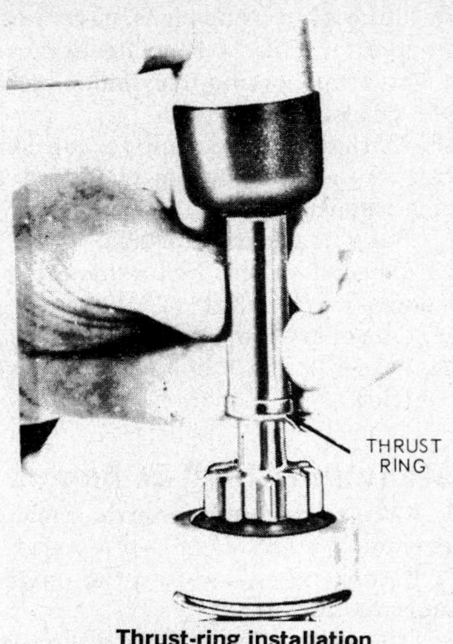

Thrust-ring installation

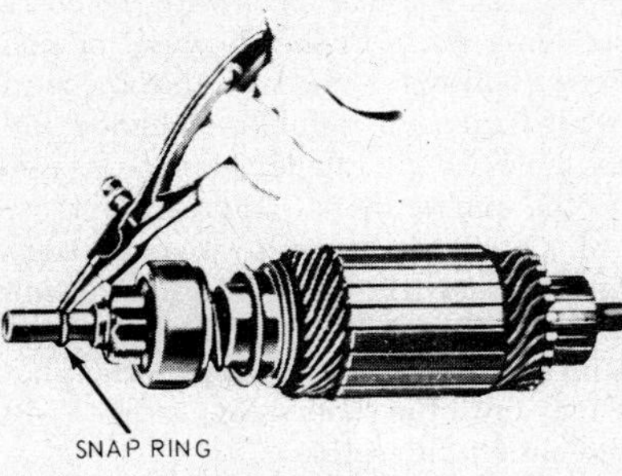

Snap-ring removal

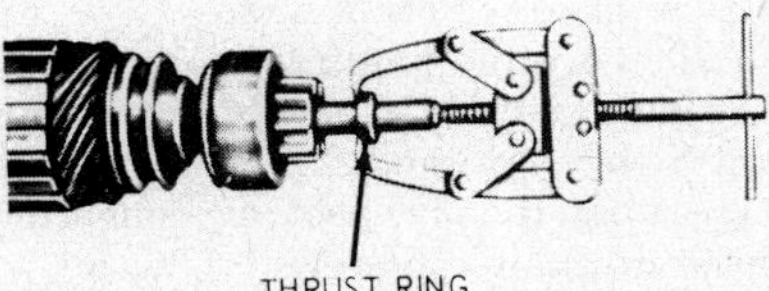

Thrust-ring removal

15. Install the housing and rubber washer.
16. Insert the end plate and bolts.
17. Hook the solenoid switch to the engaging fork and attach the screws.
18. Connect the wiring.

Starter Solenoid Replacement

Lucas

1. Disconnect the battery.
2. Disconnect the wires from the solenoid.
3. Remove the solenoid retaining nuts, washers, and connecting strap.
4. Remove the solenoid.
5. Replace the solenoid.
6. Reconnect the wires to the solenoid.
7. Reconnect the battery.

Bosch

1. Disconnect the battery.
2. Disconnect the wiring cable from the solenoid.
3. Unscrew the mounting bolts and remove the solenoid from the fender apron.
4. Attach the new switch to the fender apron.
5. Connect the wiring cable to the solenoid.
6. Connect the battery.

ENGINE MECHANICAL

DESIGN

Three different engines have been available in the Capri; a 1600 cc four, a 2000 cc four, and a 2600 cc V6.

1600 cc Engine

The 1600 cc engine is a four-cylinder, inline, overhead valve type. The cylinder head and the engine block are made of cast iron. The pistons are made of an aluminum alloy and are fitted to the steel connecting rods by full-floating piston pins. The cast-iron crankshaft is supported by five main bearings.

The camshaft is driven by a chain at one-half engine speed, by the crankshaft. A helical gear on the camshaft drives the distributor and oil pump, while the fuel pump is actuated by an eccentric on the camshaft.

NOTE: *The intake valves on the 1600 cc engine are aluminum-coated and cannot be refaced.*

2000 cc Engine

The 2000 cc engine is a four-cylinder inline engine with an overhead camshaft. The camshaft is mounted on the top of the cylinder head in three bearings and opens the valves by means of rocker arms. The overhead cam eliminates the need for valve lifters and pushrods. The cylinder head and engine block are made of cast-iron, while the intake manifold is aluminum.

The pistons are made from an aluminum alloy with steel struts. The cast iron crankshaft is supported by five main bearings. The camshaft is driven at one-half engine speed by a rubber belt. Since the camshaft is mounted on the top of the engine, the oil pump, fuel pump, and distributor must be driven by an auxiliary shaft off the camshaft belt.

2600 cc Engine

The 2600 cc engine is a V6 overhead valve design. The cylinder heads and engine block are made of cast iron. Four main bearings support the crankshaft. The distributor and the oil pump are driven by an eccentric at the front of the camshaft. The connecting rods are forged steel with replaceable copper-lead alloy insert bearings. The intake manifold is made from aluminum and has individual passages to the openings in the cylinder heads. The V6 has a full pressure lubrication system fed by a rotor type oil pump mounted at the rear of the crankcase.

Engine Cautions

Metric and standard thread bolts are mixed throughout the engine and transmission. Since some of the metric threads are very similar to the standard threads, caution should be used when installing or removing bolts.

Metric bolts and screws will have the letters "M" or "ISOM" embossed on the head. Metric nuts will have the letter "M" on the sides.

If any repair operation requires the removal of any component of the air conditioning system, do not disconnect any of the lines of the system. If it is impossible to move the component out of the way with the lines attached, have the air conditioning system evacuated by a trained serviceman.

When installing nuts or bolts (refer to the torque specification chart), oil the threads with light-weight engine oil. Do not oil threads that require oil-resistant or water-resistant sealers.

Engine Removal and Installation

1600 cc

1. Remove the hood.
2. Disconnect the battery cables.
3. Drain the cooling system, from the radiator and engine block.
4. Remove the air cleaner assembly.
5. Disconnect the radiator hoses and remove the radiator.
6. Disconnect the heater hoses from the water pump and the intake manifold.
7. Disconnect the accelerator linkage from the carburetor.
8. Disconnect the temperature gauge, oil pressure sending unit, and the alternator wires.
9. Remove the exhaust pipes from the manifold and the hot air pipes from the manifold, where applicable.
10. Disconnect the fuel line from the fuel pump.
11. Disconnect the distributor wires from the coil and the high-tension leads from the spark plugs. Remove the distributor cap.
12. Jack up the front of the car and support it with jackstands.
13. Remove the starter motor.
14. Remove the lower bolts and cover of the clutch housing.
15. Drain the crankcase oil.
16. Put the car back on the ground.
17. Support the transmission.
18. Remove the bolts which attach the clutch housing to the engine.

1600 cc engine removal

19. Install a lifting device.

20. Remove the front motor mounts while supporting the engine with the chain hoist or other lifting apparatus.

21. Pull the engine slightly forward to separate the transmission imput shaft from the clutch, and then lift the engine out of the car.

Installation, 1600 cc Engine

22. Attach a chain hoist to the engine.

23. Position the engine assembly in the engine compartment and engage the unit on the transmission shaft. Make sure that the engine flywheel cover is located on the dowel pins. If the drive gear does not mesh, turn the crankshaft pulley slowly until the gear meshes.

24. Reconnect the motor mounts.

25. Position the engine to the clutch housing bolts. Make sure that the engine ground wire is held in place by the top left bolt.

26. Remove the chain hoist.

27. Remove the transmission support.

28. Connect the fuel line to the fuel pump.

29. Install the distributor cap. Connect the wires from the coil to the distributor. Connect the high-tension leads to the spark plugs.

30. Connect the alternator wires, the temperature gauge, and the oil pressure sending unit.

31. Connect the exhaust pipe and tighten the clamp bolts.

32. Connect the accelerator linkage to the carburetor.

33. Connect the heater hoses and the automatic choke hose.

34. Install the radiator and connect the hoses.

35. After you have made sure that the drain plugs are closed, open the cooling system. Refill the cooling system.

36. Install the air cleaner assembly.

37. Jack up the front of the car and support it with jackstands.

38. Install the starter motor and wires.

39. Install the clutch housing, lower cover, and bolts.

40. Put the front of the car back on the ground.

41. Connect the battery.

42. Refill the engine with oil.

43. Install the hood.

44. Run the engine, check it for leaks, and adjust the applicable components.

2000 cc

1. Remove the hood.

2. Remove the lower splash shield from the radiator and drain the coolant.

3. Remove the air cleaner assembly.

4. Disconnect the battery.

5. Remove the upper radiator shield, disconnect the upper and lower radiator hoses, and remove the radiator.

6. Disconnect the heater hoses from the water pump and the carburetor choke fitting.

7. Disconnect the alternator wiring.

8. Disconnect the accelerator cable from the bellcrank assembly. Disconnect the bellcrank-to-carburetor shaft swivel. Remove the two capscrews which retain the bellcrank to the intake manifold. Set the bellcrank aside.

9. Disconnect the flexible fuel line at the fuel tank line and plug the fuel tank line.

10. Disconnect the coil wires.

11. Disconnect the oil pressure and the water temperature sending unit wires at the sending units.

12. Jack up the front of the car and support it with jackstands.

13. Remove the starter motor.

14. Disconnect the tailpipe at the exhaust manifold.

15. Remove the flywheel or converter housing lower front cover. On vehicles with automatic transmissions, disconnect the converter from the flexplate. Remove the converter housing-to-cylinder block lower attaching screws.

16. Mark the flywheel and torque converter so they can be correctly mated during installation.

17. Support the transmission.

18. Disconnect the motor mounts at the underbody bracket.

19. Lower the car to the ground.

20. Attach a chain hoist and remove the engine.

Installation, 2000 cc Engine

1. Place a new gasket over the exhaust inlet pipe.

2. Lower the engine into the engine compartment.

3. Line up the dowel pins on the rear face of the cylinder block with the corresponding holes in the flywheel or converter housing. Make sure that the studs in the exhaust manifold are aligned with the holes in the muffler inlet pipe. Line up the engine mount studs.

4. On a vehicle with a manual transmission, start the transmission shaft into the clutch disc. If the engine hangs up after the shaft enters, turn the crankshaft slowly until the shaft spline meshes with the clutch disc splines.

5. Install the flywheel or converter housing upper attaching screws.

6. Remove the chain hoist.

7. Remove the transmission support.

8. Jack up the front of the car and support it with jackstands.

9. Install the flywheel or converter lower attaching capscrews.

10. On a vehicle with an automatic transmission, install the converter-to-flexplate capscrews and torque them to the proper specifications.

11. Install the flywheel converter housing front cover.

12. Install the engine mounts.

13. Install the starter and wires.

14. Install the exhaust manifold-to-muffler inlet pipe retaining nuts.

15. Lower the car to the ground.

16. Connect the flexible fuel line to the fuel tank line.

17. Connect the oil pressure and temperature sending unit wires.

18. Connect the coil wires and the battery.

19. Install the bellcrank assembly to the intake manifold and connect the accelerator cable to the bellcrank assembly.

20. Connect the heater hose to the water pump and choke housing.

21. Connect the alternator wires.

22. Install the radiator and connect the hoses.

23. Fill the crankcase with oil.

24. Refill the cooling system.

25. Run the engine, check for leaks, and adjust any applicable components.

26. Install the upper and lower radiator shields.

27. Install the air cleaner assembly and hood.

Removal, 2600 cc Engine

1. Remove the hood.
2. Disconnect the battery and drain the cooling system.
3. Remove the air cleaner assembly and remove the radiator hoses.
4. Remove the fan shroud attaching bolts and position the shroud over the fan. Remove the radiator and shroud.
5. Remove the alternator and bracket and remove the alternator ground wire.
6. Disconnect the fuel line from the fuel pump and plug the fuel tank line.
7. Disconnect the accelerator linkage at the carburetor and intake manifold. Disconnect the transmission downshift linkage if so equipped.
8. Disconnect the coil wires and the brake booster lines.
9. Jack up the front of the car and support it with jackstands.
10. Disconnect the muffler inlet pipes at the exhaust manifold.
11. Remove the starter.
12. Disconnect the engine from the motor mounts.

2600 cc engine removal

13. If equipped with an automatic transmission, remove the converter inspection cover and disconnect the flywheel from the converter. Remove the downshift rod.
14. Remove the converter housing-to-engine block bolts and the adaptor plate-to-converter housing bolt.

On vehicles equipped with manual transmissions, remove the clutch linkage and remove the bell housing-to-engine block bolts.

15. Support the transmission.
16. Install a chain hoist and remove the engine.
17. Lower the engine into the compartment.
18. Start the transmission shaft into the clutch disc. If the engine hangs up, turn the crankshaft until the gear meshes. On a vehicle with an automatic transmission, start the converter pilot into the crankshaft.
19. Install the bell housing or converter housing upper bolts, making sure that the dowel pins in the cylinder block engage the flywheel housing. Remove the transmission support.
20. Remove the hoist.
21. On vehicles with an automatic transmission, position the downshift rod on the transmission and engine.
22. Jack up the car and support it with stands.
23. On a vehicle with an automatic transmission, position the transmission linkage bracket and install the remaining converter housing bolts. Install the adaptor plate-to-converter housing bolt. Install the converter-to-flywheel nuts and install the inspection cover. Connect the downshift rod on the transmission.

On a vehicle with a manual transmission, remove the the pilot studs, and then install the lower bell housing bolts and connect the clutch linkage to the engine block.

24. Install the starter and connect the wires.
25. Connect the muffler inlet pipes at the exhaust manifold.
26. Install the front motor mounts.
27. Lower the car to the ground.
28. Install the wires to the coil, and connect the wires to the temperature sending unit and the oil pressure sending unit. Connect the brake booster line.
29. Install the accelerator linkage and connect the downshift rod if so equipped. Connect the vacuum lines. Connect the fuel tank line at the fuel pump.
30. Connect the ground wire at the cylinder block. Install the heater hoses at the water pump and cylinder block.
31. Install the alternator and bracket. Connect the alternator ground wire to the cylinder block. Install the fan belts and adjust them to the proper specifications.
32. Position the fan shroud over the fan. Install the radiator and connect the hoses. Install the fan shroud attaching bolts.
33. Refill the cooling system. Fill the crankcase with oil. Adjust the transmission downshift linkage if so equipped.
34. Run the engine and check for leaks.
35. Install the air cleaner assembly and adjust any applicable components.
36. Install the hood.

Cylinder Head

NOTE: *To prevent distortion or warping of the cylinder head, allow the engine to cool completely before removing the head bolts.*

Removal and Installation

1600 cc Engine

1. Remove the air cleaner assembly.
2. Drain the cooling system.
3. Disconnect the fuel line at the fuel pump and carburetor.
4. Disconnect the spark plug leads and position them out of the way.
5. Disconnect the heater and vacuum hoses at the intake manifold and the hoses at the choke housing.
6. Disconnect the wire from the temperature sending unit.
7. Disconnect the exhaust pipe from the exhaust manifold.
8. Disconnect the throttle from the carburetor and disconnect the carburetor vacuum line from the distributor.
9. Remove the thermostat housing and the thermostat.
10. Remove the rocker arm cover and the gasket.
11. Remove the rocker arm shaft bolts evenly, and lift off the rocker arm assembly.

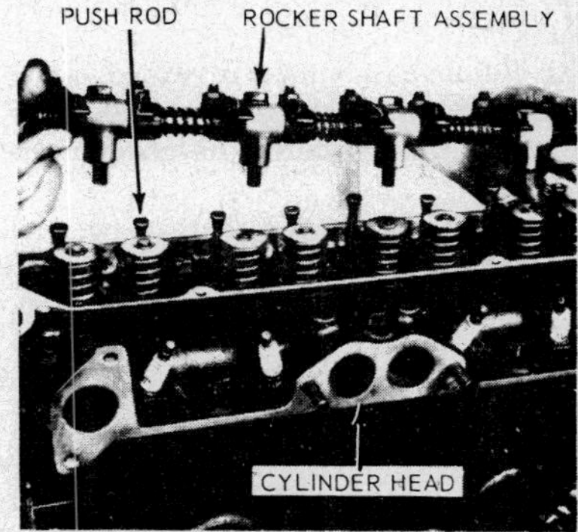

Removing or installing rocker arm assembly —1600 cc engine.

12. Lift out the pushrods and keep them in the order in which they were removed.
13. Remove the cylinder head bolts and lift off the cylinder head and gasket.

CAUTION: *Do not lay the cylinder head flat on its face or damage may result to the spark plugs or gasket surface.*

14. Clean the bottom of the head and the top of the cylinder block of all gasket material.
15. Position a new head gasket on the engine block.
16. Install the cylinder head on the engine and install the bolts hand tight.
17. Follow the proper order to tighten the bolts, in stages, to 65–70 ft lbs. with a torque wrench.

18. Install the pushrods in their original locations.

19. Install the rocker arm assembly and tighten the bolts evenly to 25–30 ft lbs.

20. Adjust the valve clearances.

21. Connect the exhaust pipe.

22. Connect the distributor vacuum advance line and the throttle linkage to the carburetor. Connect the vacuum line at the intake manifold.

23. Connect the wire to the temperature sending unit.

24. Connect the heater and vacuum hoses to the intake manifold. Connect the hoses to the choke housing.

25. Replace the thermostat and housing and use a new gasket.

26. Refill the cooling system.

27. Connect the fuel lines.

28. Connect the spark plug wires.

29. Install the rocker arm cover and the air cleaner assembly.

30. Adjust the idle speed and mixture settings.

2000 cc Engine

1. Drain the cooling system.

2. Remove the air cleaner assembly.

3. Remove the valve cover. Note the location of the valve cover attaching screws that have rubber grommets.

4. Remove the exhaust manifold. (See the Exhaust Manifold Removal procedures.)

5. Remove the intake manifold, carburetor, and the decel valve as an assembly. (See the Intake Manifold Removal procedures.)

6. Remove the camshaft drive belt cover. Note the location of the belt cover attaching bolts that have rubber grommets.

7. Loosen the drive belt tensioner and remove the drive belt.

8. Remove the water outlet elbow from the cylinder head with the hose attached.

9. Using an Allen socket, remove the cylinder head bolts. (This tool is available at automotive stores and parts houses.)

10. Lift the cylinder head and camshaft assembly from the engine.

11. Remove all the gasket material and carbon from the top of the engine block and pistons and from the bottom of the cylinder head.

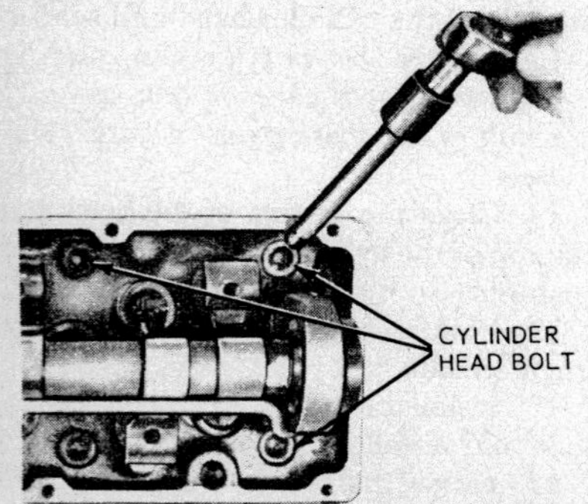

Removing or installating cylinder head bolts—2000 cc engine.

12. Place a new cylinder head gasket on the engine block and position the cylinder head on the engine.

NOTE: *If you encounter difficulty in positioning the cylinder head on the engine block, it may be necessary to install guide studs in the engine block to correctly align the head on the block.*

Cylinder head bolts installed—2000 cc engine.

13. Tighten the head bolts in sequence, and in steps, to 65–80 ft lbs. with a torque wrench.

14. Install the camshaft drive belt. (See the Camshaft Drive Belt Installation procedures in the following sections.)

15. Install the camshaft drive belt cover with its attaching bolts. Make sure that the rubber grommets are installed on the bolts. Tighten them to 6–13 ft lbs.

16. Install the water outlet elbow and a new gasket.

17. Install the intake and exhaust manifolds. (See the Intake and Exhaust Manifold installation sections.)

18. Adjust the valve clearance.

19. Install the valve cover and air cleaner assembly.

20. Fill the cooling system.

2600 cc Engine

1. Remove the air cleaner assembly and disconnect the battery and accelerator linkage. Drain the cooling system.

2. Remove the distributor cap with the spark plug wires attached. Remove the distributor vacuum line and the distributor. Remove the hose from the water pump to the water outlet which is on the carburetor.

3. Remove the valve covers, fuel line and filter, carburetor, and the intake manifold.

4. Remove the rocker arm shaft and oil baffles. Remove the pushrods, keeping them in the proper sequence for installation.

5. Remove the exhaust manifold, referring to the appropriate procedures.

6. Remove the cylinder head retaining bolts and remove the cylinder heads and gaskets.

CAUTION: *Do not lay the cylinder head flat on its surface.*

7. Remove all gasket material and carbon from the engine block and cylinder heads.

8. Place the head gaskets on the engine block.

NOTE: *The left and right gaskets are not interchangeable.*

9. Install guide studs in the engine block. Install the cylinder head assemblies on the engine block one at a time. Tighten the cylinder head bolts in sequence, and in steps, to 65–80 ft lbs.

Cylinder head guide studs installed—2600 cc engine.

10. Install the intake and exhaust manifolds.

11. Install the pushrods in the proper sequence. Install the oil baffles and the rocker arm shaft assemblies. Adjust the valve clearances.

12. Install the valve covers with new gaskets.

13. Install the distributor and set the ignition timing.

14. Install the carburetor and the distributor cap with the spark plug wires.

15. Connect the accelerator linkage, fuel line, with fuel filter installed, and distributor vacuum line to the carburetor. Fill the cooling system.

Cylinder Head Overhaul

See the "Engine Rebuilding" section. The procedure for the 2000 cc engine is the same as in the "Engine Rebuilding" section with this exception; if the camshaft is removed from the cylinder head, it must be installed along with the camshaft thrust plate and the camshaft drive gear and attaching bolt. The cylinder head must be removed to remove the camshaft.

Rocker Shaft

Disassembly and Assembly

These procedures do not apply to the 2000 cc engine because it is equipped with an overhead camshaft and does not employ a rocker arm assembly.

1. Remove the air cleaner assembly.

2. Disconnect the spark plug wires and move them aside.

3. Remove the rocker arm cover and its gasket.

4. Remove the rocker arm attaching bolts and lift off the rocker arm assembly.

5. Remove the cotter pin from one end of the shaft and slip off the flat washer, crimped washer, and the other flat washer from the shaft. The supports, springs, and rocker arms may now be removed.

6. Check the shaft and its component

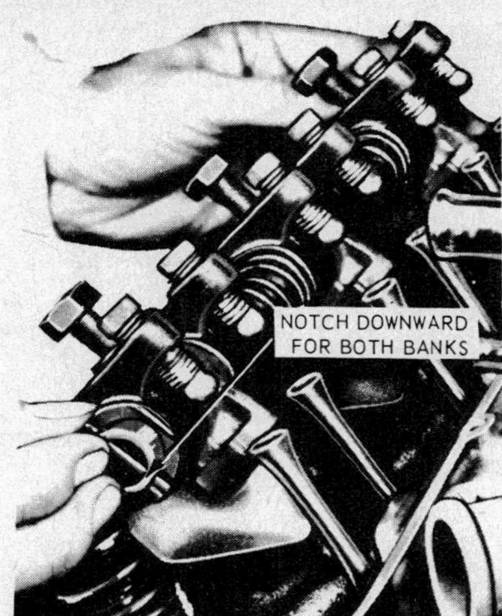

Removing rocker arm shaft assembly—2600 cc engine.

parts for excessive wear or damage. Replace any parts that show these conditions.

7. Clean the component parts of the shaft assembly in a suitable degreasing solvent.

NOTE: *Ordinarily, the rocker shaft itself is not cleaned. If there is an insufficient amount of engine oil being circulated through the rocker arm assembly, however, the inside of the shaft should be cleaned in this manner:* Remove the plugs in the rocker shaft ends by drilling a hole in one plug. Insert a long rod through the drilled hole and knock out the opposite plug. Remove the drilled plug in the same manner. Clean the shaft in a degreasing solvent and replace the plugs.

8. Assemble the rocker arm shaft. Install the cotter pins with the heads upward and bend the legs over to secure them.

9. Replace the rocker assemby on the cylinder head. Install the attaching bolts hand tight and then torque them down evenly to 25–30 ft lbs.

10. Adjust the valve clearances. (Be sure to set the valves on the 2600 cc engine when it is cold and then again, when it is hot.)

11. Clean the cylinder head and valve cover of any dirt or gasket material and replace the valve cover.

12. Replace the spark plug wires.

Intake Manifold

Removal and Installation

1600 cc Engine

1. Remove the air cleaner assembly.
2. Partially drain the cooling system.
3. Disconnect the throttle shaft from the carburetor throttle lever.
4. Disconnect the fuel and vacuum lines from the carburetor.
5. Remove the thermostatic spring and water housing.

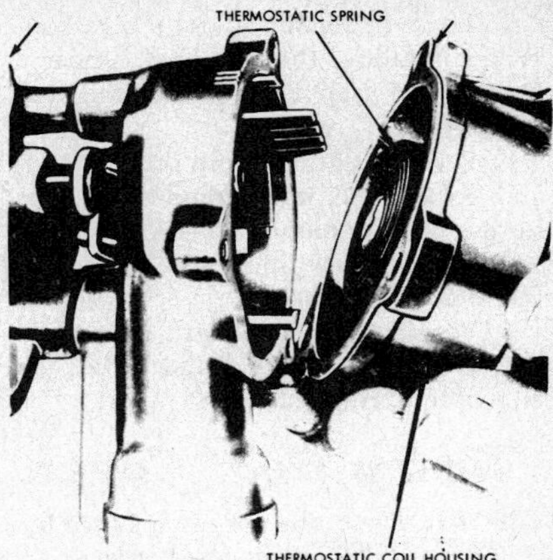

Thermostatic spring and housing

6. Disconnect the water outlet hose and the crankcase ventilation hose from the intake manifold.
7. Disconnect the decel valve to the carburetor pipe at the carburetor.
8. Remove the attaching nut and bolts and remove the intake manifold and gasket.
9. If a new manifold is being installed, transfer all the necessary components to the new manifold.
10. Use a large allen wrench to remove the decel valve adaptor from the manifold.
11. Position the decel valve against the adaptor face, engage and tighten the securing nut, and torque to 1 ft lb with the valve held in a vertical position.
12. Apply a sealing compound on both sides of the gasket around the water port and fit it to the cylinder head.
13. Install the intake manifold and tighten the nuts and bolts evenly to 15–18 ft lbs.
14. Connect the water hose and the crankcase ventilation hose to the intake manifold.
15. Connect the distributor vacuum line and fuel line to the carburetor.
16. Connect the decel vavle to the carburetor.
17. Connect the throttle lever.
18. Install the thermostatic spring and water housing, locate the spring in the center slot, and align the housing marks before tightening the screws.
19. Install the air cleaner assembly and refill the cooling system.

2000 cc Engine

1. Remove the air cleaner assembly.
2. Disconnect the fuel line from the carburetor.
3. Disconnect the two vacuum lines from the distributor at the intake manifold.
4. Disconnect the crankcase ventilation hose at the intake manifold.
5. Remove the intake manifold attaching bolts and remove the manifold, carburetor, and decel valve from the studs, as an assembly.
6. Clean all dirt and gasket material from the surfaces on the cylinder head and intake manifold.
7. Position a new gasket and the manifold on the studs. Torque the bolts and nuts to 12–15 ft lbs.
8. Connect the crankcase ventilation hose to the manifold.
9. Connect the distributor vacuum lines to the manifold.
10. Connect the fuel line to the carburetor.
11. Install the air cleaner assembly.

2600 cc Engine

1. Remove the air cleaner assembly and disconnect the battery.
2. Disconnect the throttle cables.
3. Drain the cooling system. Disconnect and remove the hose from the water outlet to the radiator and the hoses and the line from the water oulet to the water pump.
4. Remove the distributor cap and spark plug wires as an assembly. Disconnect the distributor wire and the vacuum line.
5. Mark the position of the distributor and remove it.
6. Remove the fuel line and filter between the fuel pump and the carburetor and then remove the rocker arm covers.
7. Remove the intake manifold bolts and nuts. Tap the manifold lightly with a plastic hammer to break the gasket seal; and then lift off the manifold.
8. Remove all the gasket material and dirt from the manifold and cylinder heads.
9. Apply sealing compound to the joining surfaces. Place the manifold gasket in place. (Make sure that the tap on the right bank of the cylinder head gasket fits into the cutout of the manifold gasket.)
10. Install the intake manifold. Tighten the attaching bolts until they are hand tight, and then torque them, in sequence, to 15–18 ft lbs.

NOTE: *Tightening bolt no. 7 with a torque wrench will require a "crow's foot." This tool can be obtained from an automotive supply house or parts store.*

11. Install the distributor so the rotor is pointing to the mark made previously.
12. Connect the distributor wire and vacuum line.
13. Install the carburetor, fuel line, fuel filter, and the rocker arm covers.
14. Install the distributor cap and wires.
15. Install and adjust the carburetor linkage.
16. Install the air cleaner assembly and air cleaner tube to the carburetor. Connect the battery.
17. Adjust the ignition timing.

Exhaust Manifold

Removal and Installation

1600 cc Engine

1. Support the front muffler pipe and remove the two nuts which hold the manifold to the muffler pipe flange. Separate the joint.
2. Disconnect the hot air pipe from the air cleaner to the manifold.
3. Remove the nuts and bolts which hold the manifold to the cylinder head and remove the manifold.
4. Discard the old gaskets and clean all mating surfaces of any gasket material.
5. If the manifold is to be replaced, remove the heat baffle and transfer it to the new manifold.
6. Position the center gasket on the studs, then locate the manifold on the studs.
7. Position the other gaskets between the manifold flanges and the cylinder head.
8. Install the nuts and bolts hand tight and then torque them evenly to 15–18 ft lbs.
9. Position the manifold and muffler pipe flanges together and secure them with the two nuts.
10. Connect the hot air pipe at the manifold.
11. Start the engine and check for leaks.

2000 cc Engine

1. Remove the air cleaner.
2. Remove the two attaching nuts from the top of the exhaust manifold shroud.
3. Disconnect the two attaching nuts from the muffler inlet pipe.
4. Remove the manifold attaching nuts and remove the manifold from the cylinder head.
5. This manifold does not use a gasket. When installing the manifold, smear a light coat of graphite grease on the mating surfaces of the exhaust manifold.
6. Position the manifold on the guide studs and install the attaching bolts hand tight, then torque them as shown to 12–15 ft lbs.
7. Install a new exhaust pipe gasket and install the two nuts.
8. Position the exhaust manifold shroud on the manifold and install the two nuts.
9. Install the air cleaner.

2600 cc Engine

1. Remove the air cleaner.
2. Remove the four attaching nuts from the exhaust manifold shroud (right side only).
3. Disconnect the attaching nuts from the muffler inlet pipe.
4. Remove the exhaust manifold attaching nuts and remove the manifold.
5. These manifolds do not use gaskets. When installing the manifold, smear a light coat of graphite grease on the mating surfaces.
6. Position the manifold on the studs and install the bolts hand-tight then torque them evenly to 15–18 ft lbs.
7. Install a new inlet pipe gasket and the attaching nuts.
8. Position the exhaust manifold shroud on the manifold and install the attaching nuts (right side).

Timing Gear Cover

NOTE: *These procedures apply to the 1600 and 2600 cc engines only.*

Removal and Installation

1600 cc Engine

1. Drain the cooling system and remove the radiator hoses.
2. Remove the radiator assembly.
3. Remove the fan belt and then the fan and the water pump pulley.
4. Remove the water pump. (See the Cooling System Section in this chapter.)
5. Remove the crankshaft pulley using a two-jawed puller. Remove the four front oil pan bolts and the oil dipstick. Remove the attaching bolts of the front cover and remove the front cover.

Reverse the procedure to install the cover. Torque the attaching bolts to 7–9 ft lbs. and the oil pan bolts to 7–9 ft lbs. Be sure to clean all gasket material from the cover and joining places on the block. Use a new gasket on the cover and, if necessary, replace the cork packing strip on the front cover.

2600 cc Engine

1. Remove the oil pan as described in the following section.
2. Remove the radiator and any other necessary parts to allow clearance.

Removing or installing guide sleeves—2600 cc engine.

Removing or installing front cover plate—2600 cc engine.

3. Remove the alternator and drive belts. Remove the water pump and water lines.
4. Remove the fan.
5. Remove the crankshaft pulley with a puller and, if necessary, remove the guide sleeves from the cylinder block.
6. Remove the front cover retaining bolts and remove the front cover. If the front cover plate gasket needs replacement, remove the two screws and the plate to replace the gasket.
7. To install, reverse the procedures,

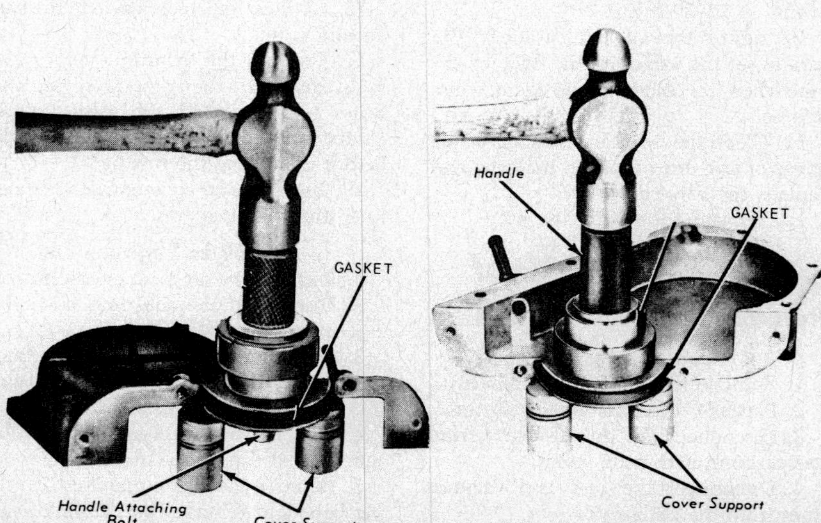

Removing or installing front cover oil seal—1600 cc engine

cleaning all surfaces of gasket material and installing new gaskets and sealing compound.

NOTE: *If the guide sleeves were removed, install them with new seal rings but do not use sealing compound.*

Oil Seal Replacement

1600 cc Engine

The oil seal can be removed after the timing chain cover has been removed. Support the front cover and drive out the seal using a suitably sized socket.

Drive the new seal into the housing from the rear while supporting the housing around the seal. When fitting the cover to the engine, be sure that the seal is lined up with the crankshaft and pulley boss.

2600 cc Engine

Remove the front cover as previously described. Support the front cover and drive out the seal with a socket of a suitable size. To install the new seal, support the cover and drive the new seal in with a socket.

Removing front oil Seal—2600 cc engine

Timing Chain, Gears, and Tensioner

Removal and Installation

1600 cc Engine

Remove the timing gear cover as previously explained. Also remove the camshaft oil slinger and camshaft sprocket retainer and bolts. Remove the camshaft sprocket and disconnect the timing chain. Remove the timing chain tensioner and bolts.

Timing chain tensioner—1600 cc engine

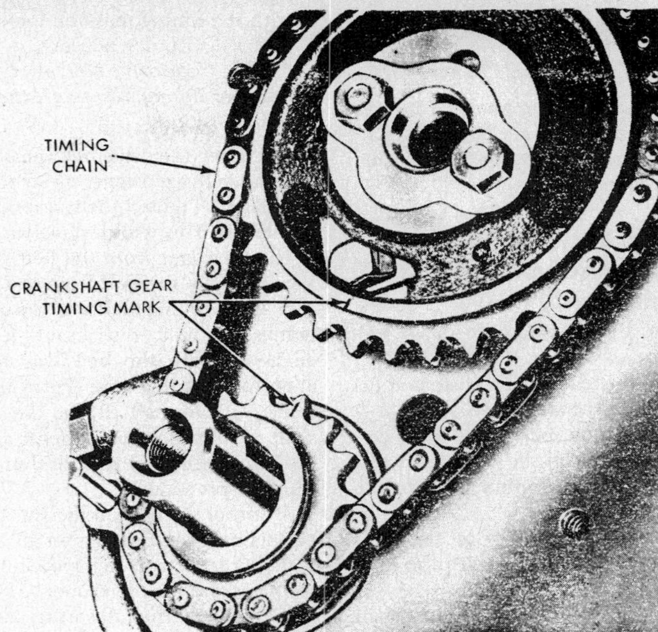

Timing marks—1600 cc engine

1. Position the timing chain over the camshaft and crankshaft sprockets so that the timing marks are aligned when the sprocket is fitted. Tighten the bolts to 12–15 ft lbs. and bend up the locking pads.
2. Install the oil slinger on the crankshaft. Install the camshaft sprocket retainer and bolts. Torque the bolts to 12–15 ft lbs. Install the timing chain tensioner.
3. Clean all surfaces of old gasket material. Install new gaskets with sealer.
4. Tighten the cover attaching bolts to 7–9 ft lbs. and the oil pan bolts to 7–9 ft lbs.
5. Position the crankshaft pulley, aligning the pulley slot with the crankshaft key. Tighten the bolts to 24–28 ft lbs.
6. Install the water pump, pulley, water pump, fan belt, fan, radiator, and hoses. Fill the cooling system.
7. Set the ignition timing as previously outlined.

2600 cc Engine

1. Drain the cooling system.
2. Remove the timing chain cover as previously described.
3. Remove the crankshaft gear with a puller. Remove the key from the crankshaft.
4. Remove the bolt and washer which hold the camshaft gear, then pry the camshaft gear from the camshaft. Pry off the gear carefully. Do not push the camshaft toward the rear of the engine or you might knock out the oil plug at the rear of the engine.
5. Install the crankshaft gear using the special Ford tool. (This tool may be ordered from a Ford dealer.)

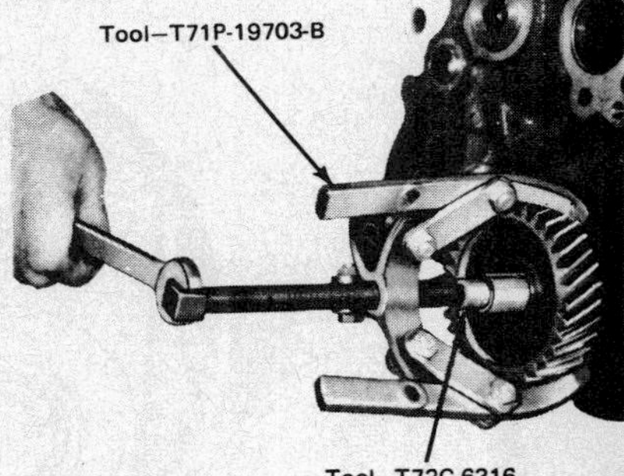

Removing the crankshaft gear—2600 cc engine.

6. Install the crankcase gear, and its attaching nut and washer. Make sure that the timing marks are aligned when the gears are engaged.
7. Install the timing chain cover and fill the cooling system.
8. Set the ignition timing.

Aligning timing marks—2600 cc engine

Timing Belt Cover, Belt, and Tensioner

These procedures apply only to the 2000 cc engine because it has a camshaft belt and an overhead camshaft, rather than timing gears or chains.

Removal and Installation; Tensioner Adjustment (2000 cc Engine only)

1. Remove the camshaft drive belt cover.
2. Remove the distributor cap and position it out of the way.
3. Using a large socket and a breaker bar, turn the bolt on the crankshaft pulley in a clockwise direction until the following conditions exist.

   A. The timing pointer on the front of the engine is aligned with the O or V mark on the pulley.

   B. The pointer on the camshaft sprocket is aligned with the ball in the belt guide plate.

   C. The distributor rotor is aligned with the timing mark on the upper lip of the distributor housing.

NOTE: *If the drive belt has slipped and is out of timing, disregard the preceding operations.*

4. Loosen the drive belt tensioner bolt and move the tensioner as far to the left as possible. Tighten the tensioner adjustment bolt. This will remove the preload of the tensioner from the belt.
5. Remove the belt from the pulleys.
6. If the timing marks on the camshaft, crankshaft, and distributor were not aligned before the belt was removed, align them at this time. Turn the crankshaft (A), camshaft (B), or the auxiliary shaft (C) until the components are in the positions described in Step 3 of the belt removal procedure.
7. Install the belt on the three sprockets, making sure the cogs on the belt fully engage the slots in the sprockets.
8. Loosen the tensioner adjustment bolt and allow the full spring pressure of the tensioner to force the tensioner against the belt.
9. Using a socket and breaker bar on the crankshaft pulley bolt, turn the crankshaft two complete turns in a clockwise direction to remove all slack from the belt.
10. Continue to turn the crankshaft until the three marks described in step 3 of the belt removal procedure are aligned. If the belt has slipped, remove the belt and repeat the installation procedure.
11. Position the drive belt tensioner so there is no free-play in the drive belt and tighten the tensioner adjustment bolt.
12. Install the distributor cap and the drive belt cover.

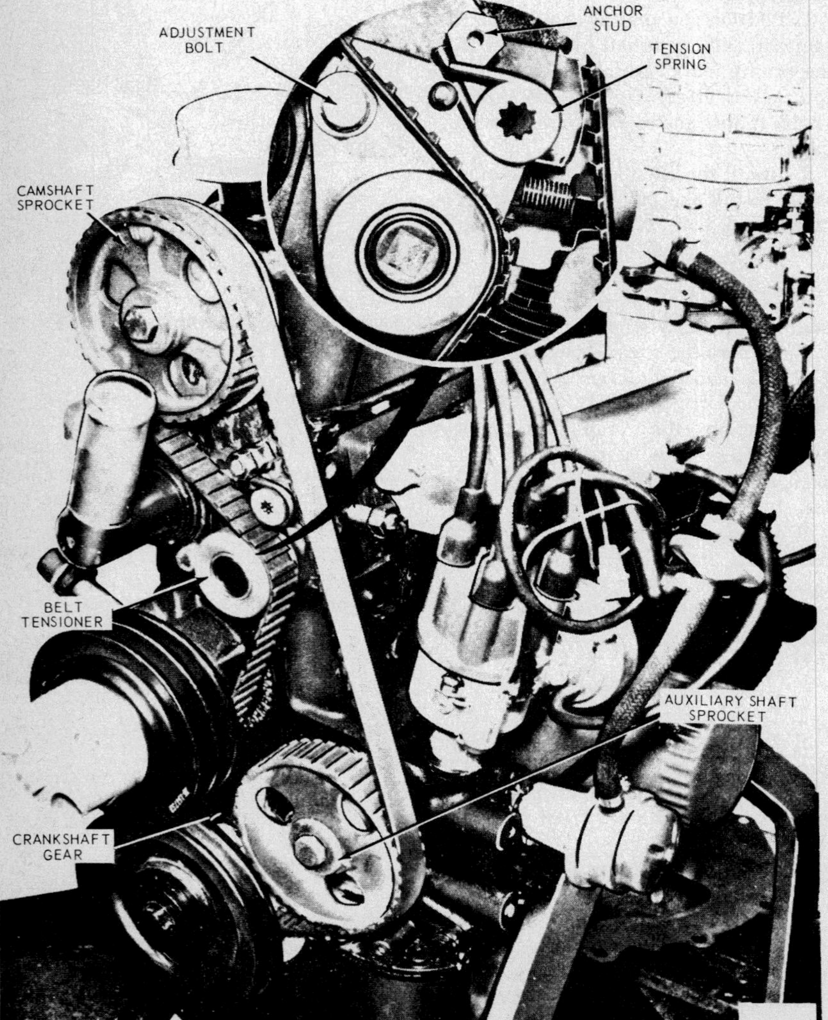

Camshaft drive train—2000 cc engine

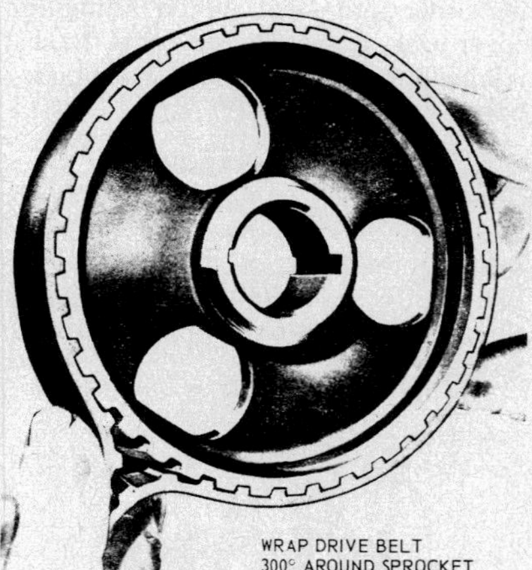

Correct fitting of camshaft drive belt sprocket 2000 cc engine

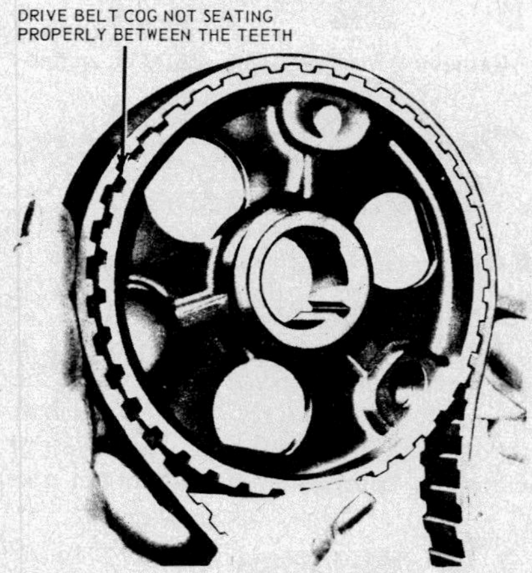

Incorrect fitting of camshaft drive belt sprocket 2000 cc engine

On vehicles where the timing belt has jumped engine timing without a known cause e.g., foreign material, snow or ice, behind the belt, or a loose tensioner, remove the camshaft sprocket from the engine. Wrap the drive belt around the sprocket for at least 300 degrees (300°). Visually check to make sure that each cog of the belt is properly seated in the valley between the teeth on the camshaft sprocket. An oversized sprocket will not permit each cog of the belt to seat between the teeth and, therefore, must be replaced with a new sprocket.

Timing marks—2000 cc engine

Auxiliary Shaft

Removal and Installation (2000 cc Engine only)

1. Remove the camshaft drive belt cover.
2. Remove the drive belt and auxiliary shaft sprocket.
3. Remove the distributor and fuel pump.
4. Remove the auxiliary shaft cover and thrust plate.
5. Withdraw the auxiliary shaft from the engine block.
6. Slide the auxiliary shaft into the housing and insert the thrust plate to hold the shaft.
7. Install a new gasket and auxiliary shaft cover.
8. Fit a new gasket to the fuel pump and install the fuel pump.
9. Insert the distributor and install the auxiliary shaft sprocket.
10. Align the timing marks and install the drive belt.
11. Install the drive belt cover.
12. Set the ignition timing.

Camshaft and/or Valve Lifters

Removal and Installation

1600 cc Engine

The mechanical lifters have an inverted, "mushroom" design. This means that the portion of the valve lifter that contacts the camshaft has a larger diameter than the top of the lifter. Because of this it is necessary to remove the engine from the car, remove most of the external components from the engine, and invert the engine, to remove the lifters and/or the camshaft.

Engine removal procedures have been described earlier; therefore, the following operations will only cover details not previously mentioned.

1. Remove the engine from the car and place it on a work stand.
2. Remove the fuel and oil pumps.
3. Remove the distributor.
4. Remove the valve cover, rocker arm shaft, and pushrods.
5. Remove the front cover and timing chain.
6. Place a drain pan under the engine and invert the engine on the stand.
7. Remove the oil pan.
8. Remove the camshaft thrust plate and the camshaft and lifters.

Installation is generally the reverse of the removal procedure. Several things should be kept in mind when replacing certain parts of the engine.

1. Make sure the timing marks on the timing sprockets are aligned.
2. The distributor should be installed with the rotor pointing in the same direction as it did when removed.
3. Replace the pushrods in the same bores from which they were removed.
4. Set the ignition timing.
5. Run the engine and check for leaks.

2000 cc Engine

The camshaft is mounted on the cylinder head in three bearings. The bearings are mounted in carriers that are an integral part of the cylinder head. The bearings and their journals have a progressively larger diameter from front to rear; therefore, the cylinder head must be removed and the camshaft must be removed from the rear.

1. Remove the cylinder head.
2. Remove the rocker arms.
3. Remove the camshaft drive gear attaching bolt and washer, and remove the gear and belt guide plate.
4. Remove the camshaft thrust plate from the rear of the cylinder head.
5. Carefully slide the camshaft out of the rear of the cylinder head.

To install, reverse the procedures.

2600 cc Engine

1. Drain the cooling system.
2. Remove the radiator.
3. Remove the distributor cap, with the spark plug wires attached. Remove the distributor vacuum line, distributor, alternator, rocker arm covers, fuel line and filter, carburetor, and intake manifold.
4. Remove the rocker arm and shaft assemblies. Lift out the pushrods and mark them so they can be replaced in the same location.
5. Remove the oil pan.
6. Remove the timing chain cover.
7. Remove the camshaft gear retaining bolt and slide the gear off the camshaft. Remove the camshaft thrust plate.
8. Remove the valve lifters from the engine block with a magnet. Lifters should be identified to permit installation in the same location.
9. Carefully pull the camshaft from the engine block, avoiding damage to the camshaft bearings. Remove the key and spacer ring.
10. Coat the camshaft with a cam lubricant or SAE 90 gear oil.
11. Install the camshaft, carefully avoiding damage to the bearings.

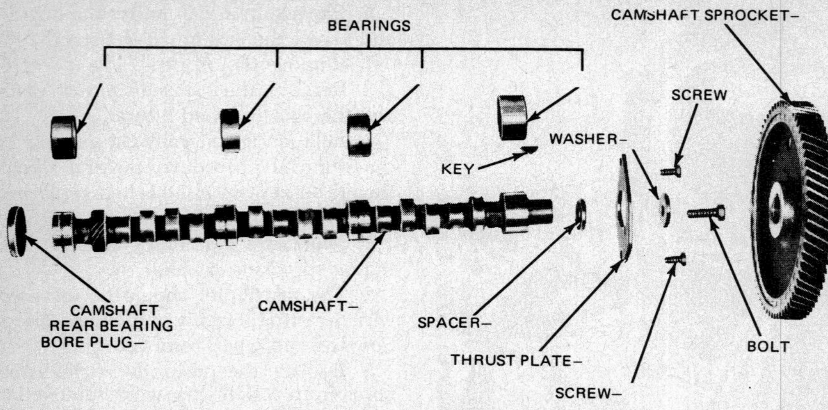

Camshaft and related parts—2600 cc engine

NOTE: *When installing the camshaft, do not push it hard into the engine. There is an oil plug at the rear of the engine block called the "bore plug". If the camshaft is installed too far into the engine or forced into the engine, it could push this plug out, resulting in oil leaking on the clutch and pressure plate and causing serious damage.*

12. Install the spacer ring with the worn side toward the engine. Insert the camshaft key. Install the thrust plate.

Thrust plate installed—2600 cc engine

13. Install the camshaft timing gear and align the timing marks. Install the retaining washer and bolt.
14. Install the valve lifters.
15. Install the timing cover.
16. Install the belt drive pulley and secure it with the washer and retaining bolt.
17. Install the oil pan.
18. Install the pushrods in the same locations from which they were removed. Install the intake manifold.
19. Install the oil baffles and rocker arm shaft assemblies. Adjust the valves to the cold setting.
20. Install the carburetor, fuel line and filter, alternator, distributor cap, and wires.
21. Fill the cooling system.
22. Install the rocker arm covers but not permanently. Run the engine, check for leaks, and set the ignition timing.
23. Set the valves at their hot setting. Install the valve covers permanently.

Pistons and Connecting Rods

These are general procedures. For further details, see the "Engine Rebuilding Section."

Removal and Installation

1600, 2000, and 2600 cc Engines

1. Drain the cooling system and the crankcase oil.
2. Remove the cylinder head(s) and manifold(s).
3. Remove the oil pan and oil pump.
4. Turn the crankshaft until the piston to be removed is at the bottom of its stroke.
5. Mark all connecting rod caps so they may be returned to their original locations in the engine. Remove the connecting rod caps.
6. Push the connecting rod and piston through the top of the cylinder with a hammer handle.
7. Install the piston rings and the pistons in their same bore. Install short lengths of rubber tubing over the connecting rod bolts to avoid damage to the rod journal.
8. Install a ring compressor over the piston. Lower the piston into the bore until the ring compressor contacts the block. Push the piston into the bore with a hammer while guiding the rod onto the journal.

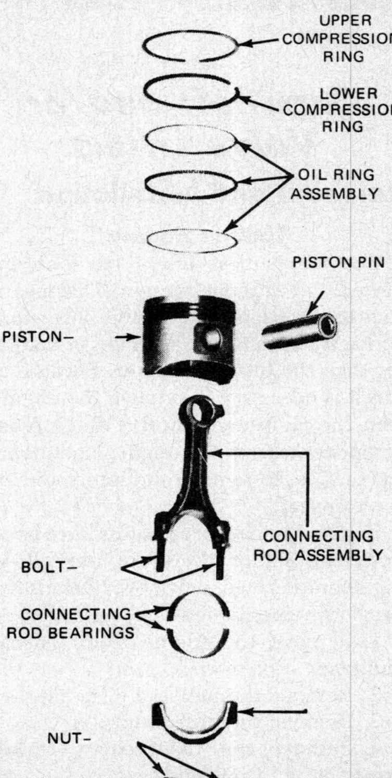

Piston, connecting rod and related parts

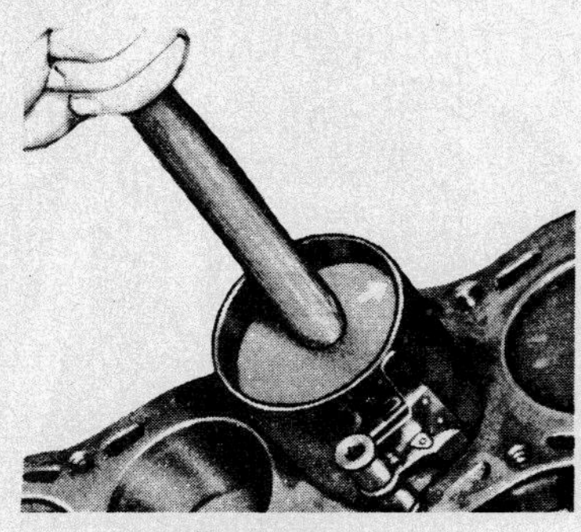

Installing piston and rod

Piston and Connecting Rod Identification and Positioning

1600 cc Engine

When assembling a connecting rod to the piston, make sure it is positioned correctly. The marking "front" is stamped on the web to facilitate this.

Connecting rods and caps are numbered. The number is stamped on the camshaft side of the big end so that the cap installed with its numbers together must be in its original position. *Never assemble a bearing cap to another connecting rod.*

The wrist pins are selected to give the correct fit in the piston bore and bushing in the connecting rod. Pistons are only supplied complete with the piston pin to ensure the correct fit. The piston pins should not be interchanged.

Three piston rings are used: one for oil and two for compression. The two compression rings have a top marking and must be installed with the mark pointing up.

Always make sure that the arrow on the piston is pointing toward the front of the engine.

2000 cc Engine

Install the pistons in the same cylinders from which they were removed. The connecting rod and bearing caps are numbered on the left side from one to four, beginning at the front of the engine. The numbers on the connecting rods and bearing cap must be on the same side when installed in the cylinder bore. If a connecting rod is transferred from one engine block or cylinder to another, new bearings should be fitted and the connecting rod should be numbered to correspond with the new cylinder.

Install the pistons with the arrow on the top facing toward the front of the engine.

Correct piston and rod location—2000 cc engine.

2600 cc Engine

Pistons must be installed in the same cylinders from which they were removed. The connecting rod and bearing caps are numbered from one to three in the right bank and from four to six in the left bank, beginning at the front of the engine. The numbers on the connecting rod and bearing cap must be on the same side when installed in the cylinder bore. If a connecting rod is ever transposed from one block or cylinder to another, new bearings should be fitted and the connecting rod should be numbered to correspond with the new cylinder number.

Install the pistons with the indentation notch on the top of the piston facing toward the front of the engine.

Connecting rod and cap numbering—2600 cc engine.

ENGINE LUBRICATION

Oil Pan

Removal and Installation

1600 cc and 2000 cc Engines

1. Remove the dipstick and drain the crankcase oil.
2. On 1600 cc engines, disconnect the ground cable of the battery and remove the starter motor from the engine.
3. Disconnect the steering shaft connection from the rack and pinion.
4. Disconnect the rack and pinion from the crossmember and move it forward to provide clearance.
5. Remove the flywheel housing inspection cover.
6. Remove the oil pan attaching bolts and also remove the pan.
7. Clean the gasket mounting surfaces on the pan and block.
8. Coat the block surfaces and oil pan mounting surfaces with an oil-resistant sealer and position the pan gasket on the engine block.
9. Coat the oil pan front seal and the front cylinder cover with a sealer, and position the seal on the front cover. Coat the rear oil pan seal with sealer and install the seal in the rear main bearing cap.
10. Position the oil pan on the engine and tighten the bolts finger-tight.
11. Tighten the bolts in sequence. On the 1600 cc engine, follow the alphabetical order, and then the numerical order. Tighten the bolts in two steps:
    A. tighten all bolts to 1–2 ft lbs
    B. on the 1600 cc engines, tighten all the bolts to 6–8 ft lbs; on the 2000 cc engines to 4–6 ft lbs.
12. Install the flywheel housing inspection cover.
13. Connect the rack and pinion to the crossmember, and the steering shaft to the rack and pinion.
14. On the 1600 cc engines, install the starter and the battery cable.
15. Install the dipstick and fill the crankcase with oil.
16. Run the engine and check for leaks.

2600 cc Engine

1. Remove the dipstick. Remove the radiator shroud and position it over the radiator. Disconnect the battery ground wire and loosen the alternator bracket and adjusting bolts.
2. Raise the vehicle and drain the oil.
3. Remove the splash pan and starter.
4. Remove the engine front support nuts. Raise the engine and place wood blocks between the engine supports and the engine.
5. Remove the clutch or converter housing cover.
6. Remove the oil pan retaining bolts and the pan.
7. Clean the surfaces of the oil pan and the engine block. Coat the block surface and the oil pan gasket with sealer. Position the pan gasket on the engine block.
8. Position the oil pan front seal on the cylinder front cover. Position the oil pan rear seal on the rear main bearing cap.
9. Position the oil pan on the engine block and tighten the bolts hand tight.

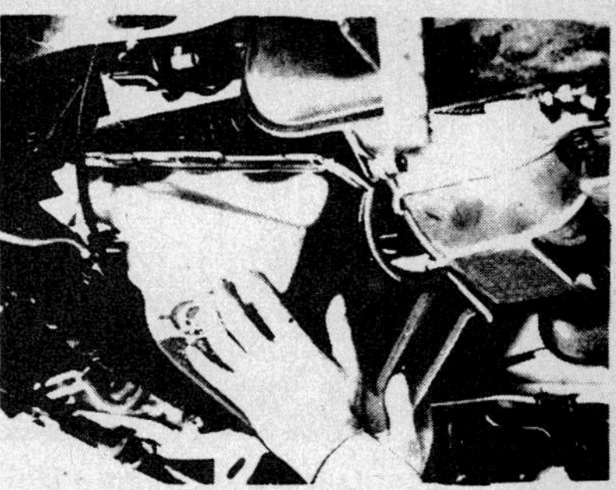

Removing or installing oil pan—2600 cc engine.

Torque the bolts in steps starting at the center and working outward in each direction (2–4 ft lbs, then 5–8 ft lbs).

10. Replace the converter housing or clutch cover.
11. Remove the wood blocks and install the support nuts.
12. Replace the starter and splash shield.
13. Lower the car. Position the alternator and tighten the bolts. Adjust the belt tension and connect the battery cable.
14. Install the fan shroud.
15. Install the dipstick. Fill the crankcase with oil. Run the engine and check for leaks.

Oil Pump

Removal and Installation

1600 cc Engine

The oil pump is mounted on the left side of the engine and is attached to the engine by three bolts. To remove the pump, remove the three bolts and the pump and oil filter as an assembly. Use a new gasket and fill the pump with oil when reinstalling.

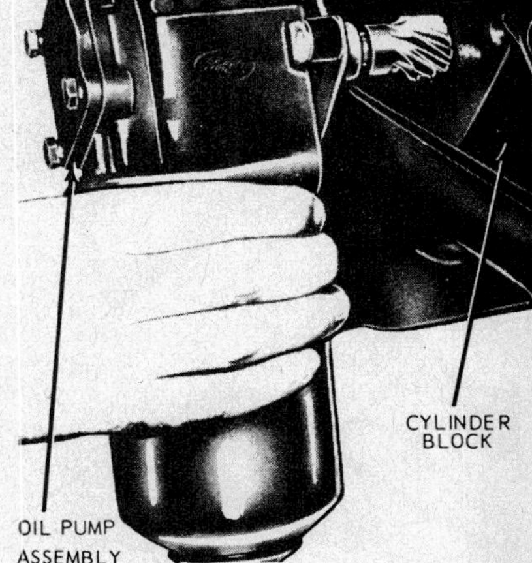

Removing oil pump—1600 cc engine

2000 cc Engine

The oil pump is mounted on the bottom of the engine block and is enclosed by the oil pan. To remove the pump, remove the oil pan, the attaching bolts, and the pump. When installing, use a new gasket and fill the pump with oil to prime it.

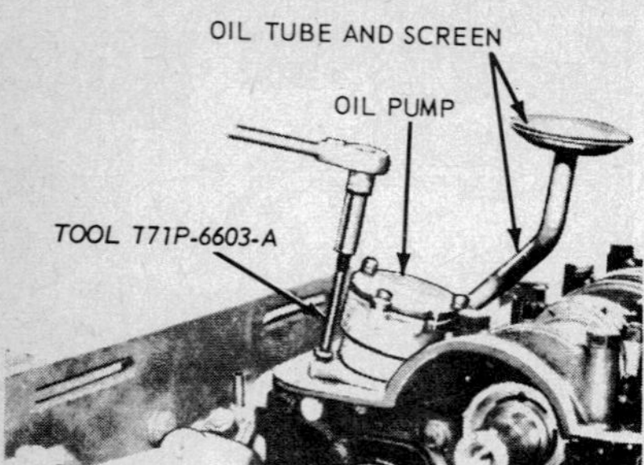

Removing or installaling oil pump—2000 cc engine.

2600 cc Engine

Remove the oil pan and remove the bolt that retains the oil pick-up screen to the main bearing cap. Remove the oil pump retaining bolts. Lift off the oil pump and withdraw the oil pump driveshaft. When installing the pump, insert the drive shaft into the engine block with the pointed end facing inward. Use a new gasket and fill the pump with oil to prime it.

Checking Clearances

Inspect the inside of the oil pump housing, the outer race, and the rotor, for wear or damage. Measure the outer race-to-housing clearance.

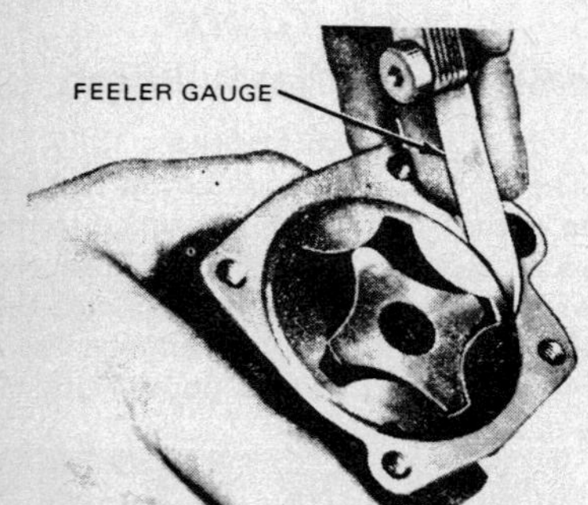

Checking oil pump clearances

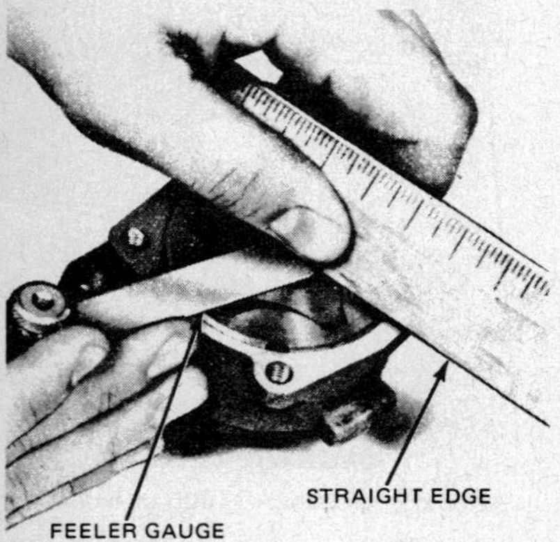

Checking oil pump clearances

With the rotor assembly installed in the housing, place a ruler over the rotor assembly and the housing. Check the clearance between the ruler and the rotor outer race.

Oil pump and inlet tube installed—2600 cc engine.

Oil Pump Clearance Specification (All Models)

Model	Outer Race-to-Housing	Rotor Assembly End Clearance
All Models	0.005-0.0075	0.001-0.004

ENGINE COOLING

The four-cylinder engines employ a pressurized cooling system with the pump fan assembly bolted to the front face of the cylinder block. Coolant is circulated from the base of the radiator up through the water pump and into the cylinder block. The coolant circulates through the engine block and cylinder head to the thermostat, located at the front of the cylinder head. It then returns to the top radiator tank, flows down the radiator tubes, and is cooled by passing air.

The V6 system has a three-staged system which uses a centrifugal type water pump with the thermostat located in the lower left corner of the cylinder front cover.

Radiator

Removal and Installation

1600, 2000, and 2600 cc Engines

1. On the 2000 and 2600 cc engines, remove the radiator upper splash shield.
2. Place a drain pan under the radiator, remove the cap, open the drain plug, and drain the radiator.
3. Disconnect the upper and lower radiator hoses.
4. Disconnect the automatic transmission cooling lines from the radiator, if so equipped.
5. Remove the retaining screws and lift out the radiator.
6. Reverse the procedures to install.
7. Refill the cooling system with an antifreeze solution.
8. Run the engine, with the cap off, to relieve any air pockets, then install the radiator cap, run the engine, and check for leaks.

Water Pump

Removal and Installation

1600, 2000, and 2600 cc Engines

1. Drain the cooling system.

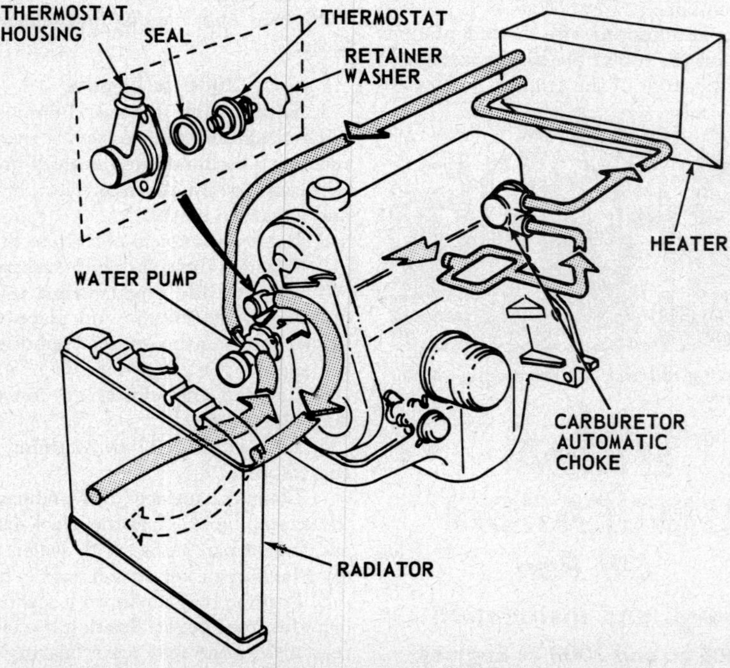

Four cylinder engine cooling system

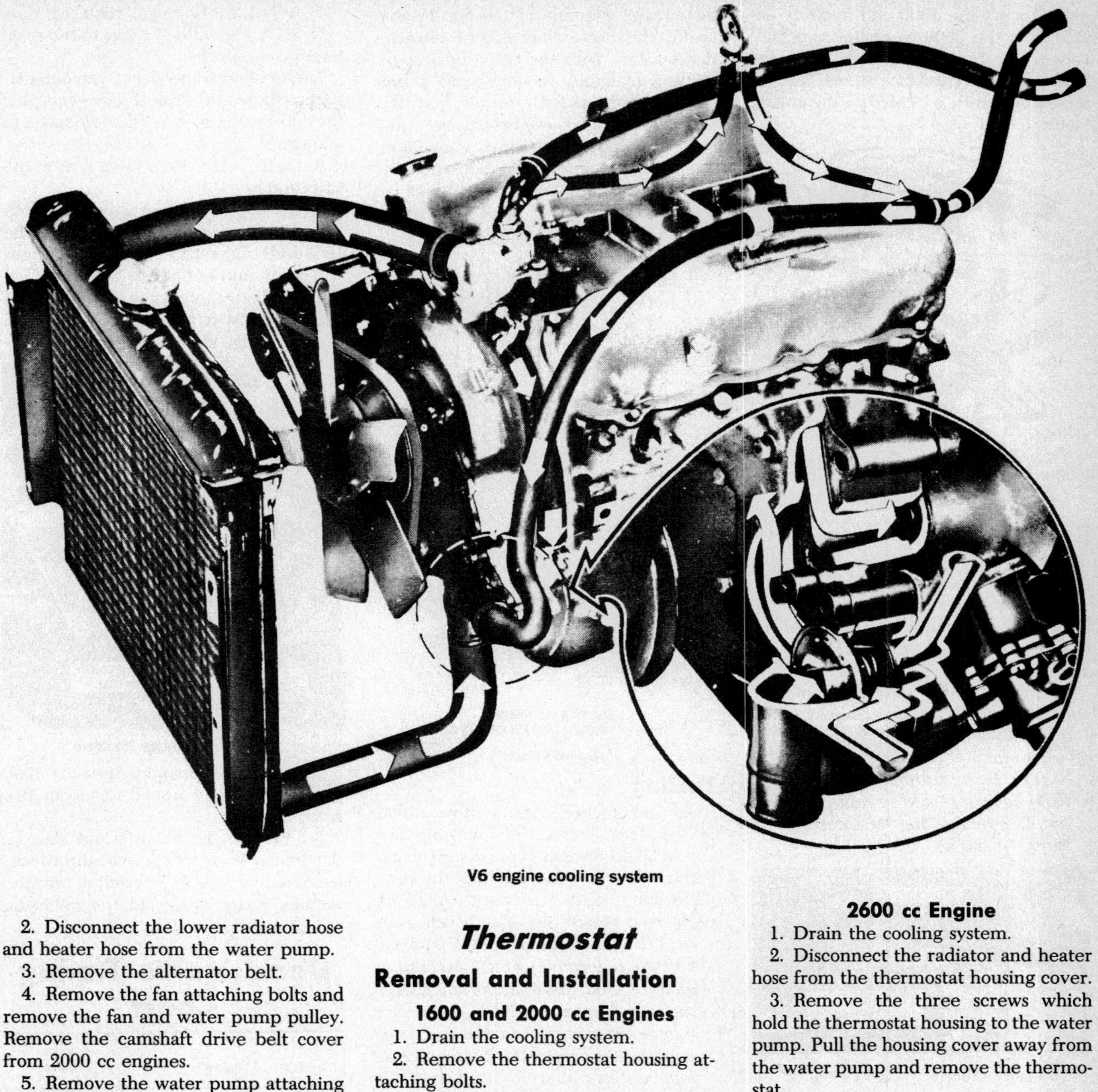

V6 engine cooling system

2. Disconnect the lower radiator hose and heater hose from the water pump.

3. Remove the alternator belt.

4. Remove the fan attaching bolts and remove the fan and water pump pulley. Remove the camshaft drive belt cover from 2000 cc engines.

5. Remove the water pump attaching bolts and also the water pump.

6. Clean all gasket material from all mounting surfaces.

7. Transfer the heater hose fitting to the new water pump.

8. Coat the new gasket with sealer and position the pump and gasket on the engine.

9. Install the pump mounting bolts. Install the camshaft drive belt on the 2000 cc engine.

10. Install the fan and water pump pulley.

11. Install the alternator belt.

12. Connect the heater and radiator hoses.

13. Fill the cooling system, run the engine, and check for leaks. (Retighten the radiator drain plug.)

Thermostat

Removal and Installation

1600 and 2000 cc Engines

1. Drain the cooling system.

2. Remove the thermostat housing attaching bolts.

3. Lift the thermostat housing from the engine and remove the thermostat and gasket from the engine.

4. Clean all gasket material from the engine and thermostat housing.

5. Coat the gasket with sealer and install it in the thermostat housing.

6. Install the housing bolts and torque them to 12–15 ft lbs.

7. Fill the cooling system.

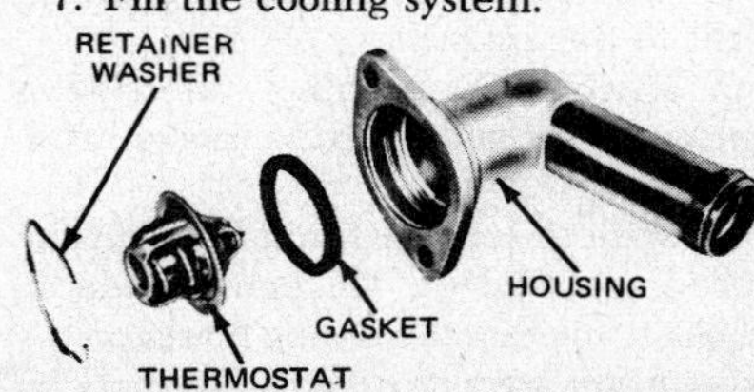

Thermostat and housing—2000 cc engine

2600 cc Engine

1. Drain the cooling system.

2. Disconnect the radiator and heater hose from the thermostat housing cover.

3. Remove the three screws which hold the thermostat housing to the water pump. Pull the housing cover away from the water pump and remove the thermostat.

4. Clean the thermostat housing cover and water pump surfaces of all gasket material.

5. Position the thermostat in the water pump and install a new gasket and thermostat housing cover.

6. Connect the radiator and heater hoses. Fill the cooling system, run the engine, and check for leaks.

EMISSION CONTROLS

PCV Valve (Positive Crankcase Ventilation Valve)

The PCV valve is located in the oil

separator on the 1600 and 2000 cc engines. On the 2600 cc engine the PCV valve is located at the left front of the intake manifold and screws out. The oil separator in turn is located on the engine block.

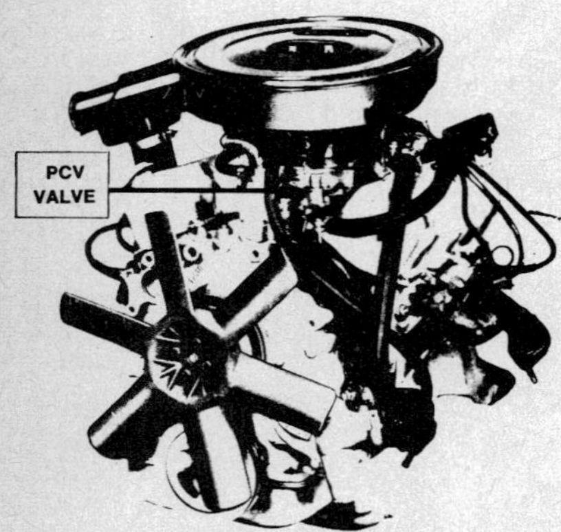

PCV valve—2600 cc engine

Removal and Replacement

1. Pull or screw out the PCV valve from the oil separator.
2. Remove the PCV valve from the hose. Inspect the inside and if it is dirty, disconnect it from the intake manifold and clean it.
3. If the PCV valve hose was removed, connect it to the intake manifold.
4. Install the new PCV valve into the oil separator.

NOTE: *Do not attempt to clean the PCV valve; it should be replaced at the proper interval. (See "Maintenance Interval Chart.")*

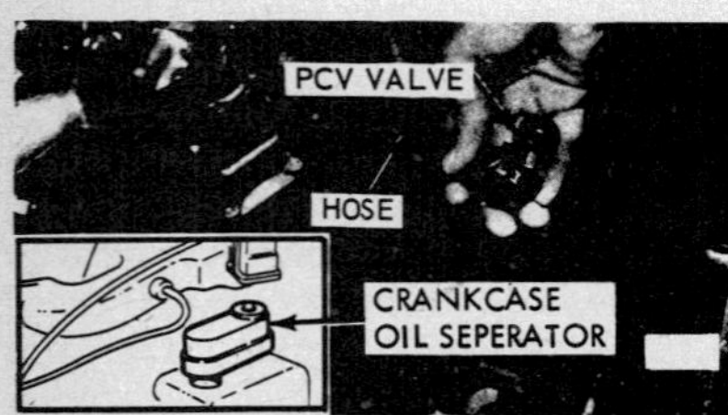

PCV valve removal—1600 cc engine

Testing

With the engine running, pull the PCV valve out of the oil separator. Block off the end of the valve with your finger. The engine speed should drop at least 50 rpm when the valve is blocked. If the engine speed does not drop 50 rpm, the PCV valve is defective and should be replaced.

Decel Valve

The decel valve is mounted on the intake manifold, adjacent to the carburetor. The purpose of this valve is to meter an additional amount of fuel and air to the engine during deceleration. Additional fuel and air permits a more complete combustion, resulting in lower levels of exhaust emissions. During deceleration, the manifold vacuum forces the diaphragm assembly in the decel valve against the spring which in turn raises the decel valve. With the valve now open, existing manifold vacuum pulls a metered amount of fuel and air from the carburetor and travels through the valve body assembly into the intake manifold. The decel valve remains open and continues to feed additional fuel and air for a specified time.

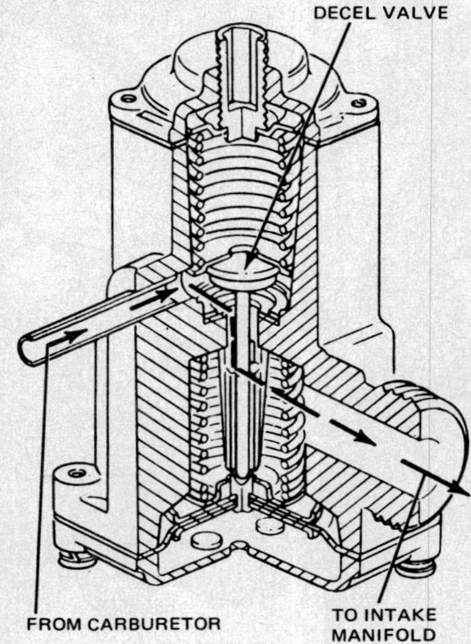

Decel valve

Testing

To prevent unnecessary replacement of the decel valve, the following test should be performed. If the decel valve is found to be out of adjustment, the complete adjustment procedure should be performed before the valve is replaced.

NOTE: *On 1600 cc engines, it is important to determine which carburetor model is used, due to important specification differences. The carburetor number is stamped on the fuel bowl opposite the accelerator pump. The 28 mm venturi carburetor used on earlier models is 701W-9510-EA; the 25 mm venturi carburetor used on later models is 701W-9510-EB.*

Idle speed and initial ignition timing settings are detailed for all engines on the emission decal located in the engine compartment.

1. Run the engine until it reaches operating temperature and then turn it off.
2. Connect a tachometer and timing light to the engine.
3. Disconnect both distributor vacuum lines and plug the intake manifold line.
4. With the engine running at the idle speed specified on the emission decal, check to see that the timing marks on the front cover are aligned with the mark on the crankshaft pulley, according to specification.
5. Adjust the timing as required.
6. Set the idle limiter cap to the maximum rich position.
7. Disconnect the decel valve-to-carburetor hose at the decel valve and plug the decel valve inlet. Set the idle speed to 600 rpm.
8. Connect the decel valve hose at the carburetor.
9. Connect a vacuum gauge between the carburetor and the decel valve. The ID (inside diameter) of the connections and pipes must not be less than the ID of the decel valve inlet tube. The length of the tube between the decel valve and the vacuum gauge should not exceed 60 in.

Pressure gauge hook-up

10. Increase the engine speed to 3000 rpm and hold this speed for about two seconds.
11. Release the throttle and observe the time interval between the throttle release and a zero (0) reading on the vacuum gauge. Refer to the following chart for proper timing.

Decel Valve Timing Chart

Engine	Valve Timing
1600 (28 mm carb)	3-5 sec
1600 (25 mm carb)	2.5-3.5 sec
2000 (manual trans)	2.5-3.5 sec
2000 (auto. trans)	1.5-3.5 sec
2600 (manual trans)	1.5-3.5 sec
2600 (auto. trans)	1.5-3.5 sec

12. If the decel valve needs adjustment, remove and discard the colored cap (if so equipped) for access to the nylon adjuster. Use the tool shown in the illustration to adjust the decel valve. This tool can be made by grinding down a ⅜ in. allen wrench to the dimensions shown.
13. Insert the tool into the decel valve nylon adjusting screw. To increase the valve timing, back out the screw (coun-

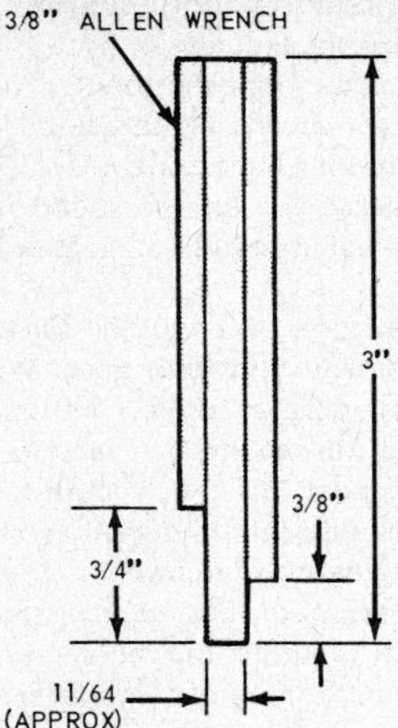

Decel valve adjusting tool

terclockwise). To decrease the valve timing, turn the adjusting screw inward (clockwise). One turn of the adjuster in either direction will increase or decrease the valve timing approximately ½ second.

14. Snap in a new colored cap in the top of the decel valve, if so equipped.

15. Remove the vacuum gauge and connect the tube between the carburetor and the decel valve. Remove the tachometer and the timing light. Connect the vacuum lines.

Removal and Installation

1. Disconnect the air-fuel hose from the decel valve.
2. Loosen the union nut that attaches the decel valve to the intake manifold and remove the decel valve.
3. Position the decel valve on the intake manifold and tighten the union nut.
4. Connect the air-fuel hose to the valve.
5. Test and adjust the valve as required. (See the previous section.)

Dual-Distributor Diaphragm

The dual-distributor diaphragm is a two-chambered housing which is mounted on the side of the distributor. The outer side of the housing is a distributor vacuum advance mechanism. The vacuum advance is connected to the carburetor by a vacuum hose. The purpose of the vacuum advance is to advance the ignition timing according to the conditions under which the engine is operating.

The second side of the dual diaphragm has been added to the older type of distributor to help control engine exhaust emissions at idle. This inner side of the diaphragm is connected by a vacuum hose to the intake manifold. When the engine is idling, intake manifold vacuum is high and the carburetor vacuum is low. Under these conditions, intake manifold vacuum, applied to the inner side of the dual diaphragm, retards the ignition timing to promote more complete combustion of the air-fuel mixture in the engine combustion chambers.

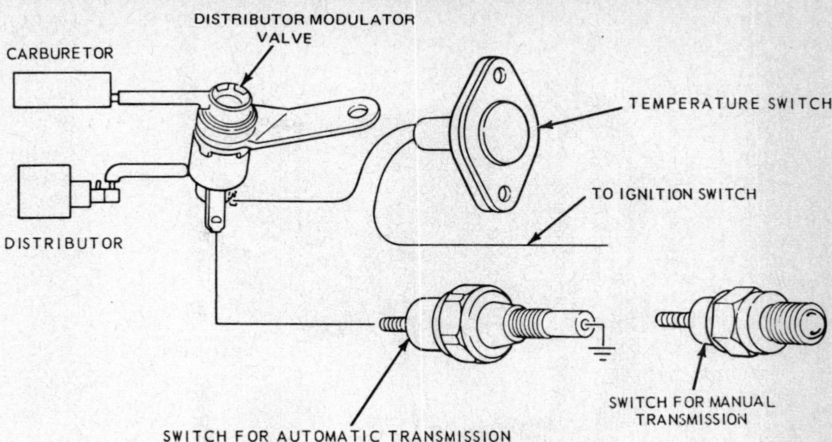

TRS system

Testing and adjustments of these distributors requires the use of an off-the-car distributor machine. You can remove the distributor from the car and take it to a qualified repair shop or you can take the car to the repair shop and have them remove and repair the distributor.

TRS (Transmission Regulated Spark Control System)

This system is used on all 1600 cc engines sold in California. The complete system consists of a distributor modulator valve, ambient temperature switch, transmission switch, the necessary vacuum hose, and the electrical wiring to connect the three components.

The TRS system reduces the exhaust emissions of an engine by retarding the distributor vacuum advance while the car is in First and Second gears. A transmission-operated switch activates the distributor modulator (solenoid) valve and advances the spark when the car is in high gear.

The vacuum is retarded through the use of a distributor modulator valve inserted in the vacuum line between the carburetor port and the distributor primary (outer diaphragm) vacuum advance connection. The modulator valve is located in the engine compartment and is normally open. When energized electrically, it closes off to cut the vacuum supply from the carburetor to the primary vacuum advance unit on the distributor (outer diaphragm) and prevents vacuum advance.

A temperature switch and connector is located under the right-side kick panel within the front passenger compartment, with the sensor of the switch assembly protruding outward to the outside atmosphere, at the right front door hinge. The function of the temperature switch is to close the electrical circuit at approximately 65° F or higher, and to open the circuit at approximately 49° F or lower. Remember; the spark can be retarded only with warm outside air available.

With a vacuum gauge connected to the TRS system as shown in the following illustrations and the temperature switch above 65° F (use a hot sponge on the

Vacuum control valve location

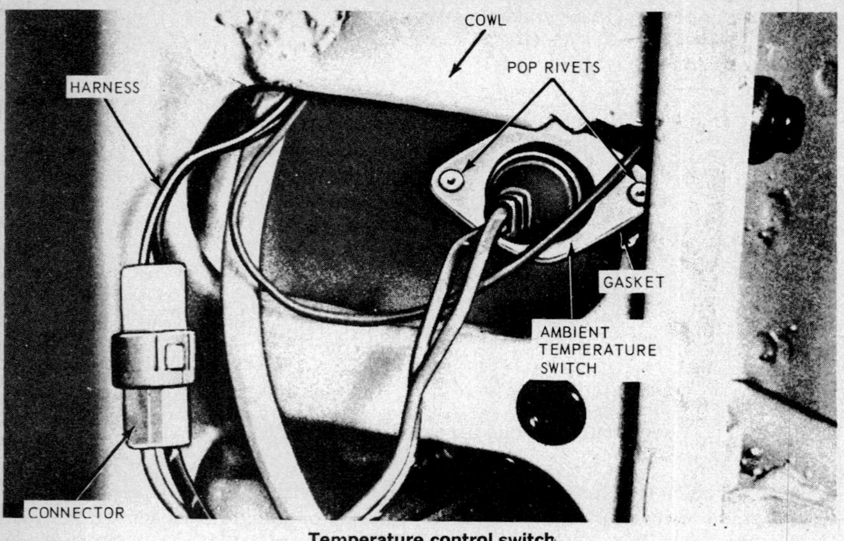

Temperature control switch

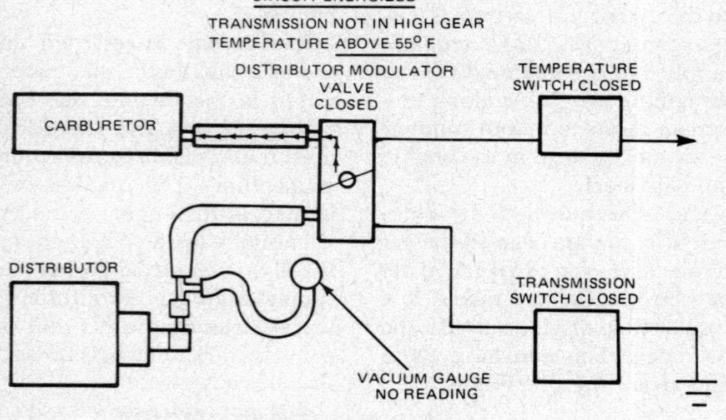

TRS circuit energized

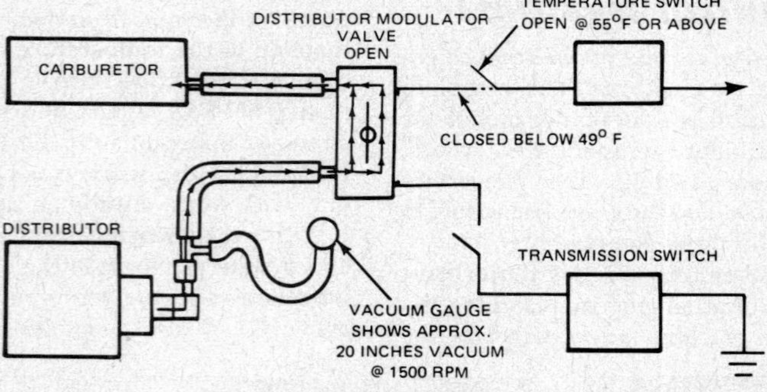

TRS circuit de-energized

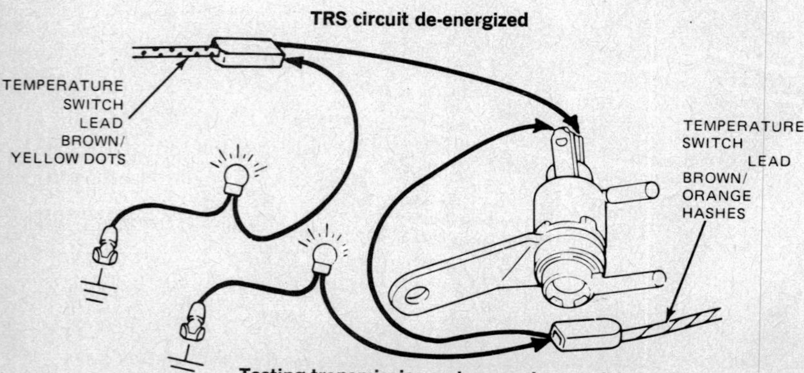

Testing transmission or temperature system

switch to raise the temperature if necessary), proceed as follows:

1. Start the engine in neutral or park. No vacuum should be indicated on the gauge (circuit energized).
2. Increase the engine speed to 1000 rpm. The vacuum indication should read zero.
3. Disengage the clutch, then place the transmission in high gear. With the engine running at 1000–1500 rpm and the clutch disengaged, at least 6 in. Hg should appear on the vacuum gauge. Make sure that the engine is stopped before engaging the clutch.

Malfunction of the electrical circuit affects the vacuum, but the vacuum portion has no effect on the electrical circuit. Therefore, if the distributor modulator valve does not function as outlined above, neither will the vacuum. In this event, there is either an absence of electrical feed or poor ground is indicated and a functional check of each component is necessary. Should the system fail to function according to the "System Test," it will be necessary to investigate the operation of each of the individual system components and their interrelated circuitry, both vacuum and electrical.

Testing

Transmission Switch Test

Disconnect the transmission switch lead from the modulator valve blade terminal and connect it in series with a test light to the positive terminal of the battery. With the engine and ignition off, move the gears through all positions. The light should stay on until high gear is entered (when the switch is open). If the light stays on, the circuit is grounded or the switch is inoperative. If it does not go on at all, the circuit is open or the switch again is inoperative. Replace the switch as necessary.

Temperature Switch Test

To test the temperature switch, disconnect the temperature switch lead from the blade terminal of the distributor modulator valve and connect it in series with a test light to a good ground. (See the previous illustration.) Turn on the ignition switch and warm the temperature switch with a hot sponge. The light should go on when the temperature of the switch reaches 65° F. (Anything approaching body temperature is sufficient.) Cool the switch until its temperature reaches below 49° F and then the light should go out. (An aerosol spray, such as starting fluid, should provide sufficient cooling to perform this exercise.) If the light does not go *on* when *warmed,* the circuit is either open or grounded or else the switch is inoperative. If it does not go *out* when *cooled,* either it is not cold enough or the switch is inoperative. Reconnect the blade terminal to the modulator valve when the tests are completed.

Distributor Modulator Valve Test

With two of the three variables known to be good (the transmission and temperature switches) the distributor modulator valve can be tested by conducting the "System Test" again. If vacuum is not present when it should be, or vice versa, either the valve is inoperative, the hoses are pinched, plugged, or improperly connected, or there is no venturi vacuum from the carburetor.

Removal and Installation

Distributor Modulator Valve

1. Remove the two wires from the distributor modulator valve.
2. Disconnect each vacuum line from the valve. Tag the vacuum lines so they can be installed in their original position.
3. Remove the attaching screw, valve, and bracket.
4. Position the new modulator valve and install the attaching screw.
5. Connect the two vacuum lines to their respective ports.
6. Connect the two wires to their respective terminals.

Temperature Switch

1. Open the right door.
2. Remove the two-step plate from the holding screws and remove the kick-pad retainer and weatherstrip.
3. Lift the floor mat and support the kick-pad in the raised position. Disconnect the switch at the connector.
4. Drill the two pop rivets from the switch.
5. Remove the switch and gasket.
6. Secure the switch and gasket with two new pop-rivet bolts.
7. Connect the switch to the harness.
8. Position the kick-pad and the floor mat, then install the retainer and step plate.

TRS Troubleshooting Chart

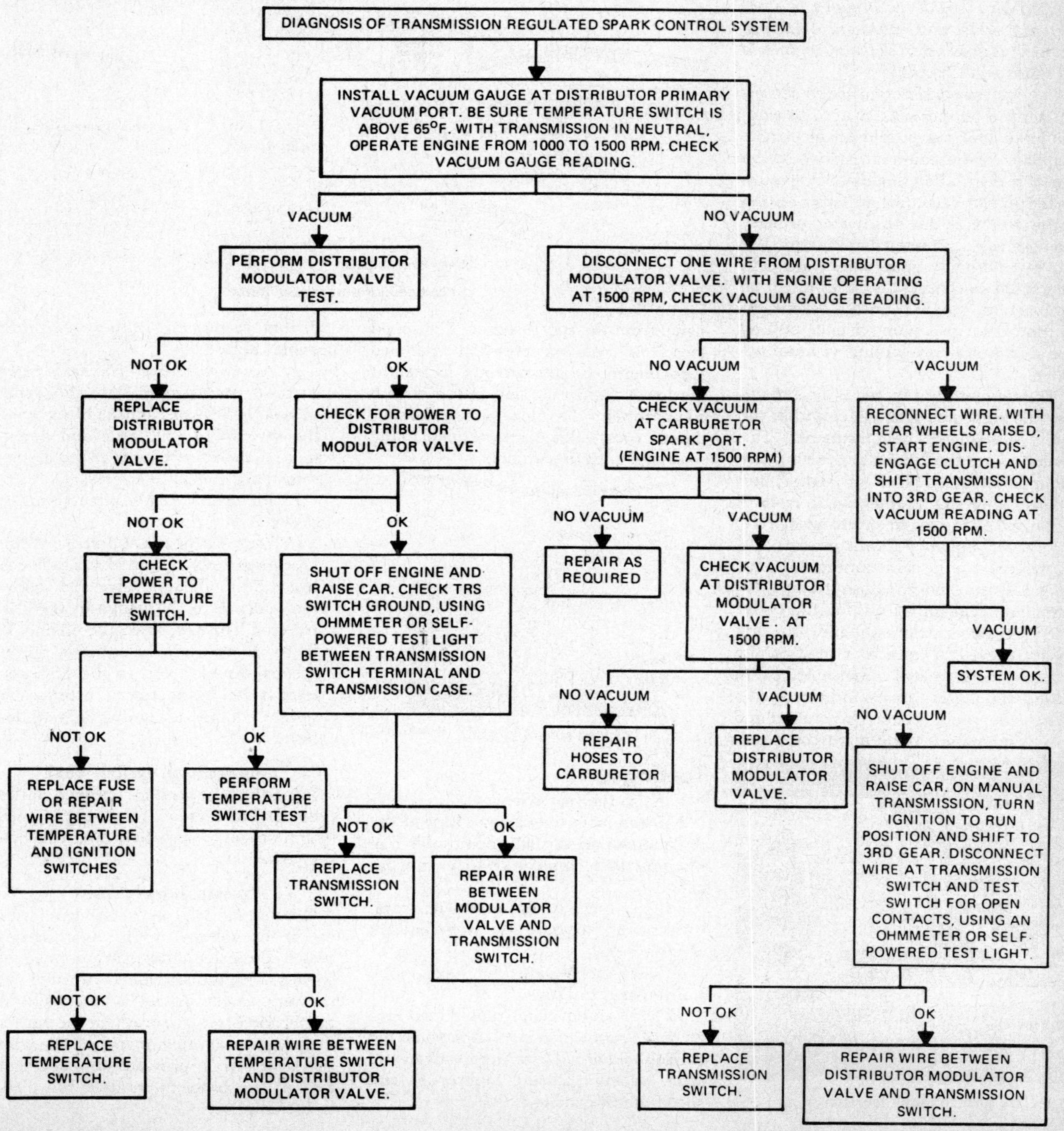

Transmission Switch

1. Remove the electrical connector from the switch.
2. Remove the switch with a large open-end wrench.
3. Replace the switch and tighten it snugly.
4. Replace the electrical connector.

ESC System (Electronic Spark Control)

The purpose of this system is to help control exhaust emissions by delaying vacuum advance to the engine distributor vacuum advance unit, as required. *It is used on all 2000 cc engines in California (manual and automatic transmissions). It is used on all 2600 cc engines in all states and Canada.*

The system consists of a speed sensor, ambient air temperature switch, distributor modulator valve, and an electronic amplifier. The vacuum is retarded by the use of a distributor modulator valve inserted in the vacuum line between the carburetor and the distributor primary vacuum advance(outer diaphragm). The valve is normally open and, when it is energized electrically, it closes to cut off the vacuum supply from the carburetor to the primary vacuum advance unit on the distributor, preventing vacuum advance.

The temperature switch is located under the right-side kick panel within the front passenger compartment. This switch closes the circuit to the amplifier at approximately 65° F or higher, and opens the circuit at approximately 49° F or lower. As the car begins to accelerate, a voltage frequency that is proportional to the speed of the car is generated by the speed sensor and is transmitted to the amplifier. The amplifier is located under the right-side instrument panel. The amplifier opens the ground circuit to the vacuum control valve at a specified cut-in speed and closes the ground circuit at a specified cut-out speed. This cut-out and cut-in function is done in response to a signal from the speed sensor. The speed sensor is installed between the two speedometer cable segments, located at the lower right rear side of the engine compartment. Two lead wires transmit the electrical voltage, proportional to the road speed, to the amplifier.

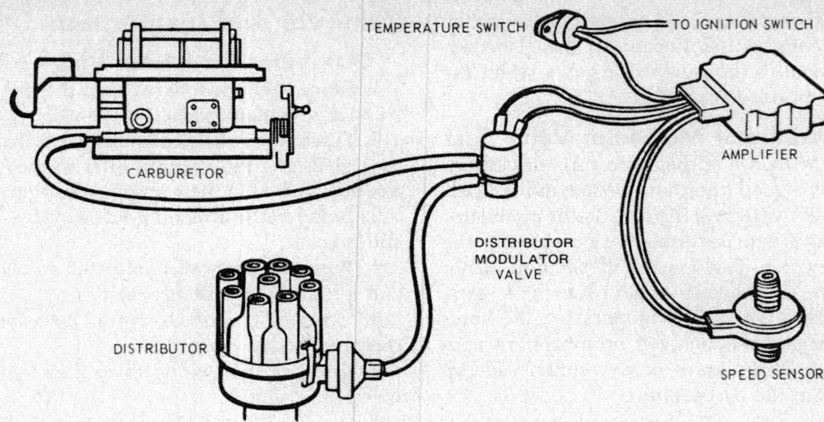

Electronic spark control system

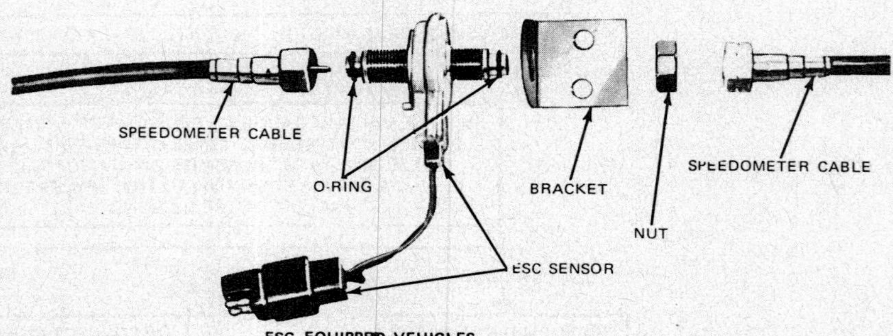

Speed sensor and related parts

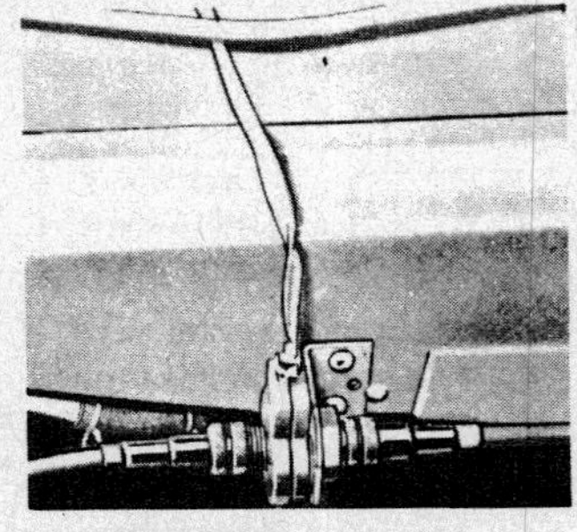
Speed sensor location

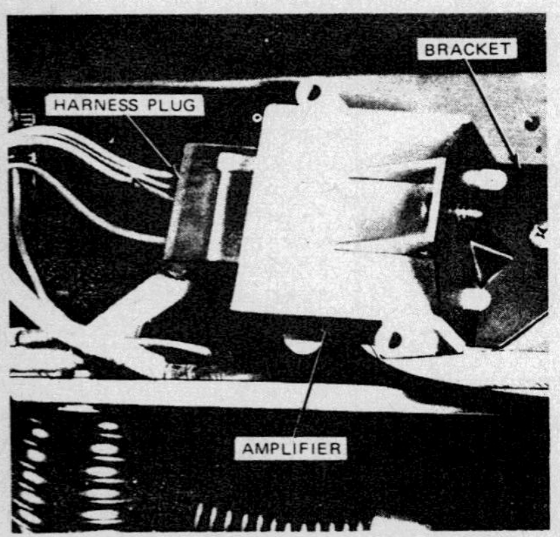

ESC amplifier location

Testing

1. Raise the rear wheels.
2. Disconnect the vacuum hose at the distributor primary advance (outer diaphragm) and connect it to a vacuum gauge.
3. Use a warm sponge on the temperature switch to raise the temperature above 65° F.
4. Start the engine and engage the transmission in Drive.
5. The vacuum gauge should read zero (0) until approximately 40 mph when the gauge should read 6 in. Hg. In any event, some vacuum should register at this speed unless trouble exists.
6. If no vacuum exists, there are three possible causes:

A. *No vacuum from the carburetor vacuum venturi port.* With the transmission in Park or Neutral, block open the throttle to 1500 rpm and determine if there is vacuum at the carburetor port. Repair as necessary.

B. *Pinched, blocked, misrouted, or disconnected hoses.*

C. *Inoperative ESC Control System.* Disconnect one or both electrical leads from the modulator valve and follow the vacuum to the gauge at the distributor. Throttle down the engine. If there is vacuum below the cut-in speeds, trouble exists in the ESC system. It will be necessary to test each system component individually to determine the cause.

Temperature Switch Test

Refer to the procedure outlined in the previous TRS section. If the temperature switch proves to operate properly, check the power supply.

Power Supply Test

Ground the lead on a test lamp and check for voltage at the temperature switch connector of the instrument panel wiring. With the ignition key turned on, the lamp should light. If no voltage is at the terminal, replace or repair the wiring to the ignition switch or replace the ignition switch. If the previous steps have not located the problem, replace the electronic amplifier.

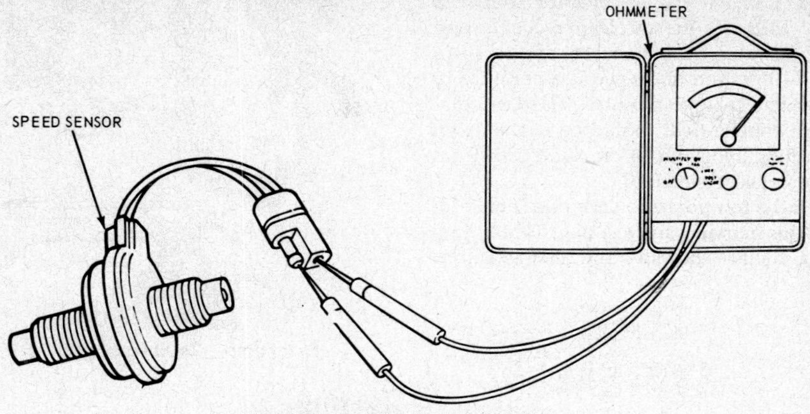

Checking speed sensor continunity

Checking speed sensor for ground

Speed Sensor Test

Disconnect the speed sensor at the multiple plug and check the sensor for continuity with an ohmmeter. Resistance of the speed sensor at room temperature is 40—60 ohms.

Check the resistance of the speed sensor to ground. The resistance should be an open circuit because no continuity is permitted between the black wire and the case. Replace the black wire if the resistance readings are incorrect.

Removal and Replacement

Speed Sensor

1. Disconnect the speed sensor lead wires at the connector.
2. Disconnect the speedometer cable nut from each side of the sensor.
3. Remove the two attaching screws, then remove the sensor and the bracket.
4. Place an O-ring on each end of the speed sensor.
5. Connect the speedometer cable to each end of the sensor.
6. Connect the sensor leads to the harness.

Electronic Amplifier

1. Remove the access cover from the instrument panel.
2. Disconnect the harness plug from the amplifier.
3. Remove the attaching screw and then remove the amplifier from the mounting bracket.
4. Hold the new amplifier in position and install the attaching screw.
5. Plug the harness into the amplifier.
6. Install the instrument panel access cover.

Temperature switch and Distributor Valve

To remove these components refer to the removal and replacement procedures outlined in the TRS system.

Evaporative Emission System

This emission system is designed to limit the emission of fuel vapors into the atmosphere and prevent raw gas from escaping from the fuel tank. The system consists of four components: the fuel tank; a pressure-sensitive and vacuum-sensitive fuel tank cap; a restrictor in the vapor line; and a vapor-absorbing charcoal canister.

This system allows fuel vapors to escape but prevents liquid gasoline from escaping. The fuel vapors enter the vapor separator outlet hose to the charcoal canister which is mounted in the engine compartment. The vapors enter the canister, pass through a charcoal filter, and then exit through a hole in the bottom. As the vapors pass through the charcoal they are cleansed of hydrocarbons so the air that passes from the canister is free of pollutants.

When the engine is running, vacuum from the carburetor draws fresh air into the charcoal canister. As the entering air passes through the charcoal in the canister, it picks up the hydrocarbons that were deposited by the gasoline vapors. This gas mixture is then carried to the carburetor where it combines with incoming air and enters the combustion chambers of the engine to be burned.

Removal and Installation

Charcoal Canister

1. Slacken the clip retaining the large hose at the charcoal canister and remove the hose.
2. Release the spring clip retaining the vapor line hose and disconnect the hose from the canister.
3. Remove the center holding bolt and remove the canister.
4. Position the canister and install the center bolt to 15–18 ft lbs.

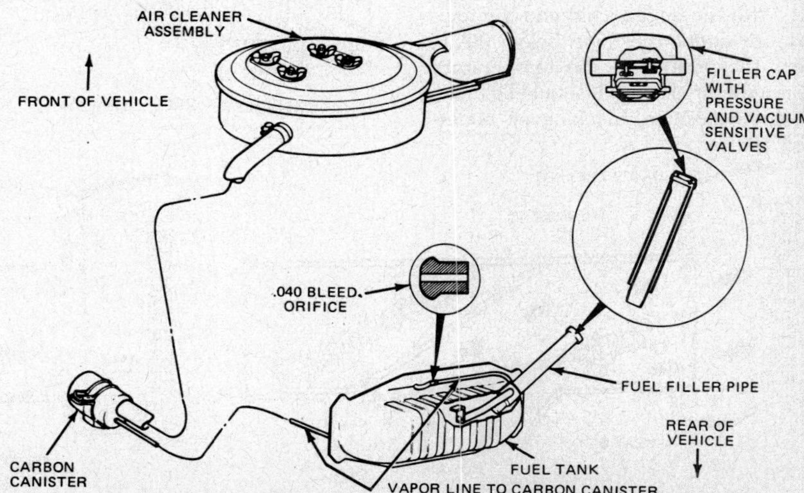

Fuel evaporative system—2600 cc engine

Charcoal canister—1600 cc engine

5. Reconnect the two hoses to the canister and secure them to their respective retaining clips.

Heated Air Intake Duct

The heated air intake portion of the air cleaner consists of a thermostat and a spring-loaded temperature control door in the snorkel of the air cleaner. The temperature control door is located between the end of the air cleaner snorkel, which draws in air from the engine compartment, and the duct that carries heated air up from the exhaust manifold. When the temperature under the hood is below 90° F, the temperature control door blocks off under-hood air from entering the air cleaner and allows only heated air from the exhaust manifold to be drawn into the air cleaner. When the temperature under the hood rises above 110° F, the temperature control door blocks off heated air from the exhaust manifold and allows only under-hood air to be drawn into the air cleaner. By controlling the temperature of the engine intake air this way, exhaust emissions are lowered and fuel economy increased.

Testing

1. With the engine cold and the temperature under the hood below 90° F, check the position of the temperature door in the air cleaner. It should be in the up (open) position, blocking off under-hood air.

2. Remove the air cleaner from the car. Immerse the air cleaner duct assembly in water, raise the water temperature to 110° F, and allow the temperature to stabilize for five minutes. The temperature control door should be in the down position, blocking off the heated air from the exhaust manifold.

If the temperature door does not react in this manner, and the door is not binding, replace the valve and duct assembly.

FUEL SYSTEM

Fuel Pump

A single-action fuel pump is used on all models. On the 1600 cc engine, the fuel pump is located on the right side of the engine and is operated by the camshaft. On the 2000 and 2600 cc engines, the fuel pump is located on the left side of the engine and is actuated by a rod driven by an eccentric on the auxiliary shaft (2000 cc engine) or the camshaft (2600 cc engine).

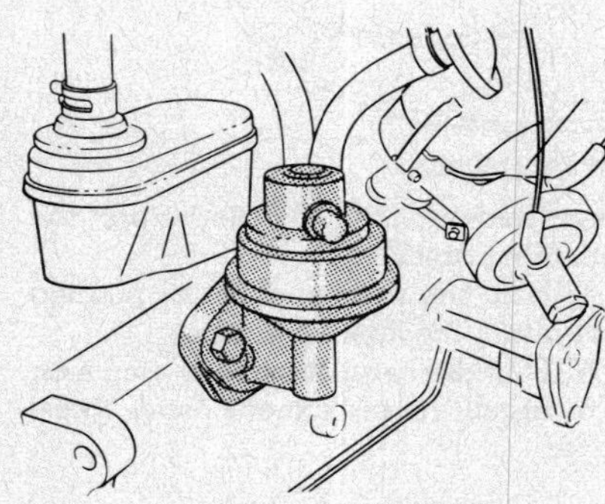
Fuel pump—1600 cc engine

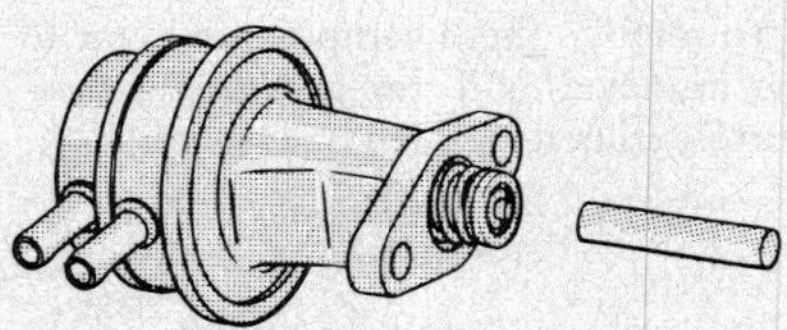
Fuel pump—2000 cc engine

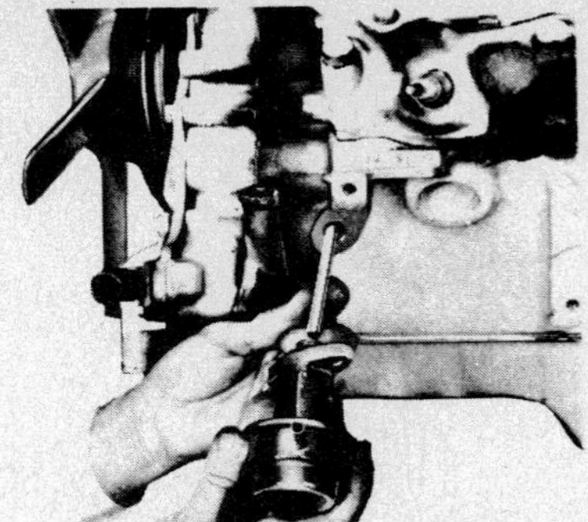
Fuel pump—2600 cc engine

Testing

Pressure Test

Disconnect the fuel line from the carburetor and attach a pressure tester to the end of the line. Crank the engine over and note the reading on the tester. The readings should be 3.5–5.0 psi for the 1600 cc engine, 3.8–5.0 for the 2000 cc engine, and 3.8–5.0 psi for the 2600 cc engine.

Capacity Test

Disconnect the fuel line from the carburetor and insert it into a one quart container. Crank the 1600 cc engine for 38 seconds, the 2000 cc engine for 43 seconds, and the 2600 cc engine for 43 seconds. The bottle should be half-full (one pint).

Removal and Installation

1. Disconnect the inlet line and outlet fuel lines at the fuel pump.

2. Remove the fuel pump retaining bolts and remove the pump and gasket. Discard the gasket.

3. Remove all the gasket material from the engine block and pump mounting surface. Apply oil-resistant sealer to both sides of the new gasket. Position the gasket on the fuel pump flange and hold the pump in position against the engine block.

NOTE: *Make sure the rocker arm or rod is riding on the camshaft eccentric.*

4. Press the pump tightly against the engine block, install the retaining bolts and tighten them securely.

5. Connect the fuel lines. Start the engine and check for leaks.

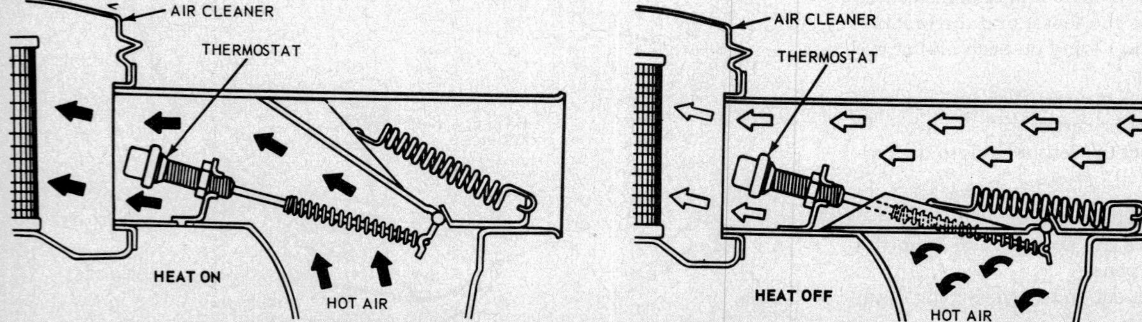

Operation of heated air intake duct on the air cleaner

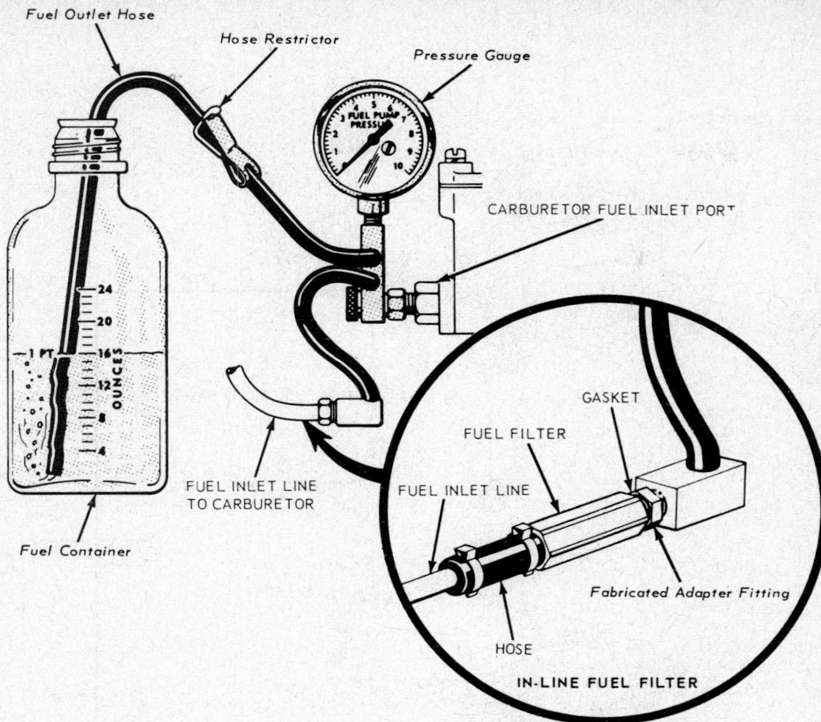

Fuel pump pressure and capacity test

Carburetors

The 1600 cc engine is equipped with a model 1250 single-venturi Barrel The 2000 and 2600 cc engines are equipped with a model 5200 two barrel carburetor. On the 5200 carburetor, the primary venturi is smaller than the secondary venturi. The two are connected by mechanical linkage and, when the primary throttle plate opens approximately 45° the secondary plate begins to open.

Removal and Installation

1. Remove the air cleaner.
2. On the 2000 and 2600 cc engines, remove the bolt that attaches the choke water housing to the carburetor and remove the water cover with its hoses attached. On the 1600 cc engine, remove the three screws that attach the water housing to the carburetor. Remove the housing.
3. Note the location of all fuel lines and vacuum hoses that attach to the carburetor, then disconnect them from the carburetor.
4. Disconnect the throttle linkage from the carburetor.
5. On all 1600 cc engines and those 2000 and 2600 cc engines with air conditioning, disconnect the throttle solenoid wire at the push-on connection.
6. On all 1600 cc engines, remove the two nuts that attach the carburetor to the intake manifold. On the 2000 and the 2600 cc engines, remove the four nuts that attach the carburetor to the intake manifold.
7. Inspect the carburetor base gasket. If it is damaged in any way, replace it. Clean any foreign matter from the base of the carburetor.
8. Position the carburetor on the intake manifold and tighten the nuts.
9. Connect the vacuum lines and the fuel lines to the carburetor.
10. Connect the throttle linkage to the carburetor.
11. Connect the water housing to the carburetor.
12. On those models equipped with a throttle solenoid, connect the lead wire at the push-on connector.
13. Replace any coolant that was lost in the removal of the water hoses.

Overhaul

All Types

Efficient carburetion depends greatly on careful cleaning and inspection during overhaul since dirt, gum, water, or varnish in or on the carburetor parts are often responsible for poor performance.

Overhaul your carburetor in a clean, dust-free area. Carefully disassemble the carburetor, referring often to the exploded views. Keep all similar and look-alike parts segregated during disassembly and cleaning to avoid accidental interchange during assembly. Make a note of all jet sizes.

When the carburetor is disassembled, wash all parts (except diaphragms, electric choke units, pump plunger, and any other plastic, leather, fiber, or rubber parts) in clean carburetor solvent. Do not leave parts in the solvent any longer than is necessary to sufficiently loosen the deposits. Excessive cleaning may remove the special finish from the float bowl and choke valve bodies, leaving these parts unfit for service. Rinse all parts in clean solvent and blow them dry with compressed air or allow them to air dry. Wipe clean all cork, plastic, leather, and fiber parts with a clean, lint-free cloth.

Blow out all passages and jets with compressed air and be sure that there are no restrictions or blockages. Never use wire or similar tools to clean jets, fuel passages, or air bleeds. Clean all jets and valves separately to avoid accidental interchange.

Check all parts for wear or damage. If wear or damage is found, replace the defective parts. Especially check the following:

1. Check the float needle and seat for wear. If wear is found, replace the complete assembly.
2. Check the float hinge pin for wear and the float(s) for dents or distortion. Replace the float if fuel has leaked into it.
3. Check the throttle and choke shaft bores for wear or an out-of-round condition. Damage or wear to the throttle arm, shaft, or shaft bore will often require replacement of the throttle body. These parts require a close tolerance of fit; wear may allow air leakage, which could affect starting and idling.

NOTE: *Throttle shafts and bushings are not included in overhaul kits. They can be purchased separately.*

4. Inspect the idle mixture adjusting needles for burrs or grooves. Any such condition requires replacement of the needle, since you will not be able to obtain a satisfactory idle.
5. Test the accelerator pump check valves. They should pass air one way but not the other. Test for proper seating by blowing and sucking on the valve. Replace the valve if necessary. If the valve is satisfactory, wash the valve again to remove breath moisture.
6. Check the bowl cover for warped surfaces with a straightedge.
7. Closely inspect the valves and seats for wear and damage, replacing as necessary.
8. After the carburetor is assembled, check the choke valve for freedom of operation.

Carburetor overhaul kits are recommended for each overhaul. These kits contain all gaskets and new parts to replace those that deteriorate most rapidly. Failure to replace all parts supplied with the kit (especially gaskets) can result in poor performance later.

Some carburetor manufacturers supply overhaul kits of three basic types: minor repair; major repair; and gasket kits.

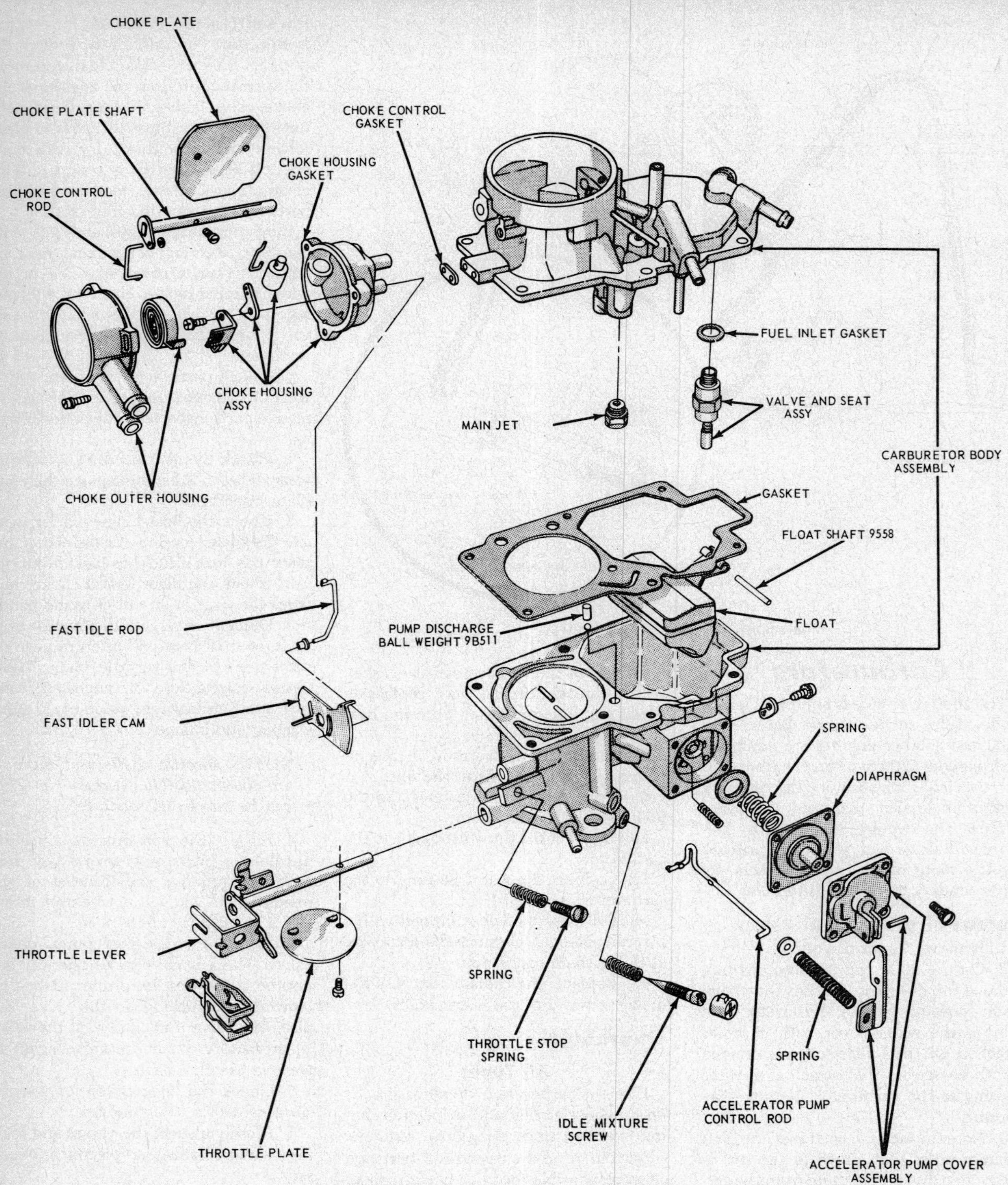

Exploded view—1250 carburetor

Basically, they contain the following:

Minor Repair Kits:
- All gaskets
- Float needle valve
- Volume control screw
- All diaphragms
- Spring for the pump diaphragm

Major Repair Kits:
- All jets and gaskets
- All diaphragms
- Float needle valve
- Volume control screw
- Pump ball valve
- Main jet carrier
- Float
- Complete intermediate rod
- Intermediate pump lever
- Complete injector tube
- Some cover hold-down screws and washers

Gasket Kits:
- All gaskets

After cleaning and checking all components, reassemble the carburetor, using new parts and referring to the exploded view. When reassembling, make sure that all screws and jets are tight in their seats, but do not overtighten, as the tips will be distorted. Tighten all screws gradually, in rotation. Do not tighten

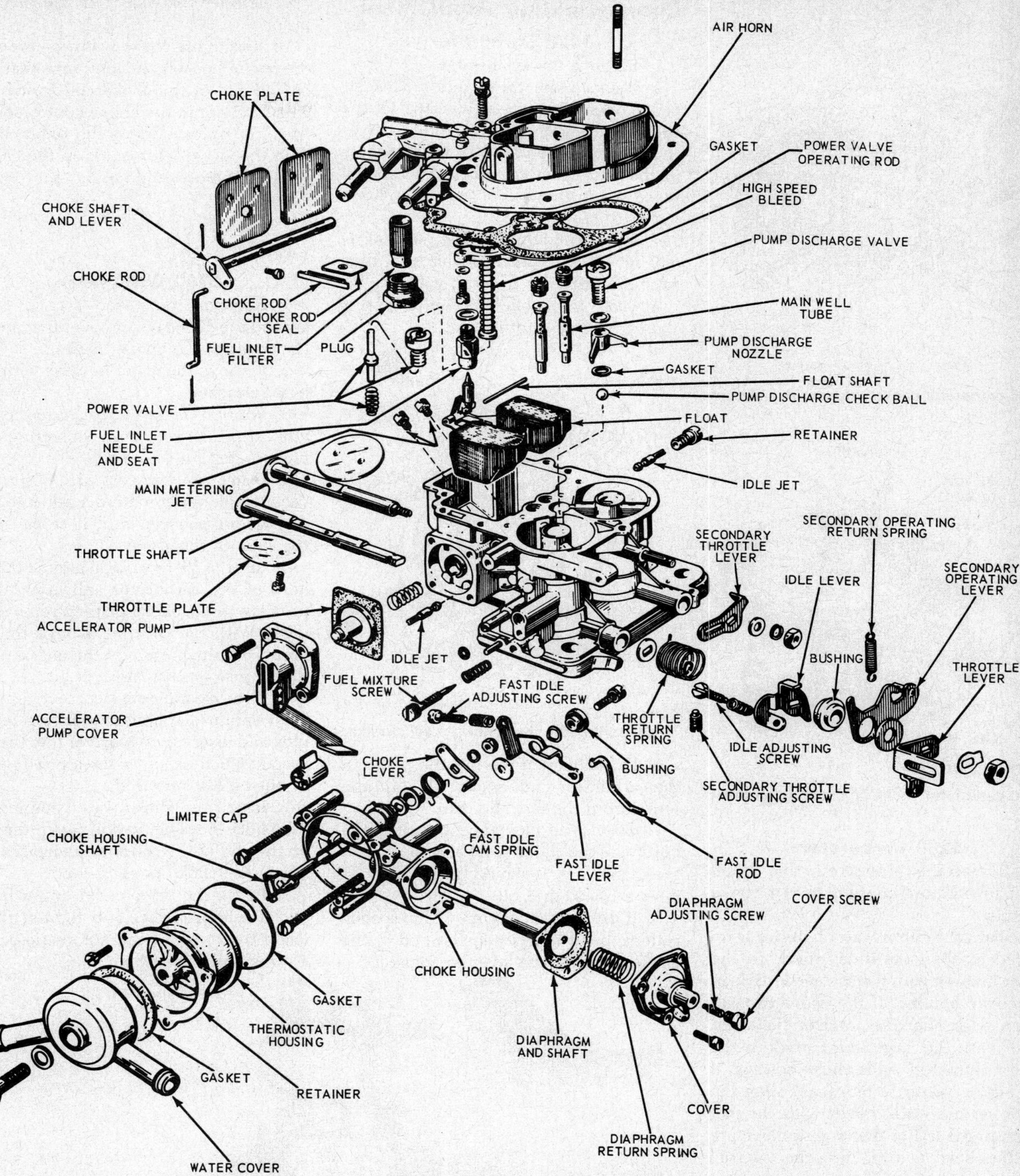

Exploded view—5200 carburetor

needle valves into their seats; uneven jetting will result. Always use new gaskets. Be sure to adjust the float level when reassembling. S.U. (Skinners Union) Carburetors Only

Choke Unloader Adjustment

1250 Carburetor

1. Remove the air cleaner and fully depress the throttle control lever.

2. Measure the clearance between the bottom of the choke plate and the carburetor wall. The clearance should be 0.210 in. (no. 4 drill bit).

3. If the clearance is not within specifications, bend the fast idle cam to adjust it.

5200 Carburetor

1. Hold the carburetor throttle lever in the wide-open position.

2. Insert a 9/32 in. drill bit (0.282 in.) into the air horn of the carburetor.

3. Apply light pressure to the choke plate to remove all slack.

4. With the drill bit against the carburetor wall, the bottom of the choke plate should just contact the drill. If it does not, bend the tab on the fast idle lever where it contacts the fast idle cam to correct it.

Automatic Choke Adjustment

1250 Carburetor

1. Remove the air cleaner.

2. Loosen the three screws that attach the choke water housing to the choke housing.

3. Turn the choke water housing to align the index mark on the water housing with the large index mark on the choke housing and tighten the water cover attaching screws.

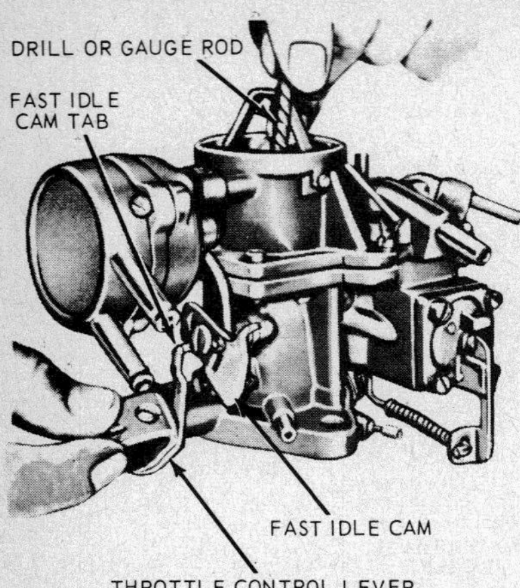

1250 carburetor choke unloader adjustment

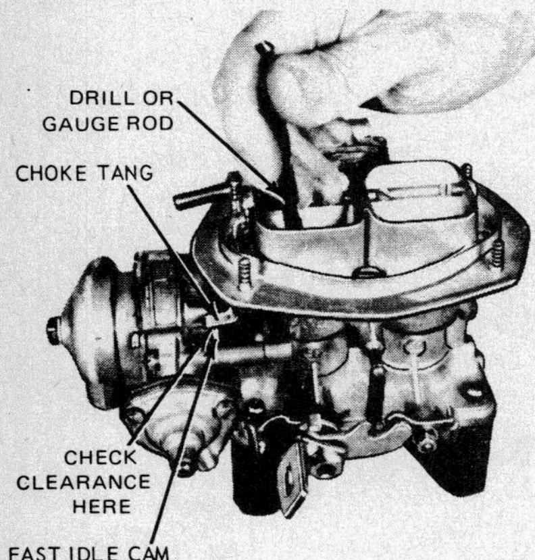

5200 carburetor choke unloader adjustment

5200 Carburetor

1. Loosen the three screws that attach the choke water housing to the choke housing.
2. Turn the choke water housing as required to align the index mark on the water housing with the specified mark on the choke housing. If the choke cap setting is index, align the notch on the water cover with the large index mark in the center of the top of the choke housing. If the choke setting is one lean, align the notch on the water cover with the first notch to the left of the large index mark on the choke housing. See the "Carburetor Specifications" chart for the proper choke settings.

Carburetor Choke Specifications Chart

Model	Carburetor	Setting
1600	701-9510-EA	Index
1600	701-9510-EB	Index
2000	All Models	1 Lean
2600	72TF-BEA	1 Lean
2600	72TF-BFA	Index

Choke Linkage Adjustment

1250 Carburetor

1. Remove the air cleaner.
2. Remove the three screws that attach the choke water housing to the choke housing.
3. Depress the choke piston assembly in the choke housing until the vacuum bleed slot in the wall of the piston housing is exposed.
4. Insert the bent tip of a piece of 0.-040 in. (thick) wire into this slot, then raise the piston to trap the wire.
5. Close the choke plate in the top of the carburetor until it stops.

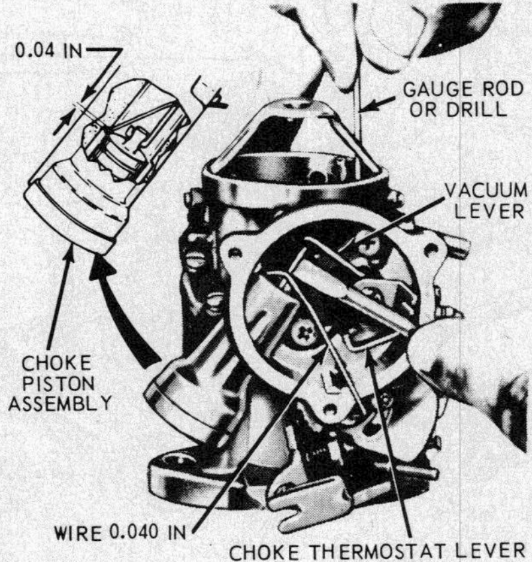

1250 carburetor choke linkage adjustment

6. Partially open the throttle plates in the carburetor to disengage the fast idle screw from the fast idle cam.
7. Check the clearance between the bottom of the choke plate and the wall of the carburetor. It should be 0.064–0.085 in. (no. 51–46 drill bit).
8. If the clearance is not within specifications, bend the tab on the end of the choke thermostatic lever to adjust it.
9. Remove the wire from the vacuum piston.
10. Install the choke water housing on the choke housing, making sure that tab on the end of the choke coil spring engages the slot in the choke control lever. Align the index mark on the water cover with the large index mark on the choke housing before tightening the water cover.

5200 Carburetor

1. Remove the three screws from around the choke water cover that attach the cover to the choke housing.
2. Remove the water housing with the hoses attached.
3. Position the fast idle cam so the fast idle adjusting screw is contacting the highest step on the cam.
4. Using a screwdriver, push the vacuum diaphragm stem back into the diaphragm housing until it stops. Hold the stem in this position.
5. Insert a 15/64 in. drill bit into the air horn of the carburetor and apply light pressure to the choke plate to remove all slack. With the drill bit against the air horn wall, the bottom of the choke plate should just contact the drill bit.
6. If the clearance is incorrect, remove the vacuum diaphragm adjusting screw plug and insert a screwdriver into the exposed hole, then adjust the screw inward or outward as required.
7. Install the choke water housing on the choke housing, making sure the tab on the end of the coil spring engages the slot in the choke housing shaft.
8. Install the three choke water housing attaching screws and tighten them finger-tight. Adjust the automatic choke as previously described.

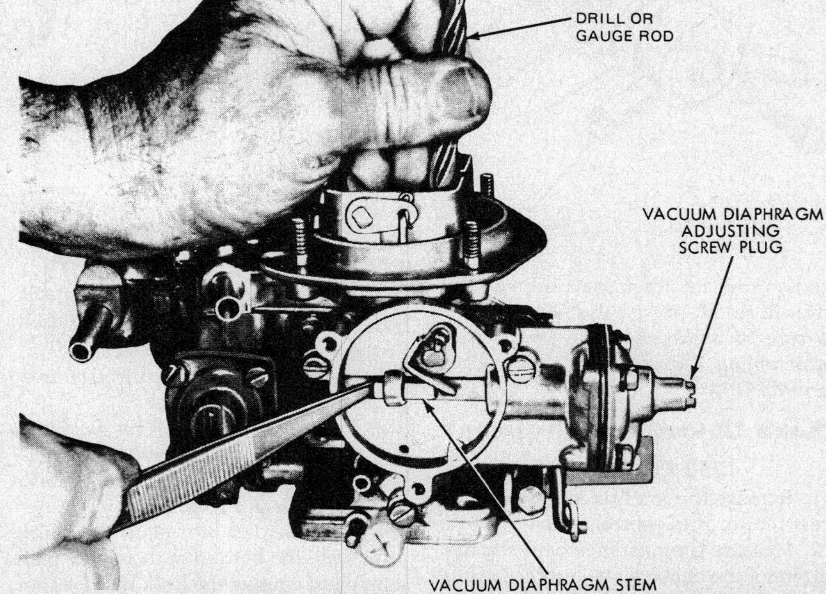

5200 carburetor choke linkage adjustment

Float Level Adjustments

1250 Carburetor

1. Remove the air cleaner.
2. Disconnect the fuel inlet hose and the decel valve hose at the carburetor.
3. Remove the choke fast idle cam pivot screw.
4. Remove the screws retaining the thermostatic spring housing and spring and then remove the spring.
5. Remove the screws and spring washers retaining the carburetor upper body to the lower body. Carefully lift off the body.
6. Hold the carburetor upper body in a vertical position with the float hanging down.

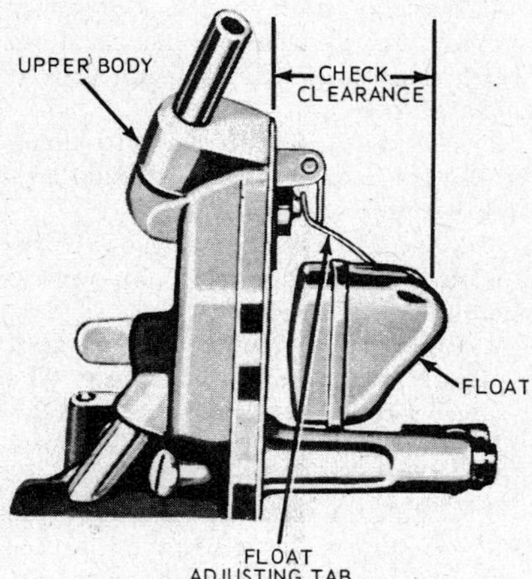

1250 carburetor float level adjustment

7. Measure the distance from the bottom of the float to the upper body gasket. Adjust the distance to 1.20 in. by bending the tab which rests against the needle valve.
8. Turn the upper body to the upright position and again measure the distance from the bottom of the float to the gasket. Adjust the distance to 1.40 in. by bending the tab which rests on the needle valve housing.
9. Position the air horn gasket to the upper body.
10. Carefully position the upper body to the lower body and install the retaining screws.
11. Install the fuel inlet hose and decel valve hose to the carburetor.
12. Install the choke thermostatic housing with the bimetallic spring in the center slot of the lever. The index mark on the housing should be aligned with the specified mark on the body. Secure the housing with the retaining screws.
13. Replace the air cleaner assembly.

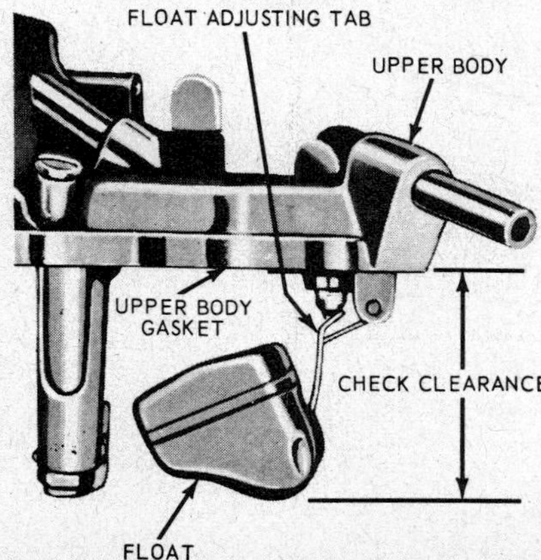

1250 carburetor float drop adjustment

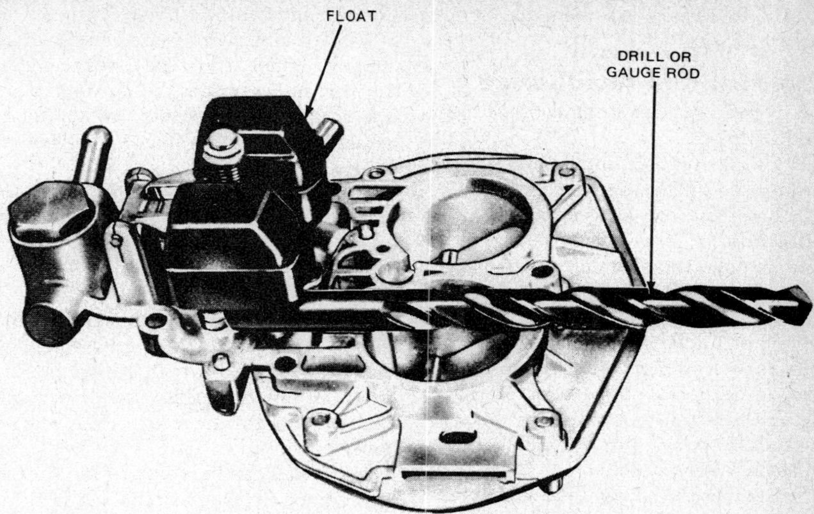

5200 carburetor float level adjustment

5200 Carburetor

1. Remove the air cleaner.
2. Disconnect the fuel and decel valve hoses from the carburetor.
3. Remove the small clip that attaches the choke rod to the choke plate shaft and disconnect the rod from the shaft.
4. Remove the screws that attach the upper body of the carburetor to the main body of the carburetor and carefully lift the upper body off the main body. Be careful not to tear the upper body gasket.
5. Turn the carburetor upper body upside down and measure the clearance between the bottom of each float and the bottom of the carburetor upper body. The clearance should be 0.420 in. (no. 58 drill bit).
6. If the clearance is incorrect, bend the float level adjusting tang to correct it.

NOTE: *Both floats must be adjusted to the same clearance.*

7. With the upper body still in the inverted position, measure the clearance between the tang on the rear of the float mounting bracket and the bumper spring on the float pivot pin. The clearance should be 0.020–0.050 in. If the clearance is incorrect, bend the float drop tang to adjust it.
8. Position the upper body and gasket of the main body of the carburetor and connect the choke rod to the choke plate lever. Install the choke rod attaching clip in the hole in the rod.

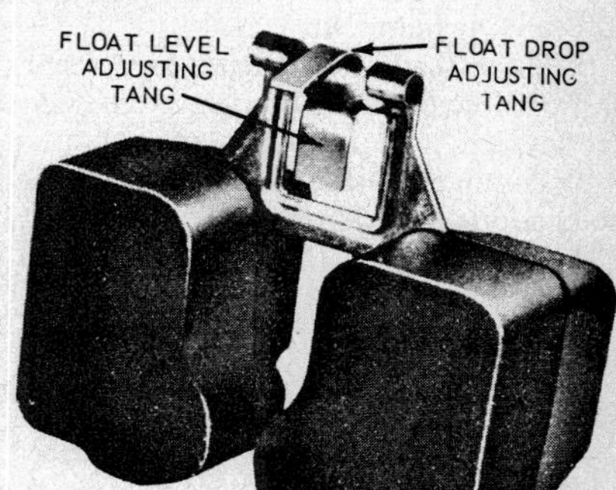

5200 carburetor float drop adjustment

9. Install the upper body attaching screws.
10. Connect the fuel and decel valve hoses to the carburetor.
11. Install the air cleaner.

Throttle Linkage Adjustments

1. Position a 0.015 in. feeler gauge between the return stop and the accelerator pedal arm.
2. Unclip the outer cable retainer from the rocker arm cover bracket.
3. Allow the outer cable to take up its natural position and reclip it to the rocker cover bracket.
4. Remove the feeler gauge and check the throttle operation. Make sure that full movement can be obtained from idling to full throttle.

MANUAL TRANSMISSION

There are two types of transmissions used on the Capri. On Capri's with the 1600 cc engine shift linkage is located inside the tailshaft. Manual transmissions used on the 2000 and 2600 cc engines have their shift linkage located externally. Before removing these transmissions it is necessary to remove the shifter and/or linkage.

Removal and Installation

1. Disconnect the ground cable from the battery.
2. On the 1600 cc engine, disconnect the throttle linkage at the carburetor.
3. Raise the car and support it with jackstands.
4. Remove the gearshift lever or disconnect the shift levers.
5. Remove the four bolts joining the driveshaft to the rear axle pinion. Also remove the two bolts securing the center bearing carrier to its bracket. Remove the driveshaft. Install a dummy yoke in the transmission to prevent oil loss if the oil has not been drained.
6. Remove the clip and the speedometer cable from the transmission.
7. Disconnect the exhaust pipe(s) from the exhaust manifold.
8. Move the clutch release lever boot and free the clutch operating cable from the lever.
9. Remove the starter motor attaching bolts and move the starter to one side.
10. Remove the bolts holding the clutch housing to the engine.
11. Remove the bolts holding the lower dust cover from the clutch housing and detach the cover.
12. Support the rear of the engine with a jack.
13. Remove the four bolts attaching the transmission crossmember to the body. Slide the transmission toward the rear of the car while supporting its weight, and remove it from the car.
14. Position the transmission assembly on the engine. Make sure that the clutch housing fully engages the dowel pins on the rear of the engine. Install the bolts attaching the clutch housing to the engine.
15. Install the four crossmember-to-body bolts and lockwashers. Remove the jack from beneath the engine.
16. Install the starter motor.
17. Replace the lower dust cover.
18. Coat the ball on the end of the clutch cable with chassis grease and install the clutch cable to the clutch release lever. Adjust the cable. (See the clutch section.) Locate the boot in the release lever opening.
19. Install the shift rods to the shifter, if so equipped (See the following section.)
20. Connect the exhaust pipe(s) to the exhaust manifold.
21. Install the speedometer cable and secure it with the retaining clip.
22. Install the driveshaft, aligning the mating marks. Replace the four nuts and bolts at the rear axle pinion. Locate the center bearing carrier in position and attach it to its bracket with the two bolts.
23. On the 1600 cc engine, install the gearshift lever.
24. Refill the transmission if the oil was drained.
25. Remove the jackstands and lower the car to the ground. Check the transmission and the clutch for proper operation.

NOTE: *Two types of manual transmissions are used on the Capri. The 2000 and 2600 cc engines use transmissions that have the shift linkage located on the outside. The 1600 cc engine uses a transmission that has the linkage located inside the top. Follow the procedure that applies to your transmission.*

Overhaul

Transmission Disassembly

1600 cc. Engine

1. Remove four bolts and top cover plate.
2. Pry the plug from the rear of the extension housing.
3. Remove the plunger screw from the right side of the case.
4. Working through the top cover opening, use a punch to remove the pin which secures the shift selector arm to the shift shaft.
5. Pull the shift shaft rearward, being careful not to drop the shift selector arm and the interlock plate.
6. Move the First-Second and Third-Fourth gear synchronizer hubs toward the input shaft bearing.
7. If necessary, remove the shift shaft plunger spring from the case. The plunger screw was removed in Step 3.
8. Remove the pin from the Third-Fourth shift fork. Remove the fork.
9. Unbolt the extension housing from the case. With a plastic hammer, tap the extension housing slightly rearward. Rotate the housing until the countershaft lines up with the notch in the housing flange.

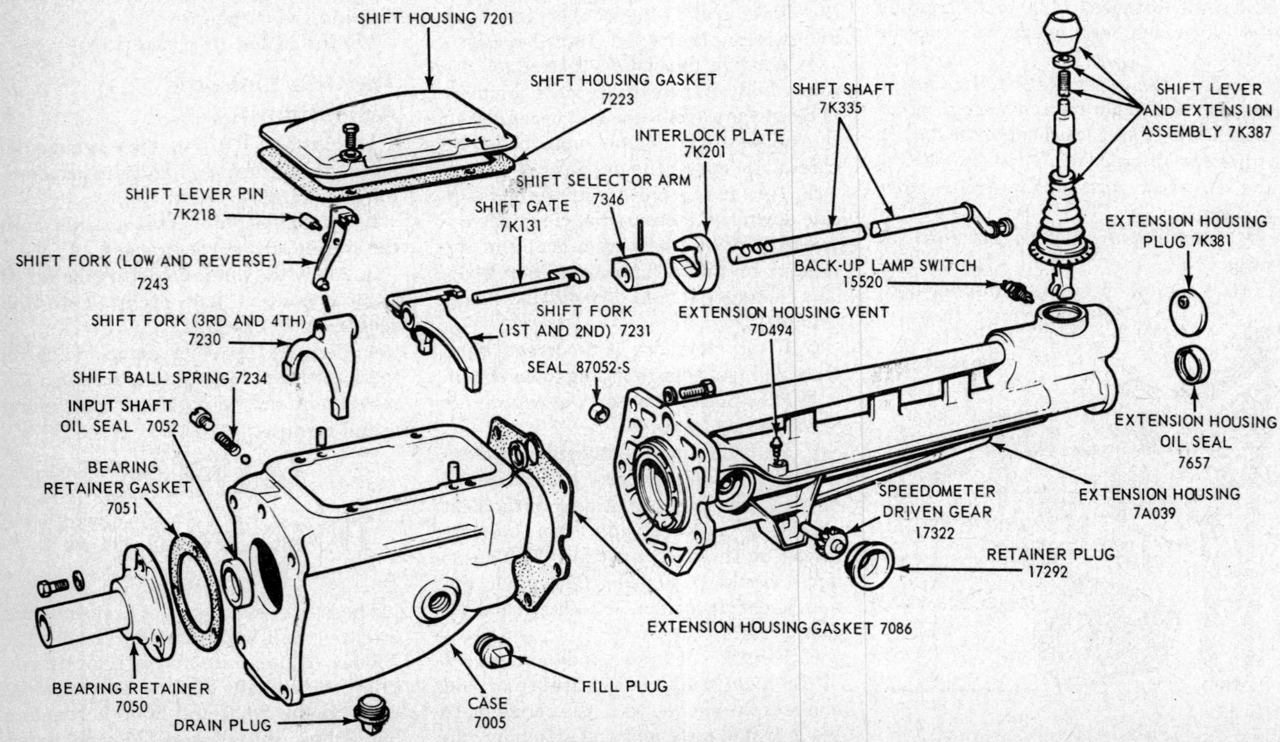

1600 cc engine transmission

10. Tap the countershaft rearward with a brass drift until it is just clear of the front of the case. Push the countershaft out with a dummy shaft. Lower the cluster gear to the bottom of the case.

11. Remove the extension housing and output shaft assembly. The third-fourth synchronizer sleeve must be pushed forward for clearance.

12. Unbolt the front bearing retainer from the case. Remove the retainer and the gasket.

13. Remove the input shaft oil seal.

14. Remove the snap-ring from around the input shaft bearing. Tap the input shaft gear and bearing assembly out of the transmission with a brass drift. Remove the needle roller bearing from the recess in the end of the input shaft gear.

15. Remove the cluster gear, two thrust washers, and the dummy shaft, from the case. Remove 20 needle rollers and a retaining washer from each end of the cluster gear.

16. Assemble a nut, a flat washer, and a sleeve on a 5/16 in. x 24 UNF threaded bolt. Screw the bolt into the reverse idler shaft and tighten to pull out the shaft.

17. Remove the low-reverse shift fork from the lever pin inside the case. Do not remove the pin.

Component Disassembly

Third-Fourth Synchronizer

1. Remove fourth gear blocking ring from the input shaft gear side of the assembly.

2. Remove the synchronizer hub snap-ring from the forward end of the output shaft and discard.

3. Support third gear. Press the output shaft out of the third-fourth gear synchronizer and third gear. Be careful not to drop the output shaft.

4. Pull the sleeve from the hub. Remove the inserts and springs.

5. Check all parts for wear. The synchronizer hub and sleeve should be replaced if worn or damaged.

First-Second Synchronizer

1. Remove the plug in the extension housing. Remove the speedometer driven gear.

2. Remove the snap-ring which holds the output shaft bearing to the extension housing. With a plastic hammer, tap the output shaft assembly out of housing.

3. Remove the snap-ring which holds the speedometer drive gear. Pull off the gear. Remove the snap-ring which holds the output shaft bearing.

4. Support low and reverse sliding gear. Press low and reverse sliding gear, spacer, and output shaft bearing from the output shaft.

5. Remove the snap-ring which holds the first-second synchronizer assembly to the output shaft.

6. Support second gear. Press the Second gear and First-Second synchronizer assembly from the output shaft.

7. Dismantle the synchronizer assembly. Replace the synchronizer hub or sleeve if worn or damaged. The output shaft bearing must be replaced.

Input Shaft and Gear

1. Remove and discard the input shaft snap-ring.

2. Press off the input shaft bearing.

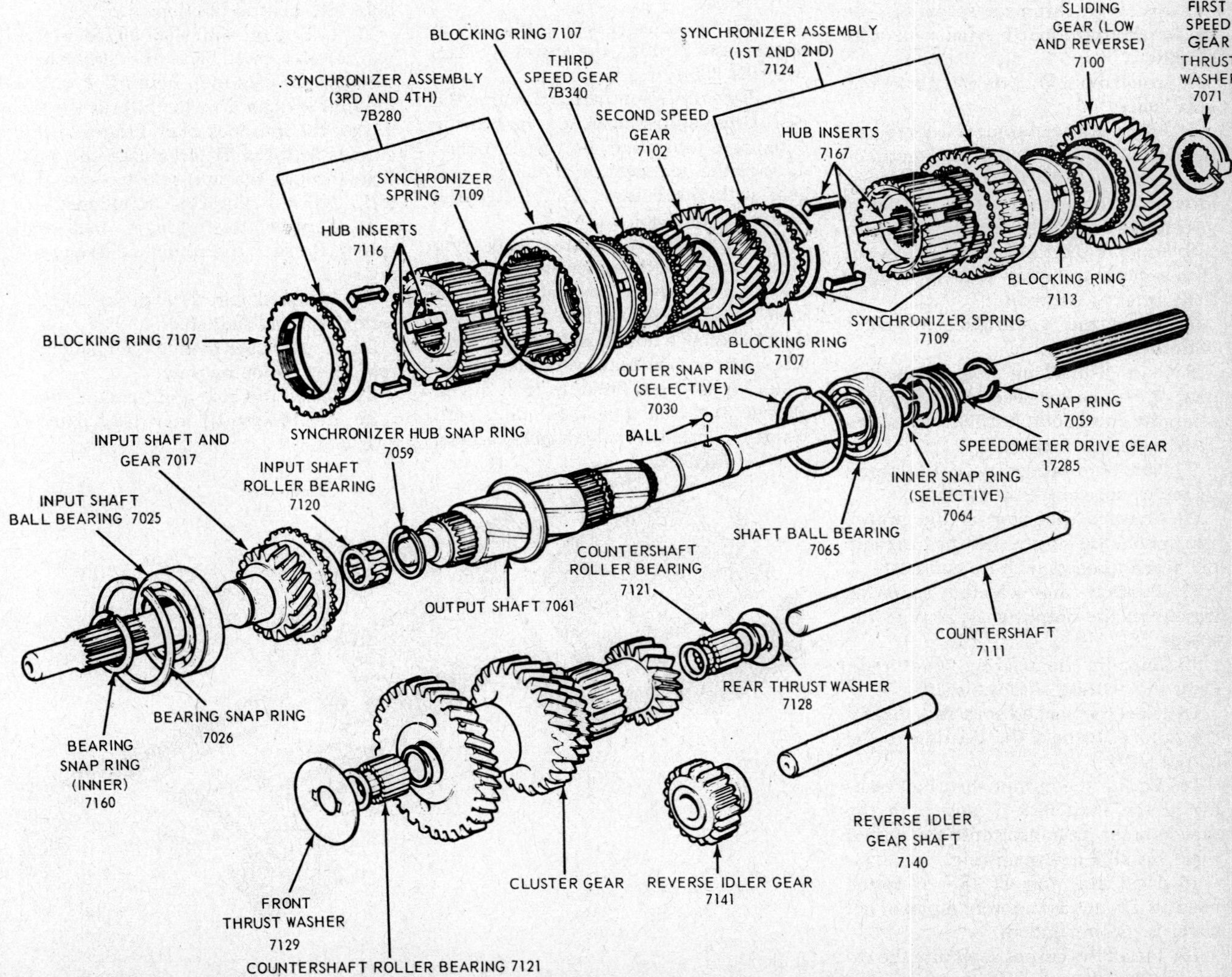

Mainshaft and countershaft—1600 cc engine.

Component Assembly

Third-Fourth Synchronizer

1. Slide the gear over the hub. Place an insert in each slot.
2. Install a synchronizer spring inside the sleeve beneath the inserts; the spring tang should fit into an insert. Install the other spring on the opposite side, fitting the tang into the same insert. When viewed from the edge, the springs should run in opposite directions.
3. Place the third gear on the output shaft with the dog teeth forward. Assemble the blocking ring on the third gear cone.
4. Place the synchronizer assembly on the output shaft with the boss forward.
5. Support the hub. Press the hub on the output shaft and install a new snap-ring.

First-Second Synchronizer

1. Install the second gear on the output shaft with the cone and dog teeth to the rear.
2. Slide the synchronizer sleeve over the hub. Place an insert in each of the three slots.
3. Install synchronizer springs as you did for the third-fourth synchronizer assembly.
4. Install a blocking ring to the second gear cone.
5. Install the synchronizer assembly on the output shaft with the gear teeth, on the periphery of the synchronizer sleeve, forward. Slide low and reverse sliding gear to the rear of the synchronizer hub.
6. Support the sliding gear. Press the synchronizer assembly onto the output shaft as far as possible.
7. Secure the synchronizer assembly with the snap-ring.
8. Place a blocking ring on the first gear side of the first-second synchronizer assembly on the output shaft. Install first gear, cone side forward.
9. Place the spacer with the larger diameter adjacent to first gear.
10. Select a snap-ring of the proper size to hold the output shaft bearing into the bearing recess with no end float.
11. Position the selected snap-ring loosely on the output shaft next to the spacer.
12. Support the bearing inner race. Press the bearing onto the shaft.
13. Select the thickest snap-ring that fits the groove, to hold the bearing to the output shaft.
14. Locate the output shaft ball bearing in the shaft indent, and push the speedometer drive gear onto the output shaft. Install a new snap-ring.
15. Heat the end of the extension housing. Do not use a torch. A pan of hot water is recommended.
16. Install the output shaft into the extension housing. Install the snap-ring which secures the output shaft bearing to the housing.
17. Replace the speedometer driven gear. Install a new plug, using sealer.

Input Shaft and Gear

1. Support the input shaft bearing inner race. Press the bearing onto the shaft.
2. Install the snap-ring which secures the bearing to the input shaft.

Transmission Assembly

1600 cc Engine

1. Slide the low-reverse lever onto the lever pin inside the case.
2. Push the idler shaft into the case. Place the reverse idler gear on the shaft. Locate the low-reverse lever in the gear groove. Tap the reverse idler shaft into position with a soft hammer.
3. Slide a dummy shaft into the cluster gear. Push a retainer washer into the gear bore. Grease and install 20 needle rollers and the second retaining washer. Install the washers and rollers at the other end of the gear. Grease and install the thrust washers with their convex side into the gear recess.
4. Place the cluster gear in the bottom of the case. Position the thrust washers with the flat upward.
5. Place the input shaft and gear in the case. Using a brass drift, tap the bearing outer race into place. Be careful not to damage the dog teeth on the input shaft gear with the cluster gear. Install the bearing snap-ring.
6. Place the input shaft needle bearing in the input shaft gear recess.
7. Drive a new oil seal into the input shaft retainer. Cover the input shaft splines. Install a new gasket on the transmission front face. Make sure that the retainer oil groove is lined up with the oil passage in the case. Coat the bolts with sealer and install them with lock-washers.
8. Locate the fourth gear blocking ring on the input shaft gear cone.
9. Install a new oil seal in the shift shaft aperture. Drive the seal in with a socket.
10. Install a new sealer coated gasket to the extension housing.
11. Pull the third-fourth synchronizer sleeve forward. Slide the extension housing and output shaft into position. Align the cutaway on the extension housing with the countershaft aperture in the rear face of the case.
12. Using loops of cord, lift the cluster gear into mesh with the output and input shaft gears. Take care not to drop the countershaft thrust washers.
13. Tap the countershaft into place, driving out the dummy shaft, and make sure that the lug on the rear of the countershaft fits into the recess on the extension housing flange.
14. Push the extension housing onto the transmission case. Apply sealer to bolts. Torque to 30–35 ft lbs.
15. Replace both shift forks. Secure the third-fourth fork with a new pin.
16. Position the shift forks to the synchronizer sleeves. Move synchronizer hubs into neutral positions.
17. Grease the shift shaft oil seal in the rear of the case. Slide the shift shaft through the extension housing. Position the shift selector arm and interlock plate so that the interlock plate locates in the cutouts in the shift forks. Pass the shift shaft through the shift selector arm and forks until the pin holes are aligned.
18. Replace the plunger ball and spring. Replace the retaining screw, using sealer.
19. Install the pin through the shift selector arm and shift shaft.
20. Apply sealer to plug. Tap plug into rear of extension housing.
21. Install top cover and gasket.
22. Refill transmission with 2.8 pints of SAE 80 oil.

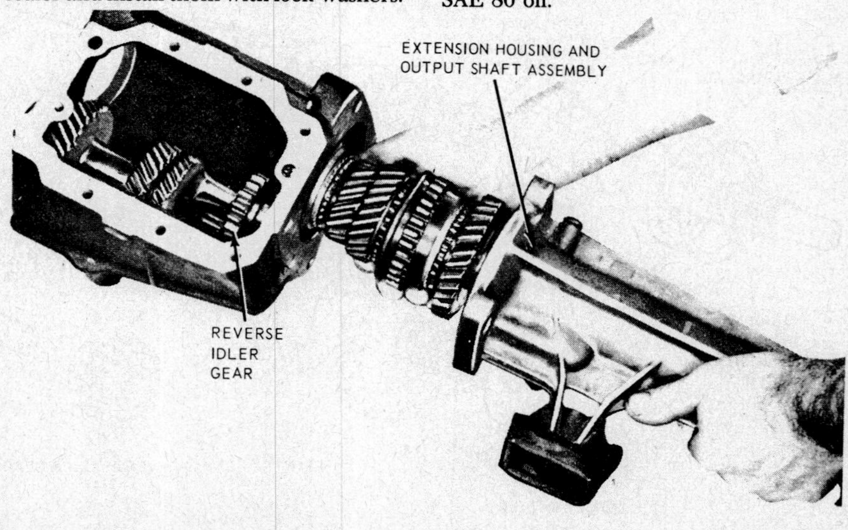

Removing tailshaft—2000 and 2600 transmissions

Transmission Disassembly

2000 and 2600 cc Engines

1. Remove the retaining clips and the flat washers from the shift rods at the shift levers. Remove the rods.

2. Remove the bolts which secure the shift linkage cover and remove the cover from the side of the transmission. Remove the shifter forks from the gear box.

3. Remove the bolts which hold the tailshaft to the gear box and twist the tailshaft until the countershaft becomes fully visible.

4. Remove the countershaft by driving it from the front of the gear box toward the rear using a brass drift. The countershaft should just clear the front of the case. Push the countershaft out the rest of the way with a dummy shaft. Lower the cluster gear to the bottom of the gear box.

5. Remove the snap ring which secures the input shaft bearing and press off the bearing.

6. Remove the tailshaft and the output shaft assembly from the gearbox.

7. Disassemble the cluster gear by allowing the dummy countershaft to fall out. Remove the needle bearings and the spacers from the cluster gear.

8. Drive out the reverse idler gear shaft toward the rear of the gear box.

9. Remove the snap-ring, in front of the third and fourth gear synchronizer, from the output shaft assembly. Remove the synchronizer assembly including third gear.

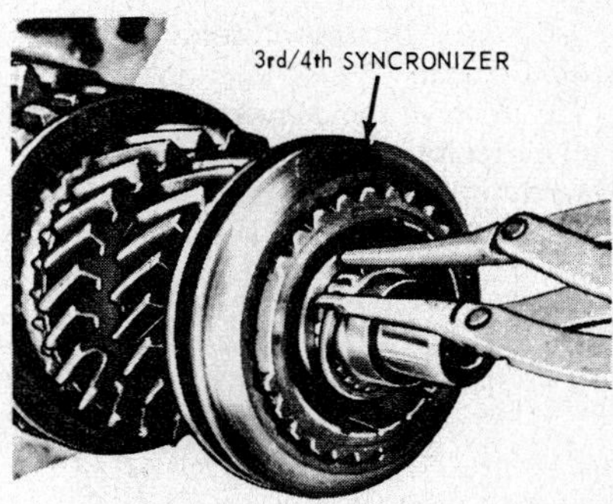

Removing third gear snap-ring—2000 and 2600 transmissions

10. Remove the snap-ring and the thrust washer in front of the second gear. Remove second gear and the blocking ring.

11. Remove the first and second gear synchronizer sleeve and remove the synchronizer inserts.

12. Remove the speedometer drive gear.

13. Remove the snap-ring which retains the output bearing in the tailshaft.

14. Using a soft faced mallet, remove the output shaft from the tail shaft.

15. Remove the snap-ring from the output shaft and press off the bearing using an arbor press. Remove the spacer and first gear with the blocking ring and insert spring.

Transmission Assembly

2000 and 2600 cc Engines

NOTE: *Before assembling the transmission, clean all parts in a suitable solvent and check them for wear and damage. Use sealer on bolts which extend into the transmission case.*

1. Slide the insert spring, blocking ring, first gear, and the spacer onto the rear of the output shaft. Make sure that the broad side of the spacer is pointing toward the shaft bearing.

2. Install a new snap-ring on the tailshaft output shaft.

When installing a new bearing on the tail shaft, a new snap-ring should be selected as follows: Place a dummy bearing into the tailshaft and determine the distance between the top face of the bearing and the outer edge of the retaining groove, using a feeler gauge.

The thickness of the dummy bearing (0.688 in.) plus the feeler gauge blades is the total width between the stop for the bearing, and the outer edge of the snap-ring retaining groove. Measure the width of the new bearing and subtract that number from the total width just obtained. This figure is the thickness that the new snap-ring should be.

3. Install the speedometer gear along the output shaft by pressing it into place.

4. Position the first and second gear synchronizer springs in the synchronizer hub by placing one end of each spring into the same groove.

5. Position the inserts in their grooves and then slide the first and second gear synchronizer sleeve onto the synchronizer hub.

6. Slide the blocking ring, second gear and the thrust washer onto the output shaft. Install the snap-ring.

7. Heat the tailshaft. Do not use a torch. A pan of hot water is recommended. Install the output shaft and bearing into the tailshaft. Do not use a press.

8. Install the snap-ring which you had previously measured, in the tailshaft.

9. Position the synchronizer springs as described in step 4. Install the inserts in their groove. Slide the third and fourth gear synchronizer sleeve onto the hub.

10. Install the third and fourth gear synchronizer assembly by sliding it onto the output shaft and install the snap-ring.

11. Press the input shaft bearing onto the input shaft and install a snap-ring that gives the least possible end-play.

12. Install the input shaft and gear to the gear box using a brass drift. Install the snap-ring.

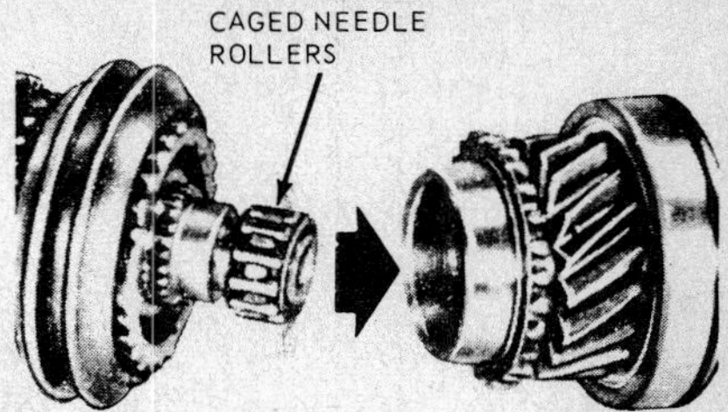

Installing caged roller bearing—2000 and 2600 transmissions

13. Install the front bearing retainer to the gear box with the gasket in place. The oil groove in the retainer should be in line with the oil passage in the gear box.

14. Install the reverse idler gear, with the collar for the selector fork facing rearward, then drive the idler gear shaft into position until it is flush against the case.

15. With a dummy pinion installed in the bottom of the gear box, install the countershaft. Position the thrust washers in the gear box.

16. Install the tailshaft using sealer on both ends. Slide the tailshaft and the output shaft into position.

17. Using cords, raise the cluster gear into mesh with the main gear train and install the countershaft. The offset lug on the rear of the countershaft must be positioned to allow final installation of the tailshaft.

18. Use a sealer and install the tailshaft bolts, torquing them to 30–35 ft lbs. Install the speedometer drive gear.

19. Install the shifter forks for first–second, and third–fourth gears so that the numbers stamped on the forks face the front of the transmission. Install the reverse fork with the number facing the *rear.*

20. Install the retaining clips and the flat washers on the shift levers and install the shift rods to the shift levers.

Linkage Adjustment

NOTE: *This procedure applies only to the 2000 and 2600 cc engines.*

1. Make an alignment pin out of 3/16 in. rod stock.

2. Place the gearshift lever in neutral and raise the car off the ground.

3. Remove the spring retainers and disconnect the shifter rods from the transmission shift levers.

4. Insert the alignment pin in the shift levers.

5. Place all the transmission shift levers in the neutral position.

6. Adjust the length of the shifter rods so they fit into the holes in the transmission shift levers. Install the shifter rods and the spring retainers.

7. Remove the alignment pin and lower the car to the ground. Check the transmission for proper operation.

Shifter alignment pin

CLUTCH

Removal and Installation

1. Remove the transmission from the car.
2. Loosen each of the pressure plate-to-flywheel attaching bolts gradually to relieve the spring pressure.
3. If the same pressure plate is being used again, match-mark it with the flywheel so it may be installed in its original position.
4. Remove the clutch disc and the pressure plate from the car.
5. Position the pressure plate and the clutch disc on the flywheel and install the attaching bolts by hand, but do not tighten them with a wrench.
6. Install a clutch (dummy or pilot) shaft to the center of the clutch disc.
7. Tighten the pressure plate attaching bolts evenly to 12–15 ft lbs.
8. Remove the dummy shaft.
9. Install the transmission.

Clutch Adjustment

1. Loosen the locknut and position the clutch pedal onto the stop, on the pedal bracket; turn the adjusting nut as necessary to obtain a clearance of 0.138–0.144 in. between the nut and the clutch housing. With this setting, there should be 0.-5–0.75 in. clutch pedal free-play.
3. Lock the locknut but do not overtighten it.
4. Lubricate the pedal end of the clutch cable.

AUTOMATIC TRANSMISSION

Removal and Installation

C4 Transmission

1. Raise the car on a lift.
2. Drain the fluid from the transmission. Place a pan under the transmission. Loosen the transmission pan attaching bolts and allow the fluid to drain. After some fluid has drained remove all the bolts and remove the pan.
3. Remove the ground cable from the battery at the engine block. Disconnect the starter cable from the starter. Remove the starter attaching bolts and remove the starter.
4. Remove the access cover from the lower part of the converter housing.
5. Remove the nuts which held the converter to the flywheel. You must rotate the flywheel in order to gain access to those bolts not made available through the access cover. To rotate the flywheel, place a socket on the crankcase attaching bolt and turn it.
5. Cars equipped with a V6 engine have a drain plug on the converter. Rotate the flywheel as previously described to gain access to the converter plug. Remove the plug and drain the fluid. Replace the plug after draining the fluid.
6. Mark the driveshaft for correct alignment when installing.
7. Remove the bolts which hold the driveshaft center bearing to the body.
8. Lower the driveshaft assembly and remove it from the car.
9. Remove the speedometer cable from the tailshaft.
10. Disconnect the shift cable from the lever on the transmission.
11. Remove the shift cable bracket from the converter housing.
12. Disconnect the downshift cable from the transmission downshift lever bracket.
13. Disconnect the neutral safety switch wires and the connectors from the switch.
14. Remove the vacuum line from the modulator on the transmission.
15. Support the transmission with a transmission jack and then remove the crossmember bolts and the crossmember.
16. Disconnect the transmission fluid cooler lines at the transmission.
17. Remove the transmission filler tube.
18. Secure the transmission to the jack with a chain.
19. Remove the converter housing attaching bolts. Move the transmission to the rear and down in order to remove it.
20. To install, move the transmission

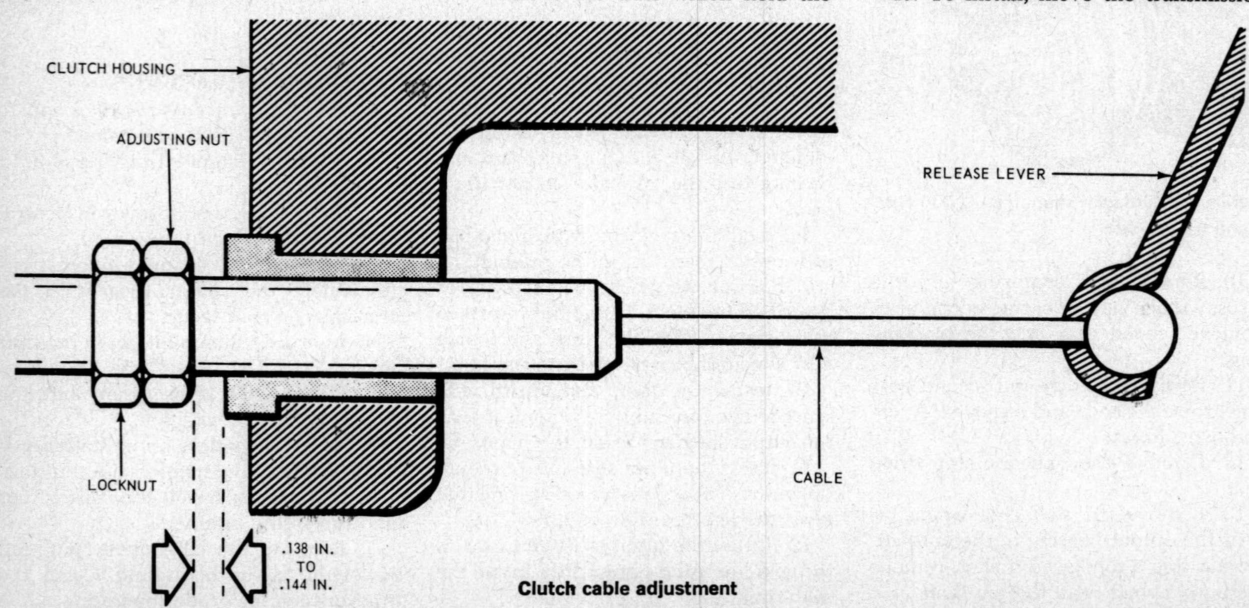

Clutch cable adjustment

into position. The converter must rest squarely against the flywheel.

21. Install the converter attaching bolts and tighten them to 23–33 ft lbs. Remove the chain from the transmission.
22. Install the transmission filler tube.
23. Install the transmission fluid cooler lines to the transmission.
24. Position the crossmember to the frame and install the bolts.
25. Install the flywheel-to-converter nuts and tighten them to 23–28 ft lbs.
26. Remove the transmission jack. Install the vacuum hose to the modulator.
27. Connect the neutral safety switch.
28. Connect the downshift cable to the downshift bracket. Connect the shift cable bracket to the converter housing.
29. Connect the shift cable to the lever on the transmission.
30. Connect the speedometer to the tailshaft.
31. Install the driveshaft and align the marks. Install the center driveshaft bearing.
32. Install the converter housing access cover. Install the starter and the starter cable. Install the battery ground cable.
33. Lower the car to the ground and fill the transmission to the correct level with the proper fluid.

Borg Warner Transmission

1. Remove the transmission dipstick and disconnect the downshift valve cable.
2. Raise the car on a hoist and remove the transmission pan drain plug and drain the oil.
3. Mark the driveshaft with paint, for correct alignment when installing. Remove the bolts from the flange.
4. Remove the bolts which hold the driveshaft center bearing to the body.
5. Lower the driveshaft assembly and remove it from the car.
6. Disconnect the exhaust pipe bracket from the transmission. Loosen the exhaust pipe and move it to one side.
7. Remove the speedometer cable from the transmission.
8. Disconnect the starter wires and remove the starter.
9. Remove the torque converter front cover. Remove the screws which hold the flex plate to the converter.
10. Disconnect the linkage control cable at the transmission.
11. Place a transmission jack under the transmission to support the transmission, and secure the transmission to the jack with a chain.
12. Remove the bolts that support the engine to the body.
13. Remove the converter housing bolts. Remove the transmission filler tube. Using a bar, apply pressure to the converter to prevent the converter from coming off the transmission when the assembly is removed.
14. Lower the transmission and converter assembly and remove it from the car.
15. To install, raise the transmission into position and install five of the six housing attaching bolts and tighten them to 30–33 ft lbs. Position the rear engine support to the body and install the bolts.
16. Remove the chain from the transmission.
17. Install the bolts which hold the flex plate to the converter. Install the converter front cover.
18. Install the starter and connect the wires.
19. Install the exhaust pipe bracket to the transmission.
20. Install the speedometer cable. Install the manual linkage control cable.
21. Connect the wires to the neutral safety switch. Install the driveshaft, aligning the marks then install the retaining bolts. Position the center bearing to the body and install the holding bolts.
22. Lower the car to the ground and install the downshift cable.
23. Fill the transmission to the proper level with specified transmission fluid.
24. Adjust the downshift cable.

Pan Removal & Installation

C4 Transmission

1. Raise the car on a hoist.
2. Place a drain pan under the transmission.
3. Starting at the rear of the pan and working toward the front, loosen the attaching bolts and allow the transmission fluid to drain. Finally, remove all the bolts except two bolts at the front, to allow the fluid to further drain.
4. Remove the last two bolts and remove the oil pan.
5. Remove all gasket material from the pan and the transmission mounting surface.
6. Apply gasket sealer to the oil pan and position the gasket on the pan.
7. Position the pan on the transmission and install the bolts hand-tight.
8. Torque the bolts evenly to 12–16 ft lbs. Fill the transmission to the proper level with the specified fluid.

Borg Warner Transmission

Follow the previous procedures for removal and installation. The fluid should be removed through the drainplug. Make sure that the drainplug has been replaced when installing the pan. The torque for the pan bolts is 8–13 ft lbs.

Filter Service

C4 and Borg Warner Transmissions

Remove the transmission oil pan. Remove the screws attaching the filter screen to the transmission. Wash the filter in a solvent and blow it clean of solvent with an air gun. Install the filter screen and replace the oil pan.

NOTE: *Cleaning the filter screen is not a regular maintenance procedure. It should be cleaned when the oil pan has been removed for other service procedures.*

Intermediate Band Adjustment

C4 Transmission

1. Wipe the area clean around the adjusting screw on the side of the transmission.
2. Remove the adjusting screw locknut and discard it.
3. Install a new locknut on the adjusting screw but do not tighten it.
4. Tighten the adjusting screw to exactly 10 ft lbs.
5. Back off the adjusting screw exactly 1 ¾ turns.
6. Hold the adjusting screw so that it does not turn and tighten the locknut to 35–45 ft lbs.

NOTE: *The tools used in the illustrations of band adjustments are: a torque wrench, an extension, and an allen socket.*

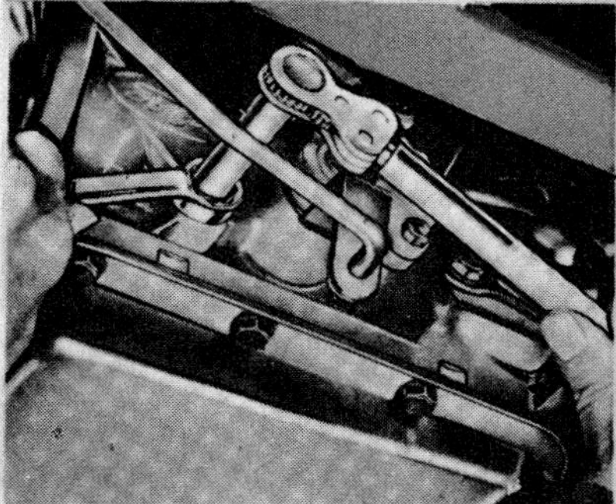

Adjusting intermediate band—C4 transmission.

Borg Warner Transmission

The intermediate and the low-reverse band adjustments for these transmissions require the use of special tools. These adjustments should be left to a qualified repair shop or a dealer.

Low-Reverse Band Adjustment

C4 Transmission

1. Wipe the area clean around the adjustment screw on the side of the transmission.
2. Remove the adjusting screw locknut and discard it.
3. Install a new locknut but do not tighten it.
4. Tighten the adjusting screw to exactly 10 ft lbs.
5. Back off the adjusting screw exactly three full turns.

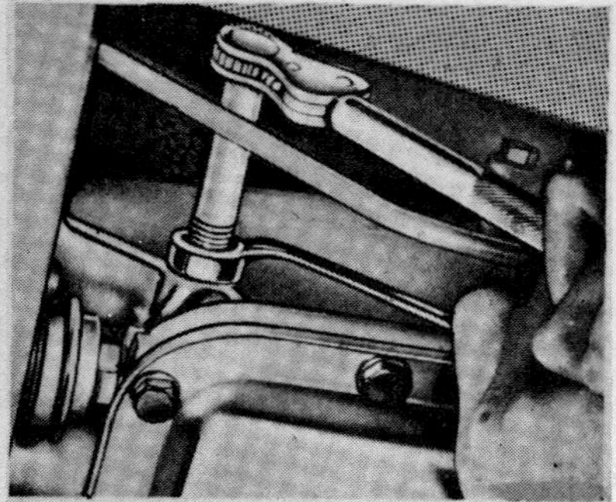

Adjusting lower reverse band—C4 transmission.

6. Hold the adjusting screw so that it does not turn and tighten the locknut to 35–45 ft lbs.

Shift Linkage Adjustment

1. Position the transmission selector lever in the Drive position.

2. Raise the car and remove the clevis pin and disconnect the cable and the bushing from the transmission.

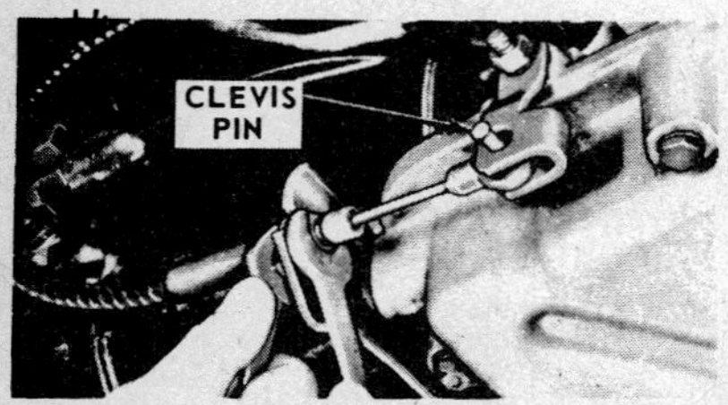

Manual linkage control cable adjustment

3. Move the transmission manual lever to the Drive position, which is the third detent from the back of the transmission.

4. With the transmission selector lever and the manual lever in the Drive positions, adjust the cable length until the clevis pin holes in the *manual* lever and the end of the cable are aligned.

5. Connect the cable, lower the car, and check the operation of the transmission in each selector lever position.

Downshift Linkage Adjustment

C4 Transmission

1. Press the gas pedal to the floor to completely open the throttle.

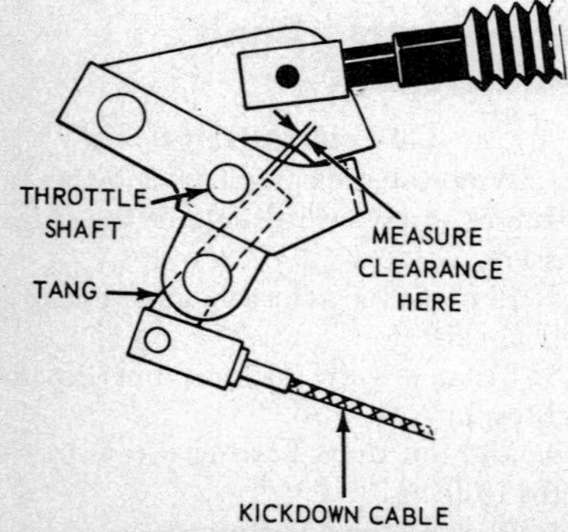

Kickdown linkage adjustment

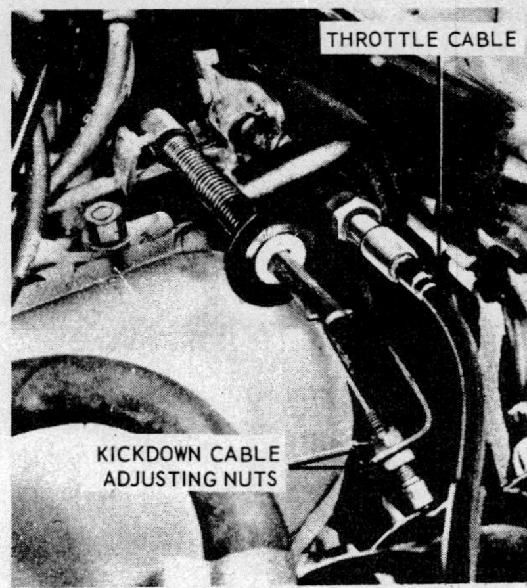

Kickdown linkage adjustment nuts

2. Position the kick-down cable so that the tang just contacts the throttle shaft.

3. If an adjustment is required, loosen the two kick-down cable adjusting nuts at the bracket and move the cable as required. Tighten the adjusting nuts.

Borg Warner Transmission

The downshift valve control cable governs the transmission control pressure which, in turn, determines the shift points. It also manually downshifts the transmission at full throttle. In order to adjust the cable you must adjust the downshift valve to the proper pressure and perform a transmission control pressure test. This test requires the use of special equipment and should be performed by a qualified repair shop or a dealer.

Neutral Safety Switch

Removal and Installation

C4 Transmission

1. Remove the downshift cable from the transmission downshift lever.

2. Remove the transmission downshift outer lever retaining nut and lever. It may be necessary to apply penetrating oil to the lever shaft and nut in order to remove the nut and lever.

3. Remove the neutral safety switch attaching bolts.

4. Disconnect the multiple wire connector. Remove the switch.

5. Install the new switch on the transmission. Install the attaching bolts.

6. With the transmission lever in neutral, rotate the switch and insert a gauge pin (no. 43 drill) into the gauge pin hole.

7. Tighten the switch attaching bolts to 4–8 ft lbs and remove the gauge pin.

8. Install the outer downshift lever and attaching nut, and install the downshift cable to the downshift lever.

9. Install the switch wires. Connect the multiple wire connector. Check the operation of the switch in each lever position. The engine should start only with the transmission lever in the neutral position.

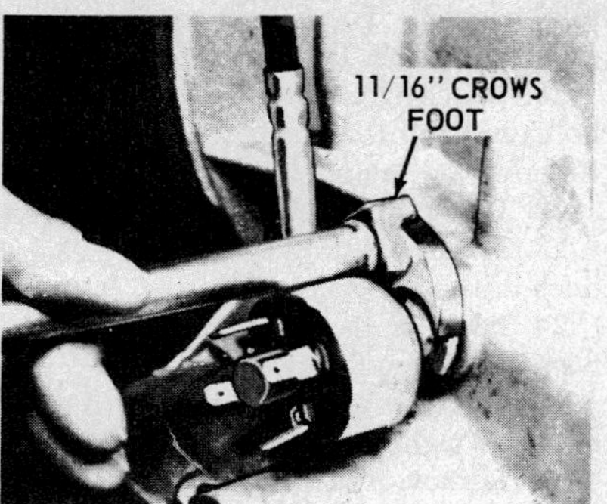

Removing neutral safety switch—Borg Warner Transmission.

Borg-Warner Transmission

1. Place the transmission lever in Drive.

2. Raise the car and disconnect the four leads from the neutral safety switch.

3. Loosen the locknut using a 11/16 in. "crow's foot" and unscrew the switch from the transmission. Remember the number of turns required to remove it.

4. Screw the new switch into the transmission the same number of turns as required to remove it.

DRIVE AXLE

Driveshaft and Universal Joints

A two-piece, tubular driveshaft is splined to the transmission output shaft and transmits power through three universal joints and a center bearing, situated in front of the middle universal joint, to the rear axle pinion flange.

Driveshaft

Removal and Installation

1. Mark the driveshaft and the rear axle pinion flange for correct realignment when installing and then remove the four attaching bolts and lockwashers.

2. Remove the two bolts and the lockwashers securing the center bearing to the body.

3. Lower the driveshaft assembly and withdraw it from the transmission. A slight amount of oil may leak from the transmission.

4. Slide the front yoke into the transmission, engaging the output shaft splines, taking care not to damage the oil seal or bearing in the tail shaft.

5. Lift the rear of the driveshaft assembly, and align the marks on the driveshaft and the rear axle pinion flange. Fit the four bolts and the lockwashers, and tighten them to 43–47 ft lbs.

6. Secure the center bearing carrier to its bracket and tighten the attaching bolts to 13–17 ft lbs.

7. Check the level of the transmission oil.

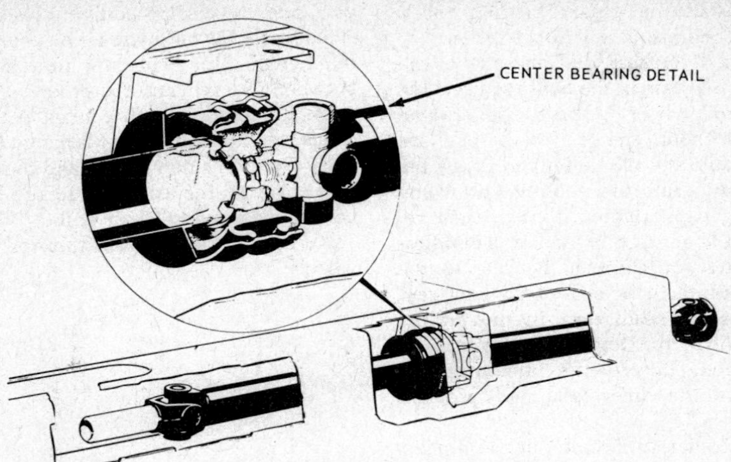

Driveshaft assembly showing center bearing

Universal Joint Overhaul

1. Remove the driveshaft.
2. Position the driveshaft assembly in a vise.
3. Remove the snap-rings which retain the bearing caps.
4. Using a suitably sized socket or an arbor press, drive one of the bearing caps in toward the center of the universal joint. This will force the opposite bearing cap out.

Universal joint—exploded view

5. As each bearing cap is pressed or punched far enough out of the universal joint assembly so that it is accessible, grip it with a pair of pliers and pull it from the driveshaft yoke. Drive or press the spider in the opposite direction in order to make the opposite bearing cap accessible and pull it free with a pair of pliers. Use this procedure to remove all bearings from the universal joints.
6. After removing the bearings, lift the spider from the yoke.
7. Thoroughly clean the yoke areas on the driveshaft.

CAUTION: *Use extreme care when installing a new bearing into position. A heavy jolt can cause one or more of the needle bearings to fall out of place which will stop the cap from sitting properly on the spider.*

8. Start a new bearing into the yoke.
9. Position the spider in the yoke and press or drive the new bearing cap ¼ in. below the surface of the yoke.
10. With the bearing cap in position, install a new snap-ring.
11. Start a new bearing cap into the opposite side of the yoke.
12. Press or drive the bearing cap until the opposite bearing—which you have just installed—contacts the inner surface of the snap-ring.
13. Install a new snap-ring on the second bearing cap.
14. Position the slip yoke on the spider and install new bearings and snap-rings.
15. Check the reassembled joints for freedom of movement. Never install a driveshaft in a car if there is any binding in the universal joints.

Center Bearing

Removal and Installation

1. Remove the driveshaft.
2. Mark the center universal yoke and the front universal yoke for correct realignment when installing. Bend back the locktab in the center of the universal yoke and loosen the retaining bolt. Remove the U-shaped plate and separate the two halves of the driveshaft.
3. Remove the driveshaft and the bearing assembly from the rubber insulator.
4. Bend back the tabs securing the rubber insulator into its carrier and then remove the insulator.
5. Remove the bearing and the protective caps from the driveshaft with a puller.
6. Drive the ball bearing and the protective caps onto the driveshaft.

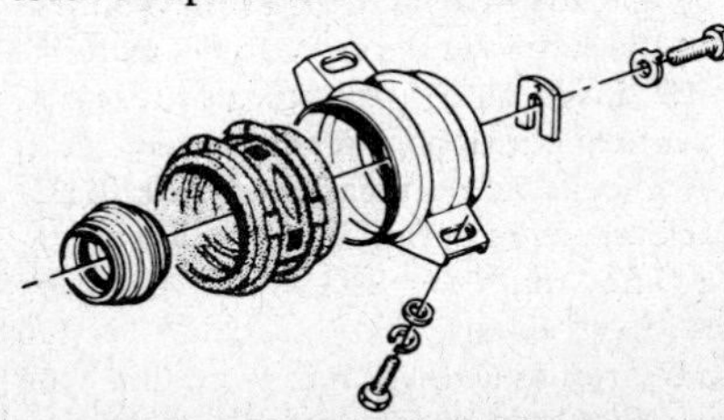
Center bearing—exploded view

7. Insert the rubber insulator into its carrier with the boss upward. Bend the tabs on the carrier back over the beaded edge of the rubber insulator.
8. Slide the carrier and the rubber insulator over the bearing assembly.
9. Screw the retaining bolt with a new locktab onto the end of the front driveshaft, leaving enough space to allow for the U-shaped plate.
10. Align the mating marks on the two universal joint yokes and assemble the driveshaft. Insert the U-shaped plate, with the smooth surface facing the fork, under the retaining bolt head and tighten the bolt to 25–30 ft lbs. Bend the locktab up.
11. Install the driveshaft.

Axle Shaft and/or Bearing Replacement

Removal and Installation

1. Jack up the rear of the car and support it with jackstands.
2. Remove the wheel, brake drum securing screw, and the brake drum. Be sure that the parking brake is released.
3. Remove the bolts that secure the axle retaining plate to the backing plate. These bolts are accessible through holes in the axle shaft flange.
4. Pull the axle and bearing assembly out of the axle housing with a slide hammer.

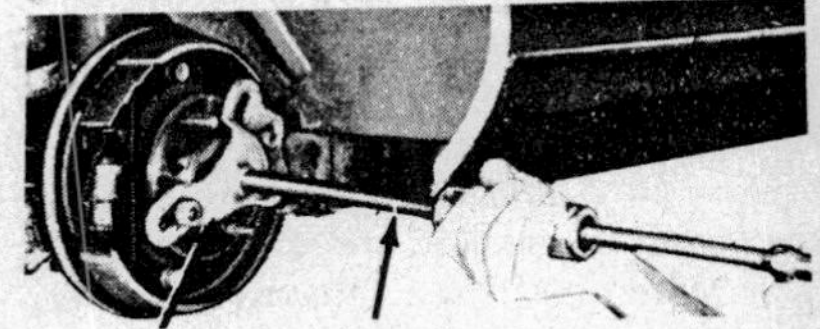
Axle shaft removal

NOTE: *If a slide hammer is not available, the axle can sometimes be pried out of the housing by using pry bars on opposing sides of the hub.*

5. Loosen the inner retaining ring by nicking it deeply with a chisel in several places. It will then slide off easily.
6. Press off the bearing and install the new one by pressing it into position.
7. Press on the new retainer.

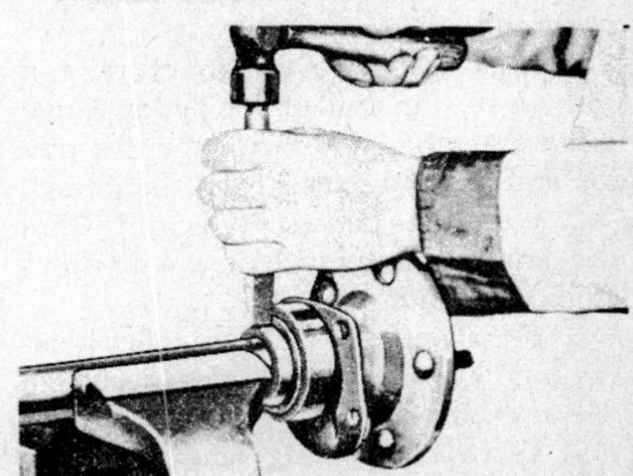
Rear wheel retaining nut removal

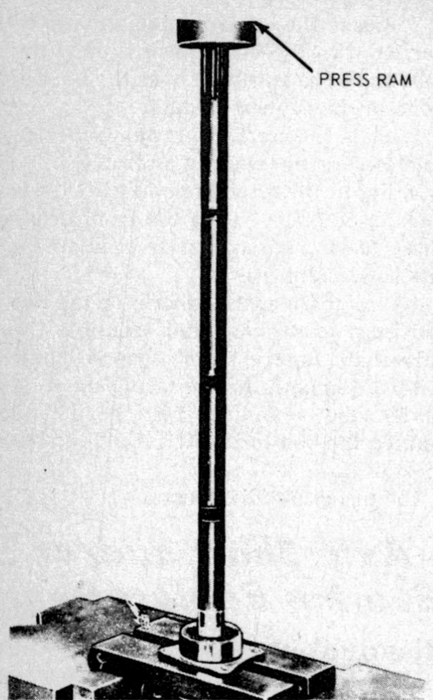

Rear wheel bearing removal

8. Assemble the shaft and the bearing in the housing.

9. Install the retaining nuts, drum, wheel, and tire.

Differential

Removal

1. Jack up the car and pull the axle shafts.

2. Mark the driveshaft and pinion flanges for realignment. Remove the four bolts and washers, the ten retaining bolts, the cover, the gasket, and drain the axle.

3. Match mark and remove the differential bearing caps. Using two pry bars, remove the differential.

Overhaul

1. Remove the bearings from each side of the differential assembly. Remove the shims.

2. Unscrew the ring gear retaining bolts and remove the ring gear from the differential assembly.

3. Remove the locking pin which secures the differential pinion shaft in the differential case. Remove the pinion shaft, differential pinions, differential side gears and adjusting shims.

4. Hold the drive pinion flange and remove the nut. Pull off the pinion flange using a suitable puller. Remove the pinion and bearing spacer from the pinion.

5. Pull off the large roller bearing from the pinion shaft, remove the spacer shims from the pinion shaft.

6. Remove the small taper roller bearing together with the radial oil seal from the axle housing.

7. Drive the bearing races out from the axle housing.

8. Install the pinion bearing races, pulling them squarely into position.

9. To determine total side play of the differential case in the housing, press the taper roller bearings on the differential case without shims. Install pressure blocks into the axle tubes and install the differential into the housing. Install the bearing caps, tighten, loosen, then retighten finger tight. Mount a dial indicator gauge on the axle housing so the feeler contacts the side of the ring gear and the dial reads zero. By moving the differential, the total side play can be measured. Record this measurement. Remove the differential and pressure blocks.

10. To determine the thickness of the pinion bearing spacer, use the trial and error method. Install the pinion with a selected spacer, small taper bearing, drive pinion flange, and the old self-locking nut. Tighten the nut to 72–87 ft lbs. and rotate the pinion several times using an in. lbs. torque wrench. If the rotating torque required is too high, the spacer is too thin, and should be replaced with a thicker one. If the torque is too low, a thinner spacer should be used. Correct torque is 13–19 in. lbs. Remove the old nut. To check the spacer thickness, use the method described in "Pinion Mesh Markings."

Measuring ring gear backlash

11. Make sure that the new oil seal has grease between the two sealing lips and is coated with sealing compound. Install it with a new self locking nut and torque to 72–87 ft lbs.

12. Remove the differential case bearings. Position the shims as indicated by the total side play figure, one half of the required amount on each side, on the differential case. Press the taper roller bearings on the differential case. Insert the case in the axle housing and center it. Position the bearing caps as marked. Insert the screws and torque to 43–49 ft lbs.

13. Position the dial indicator feeler in a vertical position on one ring gear tooth and check the tooth flank backlash. If the backlash is not within 0.005–0.009 in. (0.-12–0.22 mm.) the differential must be removed again. If the backlash is too large, remove the shims from the ring gear face side and transfer to ring gear back side. Reverse procedure if backlash is too small. Do not increase or decrease number of shims, but only interchange between one side and the other.

14. For proper tooth contact pattern check, see "Pinion Mesh Markings."

15. Position a new gasket and the axle case cover on the axle case, secure with bolts and torque to 22–29 ft lbs.

16. Install the driveshaft, axles and wheels.

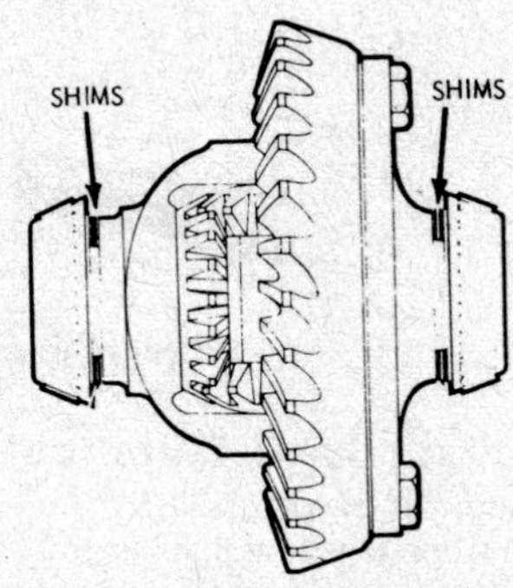

Location of differential case side shims

Pinion Mesh Markings

The following method of determining the relative position of the ring gear and pinion, and whether or not they are in proper mesh, will prove satisfactory for all pinion and ring gears. This should be followed by a final check, even when the pinion depth has been determined by special tools. Assemble the pinion in the housing, without preload, and tighten the pinion nut until a preload of about 10 in. lbs. is developed on the bearings to insure that they are completely free of end play.

This, of course, is not the final bearing preload setting, but is a good one for checking the pinion mesh markings.

Install the differential assembly and adjust it to provide from 0.004–0.008 in. backlash of the ring gear, measured at the rim of the gear.

Paint five or six of the ring gear teeth with red lead and, while the helper brakes the ring gear with a piece of wood, slowly turn the pinion until the ring gear makes at least one full revolution. The mesh of the pinion with the ring gear will be indicated as a mark in the red lead on the ring gear teeth. Compare this mark with the accompanying photographs. The caption on each photograph explains whether the mark indicates the pinion is too deep or too shallow, the ring gear too close or too far away.

When the marking is found to be improper, it is customary to make trial changes in increments of 0.005 or 0.007 in. If changing the shim 0.005–0.007 throws the marking from too deep to too shallow, the proper distance is about halfway between.

If, after changing this increment of shims, the mark still indicates that more must be changed, it is advisable to con-

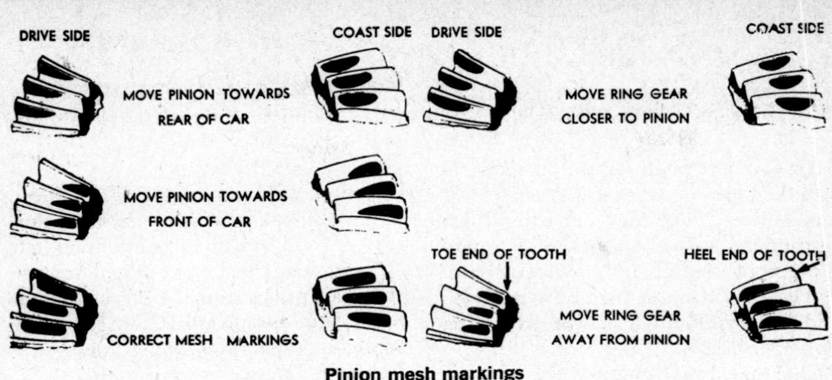

Pinion mesh markings

tinue changing in the same increments.

While considerable time is generally required to disassemble the rear, press off the bearings, change the shims, press the bearing back on and reassemble the rear, this is still the only positive method of determining if the rear will operate quietly after it is finally installed in the car

Differential Specifications

	1600	2000	2600
Axle Ratio	3.89:1	3.44:1	3.22:1
No. Teeth in Pinion	9	9	9
No. Teeth Ring Gear	35	31	29
Oil Cap.	2.3 pts.		
Side Gear Play	0.0004-0.006 in.		
Bearing Pre-load	0.0012-0.0031 in.		

REAR SUSPENSION

The rear axle is suspended by two three leaf springs. Two radius arms, which are attached to the body at one end and the rear axle at the other, assist the springs in controlling lateral movement of the rear axle. Sealed, hydraulic shock absorbers are positioned between the rear axle and the reinforced mountings on the floor pan. The shock absorbers are staggered on the axle. The right-hand shock absorber axle mounting is located in front of the rear axle and the left-hand shock is mounted to the rear of the axle.

Springs

Removal and Installation

1. Place a block under each front wheel.
2. Jack up the rear of the car and support it with jackstands.
3. Position a jack under the rear axle and extend it sufficiently to support the axle.
4. Remove the rear shackle nuts and the washers and then detach the combined shackle bolt and the plate assemblies. Remove the two rubber bushings.

NOTE: *Skip steps 5–10 if you are not replacing the bushings.*

5. Unscrew the nut from the front mounting bracket and then withdraw the thru-bolt.
6. Remove the U-bolts and then the attaching plate.
7. Remove the spring assembly.
8. Remove the insulator sleeve and the retaining plate from the spring.
9. Use a bushing remover (available at auto supply stores) to pull the bushings out of the spring eyes.

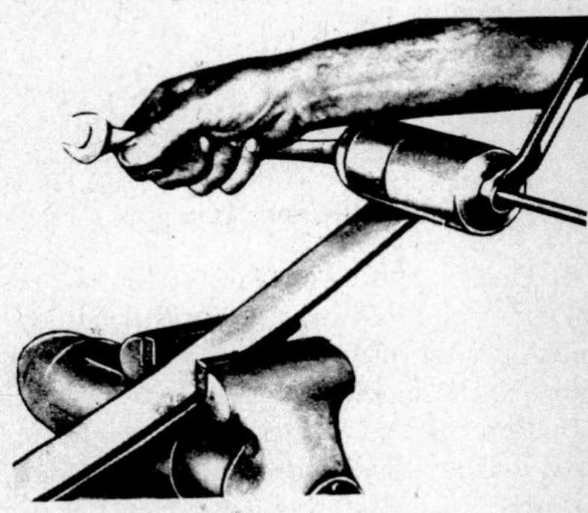

Removing spring bushing

10. Replace the bushings in the front and the rear eyes.
11. Position the front of the spring in its body mounting bracket. Install the thru-bolt and loosely assemble the nut and washer.
12. Position the rubber insulator sleeve around the spring and then place the retainer plate over the insulator.
13. Position the spring assembly to the axle and install the U-bolts, plate, and the nuts. Tighten the nuts initially to about 5 ft lbs to compress the rubber insulators.
14. Place the spring into position and assemble the rear shackle bolt and plate assemblies. Install the nuts and washers but do not tighten them.
15. Remove the trolley jack supporting the rear axle.
16. Lower the car to the ground.
17. Tighten the U-bolts, front hanger nuts, and the axle shackle nuts. Refer to the following chart for torque specifications.

Rear suspension—exploded view

Rear Suspension Torque Chart

Rear spring plate U-bolts	18–26 ft lbs
Rear spring front hanger	27–32 ft lbs
Rear spring axle shackle nuts	8–10 ft lbs

Shock Absorbers

Removal and Installation

1. Place a block under each front wheel.
2. Jack up the rear of the car and support it with jackstands.
3. From inside the trunk, remove the two nuts from the top of the shock absorbers.
4. Lift off the top steel washer and the rubber bushing.

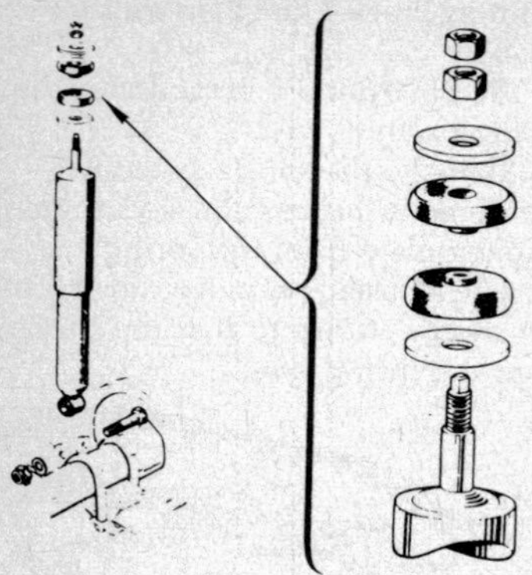

Rear shock absorber assembly

5. Detach the lower end of the shock absorber from the bracket on the axle by removing the nut, lockwasher, and bolt. Remove the shock absorber from the car.

6. Remove the rubber bushing and the steel washer from the top of the shock absorber.

7. Assemble the large steel washer and the rubber bushing on the top of the shock absorber.

8. Extend the upper end of the shock absorber through the mounting hole in the body. Position the rubber bushing and the washer over the piston rod and hold it in place by installing the nut, but do not tighten it.

9. Install the lower end of the shock abosrber into the bracket on the axle and line up the holes in the bracket with the hole in the shock absorber. Install the bolt, lockwasher, and nut. Tighten the bolt to 40–45 ft lbs.

10. Remove the jackstands and lower the car to the ground.

11. Tighten the shock absorber retaining nut, from inside the trunk, to 15–20 ft lbs. Install the locknut and tighten it securely.

Radius Arm

Removal and Installation

1. Place a block under each front wheel. Jack up the rear of the car and support it with jackstands.

2. Remove the rear end of the radius arm from the rear axle by removing the nut, washer, and bolt. Use a C-clamp and a screwdriver (if required) to remove the load from the arm.

3. Remove the front end of the radius arm.

4. Position the front end of the radius arm to the body mounting.

5. Pull the radius arm back, using a C-clamp (if required) to align the radius arm bushing with the mounting arm bracket on the rear axle. Slide the thru-bolt into position and loosely assemble the nut and washer.

6. Remove the jackstands and lower the car to the ground.

7. Tighten the securing nut to 25–30 ft lbs.

FRONT SUSPENSION

This independent front suspension uses Mc Pherson struts. These units combine vertically mounted shock absorbers surrounded by coil springs. Side-to-side movement of each front wheel is controlled by a track control arm, and fore and aft movement is controlled by the stabilizer bar.

Downward movement of the wheel is limited by a rebound stop inside the shock absorber, and the upward movement by the spring reaching its limit of compression.

Front suspension geometry figures (i.e. camber, caster, and the kingpin inclination angles) are set when the car is manufactured and are not adjustable. Toe-in, however, is adjustable and will be covered in a following section. The shock absorbers are sealed and do not need to be filled.

Strut Assembly

Removal and Installation

1. Jack up the front of the car and support it with jackstands.

2. Remove the wheel.

3. Remove and plug the brake line.

4. Position a jack under the track control arm and jack up the suspension unit.

5. Remove the cotter pin and unscrew the castle nut holding the connecting rod end to the steering arm. Using a ball joint separator, separate the joint. Remove the jack from under the control arm.

6. Remove the cotter pin and unscrew the castle nut holding the track control arm to the base of the suspension unit and disconnect the track control arm.

8. Remove the three bolts holding the top mount assembly to the side apron panel and remove the suspension assem-

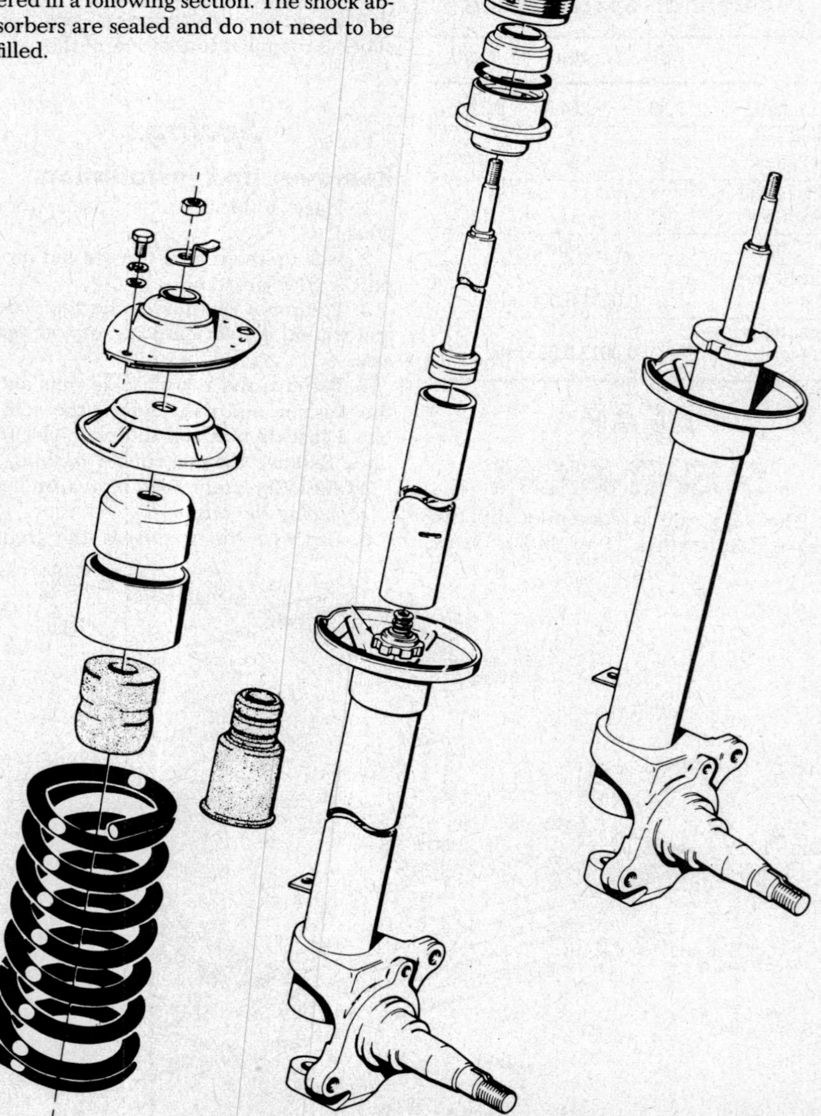

Strut assembly—exploded view

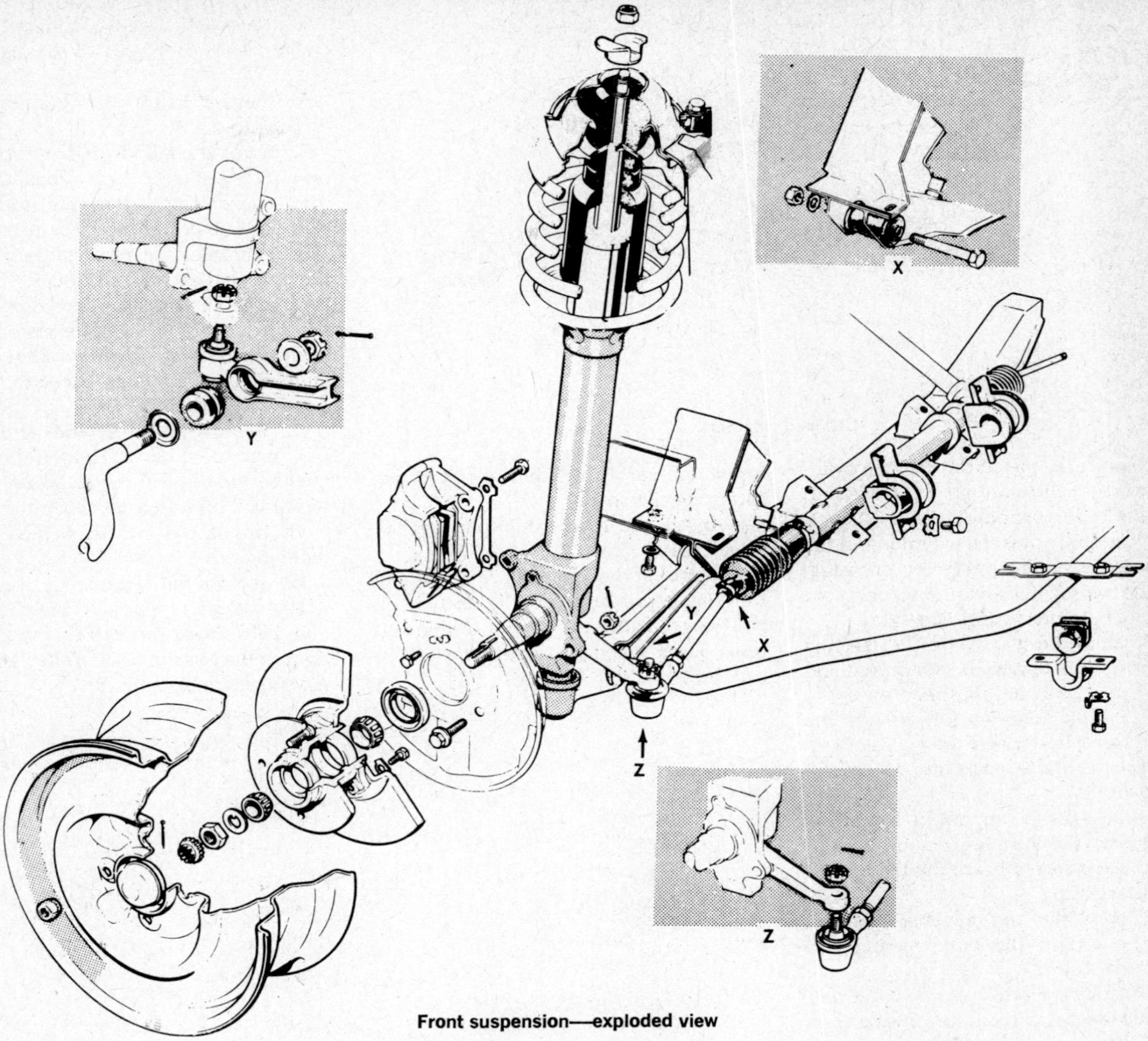

Front suspension—exploded view

bly from the car, complete with the disc brake caliper.

9. Lift the suspension assembly into position and secure it with the three bolts through the side apron panel, to the top mount assembly. Tighten the bolts to 15–18 ft lbs.

10. Assemble the track control arm ball stud to the base of the suspension unit and tighten the securing nut to 30–35 ft lbs.

11. Install the connecting rod end to the steering arm and tighten the castle nut to 18–22 ft lbs.

12. Remove the brake line plug and install the brake line.

13. Bleed the brakes.

14. Replace the wheel, jack up the car, and remove the jackstands.

Disassembly and Assembly

1. Remove the strut assembly.

2. Install a coil spring compressor (available at large auto supply stores) on the spring.

3. Unscrew the piston rod nut and then remove the cranked retainers at the top.

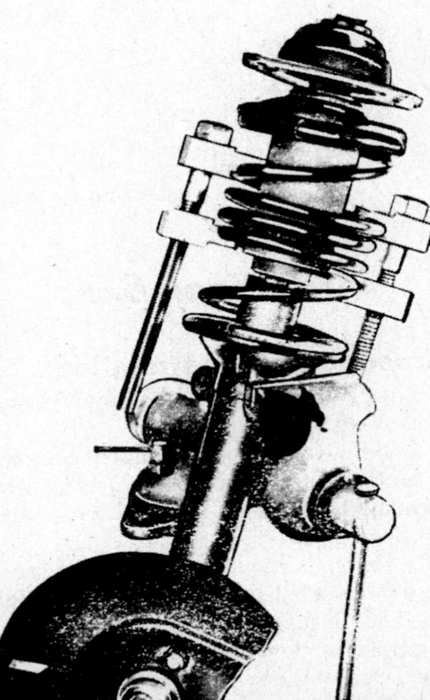

Coil spring compressor installation

4. Detach the top mount and lift off the spring upper seat, the coil spring, and the rubber bumper.

5. Using a suitable size pipe wrench, carefully unscrew the bumper stop platform and then lift it off.

6. Remove the O-ring from the upper guide and gland assembly.

7. Lift the piston rod upward until the gland and the bushing assembly are clear of the outer casing. Slide the gland assembly off the rod.

8. Empty the fluid into a suitable waste container.

9. Pull the piston rod, complete with the piston, cylinder, and the compression valve, out of the casing.

10. Remove the piston rod from the cylinder by pushing the compression valve out of the base and then pushing the rod inward and withdrawing it from the cylinder.

11. Wash all components in a suitable solvent and examine them for wear or damage. Replace any worn or damaged parts. Do not remove the piston from the piston rod.

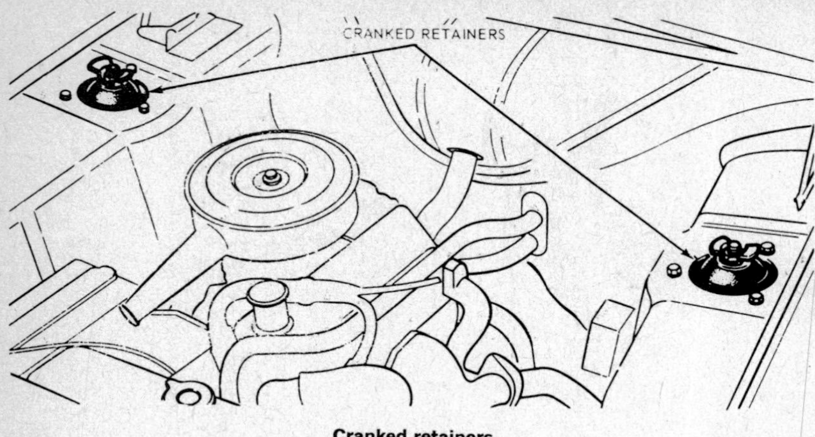

Cranked retainers

12. Insert the piston rod into the cylinder and push the compression valve into the base of the cylinder.

13. Carefully pass the cylinder and the piston rod assembly into the outer casing. Fill the unit with shock absorber fluid (available at auto supply stores).

14. Install the gland and the bushing guide onto the end of the piston rod and slide the gland and bushing over the guide. Push it down until it fits into the end of the cylinder and the complete internal assembly is below the top of the outer casing.

15. Place the O-ring on the top of the gland and the bushing assembly, and then place it correctly around the bore of the outer casing.

16. Screw the bumper stop platform into the top of the outer casing and tighten it securely.

17. Install the other parts of the unit and pull the piston rod fully upward, then install the rubber bumper, suspension spring, spring upper seat, and dished washer.

18. Assemble the top mount and the cranked retainer. Install the piston rod nut and tighten it to 5–10 ft lbs.

19. Remove the spring retainer tool.

20. Loosen the piston rod and retighten the nut to 28–32 ft lbs. When tightening the piston rod nut with the car on the ground, the wheels must be facing straight-ahead and the cranked retainer must face inward.

Coil Springs

Removal and Installation

1. Remove the strut assembly and install a spring retainer tool (as previously described).

2. Unscrew the piston rod nut and remove the cranked retainer.

3. Detach the top mount and lift off the spring upper seat, coil spring, and the rubber bumper.

4. Mount the spring in a vise and remove the adjustable spring retainers.

5. Install the new spring in a vise and install the spring retainer. Replace the spring on the strut.

6. Install the rubber bumper and the upper seat.

7. Replace the cranked retainer and the piston rod nut. See the section on strut assembly for the proper torque and procedures when installing the piston rod nut.

Stabilizer Bar

Removal and Installation

1. Jack up the front of the car and support it with jackstands.

2. Remove the two attachment clamps from the front of the stabilizer bar after bending back the locktabs and removing the four bolts.

3. Remove the cotter pins and unscrew the stabilizer bar nuts which hold the ends of the stabilizer bar to the track control arm. Remove the nuts and pull off the large washers.

4. Pull the stabilizer bar forward and remove it.

5. Remove the sleeve and the large washer from each end of the stabilizer bar.

6. Remove the stabilizer bar mounting bushings.

7. Install the stabilizer bar mounting bushing by sliding them along the bar from one end until they are under the clamp bolt holes in the body bracket.

8. Assemble a large washer and a sleeve to one end of the stabilizer bar and then insert the stabilizer bar through the holes in the track control arms.

9. Assemble the large washers to the ends of the stabilizer bar and secure them with the castle nuts.

10. Remove the jackstands and lower the car to the ground. Tighten the castle nuts on the ends of the stabilizer bar to 15–30 ft lbs. and install the cotter pins.

11. Install the stabilizer bar attachment clamps.

12. Secure the bar to the mounting points using a two new lockwashers and new bolts. With the car on the ground, tighten the bolts to 15–18 ft lbs. Turn the tabs on the lockwashers.

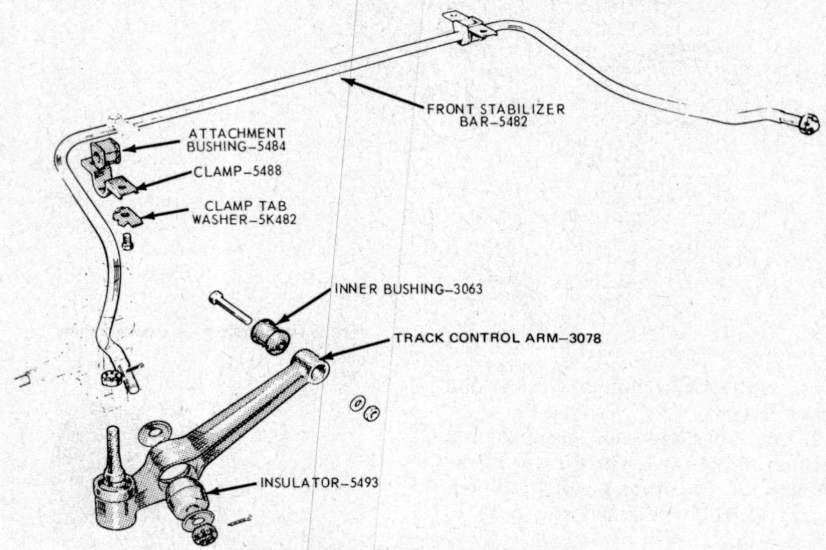

Stabilizer bar and track control arm

Lower Control Arm

Removal and Installation

1. Jack up the front of the car and support it with jackstands.

2. Remove the cotter pin and unscrew the castle nut holding the control arm to the stabilizer bar. Pull off the large dish washer.

3. Remove the self-locking nut and the flat washer from the rear of the lower control arm pivot and release the inner end of the control arm.

4. Remove the cotter pin and unscrew the nut securing the control arm ball joint to the base of the strut unit and then separate the joint.

5. Assemble the control arm ball stud to the base of the strut unit, and tighten it to 30–35 ft lbs.

6. Position the control arm so that it is in place over the stabilizer bar and then secure the inner end. Slide the pivot bolt into position from the front and install the flat washer and the self-locking nut from the rear. Tighten the nut to 22–27 ft lbs.

7. Assemble the dished washer to the end of the stabilizer bar. Install the castle nut, lower the car to the ground, and tighten the nut to 15–45 ft lbs. Install a new cotter pin.

Front-End Alignment

Before any alignment checks are made, the following points should be checked and, if necessary, corrected.

1. Correct tire inflation.
2. Front wheel bearing adjustment.
3. Stabilizer bar brackets to body crossmember nuts for tightness.
4. Front suspension springs for proper seating.
5. The car should be unloaded.

The caster, camber, and the king pin inclination angles are not adjustable, but they should be checked and, when the readings differ from those specified, the related parts should be replaced to correct the condition.

Toe-in Adjustment

Toe-in is the difference of the distance between the centers of the front and rear, of the front wheels. Toe-in is necessary to compensate for the tendency of the wheels to deflect toward the rear while in motion. Toe-in is adjusted by changing the length of the tie rod ends. When adjusting the tie rod ends, adjust each an equal amount (in the opposite direction) to increase or to decrease the toe-in.

STEERING

Rack and pinion steering gear is used on all Capris. It is mounted in rubber insulators on brackets attached to the front crossmember.

The steering wheel is mounted on a collapsible can, so that it will collapse under a heavy impact. Movement of the steering wheel is transmitted by the steering shaft through a universal joint and a flexible coupling to the pinion. Rotation of the pinion causes the rack to move from side-to-side and the connecting rods, attached to the ends of the rack, transmit this movement to the spindle arms and cause the wheels to turn.

The steering gear holds three tenths (0.3) of a pint of SAE 90 weight oil. Never fill the gear completely with oil. This would result in a buildup of pressure which could burst or blow off the bellows in the gear.

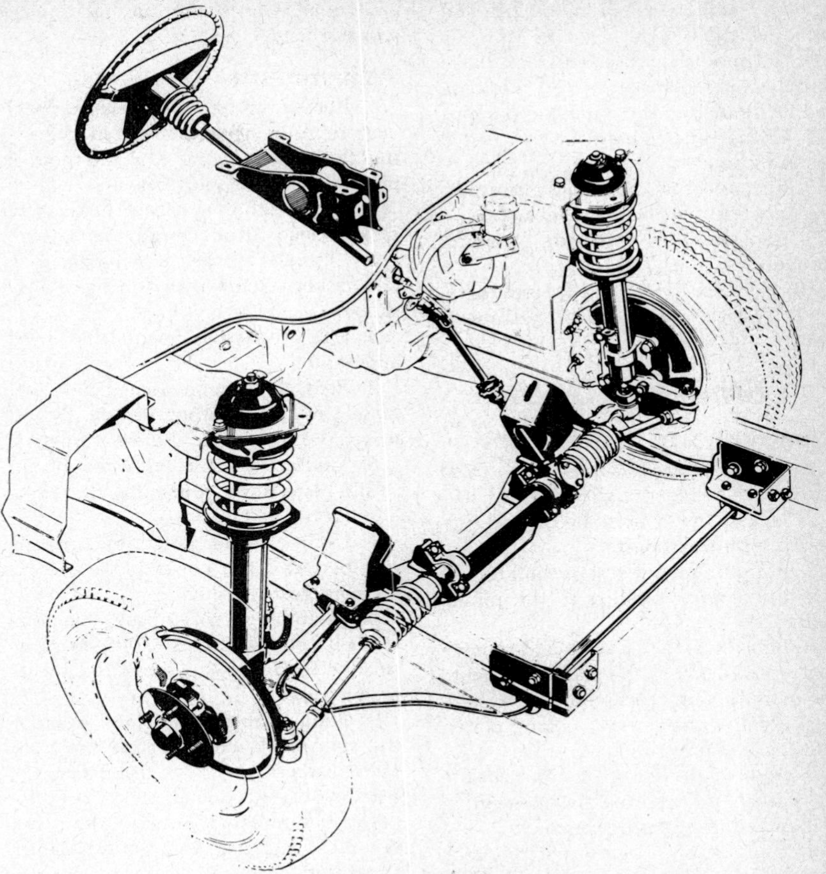

Steering gear and linkage

Steering Wheel

Removal and Installation

1. Make sure that the front wheels are facing straight ahead.
2. Pry out the steering wheel center emblem. Matchmark the steering shaft and wheel so they can be correctly realigned.
3. Remove the steering wheel retaining nut and then pull the steering wheel off the steering shaft. A steering wheel puller may be required.
4. Align the steering wheel in the correct position and push it onto the shaft.
5. Install the steering wheel retaining nut and tighten it to 20–25 ft lbs.
6. Install the steering wheel center emblem.

Turn Signal Switch

Removal and Installation

1. Disconnect the battery ground cable.
2. Remove the bolts securing the column to the underside of the instrument panel and the lower column.
3. Remove the two screws securing the steering column shrouds and remove the shrouds.
4. Remove the two screws holding the switch to the steering column.
5. Disconnect the multipin plug and remove the switch.
6. Connect the multipin plug to the harness.
7. Position the switch on the steering column and secure it with the two screws.
8. Locate the steering column shrouds and secure them with the two screws.
9. Secure the steering column to the underside of the instrument panel with the two bolts.
10. Connect the battery ground cable and check the operation of the switch.

Ignition Switch

Removal and Installation

1. Disconnect the battery ground cable.
2. Unscrew the steering column shroud retaining screw and remove the steering column shroud.
3. Make sure that the ignition key is in the "O" position.
4. Disconnect the leads at the ignition switch, noting their positions.
5. Remove the two screws which se-

cure the ignition switch to the lock and withdraw the switch.

6. Assemble the switch and lock, make sure the key remains in the "O" position, and is installed in the correct direction.

7. Engage and tighten the two switch retaining screws.

8. Reconnect the wires to their respective terminals on the ignition switch.

9. Replace the steering column shroud.

10. Connect the battery ground cable.

11. Test the switch for proper operation.

Steering Gear

Removal and Installation

1. Set the steering wheel so the front wheels are facing straight ahead.

2. Jack up the front of the car and support it with jackstands.

3. Remove the nut and the bolt retaining the flexible coupling to the pinion splines.

4. Bend back the locktabs and remove the screws holding the steering gear to the mounting brackets on the crossmember. Remove the screws, locking plates, and the U-clamps.

5. Remove the cotter pins and slacken the castle nuts securing the connecting rod ends to the spindle arms.

6. Using a ball joint separator tool, separate the connecting rod ends from the spindle arms. Remove the castle nuts and withdraw the steering gear from the car. It may be necessary to turn one wheel onto lock to permit the steering gear assembly to be moved sideways enough to allow the other end to clear the stabilizer bar.

7. Remove the connecting rods and the locknuts. Remember the number of turns required to unscrew them.

8. Replace the locknuts and the connecting rods ends; screw them in the same number of turns required to take them out.

9. Make sure the steering wheel is facing straight ahead.

10. Set the steering gear in the straight ahead position.

11. Position the steering gear and align the mating splines on the flexible coupling and the pinion shaft.

12. Secure the steering gear assembly to its mounting brackets on the crossmember. Tighten the screws to 15–18 ft lbs.

13. Assemble the connecting rod ends to the spindle arms. Install the castle nuts and tighten them to 18–22 ft lbs. Install new cotter pins.

14. Tighten the flexible coupling-to-pinion shaft securing bolt to 12–15 ft lbs.

15. Remove the jackstands and lower the car to the ground.

16. Check the front end for wheel alignment. Check the position of the steering wheel.

Adjustments

1. Remove the steering gear (as previously described) and mount it in a vise, so that the pinion is horizontal and the rack preload cover is facing upward.

2. Remove the two screws holding the rack preload cover plate to the housing.

3. Lift off the cover plate, shim pack, and gaskets. Remove the spring and the slipper.

4. Lift off the cover plate, shim pack, and gasket.

5. Refit the pinion cover plate and loosely fit the retaining screws. Do not install the shim pack and the gaskets.

6. Tighten the cover screws evenly until the plate is just contacting the pinion bearing.

7. Using a feeler gauge, measure the gap between the cover plate and the steering gear housing.

8. Assemble a shim pack, including two gaskets, which is 0.002–0.004 in. smaller than the gap measured by the feeler gauge.

9. Remove the cover plate, assemble the shim pack, and reinstall the cover plate. Install the screws, using sealer on the threads, and tighten them 6–8 ft lbs.

10. Assemble the slipper to the rear of the rack and push it in fully. Using a straightedge and a feeler gauge, measure the distance between the top of the slipper and the surface of the steering gear housing onto which the cover plate is retained.

11. Assemble a shim pack, including two gaskets, which measures 0.0005–0.0035 in. greater than the dimensions obtained in the previous paragraph.

12. Install the spring into the recess in the slipper.

13. Position the shim pack and the gaskets, and install the cover plate.

14. Install the holding screws, using sealer on the threads, and tighten them to 6–8 ft lbs.

15. Install an *in. lbs* torque wrench on the splined end of the pinion shaft.

BRAKE SYSTEMS

Brakes

All Capris are equipped with floating, caliper type disc brakes on the front wheels and conventional drum brakes on the rear. A twin-reservoir hydraulic system is used to operate the brakes. This provides separate hydraulic circuits for the front and rear brakes. If one circuit fails, the driver is still able to stop the car by using the other system which is still intact.

All models use a floor-mounted handbrake which is located between the front seats. This parking brake operates through a two-cable linkage and its operation causes the self-adjusting mechanism in the rear brakes to operate when required.

A power brake vacuum booster is installed to a bracket in the engine compartment. The booster operates through a rod and clevis assembly which is attached to the brake pedal at one end and the brake master cylinder at the other end. The power brake booster and the master cylinder are replaced as a unit. When replacing or overhauling any brake system components, make sure that only the correct replacement parts are used.

Adjustment

The front disc brakes are not adjustable. The rear drum brakes can be adjusted by the use of the parking brake lever. Operate the parking brake lever at the rear wheel backing plate. Pull and then release the lever until the clicking of the adjuster stops. The brakes should then be sufficiently adjusted. Each rear wheel brake should be adjusted in this manner.

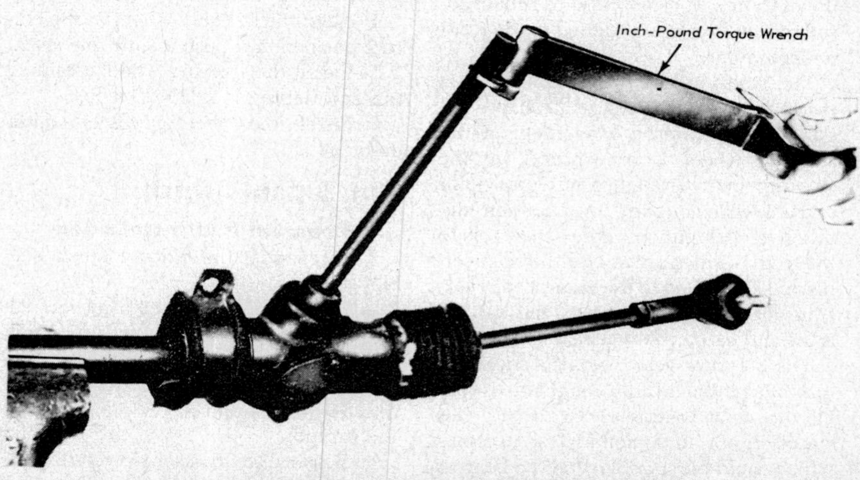

Measuring pinion and turning torque

HYDRAULIC SYSTEM

Master Cylinder

Removal and Installation

1. Siphon the fluid from the reservoir.
2. Disconnect the brake lines from the master cylinder.
3. Remove the master cylinder-to-brake booster retaining nuts.
4. Lift the master cylinder away from the brake booster, being careful not to damage the vacuum seal.
5. Position the master cylinder, including the fluid seal, correctly onto the pushrod and hold it in position. With the cylinder in this position, screw in all union nuts of the brake lines a few turns.
6. Connect the master cylinder to the brake booster and tighten the nuts.
7. Connect the brake lines.
8. Fill the reservoir with heavy-duty brake fluid. Bleed the entire brake system.
9. Check the operation of the brakes.

Overhaul

1. Remove the master cylinder.
2. Remove the reservoir from the cylinder assembly. Remove the rubber plugs.
3. Loosen the stopscrew at the center of the cylinder.
4. Push the piston inward and, using snap-ring pliers, remove the cylinder retaining snap-ring.
5. Remove the stopwasher and the primary piston assembly from the first chamber.
6. Press the secondary piston assembly out of the second chamber of the cylinder with compressed air.

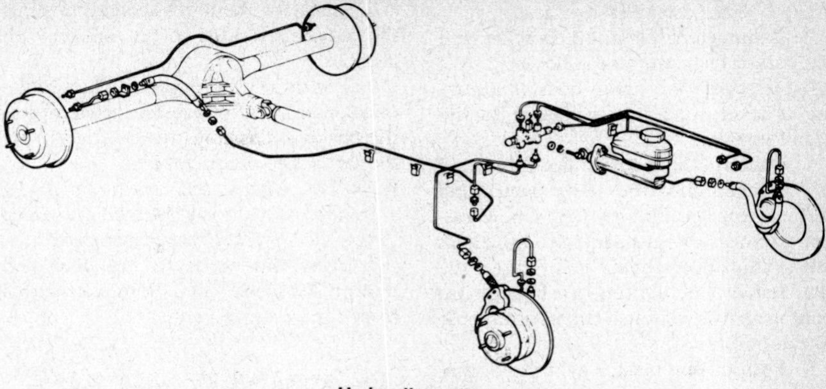

Hydraulic system

7. Clean the master cylinder and the pistons with commercial alcohol or methylated spirit. Blow the parts dry with moisture-free air. Master cylinders with scored or otherwise damaged surfaces must not be reused.
8. Lightly coat the inner surfaces, pistons, and cups with brake fluid.
9. Assemble the piston of the second chamber with the filler washer, cups, pressure disc, pressure spring, and spring seat, and carefully insert the piston into the cylinder. Press the piston inward slightly and screw in the stopscrew, with the seal. Release the piston and let it contact the stopscrew.
10. Assemble the piston of the first chamber. Do not overtighten the retainer screw.
11. Insert the piston and press it in slightly. Install the rubber plug and the reservoir.

Pressure Valve and Switch

Removal and Installation

1. Disconnect the five brake lines from the ports on the valve and the switch assembly. Plug the end of the lines from the master cylinder.
2. Disconnect the wire from the switch.
3. Unscrew the bolt securing the assembly to the rear of the engine compartment. Remove the assembly.
4. Position the assembly in place on the engine compartment dash panel and loosely install the attaching bolt.
5. Connect the hydraulic lines. Tighten the attaching bolt.
6. Connect the wiring to the switch.

Power Brake Booster

Removal and Installation

1. Remove the brake pushrod clevis pin from the brake pedal and remove the pin.
2. Remove the master cylinder retaining nuts and position the master assembly away from the brake booster.
3. Remove the vacuum hose from the brake booster.
4 Remove the brake booster-to-dash panel retaining screws and remove the

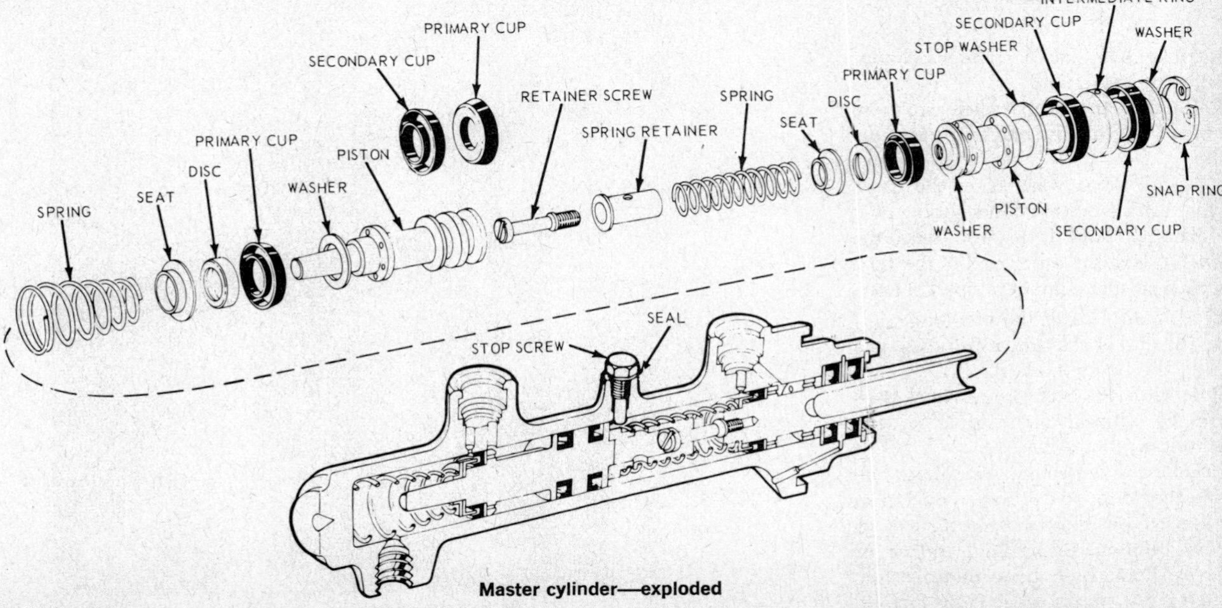

Master cylinder—exploded

brake booster assembly and seal.

5. Remove the retaining bracket and the gasket from the brake booster.

6. Assemble the brake booster retaining bracket with a new gasket to the brake booster.

7. Position the booster assembly and the bracket onto the bolts protruding through the dash panel. Use a new gasket. Connect the pushrod with the clevis pin to the brake pedal.

8. Install and tighten the bracket retaining screws. Connect the vacuum hose to the booster.

9. Position the master cylinder assembly with a new seal ring on the booster and tighten the master cylinder-to-booster retaining nuts.

Bleeding

To make sure that the brake warning light will go out after bleeding the brakes, the piston in the pressure valve must be centralized. Fabricate the tool shown in the illustration from a screwdriver. Insert the tool in the base of the pressure valve during the bleeding operation.

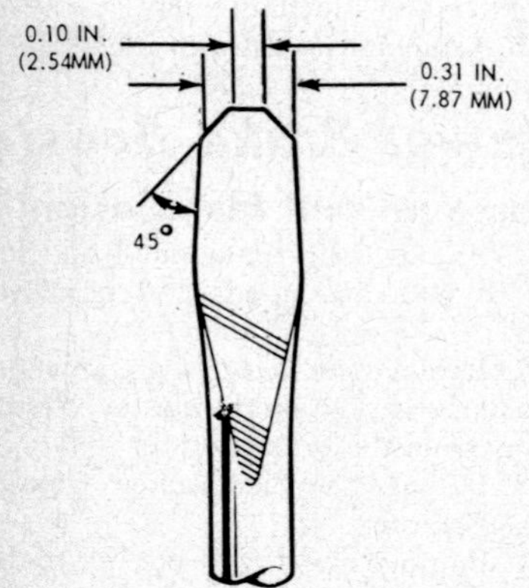

Piston centralizing tool

1. Make sure that the master cylinder is full with brake fluid.

2. Remove the rubber dust cap from the bleed valve on the rear of the backing plate.

3. Install a box wrench on the bleed valve. Push a piece of rubber tubing over the bleeder until it is flush with the wrench. Place the other end of the tube in a glass jar that contains a small amount of brake fluid. During the bleeding operation the end of the tube must always be kept in the brake fluid.

Start with the right-rear wheel then bleed the left-rear, right-front, and the left-front, in that order.

4. Unscrew the bleed valve about half a turn, then depress the brake pedal fully, release it, and allow it to return to its normal position. Brake fluid and/or air bubbles should have been pumped into the jar; if not, unscrew the valve further.

5. Pause for about five seconds to allow the master cylinder to be refilled with fluid.

6. Continue to depress the brake pedal, pausing after each return stroke of the brake pedal, until the fluid entering the jar is free of air bubbles.

NOTE: *Check the master cylinder periodically during bleeding, making sure not to let it run out of fluid.*

7. Press the pedal to the floor and tighten the bleed valve. Remove the tool from the pressure valve.

FRONT BRAKE

Disc Brake Pads

Removal and Installation

1. Jack up the front of the car and support it with jackstands.

2. Remove the front wheels.

3. Pull out the retaining clips and retaining pins, and remove the brake pads from the caliper. Remove the brake pad tension springs and shims. (It may be necessary to use a pair of thin-nosed pliers.) Remove the master cylinder reservoir cap and siphon off a third of the fluid in the reservoir.

3. Push the pistons into their bores with a screwdriver.

4. Place the brake pad tension springs on the brake pads and shims. Install new brake pads and shims. The shims may be installed either way up.

5. Install the retaining pins and clips. Refill the reservoir to the proper level.

6. Operate the brake pedal several times to bring the pads into correct adjustment.

7. Install the wheel and lower the car to the ground.

Disc Brake Calipers

Removal and Installation

1. Jack up the front of the car and support it with jackstands. Remove the wheels.

2. Remove the brake pads.

3. Remove the brake line from the rear of the caliper and install a plug into each open end.

4. Bend back the locktabs and remove the two caliper retaining bolts and the caliper assembly.

5. Replace the caliper assembly, using a new locking plate, and tighten the retaining bolts to 45–50 ft lbs. Bend up the locktabs.

6. Install the brake lines. Install the brake pads and bleed the brakes.

Overhaul

The caliper is made in two paired halves, which are bolted together. Under no circumstances should the halves be separated.

1. Remove the caliper assembly.

2. Partially remove the piston from one cylinder bore. Remove the securing circlip and also the sealing bellows from its location in the lower part of the piston skirt.

3. Pull the sealing bellows from its location in the annular ring machined in the cylinder bore.

4. Repeat these operations for the other cylinders.

5. Wash the pistons and the piston bores in commercial alcohol, methylated spirits, or brake fluid.

6. Check the pistons and their bores for score marks or other imperfections.

7. Assemble a piston seal in the groove of the piston bore.

8. Install the rubber bellows to the cyl-

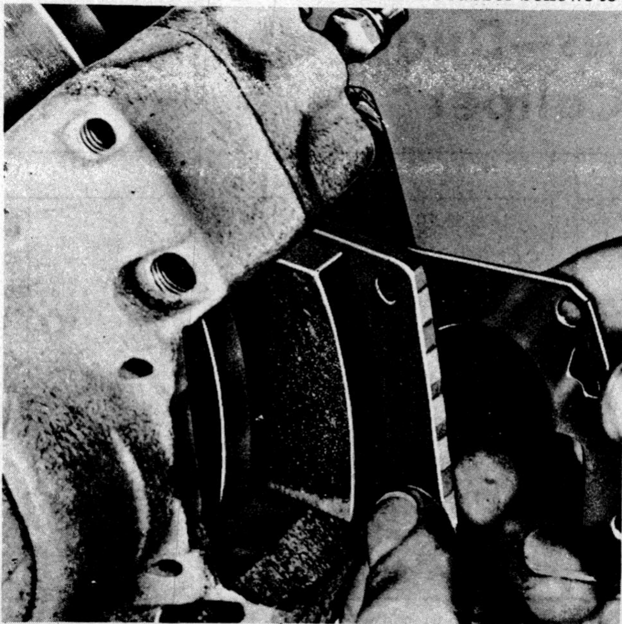

Brake pads and shims—installed

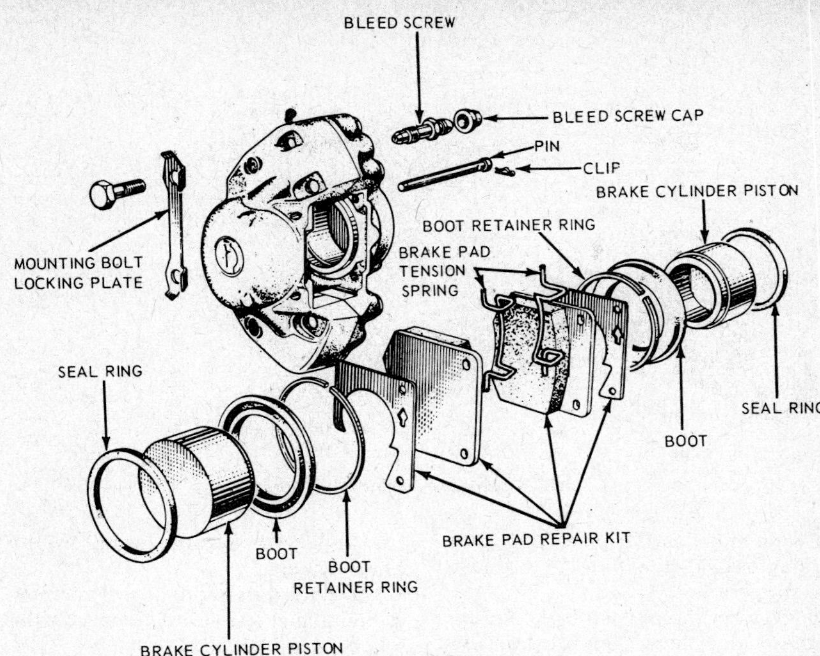

Caliper assembly—exploded view

inder, with the lip that is turned outward installed in the groove provided in the cylinder.

9. Lubricate the piston with clean brake fluid. Place the piston—crown first —through the rubber sealing bellows and into the cylinder.

10. When the piston is located in the cylinder, install the inner edge of the bellows in the groove in the piston skirt.

11. Push the piston as far down in the cylinder as possible.

12. Secure the sealing bellows to the caliper with the circlip.

13. Install the caliper assembly.

14. Bleed the brakes.

Brake Disc

Removal and Installation

1. Jack up the front of the car and support it with jackstands.

2. Remove the front wheels.

NOTE: *In order to remove the disc, the caliper must be removed.*

3. Loosen, but do not remove, the upper caliper attaching bolt.

4. Remove the lower attaching bolt.

When the caliper is removed from the disc, it must be wired out of the way of the disc. Also, the brake pads will fall out if they are not held in place when the caliper is removed. Insert a small piece of wood or fold a piece of heavy carcboard to fit between the shoes to hold them in place.

5. Hold the caliper in place and remove the upper attaching bolt.

6. Slide the caliper off the brake disc, inserting a piece of wood between the brake pads.

7. When the caliper is clear of the disc, wire it out of the way.

8. Remove the dust cap from the wheel hub. Remove the wheel bearing. (See chapter 1.)

9. Remove the disc from the spindle. Reverse the procedures to install.

Wheel Bearings

1. Remove the wheel cover and dust cap.

2. Jack up the car.

3. Remove the cotter pin, nut retainer, adjusting nut, washer, and bearing.

4. Wash all parts in a solvent.

5. Hand-pack the wheel bearing with wheel bearing grease.

6. Reassemble, reversing the removal procedure.

NOTE: *When installing the cotter pin it may be necessary to move the nut retainer in various positions on the nut to allow the cotter pin to go through the hole in the axle.*

7. Torque the adjusting nut to 17–25 ft lbs. Back the nut off one-half turn then tighten it hand-tight or 10–15 in. lbs.

REAR BRAKES

Brake Drums

Removal and Installation

1. Place blocks under the front wheels. Jack up the rear of the car and support it with jackstands.

2. Remove the wheel. Make sure that the parking brake is fully released.

3. Remove the screw holding the brake drum to the half-shaft and remove the brake drum by pulling it off the lug-nut studs.

4. Inspect the inside of the drum. It should be smooth with no ridges and with no excessive glazing. If the inside of the drum is slightly glazed, it can be cleaned with medium grade sandpaper. If any of these conditions are excessively severe, the brake should be taken to a machine shop and turned down.

5. Replace the drum and install the holding screw. Install the tire and lower the car to the ground.

Brake Shoes

Removal and Installation

Remove and replace only one side at a time. This will allow you to see how to replace parts by referring to the side that is still intact as a reference.

1. Jack up the rear of the car and sup-

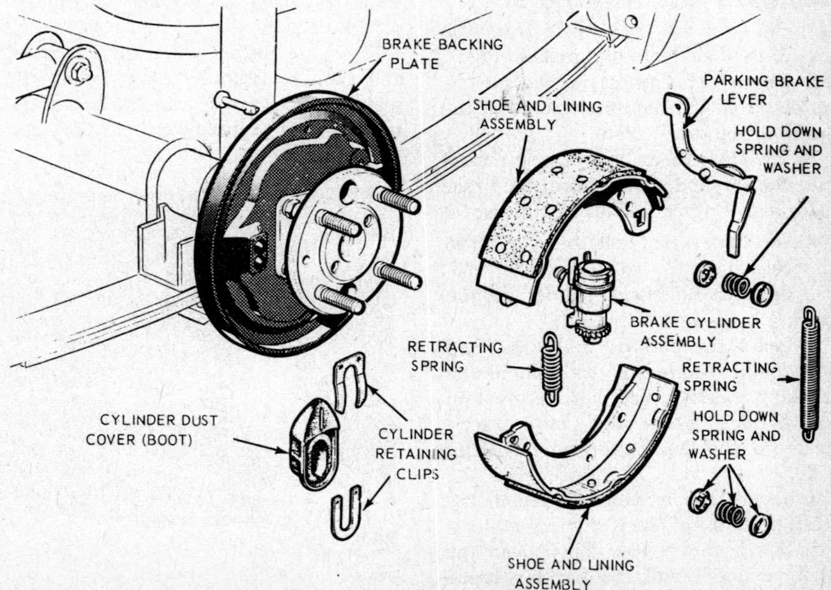

Rear brake—exploded view

port it with jackstands. Remove the rear wheels and remove the brake drums (as previously described).

2. Using a brake spring tool (available at auto supply stores), remove the shoe holding down springs by pushing in on the top washer, one on each shoe, ½ turn and pull off the washer and the spring.

3. Disengage each shoe from its slot and remove it from the wheel cylinder. Remove the shoes. To prevent the piston from falling out of the wheel cylinder, it should be held in place with a clip or a rubber band around the cylinder.

4. Remove the retracting spring from the brake shoes.

5. Turn the adjustment wheel on the wheel cylinder until it becomes flush with the cylinder shoulder. This moves the brake shoes (when installing) to the fully off adjustment. If this is not done, difficulty may be encountered when installing the brake drum.

6. Assemble the retracting springs between the two shoes. Smear white grease on the brake shoe support pads, brake shoe pivots, and to the adjustment wheel threads of the wheel cylinder.

7. Fit the shoe assembly to the backplate with the hold-down springs and washers.

8. Check to see that the shoes are seated firmly and that the springs are not binding. Install the brake drum and the holding screw.

9. Operate the parking brake lever at the backplate for as long as necessary to adjust the brakes, until the clicking stops.

10. Install the wheel. Remove the jackstands and lower the car to the ground. Check the operation of the brakes on a road test.

Wheel Cylinders

Removal and Installation

1. Remove the brake line from the rear of the backplate and install plugs.

2. Remove the spring pin and the clevis pin from the handbrake link on the inside of the brake plate.

3. Pry the rubber boot on the rear of the wheel cylinder away from the brake plate and remove it. Pull off the two U-shaped retainers that hold the cylinder to the brake plate.

4. Remove the wheel cylinder and the parking brake link.

5. Install the parking brake link and the wheel cylinder in the hole in the brake plate. Make sure that the pivot on the parking brake link is correctly located in the slot in the wheel cylinder body.

6. Secure the wheel cylinder to the brake plate using the U-shaped retainer.

7. Install the rubber boot over the wheel cylinder and the parking brake link. Make sure that the wheel cylinder can slide in the carrier plate. Check the parking brake link and see that it operates properly.

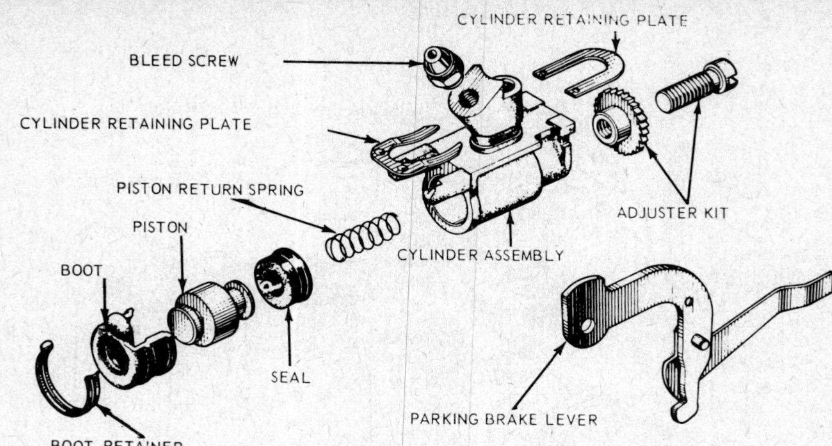

Wheel cylinder—exploded view

8. Connect the parking brake linkage to the parking brake link using a clevis pin, and retain it in position with the spring clip.

9. Remove the plug and connect the brake line to the wheel cylinder. Bleed the brake system.

Overhaul

1. Remove the wheel cylinder.

2. Remove the boot retainer, pry off the boot, and withdraw the piston—complete with seal—from the wheel cylinder bore.

3. Detach the seal from the piston.

4. Remove the return spring from the cylinder bore.

5. Remove the adjustment wheel and the screw assembly from the other end of the wheel cylinder.

6. Wash all parts in commercial alcohol or brake fluid, inspect them for wear or damage, and replace any necessary parts.

7. Dip the piston and seal in brake fluid and then reassemble them. Install the seal to the piston with the flat face of the seal adjacent to the piston rear shoulder.

8. Install the return spring in the wheel cylinder.

9. Dip the piston and the seal assembly in brake fluid and insert them into the cylinder bore, seal end first.

10. Install the dust cover on the wheel cylinder and then install the retainer.

11. Replace the adjustment wheel and screw the assembly into the wheel cylinder. Replace the wheel cylinder as previously described.

Handbrake

Cable Removal and Installation

1. Place blocks under the front wheels. Jack up the rear of the car and support it with jackstands. Release the parking brake.

2. Unscrew the nuts holding the end of the primary brake cable to the relay lever on the rear of the axle housing.

3. Remove the primary cable from the end of the parking brake lever by removing the spring and the clevis pin.

4. Free the cable from its guides on the underbody and then remove it from under the car.

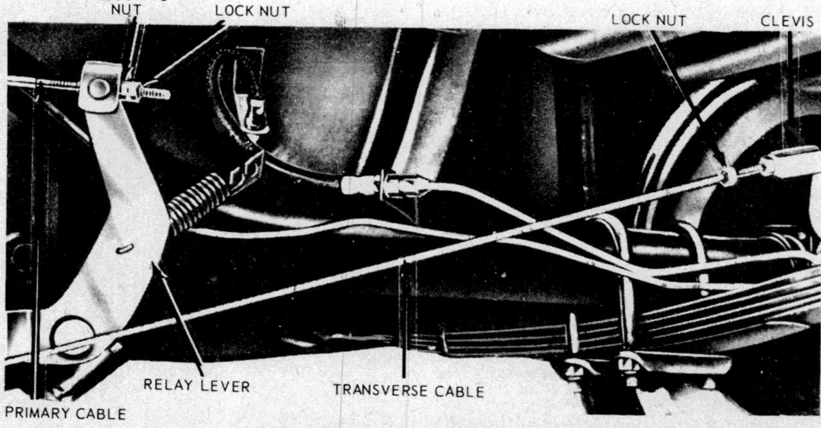

Parking brake adjusting points

5. Attach the cable to the end of the parking brake lever by installing the clevis pin and securing it with the spring clip.

6. Apply grease to the cable guides and thread the cable through the guides.

7. Connect the cable to the relay lever by threading it through the pivot pin, installing the spacer, and securing it with the two nuts. Adjust the cable. (See the next section.)

8. Remove the jackstands and lower the car to the ground. Remove the blocks from the front wheels.

Adjustment

1. Place blocks under the front wheels of the car. Jack up the rear of the car and support it with jackstands.

2. Adjust the length of the primary cable by tightening or loosening the adjusting nut on the relay lever so the cable has no slack.

3. Adjust the length of the transverse cable so that the cable has no slack in it. Do this by adjusting the nut on the end of the cable adjacent to the right-hand rear brake.

Remove the jackstands and lower the car to the ground. Remove the blocks from the front wheels. Check the operation of the parking brake.

CHASSIS ELECTRICAL

Heater

Removal and Installation

1. Disconnect the battery ground cable and drain the cooling system.

2. Disconnect the two heater hoses from the heater core.

3. Remove the cover plate and the gasket from around the core tubes at the dash panel.

4. Remove the package tray.

5. If the car is equipped with a console, it will be necessary to remove it.

a. Remove the two screws at the forward end of the console (console to floor).

b. Lift up the gearshift lever boot and remove the two screws at the rear end of the console.

c. Pry up the rear panel and remove the two attaching screws.

d. Gently pry up the clock panel and disconnect the two electrical connectors and the light bulb.

e. Remove the main screw at the rear end of the area under the clock panel.

f. Slide the plastic brace below the handbrake lever forward and remove it. Then lift the console out of the car.

6. Remove the control cable retaining clips and disconnect the cables from the control levers.

7. Disconnect the three wire connectors from the terminals on the heater and disconnect the bullet connector from the other wire.

8. Disconnect the left and right vent ducts and the left and right defroster ducts from the heater.

9. Remove the windshield wiper motor for better access to one of the mounting screws at the left side of the heater. (See the following section.)

10. Remove the four heater-to-dash panel mounting screws and then remove the heater assembly from the car.

11. Position the heater assembly to the dash panel and install the four mounting screws.

12. Install the windshield wiper motor.

13. Connect the left and right vent ducts and the left and right defroster ducts to the assembly.

14. Connect the three wire connectors to the terminals on the heater and connect the wire with the bullet connectors.

15. Connect the control cables to the levers and adjust them. (See the section on adjustment.)

16. Install the gasket and the cover plate around the heater core tubes at the engine side of the dash panel.

17. Connect the heater hoses to the heater core tubes and secure them with wire clips.

18. On those models that are equipped with a console, make the proper electrical connections and replace the console.

19. Install the package tray.

20. Fill the cooling system and connect the battery cable. Run the engine and check the operation of the cooling system. Check for leaks and once removed, the two halves must be separated.

Fan Motor

Removal and Installation

1. Separate the two halves of the heater.

2. Disconnect the two motor wires and remove the four retaining clips.

3. Remove the motor and the wheel assembly from the upper half of the heater.

4. Install the replacement assembly into the upper half of the heater and secure it with the four clips.

5. Connect the two motor wires.

6. Assemble the two halves of the heater and install it into the car.

Heater Core

Removal and Installation

1. Separate the two halves of the heater.

2. Slide the core out of the lower half of the heater.

3. Slide the replacement core into the lower half of the heater and assemble the two heater halves.

Radio

Removal and Installation

1. Remove the package tray.

2. Remove the radio knobs and unscrew the retaining nuts.

3. Remove the wire connectors from the radio and remove the brackets from the rear of the radio.

4. Remove the radio.

5. Place the radio in position and install the brackets and the wiring connectors.

6. Install the package tray.

Windshield Wiper Motor

Removal and Installation

1. Disconnect the battery ground cable.

2. Remove the package tray.

3. Remove the wiper arms and the two nuts securing the wiper pivots to the body.

4. Detach the heater-to-defroster vent hose.

5. Disconnect the two control cables from the heater.

6. Remove the attaching screws holding the wiper motor to the mounting bracket.

7. Disconnect the wiper motor wires, making note of their position.

8. Remove the wiper motor assembly.

9. Position the wiper motor behind the instrument panel.

10. Secure the motor to the body with the two wiper pivot nuts.

11. Connect the wiper motor wiring.

12. Position the wiper motor and install the attaching bolt.

13. Connect the two heater control cables.

14. Install the package tray.

15. Replace the wiper arm and blades.

16. Connect the battery ground cable.

Instrument Cluster

Removal and Installation

Standard Instrument Cluster

1. Disconnect the battery ground cable.

2. Remove the two bolts attaching the steering column to the underside of the dash panel and then lower the column.

CAUTION: *Support the column and disturb the column as little as possible, as it is collapsible.*

3. Remove the five screws attaching

the cluster and the pad assembly to the instrument panel.

4. Carefully pull the cluster and the pad assembly slightly toward you to gain access to the electrical connections at the rear of the panel.

5. Disconnect the wire connectors.

6. Disconnect the speedometer cable.

7. Carefully remove the cluster and the pad assembly.

8. Remove the four cluster-to-pad attaching screws and remove the cluster assembly.

9. Position the cluster assembly to the pad and install the four attaching screws.

10. Position the cluster and the pad assembly to the opening and connect the wire connectors to the gauges and the switches.

11. Connect the speedometer cable.

12. Install the five attaching screws that hold the cluster to the instrument panel.

13. Install the two steering column attaching bolts.

14. Connect the battery ground cable and check the operation of the instruments and the switches.

GT Instrument Cluster

1. Disconnect the battery ground cable.

2. Remove the two heater control knobs.

3. Remove the four attaching screws holding the access cover at the right of the instrument panel and remove the cover.

4. Remove the three screws and loosen (do not remove) the one nut retaining the instrument cluster and the pad assembly to the instrument panel.

5. Remove the two fuse panel attaching screws and lower the fuse panel assembly.

6. Carefully pull the cluster and the pad assembly toward you to gain access to the connections at the back of the panel.

7. Disconnect all the wire connectors at the rear of the gauges and the switches.

8. Disconnect the speedometer cable.

9. Disconnect the oil pressure gauge tube, at the gauge. Be careful not to bend or twist the tube.

10. Carefully remove the cluster and the pad assembly from the car.

11. Remove the four cluster-to-pad attaching screws and remove the cluster assembly.

12. Position the cluster assembly to the pad and install the four attaching screws.

13. Position the cluster and the pad assembly to the opening and connect the wire connectors to the gauges and the switches.

14. Connect the speedometer cable.

15. Install the three cluster and pad retaining screws, and tighten the one retaining nut.

16. Position the fuse panel and install the two retaining screws.

17. Position the access cover at the right of the instrument panel and install the four attaching screws.

18. Install the two heater knobs.

19. Connect the battery ground cable and check the operation of the gauges and the switches.

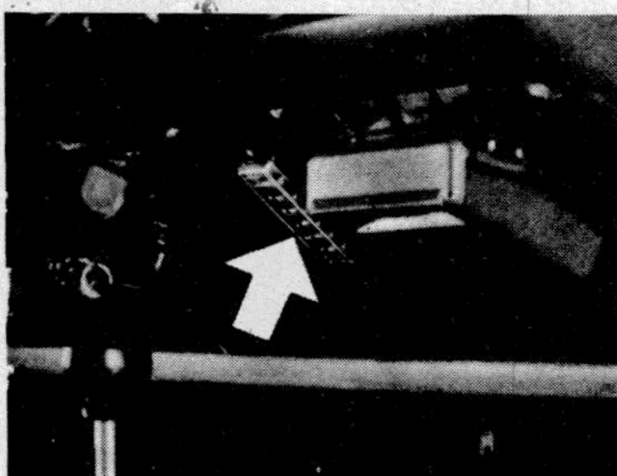

Fuse box location

Fuses

The fuse box is located under the instrument panel to the left of the ashtray. All the fuses are 8A.

Fuse Identification Chart

1. Interior Light
   Clock
   Hazard Lights
   Buzzer
   Cigar Lighter
2. Parking and Rear Lights
   Side Markers
3. Instrument Lights
   Parking and Rear Lights
   Side Markers
   License Plate Light
4. High Beam
5. Low Beam
6. Stop Light
   Back-up Lights
   Heater Motor
   Turn Signals
7. Wiper Motor

COLT

Index

INTRODUCTION

The Dodge Colt is the first combined effort of Dodge and Mitsubishi Heavy Industries, Ltd. It is a descendant of the Mitsubishi Colt, which has been sold in Japan for several years. The Colt joins a growing field of small, low priced, but well equipped economy cars which are becoming popular in the United States. The Colt is sold and serviced as part of the Dodge dealer network, rather than having its own, and is considered a Dodge product.

Engine model number

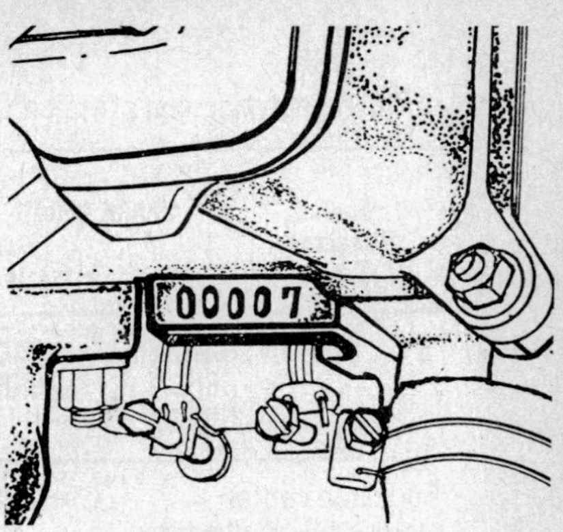

Engine number location

SERIAL NUMBER IDENTIFICATION

Vehicle Number

The vehicle identification plate is mounted on the instrument panel, adjacent to the lower corner of the windshield on the driver's side, and is visible through the windshield. The thirteen digit vehicle number is composed of a seven digit identification code, and a six digit sequential number. The code is interpreted as follows:

Serial number location

Year	Code	Body Style	Trans. Type
1971	6H21K19	2 Door coupe	Auto.
	6H21K15	2 Door coupe	Man.
	6H23K19	2 Door hardtop	Auto.
	6H23K15	2 Door hardtop	Man.
	6H41K19	4 Door sedan	Auto.
	6H41K15	4 Door sedan	Man.
	6H45K19	Station wagon	Auto.
	6H45K15	Station wagon	Man.

Engine Number

The engine model number is embossed on the lower left side of the block. The sequential engine number is stamped on a pad at the upper right front of the engine, adjacent to the exhaust manifold.

MODEL IDENTIFICATION

1971-73 Colt Sedan

1971-73 Colt Hardtop

TUNE-UP SPECIFICATIONS

When analyzing compression test results, look for uniformity among cylinders, rather than specific pressures.

Year	Engine Displace. (Cu In.)	SPARK PLUGS Type	SPARK PLUGS Gap (in.)	DISTRIBUTOR Point Dwell (deg)	DISTRIBUTOR Point Gap (in.)	IGNITION TIMING (deg) MT	IGNITION TIMING (deg) AT	Intake Valve Opens (deg)	Fuel Pump Pressure (psi)	Idle Speed (rpm)	VALVE CLEAR (in) In	VALVE CLEAR (in) Ex
1971-73	97.5	NGK, B6E, B6ES, BP6ES	0.028-0.032	49-55	0.018	TDC	N.A.	32	3.7-5.1	700-750① 1350-1450② 800-850③	0.003 cold	0.007 cold

TDC Top dead center
BTDC Before top dead center
① With solenoid off
② With solenoid on
③ Idle speed for 1972 model

NOTE: See engine compartment stickers on all models for tune-up specifications. Information on engine compartment stickers supersedes information in the above chart.

TORQUE SPECIFICATIONS

All readings in ft lbs

Year	Engine Displace. (Cu In.)	Cylinder Head Bolts	Rod Bearing Bolts	Main Bearing Bolts	Crankshaft Pulley Bolt	Flywheel To Crankshaft Bolts	MANIFOLD Intake	MANIFOLD Exhaust
1971-73	97.5	51-55① (cold) 7-9②	23-25	36-40	43-51	69-76	11-14	11-14

① bolts ②nuts

CRANKSHAFT AND CONNECTING ROD SPECIFICATIONS

All measurements are given in inches

Year	Engine Displace. (Cu In.)	CRANKSHAFT Main Brg. Journal Dia.	CRANKSHAFT Main Brg. Oil Clearance	CRANKSHAFT Shaft End-Play	CRANKSHAFT Thrust on No.	CONNECTING ROD Journal Diameter	CONNECTING ROD Oil Clearance	CONNECTING ROD Side Clearance
1971-73	97.5	2.2433-2.2441	0.0006-0.0030	0.002-0.007	3	1.7709-1.7717	0.0003-0.0028	0.0039-0.0098

ALTERNATOR AND REGULATOR SPECIFICATIONS

Year	ALTERNATOR Part No. or Manufacturer	ALTERNATOR Field Current @ 12 v	ALTERNATOR Output (amps.)	REGULATOR Part No. or Manufacturer	REGULATOR Field Relay Air Gap (in.)	REGULATOR Field Relay Point Gap (in.)	REGULATOR Field Relay Volts to Close	REGULATOR Regulator Air Gap (in.)	REGULATOR Regulator Point Gap (in.)	REGULATOR Regulator Volts
1971-73	AC2040k	N.A.	16.5① 32②	RQB2220D	0.035-0.047	0.030-0.043	14.3-15.3	0.032-0.047	0.012-0.016	—

① No Load ② Load
— Not Available

BRAKE SPECIFICATIONS

All measurements are given in inches

Year	Model	Master Cylinder Bore	WHEEL CYLINDER OR CALIPER PISTON BORE Front Disc	WHEEL CYLINDER OR CALIPER PISTON BORE Rear Drum	BRAKE DISC OR DRUM DIAMETER Front Disc	BRAKE DISC OR DRUM DIAMETER Rear
1971-73	All	11/16	1.8	0.75	—	9.0

— Not Available

CAPACITIES

Year	Model	Engine Displacement (Cu In.)	ENGINE CRANKCASE (qts) With Filter	Without Filter	TRANSMISSION (pts) Manual 4-spd	Automatic	Drive Axle (pts)	Gasoline Tank (gals)	Cooling System (qts)
1971-73	all	97.5	4.2	1.8	1.8	6.2	2.0	13 11①	7.2

① Station wagon

GENERAL ENGINE SPECIFICATIONS

Year	Engine Displacement (Cu In.)	Carburetor Type	Horsepower @ rpm	Torque @ rpm (ft lbs)	Bore x Stroke (in.)	Compression Ratio	Oil Pressure @ rpm (psi)
1971-73	97.5	1 x 2 bbl	100 @ 6300	101 @ 4000	3.03 x 3.39	8.5:1	28-57

BATTERY AND STARTER SPECIFICATIONS

		BATTERY			STARTERS						
					Lock Test			No-Load Test			
Year	Engine Displacement (Cu In.)	Ampere Hour Capacity	Volts	Terminal Grounded	Amps.	Volts	Torque (ft lbs)	Amps.	Volts	RPM	Brush Spring Tension (oz)
1971-73	97.5	60	12	Neg	500	6	11.2	55	11	5500	56

PISTON AND RING SPECIFICATIONS

All measurements in inches

			RING GAP			RING SIDE CLEARANCE		
Year	Engine Displace. (Cu In.)	Piston Clearance	Top Compression	Bottom Compression	Oil Control	Top Compression	Bottom Compression	Oil Control
1971-73	97.5	—	0.006-0.014	0.006-0.014	0.006-0.014	0.0012-0.0028	0.0008-0.0024	0.0010-0.0030

— Not Available

VALVE SPECIFICATIONS

						STEM TO GUIDE CLEARANCE (in.)		STEM DIAMETER (in.)	
Year	Engine Displace-ment (Cu In.)	Seat Angle (deg)	Face Angle (deg)	Spring Test Pressure (lbs @ in.)	Spring Installed Height (in.)	Intake	Exhaust	Intake	Exhaust
1971-73	97.5	45	44	59-65 1.47	1.47	0.0010-0.0022	0.3121-0.3129	0.3133-0.3139	0.3121-0.0033

WHEEL ALIGNMENT

		CASTER		CAMBER				WHEEL PIVOT RATIO (deg)	
Year	Model	Range (deg)	Pref Setting (deg)	Range (deg)	Pref. Setting (deg)	Toe-in (in.)	Steering Axis Inclination	Inner Wheel	Outer Wheel
1971-73	All	$1\frac{1}{4}$-$1\frac{1}{2}$	—	—	$1\frac{1}{2}$	0.08-0.23	8°50′	43°	32°

— Not Available

Wiring Diagrams

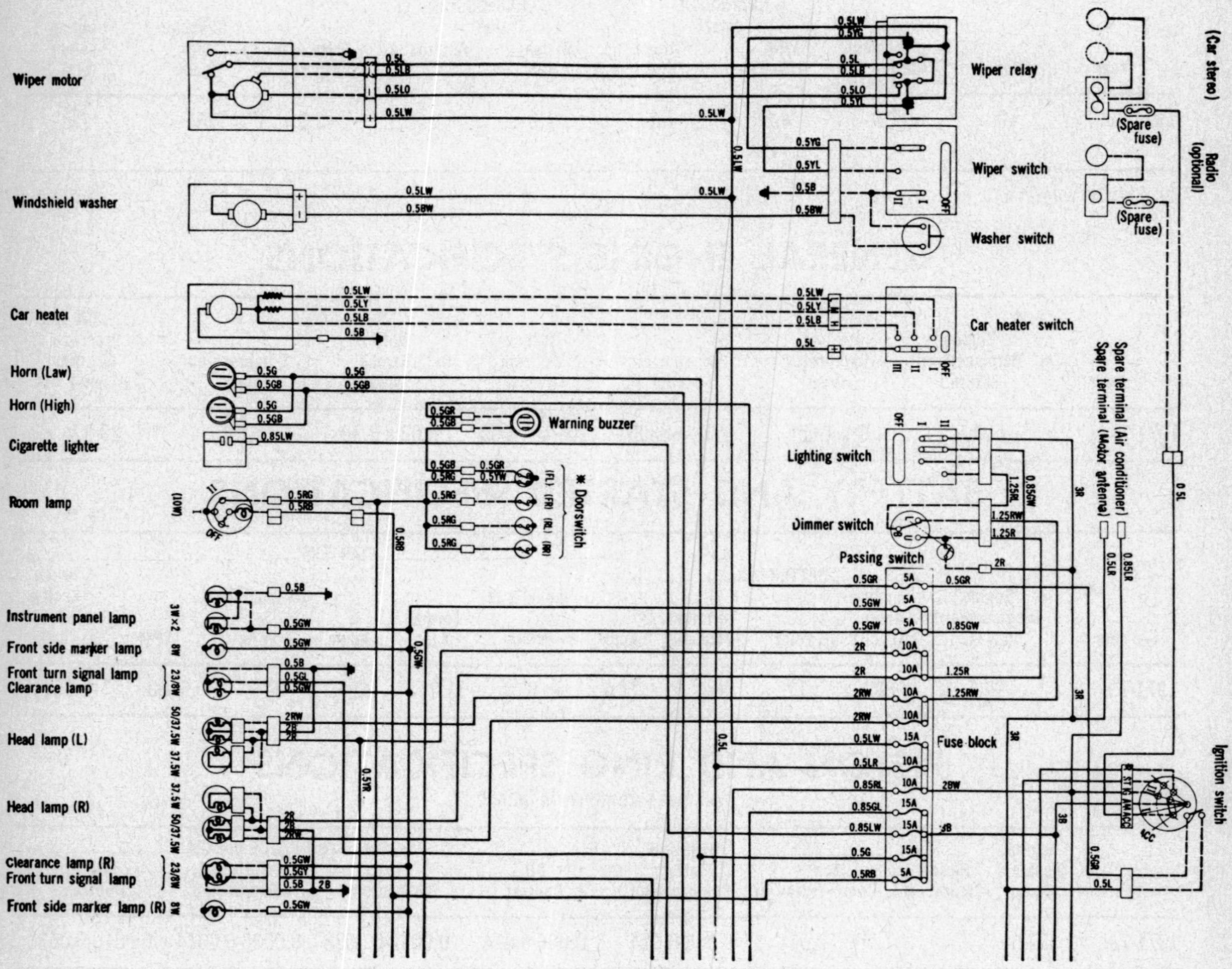

Sedan and Hardtop with manual transmission

Fuses and Circuit Breakers

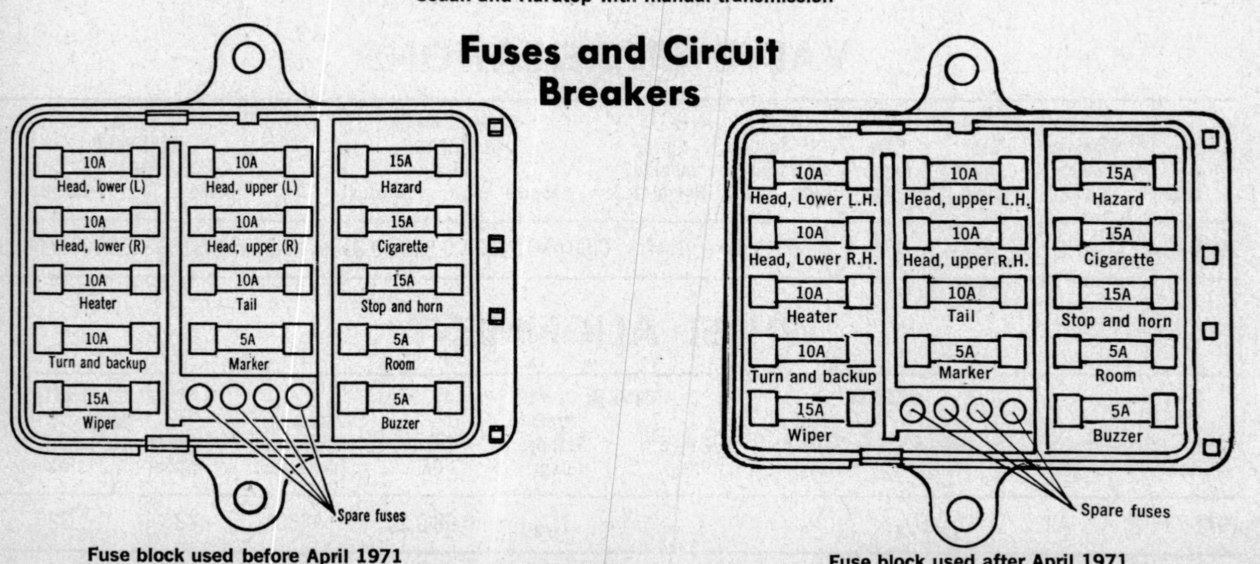

Fuse block used before April 1971

Fuse block used after April 1971

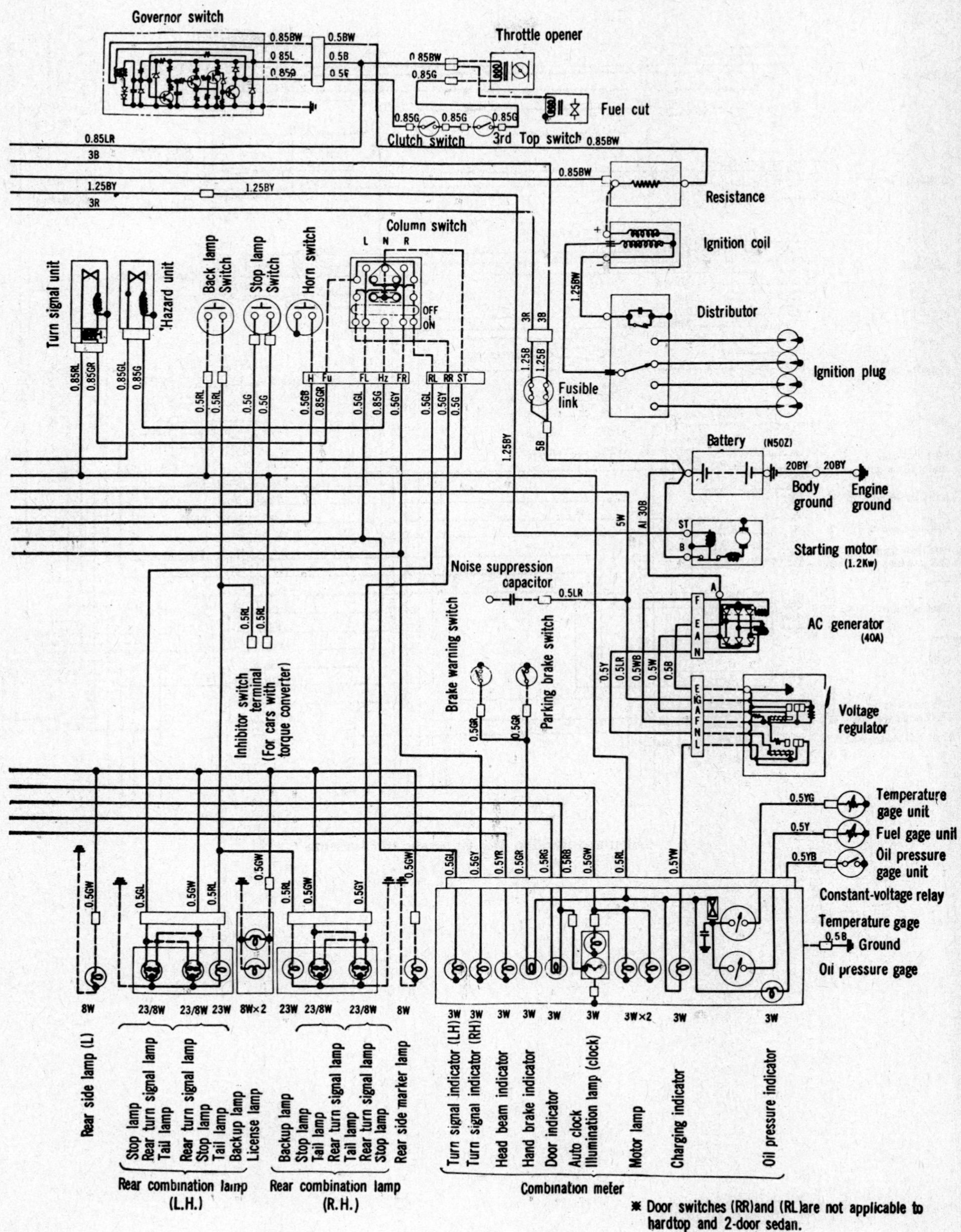

Sedan and Hardtop with manual transmission

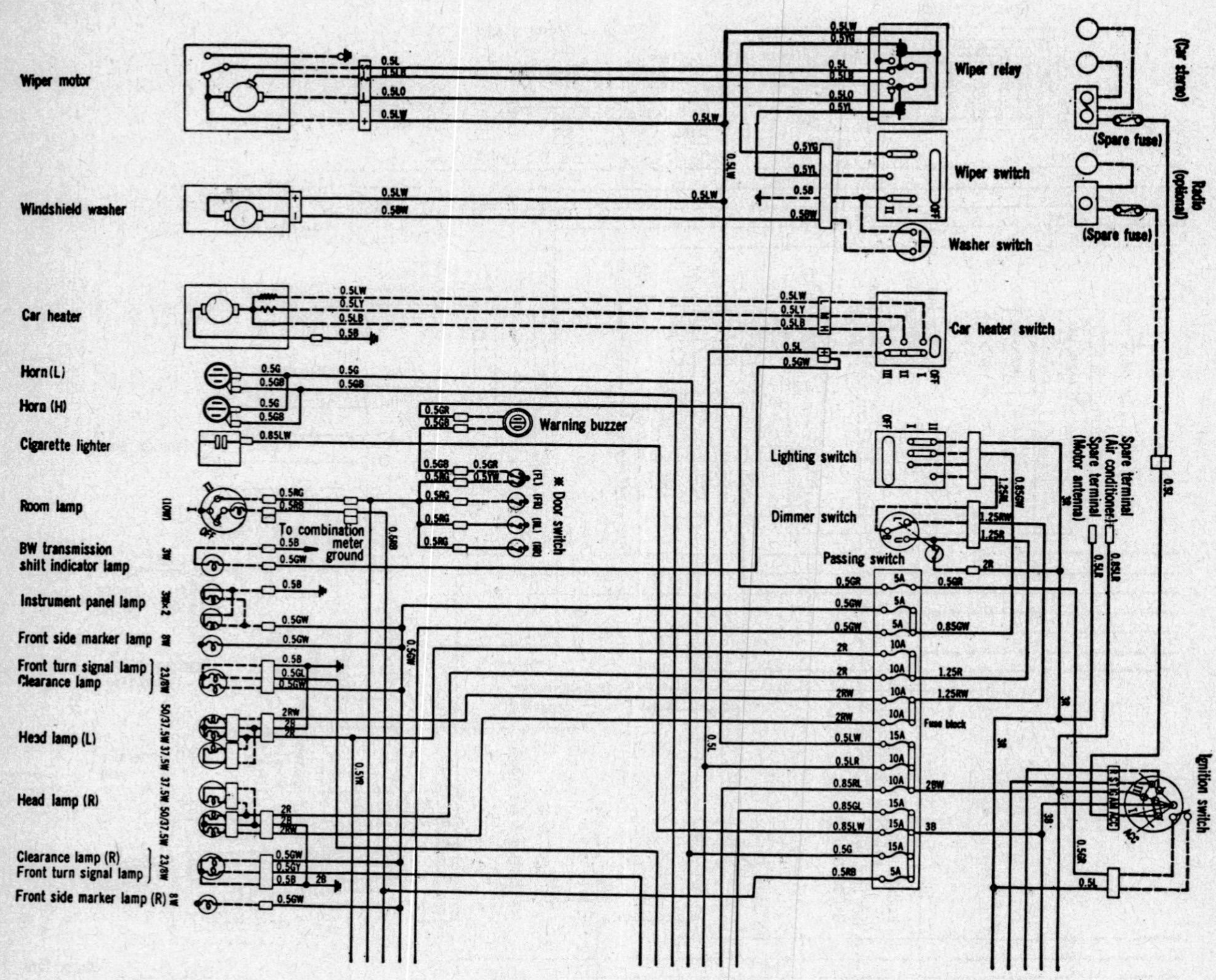

Sedan and Hardtop with automatic transmission

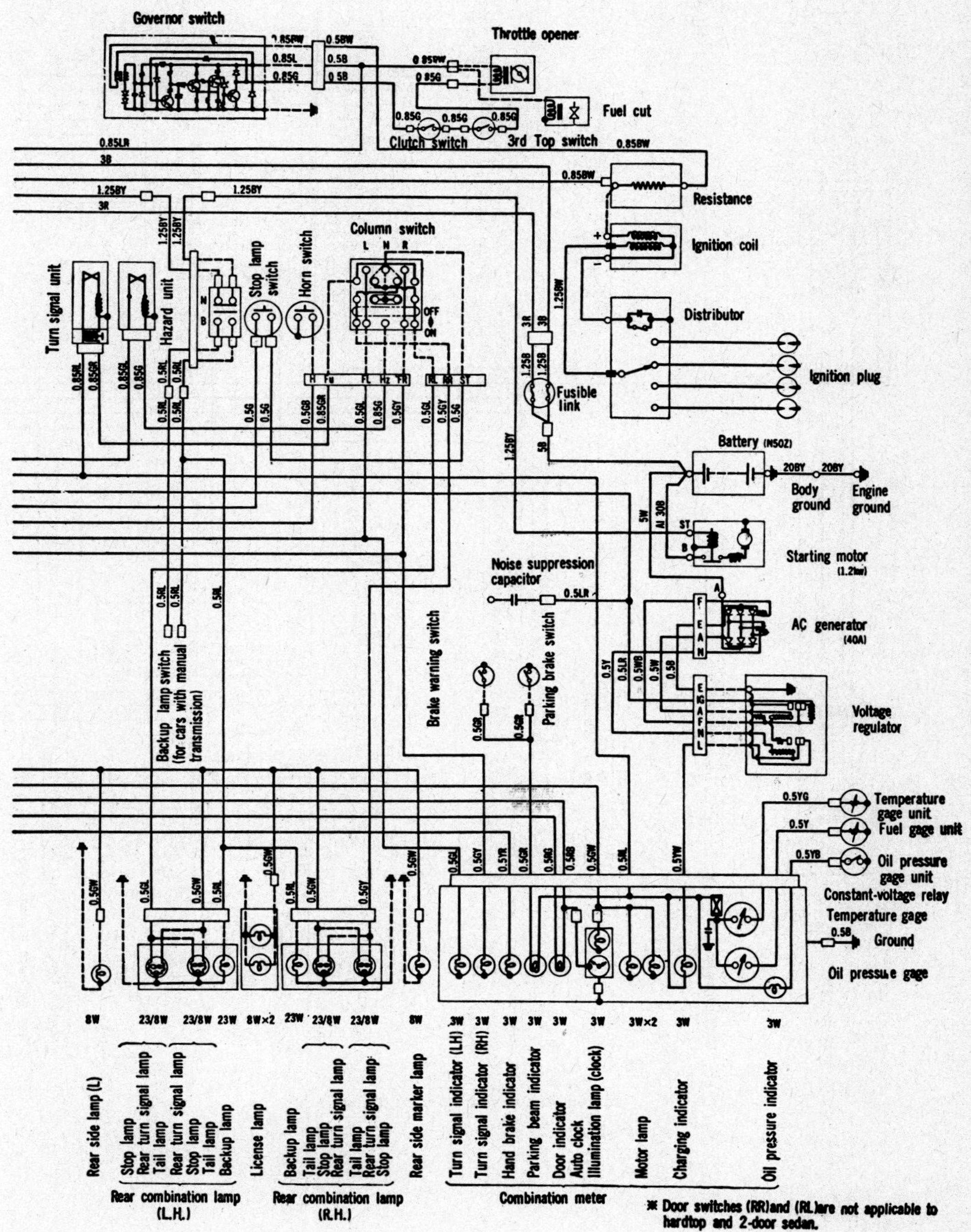

Sedan and Hardtop with automatic transmission

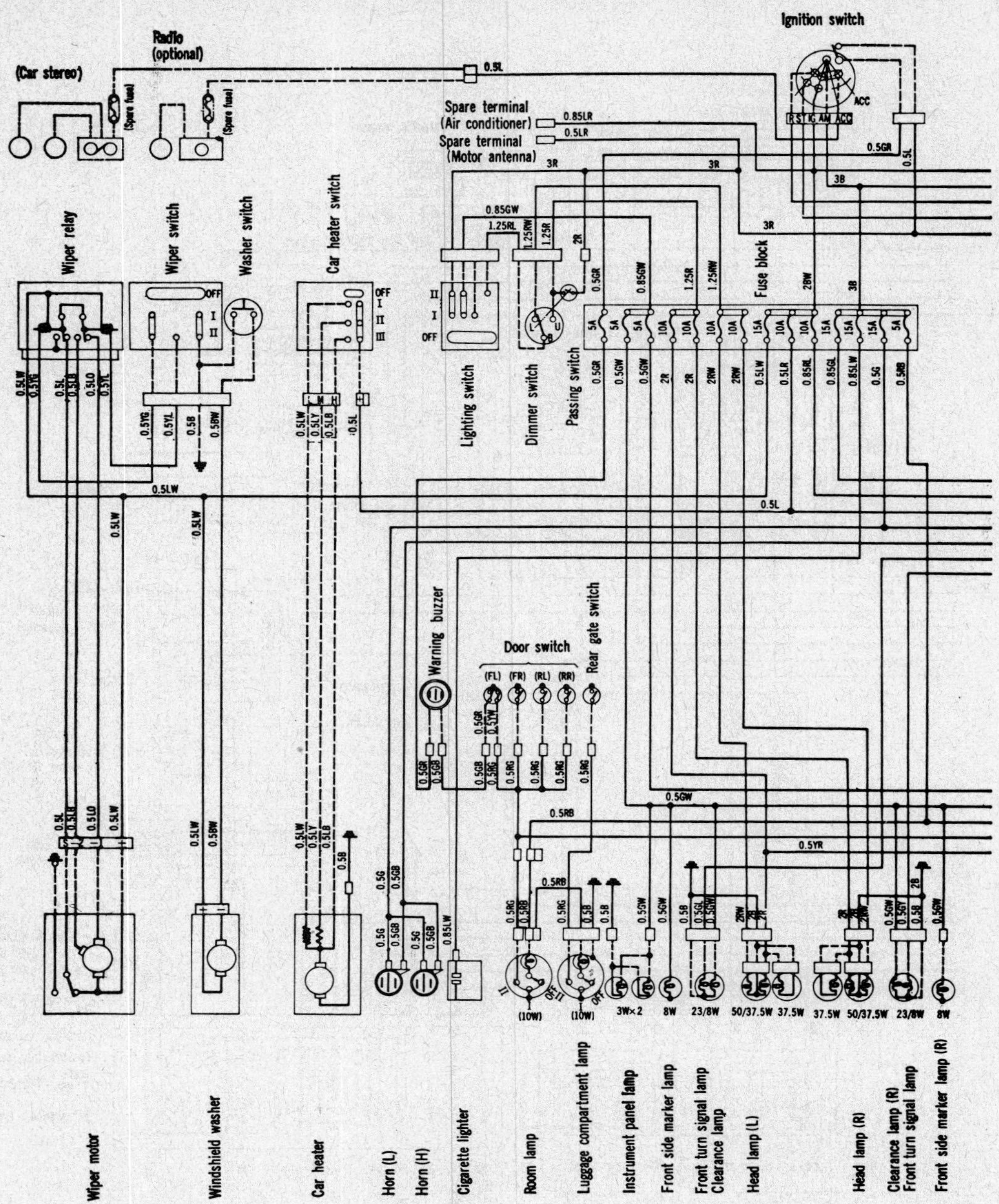

Station Wagon with manual transmission

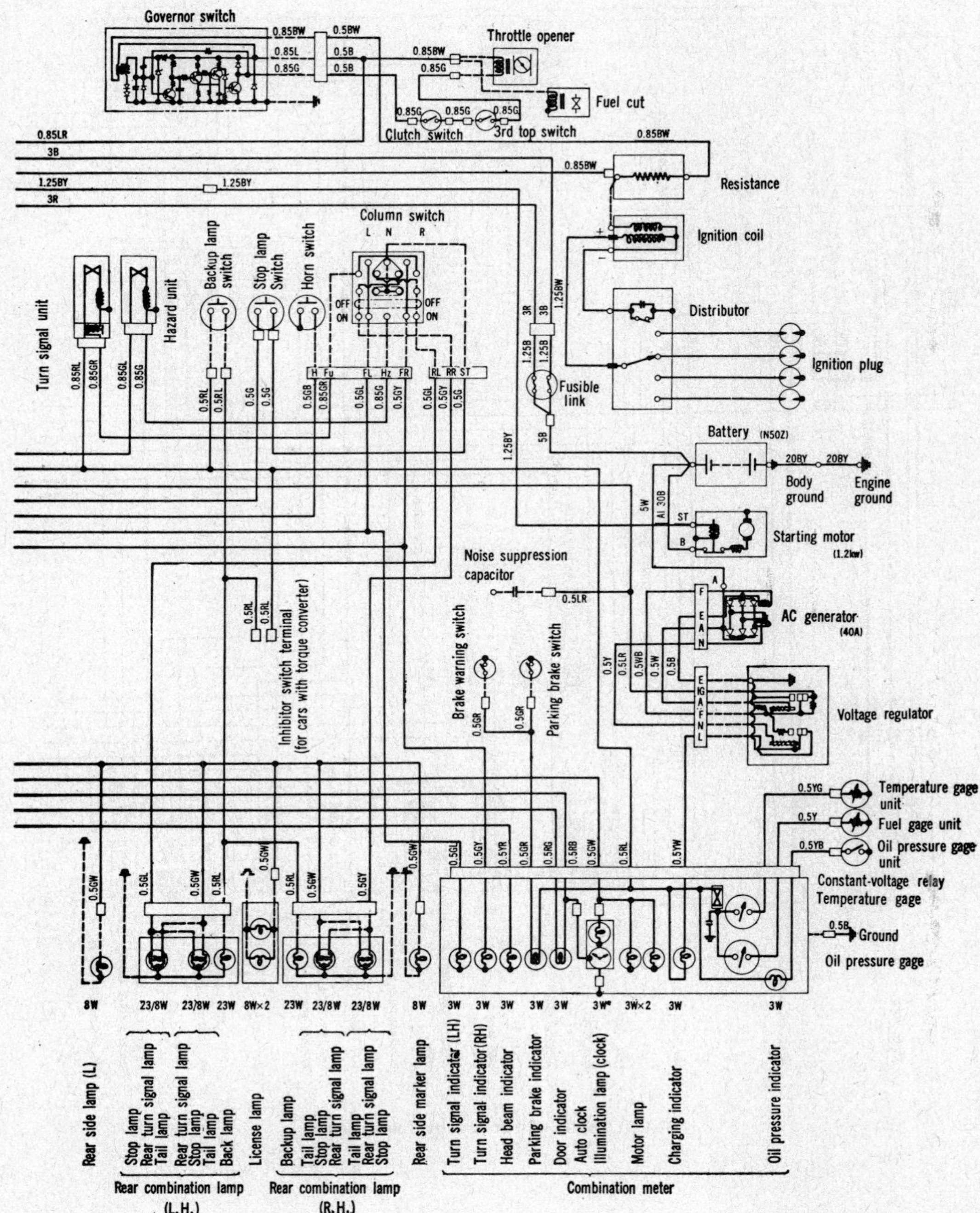

Station Wagon with manual transmission

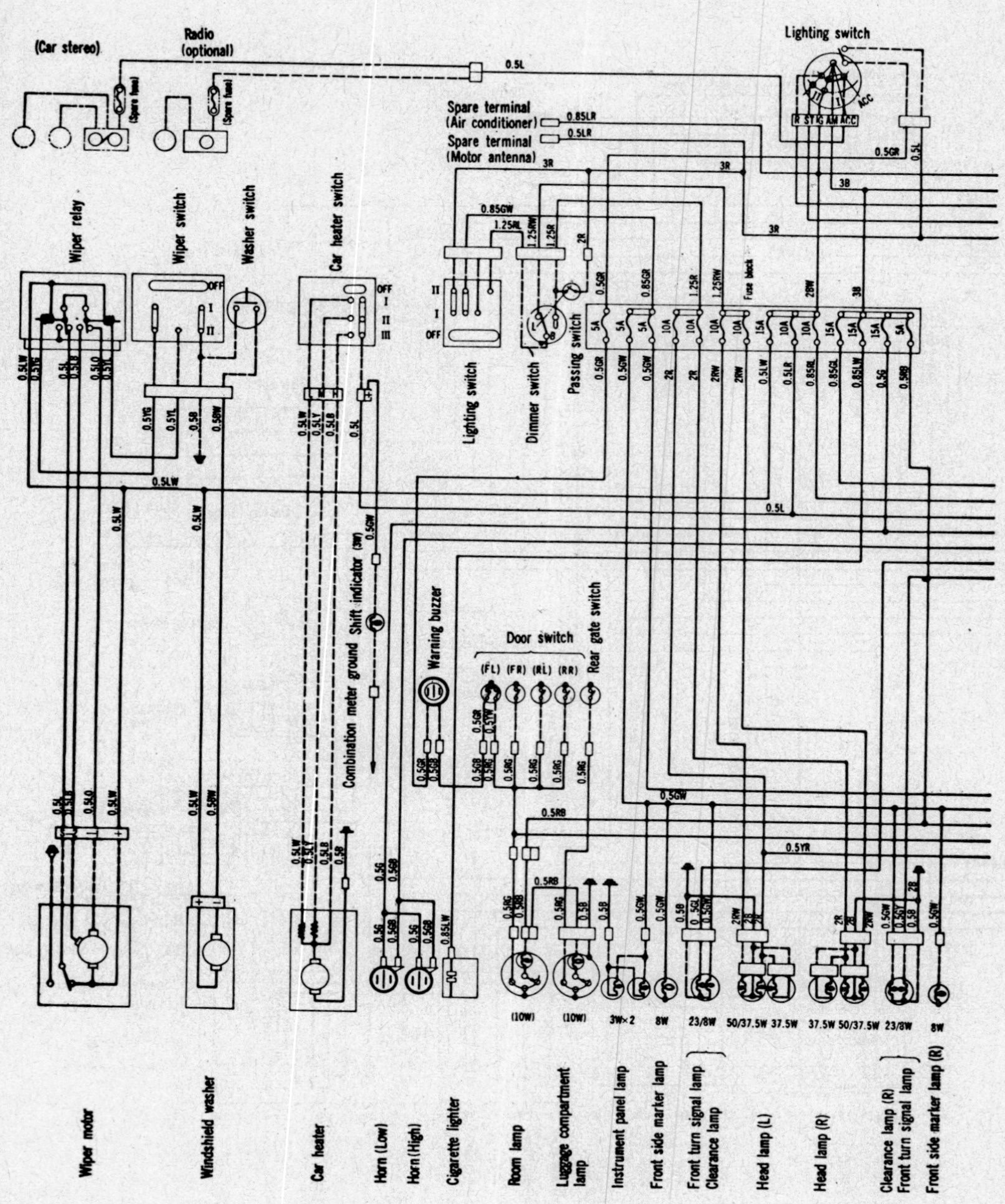

Station Wagon with automatic transmission

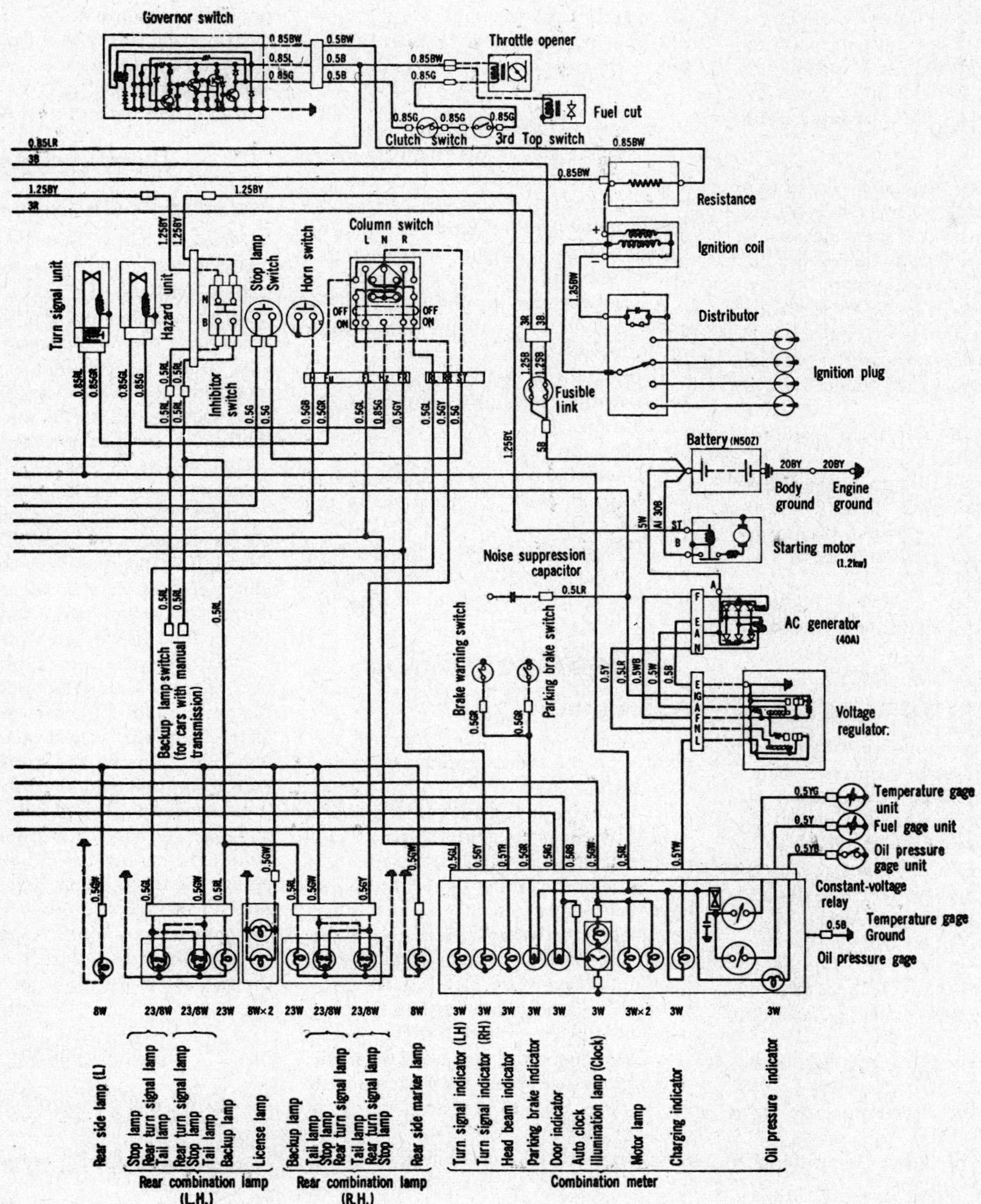

Station Wagon with automatic transmission

TUNE-UP PROCEDURES

Spark Plugs

The average life of a spark plug is 12,-000 miles. This is, however, dependent on the mechanical condition of the engine, the type of fuel used, and the driving conditions. A drop in gas mileage is the first indication of worn spark plugs.

Removal

1. If the spark plug wires are not numbered by cylinder, place a piece of masking tape on each wire and number it.
2. Grasp each wire by the rubber boot on the end. Pull the wires from the spark plugs. If the boots stick to the plugs, remove them with a twisting motion. Do not try to pull the wire by any area except the boot or you may damage the wire end.
3. Using a spark plug socket, loosen all the plugs a few turns.
4. Remove all foreign matter from around the spark plug.
5. Unscrew the spark plugs and remove them from the engine.

Installation

Installation is the reverse of removal.

Points and Condenser

The points and condenser function as a circuit breaker for the primary circuit of the ignition system. The ignition coil must boost the 12 volts of electrical current supplied to it by the battery, to about 20,000 volts in order to fire the spark plugs. To do this, the coil depends upon the points and condenser.

Removal

1. Disconnect the wire that runs from the coil to the center of the distributor cap.
2. Unsnap the distributor cap retaining clips or remove the screws.
3. Remove the distributor cap from the distributor.
4. Remove the rotor by pulling it straight up.
5. Remove the hot lead which is attached to the points.
6. Remove the points and condenser attaching screws.
7. Remove the points and condenser.

Installation

Installation is the reverse of the above procedure but includes the following adjustments.

Adjustments

Feeler Gauge

1. Turn the engine until the high spot of the distributor cam is in direct contact with the breaker point arm. This can be done by quickly turning the ignition switch to start and then releasing it until the distribution cam is properly positioned.
2. Insert the feeler gauge between the open contacts of the points. See "Tune-Up Specifications" for proper feeler gauge thickness.

Dwell Meter

1. Adjust the points with a feeler gauge as described above.
2. Connect the positive lead of the dwell meter to the post on the coil marked (dist) or to the same post that takes the distributor lead wire.
3. Connect the ground lead to any good ground such as the air cleaner mounting stud.
4. If the dwell meter has a set line be sure that the indicator is adjusted to the set position.
5. Start the engine.
6. Check the reading on the dwell meter with the dwell specifications in the tune-up chart.
7. If the reading is above the specified range, the point gap should be opened. If it is below, the points should be closed.

Ignition Timing

Adjustment

1. Locate the timing marks and pointer on the lower engine pulley and engine front cover.
2. Clean the timing marks and pointer.
3. Mark the proper timing marks with a piece of white chalk or florescent paint.
4. Attach the timing light. Most lights have three wires; Red goes to the positive terminal on the battery. Black goes to the negative terminal on the battery. The remaining clip goes on No. 1 spark plug. Insert the clip onto the plug and the plug wire onto the clip to complete the circuit.
5. Disconnect the vacuum line if the distributor is equipped with vacuum advance. Also, plug the vacuum line so it does not suck air.
6. Check to be sure that the timing light wires are clear of the fan and then start the engine.
7. Adjust the idle, using a tach and dwell meter, to the specified rpm.
8. Aim the timing light at the timing mark and pointer on the front of the engine. If the timing marks are aligned, the timing is correct.
8. If the timing marks are not aligned, loosen the distributor and by turning the distributor clockwise or counterclockwise you will be able to align the marks.
9. After aligning the marks, retighten the distributor.
10. Recheck the timing.

Valve Adjustment

Rotate the engine to TDC of each cylinder. Loosen the rocker arm nuts. Adjust the valves (cold) to 0.003 in. intake and 0.007 in. exhaust. Tighten the adjusting nuts. Start the engine and run it to operating temperature. Loosen the rocker arm nuts and adjust the valve clearance to the specified hot clearance. (See "specifications"). Tighten the rocker arm nuts and install the valve cover.

Carburetor

Throttle Positioner and Idle Speed Adjustments

Run the engine at idle speed for two minutes with the engine at 170°–190°. Initially operate the pilot and primary throttle stop screw. Temporarily adjust the idle speed to 700–750 rpm. Carbon monoxide reading should be no higher than specified. Place the idle limiter cap on the top end of the pilot screw.

CAUTION: *Be sure not to damage the screw during this operation.*

Adjust the throttle and pilot screw to obtain a reading of LESS THAN 3.5–5% CO at 700–750 rpm. Run the engine at idle speed for six minutes. After six minutes of operation, adjust the throttle position in the following manner.

Disconnect the boost pipe which runs between the intake manifold and air cleaner. Remove the air cleaner. Block off the boost pipe hole at the intake manifold side. Remove the green (negative) wire of the solenoid at its solenoid juncture. Accelerate the engine at 2,500–3,-000 rpm. Ground the green (negative) wire to the carburetor and place the solenoid in the ON position. Release the pressure on the throttle lever. Be sure that the throttle positioner is set for 1,350–1,450 rpm. If it is incorrect, adjust it with the throttle positioning nut.

ENGINE ELECTRICAL

Distributor

Removal and Installation

1. Remove the distributor cap.
2. Disconnect the distributor primary lead from the coil.
3. Rotate the engine until the rotor points toward the No. 1 tower in the distributor cap.
4. Mark the relative position of the rotor to the distributor body, and the distributor body to the engine block.
5. Remove the retaining nut and lift out the distributor.

When installing, rotate the crankshaft so that the No. 1 cylinder is on the compression stroke, and the basic ignition timing is indicated by the timing marks. Point the rotor 15° counterclockwise of the No. 1 tower in the distributor cap, and insert the distributor into the block. If the oil pump drive will not engage (the distributor will not seat), remove the distributor, and turn the pump drive with a long screwdriver, so that it is perpendicular to the crankshaft centerline. Align the distributor body index marks, install and tighten the retaining nut. Check the ignition timing, and adjust if necessary.

Breaker Points

The breaker points are retained in the distributor by two screws. A spring loaded, felt wiper arm, which lubricates the distributor cam, is also retained by the screws. An eccentric screw, positioned in a slot in the base of the stationary point, is used to adjust point gap.

Ignition Timing

The ignition timing is adjusted with the vacuum advance hose disconnected and the engine running at idle speed. To adjust the timing, insert a Phillips head screwdriver into the hole provided in the vacuum advance mounting boss. Turning the screwdriver counterclockwise advances timing, clockwise retards timing. If correct ignition timing is outside the range of adjustment provided, loosen the distributor retaining nut, and rotate the distributor body in the appropriate direction to bring the correct timing within the adjustment range.

Ignition Timing Marks

The ignition timing marks are located at the front of the engine. A notch on the front edge of the fan pulley aligns with a scale integral with the timing cover. The marks are visible from the right side of the engine.

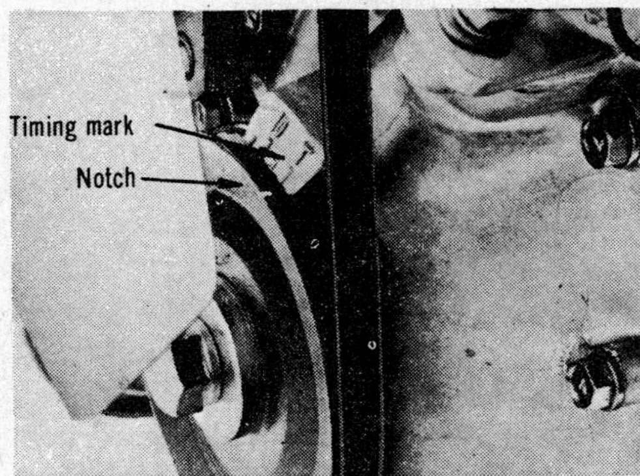

Timing marks

Adjusting timing

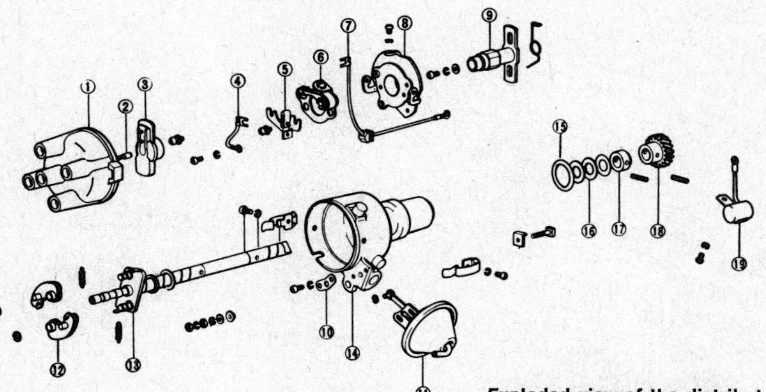

Exploded view of the distributor

1. Cap
2. Carbon
3. Rotor
4. Ground wire
5. Cam felt
6. Arm support
7. Lead wire
8. Breaker base
9. Cam
10. Locking plate
11. Vacuum control
12. Governor weight
13. Shaft
14. Housing
15. O-ring
16. Washer
17. Thrust collar
18. Gear
19. Condenser

Alternator

When servicing the charging system of vehicles equipped with an alternator the following precautions should be taken to avoid damaging the system.

1. Never operate the alternator on an open circuit (battery disconnected).
2. When installing a battery, connect the ground terminal (negative) before connecting the positive terminal.
3. When arc welding anywhere in the vehicle, always disconnect the alternator.

Removal and Installation

1. Disconnect the battery ground cable and all wires from the alternator.
2. Loosen the mounting bolts, and remove the fan belt.
3. Remove the mounting bolts, and remove the alternator.

Install in the reverse order of removal.

NOTE: *Shims must be installed between the timing cover and the alternator mounting bracket.*

AC Regulator

A dual element Tirrill type regulator, with temperature compensation, is used.

To check the voltage control relay, connect a voltmeter between terminals A and E of the regulator connector, by inserting clips into the gaps in the connector.

NOTE: *Do not disconnect the connector.*

Start the engine, run at 2000 rpm and observe the voltage reading. If the reading is outside specifications, remove the regulator cover and adjust the voltage by bending the spring tensioner. Bending the tensioner downward will lower voltage, and upward will raise voltage.

NOTE: *After making each adjustment, lower the engine speed to idle to avoid the influence of residual magnetism in the regulator core on voltage readings.*

Battery

The battery electrolyte level must be maintained, and the terminals kept clean, tight and free of corrosion. Should the specific gravity of the battery electrolyte fall below 1.19 at 68° F., the battery must be charged. If the battery takes the charge, and specific gravity repeatedly falls to this level, the charging system should be investigated.

CAUTION: *When jump starting, ensure that proper polarity is observed, and that the jumper battery is disconnected as soon as possible after starting to prevent damaging the charging system.*

Hydrometer Readings	Condition
1.260-1.310	Fully charged
1.230-1.250	¾ charged
1.200-1.220	½ charged
1.170-1.190	¼ charged
1.140-1.160	Almost discharged
1.110-1.130	Fully discharged

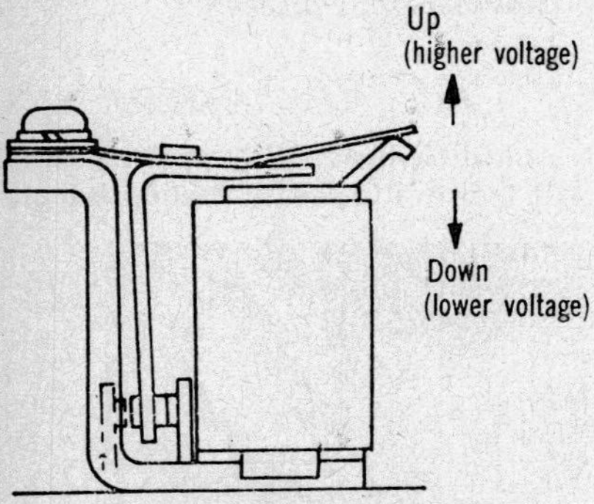

Up (higher voltage)

Down (lower voltage)

Adjusting the voltage

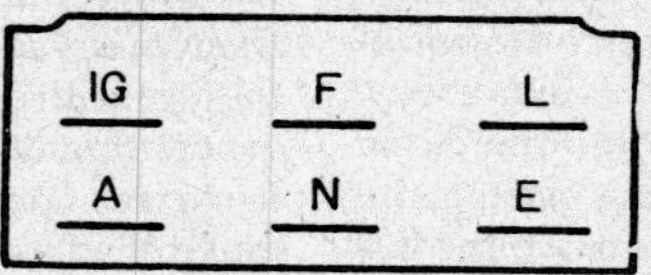

Regulator terminals

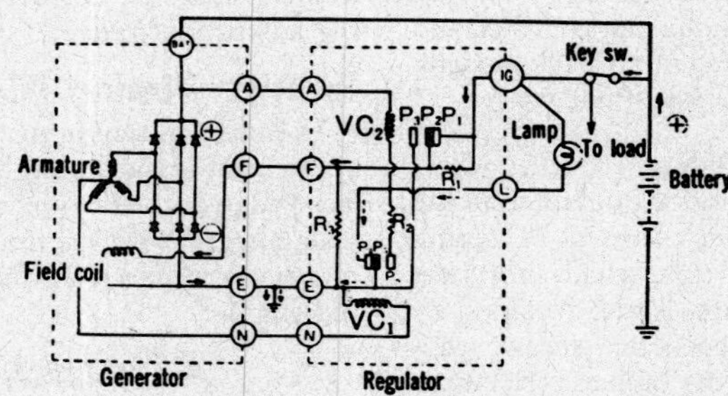

Schematic diagram of the regulator

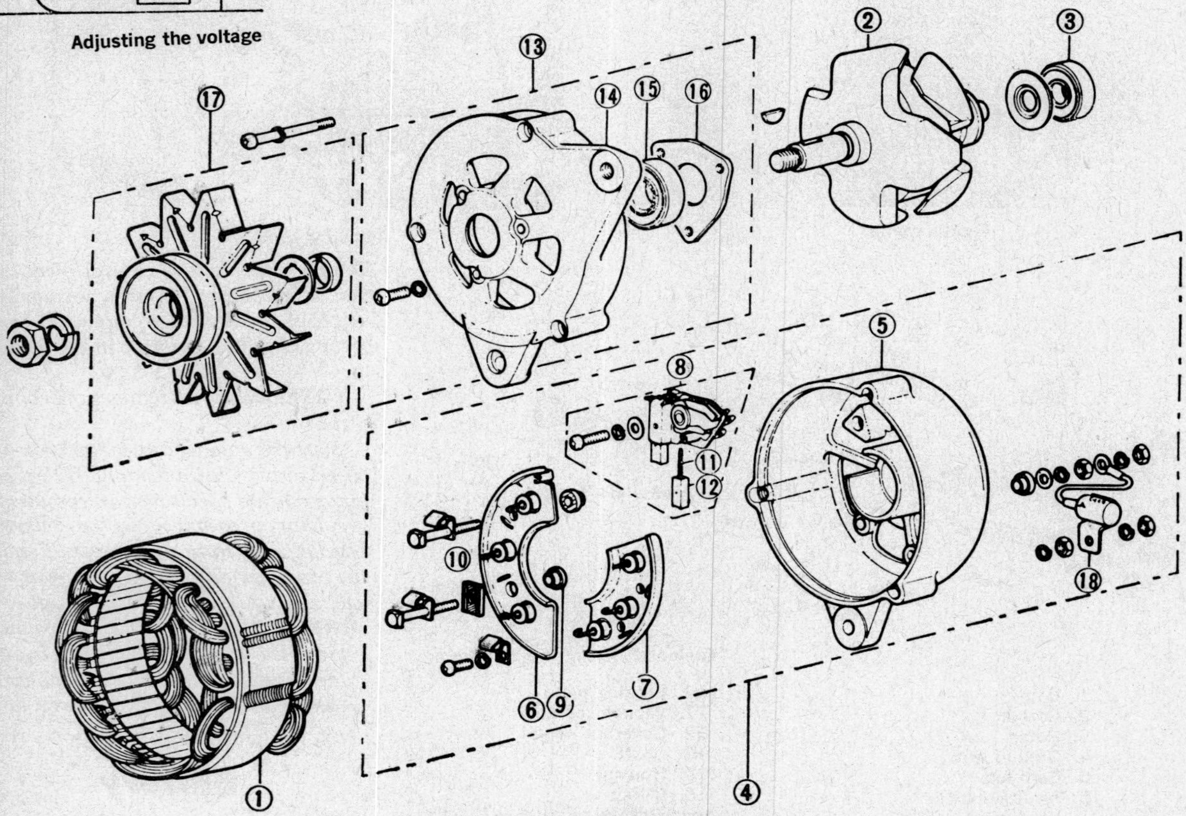

Exploded view of an AC generator

1. Stator
2. Rotor
3. Ball bearing
4. Rear bracket assembly
5. Rear bracket
6. Heat sink complete (+)
7. Heat sink complete (−)
8. Brush holder assembly
9. Insulator
10. Insulator
11. Brush spring
12. Brush
13. Front bracket assembly
14. Front bracket
15. Ball bearing
16. Bearing retainer
17. Pulley
18. Condenser

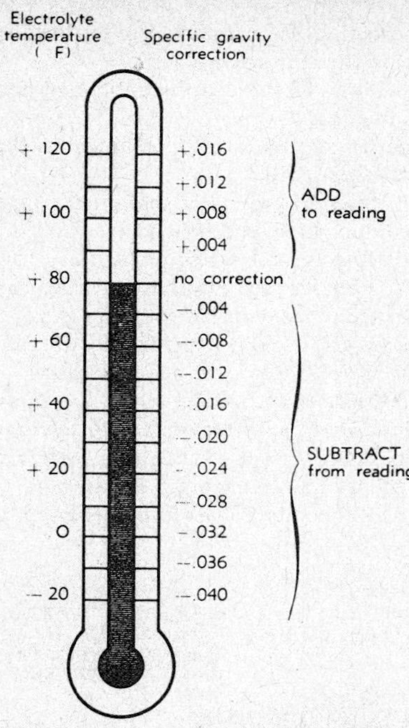

Effect of temperature on battery specific gravity.

Starter

Removal and Installation

1. Disconnect the battery ground cable.
2. Code for identification and remove all starter wires
3. Remove the starter mounting bolts, and lift out the starter.

Before installing the starter, clean the mating surfaces on the engine and the starter mounting bracket. Install in the reverse order of removal.

ENGINE MECHANICAL

Engine/Transmission Removal

1. Loosen the attaching bolts and remove the hood. Remove the bridge panel and front grill. Drain the radiator and remove it from the vehicle. On automatic transmission equipped vehicles, be sure to use a catch pan when removing the oil line from the radiator. Disconnect and remove the battery.
2. Disconnect the ground strap, ignition coil wiring and vacuum and fuel solenoid valves.
3. Disconnect the following: generator, starter, transmission switch, back-up light switch, temperature gauge and oil pressure gauge.
4. Disconnect all hoses and remove the air cleaner.
5. Disconnect all carburetor linkage at the rear of the engine. Remove the heater hose.
6. Unbolt the exhaust pipe at the manifold flange and disconnect the muffler pipe bracket at the transmission.
7. Remove the hose between the fuel filter and the fuel pump return line. Be sure that gas spillage is held to a minimum
8. Remove the vacuum hose from the purge control valve.
6. Disconnect the speedometer cable, backup light and distributor switches.
10. Disconnect the clutch cable and shift lever.
11. Remove the cross shaft and control rod from the bracket under the transmission.
12. Gently take off the leatherette cover (inside the car) and remove the shifter assembly.
13. Attach a hoist to the engine and tension it slightly to remove weight from the engine mounts. Remove the attaching bolts from the engine mounts, and lift the engine upward and forward.

Installation

To replace the engine, reverse the order of removal. Note the following when installing the engine.

Drape clean rags at the rear of the cylinder head to prevent damage to the firewall when lowering the engine into position.

Bolt the front of the engine in place first.

Torque Specifications

Engine support bracket nuts: 14–18 ft lbs.

Front insulator-to-sub frame bolts:

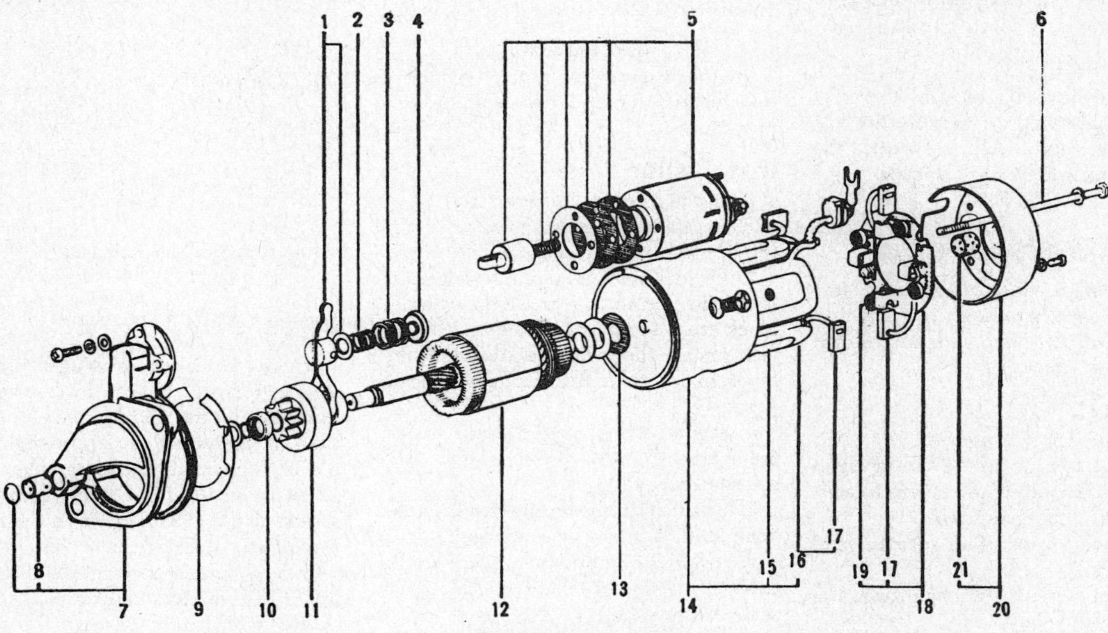

Exploded view of starter

1. Lever assembly
2. Lever spring (A)
3. Lever spring (B)
4. Spring retainer
5. Electromagnetic switch
6. Through bolt
7. Front bracket
8. Front bracket bearing
9. Plate
10. Stop ring
11. Overrunning clutch
12. Armature
13. Insulating washer
14. Yoke assembly
15. Pole piece
16. Field coil
17. Brush
18. Brush holder
19. Brush spring
20. Rear bracket
21. Rear bracket bearing

15–17 ft lbs.

Front insulator-to-engine bracket nut 15–17 ft lbs.

Front bolt, cylinder block-to-engine bracket: 29–36 ft lbs.

Rear insulator support bracket bolt: 7–8.5 ft lbs.

Support bracket-to-body bolt: 7–8.5 ft lbs.

Rear insulator-to-frame bolt:

Manual transmission: 15–17 ft lbs.

Automatic transmission: 9–11.5 ft lbs.

Intake Manifold

Removal

1. Drain the cooling system.
2. Be sure to keep the water for later use.
3. Remove the water outlet and heater hoses.
4. Disconnect the accelerator and choke linkages.
5. Remove the vacuum, fuel, and water connections at the carburetor.
6. Disconnect the water temperature gauge.
7. Loosen the attaching bolts and remove the intake manifold.

Inspection

Check the manifold mounting face for distortion. A tolerance of 0.006–0.012 in. is permissible. If the distortion exceeds the tolerance, mill the intake manifold mounting face.

Installation

To install the intake manifold, reverse the removal procedure. Be sure to use a new gasket and sealer. Torque the mounting nuts to 10.8–14.5 ft lbs.

Cylinder Head

CAUTION: *Because of the aluminum construction of the head, use extreme care when tightening bolts and during general handling.*

Removal

1. Remove the valve cover.
2. Relieve tension on the timing chain by turning the tensioner lever, located inside the timing chain case.
3. Remove the camshaft sprocket and timing chain.
4. Do not remove the chain from the crankshaft sprocket.
5. Remove the head bolts reversing the order of the tightening sequence.
6. They should be removed in three stages with the engine cold.
7. The cylinder head is positioned by four dowel pins (two front, two rear).
8. When removing the head from the engine deck, lift it straight up to prevent damaging the locating dowels.

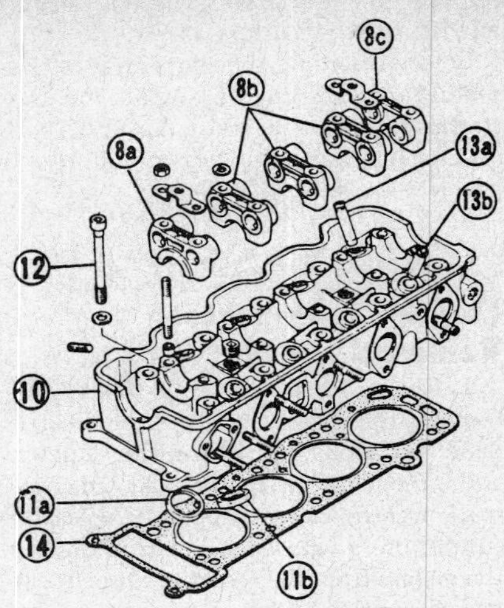

Exploded view of the cylinder head

8a. Camshaft bearing cap
8b. No. 2, 3 and 4 caps
8c. Camshaft bearing cap (rear)
10. Cylinder head
11a. Intake valve seat ring
11b. Exhaust valve seat ring
12. Cylinder head bolt
13a. Exhaust valve guide
13b. Intake valve guide
14. Cylinder head gasket

Inspection

After removal, visually inspect the head for cracks or scoring on the mounting surface. Check the cylinder head face for warpage, which should not exceed. 0.002 in. The head may be milled a maximum of 0.012 in. to correct deep scoring.

Disassembly

See the "Engine Rebuilding" section of this manual for cylinder head service procedures.

Installation

1. Install the gasket onto the block with reference to a matchmark on the top of the block.
2. Be sure that the joining surfaces of the chain case and the top of the cylinder block are smooth and parallel.
3. Install the cylinder head on the block, making sure that the dowels locate properly.
4. Tighten the bolts in three stages, finger-tight at first, progressing to the specified torque.
5. Be sure that the timing marks on the chain and camshaft gear are aligned.
6. Install the camshaft sprocket on the camshaft, being sure that the locating pin seats in the hole.
7. If it is hard to install the sprocket loosen the timing chain tensioner.

Camshaft and Rocker Arm

Removal

1. Remove the valve cover.
2. Relieve tension on the timing chain by turning the tensioner lever, located inside the timing case.
3. Remove the camshaft sprocket and timing chain.
4. Do not remove the chain from the crankshaft sprocket.
5. Support the camshaft gear and chain on the cylinder head.
6. Remove the spark plugs.
7. Remove the camshaft bearing cap nuts from the camshaft bearing caps.
8. While holding the front and rear cap, lift off the rocker arm assembly.

NOTE: *If the rocker arms are disassembled, be sure to replace the components in the same order. Be careful not to lose the bearing cap dowel pins*

9. Lift the camshaft from the head.

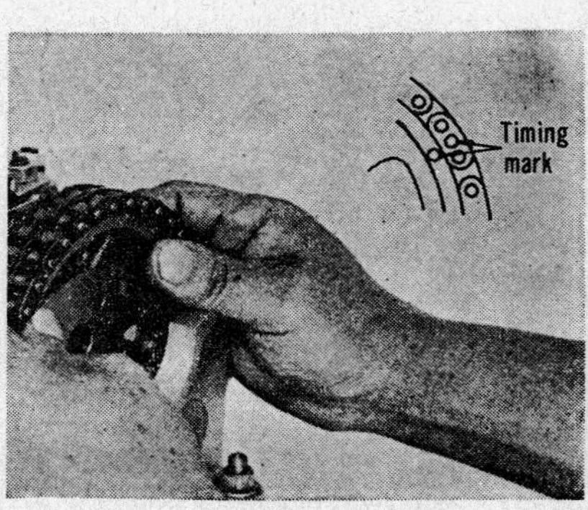

Camshaft sprocket installation

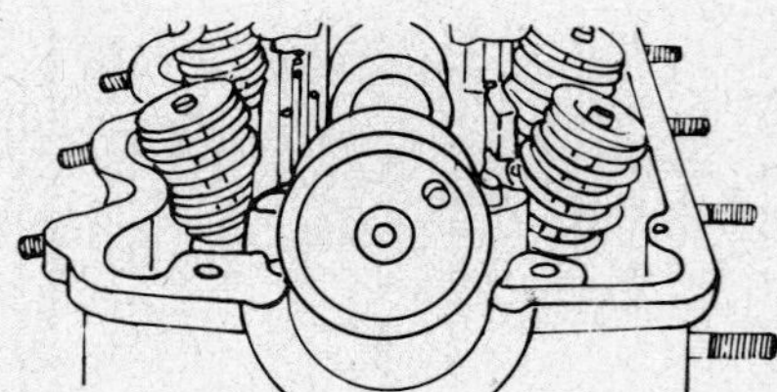

Position of installed camshaft dowel pin

Installation

Installation is the reverse of removal. Be sure to install the camshaft so that the dowel pin on the leading face of the camshaft is positioned at approximately 2 o'clock. The front bearing cap has a 0.079 in. mark on the front side which corresponds to a 0.118 in. mark on the rocker arm shaft. Rocker shafts are installed with 8 oil holes to the right and 4 to the left. These marks should be aligned. Install the bearing caps with the arrows pointing to the front of the engine. Check the camshaft end-play, which should be 0.002–.0059 in. If the camshaft end-play exceeds the limits, either the camshaft or the cylinder head must be replaced. Install the rocker arm washers with the bulged side toward the front of the engine. Torque the cap nuts in the order of 3, 2, 4, 1, 5 to 13–14.5 ft lbs.

Pistons, Rings, Connecting Rods

Pistons used in all Colt models are aluminum with press fit, forged pins. In addition, they utilize three cast iron rings: two compression and one oil control. The top and oil rings are hard chromed. Connecting rods are carbon steel forgings. Bearings are copper alloy lined for good wear qualities

NOTE: *When the engines are assembled, the cylinder/piston matchings are determined by dimensions. Matching piston-bore assemblies are stamped with A, B, or C. When assembling the engine, bore-piston letters must agree.*

1. Remove the engine from the vehicle.
2. Drain the oil and remove the oil pan
3. Remove the manifolds and the cylinder head.
4. Remove the carbon deposits from the top of the cylinder bore, using a ridge reamer.
5. Unbolt the connecting rod caps and install a short length of rubber hose over the connecting rod bolts.
6. Push the connecting rod and piston assembly out through the top of the block.
7. Remove in the order of 1, 4, 2, 3. See the "Engine Rebuilding" section of this manual for service procedures associated with pistons, connecting rods or rings.

Installation

Assemble the piston and connecting rod unit with the front marking facing toward the front of the engine. Lubricate the entire assembly.

NOTE: *The front piston mark consists of a small arrow; the connecting rod mark is an embossed numeral.*

Position the assembly in the cylinder bore with the rings in position. The piston letters must agree with the cylinder bore letters. Installation is the reverse of removal.

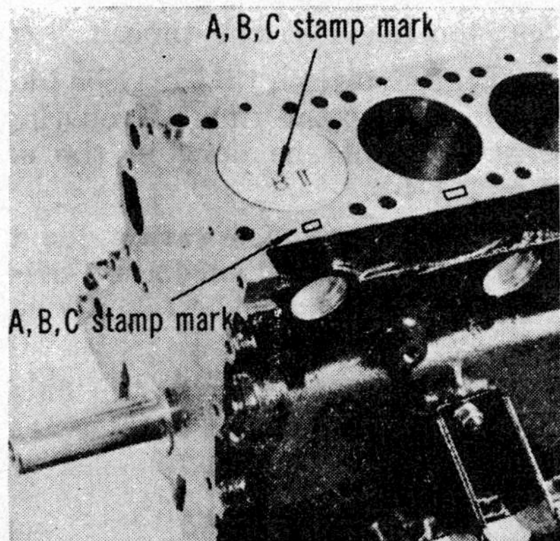

Cylinder block and piston identification

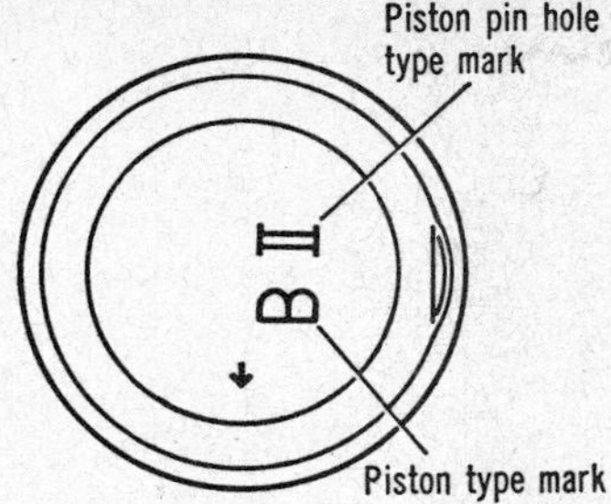

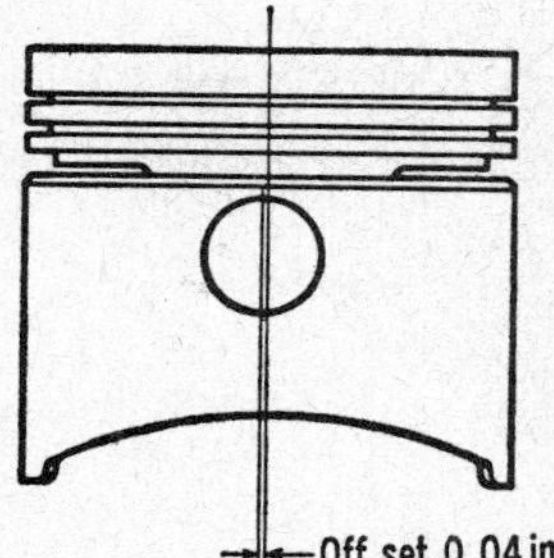

Piston markings and pin offset

Piston Specifications

The following information is in addition to that supplied in the specifications section.

Connecting rod side clearance: 0.-0039–0.0098 in.

Piston clearance: 0.0016–0.0079 in.

ENGINE LUBRICATION

The Colt lubrication system consists of a full flow canister type oil filter and a Trochoid gear type oil pump. Only oil graded Api Dg-Ms or higher should be used in this vehicle. Oil change intervals are after the first 600 miles and every 3 months or 4000 miles thereafter. The oil filter must be replaced at every other oil

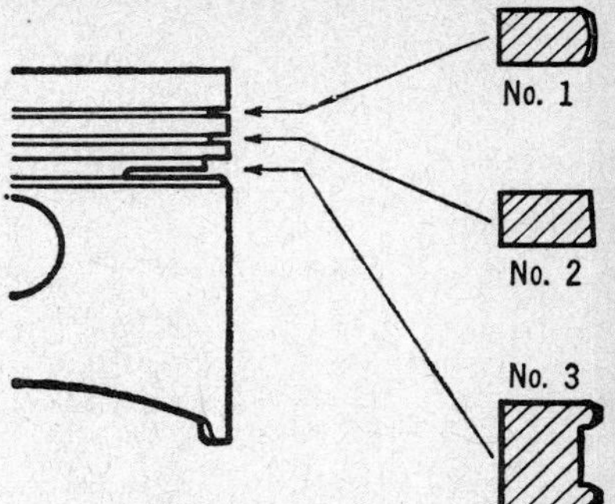

Piston ring installation

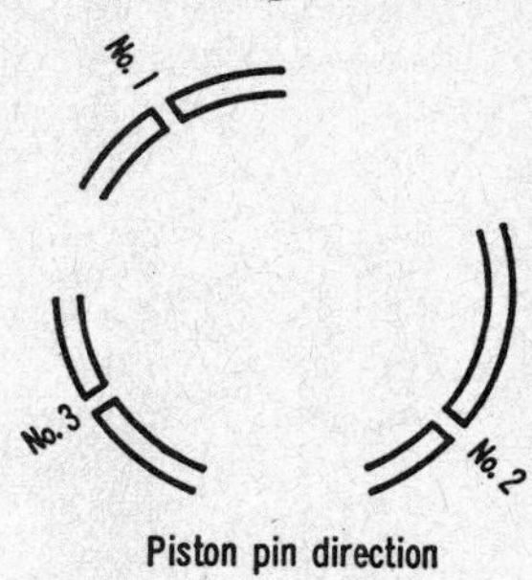

Ring end-gap positioning

change. If the car is driven exceptionally hard, or under adverse conditions, oil and filter changes should be performed more often. Both multi and single weight oils are acceptable for service.

Oil Pump

The pump is located inside the timing chain case at the bottom. Pressures higher than 56.8 psi are indicative of a clogged oil filter.

Removal

1. Unbolt the skid pan from the body underside.
2. Remove the oil filter.
3. Loosen the oil pump cover bolts and the rotor assembly fastenings.
4. Remove all the above and lift off the pump.

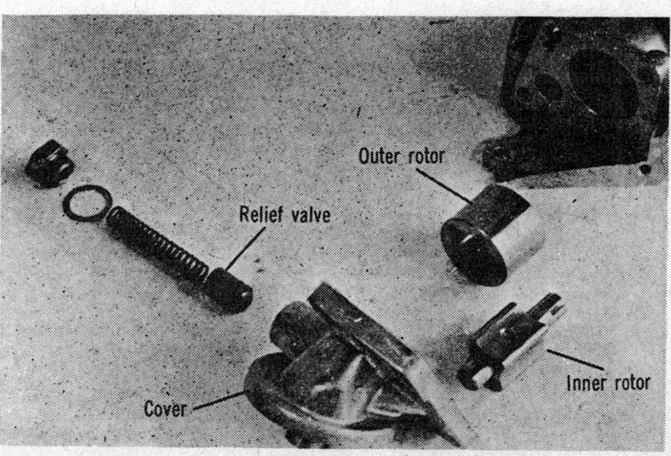

Exploded view of oil pump

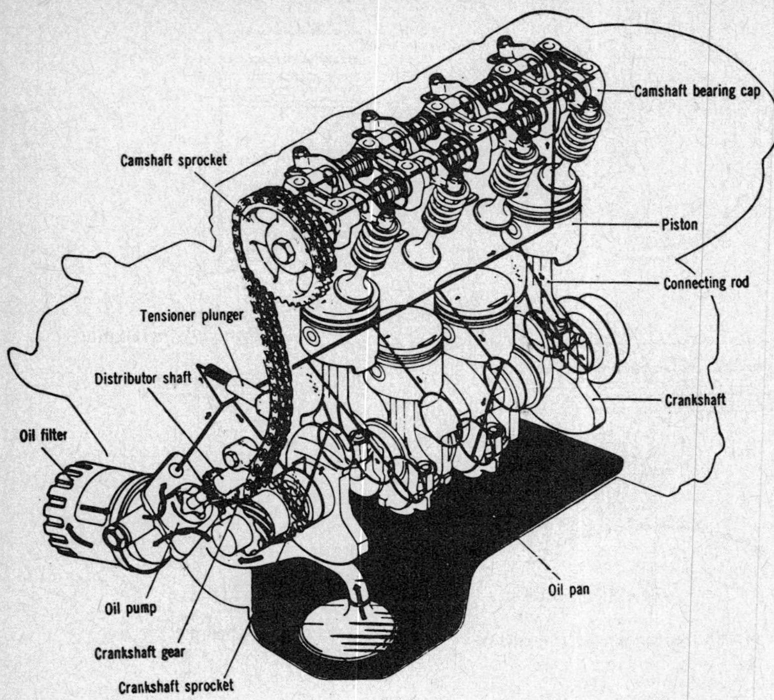

Engine oil circulation

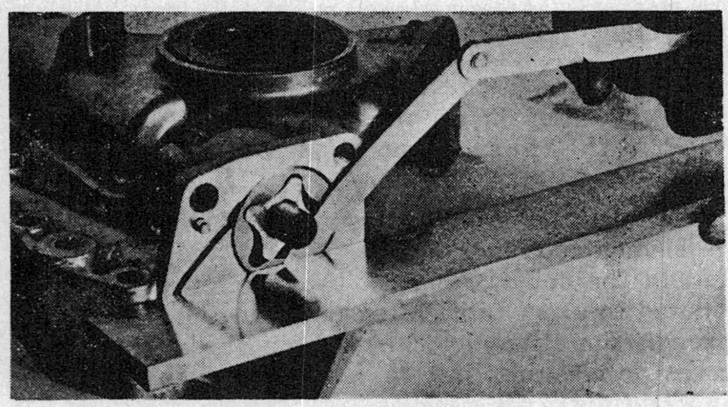

Oil pump gear end play

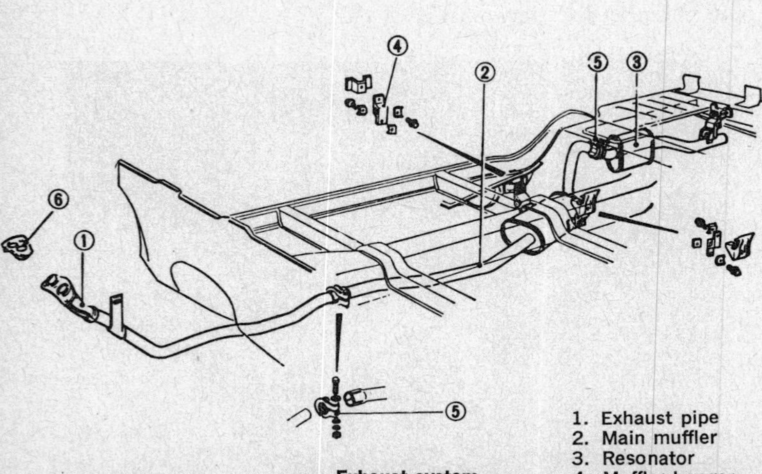

Exhaust system

1. Exhaust pipe
2. Main muffler
3. Resonator
4. Muffler hanger
5. Clamp
6. Exhaust pipe gasket

Rebuilding

Visually check all parts for defects. Insert the rotor assembly into the case and tighten to 10.8–14.5 ft lbs. Apply oil to the rotor shaft. When installing the pump cover gasket, be sure that both faces are entirely clean. Coat the gasket with commercial sealant. When assembling, adhere to the following specifications.

Chain case to shaft clearance: 0.0008–0.0022 in.

Inner rotor-to-outer rotor clearance: 0.0047 in. or less.

Rotor-to-cover end-play: 0.0027–0.0051 in.

Outer rotor-to-chain case clearance: 0.0039–0.0051 in.

Oil pump pressure relief spring

Free length: 2.351 in.

Tension: 16.6–17.8 lbs at 1.698 in. length.

Installation

Installation is the reverse of removal.

EXHAUST SYSTEM

All Colt exhaust manifolds are made from cast iron. Cylinders No. 1 and No. 4 are grouped together in the manifold as are No. 2 and No. 3. This prevents overlapping exhaust pulses from interfering with each other and causing back pressure. A conventional muffler-resonator combination is employed.

Manifold

Removal

1. Disconnect the air cleaner and remove all tubing.
2. Remove the air filter and jack the front of the vehicle.
3. Disconnect the exhaust pipe at the exhaust manifold flange.
4. Loosen the bolts and remove the manifold.

Installation

Reverse the removal procedures and torque the bolts to 10.8–14.5 ft lbs. Be sure to use a new exhaust manifold gasket and an appropriate sealer on both sides.

Manifold Warpage

On occasion, exhaust manifolds may warp. For safety reasons, this warpage should be less than 0.006 in. Under no circumstances may it exceed 0.012 in.

ENGINE COOLING

Radiator

Removal

1. Loosen the drain plug and drain the coolant. Remove all radiator hoses at the engine end.
2. Take the four attaching bolts from the radiator sides and lift the radiator

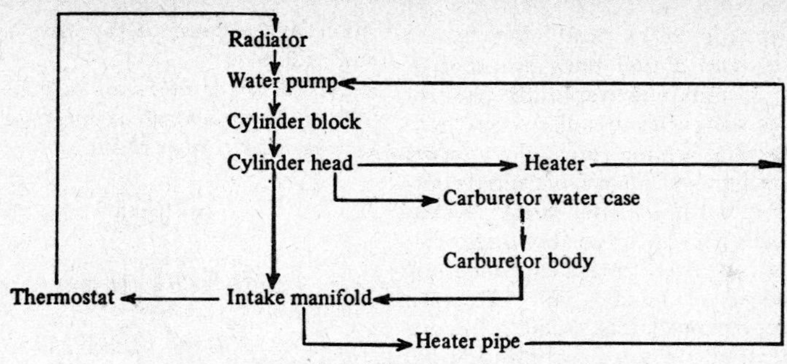

Schematic diagram of coolant flow

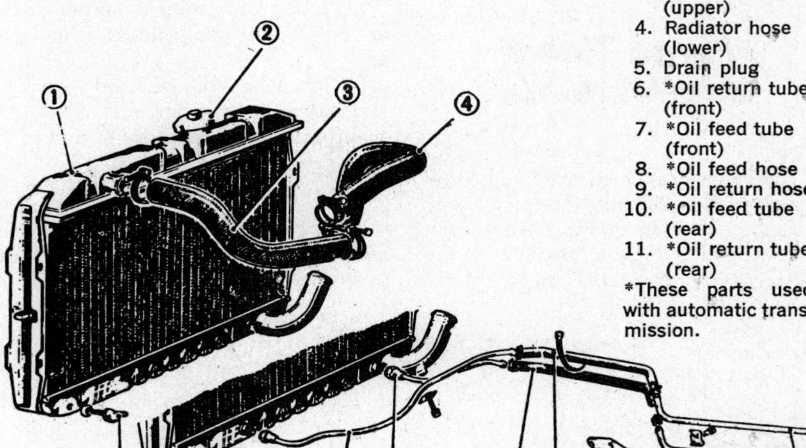

1. Radiator
2. Radiator cap
3. Radiator hose (upper)
4. Radiator hose (lower)
5. Drain plug
6. *Oil return tube (front)
7. *Oil feed tube (front)
8. *Oil feed hose
9. *Oil return hose
10. *Oil feed tube (rear)
11. *Oil return tube (rear)

*These parts used with automatic transmission.

Radiator parts

Water pump impeller installation—Dimension A = 0.772-778 in.

from the vehicle.

CAUTION: *If the car is equipped with an automatic transmission, remove the front oil tube. Be aware of possible fluid spillage when disconnecting the cover tube end to prevent entry of foreign matter. Also, when lifting the radiator from the car, use caution as the core is easily damaged.*

Installation

When replacing the radiator, be sure to align the white marks on the lower radiator hose. If the car is equipped with an automatic transmission, be sure to replace all lost transmission fluid. To replace the radiator, reverse the removal procedure.

Water Pump

Removal

1. Drain the engine cooling system (the coolant may be used again).
2. Swing the alternator from position and remove the fan pulley and belt.
3. Remove the attachments and lift off the water pump.

Disassembly

1. Remove the impeller from the pump body.
2. Using the minimum necessary force, drive the seal from body.
3. Heat the pump body to 212° F and press the shaft assembly toward the pulley.
4. Check the bearings for excessive wear. Closely inspect other parts and replace as necessary.
5. If the pump has a history of leaking, replace all seals.

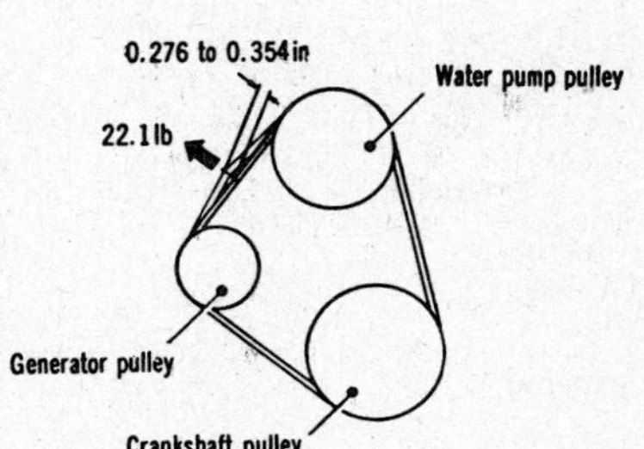

Fan belt adjustment

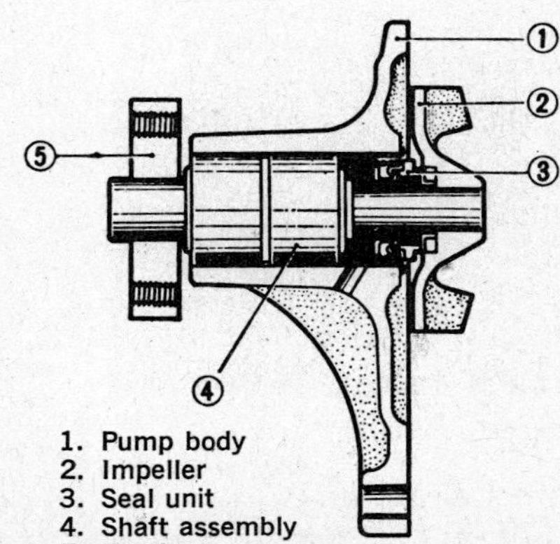

1. Pump body
2. Impeller
3. Seal unit
4. Shaft assembly
5. Bracket

Cross-section of the water pump

Assembly

1. Heat the body of the pump to 212° F.
2. Using a press, drive the shaft assembly into the body unit.
3. Be sure it is flush with the bearing face.

NOTE: *Do not attempt this operation without heating the pump body.*

4. Use new seals on the body and impeller sides.
5. Drive the impeller onto the shaft until it is flush with the end.
6. Body end face-to-shaft end dimension should be 0.772–0.788 in.

Installation

To replace the pump, reverse the removal procedure. When installing the pump body onto the timing chain case, be sure to use new packing and an adequate amount of sealant. Rotate the shaft to be sure the impeller does not interfere with the case. Install the fan pulley and belt. Adjust the belt tension using the illustration. Replace the coolant and check for leaks with the engine running.

Thermostat R&R

1. Drain the coolant from the engine.

2. Remove the water outlet hose from the fitting, located next to the intake manifold.

3. Remove the thermostat. To replace, reverse the removal procedure.

4. Be sure to use a good sealant on the water outlet fitting.

Testing

1. Immerse the thermostat in water.

2. The thermostat should begin to open when the water temperature reaches 179–182° F.

3. The fully open position should be reached at 203° F.

4. If the thermostat is defective, it must be replaced.

EMISSION CONTROLS

In order to comply with Federal air pollution standards, all Colt automobiles incorporate a Cleaner Air System. This consists of various carburetor modifications (throttle valve positioner, leaner jets, etc.) and a fuel tank evaporative emission system. The evaporative control system consists of a sub tank to trap vaporized gas and a filter canister equipped with a purge valve. This valve admits outside air into the canister to force condensed gas back into the fuel lines. The charcoal contained in this canister must be serviced at 50,000 mile intervals. When replacing charcoal (8.802.), be sure to remove all carbon dust. In addition, this canister contains a filter paper and air cleaner. These must be replaced yearly or at 12,000 mile intervals.

Purge Valve Maintenance

This valve must be checked for proper operation at 24,000 mile intervals. Apply a vacuum of -19.69 in. Hg. to the carburetor side of the intake manifold. If the purge valve air flow rate is *less* than 0.071 cubic feet per minute, the valve is operating properly.

NOTE: *Poor idle may also be indicative of an inoperative purge valve. Service is by replacement.*

FUEL SYSTEM

Fuel Pump

Removal and Installation

1. Remove the fuel lines from the pump and cover the ends.

2. Unbolt the pump mounting bolts, and remove the pump, insulator, and gasket.

3. Coat both sides of a new insulator and gasket with sealer, and install the pump in the reverse order of removal.

Carburetors

The carburetor used on all Colt vehicles consists of an emission controlled, downdraft, two barrel unit.

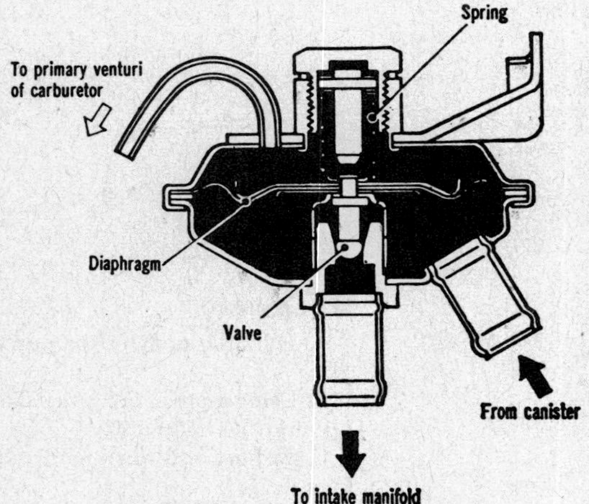

Evaporative emission system schematic diagram.

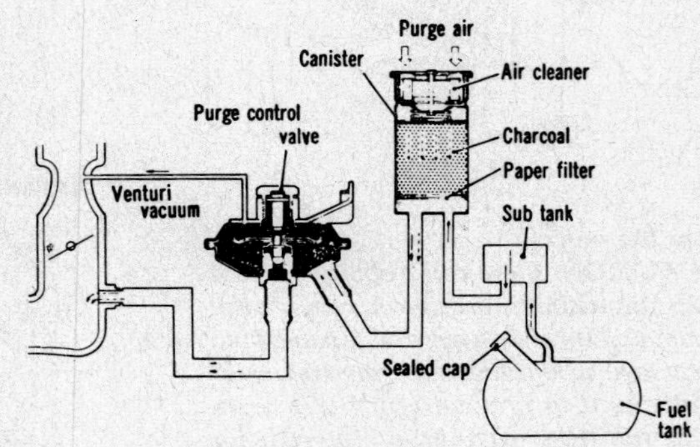

Purge valve schematic diagram

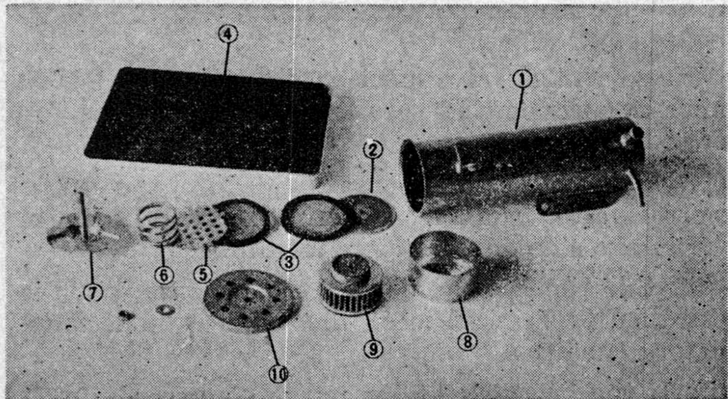

Exploded view of charcoal canister

1. Canister body
2. Filter
3. Strainer
4. Charcoal
5. Plate
6. Spring
7. Plate
8. Spacer
9. Air cleaner element
10. Cup

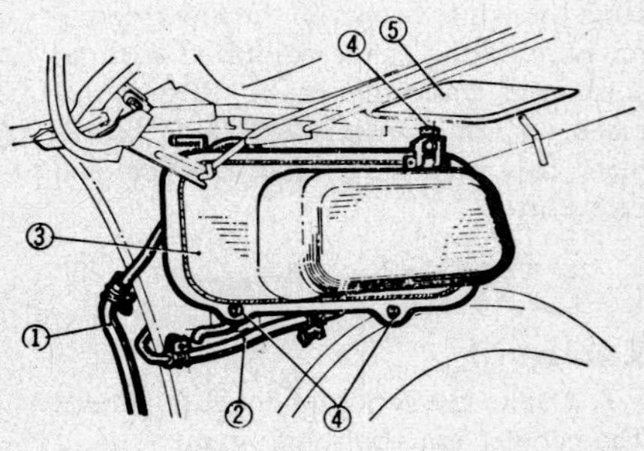

Sub tank schematic diagram

1. Liquid tube
2. Vapor tube
3. Sub tank
4. Attaching bolt
5. Shelf trim

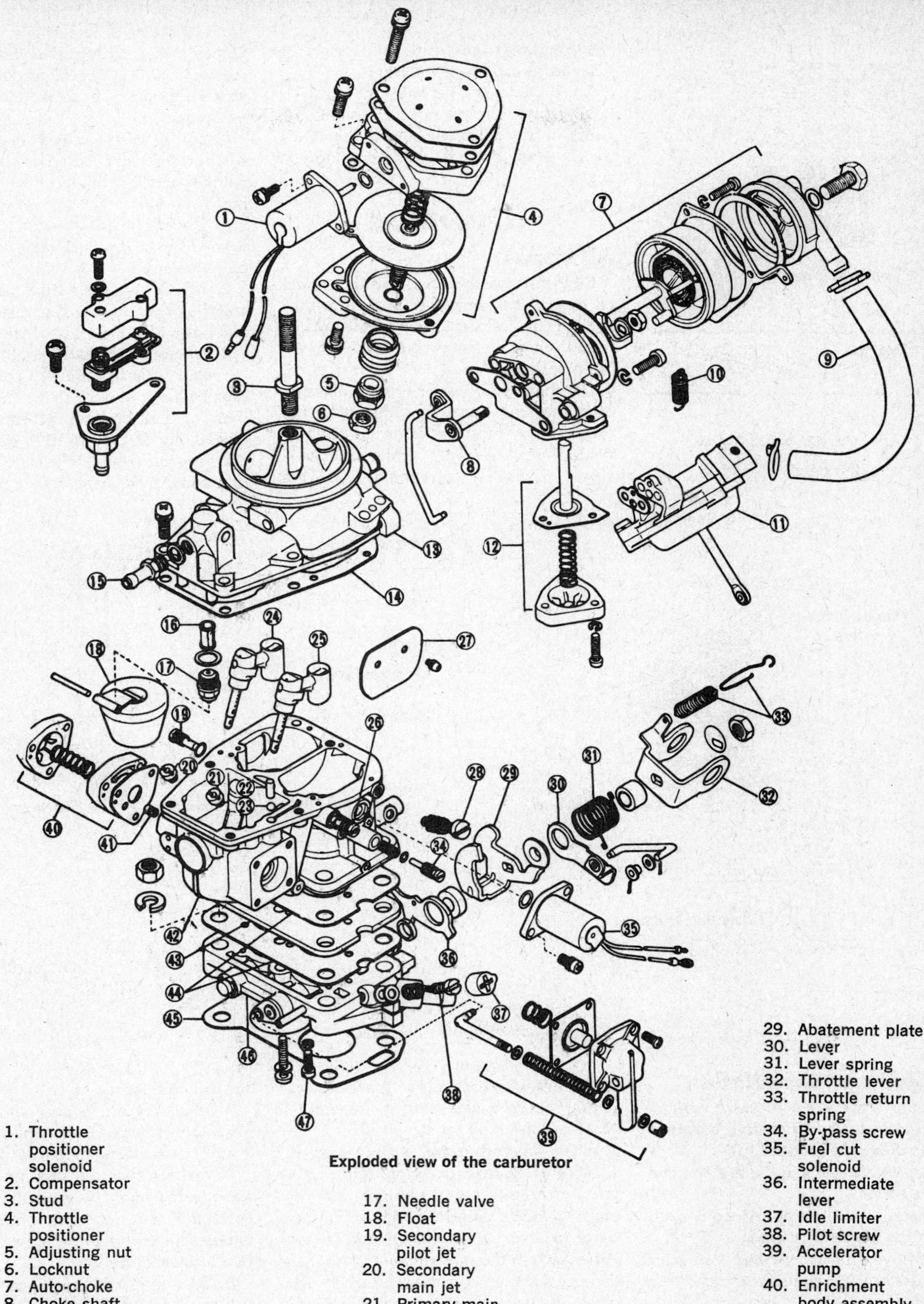

Exploded view of the carburetor

1. Throttle positioner solenoid
2. Compensator
3. Stud
4. Throttle positioner
5. Adjusting nut
6. Locknut
7. Auto-choke
8. Choke shaft
9. Water hose
10. Return spring
11. Depression chamber
12. Piston chamber
13. Float chamber cover
14. Float chamber packing
15. Fuel joint
16. Filter
17. Needle valve
18. Float
19. Secondary pilot jet
20. Secondary main jet
21. Primary main jet
22. Pump weight
23. Steel ball
24. Inner secondary venturi
25. Inner primary venturi
26. Primary pilot jet
27. Choke valve
28. Throttle stop screw
29. Abatement plate
30. Lever
31. Lever spring
32. Throttle lever
33. Throttle return spring
34. By-pass screw
35. Fuel cut solenoid
36. Intermediate lever
37. Idle limiter
38. Pilot screw
39. Accelerator pump
40. Enrichment body assembly
41. Enrichment jet
42. Main body
43. Insulator
44. Throttle chamber packing
45. Carburetor gasket
46. Throttle body
47. Throttle stop screw

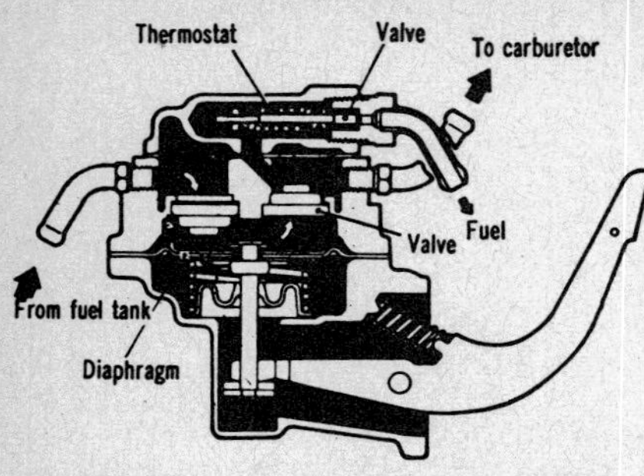

Fuel pump showing internal parts

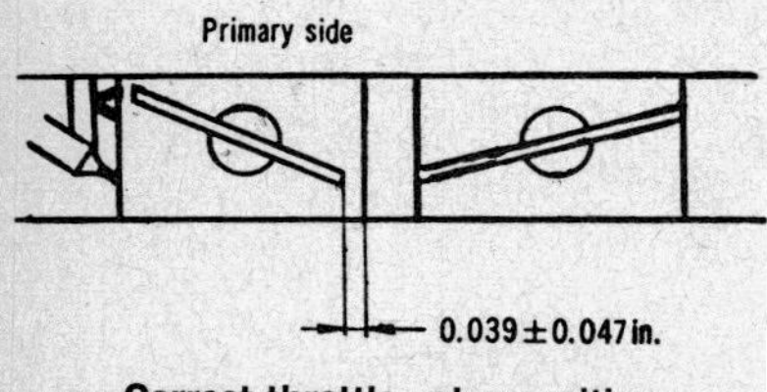

Correct throttle valve position

head.

9. Be sure to have some clean, dry rags at hand to catch any overflow.

10. Remove the carburetor.

To replace the carburetor, reverse the removal procedure. Be sure to use a new gasket and coat it with commercial sealer.

Overhaul

All Types

Efficient carburetion depends greatly on careful cleaning and inspection during overhaul since dirt, gum, water, or varnish in or on the carburetor parts are often responsible for poor performance.

Overhaul your carburetor in a clean, dust-free area. Carefully disassemble the carburetor, referring often to the exploded views. Keep all similar and look-alike parts segregated during disassembly and cleaning to avoid accidental interchange during assembly. Make a note of all jet sizes.

When the carburetor is disassembled, wash all parts (except diaphragms, electric choke units, pump plunger, and any other plastic, leather, fiber, or rubber parts) in clean carburetor solvent. Do not leave parts in the solvent any longer than is necessary to sufficiently loosen the deposits. Excessive cleaning may remove the special finish from the float bowl and choke valve bodies, leaving these parts unfit for service. Rinse all parts in clean solvent and blow them dry with compressed air or allow them to air dry. Wipe clean all cork, plastic, leather, and fiber parts with a clean, lint-free cloth.

Blow out all passages and jets with compressed air and be sure that there are no restrictions or blockages. Never use wire or similar tools to clean jets, fuel passages, or air bleeds. Clean all jets and valves separately to avoid accidental interchange.

Check all parts for wear or damage. If wear or damage is found, replace the defective parts. Especially check the following:

1. Check the float needle and seat for wear. If wear is found, replace the complete assembly.
2. Check the float hinge pin for wear and the float(s) for dents or distortion. Replace the float if fuel has leaked into it.
3. Check the throttle and choke shaft bores for wear or an out-of-round condition. Damage or wear to the throttle arm, shaft, or shaft bore will often require replacement of the throttle body. These parts require a close tolerance of fit; wear may allow air leakage, which could affect starting and idling.

NOTE: *Throttle shafts and bushings are not included in overhaul kits. They can be purchased separately.*

4. Inspect the idle mixture adjusting needles for burrs or grooves. Any such condition requires replacement of the needle, since you will not be able to obtain a satisfactory idle.
5. Test the accelerator pump check valves. They should pass air one way but not the other. Test for proper seating by blowing and sucking on the valve. Replace the valve if necessary. If the valve is satisfactory, wash the valve again to remove breath moisture.
6. Check the bowl cover for warped surfaces with a straightedge.
7. Closely inspect the valves and seats for wear and damage, replacing as neces-

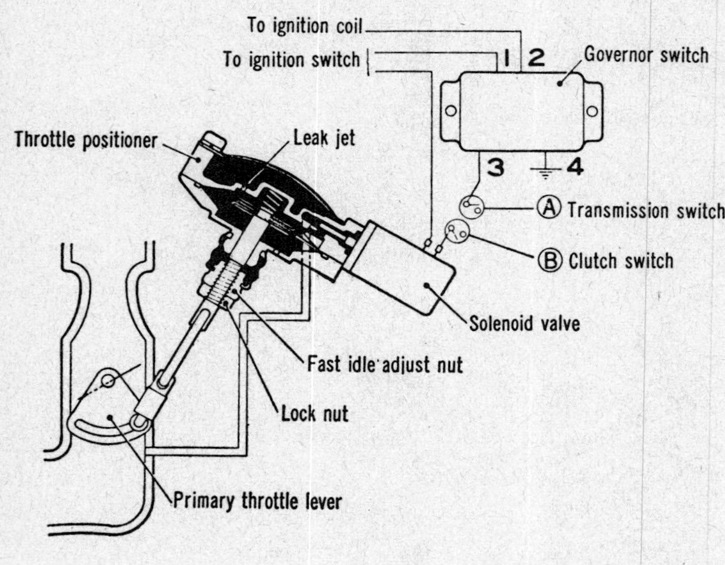

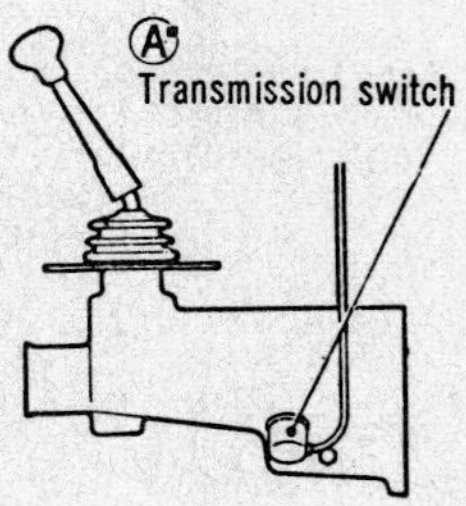

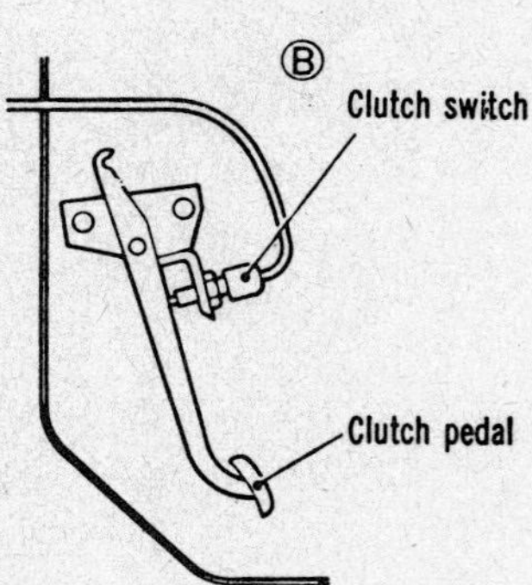

Operation of throttle positioner

Removal and Installation

1. Remove the solenoid valve wiring.
2. Disconnect the air cleaner breather hose, air duct and vacuum tube.
3. Loosen the wing nuts and remove the air cleaner.
4. Unscrew the support bolts and remove the air cleaner case.
5. Remove the accelerator and shift cables (automatic transmission) at the carburetor
6. Disconnect the purge valve hose; remove the vacuum compensator, and fuel lines.
7. Loosen the drain plug (on the right side of the block) and drain the water.

NOTE: *The water contains anti-freeze and may be reused.*

8. Remove the water hose from between the carburetor and the cylinder

sary.

8. After the carburetor is assembled, check the choke valve for freedom of operation.

Carburetor overhaul kits are recommended for each overhaul. These kits contain all gaskets and new parts to replace those that deteriorate most rapidly. Failure to replace all parts supplied with the kit (especially gaskets) can result in poor performance later.

Some carburetor manufacturers supply overhaul kits of three basic types: minor repair; major repair; and gasket kits. Basically, they contain the following:

Minor Repair Kits:
- All gaskets
- Float needle valve
- Volume control screw
- All diaphragms
- Spring for the pump diaphragm

Major Repair Kits:
- All jets and gaskets
- All diaphragms
- Float needle valve
- Volume control screw
- Pump ball valve
- Main jet carrier
- Float
- Complete intermediate rod
- Intermediate pump lever
- Complete injector tube
- Some cover hold-down screws and washers

Gasket Kits:
- All gaskets

After cleaning and checking all components, reassemble the carburetor, using new parts and referring to the exploded view. When reassembling, make sure that all screws and jets are right in their seats, but do not overtighten, as the tips will be distorted. Tighten all screws gradually, in rotation. Do not tighten needle valves into their seats; uneven jetting will result. Always use new gaskets. Be sure to adjust the float level when reassembling.

MANUAL TRANSMISSION

All Colt manual transmissions are four speed, fully synchromeshed units. Lubricant to be used in this transmission should be an SAE 80 multipurpose type with a grade of GL4 or higher. This lubricant should be changed after the first 600 miles and at 36,000 mile intervals thereafter.

Removal

1. Disconnect and remove the battery. Remove the starter. Withdraw the two large transmission top bolts (located in the engine compartment).
2. Remove the gearshift assembly and related parts from inside the vehicle.
3. Place the vehicle on jack stands and drain the transmission. Disconnect the speedometer and back-up light switch.
4. Disconnect the driveshaft at the transmission. Remove the muffler pipe and clutch cables.
5. With the transmission fully supported, unbolt the rear support (insulator).
6. Unbolt the bellhousing.
7. Remove the remaining nuts and pull the transmission rearward.

CAUTION: *Be certain not to damage the transmission when withdrawing it.*

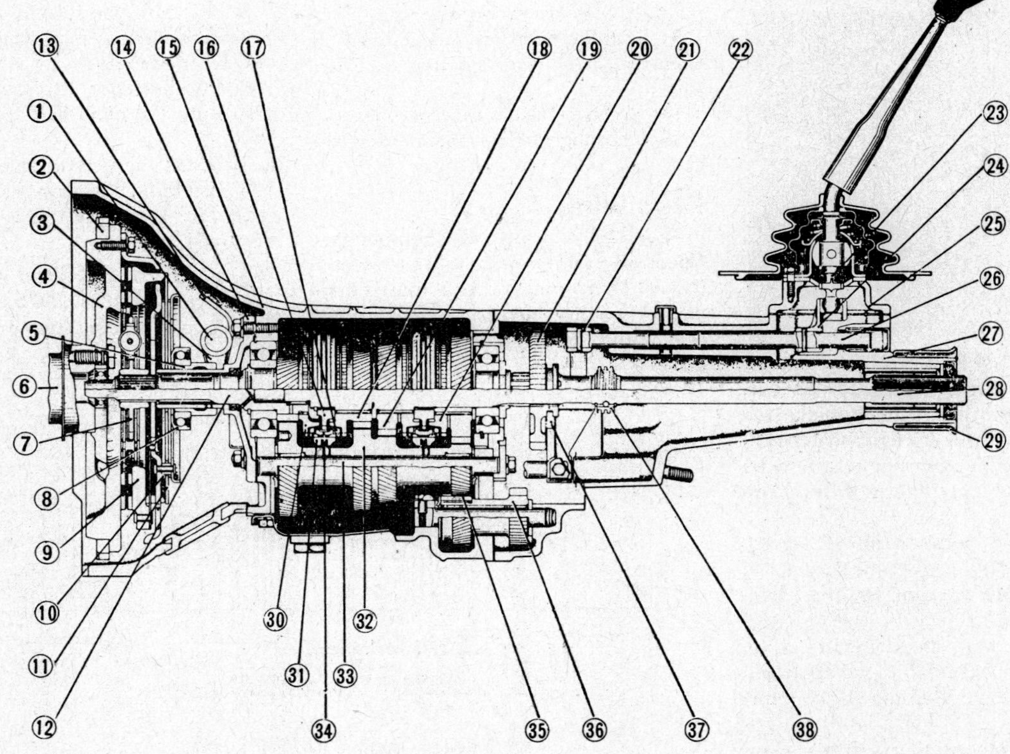

Cross-section of a four-speed transmission

1. Clutch shaft
2. Flywheel gear
3. Clutch shift arm
4. Flywheel
5. Release bearing carrier
6. Crankshaft
7. Clutch disc
8. Release bearing
9. Pressure plate
10. Wire
11. Diaphragm spring
12. Main drive gear
13. Return spring
14. Front bearing retainer
15. Transmission case
16. Synchronizer hub
17. Blocking ring
18. Third speed gear
19. Second speed gear
20. First speed gear
21. Reverse gear
22. Shift lever
23. Control housing
24. Shifter
25. Control housing
26. Control shaft
27. Extension housing
28. Main shaft
29. Dust seal guard
30. Clutch gear
31. Synchronizer sleeve
32. Countergear
33. Countergear shaft
34. Synchronizer piece
35. Reverse idler gear front
36. Reverse idler gear rear
37. Shift fork
38. Speedometer drive gear

Installation

To install the transmission, reverse the removal procedure. When replacing the gearshift assembly, place the shifter in first gear. This will align the bushing holes. Be sure that all operations are performed so that no foreign matter enters the transmission. After installation, adjust the clutch and refill the transmission with lubricant.

Torque Specifications

Transmission mounting bolts:
18.1–21.7 ft lbs (NO. 7 on head of bolt)
8.7–10.8 ft lbs (NO. 4 on head of bolt)
Starter bolts: 14.5–21.7 ft lbs
Transmission-insulator bolts: 7.2–8.7 ft lbs
Insulator-frame bolts: 14.5–17.4 ft lbs
Frame bolts: 14.5–17.4 ft lbs

Disassembly

Thoroughly clean the outside of the transmission before disassembly.

1. Using a 3/16 in. punch, drive out the clutch spring pins. Remove the clutch shaft with release fork and springs.

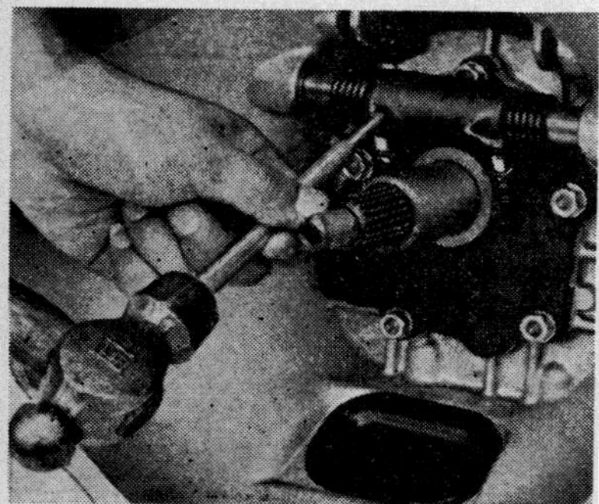

Spring pin removal

2. Remove the speedometer gear assembly and the lockplate. Remove the clutch and the back-up light switches.
3. The extension housing may now be removed by tapping lightly with a hammer.
4. With the transmission inverted, remove the bottom cover. Be sure not to support the transmission on the mainshaft.
5. Remove the speedometer drive, snap-rings, and gear. Remove the main drive gear retainer. Remove the countershaft stopper.
6. Remove the countershaft rearward. Remove the counter gear, 40 roller bearings, spacers, and front and rear washers.
7. Lift out the thrust washer, rear idler gear, needle bearings, and spacer located on the reverse idler gear shaft.
8. Withdraw the gear shaft bolt and pull the shaft from the case. Remove the front idler gear.
9. Locate the three plugs on the left case side. Remove them with the poppet springs and balls.

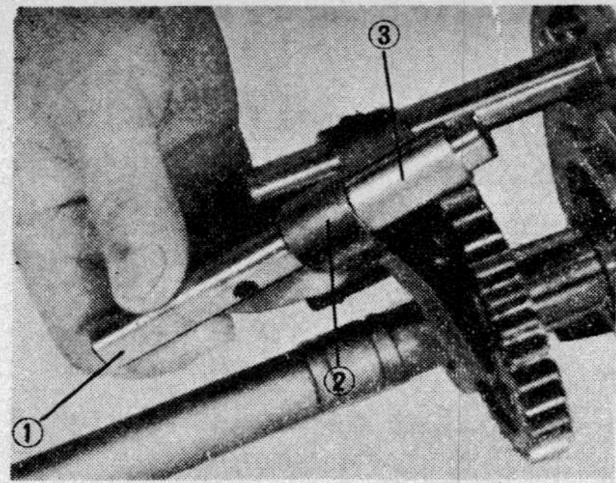

Reverse shifter fork removal

1. Reverse shift bar
2. Reverse shift fork
3. Spacer

10. Loosen the reverse shift bar and reverse locking bolt. Pull out the reverse shift bar. Remove the reverse shaft fork and spacer.
11. Using a 3/16 in. punch, drive the fork spring pins and shift bar from the mount. Remove the shift bar and shaft fork. Do not disassemble the shift bar.
12. Remove the reverse gear from case.
13. Remove the mainshaft and the main drive gear synchronizer ring.
14. Pull the main drive gear assembly from the case front. Remove all snap-rings.
15. Remove the shifter assembly.
16. Thoroughly clean the inside of the case.

Rebuilding

Thoroughly wash all components. Check all parts for wear and serviceability. All shims and oil seals must be replaced with new pieces. When assembling, lubricate all parts as necessary.

Four-Speed Transmission Specifications

Helical gear backlash: 0.002–0.006 in.
Shift fork to sleeve clearance: 0.004–0.008 in.
Spur gear backlash: 0.004–0.008 in.
Gear change lever-selector groove clearance: 0.004–0.012 in.
Reverse shift fork-reverse gear groove clearance: 0.004–0.012 in.

Main Drive Gear Unit

1. Press the bearing onto the main drive gear.
2. Secure it with a snap-ring of appropriate thickness to give an end-play of 0.002 in.

Snap-Ring Code (in.)
White 0.091
None 0.093
Red 0.094
Yellow 0.098

3. Assemble the hub and synchronizer ring.
4. Place the front and rear springs on the shaft in opposite directions.
5. Assemble the second gear synchronizer hub with the stepped gear end (narrow toothed side) rearward.
6. Install the needle bearings and third gear onto the mainshaft from the front end.
7. Install the synchronizer assembly.
8. Assemble the first-second synchronizer in the same direction it was removed.
9. Fit the snap-rings to give a proper end-play of 0.0012–0.0075 in. The third-fourth gear hub end-play is 0.00–0.0043 in.

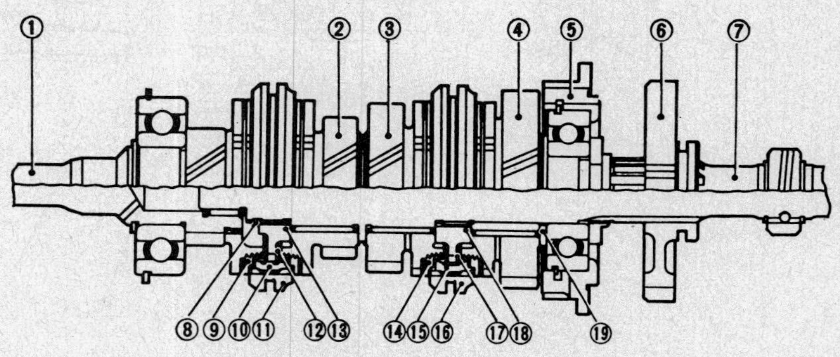

Assembled view of the mainshaft

1. Main drive gear
2. Third speed gear
3. Second speed gear
4. First speed gear
5. Rear bearing retainer
6. Reverse gear
7. Mainshaft
8. Snap-ring
9. Synchronizer ring
10. Synchronizer piece
11. Synchronizer sleeve
12. Synchronizer spring
13. Synchronizer hub (third-fourth)
14. Synchronizer ring
15. Synchronizer piece
16. Synchronizer sleeve
17. Synchronizer spring
18. Synchronizer hub (first-second)
19. Spacer

Snap Ring Code (in.)
None 0.085
Yellow 0.087
Green 0.090
Blue 0.093

10. Place the needle bearings and second gear on the mainshaft from the rear.
11. Install the synchronizer assembly.
12. Check and adjust the end-play to 0.0012–0.0075 in.
13. Place the first gear spacer, needle bearings, synchronizer, and first gear on the shaft.
14. Adjust end-play to 0.0012–0.0075 in.
15. Spacer must be installed with the I mark in the direction of the ball bearing
16. Install the mainshaft bearing with a suitable driver and tighten the locknut.
17. Install the snap-ring and retainer.
18. Adjust to give a mainshaft bearing end-play of 0.00–0.006 in.

Snap-Rings (in.)
None 0.057
Red 0.060
White 0.064
Yellow 0.067
Blue 0.071

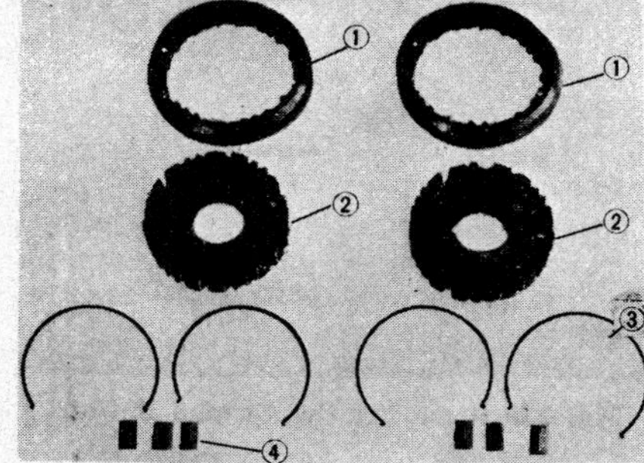

Exploded view of synchronizers

1. Synchronizer sleeve
2. Synchronizer hub
3. Springs
4. Synchronizer pieces

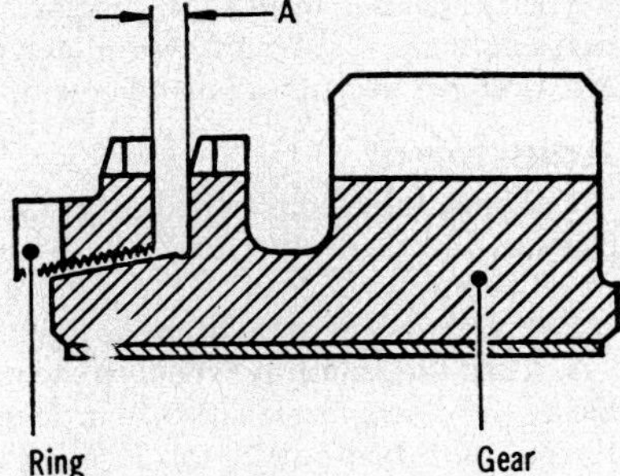

Synchronizer inspection—Dimension A = 0.059 in.

19. Invert the transmission case.
20. Install the main drive gear assembly into the transmission case.
21. Place the needle bearings on the main drive gear front end.
22. Install the synchronizer ring.
23. Be certain that all synchronizer rings are in proper mesh.
24. Install the rear bearing retainer in the case.

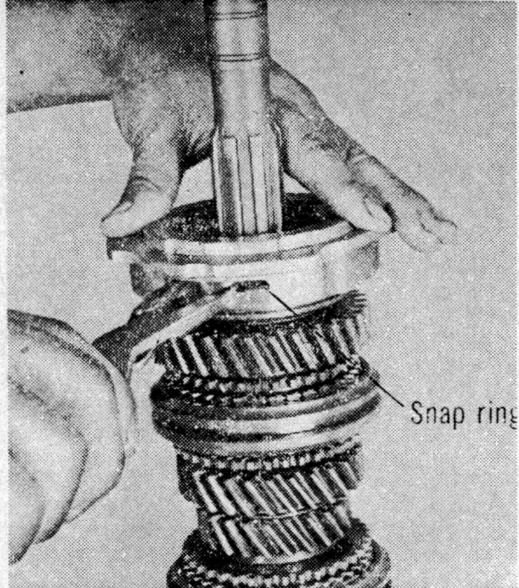

Snap ring installation

Shifter Fork and Bar Installation

1. Place the reverse gear in position on the mainshaft. Install the shift fork into the shift fork groove in the synchronizer sleeve. While holding the forks, place the third-fourth shift bar assembly into the case through the lower rear hole.
2. Insert the first interlock plunger in the case; drive the plunger into position with the use of an appropriate driver.
3. Place the first-second gear shift bar assembly into the case. Position the shift forks so that the pin holes are aligned with the shift bar holes. Secure the shift forks to the shift bars with spring pins. Be sure to drive the spring pins into position with the slot on the centerline of the shift bar.
4. Insert the second interlock plunger into the case.
5. Place the reverse shift fork ends in the reverse gear groove. Insert the reverse gear bar into the fork. Install the spacer on the shift bar and place the reverse shift bar assembly into the case. Secure the fork to the bar with a locking bolt.
6. Position the poppet balls and springs. Insert the plugs with commercial sealant. Be certain to install the tapered end of the poppet spring toward the poppet balls.

Reverse Idler Gear Installation

Place the needle bearings and spacers in position on the rear reverse idler gear. Insert the assembly into the rear of the case. Place the front idler gear with the thrust washer onto the rear shaft end. Insert the gear shaft in the case and secure with a bolt.

Rear Thrust Washer Installation

1. Measure the size from the rear surface of the transmission case to the rear of the reverse idler gear.
2. Measure the depth from the extension housing end to the idler gear shaft end. Add 0.004 in. This figure is the extension housing packing thickness.
3. Subtract NO. 2 from NO. 1. Subtract 0.009–0.012 in. (thrust washer clearance) from the result.

Example:

Dimension 1	0.863 in.
Dimension 2 (includes 0.004 in.)	—0.774 in.
	0.089 in.
Minus 0.009-0.012 in. in clearance	—0.011 in.
Thickness of thrust washer required	0.078 in.

Thrust washer identification (in.)

A—0.078	C—0.093
B—0.085	D—0.100

(This figure is the thickness of the thrust washer required.)

Thrust Washer Identification (in.)
A-0.078
B-0.085
C-0.093
D-0.100

Counter Gear Installation

1. Insert the needle roller bearings (20 front, 20 rear) and spacers in the front and rear holes of the counter gear.
2. Lubricate as necessary.
3. Be sure the spacers are installed on the outside of the roller bearings.
4. Install a 1.378 in. OD thrust washer on the front end of the countergear.
5. Install a 1.181 in. ID thrust washer on the rear end.
6. Holding the countergear cluster inside the case, install the countergear shaft

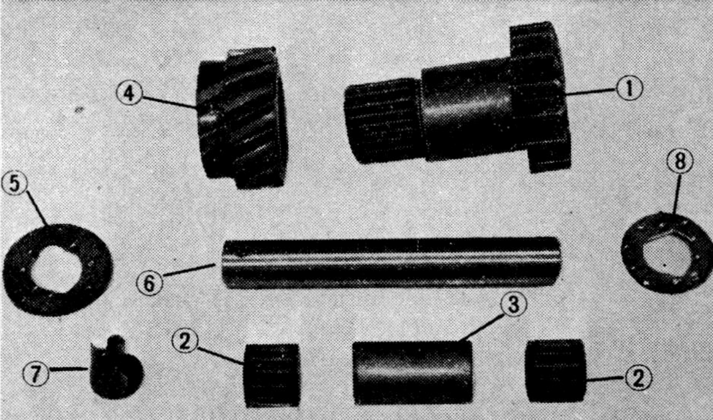

1. Reverse idler gear
2. Needle bearing
3. Spacer
4. Front idler gear
5. Thrust washer
6. Gear shaft
7. Bolt
8. Selective rear thrust washer

Exploded view of the reverse idler gear

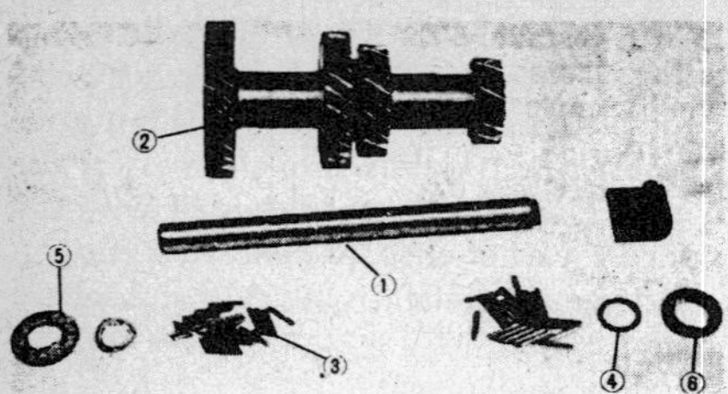

Exploded view of the counter gear

1. Countershaft
2. Counter gear
3. Needle rollers
4. Spacer
5. Thrust washer
6. Thrust washer

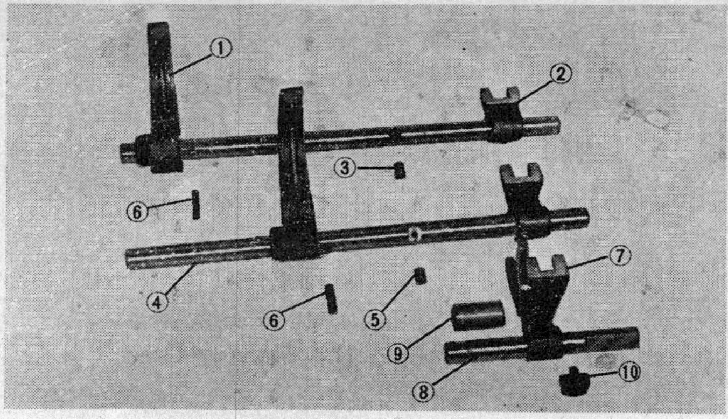

Exploded view of the shift bar

1. Shift fork
2. Third-fourth shift bar
3. Interlock plunger
4. First-second speed shift bear
5. Interlock plunger
6. Spring pins
7. Reverse shift fork
8. Reverse shift bar
9. Spacer
10. Locking bolt

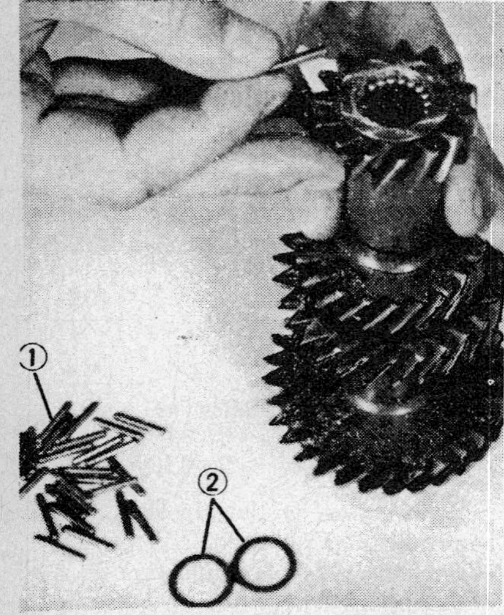

Needle bearing installation

1. Needle rollers
2. Bearing spacers

Counter gear installation

from the rear and properly mesh the gears.

7. Select a rear thrust washer to give 0.002–0.007 in. countergear end-play.
   A-0.080
   B-0.083
   C-0.086
   D-0.089
   E-0.092
8. Secure the rear shaft end with a stopper plate.
9. Place the front bearing retainer in position and install the front bearing.
10. Bearing-to-retainer clearance should be 0.002–0.0012 in.
11. Place the speedometer driven gear on the mainshaft.
12. There should be no clearance between the speedometer gear and the snap-ring.
13. Shim if necessary.
14. Connect the extension housing to the transmission case.
15. Be sure to apply sealant.
16. When installing the washers, install with the bulged side toward the bolt head.
17. Install the transmission and back-up light switch.
18. Next, install the locking plate and the transmission driven gear.

9. Finally, secure the under-cover to the transmission.
10. Torque the bolts to 5.8–7.2 ft lbs.
11. Tighten in a criss-cross pattern in two stages.
12. Fill the transmission with an appropriate lubricant.

Shifter Installation

1. Place the gear lever in the first gear gate.
2. Be sure the nylon bushing is in the vertical position.
3. With the transmission in the car, apply sealant to the packings and grease bushings.
4. Insert the clutch control shaft into the transmission from the left-hand side.
5. Assemble the shift fork and springs onto the shaft.
6. Align the shift fork with the clutch control shaft.
7. Drive the spring pin into the pin hole and set the spring.
8. Be certain that the spring pin has its slot on the centerline of the clutch control shaft.
9. Grease all appropriate parts and check the operation of the shifter.

CLUTCH

The clutch used in all Colt vehicles is a dry, single disc diaphragm type clutch of conventional design and construction.

Adjustment

1. Adjust the clutch switch so that the distance between the toe board and pedal face is 6.7 in.
2. Pull the outer cable from the holder.
3. Turn the adjusting wheel so the cable holder clearance is 0.20–0.24 in. (each turn of the wheel is 0.06 in).
4. Check the clutch free play. This is the distance between the release bearing and the diaphragm spring operation. It should be 0.079 in. Pedal free play should be 0.8–1.2 in.

Removal

1. Remove the transmission.
2. Loosen the six bolts on the pressure plate assembly and remove the pressure plate.
3. Be certain not to damage the clutch components.

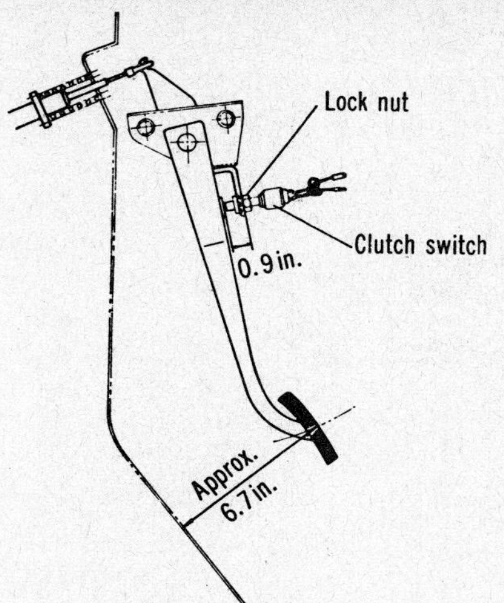

Clutch switch adjustments

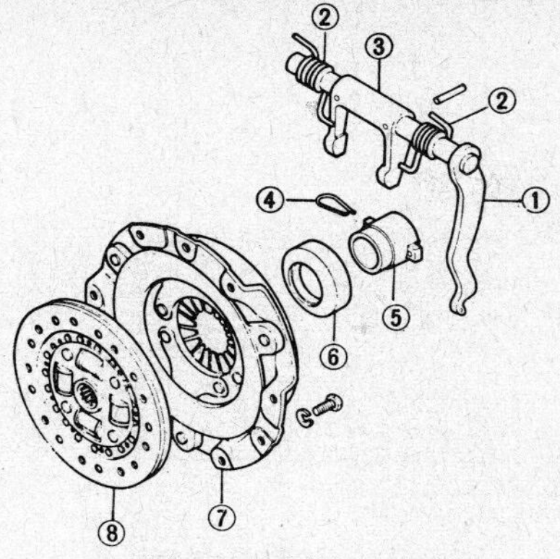

Exploded view of the clutch

1. Clutch control shaft
2. Return spring
3. Clutch shift arm
4. Return clip
5. Release bearing carrier
6. Release bearing
7. Pressure plate assembly
8. Clutch disc

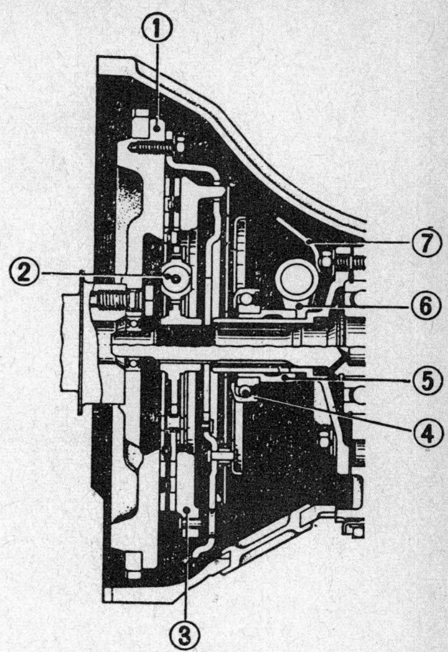

Cross-section of the clutch

1. Flywheel
2. Clutch disc
3. Pressure plate
4. Release bearing
5. Release bearing carrier
6. Clutch shift arm
7. Return spring

Clutch pedal components

1. Clutch cable
2. Spring
3. Pedal support
4. Spacer
5. Bushing
6. Spring
7. Clutch pedal
8. Pedal pad
10. Silencer
11. Brake pedal

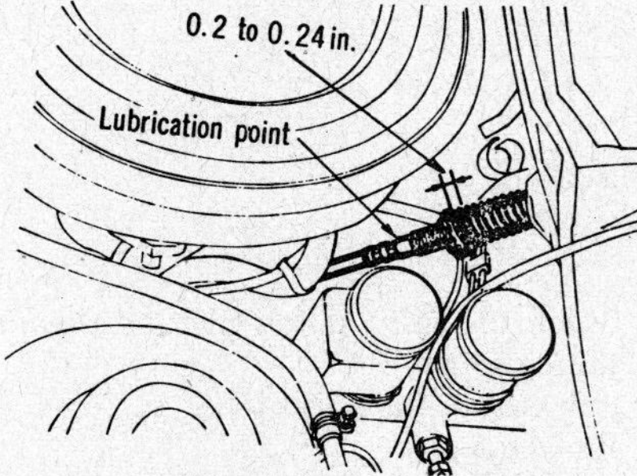

Clutch lubrication and adjustment

4. Lift off the return clip on the transmission side and remove the release bearing and carrier.

5. Utilizing a 3/16 in. punch, loosen and remove the control lever and the spring pin.

6. The shift arm and return spring are now free to remove.

Installation

1. Insert the control lever tongue into the transmission with the springs and arm.

2. Fill the shaft oil seal with lubricant.

3. Be certain that the spring pins are aligned.

4. Install the release bearing, carrier, and return clip.

5. Lubricate the carrier groove, inner wall, and clutch disc spine.

6. Place the disc and pressure plate on the flywheel and center the disc with an old mainshaft.

7. Be certain to install the disc with the larger boss facing the transmission.

8. Install the transmission and adjust the clutch assembly.

AUTOMATIC TRANSMISSION

The automatic transmission used in all Colt models is a Borg Warner, with an aluminum case. This transmission is cooled by a separate cooler/filter assembly located in the radiator bottom. Fluid capacity is 1.4 gallons (plus cooler capacity).

Removal

1. Remove: the air cleaner, battery with cables, starter, and the upper bolts which attach the engine to the transmission.

2. Place the car on jack stands. Drain the transmission. Remove the speedometer cable and disconnect the driveshaft.

3. Remove the exhaust system from the connecting pipe rearward to the muffler.

4. Remove the transmission oil lines.

5. Remove the control rod from its attachment to the arm.

6. Loosen and remove the bellhousing. While rotating the torque converter, remove the four exposed bolts.

7. Place a jack under the transmission. **NOTE:** *Do not support the transmission on the oil pan.*

8. Remove the insulator attaching bolts, ground cable, and spacer. Remove the insulator.

9. Remove the torque converter and pull out the transmission.

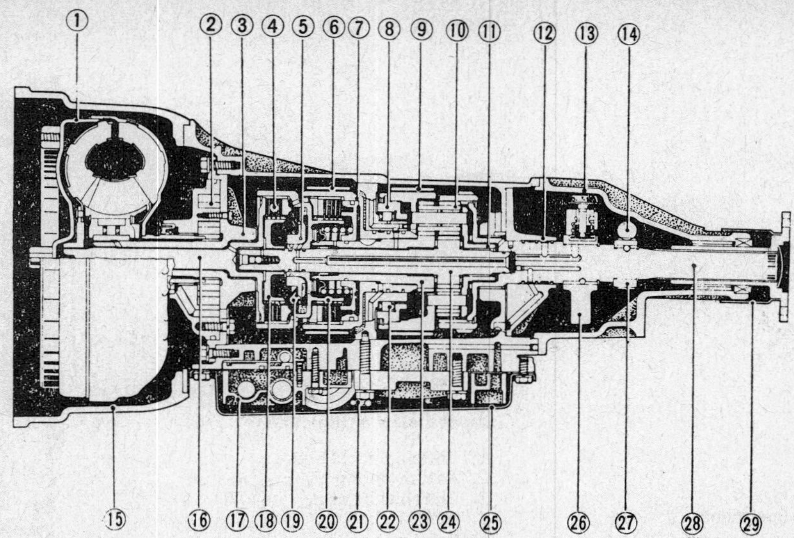

Automatic transmission

1. Torque converter
2. Oil pump gear
3. Pump adapter and converter support
4. Front clutch plate
5. Front clutch piston
6. Front brake band
7. Front drum
8. One-way clutch outer race
9. Rear brake band
10. Long pinion
11. Planet cover
12. Rear adapter
13. Extension housing
14. Speedometer driven gear
15. Converter housing
16. Input shaft
17. Valve body assembly
18. Front clutch hub
19. Front clutch spring
20. Front clutch cylinder
21. Oil tube
22. One-way clutch assembly
23. Reverse sun gear
24. Forward sun gear
25. Oil pan
26. Governor assembly
27. Speedometer drive gear
28. Output shaft
29. Coupling flange

Installation

To install the transmission, reverse the removal procedure.

Torque Specifications

Insulator attaching bolts: 14.5–17.4 ft lbs.

Insulator-to-transmission bolts: 9.4–11.6 ft lbs

Oil pan bolts: 8–13 ft lbs

Converter housing bolts: 8–13 ft lbs

Maintenance and Adjustment

Automatic transmission fluid should be changed at 2 year or 24,000 mile intervals. This should be performed more often if the vehicle is used in severe service. When the oil is replaced, the transmission bands should be adjusted

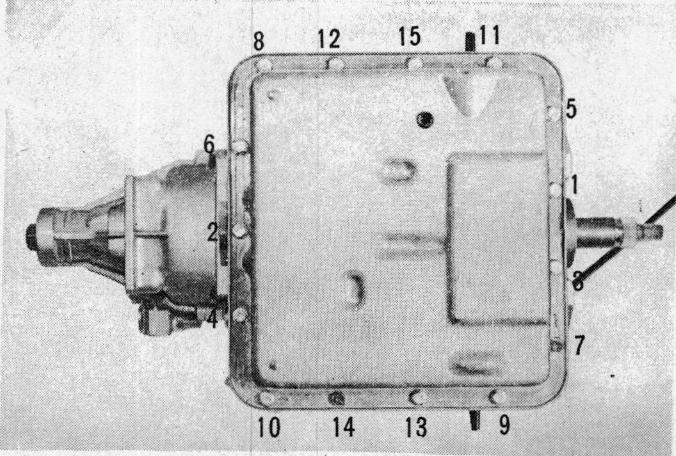

Oil pan removal sequence

Adjusting the Downshift Cable

Run the engine to operating temperature. Adjust the cable by turning the outer adjusting screw until the bottom just contacts the caulked stopper. Adjust to 0.002–0.004 in. clearance. If further adjustment is necessary, perform the following: Remove the transmission pipe plug with a 3/16 in. Allen wrench. Connect the transmission pressure gauge. Set both the parking and the foot brake. With the engine at idle, place the car in gear. Check the line pressure. Normal is 49.-7–65.3 psi. Increase the engine speed to 1,000 rpm. Line pressure should be 65.-3–85.2 psi. The difference in pressure readings should be 15.6–19.6 psi. If it is not, tighten the outer cable with the adjusting screw. This will increase the pressure. To decrease the pressure, reverse this procedure.

Front Band Adjustment

1. Remove the transmission oil pan.
2. Loosen the locknut and move the servo lever out of the way.
3. Insert a 0.35 in. feeler gauge between the servo piston pin and the adjusting screw.
4. Adjust the servo screw to 10.44 in. lbs torque.
5. Tighten the locknut and remove the feeler gauge.

Rear Band Adjustment

This screw is located on the right-hand outer wall of the transmission case. Loosen the locknut. Tighten the nut to 10 ft lbs. Loosen the nut ¾ turn. Tighten down the locknut.

Rear band adjusting screw location

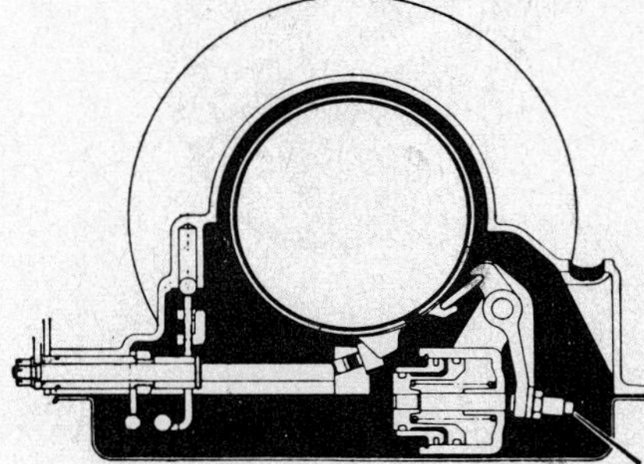

Front band adjusting screw location

Driveshafts and U-Joints

The driveshaft and U-joints used in all Colt models are of conventional design and construction. Driveshaft length differs between the manual and automatic transmission equipped vehicles; therefore, when replacing be sure to specify the transmission type. Normally, no maintenance is required of either the driveshafts or the U-joints.

Driveshaft Removal

1. Place the car on jack stands.
2. Drain the transmission fluid.
3. Remove the flange yoke bolts at the differential pinion flange.
4. Remove the driveshaft from the transmission end by withdrawing it rearward.
5. Be sure not to damage any transmission components.

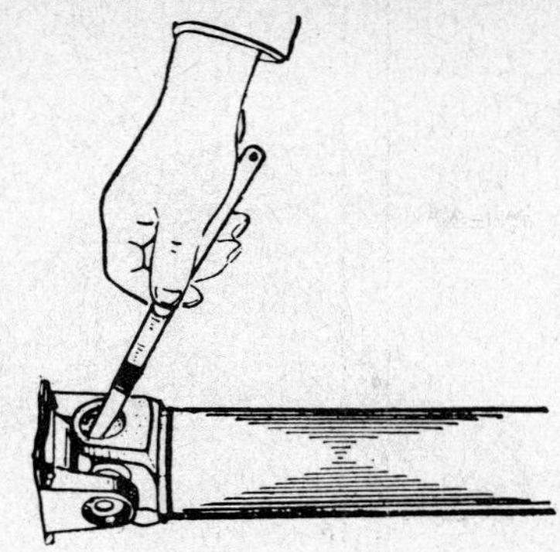
Measure the snap-ring clearance

U-Joint bearing removal

Driveshaft Installation

To replace the driveshaft, reverse the removal procedure. Torque the flange yoke bolts to 11–14.5 ft lbs.

U-Joints and Bearing Removal

1. Remove the driveshaft.
2. Remove the U-joint snap rings.
3. Be sure to note the exact position of the removed parts.
4. With suitable tools, hold the driveshaft flange yoke stationary.
5. Drive out the needle bearings. The U-joint is now free to be removed.

Assembly

1. Pack the U-joint journals, needle bearings, and trunnion with grease.
2. Be sure not to over-lubricate.
3. In addition, apply a thin coating of grease to the dust seal lips.
4. Install the bearings on the U-joint journals using a vise and the appropriate sockets.

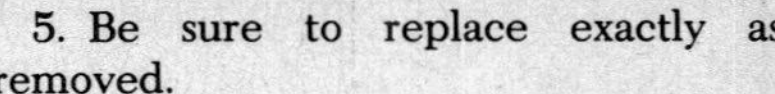

5. Be sure to replace exactly as removed.
6. Install the snap-rings to give the proper bearing-to-snap-ring clearance.
7. Snap-rings selected must be of the same or nearly the same thickness for both shaft ends.
8. This will guarantee proper shaft balance.

Snap-Ring Code (in.)

Yellow-0.0516
None-0.0504
Blue-0.0528
Purple-0.0539

Bearing-to-snap-ring clearance is 0.00–0.001 in. When the snap-rings are installed, press each bearing toward the opposite shaft ends to measure the maximum clearance.

REAR AXLE

All Colt models utilize a banjo type rear axle and a hypoid final drive. Axle shafts are semi-floating; pressure type ball bearing retainers are employed at each axle housing end. Final drive ratio is 3.89:1.

Removal

1. Jack the vehicle and remove the rear wheels. Place jack stands under the rear frame members. With the car resting on jack stands, place a slight upward pressure on the rear axle housing with the jack saddle.
2. Remove the driveshaft.
3. Disconnect all foot and parking rear brake lines. Be sure not to spill brake fluid.
4. Remove the rear U-bolts and the shock absorbers.
5. From the attachment, remove the spring shackle pin nuts and the shackle

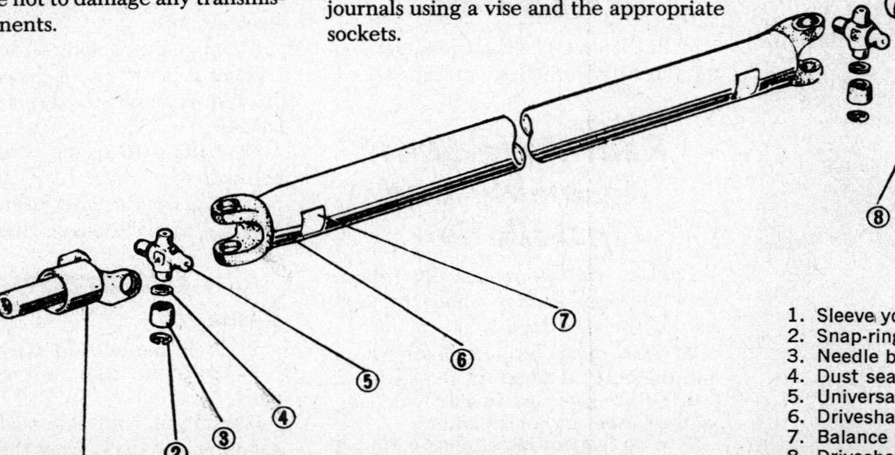

1. Sleeve yoke
2. Snap-ring
3. Needle bearing
4. Dust seal
5. Universal joint journal
6. Driveshaft
7. Balance weight
8. Driveshaft flange yoke

Driveshaft components

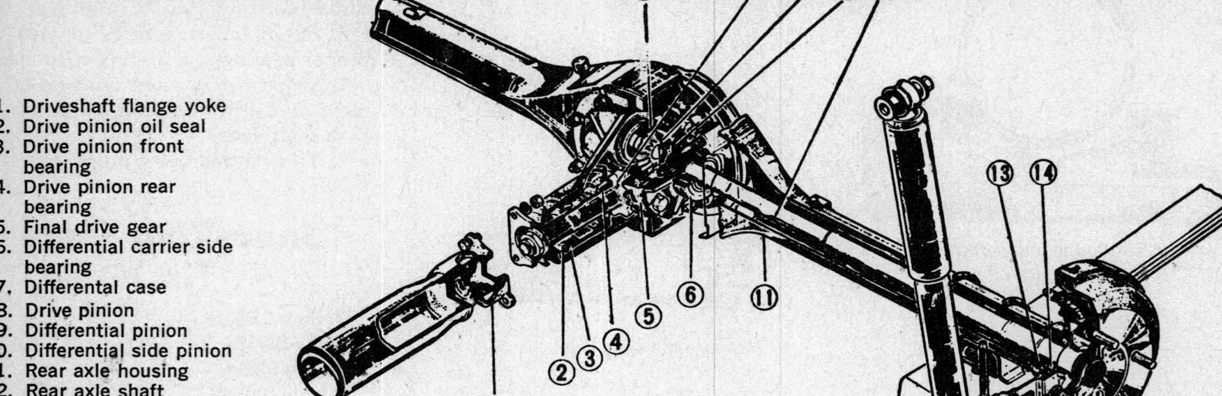

1. Driveshaft flange yoke
2. Drive pinion oil seal
3. Drive pinion front bearing
4. Drive pinion rear bearing
5. Final drive gear
6. Differential carrier side bearing
7. Differental case
8. Drive pinion
9. Differential pinion
10. Differential side pinion
11. Rear axle housing
12. Rear axle shaft
13. Rear axle shaft oil seal
14. Rear axle shaft bearing

Exploded view of the rear axle

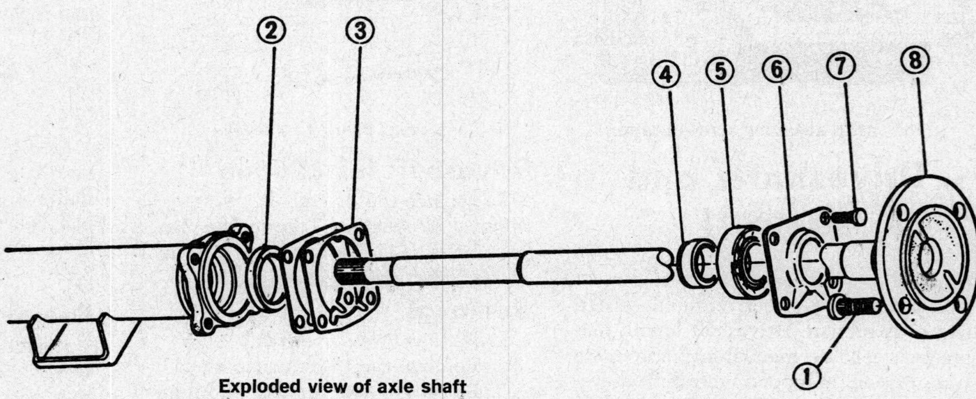

1. Wheel hub bolt
2. Rear axle shaft oil seal
3. Packing
4. Bearing retainer (inner)
5. Bearing
6. Bearing retainer (outer)
7. Bearing retainer bolt
8. Rear axle shaft

Exploded view of axle shaft

plate. With the axle housing resting on the jack, remove the rear springs. The axle housing is now free. Slowly lower the jack with the axle housing.

Installation

To replace the axle assembly, reverse the removal procedure.

Rear Axle Shaft Removal

1. Jack up the vehicle on the rear axle housing.
2. Remove the rear wheels and the brake backing plate.
3. The axle shaft may be pulled out manually or with a slide hammer.

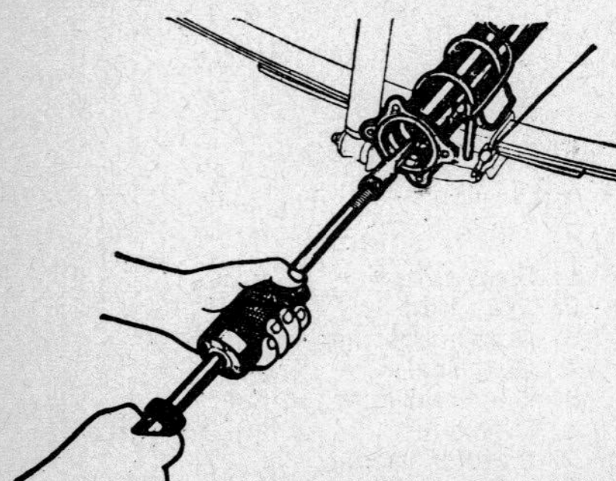

Oil seal removal

Axle Shaft Bearing Removal

Utilizing a grinder, grind a spot on the inner bearing retainer to a depth of about 0.04–0.06 in. With a chisel, lightly strike the ground portion of the inner bearing retainer. When the retainer cracks, remove the bearing.

Axle Shaft Oil Seal Removal

With the rear axle shaft removed, pull out the oil seal using an appropriate tool

Rear Axle Shaft Assembly and Installation

1. Place the outer bearing retainer with the raised surface facing the wheel hub on the axle shaft.
2. Next, install the axle shaft bearing and the outer retainer on the shaft.
3. Locate the smaller machined side of the inner bearing retainer.
4. With this side facing the bearing, install the retainer using a hydraulic press, capable of developing at least 13,000 lbs.
5. Be sure the bearing is firmly seated.
6. Clean the rear axle oil seal seat and lightly grease.
7. Using a suitable tool, drive the oil seal into the rear axle housing.
8. Lightly grease the oil seal outer lip.
9. Using packings, set the clearance between the outer bearing retainer and bearing to 0.00–0.01 in.
10. Install the brake backing plate on the shaft.
11. Install the shaft assembly into the axle housing, making sure the splines align properly.
12. Align the packing oil holes with the bearing retainer and lightly secure the bearing retainer to the axle housing flange.
13. Bolts with spring washers should be used.
14. Tighten the outer bearing retainer nuts in diagonal sequence to 25–29 ft lbs.

Differential

Removal

1. Drain the oil from the rear axle.
2. Disconnect and remove the driveshaft.
3. Pull out both axle shafts to disengage the axle shafts from the differential gears. They need only be pulled out about 2 in.

4. Unbolt and remove the differential carrier.

Disassembly

1. Remove the bearing caps and gently pry the differential from the carrier. A wooden hammer handle does this job well.

2. Using a bearing puller, remove the differential side bearings. Be sure to keep the right and left bearing shims separated to avoid confusion.

1. Locknut
2. Washer
3. End yoke
4. Slinger
5. Oil seal
6. Drive pinion bearing (front)
7. Gear carrier
8. Carrier cap
9. Preload adjusting shim
10. Drive pinion spacer
11. Drive pinion bearing (rear)
12. Drive pinion adjusting shim
13. Side bearing
14. Side bearing adjusting shim
15. Differential pinion
16. Differential pinion washer
17. Air breather
18. Final drive gear set
19. Differential pinion shaft
20. Differential case
21. Lockwasher
22. Differential side gear
23. Side gear spacer
24. Packing
25. Rear axle housing

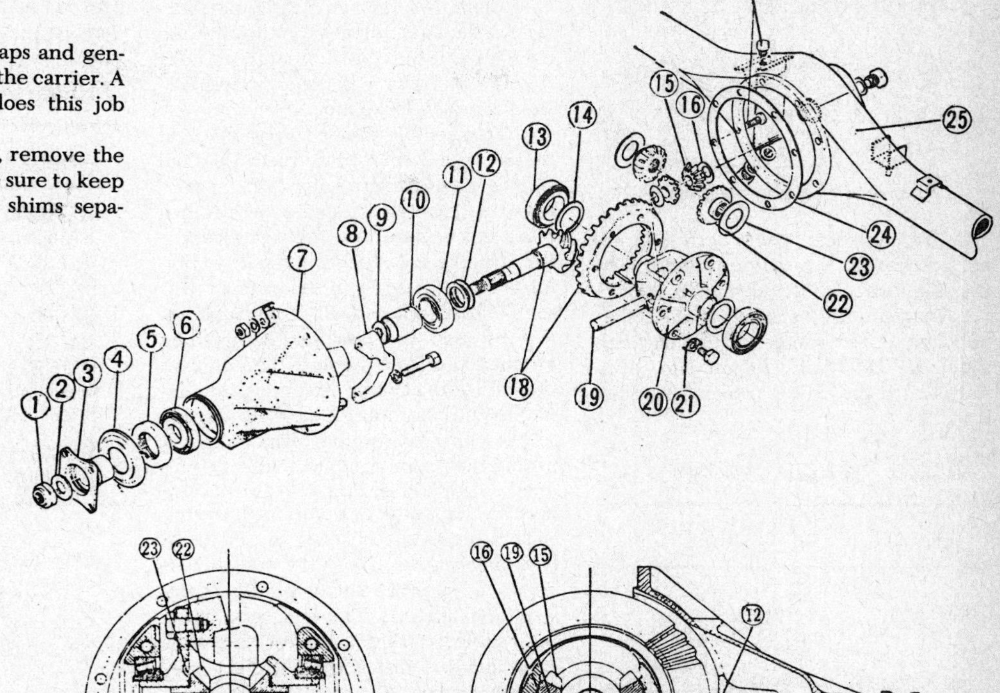
Exploded view of differential

3. Pry up the lockwashers on the ring gear bolts. Remove the ring gear bolts in a diagonal sequence and remove the ring gear.

4. Drive out the pinion shaft lockpin from the rear of the ring gear, and remove the pinion shaft.

5. Remove the pinions and side gears with spacers. Note the position of the side gear spacers so that they may be assembled in the same place.

6. Hold the end yoke with a pipe wrench and remove the pinion nut.

7. Remove the end yoke.

8. Tap the drive pinion shaft with a plastic faced mallet and remove the drive pinion with the adjusting shim, rear inner race, spacer and preload adjusting shim.

9. Remove the front pinion bearing outer race and oil seal. Discard the oil seal.

10. Remove the pinion bearing rear outer race.

Assembly

NOTE: *If the unit is to be assembled using no replacement parts, the same spacers and shims can generally be used. If either pinion bearing or ring gear and drive pinion are being replaced, new shims should be used. Only replace the drive pinion and ring gear in matched sets.*

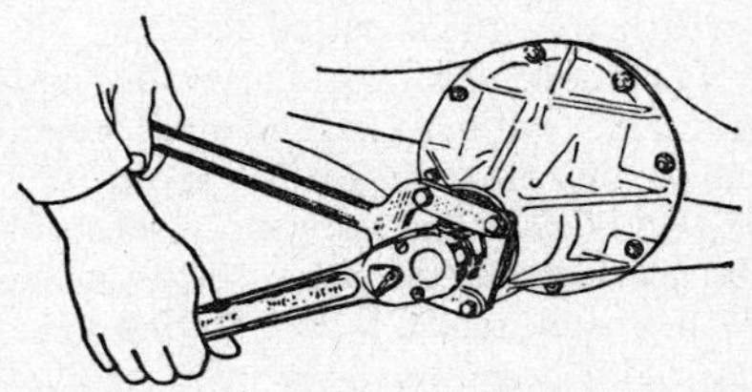
Drive pinion outer race removal

1. Assemble the side gears in the differential case. Install the thrust washers in the same place as they were installed.

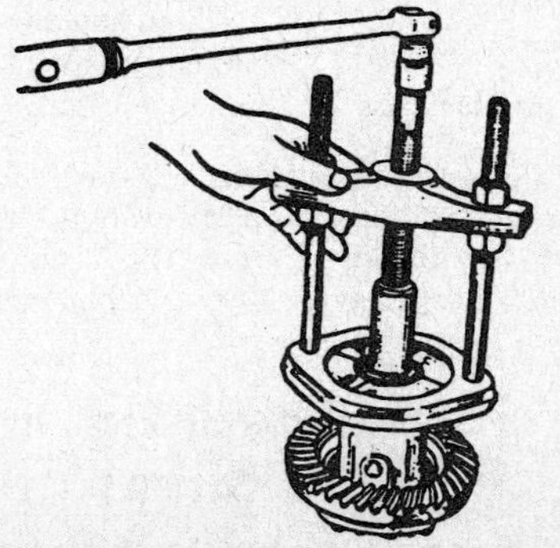
Side bearing removal

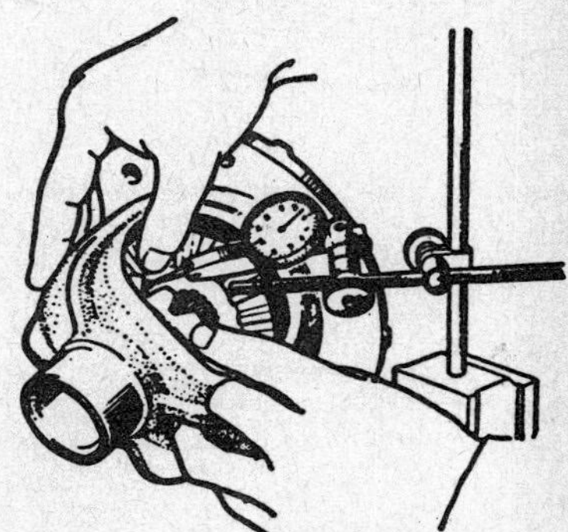
Checking pinion gear and side gear backlash

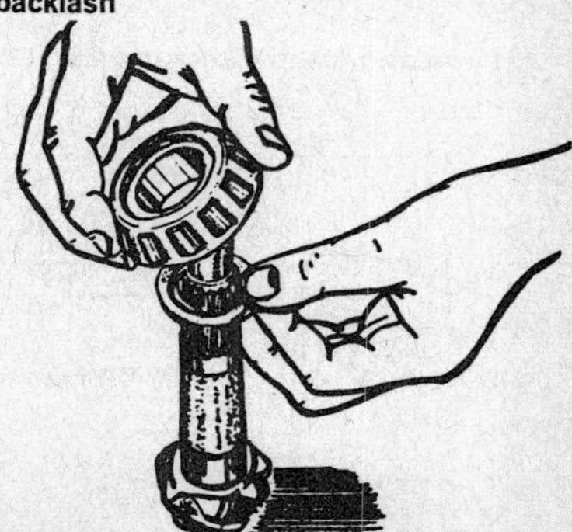
Pinion height shim installation

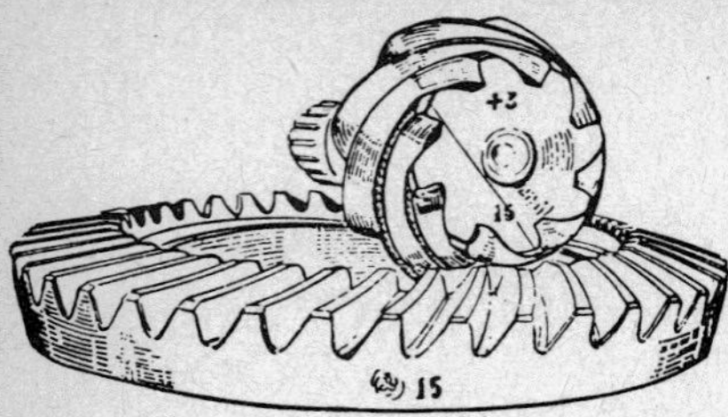

Pinion and ring gear markings

2. With washers, insert both differential gears at the same time to mesh with the side gears. Insert the pinion shaft.

3. Measure the backlash of the differential gears and side gears. The backlash should be 0.003–0.005 in. and can be adjusted with the use of spacers listed below.

Side Gear Spacers

Part No.	Thickness of spacer (in.)
MA180860	0.0394 $^{0}_{-0.0028}$
MA180861	0.0394 $^{-0.0031}_{-0.0067}$
MA180862	0.0394 $^{-0.0071}_{-0.0098}$

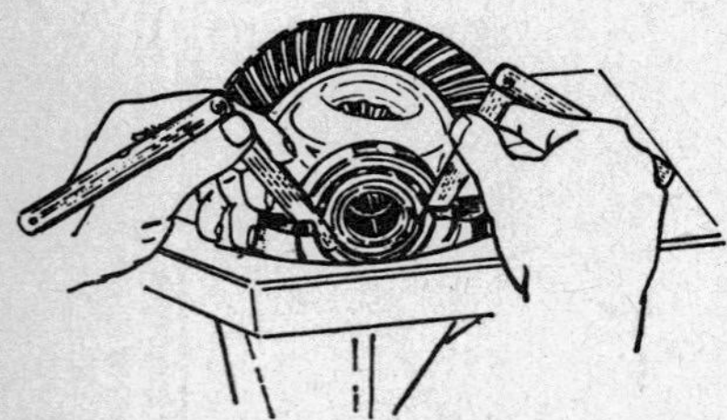

Measuring side bearing-to-carrier clearance

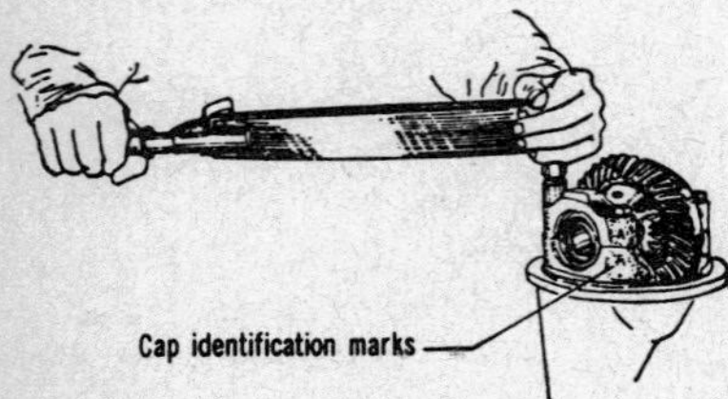

Bearing cap identification marks

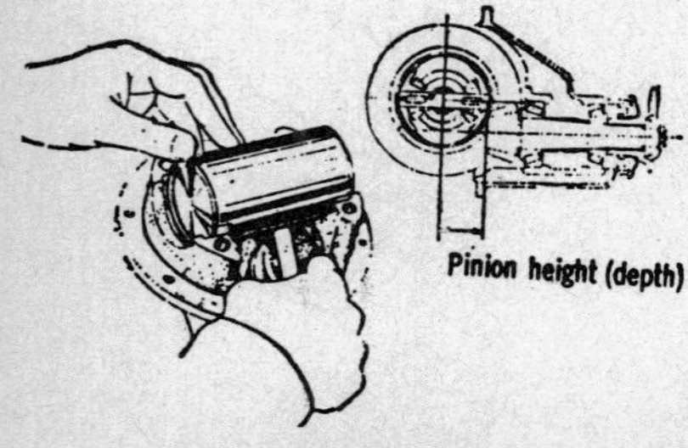

Measuring pinion height

4. Align the pinion shaft hole with the case and drive the lockpin in.

5. Clean the ring gear mounting surfaces. Install the ring gear on the differential case and tighten the mounting bolts to 50–58 ft lbs. in a diagonal pattern. Always use new lockplates.

6. To assemble the drive pinion, press the front and rear outer races into the gear carrier with a press or drift. Be sure not to use excessive pressure on the outer races and be sure they are not cocked.

7. Insert a shim between the drive pinion and rear bearing. If the original gear set is being replaced, the original shims may be used. If a new gear set is being installed, calculate the shim dimension in the following manner. Assuming the pinion height before disassembly is correct, subtract the new pinion variation marking (on the pinion head) from the old pinion variation marking. Be careful of positive and negative numbers. If the answer is positive, add shims in the corresponding amount. If the answer is negative, subtract shims in the corresponding amount. This will produce a reasonable starting point for assembly. Bear in mind that if the shim is subsequently proved incorrect, the entire pinion must be disassembled, and the shim changed accordingly. The etched marking on the face of the pinion represents a positive or negative variation from the standard in millimeters.

8. Assemble the front bearing, end yoke, pinion spacer and washer and torque the pinion nut gradually. Torque the pinion nut constantly checking the preload, until a preload of 6.1–8.7 in. lbs is reached (without the oil seal).

9. To determine the spacer thickness accurately, without trial and error mount the pinion height gauge (Colt special tool CT-1096-72) on the side bearing seats of the gear carrier and place a block gauge (Colt special tool CT-1096-D16) on the top end of the face of the drive pinion.

10. Measure the clearance between the gauges.

11. The clearance between the two gauges is set at 0.0118 in. if the pinion height is standard. The following formula may be used to determine the thickness of the preload shim thickness:

$$\text{Feeler gauge reading)} - \frac{\text{Etched value}}{25.4 \times 1000} - .0118 = \text{Thickness of shim to be added}$$

If the answer is positive, add the thickness to the original shim; if negative, subtract the thickness from the original shim. Shims are available in the following sizes:

Pinion Bearing Preload Shims

12. Remove the end yoke and insert the bearing preload adjusting shim between the pinion spacer and the bearing and torque the pinion nut to the prescribed preload (8.7–11.3 in. lbs with oil seal).

Pinion Bearing Preload Shims

Part No.	Thickness of shim (in.)
MA180842	0.0543 ± 0.0004
MA180843	0.0555 ± 0.0004
MA180844	0.0567 ± 0.0004
MA180845	0.0579 ± 0.0004
MA180846	0.0591 ± 0.0004
MA180847	0.0603 ± 0.0004
MA180848	0.0614 ± 0.0004
MA180849	0.0626 ± 0.0004
MA180850	0.0638 ± 0.0004
MA180851	0.0650 ± 0.0004
MA180852	0.0118 ± 0.0005

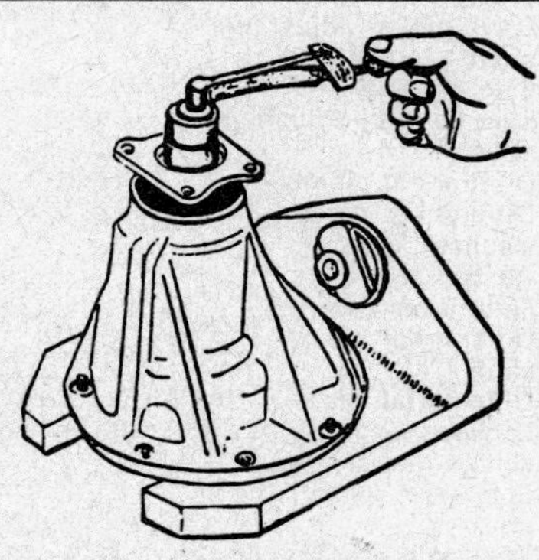

Measuring pinion preload

13. The pinion nut torque should be 100–145 ft lbs.

14. Install each side bearing into the differential case without the adjusting shim.

15. Install the differential case assembly on the gear carrier and measure the clearance between the side bearing outer race and the gear carrier.

16. The thickness of the shim on each side is determined by the following formula:

$$\frac{\text{Measured clearance} + 0.004\text{ in.}}{2} = \text{Thickness of shims on one side.}$$

The 0.004 in. dimension is added as the side bearing preload (0.002 in. on each side). Side bearing preload shims are available in the following sizes:

Side Bearing Preload Shims

17. Align the gear carrier and bearing cap positioning marks and torque the cap bolts to 25–29 ft lbs.

18. Mount a dial indicator with the pin registering on the rear face of the ring gear. Zero the dial indicator.

Side Bearing Preload Shims

Part No.	Shim thickness (in.)
MA180828	0.0787 ± 0.0004
MA180829	0.0799 ± 0.0004
MA180830	0.0811 ± 0.0004
MA180831	0.0823 ± 0.0004
MA180832	0.0835 ± 0.0004
MA180833	0.0846 ± 0.0004
MA180834	0.0858 ± 0.0004
MA180835	0.0870 ± 0.0004
MA180836	0.0882 ± 0.0004
MA180837	0.0894 ± 0.0004
MA180838	0.0906 ± 0.0004
MA180839	0.0917 ± 0.0004

19. Measure the run-out of the ring gear. If the run-out exceeds 0.002 in., change the position of the ring gear on the differential carrier by 90°. If the run-out still exceeds 0.002 in., replace the ring gear or differential carrier.

20. Measure the backlash of the ring gear at four points, 90° apart. Ring gear backlash should not exceed 0.005–0.007 in. If the measured backlash is greater than the specification, shift shims in a corresponding thickness from the ring gear tooth side to the rear of the ring gear. If backlash is less than specified, shift shims from the rear side of the ring gear to the tooth side. Side gear adjusting shims are available in the following sizes:

Side Bearing Adjusting Shims

Part No.	Thickness (in.)
MA180822	0.0028 ± 0.0004
MA180823	0.0051 ± 0.0006
MA180824	0.0098 ± 0.0010
MA180825	0.0020 ± 0.0002
MA180826	0.0062 ± 0.0008
MA180827	0.0157 ± 0.0012

21. Paint the ring gear teeth with red lead or similar testing compound. Use a socket and breaker bar on the pinion nut and rock the drive pinion back and forth on the ring gear teeth. Compare the results of this test with the following illustrations and note the corrective procedure.

A. Proper gear tooth contact pattern—a pattern of 50–70% of gear tooth contact on the ring gear, centered or slightly inclined toward the toe.

B. Face contact—indicates backlash is too large; increase the shim thickness to move the drive pinion toward the ring gear axis. This will reduce backlash, necessitating side gear shim adjustment to compensate the backlash.

Proper tooth contact

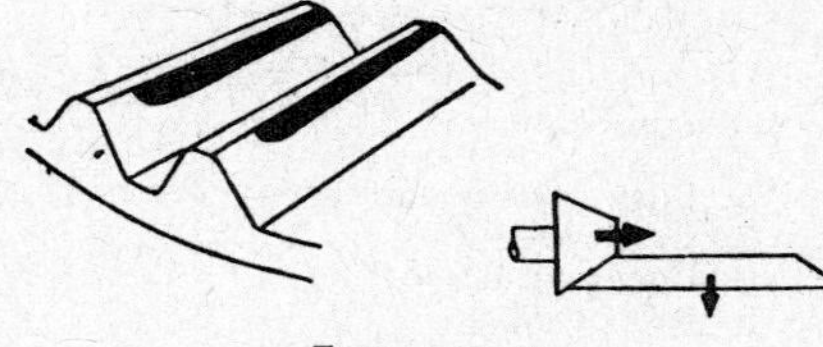

Face contact

Heel contact

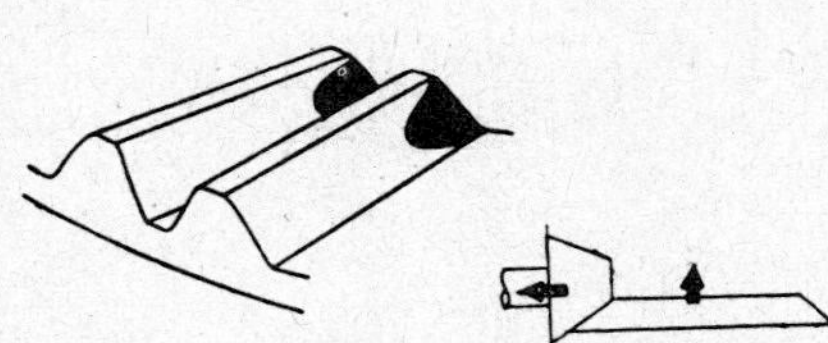

Toe contact

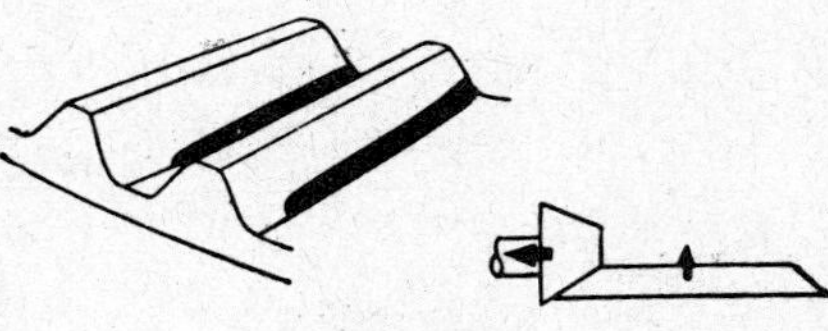

Flank contact

C. Flank contact—indicates too little backlash; decrease the shim thickness to move the pinion away from the ring gear axis. Be sure to compensate for backlash changes by altering the side gear shim positioning, to bring backlash to specification.

D. Toe contact—too little contact; adjust in the same manner as Step C.

E. Heel contact—too little contact on the heel side; adjust in same manner as Step B.

Installation

Installation is the reverse of removal. Torque the carrier-to-axle housing bolts to 11–14.5 ft lbs.

FRONT SUSPENSION

All Colt models utilize a strut type front suspension, with a coil-over-shock system and a front stabilizer bar. Caster and camber are factory set; no adjustment should be made.

Lower Arm Disassembly

1. Unscrew the bolts from the opposite ends of the lower arm shaft. Remove the lower arm shaft with the bushings. Remove the rubber stopper and the arm bushing.
2. Remove the joint cover by wedging a screwdriver in the lower ball joint ring and gently prying upward.
3. Remove the ball joint.

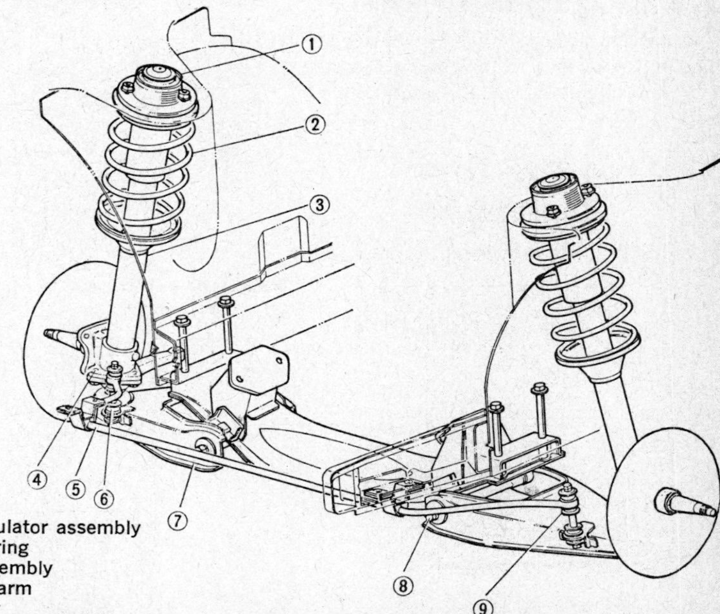

1. Strut insulator assembly
2. Front spring
3. Strut assembly
4. Knuckle arm
5. Stabilizer
6. Ball joint
7. Lower arm assembly
8. Lower arm shaft
9. Stabilizer link kit

Front suspension

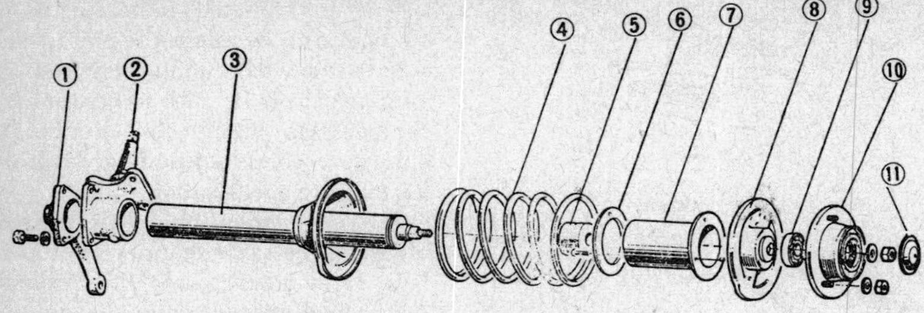

Exploded view of the front suspension

1. Knuckle arm
2. Knuckle
3. Strut sub-assembly (shock absorber)
4. Front suspension spring
5. Rubber bumper
6. Dust cover plate
7. Dust cover
8. Upper spring seat
9. Ball bearing
10. Insulator
11. Dust cover

2. Follow this with replacement of the stopper washer and the other front bushing.

3. Install the rear lower arm shaft bushing with the bushing bore center toward axle shaft.

4. Drive the bushing in until the flange contacts the lower arm bore edge.

5. Be sure not to damage the lower arm.

6. Replace the lower arm shaft retaining bolts and torque to 40–47 ft lbs. Be sure to use new washers.

NOTE: *Torque only with the wheels on the ground and the remainder of the front suspension fully assembled.*

7. Using a hydraulic press, install the ball joints.

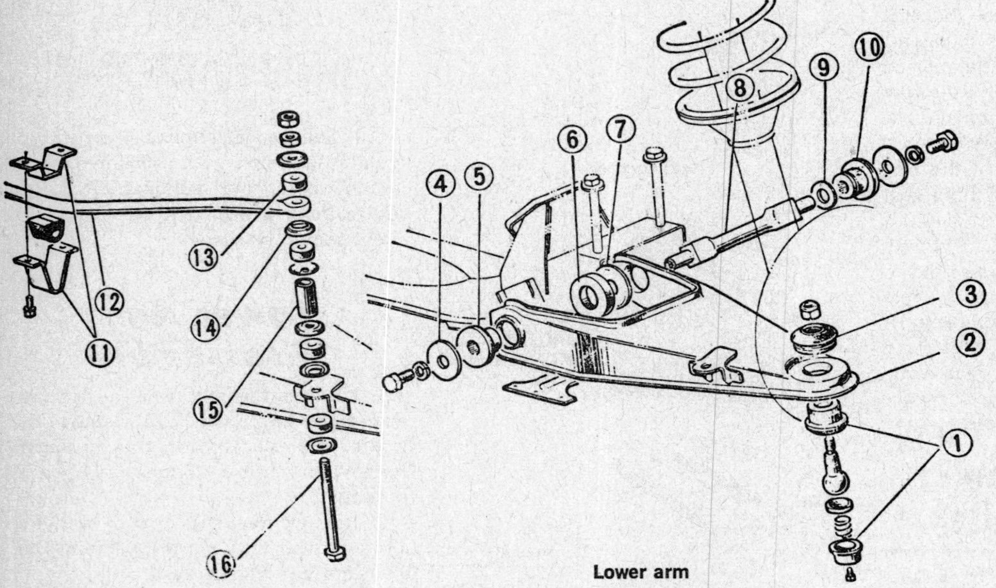

1. Joint assembly
2. Lower arm
3. Joint cover
4. Washer
5. Bushing (front)
6. Stopper rubber
7. Stopper washer
8. Lower arm shaft
9. Spacer
10. Bushing (rear)
11. Stabilizer fixture
12. Stabilizer
13. Rubber bushing
14. Seat
15. Collar
16. Stabilizer bolt

Lower arm

Rebuilding

Removed bushings must be replaced. Check the lower arm for cracks, bends, etc. Thoroughly clean all components with solvent.

Lower Arm Assembly

1. Install lower arm front bushing.

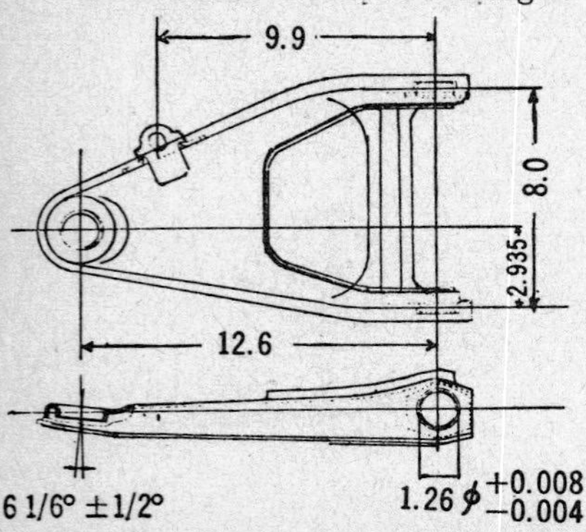

Alignment of the lower arm

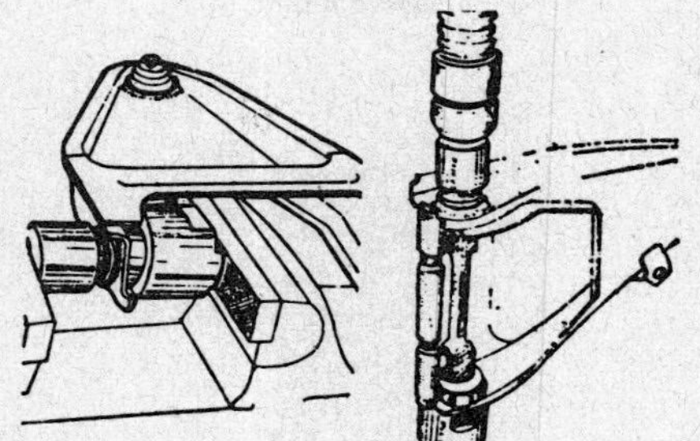

Installation of the lower arm shaft bushing

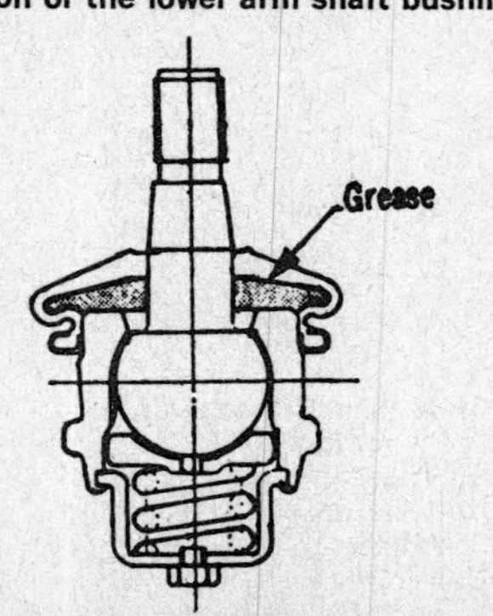

Front view of the ball joint

8. Be sure to align the lower arm end mark with the ball joint.

9. Replace the joint cover—be sure it contacts the lower arm surface

NOTE: *Once removed, a new cover should be installed. Lubricate the joint cover with grease.*

STEERING

The steering system of all Colt automobiles is a variable ratio recirculating ball type unit. Use of resin bearings eliminates the need for lubrication. In addition, a bellows type collapsible steering tube is incorporated to comply with U.S. safety regulations.

Steering Wheel

Removal

1. Gently pry off the steering wheel center foam pad.

2. Loosen and remove the large steering wheel retaining nut.

3. Using a steering wheel puller, remove the wheel.

CAUTION: *Under no conditions should a hammer be used to assist steering wheel removal.*

Installation

Be sure the front wheels are in a straight ahead position. Reverse the removal procedure. Torque the steering wheel nut to 14.5–18.0 ft lbs.

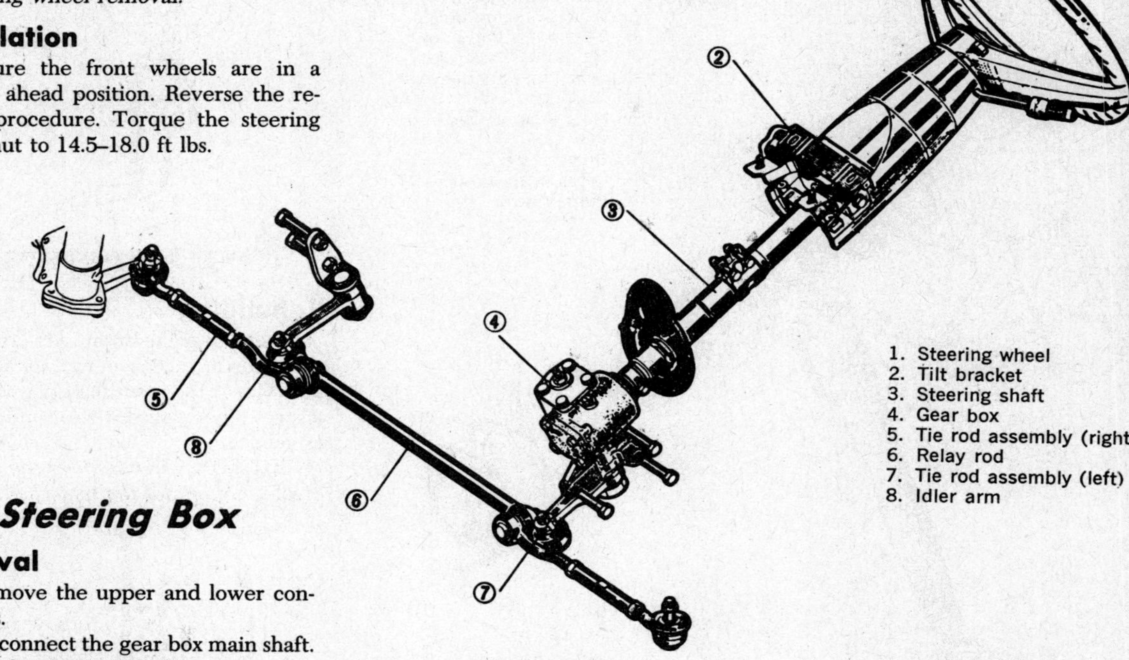

Steering system

Steering Box

Removal

1. Remove the upper and lower control rods.
2. Disconnect the gear box main shaft. Pull out the steering shaft.
3. Disconnect, but do not remove, the pitman arm and relay rod.

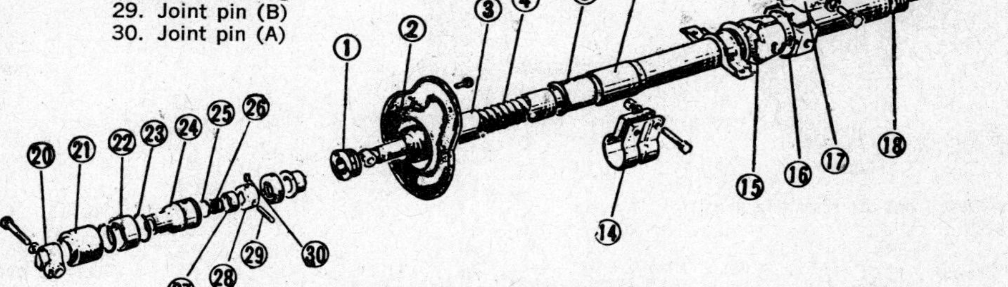

Exploded view of the steering shaft

Installation

To install the gearbox, note the information given below and reverse the above procedure. Be sure to align the pitman arm and cross shaft. When installing the upper control rod, be sure to adjust to proper end clearance (0.532–0.571 in.).

Torque values

Gear box bolts: 25–29 ft lbs

Pitman arm: 94–108 ft lbs.

Tie rod and relay rod sockets: 29–36 ft lbs.

Disassembly

Before proceeding, record the main shaft torque and shim height. This will be used as an assembly guide.

1. Unscrew the locknut on the gear box adjusting bolt and turn the bolt counterclockwise until the upper cover is free to remove. Lift the upper cover from the cross-shaft.
2. Remove the adjusting bolt from the upper cover.
3. Move the cross-shaft to the straight ahead position and remove the main shaft from the steering box.

CAUTION: *Be gentle in all operations, since cross-shaft serrations and seals damage easily.*

4. Again measure the main shaft torque with the cross-shaft removed.
5. Remove the gear box end cover. Take note of the number and thickness of shims.

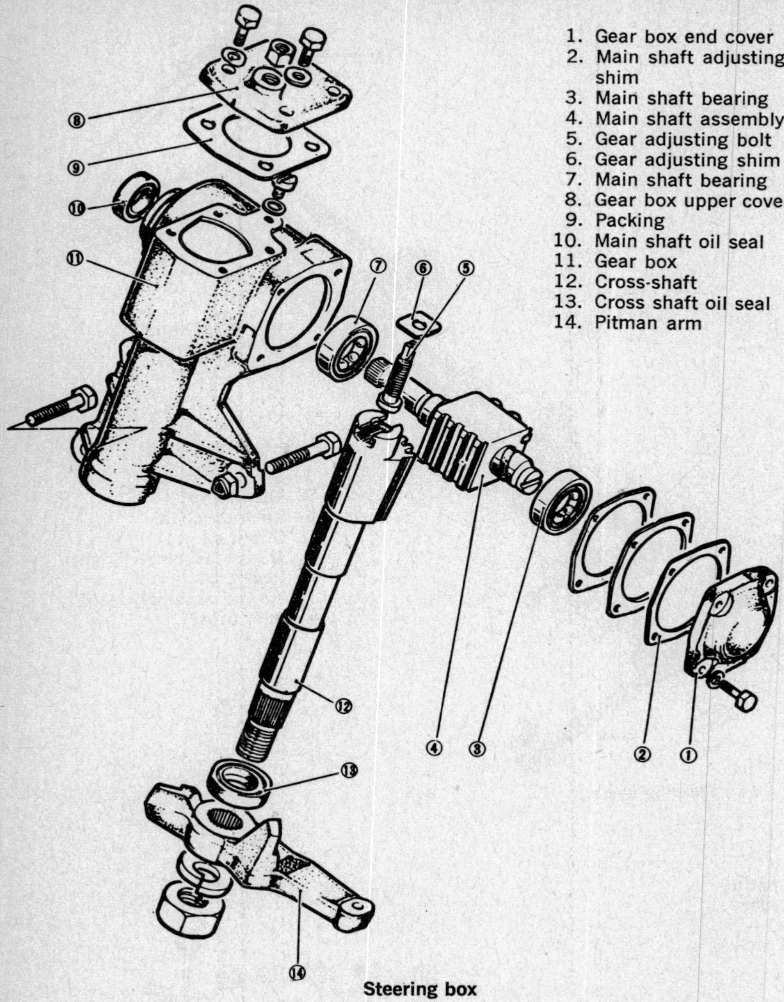

Steering box

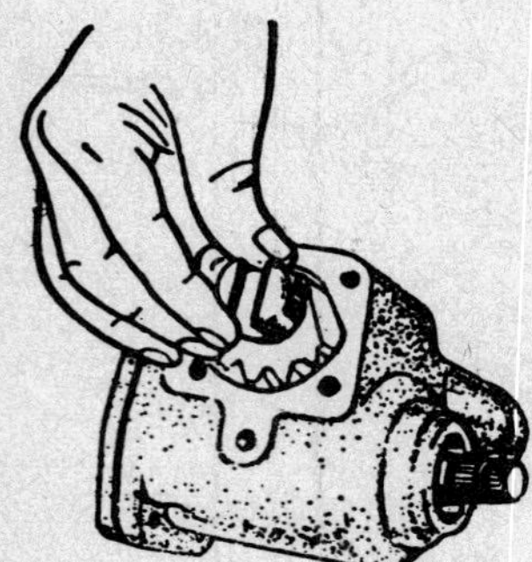
Removing cross-shaft from the sheering shaft

Main shaft removal

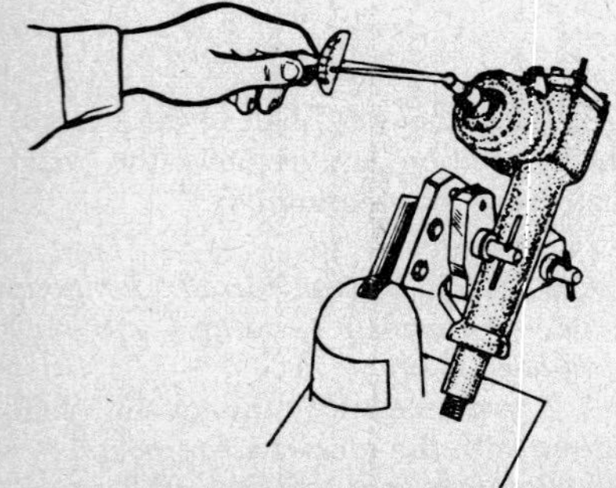
Measuring mainshaft preload

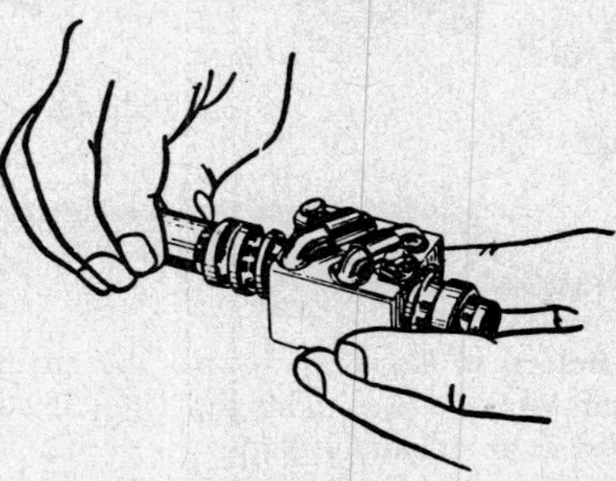
Ball nut removal

CAUTION: *Remove the ball nut assembly, bearing, and main shaft. Do not disassemble the main shaft and ballnut assembly.*

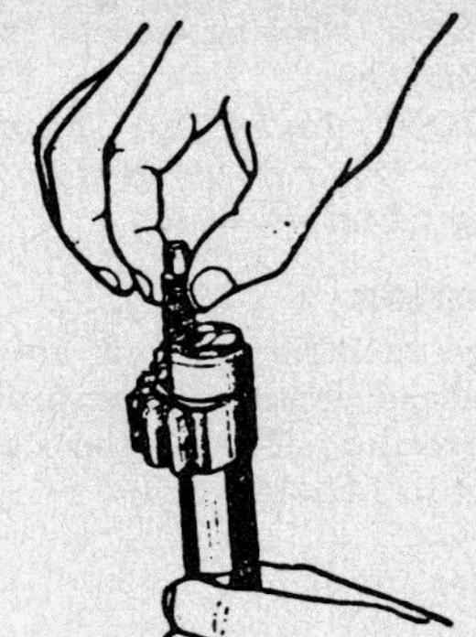
Cross shaft T-groove adjustment

Rebuilding

Take note of the bushing-to-cross-shaft clearance. If excessive, replace as necessary. Check the main shaft play. Visually inspect other parts for wear and replace as needed.

CAUTION: *Do not move the ball nut to either end of the mainshaft.*

Main shaft free play adjustment

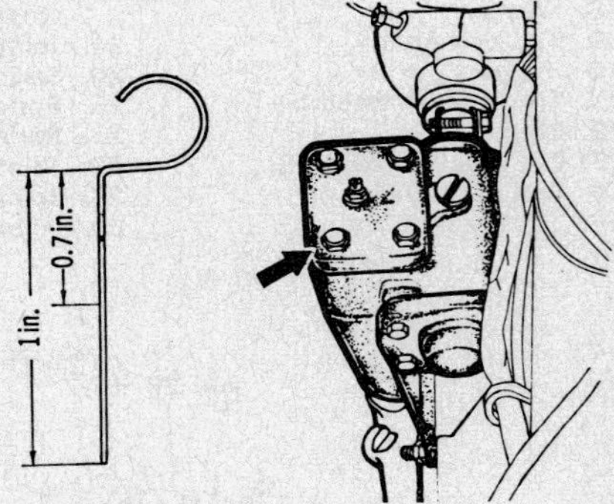

Steering gear oil level check

1. Place the gear box in a vise.
2. Positioning the main shaft horizontally, tighten the shim to the proper torque.
3. The shim height and torque were recorded during disassembly. As a guide, the usual shim used is 0.020 in.
4. Apply a bonding agent to both sides of the shim and bolts when replacing the end cover.
5. Check the main shaft preload. If not 3.5–4.4 in. lbs, adjust by the use of shims.

6. Place the adjusting bolt and shim in the T groove on the cross-shaft (upper end).

7. Adjust the shim height to give a play of 0–0.002 in.

8. Install the cross-shaft and tighten the upper cover to 10.8–14.5 ft lbs.

CAUTION: *Be sure not to damage the oil seals and bushings when installing the cross-shaft.*

9. Be certain to apply adequate lubrication to the cross-shaft gears. Also, coat the oil seal lip with grease.

10. Using sealant, install the side cover.

11. Move the cross-shaft in the housing.

12. Screw the adjusting bolt in two–three turns to push the cross-shaft into the proper mesh.

13. Back off the bolt until the main shaft shows no free play at the center position.

14. Check the main shaft preload.

15. If incorrect, be sure that the cross-shaft bushing is not damaged and that the end-cover is installed correctly.

16. Fill the unit to the proper level with hypoid gear oil No. 90 GS type.

BRAKE SYSTEMS

All Colt vehicles utilize a front disc and rear drum brake system with a tandem type master cylinder, using independent front and rear cylinders.

Master Cylinder Removal and Disassembly

1. Remove all lines connected to the master cylinder. Slowly depress the brake pedal to remove the fluid.

2. Remove the clevis pin from between the master cylinder push rod and the pedal.

3. Remove the master cylinder from the firewall and thoroughly clean it.

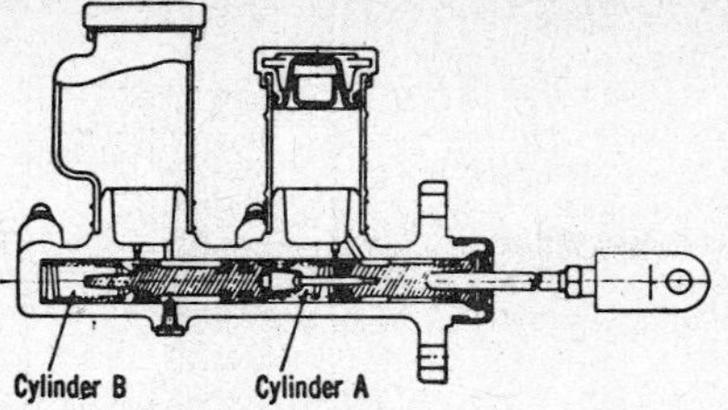

Master cylinder

4. Remove the boots, stopper ring, primary and secondary piston assembly. Remove the return spring.

5. Loosen the valve case and remove the check valve and spring. Do not attempt to disassemble the primary piston assembly.

Inspection

Visually inspect all parts. Replace as necessary. Check the clearance between the piston and the master cylinder. If it exceeds 0.001–0.006 in., replace the piston or the master cylinder. Check the primary spring free length. It should be 1.6–1.75 in. Measure the secondary spring free length which should be 2.-2–2.4 in. Replace if not according to specifications.

Assembly

To assemble the master cylinder, reverse the removal procedure. Lubricate the master cylinder parts (excluding the boots) before assembly. Be certain the return port is not obstructed by the piston cup when in the return position. Torque the master cylinder to 5.8–8.7 ft lbs.

Front Disc Brakes

Caliper, Pad and Disc Removal

1. Remove the wheel.

2. Disconnect the brake line from the brake hose.

3. Remove the flexible hose from the caliper.

4. Pull out the clip and remove the retaining pin and cross-spring.

Measuring brake disc run-out

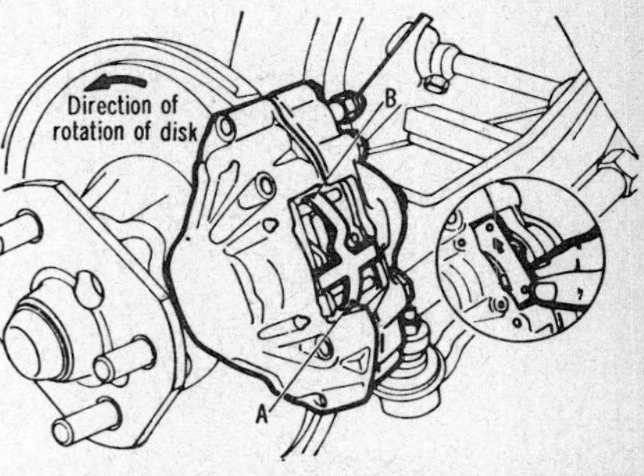

Cross-spring and shim installation

5. Hold the pad backing plate with pliers and remove the pad and shim.

6. Remove the caliper assembly from the disc.

7. Remove the hub assembly and remove the hub from the disc. A soft jawed vise should be used for this.

Caliper Disassembly

1. Remove the retaining ring and dust seal.

2. Remove the piston on the outer side holding the inner piston in place. If the piston on one side is not held in place, both pistons may jump out simultaneously, causing injury.

NOTE: *Do not loosen the bridge bolts or attempt to separate the calipers.*

3. Remove the inner piston through the cavity by gently tapping with a soft instrument.

4. Carefully remove the piston seal.

5. Clean all parts in brake fluid.

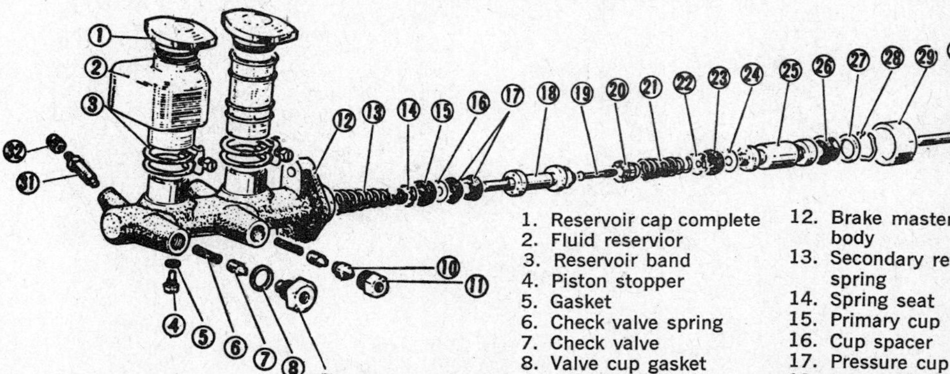

1. Reservoir cap complete
2. Fluid reservior
3. Reservoir band
4. Piston stopper
5. Gasket
6. Check valve spring
7. Check valve
8. Valve cup gasket
9. Valve case
10. Outer pipe seat
11. Check valve cap
12. Brake master cylinder body
13. Secondary return spring
14. Spring seat
15. Primary cup
16. Cup spacer
17. Pressure cup
18. Secondary piston
19. Screw
20. Spring seat (B)
21. Primary return spring
22. Spring seat (A)
23. Primary cup
24. Cup spacer
25. Primary piston
26. Secondary cup
27. Piston stopper
28. Stopper ring
29. Master cylinder boots
30. Pushrod assembly

Exploded view of master cylinder

1. Pin retaining clip
2. Pad retaining pin
3. Connector bolt
4. Gasket
5. Connector
6. Gasket
7. Caliper seal
8. Bleeder cap
9. Bleeder screw
10. Cross-spring
11. Pad shim
12. Retaining ring
13. Dust seal
14. Front brake piston
15. Piston seal
16. Caliper (outer)
17. Caliper (inner)
18. Pad assembly

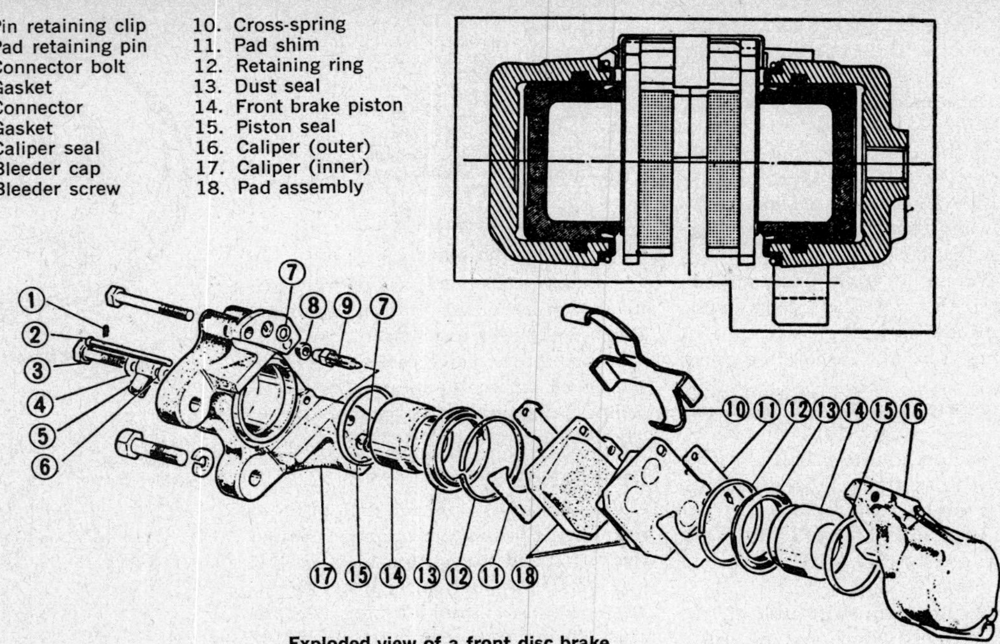

Exploded view of a front disc brake

Caliper Assembly

1. Install the piston seal and dust seal where removed.
2. Apply rubber grease to the surfaces of the piston seal and the inner side of the dust seal.
3. Apply rust preventive oil and insert the piston. Do not twist the piston.

Caliper, Pad and Disc Installation

1. Install the caliper adapter and dust cover to the knuckle arm and torque the mounting bolts to 30–36 ft lbs.
2. Install the disc on the hub and torque the bolts to 25–29 ft lbs.
3. Check the disc run-out, which should be no more than 0.006 in. If run-out cannot be brought below 0.006 in., replace the disc.
4. Install the caliper on the adapter and torque the bolts to 29–36 ft lbs.
5. Spread the piston and insert the pad and shim. The shim is installed between the pad and piston with the arrow pointing forward.
6. Install the cross-spring and attach it to the retaining pin.
7. Attach the brake hose to the caliper and connect the brake line to the hose.
8. Bleed the brakes.
9. Install the wheels.

Rear Drum Brakes

Removal

1. Remove the wheel, brake drum, and hold-down spring.
2. Disassemble the shoe return spring.
3. Remove the clevis pin from between the extension lever and the parking brake cable. Remove the adjusting assembly.
4. Remove the brake lines from the wheel.
5. Remove the wheel cylinder from the backing plate.

1. Backing plate
2. Wheel cylinder boot
3. Bleeder screw cap
4. Bleeder screw
5. Wheel cylinder piston
6. Piston cup
7. Wheel cylinder body
8. Shoe hold-down spring pin
9. Brake shoe assembly
10. Brake lining
11. Parking brake extension lever
12. Shoe hold-down spring seat
13. Shoe hold-down spring
14. Slack adjuster anchor
15. Slack adjuster body
16. Slack adjuster
17. Shoe return spring

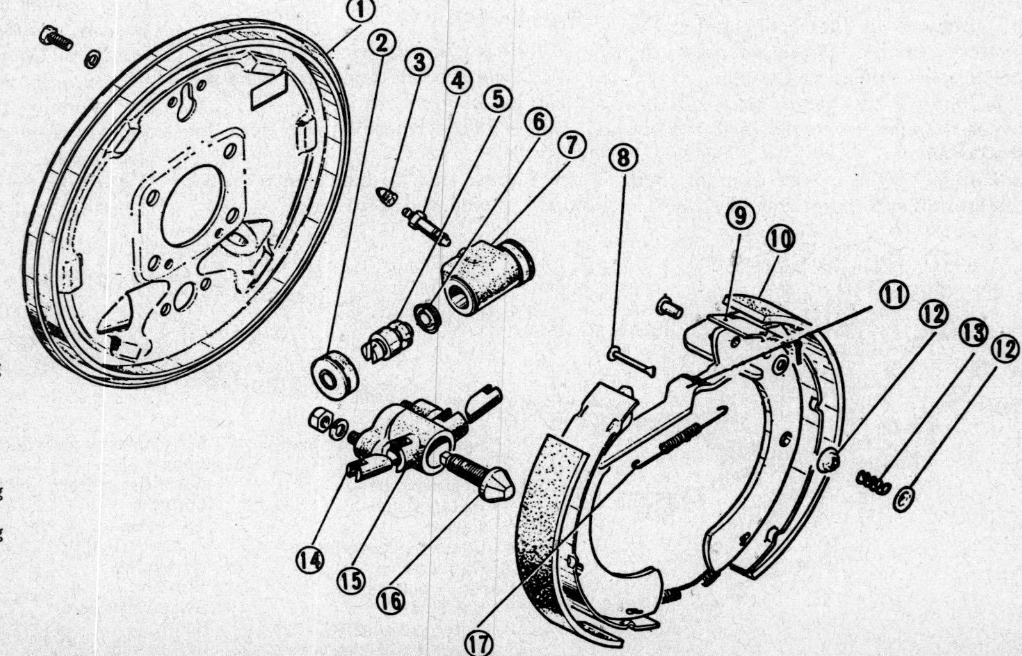

Exploded view of the rear brakes

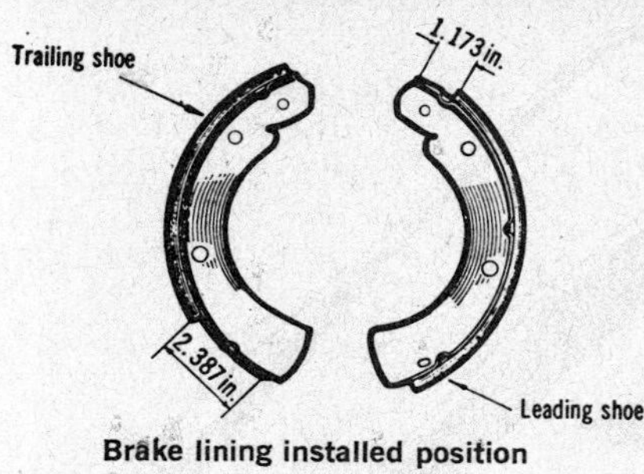

Brake lining installed position

Inspection

Thoroughly clean all components. Brake lining thickness may be no less than 0.04 in. Check the inner wall of the brake drum for scoring. Repair limit is 9.079 in.

Installation

Installation is the reverse of removal. Lease the adjuster slack.

Brake Shoe-to-Drum Clearance Adjustment

1. Move the parking brake lever to release the brake cable.
2. Turning clockwise, fully tighten the adjuster.
3. Back the adjuster off to free the linings from contact with the brake drum.
4. Maximum brake shoe-to-drum clearance is 0.012 in.

Parking Brake Adjustment

1. Release the brake cable.
2. Loosen the adjusting nuts on either side of the cable.
3. Move the cable lever to each side and tighten the nuts to the tension.

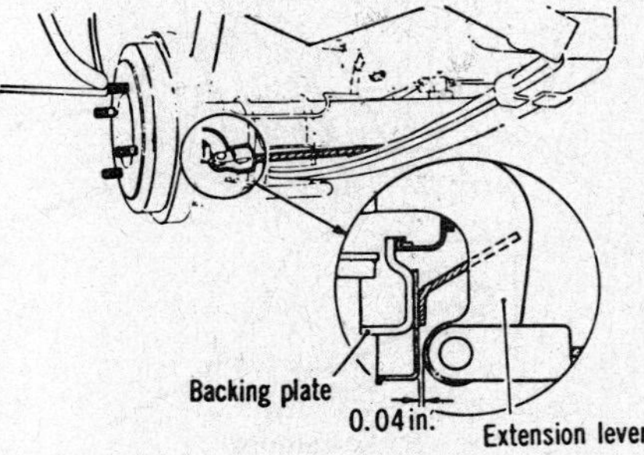

Parking brake adjustment

4. Cable tightening should provide backing plate and extension lever clearance of *less* than 0.04 in.
5. Be certain the drum does not contact the lining. Standard parking brake lever travel is 10 notches.

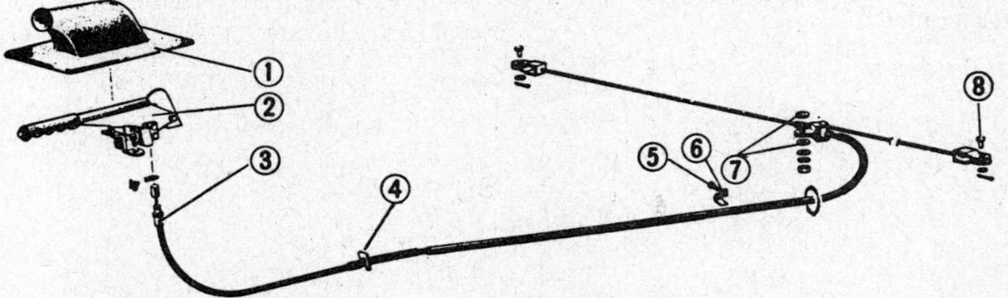
Exploded view of parking brake linkage

1. Parking brake lever cover
2. Parking brake lever assembly
3. Parking brake cable
4. Clip
5. Bolt
6. Clip
7. Bushing
8. Clevis pin

Exploded view of the heater

1. Ventilator duct assembly
2. Defroster nozzle
3. Heater assembly
4. Turbo fan
5. Motor
6. Fan motor switch
7. Air control level
8. Heater-defroster changeover and fan motor switch lever
9. Temperature control lever
10. Upper panel
11. Plate
12. Non-return valve
13. Lower panel

CHASSIS ELECTRICAL

Heater

Removal

1. Drain the cooling system.
2. Remove the center console assembly from the car interior.
3. Disconnect all heater wiring.
4. Remove the heater control assembly.
5. Disconnect all heater hoses and ducts.
6. Pull the heater from the car.

Installation

To replace the heater, reverse the removal procedure. Be sure to adjust the screws at the heater control assembly bottom. This will prevent the control lever from contacting the center console indentation.

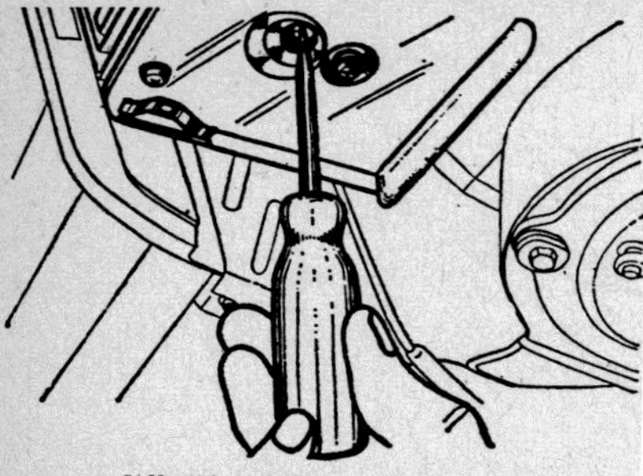
Adjusting heater control position

Windshield Wipers

Motor Removal

1. Remove the bolts which hold the motor to the body.
2. Loosen and remove the nut on the wiper arm shaft on the driver's side. Pull the motor assembly from position. Motor crank arm and linkage may be removed by extracting the bushing.

Installation

To replace the wiper motor, reverse the removal procedure

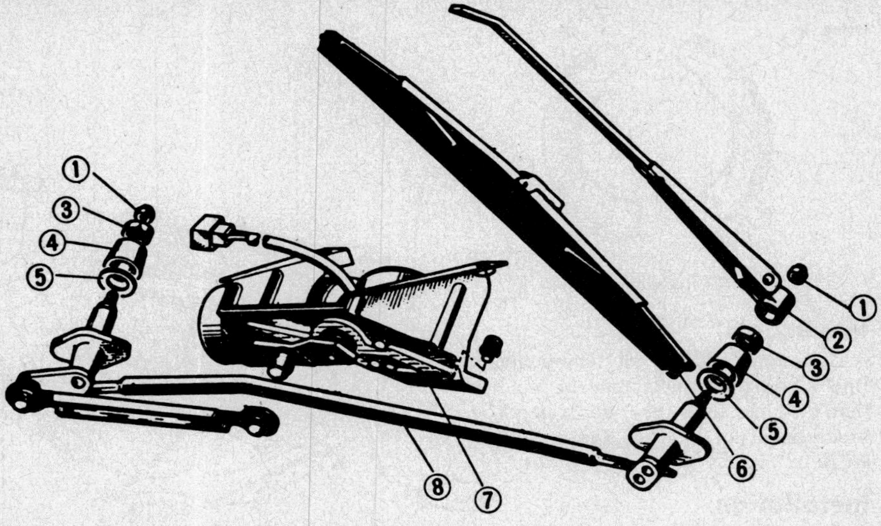

Windshield wiper motor location

1. Nut
2. Wiper arm
3. Nut
4. Collar
5. Washer
6. Wiper blade assembly
7. Wiper motor assembly
8. Wiper link assembly

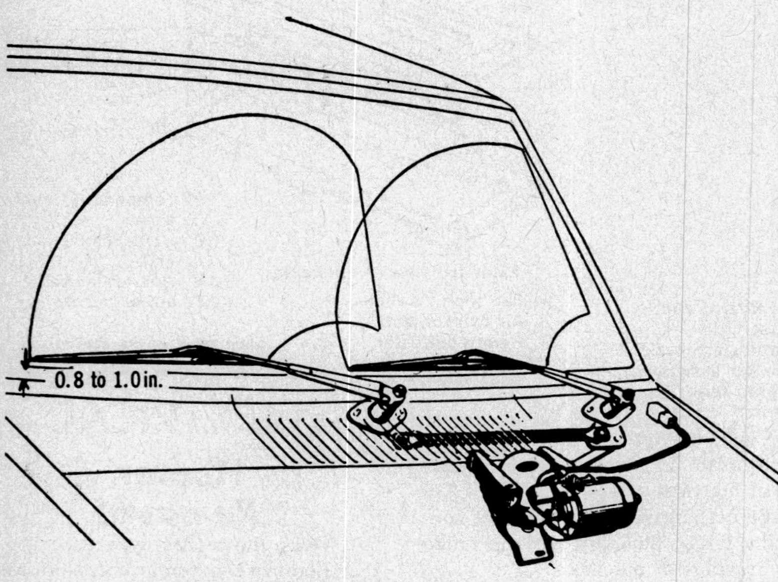

Windshield wiper motor location

Radio

Removal

1. Remove the fastenings and extract the padding from on top of the radio. This may be accomplished by withdrawing the screws at the radio bottom, which are also connected to the console.
2. Remove all radio switches. In addition, remove all heater control levers and knobs. Remove the wing nut on the radio right-hand side.
3. Remove the screws at the bottom of the ash tray and console cover.
4. Pull the radio slightly forward. Disconnect all wiring and lift out.

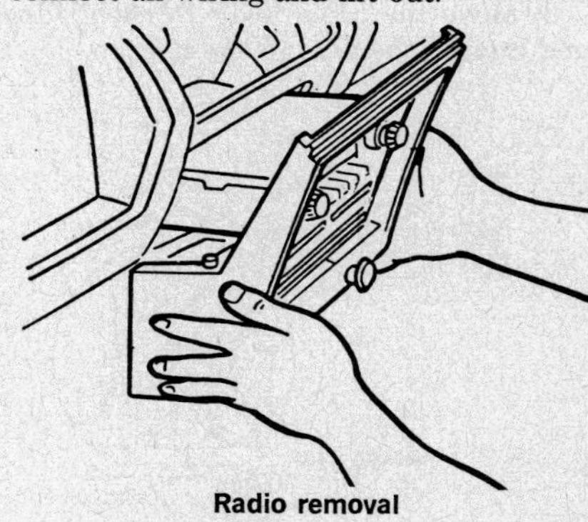
Radio removal

Installation

To replace the radio, reverse the removal procedure.

DATSUN

Index

GENERAL ENGINE SPECIFICATIONS

Year and Model	Type (model)	Engine Displacement cu. in. (cc)	Carburetor Type	Horsepower (SAE) @ rpm	Torque @ rpm (ft lbs)	Bore x Stroke (in.)	Compression Ratio	Normal Oil Pressure (psi)
1965-1968 L520 1300 Pickup 1968-1969 L521 1300 Pickup	OHV 4 (J)	79.0 (1,299)	Dual throat downdraft	67 @ 5,200	77 @ 2,800	2.89 x 3.06	8.2:1	54-57
1965-1969 SPL311 1600 Roadster	OHV 4 (R)	97.3 (1,595)	Two SU type sidedraft	96 @ 6,000	103 @ 4,000	3.43 x 2.63	9.0:1	54-57
1967-1969 SRL311 2000 Roadster	OHC 4 (U20)	120.9 (1,982)	Two SU type sidedraft	135 @ 6,000	132 @ 4,400	3.43 x 3.27	9.5:1	54-57
1967-1969 SRL311 2000 Roadster	OHC 4 (U20)	120.9 (1,982)	Two Solex type twin-choke sidedraft	150 @ 6,000	138 @ 4,800	3.43 x 3.27	9.5:1	54-57
1968-1973 PL510 1600 Sedan 1968-1972 WPL510 1600 Wagon 1970-1972 PL521 1600 Pickup 1973 PL620 1800 Pickup	OHC 4 (L16)	97.3 (1,595)	Dual throat downdraft	96 @ 5,600	100 @ 3,600	3.27 x 2.90	8.5:1	54-57
1971 240 Z Coupe	OHC 6 (L24)	146.0 (2,393)	Two SU type sidedraft	151 @ 5,600	146 @ 4,400	3.27 x 2.90	9.0:1	54-60
1972-1973 240 Z Coupe	OHC 6 (L24)	146.0 (2,393)	Two Su type sidedraft	151 @ 5,600	146 @ 4,400	3.27 x 2.90	8.8:1	50-57
1971 LB110 1200 Sedan KLB110 1200 Coupe	OHV 4 (A12)	71.5 (1,171)	Dual throat downdraft	69 @ 6,000	70 @ 4,000	2.87 x 2.76	9.0:1	54-60
1972-1973 LB110 1200 Sedan KLB110 1200 Coupe	OHV 4 (A12)	71.5 (1,171)	Dual throat downdraft	69 @ 6,000	70 @ 4,000	2.87 x 2.76	8.5:1	54-60
1973 PL610 1800 Sedan KPL610 1800 Hardtop WPL610 1800 Wagon	OHC 4 (L18)	108.0 (1,770)	Dual throat downdraft	100 @ 5,600	100 @ 3,600	3.35 x 3.307	8.5:1	50-57

CRANKSHAFT AND CONNECTING ROD SPECIFICATIONS

All measurements are given in inches.

Engine Model	CRANKSHAFT				CONNECTING ROD BEARINGS		
	Main Brg. Journal Dia.	Main Brg. Oil Clearance	Shaft End-Play	Thrust on No.	Journal Dia.	Oil Clearance	Side Clearance
J	2.0021-2.0025	0.001-0.002	0.002-0.003	Center	1.860-1.878	N.A.	0.008-0.012
R	2.3598-2.3602	0.001-0.003	0.002-0.006	Center	2.0457-2.0463	0.001-0.002	0.008-0.012
U20	2.4780-2.4785	0.001-0.003	0.002-0.007	Center	2.0449-2.0454	0.001-0.003	0.008-0.012
L16	2.1631-2.1636	0.001-0.003	0.002-0.006	3	1.9670-1.9675	0.001-0.003	0.008-0.012
L24	2.1631-2.1636	0.001-0.003	0.002-0.007	Center	1.9670-1.9675	0.001-0.002	0.008-0.012
A12	1.9671-1.9668	0.001-0.002	0.002-0.006	3	1.7701-1.7706	0.001-0.002	0.008-0.012
L18	2.1631-2.1636	0.001-0.002	0.002-0.007	3	1.9670-1.9675	0.001-0.002	0.008-0.012

TUNE-UP SPECIFICATIONS

When analyzing compression test results, look for uniformity among cylinders, rather than specific pressures.

Year	Model	SPARK PLUGS Type	SPARK PLUGS Gap (in.)	DISTRIBUTOR Point Dwell (deg)	DISTRIBUTOR Point Gap (in.)	IGNITION TIMING (deg) MT	IGNITION TIMING (deg) AT	Intake Valve Opens (deg)	Fuel Pump Pressure (psi)	IDLE SPEED (rpm) MT	IDLE SPEED (rpm) AT①	VALVE CLEARANCE (in.) In	VALVE CLEARANCE (in.) Ex	Percentage of CO at idle
1965- 1969	SPL311	NGK BP-6E	0.028- 0.032	49-55	0.018- 0.022	16B@ 600	—	20	3.4- 4.3	600	—	0.017	0.017	N.A.
1969	SPL311 with emiss. control	NGK BP-6E	0.032- 0.036	49-55	0.018- 0.022	TDC@ 700	—	20	3.4- 4.3	700	—	0.017	0.017	5-7② 1.8- 2.2④
1967- 1969	SRL311	NGK BP-6E	0.028- 0.032	49-55	0.018- 0.022	16B@ 600	—	18	3.4- 4.3	600	—	0.008 hot	0.012 hot	N.A.
1969	SRL311 with emiss. control	NGK BP-6E	0.028- 0.032	49-55	0.018- 0.022	TDC@ 700	—	18	3.4- 4.3	700	—	0.008 hot	0.012 hot	5-7② 1.8- 2.2④
1967- 1969	SRL311 with Mikuni/Solex carburetors	N.A.	0.028- 0.032	51-58	0.016- 0.022	20B@ 700	—	30	3.4- 4.3	700	—	0.008 hot	0.012 hot	N.A.
1965- 1968	L520	NGK BP-6E	0.028- 0.032	50-55	0.018- 0.022	8B@ 600 ③	—	14	2.1- 2.5	600	—	0.014	0.014	N.A.
1969	L520 with emiss. control L521	NGK BP-6E	0.028- 0.032	50-55	0.018- 0.022	TDC@ 700	—	14	2.1- 2.5	700	—	0.014	0.014	1-3
1970- 1971	PL521	NGK BP-6E	0.032- 0.036	49-55	0.018- 0.022	10B@ 700	—	12	2.6- 3.4	700	—	0.008 cold, 0.010 hot	0.010 cold, 0.012 hot	2.4②
1972	PL521	NGK BP-5ES	0.032- 0.036	49-55	0.018- 0.022	7B@ 700	7B@ 600	N.A.	2.6- 3.4	700	600	0.008 cold, 0.010 hot	0.010 cold, 0.012 hot	2
1973	PL620	NGK BP-6ES	0.028- 0.031	49-55	0.018- 0.022	5B@ 800	5B@ 650	N.A.	2.6- 3.4	800	650	0.008 cold, 0.010 hot	0.010 cold, 0.012 hot	1.5
1968- 1971	PL510, WPL510	NGK BP-6E	0.028- 0.032	49-55	0.018- 0.022	10B@ 600- 700	10B@ 575- 650	16 ⑦, 12 ⑧	2.6- 3.4	600- 700	575- 650	0.008 cold, 0.010 hot	0.010 cold, 0.012 hot	N.A.
1969- 1971	PL510, WPL510 with emiss. control	NGK BP-6E	0.032- 0.036	49-55	0.018- 0.022	5A@ 700	5A@ 600	16 ⑦, 12 ⑧	2.6- 3.4	700	600	0.008 cold, 0.010 hot	0.010 cold, 0.012 hot	1969 2.0- 2.4, 1970 2-4②
1972	PL510, WPL510	NGK BP-5ES	0.032- 0.036	49-55	0.018- 0.022	7B@ 700	7B@ 600	N.A.	2.6- 3.4	700	600	0.008 cold, 0.010 hot	0.010 cold, 0.012 hot	2
1973	PL510	NGK BP-6ES	0.028- 0.031	49-55	0.018- 0.022	5B@ 800	5B@ 650	N.A.	2.6- 3.4	800	650	0.008 cold, 0.010 hot	0.010 cold, 0.012 hot	1.5
1971	240 Z	NGK BP-6E	0.031- 0.035	35-41	0.018- 0.022	17B@ 550	—	16	3.4- 4.3	550	—	0.008 cold, 0.010 hot	0.010 cold, 0.012 hot	N.A.

TUNE-UP SPECIFICATIONS—(Continued)

Year	Model	Spark Plugs Type	Spark Plugs Gap (in.)	Distributor Point Dwell (deg)	Distributor Point Gap (in.)	Ignition Timing (deg) MT	Ignition Timing (deg) AT	Intake Valve Opens (deg)	Fuel Pump Pressure (psi)	Idle Speed (rpm) MT	Idle Speed (rpm) AT①	Valve Clearance (in.) In	Valve Clearance (in.) Ex	Percentage of CO at idle
1971	240 Z with emiss. control	NGK BP-6E	N.A.	35-41	0.016-0.020	5B@ 750	TDC@ 600 ⑤	16	3.4-4.3	750	600	0.008 cold, 0.010 hot	0.010 cold, 0.012 hot	5-7②
1972	240 Z	NGK BP-6ES	0.032-0.036	35-41 man., 33-39 auto.	0.018-0.022	5B@ 750	TDC@ 600 ⑤	N.A.	3.4-4.3	750	600	0.008 cold, 0.010 hot	0.010 cold, 0.012 hot	6②
1973	240 Z	NGK BP-6ES	0.032-0.036	35-41 man., 33-39 auto.	0.018-0.022	7B@ 750	5B@ 600 ⑥	N.A.	3.4-4.3	750	600	0.008 cold, 0.010 hot	0.010 cold, 0.012 hot	3②
1971	LB110, KLB110	NGK BP-6E	0.031-0.035	49-55	0.018-0.022	5B@ 700	—	14	N.A.	700	—	0.010 cold, 0.014 hot	0.010 cold, 0.014 hot	2-3
1972	LB110, KLB110	NGK BP-5ES	0.032-0.036	49-55	0.020	5B@ 700	5B@ 600	N.A.	N.A.	700	600	0.010 cold, 0.014 hot	0.012 cold, 0.014 hot	2
1973	LB110, KLB110	NGK BP-5ES	0.032-0.036	49-55	0.020	5B@ 700	5B@ 600	N.A.	N.A.	700	600	0.010 cold, 0.014 hot	0.010 cold, 0.014 hot	1.5
1973	PL610, KPL610, WPL610	NGK BP-6ES	0.028-0.031	49-55	0.018-0.022	5B@ 800	5B@ 650	N.A.	2.6-3.4	800	650	0.008 cold, 0.010 hot	0.010 cold, 0.012 hot	1.5

NOTE: Emission control requires a very precise approach to tune-up. Timing and idle speed are peculiar to the engine and its application, rather than to the engine alone. Data for the particular application is on a sticker in the engine compartment on all late models. If the sticker disagrees with this chart, use the sticker figures. The results of any adjustments or modifications should be checked with a CO meter.

① In Drive
② Air pump disconnected
③ Early models are set at 15B @ 600
④ Air pump connected
⑤ Automatic—10B @ 600 below 30°F
⑥ Automatic—15B @ 600 below 30°F
⑦ PL510
⑧ WPL510

PISTON AND RING SPECIFICATIONS

All measurements in inches

Engine Model	Piston Clearance	Ring Gap Top Compression	Ring Gap Bottom Compression	Ring Gap Oil Control	Ring Side Clearance Top Compression	Ring Side Clearance Bottom Compression	Ring Side Clearance Oil Control
J	0.001-0.002	0.008-0.013	0.008-0.013	0.008-0.013	0.002-0.004	0.002-0.004	0.002-0.004
R	0.001-0.002	0.010-0.016	0.006-0.012	0.006-0.012	0.002-0.003	0.001	0.001
U20	0.001-0.002	0.010-0.016	0.006-0.012	0.006-0.012	0.002-0.003	0.001-0.003	0.001-0.003
L16	0.001-0.002	0.009-0.015	0.006-0.012	0.006-0.012	0.002-0.003	0.001-0.003	0.001-0.003
L24	0.001-0.002	0.009-0.015	0.006-0.012	0.006-0.012	0.002-0.003	0.001-0.003	0.001-0.003
A12	0.001-0.002	0.008-0.014	0.008-0.014	0.010-0.014	0.002-0.003	0.002-0.003	0.002-0.003
L18	0.001-0.002	0.014-0.022	0.012-0.020	0.012-0.035	0.002-0.003	0.002-0.003	0.002-0.003

VALVE SPECIFICATIONS

Engine Model	Seat Angle (deg)	Valve Spring Pressure (lb. @ in.) Outer	Valve Spring Pressure (lb. @ in.) Inner	Valve Spring Free Length (in.) Outer	Valve Spring Free Length (in.) Inner	Stem to Guide Clearance (in.) Intake	Stem to Guide Clearance (in.) Exhaust	Valve Guide Removable
J	45	N.A.	N.A.	1.97	2.05	0.002-0.003	0.002-0.003	Yes
R	45	N.A.	N.A.	1.97	1.93	0.001-0.002	0.002-0.003	Yes
U20	45	168 @ 1.17 71 @ 1.62	29 @ 1.54	1.96	1.91	0.001-0.002	0.002-0.003	Yes
L16	45	105 @ 1.21 64 @ 1.53	56 @ .96 27 @ 1.38	2.05	1.77	0.001-0.002	0.002-0.003	Yes
L24	45	47 @ 1.57 108 @ 1.16	56 @ .96	1.97	1.76	0.001-0.002	0.002-0.003	Yes
A12	45	66 @ 1.52 135 @ 1.23	None	1.80	None	0.001-0.002	0.002-0.003	Yes
L18	45	108 @ 1.16	56 @ .97	1.97	1.77	0.001-0.002	0.002-0.003	Yes

FIRING ORDER

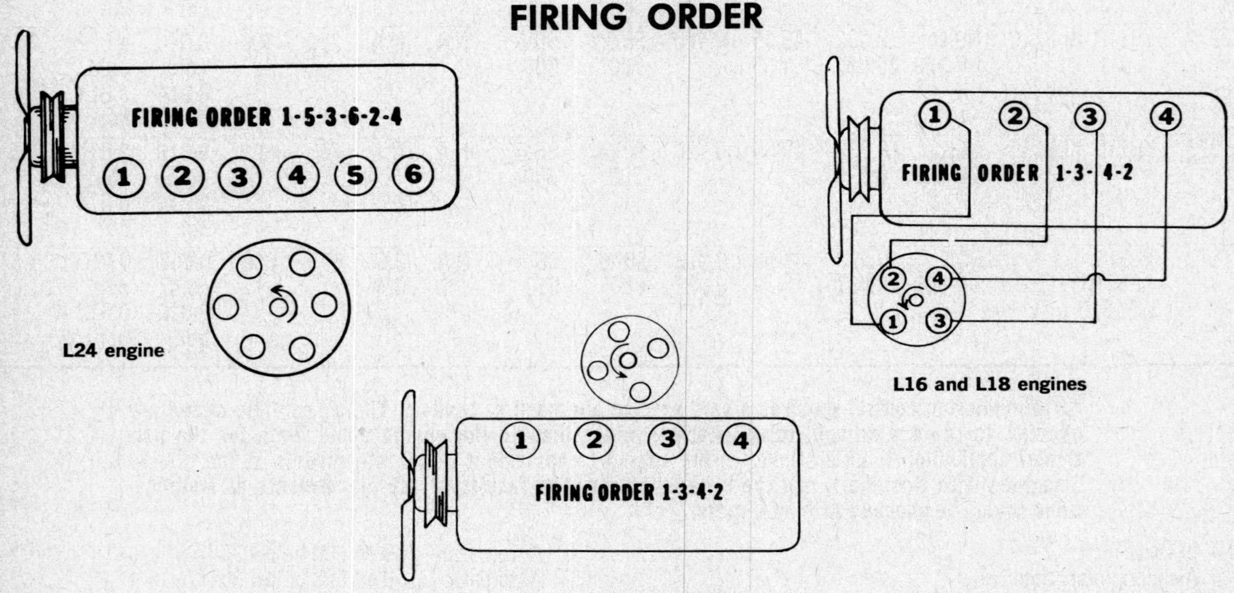

L24 engine

L16 and L18 engines

J, R, U20, and A12 engines

TORQUE SPECIFICATIONS

All readings in ft lbs

Engine Model	Cylinder Head Bolts	Main Bearing Bolts	Rod Bearing Bolts	Crankshaft Pulley Bolt	Flywheel to Crankshaft Bolts
J	45	75-80	22-25	N.A.	35-44
R	45-50	71-81	35-45	N.A.	35-44
U20	65	65	65	145	58
L16	40	33-40	20-24	116-130	69-76
L24	47	33-40	20-24	116-130	101
A12	33-35	36-38	25-26	108-116	47-54
L18	47-62	33-40	33-40	87-116	101-116

CYLINDER HEAD BOLT TIGHTENING SEQUENCE

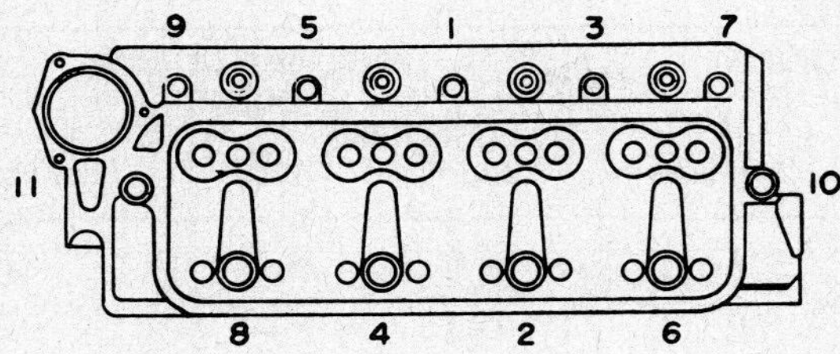

J engine

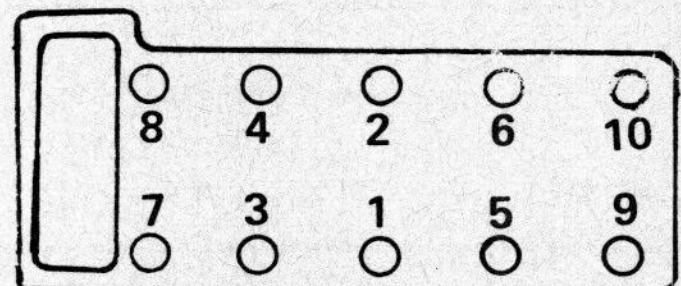

L16, L18, and U20 engines

12 8 4 2 6 10 14
11 7 3 1 5 9 13

Cylinder head, L16 and U20 engines

L24 engine

A12 and R engines

CAPACITIES

Model	ENGINE CRANKCASE With Filter	ENGINE CRANKCASE Without Filter	TRANSMISSION (pts) MANUAL 4-Sp	TRANSMISSION (pts) MANUAL 5-Sp	TRANSMISSION (pts) Automatic (total capacity)	Drive Axle (pts)	Gas Tank (gals)	Cool. Syst. (qts)
SPL311	N.A.	4.3	4.6	—	—	2.0	11.4	8.4
SRL311	N.A.	4.3	—	5.4	—	2.0	11.4	9.0
SRL311 with two twin-ch. carb.	N.A.	7.5	—	5.4	—	2.0	11.4	9.0
L520 L521	3.8	3.2	4.2	—	—	1.7	10.8	5.9
PL510	5.2	4.4	6.4	—	11.4 ①	1.7	11.9	6.8, 7.2 ②
WPL510	5.2	4.4	6.4	—	11.4 ①	2.1	11.9	6.8, 7.2 ②
PL521	4.4	3.6	4.2	—	—	1.7	10.8	6.8, 7.4 ②
240 Z	4.7	4.3	3.2	3.2	12.8	2.1	15.9	8.5
LB110, KLB110	N.A.	2.9	4.3	—	11.8	1.8	9.3	5.7
PL610 KPL610	5.0	4.5	4.0	—	11.8	1.8	13.8	9.0
WPL610	5.0	4.5	4.0	—	11.8	2.8	13.8	9.0
PL620	5.0	4.5	4.0	—	11.8	2.0	11.8	6.5

① 1.5 pts—oil cooler
② With heater

BRAKE SPECIFICATIONS

All measurements are given in inches

Model	Master Cylinder Bore	Wheel Cylinder or Caliper Piston Bore: Front Disc	Wheel Cylinder or Caliper Piston Bore: Front Drum	Wheel Cylinder or Caliper Piston Bore: Rear Drum	Brake Disc or Drum Diameter: Front Disc	Brake Disc or Drum Diameter: Front Drum	Brake Disc or Drum Diameter: Rear Drum
SPL311	0.750	2.125	—	0.813	11.2	—	9.0
SRL311	0.750	2.125	—	0.713	11.2	—	9.0
L520, L521	0.750	—	0.750	0.750	—	10.0	10.0
PL510, WPL510	0.750	2.000	—	0.813	9.1	—	9.0
PL521	N.A.	—	N.A.	N.A.	—	10.0	10.0
240 Z	0.875	2.125	—	0.875	10.7	—	9.0
LB110, KLB110	0.688	1.894	—	0.688	8.4	—	8.0
PL610, KPL610, WPL610	0.750	2.000	—	0.875	9.1	—	9.0
PL620	0.750	—	0.750	0.750	—	10.0	10.0

BATTERY AND STARTER SPECIFICATIONS

Engine Model	Battery: Ampere Hour Capacity	Battery: Volts	Battery: Terminal Grounded	Starter Lock Test: Amps	Starter Lock Test: Volts	Starter Lock Test: Torque (ft lbs)	Starter No Load Test: Amps	Starter No Load Test: Volts	Starter No Load Test: rpm	Brush Minimum Length (in.)
J	40,50	12	Neg.	N.A.	N.A.	N.A.	60	12	7,000	0.37
R	40,50	12	Neg.	500	9.5	6.5	N.A.	N.A.	N.A.	N.A.
U20	50	12	Neg.	500	6.0	7.2	60	11	6,000	0.30
L16	50,60 PL510, WPL510 40,50 L520 40,50,60 PL521, L521	12	Neg.	480	6.0	7.9	60	12	7,000	0.28
L24	N.A.	12	Neg.	460	6.0	10.1	60	12	5,000	0.49
A12	N.A.	12	Neg.	420	6.3	6.5	60	12	7,000	0.37
L18	N.A.	12	Neg.	—	—	—	60	12	6,000	0.24

ALTERNATOR AND REGULATOR SPECIFICATIONS

Engine Model	Alternator: Part Number	Alternator: Output @ 2,500 Alternator rpm (amps)	Regulator: Part Number	Charge Relay① Core Gap (in.)	Charge Relay① Back Gap (in.)	Charge Relay① Air Gap (in.)	Charge Relay① Point Gap (in.)	Voltage Regulator② Core Gap (in.)	Voltage Regulator② Back Gap (in.)	Voltage Regulator② Air Gap (in.)	Voltage Regulator② Point Gap (in.)	Regulated Voltage
J	Mitsubishi AS203A1	24.5	Mitsubishi RL2220B5	—	0.032-0.043	0.032-0.047	0.032-0.043	—	0.028-0.035	0.032-0.039	0.012-0.016	14-15
R	Mitsubishi AC300/12X2R	24.5, 21.5 @ high temp.	Mitsubishi RL-2B	—	0.032-0.043	0.032-0.047	0.032-0.043	— —	0.028-0.035	0.032-0.035	0.012-0.016	14-15
U20	Mitsubishi AS2030A2	23	Mitsubishi RL2220B5	—	0.035-0.047	0.030-0.043	0.030-0.043	— —	0.032-0.047	0.032-0.043	0.012-0.016	13.5-14.5
L16	Hitachi LT130-41	22	Hitachi TL1Z-17	—	0.007	0.020-0.024	0.016-0.020	—	0.035-0.039	0.032-0.047	0.012-0.016	14-15
L24	Hitachi LT145-35	34	Hitachi TL1Z-37	0.032-0.039	—	—	0.016-0.024	0.024-0.039	—	—	0.012-0.016	14.3 15.3 @ 50°F

ALTERNATOR AND REGULATOR SPECIFICATIONS (Continued)

	ALTERNATOR		REGULATOR									
				CHARGE RELAY①			VOLTAGE REGULATOR②					
Engine Model	Part Number	Output @ 2,500 Alternator rpm (amps)	Part Number	Core Gap (in.)	Back Gap (in.)	Air Gap (in.)	Point Gap (in.)	Core Gap (in.)	Back Gap (in.)	Air Gap (in.)	Point Gap (in.)	Regulated Voltage
A12	Hitachi LT135-05	24	Hitachi TL1Z-37	0.032-0.039	—	—	0.016-0.024	0.024-0.039	—	—	0.012-0.016	14.3-15.3 @ 50°F
L16, L18	Hitachi LT150-05B	50	Hitachi TL1Z-58	0.032-0.039	—	—	0.016-0.024	0.024-0.039	—	—	0.012-0.016	14.3-15.3 @ 68°F
L18	Hitachi LT135-13B	35	Hitachi TL1Z-57	0.032-0.039	—	—	0.016-0.024	0.024-0.039	—	—	0.012-0.016	14.3-15.3 @ 68°F

— Not Applicable

① Right unit in regulator case (left unit in TL1Z-17, upper unit in TL1Z-57/58)
② Left unit in regulator case (right unit in TL1Z-17, lower unit in TL1Z-57/58)
NOTE: Right and left are determined with the regulator terminals or harness plug downward.

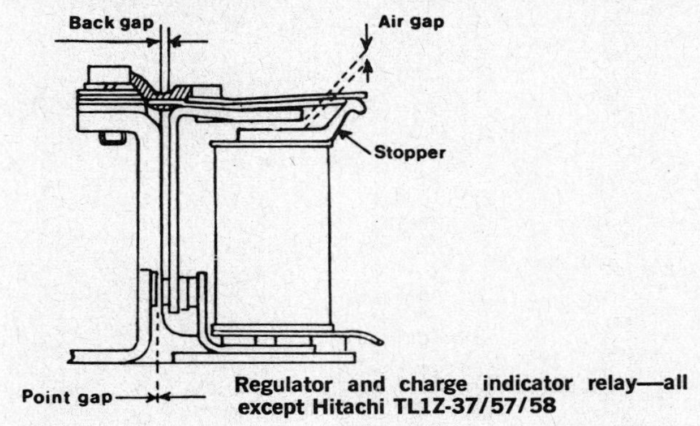

Regulator and charge indicator relay—all except Hitachi TL1Z-37/57/58

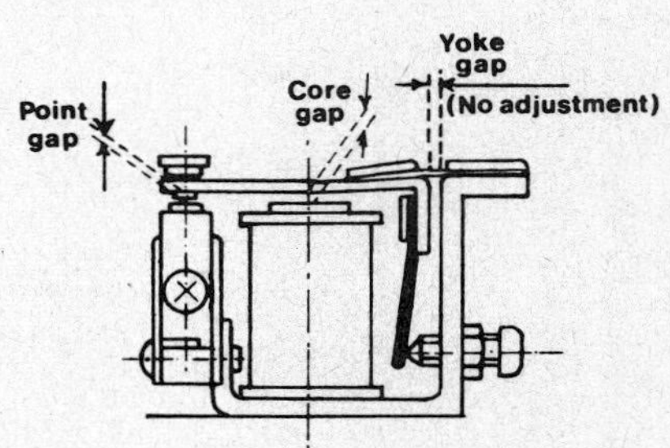

Regulator and charge indicator relay—Hitachi TL1Z-37/57/58

WHEEL ALIGNMENT SPECIFICATIONS

	CASTER		CAMBER				WHEEL PIVOT RATIO (deg)	
Model	Range (deg)	Preferred Setting (deg)	Range (deg)	Preferred Setting (deg)	Toe-In (in.)	Steering Axis Inclination (deg)	Inner Wheel	Outer Wheel
SPL311	—	1°30′	—	1°25′	0.08-0.12	6°35′	36°16′	29°20′
SRL311	—	1°30′	—	1°25′	0.08-0.12	6°35′	36°16′	29°20′
L520	—	1°50′	50′-1°50′	1°20′	0.08-0.12	6	34	29°30′
PL510	—	1°40′	—	1	0.35-0.47	8	38-39	22°30′-33°30′
WPL510	—	2	—	1°10′	0.12-0.24	7°50′	38-39	22°30′-33°30′
L521, PL521	—	3°50′	50′-1°50′	1°20′	0.08-0.12	6	34	29°30′
240 Z	2°25′-3°25′	2°55′	20′-1°20′	50′	0.08-0.20	11°40′-12°40′	32-33	31°24′ 32°24′
LB110, KLB110	40′-1°40′	1°10′	35′-1°35′	1°05′	0.16-0.24	7°55′	42-44	35-37
PL610, KPL610	0°45′-2°15′	—	1°-2°30′	—	0.24-0.35	7°05′	37-38	30°40′-32°40′
WPL610	0°55′-2°25′	—	1°10′-2°40′	—	0.32-0.43	6°55′	37-38	30°40′-32°40′
PL620	—	1°50′	—	1°15′	0.08-0.12	6°15′	36	31

— Information not applicable

WIRING DIAGRAMS

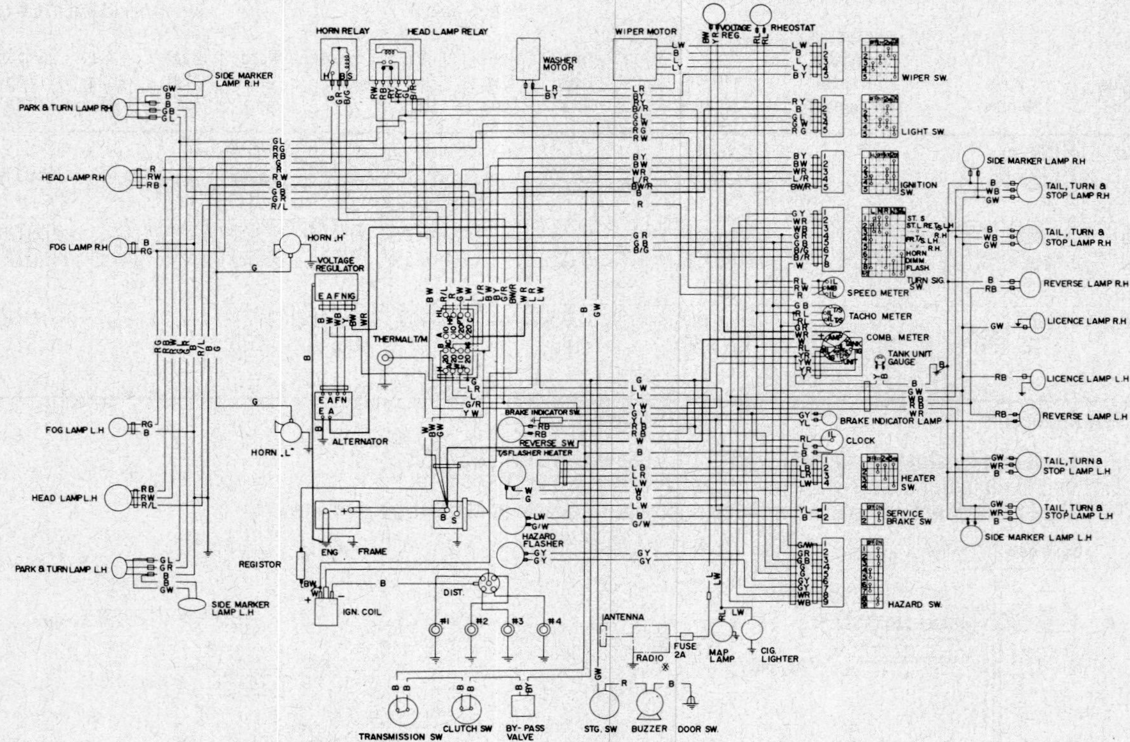

SPL311 sportscar

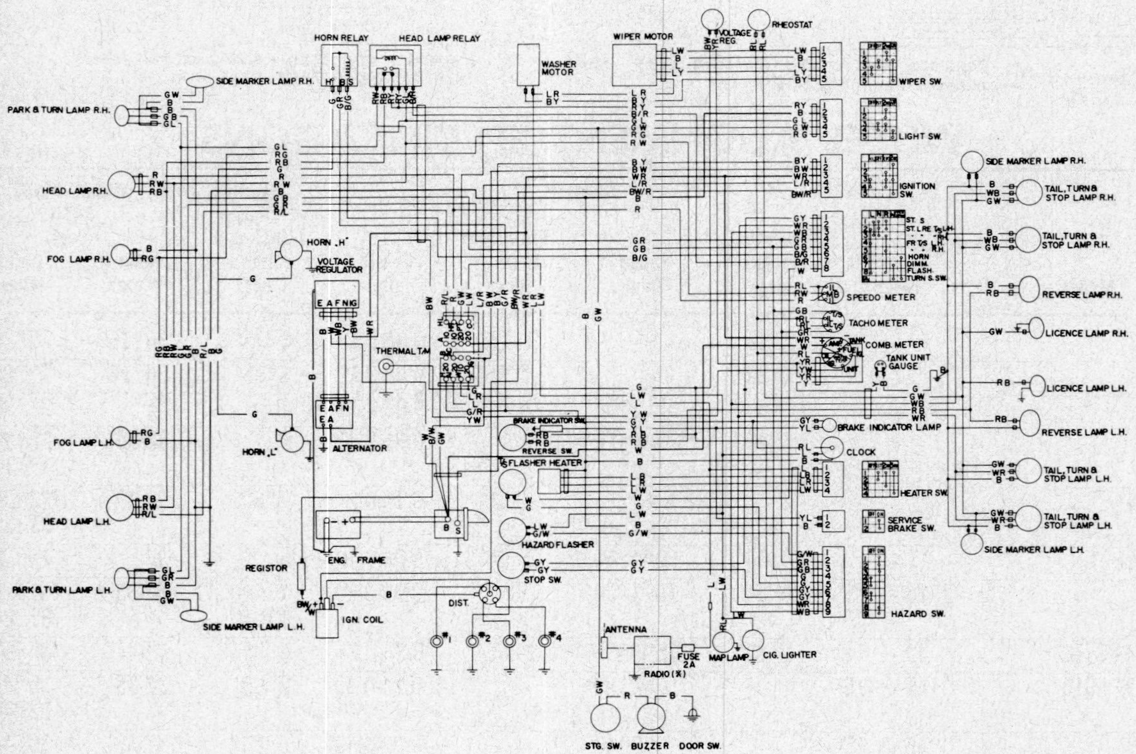

SRL311 sportscar

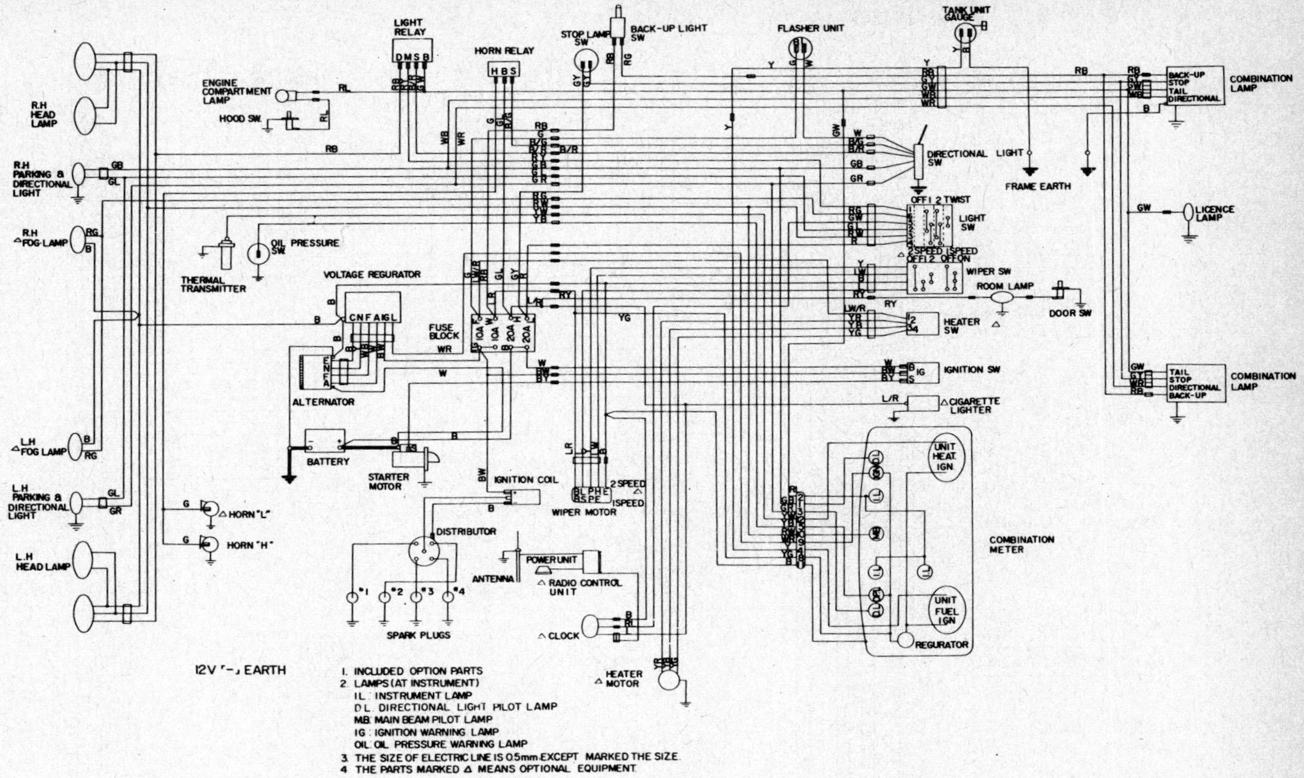

L520 pickup

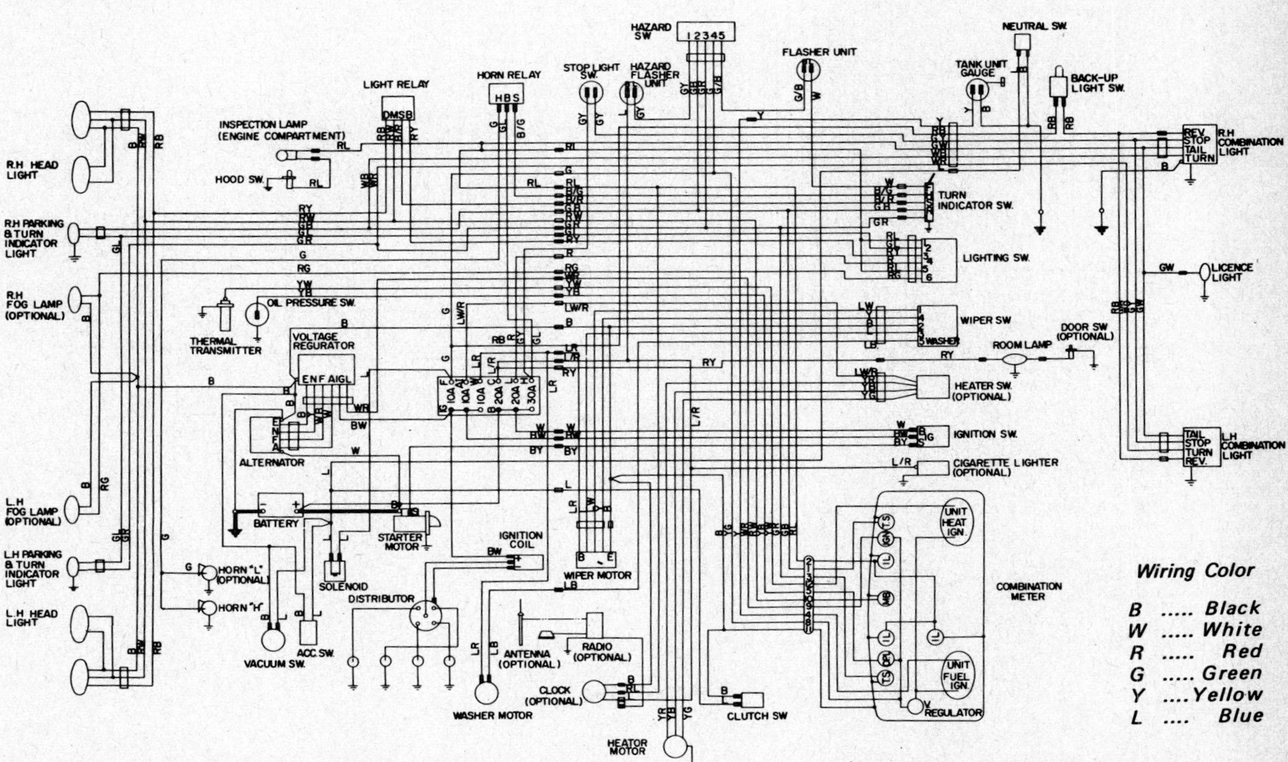

L521 pickup

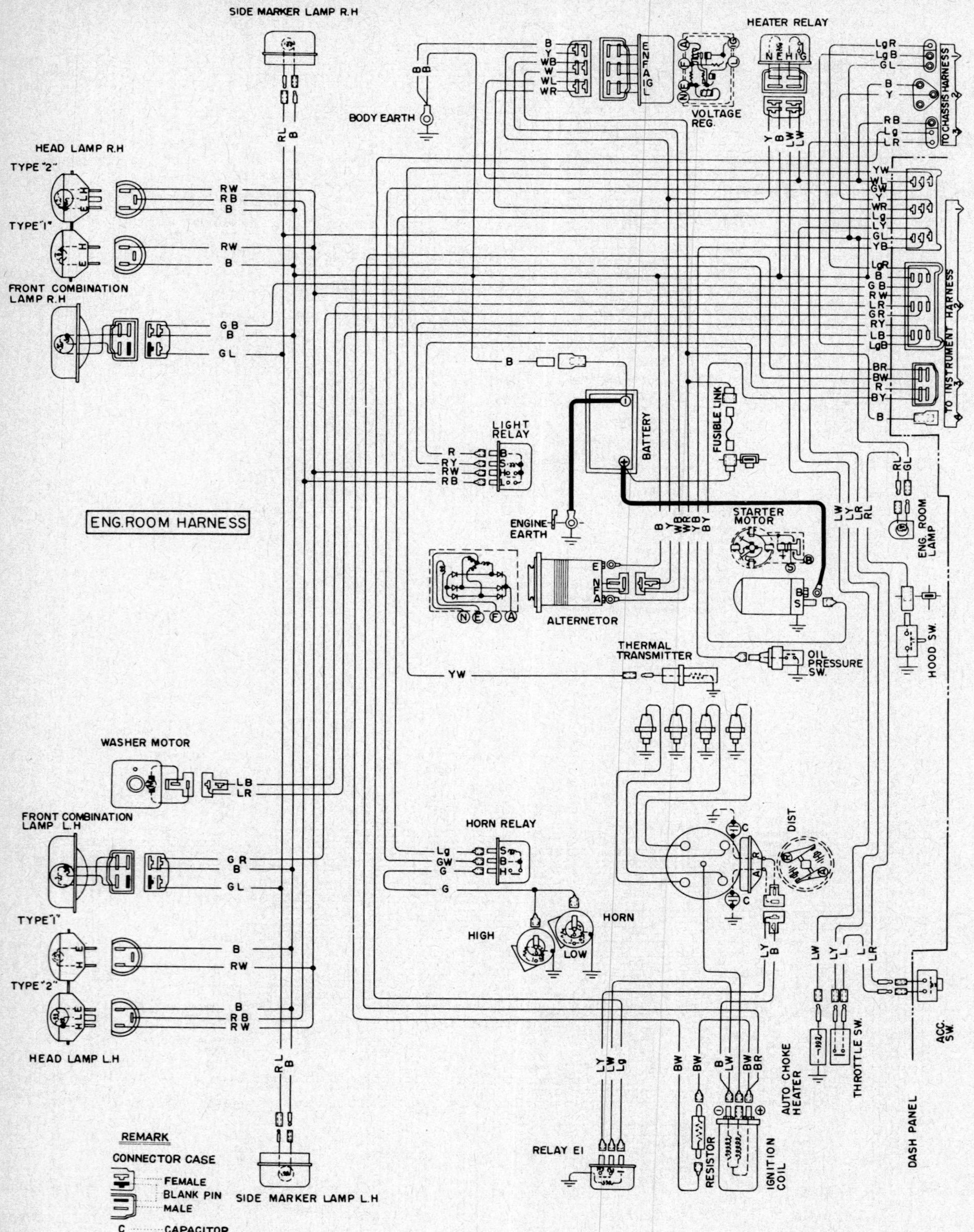

PL620 pickup

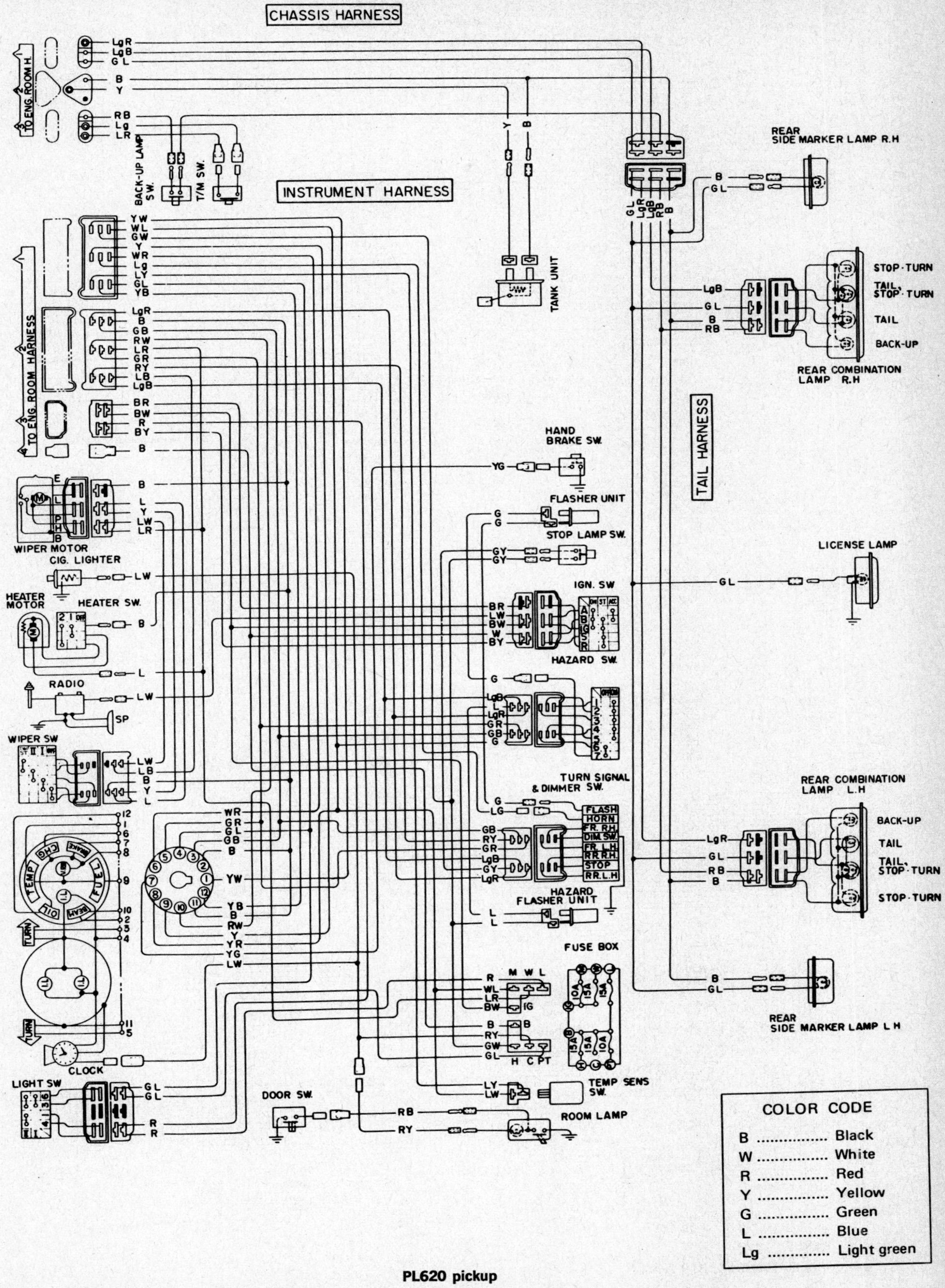

PL620 pickup

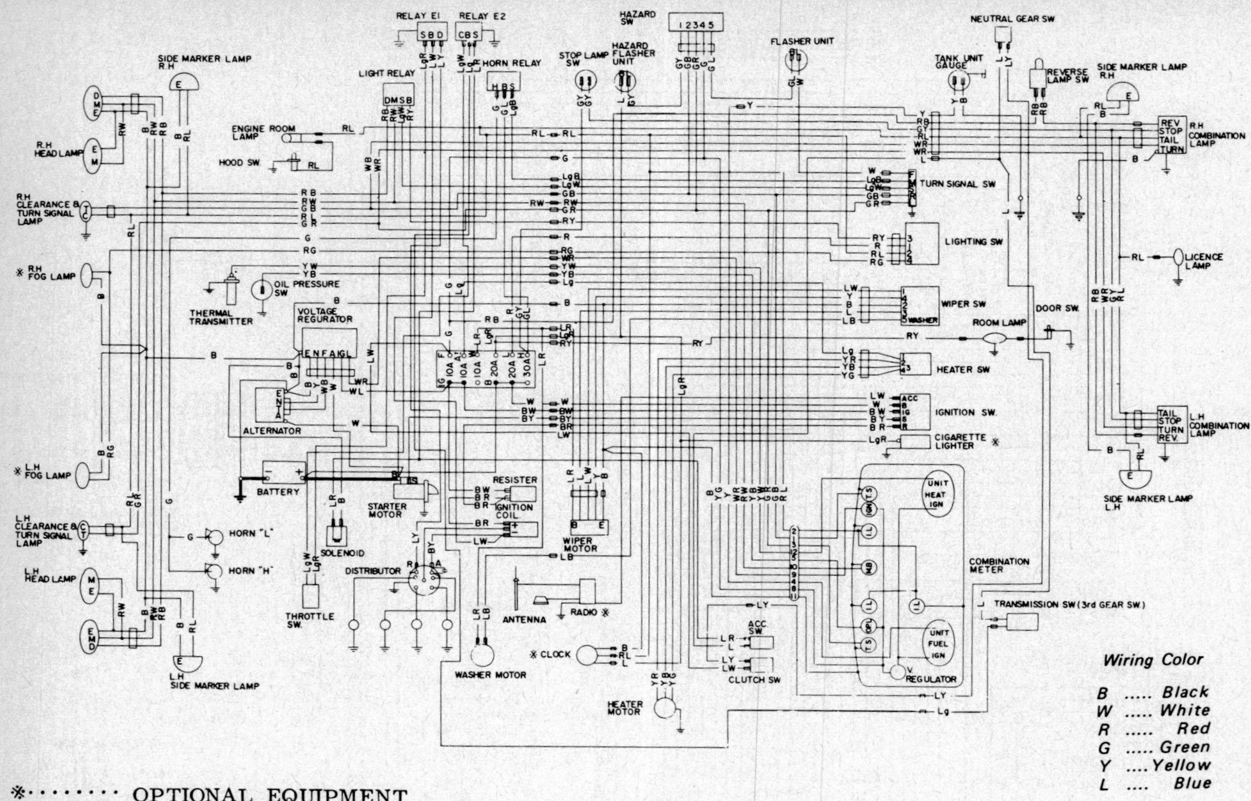

※········ OPTIONAL EQUIPMENT

PL521 pickup

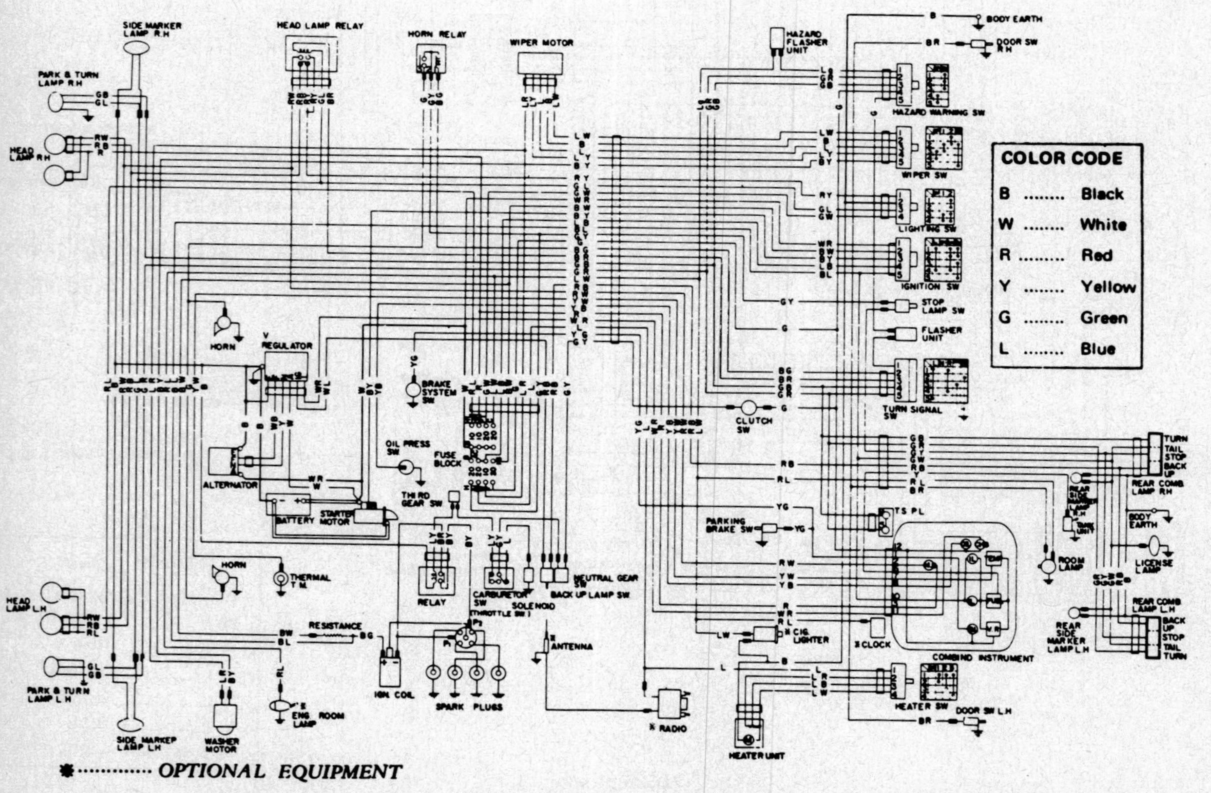

✱············ *OPTIONAL EQUIPMENT*

PL510 sedan, standard transmission

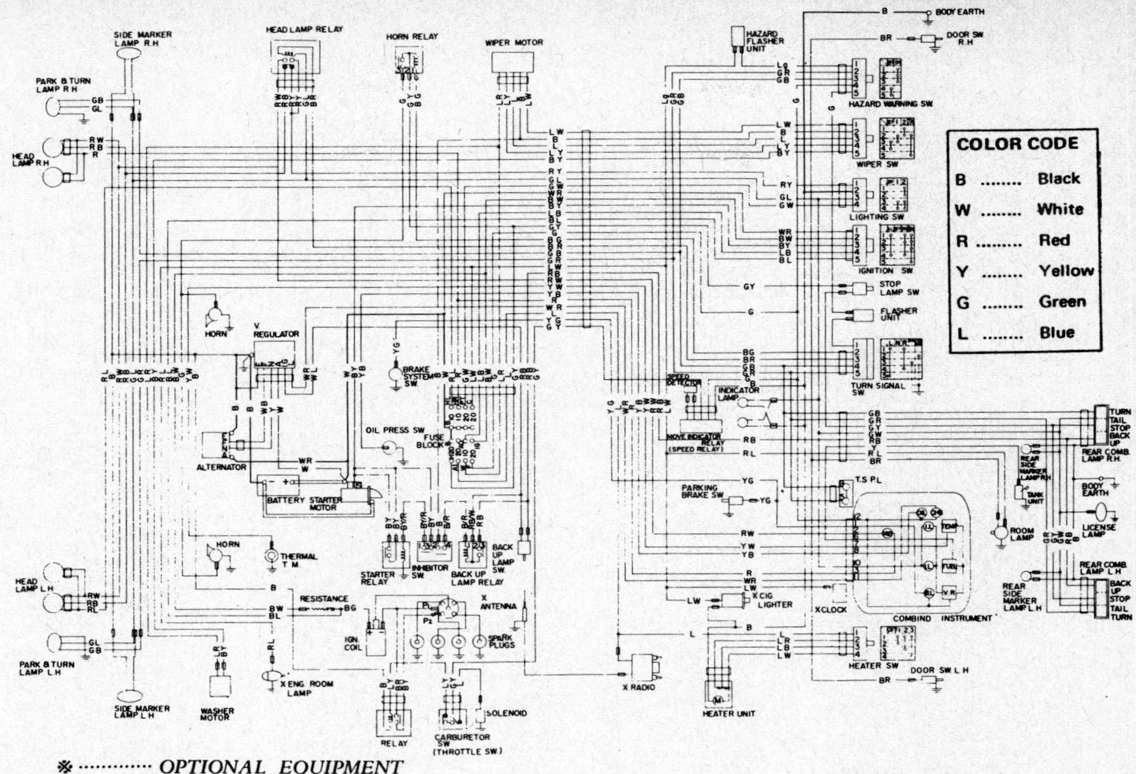

PL510 sedan, automatic transmission

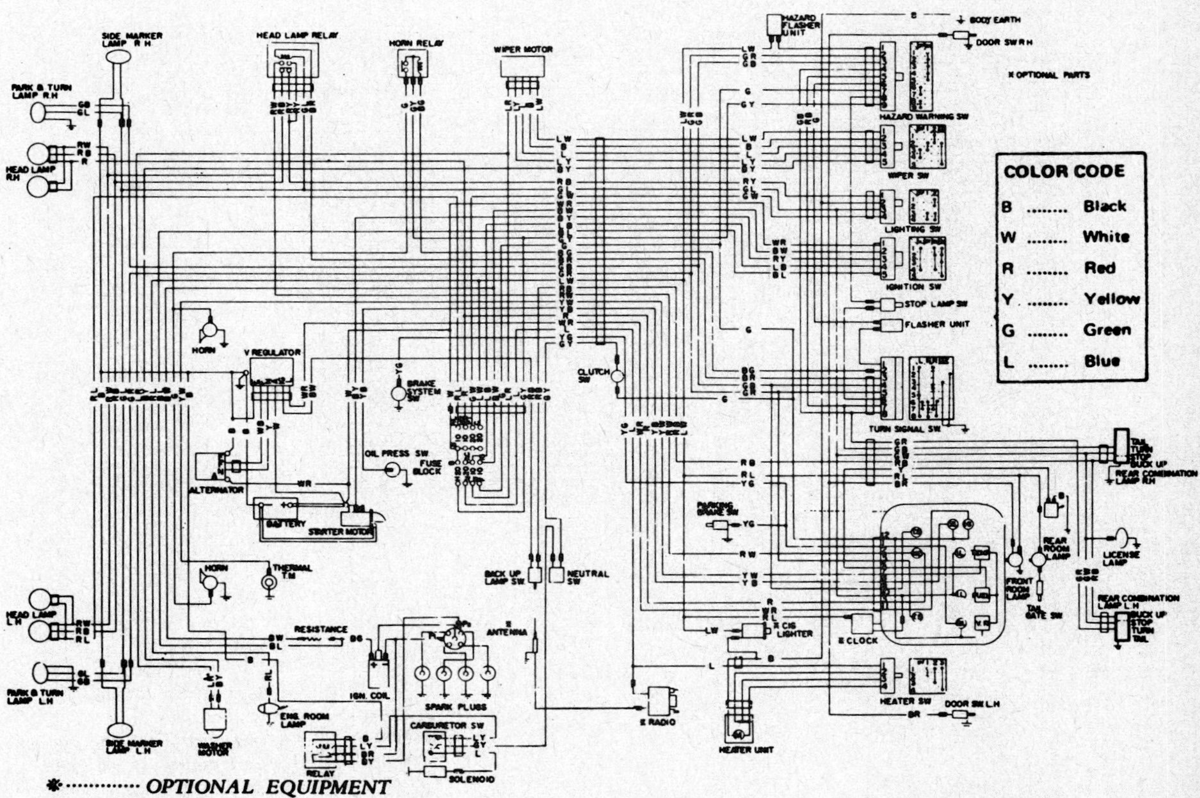

WPL510 wagon, standard transmission

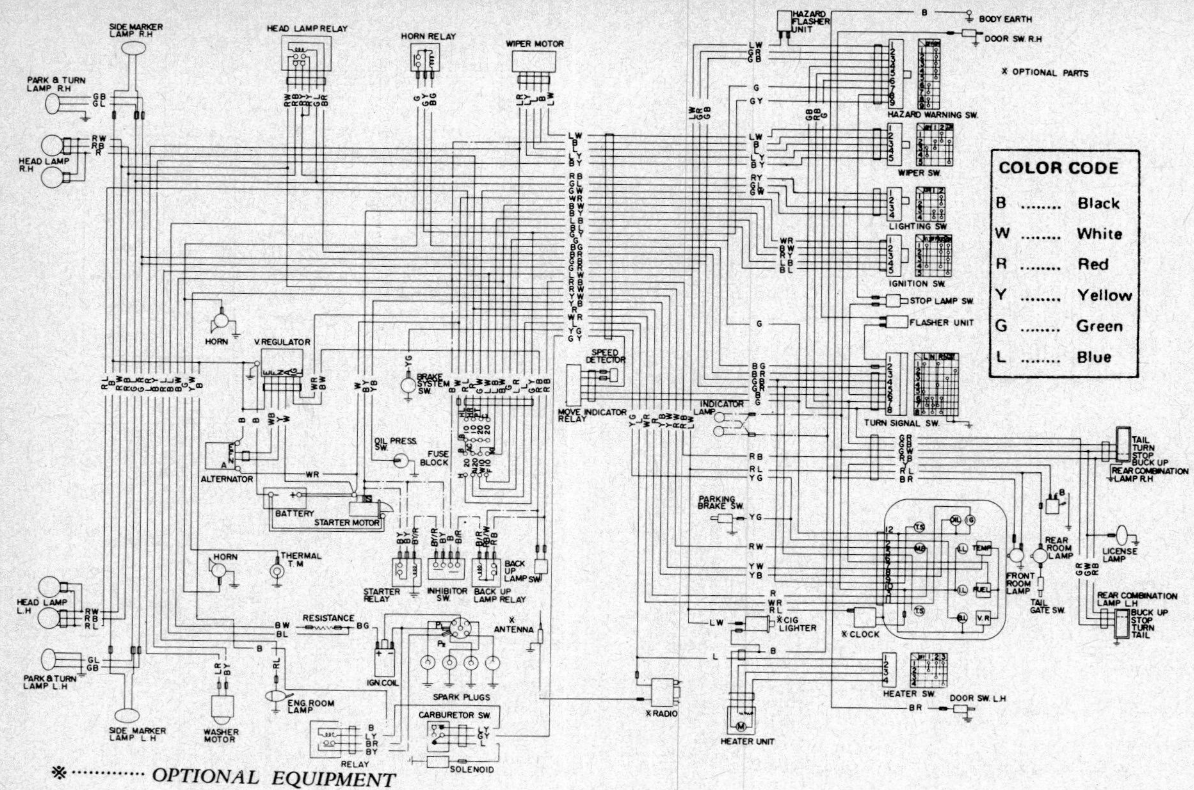

WPL510 wagon, automatic transmission

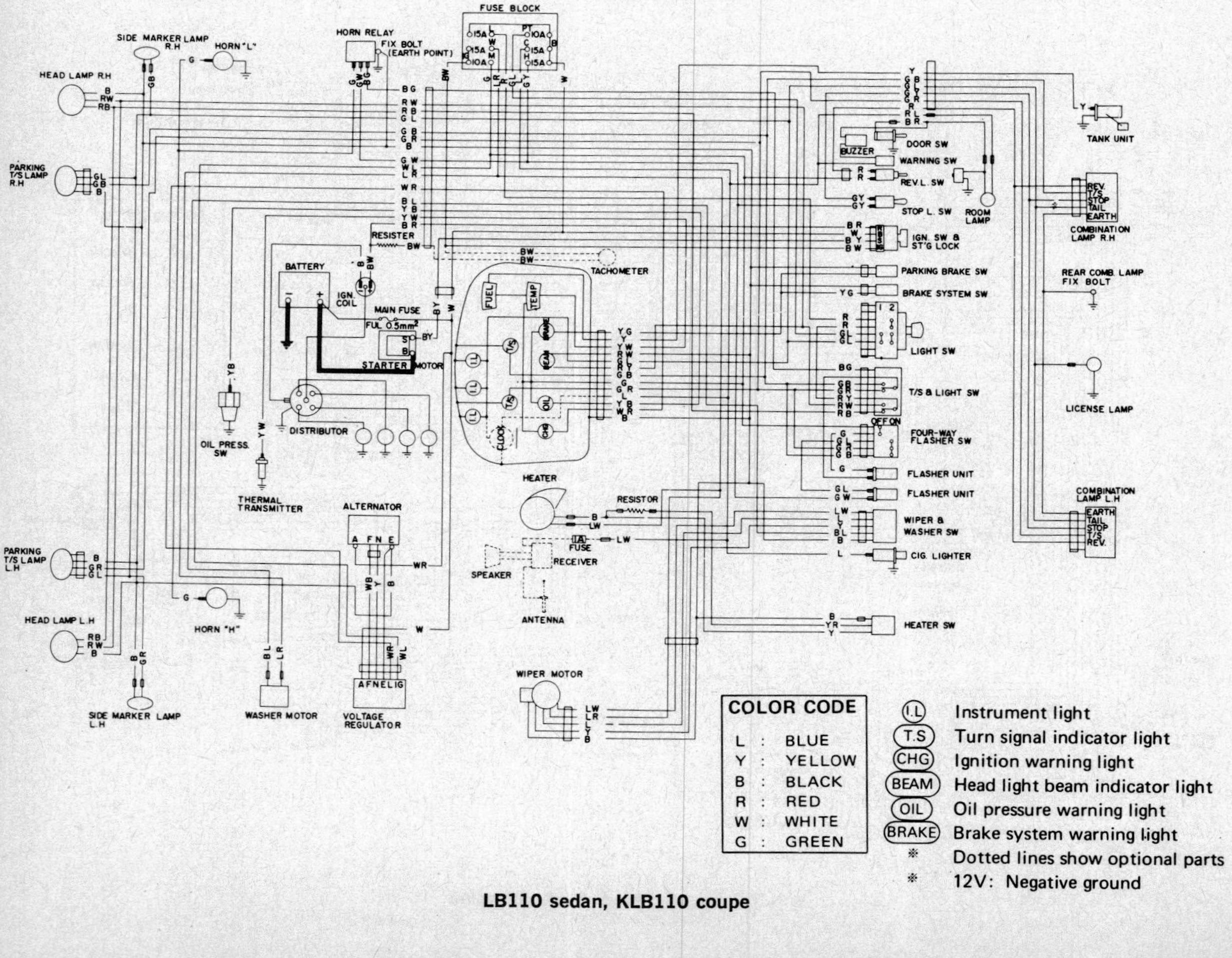

COLOR CODE	
L :	BLUE
Y :	YELLOW
B :	BLACK
R :	RED
W :	WHITE
G :	GREEN

(I.L) Instrument light
(T.S) Turn signal indicator light
(CHG) Ignition warning light
(BEAM) Head light beam indicator light
(OIL) Oil pressure warning light
(BRAKE) Brake system warning light
※ Dotted lines show optional parts
※ 12V: Negative ground

LB110 sedan, KLB110 coupe

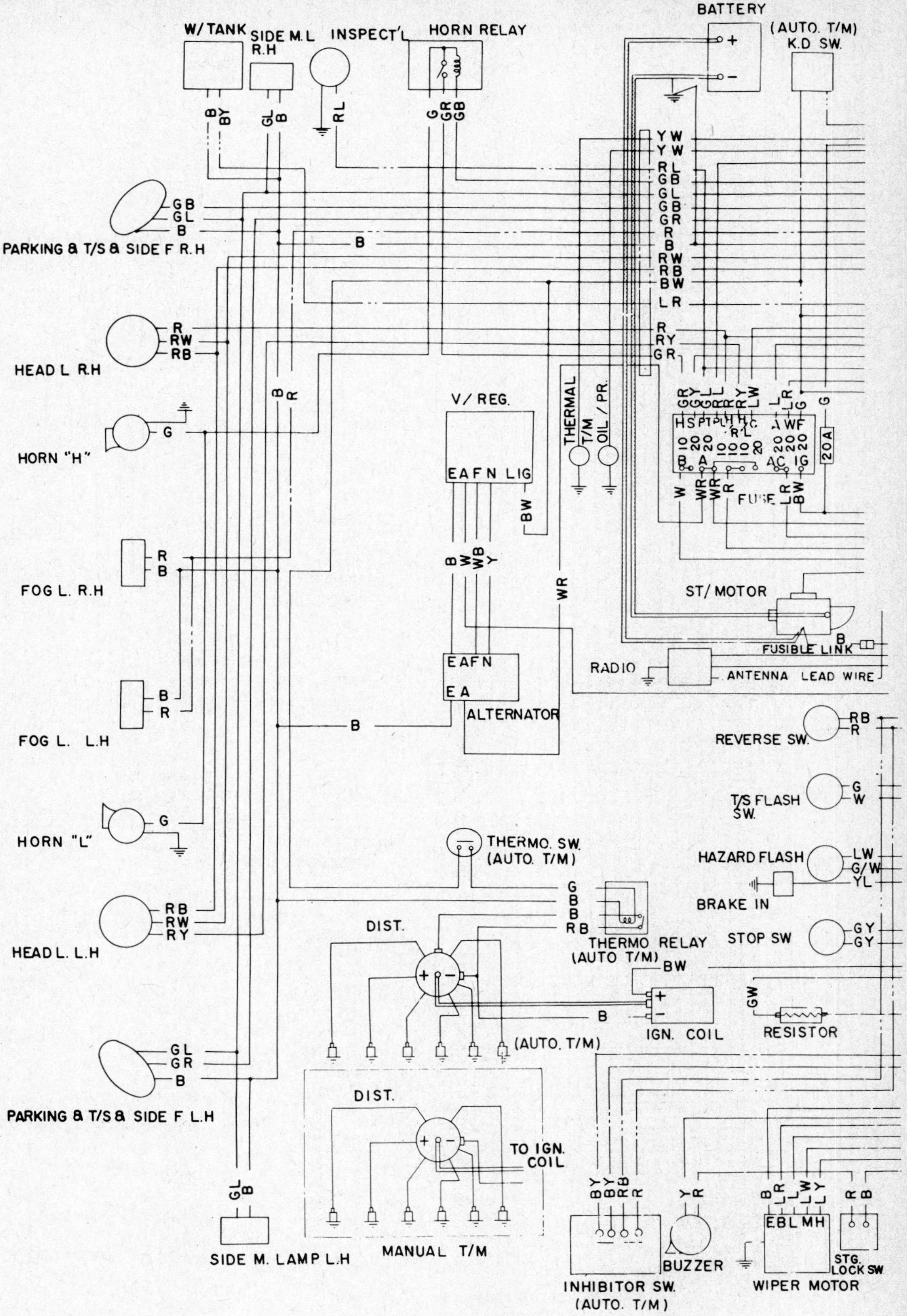

240 Z sports coupe

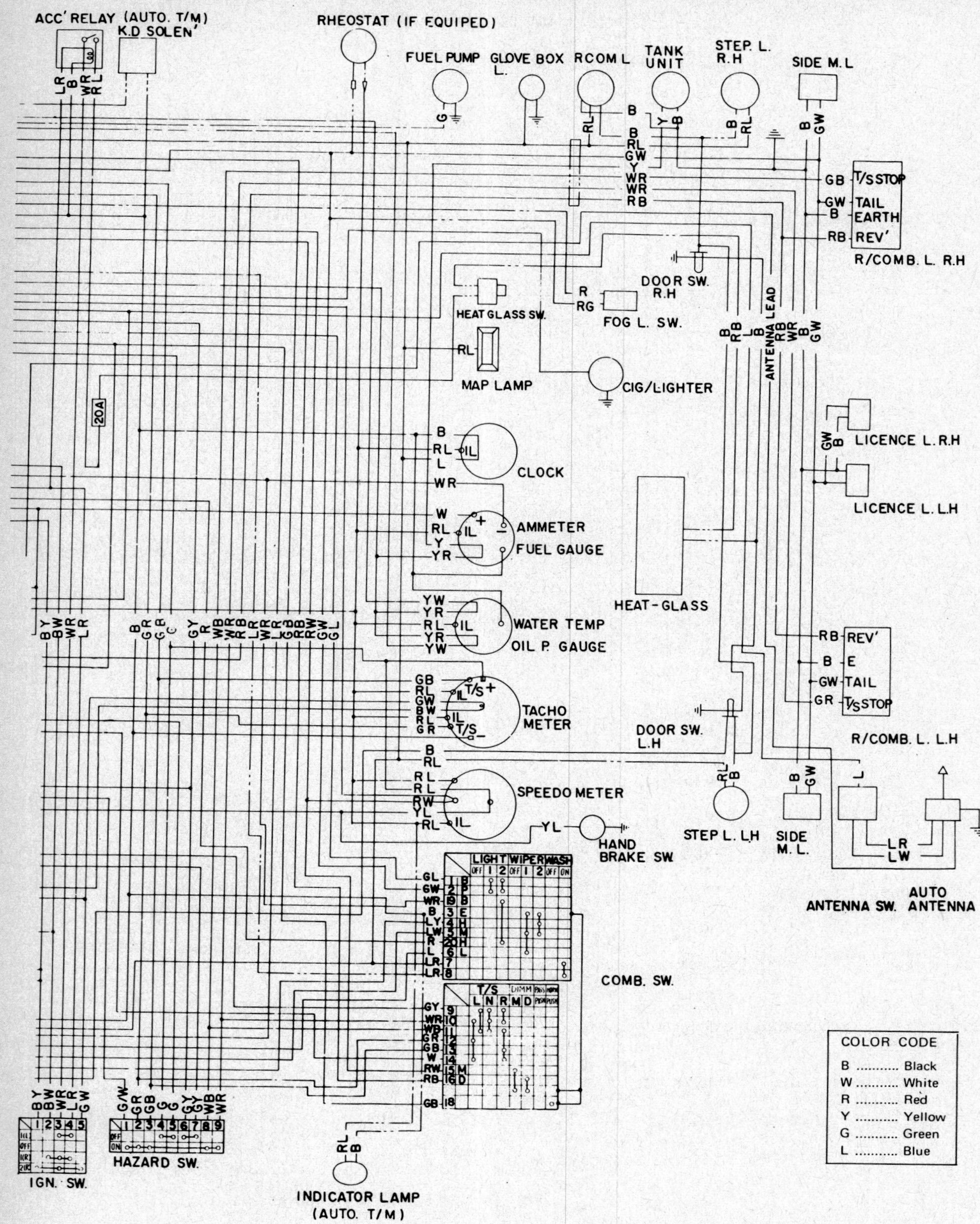

240 Z sports coupe

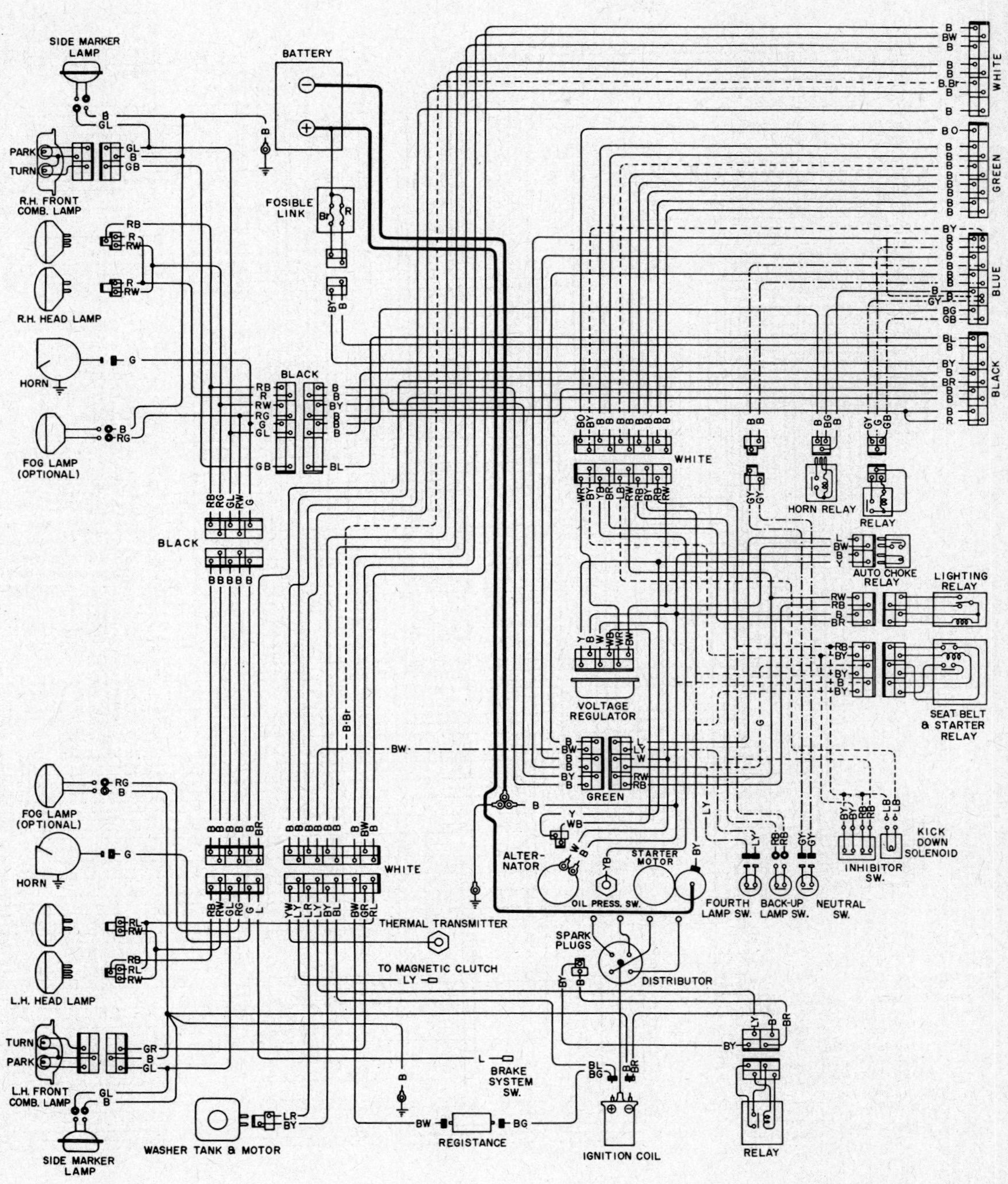

PL610 sedan, KPL610 fastback, WPL610 wagon

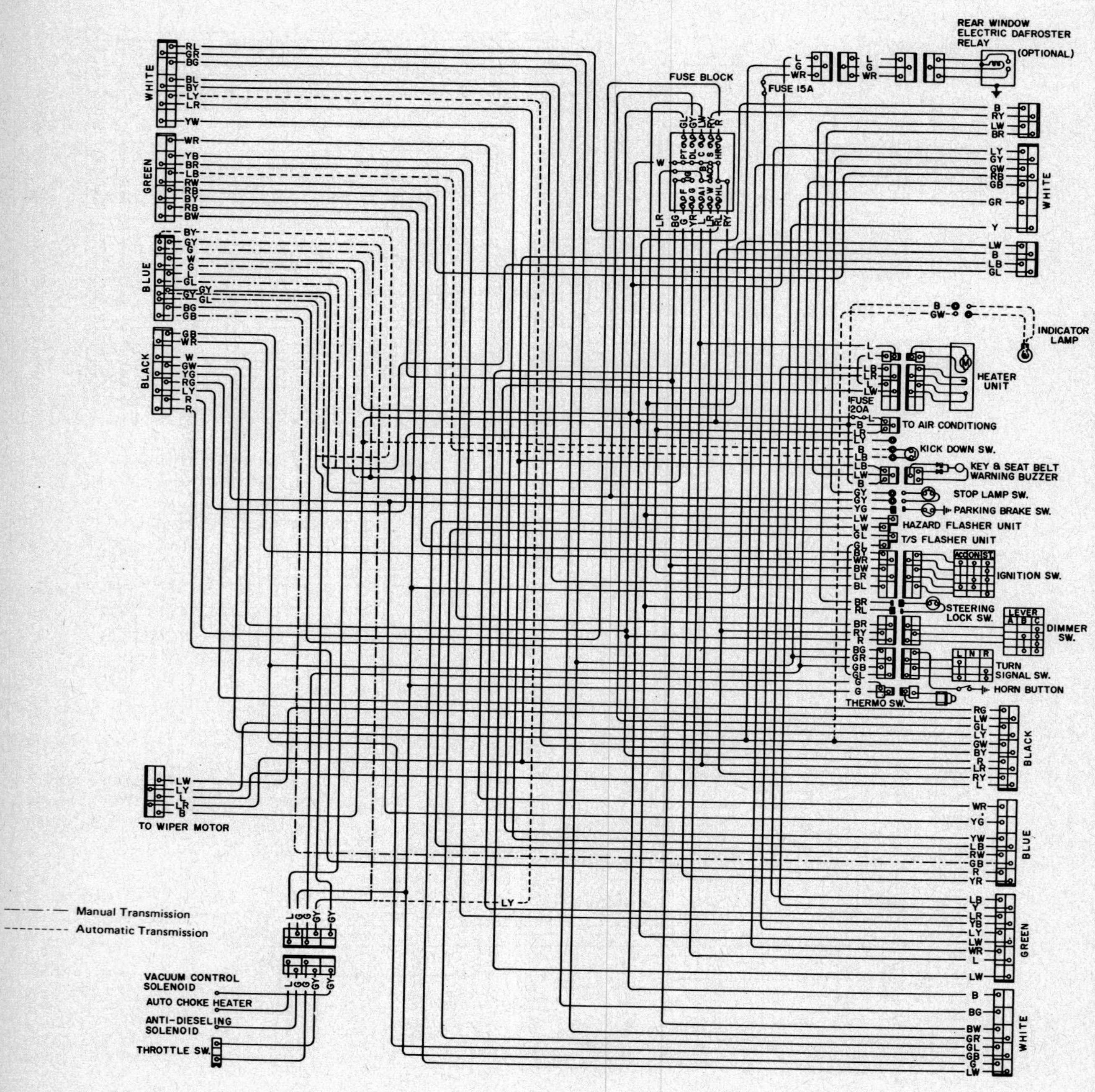

PL610 sedan, KPL610 fastback, WPL610 wagon

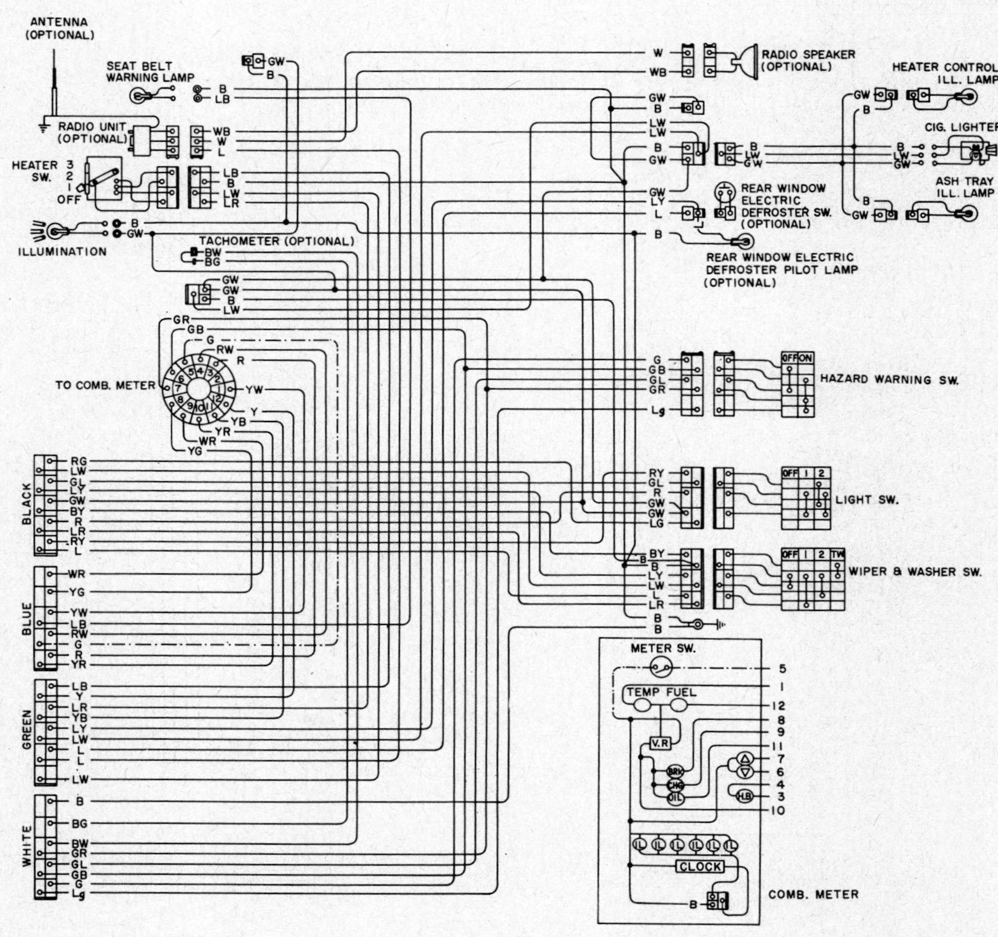

PL610 sedan, KPL610 fastback, WPL610 wagon

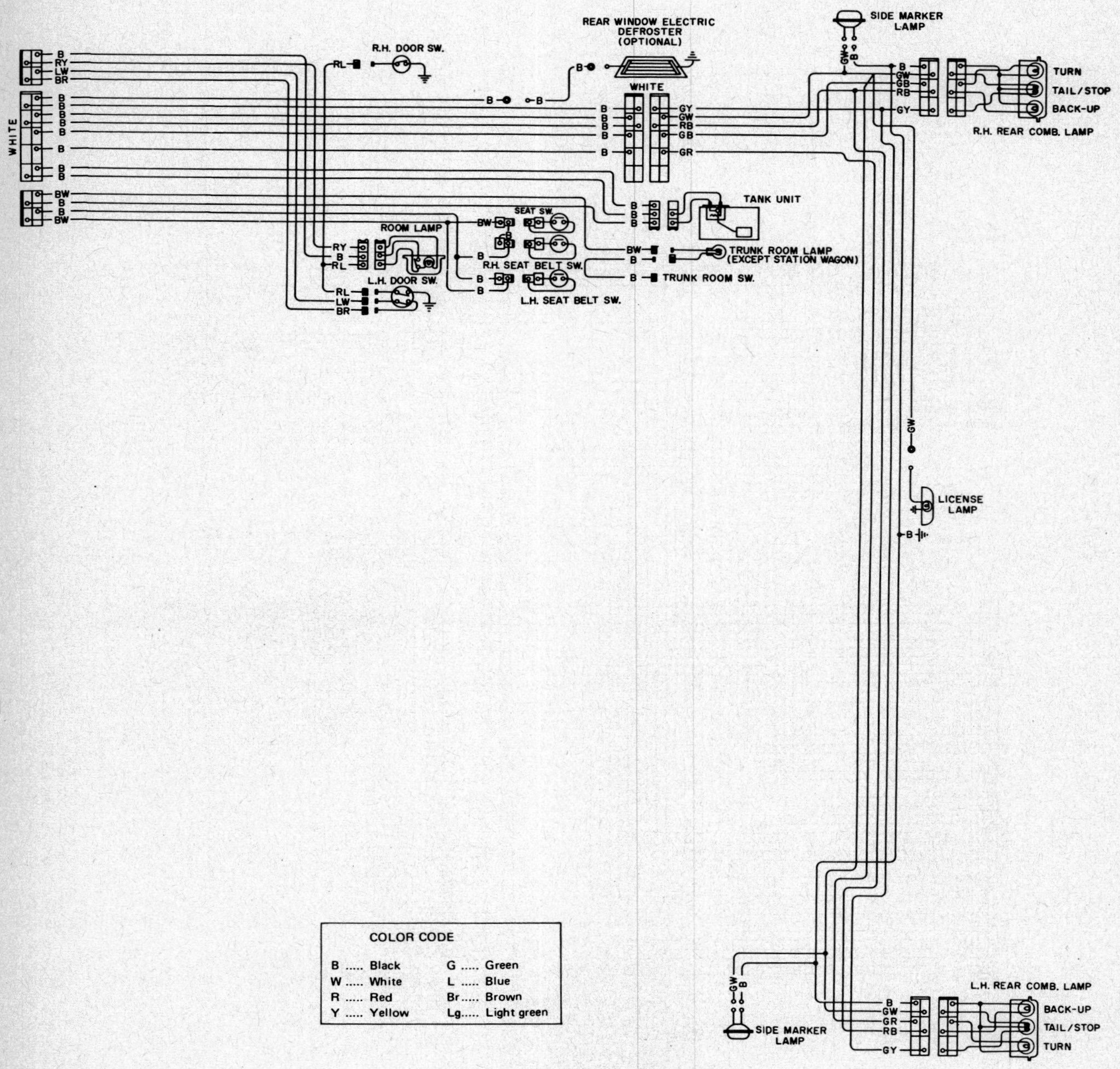

PL610 sedan, KPL610 fastback, WPL610 wagon

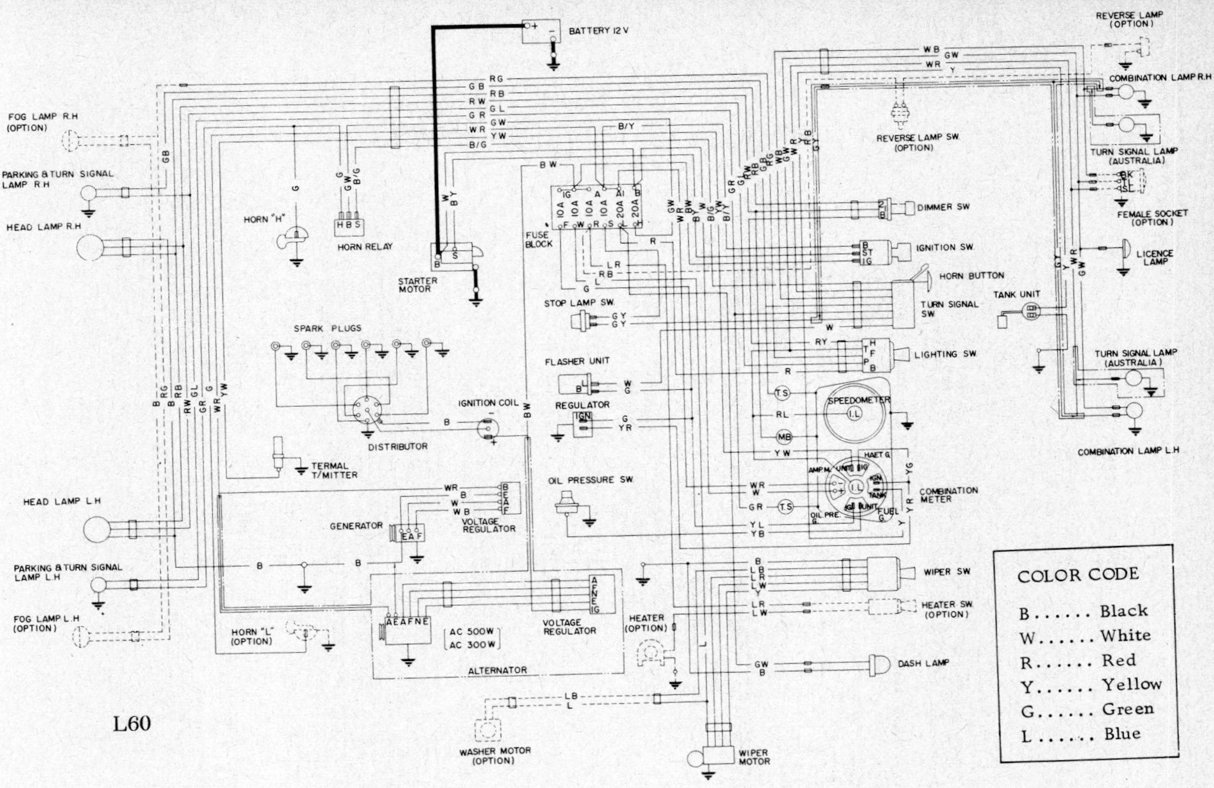
BATTERY 12V
FOG LAMP R.H (OPTION)
PARKING & TURN SIGNAL LAMP R.H
HEAD LAMP R.H
HORN "H"
HORN RELAY
STARTER MOTOR
FUSE BLOCK
REVERSE LAMP (OPTION)
COMBINATION LAMP R.H
REVERSE LAMP SW. (OPTION)
TURN SIGNAL LAMP (AUSTRALIA)
FEMALE SOCKET (OPTION)
DIMMER SW.
IGNITION SW.
HORN BUTTON
LICENCE LAMP
STOP LAMP SW.
TURN SIGNAL SW.
TANK UNIT
SPARK PLUGS
LIGHTING SW.
FLASHER UNIT
TURN SIGNAL LAMP (AUSTRALIA)
IGNITION COIL
REGULATOR
SPEEDOMETER
DISTRIBUTOR
TERMAL T/MITTER
COMBINATION LAMP L.H
OIL PRESSURE SW.
COMBINATION METER
HEAD LAMP L.H
GENERATOR
VOLTAGE REGULATOR
PARKING & TURN SIGNAL LAMP L.H
WIPER SW.
HEATER SW. (OPTION)
FOG LAMP L.H (OPTION)
HORN "L" (OPTION)
AC 500W
AC 300W
VOLTAGE REGULATOR
HEATER (OPTION)
ALTERNATOR
DASH LAMP
WASHER MOTOR (OPTION)
WIPER MOTOR
L60
COLOR CODE
B...... Black
W...... White
R...... Red
Y...... Yellow
G...... Green
L...... Blue

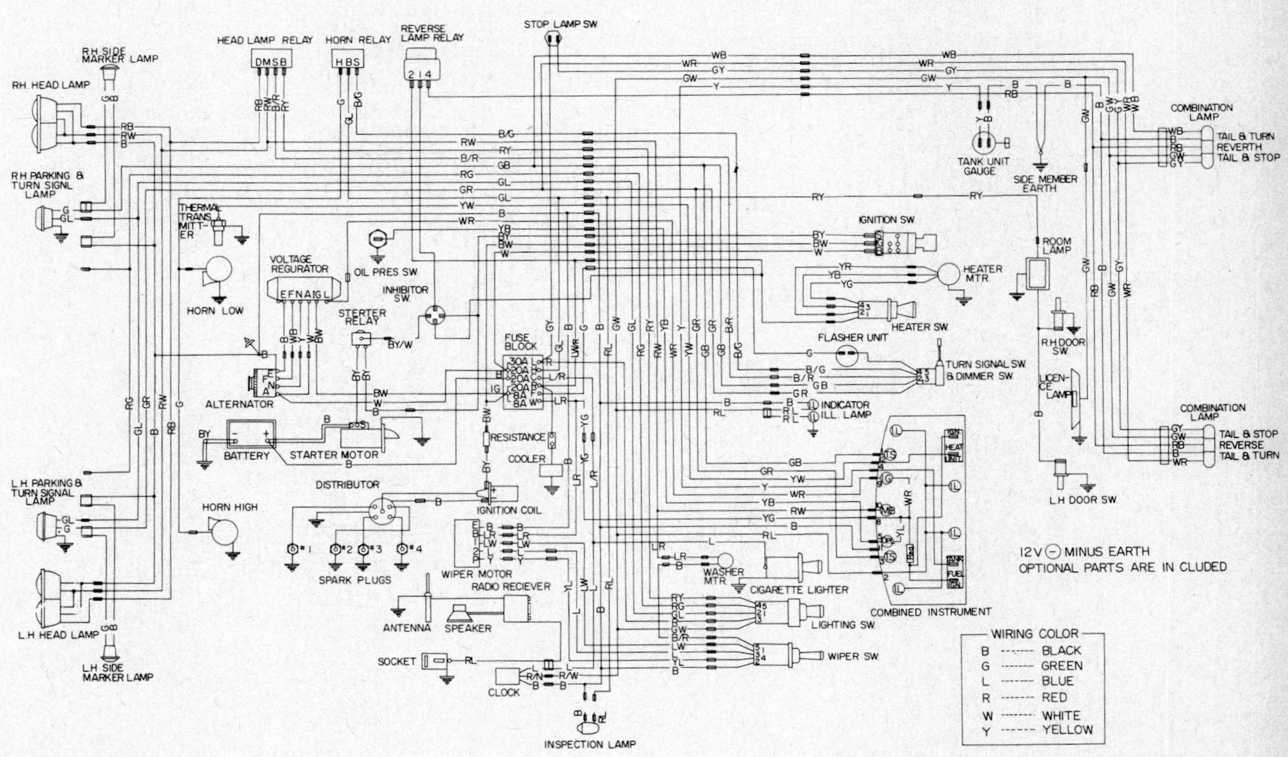
HEAD LAMP RELAY
HORN RELAY
REVERSE LAMP RELAY
STOP LAMP SW.
R.H SIDE MARKER LAMP
RH HEAD LAMP
COMBINATION LAMP
TAIL & TURN
REVERTH
TAIL & STOP
TANK UNIT GAUGE
SIDE MEMBER EARTH
RH PARKING & TURN SIGNL LAMP
THERMAL TRANS-MITTER
IGNITION SW.
ROOM LAMP
VOLTAGE REGURATOR
OIL PRES SW.
INHIBITOR SW.
HEATER MTR.
HORN LOW
STERTER RELAY
HEATER SW.
FUSE BLOCK
FLASHER UNIT
R H DOOR SW.
TURN SIGNAL SW. & DIMMER SW.
ALTERNATOR
INDICATOR ILL. LAMP
LICEN-CE LAMP
BATTERY
STARTER MOTOR
RESISTANCE
COOLER
COMBINATION LAMP
TAIL & STOP
REVERSE
TAIL & TURN
L.H PARKING & TURN SIGNAL LAMP
DISTRIBUTOR
IGNITION COIL
L.H DOOR SW.
HORN HIGH
SPARK PLUGS
WIPER MOTOR
WASHER MTR.
CIGARETTE LIGHTER
12V ⊖ MINUS EARTH
OPTIONAL PARTS ARE IN CLUDED
RADIO RECIEVER
ANTENNA
SPEAKER
COMBINED INSTRUMENT
LIGHTING SW.
L.H HEAD LAMP
WIPER SW.
L.H SIDE MARKER LAMP
SOCKET
CLOCK
INSPECTION LAMP
WIRING COLOR
B ------ BLACK
G ------ GREEN
L ------ BLUE
R ------ RED
W ------ WHITE
Y ------ YELLOW

RL411

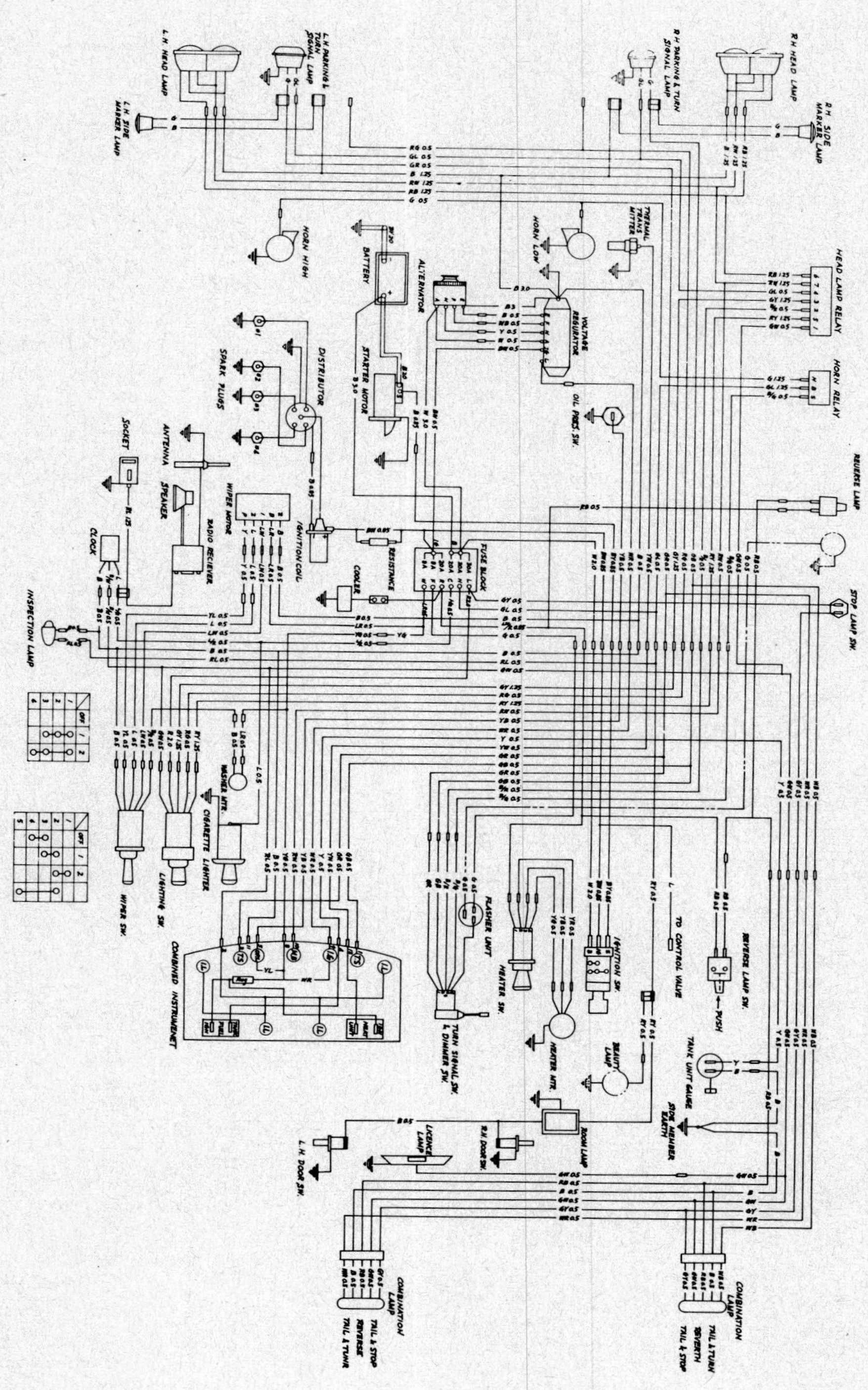
L.H. HEAD LAMP
L.H. SIDE MARKER LAMP
L.H. PARKING & TURN SIGNAL LAMP
R.H. PARKING & TURN SIGNAL LAMP
R.H. HEAD LAMP
R.H. SIDE MARKER LAMP
HORN HIGH
HORN LOW
THERMAL TRANSMITTER
BATTERY
ALTERNATOR
VOLTAGE REGULATOR
HEAD LAMP RELAY
HORN RELAY
DISTRIBUTOR
SPARK PLUGS
STARTER MOTOR
OIL PRES. SW.
REVERSE LAMP
STOP LAMP SW.
ANTENNA
SPEAKER
SOCKET
RADIO RECEIVER
CLOCK
WIPER MOTOR
IGNITION COIL
RESISTANCE
FUSE BLOCK
COOLER
INSPECTION LAMP
WASHER MTR.
CIGARETTE LIGHTER
LIGHTING SW.
WIPER SW.
COMBINED INSTRUMENT
FLASHER UNIT
HEATER SW.
IGNITION SW.
TO CONTROL VALVE
REVERSE LAMP SW.
PUSH
TANK UNIT GAUGE
HEATER MTR.
TURN SIGNAL SW. & DIMMER SW.
ROOM LAMP
R.H. DOOR SW.
LICENCE LAMP
L.H. DOOR SW.
COMBINATION LAMP
PL411

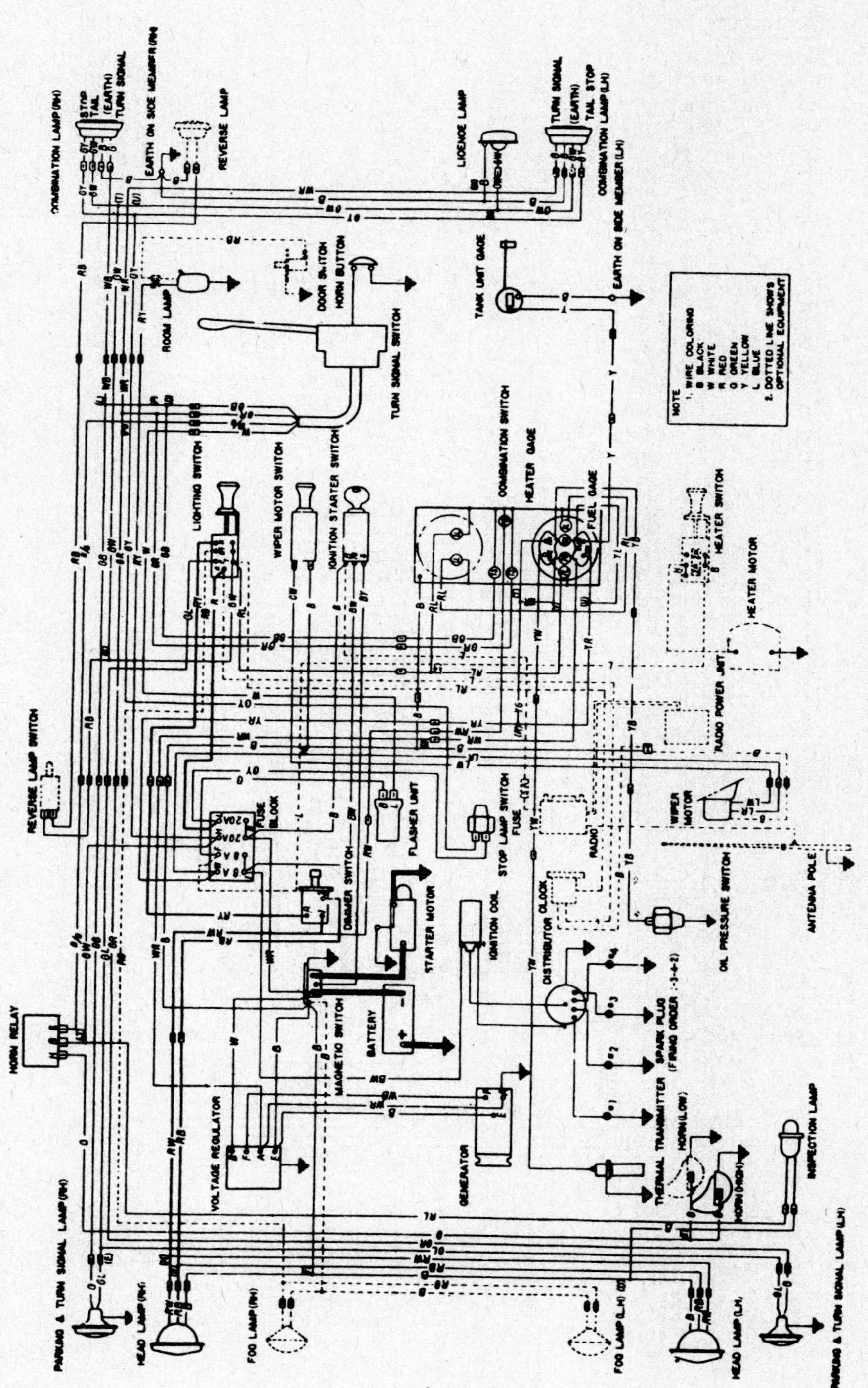
NOTE
1. WIRE COLORING
B BLACK
W WHITE
R RED
G GREEN
Y YELLOW
L BLUE
2. DOTTED LINE SHOWS OPTIONAL EQUIPMENT

L320

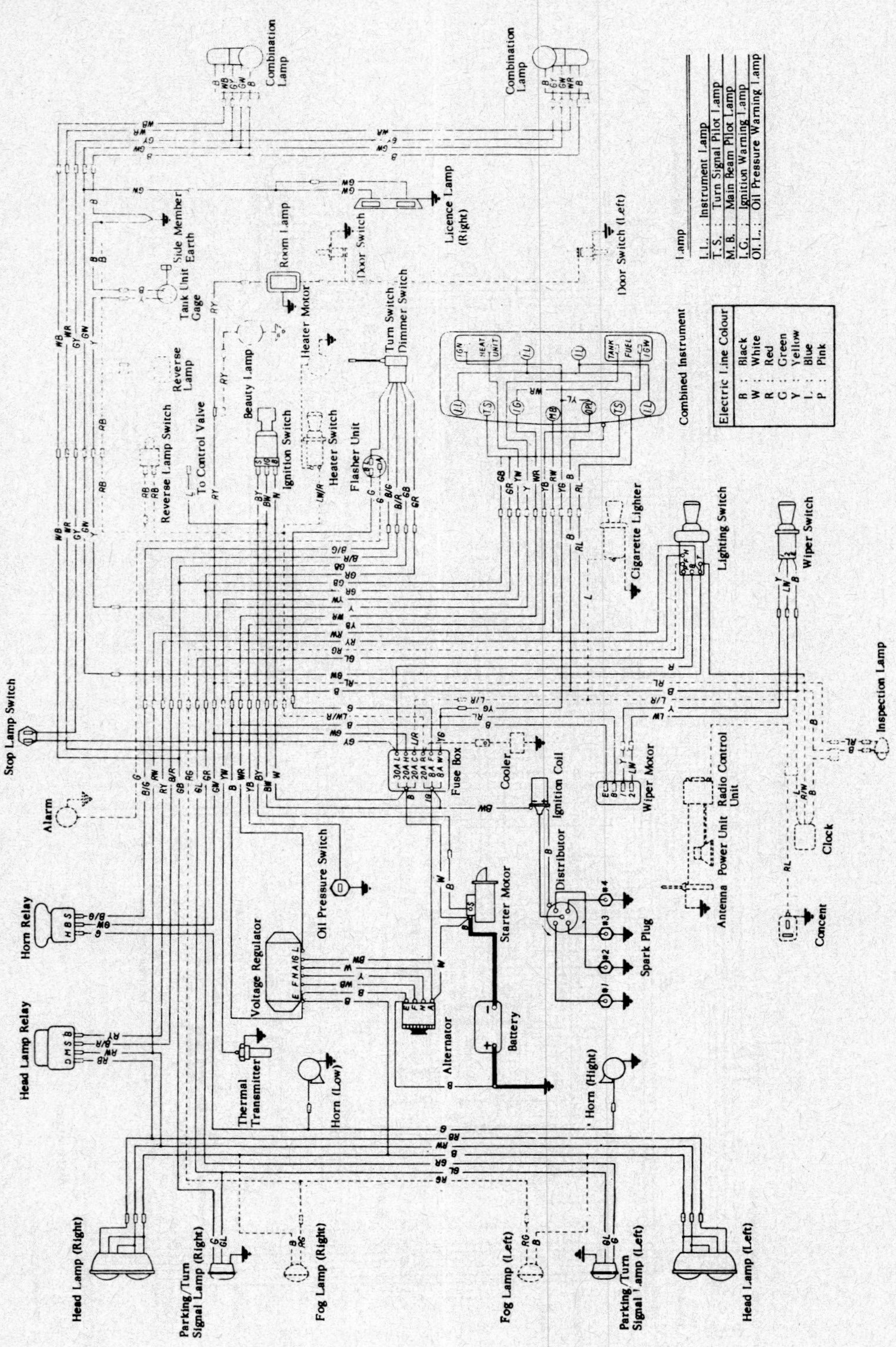
Combination Lamp
Combination Lamp
Licence Lamp (Right)
Side Member Earth
Tank Unit Gage
Room Lamp
Door Switch
Door Switch (Left)
Heater Motor
Turn Switch
Dimmer Switch
Reverse Lamp
Beauty Lamp
Reverse Lamp Switch
To Control Valve
Ignition Switch
Heater Switch
Flasher Unit
Combined Instrument
Electric Line Colour
B : Black
W : White
R : Red
G : Green
Y : Yellow
L : Blue
P : Pink
Lamp
I.L. : Instrument Lamp
T.S. : Turn Signal Pilot Lamp
M.B. : Main Beam Pilot Lamp
I.G. : Ignition Warning Lamp
Ol.L. : Oil Pressure Warning Lamp
Cigarette Lighter
Lighting Switch
Wiper Switch
PL410
Stop Lamp Switch
Alarm
Fuse Box
Cooler
Ignition Coil
Wiper Motor
Radio Control Unit
Inspection Lamp
Clock
Oil Pressure Switch
Distributor
Starter Motor
Power Unit
Antenna
Concent
Horn Relay
Voltage Regulator
Spark Plug
Head Lamp Relay
Alternator
Battery
Thermal Transmitter
Horn (Low)
Horn (Hight)
Head Lamp (Right)
Parking/Turn Signal Lamp (Right)
Fog Lamp (Right)
Fog Lamp (Left)
Parking/Turn Signal Lamp (Left)
Head Lamp (Left)

INTRODUCTION

Nissan Motor Company Limited, the producer of Datsun vehicles, was established in 1933. Nissan is Japan's first mass producer and exporter of cars and trucks. The 5,000,000th Nissan-built vehicle was produced in 1969. Small economy sedans, pickup trucks, and sportscars are included in the Datsun line imported to the United States. In 1970, Datsun moved into third place in import sales. Datsun gained international recognition in 1969 by winning the team championship in the East African Safari Rally. The Datsun team took the first six places in its class. Datsun is also a frequent entrant in the grueling Mexican 1000 mile off-road race and has won the 1970 SCCA C-production championship.

MODEL IDENTIFICATION

SPL311 1,600 cc sportscar, SRL311, 2000 cc sportscar

PL521 1,600 cc pickup, PL520 and L521 are similar

PL510 sedan, two-door and wagon are similar

KLB110 coupe, sedan is similar

240 Z sports coupe

KPL610 fastback coupe, sedan and wagon are similar with vertical grille bars added

SERIAL NUMBER IDENTIFICATION

Engine Number

The engine number is stamped on the right side top edge of the cylinder block. The engine serial number is preceded by the engine model code.

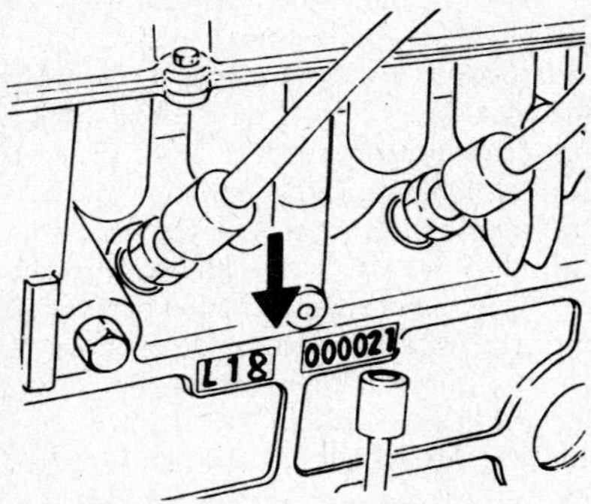

Engine serial and code number

Chassis Number

The chassis number is on the firewall under the hood. On pickups, it is on top of the right frame member, in the engine compartment. Late model vehicles also have the chassis number on a plate attached to the top of the instrument panel on the driver's side. The chassis serial number is preceded by the model designation.

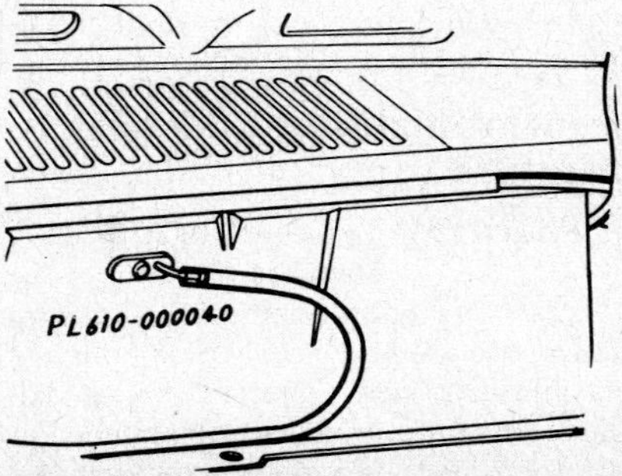

Chassis number location for all models except pickup

Vehicle Identification Plate

The vehicle identification plate is attached to the hood ledge or the firewall. This plate is mounted on the right front suspension strut housing on the 240 Z. The identification plate gives the vehicle model, engine displacement in cc., SAE horsepower rating, wheelbase, engine number, and chassis number.

Engine Identification

Number of Cylinders	Displacement cu. in. (cc)	Type	Engine Model Code
4	79.0 (1,299)	OHV	J
4	97.3 (1,595)	OHV	R
4	120.9 (1,982)	OHC	U20
4	97.3 (1,595)	OHC	L16
6	146.0 (2,393)	OHC	L24
4	71.5 (1,171)	OHV	A12
4	108.0 (1,770)	OHC	L18

DATSUN TYPE HLS30

ENGINE CAPACITY	2,393 cc
MAX. HP at RPM	151 HP at 5,600 rpm
WHEEL BASE	2,305 mm
ENGINE NO.	L24- □□□□□□
CAR NO.	HLS30- □□□□□

NISSAN MOTOR CO., LTD.
YOKOHAMA JAPAN

Vehicle identification plate

TUNE-UP PROCEDURES

Spark Plugs

Clean any foreign material from around the spark plugs prior to removing them. Use a spark plug socket with a rubber insert to remove the plugs. This will prevent cracking the porcelain insulator. Each spark plug should be individually inspected and, if necessary, replaced. Refer to the Troubleshooting Section for an analysis of plug tip conditions. Clean reusable spark plugs and file the center electrode flat. Adjust the spark plug gap, according to the Tune-Up Specifications chart, with a wire type feeler gauge. Lightly oil the threads and torque the spark plugs to 11–15 ft lbs.

Breaker Points and Condenser

Release the distributor cap latches and remove the cap and rotor. Check the points for pitting or burning. Use a point file to clean the points. Turn the engine by hand until the distributor cam opens the breaker points. Loosen the setscrew.

Adjust the points to the specified gap using a feeler gauge. Tighten the setscrew and recheck the gap. Apply a trace of bearing lubricant to the breaker cam. Replace the cap and rotor. Point dwell should be checked at this time. Point dwell figures are given in the Tune-Up Specifications Chart. The ignition timing should be checked each time the breaker points are adjusted.

NOTE: *Some distributors are equipped with dual points.*

Dwell Angle

A dwell meter hookup is shown in the Troubleshooting section. If the distributor has two sets of points, proceed as follows:

1. Unplug the distributor from the engine wiring harness.
2. Connect the two black wires with a jumper wire. This activates the advanced set of points.
3. Check and adjust the dwell of the advanced set of points.
4. Take one end of the jumper wire from the distributor side of the plug. Connect the black wire in the engine harness to the yellow wire from the distributor. This activates the retarded set of points.
5. Check and adjust the dwell of the retarded set of points.
6. Reconnect the plug. Adjust both point sets to the specified gap.

Ignition Timing

Ignition timing should be adjusted with the distributor vacuum line disconnected and plugged and the engine running at idle speed. A stroboscopic timing light must be used to obtain an accurate setting. The setting is indicated by the pointer on the engine front cover and the markings on the crankshaft pulley. The top dead center, or 0°, mark is located at the extreme left. The next mark may be either 5° or 10° before top dead center, depending on the engine model. The succeeding marks are 5° apart. To set the timing, disconnect the vacuum line and loosen the distributor clamp. Connect the timing light, start the engine, and allow it to idle. Direct the timing light at the pulley markings. Turn the distributor head until the timing pointer and the correct pulley mark are aligned. Some early distributors have a knurled knob for fine adjustments. Tighten the clamp and replace the vacuum line. Timing settings for each model are given in the Tune-Up Specifications Chart. Engines with emission controls must be set exactly to the manufacturer's recommendations.

NOTE: *There are two different timing settings for the 240 Z with automatic transmission: an advanced setting for temperatures below 30°F, and a retarded setting for temperatures above 50°F*

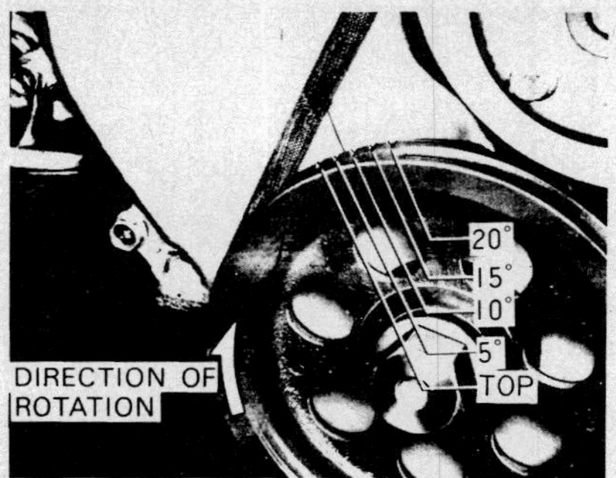

Timing marks, A12 engine

Valve Lash

Remove the rocker arm cover or camshaft cover. Both valves for each cylinder may be adjusted while they are fully closed, on the compression stroke. After the valves have closed, turn the engine another quarter turn to insure that the cam lobes are not exerting pressure on the valves. This can readily be seen on overhead camshaft engines. Loosen the locknuts. Insert the proper size feeler gauge between the valve stem and rocker arm on overhead valve engines, or between the cam lobe and cam follower on overhead cam engines. Valve clearance figures are given in the Tune-Up Specifications Chart. Tighten the adjusting screw until there is a slight drag on the feeler gauge. Tighten the locknut and recheck the clearance. After adjusting the valves for the first cylinder, turn the engine in the normal direction of rotation until the valves for the next cylinder in the firing order close. Repeat the adjusting procedure until all valves have been adjusted. Install a new gasket and replace the rocker arm or camshaft cover.

NOTE: *Do not run the engine with the rocker arm or camshaft cover removed. Do not adjust the valves with the engine running.*

Carburetor

See the Fuel System Section for further adjustments. Two Hitachi sidedraft carburetors are used on R, U20, and L24 engines. A few high performance U20 engines are equipped with two twin-choke sidedraft Mikuni carburetors. All other engines use one down-draft carburetor of various makes and types.

Synchronization and Idle Mixture

Hitachi/SU Type—R, U20, L24 Engines

Two types of dual carburetor linkages have been used. The early type utilizes a flexible cable from the accelerator pedal. The cable turns a cable drum attached to a throttle shaft, which is mounted on the intake manifold. The throttle shaft is connected to each carburetor throttle by a threaded turnbuckle. Each carburetor has an individual throttle adjusting (idle speed) screw. Some models have another idle adjusting screw on the throttle shaft. Synchronization adjustments are made at the turnbuckles. The late type uses a rod linkage from the accelerator pedal to turn an auxiliary throttle shaft. This shaft is connected by a nonadjustable link rod to a throttle shaft linking the carburetor throttles. Each carburetor has an individual throttle adjusting (idle speed) screw. There is also an idle speed adjusting screw on the auxiliary throttle shaft. Synchronizing adjustments are made at a balance screw on the throttle shaft. 1972–1973 models have a fast idle setting screw which is not to be disturbed.

The engine must be at normal operating temperature to perform carburetor adjustments. Make sure that the piston damper oil level is correct. If the plunger has one mark, the oil level should be within 0.2 in. of the mark. If the rod has two marks, the oil level should be between the marks. SAE 20 oil should be used in the dampers, except in extremely cold areas where a lighter viscosity may be necessary. To adjust the carburetors:

1. Remove the air cleaner.
2. Back out the individual carburetor throttle adjusting screws.
3. On early linkage, disconnect the front turnbuckle. On late linkage, back out the balance screw.

Early Hitachi/SU throttle linkage

4. On early linkage, adjust the rear turnbuckle to the standard measurement.

Engine	*Vehicle*	*Std. measurement*
G	SPL310	3.4-3.6"
R	SPL311	2.8"
R	RL411	3.1"
U20	SRL311	2.8"

5. Tighten both carburetor mixture adjusting nuts fully. Back them off an equal number of turns (2–3) until they reach their stops. Tighten both nuts about ½ turn.
6. Turn in the individual carburetor throttle adjusting screws a few turns and start the engine. Adjust both screws equally to obtain a reasonable idle speed.
7. Using an air flow meter (Unisyn), measure air flow through each carburetor. Equalize the readings at each car-

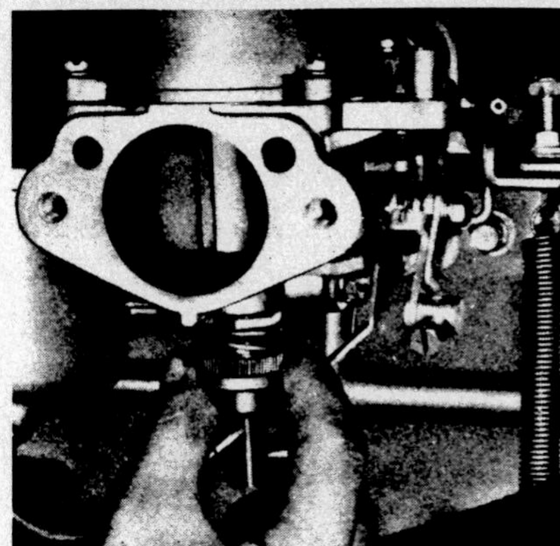

Hitachi/SU carburetor mixture adjusting nut

buretor by adjusting the individual throttle adjusting screws. An alternate, and more difficult, method is to equalize air flow by listening to the hiss of each carburetor air intake through a length of rubber hose. The carburetors are now synchronized. This can be checked visually by stopping the engine, raising both carburetor pistons, and observing whether the throttle plates are parallel.

8. Tighten both mixture adjusting nuts simultaneously in increments of ⅛ turn. Tightening the nut leans the mixture. Stop at the point which gives the fastest smooth idle. If the nuts are tightened all the way and idle is still unsatisfactory, return the nuts to their initial positions as in Step 5. Loosen the nuts simultaneously in increments of ⅛ turn. Loosening the nuts richens the mixture. Stop at the point which gives the fastest smooth idle.

NOTE: *On engines with emission control, the mixture adjusting nuts are held by locknuts and are not to be adjusted, except after carburetor overhaul. Adjust the mixture to obtain the percentage of CO at idle speed specified in the Tune-Up Specifications Chart.*

9. Lift the piston of the rear carburetor ½ in. This makes the carburetor inoperative. If the engine stalls, richen the front carburetor until it will keep the engine running. Now lift the piston of the front carburetor, and adjust the mixture of the back carburetor. The mixture adjustment is now completed.

10. On early linkage, adjust and connect the front turnbuckle. On late linkage, turn in the balance screw to interlock the front and rear throttle shafts.

11. Open the throttle suddenly. The engine should accelerate immediately with no hesitation. Both pistons should rise an equal amount. If this is not the case, recheck the synchronization and mixture adjustments.

12. Adjust the idle speed to that specified in the Tune-Up Specifications Chart. If there is a manufacturer's sticker

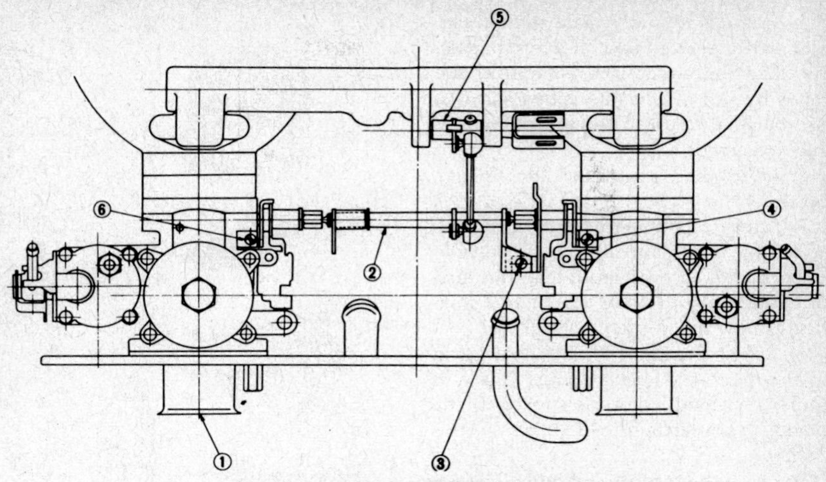

Late Hitachi/SU throttle linkage—1971

1. Air horn
2. Throttle shaft
3. Balance screw
4. Throttle adjusting screw
5. Auxiliary throttle shaft
6. Throttle adjusting screw

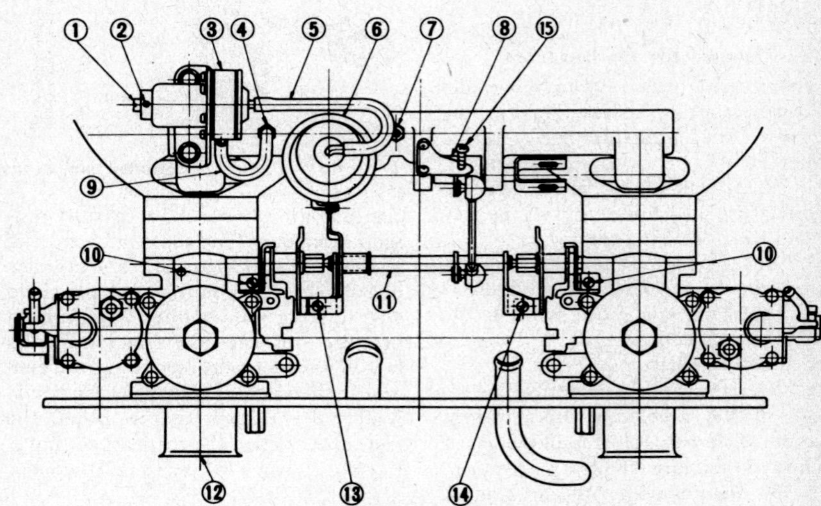

Late Hitachi/SU throttle linkage—1972-73

1. Vacuum adjusting screw
2. Lock screw
3. Control valve
4. Connector-control valve
5. Vacuum tube-servo diaphragm
6. Throttle positioner servo diaphragm
7. Connector-anti-backfire valve
8. Auxiliary throttle shaft
9. Vacuum tube-control weights
10. Throttle adjusting screw
11. Throttle shaft
12. Air cleaner air horn
13. Positioner adjusting screw
14. Balance screw
15. Fast idle setting screw

in the engine compartment, it takes precedence.

Mikuni/Solex Twin Choke—U20 Engine

The engine must be at normal operating temperature before making any carburetor adjustments. There is a separate idle mixture adjusting screw for each of the four choke tubes. The relationship between the throttle shafts for the two carburetors is adjusted by a balance screw. A throttle (idle speed) adjusting screw is provided on the linkage between the carburetors. Some installations may also have an individual idle speed adjusting screw for each carburetor.

1. Remove the air cleaner. Disconnect the turnbuckles from the throttle linkage. Back out the idle speed adjusting screw(s).

2. Gently screw the idle mixture screws in all the way, then back them out about 1–1 ½ turns.

3. Turn in the idle speed screw(s) until it just contacts the lever, then tighten it one turn.

4. Start the engine. Adjust the idle speed screw(s) to obtain a reasonable idle speed.

5. Measure the air flow at each choke tube with an air flow meter (Unisyn). Equalize the air flow in all four choke tubes by use of the idle speed screw(s) and balance screw. The carburetors are now balanced.

6. Adjust and reconnect the linkage turnbuckles.

7. Adjust each idle mixture screw, one at a time, to obtain the fastest possible smooth idle. Screw it in to lean the mixture, and out to richen it. The idle mixture is now set.

8. Adjust the idle speed to that given in the Tune-Up Specifications Chart. If there is a manufacturer's sticker in the engine compartment, it takes precedence.

9. Open the throttle suddenly. The engine should accelerate immediately with no hesitation. If this is not the case, recheck first the idle mixture and then the synchronization adjustments.

10. Stop the engine and replace the air cleaner.

Downdraft Carburetors

These carburetors have only one idle mixture adjusting screw. Tighten the screw to lean the mixture and loosen to richen it.

1. For a starting point, gently turn the idle mixture adjusting screw all the way in and back out 2–3 turns.

2. Start the engine and adjust the mixture screw for the fastest smooth idle.

3. Adjust the idle speed screw to obtain the idle speed given in the Tune-Up Specifications Chart.

4. Open the throttle suddenly. The engine should accelerate immediately, without hesitation. If it stumbles or stalls, richen the mixture slightly.

5. On engines with emission control, adjust the idle mixture to obtain the percentage of CO at idle speed given in the Tune-Up Specifications Chart. Some carburetors have idle mixture limiter caps to prevent excessive idle mixture adjustments.

NOTE: *If turning the idle mixture screw has no effect, the idling passages are probably clogged.*

ENGINE ELECTRICAL

Distributor

Removal and Installation

When removing the distributor for any reason, note the location of the rotor and mark the relationship of the distributor body to the engine. The distributor can then be replaced precisely in its original location, if the engine has not been turned. If the engine has been turned while the distributor was removed, or the distributor location was not marked, proceed as follows: Find top dead center of the compression stroke of No. 1 cylinder by holding a finger in the spark plug hole and rotating the engine. Compression pressure will force the finger from the hole. The exact location of top dead center can then be found by use of the crankshaft pulley timing marks. Install the distributor so that the rotor is pointing at the No. 1 spark plug wire and the points are just opening. The ignition wires may now be installed in the distributor cap, following the firing order in the direction of rotation. Set the timing to specifications.

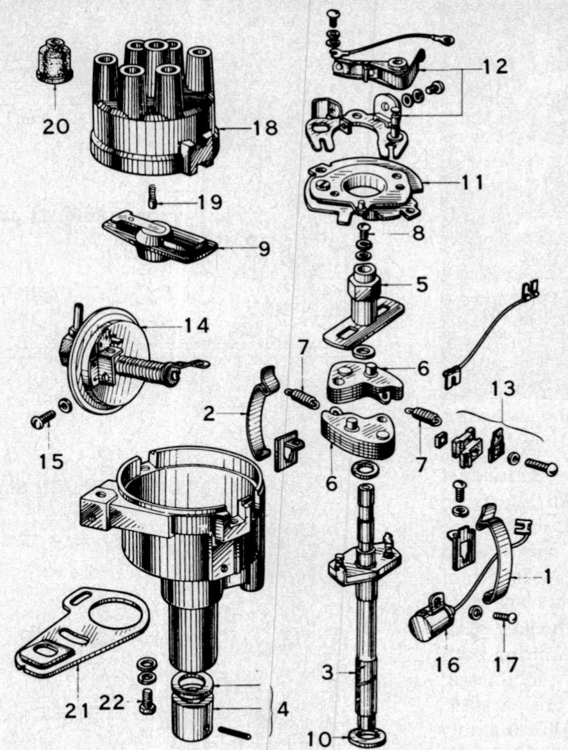

Exploded view of distributor, L16 engine

1. Cap holddown spring
2. Cap holddown spring
3. Shaft
4. Drive pinion
5. Cam
6. Centrifugal advance weights
7. Centrifugal advance springs
8. Screw
9. Rotor
10. Thrust washer
11. Breaker plate
12. Contact set
13. Terminal assembly
14. Vacuum control unit
15. Screw
16. Condenser
17. Screw
18. Cap
19. Carbon brush
20. Rubber boot
21. Holddown plate
22. Bolt

Alternator

An alternator is used on all current models. The following precautions must be observed to prevent alternator and regulator damage:

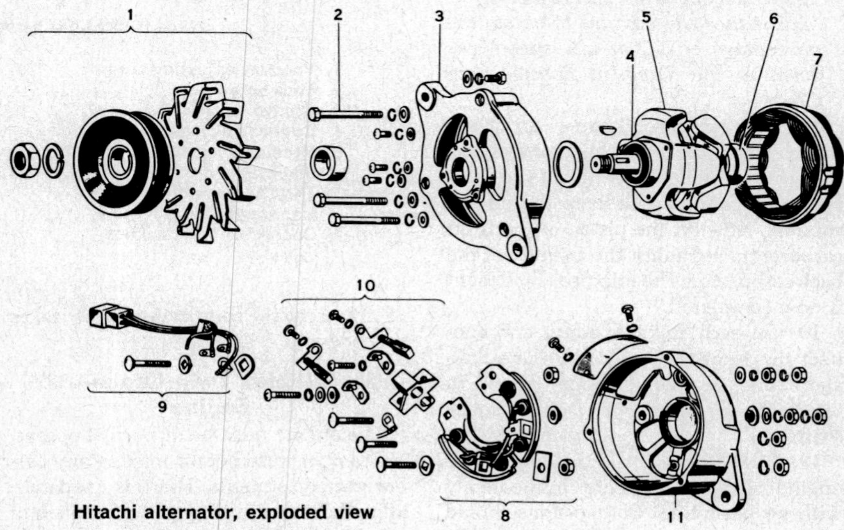

Hitachi alternator, exploded view

1. Pulley assembly
2. Through bolt
3. Front cover
4. Front bearing
5. Rotor
6. Rear bearing
7. Stator
8. Diode plate assembly
9. Lead wire assembly
10. Brush assembly
11. Rear cover

1. Be absolutely sure of correct polarity when installing a new battery, or connecting a battery charger.
2. Do not short across or ground any alternator or regulator terminals.
3. Disconnect the battery ground cable before replacing any electrical unit.
4. Never operate the alternator with any of the leads disconnected.
5. When steam cleaning the engine, be careful not to subject the alternator to excessive heat.
6. When charging the battery, remove it from the car or disconnect the alternator output terminal.

Belt Tension Adjustment

The correct belt tension for all alternators gives about ½ in. play on the longest span of the belt. The adjustment is usually made by pivoting the alternator. Overtightening the belt will cause rapid wear to the alternator and water pump bearings.

Regulator

Adjustment

All Regulators Except Hitachi TL1Z–37/57/58

1. Perform this test with the regulator cool. If voltage is not measured within one minute after starting the engine, stop the engine and allow the regulator to cool. It is imperative that the battery be fully charged.
2. Connect an ammeter and voltmeter as shown.
3. Run the engine at 2,500 rpm. Make sure that the charging current is less than 5 amps, and that the regulated voltage is as specified in the Alternator and Regulator Specifications Chart. If the charging current is too high, replace the battery with a fully charged one.
4. If the voltage is incorrect, set the regulator unit gaps to the specified clearances.
5. Recheck the voltage. If it is still incorrect, readjust the air gap. Bend the stopper up to raise the voltage and down to lower.

Hitachi TL1Z–37/57/58 Regulator

1. Connect an ammeter, voltmeter, fully charged battery, and resistor as shown.
2. Since this regulator is temperature compensated, the temperature of the regulator cover must be noted. Regulated voltage varies with ambient temperature.
3. Before starting the check, bypass the ammeter as shown to prevent ammeter damage.
4. Start the engine, increase engine speed to 2,500 rpm gradually, and continue for several minutes.
5. If ammeter reading is not below 5 amps, the battery is not fully charged. Replace it with a good one.
6. Return the engine to idle speed.
7. Increase engine speed to 2,500 rpm and check the voltage.

Ambient temperature (°F)	Regulated voltage
14	14.6-15.6
32	14.5-15.5
50	14.3-15.3
68	14.2-15.2
86	14.0-15.0
104	13.9-14.9

8. If the voltage is incorrect, set the regulator unit gaps to the specified figures.
9. Recheck the voltage. If it is still incorrect, turn in the adjusting screw on the voltage regulator unit to increase voltage, and turn it out to decrease voltage.

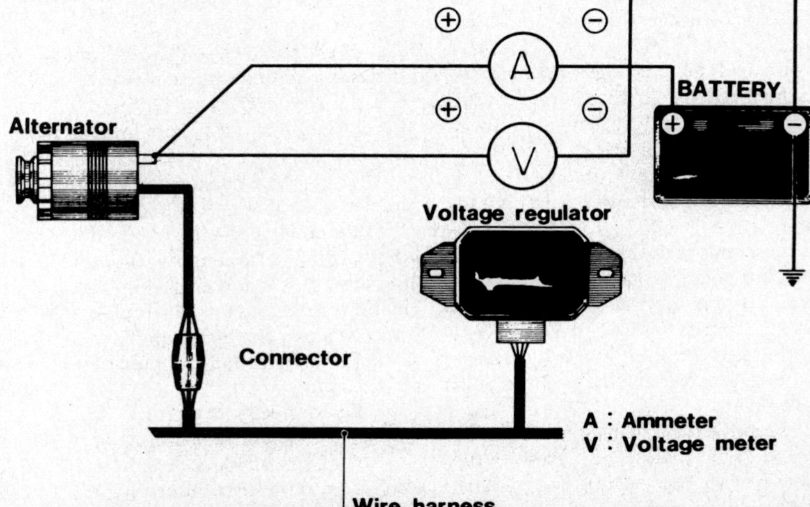

Test setup for all regulators except Hitachi TLIZ-37/57/58

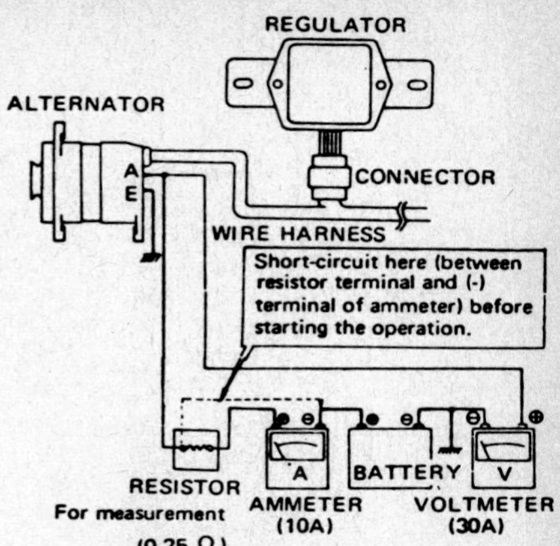

Test setup for Hitachi TL1Z-37/57/58 regulator

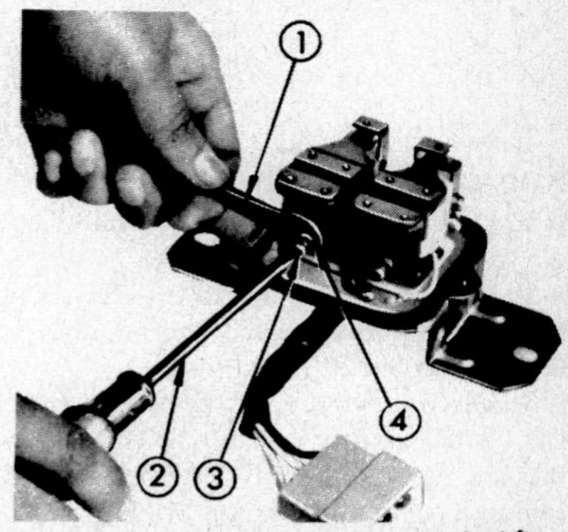

Adjustment of voltage on TL1Z-37/57/58 regulator. Wrench (1) is used to loosen the lock-nut (4) Screwdriver (2) is used to turn the adjusting screw (3)

Starter

The starter is mounted at the right rear of the engine. The solenoid is mounted on top of the starter and engages the drive pinion through a pivot yoke shift lever.

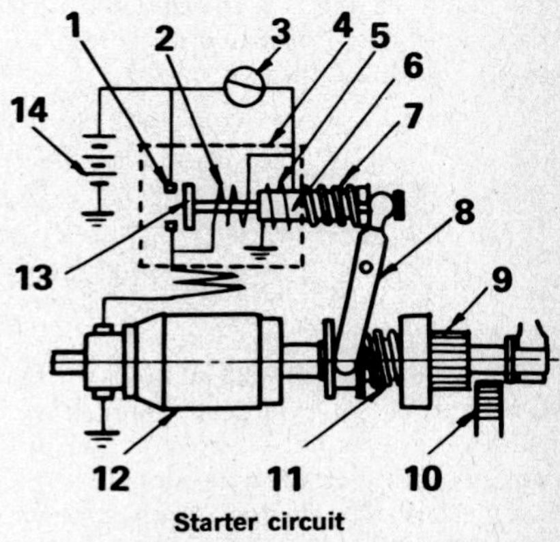

Starter circuit

1. Stationary contact
2. Series coil
3. Ignition switch
4. Solenoid
5. Shunt coil
6. Plunger
7. Return spring
8. Shift lever
9. Drive pinion
10. Ring gear
11. Pinion sleeve spring
12. Armature
13. Moveable contact
14. Battery

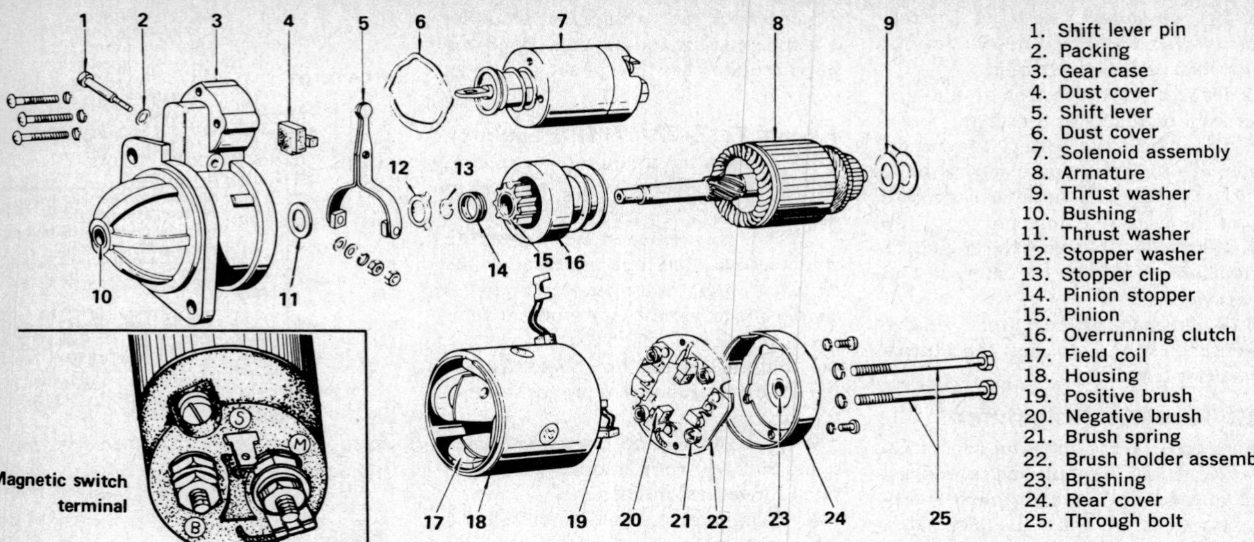

Starter with top-mounted solenoid (magnetic switch). The L16 engine starter is shown.

Removal and Installation

1. Disconnect the battery ground cable.
2. Disconnect the switch lead from the solenoid switch terminal. This terminal is usually labeled S.
3. Disconnect the battery cable from the solenoid battery terminal. This terminal is usually labeled B. There is a third solenoid terminal, labeled M, connected to the starter motor.
4. Remove both starter mounting bolts. Pull the starter assembly forward and out.
5. Reverse the procedure to install.

Battery

All Datsun models are equipped with a 12-volt battery. The battery is located under the hood in all models. To gain access to the battery in the 240 Z coupe, first open the hood, then the inspection flap in the fender. The inspection flap must be closed before the hood.

ENGINE MECHANICAL

Datsun engines are all inline, with either four or six cylinders. Some have overhead valves with a rocker arm arrangement and others have a single overhead camshaft. Engine displacements range from 1,171 to 2,393 cc. Refer to the Engine Identification Chart for identification of engines by model, number of cylinders, displacement, and camshaft location. Engines are referred to by model designation codes throughout this section.

Engine Removal and Installation

SPL311, SRL311, L520, L521

It is best to remove the engine and transmission as a unit. On the sportscars, this must be done.

1. Mark the location of the hinges on the hood. Unbolt and remove the hood.
2. Drain the coolant. Drain the automatic transmission.
3. Remove the air cleaner, battery, and tray.
4. Remove the radiator hoses. Remove the radiator. On automatic transmission models disconnect the oil cooler lines from the bottom of the radiator, remove the oil filler tube and cooler lines from the transmission case, and disconnect the shift linkage.
5. Disconnect the heater hoses.
6. Disconnect the fuel line(s) at the pump.
7. Disconnect the throttle and choke linkage.
8. Remove all electrical connections from the ignition coil, distributor, starter, alternator, and oil pressure and water temperature sending units.
9. Remove the clutch linkage or slave cylinder. Do not disconnect the hydraulic line.
10. Disconnect the speedometer cable and backup switch from the transmission. Disconnect the neutral start switch on automatic transmission models.
11. Remove the shift lever from floor-shift units. Disconnect the column shift linkage.
12. Remove the exhaust pipe from the manifold. On sportscars, remove the manifold from the engine first, detach the bottom of the left rear shock absorber so the exhaust system can be pulled to one side, then separate the manifold and exhaust pipe.
13. Mark the relationship of the driveshaft flanges at the rear end. Unbolt the flanges and remove the driveshaft.
14. Jack up the rear of the transmission. Unbolt the crossmember from the frame, then from the transmission. Detach the handbrake cable clamp from the transmission.
15. Unbolt the front motor mounts. Remove them if necessary.
16. Attach a hoist to lifting hooks on the engine. As the engine is hoisted, lower the jack under the transmission. It will be necessary to tilt the engine rather steeply to remove it.
17. Reverse the procedure to install the engine.

PL510, PL610, KPL610, WPL510, WPL610, PL521, PL620, LB110, KLB110, 240 Z

It is best to remove the engine and transmission as a unit.

1. Mark the location of the hinges on the hood. Unbolt and remove the hood.
2. Disconnect the battery cables. Remove the battery from models with the L16 engine.
3. Drain the coolant and automatic transmission fluid.
4. Remove the grille on models with the L16 or L18 engine. Remove the radiator after disconnecting the automatic transmission coolant tubes.
5. Remove the air cleaner.
6. Remove the fan and pulley from the L16 engine.
7. Disconnect:
    a. water temperature gauge wire
    b. oil pressure sending unit wire
    c. ignition distributor primary wire
    d. starter motor connections
    e. fuel hose

f. alternator leads
g. heater hoses
h. throttle and choke connections

8. Disconnect the power brake booster hose from the engine.

9. Remove the clutch operating cylinder and return spring.

10. Disconnect the speedometer cable from the transmission. Disconnect the backup light switch and any other wiring or attachments to the transmission. On cars with the L18 engine, disconnect the parking brake cable at the rear adjuster.

11. Disconnect the column shift linkage. Remove the floorshift lever. On LB110 and KLB110 models, remove the boot, withdraw the lock pin, and remove the lever from inside the car.

12. Detach the exhaust pipe from the exhaust manifold. Remove the front section of the exhaust system.

13. Mark the relationship of the driveshaft flanges and remove the driveshaft.

14. Place a jack under the transmission. Remove the rear crossmember. On LB110 and KLB110 models, remove the rear engine mounting nuts.

15. Attach a hoist to the lifting hooks on the engine (at either end of the cylinder head). Support the engine.

16. Unbolt the front engine mounts. Tilt the engine by lowering the jack under the transmission and raising the hoist.

17. Reverse the procedure to install the engine.

Cylinder Head

Removal and Installation

NOTE: *To prevent distortion or warping of the cylinder head, allow the engine to cool completely before removing the head bolts.*

J, R, A12 Overhead Valve Engines

To remove the cylinder head on OHV engines:

1. Drain the coolant.
2. Disconnect the battery ground cable.
3. Remove the upper radiator hose. Remove the water outlet elbow and the thermostat.
4. Remove the air cleaner, carburetor, rocker arm cover, and both manifolds.
5. Remove the spark plugs.
6. Disconnect the temperature gauge connection.
7. On A12 engines, remove the head bolts and remove the head and rocker arm assembly together. On the other OHV engines, the rocker arm assembly is held down by four of the head bolts and must be removed before the cylinder head. There is a special locking plate under the right rear rocker stud nut. Rap the head with a mallet to loosen it from the block. Remove the head and discard the gasket.
8. Remove the pushrods, keeping them in order.

To replace the cylinder head on OHV engines:

1. Make sure that head and block surfaces are clean. Check the cylinder head surface with a straightedge and a feeler gauge for flatness. If the head is warped more than 0.003 in., it must be trued. If this is not done, there will probably be a leak. The block surface should also be checked in the same way. If the block is warped more than 0.003 in., it must be trued.
2. Install a new head gasket. Most gaskets have a TOP marking. Make sure that the proper head gasket is used on the A12 so that no water passages are blocked off.
3. Install the head. Install the pushrods in their original locations. Install the rocker arm assembly. Loosen the rocker arm adjusting screws to prevent bending pushrods when tightening the head bolts. Tighten the head bolts finger tight. On A12 engines, the single bolt marked T must go in the No. 1 position on the center right side of the engine.
4. Refer to the Torque Specifications Chart for the correct head bolt torque. Tighten the bolts to one third of the specified torque in the order shown in the head bolt tightening sequence illustration. On A12 engines, torque the rocker arm mounting bolts to 15–18 ft lbs.
5. Tighten the bolts to two thirds of the specified torque in sequence.
6. Tighten the bolts to the full specified torque in sequence.
7. Adjust the valves. If no cold setting is given, adjust the valves to the normal hot setting.
8. Reassemble the engine. On A12 engines, intake and exhaust manifold bolt torque is 7–10 ft lbs. Fill the cooling system. Start the engine and run it until normal temperature is reached. Remove the rocker arm cover. Torque the bolts in sequence once more. Check the valve clearances.
9. Retorque the head bolts after 600 miles of driving. Check the valve clearances after torquing, as this may disturb the settings.

U20, L16, L18, L24 Overhead Cam Engines

To remove the cylinder head on OHC engines:

1. Drain the coolant.
2. Disconnect the battery ground cable.
3. Remove the upper radiator hose. Remove the water outlet elbow and thermostat.
4. Remove the air cleaner, carburetor, camshaft cover, and both manifolds.
5. Disconnect the temperature gauge at the head.
6. Remove the spark plugs.
7. Mark the relationship between the camshaft, camshaft sprocket, and timing chain. Remove the camshaft sprocket. On L16, L18, and L24 engines, a wooden wedge may be used to prevent the timing chain from slipping off the crankshaft sprocket. If this tool is not available, support the timing chain in some way so that the relationship of the crankshaft sprocket and the timing chain will be unchanged. On U20 engines, unbolt the camshaft sprocket, remove the cylinder head front cover plate and upper chain tensioner. Attach the camshaft sprocket to the chain guide with a bolt. The camshaft sprocket and chain will be left in place when the head is removed.

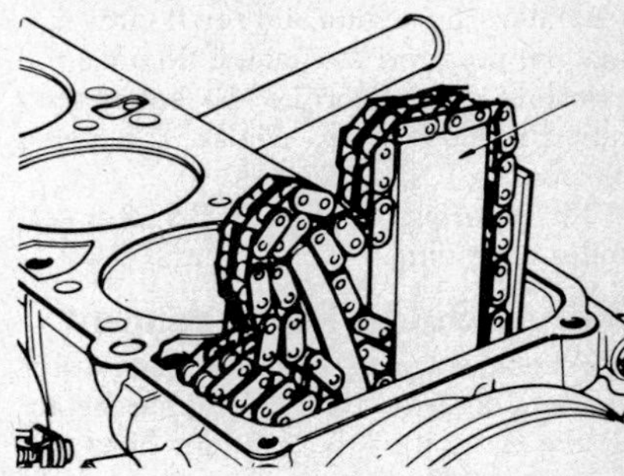

On overhead cam engines, the wedge shown by the arrow can be used to prevent the timing chain from slipping off the crankshaft sprocket.

8. Remove the cylinder head front plate and chain tensioner on L16, L18, and L24 engines.
9. Unbolt the cylinder head from the block and from the front timing cover. The L16, L18, and L24 engines use three different size head bolts. Note the original locations of these bolts.

To replace the cylinder head on OHC engines:

1. Make sure that the head and block surfaces are clean. Check the cylinder head surface for flatness. If the head is warped more than 0.003 in., it must be trued. If this is not done, there will probably be a leak. The block surface should also be checked. If the block is warped more than 0.003 in., it must be trued.
2. Install the new gasket. On L16 engines, apply sealant to both sides of the gasket.
3. Install the head. Install the bolts in their proper locations. Tighten the bolts finger tight.
4. Refer to the Torque Specifications Chart for the correct bolt torque. Tighten the bolts to one third of the specified torque in the order shown in the head bolt tightening sequence illustration.
5. Tighten the bolts to two thirds of the specified torque in sequence.
6. Tighten the bolts to the full specified torque in sequence.
7. If the engine has not been disturbed, and the timing chain has not slipped off the crankshaft sprocket (jackshaft sprocket on U20 engine), reinstall

the camshaft sprocket, aligning the marks made on disassembly. On L16, L18, and L24 engines, replace the fuel pump drive cam. Camshaft sprocket torque is 13 ft lbs on the U20 and 36–43 ft lbs on the L16, L18, and L24 engines. If the relationship of the crankshaft, camshaft, and timing chain has been disturbed, correct this relationship as described later.

8. Adjust the valves. If no cold setting is given, adjust the valves to the normal hot setting.

9. Reassemble the engine. On U20 engines, intake and exhaust manifold bolt torque is 10–20 ft lbs. Fill the cooling system. Start the engine and run it until normal temperature is reached. Remove the camshaft cover. Torque the bolts in sequence once more. Check the valve clearances.

10. Retorque the head bolts after 600 miles of driving.

Valve Guide Replacement

When replacing cylinder head valve guides, be sure that the guide height above the top of the cylinder head surface is as follows.

Engine	Guide height (in.)
J	0.610-0.626
U20	0.508-0.516
L16, L18, L24	0.409-0.417
A12	0.709
R	not specified

Timing Chain Cover

Removal and Installation, Oil Seal Replacement

J, R, A12 Overhead Valve Engines

1. Remove the radiator. Loosen the alternator adjustment and remove the belt. Loosen the air pump adjustment and remove the belt on engines with the air pump system.

2. Remove the fan and/or water pump. The water pump should be removed from A12 engine.

3. Bend back the lock tab from the crankshaft pulley nut. Remove the nut by affixing a heavy wrench and rapping the wrench with a hammer. The nut must be unscrewed in the opposite direction of normal engine rotation. Pull off the pulley.

4. On A12 engines, it is recommended that the oil pan be removed or loosened before the front cover is removed.

5. Unbolt and remove the timing chain cover.

6. Replace the crankshaft oil seal in the cover. Most models use a felt seal.

7. Reverse the procedure to install, using new gaskets. Apply sealant to both sides of the timing cover gasket. On A12 engines, front cover bolt torque is 4 ft lbs, water pump bolt torque is 7–10 ft lbs, and oil pan bolt torque is 4 ft lbs.

U20, L16, L18, L24 Overhead Cam Engines

While it may be possible to perform this operation with the engine in place, Datsun recommends that the engine be removed from the vehicle.

1. Loosen and remove the alternator and air pump belts. Remove the alternator and air pump.

2. Remove the distributor on L16, L18, and L24 engines. Remove the cylinder head. This may not be necessary on some engines.

3. Remove the fan and pulley.

4. Bend back the lock tab from the crankshaft pulley nut. Remove the nut by affixing a heavy wrench and rapping the wrench with a hammer. The nut must be unscrewed in the opposite direction of normal engine rotation.

5. Remove the water pump.

6. Remove the oil pan.

7. Remove the timing chain cover.

8. Remove the old crankshaft oil seal from the cover. Press in a new seal.

9. Reverse the procedure to install, applying sealant to both sides of the cover gasket. On L16 and L18 engines, check that the height difference between the cylinder block upper surface and the front cover upper surface is less than 0.006 in. Oil pan bolt torque is 4–5 ft lbs for all three engines.

Timing Chain and Camshaft

Removal and Installation

J, R, A12 Overhead Valve Engines

It is recommended that this operation be done with the engine removed from the vehicle.

1. Remove the timing chain cover.

2. Unbolt and remove the chain tensioner.

3. Remove the camshaft sprocket retaining bolt.

4. Pull off the camshaft sprocket, easing off the crankshaft sprocket at the same time. Remove both sprockets and chain as an assembly. Be careful not to lose the shims and oil slinger from behind the crankshaft sprocket.

5. Remove the distributor, distributor drive spindle, pushrods, and valve lifters.

NOTE: *On G, R, and A12 engines, the lifters cannot be removed until the camshaft has been removed.*

Remove the oil pump and pump driveshaft.

6. Remove the engine front mounting plate on J engines.

7. Unbolt and remove the camshaft locating plate.

8. Remove the camshaft carefully. On R and A12 engines, this will be easier if the block is inverted to prevent the lifters from falling down.

9. The camshaft bearings can be pressed out and replaced. They are available in undersizes, should it be necessary to regrind the camshaft journals.

10. Reinstall the camshaft. If the locating plate has an oil hole, it should be to the right of the engine. On A12 engines, the locating plate is marked with the word LOWER and an arrow. A12 engine locating plate bolt torque is 3–4 ft lbs. Be careful to engage the drive pin in the rear end of the camshaft with the slot in the oil pump driveshaft.

11. Camshaft end-play can be measured after temporarily replacing the camshaft sprocket and securing bolt.

Engine	Camshaft end-play (in.)
J	0.003-0.007
R	0.002-0.011
A12	0.001-0.003

If end-play is excessive, replace the locating plate. They are available in several sizes.

12. On J engines, replace the engine front mounting plate.

13. If the crankshaft or camshaft has been replaced, install the sprockets temporarily and make sure that they are parallel. Adjust by shimming under the crankshaft sprocket.

14. Assemble the sprockets and chain, aligning them.

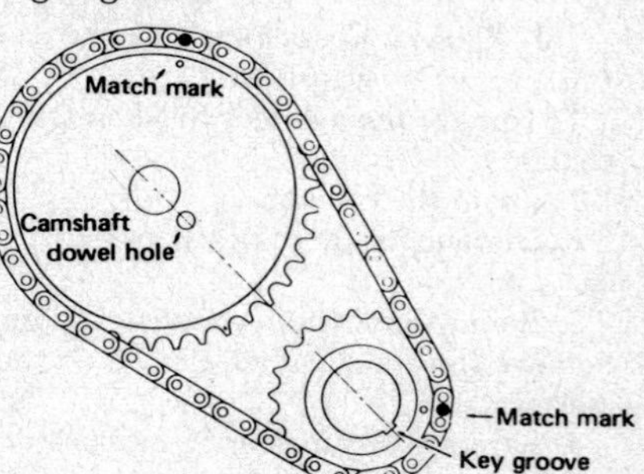

Assembly of sprockets and timing chain, A12 engine

15. Turn the crankshaft until the keyway and No. 1 piston is at top dead center. Install the sprockets and chain. The oil slinger behind the crankshaft sprocket must be replaced with the concave surface to the front. If the chain and sprocket installation is correct, the sprocket marks must be aligned between the shaft centers when No. 1 piston is at top dead center. A12 engine camshaft sprocket retaining bolt torque is 33–36 ft lbs.

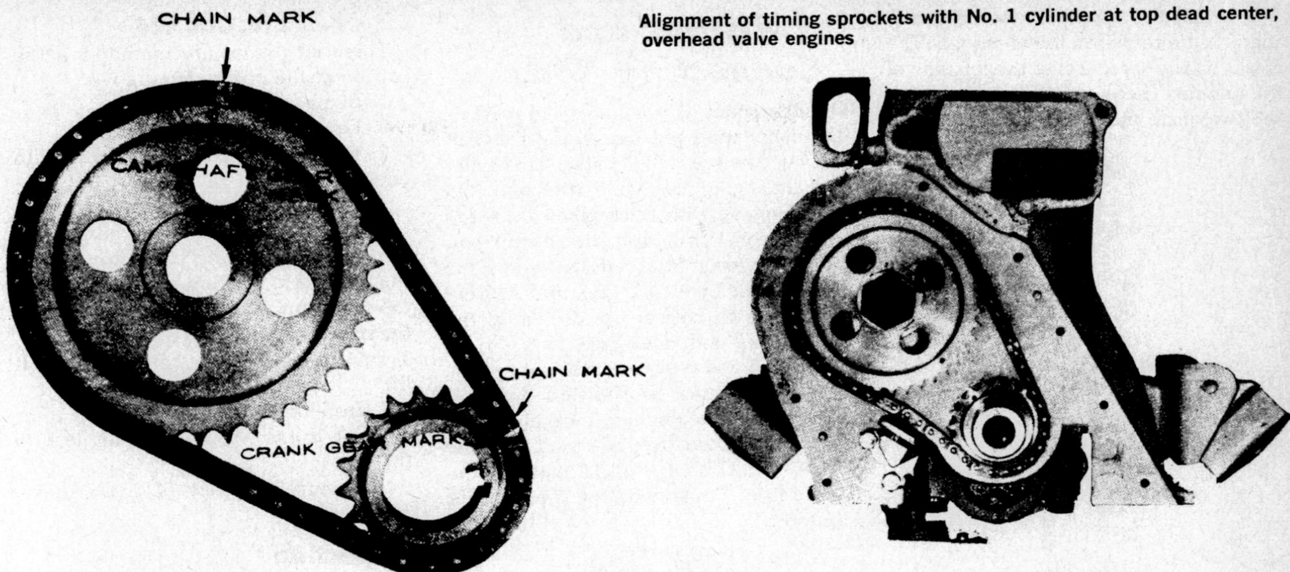

Alignment of timing sprockets with No. 1 cylinder at top dead center, overhead valve engines

Assembly of sprockets and timing chain, J and R engines

16. The rest of the reassembly procedure is the reverse of disassembly. A12 engine chain tensioner bolt torque is 4–6 ft lbs.

U20 Overhead Cam Engine

This engine is basically an overhead valve type redesigned to use an overhead camshaft cylinder head. A jackshaft replaces the camshaft in the cylinder block. The overhead camshaft is chain driven from the jackshaft. Thus there are two timing chains. To remove the timing chains:

1. Remove the timing chain cover.
2. Remove the lower chain tensioner.
3. Remove the jackshaft outer sprocket retaining bolt.
4. Pull off the jackshaft outer sprocket, easing off the crankshaft sprocket at the same time. Remove both sprockets and chain as an assembly.
5. Remove the bolt which was installed during cylinder head removal, holding the camshaft sprocket to the chain guide. If the head was not removed, unbolt the camshaft sprocket.
6. Remove the camshaft chain. Remove the jackshaft inner sprocket.
7. The jackshaft may now be removed if necessary.

To replace the timing chains:

8. Place the camshaft sprocket and jackshaft inner sprocket in the camshaft chain, aligning the timing marks on the sprockets with the marks on the chain.
9. Holding the sprockets in position, engage the jackshaft inner sprocket keyway with the key on the jackshaft.
10. Replace the bolt removed in Step 5.
11. Assemble the jackshaft outer sprocket and crankshaft sprocket to the chain. Install the sprockets and chain on the shafts. Jackshaft bolt torque is 33–36 ft lbs. If the assembly is correct, the lower chain sprocket marks will be aligned between the shaft centers when No. 1 piston and the crankshaft key are at top dead center.
12. Replace the lower chain tensioner and timing chain cover.

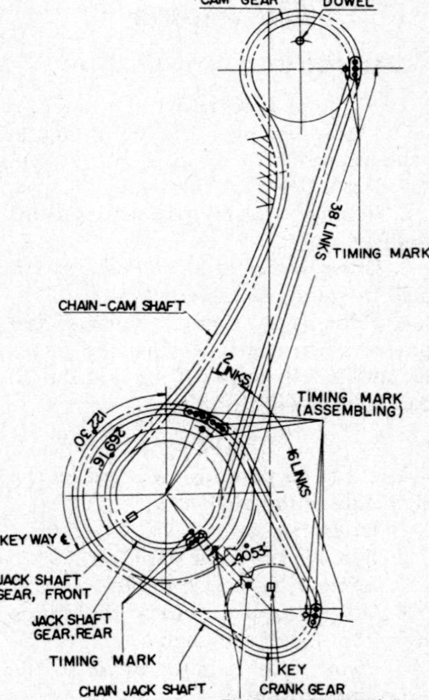

Timing marks for camshaft sprockets and chain, assembling and timing marks for jackshaft sprockets and chain, U20 engine

The camshaft can be removed from the cylinder head with the head either in place on the engine or removed. To remove the camshaft:

1. Remove the cylinder head or remove the camshaft cover, unbolt the camshaft sprocket, and support the sprocket with a bolt to the chain guide.
2. Unbolt all camshaft bearing caps. Do not remove the lower camshaft bearings. If these bearings are removed, an alignment boring procedure will be required to properly realign them.
3. Remove the camshaft.

To replace the camshaft:

4. Replace the camshaft. Torque the large bearing cap nuts to 13 ft lbs. and the small nuts to 5 ft lbs.
5. Check camshaft end-play. It should be 0.004–0.012 in.
6. Replace the camshaft sprocket, torquing the bolts to 13 ft lbs.
7. Press down the valve springs and reinstall the rocker arms.
8. Adjust the valves.

L16, L18, L24 Overhead Cam Engines

These engines are of true overhead camshaft design, using only a single timing chain. The L16, L18, and L24 are very similar in appearance and construction. To remove the timing chain:

1. Remove the timing chain cover. Remove the camshaft sprocket if the head has not been removed.
2. Remove the chain and tensioner.
3. Remove the oil slinger and distributor drive gear from the crankshaft. Pull off the sprocket.

To replace the chain:

4. Install the cylinder head (removed during timing chain cover removal).
5. Install the crankshaft sprocket, distributor drive gear, and oil slinger with the concave side out.
6. Set the crankshaft and camshaft keys upward. When turning the shafts, be careful not to force the valves against the pistons.

7. Install the sprockets to the chain, aligning the marks on the chain with the marks on the sprockets at the left side of the engine. There are 42 links between the two chain marks.

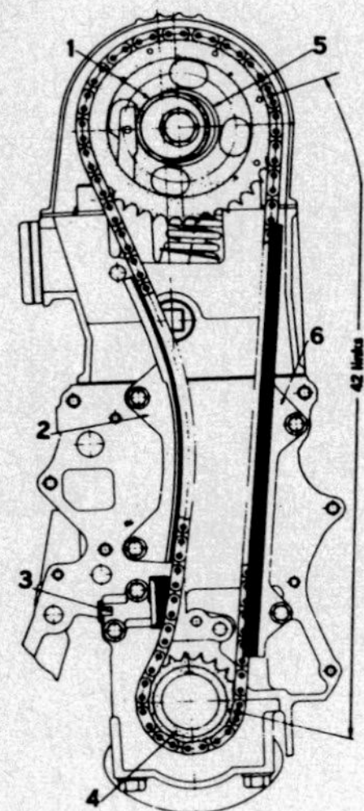

Camshaft chain installation, L16, L18, and L24 engines

1. Fuel pump drive cam
2. Chain guide
3. Chain tensioner
4. Crankshaft sprocket
5. Camshaft sprocket
6. Chain guide

8. Install the chain and sprockets to the engine. Install the fuel pump drive cam. Torque the camshaft sprocket bolt to 36–43 ft lbs.

9. Install the chain tensioner.

10. Replace the timing chain cover.

The camshaft can be removed from the cylinder head with the head either in place on the engine or removed. To remove the camshaft:

1. Remove the camshaft cover or cylinder head. Remove the fuel pump drive cam and camshaft sprocket. Remove the rocker arm springs.

2. Loosen the rocker pivot lock nuts and remove the rocker arms by pressing down the valve springs.

3. Remove the camshaft locating plate.

4. Withdraw the camshaft carefully. Do not remove the camshaft bearings. If these bearings are removed, an alignment boring procedure will be required to properly realign them.

To replace the camshaft:

5. Replace the camshaft. Install the locating plate.

6. Check camshaft end-play. It should be 0.003–0.015 in. Adjust by replacing the locating plate.

7. Replace the sprocket, torquing the bolt to 36–43 ft lbs.

8. Install the rocker arms, pressing down the valve springs with a screwdriver. Install the rocker arm springs.

9. Adjust the valves.

Pistons and Connecting Rods

On all engines, it is advisable to mark the connecting rods on removal so that they will be reinstalled in the same cylinder, facing in the same direction. On early engines with a clamp bolt at the top of the connecting rod, the clamp bolt must face toward the camshaft side of the engine. On L16, L18, L24, and A12 engines, the oil hole at the bottom of the connecting rod must face to the right side. On J and R engines, the split in the piston skirt must face toward the camshaft side of the engine. If the piston has a mark on its top, the mark must be to the front. U20, L16, L18, L24, and A12 engines have F marks on the tops of their pistons.

ENGINE LUBRICATION

Oil Pump

Removal and Installation

J, R, U20

On these engines, the oil pump is mounted inside the oil pan.

1. Drain the oil.
2. Remove the oil pan and pickup strainer.
3. Unscrew the three long bolts which hold the pump to the crankcase.
4. Prime the pump. Reverse the procedure to install. Torque the pump mounting bolts to 6–7 ft lbs. and the oil pan bolts to 4–5 ft lbs.

A12

The A12 oil pump is mounted on the right side of the engine.

1. Drain the oil.
2. Remove the front stabilizer.
3. Remove the splash shield.
4. Unbolt and withdraw the pump from the side of the engine.
5. Prime the pump. Reverse the procedure to install. Torque the pump mounting bolts to 9–11 ft lbs.

L16, L18, L24

These oil pumps are mounted at the bottom of the engine front cover.

1. Remove the distributor.
2. Drain the oil.
3. Remove the front stabilizer on L16 engine models.
4. Remove the splash shield.
5. Unbolt and remove the oil pump.
6. Before replacing the pump, prime the pump and position No. 1 cylinder at top dead center. Install the oil pump with the spindle punch mark toward the front. Torque the mounting bolts to 11–15 ft lbs.
7. Install the distributor with the rotor pointing to the No. 1 spark plug lead in the cap.
8. Reverse the rest of the removal procedure.

Inspection

The pump can readily be disassembled and checked for wear. Refer to the Oil Pump Specifications Chart for clearances. The rotor pump used on J engines has a chamfered edge on the outer rotor. On reassembly, the chamfer must be toward the base of the pump body.

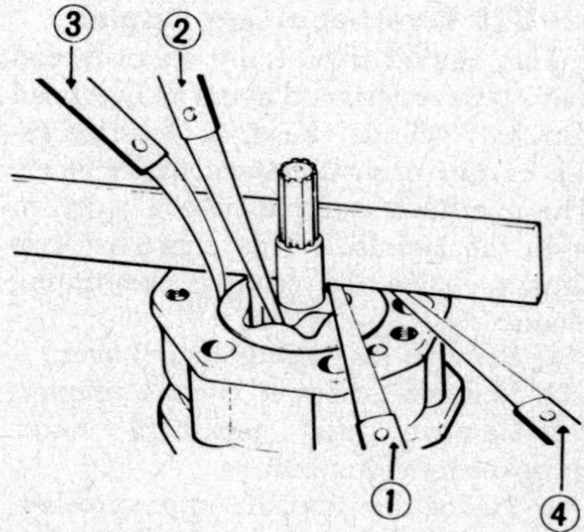

Clearances to be checked in rotor oil pumps

1. Side clearance
2. Tip clearance
3. Outer rotor to pump body clearance
4. Rotor to cover clearance

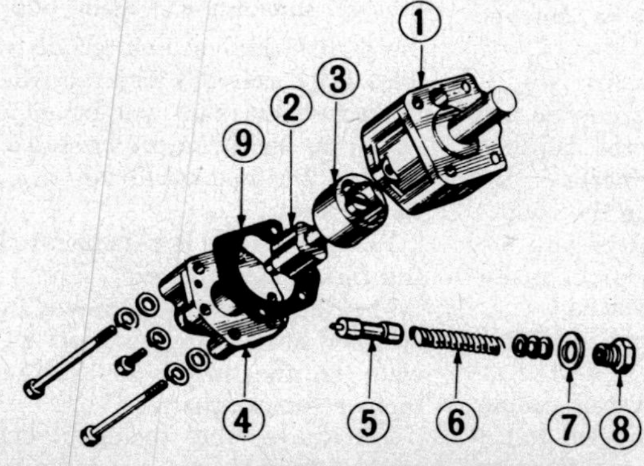

1. Pump body
2. Inner rotor and shaft
3. Outer rotor
4. Pump cover
5. Pressure regulator valve
6. Valve spring
7. Washer
8. Cap
9. Gasket

Oil pump, L16 and L18 engines

OIL PUMP SPECIFICATIONS

Engine	Pump type	Clearance between inner and outer rotor (in.)	Tip clearance—gear or rotor to cover or outer rotor (in.)	Clearance between outer rotor and body (in.)	Gear backlash (in.)	Side clearance—gear to body (in.)	Maximum oil pressure (psi)	Minimum oil pressure (psi) at idle	Relief valve spring free length (in.)	Relief valve opening pressure (psi)
J	Rotor	0.002-0.005	0.005-0.008	N.A.	—	—	54-57	14-17	N.A.	N.A.
R	Gear	—	0.002-0.004	—	0.010-0.012	N.A.	54-57	7-10	N.A.	N.A.
U20	Gear	—	0.006-0.009	—	0.012-0.016	0.002-0.004	54-57	7-10	2.453	63.9
L16, L18, L24	Rotor	0.002-0.005	0.005	0.006-0.008	—	—	54-60	14-17	2.24	54.0-59.7
A12	Rotor	0.002-0.005	0.005	0.006-0.008	—	—	54-60	13-17	1.71	54.0-59.7

ENGINE COOLING

Water Pump

Removal and Installation

1. Drain the coolant.
2. Loosen the adjusting bolt at the alternator and remove the fan belt.
3. Remove the fan and pulley and unbolt the pump. This job will be made easier by removing the radiator beforehand.
4. Reverse the procedure for installation.

Thermostat

Removal and Installation

The engine thermostat is housed in the water outlet casting on the cylinder head.

1. Drain the coolant.
2. Remove the upper radiator hose and unbolt the water outlet elbow.
3. The thermostat may now be removed.
4. Refer to the accompanying chart for data on original equipment thermostats.

Engine	Opening Temperature of Thermostat (°F)	Full Opening of Thermostat (in.)
J	170 or 180	—
R	176	0.374
U20, L16, L18, L24, A12	180	0.315 @ 203°F

5. Reverse the removal procedure to replace the thermostat. When installing be sure that the side with the spring faces into the engine. Use a new gasket.

Correct thermostat installation

Radiator

Removal and Installation

To remove the radiator:

1. Drain the coolant.
2. Disconnect the upper hose, lower hose, and expansion tank hose.
3. Disconnect the automatic transmission oil cooler lines after draining the transmission. Cap the lines to exclude dirt.
4. Remove the radiator mounting bolts and radiator.
5. Reverse the procedure to replace the radiator. Fill the automatic transmission to the to proper level. Fill the cooling system.

EMISSION CONTROLS

Various systems are used to control crankcase vapors, exhaust emissions, and fuel vapors. The accompanying chart shows the systems used with various models and engines.

Year (approx.)	Model	Engine	Emission Control Systems
1969	PL510 WPL510	L16	1,3
1969	SPL311	R	2,3
1969	SRL311	U20	2,3
1969	L520, L521	J	2,4
1970-1971	PL510 WPL510 PL521	L16	1,3,4,5
1972-1973	PL510 WPL510 PL521	L16	1,4,5
1973	PL610 KPL610 WPL610 PL620	L18	1,4,5
1969	SPL311	R	2,3,4,5
1969	SRL311	U20	2,3,5
1971-1973	240 Z	L24	1,3,4,5
1971-1973	LB110 KLB110	A12	1,4,5

1. Closed crankcase ventilation system
2. Sealed crankcase ventilation system
3. Air pump system
4. Engine modification system
5. Fuel vapor control system

Crankcase Ventilation System

The sealed system consists simply of a tube connecting the valve cover to the carburetor air cleaner. The oil filler cap and the dipstick are sealed. No provision is made for admitting ventilation air into the crankcase. Crankcase vapors are drawn through the carburetor and burned along with the air/fuel mixture.

The closed system is identical to the sealed system, with the addition of a tube containing a variable orifice valve between the crankcase and the intake manifold. Under high vacuum conditions (idle), vapors are drawn into the intake manifold through the valve. The tube connected to the air cleaner admits ventilation air through the crankcase. Under low vacuum conditions (full-throttle), vapors are drawn through the carburetor as in the sealed system.

The crankcase ventilation system requires no periodic maintenance other than replacement of the variable orifice valve, should it become clogged.

Variable Orifice Valve Test

1. With the engine idling, remove the hose from the valve on the intake manifold.
2. A hissing sound should be heard and a vacuum felt at the valve inlet.

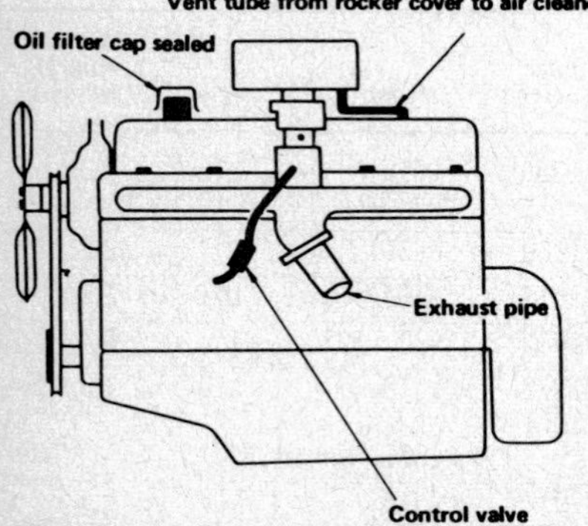

Closed crankcase ventilation system. The control valve is the variable orifice valve referred to in the text

Air Pump System

In this system, an air injection pump, driven by the engine, compresses, distributes, and injects filtered air into the exhaust port of each cylinder. The air combines with unburned hydrocarbons and carbon monoxide to produce harmless compounds. The system includes an air cleaner, the belt driven air pump, a check valve, and an anti-backfire valve.

The air pump draws air through a hose connected to the carburetor air cleaner or to a separate air cleaner. The pump is a rotary vane unit with an integral pressure regulating valve. The pump outlet pressure passes through a check valve which prevents exhaust gas from entering the pump in case of insufficient pump outlet pressure. An anti-backfire valve admits air from the air pump into the intake manifold on deceleration to prevent backfiring in the exhaust manifold.

All engines with the air pump system have a series of minor alterations to accommodate the system. These are:

1. Special close-tolerance carburetor. Most engines, except the L16, require a slightly rich idle mixture adjustment.
2. Distributor with special advance curve. Ignition timing is retarded about 10° at idle in most cases.

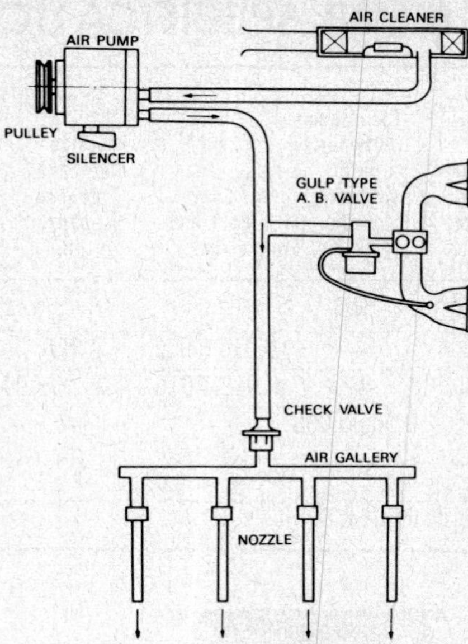

Air pump system

3. Cooling system changes such as larger fan, higher fan speed, and thermostatic fan clutch. This is required to offset the increase in temperature caused by retarded timing at idle. The U20 engine has a thermal modulator valve which gives full distributor vacuum advance at idle if engine temperature becomes excessive.
4. Faster idle speed.
5. Heated air intake on some engines.

The only periodic maintenance required on the air pump system is replacement of the air filter element and adjustment of the drive belt.

Air Pump System Tests and Repairs

Air Pump Test, Removal and Installation

To test air pump output pressure:

1. The engine must be at normal operating temperature.
2. Stop the engine. Disconnect the air supply hose from the check valve at the exhaust manifold.
3. Start the engine. Check the pump pressure output at 1,500 rpm. With the L16 engine, the pressure should be 0.47 in. (12 mm.) Hg or more. With an R, U20, or L24 engine, the pressure should be 0.063 in. (16 mm.) Hg or more.

To remove and replace the air pump:

1. Disconnect the hoses from the pump.
2. Remove the bolt holding the pump to the belt adjustment arm or adjusting bracket.
3. Unbolt the pump from the mounting bracket. Remove the belt.
4. Remove the pump from the car.
5. Reverse the procedure to install, adjusting the belt to have about ½ in. play under thumb pressure at the longest span between pulleys.

Check Valve Test, Removal and Installation

To test the check valve action:

1. The engine must be at normal operating temperature.
2. Stop the engine. Disconnect the air supply hose from the check valve at the exhaust manifold.
3. The valve plate inside the valve body should be lightly positioned against the valve seat away from the air distributor manifold.
4. Insert a small screwdriver into the valve and depress the valve plate. The plate should reset freely when released.
5. Start the engine. Increase the idle speed to 1,500 rpm and check for exhaust leakage. Valve pulsation or vibration at idle is a normal condition.

To remove and replace the check valve:

1. Remove the check valve from the air gallery pipe, holding the air gallery flange with a wrench.
2. On reinstallation, the proper torque is 65–76 ft lbs.

Anti-Backfire Valve Test, Removal and Installation

To test the anti-backfire valve:

1. The engine must be at normal operating temperature.
2. Disconnect the air hose to the intake manifold at the anti-backfire valve. Plug the hose.
3. Open and close the throttle rapidly. Air flow should be felt at the valve for 1–2 seconds on deceleration. If no air flow is felt or flow is felt continuously for more than 2 seconds, replace the valve.

To remove the anti-backfire valve, simply disconnect the hoses.

Thermal Modulator Test

The thermal modulator is used only on the U20 engine. It provides full vacuum advance at idle if coolant temperature exceeds about 220°F. To test the unit:

1. Remove the vacuum tube at the distributor.
2. Connect a vacuum gauge to the tube.
3. Run the engine until it reaches normal operating temperature.
4. Vacuum should be no more than 4 in. (102 mm.) Hg. If it is excessive, the modulator is leaking internally and must be replaced.

Engine Modification System

Engine modifications used on the L520 0r L521 pickup with the J engine are:

1. A special carburetor calibrated about three percent leaner than normal for cruise conditions. The idle speed is higher than normal and the extent of idle mixture adjustment is limited. A solenoid valve shuts off the idle fuel system on de-

celeration. The solenoid valve is regulated by four switches. The throttle valve switch attached to the carburetor is on when the throttle valve is open. The vacuum switch connected to the intake manifold is on when manifold vacuum is less than 22.8 in. Hg. The clutch switch on the pedal bracket is on when the pedal is depressed. The neutral switch on the transmission rear extension is on when the transmission is in neutral. If any of these switches are on, the solenoid valve will not shut off the fuel.

2. A heated air intake to prevent icing with the leaner carburetor mixture.

3. Maximum ignition timing retard at low speed and small retard at middle speed ranges. Normal advance is provided at high speeds.

Engine modification system, pickup with J engine

Engine modifications used on vehicles with the L16 or L18 engine are:

1. A distributor with a secondary set of contact points which are retarded 5° (7° in 1972–1973). These secondary points are operational only when cruising or accelerating with a partially open throttle in third gear with manual transmission, or over 13 mph with automatic transmission. For 1973, the timing is advanced only at idle, full throttle, and in fourth gear. A speed sensor is located at the speedometer on automatic transmission models. On 1972–1973 models, a temperature sensor in the engine compartment allows retarded timing only when the temperature inside the car is 50°F or above.

2. A solenoid valve in the carburetor opens to supply a lean fuel and air mixture, bypassing the throttle valve, in third gear or over 13 mph as above. The solenoid valve will not open if overridden by a closed throttle switch, a wide open throttle switch, a neutral switch, or a clutch disengaged switch. This arrangement is operational primarily during deceleration, when high intake manifold vacuum is present. For 1972–1973, this system is replaced with a vacuum controlled device in the carburetor to perform the same function.

Engine modifications on the SPL311 sports roadster with the R engine consist only of a solenoid valve which bypasses a lean fuel and air mixture into the intake manifold for improved combustion. The solenoid valve is overridden if the clutch is not depressed or the transmission is not in third or fourth gear. This arrangement is operational primarily during deceleration, when high intake manifold vacuum is present.

The engine modification system used on the LB110 and KLB110 1200 series with the A12 engine is relatively simple. It requires only a throttle positioner which holds the throttle slightly open on deceleration. A vacuum control valve connected to the intake manifold causes a vacuum servo to hold the throttle open slightly during the high vacuum condition of deceleration. The control valve is compensated for the effects of altitude and atmospheric pressure. The carburetor and distributor are specially calibrated for this engine. A transmission-controlled vacuum advance system is used on 1972–1973 manual transmission models.

The engine modification system for the 240 Z sports coupe with the L24 engine is quite similar to that for the A12 engine, using a vacuum control valve, vacuum servo, and throttle positioner. 1973 models have a solenoid to prevent running on, mounted on the vacuum control valve. The 240 Z with automatic transmission has a dual point distributor. One set of points has a timing setting of 0°TDC and the other a setting of 10°BTDC. A thermo-switch under the instrument panel activates the advanced timing set of points for easier starting and warmup when the temperature inside the car drops below 30°F.

For 1973, exhaust gas recirculation (EGR) is used on the 240 Z. This system uses vacuum from the rear carburetor to actuate a valve which allows a small amount of exhaust gases to be drawn into the intake manifold. This results in a decrease in oxides of nitrogen in the exhaust gases. The vacuum required to operate the system is not available at idle or wide throttle openings. A thermostatic switch inside the car shuts off the vacuum to the system when the temperature is below 30°F, thus allowing good cold starting and driveability.

Engine Modification System Tests, Adjustments

Throttle Positioner Adjustment—L24, A12 Engines

Only the A12 and L24 engines use a throttle positioner. This device is regulated by a vacuum control valve with an adjusting screw.

1. The engine must be at normal operating temperature. A tachometer must be connected. If there is a dashpot, back off its adjustment to prevent interference.

2. Increase engine speed to 3,000 rpm for the A12 or 2,000 rpm for the L24.

3. Release the throttle. The time required to slow to 1,000 rpm should be:

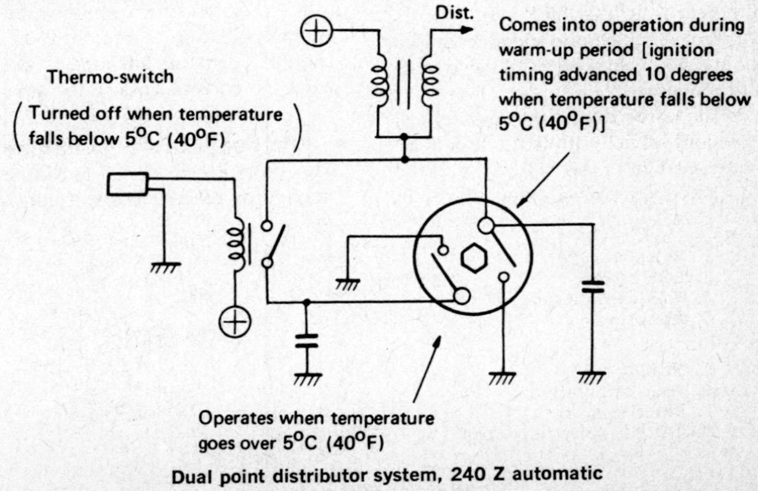

Dual point distributor system, 240 Z automatic

Engine	Transmission	Time in seconds
A12	Manual	3.5-4.5
A12	Automatic	2.5-3.5
L24	Manual	3.0

4. To adjust the time lag, first loosen the lockscrew on the vacuum control valve. Turn the adjusting screw clockwise to increase time lag, and counterclockwise to decrease.
5. Tighten the lockscrew.
6. Repeat Steps 2–5 to check the adjustment. If the adjustment is correct, the engine will settle down to the correct idle speed.

Transmission Controlled Vacuum Advance—1972–1973 A12 Engine With Manual Transmission

1. Place the car on a lift with the rear wheels free.
2. Pull off the distributor vacuum hose.
3. Place the transmission in high gear.
4. Run the engine to about 3,000 rpm.
5. Vacuum should be available at the hose. It should be available only in high gear, unless the temperature inside the car is above 50°F. If this is the case, vacuum should be available regardless of the gear selected.
6. If the system does not function properly, check:
   a. the fuse. If it is blown, the electric choke won't work either.
   b. the high gear switch on the right side of the transmission.

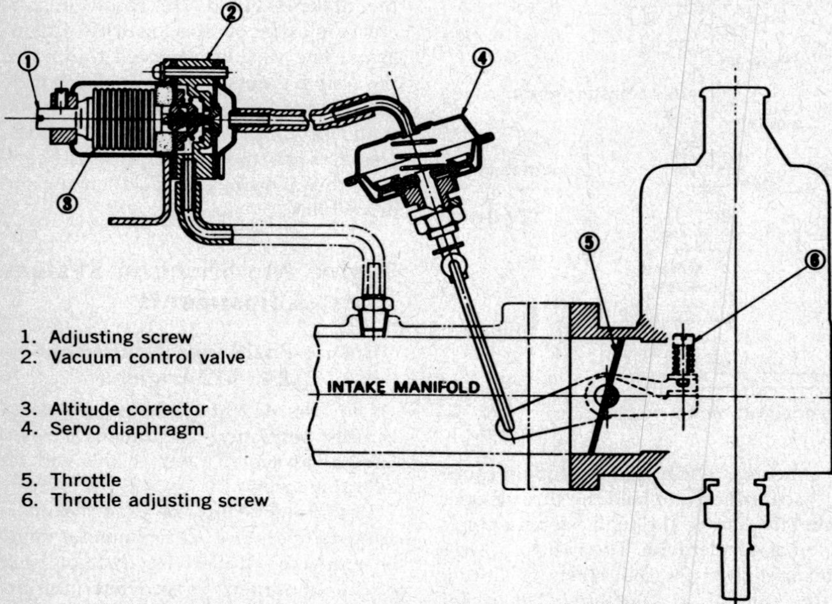

Engine modification system, 240 Z. The 1973 model has a solenoid on the vacuum control valve.

EGR System—1973 L24 Engine

1. Make sure that the temperature inside the car is at least 55°F.
2. Increase the engine speed from idle to about 3,500 rpm. The EGR valve shaft should move up.
3. If the valve does not move, check the solenoid valve by applying direct battery current. Check the EGR valve. If the valve sticks open, a rough idle will result.

   c. the temperature sensing switch inside the passenger compartment.
   d. the solenoid valve between the engine vacuum source and the distributor. Vacuum advance is allowed when no current goes to the solenoid.

Idle Fuel Cutoff—J Engine

The solenoid valve used in this system is opened by electric current and spring-loaded to the closed position. If the solenoid valve circuit is shorted to ground by any one of the four circuit switches being in its on position, the idle fuel supply is cut off. Thus a short circuit or a sticking switch in the circuit will cause the engine to give the symptoms of a clogged idle fuel system. These are stalling, rough idle and low speed operation, but normal operation at higher speeds.

To test the solenoid valve:

1. With the engine running, disconnect the solenoid wires. The valve should cut off the fuel and stall the engine.
2. Ground one solenoid terminal. Connect battery voltage to the other. The valve should click open.

To test the function of all the system switches, disconnect the wires of the solenoid valve and connect them to a test light. Disconnect the wires of the clutch switch, vacuum switch, and neutral switch.

1. Turn the ignition switch on. Do not start the engine.
2. Reconnect the transmission neutral switch. Make sure that the test light is on with the transmission in neutral and off in all other positions. Disconnect the transmission neutral switch.
3. Reconnect the throttle valve switch. Depress the accelerator pedal. The test light should be on. Release the accelerator. The light should be off. Disconnect the throttle valve switch. Correct adjustment requires that the throttle arm depress the contact arm of the switch about 0.02 in. at rest.
4. Reconnect the clutch switch. Make sure that the test light is on when the pedal is down and off when pedal is released. Disconnect the clutch switch.
5. Reconnect the solenoid valve, installing the test lamp in series with the solenoid so that it will indicate when current is supplied. Reconnect the transmission neutral switch, throttle valve switch, and vacuum switch but not the clutch switch. T-connect a vacuum gauge into the vacuum line between the intake manifold and the vacuum switch. Start and warm up the engine. Depress the clutch pedal and shift the transmission into gear. Race the engine and close the throttle rapidly. On deceleration, the vacuum should rise and the test light should go off. The light should go back on when the gauge drops to 20.9–21.6 in. Hg.
6. Reconnect all leads.

Solenoid Bypass Valve—R Engine

This system uses a solenoid valve which is opened by electric current and spring loaded to the closed position. To test system operation:

1. Switch the ignition on.
2. Shift into third or fourth gear.
3. Release the clutch pedal slowly.

1. Solenoid valve
2. EGR valve
3. EGR vacuum tube
4. Attaching nut
5. Sealing nut
6. Rear carburetor
7. Throttle valve
8. Throttle valve fully open

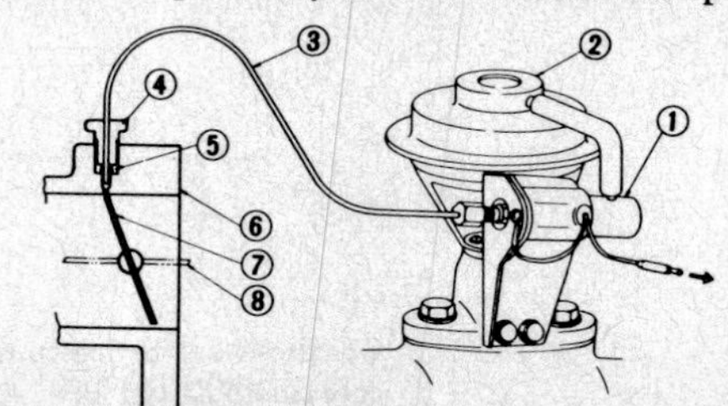

L24 engine EGR system

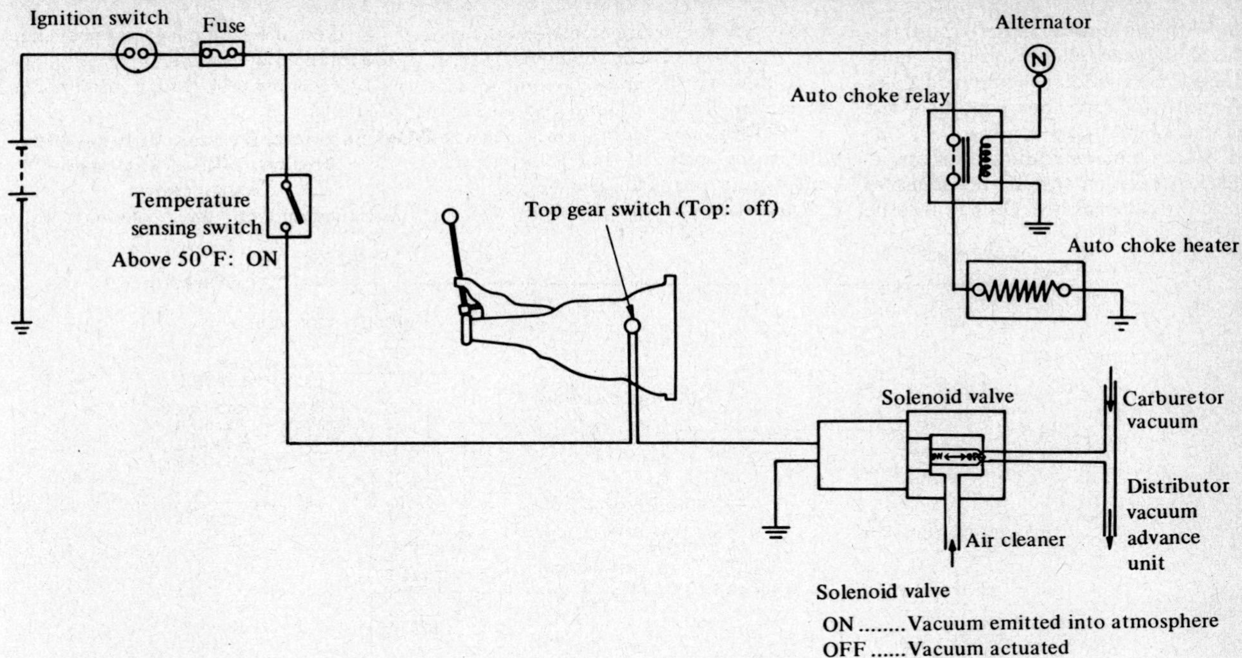

Transmission controlled vacuum advance arrangement introduced in 1972 on the A12 engine

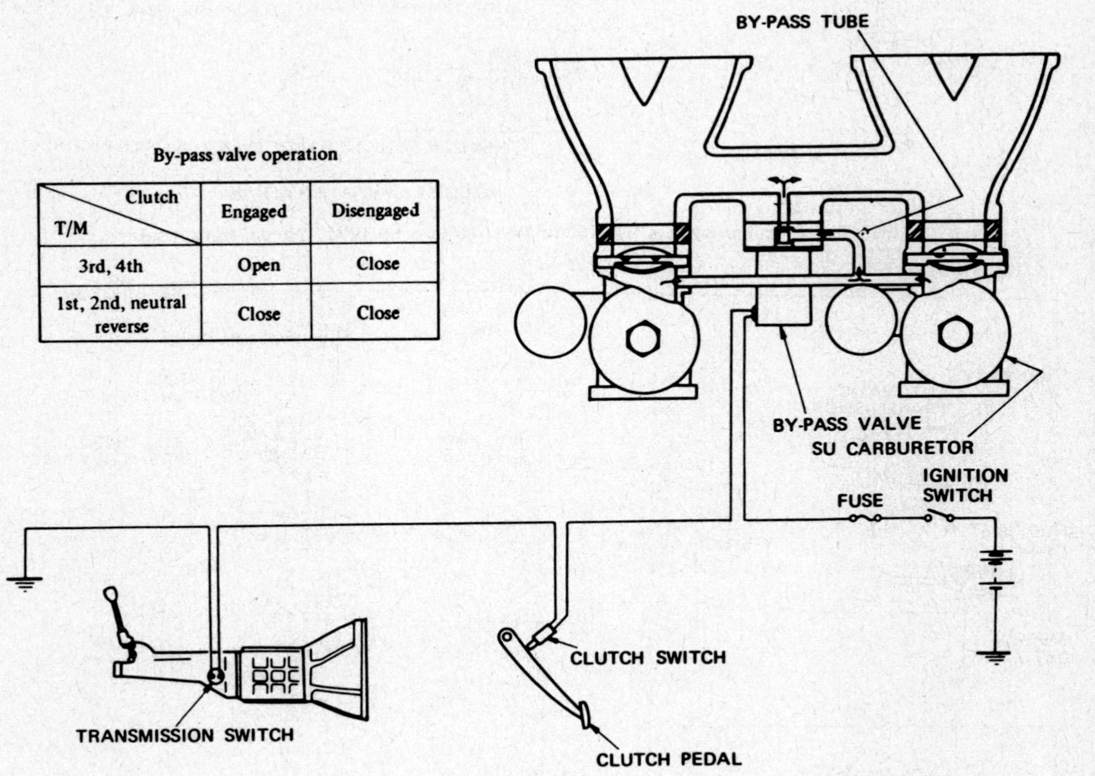

By-pass valve operation

T/M \ Clutch	Engaged	Disengaged
3rd, 4th	Open	Close
1st, 2nd, neutral reverse	Close	Close

Engine modification system, SPL311 sportscar, R engine

When the clutch switch reaches its closed position, the bypass valve should make an audible click.

4. The operation of the two individual switches can be tested by use of a test light or an ohmmeter. The clutch switch should be closed when the pedal is released. The transmission switch should be closed only in third and fourth gears.

Solenoid Bypass Valve—L16 Engine With Manual Transmission

The solenoid valve is opened by electric current and spring-loaded to the closed position. To test system operation:

1. Disconnect the solenoid valve ground lead (black wire). Connect an ammeter between the lead terminal and ground. A test light can also be used, but this only indicates whether current is present or not, while an ammeter measures the amount of current.

2. Switch the ignition on.

3. With the throttle closed, the transmission in gear, and the clutch pedal released, the ammeter should read about 0.4 amps. In any other condition, the ammeter should read 0 amps.

4. If the ammeter reading is not as specified, check each switch and adjust or replace it as necessary. On the throttle valve switch, clearance between the cam and microswitch body should be 0.032 in.

5. Remove the ammeter and replace the solenoid valve ground lead. Start the engine. Connect a jumper wire between the battery output terminal and the solenoid input terminal. The engine speed should rise to about 1,100 rpm.

6. If engine speed does not rise, check the solenoid operation.

7. Reconnect the leads in their normal locations.

Solenoid Bypass Valve—L16 Engine With Automatic Transmission

1. Disconnect the solenoid valve

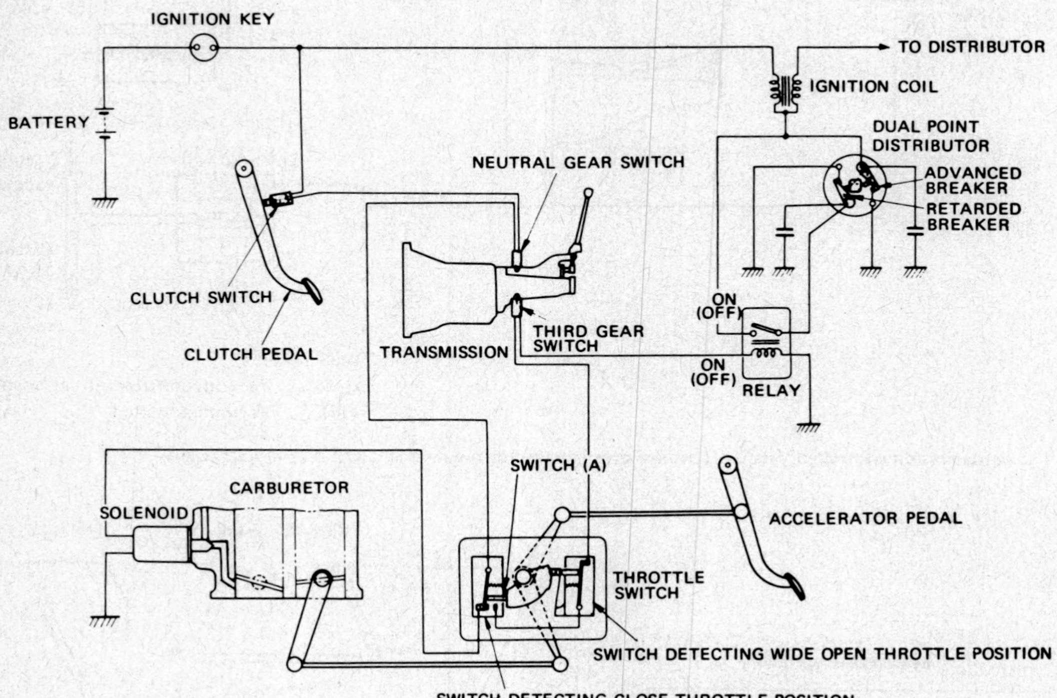

Engine modification system, PL510 and WPL510 through 1971, manual transmission

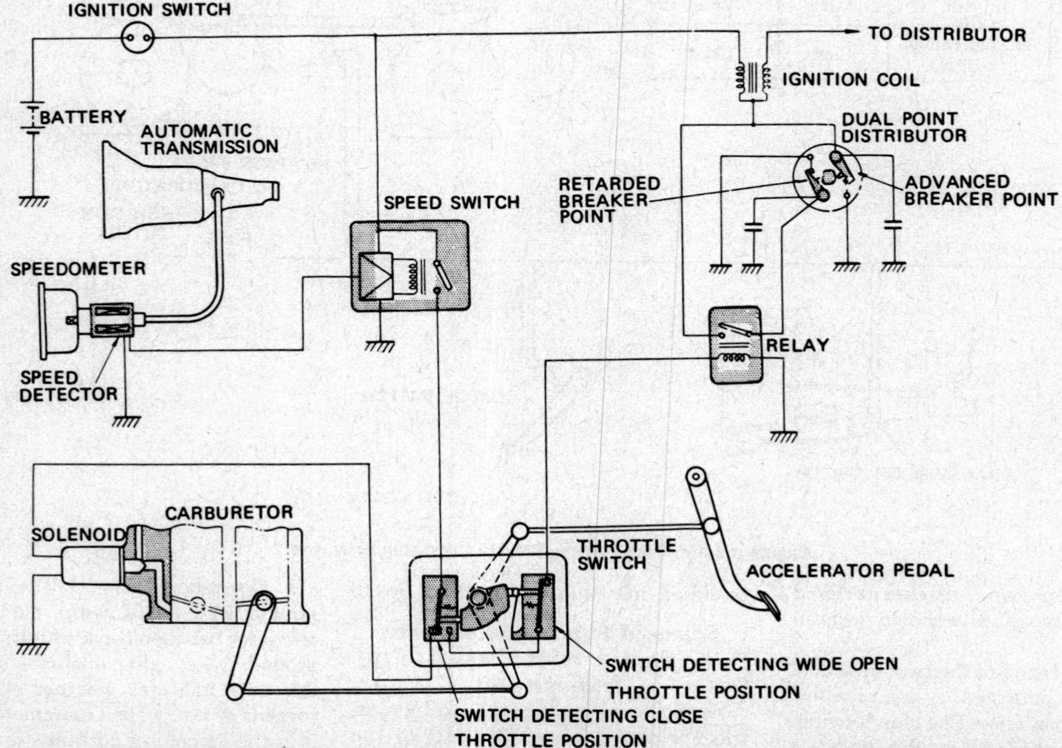

Engine modification system, PL510 and WPL510 through 1971, automatic transmission

ground lead (black wire). Connect an ammeter between the lead terminal and ground. A test light can also be used, but this only indicates whether current is present or not, while an ammeter measures the amount of current.

2. When speed is over 13 mph with a closed throttle, the ammeter should read about 0.4 amps. Below 13 mph or with the throttle open, the ammeter should read 0 amps.

3. If the ammeter reading is not as specified, check each switch and adjust or replace it as necessary.

4. Remove the ammeter and replace the solenoid valve ground lead. Start the engine. Connect a jumper wire between the battery output terminal and the solenoid input terminal. The engine speed should rise to about 1,100 rpm.

5. If engine speed does not rise, check the solenoid operation.

6. Reconnect the leads in their normal locations.

Vacuum Bypass Valve—1972–73 L16 and L18 Engine

If this device is not adjusted correctly,

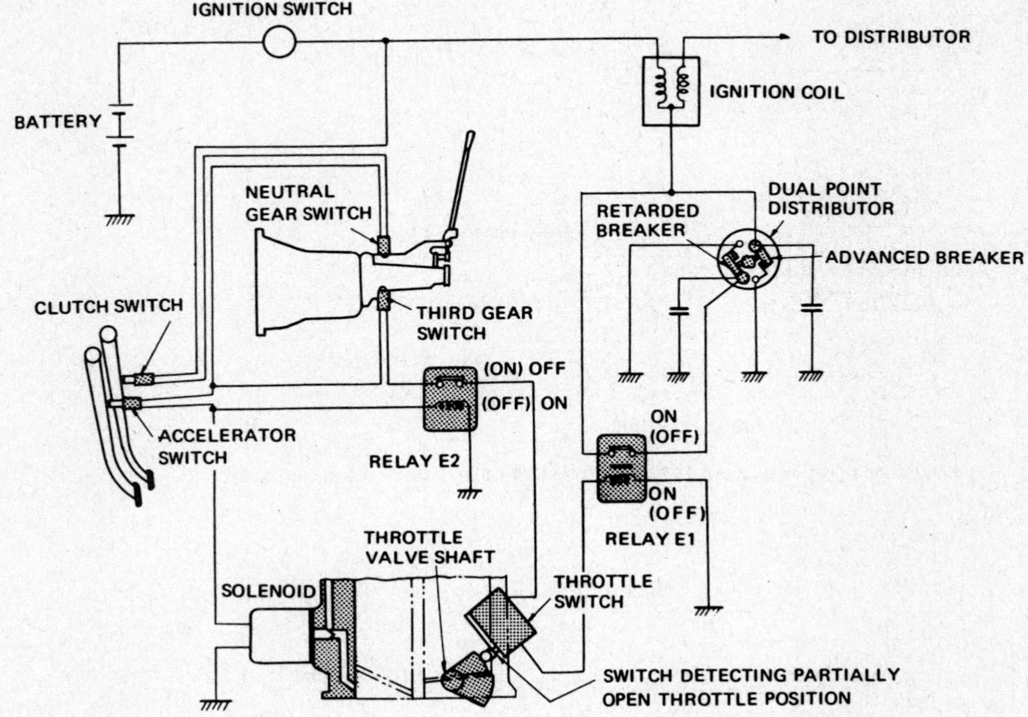

Engine modification system, PL521 pickup through 1971

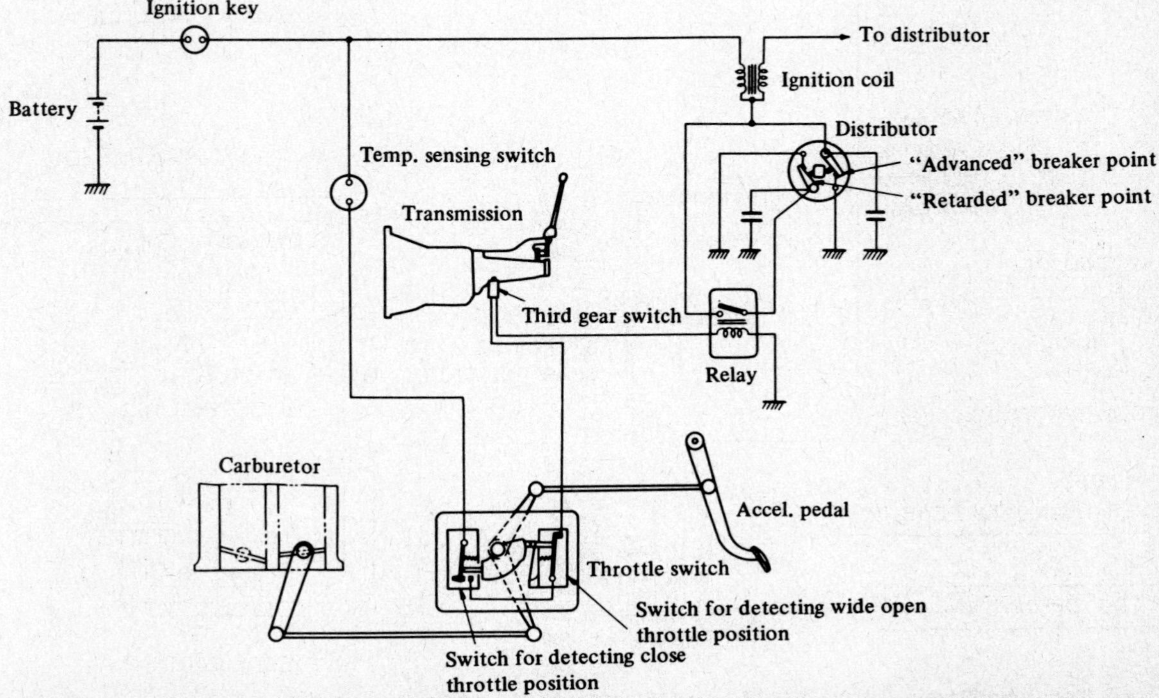

Engine modification system, 1972 PL510 and WPL510, manual transmission

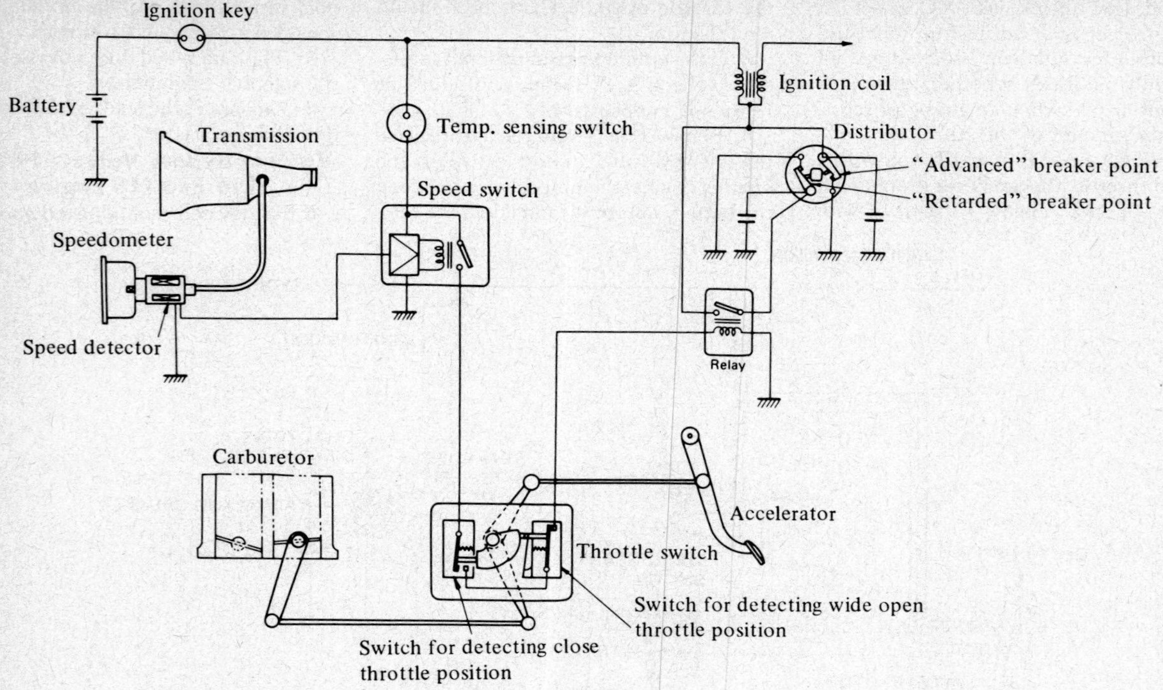

Ignition key
Battery
Transmission
Temp. sensing switch
Ignition coil
Distributor
"Advanced" breaker point
"Retarded" breaker point
Speed switch
Speedometer
Speed detector
Relay
Carburetor
Accelerator
Throttle switch
Switch for detecting wide open throttle position
Switch for detecting close throttle position

Engine modification system, 1972 PL510 and WPL510, automatic transmission

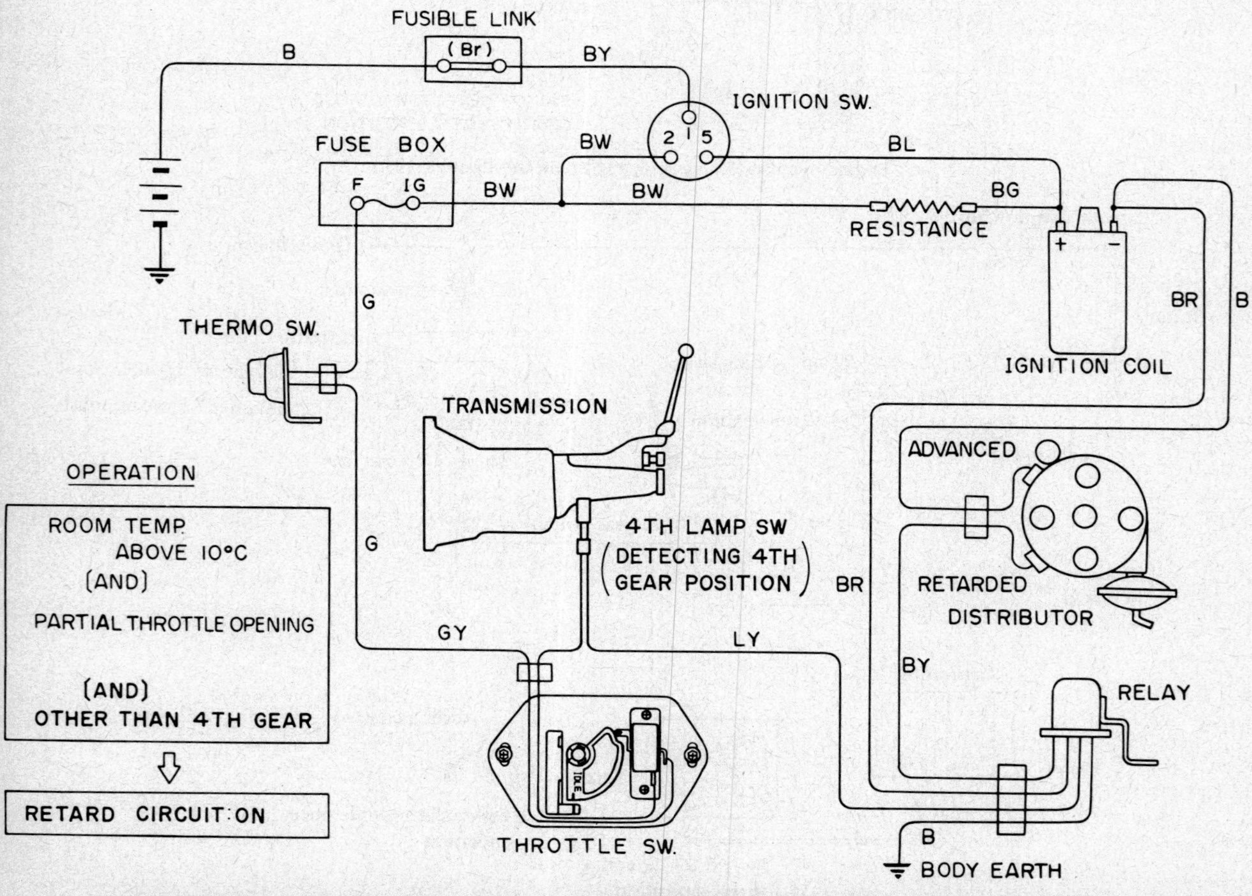
FUSIBLE LINK
(Br)
B
BY
IGNITION SW.
2 1 5
FUSE BOX
F IG
BW
BL
BW
BW
BG
RESISTANCE
+ −
G
THERMO SW.
BR
B
IGNITION COIL
TRANSMISSION
OPERATION
ROOM TEMP. ABOVE 10°C
(AND)
PARTIAL THROTTLE OPENING
(AND)
OTHER THAN 4TH GEAR
RETARD CIRCUIT ON
ADVANCED
G
4TH LAMP SW (DETECTING 4TH GEAR POSITION)
BR
RETARDED
DISTRIBUTOR
GY
LY
BY
RELAY
IDLE
THROTTLE SW.
B
BODY EARTH

Engine modification system, 1973 L16 and L18 engine models. Automatic transmission vehicles don't have the transmission switch shown

the engine will take a long time to settle down to idle speed after the throttle is released.

1. With the engine warmed up, it should take 4–5 seconds for the engine speed to fall from 3,000 rpm to 1,000 rpm after the throttle is released. If it does not, proceed with the following.

2. Loosen the lock screw at the bottom of the vacuum bypass valve on the carburetor.

3. Remove the vacuum bypass valve cover.

4. Turn the adjusting screw clockwise to increase the time lag, and counterclockwise to decrease. Do not fit the screwdriver tightly into the slot.

5. Replace the cover and tighten the lock screw.

Dual Point Distributor—L16 Engine With Manual Transmission through 1972

1. Disconnect the lead wires from the retarded and advanced terminals on the distributor. Connect an ammeter between the lead wire for the retarded points and ground.

2. Switch the ignition on.

3. With the throttle partially open, the shift lever in third gear, and the clutch pedal released, the ammeter should indicate about 3 amps. The temperature must be above 50°F in the passenger compartment on 1972–1973 models.

4. With the throttle valve wide open or nearly closed, or the shift lever in some position other than third, or the clutch pedal depressed, the ammeter should indicate 0 amps.

5. If the ammeter reads 0 amps in Step 3, disconnect the terminals of the relay (relay E1 on PL521) and measure the voltage between the terminal with the No. 1 punch mark and ground. If voltage is about 12 volts, replace the relay. If voltage is 0 volts, check each switch and wiring.

6. If the ammeter reads 3 amps in Step 4, check the clutch switch, neutral switch, and third gear switch. On the PL510 and WPL510, check the throttle switch. On the PL521, check the throttle switch and accelrator switch.

Dual Point Distributor—L16 Engine With Automatic Transmission through 1972

1. Disconnect the lead wire of the retarded side of the distributor. Connect an ammeter between the lead wire and the retarded side terminal.

2. Start the engine and drive the vehicle.

3. The ammeter should not read 0 amps when speed is over 13 mph with a partially open throttle. Otherwise, the ammeter should read 0 amps.

4. If the ammeter reading is not as specified, check the speed switch, throttle switch, speed detector, and relay.

Fuel Vapor Control System

The fuel vapor control system is used on all vehicles sold in the U.S., starting 1970. It has four major components:

1. A sealed gas tank filler cap to prevent vapors from escaping at this point.

2. A vapor separator which returns liquid fuel to the fuel tank, but allows vapors to pass into the system.

3. A vapor vent line connecting the vapor separator to a flow guide valve.

4. A flow guide valve which allows air into the fuel tank and prevents vapors from the crankcase ventilation system from passing into the vapor vent line and fuel tank.

When the engine is not running, fuel vapors accumulate in the fuel tank, vapor separator, and vapor vent line. When the vapor pressure exceeds 0.4 in. (10 mm) Hg, the flow guide valve opens to allow the vapors to pass into the crankcase ventilation system. Fuel vapors are thus accumulated in the crankcase. When the engine starts, the vapors are disposed of by the crankcase ventilation system. When enough fuel has been used to create a slight vacuum in the fuel tank and fuel vapor control system, the flow guide valve opens to let fresh air from the carburetor air cleaner into the tank.

On engines with sidedraft carburetors, float bowl vapors are routed through the float bowl overflow tubes to the carburetor air cleaner.

Flow Guide Valve Test

The flow guide valve is mounted in the engine compartment. The valve fittings are usually marked A, from air cleaner; F, from fuel tank; and C, to crankcase.

1. Blow into the F fitting. Air should come out the C fitting.

2. Blow into the C fitting. Air should not escape.

3. Blow into the A fitting. Air should come out either the F or C fitting, or both.

4. Replace the valve if defective.

FUEL SYSTEM

Fuel Pump

The diaphragm fuel pump is driven from the engine camshaft on all engines except the U20. On the U20 engine, the pump is driven off the engine jackshaft. It is mounted on the side of the engine block on overhead valve engines and the U20 and on the side of the cylinder head on all other overhead camshaft engines. The pump is on the left side of J engines and on the right side of all others. The pump on J engines has a primer lever which is useful in cold weather and in restarting after running out of fuel.

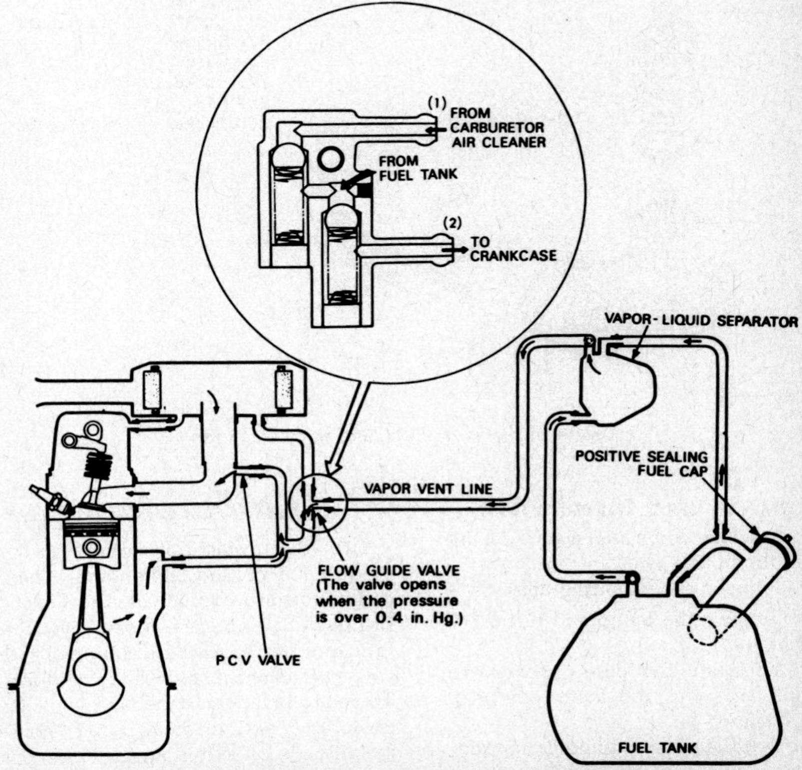

Fuel vapor control system for engines with downdraft carburetors

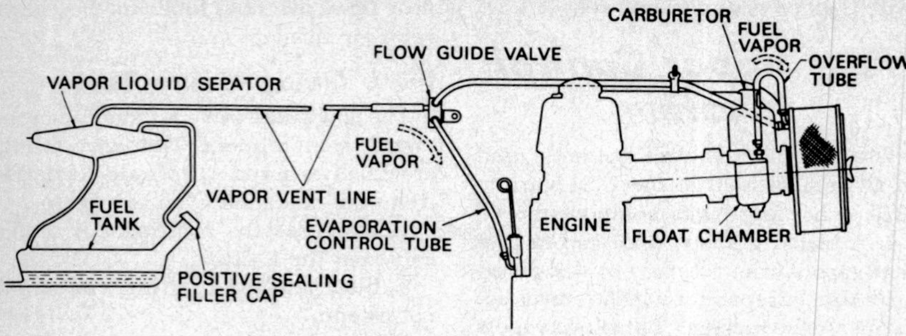

Fuel vapor control system for engines with sidedraft carburetors

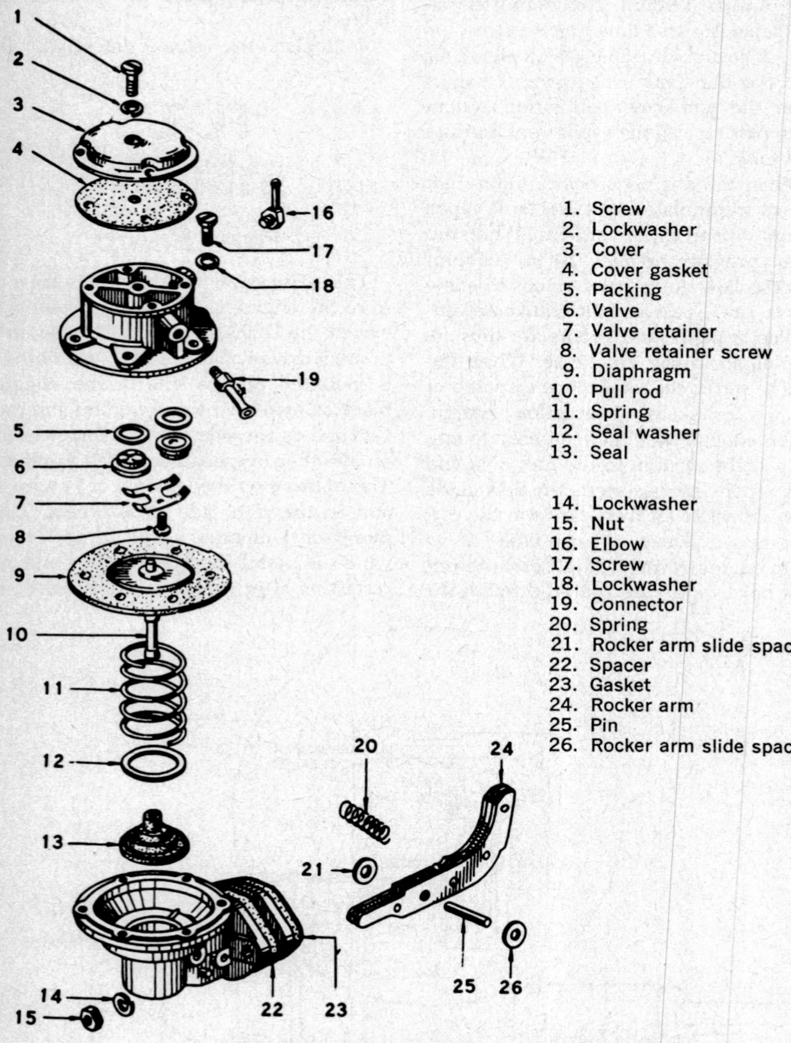

1. Screw
2. Lockwasher
3. Cover
4. Cover gasket
5. Packing
6. Valve
7. Valve retainer
8. Valve retainer screw
9. Diaphragm
10. Pull rod
11. Spring
12. Seal washer
13. Seal
14. Lockwasher
15. Nut
16. Elbow
17. Screw
18. Lockwasher
19. Connector
20. Spring
21. Rocker arm slide spacer
22. Spacer
23. Gasket
24. Rocker arm
25. Pin
26. Rocker arm slide spacer

Details of fuel pump, L16 engine pump shown

Removal and Installation

1. Disconnect the inlet and outlet lines from the pump.
2. Remove the mounting bolts.
3. Remove the pump and discard the gasket.
4. Lubricate the pump rocker arm, rocker arm pin, and lever pin before reinstallation.
5. Bolt the pump into position, using a new gasket.
6. Connect the fuel lines.

Carburetors

Two Hitachi sidedraft carburetors are used on R, U20, and L24 engines. These carburetors are virtually identical to the British SU carburetors. A few high performance U20 engines are equipped with two twin-choke sidedraft carburetors. These are identical to the German Solex carburetors and are built under license by Mikuni. All other engines use one downdraft carburetor of various makes and types.

Hitachi/SU Type

Fuel Level Adjustment

Float bowl fuel level should be 0.87–0.95 in. from the top edge of the bowl with the float in place.

To adjust the level:

1. Remove the float chamber covers.
2. Place the covers upside down.
3. Lift the float lever and slowly lower it until the float lever seat just contacts the valve stem.
4. Check dimension H. It should be 0.-55–0.59 in. Note that some carburetors have free floats and others have the float in unit with the float lever.

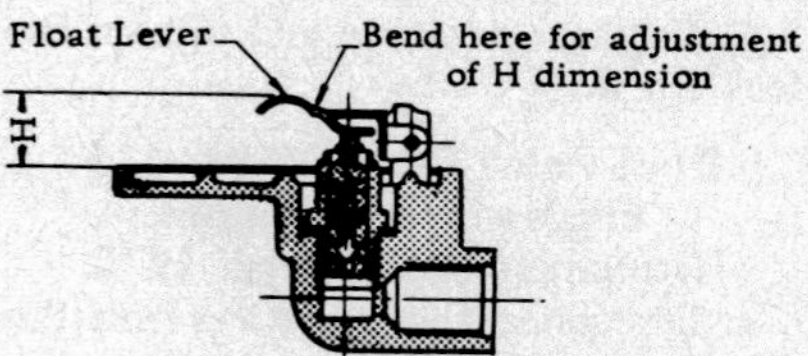

Float bowl fuel level adjustment for Hitachi/SU type carburetor with free float

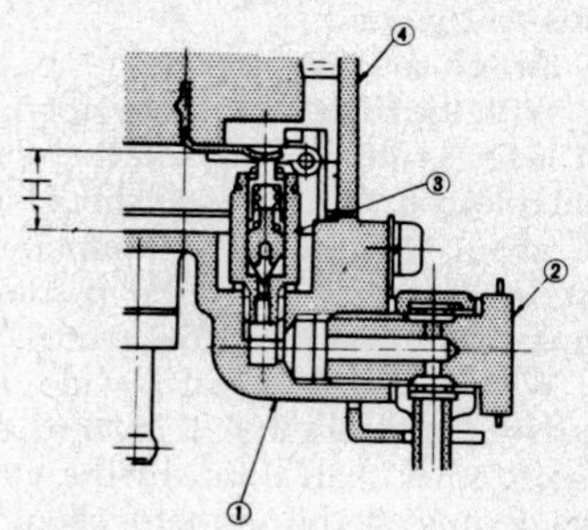

Float bowl fuel level adjustment for Hitachi/SU type carburetor with float in unit with float lever

1. Float chamber cover (unit shown inverted)
2. Filter bolt
3. Needle valve
4. Float chamber

Overhaul

These carburetors, being precision devices, are capable of being very finely adjusted. For the same reason, they require periodic attention. The factory recommends that they be disassembled and cleaned every six months. The suction piston and chamber often accumulate deposits of grit and varnish. To check for this condition, remove the air cleaner and raise the suction piston about ½ in. with a finger. Release the piston. It should come down smoothly and evenly. If not, the carburetor must be disassembled and cleaned. If turning the mixture nuts seems to have no effect, the difficulty is probably an air leak at some point. The remedy for this is to replace all packings and gaskets. The same applies to fuel leaks. A common cause of air leaks is wear of the throttle shafts and the throttle shaft bore itself. The remedy for this condition is to install new throttle shafts and bushings. If the carburetor has no throttle shaft bushings, it may be necessary to drill out the throttie shaft bore to install bushings, The float chambers of these carburetors are very similar to those in conventional carburetors. However, the venturi and fuel system are precision made and require careful handling.

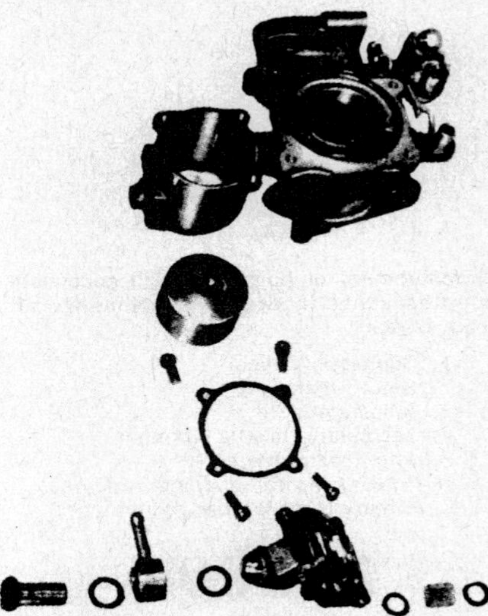

Hitachi/SU float bowl assembly

To disassemble the carburetors:

1. Remove the screws and the suction chamber.
2. Remove the suction spring, nylon packing, and suction piston from the chamber. Be extremely careful not to bend the jet needle.
3. Do not remove the jet needle from the suction piston unless it must be replaced. To remove it, loosen the jet needle setscrew. Hold the needle with pliers at a point no more than 0.1 in. from the piston. Remove the needle by pulling and turning slowly. Replace the needle with the shoulder portion flush with the piston surface. Check this with a straightedge. Tighten the setscrew.
4. Clean all parts of the suction chamber assembly with a safe solvent. Reassemble, using all the new parts supplied in the overhaul kit. Do not lubricate the piston.
5. To dismantle the nozzle assembly, remove the 4 mm. screw and remove the connecting plate from the nozzle head by pulling lightly on the starter (choke) lever. Remove the fuel line and nozzle. Be careful not to bend the jet needle if the suction chamber assembly is mounted on the carburetor. Remove the idle (mixture) adjusting nut and spring. Do not remove the nozzle sleeve unless absolutely necessary. Special care is required to replace this part. Remove the nozzle sleeve setscrew and nozzle sleeve.
6. Clean all parts of the nozzle assembly with a safe solvent. Be very careful of the nozzle. Do not pass anything through the nozzle for cleaning purposes.
7. The jet needle must now be carefully centered in the nozzle, unless the nozzle sleeve and setscrew were not disturbed. Even so, it is a good idea to check this. To center the jet needle, insert the nozzle sleeve into the carburetor body with the setscrew loose. Carefully install the suction piston assembly without the plunger rod. Insert the nozzle without the spring and mixture adjusting nut until the nozzle contacts the nozzle sleeve. Position the nozzle sleeve so that the jet needle is centered inside the sleeve and does not contact the sleeve. Test centering by raising and releasing the suction piston. It should drop smoothly, making a metallic sound when it hits the stop.

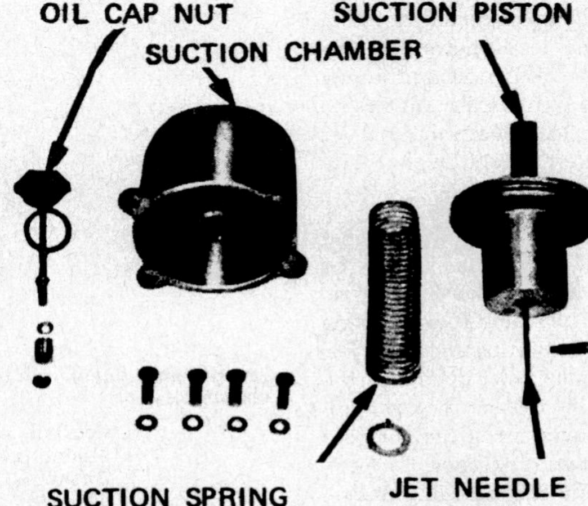

Hitachi/SU suction chamber assembly

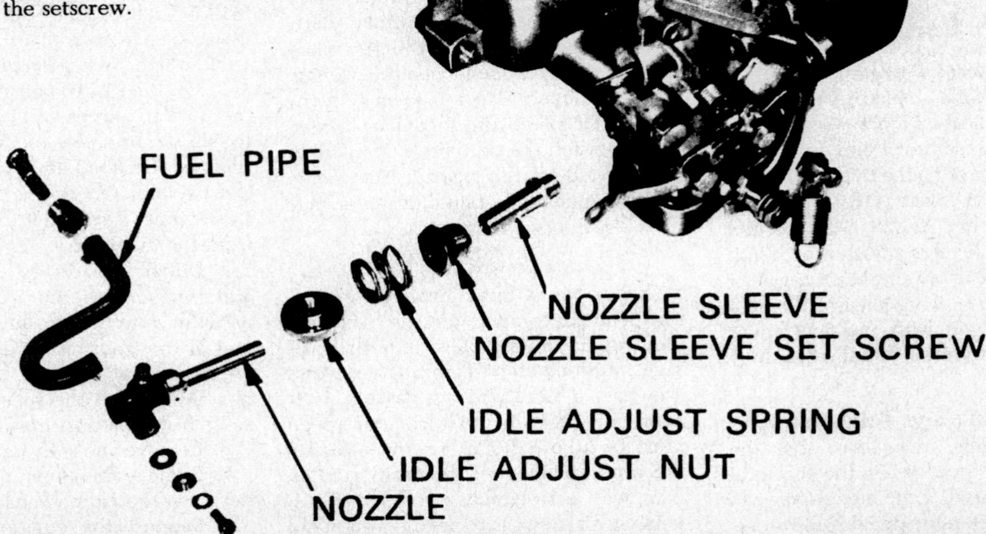

Hitachi/SU nozzle assembly

Tighten the nozzle sleeve setscrew when the needle is centered.

8. Reassemble the nozzle assembly. Replace the fuel line. Replace the damper plunger rod.

9. Pull the starter lever slightly, replace the connecting plate and 4 mm. screw.

10. Carburetor synchronization and mixture adjustments must be performed after reinstalling the carburetors.

Mikuni/Solex Twin-Choke

Fuel Level Adjustment

Float bowl fuel level is controlled by the thickness of the washer under the float needle valve. The standard washer thickness is 0.04 in. (1 mm.). A 0.02 in. (0.5 mm.) thick washer is available to raise the fuel level 0.08 in. (2 mm.), and a 0.06 in. (1.5 mm.) washer is available to lower it 0.08 in (2 mm.). Normal fuel level is 0.79 in. above the center of the main bore. A special fuel level meter is available to measure this. When using the meter, fuel level on the scale should be 0.67–0.75 in. The float lever should never be bent to change the fuel level.

Jet Replacement

These carburetors are unique in that jet changes can be made simply by removing a jet chamber cover and replacing the main air, main fuel, or idling (pilot) jets. To maintain balance, the jets for each of the choke tubes in both carburetors must all be the same size. This means that four main air or fuel, or pilot jets must be changed together. Jet numbers relate directly to jet drilling diameter, except in the case of main fuel jets which are rated by flow. The larger the main air or pilot jet number, the leaner the mixture. The larger the main fuel jet number, the richer the mixture.

The carburetor venturi tubes can also be replaced readily and are available in a number of sizes.

Downdraft Carburetors

Fuel Level Adjustment

All Nihonkikaki (Nikki) carburetors have a glass float chamber side cover marked with a fuel level line. Fuel level is adjusted by varying the thickness of the washer under the float valve.

On the Hitachi DAF328, DCG306, and DCH340, fuel level is adjusted by bending the float seat tab to obtain a gap of 0.051–0.067 in. between the needle valve and float seat tab with the float cover removed and inverted, and the float fully raised.

Throttle Linkage Adjustment

On all models, make sure that the throttle is wide open when the accelerator pedal is floored. Some models have an adjustable accelerator pedal stop to prevent strain on the linkage.

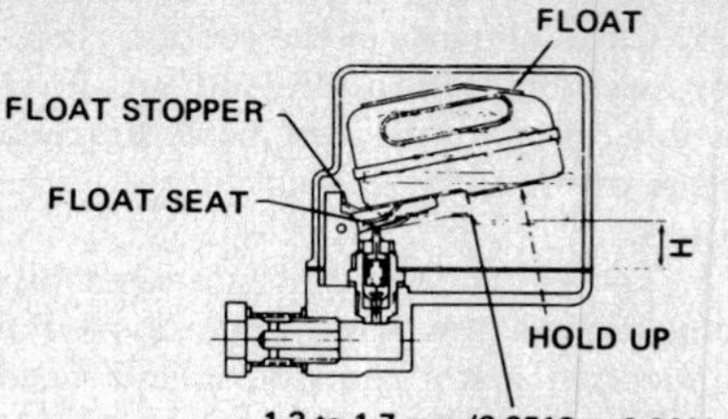

Hitachi downdraft carburetor float level adjustment

Dashpot Adjustment

A dashpot is used on carburetors with automatic transmissions. The dashpot slows the closing of the throttle valve to prevent stalling. The dashpot should be adjusted so that it contacts the throttle lever at about 2,000–2,500 rpm on deceleration.

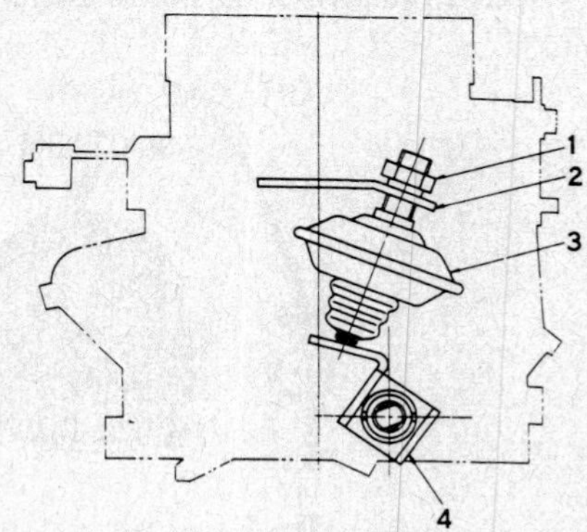

Dashpot installation on Hitachi downdraft carburetor

1. Locknut
2. Mounting arm
3. Dashpot
4. Throttle lever

Secondary Throttle Adjustment

On most two throat carburetors the secondary throttle should begin to open when the primary throttle is open 48°. On the Hitachi DCG306, 48° corresponds to a measurement of 0.23 in. between the lower edge of the primary throttle valve and the inside edge of the primary bore. On the Hitachi DAF328, the secondary throttle begins to open when the primary throttle is open 59° or 0.35 in. On the Hitachi DCH340, the secondary begins to open when the primary is open 50° or 0.29 in. Adjust the point of secondary throttle opening by bending the linkage between the two throttles.

Overhaul

Carburetor overhaul involves separating the major components, removing and blowing out all jets, blowing out all passages, washing all parts in a safe solvent, and reassembling with new gaskets. After overhaul, the idle mixture and speed must be adjusted. Carburetor overhaul kits are available, and generally contain complete instructions, a full set of gaskets, and a new float needle valve and accelerator pump parts.

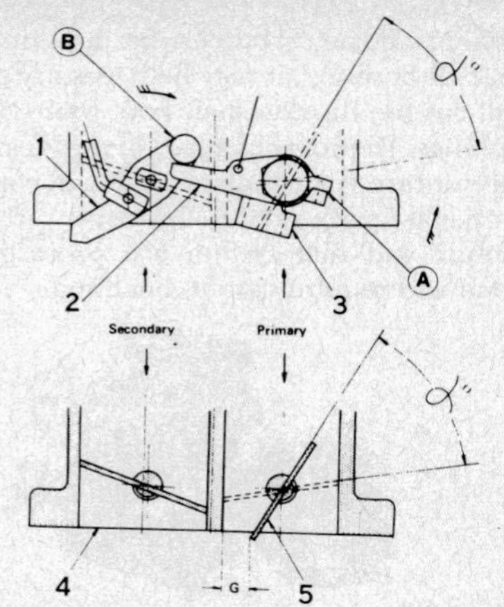

Measurement of point at which secondary throttle starts to open, Hitachi downdraft carburetor

1. Connecting lever
2. Return plate
3. Adjusting plate
4. Secondary throttle chamber
5. Primary throttle valve

a. Primary throttle opening in degrees
G. Primary throttle opening in inches

MANUAL TRANSMISSION

Removal and Installation

On SPL311 and SRL311 sportscars, the transmission must be removed in unit with the engine; it cannot be removed separately. On all other models, the transmission may be removed separately from under the vehicle. Transmission removal and replacement procedure for early models is generally similar to that given here.

PL510, PL610, KPL610, WPL510, WPL610, PL521, PL620, LB110, KLB110, 240 Z

1. Raise and support the vehicle. Disconnect the battery. On the PL510 and WPL510, disconnect the handbrake cable at the equalizer pivot. Disconnect the backup light switch on all models.

3. On the PL510 and WPL510, loosen the muffler clamps and turn the muffler to one side to allow room for driveshaft removal. On the 240 Z, remove the exhaust system. On models with the A12 or L18 engine, disconnect the exhaust pipe from the manifold.

4. Unbolt the driveshaft at the rear and remove. If there is a center bearing, unbolt it from the crossmember. Seal the end of the transmission extension housing to prevent leakage.

5. Disconnect the speedometer drive cable from the transmission.

6. Remove the shift lever.

7. Remove the clutch operating cylinder from the clutch housing.

8. Support the engine with a large wood block and a jack under the oil pan.

9. Unbolt the transmission from the crossmember. Support the transmission with a jack. Remove the crossmember.

10. Lower the rear of the engine to allow clearance.

11. Remove the starter.

12. Unbolt the transmission. Lower and remove it to the rear.

13. Reverse the procedure for reinstallation. Check the clutch linkage adjustment.

Four Speed, Bottom Cover Transmission Overhaul—L520, L521, PL521, PL620, SPL311, PL510, PL610, KPL610, WPL510, WPL610

The reverse and reverse idler drive gears are contained in the extension housing of this transmission. On late units, the cast, ribbed bottom cover is replaced by a stamped steel cover. Virtually all of these transmissions imported to the US have a modified extension housing incorporating a floorshift mechanism. The transmission model number is F4W63.

Disassembly

1. Drain the transmission.

2. Remove the clutch withdrawal lever and release bearing.

3. Remove the clevis pin which connects the striker rod to the shift lever.

4. Remove the speedometer drive pinion assembly.

5. Unbolt and remove the extension housing, disengaging the striker rod from the shift rod gates.

6. Remove the bottom and front covers.

7. Remove the three detent plugs, springs, and balls.

8. Drive out the shift fork retaining pins. Remove the rods and forks.

9. Move the first/second and third/fourth coupling sleeves into gear at the same time to lock the mainshaft.

10. Pull out the countershaft and countergear with the two needle roller bearings and spacers.

11. Remove the snap-ring, reverse idler gears, and shaft.

12. Unbolt the mainshaft rear bearing retainer.

13. Pull out the mainshaft assembly to the rear. Pull out the clutch shaft to the front.

14. To disassemble the mainshaft, remove the snap-ring, third/fourth synchronizer hub and coupling sleeve. Remove third gear, with the roller bearing. Remove the mainshaft nut, lockplate, speedometer drive gear, and steel ball. Take off reverse gear and the hub. Press off the bearing and retainer. Remove the thrust washer and first gear with the needle roller bearing and bushing. Be careful not to lose the steel ball which locates the thrust washer. Take off the first/second synchronizer and hub. Remove second gear with the needle roller bearing.

Inspection

1. Clean all parts with a safe solvent. Lubricate the bearings with gear oil.

2. Check the mainshaft for straightness. Runout at the rear of the shaft should not exceed 0.0059 in. (0.15 mm.). Make sure that the synchronizer hubs slide freely without excessive clearance.

3. Place the synchronizer baulk ring in position on the cone of its gear. Check the gap between the baulk ring end face and the front face of the clutch teeth. The gap should be 0.0472–0.0360 in. (1.2–1.6 mm.). If it is less than 0.0315 in. (0.8 mm.), replace the ring.

4. The clearance between the shift

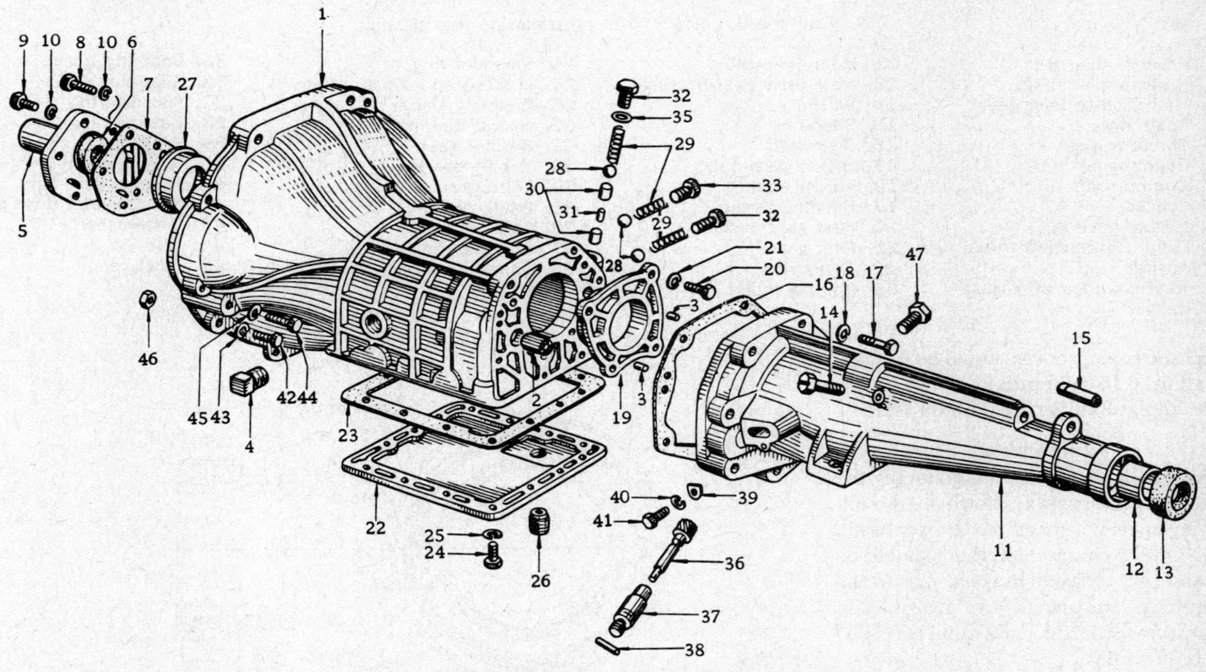

Four speed, bottom cover transmission case details

1. Case
2. Needle bearing
3. Dowel pin
4. Plug
5. Front cover assembly
6. Oil seal
7. Gasket
8. Bolt
9. Bolt
10. Lockwasher
11. Extension housing
12. Bushing
13. Oil seal
14. Breather
15. Striker bushing
16. Gasket
17. Bolt
18. Lockwasher
19. Bearing retainer
20. Bolt
21. Lockwasher
22. Bottom cover
23. Gasket
24. Bolt
25. Lockwasher
26. Drain plug
27. Bearing retainer
28. Detent ball
29. Detent spring
30. Interlock plunger
31. Interlock pin
32. Detent plug
33. Detent plug
34. Not used
35. Washer
36. Speedometer pinion
37. Pinion sleeve
38. Pin
39. Lockplate
40. Lockwasher
41. Bolt
42. Bolt
43. Lockwasher
44. Bolt
45. Lockwasher
46. Nut
47. Plug for backup light switch

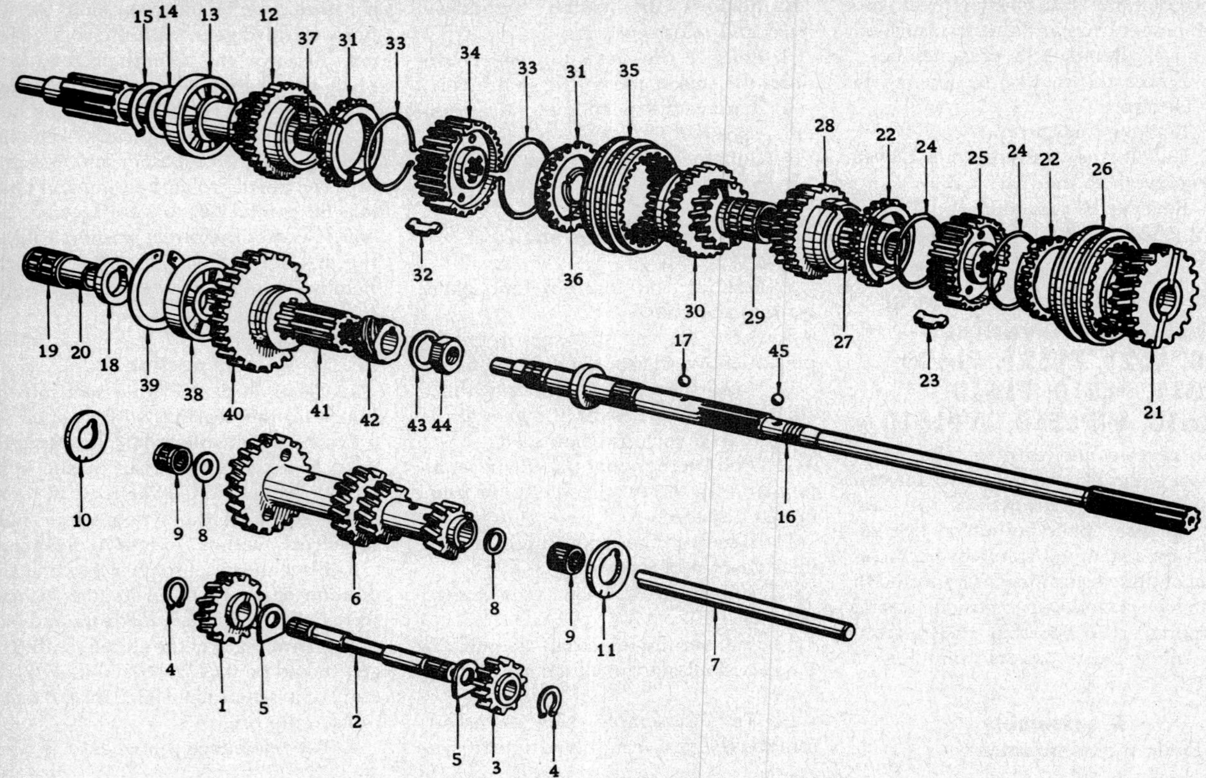

Four speed, bottom cover transmission gear details

1. Reverse idler gear
2. Reverse idler shaft
3. Main reverse idler gear
4. Snap-ring
5. Thrust washer
6. Countergear
7. Countershaft
8. Spacer
9. Needle bearing
10. Front countershaft thrust washer
11. Rear countershaft thrust washer
12. Main drive gear
13. Main drive gear bearing
14. Washer
15. Snap-ring
16. Mainshaft
17. 5/32" steel ball
18. Thrust washer
19. Needle bearing
20. First gear bushing
21. First gear
22. Baulk ring
23. Shifting insert
24. Spreader ring
25. First/second synchro hub
26. Coupling sleeve
27. Needle bearing
28. Second gear
29. Needle bearing
30. Third gear
31. Baulk ring
32. Shifting insert
33. Spreader ring
34. Third/fourth synchro hub
35. Coupling sleeve
36. Snap-ring
37. Pilot bearing
38. Bearing
39. Snap-ring
40. Reverse gear
41. Reverse gear hub
42. Speedometer drive gear
43. Lockwasher
44. Nut
45. Steel ball

forks and their grooves should be 0.0059–.0118 in (0.15–0.30 mm.).

5. Replace all O-rings and oil seals.

Assembly

Assembly procedures are generally the reverse of disassembly, however the following special instructions are required.

1. On the clutch shaft, there should be no end-play between the bearing and the snap-ring. Snap-rings are available in sizes from 0.0598 in. (1.52 mm.) to 0.0697 in. (1.77 mm.).

2. Some of these transmissions use a servo type synchronizer which utilizes brake bands. To assemble these synchronizers, place each gear on a flat surface. Install the synchronizer ring into the clutch gear. Place the thrust block and anchor block as shown and install the circlip into the groove.

3. Third gear should be adjusted to give an end-play of 0.0020–0.0059 in. (0.05–0.15 mm.). Snap-rings for adjustment are available in sizes from 0.0551 in. (1.40 mm.) to 0.0630 in. (1.60 mm.).

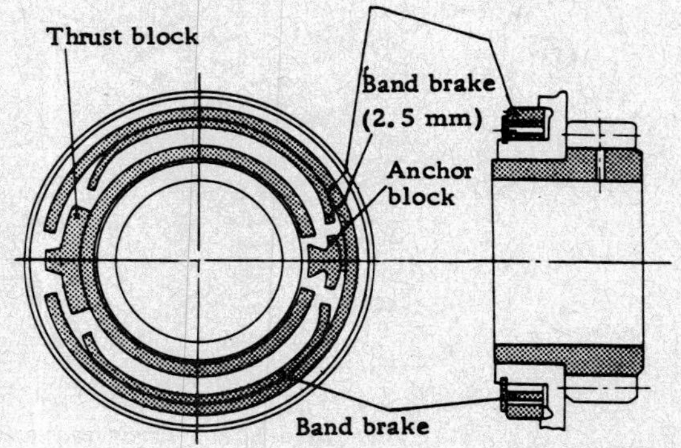

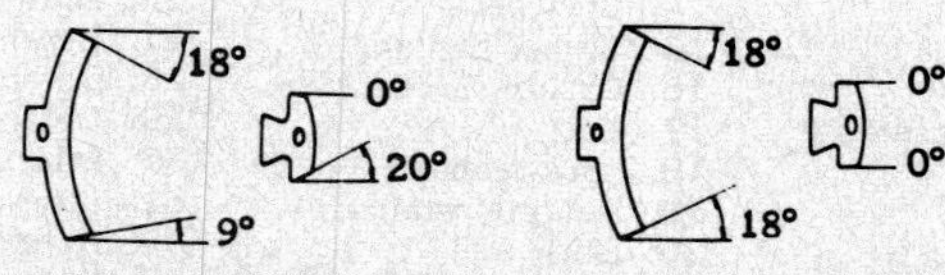

Servo type synchronizer assembly details

4. Tighten the mainshaft nut to 65–80 ft lbs.

5. Install the reverse idler driving gear on the reverse shaft and fasten with a snap-ring. Install the shaft and gear into the case, placing a thrust washer between the gear and case. Place a thrust washer, idler gear, and snap-ring on the inside end of the shaft. Idler gear end-play should be 0.0039–0.0118 in. (0.1–0.3 mm.). Snap-rings are available in sizes from 0.0433 in. (1.1 mm.) to 0.0591 in. (1.5 mm.).

6. Countergear end-play should be 0.-0020–.0059 in. (0.05–0.15 mm.). Thrust washers for adjustment are available from 0.0945 in. (2.40 mm.) to 0.1024 in. (2.60 mm.).

7. To assemble the shift mechanism, place the first/second and third/fourth forks onto their sleeves. Insert the first/second shift rod. Install an interlock plunger and then the third/fourth shift rod with the interlock pin. Install the other interlock plunger and then the reverse shift fork and rod. Place a detent ball and spring into each detent hole. Use sealant on the plug threads and torque the plug to 12–15 ft lbs.

8. Install the extension housing, engaging the striker rod with the shift rod gates. Torque the bolts to 16–22 ft lbs. Torque the front cover bolts to 8–12 ft lbs. Torque the bottom cover bolts to 8–12 ft lbs. See the Capacities Chart for refill capacity.

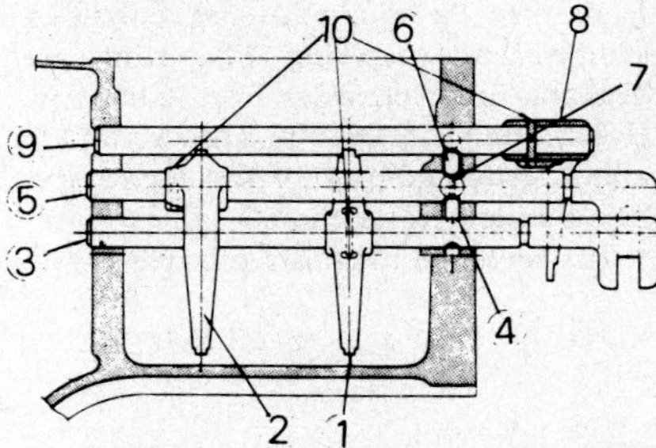

Shift rod and fork details, four speed bottom cover transmission

1. First/second shift fork
2. Third/fourth shift fork
3. First/second shift rod
4. Interlock plunger
5. Third/fourth shift rod
6. Interlock plunger
7. Interlock pin
8. Reverse shift fork
9. Reverse shift rod
10. Fork retaining pin

Four Speed Transmission Overhaul—240 Z

This transmission is constructed in three sections: clutch housing, transmission housing, and extension housing. There are no case cover plates. There is a cast iron adapter plate between the transmission and extension housings. The transmission model number is F4W71.

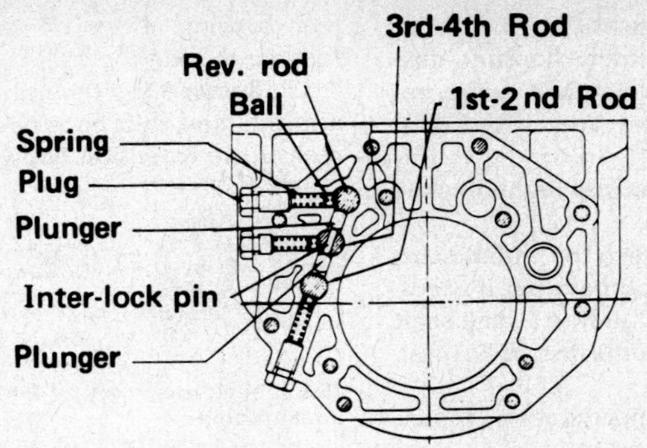

Shift rod interlock details for four speed bottom cover transmission

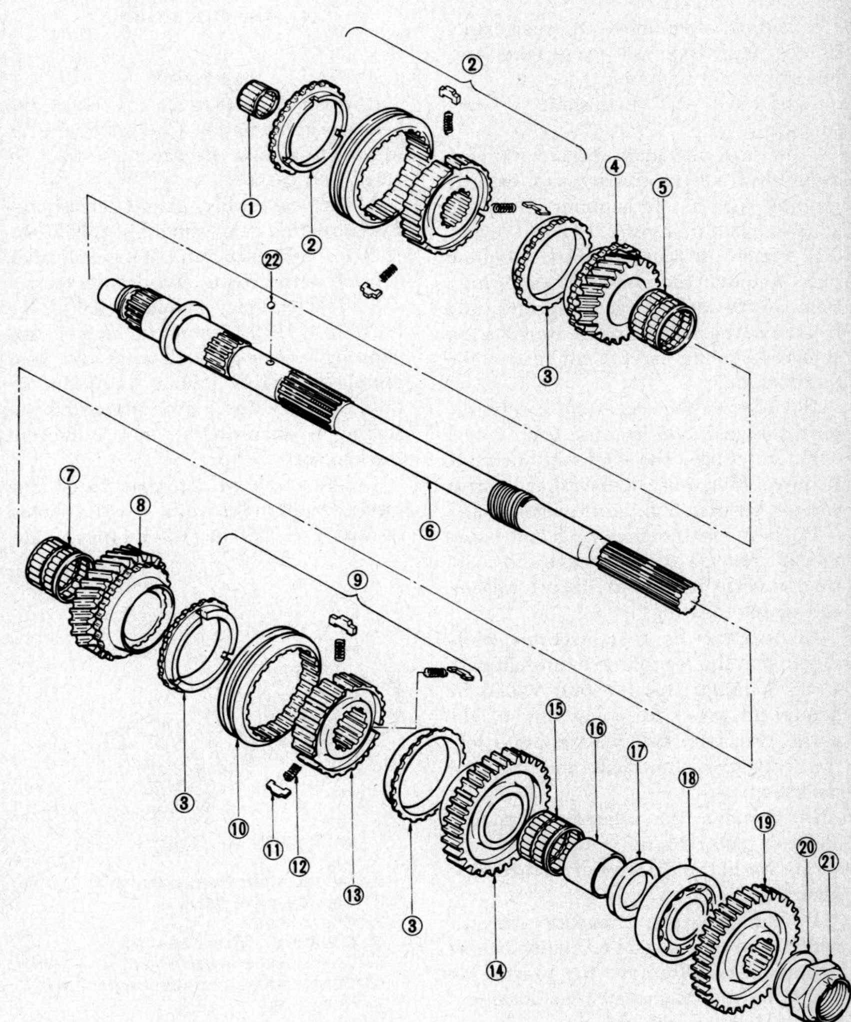

Mainshaft assembly of 240 Z four speed transmission

1. Pilot bearing
2. 3rd & 4th synchromesh assembly
3. Baulk ring
4. 3rd gear, mainshaft
5. Needle bearing
6. Mainshaft
7. Needle bearing
8. 2nd gear, mainshaft
9. 1st & 2nd synchromesh assembly
10. Coupling sleeve
11. Shifting insert
12. Spread spring
13. Synchronizer hub
14. 1st gear, mainshaft
15. Needle bearing
16. Bushing, 1st gear
17. Thrust washer, mainshaft
18. Mainshaft bearing
19. Reverse gear, mainshaft
10. Thrust washer
21. Nut
22. Steel ball

Disassembly

1. Remove the clutch housing dust cover. Remove the retaining spring, release bearing sleeve, and withdrawal lever.

2. Remove the backup light/neutral safety switch.

3. Unbolt and remove the clutch housing, rapping with a soft hammer if necessary. Remove the gasket, mainshaft bearing shim, and countershaft bearing shim.

4. Remove the speedometer pinion sleeve.

5. Remove the striker rod pin from the rod. Separate the striker rod from the shift lever bracket.

6. Unbolt and remove the rear extension. It may be necessary to rap the housing with a soft hammer.

7. Remove the mainshaft bearing snap-ring.

8. Remove the adapter plate and gear assembly from the transmission case by rapping with a soft hammer. Hold the adapter plate in a vise.

9. Punch out the shift fork retaining pins. Remove the shift rod snap-rings. Remove the detent plugs, springs, and balls from the adapter plate. Remove the shift rods, being careful not to lose the interlock balls.

10. Remove the snap-ring, speedometer drive gear, and locating ball.

11. Bend back the mainshaft lock tab. Remove the nut, lockwasher, thrust washer, reverse hub, and reverse gear.

12. Remove the snap-ring and countershaft reverse gear. Remove the snap-ring, reverse idler gear, thrust washer, and needle bearing.

13. Support the gear assembly while rapping on the rear of the mainshaft with a soft hammer. An assistant would be helpful to avoid dropping any of the parts. The mainshaft will separate into the forward clutch shaft and the rear mainshaft.

14. Remove the setscrew from the adapter plate. Remove the shaft nut, spring washer, plain washer, and reverse idler shaft.

15. Remove the machine screws, which hold the bearing retainer, with an an impact tool. Remove the bearing retainer and the mainshaft rear bushing.

16. To disassemble the mainshaft (rear section), remove the front snap-ring, third/fourth synchronizer assembly, third gear, and needle bearing. From the rear, remove the thrust washer, locating ball, first gear, needle bearing, first gear bushing, first/second synchronizer assembly, second gear, and needle bearing.

17. To disassemble the clutch shaft, remove the snap-ring and bearing spacer. Press off the bearing.

18. To disassemble the countershaft, press off the front bearing. Press off the rear bearing. Press off the gears and remove the keys.

19. Remove the retaining pin, control arm pin, and shift control arm from the rear of the extension housing.

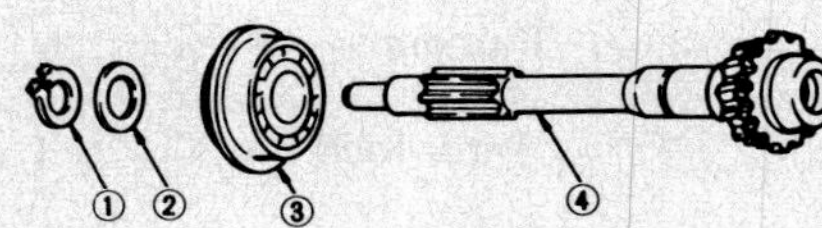

Clutch shaft assembly of 240 Z four speed transmission

1. Snap ring
2. Spacer
3. Main drive bearing with snap ring
4. Main drive shaft

Inspection

1. Wash all parts in a safe solvent. Oil bearings immediately. Check all parts for wear or damage. Replace all seals, O-rings, and gaskets.

2. On reassembly, gear backlash between mating gears should be 0.0020–0.0059 in. (0.05–0.15 mm.). If it is excessive, replace both driving and driven gears.

3. Gear end-play should be 0.0047–0.0075 in. (0.12–0.19 mm.) for all gears except the reverse idler. Reverse idler gear endplay should be 0.0020–0.0138 in. (0.05–0.35 mm.). End-play is adjusted by installing snap-rings of different thicknesses.

4. Check the synchronizer baulk ring inside serration for wear. The slot should be 0.0472–0.0550 in. (1.2–1.4 mm.) wide.

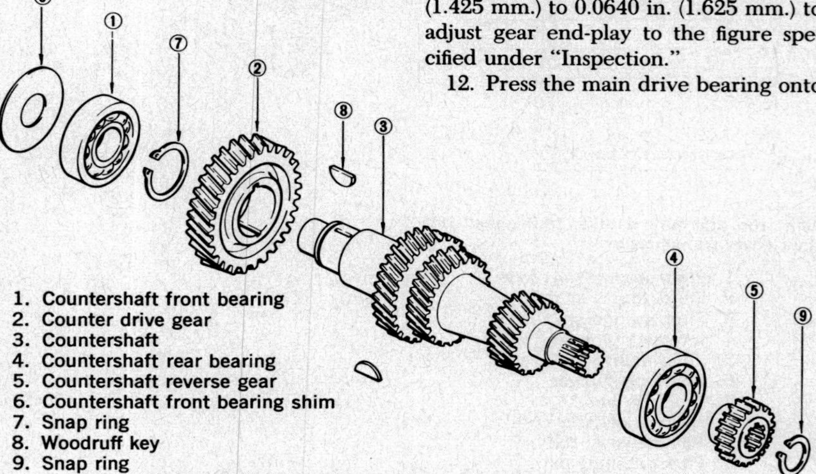

1. Countershaft front bearing
2. Counter drive gear
3. Countershaft
4. Countershaft rear bearing
5. Countershaft reverse gear
6. Countershaft front bearing shim
7. Snap ring
8. Woodruff key
9. Snap ring

Countershaft assembly of 240 Z four speed transmission

Assembly

1. Place the O-ring in the front cover. Install the front cover to the clutch housing with a press. Install the front cover oil seal.

2. Install the rear extension oil seal with a drift.

3. Assemble the first/second and third-/fourth synchronizer assemblies. Make sure that the spreader ring gaps are not both on the same side of the unit.

4. On the rear end of the mainshaft, install the needle bearing, second gear, baulk ring, first/second synchronizer assembly, baulk ring, first gear bushing, needle bearing, first gear, locating ball, and thrust washer.

5. Drive or press on the mainshaft rear bearing.

6. Install the countershaft rear bearing to the adapter plate. Drive or press the mainshaft rear bearing into the adapter plate until the bearing snap-ring groove comes through the rear side of the plate. Install the snap-ring. If it is not tight against the plate, press the bearing back in slightly.

7. Insert the countershaft bearing ring between the countershaft rear bearing and bearing retainer. Install the bearing retainer to the adapter plate, torquing the screws to 9–13 ft lbs. Stake both ends of the screws with a punch.

8. Insert the reverse idler shaft from the rear of the adapter plate. Torque the setscrew to 9–13 ft lbs. Install the spring washer and plain washer to the idler shaft. Torque the shaft nut to 43–58 ft lbs.

9. Place the two keys on the countershaft and oil the shaft lightly. Press on third gear and install a snap-ring.

10. Install the countershaft into its rear bearing.

11. From the front of the mainshaft, install the needle bearing, third gear, baulk ring, third/fourth synchronizer assembly, and snap-ring. Snap-rings are available in thicknesses from 0.0561 in. (1.425 mm.) to 0.0640 in. (1.625 mm.) to adjust gear end-play to the figure specified under "Inspection."

12. Press the main drive bearing onto the clutch shaft. Install the main drive gear spacer and a snap-ring. Snap-rings are available in thicknesses from 0.0710 in. (1.80 mm.) to 0.0820 in. (2.08 mm.) to adjust gear end-play to the figure specified under "Inspection."

13. Insert a key into the countershaft. Insert the pilot bearing in the clutch shaft assembly. Engage the countershaft drive

gear with fourth gear and drive on the countershaft fourth gear with a drift. The rear end of the countershaft should be held steady while driving on the gear, to prevent rear bearing damage.

14. Install the reverse hub, reverse gear, thrust washer, and lock tab on the rear of the mainshaft. Install the shaft nut temporarily.

15. Oil the reverse idler shaft lightly. Install the needle bearing, reverse idler gear, thrust washer, and snap-ring.

16. Place the countershaft reverse gear and snap-ring on the rear of the countershaft. Snap-rings are available in thicknesses from 0.0433 in. (1.1 mm.) to 0.0590 in. (1.5 mm.) to adjust gear end-play to the figure specified under "Inspection."

17. Engage both first and second gears to lock the shaft. Torque the mainshaft nut to 130–152 ft lbs. and bend up the lock tab.

18. On the rear of the mainshaft, install the snap-ring, locating ball, speedometer drive gear, and snap-ring. Snap-rings are available in thicknesses from 0.0433 in. (1.1 mm.) to 0.0590 in. (1.5 mm.).

19. Recheck end-play and backlash of all gears. See "Inspection."

20. Place the reverse shift fork on the reverse gear and install the reverse shift rod. Install the detent ball, spring, and plug. Install the fork retaining pin. Place two interlock balls between the reverse shift rod and the third/fourth shift rod location. Install the third/fourth shift fork and rod. Install the detent ball, spring, and plug. This plug is shorter than the other two. Install the fork retaining pin. Place two interlock balls between the first/second shift rod location and the third/fourth shift rod. Install the first/second shift fork and rod. Install the detent ball, spring, and plug. Apply locking agent to each detent plug and torque them to 16–22 ft lbs. Install the fork retaining pin.

21. Install the shift rod snap-rings.

22. Oil all moving parts and make sure that all gears can be shifted smoothly.

23. Apply sealant sparingly to the adapter plate and transmission housing.

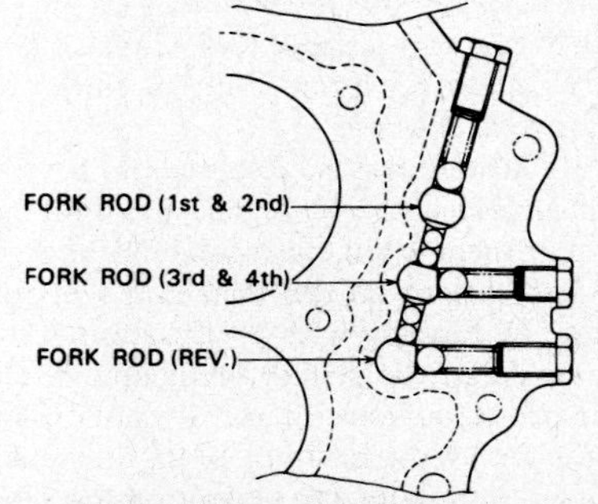

Interlock and detent arrangement, 240 Z four speed transmission

Install the transmission housing to the adapter plate and bolt it down temporarily.

24. Drive in the countershaft front bearing with a drift. Place the snap-ring in the mainshaft front bearing.

25. Apply sealant sparingly to the adapter plate and extension housing. Align the shift rods in the neutral positions. Position the striker rod to the shift rods and bolt down the extension housing. Torque to 11–16 ft lbs. Be careful not to damage the extension housing oil seal in installation.

26. Insert the striker rod pin, connect the rod to the shift lever bracket, and install the striker rod pin retaining ring. Replace the shift control arm.

27. To select the proper mainshaft bearing shim, first measure the amount the bearing protrudes from the front of the transmission case. This is measurement (B). Then measure the depth of the bearing recess in the rear of the clutch housing. This is measurement (A). Required shim thickness is found by subtracting (B) from (A). Shims are available in thicknesses of 0.0551 in. (1.4 mm.) and 0.0630 in. (1.6 mm.).

28. To select the proper countershaft front bearing shim, measure the amount that the bearing is recessed into the transmission case. Shim thickness should equal this measurement. Shims are available in thicknesses from 0.0157 in. (.4 mm.) to 0.0394 in. (1.0 mm.).

29. Apply sealant sparingly to the clutch and transmission housing mating surfaces and torque the bolts to 11–16 ft lbs.

30. Replace the clutch operating mechanism.

31. Install the shift lever temporarily and check shifting action.

32. Refill the transmission. See the Capacities Chart.

Five Speed Transmission Overhaul—SRL311, 240 Z

This transmission is quite similar to the four speed 240 Z unit. The model number is FS5C71A. Servo type synchromesh is used, instead of the Borg Warner type in the four speed. Shift linkage and interlock arrangements are the same, except that the reverse shift rod also operates fifth gear. Most service procedures are identical to those for the four speed unit. Those unique to the five speed follow.

Disassembly

1. To disassemble the synchronizers, remove the circlip, synchronizer ring, thrust block, brake band, and anchor block. Be careful not to mix parts of the different synchronizer assemblies.

Inspection

1. Gear backlash should be 0.0016–0.0059 in. (0.04–0.15 mm.) for the main drive gear and reverse gear. For first, second, third, and fifth gears it should be 0.0016–0.0079 in. (0.04–0.20 mm.).

2. Gear end-play should be:

Gear	End-Play in. (mm.)
First, Second, Fifth	0.0039-0.0075 (0.12-0.19)
Third	0.0039-0.0094 (0.12-0.24)
Reverse Idler	0.0019-0.0137 (0.05-0.35)

Assembly

1. The synchronizer assemblies for second, third, and fourth are identical. When assembling the first gear synchronizer, be sure to install the 0.0866 in. (2.2 mm.) thick brake band at the bottom.

2. When assembling the mainshaft, select a third gear synchronizer hub snap-ring to minimize hub end-play. Snap-rings are available in thicknesses of 0.0610–0.0630 in. (1.55–1.60 mm.), 0.-0591–0.0610 in. (1.50–1.55 mm.), and 0.-0571–0.0591 in. (1.45–1.50 mm.). The synchronizer hub must be installed with the longer boss to the rear.

3. When reassembling the gear train, install the mainshaft, countershaft, and gears to the adapter plate. To tighten the mainshaft locknuts, tighten the front nut to 15–22 ft lbs. and the rear nut to 7–15 ft lbs. Hold the rear nut and force the front nut against it to a torque of 217 ft lbs. Select a snap-ring to minimize end-play of the fifth gear bearing at the rear of the mainshaft. Snap-rings are available in thicknesses from 0.0433 in. (1.1 mm.) to 0.0551 in. (1.4 mm.).

Four Speed Transmission Overhaul—LB110, KLB110

This transmission is constructed in two sections: a combined clutch and transmission housing, and an extension housing. There is a cast iron adapter plate between the housings. There are no case cover plates. The transmission model number is F4W56.

Disassembly

1. Drain the oil.

2. Remove the dust cover, spring, clutch withdrawal lever, and release bearing.

3. Remove the front cover from inside the clutch housing.

4. From the extension housing, remove the speedometer drive pinion. Remove the striker rod return spring plug, spring, plunger, and bushing. Remove the striker rod pin and separate the striker rod from the shift lever bracket.

5. Unbolt the extension housing and remove it. Tap it with a soft hammer, if

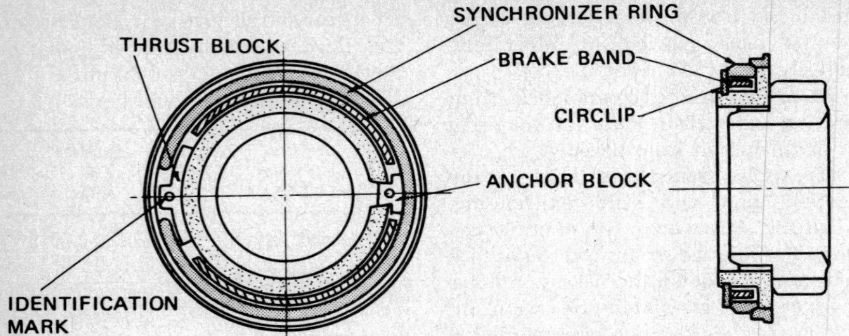

Servo type synchronizer assembled

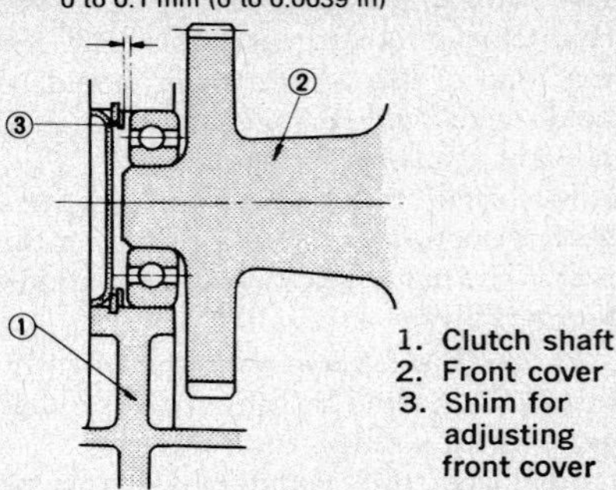

Selecting the countershaft front bearing shim

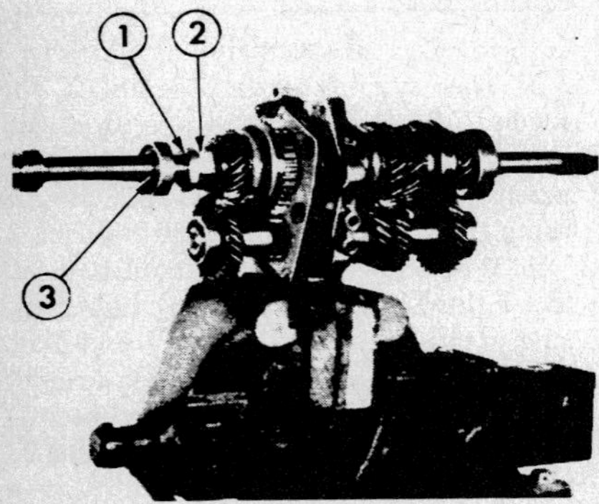

Mainshaft locknuts, 1 and 2, and snap-ring, 3

necessary.

6. Separate the adapter plate from the transmission case, being careful not to lose the countershaft bearing washer.

7. Clamp the adapter plate in a vise with the reverse idler gear up.

8. Drive out the retaining pin and remove the reverse shift fork and reverse idler gear.

9. Remove the mainshaft rear snap-ring, washer, and reverse gear.

10. Drive out the remaining shift fork retaining pins. Remove all three detent plugs, springs, and balls. Remove the forks and shift rods. Be careful not to lose the interlock plungers.

11. Tap the rear of the mainshaft with a soft hammer to separate the mainshaft and countershaft from the adapter plate. Be careful not to drop the shafts. Separate the clutch shaft from the mainshaft.

12. From the front of the mainshaft, remove the needle bearing, synchronizer hub thrust washer, steel locating ball, third/fourth synchronizer, baulk ring, third gear, and needle bearing.

13. Press off the mainshaft bearing to the rear. Remove the thrust washer, first gear, needle bearing, baulk ring, first/second synchronizer, baulk ring, second gear, and needle bearing.

14. Remove the countergear bearing.

15. Remove the clutch shaft snap-ring and bearing.

Inspection

1. Clean all parts in a safe solvent. Oil the bearings immediately. Check all parts for wear or damage.

2. Backlash for each pair of gears should be 0.0031–0.0059 in. (0.08–0.15 mm.). If it is excessive, replace both drive and driven gears.

3. Gear end-play is adjusted by using snap-rings of different thicknesses.

Gear	*End-Play*
First, Second	.0059-.0098" (.15-.25 mm.)
Third	.0059-.0138" (1.5-.35 mm.)

4. Place each baulk ring on the cone of its gear. Check the gap between the baulk ring end face and the clutch teeth front face. The gap should be 0.0413–0.-0551 in. (1.05–1.40 mm.). If it is less than 0.0197 in. (0.5 mm.), replace the baulk ring.

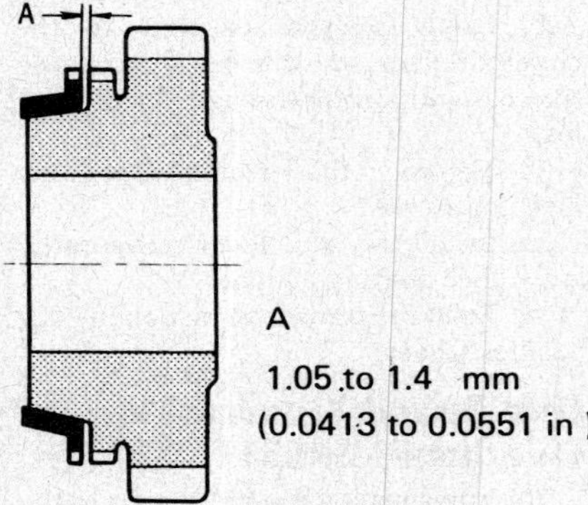

Checking the baulk ring gap

Assembly

1. Press on the countershaft bearings. Install the countershaft assembly into the transmission case and replace the adapter plate temporarily. Countershaft end-play should be 0–0.0079 in. (0–0.2 mm.). Front bearing shims are available for adjustment in thicknesses from 0.-0315 in. (0.8 mm.) to 0.0512 in. (1.3 mm.). Remove the countershaft assembly from the case.

2. Oil all moving parts on installation.

3. Install the coupling sleeve, shifting inserts, and spring on the synchronizer hub. Be careful not to hook the front and rear ends of the spring to the same insert. Make sure that the hub and sleeve operate smoothly.

4. Install the needle bearing from the rear of the mainshaft. Install second gear, the baulk ring, and synchronizer hub assembly. Align the shifting insert to the baulk ring groove. Install the first gear side needle bearing, baulk ring, and first gear. Install the mainshaft thrust washer and press on the rear bearing. On the mainshaft front end, replace the needle bearing, third gear, baulk ring, synchronizer hub assembly, steel locating ball, thrust washer, and pilot bearing. Be sure to grease the sliding surface of the steel ball and thrust washer. The dimpled side of the thrust washer must face to the front and the oil grooved side to the rear.

5. Replace the main bearing, washer, and snap-ring onto clutch shaft. The web side of the washer must face the bearing. Place the baulk ring on the clutch shaft and assemble the clutch shaft to the mainshaft.

6. Align the mainshaft assembly with the countershaft assembly and install them to the adapter plate by lightly tapping on the clutch shaft with a soft hammer.

7. Place the first/second and third-/fourth shift forks on the shift rods, being careful that the forks are not reversed. Install all three shift rods and the detent and interlock parts. Apply locking agent to the detent plug threads and screw the plugs in flush. Make sure that the shift forks are in their grooves and drive in the retaining pins.

8. Install the mainshaft reverse gear, thrust washer, and snap-ring. Face the web side of the thrust washer to the gear.

9. Replace the reverse idler gear and pin on the reverse shift fork. Check interlock action by attempting to shift two shift rods at once.

10. Install the adapter plate to the transmission case. Make sure to install the countergear front shim selected in Step 1. Use sealant on the joint and seat the plate by tapping with a soft hammer.

11. Align the striker lever and install the extension housing. Use sealant on the joint. Install the bushing, plunger, return spring, and plug. Use sealant on the plug threads. Install the striker rod pin and the speedometer drive pinion.

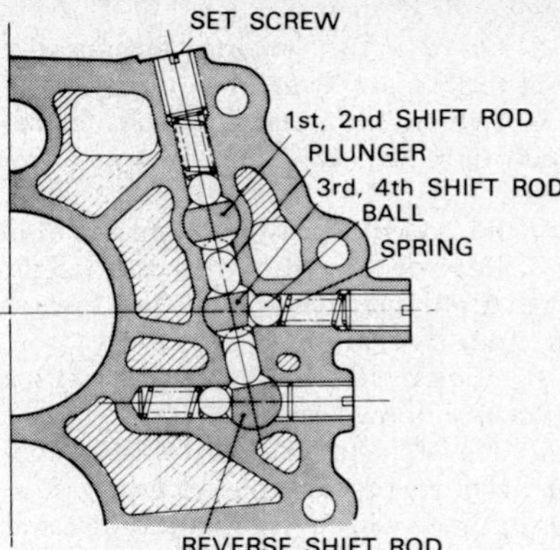

Detent ball and interlock details, LB110 and KLB110 four speed

12. Select clutch shaft bearing shim(s) by measuring the amount the bearing outer race is recessed below the machined surface for the front cover. The depth should be 0.1969–0.2028 in. (5.00–5.15 mm.). Shims are available for adjustment in thicknesses of 0.0039 in (0.1 mm.), 0.0079 in. (0.2 mm.), and 0.0197 in. (0.5 mm.).

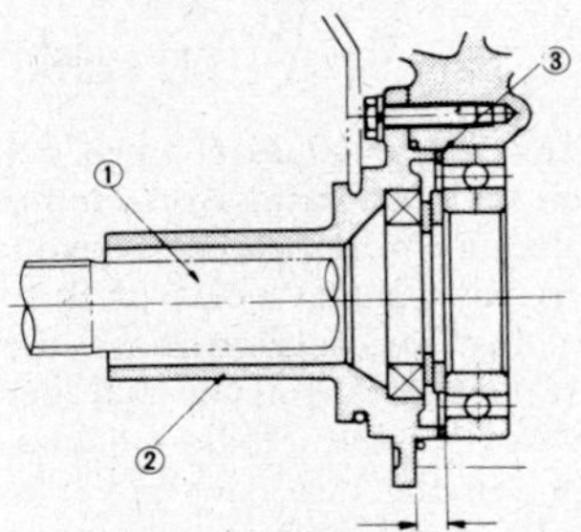

Selecting clutch shaft bearing shims

1. Transmission case
2. Counter-shaft
3. Shim

13. Place the oil seal in the front cover, grease the seal lip, and install the cover and O-ring with the shim(s) selected in Step 12.

14. Replace the clutch release bearing, return spring, and withdrawal lever.

15. Check shifting action. Rotate the clutch shaft slowly in neutral. The rear of the mainshaft should not turn.

16. Refer to the Capacities Chart for refill capacity.

Four Speed, Top Cover Transmission Overhaul L520

This transmission may be found in some early L520 models. The transmission and clutch housings are combined in one piece. The floorshift mechanism is integrated with the top cover. On some models, the shift lever is located further back, above the extension housing.

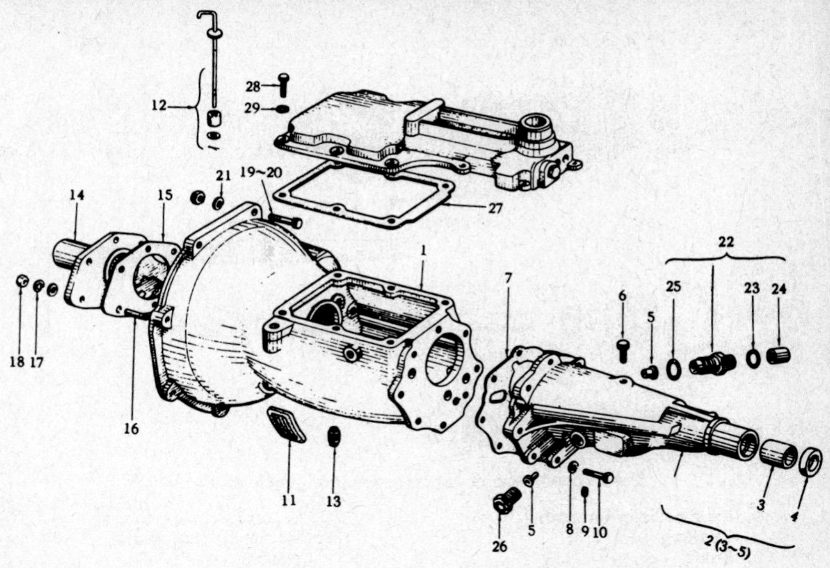

Four speed, top cover transmission case details

1. Case
2. Extension housing
3. Bushing
4. Oil seal
5. Speedometer pinion bushing
6. Breather
7. Gasket
8. Lockwasher
9. Plain washer
10. Bolt
11. Rubber boot
12. Dipstick assembly
13. Drain plug
14. Front cover
15. Gasket
16. Stud
17. Lockwasher
18. Nut
19. Bolt
20. Bolt
21. Lockwasher
22. Speedometer pinion sleeve assembly
23. O-ring
24. O-ring retainer
25. O-ring
26. Speedometer pinion plug
27. Cover gasket
28. Bolt
29. Lockwasher

Disassembly

1. Drain the oil.

2. Remove the clutch withdrawal lever. Remove the transmission top cover.

3. Twist the cap at the base of the shift lever counterclockwise while pressing down.

4. Unbolt and remove the top cover.

5. Straighten the lock tab, remove the setscrew, and tap the reverse idler shaft forward. Remove the shaft and gear.

6. Drive the countershaft forward and out. Remove the thrust washers. The countergear cannot be removed yet.

7. Pull the mainshaft out through the rear of the case.

8. Tilt the countergear to clear the clutch shaft gear. Insert a long drift through the mainshaft opening and drive the clutch shaft and bearing forward out of the case.

9. Remove the countergear from the case. To remove the needle roller bearing, break the retaining clips and drive out the bearing.

10. To disassemble the mainshaft, slide off the third/fourth synchronizer from the front. Insert a wire through the hole in the gear cone and depress the spring loaded plunger which locates the splined washer, aligning the washer with the splines. Pull third and second gears, with their bronze sleeves, over the plunger and off the shaft. It may be necessary to immerse the shaft in warm oil to expand the sleeve slightly. Remove the plunger and spring. Remove the splined washer and first gear. At the rear of the shaft, straighten the lock tab, remove the nut, speedometer drive gear, and key. Remove the distance piece (spacer) and bearing.

11. To dismantle the clutch shaft, first remove the needle roller bearings from the rear. Bend back the lock tab, unscrew the left hand threaded nut, and press off the bearing.

Inspection

1. Wash all parts in a safe solvent. Oil bearings immediately.

2. Check all parts for wear or damage.

3. Pry out extension housing oil seal and install a new one.

4. Replace all gaskets.

5. Gear backlash should be 0.003–0.005 in. (0.075–.125 mm.) between all pairs of gears.

Assembly

1. Install the countergear in the case with the thrust washers. The larger washer must be at the front. Install the countershaft. Countergear end-play

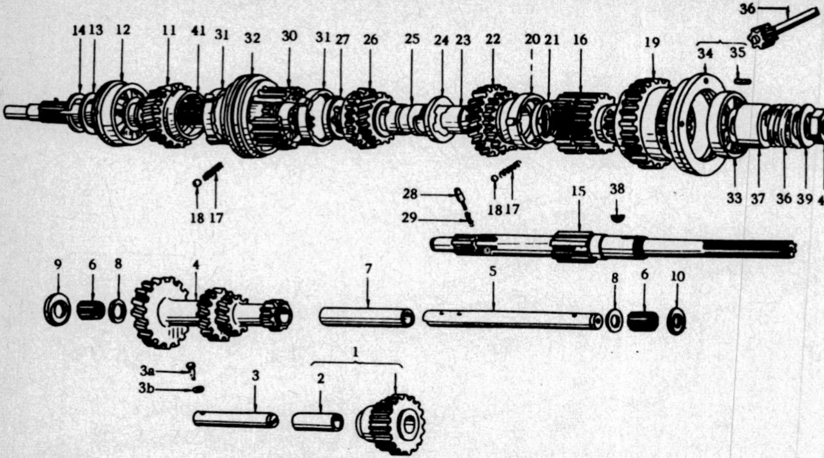

Four speed, top cover transmission gear details

1. Reverse idler assembly
2. Bushing
3. Shaft
3a. Setscrew
3b. Lock tab
4. Countergear
5. Countershaft
6. Needle roller
7. Countershaft spacer
8. Needle roller retainer ring
9. Countergear front thrust washer
10. Countergear rear thrust washer
11. Main drive (clutch shaft) gear
12. Bearing
13. Bearing spacer
14. Snap-ring
15. Mainshaft
16. Synchronizer hub
17. Synchronizer spring
18. Synchronizer ball
19. Mainshaft gear
20. Second gear baulk ring
21. Mainshaft rear thrust washer
22. Second gear
23. Second gear bushing
24. Thrust washer
25. Third gear bushing
26. Third gear
27. Mainshaft front thrust washer
28. Locking peg
29. Spring
30. Third/fourth synchronizer
31. Third/fourth baulk ring
32. Third/fourth synchronizer sleeve
33. Mainshaft bearing
34. Bearing retainer
35. Locking peg
36. Speedometer drive gears
37. Distance piece
38. Key
39. Lockwasher
40. Mainshaft nut
41. Mainshaft pilot bearing

should be 0.0015–0.0023 in. (0.04–0.06 mm.). End-play is adjusted by changing the rear thrust washer. Thrust washers are available in thicknesses from 0.0015–0.0023 in. (0.04–0.06 mm.) to 0.154–0.156 in. (3.91–3.96 mm.). Temporarily replace the countershaft with a smaller diameter rod so that the countergear will not mesh with the mainshaft and clutch shaft gears as they are installed.

2. Press the bearing onto the clutch shaft; replace the washer and nut. Some units may have a snap-ring instead of a nut. Place the 18 needle rollers into the rear of the shaft with a bit of grease. Turn the transmission housing so that the countergear is out of the way and drive in the shaft and bearing from the front.

3. Press the mainshaft bearing on from the rear. Oil the shaft ahead of the bearing and install first gear with the synchronizer forward. Replace the thrust washer and baulk ring. Expand the second gear sleeve in warm oil and slide it over the shaft. Install second gear, the washer, and the third gear sleeve. The two sleeves are locked together by the washer. Replace third gear. Place the spring and plunger into the hole in the shaft and slide on the splined washer. Depress the plunger with a wire through the hole in third gear, and slide the splined washer over the plunger. Turn the washer so that the plunger engages with a groove in the washer. Assemble the two baulk rings to the third/fourth synchronizer and coupling sleeve. The large boss of the synchronizer inner splines must face forward. The pointed ends of the baulk ring lugs must face into the synchronizer. Slide the third/fourth synchronizer forward slightly to clear the countergear and install the mainshaft. Second and third gear end-play should be 0.0048–0.0062 in. (0.12–0.16 mm.).

4. Oil and install the countershaft.

5. Replace the reverse idler gear and shaft with the setscrew and lock tab. Replace the front cover.

CLUTCH

Removal and Installation

Models With Coil Spring Clutch

1. Remove the transmission from the engine.

2. On the L16 engine, temporarily lock the release lever.

3. Loosen the retaining bolts in sequence, a turn at a time. Remove the bolts.

4. Remove the pressure plate and disc.

5. Replace the disc with the longer chamfered splined end of the hub toward the transmission.

6. Align the disc to the flywheel with a splined dummy shaft.

7. Install the pressure plate. Most models have two pressure plate locating dowels in the flywheel. Tighten the pressure plate bolts in sequence, a turn at a time. Torque to 35 ft lbs., except on the L16 engine. L16 torque is 17–19 ft lbs.

8. Remove the dummy shaft. Unlock the release lever on the L16.

9. Replace the release bearing and transmission.

Models With Diaphragm Spring Clutch

1. Remove the transmission from the engine.

2. Loosen the bolts in sequence, a turn at a time. Remove the bolts.

3. Remove the pressure plate and clutch disc.

4. On A12 and L24 engines, remove the release mechanism. Apply multi-purpose grease to the bearing sleeve inside groove, the contact point of the withdrawal lever and bearing sleeve, the contact surface of the lever ball pin and lever. Replace the release mechanism.

5. Install the disc, aligning it with a splined dummy shaft.

6. Install the pressure plate and torque the bolts to 17–18 ft lbs on L16 and L24 engines, and 11–16 ft lbs on A12 and L18 engines.

7. Remove the dummy shaft.

8. Replace the transmission.

Clutch Linkage

Adjustment

Refer to the Clutch Specifications Chart for clutch pedal height above floor and pedal free play.

All models have a hydraulically operated clutch. Pedal height is usually adjusted with an adjustable stopper which limits the upward travel of the pedal. Pedal free-play is adjusted at the master cylinder pushrod. If the pushrod is non-adjustable, free-play is adjusted by placing shims between the master cylinder and the firewall. On a few models, pedal free play can also be adjusted at the operating (slave) cylinder pushrod.

Hydraulic System Bleeding

Bleeding is required to remove air trapped in the hydraulic system. This operation is necessary whenever the system has been leaking or dismantled. The

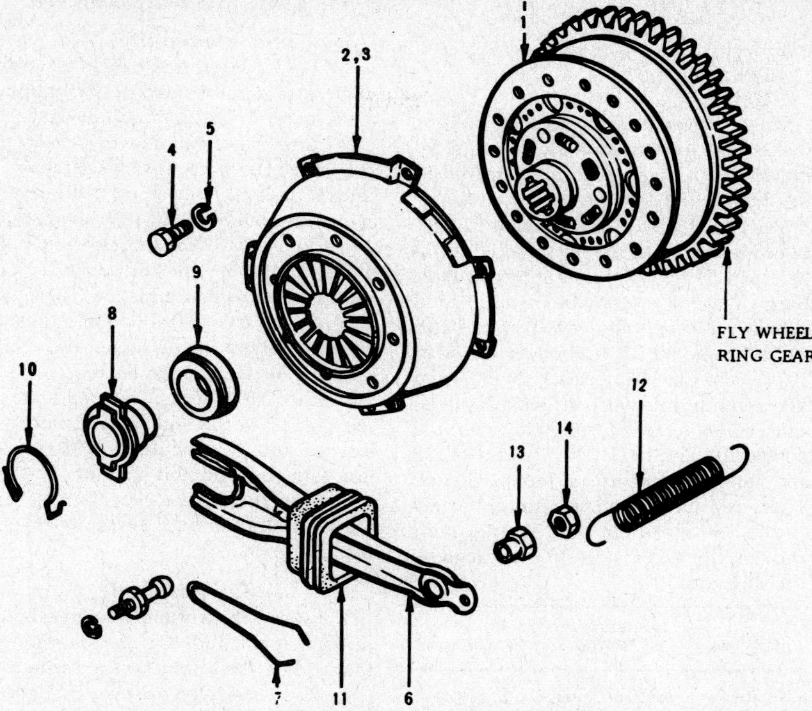

Diaphragm spring clutch, PL510 and WPL510

1. Disc
2, 3. Clutch cover assembly with pressure plate
4. Bolt
5. Lockwasher
6. Withdrawal lever
7. Retainer spring
8. Bearing sleeve
9. Release bearing
10. Bearing sleeve holder spring
11. Dust cover
12. Return spring
13. Withdrawal lever push nut
14. Locknut

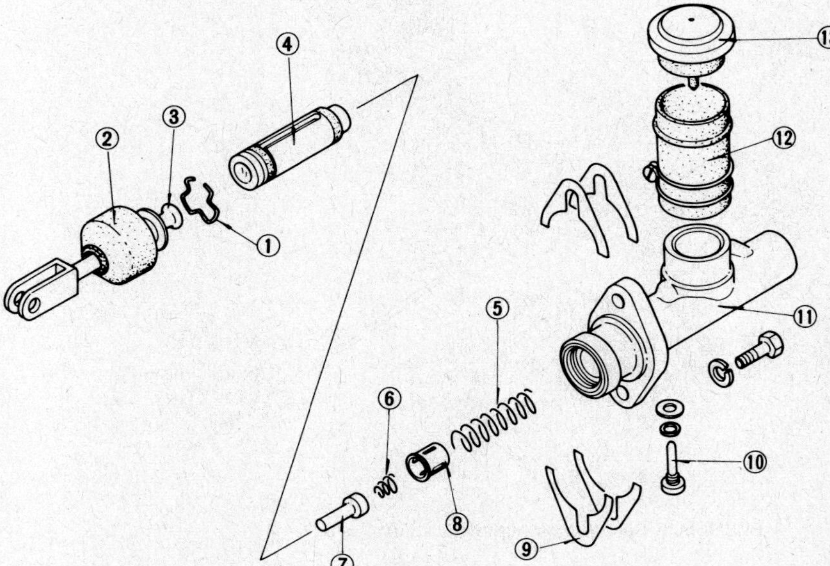

Clutch master cylinder, LB110 and KLB110

1. Snap-ring
2. Dust cover
3. Pushrod
4. Piston
5. Spring
6. Inlet valve spring
7. Inlet valve
8. Spring retainer
9. Shims
10. Inlet valve release pin
11. Housing
12. Fluid reservoir
13. Reservoir cap

Clutch release mechanism, A12 and L24 engines. (1) is withdrawal lever, (2) is return spring, and (3) is the release bearing.

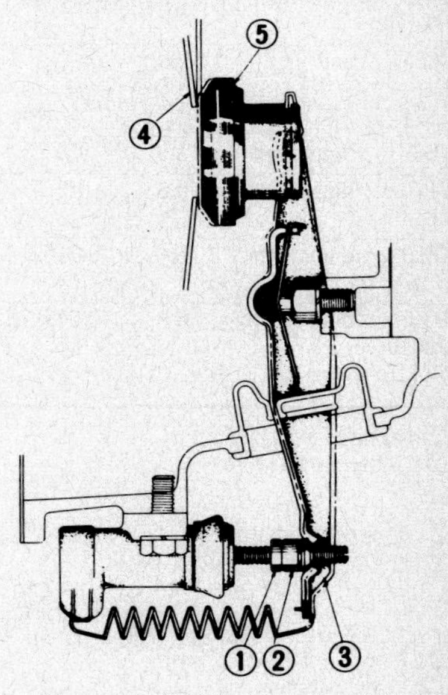

Detail of clutch operating cylinder and withdrawal lever, 240 Z. Free-play is adjusted at this point on this model

1. Locknut
2. Adjusting nut
3. Withdrawal lever
4. Diaphragm spring
5. Release bearing

bleed screw is usually located on the clutch operating (slave) cylinder.

1. Remove the bleed screw dust cap.
2. Open the bleed screw about ¾ turn.
3. Attach a tube to the bleed screw, immersing the free end in a clean container of brake fluid.
4. Fill the master cylinder with fluid.
5. Depress the clutch pedal quickly. Hold it down. Have an assistant tighten the bleed screw. Allow the pedal to return slowly.
6. Repeat Steps 2 and 5 until no more air bubbles are seen in the fluid container.
7. Remove the bleed tube. Replace the dust cap. Refill the master cylinder.

Hydraulic System Repairs

Clutch master and slave cylinders are repaired in much the same way as are brake master and wheel cylinders. Bleeding is required whenever the clutch hydraulic system has been dismantled.

Clutch Specifications

Model	Clutch Spring Type	Pedal Height Above Floor (in.)	Pedal Free-Play (in.)
SPL311 SRL311	coil	N.A.	1.9-2.1
PL510 WPL510	coil	8.2	1.0
PL510 WPL510	diaphragm	8.2	1.0
L520 L521 PL521	coil	5.3, 5.5②	1.0
240 Z	diaphragm	8.0	1.0
LB110 KLB110	diaphragm	5.6	1.2
PL620	diaphragm	6.4	0.04-0.12 ①
PL610 KPL610 WPL610	diaphragm	6.9	0.04-0.20 ①

① Measured at clevis pin
② Without pedal stop

AUTOMATIC TRANSMISSION

Only external transmission adjustments and repairs, and transmission removal and replacement, are covered in this book.

The PL510 up to serial number PL510-117464, and WPL510 up to serial number WPL510-853595 use a British built Borg Warner automatic transmission with a cable operated downshift. Later PL510 and WPL510 models (through 1971) use an American built Borg Warner transmission with vacuum pressure control and a solenoid operated downshift. The 1971 240 Z and all 1972 and later models use a Japanese unit. There is a model and serial number tag on the left side of the Borg Warner units and on the right side of the Japanese transmission.

Model no.	Nissan Part no.	Transmission
AS14-35EC	31010-24500	British built BW
AS2-41	31010A8500	American built BW
3N71		Japanese

Shift Linkage Adjustment

Floorshift

1. Loosen the trunnion locknuts at the lower end of the control lever. Remove the selector lever knob and console.
2. Place the selector lever in Neutral.
3. Place the transmission shift lever in neutral position by pushing it all the way back, then pulling it forward two stops.
4. Check the vertical clearance between the top of the shift lever pin and transmission control bracket. The clearance, should be 0.020–0.059 in. Adjust by turning the nut at the lower end of the selector lever compression rod.
5. Check the horizontal clearance, of the shift lever pin and transmission control bracket. This should be 0.020 in. Adjust with the trunnion locknuts.
6. Replace the console, making sure that the shift pointer is correctly aligned. Install the knob.

Column Shift

1. Loosen the trunnion locknuts on the upper selector rod. (On the steering column inside the engine compartment).
2. Place the selector lever in Neutral. Place the transmission shift lever in neutral position, the central of its five positions.
3. Adjust the locknuts so that the clearance between the stop pin on the lower selector lever and the position plate is 0.020–0.039 in.

1. Converter housing
2. Housing to case bolt
3. Lockwasher
4. Screen
5. Captive nut
6. Screw
7. Converter assembly
8. Not used
9. Case assembly
10. Rear band adjusting screw
11. Locknut
12. Seal
13. Adapter
14. Neutral safety switch
15. Park pawl
16. Toggle link
17. Toggle link pin
18. Washer
19. Spring
20. Toggle lever
21. Toggle pin
22. Washer
23. Retaining clip
24. Toggle pin
25. O-ring
26. Cotter pin
27. Pin
28. Toggle lift lever
29. Spring
30. Torsion lever
31. Washer
32. Retaining clip
33. Park linkage
34. Retaining clip
35. Downshift cable assembly
36. Manual valve shaft
37. Spring

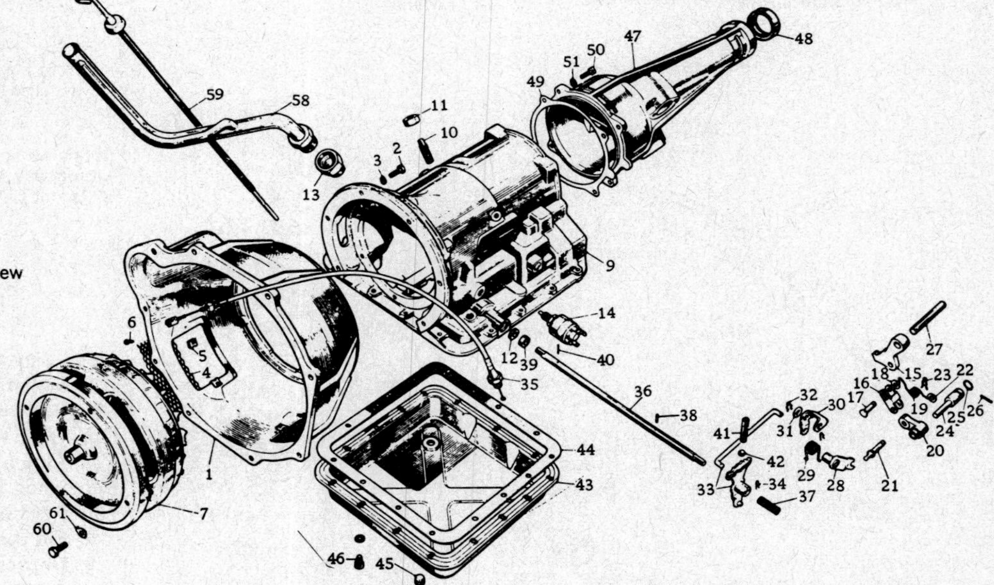

British built Borg Warner automatic transmission

38. Roll pin
39. Collar
40. Roll pin
41. Detent spring
42. Detent ball
43. Pan
44. Pan gasket
45. Drain plug
46. Bolt
47. Extension housing
48. Oil seal
49. Gasket
50. Bolt
51. Lockwasher

52-57 Not used

58. Filler, dipstick and breather tube
59. Dipstick
60. Drive plate to converter bolt
61. Lockwasher

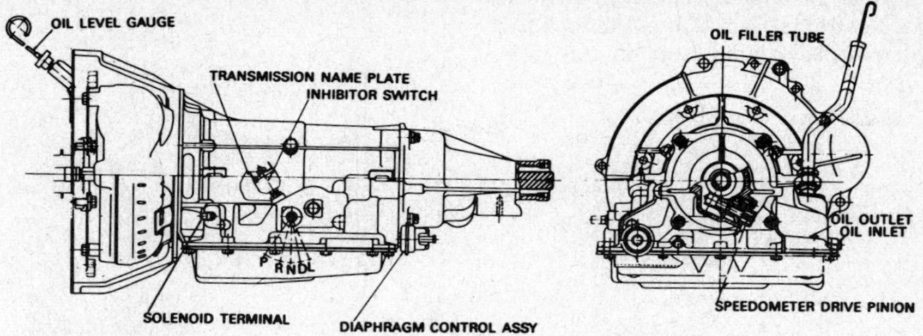

American built Borg Warner automatic transmission

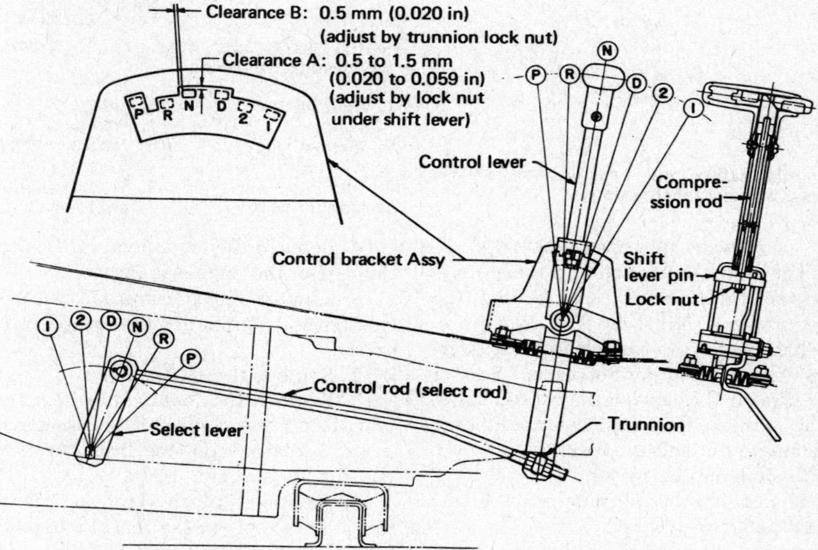

Floorshift automatic transmission linkage adjustment

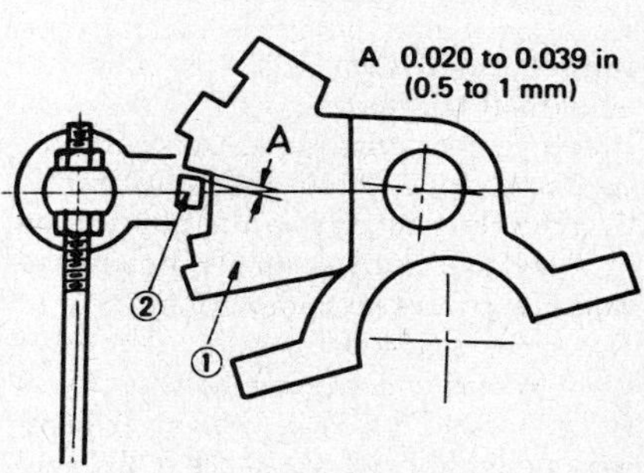

Column shift automatic transmission linkage adjustment. (1) is the selector position plate, (2) is the stop pin

Downshift Cable Adjustment

This adjustment is necessary only on early models with the British built Borg Warner transmission. The adjustment is made at the carburetor end of the cable.

1. Check the transmission fluid level. Connect a tachometer to the engine.
2. Connect a pressure gauge to the transmission line pressure outlet.
3. Start the engine and shift into Drive. The car should be safely blocked and the hand and footbrakes set.
4. Increase engine speed from 500 to 1,000 rpm. The line pressure should rise 15–20 psi.
5. If the pressure rise is less than 15–20 psi, shorten the inner cable with the adjuster.

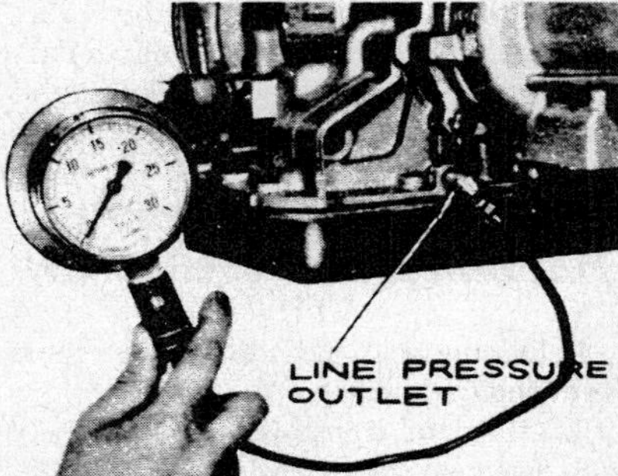

Pressure gauge connected to the British built Borg Warner automatic transmission

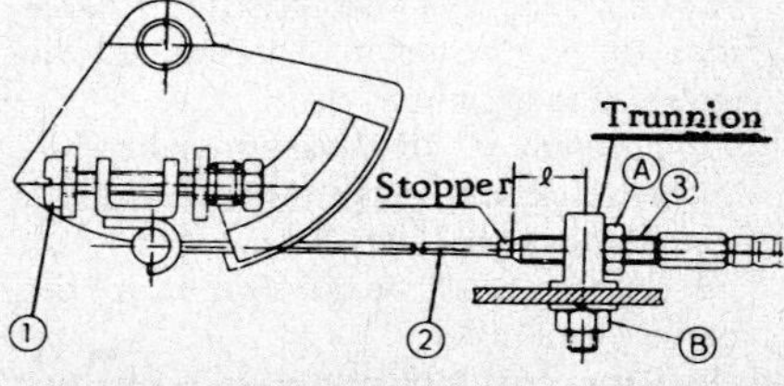

Downshift cable adjuster. (1) is adjuster, (2) is inner cable, (3) is outer cable.

6. If the pressure rise is excessive, lengthen the cable.

NOTE: *Do not oil the cable.*

Downshift Solenoid Check

This solenoid is used on the American Borg Warner and the Japanese transmissions. It is controlled by a downshift switch on the accelerator linkage inside the car. To test the switch and solenoid operation:

1. Turn the ignition on.
2. Push the accelerator all the way down to actuate the switch.
3. The solenoid should click when actuated. Since the solenoid on the Borg Warner transmission is mounted inside the pan, it may be difficult to hear the click. The Japanese transmission solenoid is screwed into the outside of the case. If there is no click, check the switch, wiring, and solenoid.

Removal of Borg Warner transmission downshift solenoid

To remove the solenoid from the Borg Warner transmission, drain and remove the pan. Then push in and turn the solenoid ½ turn clockwise to remove.

To remove the Japanese solenoid, first drain 2–3 pints of fluid, then unscrew the unit.

Front Band Adjustment

This adjustment procedure is for the Borg Warner transmissions only.

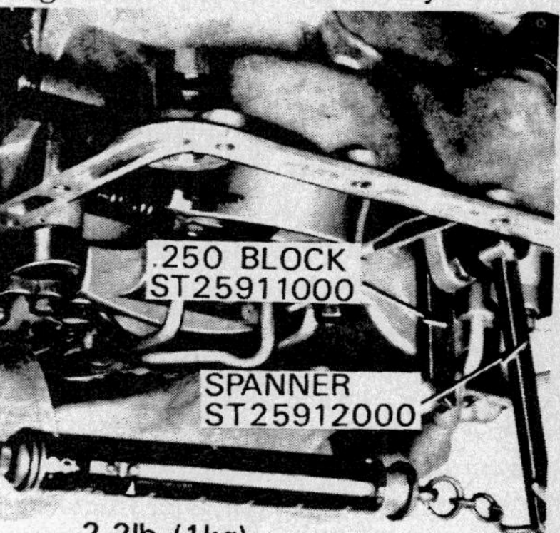

Front band adjustment on Borg Warner transmissions using a special wrench and a spring scale

1. Drain the fluid and remove the pan.
2. Clean the fluid pickup screen.
3. Loosen the locknut on the front servo adjusting screw. Loosen the adjusting screw.
4. Insert a 0.250 in. thick gauge block between the adjusting screw and the servo piston rod.
5. Tighten the adjusting screw to 10 in. lbs. Tighten the locknut to 18 ft lbs.
6. Remove the gauge block.
7. Clean and install the pan with a new gasket.

Rear Band Adjustment

This adjustment procedure is for the Borg Warner transmissions only. It may be necessary to unbolt the crossmember and lower the rear of the transmission to get at the adjusting screw on the right side of the case.

1. Loosen the locknut. Tighten the adjusting screw to 10 ft lbs.
2. Back off the adjusting screw ¾ turn on the American unit and one turn on the British unit.
3. Tighten the locknut to 28 ft lbs.

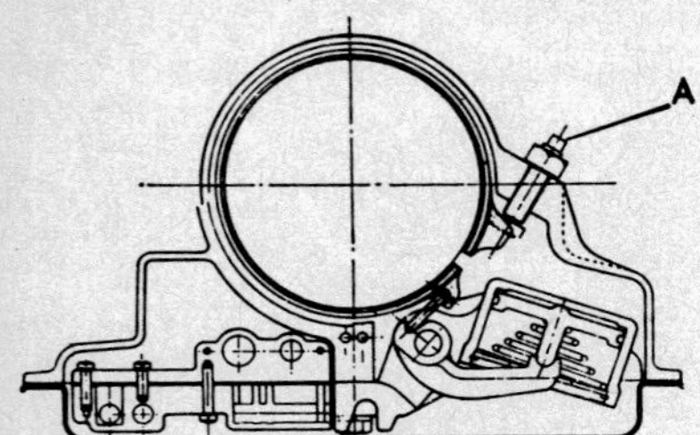

Rear band adjustment on Borg Warner transmissions. (A) is the adjusting screw.

Neutral Safety and Backup Light Switch Adjustment

Borg Warner Transmission

The switch unit is screwed into the left side of the transmission case. The switch terminals marked 1 and 3 are for the neutral safety switch which prevents the engine from being started except in Park or Neutral. The terminals 2 and 4 are for the backup light switch.

1. Shift into Drive or Low with the engine off. Disconnect the switch leads.
2. Connect a test light in series with terminals 1 and 3 and battery current.
3. Loosen the switch locknut. Screw in the switch until the light goes out. The neutral safety switch is now open. Mark the switch position in the case.
4. Connect the test light to terminals 2 and 4. Screw the switch in until the test light goes on. The backup light switch is now closed. Mark the switch position in the case.
5. Screw the switch out to a position midway between the positions marked in Steps 3 and 4. Tighten the locknut to 5 ft lbs.
6. Make sure while holding the brakes on, that the engine will start only in Park or Neutral transmission positions. Check that the backup lights go on only in Reverse.

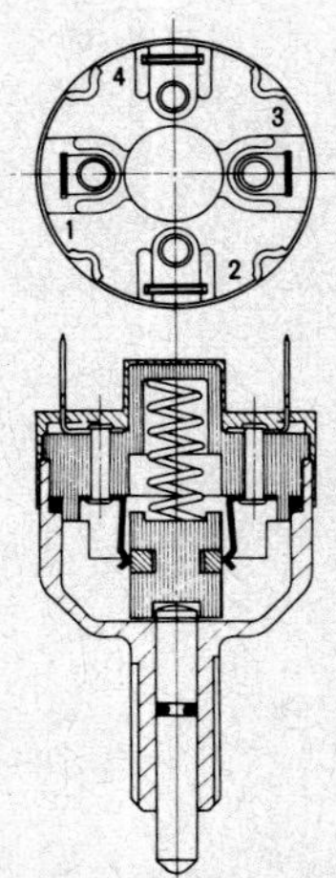

Neutral safety and backup light switch, Borg Warner transmission

Japanese Transmission

The switch unit is bolted to the left side of the transmission case, behind the transmission shift lever. The switch prevents the engine from being started in any transmission position except Park or Neutral. It also controls the backup lights.

1. Remove the transmission shift lever retaining nut and the lever.
2. Remove the switch.
3. Remove the machine screw in the case under the switch.
4. Align the switch to the case by inserting a 0.059 in. (1.5 mm.) diameter pin through the hole in the switch into the screw hole. Mark the switch location.
5. Remove the pin, replace the machine screw, install the switch as marked, and replace the transmission shift lever and retaining nut.
6. Make sure while holding the brakes on, that the engine will start only in Park or Neutral. Check that the backup lights go on only in Reverse.

Removal and Installation

PL510, WPL510 With British BW Unit

1. Disconnect the downshift cable from the carburetor.
2. Drain the transmission oil pan.
3. Remove the driveshaft.
4. Disconnect the handbrake mechanism if necessary.
5. Disconnect the speedometer cable from the transmission. Disconnect the neutral safety switch.
6. Disconnect the transmission shift linkage. Disconnect the oil cooler tubes.
7. Remove the filler tube.
8. Unbolt the transmission from the rear crossmember.
9. Support the engine with a jack under the torque converter housing.

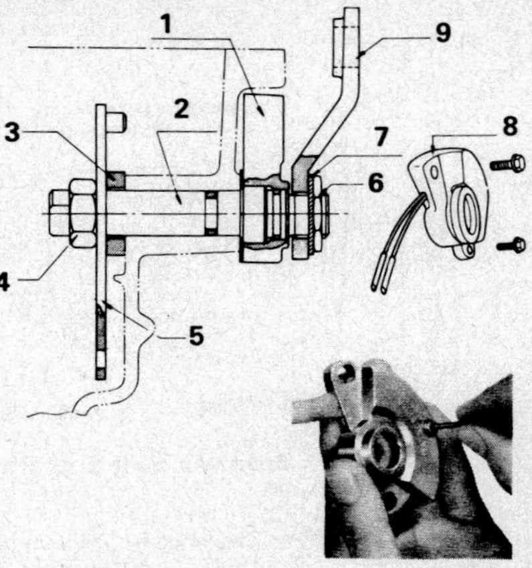

Neutral safety and backup light switch, Japanese transmission

1. Neutral safety switch
2. Manual shaft
3. Washer
4. Nut
5. Manual plate
6. Nut
7. Washer
8. Neutral safety switch
9. Transmission shift lever

10. Remove the crossmember. Lower the rear of the engine slightly.
11. Support the transmission with a jack. Place a pan under the torque converter.
12. Remove the starter.
13. Remove the four bolts which retain the torque converter to the drive plate. Access is from the front through the engine mounting plate.
14. Remove the converter and transmission assembly to the rear. Be careful not to let the converter fall when separating the assembly from the engine.
15. Reverse the procedure to install. Make sure that the drive plate is not warped more than 0.020 in. Plate-to-crankshaft bolt torque is 40–50 ft lbs. To insure correct engagement of the front oil pump drive, rotate the converter so that the drive fingers on the hub will be in 9 and 3 o'clock positions. Rotate the slots of the front oil pump driving gear to the same positions. Torque the drive plate-to-torque converter bolts to 25–30 ft lbs. Torque the ⅜ in. converter housing-to-engine bolts to 30–34 ft lbs. and the 5/16 in. bolts to 7–10 ft lbs. There are two dowels for aligning the converter housing to the engine.
16. Refill the transmission and check the fluid level.

PL510, WPL510 with American BW Unit

1. Disconnect the battery.
2. Remove the carburetor torsion shaft and starter.
3. Remove the two torque converter housing-to-engine capscrews at the top.
4. Raise and support the car.
5. Disconnect the handbrake front cable from the center lever.
6. Loosen the oil pan bolts and drain the transmission.

7. Loosen the muffler clamps and turn the muffler for clearance. Remove the driveshaft after unbolting it at the rear.

8. Disconnect the speedometer cable, vacuum hose, and neutral safety switch wiring. Disconnect the solenoid wire at the transmission.

9. Detach the oil cooler tubes. Remove the filler tube and plug opening.

10. Disconnect the lower selector rod and remove the cross shaft assembly.

11. Support the transmission with a suitable jack.

12. Remove the rear crossmember. Lower the transmission and the rear of the engine for access to the converter-to-drive plate bolts. Place a pan under the converter.

13. Remove the engine rear plate. Mark the relationship of the converter and drive plate. Remove the torque converter-to-drive plate bolts, screwing the bolts out completely one at a time. Remove the remaining converter housing-to-engine capscrews. Pull the transmission away from the engine.

To replace the American built Borg Warner transmission:

14. Make sure that the drive plate is not warped more than 0.020 in. Plate-to-crankshaft bolt torque is 50 ft lbs. Place the transmission and converter assembly on a jack. Pull the transmission forward to start the converter hub into the crankshaft. Align the engine block dowel pin with the converter housing aligning hole. Install the two lower converter housing attaching bolts and tighten to pull the transmission assembly into place. Torque the converter housing bolts to 32 ft lbs. Tighten the drive plate-to-converter bolts to 28 ft lbs.

15. Install the starter motor, shift linkage, speedometer cable, filler tube, and oil cooler tubes.

16. Connect the vacuum hose and kickdown solenoid wire.

17. Raise the transmission until it contacts the floor pan, attach the rear crossmember to the side rails, lower the transmission, and bolt the transmission to the crossmember.

18. Replace the driveshaft, exhaust pipe, and handbrake cable.

19. Lower the vehicle, replace the battery cable, and carburetor torsion shaft.

20. Pour in 3 quarts of transmission fluid. Set the handbrake and start the engine. Add 3 more quarts. Move the selector lever through all ranges. Add enough fluid to bring the level up to the F mark.

All Models with Japanese Transmission

1. Disconnect the battery cable.
2. Remove the accelerator linkage.
3. Detach the shift linakge.
4. Disconnect the neutral safety switch and downshift solenoid wiring.
5. Remove the drain plug and drain the torque converter. If there is no converter drain plug, drain the transmission. If there is no transmission drain plug, remove the pan to drain. Replace the pan to keep out dirt.
6. Remove the front exhaust pipe.
7. Remove the vacuum tube and speedometer cable.
8. Disconnect the fluid cooler tubes.
9. Remove the driveshaft and starter.
10. Support the transmission with a jack under the oil pan. Support the engine also.
11. Remove the rear crossmember.
12. Mark the relationship between the torque converter and the drive plate. Remove the four bolts holding the converter to the drive plate through the hole at the front, under the engine. Unbolt the transmission from the engine.
13. Reverse the procedure for installation. Make sure that the drive plate is warped no more than 0.020 in. Torque the drive plate-to-torque converter and converter housing-to-engine bolts to 29–36 ft lbs. Drive plate-to-crankshaft bolt torque is 101–116 ft lbs.
14. Refill the transmission and check the fluid level.

DRIVE AXLES

Driveshaft and U-Joints

Removal and Installation

L520, L521, PL521, SPL311, LB110, KLB110

These driveshafts are all one piece units with a U-joint and flange at the rear, and a U-joint and a splined sleeve yoke which fits into the rear of the transmission, at the front. Early models and trucks generally have U-joints with grease fittings. U-joints without grease fittings must be disassembled for lubrication, usually at 24,000 mile intervals. The splines are lubricated by transmission oil.

1. Be ready to catch oil coming from the rear of the transmission and to plug the extension housing.
2. Unbolt the rear flange.
3. Pull the drivehsaft down and back.
4. Plug the transmission extension housing.
5. Reverse the procedure to install, oiling the splines. Flange bolt torque is 15–20 ft lbs.

PL510, PL610, KPL610, WPL510

These driveshafts are the one piece type with a U-joint and flange at the rear, and a U-joint and a splined sleeve yoke which fits into the rear of the transmission, at the front. The U-joints must be disassembled for lubrication at 24,000 mile intervals. The splines are lubricated by transmission oil.

1. Release the handbrake.
2. Loosen the PL510 muffler and rotate it out of the way.
3. On the PL510, remove the handbrake rear cable adjusting nut and disconnect the left handbrake cable from the adjuster.
4. Unbolt the rear flange.
5. Pull the driveshaft down and back.
6. Plug the transmission extension housing.
7. Reverse the procedure to install, oiling the splines. Flange bolt torque is 29–62 ft lbs on the PL510 and WPL510, and 15–20 ft lbs on the PL610 and KPL610.

240 Z—Four Speed

This driveshaft is the same type used on the PL510 and WPL510. It is balanced as an assembly.

1. Make sure that there are spline/-flange yoke match marks in two places. If not, make some with chalk.
2. Remove the submuffler.
3. Unbolt the rear flange.
4. Pull the driveshaft down and back.
5. Plug the transmission extension housing.
6. Reverse the procedure to install, aligning the match marks and oiling the splines. Flange bolt torque is 18 ft lbs.

240 Z, SRL311—Five Speed

This driveshaft has a flange at either end and a splined coupling in the center.

1. Carry out Steps 1–3 for 240 Z—Four Speed.
2. Unbolt the front flange.
3. Remove the driveshaft.
4. Reverse the procedure to install, aligning the match marks. Flange bolt torque is 18 ft lbs.

WPL610, PL620

These models use a driveshaft with three U-joints and a center support bearing. The driveshaft is balanced as an assembly. It is not recommended that it be disassembled.

1. Mark the relationship of the driveshaft flange to the differential flange.
2. Unbolt the center bearing bracket.
3. Unbolt the driveshaft flange from the differential flange.
4. Pull the driveshaft back under the rear axle. Plug the rear of the transmission to prevent oil or fluid loss.
5. On installation, align the marks made in Step 1. Torque the flange bolts to 15–20 ft lbs. Center bearing bracket bolt torque is 12–16 ft lbs on the PL620 and 26–35 ft lbs on the WPL610.

U-Joint Overhaul

Disassembly

1. Mark the relationship of all components for reassembly.
2. Remove the snap-rings. On early units, the snap-rings are seated in the yokes. On later units, the snap-rings seat

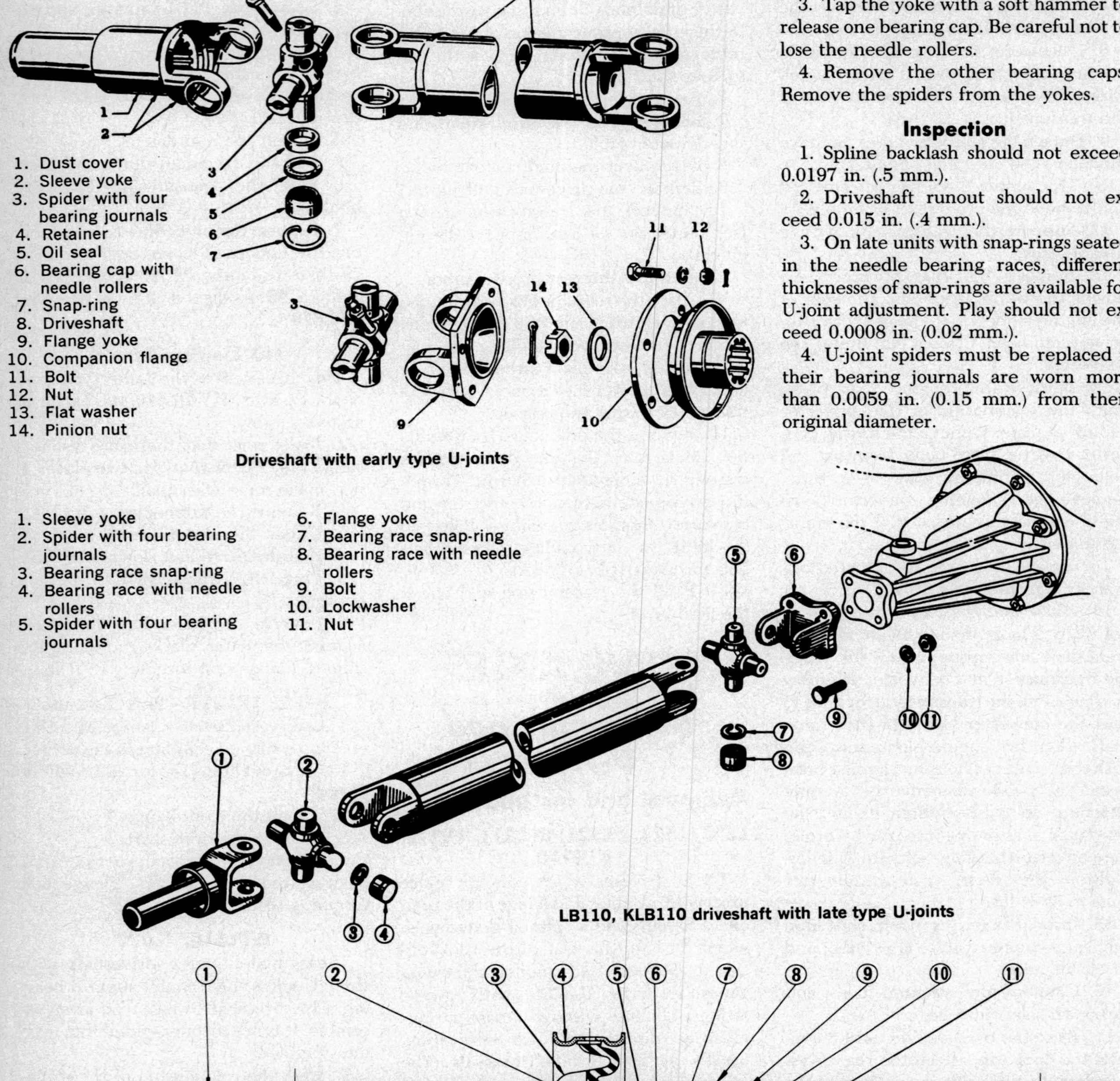

Driveshaft with early type U-joints

LB110, KLB110 driveshaft with late type U-joints

in the needle bearing races.

3. Tap the yoke with a soft hammer to release one bearing cap. Be careful not to lose the needle rollers.

4. Remove the other bearing caps. Remove the spiders from the yokes.

Inspection

1. Spline backlash should not exceed 0.0197 in. (.5 mm.).

2. Driveshaft runout should not exceed 0.015 in. (.4 mm.).

3. On late units with snap-rings seated in the needle bearing races, different thicknesses of snap-rings are available for U-joint adjustment. Play should not exceed 0.0008 in. (0.02 mm.).

4. U-joint spiders must be replaced if their bearing journals are worn more than 0.0059 in. (0.15 mm.) from their original diameter.

WPL610 and PL620 driveshaft

1. Sleeve yoke assembly
2. Center bearing
3. Center bearing insulator
4. Center bearing bracket
5. Companion flange
6. Plain washer
7. Self locking nut
8. Flange yoke
9. Bearing race assembly
10. Snap ring
11. Journal assembly

Assembly

1. Place the needle rollers in the races and hold them in place with grease.
2. Put the spider into place in its yokes.
3. Replace all seals.
4. Tap the races into position and secure with the snap-rings.

Differential

All models have solid rear drive axles except the PL510, PL610, KPL610, and 240 Z, which have independent rear suspension with the differential carrier solidly mounted.

Solid Rear Axle—L520, L521, PL521, PL620, WPL510, WPL610, LB110, KLB110, SPL311, SRL311

Axle Unit Disassembly

1. Remove the rear axle assembly from the vehicle. Disconnect the brake lines at the wheel cylinders.
2. Remove the handbrake linkage.
3. Drain the oil.
4. Unbolt the backing plate from the axle housing. Pull the axle shaft and backing plate out together with a slide hammer.
5. From the rear of the backing plate, press off the bearing collar or cut if off with a cold chisel. The collar should not be reused. Pull out the bearing.

NOTE: *Some units use a locknut instead of a bearing collar.*

6. Unbolt and pull out the differential carrier from the axle housing.

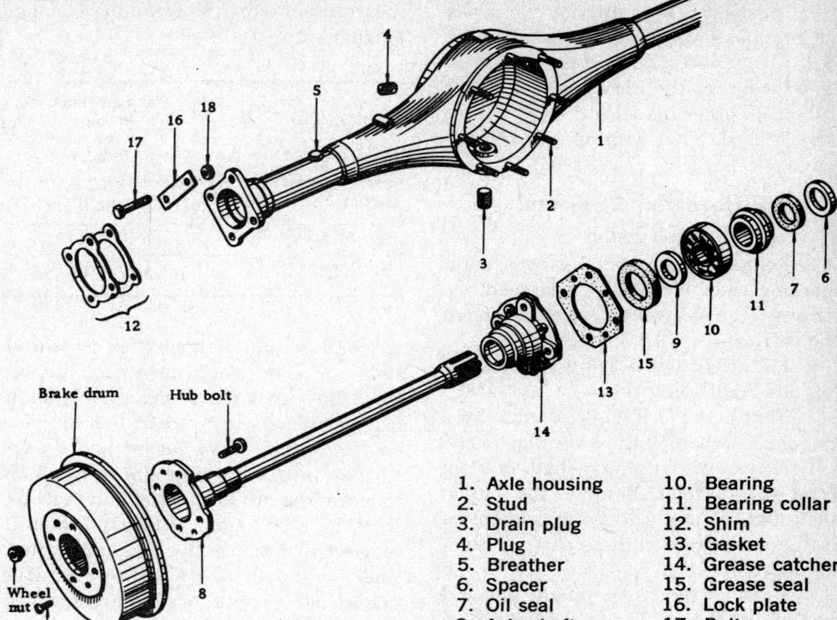

Detail of SPL311 axle shafts

Axle Unit Assembly

1. Use a new gasket between the axle housing and differential carrier. Torque the bolts to 14–18 ft lbs. in a diagonal pattern.
2. Install the grease catcher, bearing spacer, bearing packed with grease, and new bearing collar onto the axle shaft. The seal side of the wheel bearing must face the wheel. Coat the oil seal lips with grease. Press on the bearing collar.
3. Adjust the axle end-play by using shims between the backing plate and axle housing. Specified end-play is 0.012–0.-020 in. for the WPL510, 0.004 in. for the LB110 and KLB110, 0.001–0.006 in. for the PL620, and 0.004–0.018 in. for the WPL610. For the L520, the first axle shaft to be installed should have an end-play of 0.033–0.043 in., and the second 0.004 in.

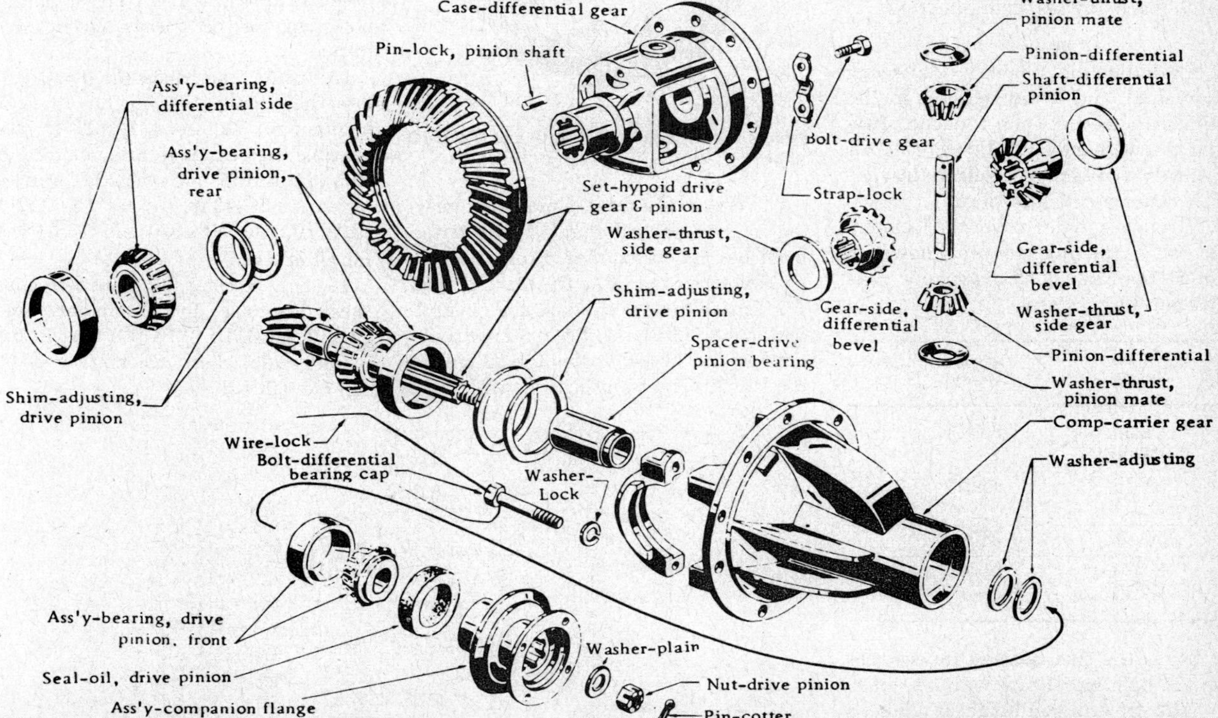

Differential details, WPL510

4. Specified bolt torque for the brake backing plate is 20–28 ft lbs. for the WPL510, 16–20 ft lbs for the WPL610, 27–35 ft lbs for the PL620, and 11–15 ft lbs. for all other models.

5. Refill the unit with oil. See the Capacities Chart.

Differential Overhaul

Disassembly

1. Remove the side bearing caps, marking their locations for reassembly. Remove the differential assembly from the carrier.

2. Pull off the side bearings. Do not mix left and right side parts.

3. Flatten the lock tabs and unbolt the ring gear, loosening the bolts diagonally.

4. Drive out the pinion shaft lock pin from left to right. Remove the pinion shaft and pinions, side gears, and thrust washers. Separate all these parts by original location.

5. Remove the drive pinion nut and pull off the flange. Tap the drive pinion back with a soft hammer and remove it with the rear bearing inner race, bearing spacer, and adjusting washer.

6. Remove and discard the oil seal. Remove the front bearing inner race.

7. Pull out the front and rear bearing outer races.

Inspection

1. Wash all parts in a safe solvent. Oil the bearings immediately.

2. Ring and pinion gears must be replaced only in pairs. If the ring gear is warped more than 0.002 in., replace it.

3. Check all parts for wear or distortion. Replace any suspected bearings.

Assembly

1. Assemble the pinions, side gears, pinion shaft, and thrust washers in the case. Clearance between the side gears and thrust washers should be 0.004–0.008 in. Thrust washers are available in various thicknesses for adjustment.

2. Drive in and peen over the lock pin.

3. Bolt on the ring gear using new lock tabs. Tighten the bolts diagonally. Specified bolt torques are:

Model	Torque (ft lbs)
L520, WPL510	35-40
LB110, KLB110	43-51
SPL311	25-30
PL620, WPL610	51-58

4. Press the side bearing inner races onto the differential case without shims.

5. The drive pinion height is adjusted with shims behind the rear bearing race. Dealers have special tools for making this measurement. Specified standard pinion heights are:

Model	Standard Pinion Height in. (mm.)
SPL311	2.0094 (51)
L520, WPL510	2.4034 (61)
LB110, KLB110	1.772 (45)

Standard pinion height is measured from the axle centerline to the pinion face. The deviation of the drive pinion from standard size is marked on the pinion face with + for larger and – for smaller. All early units are marked in thousandths of an inch. The LB110, KLB110, PL620, and WPL610 pinion is marked in hundredths of a millimeter. There is usually an M mark on pinions graded in hundreths of a millimeter. If no standard pinion height is specified, the adjustment must be made by use of special tools or by comparing the marks on the old and new drive pinion and adjusting the original shim pack to suit.

Pinion face markings, LB110 and KLB110 shown

6. Press in the drive pinion rear bearing outer race and shims. Press in the front bearing outer race. Press the rear bearing inner race onto the drive pinion.

7. Install the drive pinion and collapsible spacer into the differential carrier without the oil seal. Install the oil seal on the PL620. The front bearing inner race and the flange should be installed. Tighten the flange nut until the torque required to turn the shaft (bearing preload) is:

Model	New Bearing (in. lbs.)	Used Bearing (in. lbs.)
LB110, KLB110	5.2-6.9	2.6-3.5
WPL510	8.7-11.3	3.5-4.3
L520, SPL311	6.1-8.7	2.4-3.5
PL620	6-13	—

On the WPL610, preload is adjusted by selecting the proper size washer and spacer. This is done since this model does not use a collapsible spacer. Preload should be 6–9 in. lbs without an oil seal.

8. Check the drive pinion height again.

9. Torque the flange nut to the specified torque.

Model	Torque (ft lbs)
WPL510, WPL610	101-130
LB110, KLB110	87-123
L520, SPL311	100-120
PL620	94-145

10. Make sure that pinion bearing preload is as in Step 7. If it is excessive, a new spacer must be installed.

11. Remove the nut and flange. Press in a new oil seal. Pack grease between the seal lips. Replace the flange and nut, torquing as in Step 9. If the cotter pin does not align, file the washer. Do not overtorque.

12. Install the differential assembly into the carrier, tapping it with a soft hammer if necessary. Install the side bearing caps in their original locations and torque the bolts. Bearing cap bolt torque is 36–43 ft lbs for the LB110, KLB110, and WPL610 and 30–35 ft lbs for all others.

13. Side bearing shims are selected by these formulae, for all models except LB110, KLB110, WPL610, and PL620:

Left side shim thickness = A – C + D + E + 0.007 in.

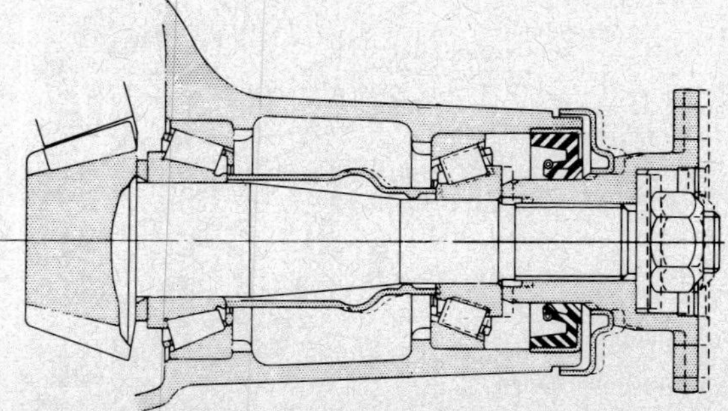

Detail of drive pinion bearing spacer, LB110 and KLB110

Right side shim thickness = B−D+F+0.006 in.

Figure	Location
A	left bearing housing of gear carrier
B	right bearing housing
C,D	differential case
E	difference from standard size (0.7874 in.) of left bearing
F	difference from standard size of right bearing

All figures are read in thousandths of an inch. If old bearings are being reused, the required shim thickness on each side should be reduced by 0.001–0.003 in. to prevent excessive bearing preload.

14. LB110 and KLB110 side bearing shims are selected by these formulae:

Left side shim thickness=A−C+-D+E+0.2 mm.

Right side shim thickness=B−D+F+0.2 mm.

Figures A, B, C, and D are as in Step 13 but are read in hundredths of a millimeter. Figures E and F are the differences of the left and right bearings from standard size (17.5 mm.), read in hundredths of a millimeter.

15. WPL610 side bearing shims are selected by these formulae:

Left side shim thickness = (A−C+D−H) X 0.01 + 0.20 +E

Right side shim thickness = (B−D+H) X 0.01 + 0.09 +F

Figures A through F are as in Step 13 but are given in hundredths of a millimeter. Figures E and F are the differences of the left and right bearings from standard size. Figure H is marked on the ring gear.

16. PL620 side bearing shims are selected by these formulae:

Left side shim thickness = (A−C+D−H) X 0.01 + 0.175 + E

Right side shim thickness = (B−D+H) X 0.01 + 0.150 + F

Figures A through H are as in Step 15.

17. Ring and pinion gear backlash should be .006–.008 in., measured with a dial indicator. It should be 0.005–0.007 on the WPL610. If it is excessive, remove some right side shims and place them on the left. If it is too small, change shims from left to right.

18. Make a tooth contact pattern check with red lead. Adjust the drive pinion height and side bearing shims as required.

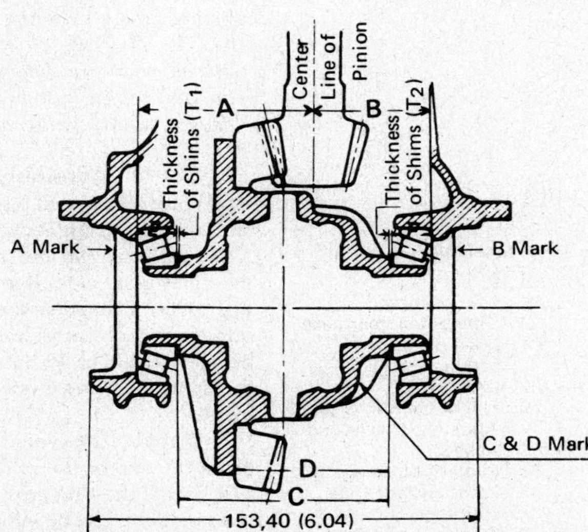

Measurements for selecting side bearing shims, LB110 and KLB110

Final Drive Unit—240Z, PL510, PL610, KPL610

These vehicles have independent rear suspension with the final drive unit mounted solidly. Although the suspension arrangements differ, the final drive units are virtually identical.

Removal and Installation

240 Z

1. Chock the front wheels. Raise and support the rear of the vehicle.
2. Remove the main muffler.
3. Unbolt the driveshaft.
4. Loosen the transverse link spindle inner bolts (on the front of the front differential mounting crossmember) enough to free the crossmember.
5. Unbolt the axle shafts.
6. Support the differential unit with a jack.
7. Remove the two mounting nuts from the rear of the rear differential mounting crossmember.
8. Remove the four nuts from the bottom of the front crossmember.
9. Lower the front crossmember and final drive unit together.
10. Unbolt the front crossmember from the differential unit.
11. Reverse the procedure to install. Tighten the transverse link spindle inner bolts with the vehicle lowered to the ground and with two 150 lb passengers.

Fastener	Torque (ft lbs)
Axle shaft bolts	36-43
Driveshaft bolts	18
Transverse link spindle inner bolts	101-116
Differential rear mounting nuts	54-69
Differential front mounting and crossmember bolts	23-31

PL510, PL610

1. Chock the front wheels. Raise and support the rear of the vehicle.
2. Disconnect the handbrake rear cable driveshaft, and axle shafts.
3. Support the differential unit with a jack.
4. Unbolt the differential rear mounting crossmember from body.
5. Remove the four bolts holding the differential to the rear suspension crossmember.
6. Remove the differential to the rear.
7. Support the rear suspension crossmember with stands to prevent damage to the insulators.
8. Unbolt the differential rear mounting crossmember from the differential.
9. Reverse the procedure to install. Pry the differential unit into position.

Fastener	Torque (ft lbs)
Differential mounting crossmember-to-differential nuts	43-58
Differential mounting crossmember-to-body nuts	51-72
Differential-to-suspension crossmember nuts	36-51
Driveshaft bolts	15-20
Axle shaft bolts	36-43

Disassembly

1. Drain the oil and remove the rear cover.
2. Clamp the housing down securely.
3. Check the tooth contact pattern with red lead.
4. Check the backlash between the ring and pinion with a dial indicator. It should be 0.004–0.008 in.
5. If the tooth contact pattern or gear backlash is incorrect, make sure that runout at the rear of the ring gear does not exceed .002 in.
6. Remove the side flange bolts and pull off the side flanges with a slide hammer.
7. Unbolt and pull off the side retainers. Note the original locations of retainers and shims.

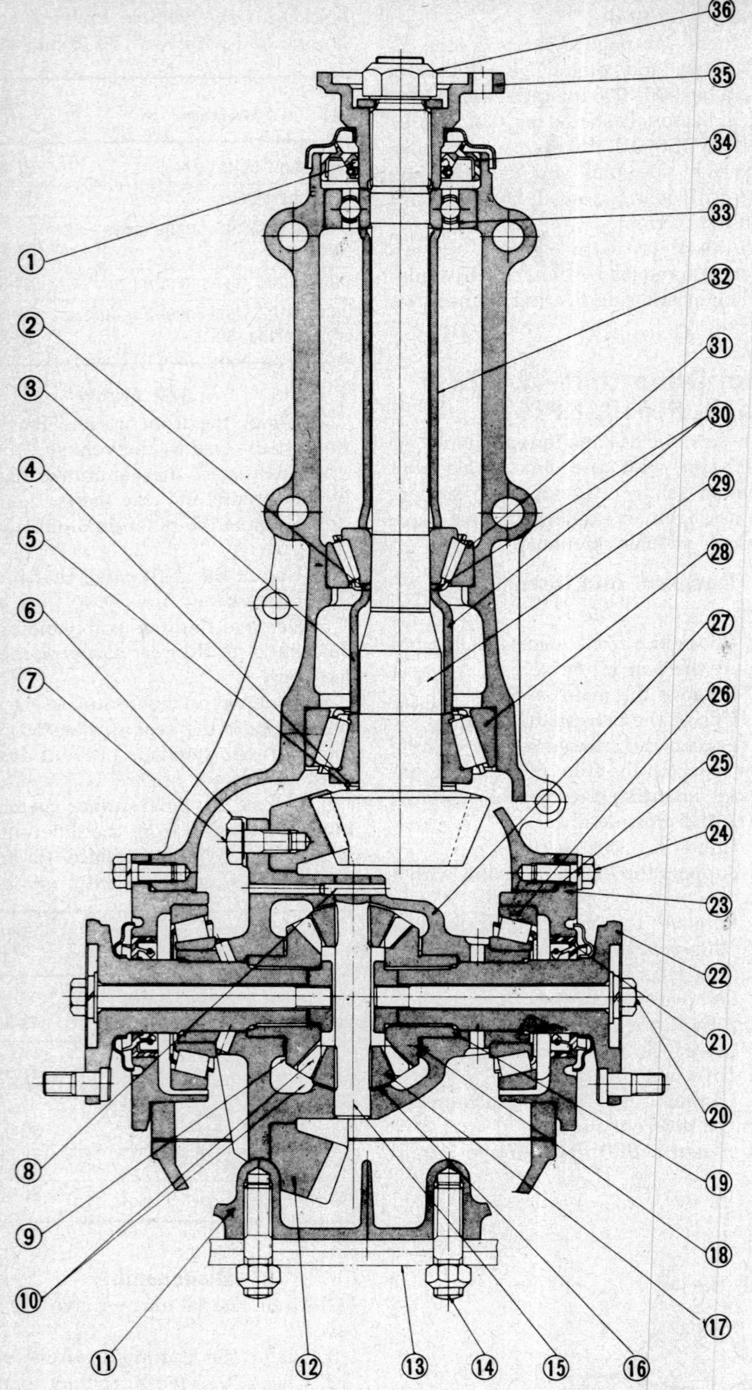

Details of independent rear suspension differential assembly

1. Oil seal
2. Pinion bearing adjusting washer
3. Pinion bearing adjusting spacer
4. Pinion height adjusting shims
5. Pinion height adjusting washer
6. Lock strap
7. Ring gear retaining bolt
8. Pinion shaft lock pin
9. Side gear thrust washer
10. Side gear
11. Rear cover
12. Ring gear
13. Differential mount
14. Nut
15. Pinion shaft
16. Thrust washer
17. Pinion gear
18. Thrust washer
19. Side gear
20. Side flange bolt
21. Oil seal
22. Side flange
23. Side retainer
24. Bolt
25. O-ring
26. Side bearing
27. Differential gear case
28. Drive pinion rear bearing
29. Drive pinion
30. Pinion bearing preload adjusting spacer and washer
31. Pinion front bearing
32. Front pilot bearing spacer
33. Front pilot bearing
34. Oil seal
35. Drive pinion flange
36. Drive pinion nut

8. Remove the differential assembly from the carrier.

9. Remove the bearing outer races from the side retainers with an oil seal puller.

10. Hold the drive pinion flange and loosen the nut. Tighten the nut to 123–145 ft lbs and check the torque required to turn the drive pinion. It should be 2.-6–13 in lbs. Remove the nut and pull off the flange.

11. Press the drive pinion from the gear carrier with the front and rear bearing inner races, bearing spacers, and adjusting washers. Press out the front pilot bearing.

12. Press the drive pinion from the rear bearing.

NOTE: *If the tooth contact pattern and backlash was correct in Steps 3 and 4 and the original ring gear, carrier, drive pinion, rear bearing, and washers are to be reused, it is not necessary to remove the rear bearing.*

13. Press the front and rear bearing outer races from the carrier.

14. Pull off the right differential side gear. Spread the lock straps, loosen and remove the ring gear bolts in a diagonal pattern. Remove the ring gear and pull off the left differential side gear. Do not mix right and left side parts.

15. Punch out the pinion shaft lock pin from the ring gear side. Remove the shaft, differential gears, and thrust washers. Note the original location of all parts.

16. To replace the front oil seal, pull off the seal retainer and pull out the seal. Apply grease between the lips of the new oil seal and drive it into place. Replace the retainer.

NOTE: *The front oil seal can be replaced with the differential mounted on the vehicle, after the driveshaft and flange are removed.*

17. To replace the side oil seals, pull out the seal and drive in the new one, applying grease between the seal lips.

NOTE: *The side oil seals can be replaced with the differential mounted on the vehicle, after the axle shafts, flanges, and retainers are removed.*

Assembly

1. Wash all parts in a safe solvent and oil the bearings immediately.

2. Install the side and pinion gears into the differential case. Replace the pinion shaft. Check the clearance between the side gears and thrust washers. It should be 0.004–0.008 in. Various thicknesses of thrust washers are available for adjustment.

3. Drive in the pinion shaft lock pin. Stake the end of the pin with a punch.

4. Install the ring gear to the differential assembly. Use new lock straps under the bolts. Torque the bolts to 51–58 ft lbs in a diagonal pattern, tapping the bolt heads lightly before final torquing.

5. Before pressing on new differential side bearings, check bearing width. Standard width is 0.787 in (20 mm.).

6. Press the front and rear drive pinion bearing outer races into the gear carrier.

7. Drive pinion bearing preload turning torque should be 6–9 in. lbs, with the pinion flange nut torqued to 123–145 ft lbs and without the oil seal. This is normally checked and adjusted with special tools.

8. Normal PL510 drive pinion height is 1.909 in. (48.5 mm.) from the axle centerline to the pinion face. Special tools are required to make this adjustment. The height is adjusted by a washer and shims between the rear bearing and the drive pinion gear. The deviation of the drive pinion from standard size, in hundredths of a millimeter, is marked on the pinion face with + for larger and – for smaller. If the drive pinion is replaced, compare the old and new marks and adjust the shim pack to suit.

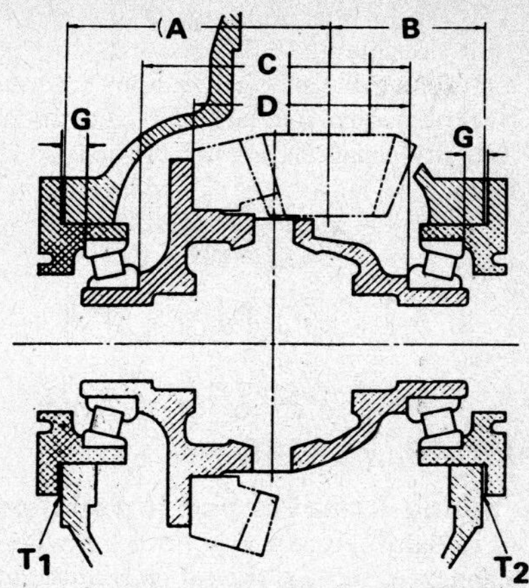

Measurements used in selecting side bearing shims

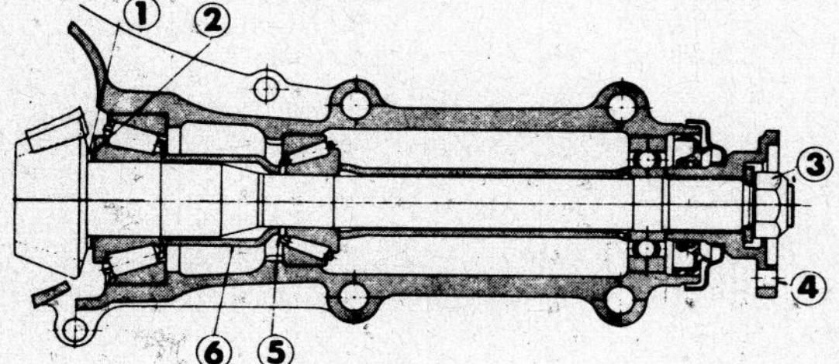

1. Pinion bearing adjusting washer
2. Pinion height adjusting shims
3. Pinion nut
4. Pinion flange
5. Pinion bearing adjusting washer
6. Pinion bearing adjusting spacer

Details of installed drive pinion

9. Install the drive pinion, front pilot bearing, and oil seal. Replace the flange and torque the bolt to 123–145 ft lbs.

10. Side bearing shims are selected by these formulae:

Left side shim thickness = A+C+G–D–E+H+.76 mm.

Right side shim thickness = B+D+G–F–H+.76 mm.

Figure	Location
A,B	on gear carriers
C,D	on differential case
E,F	difference from standard size (20 mm.) of bearing
G	on side retainers
H	on ring gear

11. Install the shims selected in Step 10 and the O-rings in the side retainers. Install the retainers. Bolt torque should be 6.5–8.7 ft lbs.

12. Check ring and pinion gear backlash. It should be 0.004–0.008 in. If less, move side retainer shims from right to left. If more, move shims from left to right.

13. Check the tooth contact pattern with red lead.

14. Replace the rear cover and torque the bolts to 54–69 ft lbs. Replace the side flanges and torque the bolts to 14–19 ft lbs.

15. Refill the differential. See the Capacities Chart.

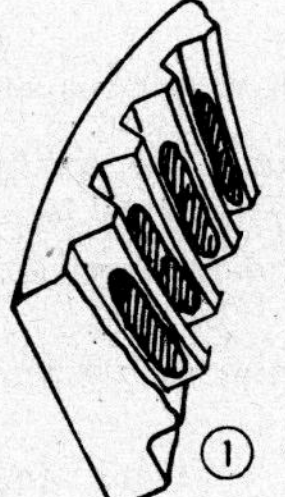

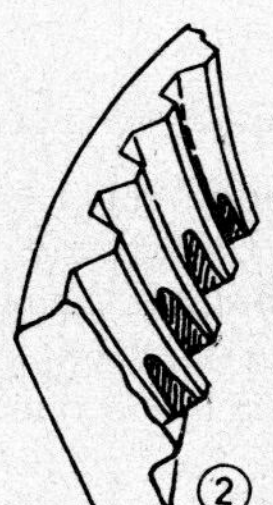

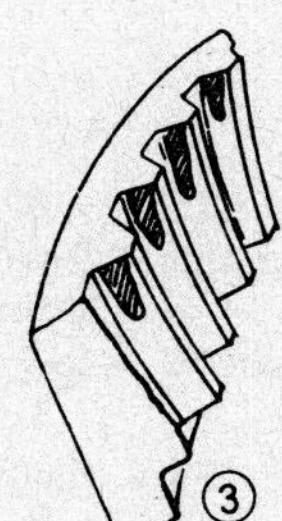

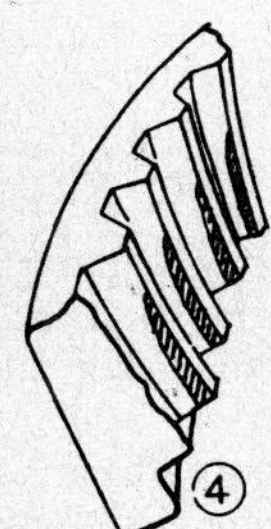

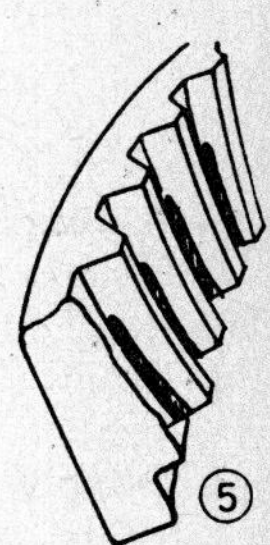

Ring gear tooth contact patterns

1. Correct tooth contact
2. Short toe contact; move ring gear away from pinion.
3. Short heel contact; move ring gear toward pinion.
4. Contact too high and narrow; pinion should be moved toward center of axle.
5. Contact too low and narrow; pinion should be moved away from center of axle.

Axle Shafts—240 Z, PL510, PL610, KPL610

Wheel Bearing, Seal, and Axle Shaft Service

1. Jack up and support the rear of the car.

2. Remove the wheel and brake drum.

3. Disconnect the axle driveshaft from the axle shaft at the flange.

4. Remove the wheel bearing locknut while holding the axle shaft outer flange from turning.

5. Pull out the axle shaft with a slide hammer. Remove the distance piece and inner flange.

6. Drive the inner wheel bearing and oil seal out toward the center of the car.

7. Press or pull the outer wheel bearing from the axle shaft.

8. Pack the wheel bearings with grease. Coat the seal lip also.

9. Reinstall the wheel bearings. Install the outer bearing on the axle shaft so that the side with the seal will be toward the wheel. Always press or drive on the inner bearing race.

10. The distance piece may be reused if it is not collapsed or deformed. The distance piece must always carry the same mark, A, B, or C, as the bearing housing.

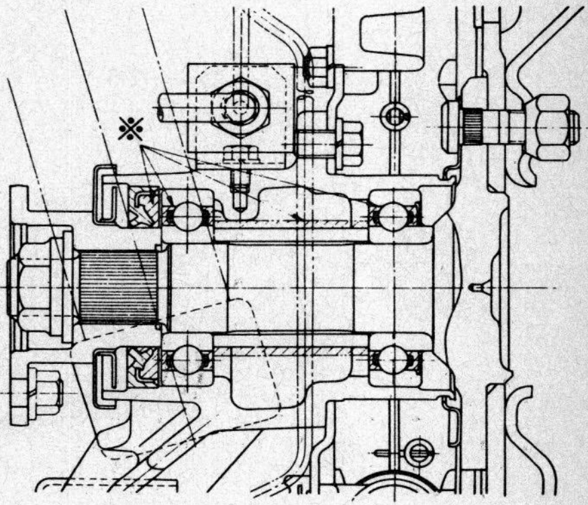

* indicates areas to receive grease

11. Fill the area illustrated with grease.

12. Replace the axle shaft and flange. Tighten the bearing locknut to the specified torque.

13. The torque required to start the axle shaft turning should be 3.9 in. lbs or less. This is a 28.7 oz or less pull at the hub bolt. Axle shaft end-play, checked with a dial indicator, should be 0–0.006 in.

14. If the turning torque or axle shaft play is incorrect, disassemble the unit and install a new distance piece.

Fastener	Torque (ft lbs)
Wheel nut	58-65
Axle driveshaft flange nuts	36-43
Bearing locknut	181-239
Axle shaft inner flange mounting nut	14-19

Driveshaft

The axle driveshafts must be removed and disassembled to lubricate the ball splines every 30,000 miles. Handle the driveshaft carefully; it is easily damaged. No repair parts for the driveshafts are available. If a driveshaft is defective in any way, it must be replaced as an assembly.

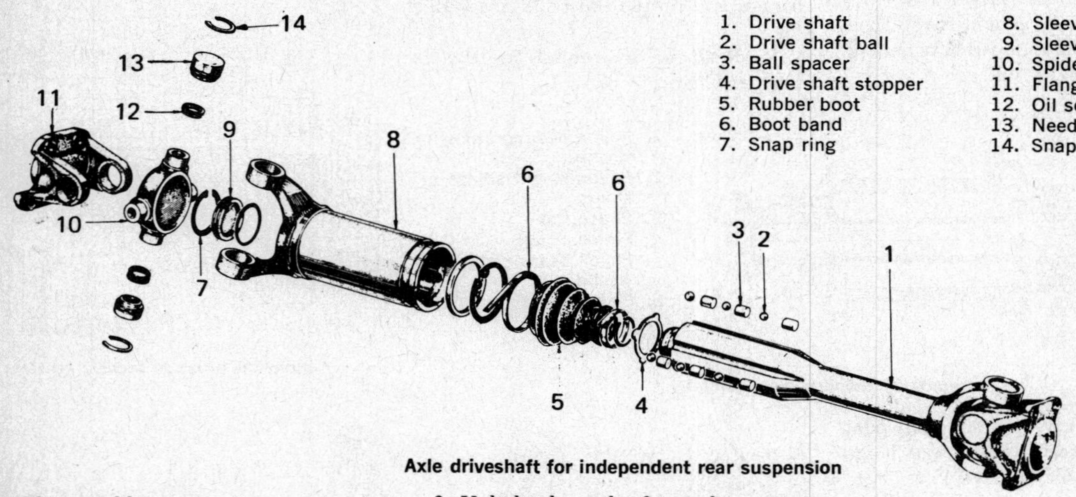

Axle driveshaft for independent rear suspension

To disassemble:

1. Remove the U-joint spider from the differential end of the shaft.
2. Remove the snap-ring and sleeve yoke plug.
3. Compress the driveshaft and remove the snap-ring and stopper.
4. Disconnect the boot and separate the driveshaft carefully so as not to lose the balls and spacer.
5. Pack about 10 grams (0.35 oz) of grease into the ball grooves. Also pack about 35 grams (1.23 oz) of grease into the area illustrated.
6. Twisting play between the two shaft halves should not exceed 0.004 in. Check play with the driveshaft completely compressed.

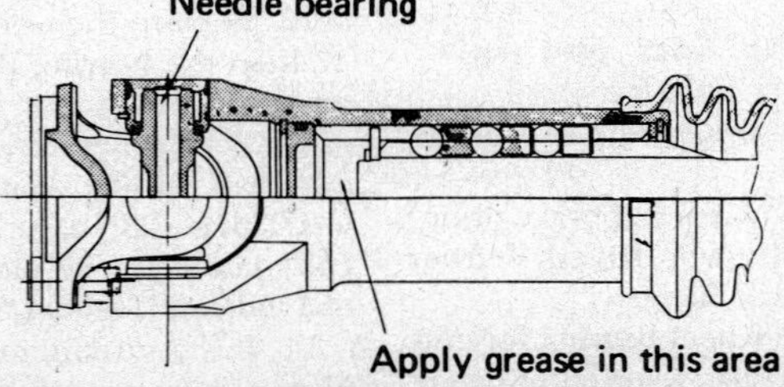

Axle driveshaft cross-section

7. While reassembling, adjust the U-joint side play to 0.001 in. or less by selecting suitable snap-rings. Four different thicknesses are available for adjustment. Axle driveshaft flange nut torque is 36–43 ft lbs.

REAR SUSPENSION

Leaf Spring Type

LB110, KLB110

Spring Removal and Installation

1. Raise the rear axle until the wheels hang free. Support the car on stands. Support the rear axle with a jack.
2. Unbolt the bottom end of shock absorber.
3. Unbolt the axle from the spring leaves. Unbolt and remove the front spring bracket. Lower the front of the spring to the floor.
4. Unbolt and remove the spring rear shackle.
5. Before reinstallation, coat the front bracket pin, bushing, shackle pin, and shackle bushing with a soap solution.
6. Reverse the procedure to install. The front pin nut and the shock absorber mounting should be tightened before the vehicle is lowered to the floor.

Shock Absorber Removal and Installation

To remove the rear shock absorbers, simply unbolt the lower and upper ends.

Fastener	Torque (ft lbs)
Axle U-bolts	23-29
Front spring bracket to body	12-15
Shackle pin nuts	12-15
LB110 Sedan shock absorber upper nuts	26-33
KLB110 Coupe shock absorber upper nuts	7-9
LB110 Sedan shock absorber lower nuts	26-33
KLB110 Coupe shock absorber lower nuts	7-9

The upper nuts are under the rear seat back. The shock absorbers are not serviceable and should be replaced if defective. Mounting bolt torques are given under "Spring Removal and Installation"

WPL510, WPL610

Spring Removal and Installation

1. Raise the rear axle until the wheels hang free. Support the car on stands. Support the rear axle with a floor jack.
2. Remove the spare tire.
3. Unbolt the bottom end of the shock absorber.
4. Unbolt the axle from the spring leaves.
5. Unbolt the front spring bracket from the body. Lower the spring end and bracket to the floor.
6. Unbolt and remove the rear shackle.
7. Unbolt the bracket from the spring.
8. Before reinstallation, coat the front bracket pin and bushing, and the shackle pin and bushing with a soap solution.
9. Reverse the procedure to install. The front pin nut and the shock absorber mounting should be tightened after the vehicle is lowered to the floor. Make sure that the elongated flange of the rubber bumper is to the rear.

Fastener	TORQUE (ft lbs) WPL510	WPL610
Axle U-bolts	43-47	43-47
Shock absorber upper bracket to body	11-18	6-9
Shock absorber to upper bracket nuts	12-16	—
Shock absorber lower nuts	25-33	25-33
Spring shackle nuts	33-36	43-47
Front pin nuts	33-36	43-47
Front bracket to body nuts	13-17	43-47

5. Unbolt the rubber bumper inside the bottom of the coil spring.

6. Jack up the suspension arm and unbolt the shock absorber lower mounting.

7. Lower the jack slowly and cautiously. Remove the coil spring, spring seat, and rubber bumper.

8. Reverse the procedure to install, making sure that the flat face of the spring is at the top.

Strut Removal and Installation—240 Z

1. Raise the rear of the vehicle and support it on stands.

2. Remove the wheels.

Fastener	TORQUE (ft lbs) PL510	PL610 KPL610
Axle driveshaft flange nuts	36-43	36-43
Rubber bumper nut	15-19	12-16
Shock absorber mounting nuts	17	12-16

3. Disconnect the brake hydraulic line and handbrake cable.

4. Remove the nuts from either end of the transverse link outer spindle. Remove the spindle center locking bolt. Pull out the spindle. Separate the bottom of the strut from the transverse link.

5. Unbolt the axle driveshaft flange at the wheel end.

6. Jack under the lower end of the strut. Remove the strut installation nuts from the tower inside the luggage area. Lower the jack and strut gradually.

NOTE: *Strut disassembly and repair requires special tools.*

7. Reverse the procedure to install. Note that the shorter part of the spindle (measured from the locking bolt notch) should be to the front. Tighten the outer spindle end nuts after the vehicle has been lowered to the floor.

Fastener	Torque (ft lbs)
Strut installation nut	12-15
Transverse link outer spindle nuts	54-69
Outer spindle locking bolt	7-9
Axle driveshaft flange nuts	36-43

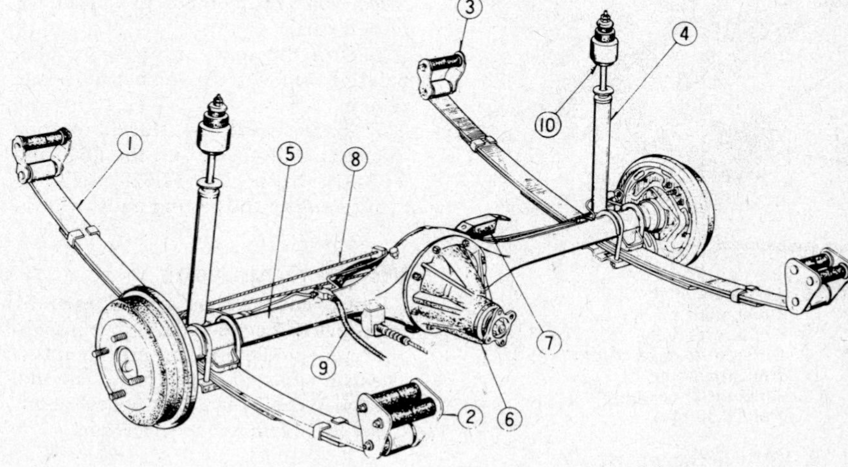

Leaf spring rear suspension, LB110 and KLB110 shown

1. Leaf spring
2. Front mounting
3. Shackle
4. Shock absorber
5. Axle housing
6. Differential carrier
7. Torque arrester
8. Handbrake cable
9. Brake hose
10. Bound bumper

Shock Absorber Removal and Installation

When removing the WPL510 shock absorber, unbolt the upper bracket from the body and remove the shock absorber and bracket as a unit. The WPL610 shock absorbers have a conventional strap mounting at the top. The shock absorbers are not serviceable and should be replaced if defective. Mounting bolt torques are given under "Spring Removal and Installation"

Independent Rear Suspension—PL510, PL610, KPL610, 240Z

Coil Spring Removal and Installation—PL510, PL610, KPL610

1. Raise the rear of the vehicle and support it on stands.

2. Remove the wheels.

3. Disconnect the handbrake linkage and return spring.

4. Unbolt the axle driveshaft flange at the wheel end.

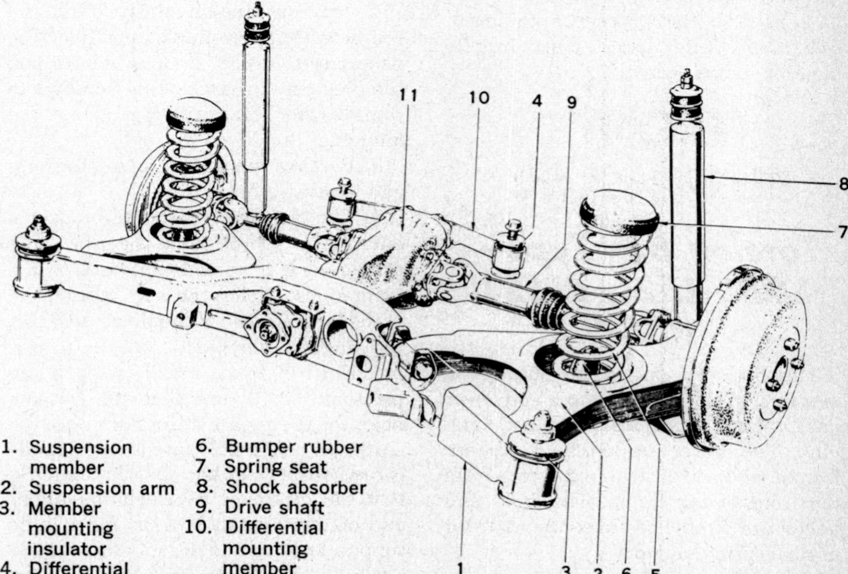

1. Suspension member
2. Suspension arm
3. Member mounting insulator
4. Differential mounting insulator
5. Coil spring
6. Bumper rubber
7. Spring seat
8. Shock absorber
9. Drive shaft
10. Differential mounting member
11. Differential carrier

Sedan independent rear suspension

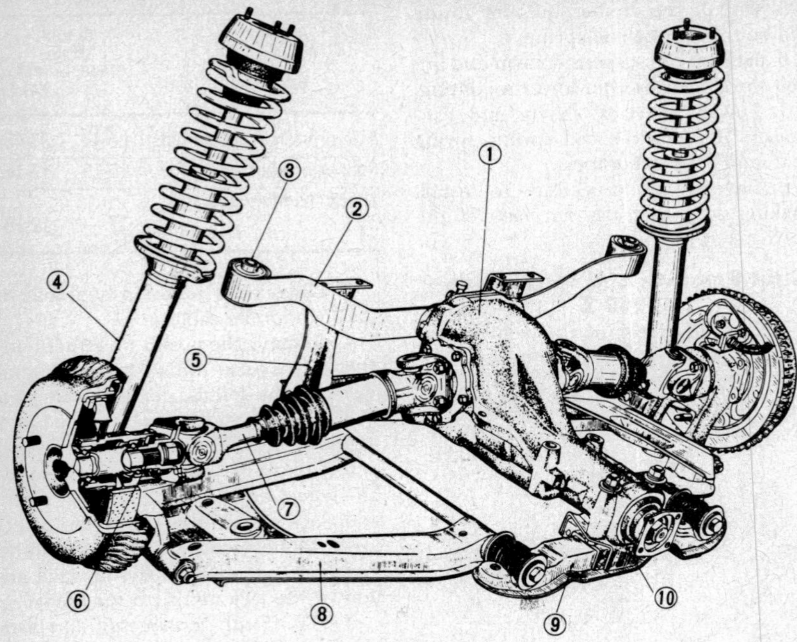

240 Z independent rear suspension

1. Differential carrier
2. Differential case mount rear member
3. Differential case mount rear insulator
4. Strut assembly
5. Link mount brace
6. Rear axle shaft
7. Drive shaft
8. Transverse link
9. Differential case mount front member
10. Differential case mount front insulator

Shock Absorber Removal and Installation—PL510, PL610, KPL610

1. Open the trunk and remove the cover panel.

2. Remove the two nuts holding the top of the shock absorber. Unbolt the bottom of the shock absorber.

3. The shock absorbers can not be repaired. Replace them if defective.

4. Reverse the procedure to install. See "Coil Spring" Removal and Installation for torque figures.

FRONT SUSPENSION

Torsion Bar Type—L520, L521, PL521, PL620

This independent front suspension uses torsion bar springs, upper and lower links, tubular shock absorbers, and kingpins. The lower suspension links are located fore and aft by tension rods from the front of the frame. The front end height can be adjusted to compensate for normal spring sagging.

Kingpin and Bushing Replacement

1. Block the front of the truck.

2. Remove the wheels.

3. Unscrew the front wheel brake hose connections.

4. Remove the hubcap and spindle nut. Remove the hub and drum with the wheel bearing.

5. Remove the brake backing plate from the spindle.

6. Disconnect the tie rod from each spindle.

7. Take out the kingpin lock bolt and remove the upper spindle plug. It may be necessary to drill and tap a hole to pull the plug out. Drive the kingpin down to remove the bottom plug. Tap out the kingpins.

8. Remove the spindle with the shims and thrust washer.

9. The old bushings should be driven out of the spindle and the new ones driven in. It is advisable to replace the kingpin also. Ream the new bushings to fit the kingpin. The fit should be such that the kingpin, when, oiled, can be turned or pushed in or out readily with thumb pressure. Make sure that the bushing holes for the grease fittings are open.

10. On reassembly, use a new spindle thrust washer. Install spindle shims so that the clearance between the upper end of the kingpin boss on the spindle support knuckle and the spindle is 0.003–0.005 in. Use new kingpin expansion plugs. Use a new front hub grease seal. Adjust the front wheel bearing by torquing it to 30 ft lbs and backing off ⅛ turn. On the PL620, the torque should be 22–25 ft lbs.

11. Grease the suspension and bleed the brake system.

Tension Rod Adjustment

There are three adjusting nuts on each tension rod. There is one at the lower suspension link end and two at the frame end. Adjust these nuts until both rubber bushings at the frame end are compressed to 0.43 in.

Suspension Height Adjustment

1. Jack up the vehicle under the front suspension crossmember to unload the torsion bars.

2. Turn the rear torsion bar anchor bolt right to lower the vehicle and left to raise it.

3. Dimension B in the illustration should be 3.07–3.09 in. on the L520 and 3.07–3.23 in. on the PL620, with the vehicle empty and resting on its wheels.

Wheel Alignment

Caster and camber are adjusted by shims placed between the upper suspension link spindle and the crossmember. Toe-in is adjusted at the center tie-rod. See the Wheel Alignment Specifications Chart for alignment specifications.

Coil Spring Type—SPL311, SRL311

This independent front suspension uses coil springs between upper and lower wishbones. The shock absorbers are mounted in the center of each spring. The spindles are connected to the wishbones by ball joints. A cross-chassis stabilizer bar is used.

Wheel Bearing Adjustment

1. Jack up the car and remove the wheel.

2. Remove the hubcap and cotter pin.

3. Torque the spindle nut to 20–30 ft lbs.

4. Turn the hub a few turns in each direction and retorque the nut.

5. Loosen the nut 40–70°. Insert the cotter pin.

6. Turn the hub a few more turns.

7. Make sure that the hub turns easily. If not, check wheel bearing condition.

8: Replace the hubcap and wheel. Lower the car.

Spring Removal and Installation

1. Raise and support the front of the car.

2. Unbolt the top and bottom mounts and remove the shock absorber.

3. Install a coil spring compressor.

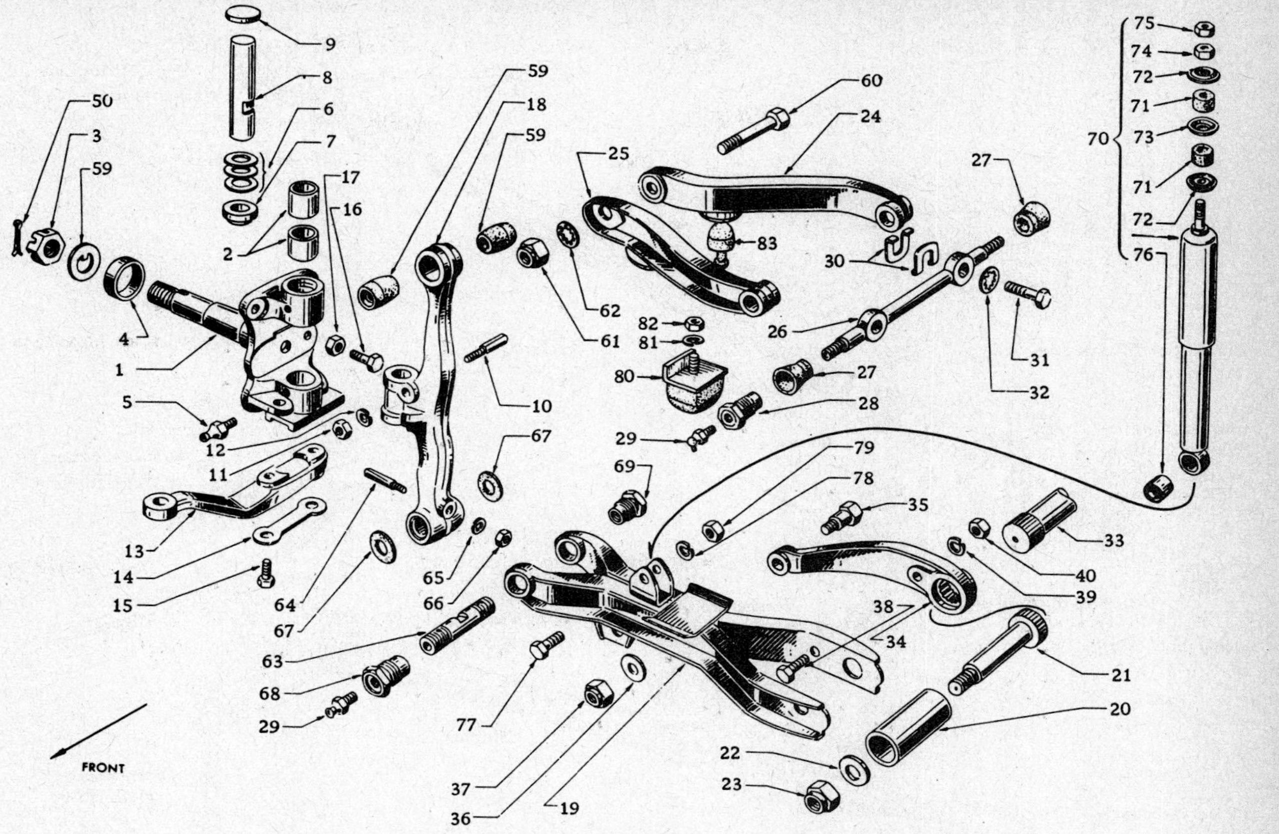

Pickup front suspension, L520 shown

1. Spindle
2. Bushing
3. Spindle nut, used to adjust front wheel bearing
4. Spindle collar
5. Grease nipple
6. Spindle shims
7. Thrust washer
8. Kingpin
9. Plug
10. Lock bolt
11. Nut
12. Lockwasher
13. Steering arm
14. Lockplate
15. Bolt
16. Bolt
17. Nut
18. Spindle support
19. Lower link
20. Lower link bushing
21. Lower link spindle
22. Washer
23. Nut
24. Rear upper link
25. Front upper link
26. Upper link spindle
27. Seal
28. Bushing assembly
29. Grease fitting
30. Camber adjusting shims
31. Spindle upper link bolt
32. Lockwasher
33. Torsion bar
34. Torsion bar front arm
35. Bolt
36. Washer
37. Nut
38. Bolt
39. Lockwasher
40. Nut
41-58. Not used
59. Bushing
60. Fulcrum bolt
61. Nut
62. Lockwasher
63. Fulcrum pin
64. Lock bolt
65. Lockwasher
66. Nut
67. Ring
68. Front bushing assembly
70. Shock absorber assembly
71. Bushing
72. Washer
73. Washer
74. Nut
75. Locknut
76. Bushing
77. Clamp bolt
78. Lockwasher
79. Nut
80. Suspension rebound bumper
81. Lockwasher
82. Nut
83. Suspension rebound bumper

NOTE: *Be extremely cautious when working with chassis coil springs.* Compress the spring.

4. Unbolt the lower link spindle from the crossmember. An alternate method is to unbolt the lower ball joint. It is also possible to unbolt the lower spring support plate.

5. Slowly and carefully release the coil spring. When the coil is fully extended, remove it.

6. On reinstallation, compress the spring and set it into place. Bolt on the part disconnected in Step 4. Release the coil spring and replace the shock absorber.

Wheel Alignment

Caster and camber are adjusted by shims placed between the crossmember and the spindle of the upper wishbone. See the Wheel Alignment Specifications Chart for alignment specifications.

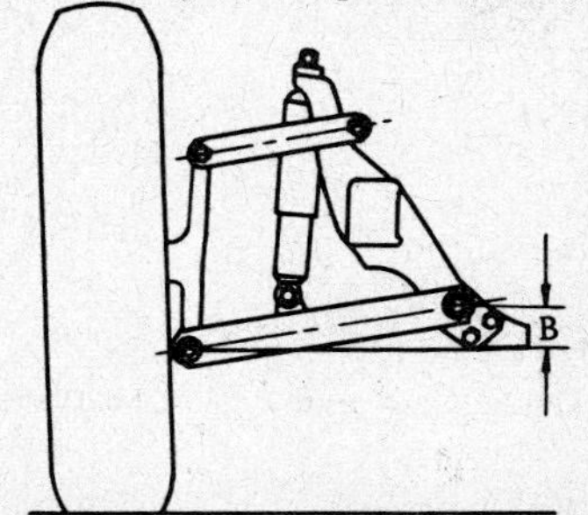

Check measurement (B) after adjusting front suspension height

Strut Type—PL510, PL610, KPL610, WPL510, WPL610, LB110, KLB110, 240 Z

This independent front suspension uses McPherson struts. Each strut combines the function of coil spring and shock absorber. The spindle is mounted to the lower part of the strut which has a single ball joint. No upper suspension arm is required in this design. The spindle and lower suspension transverse link (control arm) are located fore and aft by tension rods to the front part of the chassis on most models. Compression rods,

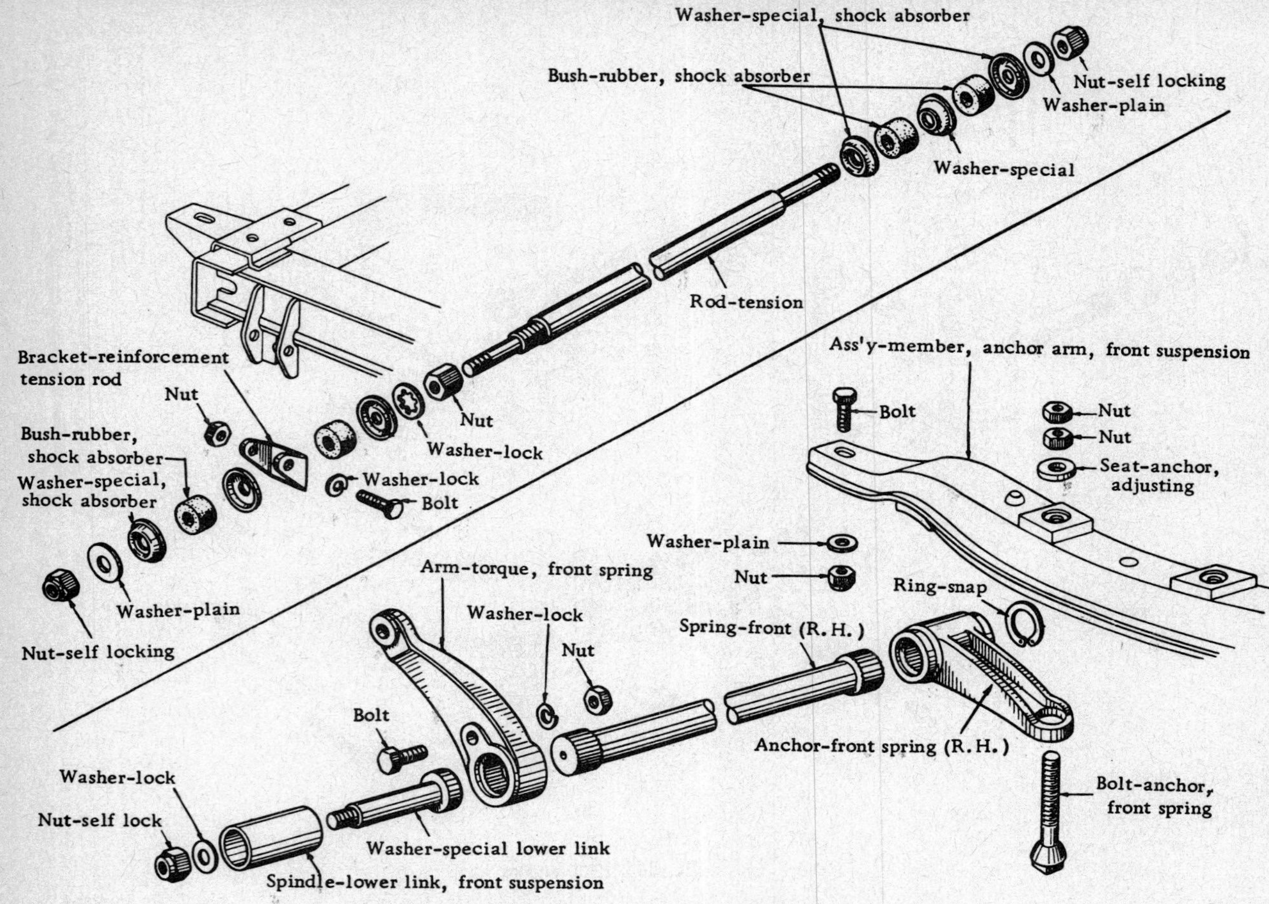

Tension rod assembly, top, and torsion bar assembly, bottom

Nut-spindle

Collar-front spindle

Pickup hub and drum details, L520 shown

1. Hub
2. Wheel bolt
3. Inner bearing
4. Outer bearing
5. Grease seal spacer
6. Grease seal
7. Brake drum
8. Screw
9. Bearing washer
10. Cotter pin
11. Hubcap
12. Wheel
13. Wheel cover
14. Wheel nut

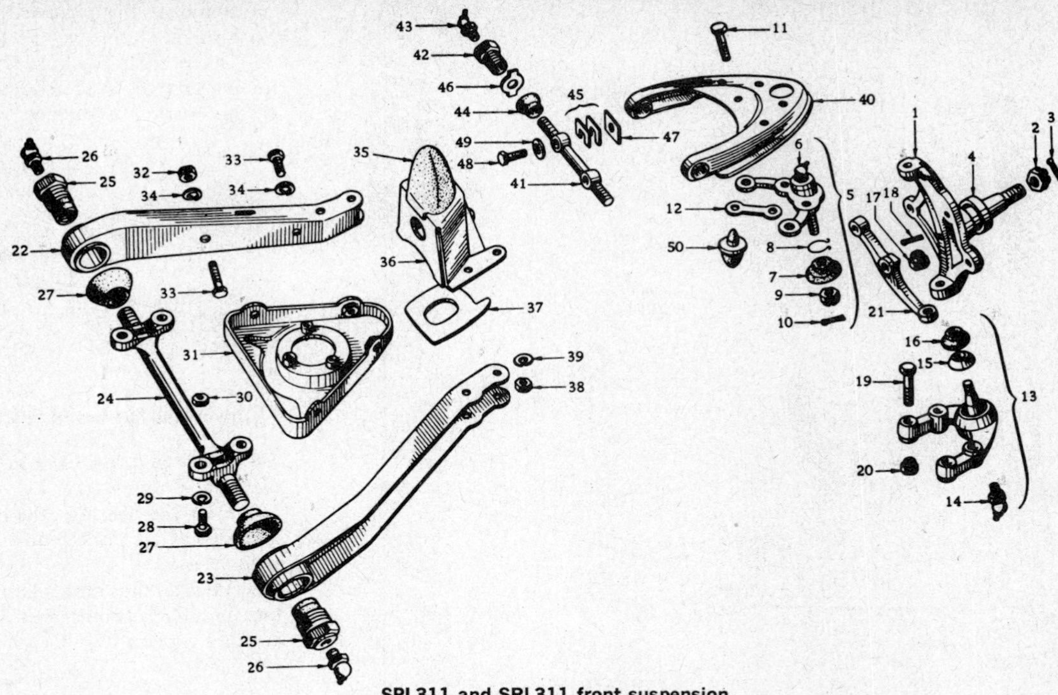

SPL311 and SRL311 front suspension

1. Spindle assembly
2. Nut
3. Cotter pin
4. Spindle collar
5. Upper ball joint assemby
6. Grease fitting
7. Dust cover
8. Clamp
9. Nut
10. Cotter pin
11. Bolt
12. Lock plate
13. Lower ball joint assembly
14. Grease fitting
15. Inner dust cover
16. Outer rubber dust cover
17. Nut
18. Cotter pin
19. Bolt
20. Nut
21. Steering arm
22. Front lower link
23. Rear lower link
24. Lower link spindle
25. Bushing assembly
26. Grease fitting
27. Dust seal
28. Bolt
29. Lockwasher
30. Nut
31. Lower spring seat
32. Nut
33. Bolt
34. Lockwasher
35. Rebound bumper
36. Bracket
37. Spacer
38. Nut
39. Lockwasher
40. Upper link
41. Upper link spindle
42. Bushing assembly
43. Grease fitting
44. Dust seal
45. Camber shims
46. Lockwasher
47. Caster shim
48. Bolt
49. Lockwasher
50. Rebound bumper

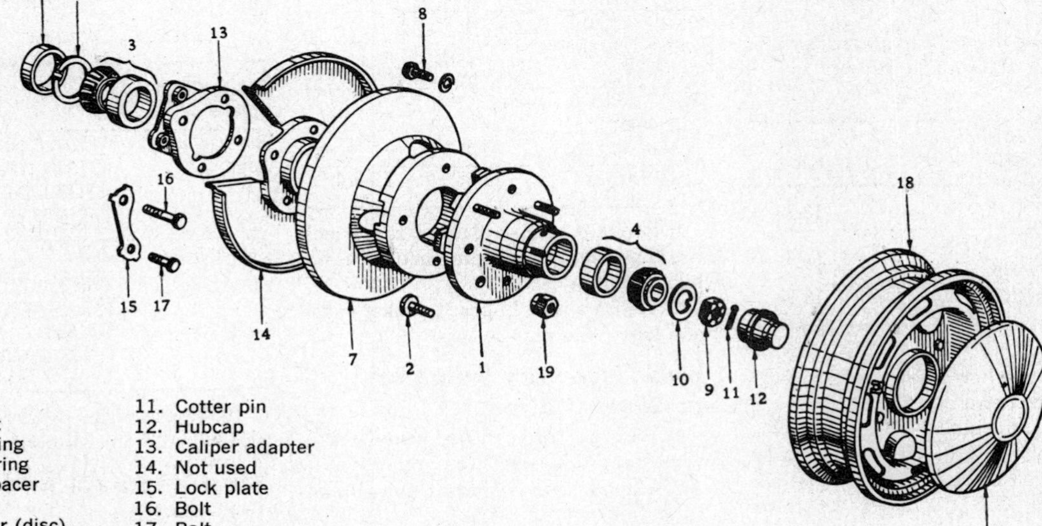

1. Hub
2. Wheel bolt
3. Inner bearing
4. Outer bearing
5. Oil seal spacer
6. Oil seal
7. Brake rotor (disc)
8. Rotor bolt
9. Spindle nut
10. Bearing washer
11. Cotter pin
12. Hubcap
13. Caliper adapter
14. Not used
15. Lock plate
16. Bolt
17. Bolt
18. Wheel
19. Wheel nut
20. Wheel cover

SPL311 and SRL311 front hub details

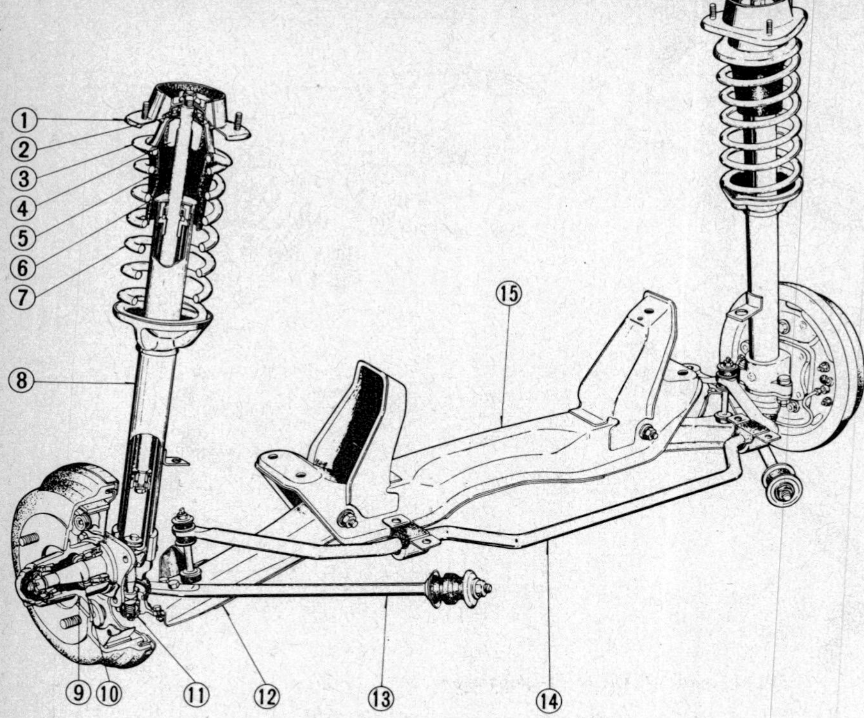

Strut type front suspension, LB110 and KLB110. Other models are quite similar. On the 240 Z, the tension rods are replaced by compression rods that run to the rear.

1. Strut mounting
2. Strut mounting bearing
3. Upper spring seat
4. Bumper rubber
5. Dust cover
6. Piston rod
7. Front spring
8. Strut assembly
9. Hub assembly
10. Spindle
11. Ball joint
12. Transverse link
13. Tension rod
14. Stabilizer
15. Suspension member

which run rearward, are used on the 240 Z. A cross-chassis sway bar is used on all models.

Wheel Bearing Adjustment

1. Jack up the car and remove the wheel.

2. Remove the hubcap and cotter pin.

3. Torque the spindle nut to:

Model	Torque (ft lbs)
240 Z	18-22
PL510, PL610, KPL610, WPL510, WPL610	22-25
LB110, KLB110	16-17

4. Turn the hub a few turns in each direction and retorque the nut.

5. Loosen the nut 60–75° on the 240 Z, 90° on the PL510, PL610, KPL610, WPL510, WPL610 and 40–70° on the LB110 and KLB110. Insert the cotter pin.

6. Turn the hub a few more turns.

7. Hub turning torque, with the disc brake pads removed, should be:

Model	Torque (in lbs)	Pull at hub bolt (lbs)
240 Z	3.5-7.4	1.5-3.3
PL610, KPL610, WPL610	—	1.5
PL510, WPL510 with new bearing and seal	6.1	—
PL510, WPL510 with original bearing and seal	3.5	—
LB110, KLB110	15.6-20.0	7.1-8.8

If torque is excessive, check the wheel bearing condition. There should be no hub end-play.

8. Replace the hubcap, brake pads, and wheel. Lower the car.

Hub Assembly Removal and Installation

1. Jack up the vehicle, remove the wheel, and disconnect the brake hose.

2. Unbolt and remove the brake caliper assembly.

3. Remove the hubcap, cotter pin, and spindle nut.

4. Remove the wheel hub with bearing washer, bearing, and brake rotor.

5. Remove the screws and brake splash shield.

6. Disassemble the hub. Use a drift in the two grooves inside the hub to drive out the bearing outer race.

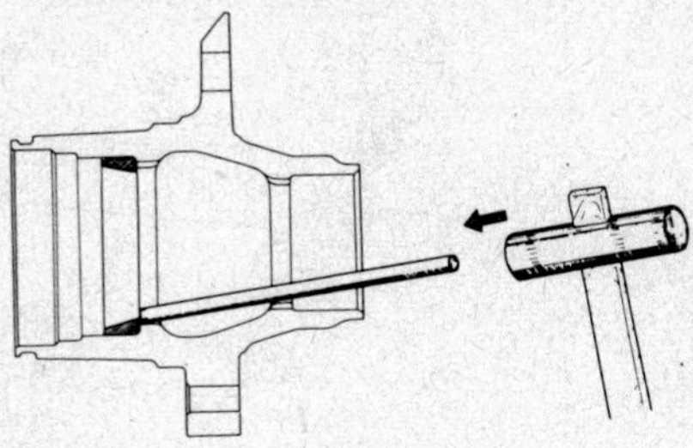

Driving out the bearing outer race

7. Drive or press back in the bearing outer race.

8. Pack the bearings, the hub, and the grease seal lip pocket (use a new seal) with grease.

9. Reassemble, and adjust the wheel bearings. Pack some grease into the hubcap and replace it.

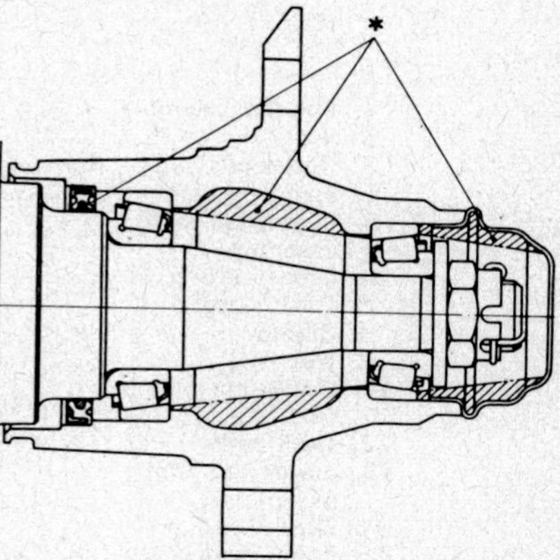

***indicates areas to be filled with grease**

Fastener	Model	Torque (ft lbs)
Splash shield screws	All	2-3
Rotor to hub bolts	PL510, PL610, KPL610, WPL510, WPL610, 240 Z	28-38
	LB110, KLB110	20-27
Caliper bolts	240 Z	11-13
	PL510, PL610, KPL610, WPL510, WPL610	53-72
	LB110, KLB110	33-44

10. Replace the caliper, brake hose, and wheel. Lower the vehicle.

Strut Removal and Installation

1. Jack up the car and support it safely. Remove the wheel.

2. Disconnect and plug the brake hose.

3. Disconnect the tension rod (com-

pression rod on 240 Z) and stabilizer bar from the transverse link.

4. Unbolt the steering arm.

5. Place a jack under the bottom of the strut.

6. Open the hood and remove the nuts holding the top of the strut.

7. Lower the jack slowly and cautiously until the strut assembly can be removed.

8. Reverse the procedure to install. The self locking nuts holding the top of the strut must be replaced.

Fastener	Model	Torque (ft lbs)
Strut-to-body nuts	PL610, KPL610, WPL610, 240 Z	18-25
	PL510, WPL510	28-38
	LB110, KLB110	12-15
Steering arm-to-strut bolts	PL610, KPL610, WPL610, 240 Z PL510, WPL510 LB110, KLB110	53-72 43-58 33-44
Tension or compression rod-to-transverse link nut	PL510, PL610, KPL610, WPL510, WPL610, 240 Z	36-46
	LB110, KLB110	16-22
Stabilizer-to-transverse link bolts	PL510, PL610, KPL610, WPL510, WPL610, 240 Z	9-12
	LB110, KLB110	7-9
Stabilizer-to-frame bracket bolts	240 Z, PL510, WPL510	14-18
	LB110, KLB110	7-9
	PL610, KPL610, WPL610	10-13

NOTE: Special tools are required to disassemble the strut.

Ball Joint Removal and Installation

The lower ball joint should be replaced when up and down (axial) play exceeds the standard play of 0.012–0.040 in. for the LB110 and KLB110, 0.040 in. for the PL610, KPL610, and WPL610 or 0.012–0.014 in. for the other models. The ball joint should be greased every 30,000 miles. There is a plugged hole in the bottom of the joint for installation of a grease fitting.

1. Raise and support the car so the wheels hang free. Remove the wheel.

2. Unbolt the tension rod (compression rod on 240 Z) and stabilizer bar from transverse link.

3. Unbolt the strut from the steering arm.

4. Remove the cotter pin and ball joint stud nut. Separate the ball joint and steering arm.

5. Unbolt the ball joint from the transverse link.

6. Reverse the procedure to install a new ball joint. Grease the joint after installation.

Fastener	Model	Torque (ft lbs)
Ball joint to transverse link bolts	PL610, KPL610, WPL610, 240 Z	36-46
	PL510, WPL510	14-18
	LB110, KLB110	16-22
Ball joint stud nut	All	40-55

Wheel Alignment

Caster and camber angles cannot be adjusted except by replacing worn or bent parts. Suspension height is adjusted by replacing the front springs. Various springs are available for adjustment. Toe-in is adjusted by changing the length of the steering side-rods. The length of these rods should always be equal. Steering angles are adjusted by means of a stop bolt on each steering arm. On the LB110 and KLB110 make sure that the clearance between the tire and tension rod is at least 1.181 in.

STEERING

Several types of steering gear are used on Datsun vehicles. These are:

Model	Type
L520	Worm and roller
SPL311, SRL311	Cam and lever
LB110, KLB110, PL510, WPL510, PL610, KPL610, WPL610, L521, PL521, PL620	Recirculating ball
240 Z	Rack and pinion

All models starting 1969 have a steering shaft lock actuated by the ignition lock and a steering column and shaft assembly designed to collapse on impact.

Steering Wheel

Removal and Installation

First remove the horn button or ring. On the L520, and other early models, the horn button assembly is retained by three screws which can be removed from the rear of the wheel. On the KLB110, LB110, and PL620 the horn ring is retained by two screws which can be removed from the rear of the wheel spokes. On the SPL311 and SRL311, the horn button is retained by a wire snap-ring and can be pried loose. To remove the PL510, PL610, KPL610, WPL510, and WPL610 horn pad, press in and turn to the left. Some can be simply pulled off. Pull the 240 Z horn button straight out to remove. Next remove the rest of the horn switching mechanism, noting the relative location of the parts. Hold the steering wheel and remove the nut. Using a puller, remove the steering wheel. Do not attempt to pry or hammer off the wheel. This is particularly important in the case of collapsible steering columns. When replacing the wheel, make sure that it is correctly aligned when the wheels are straight ahead. Do not drive or hammer the wheel into place. Tighten the nut while holding the wheel. Specified wheel nut torque is 22–25 ft lbs for the LB110 and KLB110, 51–54 ft lbs for the PL620 and 29–36 ft lbs for the 240Z, PL610, KPL610, and WPL610. Reinstall the horn button, pad, or ring.

Steering Gear

Removal and Installation

L520, L521, PL521, PL620

1. Remove the steering wheel.

2. Unbolt the steering column from the instrument panel. On models with column shift, unbolt the shift linkage from the column.

3. Disconnect the horn wire.

4. Disconnect the steering rod from the steering arm.

5. Unbolt the steering gear box from the frame.

6. Pull the box, column, and shaft down and out of the vehicle.

7. Reverse the procedure to install.

SPL311, SRL311—Rigid Column

SPL311, SRL311, PL510, PL610, KPL610, WPL510, WPL610—Collapsible Column

1. Remove the steering shaft U-joint clamp bolt.

2. Remove the stud nut and pull the steering rod ball joint from the steering arm.

3. Unbolt the steering gear box from the frame and remove. If necessary, remove the horn button and pull the steering wheel and shaft up slightly.

4. Reverse the procedure to install. Torque the U-joint clamp bolt to 22 ft lbs (29–36 ft lbs for the PL610, KPL610, and WPL610). If the upper and lower shaft sections of the collapsible column have been separated, the slit of the universal joint must align with the punch mark on the upper end of the upper steering shaft.

PL510, WPL510—Rigid Column

LB110, KLB110—Collapsible Column

1. Remove the steering wheel.

2. Separate and remove the upper steering column shell.

3. Remove the turn signal and light

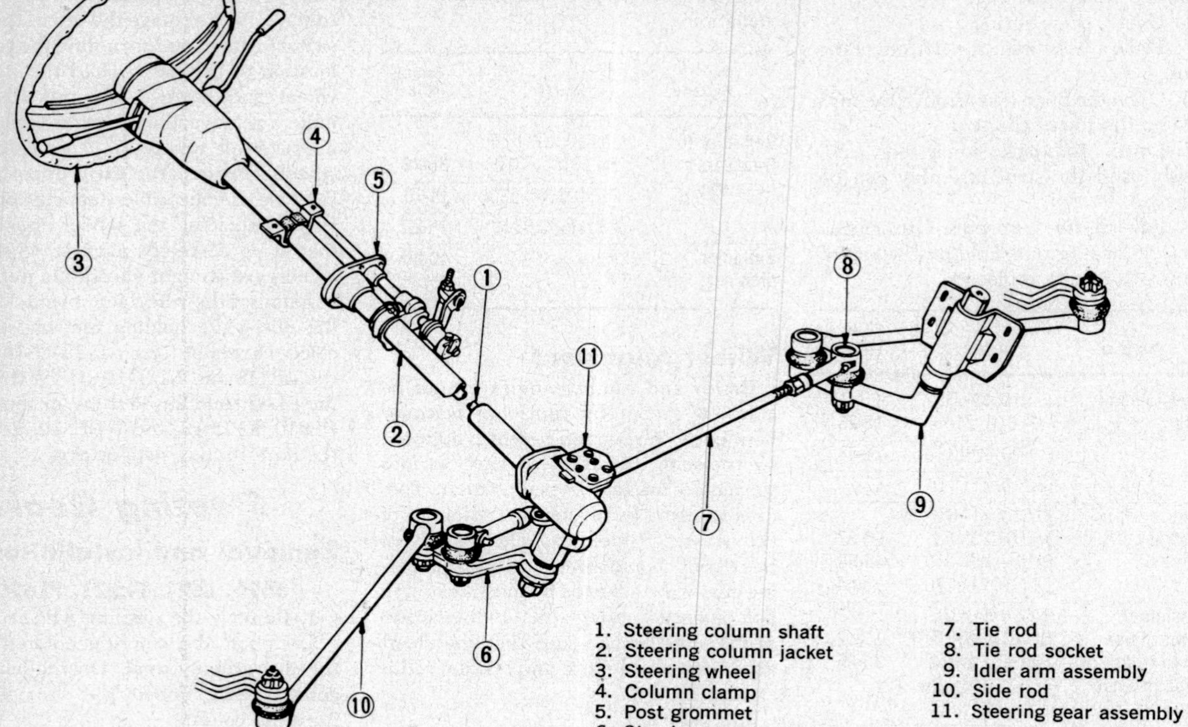

1. Steering column shaft
2. Steering column jacket
3. Steering wheel
4. Column clamp
5. Post grommet
6. Steering gear arm
7. Tie rod
8. Tie rod socket
9. Idler arm assembly
10. Side rod
11. Steering gear assembly

Steering assembly, PL620 shown. Most sedans and pickups are similar.

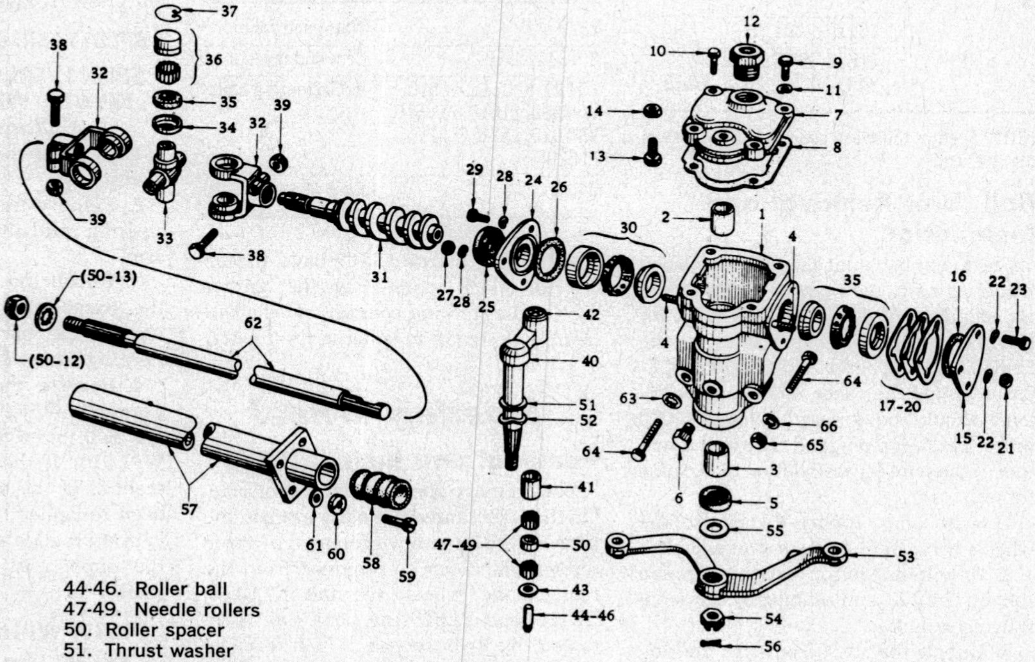

1. Steering gear housing
2. Bushing
3. Bushing
4. Stud
5. Oil seal
6. Drain plug
7. Cover
8. Gasket
9. Bolt
10. Bolt
11. Lockwasher
12. Filler plug
13. Adjusting screw
14. Locknut
15. Cover
16. O-ring

17-20. Shims

21. Nut
22. Lockwasher
23. Bolt
24. Rear cover
25. Oil seal
26. O-ring
27. Nut
38. Lockwasher
29. Bolt
30. Bearing
31. Worm gear
32. U-joint yoke
33. U-joint spider
34. Oil seal retainer
35. Oil seal
36. Bearing
37. Snap-ring
38. Bolt
39. Nut
40. Rocker shaft (lever)
41. Needle roller race
42. Roller ball pug
43. Needle roller cover

44-46. Roller ball

47-49. Needle rollers

50. Roller spacer
51. Thrust washer
52. Shaft adjusting thrust washer
53. Steering arm
54. Nut
55. Washer
56. Cotter pin
57. Steering column
58. Column bushing
59. Bolt
60. Lockwasher
61. Washer
62. Steering shaft
63. Lockwasher
64. Mounting bolt
65. Nut
66. Lockwasher

Cam and lever steering gear

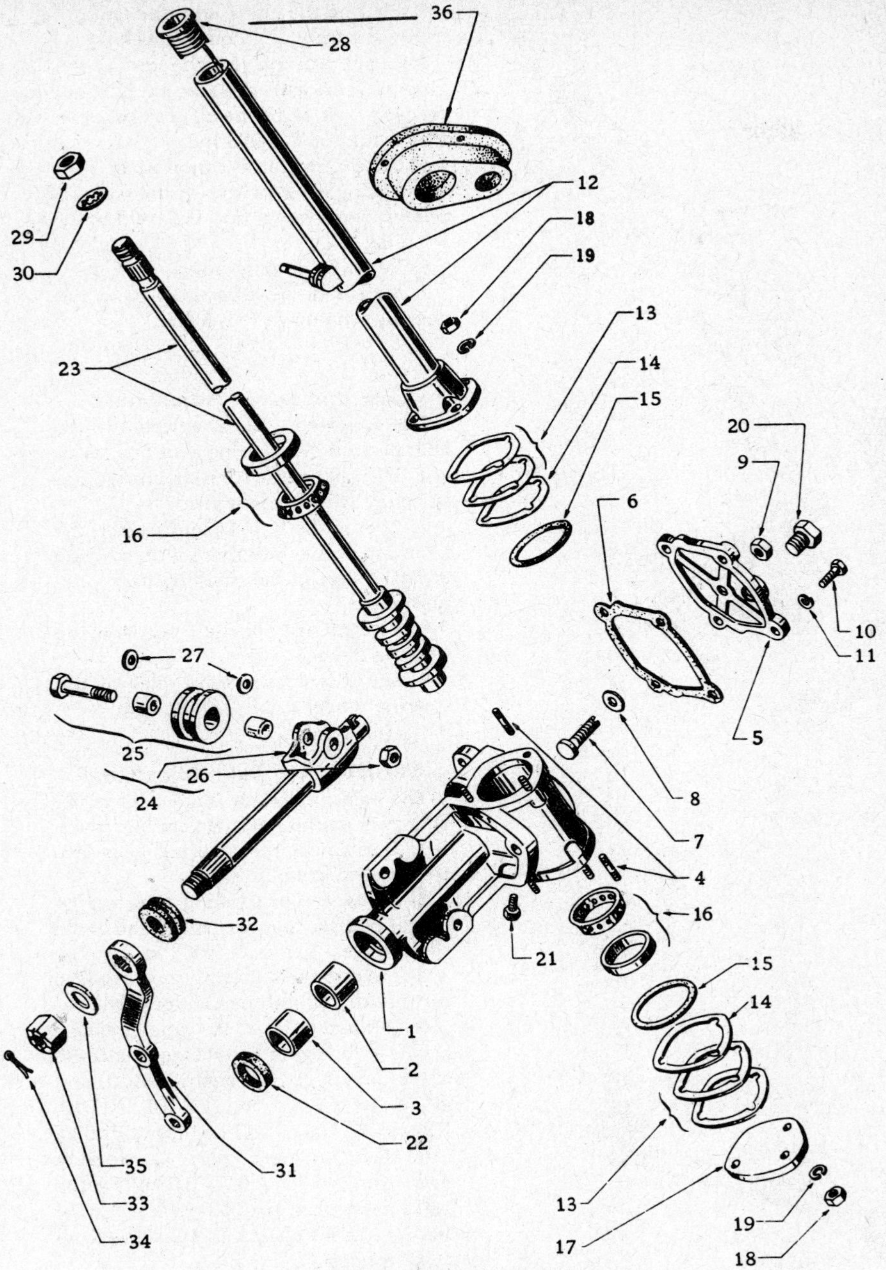

Worm and roller steering gear

1. Steering gear housing
2. Upper bushing
3. Lower bushing
4. Stud
5. Cover
6. Gasket
7. Adjusting screw
8. Adjusting shim
9. Locknut
10. Bolt
11. Lockwasher
12. Steering column
13. Worm bearing shim
14. Shims
15. O-ring
16. Worm bearing
17. Cover
18. Nut
19. Lockwasher
20. Filter plug
21. Drain plug
22. Oil seal
23. Steering shaft
24. Roller shaft
25. Roller and pin
26. Nut
27. Thrust washers
28. Column bushing
29. Wheel nut
30. Lockwasher
31. Steering arm
32. Dust seal
33. Nut
34. Cotter pin
35. Washer
36. Rubber grommet

switch assembly. Disconnect the automatic transmission linkage.

4. Unbolt the steering column from the instrument panel.

5. Remove the steering column hole cover from the floorboards.

6. Unbolt the steering box from the body.

7. Pull the assembly out of the car toward the engine compartment. Be extremely cautious with the LB110 and KLB110 collapsible column. Merely

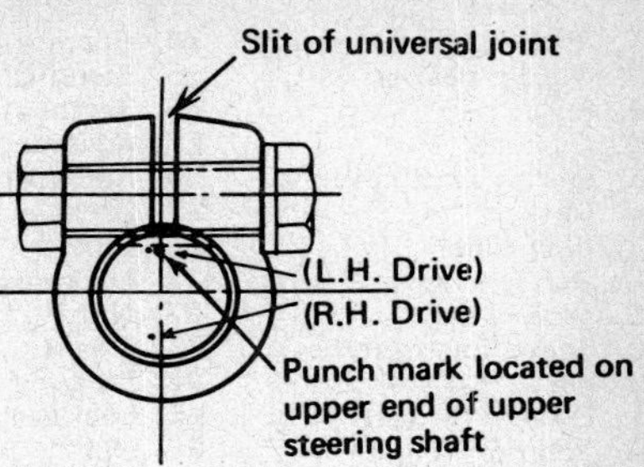

Reassembly details for collapsible column steering shaft

dropping or leaning on the assembly could cause enough damage to require replacement.

8. Reverse the procedure to install.

Fastener	Model	Torque (ft lbs)
Linkage stud nut	PL510, WPL510	40-55
	LB110, KLB110	22-36
Steering gear box bolts	PL510, WPL510	72
	LB110, KLB110	14-19
Steering column-to-instrument panel bolts	LB110, KLB110	11-13
Column clamp-to-column	LB110, KLB110	6-7

240 Z

1. Raise and support the front end. Remove the front wheels.

2. Loosen the clamp bolts at both U-joints. Remove the lower joint and shaft assembly from the engine compartment.

3. Remove the splash shields.

4. Remove the steering side rod stud nuts and pull the studs from the spindle steering arms.

5. Raise the engine slightly, being careful not to damage the accelerator linkage.

6. Unbolt the steering gear housing from the suspension crossmember.

7. Remove the rack and pinion assembly.

8. Reverse the procedure to install. If the upper and lower shaft sections of the collapsible column have been separated, the slit of the universal joint must align with the punch mark on the upper end of the upper steering shaft.

Fastener	Torque (ft lbs)
Rubber coupling bolt	11-13
Lower joint bolt	29-36
Side rod stud nut	40-55
Side rod inner socket stopper nut	53-72
Side rod locknut	65

1. Steering gear housing
2. Needle bearing
3. Plug
4. Oil seal
5. Sector shaft cover
6. Gasket
7. Plug (filler)
8. Bolt
9. Lockwasher
10. Shims for worm bearing
11. O-ring
12. Steering column
13. Bearing
14. Bearing
15. Steering shaft
16. Sector shaft
17. Adjusting screw
18. Adjusting shim
19. Locknut
20. Bolt
21. Lockwasher
22. Nut
23. Washer
24. Steering arm
25. Lockwasher
26. Nut

Recirculating ball steering gear

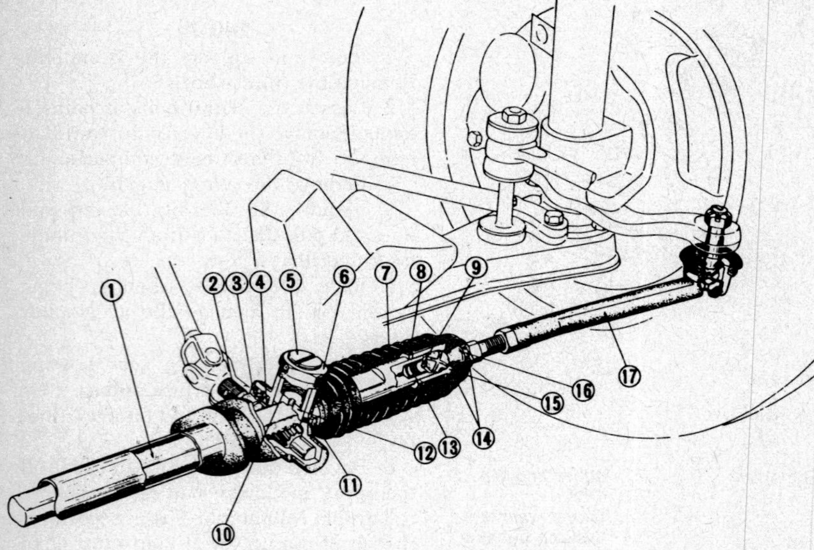

Rack and pinion steering gear, left side shown

1. Rack
2. Pinion
3. Oil seal
4. Pinion bearing
5. Retainer adjusting screw
6. Locknut
7. Boot
8. Locknut
9. Side rod spring seat
10. Retainer spring
11. Filler plug
12. Retainer
13. Side rod inner spring
14. Dust cover clamp
15. Side rod inner socket
16. Ball stud
17. Side rod

Adjustment

Worm and Roller Adjustment

The backlash adjusting screw is located next to the filler plug on the steering gear box cover.

1. Disconnect the drag link from the steering arm.
2. Loosen the locknut and turn the adjusting screw in clockwise until the mechanism binds.
3. Back off the screw until the unit operates smoothly. Tighten the locknut.
4. Check free play at the end of the steering arm, with the steering gear in the central (straight ahead) position. Free play should be 0–0.008 in.
5. Check the force required to turn the steering wheel with a spring scale attached to the wheel rim. It should be 1.-1–1.5 lbs.
6. Replace the drag link.
7. Maximum permissible play at the steering wheel rim is 1–1.4 in.

Cam and Lever Adjustment

The adjusting screw is adjacent to the filler plug on the steering gear box cover.

1. Disconnect the steering linkage ball stud from the steering arm.
2. Loosen the locknut and tighten the adjusting screw until there is no steering arm free play in the straight ahead position.
3. Tighten the locknut. Replace the steering linkage.
4. Maximum permissible play at the steering wheel rim is 0.98–1.38 in.

Recirculating Ball Adjustment

The adjusting screw is adjacent to the filler plug on the steering gear box cover.

1. Disconnect the steering gear arm from the steering linkage.
2. Adjust the backlash at the steering center point so that play at the end of the steering gear arm is 0–0.004 in.
3. Tighten the adjusting screw ⅛–1/6 turn more and tighten the locknut.
4. Reconnect the steering linkage. Specified linkage stud nut torque is 22–36 ft lbs for the LB110 and KLB110, and 40–55 ft lbs for the PL510, PL610, KPL610, WPL510, WPL610, and PL620.
5. Maximum free play at steering wheel rim should be 0.79–0.98 in. for the LB110 and KLB110, 0.98–1.18 in. for the PL510 and WPL510, and 1–1.4 in. for all other models.

Steering Lock

The steering lock/ignition switch /warning buzzer assembly is attached to the steering column by special screws whose heads shear off on installation. The screws must be drilled out to remove the assembly. The ignition switch or warning switch can be replaced without removing the assembly. The ignition switch is on the back of the assembly, and the warning switch on the side. The warning buzzer, which sounds when the driver's door is opened with the steering unlocked, is located behind the instrument panel. It is on the left side of the instrument panel on the LB110 and KLB110, and on the steering support on the 240 Z.

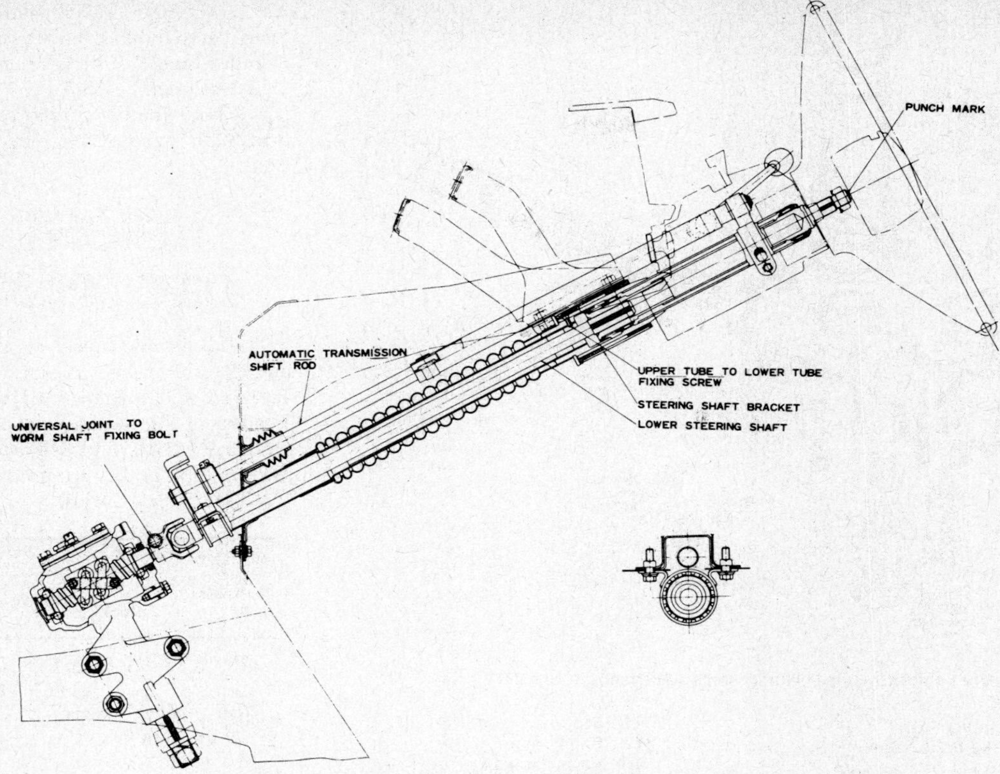

Collapsible shaft and column assemby

BRAKE SYSTEMS

Front disc brakes are used on all current car models, with drum brakes at the rear. All pickups have a drum brake system front and rear. Starting 1968, all car models are equipped with independent front and rear hydraulic systems with a warning light to indicate loss of pressure in either system. The 240 Z, PL610, KPL610, WPL610, and PL620 have a vacuum booster system to lessen required pedal pressure. The parking brake operates the rear brakes through a cable system.

Adjustment

There are four basic types of brake adjusting system used.

Adjuster type	Wheel	Model
Bolt	Rear	LB110, KLB110, PL610, KPL610, WPL610
Bolt with click arrangement	Rear	SPL311, SRL311, PL510, WPL510
Star wheel	Front and Rear	L520, L521, PL521, PL620
Self adjusting	Rear	240 Z

To adjust the brakes, raise the wheels, disconnect the handbrake linkage from the rear wheels, apply the brakes hard a few times to center the drums, and proceed as follows:

Bolt Adjuster

Turn the adjuster bolt on the backing plate until the wheel can no longer be turned, then back off until the wheel is free of drag. Repeat the procedure on the other adjuster bolt on the same wheel. Some models may have only one adjuster bolt per wheel.

Bolt Adjuster With Click Arrangement

The adjuster is located on the backing plate. The adjustment proceeds in clicks or notches. The wheel will often be locked temporarily as the adjuster passes over center for each click. Thus the adjuster is alternately hard and easy to turn. When the wheel is fully locked, back off 1–3 clicks.

Star Wheel Adjuster

Remove the rubber boot from the backing plate. Insert a screwdriver through the adjusting hole to engage the toothed wheel. Turn the adjuster teeth down until the wheel is locked, then push them up about 12 notches so that the wheel is free of drag.

Self Adjusting

No manual adjustment is required. The self adjusters operate whenever the hand or foot brakes are used.

After Adjustment

After adjusting the brakes, reconnect the handbrake linkage. Make sure that there is no rear wheel drag with the handbrake released. Loosen the handbrake adjustment if necessary.

HYDRAULIC SYSTEM

Master Cylinder

Removal and Installation

Clean the outside of the cylinder thoroughly, particularly around the cap and fluid lines. Disconnect the fluid lines and cap them to exclude dirt. Remove the clevis pin connecting the pushrod to the brake pedal arm inside the vehicle. This pin need not be removed on models with the vacuum booster. Unbolt the master cylinder from the firewall and remove. If the pushrod is not adjustable, there will be shims between the cylinder and the firewall. These shims, or the adjustable pushrod, are used to adjust brake pedal free play. After installation, bleed the system and check the pedal free play.

NOTE: *Ordinary brake fluid will boil and cause brake failure under the high temperatures developed in disc brake systems. Special fluid for disc brake systems must be used.*

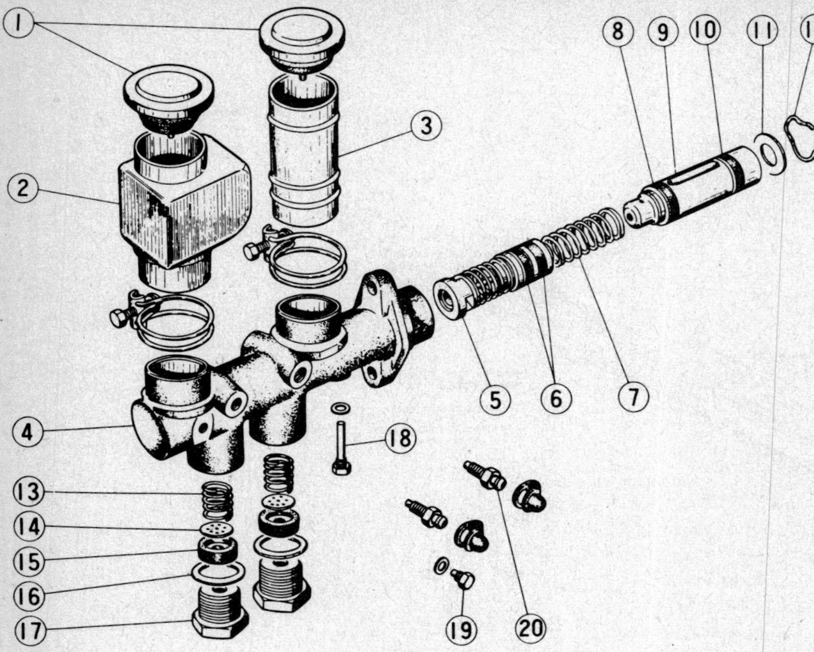

Dual circuit master cylinder used with vacuum booster

1. Reservoir cap
2. Brake fluid reservoir
3. Brake fluid reservoir
4. Brake master cylinder
5. Piston assembly
6. Piston cup
7. Cylinder spring
8. Primary piston cup
9. Pistom assembly
10. Secondary piston cup
11. Stopper
12. Snap ring
13. Valve spring
14. Check valve assembly
15. Check valve assembly
16. Packing
17. Valve cap screw
18. Stopper bolt
19. Stopper bolt
20. Bleeder

Pedal Adjustment

Before adjusting the pedal, make sure that the wheelbrakes are correctly adjusted.

Model	Pedal free play (in.)	Pedal pad free height (in.)
L520	0.39-0.55	—
SPL311, SRL311	0.31-0.47	—
PL510, WPL510	—	8.15 manual, 7.76 automatic
LB110, KLB110	0.24-0.59	5.49-6.65
240 Z	—	7.99
PL620	0.04-0.20	5.51
PL610, KPL610, WPL610	0.04-0.20	7.28

Adjust the pedal free-play by means of an adjustable pushrod or shims between the master cylinder and the firewall. Adjust the pedal height by means of the pedal arm stop pad.

Overhaul

The master cylinder can be disassembled using the illustrations as a guide. Clean all parts in clean brake fluid. Replace the cylinder or piston as necessary if clearance between the two exceeds 0.006 in. Lubricate all parts with clean brake fluid on assembly. Master cylinder rebuilding kits, containing all the wearing parts, are available to simplify overhaul.

System Bleeding

Bleeding is required whenever air in the hydraulic fluid causes a spongy feeling pedal and sluggish response. This is almost always the case after some part of the hydraulic system has been repaired or replaced.

1. Fill the master cylinder reservoir with the proper fluid. Special fluid is required for disc brakes.
2. The usual procedure is to bleed at the points furthest from the master cylinder first.
3. Fit a rubber hose over the bleeder screw. Submerge the other end of the hose in clean brake fluid in a clear glass container. Loosen the bleeder screw.
4. Slowly pump the brake pedal several times until fluid free of bubbles is discharged. An assistant is required to pump the pedal.
5. On the last pumping stroke, hold the pedal down and tighten the bleeder screw. Check the fluid level periodically during the bleeding operation.
6. Bleed the front brakes in the same way as the rear brakes. Note that some front drum brakes have two hydraulic cylinders and two bleeder screws. Both cylinders must be bled.
7. Check that the brake pedal is now firm. If not, repeat the bleeding operation.

FRONT DISC BRAKES

The disc brakes used on the SPL311 and SRL311 are the Dunlop type, manufactured under license in Japan. Lockheed type disc brakes are used on the PL610, KPL610, WPL510, and WPL610. Girling type brakes are used on the 240 Z, KLB110, and LB110.

Min. safe disc pad thickness (in.)	Model	Type brakes
0.236	SPL311, SRL311	Dunlop (Sumitomo)
0.039	PL610, KPL610, WPL510, and WPL610	Lockheed (Akebono)
0.063	LB110, KLB110	Girling (Tokiko)
0.032	240 Z	Girling (Sumitomo)

Disc Brake Pads Replacement

Removal and Installation

All four front brake pads must always be replaced as a set. Several grades of pads are available for most models for road use, or racing.

Dunlop Type

1. Jack up the car and remove the wheel.
2. Remove the keeper plate bolt and keeper plate.
3. Pull the pads out. A removal tool can easily be made.
4. Thoroughly clean the exposed end of each piston and the caliper assembly. Check the rotor (disc) for scoring. If it is badly scored, it must be removed for resurfacing or replacement.
5. Before installing the new pads, the pistons must be pushed back into their cylinders. Be careful not to scratch the pistons or bores.

NOTE: *The master cylinder may overflow when the pistons are pushed back. The bleeder screw can be loosened to prevent overflow.*

6. Install the new pads. Tighten the bleeder screw if it was loosened.
7. Replace the wheels and pump the brake pedal a few times to seat the pads.

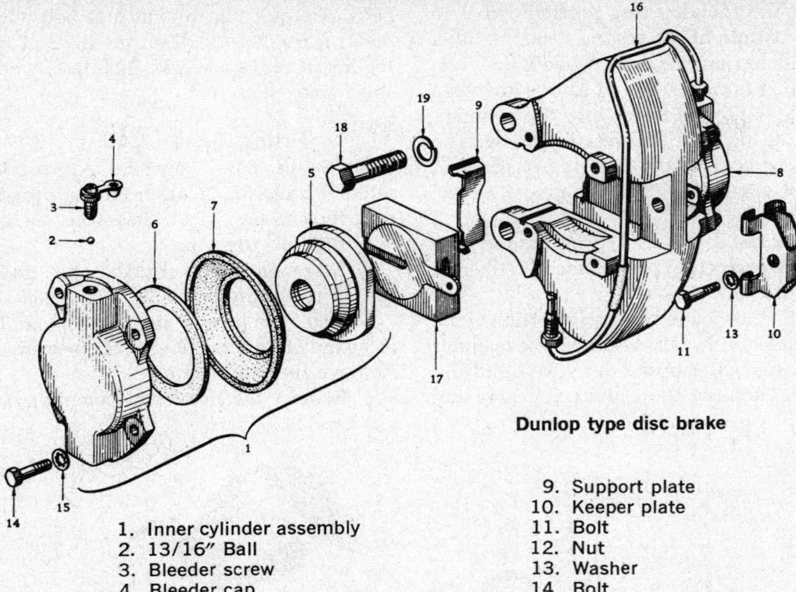

Dunlop type disc brake

1. Inner cylinder assembly
2. 13/16″ Ball
3. Bleeder screw
4. Bleeder cap
5. Piston
6. Piston packing
7. Dust cover
8. Outer cylinder assembly
9. Support plate
10. Keeper plate
11. Bolt
12. Nut
13. Washer
14. Bolt
15. Washer
16. Bridge tube
17. Pad
18. Bolt
19. Lockwasher

This must be done before the car is driven.

Lockheed Type

1. Jack up the car and remove the wheel.
2. Loosen the anti-rattle clip.
3. Loosen the bleed screw. Pull the caliper plate toward the outer end of the spindle and push the piston in 0.12–0.16 in. Be careful not to scratch the pistons or bores.
4. The outer pad can now be pulled out.
5. Pull the caliper plate inward and remove the inner pad.
6. Thoroughly clean the exposed end of each piston and the caliper assembly. Check the rotor (disc) for scoring. If it is badly scored, it must be removed for resurfacing or replacement.
7. If the piston has been pushed in far enough, the new pads can be installed.
8. Install the new pads. Tighten the bleeder screw.

Girling Type

1. Jack up the car and remove the wheel.
2. Remove the clip(s), retaining pins, and anti-squeal clips. Remove the coil spring on the LB110 and KLB110.
3. Using pliers, pull out the pads and anti-squeal shims.
4. Thoroughly clean the exposed end of each piston and the caliper assembly. Check the rotor (disc) for scoring. If it is badly scored, it must be removed for resurfacing or replacement.
5. Before installing the new pads, the pistons must be pushed back into their cylinders. Be careful not to scratch the pistons or bores.

NOTE: *The master cylinder may overflow when the pistons are pushed back. The bleeder screw can be loosened to prevent overflow.*

Be careful not to push the pistons in too far or the seals will be damaged. The pistons need not be pushed in past a position flush with the edge of the cylinder. Install the new pads and tighten the bleeder screw if it was loosened.

6. Install the anti-squeal shims with the arrow marks pointing in the direction of rotor rotation. On the LB110, the coil spring should be installed on the retaining pin furthest from the bleed screw.
7. Replace the wheels and pump the brake pedal a few times to seat the pads. This must be done before the car is driven.

Calipers and Brake Discs

Overhaul

Lockheed Type

1. Jack up and support the car. Remove the wheel.
2. Disconnect and cap the brake hose.
3. Unbolt and remove the caliper assembly.
4. Remove the spindle nut and rotor with the hub.
5. Unbolt and remove the rotor from the hub.
6. Remove the pads. Remove the tension springs and pull out the cylinder. Apply air or hydraulic pressure to the inlet hole to remove the piston from the cylinder. Remove the retainer and seals. The piston seal also serves to retract the piston and should be replaced at every overhaul.
7. If the rotor (disc) is scored, it can be machined. Minimum safe rotor thickness is 0.331 in. Rotor runout must not exceed 0.004.
8. Wash all parts in clean brake fluid. Replace all seals. If the cylinder or piston is damaged, replace both.

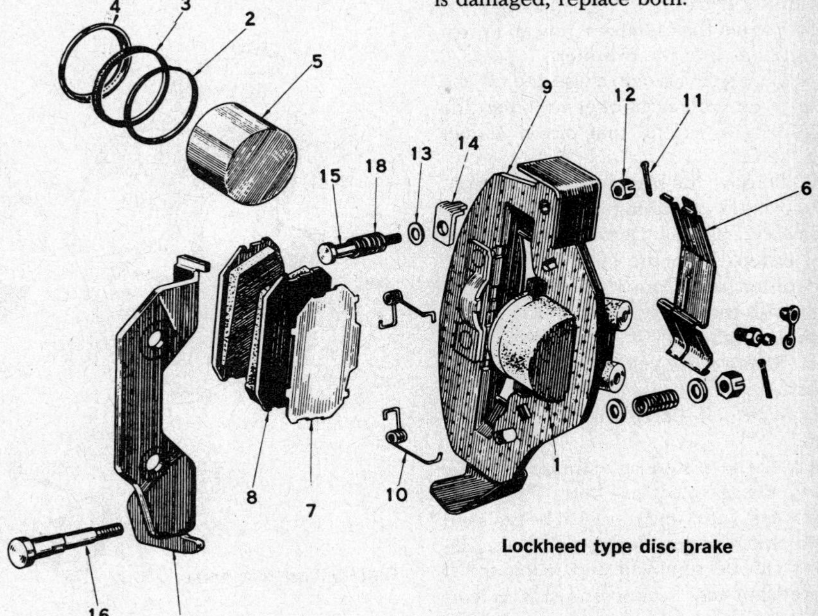

Lockheed type disc brake

1. Cylinder
2. Piston seal
3. Wiper seal
4. Retainer
5. Piston
6. Clip
7. Shim
8. Pad
9. Caliper plate
10. Tension spring
11. Cotter pin
12. Nut
13. Washer
14. Support bracket
15. Hold down pin
16. Pivot pin
17. Mounting bracket
18. Spring

9. Bolt the rotor to the hub, torquing the bolts to 28–38 ft lbs. Pack the bearings, install the hub on the spindle, and adjust the wheel bearing.

10. Insert a new seal in the cylinder groove and attach the wiper seal. Lubricate the cylinder bore with brake fluid. Insert the piston cautiously until the piston head is almost flush with the wiper seal retainer. The relieved part of the piston must face the pivot pin.

11. Install the cylinder into the caliper plate and secure it with the tension springs.

12. Install the hold down pin, washer, and nut on the support bracket. Install a new cotter pin in the nut.

13. Assemble the mounting bracket and caliper plate with the pivot pin. Install the washer, spring, washer, and nut. Tighten the nut completely and lock it with a cotter pin.

14. Install the caliper assembly to the spindle, torquing the mounting bolts to 53–65 ft lbs. Make sure that the caliper plate can slide smoothly.

15. Install the pads and shims, making sure that they are seated correctly. Seat the inner pad first. Make sure the anti-rattle clip is positioned correctly.

16. Reconnect the brake hose and bleed the system.

Girling Type—LB110, KLB110

1. Remove the pads.
2. Disconnect the brake tube.
3. Remove the two bottom strut assembly installation bolts to obtain clearance.
4. Remove the caliper assembly mounting bolts.
5. Loosen the bleeder screw and press the pistons into the cylinder.
6. Clamp the yoke in a vise and tap the yoke head with a hammer to loosen the cylinder. Be careful that piston A does not fall out.
7. Remove the bias ring from piston A. Remove the retaining rings and boots from both pistons. Depress and remove the pistons from the cylinder. Remove the piston seal from the cylinder carefully with the fingers so as not to mar the cylinder wall.
8. Remove the yoke springs from the yoke.
9. Wash all parts with clean brake fluid.
10. If the piston or cylinder is badly worn or scored, replace both. The piston surface is plated and must not be polished with emery paper. Replace all seals. The rotor can be removed and machined if scored, but final thickness must be at least 0.331 in. Runout must not exceed 0.001 in.
11. Lubricate the cylinder bore with clean brake fluid and install the piston seal.
12. Insert the bias ring into piston A so that the rounded ring portion comes to the bottom of the piston. Piston A has a small depression inside, while B does not.
13. Lubricate the pistons with clean brake fluid and insert into the cylinder. Install the boot and retaining ring. The yoke groove of the bias ring of piston A must align with the yoke groove of the cylinder.
14. Install the yoke springs to the yoke so the projecting portion faces to the disc (rotor).
15. Lubricate the sliding portion of the cylinder and yoke. Assemble the cylinder and yoke by tapping the yoke lightly.
16. Replace the caliper assembly and pads. Torque the mounting bolts to 33–41 ft lbs. Rotor bolt torque is 20–27 ft lbs. Strut bolt torque is 33–44 ft lbs. Bleed the system of air.

Girling Type—240 Z

The caliper halves must not to be separated. If brake fluid leaks from the bridge seal, replace the caliper assembly.

1. Remove the pads.
2. Disconnect the brake line and caliper mounting bolts.
3. Hold the piston in one side and force the other one out with air pressure. Remove the other piston.
4. Remove the piston seal from the cyl-

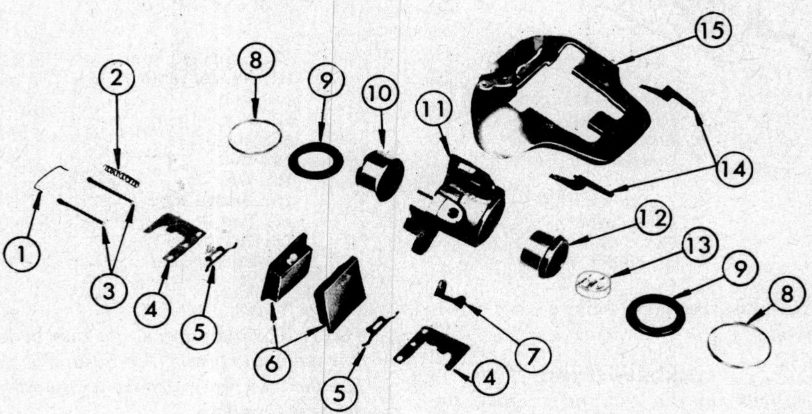

Girdling type disc brake, LB110 and KLB110

1. Clip
2. Spring
3. Pin
4. Shim
5. Hanger spring
6. Brake pad
7. Air bleeder
8. Retaining ring
9. Boot
10. Piston B
11. Cylinder
12. Piston A
13. Bias ring
14. Yoke spring
15. Yoke

Girdling type disc brake, 240 Z

1. Anti-squeal shim, right
2. Pad
3. Anti-squeal shim, left
4. Retaining ring
5. Dust cover
6. Piston
7. Piston seal
8. Anti-squeal spring
9. Caliper assembly
10. Bleeder
11. Clip
12. Retaining pin
13. Caliper fixing bolt
14. Baffle plate

inder carefully with the fingers so as not to mar the cylinder wall.

5. Wash all parts with clean brake fluid.

6. If the piston or cylinder is badly worn or scored, replace both. The piston surface is plated and must not be polished with emery paper. Replace all seals.

7. With the wheel bearing properly adjusted, runout at the center of the rotor surface should be less than 0.006 in. The rotor can be resurfaced if scored, but must be at least 0.413 in thick after resurfacing.

8. Lubricate the piston seal with clean brake fluid and install it.

9. Install dust seals on the pistons, lubricate the pistons with clean brake fluid, and install the pistons into the cylinders. Clamp the dust seals with retaining rings.

10. Reinstall the caliper assembly. Mounting bolt torque is 53–71 ft lbs. Rotor mounting bolt torque is 28–38 ft lbs.

11. Replace the pads and brake line. Bleed the system of air.

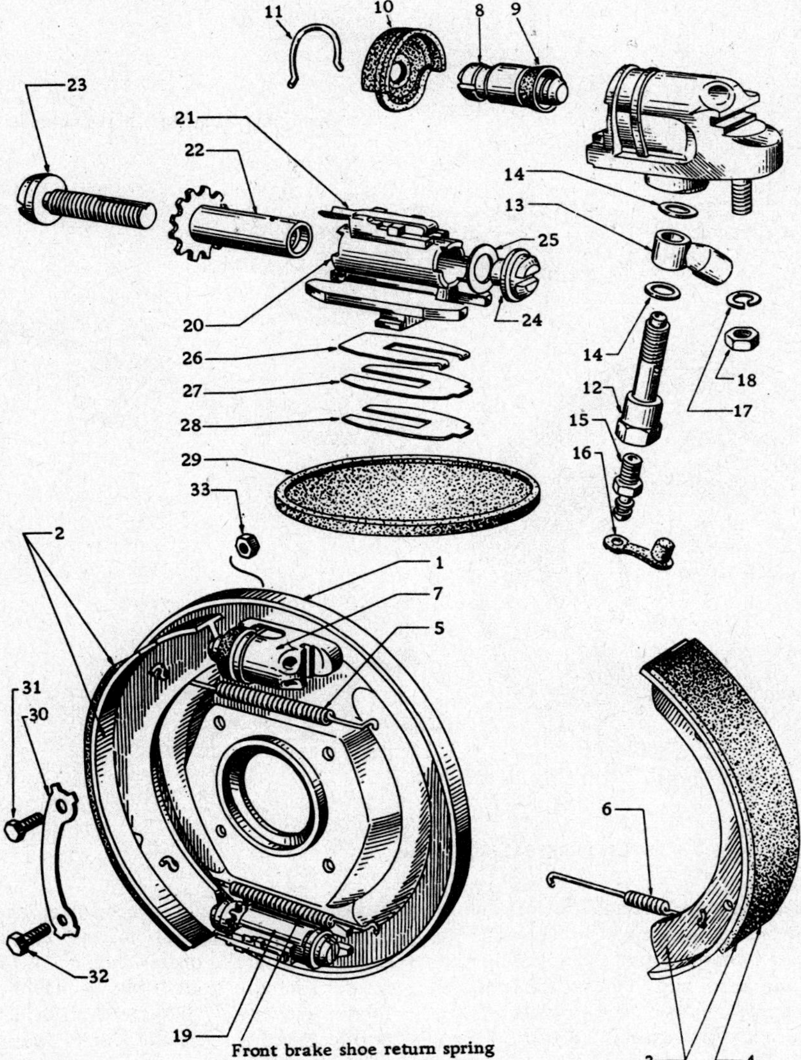

Pickup rear brake, L520 shown

1. Backing plate
2. Forward shoe
3. Rear shoe
4. Lining
5. Rear shoe return spring
6. Rear shoe return spring
7. Wheel cylinder
8. Piston
9. Piston cup
10. Dust shield
11. Dust shield retainer
12. Connector bolt
13. Connector
14. Washer
15. Bleeder screw
16. Bleeder cap
17. Lockwasher
18. Nut
19. Adjuster
20. Adjuster housing
21. Lock spring
22. Adjuster wheel
23. Adjuster screw
24. Adjuster head
25. Adjuster head shim
26. Adjuster retaining spring
27. Retaining spring lock plate
28. Retaining spring adjusting shim
29. Rubber boot
30. Lock plate
31. Bolt
32. Bolt
33. Nut

DRUM BRAKES

Front drum brakes on all models except the L520 pickups have two shoes and two hydraulic cylinders at each wheel. These pickups have two shoes and a single hydraulic cylinder at each wheel. The cylinders are bolted to the front brake backing plate. All models have rear drum brakes. Each rear brake assembly has two brake shoes and a single hydraulic cylinder which is free to slide back and forth in a slot in the brake backing plate. On some models the hydraulic cylinder is bolted fast and the adjuster slides.

Lining Replacement

PL510, PL610, KPL610, WPL510, WPL610 Rear

1. Raise the vehicle and remove the wheels.

2. Release the parking brake. Disconnect the cross rod from the lever of the brake cylinder. Remove the brake drum. Place a heavy rubber band around the cylinder to prevent the piston from coming out.

3. Remove the return springs and shoes.

4. Clean the backing plate and check the wheel cylinder for leaks. To remove the wheel cylinder, remove the brake line, dust cover, plates, and adjusting shims. Clearance between the cylinder and the piston should not exceed 0.006 in.

5. The drums must be machined if scored or out of round more than 0.002 in. The drum inside diameter should not be machined beyond 9.04 in. Minimum safe lining thickness is 0.059 in.

6. Hook the return springs into the new shoes. The springs should be between the shoes and the backing plate. The longer return spring must be adjacent to the wheel cylinder. A very thin film of grease may be applied to the pivot points at the ends of the brake shoes. Grease the shoe locating buttons on the backing plate, also. Be careful not to get grease on the linings or drums.

7. Place one shoe in the adjuster and piston slots, and pry the other shoe into position.

8. Replace the drums and wheels. Adjust the brakes. Bleed the hydraulic system of air if the brake lines were disconnected.

9. Reconnect the handbrake, making sure that it does not cause the shoes to drag when it is released.

LB110, KLB110 Rear

1. Raise the vehicle and remove the wheels.

2. Loosen the handbrake cable, remove the clevis pin from the wheel cylinder lever, disconnect the handbrake cable, and remove the return pull spring.

3. Remove the brake drum, shoe retainers, return springs, and brake shoes. Loosen the brake adjusters if the drums are difficult to remove. Place a heavy rubber band around the cylinder to prevent the piston from coming out.

4. Clean the backing plate and check the wheel cylinder for leaks. To remove the wheel cylinder, remove the brake line, dust cover, plates, and adjusting shims. Clearance between cylinder and piston should not exceed 0.006 in.

5. The drums must be machined if scored or out of round more than 0.001 in. The drum inside diameter must not be machined beyond 8.04 in. Minimum safe lining thickness is 0.059 in.

6. Follow Steps 6–9 for PL510, WPL510 Rear.

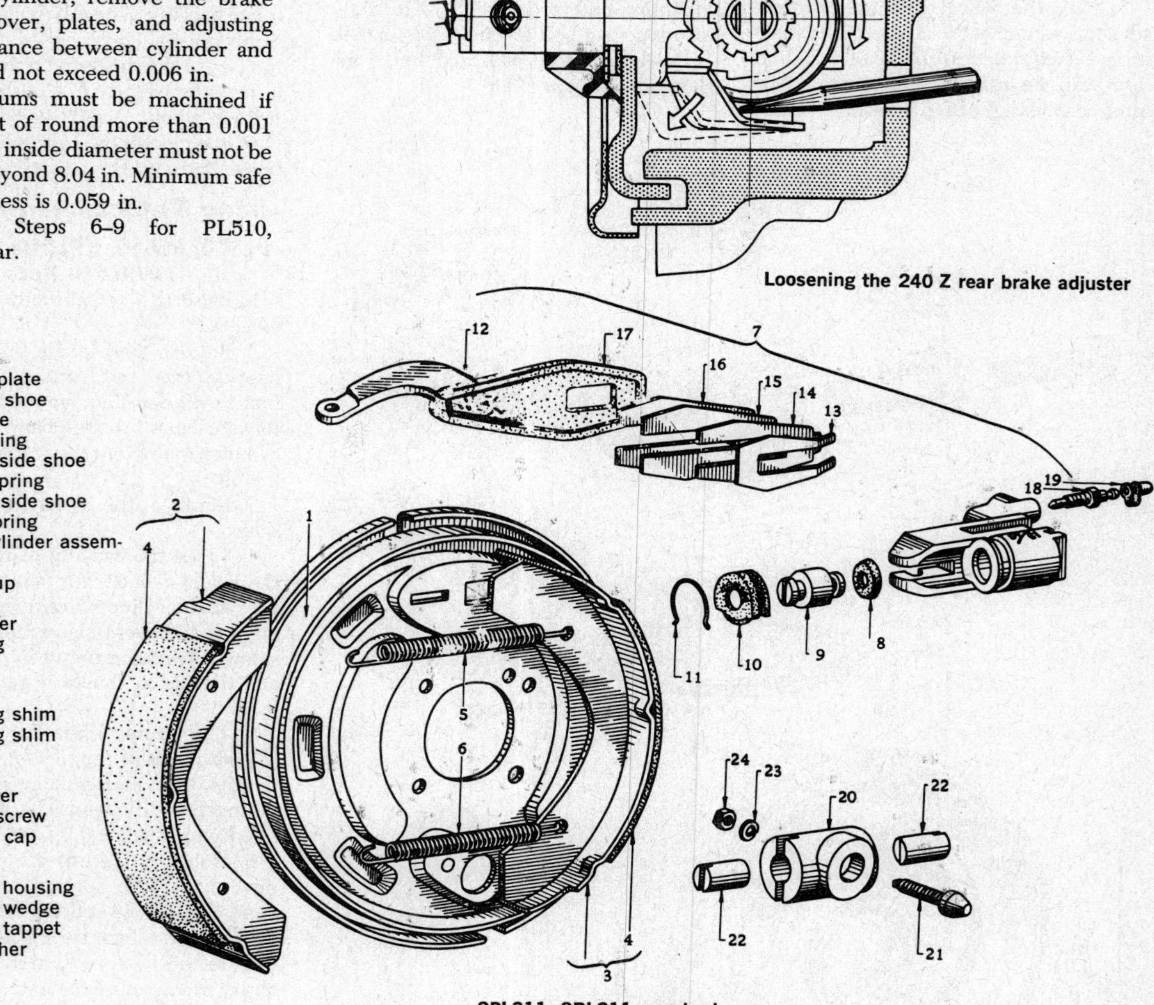

Loosening the 240 Z rear brake adjuster

1. Backing plate
2. Forward shoe
3. Rear shoe
4. Brake lining
5. Cylinder side shoe return spring
6. Adjuster side shoe return spring
7. Wheel cylinder assembly
8. Piston cup
9. Cylinder
10. Dust cover
11. Snap-ring
12. Lever
13. Adjusting shim
14. Adjusting shim
15. Plate
16. Plate
17. Dust cover
18. Bleeder screw
19. Bleeder cap
20. Adjuster housing
21. Adjuster wedge
22. Adjuster tappet
23. Lockwasher
24. Nut

SPL311, SRL311 rear brake

240 Z Rear

1. Raise and support the vehicle. Remove the wheel.

2. Remove the brake drum. If it is difficult to remove, remove the wheel cylinder lever handbrake clevis pin. Remove the brake drum adjusting hole plug and pry the adjusting lever away from the adjusting wheel with a screwdriver inserted through the adjusting hole. Turn the adjusting wheel down with the screwdriver to loosen the brake shoes. Remove the brake drum.

3. Remove the brake shoe retainers and springs. Remove the shoes and return springs. Place a heavy rubber band around the cylinder to prevent the piston from coming out.

4. Clean the backing plate and check for wheel cylinder leaks. To remove the wheel cylinder, detach the brake tube and dust cover, drive the lock plate out toward the front, pull the adjusting plate to the rear, and remove the cylinder. Clearance between the cylinder and piston should not exceed 0.006 in.

5. The drums should be machined if scored or out of round more than 0.002 in. The drum inside diameter should not be machined beyond 9.04 in. Minimum safe lining thickness is 0.060 in.

6. On reassembly, apply a very light film of grease to all sliding surfaces. Be careful not to get any on the linings or drums. The wheel cylinder must be free to slide. The longer black return spring must be adjacent to the wheel cylinder.

All Other Models

Lining replacement procedures for models not specifically covered above are generally quite similar to the above procedures. Brake drums should not be machined more than 0.040 in. beyond their original inside diameter, and should be machined if scored or out of round more than 0.002 in. Minimum safe lining thickness is 0.060 in.

PARKING BRAKE

Adjustment

Handbrake adjustments are generally not needed, unless the cables have stretched.

All Models except 240 Z

There is an adjusting nut on the cable under the car, usually at the end of the front cable and near the point at which

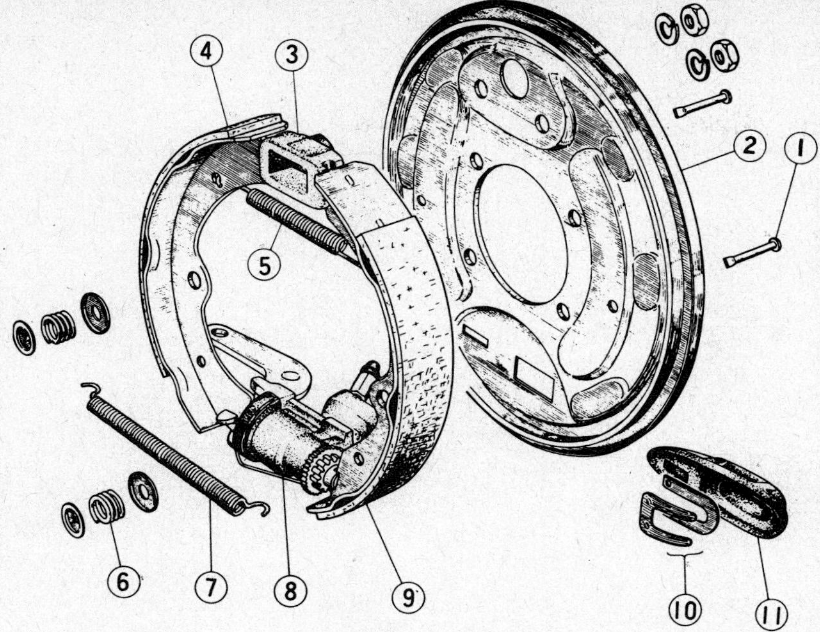

240 Z rear brake

1. Anti-rattle pin
2. Brake backing plate
3. Anchor block
4. After shoe assembly
5. Return spring
6. Anti-rattle spring
7. Return spring
8. Wheel cylinder
9. Fore shoe assembly
10. Retaining shim
11. Dust cover

the two cables from the rear wheels come together (the equalizer). The LB110 and KLB110 have a turnbuckle in the cable. LB110 and KLB110 handbrake lever stroke should be 3.1 in. or 6 notches. PL510 handle travel should be 3.4–3.7 in.; WPL510 handle travel should be 4.-3–4.7 in. PL620 handle travel should be 3.1–3.9 in.; PL610, KPL610, and WPL610 handle travel should be 3.5–3.9 in. Some models also have a turnbuckle in the rear cable to compensate for cable stretching.

240 Z

The driveshaft must be removed gain access to the adjusting nut on the front linkage rod.

CHASSIS ELECTRICAL

Heater Unit

Removal and Installation

PL510, WPL510

1. Drain the coolant.
2. Disconnect the water pipes to the engine.
3. Disconnect the blower motor electrical connector.
4. Remove the three heater control wires at the heater unit.
5. Remove the two bolts and ventilator.
6. Remove the four bolts and detach the heater unit.
7. Reverse the procedure for installation.

LB110, KLB110

1. Remove the package tray and ashtray.
2. Disconnect the two hoses between the heater and engine.
3. Disconnect the cables from the heater unit and heater controls. Disconnect the wiring.
4. Disconnect the two control wires from the water cock and interior valve, and the control rod from the shut valve. Set the heater control upper lever to DEF and lower lever to OFF.
5. Pull off the right and left defroster hoses.
6. Remove the four screws holding the heater unit to the firewall. Remove the control knob and remove the screws holding the control unit to the instrument panel. Remove the heater unit.
7. Reverse the procedure for installation.

PL610, KPL610, WPL610

1. Disconnect the battery ground cable.
2. Drain the coolant.
3. Detach the coolant inlet and outlet hoses.
4. Remove the center ventilator grille from the bottom of the instrument panel.
5. Remove the heater duct hose.
6. Detach the defroster hose from each side of the heater unit.
7. Disconnect the control cables.
8. Disconnect the wires at the connectors.
9. Remove the bolt at each side of the unit and the one on the top.
10. Remove the unit.
11. Reverse the procedure for installation. Run the engine for a few minutes with the heater on to make sure the system is filled with coolant.

PL620

1. Disconnect the battery ground cable.
2. Drain the coolant.
3. Remove the defroster hoses.
4. Disconnect the control cables.
5. Disconnect the wires at the connectors.
6. Disconnect the coolant inlet and outlet hoses.
7. Remove the three mounting bolts and remove the heater unit.
8. Reverse the procedure for installation. Run the engine for a few minutes with the heater on to make sure the system is filled with coolant.

Heater Core

Removal and Installation

PL510, WPL510

1. Remove the four clips and separate the lower cover.
2. Unbolt and remove the heater core.
3. Installation is the reverse of removal.

PL610, KPL610, WPL610, PL620

The heater unit need not be removed to remove the heater core. It must be removed to remove the blower motor.

1. Drain the coolant.
2. Detach the coolant hoses.
3. Disconnect the control cables on the sides of the heater unit.
4. Remove the clips and the cover from the front of the heater unit.
5. Pull out the core.
6. Reverse the procedure for installation. Run the engine with the heater on for a few minutes to make sure the system fills with coolant.

Radio

Removal and Installation

PL510, PL610, KPL610, WPL610, PL620

1. Detach all electrical connections.
2. Remove the radio knobs and retaining nuts.
3. Remove the mounting screws, tip the radio down at the rear, and remove.
4. Reverse the procedure for installation.

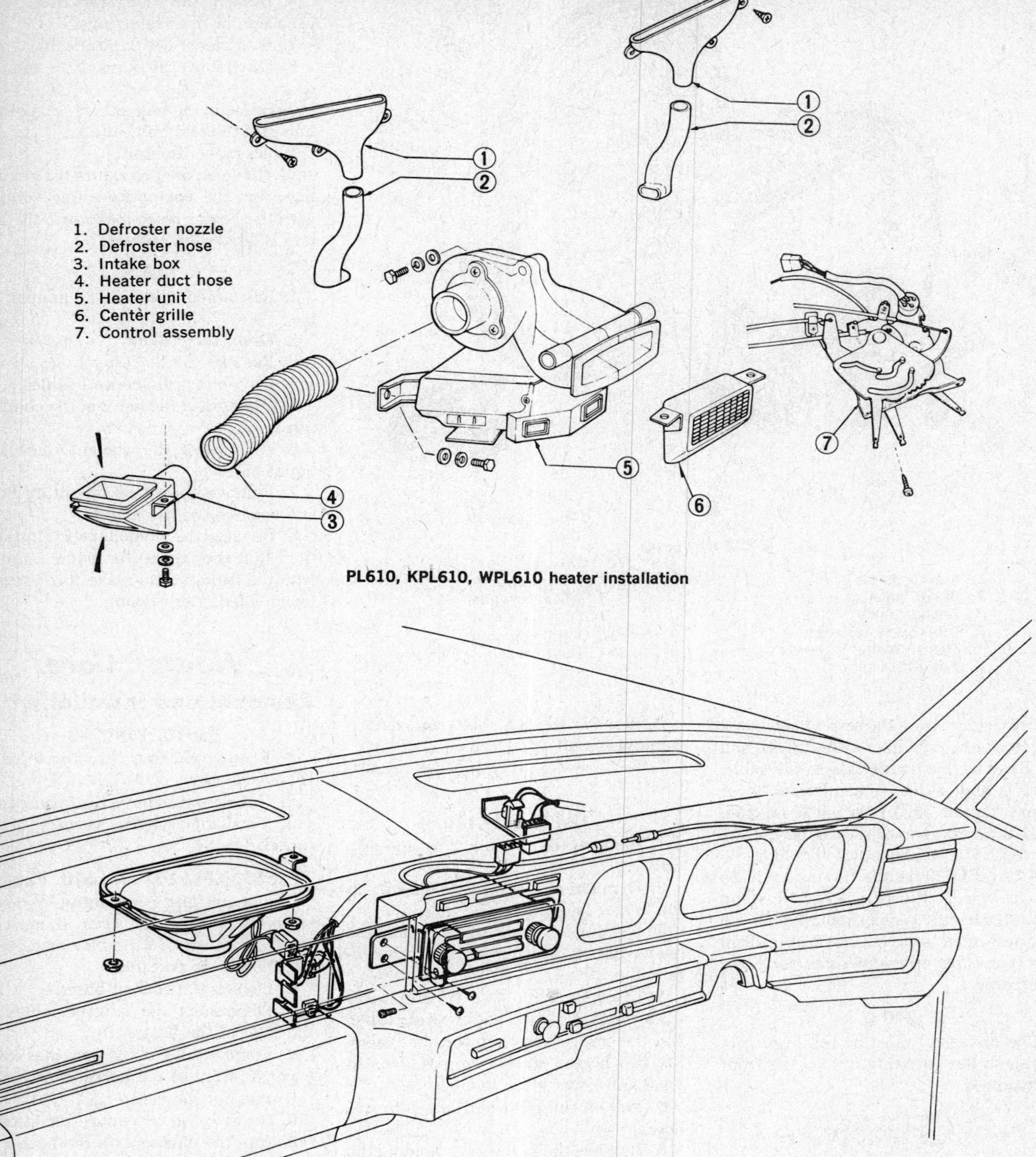

PL610, KPL610, WPL610 heater installation

PL610, KPL610, WPL610 radio installation

LB110, KLB110

1. Remove the instrument cluster.
2. Detach all electrical connections.
3. Remove the radio knobs and retaining nuts.
4. Remove the rear support bracket.
5. Remove the radio.
6. Reverse the procedure for installation.

240 Z

The radio is mounted in the center console panel and the speaker in the left fender inner panel. The front face plate of the console must be removed to remove the radio.

Windshield Wiper Motor

Removal and Installation

PL510, PL610, KPL610, WPL510, WPL610

The wiper motor and operating linkage is on the firewall under the hood.

1. Lift the wiper arms. Remove the securing nuts and detach the arms.
2. Remove the nuts holding the wiper pivots to the body. Remove the air intake grille for access.
3. Open the hood and unscrew the motor from the firewall.
4. Disconnect the wiring connector and remove the wiper motor with the linkage.

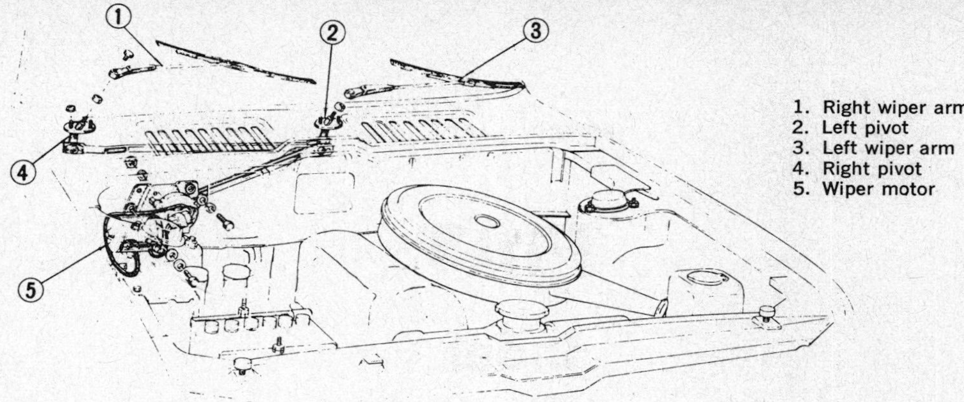

PL610, KPL610, WPL610 wiper installation

5. Reverse the procedure for installation.

NOTE: *If the wipers do not park correctly, adjust the position of the automatic stop cover on the wiper motor.*

LB110, KLB110

The wiper motor is on the firewall under the hood. The operating linkage is on the firewall inside the car.

1. Detach the motor wiring plug.
2. Inside the car, remove the nut connecting the linkage to the wiper shaft.
3. Unbolt and remove the wiper motor from the firewall.
4. Reverse the procedure for installation.

PL620

The wiper motor is on the firewall, inside the truck.

1. Remove the air intake grille in front of the windshield.
2. Detach the connecting rod from the wiper motor arm, working through the grille opening.
3. Disconnect the electrical connector at the motor.
4. Unscrew and remove the motor.
5. Reverse the procedure for installation.

Instrument Cluster

Removal and Installation

PL510, WPL510

1. Disconnect the speedometer cable by unscrewing the nut at the back of the speedometer.
2. Remove the screws holding the instrument cluster to the instrument panel.
3. Pull out the instrument cluster enough to detach the wiring.
4. Remove the cluster. Individual instrument units can be removed from the rear of the cluster.

LB110, KLB110

1. Disconnect the battery negative lead.
2. Depress the wiper, light switch, and choke knobs, turning them counterclockwise to remove.
3. From the rear, disconnect the lighter wire. Turn and remove the lighter outer case.
4. Remove the radio and heater knobs.
5. Remove the shell cover from the steering column.
6. Remove the screws which hold the instrument cluster to the instrument panel. Pull out the cluster.
7. Disconnect the wiring connector. Disconnect the speedometer cable by unscrewing the nut at the back of the speedometer.
8. Individual instruments may be removed from the rear of the cluster.

PL610, KPL610, WPL610

1. Disconnect the battery ground cable.
2. Remove the four screws and the steering column cover.
3. Remove the screws which attach the cluster face. Two are just above the steering column, and there is one inside each of the outer instrument recesses.
4. Pull the cluster lid forward.
5. Disconnect the multiple connector.
6. Disconnect the speedometer cable.
7. Disconnect any other wiring.
8. Remove the cluster face.
9. Remove the odometer knob if the vehicle has one.
10. Remove the six screws and the cluster.
11. Instruments may now be readily replaced.
12. Reverse the procedure for installation.

PL620

1. Disconnect the battery ground cable.
2. Remove the three cluster face retaining screws from inside the instrument recesses.
3. Remove the cluster face retaining screw from underneath the instrument panel.
4. Pull the cluster face outward.
5. Disconnect the speedometer cable and the multiple electrical connector. Disconnect any other wiring. Remove the four screws which hold the cluster to the cluster face. Remove the cluster.
6. Reverse the procedure for installation.

Instruments

Removal and Installation—240 Z

The speedometer and tachometer are both attached at the rear with two wingnuts. Access is from under the instrument panel. After the wingnuts are removed, the instrument can be pulled out through the instrument panel. The other three gauge units are held to brackets by slotted head hex bolts. To gain access, the center console panel must be removed.

Fuses

Model	Fuse Box Location	Fusible Link Location
L520, L521 PL521, PL510, WPL510	Engine compartment right rear	
SPL311, SRL311	Inside glove compartment	
LB110 KLB110	Under instrument panel, right of steering column	Between battery and alternator
240 Z	Under ash tray in console	At alternator, at starter
PL610, KPL610, WPL610	Below hood release knob	Adjacent to battery
PL620	Below headlight switch	Between battery and alternator

FIAT

Index

INTRODUCTION

Fiat has imported many models into the United States, among them the 124 series, 128 series, and 850 series. Most series are available in body styles ranging from roadsters and coupes to sedans and station wagons.

All Fiats are equipped with four-cylinder, inline, water cooled engines. Displacements run from 50 cu in. to as high as 98 cu in.

MODEL IDENTIFICATION

Fiat 124 Sedan

Fiat 124 Coupe

Fiat 124 Spider

Fiat 850 Sedan

Fiat 850 Coupe

Fiat 850 Spider

Fiat 850 Sport Spider

Fiat 124 Special

Fiat 124 Sport Spider

Fiat 124 Family Wagon

Fiat 128 Sedan

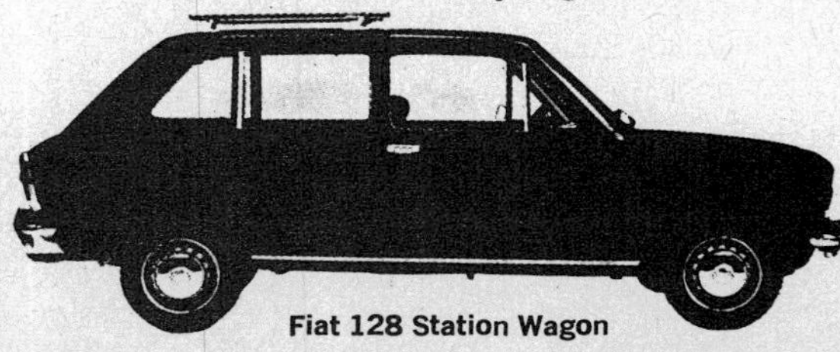

Fiat 128 Station Wagon

Vehicle and Engine Identification

An identification plate, mounted on the engine compartment wall, carries the chassis number and the spare parts ordering number. The engine number is stamped on a pad on the engine block.

Fiat 850 Identification: (A) Model number: (B) Chassis type and serial number; (C) Engine type and serial number.

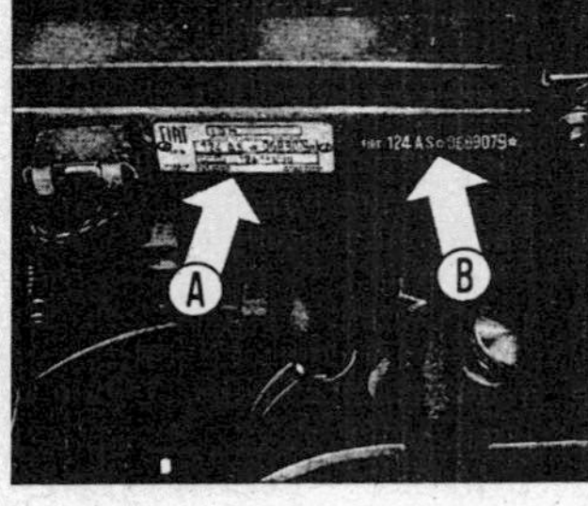

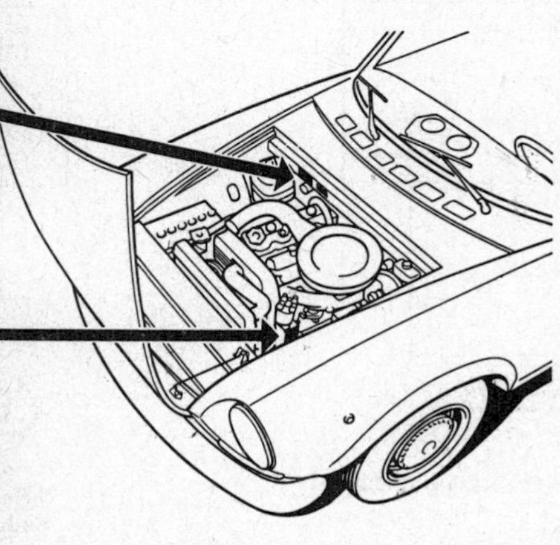

Fiat 124 Identification: (A) Chassis type and number, engine type and spares ordering number; (B) Chassis number; (C) Engine number.

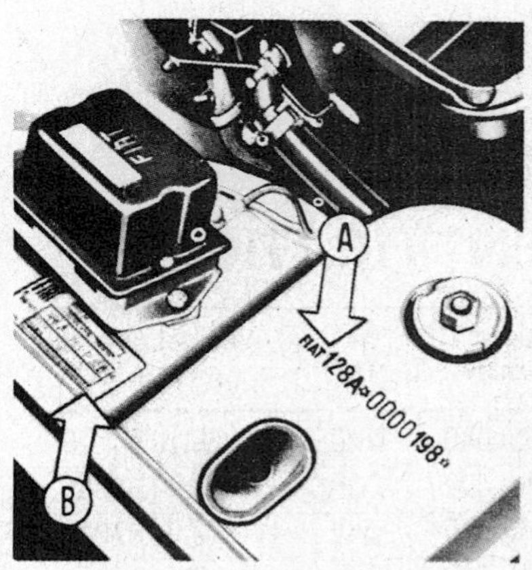

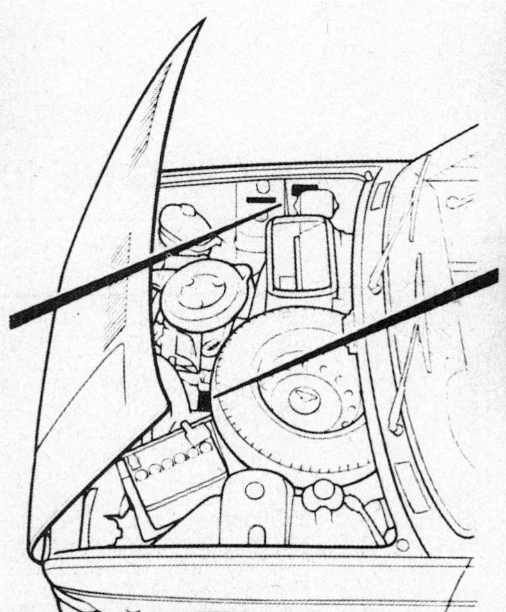

Fiat 128 Identification: (A) Chassis type and serial number; (B) Identification plate; and (C) Engine type and serial number.

Firing Order

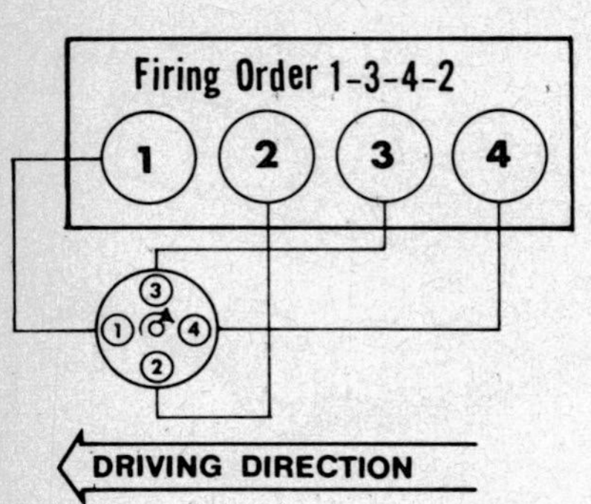

Firing order—124 Sedan, Station Wagon (1970).

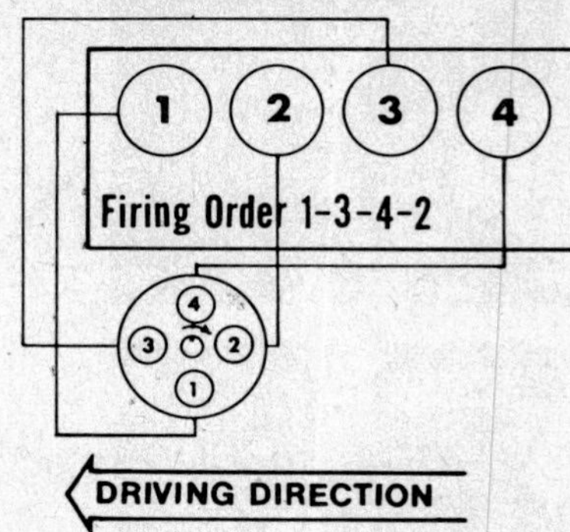

Firing order—124 Spider, Coupe

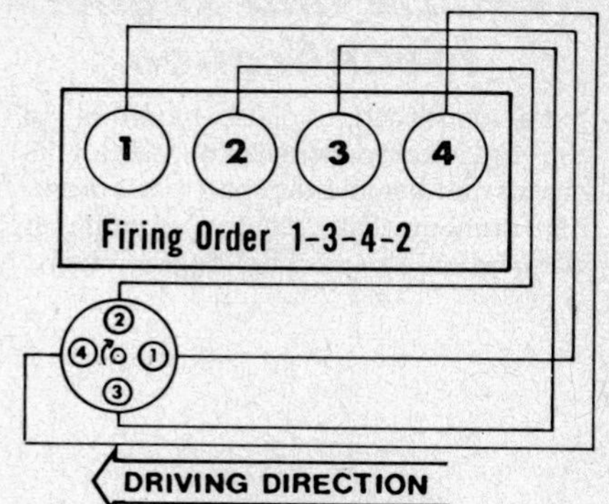

Firing order—124 Sport Coupe and Sport Spider

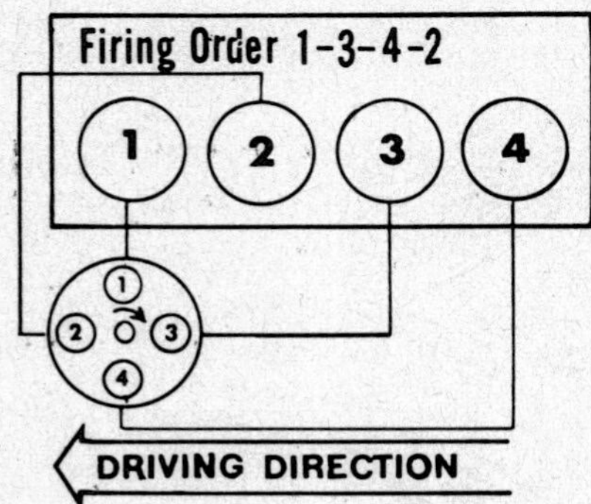

Firing order—124 Sedan, Station Wagon

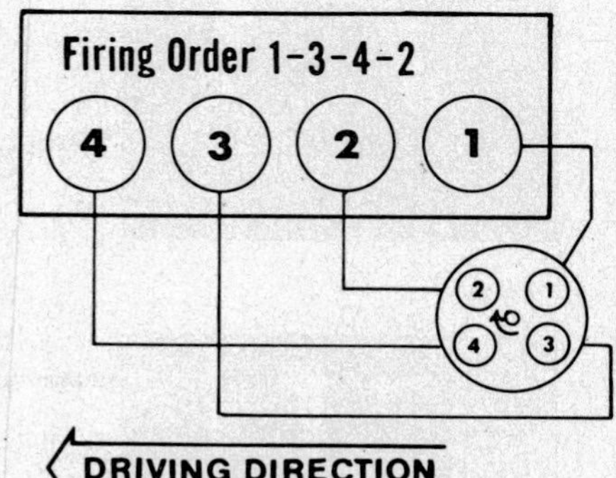

Firing order—850 Coupe, Sport Coupe, Sedan.

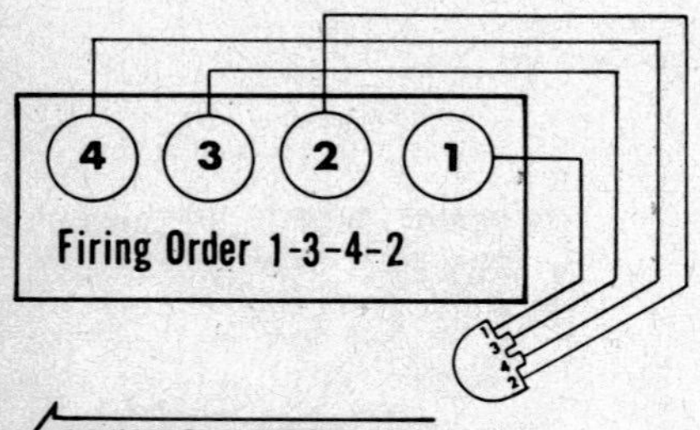

Firing order—850 Spider, Sport Spider

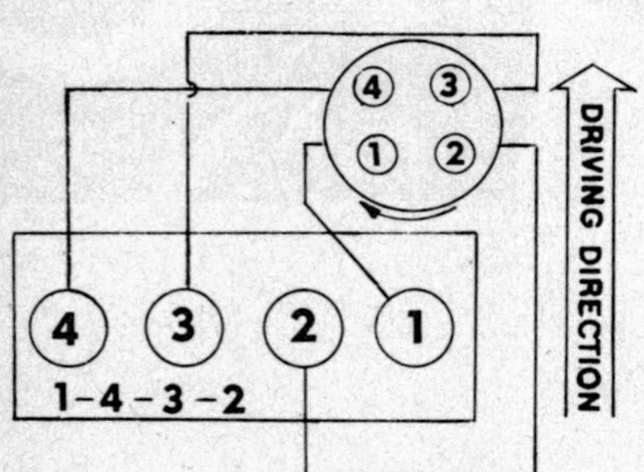

Firing order—128

ENGINE IDENTIFICATION

Car Model	Serial Number	Type	Displacement Cu. In. (cc)
128 Sedan	128A.040	OHC	68.10 (1,116)
124 Spyder Coupe	124AC.000	DOHC	87.7 (1,438)
124 Sedan, Sta Wag	124B.040	OHV	73.0 (1,197)
124 Special	124B2.040	OHV	87.7 (1,438)
124 Sport Coupe Spyder	125BC.040	DOHC	98.1 (1,608)
850 Sedan	100G3.002	OHV	49.85 (817)
850 Coupe	100GC3.040	OHV	49.85 (817)
850 Spyder	100GS3.040	OHV	49.85 (817)
850 Racer, Sp. Racer Sp. Spyder	100GBS.040	OHV	55.1 (903)
850 Sp. Coupe	100GBC.040	OHV	55.1 (903)

GENERAL ENGINE SPECIFICATIONS

Model	Displacement Cu. In.	Bore	Stroke	Compression ratio	Torque ft lbs	Oil Pressure psi
124 Spider Coupe	87.7	3.16	2.81	8.9:1	82.2/4000	50-70
124 Sp. Spider Coupe	98.1	3.15	3.15	8.5:1	94.3/4200	50-70
124 Sedan	73	2.87	2.81	8.8:1	64.4/3400	50-70
124 Sedan (1970)	87.7	3.16	2.81	NA	81.0/4000	50-70
124 Special	87.7	3.16	2.81	8.9:1	81.0/3300	50-70
128 Sedan	68.1	3.149	2.815	8.5:1	57.0/3000	50-70
850 Spider Coupe②	49.8	2.51	2.50	10.0:1	45.5/4000	40-60
850 Spider Coupe①	51.4	2.56	2.50	③	45.5/4000	40-60
850 Sp. Racer 1970 Sp. Spider 1970 Sp. Coupe 1970	55.1	2.56	2.68	9.5:1	47.7/4000	40-60
850 Sedan	51.4 49.8	2.56 2.51	2.5 2.5	8.0:1 8.9:1	42.7/3600 44.1/3600	40-60## 40-60

① 1966-67
② 1968-69
③ 1966 Coupe—8.8; 1966-67 Spider and 1967 Coupe—9.3
Super version—8.8
Super version—same as 1968-69 standard version
NA Not Available

TUNE-UP SPECIFICATIONS

Engine Cu. In.	SPARK PLUGS Type①	SPARK PLUGS Gap (in.)	DISTRIBUTOR Gap (in.)	DISTRIBUTOR Dwell (deg)	Ignition Timing (deg)	Idle Rpm ③	VALVE ADJUSTMENT Intake (in.)	VALVE ADJUSTMENT Exhaust (in.)	Intake Valve Opens (deg)
68.1 (128)	N9Y	0.024	0.015	55±3	TDC	850	0.012	0.016	12B
87.7 (124)	N9Y	0.024	0.018	57-53	5B	800	0.017	0.019	26
73 (124 Sedan)	N9Y	0.024	0.018	57-63	TDC	800	0.006	0.006	25
98.1 (124 Sp. Coupe)	N6Y	0.020-0.024	0.015	52-58	10B	900	0.018	0.020	NA
49.85 (850)	N4	0.024	0.018	60	TDC	800	0.006	0.006	16
49.85 hi perf. (850)	N7Y	0.024	0.015	60	11B	900	0.006	0.008②	NA
51.4 (850)	N3	0.020	0.018	60	10B	800-900	0.006	0.008	25
55.1 (850 Sport)	N7Y	0.020-0.024	0.015-0.017	52-58	10B	850	0.006	0.008	NA

① All Plugs Champion
② 850 Racer, Sp. Racer, Sp. Spider, Sp. Coupe are equipped with high performance valves
③ Idle speed will vary with carburetor mixture setting
NA Not Available

BATTERY AND STARTER SPECIFICATIONS

Engine	Cu In. Displacement	BATTERY Amp. Hour Cap.	BATTERY Volts	BATTERY Term Ground.	STARTERS Running Test Amps.	STARTERS Running Test Volts	STARTERS Running Test Torque (ft lbs)	STARTERS No-Load Test Amps.	STARTERS No-Load Test Volts	STARTERS No-Load Test RPM	Brush Spring Tension (oz)
128 All	68.10	48	12	N	170	9.5	2.97	30	11.9	7000	46.4
124 Sport All	98.1	48	12	N	160	9.7	2.9	25	12.0	8250	49.0
124 All Ex Sport	87.7 73.0	48	12	N	160	9.7	2.9	25	12.0	8000	49.0
850 All Ex Sport Sport	49.95 55.1	36	12	N	130	10.0	2.2	30	12.0	9500	40.0

N—Negative

VALVE SPECIFICATIONS

Model	Engine Cu. In. Displacement	VALVE LIFT Intake (in.)	VALVE LIFT Exhaust (in.)	Spring Test Pressure (lbs & in.)	Spring Installed Height (in.)	STEM TO GUIDE CLEARANCE (in.) Intake	STEM TO GUIDE CLEARANCE (in.) Exhaust	STEM DIAMETER (in.) Intake	STEM DIAMETER (in.) Exhaust
* 128 All	68.10	0.3583	0.3583	outer 1.417 in. 75.5 lbs.	1.417	0.002	0.002	0.3139	0.3145
* 124 Sport (All)	98.1 87.7	0.3760	0.3760	outer 1.417 in. 85.8 lbs.	1.417	0.002	0.002	0.3137	0.3146
* 124 All Ex Sport	73.0	0.3396	0.3396	outer 1.287 in. 67.68 lbs.	NA	0.002	0.002	0.3139	0.3145
* 850 All	49.85 55.1	0.3386	0.3386	outer 1.338 in. 46.3 lbs.	1.338	0.002	0.002	0.2750	0.2756

NOTE: All valve guides are replaceable
* All seat angles—45 degrees
All face angles—45 degrees 30 minutes
NA Not Available

TORQUE SPECIFICATIONS

All readings in ft lbs

Year	Engine Cu. In. Displacement	Cylinder Head Bolts	Rod Bearing Bolts	Main Bearing Bolts	Crankshaft Pulley Bolt	Flywheel To Crankshaft Bolts	MANIFOLD Intake	MANIFOLD Exhaust
128 All	68.1	61.0	37.6	61.0	—	61.0	22.0	22.0
124 Sport All	98.1	56.0	37.6	59.3	—	58.6	18.1	18.1
124 All Ex Sport	87.7 73.0	48.5	37.6	59.3	—	58.6	18.1	18.1
850 All Ex Sport Sport	49.85 55.1	21.7 28.9	25.3 25.3	44.8 44.8	72.3 72.3	28.9 28.9	NA NA	NA NA

NA Not Available

Torque Sequences

Cylinder Head

NOTE: *It is a common rule that most torque sequences start at the center and work outward.*

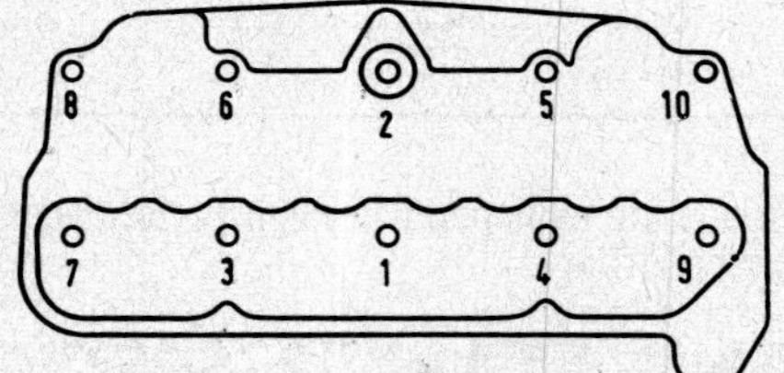

Cylinder head bolt tightening sequence, 850

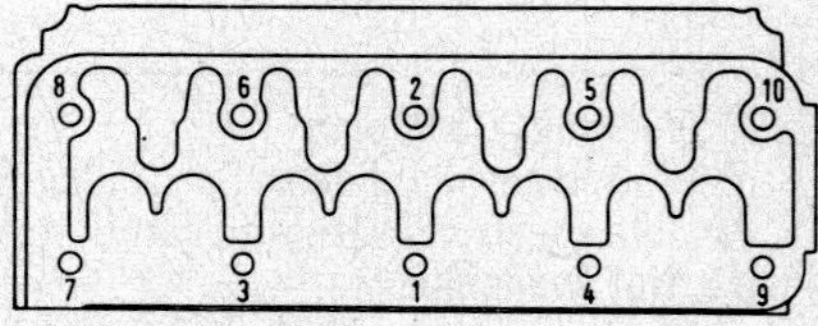

Cylinder head bolt tightening sequence, 124 Sedan.

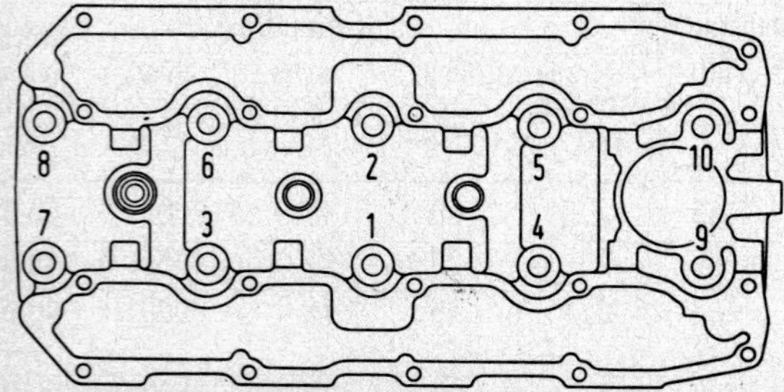

Cylinder head bolt tightening sequence, 124 Coupe, Spider.

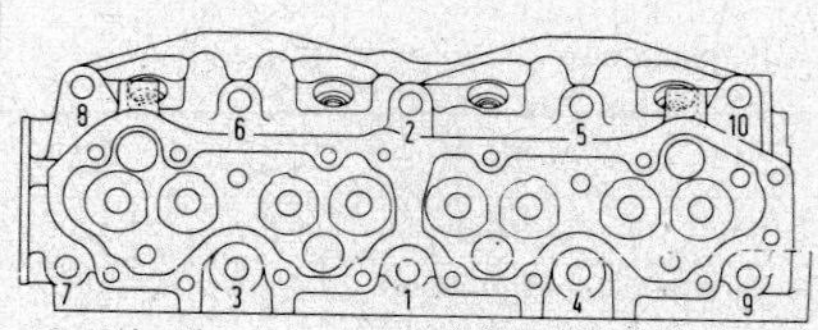

Cylinder head bolt tightening sequence, 128 Sedan.

CAPACITIES

Model	Engine Displacement (cc) Cu. In.	ENGINE CRANKCASE (qts) With Filter	Without Filter	TRANSMISSION (pts) Manual 5 spd	4 spd	Automatic	Drive Axle (pts)	Gasoline Tank (gals)	Cooling System (qts)
124 Spider Coupe	1438 cc. 87.7	5.0	4.0	3.5	3.5	9	1.5	12.0 10.0①	16.0
124 Sedan Sta. Wag.	1197 cc. 73.0	5.0	4.0	—	2.9	9	1.5	12.0	16.0
124 Special	1438 cc. 87.7	5.0	4.0	—	3.5	9	1.5	10.3	16.0
124 Sp. Coupe	1608 cc. 98.1	5.0	4.0	3.5	4.0	—	2.0	11.4	16.0
128 Sedan	1116 cc. 68.10	5.5	4.5	—	6.0	—	6.0	10.0	16.0
850 All Ex below	817 cc. 49.85	4.5	3.5	—	4.4	—	—	8.0	16.0
850 Racer Sp. Racer Sp. Coupe Sp. Spider	903 cc. 55.1	4.5	3.5	—	4.4	—	—	8.0	16.0

① Sedan
— Not Applicable

CRANKSHAFT AND CONNECTING ROD SPECIFICATIONS

All measurements in inches

Model	Displacement	Main Bearing Journal Dia	Rod Bearing Journal Dia	Shaft End Play	CONNECTING ROD Journal Dia	Oil Clearance
124 Spider, Coupe	87.7	1.999 -1.9998	1.791 -1.792	0.0024-0.0102	1.9145-1.9152	0.00102-0.00299
124 Sta. wag. Sedan	73.0	1.999 -1.9998	1.791 -1.792	0.0021-0.0104	1.9145-1.9152	0.00102-0.00299
124 Special	87.7	1.999 -1.9998	1.791 -1.792	0.0024-0.010	1.9145-1.9152	0.0010 -0.00299
124 Sp. Cpe, Sp. Spider	98.1	1.999 -1.9998	1.791 -1.792	0.0024-0.010	1.9145-1.9152	0.0010 -0.00299
128 Sedan	68.10	1.999 -1.9998	1.791 -1.792	0.0021-0.0104	1.9145-1.9152	0.0014 -0.0034
850 Sedan	49.85	1.9994-2.0002	1.5742-1.5750	0.0024-0.0102	1.7188-1.7913	0.00100-0.00280
850 Spider, Coupe	49.85	1.9994-2.0002	1.5742-1.5750	0.0024-0.0102	1.7188-1.7913	0.00100-0.00280
850 Racer, Sp. Racer Sp. Spider Sp. Coupe	55.1	1.9994-2.0002	1.5742-1.5750	0.0024-0.0102	1.7188-1.7913	0.00100-0.00280

NOTE: Thrust bearing location 128 and 124—rear main; 850—center main

WHEEL ALIGNMENT

Model	CASTER Range Min	Pref Setting (deg)	CAMBER Range Min	Pref Setting (deg)	Toe-in (in.)	Steering Axis Inclination deg
128 Sedan	15	2-15 min	±20	1.0	0.0	NA
124 Spider	−10 +30	3.5	±20	0.5	0.118	6
124 Coupe	−10 +30	3.5	±20	0.5	0.07	6
124 Sedan	−10 +30	3.5	±20	0.5	0.07	6
124 Sp. Coupe Sp.Spider	−10 +30	3.5	−10 +30	0.5	0.07	NA
850 All Ex Sport	±1 deg	9.0	±15	1.0	0.23	4 20 min
850 All Sport	±1 deg	9.0	±15	1.0	0.23	4 20 min

NA Not Available

PISTON AND RING SPECIFICATIONS

All measurements in inches

Model	Engine Cu in Displacement	Piston Clearance	RING GAP Top Compression	RING GAP Bottom Compression	RING GAP Oil Control	RING SIDE CLEARANCE Top Compression	RING SIDE CLEARANCE Bottom Compression	RING SIDE CLEARANCE Oil Control
124 Spider Coupe	87.7	0.0031-0.0039	0.012	0.007	0.007	0.003	0.002	0.002
124 Sedan, Sta Wag	73.0	0.0011-0.0020	0.007	0.007	0.007	0.003	0.002	0.002
124 Special	87.7	0.0031-0.0020	0.012	0.007	0.007	0.003	0.002	0.002
124 Sp. Coupe Sp. Spider	98.1	0.0031-0.0039	0.012	0.007	0.007	0.003	0.002	0.002
128 Sedan	68.10	0.0020-0.0028	0.012	0.007	0.007	0.003	0.002	0.002
850 Sedan	49.85	0.0007-0.0015	0.008	0.008	—	0.003	0.002	0.003
850 Coupe, Spider	49.85	0.0023-0.0031	0.008	0.008	—	0.003	0.002	0.003
850 Racer Sp. Racer Sp. Spider Sp. Coupe	55.1	0.0023-0.0031	0.008	0.008	—	0.003	0.002	0.003

BRAKE SPECIFICATIONS

Model	Master Cylinder Bore	BRAKE CYLINDER BORE Front	BRAKE CYLINDER BORE Rear	BRAKE DRUM OR DISC DIAMETER Front	BRAKE DRUM OR DISC DIAMETER Rear
124 Spider Coupe	0.75	1.875	1.375	8.94*	8.94*
124 Sedan, Sta. Wag.	0.75	1.375	1.375	8.93*	8.93*
124 Special	0.75	1.375	1.375	8.93*	8.93*
124 Sp. Coupe Sp.Spider	0.75	1.875	1.375	8.94*	8.94*
128 Sedan	0.75	1.890	0.75	8.94*	7.29*
850 Sedan	0.75	0.875	0.75	7.29	7.29
850 Coupe Spider	0.75	1.772	0.75	8.898	7.29
850 Family	1.00	1.125	0.75	8.672	8.672
850 Racer, Sp. Racer Sp. Spider	0.75	1.125	0.75	8.898	7.29
850 Sp. Coupe	0.75	1.125	0.75	8.898	7.29

* Disc Brakes

ALTERNATOR AND REGULATOR SPECIFICATIONS

ALTERNATOR Part No. or Manufacturer	ALTERNATOR Field Current 14 V	ALTERNATOR Output (amps.)	REGULATOR Part No. or Mfr.	Field Relay Air Gap (in.)	Field Relay Point Gap (in.)	Field Relay Volts to Close	Regulator Air Gap (in.)	Regulator Volts
Bosch G1-14 V 33 A 27	29A	38A	GN2/12/16	0.013	0.017	12.2-13.0	0.038	13.9-14.5
Fiat		53A	GN1/12/16	0.013	0.017	12.4-12.8	0.038	13.9-14.5
A 12 m 124/12/42	42A		GN2/12/28	0.013	0.017	12.4-12.8	0.038	13.9-14.5
Fiat	AT 12 V	22A	A/4-180/12	0.013	0.017	12.4-12.8	0.038	14.2-14.8
D 90/12/16/3 (Generator)	16A	22A	RC1/12B	0.013	0.017	12.4-12.8	0.038	13.9-14.8

Wiring Diagrams

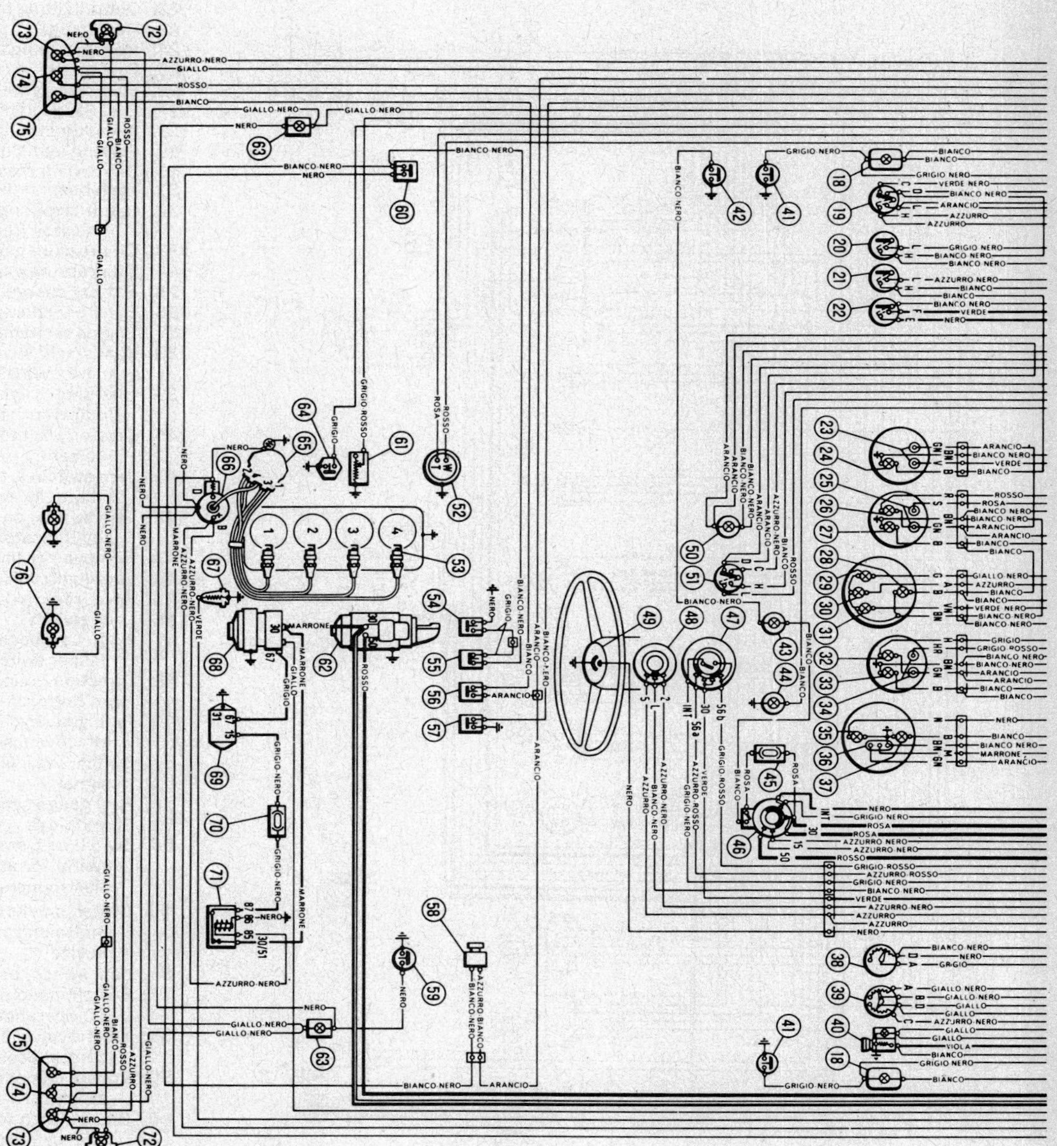

Fiat 850 Sport Spider

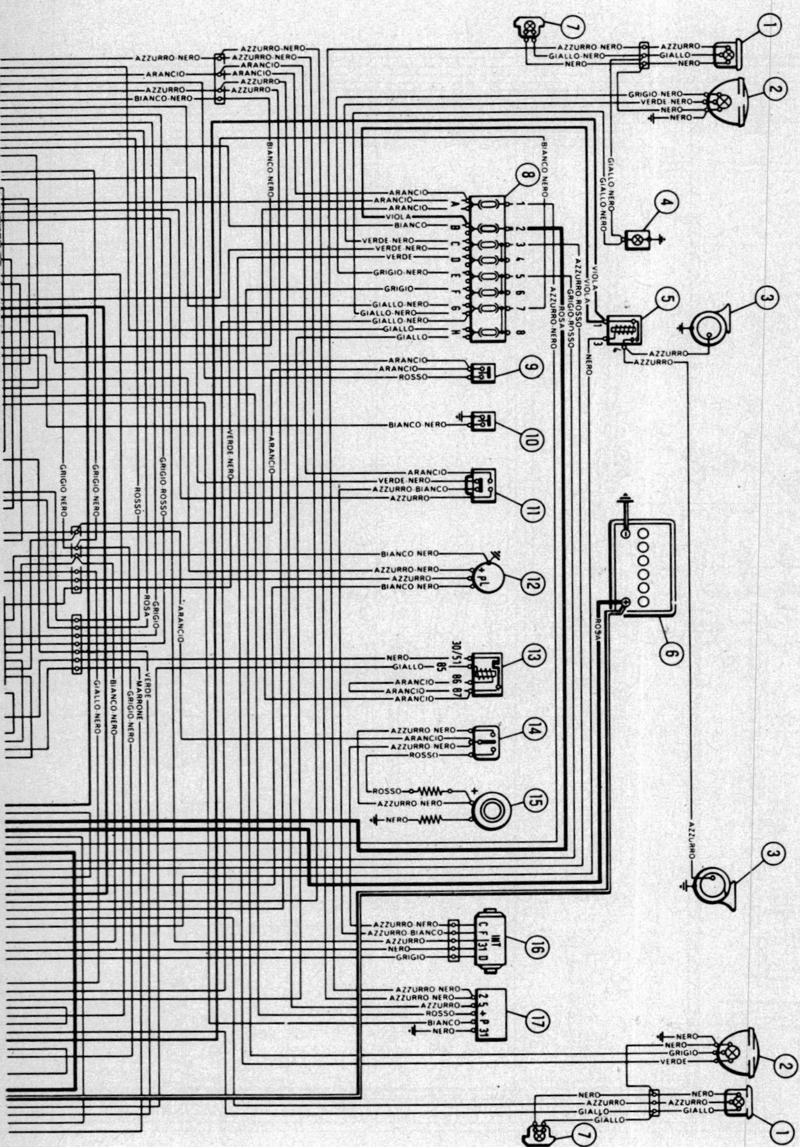

Fiat 850 Sport Spider

1. Front parking lights and direction indicators
2. Headlamp (high and low beams)
3. Horns
4. Front compartment light
5. Horn relay switch
6. Battery
7. Front side marker lights
8. Fuses
9. Stop lights pressure-operated switch
10. Switch for indicator 50
11. Windshield washer and wiper foot control
12. Flasher, direction indicators
13. Battery charge indicator relay
14. Switch, 3-position, heating and ventilation fan
15. Electrofan motor, 2-speed
16. Windshield wiper motor
17. Flasher, vehicular hazard warning signal
18. Courtesy lights under instrument panel
19. Windshield wiper switch
20. Courtesy lights toggle switch
21. Instrument cluster light switch
22. Outer lighting switch
23. Heat gauge
24. Heat gauge light
25. Fuel gauge
26. Fuel reserve indicator
27. Fuel gauge light
28. Speedometer light
29. Parking lights indicator (green)
30. Direction indicators (green)
31. High beam indicator (blue)
32. Insufficient engine oil pressure indicator (red)
33. Oil pressure gauge light
34. Oil pressure gauge
35. Battery charge indicator (red)
36. Engine tachometer
37. Engine tachometer light
38. Windshield wiper sweep rate adjustment rheostat
39. Instrument lights and parking lights indicator rheostats
40. Cigarette lighter (w/housing indicator)
41. Jam switches, between doors and pillars, for courtesy lights
42. Jam switch, on door, for remove key indicator
43. Remove key indicator
44. Pilot light, vehicular warning signal
45. Fuse, remove key indicator
46. Lock switch
47. High/Low beams change-over and flasher switch
48. Direction indicators switch
49. Horn button
50. Indicator, hydraulic service brake effectiveness and hand brake ON
51. Switch, vehicular hazard warning signal
52. Fuel gauge sending unit
53. Spark plugs
54. Switch on transmission (3rd and 4th gears) for exhaust emission control electropneumatic device
55. Switch on clutch pedal for exhaust emission control electropneumatic device
56. Jam switch, back-up lamp
57. Switch, hand brake ON and indicator 50 operation checks
58. Electrovalve, exhaust emission control device
59. Engine compartment lamps jam switch
60. Press switch for electrovalve energizing during fast idle rate adjustment
61. Sending unit, oil pressure gauge
62. Starter
63. Engine compartment lamps
64. Sending unit, insufficient oil pressure indicator
65. Ignition distributor
66. Ignition coil
67. Sending unit, heat gauge
68. Alternator
69. Voltage regulator
70. Fuse, alternator field circuit
71. Alternator, field circuit relay
72. Rear side marker lights
73. Rear direction indicators
74. Rear parking and stop lights
75. Back-up lamp
76. Number plate lights

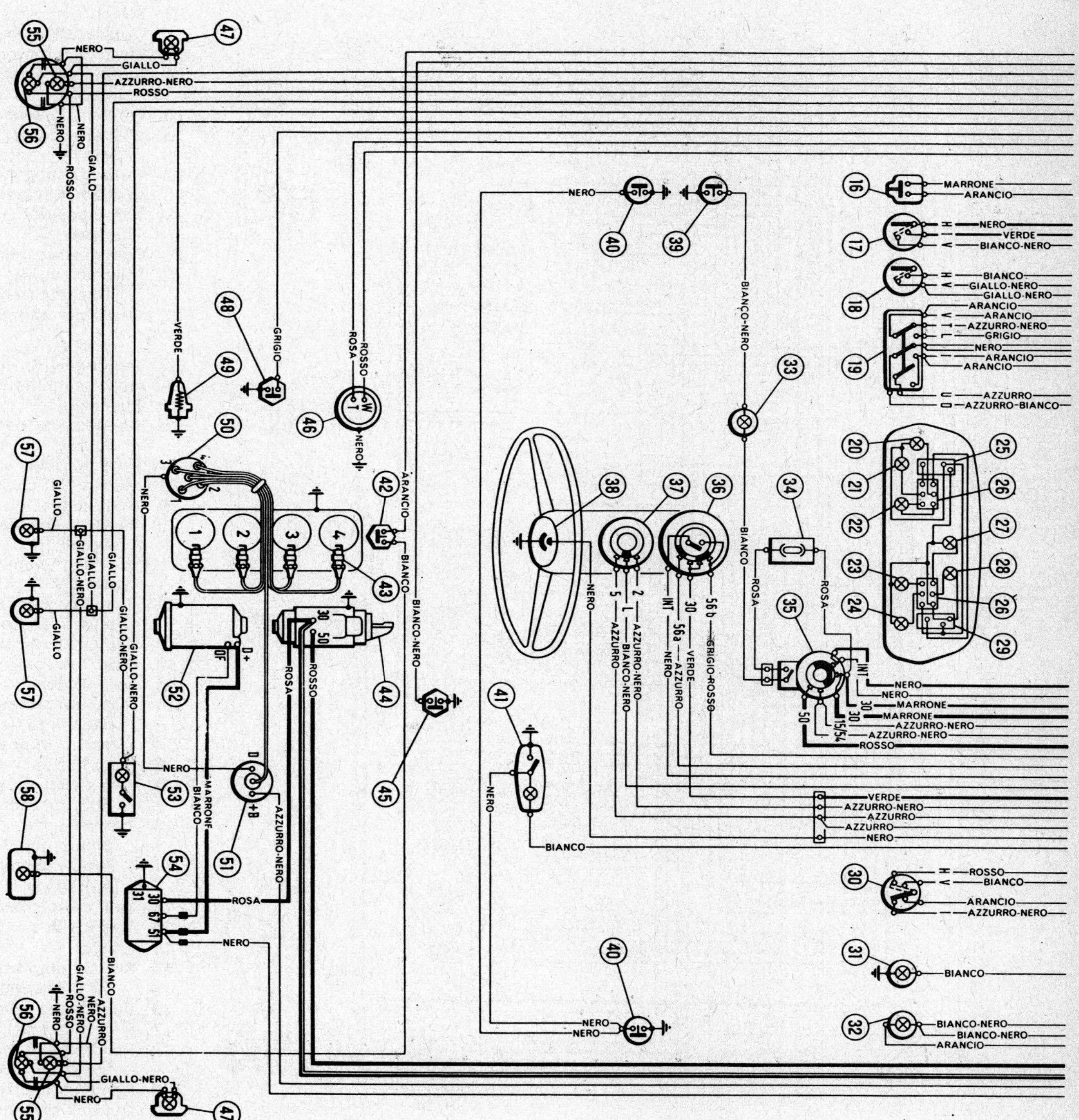

Fiat 850 Sedan

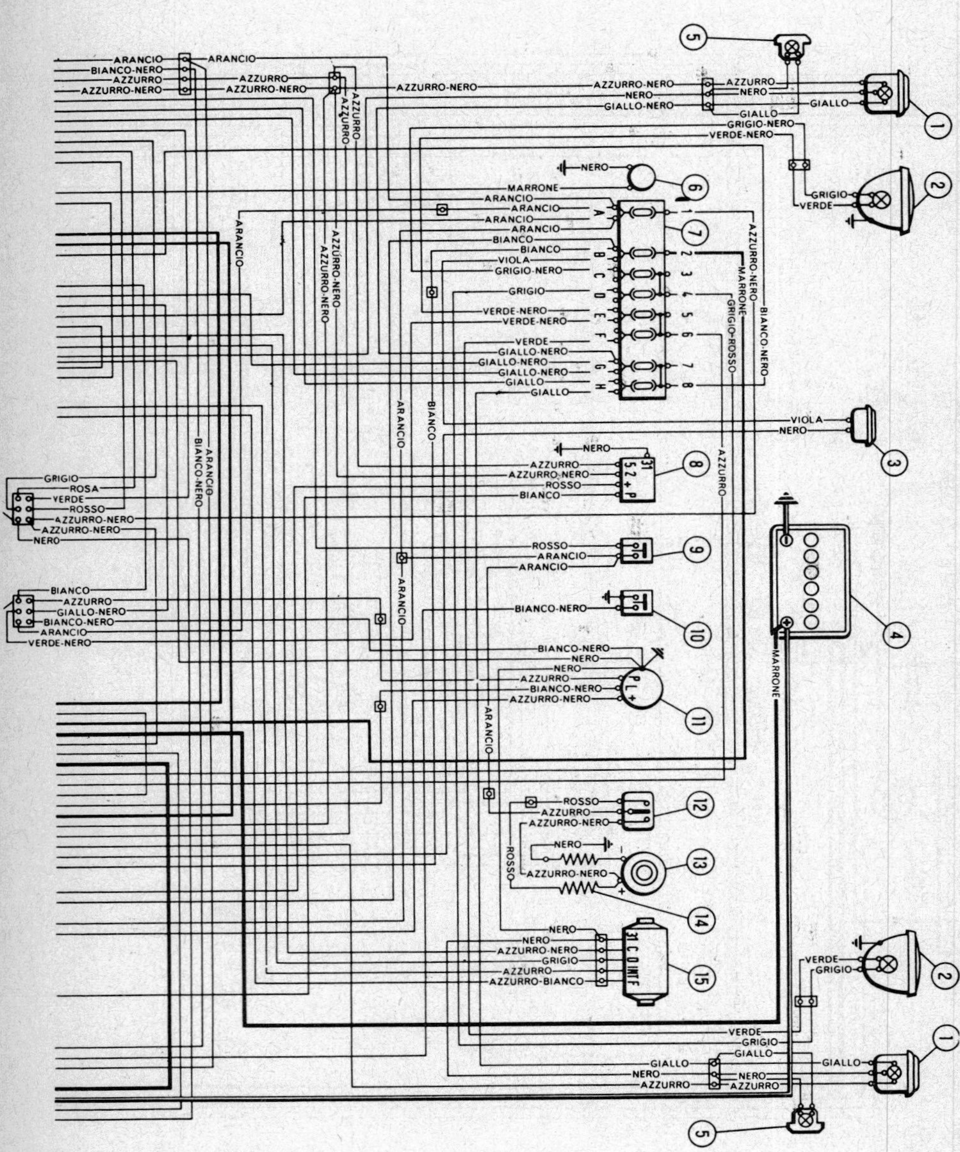

Fiat 850 Sedan

1. Front parking and direction indicator lamps
2. Headlamps (high and low beams)
3. Horn
4. Battery
5. Front side marker lamps (amber)
6. Electric pump, windshield washer
7. Fuses
8. Flasher, vehicular hazard warning signal
9. Stop lights pressure-operated switch
10. Switch for indicator 32
11. Flasher, direction indicators
12. Switch, 3-position, heating and ventilation electrofan
13. Electrofan motor, 2-speed
14. Additional resistor, for electrofan motor
15. Windshield wiper motor
16. Windshield washer pump button switch
17. Outer lighting switch
18. Instrument cluster light switch
19. Three-position, windshield wiper switch
20. Fuel reserve indicator (red)
21. Insufficient engine oil pressure indicator (red)
22. Generator charge indicator (red)
23. Parking lights indicator (green)
24. High beam indicator (blue)
25. Fuel gauge
26. Connectors, electrical, on instrument cluster
27. Direction indicator tell-tale (green)
28. Instrument cluster light
29. Heat gauge
30. Switch, vehicular hazard warning signal
31. Pilot light, vehicular hazard warning signal ON
32. Indicator, hydraulic service brake effectiveness and hand brake ON
33. Remove key indicator
34. Fuse, indicator 33 protection
35. Lock switch
36. High/low beams change-over and headlamp flashes switch
37. Direction indicators switch
38. Horn button
39. Jam switch on steering wheel side door for indicator 33
40. Jam switches, between doors and pillars, for courtesy light
41. Courtesy light with incorporated switch
42. Jam switch, back-up lamp
43. Spark plugs
44. Starter
45. Switch hand brake ON and indicator 32 operation check
46. Fuel gauge sending unit
47. Rear side marker lamps (red)
48. Sending unit, insufficient oil pressure indicator
49. Sending unit, heat gauge
50. Ignition distributor
51. Ignition coil
52. Generator
53. Engine compartment lamp with incorporated switch
54. Generator regulator
55. Rear direction indicators
56. Rear parking and stop lights
57. Number plate lights
58. Back-up lamp

NOTE: Mark — means that cable is provided with numbered strip or ferrule.

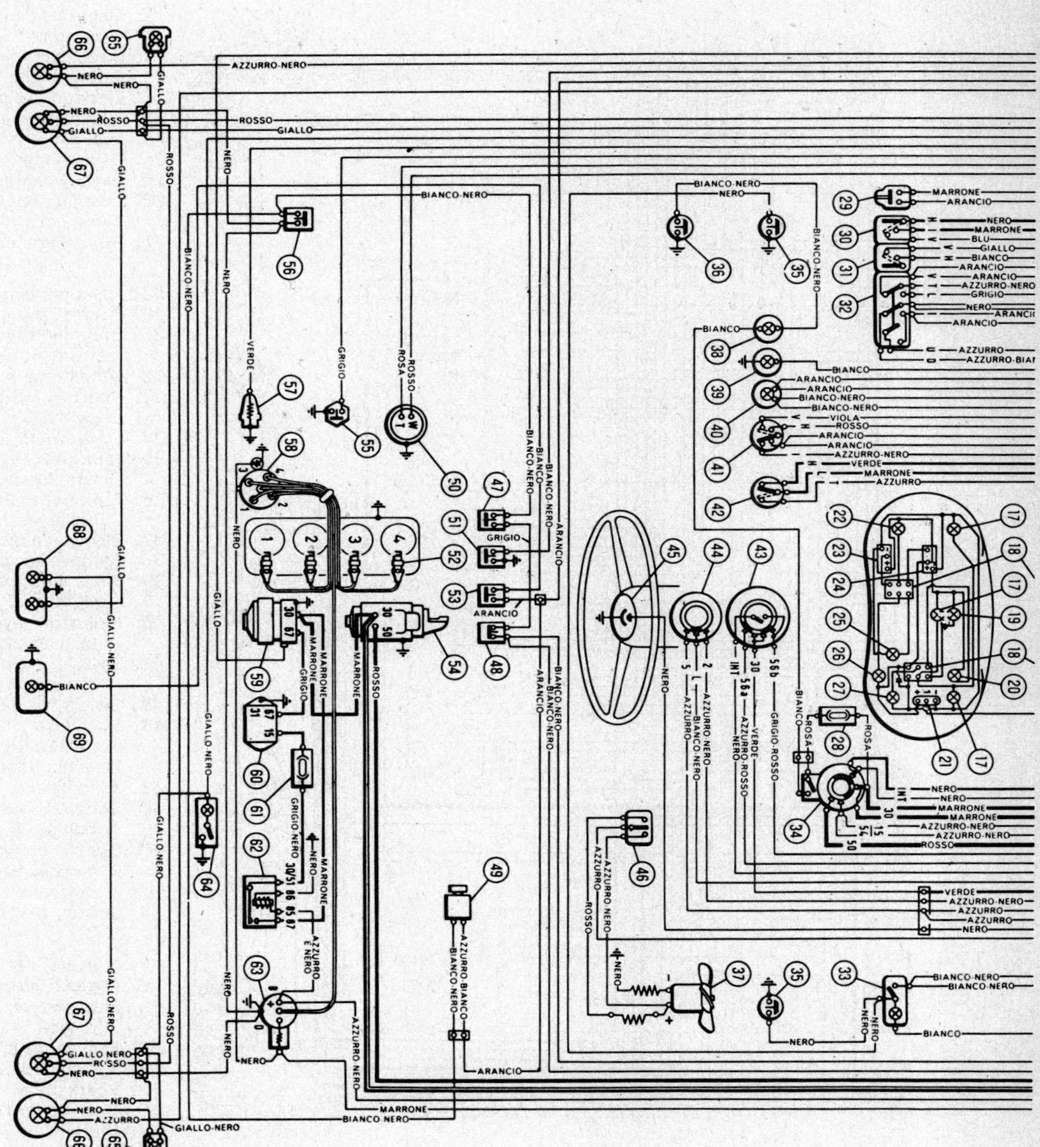

Fiat 850 Sport Coupe

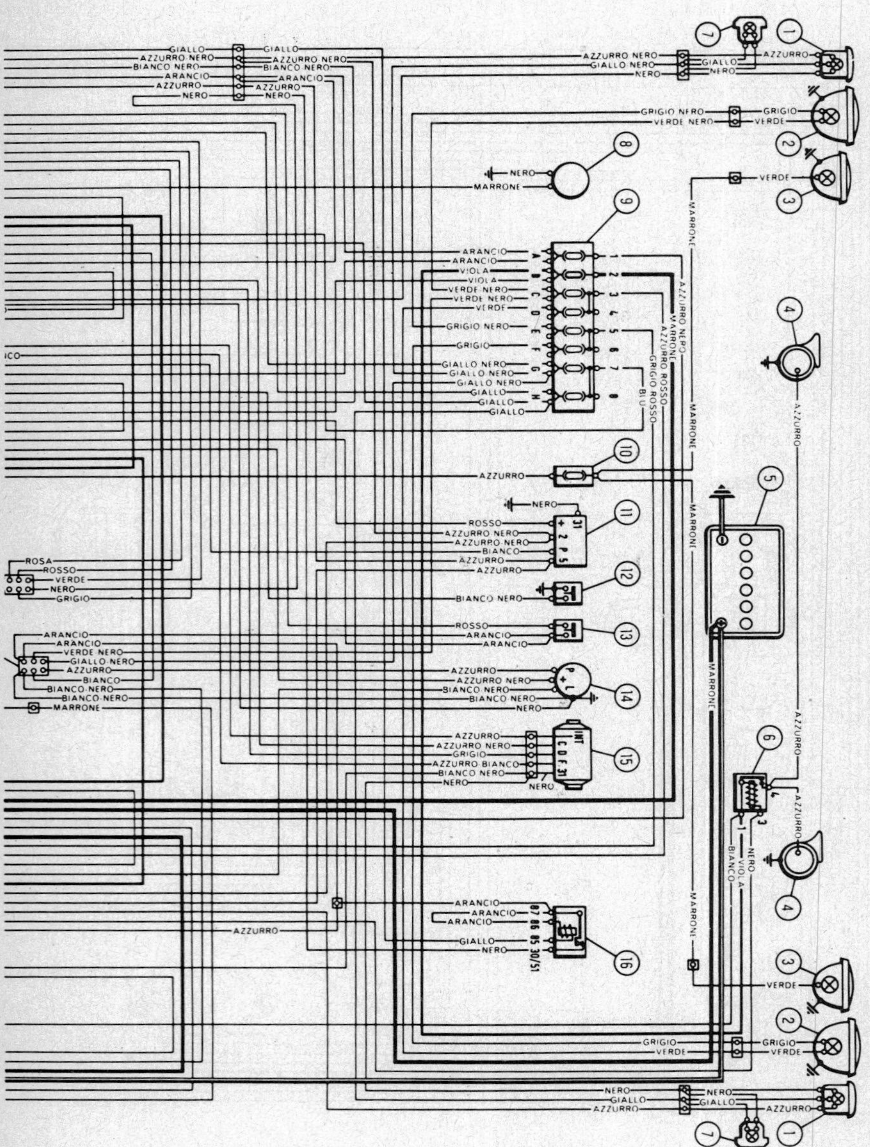

Fiat 850 Sport Coupe

1. Front parking lights and direction indicators
2. Headlamps (high and low beams)
3. Fog lamps
4. Horns
5. Battery
6. Horn relay switch
7. Front side marker lights
8. Windshield washer pump
9. Fuses.
10. Fuse, fog lamps
11. Flasher, vehicular hazard warning signal
12. Switch for indicator 40
13. Stop lights pressure operated switch
14. Flasher, direction indicators
15. Windshield wiper motor
16. Battery charge indicator relay
17. Instrument lights
18. Electrical connectors for instrument cluster
19. Direction indicators tell-tale (green)
20. Parking lights indicator (green)
21. Electronic engine tachometer
22. Fuel reserve indicator (red)
23. Fuel gauge
24. Heat gauge
25. Battery charge indicator (red)
26. Insufficient engine oil pressure indicator (red)
27. High beam indicator (blue)
28. Fuse, remove key indicator
29. Control, pump 8
30. Outer lighting switch
31. Instrument cluster light switch
32. Windshield wiper 3-position switch
33. Courtesy light with incorporated switch
34. Lock switch
35. Jam switches, between doors and pillars, for courtesy lights
36. Jam switch, on door, for remove key indicator
37. Electrofan motor
38. Remove key indicator
39. Pilot light, vehicular hazard warning signal
40. Indicator, hydraulic service brake effectiveness and hand brake ON
41. Switch, vehicular hazard warning signal
42. Switch, fog lamps.
43. High/Low beams change-over and flashes switch
44. Direction indicators switch
45. Horn button
46. Switch, 3 position, heating and ventilation fan
47. Switch on clutch pedal for exhaust emission control electropneumatic device
48. Switch, on transmission (3rd and 4th gears) for exhaust emission control electropneumatic device
49. Electrovalve, exhaust emission control device
50. Fuel gauge sending unit
51. Switch, indicator 40 operation check
52. Spark plugs
53. Back-up jam switch
54. Starter
55. Insufficient oil pressure indicator sending unit
56. Press switch for electrovalve energizing during fast idle rate adjustments
57. Heat gauge sending unit
58. Ignition distributor
59. Alternator
60. Voltage regulator
61. Fuse, alternator field circuit
62. Field circuit relay alternator
63. Ignition coil
64. Engine compartment lamp with incorporated jam switch
65. Rear side marker lights
66. Rear direction indicators
67. Rear parking and stop lights
68. Number plate lights
69. Back-up lamps

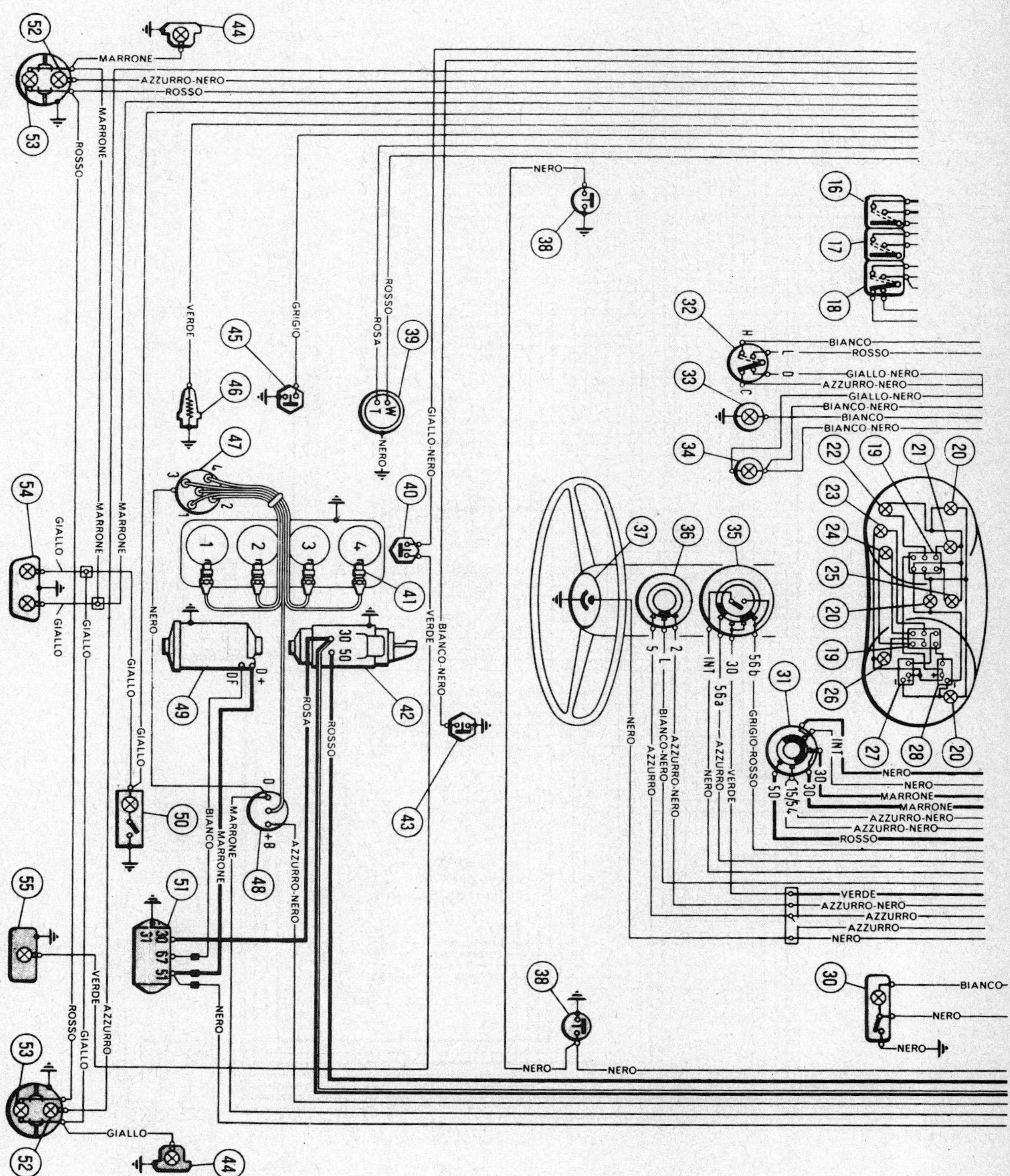

Fiat 850 Coupe

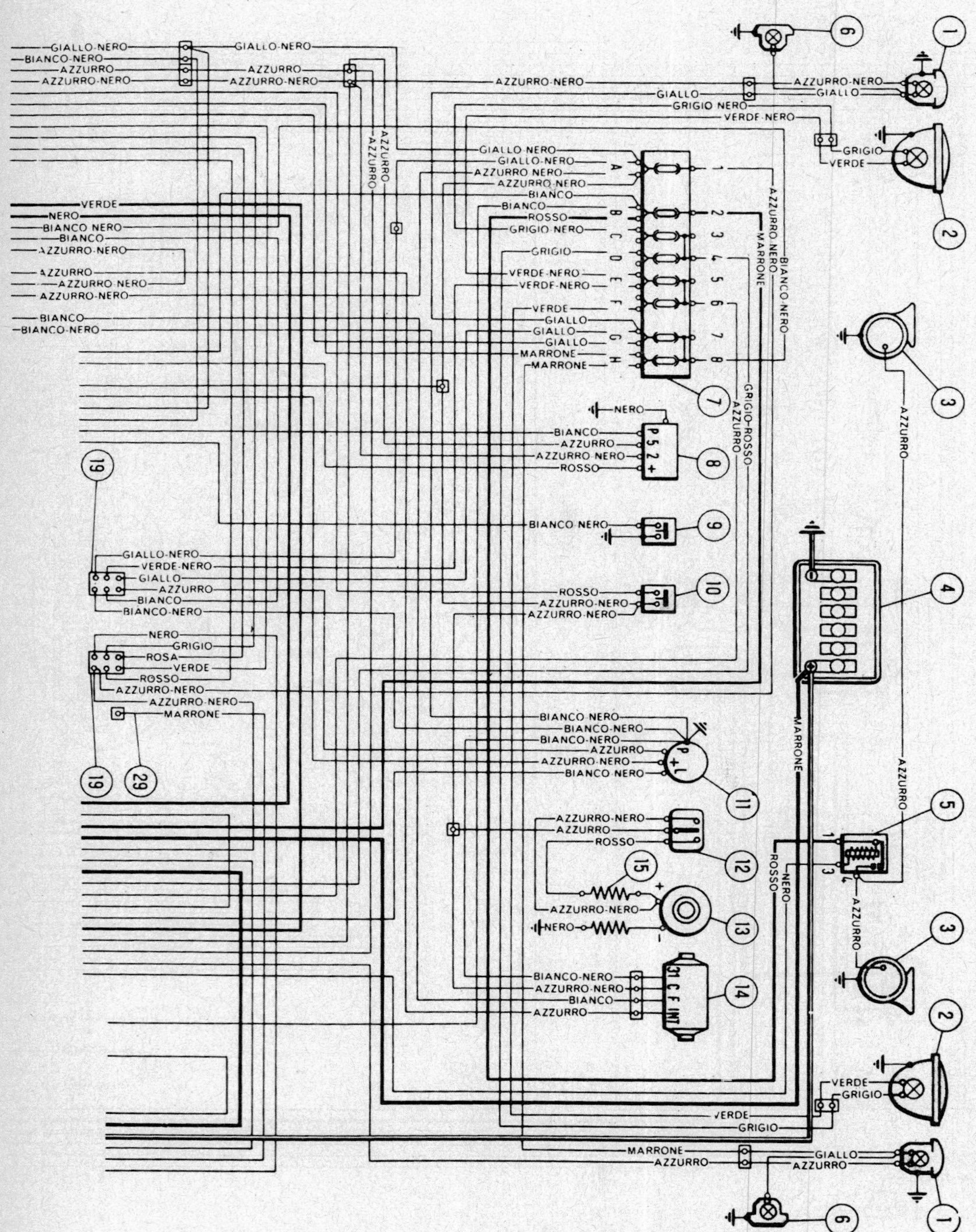

Fiat 850 Coupe

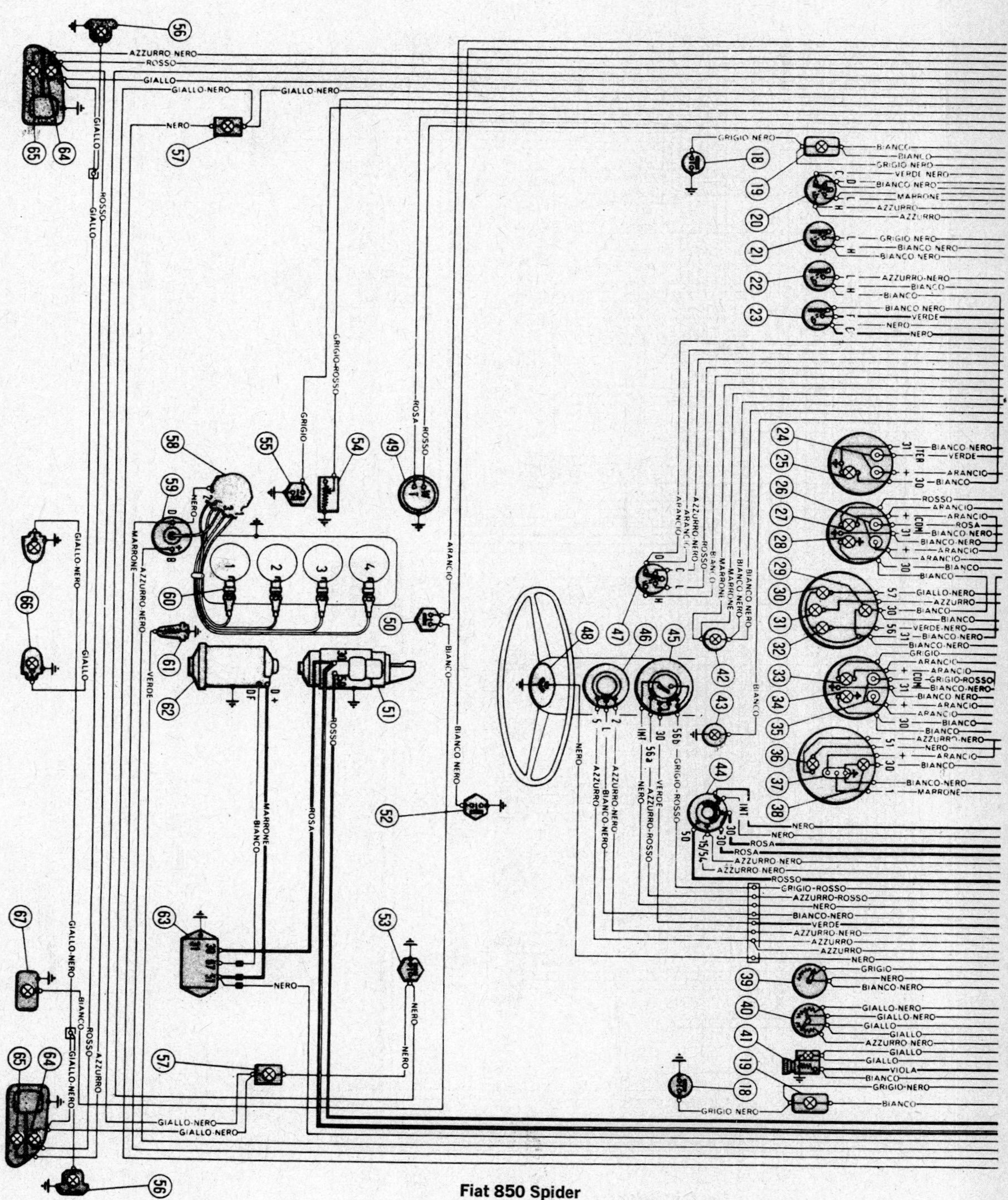

Fiat 850 Spider

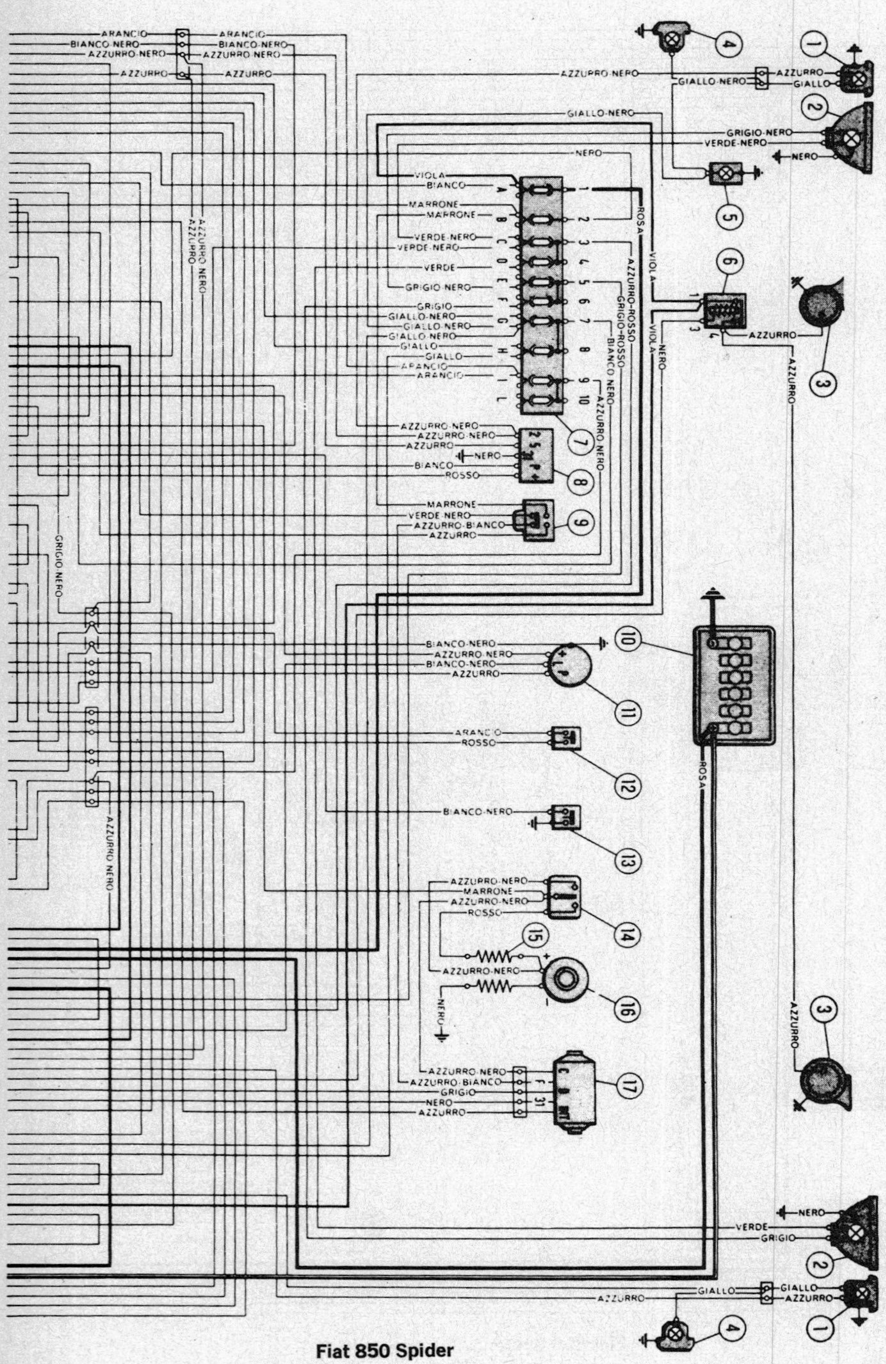

Fiat 850 Spider

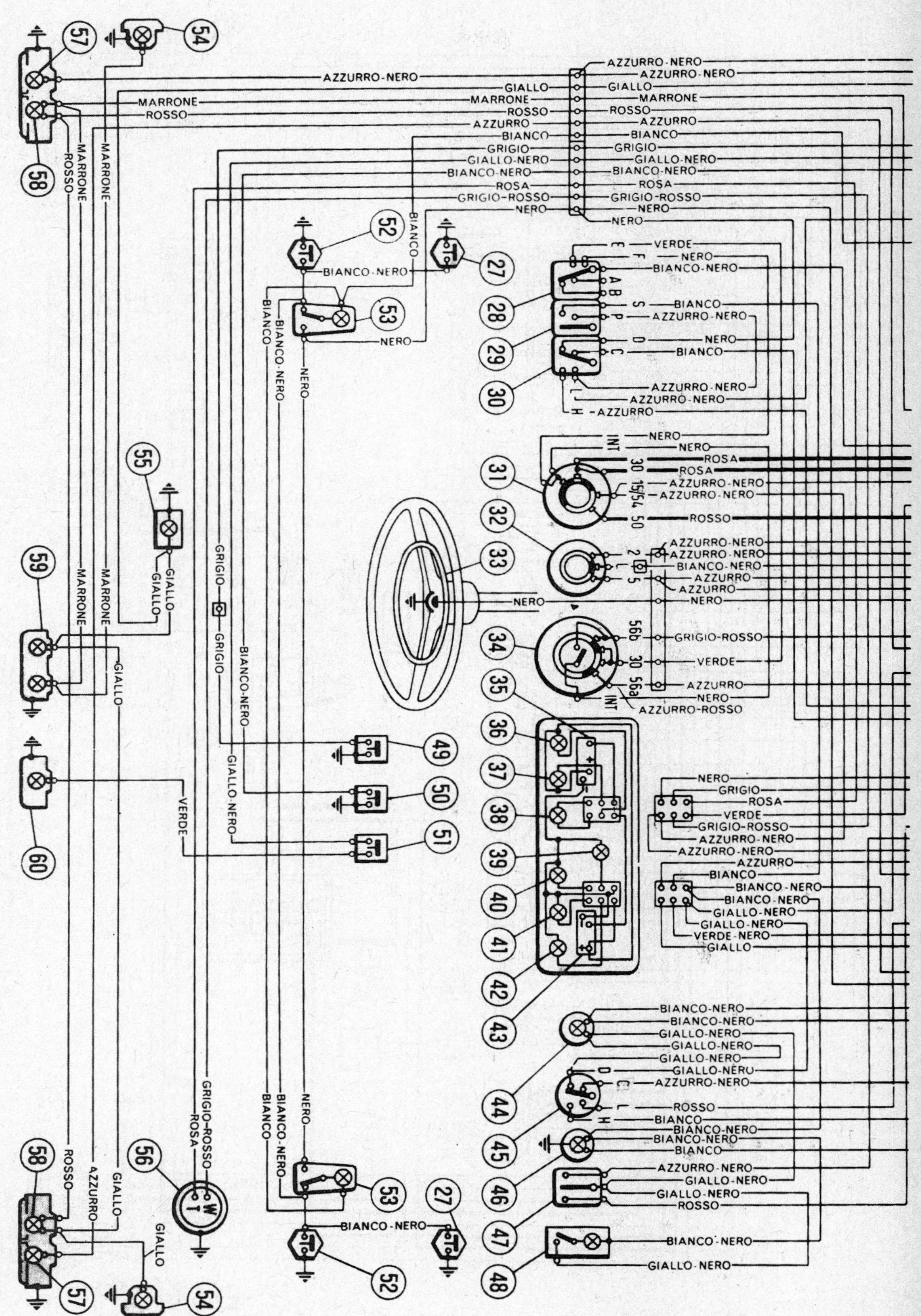

Fiat 124 Sedan and Station Wagon

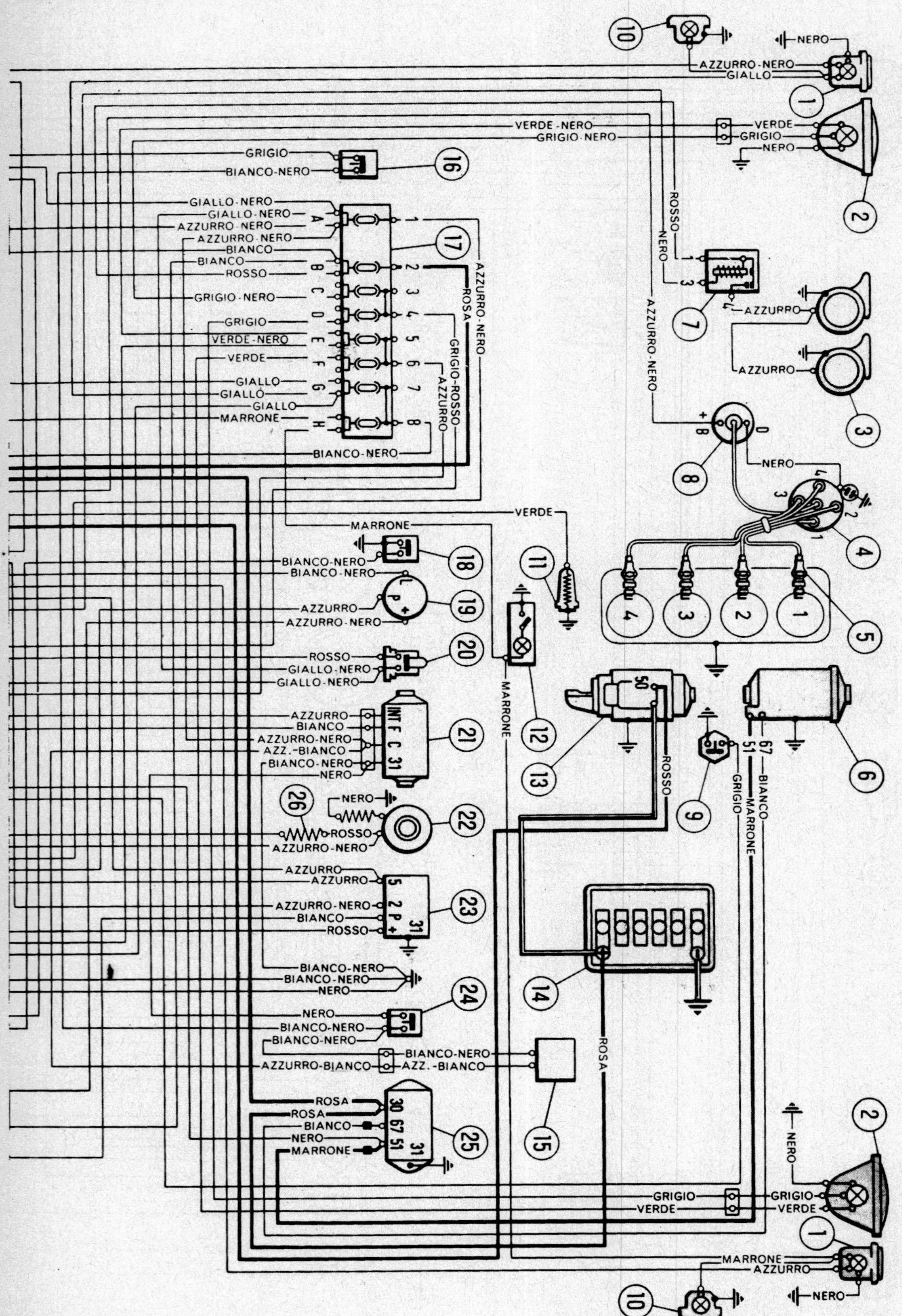

Fiat 124 Sedan and Station Wagon

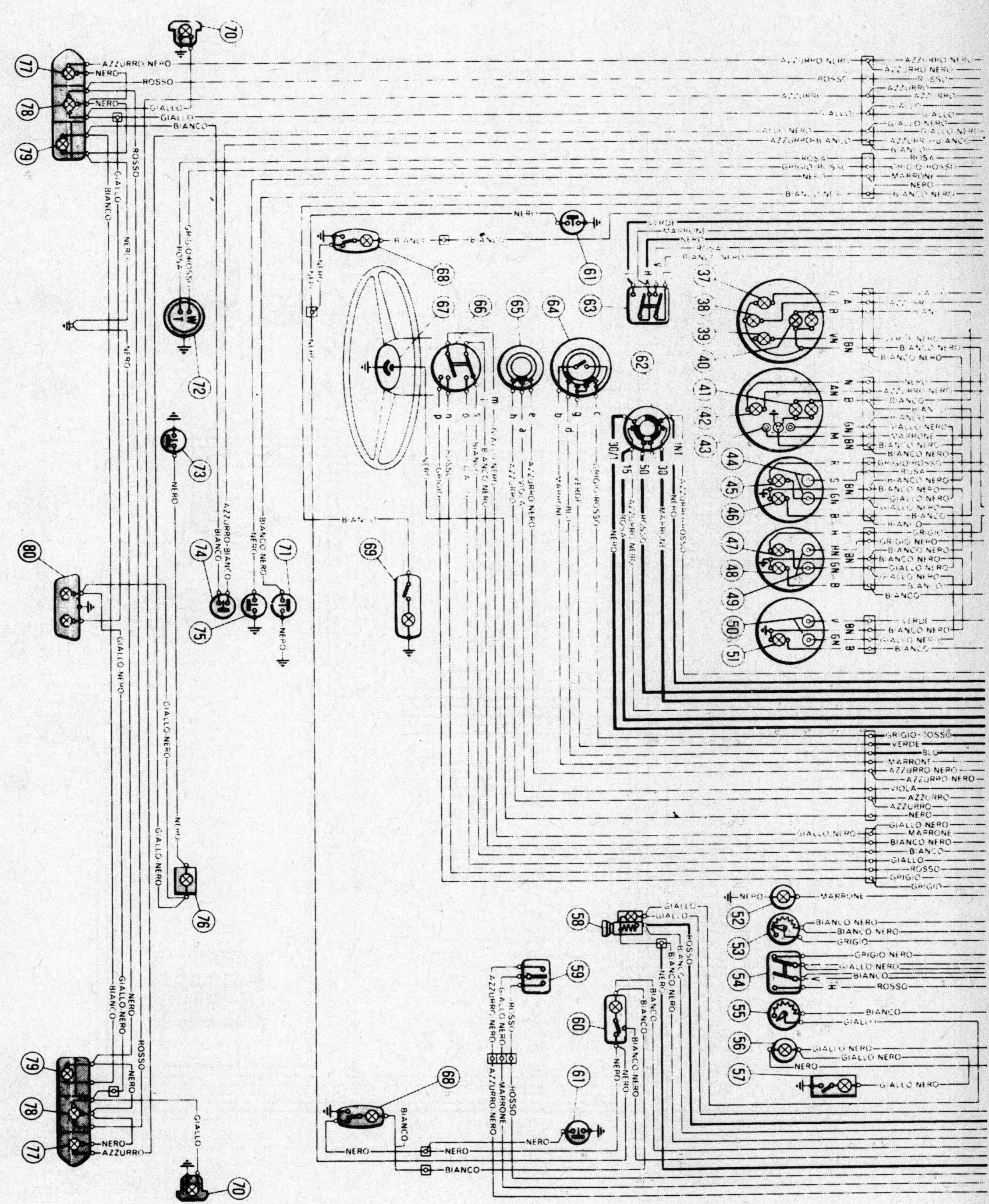

Fiat 124 Coupe

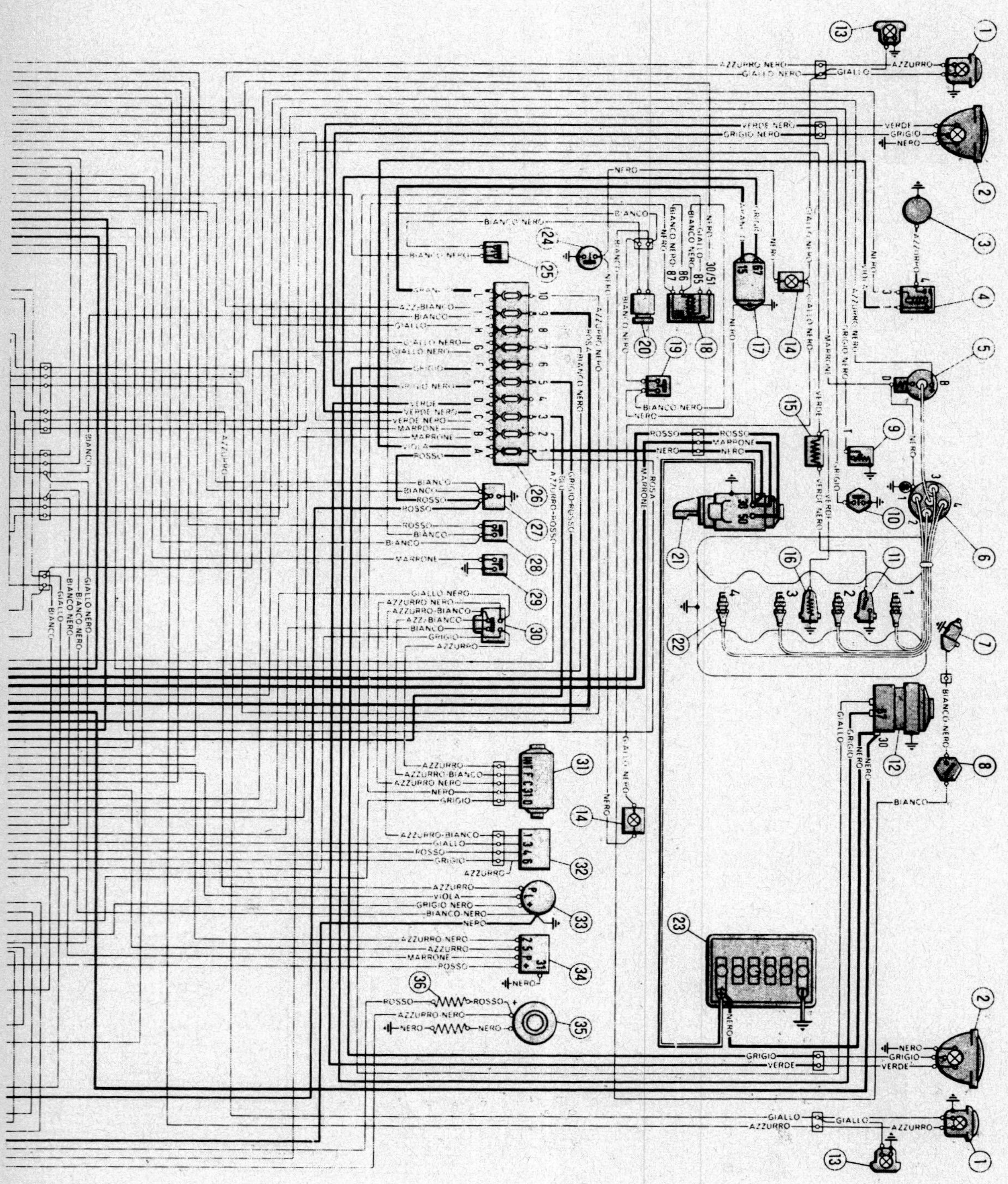

Fiat 124 Coupe

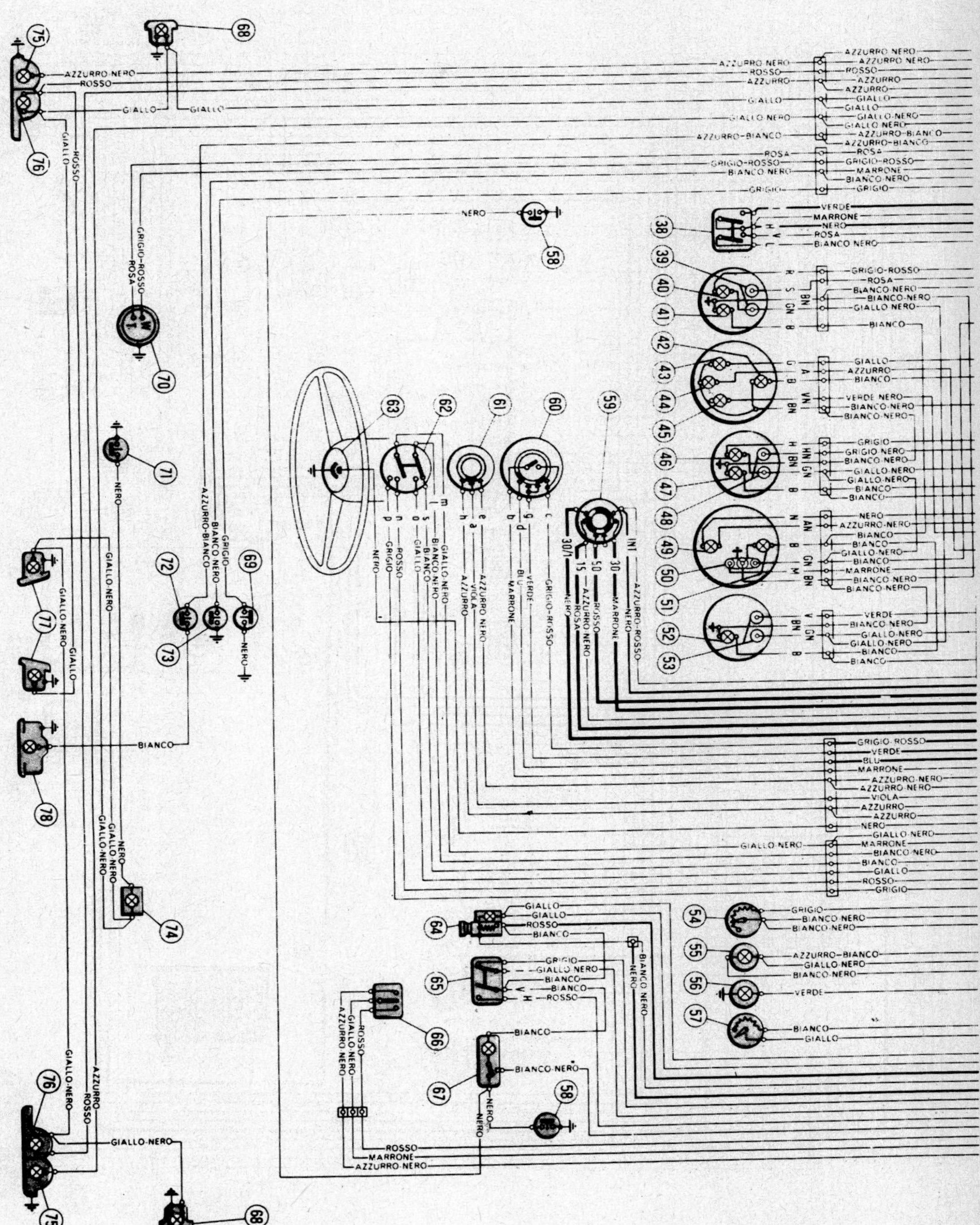

Fiat 124 Sport Spider

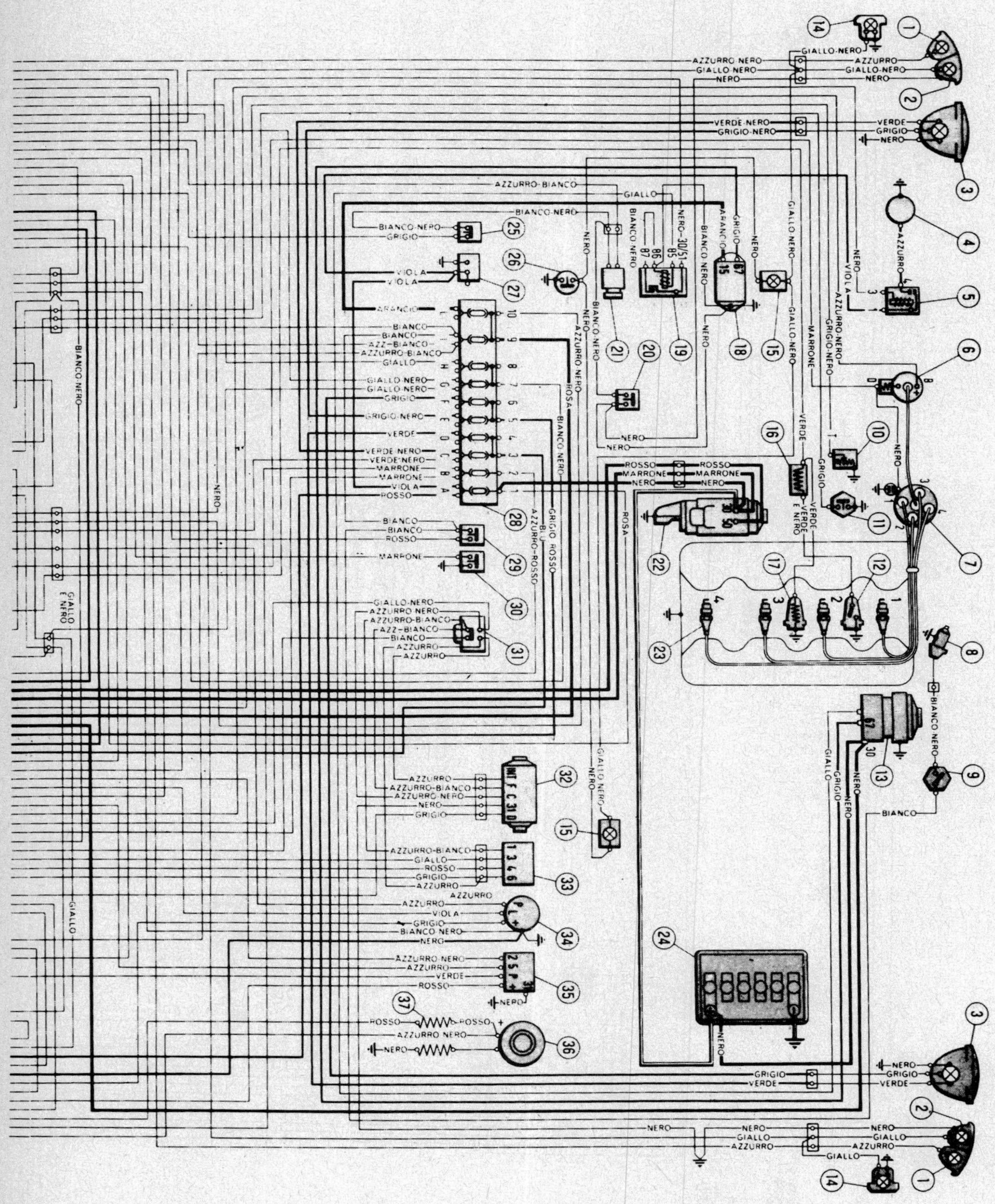

Fiat 124 Sport Spider

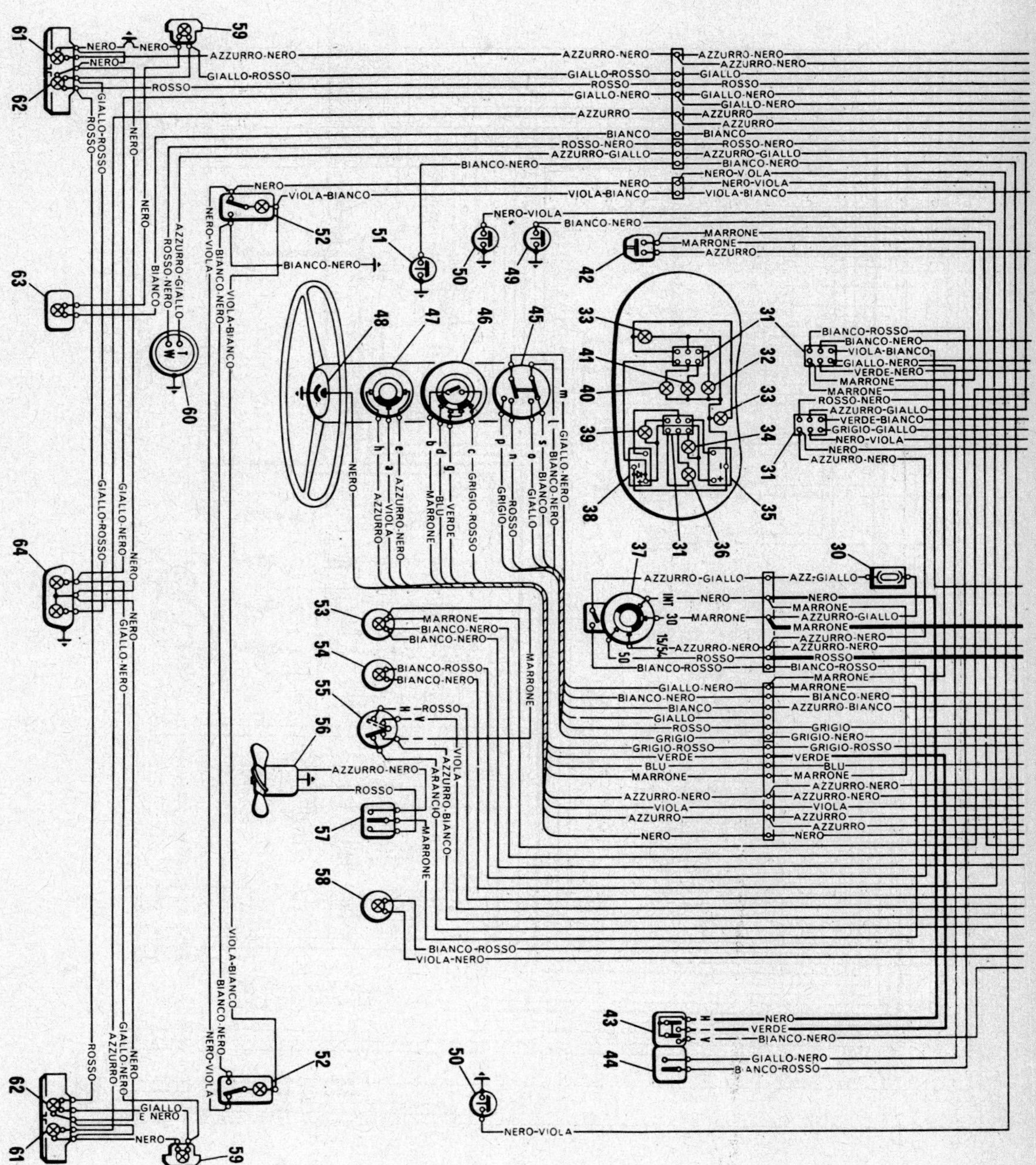

Fiat 128 Sedan

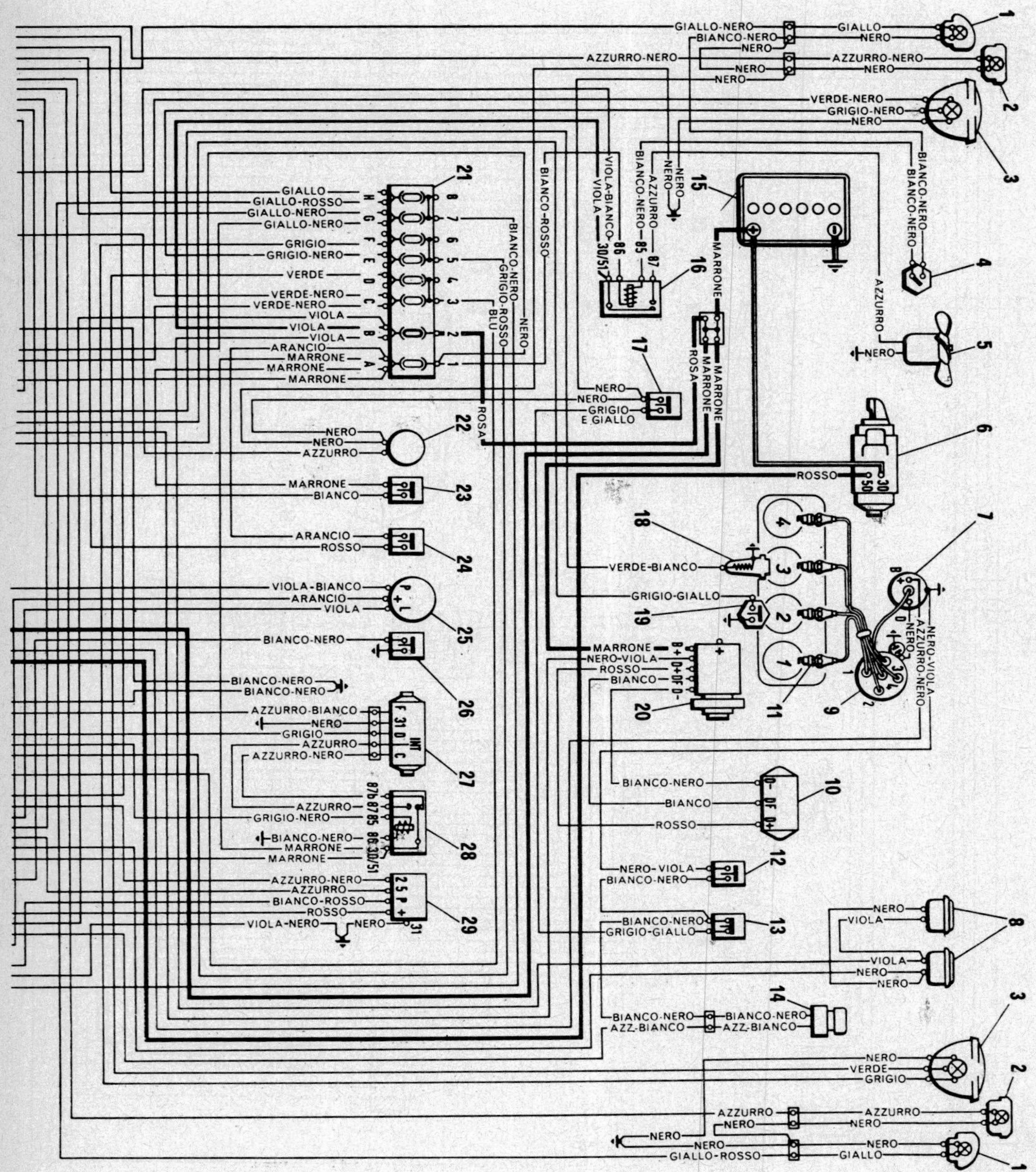

Fiat 128 Sedan

1. Front parking and direction indicator lamps
2. Headlamps (high and low beams)
3. Horns
4. Battery
5. Horn relay switch
6. Front side marker lights (amber)
7. Fuses
8. Flasher, vehicular hazard warning signal
9. Switch for indicator 34
10. Stop lights pressure-operated switch
11. Flasher, direction indicators
12. Electrofan, 3-position switch
13. Electrofan motor, 2-speed
14. Windshield wiper motor
15. Additional resistor for electrofan motor
16. Outer lighting switch
17. Instrument cluster light switch
18. Windshield wiper switch
19. Connectors, electrical, on instrument cluster
20. Instrument cluster lights
21. Parking lights indicator (green)
22. High beam indicator (blue)
23. Insufficient engine oil pressure indicator (red)
24. Generator charge indicator (red)
25. Direction indicators arrow tell-tale (green)
26. Fuel reserve indicator (red)
27. Fuel gauge
28. Heat gauge
29. Cable for tachometer
30. Courtesy light, with toggle switch
31. Lock switch
32. Switch, vehicular hazard warning signal
33. Pilot light, vehicular hazard warning signal ON
34. Indicator, hydraulic service brake effectiveness and hand brake ON
35. Outer lighting change-over and headlamp flashes switch
36. Direction indicators switch
37. Horn button
38. Jam switches, between doors and pillars, for courtesy light
39. Fuel gauge sending unit
40. Jam switch, back up lamp
41. Spark plugs
42. Starter with solenoid switch
43. Switch, hand brake ON and indicator 34 operation check
44. Rear side marker lights
45. Sending unit, for insufficient oil pressure indicator
46. Thermostatic sending unit for heat gauge
47. Ignition distributor
48. Ignition coil
49. Generator
50. Engine compartment lamp w/incorporated switch
51. Generator regulator
52. Rear direction indicators
53. Rear parking and stop lights
54. Number plate lights
55. Back up lamp

NOTE - Mark — means that cable is provided with numbered strip or ferrule.

Fiat 850 Coupe

1. Front parking and direction indicators
2. Headlamps (high and low beams)
3. Motorcompressor for electropneumatic horns
4. Horn control relay switch
5. Ignition coil
6. Ignition distributor
7. Electromagnetic fan switch brush
8. Electromagnetic fan thermostatic switch
9. Oil pressure gauge sending unit
10. Insufficient oil pressure indicator sending unit
11. Heat gauge thermostatic switch: sends heat gauge pointer to scale end (excessive water temperature) independently of sending unit 16
12. Alternator
13. Front side marker lights
14. Engine compartment lamps
15. Heat gauge additional resistor
16. Heat gauge sending unit
17. Voltage regulator
18. Battery charge indicator relay
19. Button switch for electrovalve energizing during fast idle rate adjustments
20. Electrovalve, exhaust emission control device
21. Starter motor
22. Spark plugs
23. Battery
24. Engine compartment lamps jam switch
25. Switch on clutch pedal for exhaust emission control electropneumatic device
26. Fuses
27. Inspection lamp receptacle
28. Stop lights switch
29. Switch, on the hydraulic circuit, for indicator 56
30. Windshield washer and wiper foot control
31. Windshield wiper motor
32. Windshield wiper intermittent operation cycling switch unit
33. Flasher, direction indicators
34. Flasher, indicator 56
35. Electrofan motor, two-speed
36. Electrofan motor additional resistor
37. Parking lights indicator (green)
38. Directional signal arrow tell-tale (green)
39. Headlamp high beam indicator (blue)
40. Speedometer lights
41. Engine tachometer lights
42. Battery charge indicator (red)
43. Engine tachometer
44. Fuel gauge
45. Fuel reserve indicator
46. Fuel gauge light
47. Insufficient oil pressure indicator (red)
48. Oil pressure gauge light
49. Oil pressure gauge
50. Engine water heat gauge
51. Engine water heat gauge light
52. Vehicular hazard warning signal indicator
53. Windshield wiper sweep rate rheostat
54. Vehicular hazard warning signal switch
55. Panel light rheostatic switch
56. Brake system effectiveness and hand brake ON indicator (red)
57. Glove compartment light, with incorporated switch
58. Electric cigarette lighter (with housing indicator)
59. Electrofan 3-position switch
60. Courtesy light, front, with incorporated switch
61. Jam switches, between doors and pillars, for courtesy lights
62. Lock switch
63. Outer lighting 3-position switch
64. Headlamp high/low beam change-over and low beam flashes switch
65. Direction indicators switch
66. Windshield wiper control 3-position switch
67. Electropneumatic horn control button
68. Courtesy lights, rear, with incorporated switch
69. Lamp, mirror light, with incorporated switch
70. Rear side marker lights
71. Switch, on transmission (3rd and 4th gears) for exhaust emission control electropneumatic device
72. Fuel gauge sending unit
73. Luggage compartment lamp jam switch
74. Back-up light switch
75. Switch, on hand brake lever, for indicator 56
76. Luggage compartment lamp
77. Rear direction indicators
78. Rear parking and stop lights
79. Back-up lamps
80. Number plate lights

Fiat 124 Coupe

1. Front parking and direction indicators
2. Headlamps (high and low beams)
3. Horns
4. Front side marker lights
5. Front compartment light
6. Horn relay switch
7. Fuses
8. Flasher, vehicular hazard warning signal
9. Windshield washer and wiper foot control
10. Battery
11. Flasher, direction indicators
12. Stop lights pressure-operated switch
13. Switch for indicator 42
14. Switch, 3-position, heating and ventilation fan
15. Additional resistor, for electrofan motor
16. Electrofan motor, 2-speed
17. Windshield wiper motor
18. Jam switches, between doors and pillars, for courtesy lights
19. Courtesy lights under facia
20. Windshield wiper switch
21. Courtesy lights toggle switch
22. Instrument cluster light switch
23. Outer lighting switch
24. Heat gauge
25. Heat gauge light
26. Fuel gauge
27. Fuel reserve indicator
28. Fuel gauge light
29. Speedometer light
30. Parking lights indicator (green)
31. Direction indicators tell-tale (green)
32. High beam indicator (blue)
33. Insufficient engine oil pressure indicator (red)
34. Oil pressure gauge light
35. Oil pressure gauge
36. Generator charge indicator (red)
37. Engine tachometer
38. Engine tachometer light
39. Windshield wiper sweep rate adjustment rheostat
40. Instrument lights and parking light indicator rheostats
41. Cigarette lighter (w/housing indicator)
42. Indicator, hydraulic service brake effectiveness and hand brake ON
43. Pilot light, vehicular hazard warning signal ON
44. Lock switch
45. Outer lighting change-over and headlamp flashes switch
46. Direction indicators switch
47. Switch, vehicular hazard warning signal
48. Horn button
49. Fuel gauge sending unit
50. Jam switch, back up lamp
51. Starter
52. Switch, hand brake ON and indicator 42 operation check
53. Engine compartment lamps jam switch
54. Sending unit, oil pressure gauge
55. Sending unit, insufficient oil pressure indicator
56. Rear side marker lights
57. Engine compartment lamps
58. Ignition distributor
59. Ignition coil
60. Spark plugs
61. Sending unit, heat gauge
62. Generator
63. Generator regulator
64. Rear parking and stop lights
65. Rear direction indicators
66. Number plate lights
67. Back up lamp

NOTE — Mark means that cable is provided with numbered strip or ferrule.

Fiat 850 Spider

1. Front parking and direction indicator lamps
2. Headlamps (high and low beams)
3. Horns
4. Ignition distributor
5. Spark plugs
6. Generator
7. Horn relay switch
8. Ignition coil
9. Sending unit, for insufficient oil pressure indicator
10. Side marker lamps, front (amber)
11. Heat gauge sending unit
12. Engine compartment lamp, with incorporated switch
13. Starter
14. Battery
15. Electrovalve, exhaust emission control device
16. Switch, on clutch pedal for exhaust emission control electropneumatic device
17. Fuses
18. Switch for indicator 44
19. Flasher, direction indicators
20. Stop lights mechanically-operated switch
21. Windshield wiper motor
22. Electrofan, two-speed
23. Vehicular hazard warning signal light flasher
24. Button switch for electrovalve energizing during fast idle rate adjustments
25. Generator regulator
26. Additional resistor for two-speed electrofan motor
27. Jam switches, between front doors and pillars, for lamps 53
28. Outer lighting switch
29. Instrument cluster light switch
30. Windshield wiper switch
31. Lock switch
32. Direction indicators switch
33. Horn ring
34. Switch for outer lighting change-over and headlamp flashes
35. Fuel level gauge
36. Fuel reserve indicator (red)
37. Insufficient engine oil pressure indicator (red)
38. Generator charge indicator (red)
39. Instrument cluster light
40. Direction indicators tell-tale (green)
41. Parking lights indicator (green)
42. High beam indicator (blue)
43. Heat gauge
44. Brake system effectiveness and hand brake ON indicator
45. Switch for vehicular hazard warning signal lights
46. Pilot light for vehicular hazard warning signal lights
47. Electrofan 3-position switch
48. Glove compartment light, with incorporated jam switch
49. Switch, on transmission (on 3rd and 4th gear) for exhaust emission control electropneumatic device
50. Switch, hand brake ON and efficiency check of bulb for indicator 44
51. Jam switch for back-up lamp
52. Jam switches, between rear doors and pillars, for lamps 53
53. Pillar lamps with incorporated switch
54. Rear side marker lamps (red)
55. Luggage compartment light
56. Fuel level gauge sending unit
57. Rear direction indicators
58. Rear parking and stop lights
59. Number plate lights
60. Back up lamp

NOTE - Mark—means that cable is provided with numbered strip or ferrule.

Fiat 124 Sedan and Station Wagon

1. Front direction indicators
2. Front parking lights
3. Headlamps (high and low beams)
4. Motorcompressor for electropneumatic horns
5. Horn control relay switch
6. Ignition coil
7. Ignition distributor
8. Electromagnetic fan switch brush
9. Electromagnetic fan thermostatic switch
10. Oil pressure gauge sending unit
11. Insufficient oil pressure indicator sending unit
12. Heat gauge thermostatic switch: sends heat gauge pointer to scale end (excessive water temperature) independently of sending unit 17
13. Alternator
14. Front side marker lights
15. Engine compartment lamps
16. Heat gauge additional resistor
17. Heat gauge sending unit
18. Voltage regulator
19. Battery charge indicator relay
20. Button switch for electrovalve energizing during fast idle rate adjustments
21. Electrovalve, exhaust emission control device.
22. Starter motor
23. Spark plugs
24. Battery
25. Switch on clutch pedal for exhaust emission control electropneumatic device
26. Engine compartment lamps jam switch
27. Inspection lamp receptacle
28. Fuses
29. Stop lights switch
30. Switch, on the hydraulic circuit, for indicator 55.
31. Windshield washer and wiper foot control
32. Windshield wiper motor
33. Windshield wiper intermittent operation cycling switch unit
34. Flasher, direction indicators
35. Flasher, indicator 56
36. Electrofan motor, two-speed
37. Electrofan motor additional resistor
38. Outer lighting 3-position switch
39. Fuel gauge
40. Fuel reserve indicator
41. Fuel gauge light
42. Speedometer light
43. Parking lights indicator (green)
44. Directional signal arrow tell-tale (green)
45. Headlamp high beam indicator (blue)
46. Insufficient oil pressure indicator (red)
47. Oil pressure gauge light
48. Oil pressure gauge
49. Battery charge indicator (red)
50. Engine tachometer
51. Engine tachometer light
52. Engine water heat gauge light
53. Engine water heat gauge
54. Windshield wiper sweep rate rheostat
55. Brake system effectiveness and hand brake ON indicator (red)
56. Vehicular hazard warning signal indicator
57. Panel light rheostatic switch
58. Jam switches, between doors and pillars, for courtesy lights
59. Lock switch
60. Headlamp high/low beam change-over and low beam flashes switch
61. Direction indicators switch
62. Windshield wiper control 3-position switch
63. Electropneumatic horn control button
64. Electric cigarette lighter (with housing indicator)
65. Vehicular hazard warning signal switch
66. Electrofan 3-position switch
67. Courtesy light, with incorporated switch
68. Rear side marker lights
69. Switch, on transmission (3rd and 4th gears) for exhaust emission control electropneumatic device
70. Fuel gauge sending unit
71. Luggage boot lamp jam switch
72. Back-up light switch
73. Switch, on hand brake lever, for indicator 55
74. Luggage boot lamp
75. Rear direction indicators
76. Rear parking and stop lights
77. Number plate lights
78. Back-up lamp

Fiat 124 Sport Spider

1. Front parking lamps
2. Front direction indicator lamps
3. Headlamps (high and low beams)
4. Thermostatic control switch for motor 5
5. Engine radiator cooling fan motor
6. Starter
7. Ignition coil
8. Horns
9. Ignition distributor
10. Voltage regulator
11. Spark plugs
12. Button switch for electrovalve energizing during fast idle rate adjustments
13. Switch on clutch pedal for exhaust emission control electropneumatic device
14. Electrovalve, exhaust emission control device
15. Battery
16. Relay switch for motor 5
17. Switch, on transmission (3rd and 4th gears) for exhaust emission control electropneumatic device
18. Sending unit, coolant temperature gauge
19. Sending, unit for insufficient oil pressure indicator
20. Alternator
21. Fuses.
22. Electric pump, windshield washer
23. Jam switch, back-up lamp
24. Stop lights switch
25. Flasher, direction indicators
26. Switch for indicator 53
27. Windshield wiper motor
28. Windshield washer relay switch
29. Flasher, vehicular hazard warning signal
30. Fuse, remove key indicator
31. Connectors, electrical, or instrument cluster
32. Turn signal tell-tale (green).
33. Instrument cluster lights
34. Insufficient engine oil pressure indicator (red)
35. Coolant temperature gauge
36. Battery charge indicator (red)
37. Lock switch
38. Fuel gauge
39. Fuel reserve indicator (red)
40. High beam indicator (blue)
41. Parking lights indicator (green)
42. Windshield washer pump button switch
43. Outer lighting switch
44. Instrument cluster lights switch
45. Windshield wiper 3-position switch
46. High/low beams change-over and flashes switch
47. Direction indicators switch
48. Horn button
49. Jam switch, on door, for remove key indicator
50. Jam switches, between doors and pillars, for pillar lamps
51. Switch, hand brake ON and indicator 53 operation check
52. Pillar lamps, with switch
53. Indicator, hydraulic service brake effectiveness and hand brake ON
54. Remove key indicator
55. Switch, vehicular hazard warning signal
56. Heater fan motor, 2-speed
57. Switch, 3-position, heater fan
58. Pilot light, vehicular hazard warning signal
59. Rear side marker lights
60. Fuel gauge sending unit
61. Rear direction indicators
62. Rear parking and stop lights
63. Back up lamp
64. License plate lamp

Fiat 128 Sedan

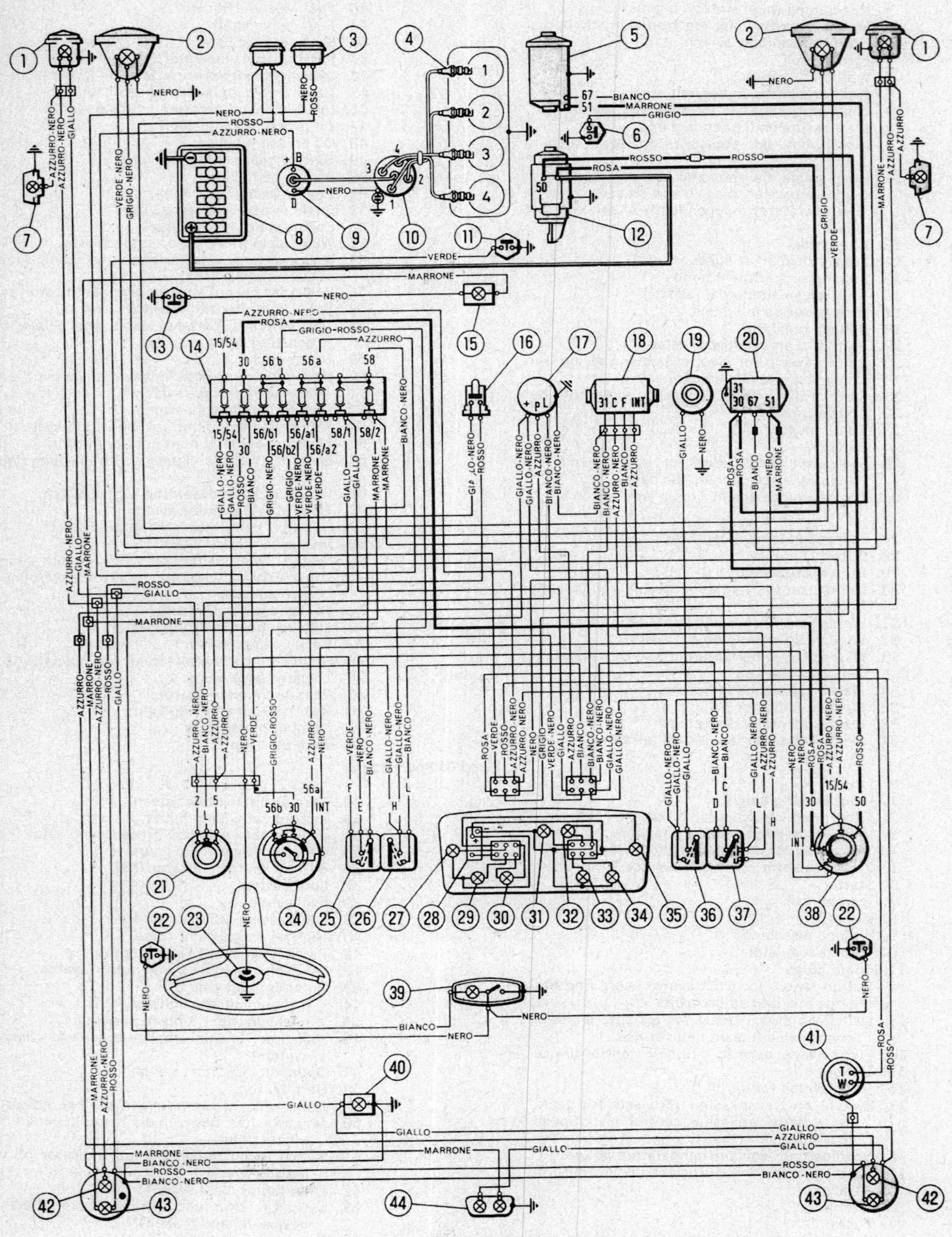

1100R wiring diagram.

1. Front parking and direction signal lights.
2. High and low beam headlamps.
3. Horns.
4. Spark plugs.
5. Generator.
6. Low oil pressure indicator sending unit.
7. Side direction signal lights.
8. Battery.
9. Ignition coil.
10. Ignition distributor.
11. Heat indicator thermal switch.
12. Starting motor.
13. Engine compartment light jam switch.
14. 8-Ampere fuses.
15. Engine compartment light.
16. Stop light jam switch.
17. Direction signal light flasher unit.
18. Wiper motor.
19. Air conditioner electro-fan.
20. Generator regulator.
21. Direction signal switch.
22. Courtesy light jam switches on front quarter door pillars.
23. Horn push button.
24. Change-over switch for outer lighting and low beam flashes.
25. Outer lights master switch.
26. Instrument light switch.
27. Fuel reserve supply indicator (red).
28. Fuel gauge.
29. Low oil pressure indicator (red).
30. No-charge indicator (red).
31. Direction signal light indicator (green).
32. Instrument light.
33. Parking light indicator (green).
34. High beam indicator (blue).
35. Heat indicator (red).
36. Air conditioner electro-fan switch.
37. Windshield wiper switch.
38. Key-type ignition switch, also energizing starting and warning lights circuits.
39. Map light and switch (in rear view mirror).
40. Trunk compartment light (this light is fitted with its own switch on cars with collapsible rear seat back).
41. Fuel gauge tank unit.
42. Rear direction signal lights.
43. Rear parking and stop lights.
44. License plate light.

NOTE - Mark ▬ means that the cable is provided with numbered strip or ferrule.

CABLE COLOUR CODE

Azzurro = **Blue**	Grigio = **Grey**	Rosa = **Pink**
Bianco = **White**	Marrone = **Brown**	Rosso = **Red**
Giallo = **Yellow**	Nero = **Black**	Verde = **Green**

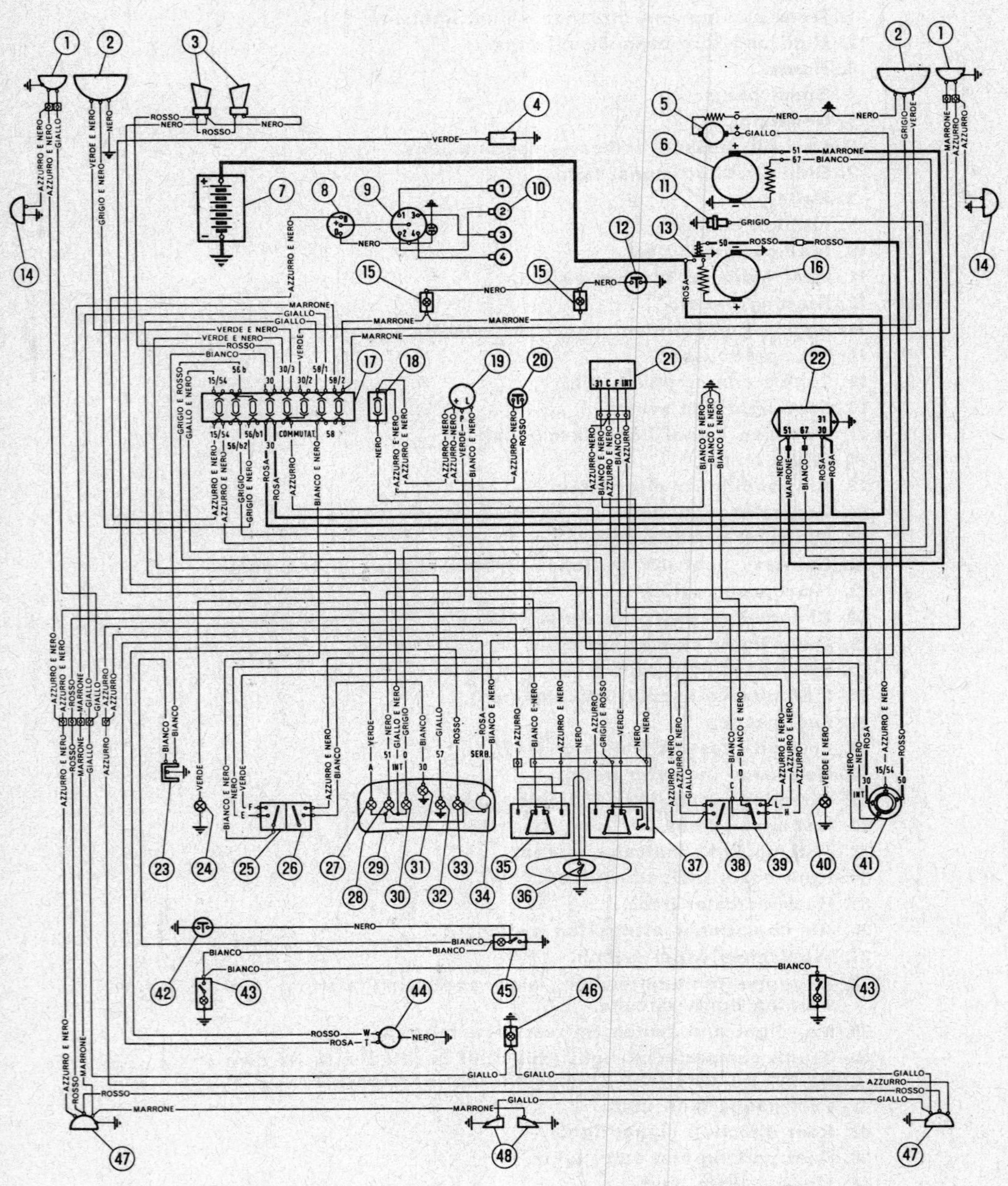

Fiat 1100D wiring diagram

1. Front turn indicator and parking lights.
2. Headlights (high and low beams).
3. Horns.
4. Engine cooling water temperature indicator sending unit.
5. Electrofan, ventilation and heating.
6. Generator.
7. Battery.
8. Ignition coil.
9. Ignition distributor.
10. Spark plugs.
11. Low oil pressure indicator sending unit.
12. Engine compartment lights jam switch.
13. Starter relay switch.
14. Turn indicator side repeaters.
15. Engine compartment lights.
16. Starter.
17. Fuses, 8 Amps.
18. Fuse, 8 Amps.
19. Flasher, turn indicators.
20. Hydraulic, pressure-operated stop lights switch.
21. Windshield wiper motor.
22. Generator regulator.
23. Inspection lamp socket.
24. Turn indicator pilot light (green).
25. Outer lighting switch.
26. Panel light switch.
27. Engine cooling water temperature indicator (red).
28. Generator charge indicator (red).
29. Instrument cluster.
30. Low oil pressure indicator (red).
31. Panel light bulb.
32. Front parking light indicator (green).
33. Low fuel indicator (red).
34. Fuel gauge.
35. Turn indicators switch.
36. Horn button.
37. Front outer lighting selector switch.
38. Electrofan switch.
39. Windshield wiper switch.
40. Headlight high beam indicator (blue).
41. Lock switch.
42. Jam switch, between door and pillar, for bulb incorporated in rear view mirror.
43. Pillar lights, with incorporated switch.
44. Fuel gauge sending unit.
45. Bulb, incorporated in rear view mirror, for courtesy lights.
46. Luggage compartment light.
47. Rear parking, stop and direction indicator lights.
48. License plate light.

NOTE: *Mark — means that the cable is provided with numbered strip or ferrule.*

CABLE COLOR CODE

Azzurro Blue

Grigio Grey

Rosso Red

Bianco White

Marrone Brown

Verde Green

Giallo Yellow

Nero Black INT-COMMUTAT Switch SERB. Tank.

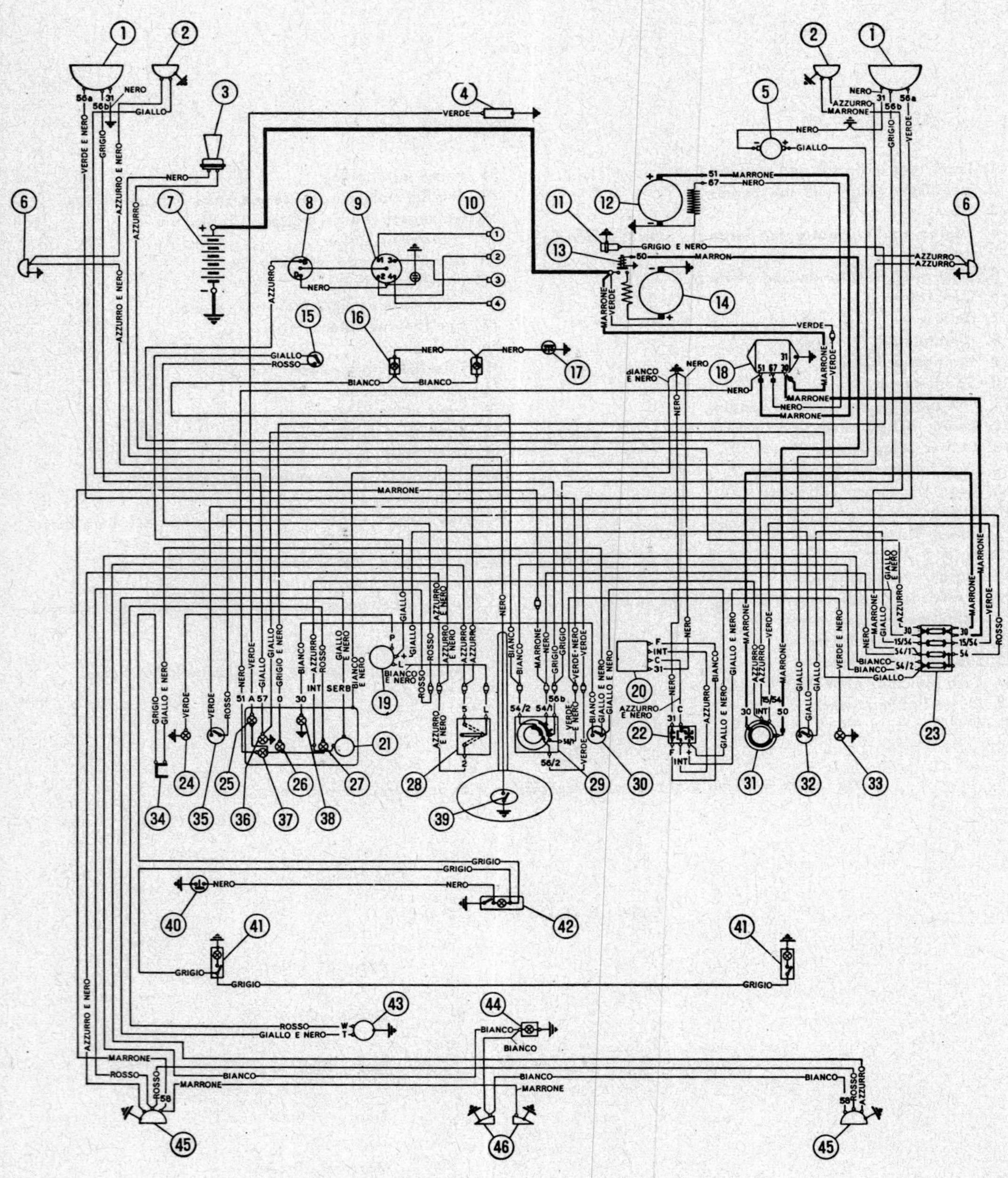

Fiat Export, Special Sedan and Family car wiring diagram

1. Headlights (high and low beams).
2. Front turn indicator and parking lights.
3. Horn.
4. High water temperature indicator sending unit.
5. Air conditioning unit electrofan.
6. Turn indicator side repeaters.
7. Battery.
8. Ignition coil.
9. Ignition distributor.
10. Spark plugs.
11. Low oil pressure indicator sending unit.
12. Generator.
13. Starter electronmagnetic switch.
14. Starter.
15. Hydraulic, pressure-operated stop lights switch.
16. Engine compartment lights.
17. Engine compartment lights jam switch.
18. Generator regular.
19. Flasher, turn indicators.
20. Windshield wiper motor.
21. Fuel gauge.
22. Windshield wiper three-position switch.
23. Fuses, 8 Amps.
24. Turn indicators pilot light (green).
25. High water temperature indicator (red).
26. Low oil pressure indicator (red).
27. Low fuel indicator (red).
28. Turn indicator switch.
29. Front outer lighting selector switch.
30. Panel light switch.
31. Lock switch.
32. Electrofan switch.
33. Headlight high beam indicator (blue).
34. Inspection lamp receptacle.
35. Outer lighting switch.
36. Front parking lights indicator (green).
37. Generator charge indicator (red).
38. Panel light bulb.
39. Horn button.
40. Jam switch, between door and pillar, for bulb incorporated in rear view mirror.
41. Pillar lights, with incorporated switch.
42. Bulb, incorporated in rear view mirror, for courtesy light.
43. Fuel gauge sending unit.
44. Luggage compartment light.
45. Rear parking, stop and turn indicator lights.
46. License plate light.

NOTE: *Cars with speedometer gauged in miles have a cluster incorporating a heat gauge instead of the temperature indicator. The gauge and its sending unit are not shown in this diagram. Mark — means that the cable is provided with numbered strip or ferrule.*

CABLE COLOR CODE

Azzurro Blue

Grigio Grey

Rosso Red

Bianco White

Marrone Brown

Verde Green

Giallo Yellow

Nero Black INT-COMMUTAT Switch SERB. Tank.

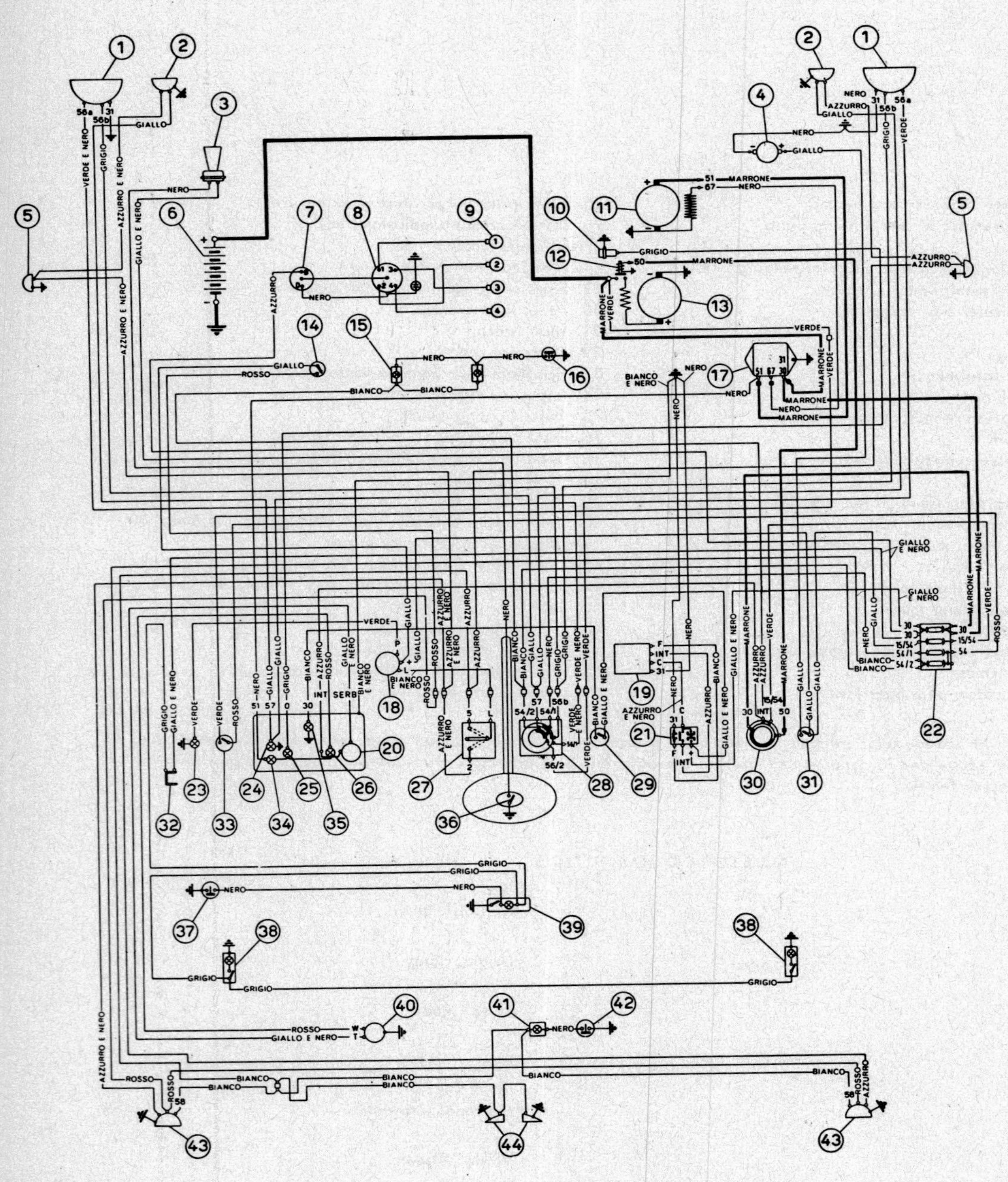

Fiat 1100/103D wiring diagram

1. Headlights (high and low beams).
2. Front turn indicator and parking lights.
3. Horn.
4. Air conditioning unit electrofan.
5. Side turn indicator repeaters.
6. Battery.
7. Ignition coil.
8. Ignition distributor.
9. Spark plugs.
10. Low oil pressure indicator sending unit.
11. Generator.
12. Starter relay switch.
13. Starter.
14. Hydraulic, pressure-operated stop light switch.
15. Engine compartment lights.
16. Engine compartment light jam switch.
17. Generator regulator.
18. Flasher, turn indicators.
19. Windshield wiper.
20. Fuel gauge.
21. Windshield wiper three-position switch.
22. 8-A fuses.
23. Turn indicators pilot light (red).
24. Front parking lights indicator (green).
25. Low oil pressure indicator (red).
26. Low fuel indicator (red).
27. Turn indicators switch.
28. Front outer lighting selector switch.
29. Panel light switch.
30. Lock switch.
31. Electrofan switch.
32. Inspection lamp receptacle.
33. Outer lighting switch.
34. Generator charge indicator (red).
35. Panel light bulb.
36. Horn control pushbutton.
37. Jam switch, between door and pillar, for courtesy light in rear view mirror.
38. Inner lights, with incorporated switch.
39. Bulb, incorporated in rear view mirror, for courtesy light.
40. Fuel gauge sending unit.
41. Luggage compartment light.
42. Jam switch, luggage compartment light.
43. Rear parking, stop and turn indicator lights.
44. License plate lights.

NOTE: *Mark — means that the cable is provided with numbered strip or ferrule.*

CABLE COLOR CODE

Azzurro Blue

Grigio Grey

Rosso Red

Bianco White

Marrone Brown

Verde Green

Giallo Yellow

Nero Black INT-COMMUTAT Switch SERB. Tank.

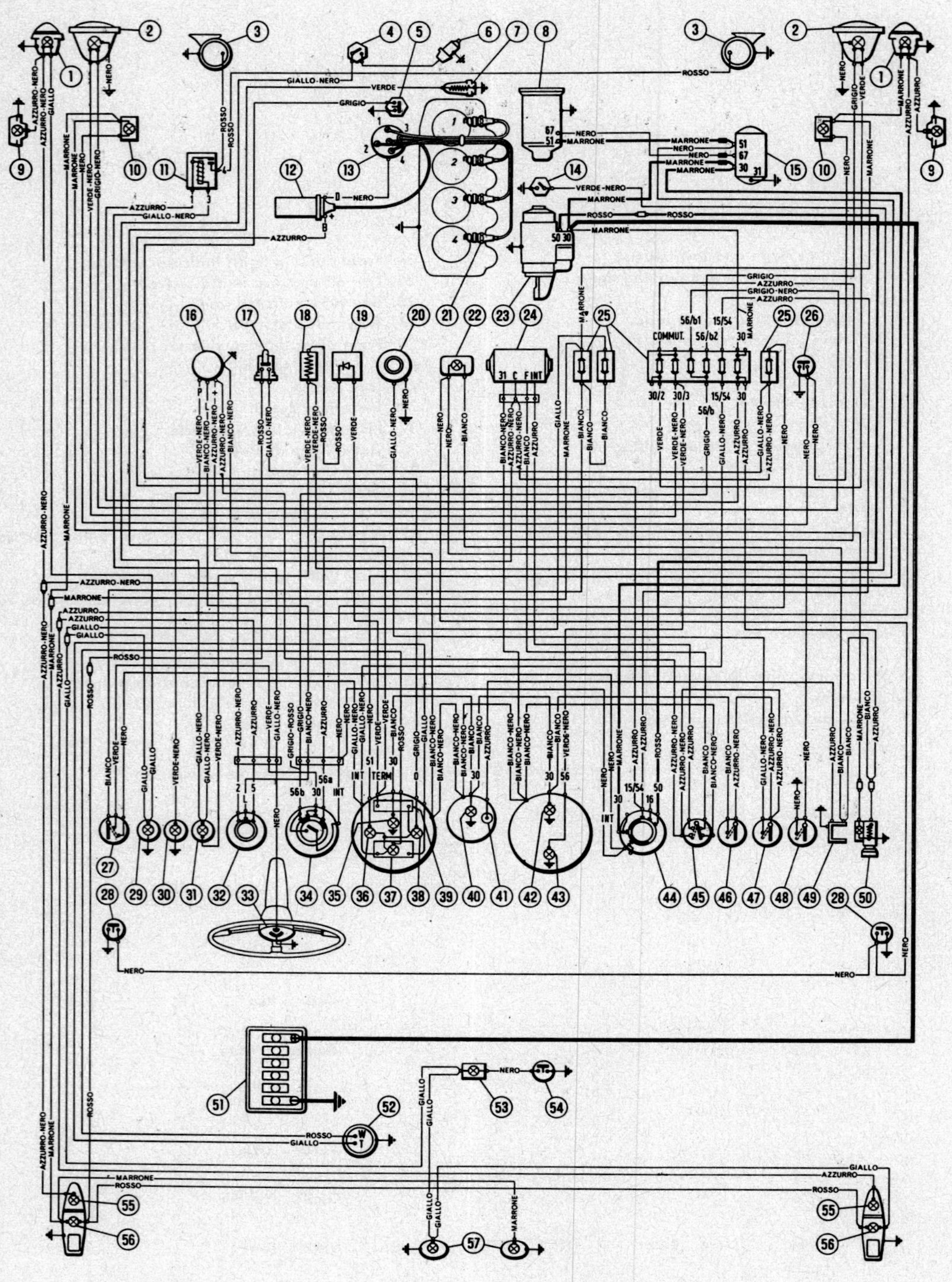

Fiat 1500 Cabriolet wiring diagram

1. Front direction signal and parking lamps.
2. Headlamps (high and low beams).
3. Horns.
4. Electromagnetic fan thermal switch.
5. Low oil pressure indicator sending unit.
6. Electromagnetic fan switch brush.
7. Temperature gauge sending unit.
8. Generator.
9. Direction signal side repeaters.
10. Engine compartment lights.
11. Horn control relay switch.
12. Ignition coil.
13. Ignition distributor.
14. Heat indicator sending unit.
15. Generator regulator.
16. Flasher unit, direction indicators.
17. Stop light jam switch.
18. Temperature gauge resistor.
19. Temperature gauge silicon diode.
20. Heater electrofan.
21. Spark plugs.
22. Map light under dashboard.
23. Starting motor.
24. Windshield wiper motor.
25. Fuses.
26. Engine compartment light jam switch.
27. Outer lighting master switch.
28. Jam switches on doors for courtesy light.
29. Direction signal pilot light (green).
30. Front parking light indicator (green).
31. Heat gauge indicator (red).
32. Direction signal switch.
33. Horn button.
34. Outer lighting change-over switch and headlamp flasher.
35. Fuel and temperature gauge light.
36. No-charge indicator (red).
37. Fuel gauge and reserve supply indicator.
38. Low oil pressure indicator (red).
39. Temperature gauge.
40. Electric clock light.
41. Electric clock.
42. Speedometer light.
43. Headlamp high beam indicator (blue).
44. Lock switch for ignition, warning lights and startng (controls also the anti-theft device).
45. Windshield wiper switch.
46. Instrument lights switch.
47. Electrofan switch.
48. Map light switch.
49. Trouble light receptacle.
50. Cigar lighter (w/spot light).
51. Battery.
52. Fuel gauge sending unit.
53. Deck light.
54. Deck light jam switch.
55. Rear direction signal lights.
56. Tail and stop lights.
57. License plate lights.

NOTE: *Mark — means that the cable is provided with numbered strip or ferrule.*

TERM Temperature gauge -- INT Switch

CABLE COLOR CODE

Azzurro	Blue
Bianco	White
Giallo	Yellow
Grigio	Grey
Marrone	Brown
Nero	Black
Rosa	Pink
Rosso	Red
Verde	Green

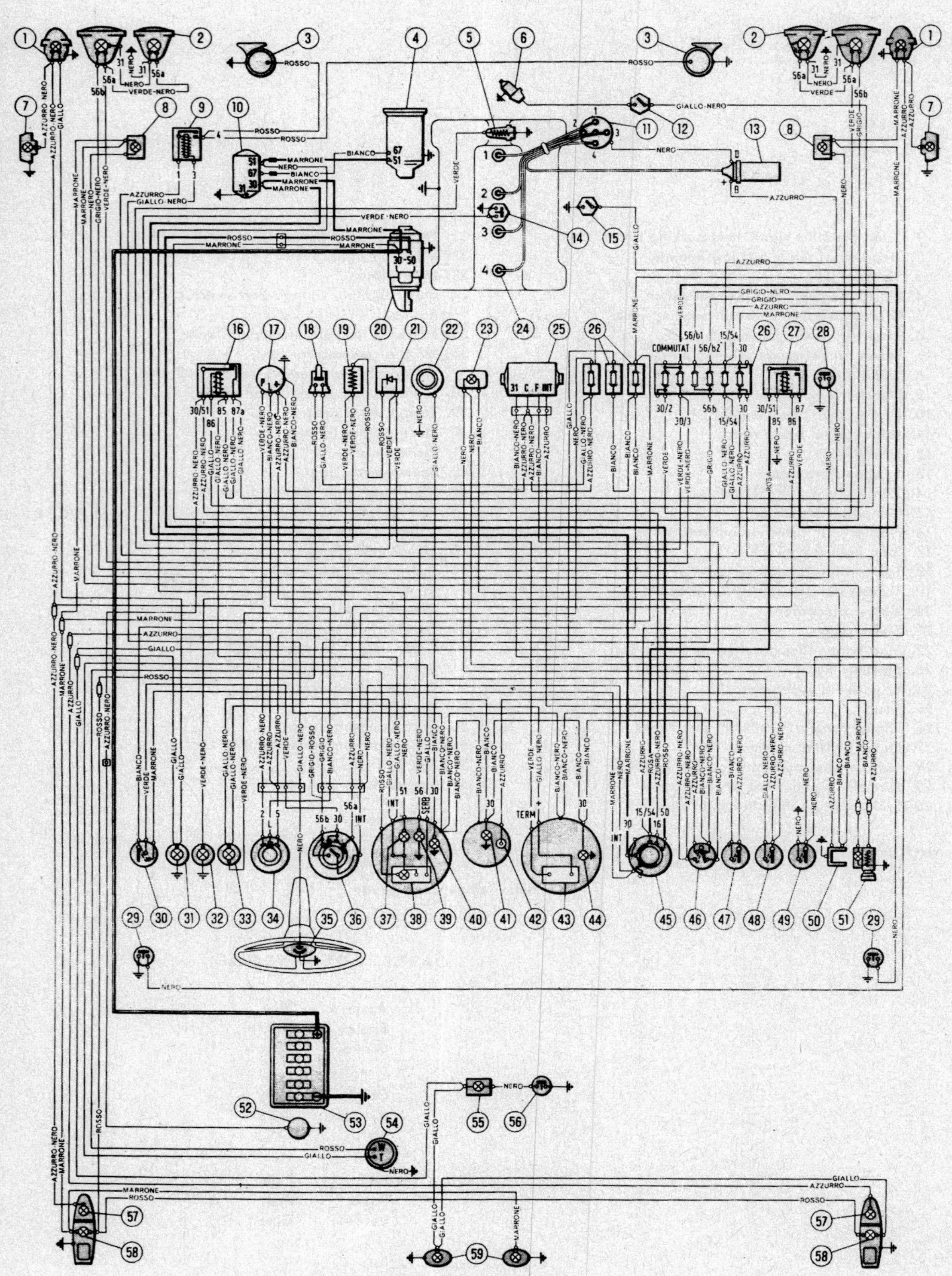

1600S Cabriolet wiring diagram.

1. Front direction signal and parking lamps.
2. Dual headlamps (high and low beam).
3. Horns.
4. Generator.
5. Temperature gauge sending unit.
6. Cooling radiator electromagnetic fan.
7. Direction signal side repeaters.
8. Engine compartment lights.
9. Horn relay switch.
10. Generator regulator.
11. Ignition distributor.
12. Thermal switch for fan 6.
13. Ignition coil.
14. Thermal switch for indicator 33.
15. Low oil pressure sending unit for relay switch 16.
16. Relay switch for pump 52.
17. Flasher unit, direction signal light.
18. Stop light jam switch.
19. Resistor for electric temperature gauge.
20. Starting motor.
21. Silicon diode for temperature gauge.
22. Ventilation and heating electrofan.
23. Map light under dashboard.
24. Spark plugs.
25. Windshield wiper motor.
26. Fuse box.
27. Headlamp high beam relay switch.
28. Engine compartment light jam switch.
29. Jam switches, between door and pillar, for courtesy light.
30. Outer lighting master switch.
31. Parking light indicator (green).
32. Direction signal pilot light (green).
33. Heat indicator (red).
34. Direction signal light switch.
35. Horn button.
36. Outer lighting change-over switch.
37. No-charge indicator (red).
38. Fuel gauge with red reserve supply indicator.
39. Headlamp high beam indicator (blue).
40. Speedometer light.
41. Electric clock light.
42. Electric clock.
43. Temperature gauge.
44. Tachometer.
45. Lock switch for ignition, warning lights and starting (controls also the anti-theft device).
46. Windshield wiper switch.
47. Instrument lights switch.
48. Electrofan switch.
49. Map light switch.
50. Trouble light receptacle.
51. Cigar lighter, with spot light.
52. Electric fuel pump.
53. Battery.
54. Fuel gauge sending unit.
55. Deck light.
56. Jam switch for lamp 55.
57. Rear direction signal lights.
58. Tail and stop lights.
59. License plate lights.

NOTE - Mark ▬ means that the cable is provided with numbered strip or ferrule.

TERM. = **Temperature gauge** — INT-COMMUTAT. = **Switch**
SERB. = **Tank**

CABLE COLOR CODE

Azzurro = **Blue**	Grigio = **Grey**	Rosa = **Pink**
Bianco = **White**	Marrone = **Brown**	Rosso = **Red**
Giallo = **Yellow**	Nero = **Black**	Verde = **Green**

1600S Cabriolet wiring diagram.

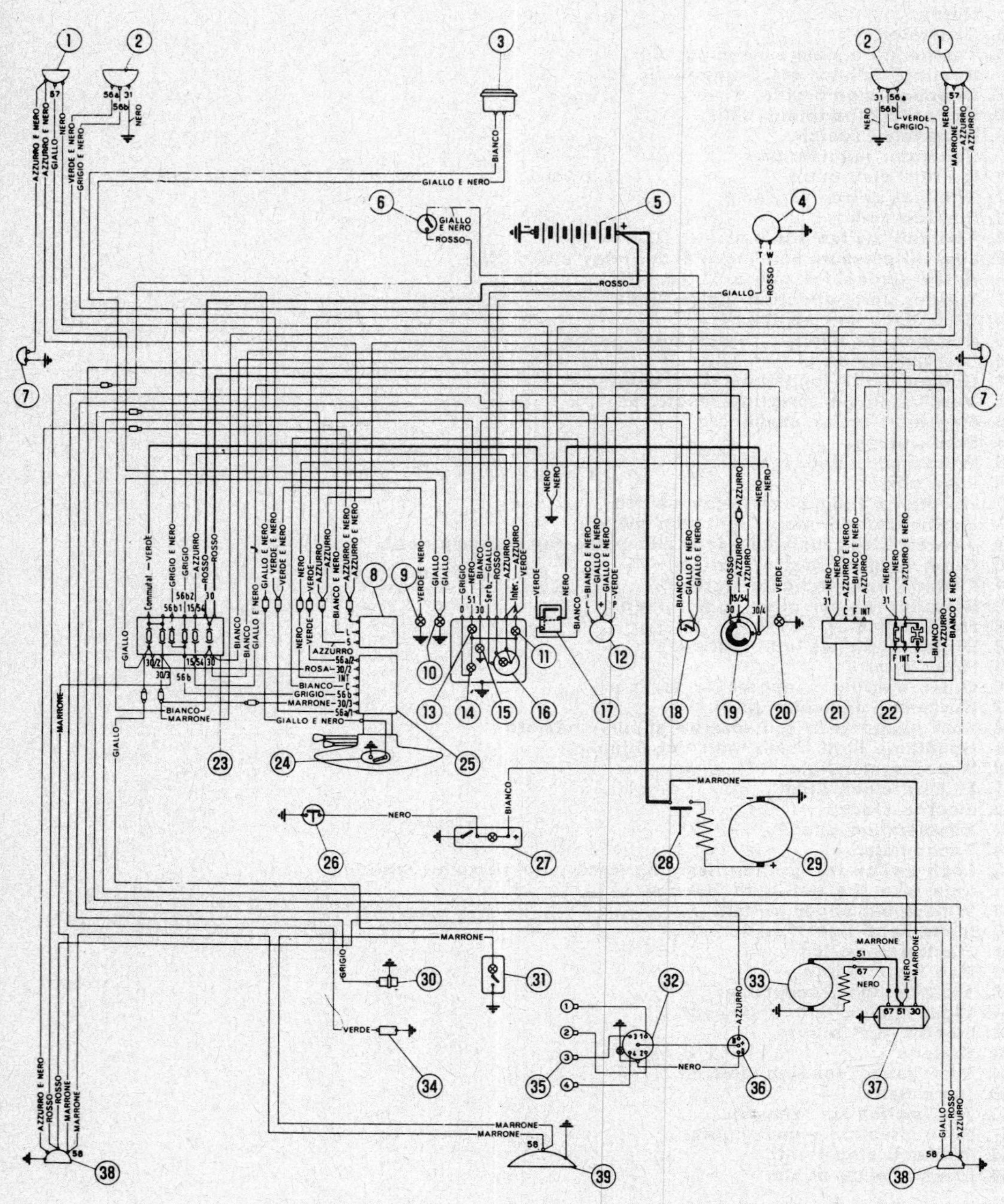

Fiat 600, 600D wiring diagram

1. Front parking and direction indicator lamps.
2. Headlamps (high and low beam).
3. Horn.
4. Fuel gauge sending unit.
5. Battery.
6. Stop lamp pedal-operated switch.
7. Side direction lights.
8. Direction indicator switch.
9. High beam indicator.
10. Parking light indicator.
11. High water temperature indicator.
12. Winking device (flasher unit).
13. Generator charge indicator.
14. Low engine oil pressure indicator.
15. Instrument cluster light.
16. Fuel gauge, with reserve supply indicator.
17. Outer lighting switch.
18. Instrument cluster light switch.
19. Ignition lock switch.
20. Direction indicator pilot light.
21. Windshield wiper motor.
22. Windshield wiper switch.
23. 8-A fuses.
24. Horn button.
25. Outer lighting change-over switch.
26. Jam switch, between door and pillar, for rear view mirror light.
27. Lamp incorporated in rear view mirror, for car in terior illumination, with toggle switch.
28. Starter switch.
29. Starter.
30. Sending unit, for low oil pressure indicator.
31. Engine compartment light, with automatic switch.
32. Ignition distributor.
33. Generator.
34. Thermostatic sending unit for excessive water temperature indicator.
35. Spark plugs.
36. Ignition coil.
37. Generator regulator.
38. Rear parking, stop and direction indicator lamps.
39. Number plate lamp.

NOTE: *Mark — means that cable is provided with numbered strip and ferrule.*

CABLE COLOR CODE

Azzurro	Blue
Bianco	White
Giallo	Yellow
Grigio	Grey
Marrone	Brown
Nero	Black
Rosa	Pink
Rosso	Red
Verde	Green
Azzurro e Nero	Black and Blue
Bianco e Nero	Black and White
Giallo e Nero	Black and Yellow
Verde e Nero	Black and Green
Grigio e Nero	Black and Grey
Commutat.	Switch
Serb.	Tank
INT.–Inter.	Switch

TUNE-UP PROCEDURES

Spark Plugs

The average life of a spark plug is 12,000 miles. This is, however, dependent on the mechanical condition of the engine and the driving conditions. The best indication of worn spark plugs is a drop in gas milage.

Spark plugs should not be filed and regapped; they should be replaced. Be sure to check the gap with a feeler gauge before installation.

Breaker Points and Condenser

Points should be replaced, not filed.

1. Remove the distributer cap and rotor.
2. Then disconnect the wires attached to the points; one from the condenser and the other from the distributor.
3. Remove the points and condenser attaching screws. When installing, be sure that the breaker arm is in contact with the high point on the distributor cam lobe. In this position, proper gap adjustment can be obtained.

Dwell Angle

Dwell angle is the most efficient way to adjust points but can only be done with a dwell meter. See "Tune-Up Specifications Chart" for proper dwell angle.

Ignition Timing

The timing marks for the various engines are as follows:

Timing Adjustment

Timing adjustments can only be made with a timing light.

1. The best way to adjust the timing is to first mark the notch on the pulley with a piece of white chalk.
2. Then go to the desired number of degrees and mark also.
3. Before starting the car loosen the distributor hold-down nut.
4. By moving the distributor clockwise or counterclockwise with the car running, align the chalk marks.
5. Tighten the distributor and recheck the alignment before shutting off the engine.

NOTE: *850 timing adjustments require that the vacuum advance be disconnected.*

Valve Adjustments

Valves can be adjusted by first removing the valve cover and then inserting a feeler gauge between the rocker arm and the valve stem with the valve in a closed position. Fiat requires that the engine be cold for this adjustment. Proper valve lash can be found in "Tune-Up Specifications."

Idle Speed and Mixture Adjustments

Weber 30DIC

This is the basic carburetor that comes on 850 models. It is a dual throat carburetor with a manual choke.

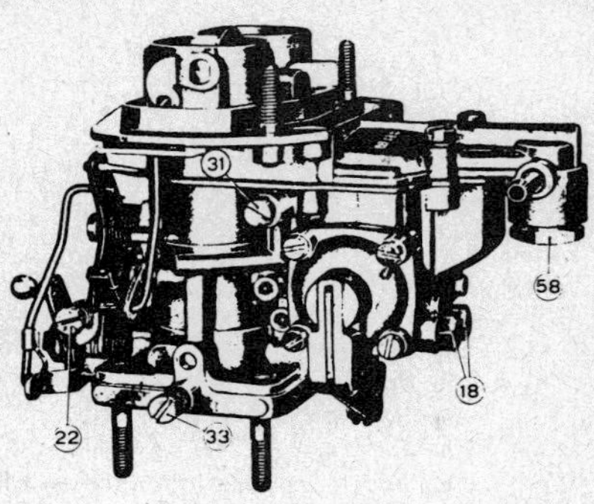

Weber 30DIC carburetor adjustments, controls and jet locations. (18) main jets (22) throttle-stop screw (31) idle jet (33) volume control screw (58) strainer inspection plug.

1. Idle is adjusted on a warm, running engine.
2. Adjust the throttle stop screw to a point where the engine runs steadily.
3. Adjust the volume control screw to the point which allows the highest steady engine speed at a selected degree of throttle restriction. Adjust the throttle opening to the best idle speed, controlling the mixture rate with the volume control screw.

Solex 32 DISA

The Solex carburetor is a single throat downdraft type and is fitted with a cold starting device.

It has three main parts:

1. The cover which contains the cold starting device and the power device.
2. The upper housing which contains the accelerator pump.
3. The lower housing which is heated

850 timing marks

Timing marks for 124: (1) Mark for 10 advance (2) mark for 5 advance (3) mark for 0 advance; (4) reference mark on fan belt pulley.

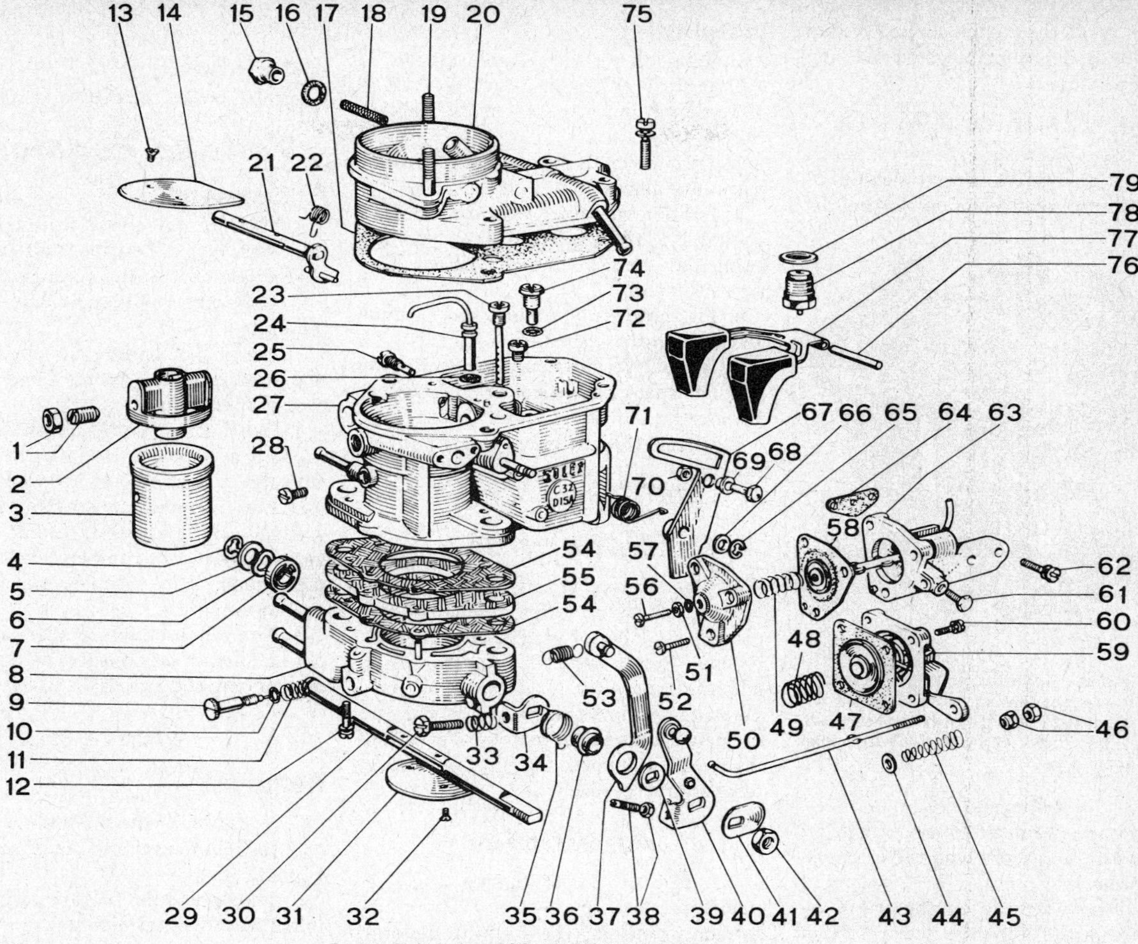

Exploded view Of Solex C 32 DISA carburetor

1. Screw and nut for attaching auxiliary venturi
2. Auxiliary venturi
3. Main venturi
4. Spring washer
5. Spacer
6. Washer
7. Disk valve for oil fumes recirculation device
8. Lower housing.
9. Idle mixture adjustment screw
10. Grommet.
11. Spring.
12. Screw and washer attaching lower to upper housing
13. Screw
14. Cold starting throttle
15. Filter plug
16. Filter plug gasket
17. Gasket
18. Fuel filter
19. Stud
20. Cover
21. Starting choke throttle shaft
22. Spring
23. Emulsion tube
24. Accelerator pump nozzle and jet
25. Idle jet
26. Gasket for nozzle 24
27. Upper housing
28. Main venturi attachment screw
29. Throttle shaft
30. Idle speed adjustment screw
31. Throttle
32. Screw attaching throttle to shaft 29
33. Spring
34. Throttle stop lever
35. Spring
36. Bushing
37. Throttle control lever
38. Throttle opening adjustment screw and nut
39. Bushing for lever 37
40. Throttle control lever
41. Washer
42. Nut locking throttle linkage to throttle shaft
43. Rod
44. Washer
45. Spring
46. Accelerator pump delivery adjustment nut and lock nut
47. Accelerator pump diaphragm
48. Diaphragm spring
49. Lean mixture device spring
50. Lean mixture device cover
51. Nut
52. Screw attaching cover 50
53. Spring returning lever 37
54. Gaskets
55. Thermal spacer
56. Starting throttle opening adjustment screw
57. Washer
58. Lean mixture device diaphragm
59. Accelerator pump cover
60. Accelerator pump cover attachment screw
61. Cold starting device control sheath attachment screw
62. Screw and washer
63. Lean mixture device housing
64. Gasket
65. Spring washer
66. Shoulder washer
67. Cold starting control wire lever
68. Cold starting device control wire locking screw
69. Bushing for screw 68
70. Nut for screw 68
71. Return spring for lever 67
72. Main jet
73. Gasket
74. Accelerator pump valve
75. Screw attaching cover to upper housing
76. Float hinge pin
77. Float
78 Needle valve
79. Needle valve gasket

by water from the engine cooling system to prevent the forming of ice while idling in cold weather.

Weber 221 M and 261 M

This is the basic carburetor on the 124 model. It is a single throat downdraft type with progressive action starting devices.

Weber 261M carburetor. Idle jet holder (1) throttle lever (2) idle speed adjustment (3) vacuum advance line (4) idle mixture adjustment (5) main jet holder (6) fuel inlet (7) strainer (8).

Adjustments

1. Idle speed adjustments are made by the throttle stop screw and the idle mixture screw.
2. Adjust, with the engine warm by first setting the idle stop screw to that minimum which allows steady operation.
3. Then turn the mixture screw in or out to achieve a fast smooth idle.
4. Readjust the throttle stop screw for proper idle speed.

Adjustments for the 128 are the same.

ENGINE ELECTRICAL

Distributor

All Fiat distributors are similar in appearance and operation. The 850 series is equipped with distributors that use a vacuum and centrifugal advance. The 124 and 128 models are fitted with distributors employing only centrifugal advance.

Removal

Removal procedures are similar for all Fiat distributors.

1. Remove the high tension wires from the distributor.
2. Remove the low tension leads and disconnect the vacuum advance (if equipped).
3. Loosen the clamp bolt at the base of the distributor and carefully remove the distributor from the engine.

Installation

1. Rotate the crankshaft to bring No. 1 cylinder to TOP DEAD CENTER (TDC) of compression stroke (both valves closed).
2. Turn the crankshaft until the timing marks are aligned.
3. Position the distributor rotor opposite the No. 1 contact in the cap. At this point the contact breaker points are about to open.
4. Fit the distributor into its housing and tighten the clamp bolt.
5. Replace the distributor cap and connect the spark plug wires in the correct firing order.
6. Check the ignition timing with a timing light and the point dwell with a dwell meter.

Generator

DC generators are two-pole, shunt-wound units with three regulators for control of generator voltage, current and cut-out. Before making regulator tests and adjustments, it is necessary to temperature-stabilize the unit. This can be done by operating the generator at 15–16 volts, with the cover on, until operating temperature is reached.

Alternator

Fiat 124 Sp. Coupe, Spider, and late models are equipped with a 770 watt alternator, replacing the 400 watt generator. The alternator is a self-rectifying, three phase current generator, using silicone diodes in a bridge circuit. The rc1/12b voltage regulator is a dual vibrating contact type, requiring no adjustment.

Certain precautions should be observed when working on this, or any other AC charging system.

1. Never switch battery polarity.
2. When installing a battery, never connect the hot cable first.
3. Never disconnect the battery while the engine is running.
4. If the molded connector is disconnected from the alternator, do not ground the hot wire.
5. Never run the alternator with the main output cable disconnected.
6. Never electric weld around the vehicle, without disconnecting the alternator.
7. Never apply any voltage, other than battery voltage, when testing.
8. Never apply more than 12 volts to jump a battery for starting purposes.

Removal

The alternator is removed by unscrewing the nut on the upper bracket and the screw which attaches the bracket to the engine. Remove the two nuts of the lower brackets, fan, generator and water pump belt.

Installation

Installation is the reverse of removal.

Voltage Regulator

Adjustments

1. Measure the air gap for the cut-out relay between the clapper and the edge of the core nearest the contacts.
2. Make the cut-in adjustment with the unit at 65–95° F.
3. Adjust by bending the spring tension arm until the points close at the proper specification.
4. Check the reverse current by connecting a two-way ammeter in series with the battery lead to the regulator.
5. Run the generator to 4500 rpm and gradually reduce speed, noting the reverse current at the point where the contacts open. (See specifications for the proper amperage.)
6. The range between cut-in and cut-out action can be adjusted by enlarging or reducing the air gap.

Starter

Removal

Front Engine Models

.1 Jack up the car and place jackstands beneath the frame.

2. Disconnect the battery positive terminal to prevent accidental shorting.
3. Remove the exhaust manifold and muffler to provide clearance.
4. Disconnect the wires from the starter, tagging each wire to facilitate later identification.
5. Remove the mounting bolts and pull the starter from the housing.

Rear Engine Models

1. Raise the car at the rear and set it on two stands at the control arms.
2. Disconnect the battery (positive) cable to prevent shorting.
3. Disconnect and remove the lower linings of the compartment.
4. If necessary, remove the exhaust manifold and muffler.
5. Disconnect the wires from the starter motor and tag each wire to facilitate later identification.
6. Remove the mounting bolts and the starter.

Disassembly

The starter can be broken down into the following subassemblies: solenoid, commutator end head, frame, armature, drive and pinion end head.

1. To disassemble, disconnect the starter motor lead from the solenoid and remove the solenoid.
2. Remove the brush cover and disconnect the brush holder.

3. Lift the brushes slightly and retain them in their holders by arranging springs against their sides.

4. Unscrew the two self-locking nuts and take off the brush holder bracket, saving the fiber and steel thrust washers.

5. Slide the frame off the pinion end.

6. Remove the cotter pin from the linkage pivot and remove the pivot. The armature can then be taken out, along with the drive and fork lever.

Assembly

Assembly is the reverse of removal.

Installation

Installation for all models is the reverse of removal.

Battery

All Fiat batteries are 12 volt units, grounded on the negative side. The only maintenance associated with the battery is to keep it filled with clean (preferably, distilled) water. The terminals should also be kept lightly coated with petroleum jelly to prevent corrosion.

ENGINE MECHANICAL

The Fiat 124, 128 and 850 all have four cylinder, inline, water cooled engines. The 124 and 128 engines are mounted in the front, and the 128 is mounted transversely.

The engine used in the 124 Spider and Coupe sport cars differs from that used in the 124 sedan and station wagon. Major differences are a larger bore in the sports models and their double overhead camshaft valve train, as opposed to the overhead valve design used in the sedan and wagon. There are also slight differences in carburetion, lubrication and cooling.

Engine Removal

All 124 Models

1. Removal of 124 sedan and sports car engines is facilitated by removing the radiator and the transmission. Proceed as follows:

2. Jack up the car and place it on jackstands.

3. Drain the radiator, auxiliary tank, block and heater system by first moving the heater lever to far right, then opening the radiator drain cock and removing the plug on the right-hand side of the block.

4. Speed drainage by removing the radiator and auxiliary tank caps.

5. Disconnect the battery leads.

6. Then disconnect the ignition coil, generator, starter, low oil pressure and water temperature indicator wires.

7. Disconnect the accelerator rod, sliding it out of the lever ball joint end toward the dash.

8. Remove the air filter.

9. Detach the choke cable from the carburetor.

10. Disconnect the line from the fuel pump and detach the exhaust pipe from the manifold.

11. Disconnect the radiator and heater hoses.

12. Remove the upper two screws that hold the radiator to the body, then remove the radiator by sliding it from the lower support bracket.

13. Working from inside the car, remove the gearshift lever by pressing down the upper part of the sleeve and, with a screwdriver, releasing the spring ring from its seating in the lower part of the lever. The upper part of lever can then be slipped from the lower part.

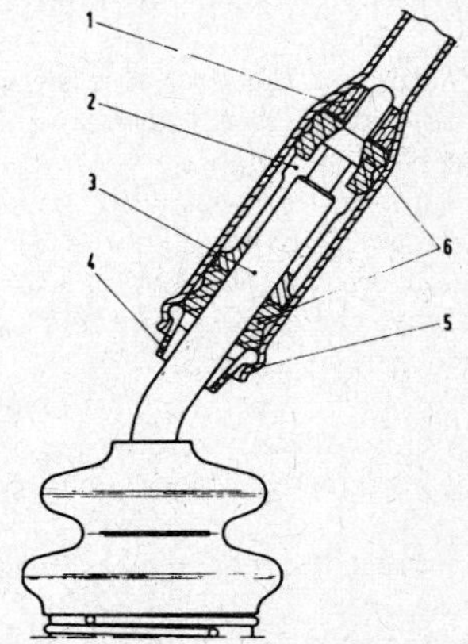

Fiat 124 gearshift lever assembly: (1) shoulder (2) spacer (3) lever (4) spring (5) sleeve (6) rubber bushings.

14. Remove the transmission cover.

15. From under the car, disconnect the driveshaft spider and transmission mainshaft from the universal.

A clamp holds universal (4) together while removing drive shaft screws (1) and transmission spider screws.

NOTE: *This is facilitated by placing the band, Tool A.70025, on the coupling itself.*

16. Disconnect the speedometer cable from the transmission and disconnect the flexible cable from the clutch fork.

17. Remove the flywheel cover, electrical ground cable and exhaust pipe bracket clip.

18. Remove the heat shield from the exhaust manifold and the three bolts that hold the starter to the front of the transmission.

19. Position a hydraulic jack under the transmission for support.

20. Remove the four bolts which mount the transmission to the crankcase.

21.Remove the crossmember that holds the transmission to the car floor.

22. Supporting the transmission jack, move it toward the rear of the car so as to withdraw the clutch shaft from the pilot bushing and clutch hub.

23. Lower the jack and pull the transmission from under the car.

24. Remove the starter from the engine compartment.

25. Using a chain hoist, pass the rear sling under the crankcase and the front sling under the thermostat housing.

26. Supporting the engine with a hoist, remove the front mounts and lift the engine clear.

Installation

Installation is the reverse of removal.

850

1. Jack up the car from the rear and place it on jackstands.

2. Disconnect the positive terminal of the battery and the fuel line at the tank.

3. Tilt the back of the rear seat forward and remove the screws and floor covering.

4. Remove the starter and the two upper bolts that hold the transmission to the engine.

5. Remove the apron from under the engine.

6. Unbolt the flywheel housing from the transmission.

7. Disconnect the exhaust pipe at the manifold and the muffler at the oil sump.

8. Drain the cooling system and disconnect the water hoses at the radiator.

9. Disconnect the fuel line at the fuel pump.

10. Disconnect the oil pressure and water temperature indicators.

11. Remove the air cleaner and disconnect the carburetor choke and accelerator linkage.

12. Disconnect the ignition coil and generator.

13. Attach a chain hoist to the engine and lightly take up the slack.

14. Remove the two bottom bolts that hold the engine to the transmission.

15. Remove the rear central engine support nut, washer and rubber bushing.

16. Remove the two nuts, one on each side, that hold the bumper to the brackets and the four nuts and two screws that hold the lower body panel.

17. Lift the engine from the car.

Disassembly

Disassembly of Fiat 850 engines is almost identical to that for the Fiat 124 OHV engine. All three engines are inline, four-cylinder, overhead valve engines, differing only in internal specifications. Basically, disassembly of all three engines is identical, excepting external attachments.

Assembly

Follow the procedure outlined for the Fiat 124 overhead valve engine.

124 Sedan, Special, Station Wagon (OHV)

Disassembly

1. To facilitate disassembly, mount the engine on some type of engine stand.
2. Drain the oil from the engine and remove the dipstick.
3. Dismantle the clutch assembly, by removing the six bolts and washers which secure it to the flywheel.
4. If the air filter was not removed earlier, remove it by disconnecting the two crankcase ventilation pipes and removing the four screws.
5. Disconnect the fuel pump-to-carburetor fuel line.
6. Remove the fuel pump from the mounting studs.
7. Remove the distributor bracket from the stud and the distributor from the engine.
8. Remove the oil and water temperature sending units.
9. Remove the generator, bracket, fan and drive belt.
10. Disconnect the accelerator rod from the carburetor throttle lever.
11. Remove the valve cover from the cylinder head.
12. Remove the heater delivery and return water pipes, which are connected to the cylinder head and water pump outlet.
13. Remove the thermostat cover and gasket and withdraw the thermostat.
14. Remove the water outlet from the cylinder head.
15. Remove the carburetor, complete with shields, spacers and gaskets.
16. Remove the intake and exhaust manifolds.
17. Unscrew the oil filter and remove the gasket.
18. Remove the water pump and fan assembly from the crankcase.
19. Loosen the four self-locking nuts and remove the rocker shaft assembly from the cylinder head.
20. Withdraw the pushrods from their bores, keeping them in the proper order for assembly.
21. Loosen the ten bolts and remove the cylinder head.
22. Withdraw the tappets from their guides, keeping them in the proper order.
23. Unlock the tap washer under the nut which secures the fan drive pulley.
24. Using a flywheel holder, remove the nut from the pulley.
25. Remove the pulley from the crankshaft.
26. Remove the oil pan from the cylinder block.
27. Loosen the bolts, and withdraw the front timing gear cover.
28. Unlock the tab washer and remove the bolt which secures the timing gear (larger) to the camshaft.
29. Remove the camshaft sprocket and timing chain.
30. Use a gear puller to remove the crankshaft sprocket from the crankshaft.
31. Remove the flywheel from the crankshaft.
32. Using a puller, withdraw the ball race which carries the transmission direct driveshaft from its seat in the crankshaft.
33. Withdraw the driven gear of the oil pump and the distributor drive from the end of its spindle.
34. Remove the oil pump assembly, complete with suction pipe and gasket.
35. Remove the connecting rod caps and bearing shells, keeping them in the proper order for assembly.
36. Carefully, push the connecting rods, complete with pistons, rings and bearings, from the upper end of the block.
37. Remove the rear cover plate of the crankcase.
38. Unbolt the five main bearing caps and remove these, keeping them in correct order.
39. Carefully, lift the crankshaft from the block and lay it down where it will not be damaged.
40. Remove the bearing shells and the thrust half bearings from the rear main bearing.
41.Remove the camshaft end plate.
42. Carefully remove the camshaft.

Assembly

1. Lubricate the camshaft bearings and journals.
2. Insert the camshaft and fit the retainer plate over the front end of the shaft.
3. Carefully, lubricate the main bearing half shells and seat them in the block.
4. Lubricate the crankshaft journals and seat the crankshaft in the block.
5. Install the thrust half-rings in the rear main bearing seat.
6. Fit the main bearing caps and half-bearings, tightening the caps to specification.
7. Replace the ball race of the transmission direct driveshaft.
8. Install the rear crankcase cover plate and tighten the six bolts.
9. Turn the crankshaft to bring the crankpins of Nos. 1 and 4 cylinders to their highest point (with the engine upside down).
10. Fit the flywheel, aligning the reference mark on the flywheel with the crankpins.
11. Torque the retaining bolts to specification.
12. Lubricate the pistons and fit the piston, ring and connecting rod assembly to their respective cylinders.
13. Refit the oil pump to the cylinder block.
14. Connect the connecting rods and torque to specifications.
15. Replace the driven gear of the oil pump and the distributor drive on its spindle.
16. Oil the camshaft journals and insert the camshaft into the block, being careful not to damage the bearings.
17. Replace the camshaft gear on the camshaft and torque the bolt to specifications.
18. Replace the key and gear on the crankshaft along with the timing chain. Be sure that the marks on the two gears align.
19. Insert the tappets into their proper bores in the cylinder block.
20. Place the cylinder head gasket on the block and fit the cylinder head, complete with valves and springs.
21. Insert the ten cylinder head bolts and torque according to specifications, in no less than two stages.
22. Insert the pushrods into their proper housings.
23. Replace the rocker assembly over the studs on the cylinder head.
24. Torque the nuts to specification.
25. Adjust the final clearance of the valves and rockers.
26. Replace the timing gear cover.
27. Install the fan drive pulley over the front end of the crankshaft with its tab washer and nut.
28. Torque to specification.
29. Replace the fuel pump, inserting a gasket and spacer between the pump and the block.
30. Fit the oil filter bracket and oil filter.
31. Replace the intake and exhaust manifolds on the cylinder head.
32. Install the water pump to the front of the cylinder block with gaskets.
33. Replace the thermostat.
34. Fit the water return pipe from the heater to the water pump and exhaust manifold.
35. Replace the water temperature sending unit in the cylinder head.
36. Fit the oil pressure sending unit to the oil filter bracket.
37. Replace the cooling system drain plug in the crankcase.
38. Replace the spacer, gasket, carbu-

retor, and heat shield over the intake manifold studs, in that order.

39. Connect the fuel line to the fuel pump and carburetor.

40. Bring No. 1 cylinder to the end of the compression stroke (both valves closed) and fit the degree wheel.

41. Turn the flywheel until the reference mark on the flywheel shows 10° B.T.D.C.

42. Mesh the oil pump and distributor drive pinion with the camshaft.

43. Turn the distributor drive spindle so that the rotor is facing No. 1 cylinder contact. The breaker points should be just beginning to open.

44. Without moving the distributor spindle, insert the distributor into the housing and insert the spindle in the toothed end of the driving gear.

45. Clamp the distributor in place, and replace the distributor cap.

46. Fit the fan pulley and fan on the hub of the water pump spindle.

47. Replace the lower generator supports, generator and upper generator support.

48. Fit the belt over the three pulleys (drive pulley, fan pulley and generator pulley).

49. Adjust the belt tension and clamp the generator to the upper bracket.

50. Fit the gasket and rocker cover to the cylinder head and replace the spark plugs.

51. Connect the accelerator control rod to the lever on the cylinder head cover.

52. Replace the clutch assembly on the flywheel.

53. Replace the oil pan on the block.

54. Fill the engine with oil and replace the dipstick.

124 Spyder, Coupe, Sport Spyder, Sport Coupe (DOHC)

Disassembly

These Fiat models use a double overhead camshaft engine. This engine is identical to the overhead valve model, except for the two camshafts. It also has a timing belt instead of a timing chain, an idler sprocket for the timing belt and an auxiliary shaft to drive the distributor and oil pump.

Follow the disassembly procedure suggested for the 124 overhead valve engine, noting the above differences.

Assembly

Assemble the engine following the procedure outlined for the 124 overhead valve engine. The following departures should be noted.

1. To install the cylinder head and time valves, crank pistons Nos. 1 and 4 to TDC.

2. Screw two dummy studs into the crankcase to index the cylinder head.

3. Align the cylinder head gasket and carefully position the cylinder head on the crankcase, piloting it over the dummy studs.

NOTE: *Care should be taken when replacing the cylinder head, since the valves protrude from the head face. These can be knocked against the block and bent.*

4. Start some of the head screws manually, and remove the pilot studs.

5. Torque the cylinder head bolts, in the proper sequence, to specification.

6. Position the camshafts, so that the reference mark on each gear is aligned with the fixed pointer at the front of the cylinder head.

NOTE: *Once the head has been fitted, avoid turning the camshafts until the timing belt is installed.*

7. Fit the timing belt, being careful not to disturb the alignment of the camshafts and fixed pointer.

8. Fix a spring balance to the upper right arm of the timing belt idler.

9. Adjust the belt tension by applying a force of 60 lbs. in a direction bisecting the angle formed by the timing belt as it passes around the idler.

10. Tighten the nuts to clamp the idler.

11. Check the belt tension at two or three points, turning the crankshaft ½ turn in the direction of rotation only.

NOTE: *The timing belt must be changed every 25,000 miles. Under no circumstances, may the timing belt be used more than 37,000 miles.*

To change the timing belt without removing the radiator or engine, follow the procedure outlined.

1. Drain part of the water in the cooling system and remove the upper radiator hose.

2. Remove the upper section of the air duct.

3. Check the ignition timing and remove the timing cover.

4. Check the valve timing and hold the camshaft gears and engage a low gear while applying the handbrake.

5. Remove the lower protection plate from the engine.

6. Loosen the generator mounting nut and tensioner bolt.

7. Remove the generator drive belt and slacken the timing belt idler locknuts.

8. Remove the timing belt and fit a new belt over the camshaft gears and idler.

9. Fix a spring scale and apply a force of 60 lbs. in a direction bisecting the angle formed by the timing belt as it passes around the idler.

10. Clamp the idler with the locknuts and check the tension at two or three places, turning the crankshaft ½ turn in the direction of rotation only.

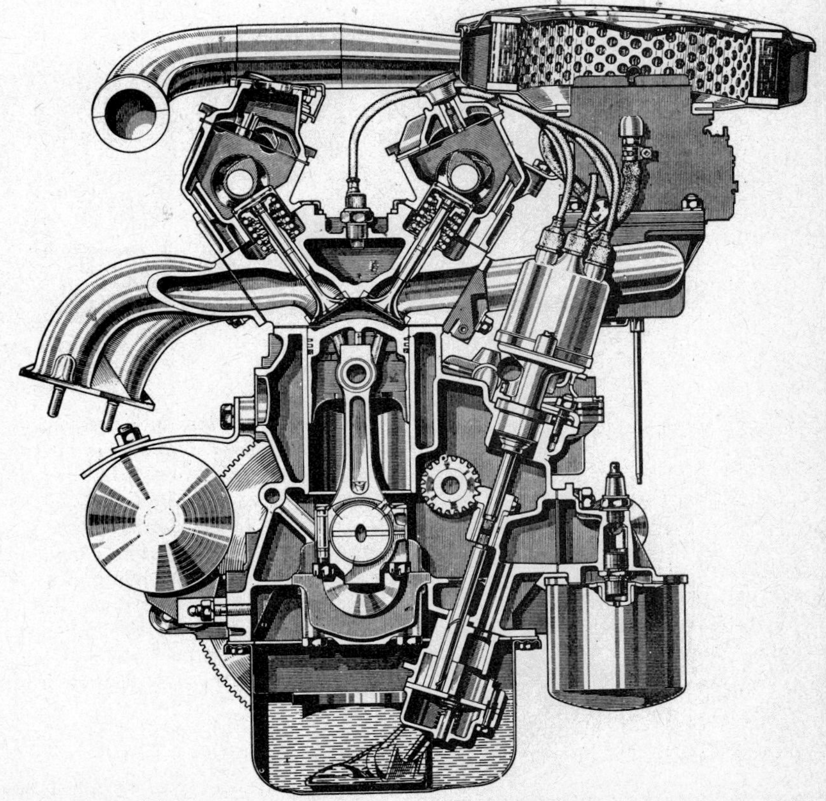

Fiat 124 Coupe and Spider overhead camshaft engine.

Valve adjustment is necessary only if the clearance is .004 in. less than the figure listed in the specifications. This applies only to overhead camshaft engines. Tappet clearance is measured between the camshaft lobe and the tappet, directly beneath it. It is not necessary to remove the camshaft to adjust clearance.

1. Check the valve clearance by removing the rocker cover.
2. Remove the covers from over the camshafts.
3. Rotate the crankshaft until the cam lobe, which controls the tappet to be checked, is perpendicular to the tappet. In this position, the valve in question is closed.
4. Use a feeler gauge to measure the clearance between the cap plate and the cam lobe.

Tappet Clearance Adjustment

1. Rotate the camshaft until the valve is fully open.
2. Hold the tappet down and rotate the camshaft to allow the extraction of the tappet by means of a jet of compressed air through the notch in the tappet.
3. Insert the new cap plate of correct thickness, determined by the feeler gauge measurement. Cap plates are available in 30 different thicknesses in graduations of 0.0019 in. The thickness is marked on the face of the plate, but it is good practice to measure the cap plate to be sure that the thickness is as marked.

128

1. Place the car on jackstands and be sure the car is in a stable position before removal.
2. Raise the hood and unhook the stay rod. Place covers on the fenders.
3. Loosen the wing nut and remove the spare tire.
4. Take off the lower guards.
5. Drain the water from the radiator, supply tank, cylinder block and passenger compartment heating system in the following way:
   a. Completely lower the heater lever inside the car.
   b. Open the cock at the bottom of the radiator and remove the radiator cap.
   c. Open the cock at the inner side of the engine block and take the cap off the supply tank to help water drainage.
6. Disconnect the battery cables.

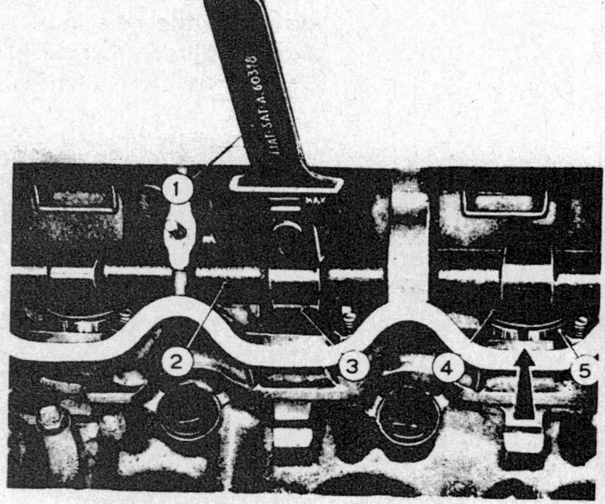

A. Use tool (1) to adjust clearance between cap plate (4) of tappet (5) and cam (3). Arrow shows notch for removing cap plate.

B. Rotate camshaft in the direction of arrow until cam meets stop (a) to free cap plate from cam.

Remove the air filter by disconnecting two crankcase ventilation pipes and removing four screws.

7. Disconnect the primary and secondary wires from the coil to the distributor.
8. Disconnect the wires from the generator.
9. Disconnect the wires from the starter, the oil pressure sending unit, and the water temperature sending unit.
10. Disconnect the air cleaner.
11. Disconnect the linkage and choke wire from the carburetor.
12. Disconnect the fuel inlet hose from the fuel pump.
13. Disconnect the exhaust pipe from the manifold.
14. Remove the two rubber hoses from the union with the thermostat to the radiator.
15. Disconnect the water inlet and outlet hoses from the engine to the passenger compartment heater.
16. Disconnect the speedometer drive from the transmission housing by unscrewing the retaining ring.
17. Remove the adjustable rod of the flexible cable from the clutch release lever by unscrewing the locknut and nut.
18. Detach the anti-roll bar by removing the screws which clamp the brackets and insulators to the body. Then unscrew the nuts which fasten the ends to the control arms.
19. Remove the exhaust pipe support bracket from the transmission housing.
20. Disconnect the rod from the gearshift control lever.
21. Remove the earth plate from the transmission housing.
22. Take off the left hand wheel. Unscrew the left tie rod-to-steering nut and disconnect the ball joint.
23. Remove the shock absorber from the pillar.
24. Unscrew the constant-speed joint nuts from both front wheels.
25. From above the car, working in the engine compartment, disconnect the reaction strut.
26. Hook up the engine and put the cable under light tension. Then, working from above, unscrew the engine to body clamping bolt and, from below, detach the crossmember from the underbody.
27. Work the shaft of each constant-speed joint out of its seat in the pillars and secure the axle shafts with wire to prevent them from coming away from their seats in the differential.
28. Using a hoist lower the engine group to remove.

Disassembly

1. Drain the oil pan.
2. Remove the clutch assembly.
3. Remove the spark plug wires.
4. Remove the distributor.

5. Remove the oil pressure sending unit and water temperature sending unit.

6. Remove the generator drive belt and generator.

7. Remove the fuel pump, insulating spacer and control plunger.

8. Slacken the retaining clamps and remove the water delivery and return pipes from the carburetor.

9. Remove the carburetor complete with guard and gaskets.

10. Remove the intake shroud.

11. Remove the intake and exhaust manifolds as a unit.

12. Disassemble the water pump unit from the engine block.

13. Remove the oil filter.

14. Remove the timing gear cover.

15. Unscrew the camshaft sprocket attachment screw and auxiliary shaft sprocket screw.

16. Unscrew the belt tensioner and drive pulley nuts.

17. Remove the sprockets, pulleys, and toothed belt.

18. Remove the tensioner support and work the tensioner from its seat on the engine mount.

19. Remove the belt guard and bracket.

20. Disassemble the cylinder head from the crankcase along with the camshaft support.

21. Remove the cylinder head and gasket.

22. Remove the auxiliary shaft lock plate and shaft.

23. Remove the crankcase breather body and gasket.

24. Remove the flywheel.

25. Remove the oil pan.

26. Remove the cover plates, gaskets, timing gear end, and flywheel end.

27. Remove the oil pump assembly.

28. Remove both oil return pipes.

29. Remove the connecting rod caps and piston rod assemblies.

30. Remove the main bearing caps and inserts.

31. Remove the crankshaft, bearing inserts and thrust ring halves.

Assembly

1. After careful lubrication, put the main bearing inserts into position and install the crankshaft.

2. Install the thrust half rings at the flywheel end.

3. Install the main bearing inserts and caps and torque to 58 ft lbs.

4. Install the flyweel cover and gasket.

5. Install the flyweel and torque to 61 ft lbs.

6. Using a ring compressor, install the piston and rod assemblies, with rings, into the cylinder bore.

7. Torque the connecting rods to 36 ft lbs.

8. Install the timing cover seal.

9. Install the timing cover.

10. Install the auxiliary shaft in its crankcase seating, complete with bushings in the two supports, and lock it in place with the cover and seal.

11. Slide the driven sprocket onto the auxiliary shaft and lock it with the plate and screw, but do not tighten fully.

12. Install the oil pump, and the gasket.

13. Before final locking, install the oil

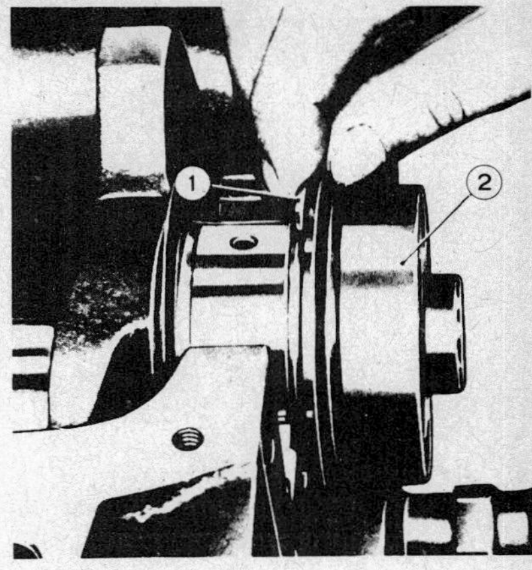

Assembly of crankshaft thrust half-rings in their seats at the flywheel end saddle bore.

1. Thrust half-ring
2. Crankshaft

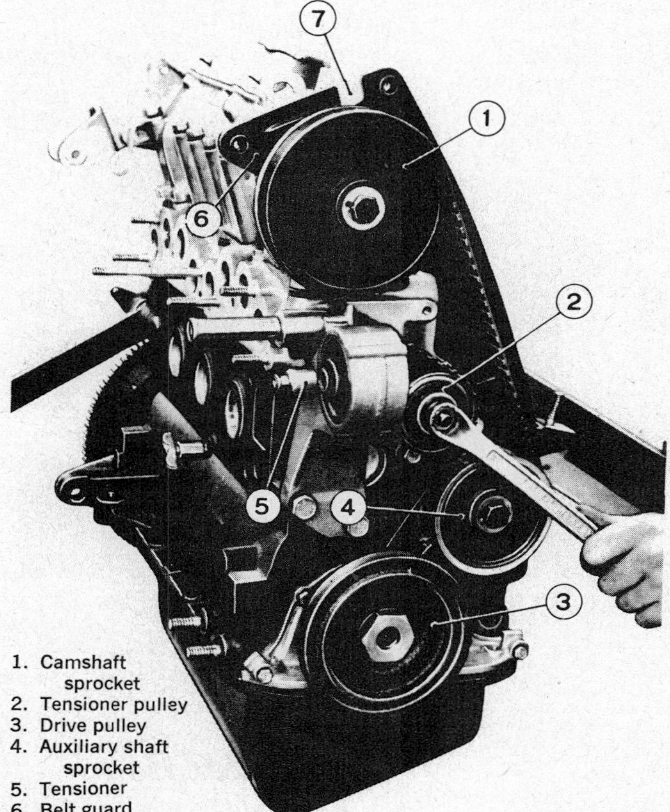

1. Camshaft sprocket
2. Tensioner pulley
3. Drive pulley
4. Auxiliary shaft sprocket
5. Tensioner
6. Belt guard
7. Bracket

Removal of belt tensioner pulley nut

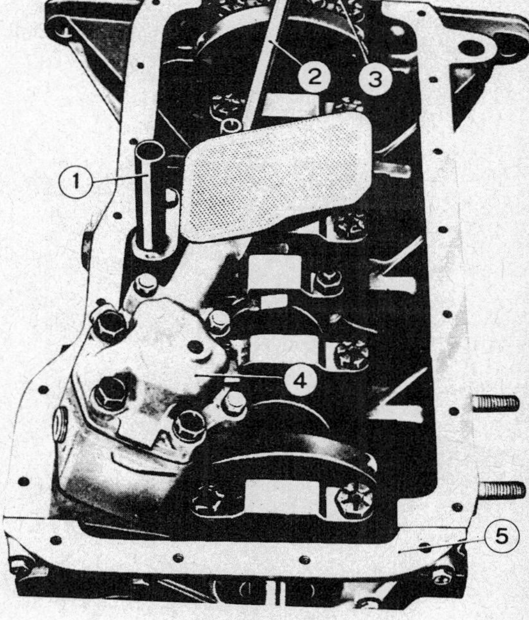

View of oil pump in crankcase

1. Oil return pipe from breather body
2. Oil return pipe from rear saddle bore
3. Flywheel end cover plate
4. Oil pump
5. Timing gear end cover plate

View of auxiliary shaft on crankcase

1. Cover
2. Seal
3. Shaft

pump and ignition distributor drive gear, coupling it to the relative gear on the auxiliary shaft. Then fit the distributor into the crankcase.

14. While using the gear to rotate the auxiliary shaft, lock the oil pump by alternately tightening the three screws.

15. Install the breather body and oil return pipes.

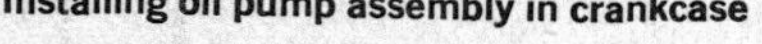

Installing oil pump assembly in crankcase

1. Oil pump
2. Auxiliary shaft sprocket
3. Ignition distributor
4. Breather body oil return pipe
5. Flywheel end bearing oil return pipe

The arrow shows the rotation of the auxiliary shaft during pump assembly to prevent drive spindle binding.

16. Install the timing gear, water pump, and alternator drive pulleys without tightening completely.

17. Install the water drain plug.

18. Assemble the oil sump.

19. Install the head gasket with the word ALTO facing upward; then install the complete head assembly.

20. Tighten the cylinder head using sequences and torque specifications.

21. Fix the bracket to the camshaft bearing assembly and install the belt guard by interposing the two insulating rings.

22. After fitting the drive plunger, the insulator and the two gaskets, install the fuel pump and lock it into its crankcase seat.

23. Install the gas and oil vapor breather body and the cartridge filter.

24. Install the water pump.

25. Install the intake and exhaust manifolds.

26. Key the sprocket to the camshaft and lock it with the screw and the lock plate. Install the belt tensioner in its seat on the crankcase support. Then install the tensioner support and lock it to the crankcase.

27. Install the tensioner pulley on the support and lock it temporarily with a nut, interposing the spacer and the flat and spring washers. Then assemble the toothed belt.

28. Attach the shroud to the intake and exhaust manifolds.

29. Install the carburetor.

30. Connect the fuel line.

31. Connect the hot water return pipe to the intake manifold.

32. Install the toothed timing belt guard, the generator complete with pulley and then fit the V-belt on the three pulleys: the drive, water pump, and generator pulleys.

33. Install the distributor.

34. Install the water temperature sending unit.

35. Install the oil pressure sending unit.

36. Install the spark plugs and wires.

37. Install the union with the thermostat at the cylinder head.

38. Fill with oil.

39. Install the filler cap and the dipstick.

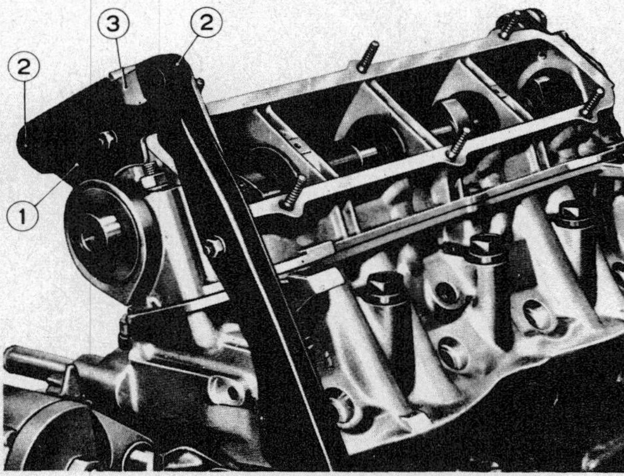

View of timing belt guard

1. Guard
2. Insulating rings
3. Bracket

Cylinder Head (DOHC)

Removal

1. Remove the air filter.
2. Disconnect all linkage and hoses connected to the head.
3. Remove the spark plugs and wires.
4. Remove, as a unit, the carburetor, intake manifold, and exhaust manifold.
5. Remove the valve cover.
6. Remove the rocker shaft assembly and pushrods.
7. Remove the ten attaching bolts and then remove the head gasket.

Installation

Clean all surfaces and inside the cylinders if necessary. Install a new head gasket and reverse the above process. Tighten all bolts to the proper torque specification and in the correct sequence.

Rocker Shafts (Except DOHC)

Removal

1. Remove the air filter.
2. Remove the valve rocker cover by unscrewing the six nuts which lock it into place on the cylinder head. Be sure to retain the flat washers.
3. Take off the four self-locking nuts and washers which fix the rocker shaft bearings, by studs, to the cylinder head. Then remove the whole assembly.

Installation

Installation is the reverse of removal.

NOTE: *Rocker stud nuts must be torqued to 29 ft lbs.*

Intake and Exhaust Manifolds

Removal

1. Remove the air filter.
2. Remove all attaching lines and linkage from the carburetor.
3. Remove the carburetor.
4. Take off both manifolds, with their gaskets, by removing the seven nuts and washers.

Installation

Installation is the reverse of removal.

Cylinder Head (OHV)

Removal

128

1. Drain the cooling system.
2. Remove the spare wheel from the engine compartment.
3. Remove the air cleaner.
4. Disconnect the spark plugs.
5. Disconnect the accelerator linkage.
6. Disconnect fuel pump-to-carburetor inlet line and choke cable.
7. Disconnect the temperature sending unit cable.
8. Disconnect the heater delivery hose.
9. Disconnect the thermostat, the water outlet and inlet hoses, and the union-to-pump delivery hose.
10. Disconnect the exhaust pipe from its manifold.
11. Remove the belt guard cover (work from below the vehicle to get at the lower screw after removing the guard).

View of timing gear

1. Tensioner pulley retaining nut
2. Belt guard lower retaining screw
3. Belt guard
4. Camshaft sprocket
5. Tensioner pulley
6. Shroud

View of generator in engine

1. Generator-to-upper bracket nut
2. Generator-to-lower bracket nuts
3. Generator

12. Slacken the tensioner pulley retainer nut.
13. Remove the toothed belt from the camshaft sprocket.
14. Unscrew the belt guard lower screw.
15. Remove the shroud by unscrewing the set screws.
16. Disconnect the reaction rod from the bracket in the cylinder head.
17. Remove the cylinder head-to-crankcase hold down nuts, using wrenches A.50131/1/2 for nuts that are inaccessible with standard wrenches, and take off the head.

Installation

Installation is the reverse of removal.

NOTE: Be sure to follow sequences and torque specifications.

Timing Belt

Removal and Replacement

128

1. Remove the timing gear cover.
2. Check the timing by aligning the timing marks.
3. Apply the hand brake and engage a low gear to prevent crankshaft rotation.
4. Slacken the lower screws and the generator-to-upper bracket nut. Remove the water pump and generator drive belt.
5. Slacken the tensioner pulley retainer nut and relieve the spring action in order to remove the toothed belt.
6. Install the new toothed belt, making sure that the belt and sprocket teeth engage perfectly.
7. Tighten the nut to 32.5 ft lbs.
8. Check valve timing.
9. Install the generator and water pump V belt and adjust its tension to 22 lbs. of pressure. Lock the screws and nut.
10. Check ignition timing.

Parts involved in adjusting toothed timing belt

1. Tensioner
2. Tensioner pulley
3. Pulley-to-support nut, to be tightened to 32.5 ft. lbs (4.5 kgm)
4. Pulley support-to-crankcase screw
5. Support

Oil Pump

Removal in Vehicle

128

In cases where only the oil pump needs attention, its removal and installation must be preceded by the attachment of an A.70526 rail to support the power plant.

Applications of rail to support the power plant

The protection shields and the power plant support crossmember can now be removed from below. Drain and remove the oil pan.

The three pump-attachment screws should now be removed in order to slide out the pump complete with its suction pipe.

View of timing gear end of engine

1. Camshaft sprocket timing mark
2. Reference index for valve timing
3. Reference index for drive sprocket timing
4. Timing mark on drive sprocket

Timing Gear Cover and Oil Seal

Replacement

See "Camshaft Removal and Installation" Steps 1–10

NOTE: *Some Fiats do not require engine removal for the above procedure but this has to be left to the discretion of the individual depending upon ability and equipment.*

Timing Chain

Replacement

See "Camshaft Removal and Installation" Steps 1–12

The above **NOTE** also applies.

Timing Belt

Replacement

DOHC engine only

NOTE: *The timing belt must be changed every 25,000 miles. Under no circumstances, may the timing belt be used more than 37,000 miles.*

To change the timing belt without removing the radiator or engine, follow the procedure outlined.

1. Drain part of the water in the cooling system and remove the upper radiator hose.
2. Remove the upper section of the air duct. Check the ignition timing and remove the timing cover.
3. Check the valve timing and hold the camshaft gears and engage a low gear while applying the handbrake.
4. Remove the lower protection plate from the engine.
5. Loosen the generator mounting nut and tensioner bolt.
6. Remove the generator drive belt and slacken the timing belt idler locknuts.
7. Remove the timing belt and fit a new belt over the camshaft gears and idler.
8. Fix a spring scale and apply a force of 60 lbs. in a direction bisecting the angle formed by the timing belt as it passes around the idler.
9. Clamp the idler with the locknuts and check the tension at two or three places, turning the crankshaft ½ turn in the direction of rotation only.

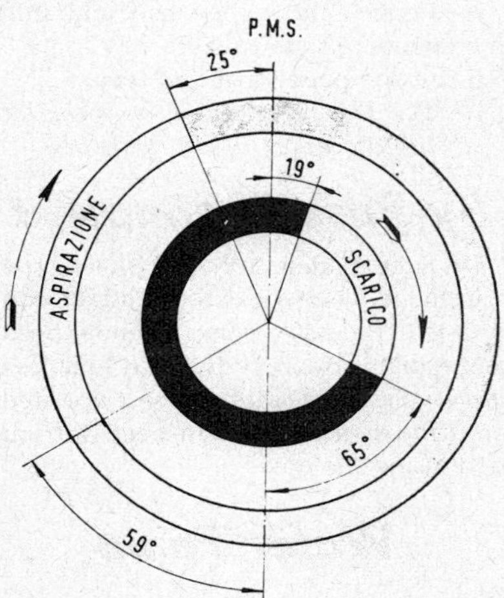

Valve timing diagram for 124 sedan, with a tappet clearance of 0.0174 in. (0.375 mm.) Outer ring is intake valve, and inner ring is exhaust valve.

NOTE: Valve adjustment is necessary only if the clearance is 0.004 in. less than the figure listed in the specifications. This applies only to overhead camshaft engines. Tappet clearance is measured between the camshaft lobe and the tappet, directly beneath it. It is not necessary to remove the camshaft to adjust clearance.

Timing marks aligned on 124 camshaft drive sprockets.

Camshaft (Except DOHC)

Removal and installation

1. See procedures for engine removal.
2. Remove the rocker shaft cover and rocker shaft.
3. Remove the ten cylinder head bolts and push rods.
4. Now, as a unit, remove the head, manifolds, and carburetor.
5. Remove the lifters.
6. Remove the water pump.
7. Unlock the tab washer under the nut that secures the fan drive pulley.
8. Using a flywheel holder, remove the nut from the pulley.
9. Remove the oil pan from the cylinder block.
10. Loosen the bolts, and withdraw the timing gear cover.
11. Unlock the tab washer and remove the bolt which secures the timing gear (larger) to the camshaft.
12. Remove the camshaft sprocket and timing chain.
13. Remove the camshaft end-plate and carefully remove the camshaft.

Installation

Installation is the reverse of removal.

NOTE: *Be sure to lubricate the camshaft lobes and align the timing marks properly during installation.*

Install timing belt (3) with camshaft gears at top (exhaust left, intake right) locked by tool (4) and positioned with reference marks opposite pointers on (1). Idler pulley (8), locked by screws (7 and 9), exerts tension on belt. Auxiliary drive gear is held in place by (6).

Pistons and Connecting Rods

Identification

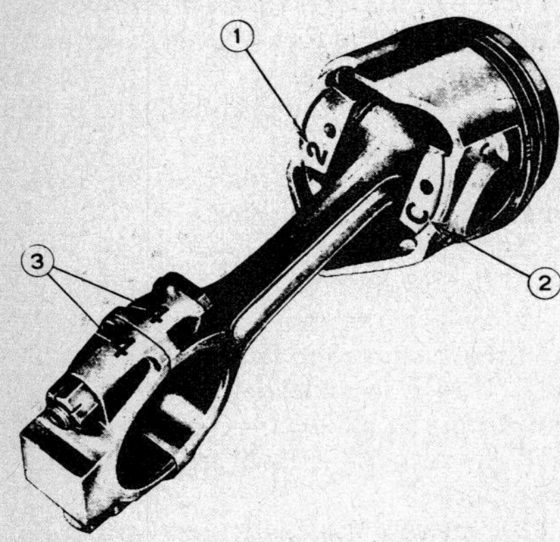

Piston and rod assemblies are marked (1) for class of bore (2) piston class, and (3) piston cylinder number. Metal may be removed from areas (1) and (2) to equalize weights.

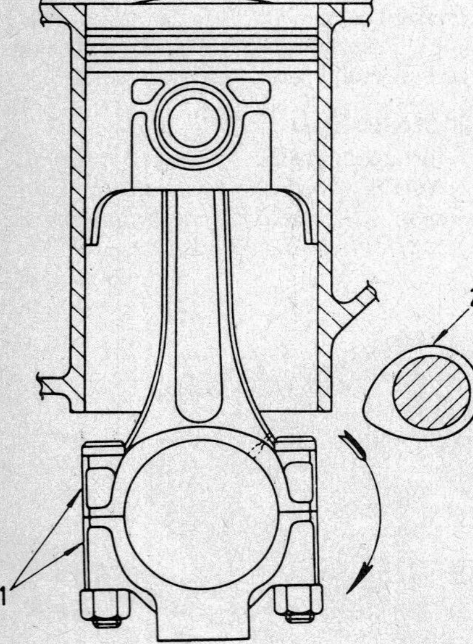

Install piston and rod assembly with cylinder number identification (1) away from camshaft (2). Arrow shows engine rotation from front.

ENGINE COOLING

124

Engine cooling is done by forced water circulation using a centrifugal pump. The cooling system consists of a water pump mounted on the crankcase, radiator in front of the engine, auxiliary tank, thermostat, fan and water temperature gauge sending unit.

Radiator

Removal

1. Open the petcock at the bottom of the radiator and drain the coolant from radiator and cylinder block.
2. Remove the hose which connects the radiator and thermostat cover.
3. Remove the hose which connects the radiator and water pump.
4. Remove the pipe which connects the radiator to the auxiliary tank.
5. Unbolt and remove the radiator.

Installation

Installation is the reverse of removal.

Water Pump

Removal

1. If necessary, remove the radiator from the vehicle.
2. Unbolt and remove the fan from the water pump flange.
3. Remove the hose which connects the water pump and radiator.
4. Remove the water pump from the mounting.

Installation

Installation is the reverse of removal.

Thermostat

Removal

1. Drain off part of the water in the radiator (to a level below the outlet in the cylinder head).
2. Remove the hose which connects the radiator to the thermostat cover. Remove the cover and withdraw the thermostat.

Inspection

Immerse the thermostat in water and heat the water. When the temperature reaches 185–192° F., the thermostat valve should begin to open. The valve should be completely open when the water temperature reaches 212° F. If the thermostat does not meet specifications, it is defective and must be replaced.

Installation

Installation is the reverse of removal.

850

The cooling system used on 850 model Fiats consists of a radiator, fan, water pump, thermostat and connecting hoses.

Radiator

Removal

1. Remove the engine right-side apron and drain the coolant from the radiator.
2. Disconnect the coolant intake and outlet hoses from the radiator.
3. Disconnect the lockring which secures the air conveyor to the radiator.
4. Disconnect the engine ground cable and the pipe from the radiator to the expansion tank.
5. Remove the radiator mounting screws and lift out the radiator.

Installation

Installation is the reverse of removal.

Water Pump

Removal

1. Remove the engine right-side apron.
2. Drain the coolant from the radiator.
3. Remove the drive belt from the pulley and disconnect the hoses at the cylinder head and radiator.
4. Remove the lockring which holds the air conveyor to the radiator.
5. Remove the securing bolts and remove the water pump and air conveyor assembly.

Installation

Installation is the reverse of removal.

Thermostat

Removal

The thermostat is situated at the front end of the cylinder head. Drain the coolant from the engine and radiator. Remove the hose from the thermostat housing and withdraw the thermostat.

Installation

Installation is the reverse of removal.

Water Pump Drive Belt

Adjust Tension

1. Correct belt tension is approximately ½ in. To adjust the tension, loosen the generator mounting bolts.
2. Correct the tension of the belt, setting the position of the generator support.
3. Remove the pulley locknuts.
4. Remove the pulley half and shift one or more shims outside.
5. Fit the pulley half and secure.

NOTE: *This procedure is only valid to stretch the water pump drive belt.*

By-Pass Thermostat

On later models, a by-pass thermostat is installed. This type of thermostat is connected to the water pump, cylinder head, and radiator by three hoses. It enables a large volume of water to be circulated, ensuring a more uniform heat distribution inside the engine.

Water Pump

Removal

128

1. Remove the spare wheel.
2. Place protective coverings on the fenders.

3. Drain the water from the cooling system.

4. Disconnect the hot air hose and the accelerator rod from the shroud.

5. Remove the shroud.

6. Disconnect the passenger compartment heater water delivery and return hoses.

7. Slacken the nuts that hold the generator on the two lower brackets and remove the top bracket.

8. Unscrew the nuts which attach the pump to the crankcase and slide off the pump assembly.

Engine compartment: parts to be disconnected when removing the water pump from the crankcase.

1. Hot air hose
2. Shroud
3. Water return hose from passenger compartment heater
4. Generator bracket to pump housing attachment nuts
5. Vee belt
6. Water pump
7. Water delivery hose to passenger compartment heater

Installation

Installation is the reverse of removal.

128

Radiator

Removal

1. Drain the radiator and the cylinder block.

2. Disconnect the thermal fan switch and the fan relay switch.

3. Disconnect the hose running from the radiator to the expansion tank.

4. Remove the hoses running from the thermostat union to the radiator.

5. Remove the screws that attach the top part of the radiator to the brackets fitted on the body, together with the rubber pads, washers, and spacers.

6. Slide the radiator, fan, and shroud out of the top of the engine compartment

Installation

Installation is the reverse of removal.

View of radiator in vehicle

1. Radiator
2. Radiator to body attachment screws
3. Hose to expansion tank
4. Hose from union (with thermostat) to radiator
5. Hose from radiator to union
6. Fan motor relay switch

Thermostat

Removal

1. Drain the water from the radiator.

2. Remove the spare wheel from the engine compartment.

3. Disconnect the hoses from the thermostat union.

4. Unscrew the attachment screws and remove the union, complete with the thermostat.

5. Unscrew the union cover and slide out the thermostat and its seal.

Installation

Installation is the reverse of removal.

Exhaust System

Removal of the exhaust system from front-engined Fiats presents no special difficulties or problems. It is a conventional exhaust system consisting of tailpipe, muffler, exhaust pipe and exhaust manifold.

The muffler and headers are removed as a unit from Fiats equipped with rear mounted engines. On the Fiat 850 the lower splash shield must be removed. The single header (or four headers, in the 850 Spyder and Coupe) are unbolted from the engine. Finally, unbolt the two mounting nuts just above the muffler.

Replace the muffler and header assembly by reversing the removal procedure.

Exhaust Emission Control

Fiat 124 and 850 (1970-on), 128

Air pollution control is provided by the Fiat FD1 system, which consists of a specially calibrated carburetor, a new water-heated intake manifold, modified centrifugal spark advance and a fast idling device to limit intake vacuum during deceleration. The second barrel of the carburetor is equipped with a vacuum diaphragm unit (H) and linkage (1), which prevents the throttle from closing completely during deceleration when the fast idling device goes into operation. Another vacuum device, in parallel with the fast idle unit, matches engine mixture requirements during warm-up.

Fast idle operation is provided by three switches and a solenoid. One switch (A) on the side of the transmission is open when the car is standing, but closed when third and fourth gears are engaged. A second switch installed near the clutch pedal closes when the pedal is released. When both these switches are closed the solenoid valve is energized, which opens the vacuum line that actuates the fast idle diaphragm unit (H) on the carburetor. The third switch (2) is a push-button switch to energize the solenoid when the car is standing still. Adjustment of the fast idle speed then can be made by turning a screw (G).

Carburetor adjustment is made by first adjusting the set screw for 800 rpm idle speed. If an analyzer is available, adjust mixture screw for the specified output of carbon monoxide. Press pushbutton, then set fast idle speed to 1500 rpm by adjusting screw. Before pressing pushbutton to release the solenoid, rev up the engine with accelerator and recheck fast idle speed. Readjust screw, if necessary, and press pushbutton to OFF position.

FUEL SYSTEM

Fuel Pump

All Fiats use mechanical type fuel pumps, operated from the camshaft or auxiliary shaft.

Removal

Mechanical

1. Remove and plug the fuel lines leading to the fuel pump.

2. Remove the mounting nuts and carefully remove the fuel pump from the block (or crankcase).

3. If the pump is equipped with a pushrod, remove the pushrod, gasket and insulator from the mounting.

Servicing the Fuel Pump

Sludge deposited in the fuel chamber or on the filter may be removed with the pump cover off. Intake and outlet valves

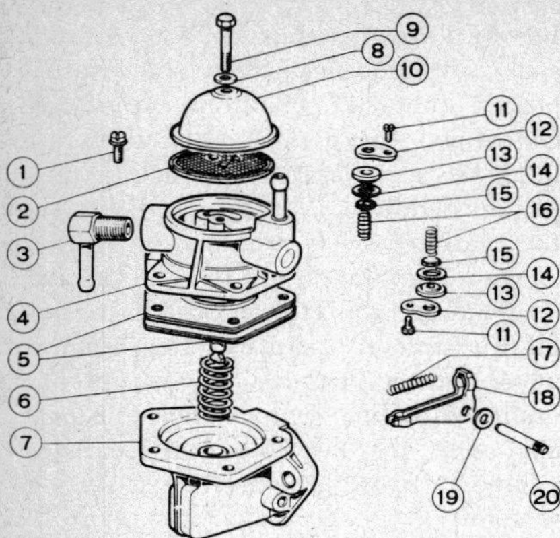

Fuel pump, 850. (1) pump bodies interlocking screws; (2) filter gauze; (3) connector; (4) upper body; (5) diaphragms; (6) spring; (7) lower body; (8) plain washer; (9) cover mounting screw; (10) pump cover; (11) valve housing locking screws; (12) valve housings; (13) valve plugs; (14) plug seals; (15) suction and delivery valves; (16) valve springs; (17) operating lever reaction spring; (18) yoke lever; (19) thrust washer; (20) yoke lever pin.

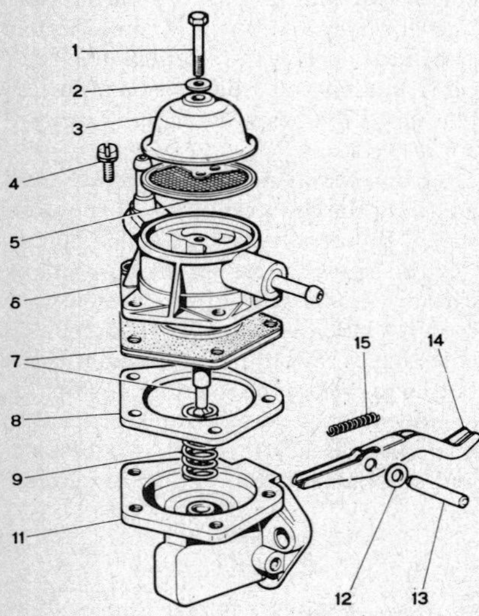

Fuel pump, 124. (1) cover fixing screw; (2) lockwasher; (3) cover; (4) screw fixing upper to lower body; (5) filter; (6) upper body; (7) diaphragm; (8) spacer; (9) spring; (11) lower body; (12) flat washer; (13) pivot pin; (14) operating lever; (15) spring.

should be inspected and replaced if damaged. Check springs for good condition.

Control mechanism for the intake chamber diaphragm should be washed in kerosene and lightly lubricated with thin oil. Lightly coat new fuel pump seals with grease before assembly. If a new diaphragm is to be installed, soak it in kerosene for a few minutes before assembly.

Installation

(Except 850)

Installation is the reverse of removal.

850

1. Before replacing the fuel pump, adjust the projection of the pump pushrod.

2. Fit the insulating spacer to its seat with a gasket.

3. Slide in the pushrod. The projection of the pushrod should be 0.0394–0.0591 in. If the projection is not within specified limits, adjust the projection by replacing the gasket with another. Service gaskets are available in the following thicknesses:

A = .0106"-.0130"
B = .0276"-.0315"
C = .0472"-.0512"

Further installation is the reverse of removal.

Air Cleaner

Removal

128

1. Disconnect the hot air intake hose from the shroud.
2. Slip off the blow-by gas recirculation pipes.
3. Unscrew the air cleaner-to-camshaft housing attachment nut.
4. Unscrew the cover attachment wing nuts. Remove the cover with the gasket and the filtering element.
5. Remove the two self-locking nuts which attach the cleaner housing to the carburetor studs. Slide off the top plate and withdraw the housing, complete with its gasket and spacers.

Installation

Installation is the reverse of removal.

Carburetors

Over the years, Fiats have been equipped with either Weber or Solex carburetors, in either one- or two-barrel models.

Removal

1. Disconnect the accelerator rod, sliding it out of the lever ball joint end, toward the dashboard.
2. Remove the air filter.
3. Detach the choke cable.
4. Disconnect the fuel line.
5. Disconnect all vacuum lines.
6. Remove the mounting bolts, or nuts if mounted by studs.
7. Remove the carburetor and gasket.

Installation

Installation is the reverse of removal.

Adjustments

See "Tune-Up Procedures".

Overhaul

All Types

Efficient carburetion depends greatly on careful cleaning and inspection during overhaul. Since dirt, gum, water, or varnish in or on the carburetor parts are often responsible for poor performance.

Overhaul your carburetor in a clean, dust-free area. Carefully disassemble the carburetor, referring often to the exploded views. Keep all similar and look-alike parts segregated during disassembly and cleaning to avoid accidental interchange during assembly. Make a note of all jet sizes.

When the carburetor is disassembled, wash all parts (except diaphragms, electric choke units, pump plunger, and any other plastic, leather, fiber, or rubber parts) in clean carburetor solvent. Do not leave parts in the solvent any longer than is necessary to sufficiently loosen the deposits. Excessive cleaning may remove the special finish from the float bowl and choke valve bodies, leaving these parts unfit for service. Rinse all parts in clean solvent and blow them dry with compressed air or allow them to air dry. Wipe clean all cork, plastic, leather, and fiber parts with a clean, lint-free cloth.

Blow out all passages and jets with compressed air and be sure that there are no restrictions or blockages. Never use wire or similar tools to clean jets, fuel passages, or air bleeds. Clean all jets and valves separately to avoid accidental interchange.

Check all parts for wear or damage. If wear or damage is found, replace the defective parts. Especially check the following:

1. Check the float needle and seat for wear. If wear is found, replace the complete assembly.
2. Check the float hinge pin for wear and the float(s) for dents or distortion. Replace the float if fuel has leaked into it.
3. Check the throttle and choke shaft bores for wear or an out-of-round condition. Damage or wear to the throttle arm, shaft, or shaft bore will often require replacement of the throttle body. These parts require a close tolerance of fit; wear may allow air leakage, which could affect starting and idling.

NOTE: *Throttle shafts and bushings are not included in overhaul kits. They can be purchased separately.*

4. Inspect the idle mixture adjusting needles for burrs or grooves. Any such condition requires replacement of the needle, since you will not be able to obtain a satisfactory idle.
5. Test the accelerator pump check valves. They should pass air one way but not the other. Test for proper seating by blowing and sucking on the valve. Replace the valve if necessary. If the valve is satisfactory, wash the valve again to remove breath moisture.
6. Check the bowl cover for warped surfaces with a straightedge.
7. Closely inspect the valves and seats for wear and damage, replacing as necessary.

8. After the carburetor is assembled, check the choke valve for freedom of operation.

Carburetor overhaul kits are recommended for each overhaul. These kits contain all gaskets and new parts to replace those that deteriorate most rapidly. Failure to replace all parts supplied with the kit (especially gaskets) can result in poor performance later.

Some carburetor manufacturers supply overhaul kits of three basic types: minor repair; major repair; and gasket kits. Basically, they contain the following:

Minor Repair Kits:

All gaskets
Float needle valve
Volume control screw
All diaphragms
Spring for the pump diaphragm

Major Repair Kits:

All jets and gaskets
All diaphragms
Float needle valve
Volume control screw
Pump ball valve
Main jet carrier
Float
Complete intermediate rod
Intermediate pump lever
Complete injector tube
Some cover hold-down screws and washers

Gasket Kits:

All gaskets

After cleaning and checking all components, reassemble the carburetor, using new parts and referring to the exploded view. When reassembling, make sure that all screws and jets are tight in their seats, but do not overtighten, as the tips will be distorted. Tighten all screws gradually, in rotation. Do not tighten needle valves into their seats; uneven jetting will result. Always use new gaskets. Be sure to adjust the float level when reassembling.

FLOAT LEVEL SPECIFICATIONS

Carburetor	*Float Level (in.) Distance from the cover with gasket*
Weber 30 DICA	.24
Weber 30 DICI	.24
Solex C30 PIB4	See Text
Weber 30ICF7	.28
Weber 26 IM	.28
Weber 22 IM	①
Weber 26/34 DHSA1	.24
Weber 32 DHSA1	.24
Weber 32DHSA	.24
Weber 26/34 DHSA	.24

① Brass—.28 in. Nylon—.20 in.

32 DISA

NOTE: *Idle adjustment must be set with engine at normal operating temperature.*

1. Turn the throttle valve stop screw to a position where the engine continues to run slowly but steadily.

2. Turn the mixture adjustment screw to the position where the fastest and the steadiest running is obtained at this throttle valve setting.

3. With the throttle stop screw reduce the idle to the specified rpm.

Float Level Adjustments

Weber Carburetors

Float level adjustments are checked with the carburetor cover held vertically. When the adjustment is correct, the float arm (5) just touches the ball (7) of the needle (2) when the float is the specified distance away from the cover gasket (9). Bend the float arms to correct the float level.

32 DISA

The position of the float is checked by resting the hinge pin seating at the end of the float against the gauge and checking that the yoke and the two floats touch the three support studs on the gauge.

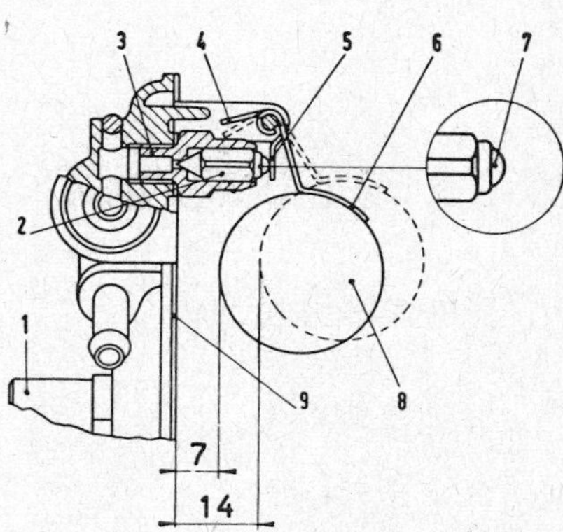

Weber carburetor float level adjustment

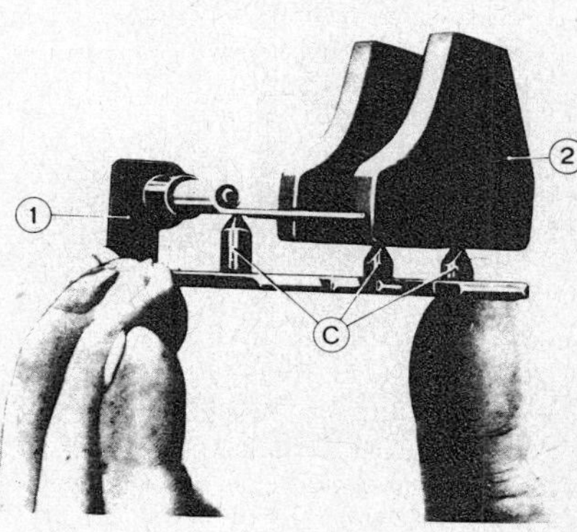

Solex carburetor float level adjustment

1. Gauge
C. Gauge points
2. Float

Clutch and Transmission

The drive train for Fiat models, except the 850, consists of the clutch, gearbox, driveshaft, and rear axle. The 850's have rear-mounted engines and utilize a clutch and transaxle (gearbox, differential and axle) assembly to transmit power to the rear wheels.

Clutch

A single-plate, dry clutch is used on all models. Pressure plates are of two types, those having conventional coil springs and those having a single diaphragm spring.

All are mechanically operated.

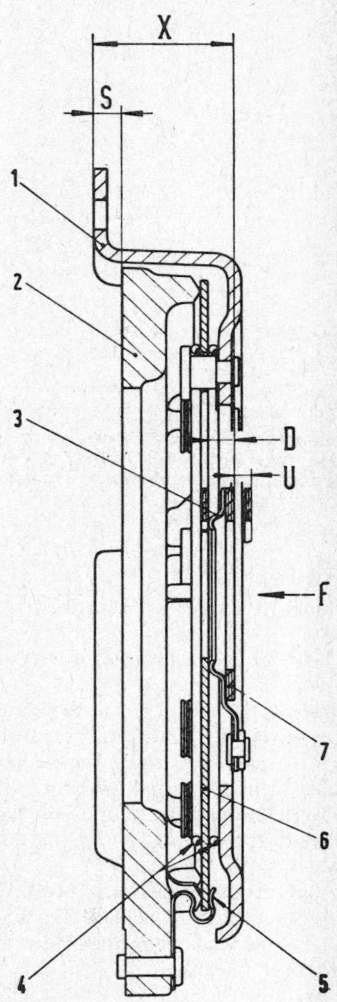

Clutch plate assembly and specifications for the 124 Coupe and Spider. (1) clutch plate; (2) thrust ring; (3) withdrawal flange; (4) spring spacers; (5) spring retainer; (5) (6) diaphragm spring; (7) friction ring; (S) thickness of ring gauge = .32" (8.2 mm.); (X) distance to be maintained = 1.57-1.68" (40-43 mm.); (D) withdrawal stroke - .31" (8 mm.); (U) maximum wear limit - .19" (5 mm.); (F) load to move withdrawal flange - 728 lbs. (330 kg.)

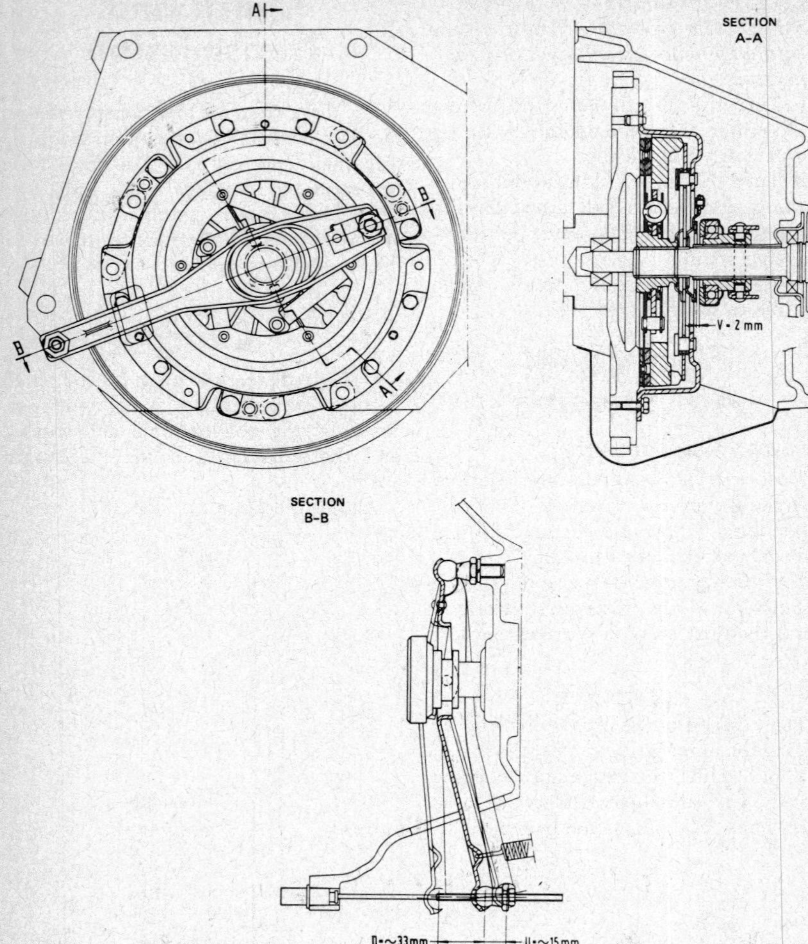

Diaphragm spring clutch assembly of 124 viewed from throwout fork side. (V) in A-A = free travel of throwout sleeve; (D) in B-B = travel of throwout lever; (U) in B-B = maximum movement of lever due to wear.

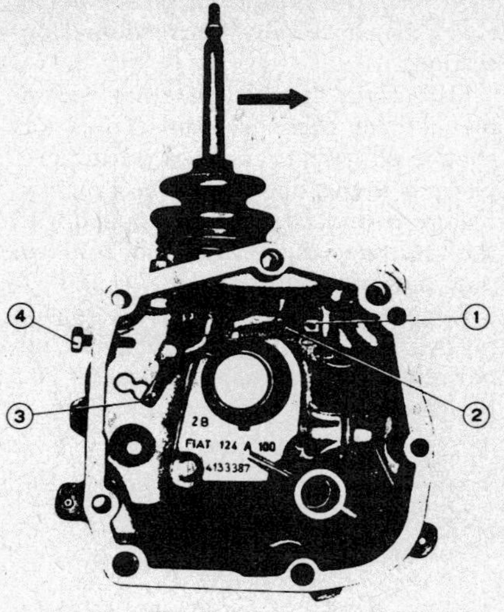

1. Anchor screw for gear lever return spring
2. Gear lever return spring
3. Gear lever
4. Gear lever sidetravel stopscrew
   The arrow shows the direction in which the lever must be moved to disengage it from the selector rods, so that the rear cover can be removed.

Inside view of rear transmission case (124 4-speed).

Removal

The clutch is removed with the transmission.

1. Jack the car and remove the transmission.

NOTE: It is important that the clutch shaft never be allowed to rest on the withdrawal flange, since the support plates of the flange will be bent.

2. Mark the position of the clutch in relation to the flywheel to facilitate assembly.

3. Remove the bolts which secure the clutch cover to the flywheel. The bolts should be removed evenly to prevent distortion of the clutch.

Installation

Check the condition of the pilot bushing which is pressed into the crankshaft. If necessary, replace this bushing. Installation of the clutch is the reverse of removal. Use an old mainshaft or wooden dummy shaft to center the clutch disc.

Removing the detent balls and springs from the central case (124 4-speed).

1. Detent ball spring, reverse gear selector rod
2. Detent ball spring for 3rd and 4th gears
3. Detent ball spring, 1st and 2nd gears

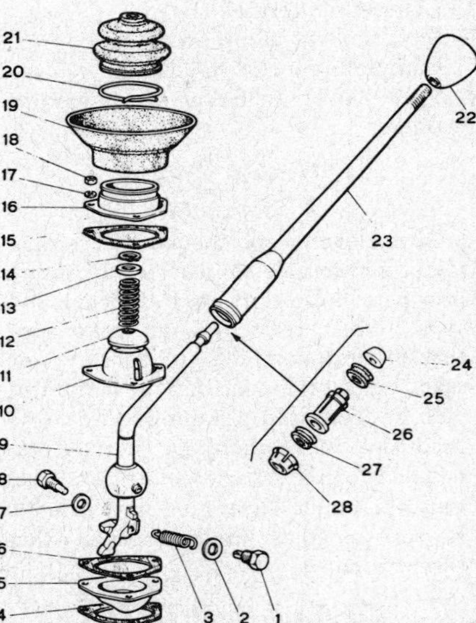

Exploded view of 124 Sedan gearshift assembly.

1. Gear lever return spring anchor screw
2. Flat washer
3. Lever return spring
4. Gasket
5. Socket plate
6. Gasket
7. Flat washer
8. Gear lever stop screw
9. Lower part of gear lever with ball
10. Upper socket plate
11. Dome washer
12. Spring
13. Cup washer
14. Retaining snap-ring
15. Gasket
16. Flange
17. Spring washer
18. Nut
19. Grommet
20. Spring clip
21. Rubber boot
22. Knob
23. Upper part of gear lever
24. Shoulder block
25. Rubber bushings
26. Spacer
27. Rubber bushings
28. Spring-ring

Cross section of 124 Sedan clutch and transmission.

Pedal Travel Adjustment

Should pedal free travel be less than specified because of clutch plate wear, adjustment should be made, otherwise the clutch will slip. Prior to making adjustments, check all cable and rod grommets and bushings for possible wear.

Removal

128

1. Disconnect the battery cable.
2. Remove the spare tire.
3. Remove the speedometer drive.

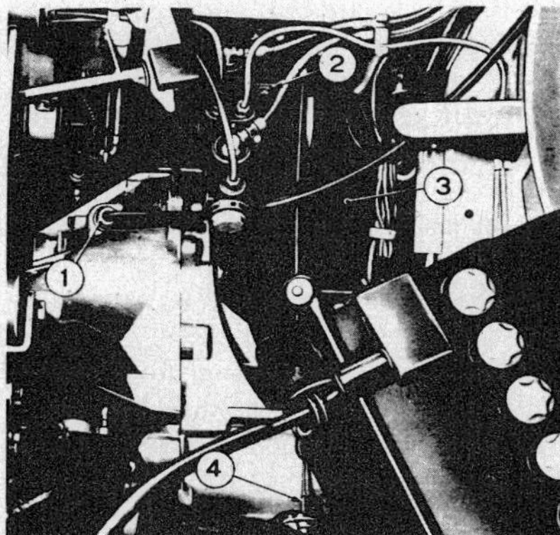

Overhead view of transmission assembly

1. Speedometer drive ring nut
2. Guard to body retaining nut
3. Guard
4. Clutch release control flexible cable

4. Disconnect the flexible cable adjusting rod from the clutch release lever and unhook the return spring.
5. Unscrew the guard-to-body nut.
6. Unscrew the transmission-to-crankcase attachment screws and nuts, accessible from above.
7. Attach the engine support crosspiece.
8. Remove the hub cabs from the front wheels and unscrew the constant speed joint-to-wheel hub nuts.
9. Remove the left front wheel.
10. Disconnect the left tie rod from the steering arm.
11. Remove the anti-roll bar.
12. Unscrew the two lower left shock absorbers-to-pillar attaching screws and nuts.
13. Remove the two lower guards.
14. Unscrew the nuts which fasten the exhaust clamping bracket to the transmission.
15. Disconnect the gearshift and selection lever control rod.
16. Unscrew the starter motor-to-transmission assembly screws.
17. Remove the power plant support crossmember.
18. Remove the flywheel cover.
19. Unscrew the remaining transmission-to-engine attachment screws.
20. Disconnect the ground cable from the transmission assembly
21. Using wire, fix the axle shafts complete with constant speed joints, to the transmission in order to prevent them from coming away from their seats in the differential.

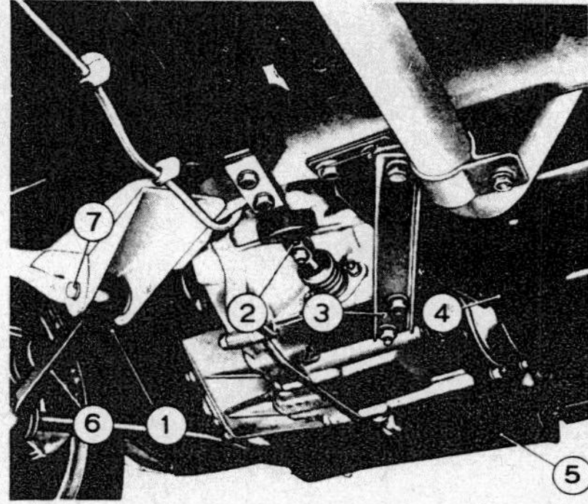

View of transmission assembly from below

1. Axle shaft
2. Engagement control rod
3. Exhaust pipe clamping bracket
4. Crosspiece
5. Guard
6. Control arm
7. Control arm to floor retaining screw with nut

22. Remove the transmission-differential assembly from beneath the car using a hydraulic jack.

Installation

Installation is the reverse of removal.

Clutch

Removal

128

1. Raise the car at the front and set it on support stands.
2. Remove the transmission.
3. Mark the clutch in respect to the flywheel so correct balance can be maintained.
4. Remove the retaining screws which secure the clutch cover to the flywheel and then remove the clutch assembly.

Installation

Installation is the reverse of removal with the following notes:

1. The clutch disc should be positioned with the protruding part of the hub facing the transmission housing.
2. Before tightening the clutch-to-flywheel mounting screws, be sure to center the disc with a dummy shaft.
3. Runout should not exceed 0.01 in.

Transmission

The transmission is a conventional type, with four forward gears and one reverse. All gears are fully synchronized. The transmission is in three parts, front bell housing, main transmission case and rear cover.

Removal

124 (4 Speed)

1. Working from inside the car, remove the gear lever and cover plate.
2. Underneath the car, remove the flexible coupling from the spider on the mainshaft.
3. Remove the speedometer drive from the support on the transmission.
4. Disconnect the clutch withdrawal fork return spring.
5. Remove the locknut and unscrew the adjusting rod from the flexible cable.
6. Remove the flywheel cover from the bell housing.
7. Remove the bolt which secures the exhaust pipe bracket to the transmission.
8. Detach the exhaust piping.
9. Remove the starter motor heat shield and starter motor.
10. Support the transmission, and remove the four bolts which secure the transmission to the engine.
11. Move the transmission carefully away from the engine and lower it to the ground.

Disassembly

1. Remove the drain plug and drain

the oil from the transmission.

2. Remove the oil filler plug.

3. Place the transmission upside down and remove the lower cover and gasket.

4. Remove the clutch withdrawal fork and slide the thrust bearing and control sleeve from the central support.

5. Remove the bell housing and gasket. At the same time remove the center cover of the direct drive shaft with the oil seal and spring washer.

6. It may be necessary to remove the seal on the bench.

7. Remove the bolts which secure the 3rd and 4th gear selector forks.

NOTE: *When the bolts have been removed the fork can be moved along the bar and the two gears can be engaged simultaneously.*

8. Slide the rubber dust cover from the end of the mainshaft.

9. Remove the snap-ring and flexible coupling ring.

10. Lock the mainshaft by proceeding according to the note above, and remove the spider from the mainshaft.

11. Remove the speedometer drive support and gasket from the rear transmission cover.

12. Remove the selector rod detent ball spring cover plate from the main casing.

13. Remove the springs from the recesses, followed by the detent balls.

NOTE: *The reverse gear selector rod ball spring is not of the same compression as the other two springs. Keep this one separate from the other two.*

14. Remove the rear cover complete with gear lever, by proceeding as follows.

15. Remove the stop screw which limits the side movement of the lever.

16. Remove the nuts which retain the cover to the main body.

17. Move the gear lever to the left to disengage it from the selector rods and remove the rear cover.

18. Remove the gear lever from the rear cover.

19. Slide the rear ball bearing and speedometer drive gear from the mainshaft.

20. Slide the reverse gear selector rod, complete with fork, from its seat in the main case and, at the same time, remove reverse gear from its spindle.

21. Remove the snap-ring which retains the reverse driving gear and remove the gear from the end of the layshaft.

22. Remove the snap-ring which retains the driven gear from the reverse gear train.

23. Remove the spring washers, driven gear of the reverse gear train, and remove the Woodruff key from its seat.

NOTE: *Before removing the retaining clip of the reverse gear driven train, the spring washer must be compressed.*

24. Engage the two gears to prevent the shafts from turning and remove the retaining bolt and front ball bearing from the layshaft.

25. Tilt the layshaft and remove it from the main case.

26. Remove the 3rd and 4th gear selector rods from the case and remove the bolt and spring washer holding the 1st and 2nd gear selector forks to the rod.

27. Remove the rod, followed by the 1st-2nd and 3rd-4th gear forks. The three safety rollers will be released as the selector rods are removed.

28. Remove the plate which retains the mainshaft intermediate ball bearing.

29. Withdraw the bearing from its housing.

NOTE: *When separating the direct drive shaft from the mainshaft, the 23 needle roller bearings will be free to spin or fall inside the case. It is advisable to remove these and check the exact number immediately.*

30. Withdraw the reverse gear spindle from the main case.

31. Remove the direct drive and 4th gear shaft from the mainshaft, complete with ball bearing and 4th gear synchronizing ring.

32. Tilt the mainshaft and remove it from the case, complete with gears, hubs, sliding sleeves and synchronizing rings.

33. Remove the following parts from the mainshaft: 1st gear and bushing, 1st gear synchronizing ring, 1st and 2nd gear hub and sliding sleeve, 2nd gear synchronizing ring and 2nd gear.

34. Remove the snap-ring from its seat in the front end of the mainshaft and remove the following parts: spring washer, 3rd-4th gear hub, sliding sleeve, synchronizing ring, and 3rd gear.

35. Remove the snap-ring from the direct drive and 4th gear shaft and remove the spring washer and ball bearing.

Assembly

1. Assemble the following parts on the mainshaft, in the order given: 3rd gear and synchronizing ring, 3rd-4th gear sliding sleeve (with three dogs and two springs) and spring washer.

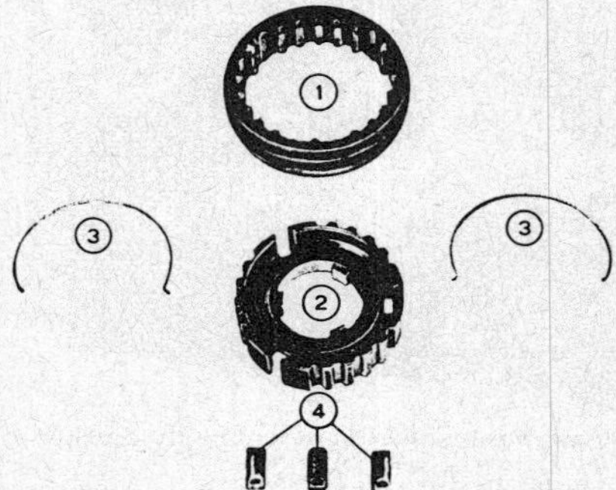

Exploded view of sliding type synchronizer

1. Sliding sleeve
2. Hub
3. Dog retaining spring
4. Dogs

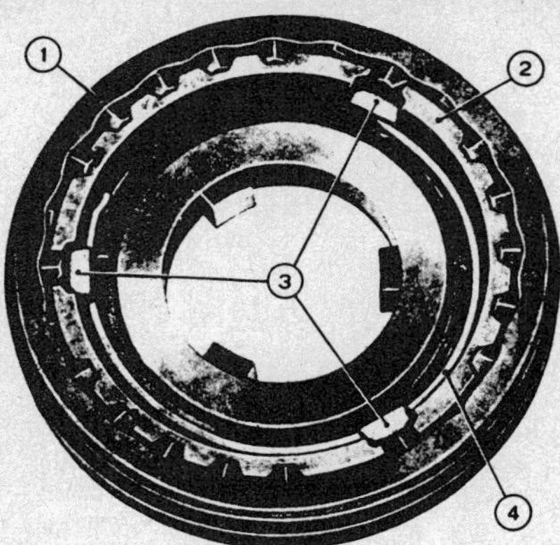

Sliding sleeve type synchronizer

1. Sliding sleeve
2. Hub
3. Dogs
4. Dog retaining spring

2. Insert the snap-ring in the groove, securing the parts listed above to the front of the mainshaft.

3. Slide the 2nd gear and synchronizing ring, 1st-2nd gear sliding sleeve and hub (with three dogs and two springs) and 1st speed synchronizing ring and gear with bushing onto the rear end of the shaft.

NOTE: *The synchronizing ring dog springs must be fitted so that the ends of the springs are not attached to the same dog.*

4. Tilt the mainshaft and insert it into the transmission case.

5. Working from the rear end of the mainshaft, use a driver and insert the intermediate ball bearing.

6. Install the reverse idler gear shaft, then fit the shaft and bearing retaining plate.

7. Secure the plate to the main case and stake the nuts in place.

8. Fit the ball bearing and spring washer to the direct drive shaft and insert the spring retaining clip of the bearing in the groove.

9. Fit the inner thrust ring in the recess of the direct drive shaft.

10. Coat the 23 needle rollers with heavy grease and insert these, followed by the outer thrust ring.

11. Insert the direct drive shaft in the main case and slide it onto the end of the mainshaft, seating the 4th gear synchronizing ring and toothed spring washer between them.

12. Fit the 1st and 2nd gear selector fork to the sliding sleeve and slide the corresponding selector rod into the fork from outside.

13. Replace the locating roller of this bar to its seat and secure the fork to the rod.

14. Install the 3rd-4th gear selector fork and rod in the same manner.

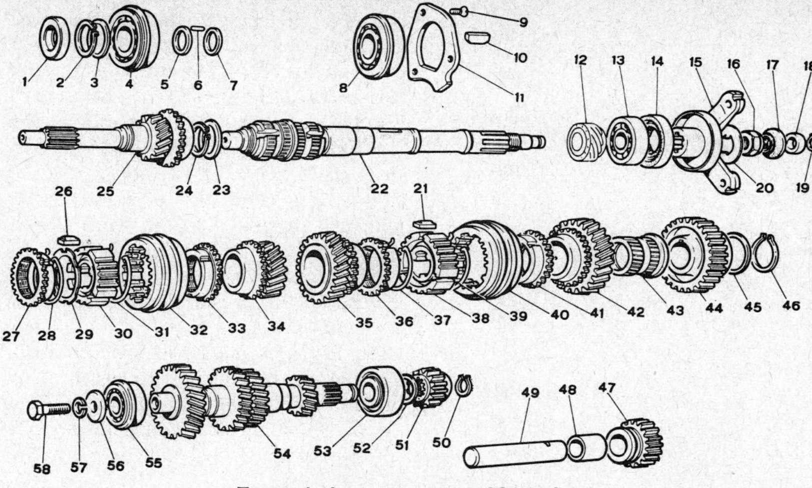

Transmission components, 124 Sedan.

1. Inner cover seal
2. Bearing retaining ring
3. Spring washer
4. Direct drive shaft ball bearing
5. Thrust rings of needle roller bearing between direct drive and mainshaft
6. Needle roller
7. Thrust rings of needle roller bearing between direct drive and mainshaft
8. Mainshaft intermediate ball bearing
9. Bearing retaining plate fixing screw
10. Key
11. Mainshaft intermediate ball bearing retaining plate
12. Speedometer drive gear
13. Mainshaft rear ball bearing
14. Rear cover oil seal
15. Flexible coupling spider
16. Spider fixing nut
17. Sealing ring
18. Flexible coupling centering ring
19. Snap-ring
20. Lockwasher
21. Sliding sleeves dogs
22. Mainshaft
23. Spring washer
24. Mainshaft assembly retaining snap-ring
25. Direct drive and fourth gear shaft
26. Sliding sleeves dogs
27. Synchronizing rings
28. Dog retaining rings
29. Spring washer
30. Third-fourth gear sliding sleeve hub
31. Dog retaining rings
32. Sliding sleeves
33. Synchronizing rings
34. Third speed driven gear
35. Second speed driven gear
36. Synchronizing rings
37. Dog retaining rings
38. First-second gear sliding sleeve hub
39. Dog retaining rings
40. Sliding sleeves
41. Synchronizing rings
42. First speed driven gear
43. First gear bush
44. Reverse driven gear
45. Spring washer
46. Reverse driven gear retaining snap-ring
47. Reverse idler gear
48. Reverse idler gear bush
49. Reverse idler gear spindle
50. Snap-ring
51. Reverse driving gear
52. Spring washer
53. Layshaft rear roller bearing
54. Layshaft with first, second and third gears
55. Layshaft front double-row ball bearing
56. Flat washer
57. Spring washer
58. Layshaft front ball bearing fixing bolt

NOTE: Do not lock the fork to the rod at this point, since it will be necessary to use this fork to lock the transmission at a later time.

15. Insert the layshaft with 1st, 2nd, 3rd and direct drive gears, into the main case.

16. Replace the front ball bearing and rear ball bearing of the layshaft.

17. Lock the shafts by engaging two gears at the same time.

18. Use the flat washer, spring washer and bolt to secure the front bearing to the layshaft.

19. Fit the key to the mainshaft and install the reverse driving gear and spring washer.

20. Retain these with a snap-ring. Fit the spring washer and reverse driving gear to the end of the layshaft and secure them with a snap-ring.

21. Insert the reverse selector rod locating roller in its seating, and fit the selector fork to the rod.

22. Retain this with a bolt and spring washer.

23. Install the selector rod in its guide and at the same time, fit the reverse idler gear to its spindle.

24. Install the speedometer drive gear and rear ball bearing on the mainshaft.

25. Fit the gear shifting assembly to the rear transmission cover, as follows.

26. Drive a new oil seal with inner spring into place.

27. Fit the gear shifting lever to the cover.

28. Attach the gear lever return spring to the lever and replace the screw in the cover.

29. Mount the lever assembly on the rear cover and fit the rear cover to the main transmission case. Be sure to fit a gasket between the two cases.

30. Replace the speedometer drive support with a gasket under it. It is held in place by a nut on a stud in the cover.

31. Install the flexible spider and flat washer on the tail of the mainshaft.

32. Lock the gears and tighten the nut, bending up the tab washer.

33. Install the dust cover on the mainshaft and drive the coupling centering ring into place and insert the snap-ring in the groove.

34. Drive an oil seal into the cover of the direct drive shaft and attach this cover to the front of the transmission body.

35. Insert a sealing ring between them.

36. Install the spring washer of the cover and fit the bell housing to the main case, with a gasket.

37. Fit the 3rd and 4th gear selector fork to the selector rod and secure with a bolt and washer.

38. Replace the three selector rod detent balls and springs in their proper bores. Note that the reverse spring is different from the other two.

39. Fit the lower cover and gasket to the main case.

40. Install the oil drain plug.

41. Fit the clutch release sleeve and thrust bearing to the cover of the direct drive shaft and install the fork lever.

42. Turn the transmission right side up, and fill with 2.75 pints of Fiat W 90/M oil. The oil must come to the brim of the filler hole.

43. Replace the filler plug.

Installation

Install the transmission in reverse order of removal. Be sure to center the clutch with an old mainshaft or wooden dummy shaft.

Specifications

Gear blacklash	0.0039 in.
Clearance between 1st gear and bushing	0.0019-0.0039 in.
2nd and 3rd gears and seats	0.0019-0.0039 in.
Clearance between reverse gear and bushing	0.0019-0.0039 in.
Clearance between flanks of sleeve splines and hub splines	0.0027-0.0063 in.
Radial bearing clearance	0.0019 in. (max.)
Axial bearing clearance	0.0196 in. (max.)
Shaft runout	0.00098 in. (max.)

124 (5-Speed)

This transmission, previously optional on 124 Spyder and Coupe models, has now become standard. Basically, it is the same unit as the 4-speed, with the addition of a fifth gear or overdrive. The transmission is in three parts. The front body is bolted to the crankcase and houses the clutch and withdrawal sleeve, with a thrust bearing. The center body is

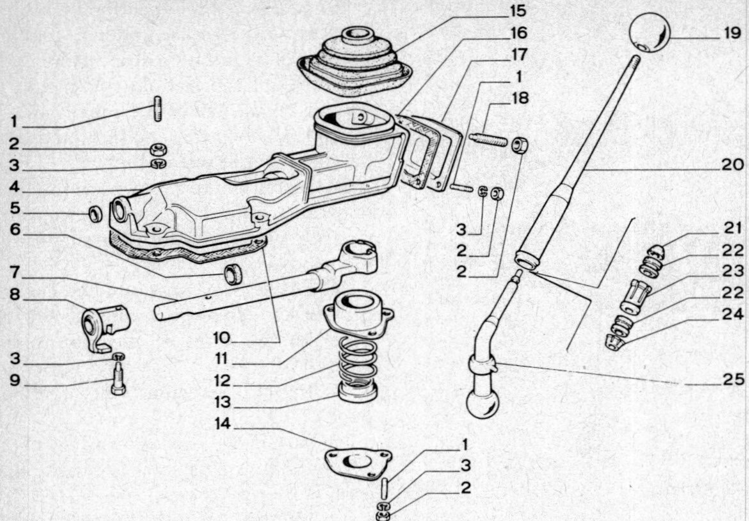

Exploded view of 124 5 speed gearshift mechanism.

1. Studs
2. Nuts
3. Spring washers
4. Support
5. Plug
6. Gasket
7. Gear selector and actuating bar
8. Dog
9. Screw
10. Gasket
11. Cover, spring retaining
12. Reverse stiffening spring
13. Upper ball socket, pivot lever
14. Lower ball socket, pivot lever
15. Boot
16. Gasket
17. Cover
18. Pin
19. Grip
20. Lever jacket
21. Pad
22. Resilient bushings
23. Spacer
24. Snap-ring, lever jacket
25. Pivot lever, gearshift

bolted to the front body and contains the 1st, 2nd, 3rd and 4th gears. The rear cover is bolted to the center body and carries 5th and reverse gears, along with the selector bars. It also contains the mainshaft roller bearing and countershaft ball bearing. The upper part of the rear cover holds the gearshift lever, which is slightly different from the 4-speed unit.

NOTE: *Starting with chassis number 0005752, a new gearshift mechanism is used in production.*

All forward gears are synchronized. The 1st, 2nd, 3rd and 4th gears use a blocker type synchronizer with a sliding sleeve. The 5th gear is synchronized by a spring-ring type synchronizer.

Overhaul

Disassembly and assembly are basically the same procedures as those outlined for the 124 (4-speed). Specifications remain identical to those for the 4-speed unit.

When assembling a synchronizer, be sure that the returned ends of the spring are inserted in the slots in the blocker ring, without distorting the normal diameter of the spring. This should be done before the circlip is fitted.

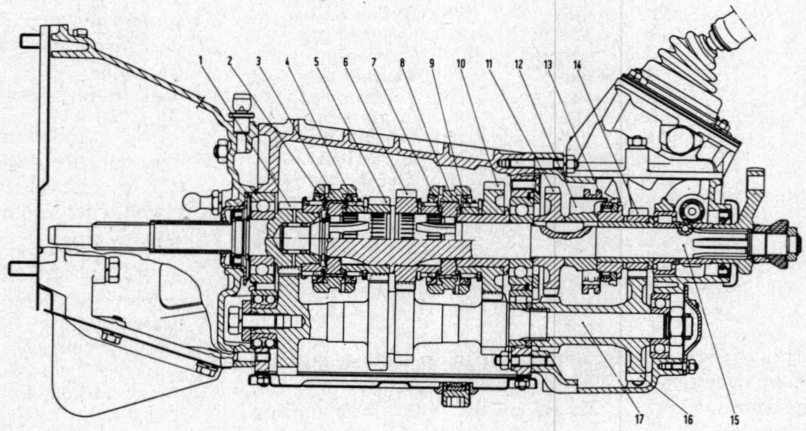

Cross-section of 124 5 -speed transmission

1. Constant mesh 4th gear pinion and main drive
2. Synchronizing ring
3. Sliding sleeve, 3rd and 4th gear
4. Synchronizing ring
5. 3rd gear pinion
6. 2nd gear pinion
7. Synchronizing ring
8. Sliding sleeve, 1st and 2nd gears
9. Synchronizing ring
10. 1st gear pinion
11. Reverse gear pinion
12. Hub
13. Sliding sleeves, 5th gear
14. Pinion and synchronizing complete, 5th gear
15. Mainshaft
16. Gear assembly for 5th and reverse gears
17. Countershaft
18. Reverse shaft
19. Reverse sliding pinion
20. 5th and reverse selector bar
21. 3rd and 4th gear selector bar
22. 1st and 2nd gear selector bar
23. 5th and reverse selector fork
24. Gear lever ball
25. Reverse spring
26. Gear lever ball socket
27. Ball socket retaining plate
28. Gear lever guide plate
29. 5th gear and reverse guard plate
30. Gear lever guide plate
31. Resistance-spring spindle, 1st, 2nd 5th and reverse
32. 3rd and 4th gear selector fork
33. 1st and 2nd gear selector fork
34. Sleeve hub, 3rd and 4th gears
    A. Stop dog
    B. Safety stop for reverse

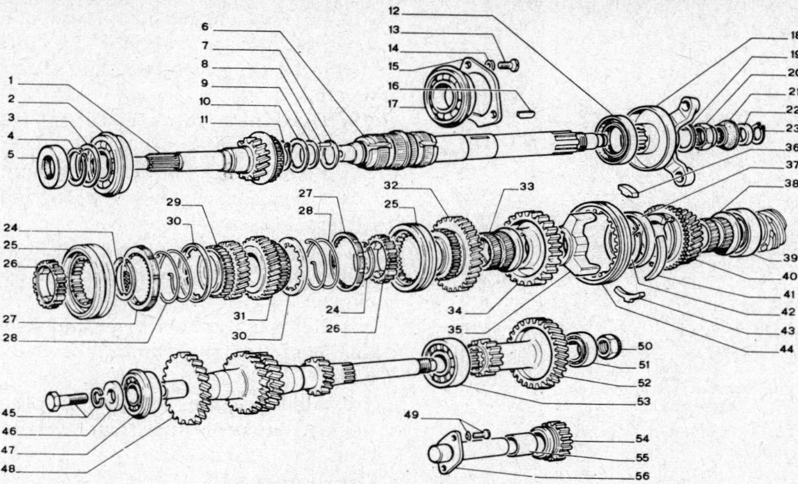

Exploded view of 124 5-speed components.

1. Constant mesh and fourth gear shaft
2. Front ball bearing
3. Spring washer
4. Snap-ring
5. Gasket
6. Mainshaft
7. Thrust washer
8. Needle rollers
9. Thrust washer
10. Spring washer
11. Snap-ring
12. Gasket
13. Plate fixing screws
14. Toothed washer
15. Bearing retainer plate
16. Woodruff key
17. Intermediate ball bearing
18. Joint sleeve
19. Lockwasher
20. Nut
21. Seal ring
22. Positioning ring
23. Snap-ring
24. Snap-ring
25. Sliding sleeves, 1st 2nd, 3rd, and 4th gears
26. Sliding sleeve hubs
27. Synchronizing ring
28. Springs
29. 3rd speed gear
30. Cup
31. 2nd speed gear
32. 1st speed gear
33. 1st speed gear bushing
34. Reverse gear
35. Sliding sleeve hub, 5th speed gear
36. Stop plate
37. 5th speed gear synchronizing ring
38. 5th speed gear bushing
39. Rear roller bearing
40. 5th speed gear
41. Spring
42. Snap-ring
43. Thrust plate
44. 5th gear sliding sleeve
45. Screws and spring washer, locking bearing
46. Plain washer
47. Front ball bearing, countershaft
48. Countershaft and gears for 1st, 2nd, 3rd and constant mesh
49. Screws and toothed washer fixing reverse gear shaft
50. Nut
51. Rear ball bearing
52. Reverse and 5th speed gears
53. Intermediate roller bearing
54. Reverse gear
55. Reverse gear bushing
56. Reverse gear shaft

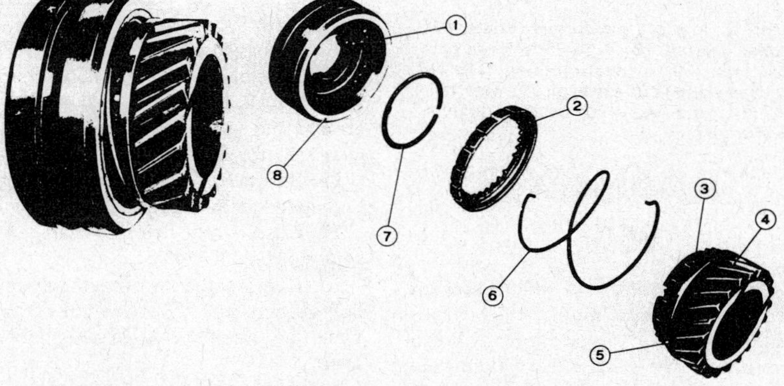

Exploded view of sliding sleeve type synchronizer used on 5 speed transmissions

1. Hub
2. Synchronizing ring
3. Blocker ring
4. Third gear pinion
5. Cup ring
6. Spring
7. Circlip
8. Sliding sleeve

REAR SUSPENSION

128

Removal

1. Set rear of vehicle on stands.
2. Remove the rear weels.
3. Stop up the outlet hole of the brake fluid reservoir.
4. Detach the flexible fluid hose from the metal pipe.
5. Release the hand brake relay lever and detach the cable from the shoe control levers on the brake backing plate.
6. Disconnect the braking regulator torsion bar from the left control arm.
7. Place a hydraulic jack under the control arm, raise the suspension, and detach the shock absorbers via the baggage compartment. Remove the jack.
8. Detach the rubber pads which attach the leaf spring to the control arms.
9. Unscrew the nuts that attach the swivels of the control arms to the screws which pass through the plate that mounts the suspension to the body.

Installation

1. Attach the control arm to the body by passing the two screws through the plate. Finger tighten the nuts.
2. Reattach the rubber pads used to anchor the leaf spring.
3. Link the braking regulator torsion bar to the left control arm.
4. Slip the bottom rubber bushing onto the top stud of the shock absorber. Apply a hydraulic jack under the suspension and lift the whole assembly to enable the top stud of the shock absorber to be inserted into the special hole provided in the baggage compartment.
5. Mount the top rubber bushings, the retainer cap, and the self-locking nut to the top stud of the shock absorber.
6. Tighten the shock absorber nuts.
7. Reattach the handbrake control cable to the lever on the brake backing plate and reconnect the brake fluid hose and metal pipe to each other.
8. Restore the brake fluid and bleed the system.

Wheel Alignment

128

Caster Adjustments

If the caster angles are incorrect, the necessary corrections must be made by varying the number of shims inserted between the end of the anti-roll bar and the rubber pad of the control arm.

The angle is reduced by about 15 minutes for each extra shim.

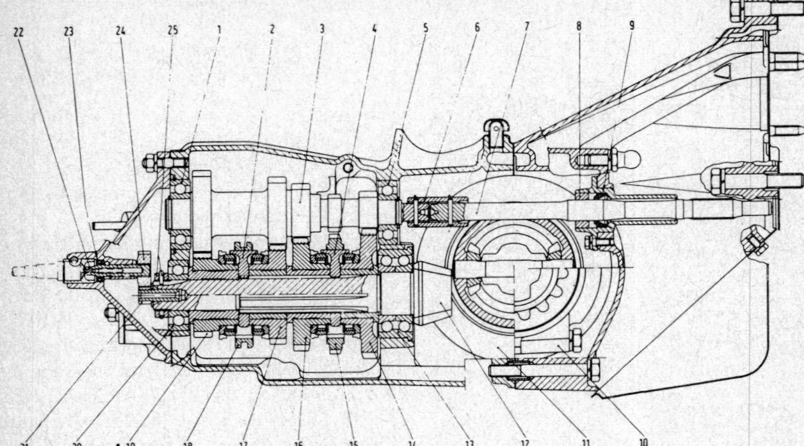

Transaxle assembly of the 850 Series. (1) front ball bearing of countershaft; (2) third and fourth slip sleeve hub; (3) countershaft with drive gears; (4) first and second slip sleeve hub; (5) rear ball bearing of countershaft; (6) countershaft-to-input shaft sleeve; (7) input shaft; (8) input shaft bushing; (9) oil seal; (10) differential carrier cap; (11) ring gear; (12) drive pinion-output shaft; (13) drive pinion rear ball bearing; (14) first driven gear; (15) first second slip sleeve and reverse gear; (16) second driven gear; (17) third driven gear; (18) third and fourth slip sleeve; (19) fourth driven gear; (20) output shaft-drive pinion front ball bearing; (21) speedometer drive gear; (22) speedometer driven shaft; (23) oil seal; (24) speedometer driven gear; (25) output shaft-drive pinion nut and retainer.

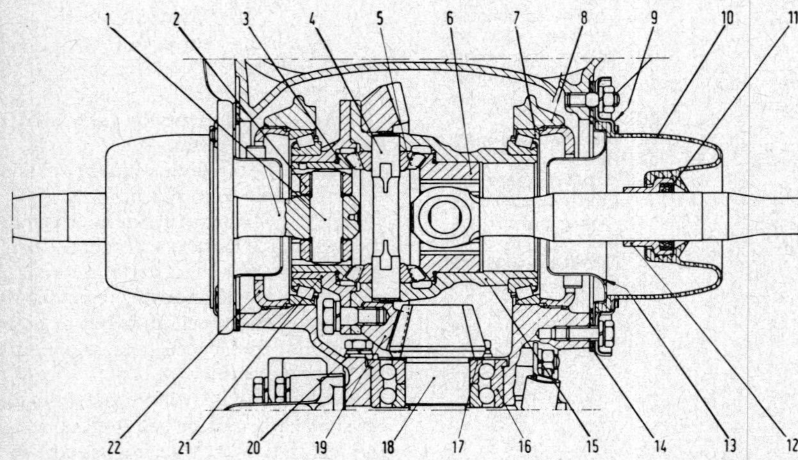

(1) axle shaft; (2) axle slip joint; (3) side gear thrust ring; (4) pinion gear shaft; (5) pinion gear; (6) side gear; (7) differential cage roller bearing; (8) differential cage carrier cap; (9) oil boot cover; (10) oil boot; (11) oil seal; (12) oil seal retainer; (13) oil boot baffle; (14) baffle gasket; (15) differential cage half; (16) drive pinion rear ball bearing; (17) drive pinion shim; (18) drive pinion; (19) ring gear; (20) bearing retainer plate; (21) differential cage half; (22) roller bearing adjuster.

1. Raise the front of the vehicle on a pneumatic jack.

2. Remove the nut which anchors the anti-roll bar to the control arm.

3. Disconnect the control arm from the body.

4. Withdraw the end of the anti-roll bar from the control arm.

5. Add or remove as many shims as may be required to correct the caster angle.

6. Reassemble the various components. Lower the vehicle and rock it a few times to settle down the suspension before tightening the two attachment nuts to their correct torque values.

TRANSAXLE
850

The transmission and differential are incorporated into a single case. The transmission uses four forward gears, all synchronized, the 4th gear being an overdrive. Synchronizing rings are of the sliding type. The transmission is controlled manually through a gearshift lever on the floor.

Removal

1. Disconnect cable from positive terminal of battery.

2. Remove engine compartment lid, upper headlining, generator and starter.

3. Jack car up at the rear and place on stands.

4. Disconnect shock absorbers from lower mountings.

5. Remove axle shaft universal joints.

6. Disconnect clutch and speedometer cables and gearshift rod.

7. Support transaxle unit with a jack and remove unit mounting screws from engine.

8. Remove flywheel cover and screws that hold transaxle support bracket to body.

9. Adjust position of jack to permit disengagement of clutch shaft from plate, then lift out transaxle.

Disassembly

1. Remove the left side mounting bracket and tie the axle shafts up, to prevent them from falling or being damaged.

2. Place the transaxle on a work stand or large smooth bench and drain the oil.

3. Carefully, dismantle the transmission and differential unit.

4. Mark the position of the differential carrier caps and bearing adjusters.

NOTE: *The transmission components can be removed from the gearbox without removing the differential unit, unless the layshaft and drive pinion are removed. If there is no evidence of malfunction in the differential, do not disturb it.*

5. Remove the support with the speedometer drive pinion.

6. Disassemble the front housing and extract the gear selector lever and gasket.

7. Lock the layshaft and drive pinion and remove the cotter pin and nut.

8. Remove the speedometer drive gear from the layshaft, followed by the retainer cover, springs and detent balls.

9. Remove the second gear sliding sleeve with fork and selector rod and the hub (with springs).

10. Slide out the reverse control upper rod and fork, red locking ball, intermediate rod and safety roller and 3rd and 4th gear selector forks.

11. Remove the synchronizer ring, 2nd speed driven gear and bushing.

12. Unscrew the primary shaft nut and remove the washer.

13. Remove the 2nd speed drive gear, ball bearing and reverse shaft retaining plate and slide out the reverse shaft with gear.

14. Remove the front housing-to-center body mounting plate and from the plate, remove the primary shaft front bearing and layshaft front bearing.

15. Remove from the layshaft: 3rd speed driven gear and bushing; synchronizer; 3rd and 4th speed sliding sleeve and hub; first and reverse driven gear;

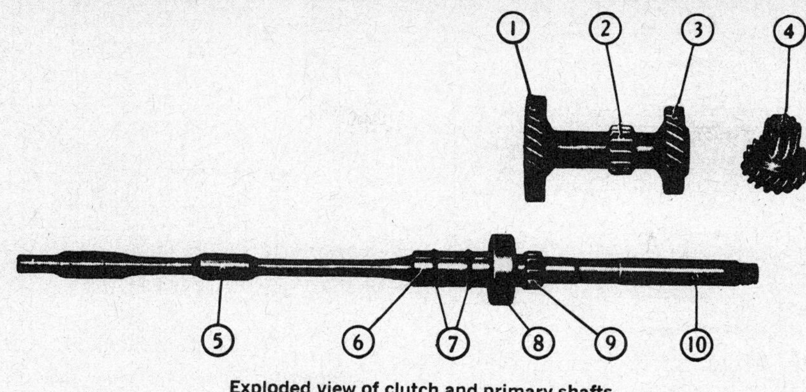

Exploded view of clutch and primary shafts

1. 4th speed driving gear
2. 1st speed and reverse driving gear
3. 3rd speed driving gear
4. 2nd speed driving gear
5. Clutch shaft
6. Sleeve, clutch shaft to primary shaft
7. Sleeve locking snap-rings
8. Primary shaft rear bearing
9. Gear cluster driving gear
10. Primary shaft

4th speed synchronizer and driven gear with bushing.

16. Through the front end, remove the primary shaft containing the 1st, 3rd, 4th and reverse drive gears, rear bearing and clutch shaft.

17. Remove the clutch release control assembly from the rear housing. The seal ring and intermediate support bushing will remain in the gearbox rear housing.

Inspection

Thoroughly clean all parts and inspect them for cracks, burrs, wear and runout. Any parts not meeting specifications should be replaced. Carefully file away all burrs with a dead file.

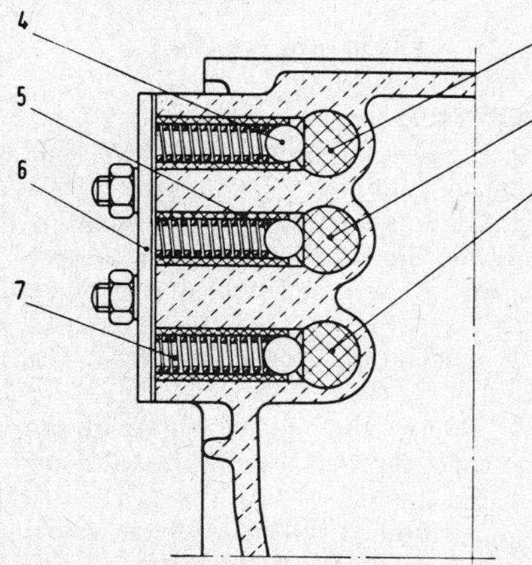

Location of transaxle dentent balls

1. Reverse selector rod
2. 3rd and 4th selector rod
3. 1st and 2nd speed selector rod
4. Selector rod positioning balls
5. Ball and spring guide bushings
6. Cover
7. Detent ball spring

850 Transmission

Assembly

1. Through the casing front end, install the primary shaft with 1st, 3rd, 4th and reverse speeds drive gear assembly, complete with rear bearing and clutch shaft.

2. Fit the layshaft with the following parts: 4th speed gear and bushing, 3rd and 4th speed gear synchronizer assembly, hub and 3rd and 4th speed sliding sleeve (to which the 1st speed driven gear must be keyed), 3rd speed synchronizer ring and driven gear with bushing.

3. Install the mounting plate for the center housing to front body.

4. Install the primary shaft front bearing and the layshaft front bearing.

5. Fit the reverse shaft with gear and bushing and install the retaining plate.

6. Key the 2nd speed driving gear in position and secure with a nut and washer.

7. Tighten this nut to a torque of 43.4 ft lbs. (early type) and 73.0 ft lbs. (later gearboxes).

8. Fit the 2nd speed driven gear, bushing, synchronizing ring and sliding sleeve hub to the layshaft.

9. Install the sliding sleeve with 1st and 2nd speed selector rod and fork.

10. Position the three synchronizer inner springs.

11. Insert the selector rod safety roller.

12. Slide the following parts into position: 3rd and 4th speed intermediate selector rod and fork; safety roller and ball set and reverse speed upper selector rod and fork.

13. Lock the forks on rods.

14. Install the three detent balls and springs and secure with the cover.

15. Install the speedometer driven gear.

16. Screw the nut into place on the layshaft and torque to 40 ft lbs.

17. Fit the speed selector lever and gasket to the front housing.

18. Fit the front housing to the central body and at the same time insert the speed selector lever on the selector lever dogs.

19. Install the speedometer drive pinion support.

20. Install the cotter pin and nut on the shaft.

Installation

Installation is the reverse of removal.

Specifications (850)

Ball bearing radial clearance	0.002 in. (max.)
Ball bearing axial clearance	0.02 in. (max.)
Shaft runout	0.0008 in. (max.)
Differential cage bearings	
Preload (divarication measured at carrier caps with dial indicator)	0.008-0.010 in.
Final drive backlash	0.004-0.006 in.
Oil	
Type	Fiat W 90M
Quantity	4.44 pts.

850 Differential

Disassembly

1. Remove the side gear lateral sleeves, bearing adjuster lockplate, bearing adjuster and bearing housing with seals from both ends of the differential.

2. Pull out the roller bearing outer ring.

3. Remove the rear body of the central case and remove the differential case.

4. Extract the bevel pinion and bearing after removing the retaining plate.

5. Disassemble the bevel pinion bearing with an arbor press.

6. Pull the roller bearing and inner rings from the differential case.

7. Loosen the screws joining the two differential halves and the ring gear.

8. Remove the idle pinion carrier shaft, idle pinions and side gears, and thrust washers.

Assembly

A shim of suitable thickness must be installed between pinion and rear ball bearing to set the pinion depth, thereby obtaining the correct backlash between ring gear and pinion. Shims are supplied in the following thicknesses: 0.108 in., 0.110 in., 0.112 in., 0.114 in., 0.116 in., 0.118 in., 0.120 in., 0.122 in., 0.124 in., 0.126 in., 0.128 in., 0.130 in., 0.132 in. and 0.134 in. Ideally, the determination of shim thickness is made with a suitably machined dummy pinion and dial indicator. In the absence of a dummy pinion, the following method may be used.

If the original ring gear and drive pinion are being replaced, install the same shim as was removed. This should give an adequate setting of pinion depth. If either a new ring gear or drive pinion are being replaced (they should be replaced in matched sets), compare the number stamped on the drive pinion and ring gear being replaced with that stamped on the original ring gear and drive pin-

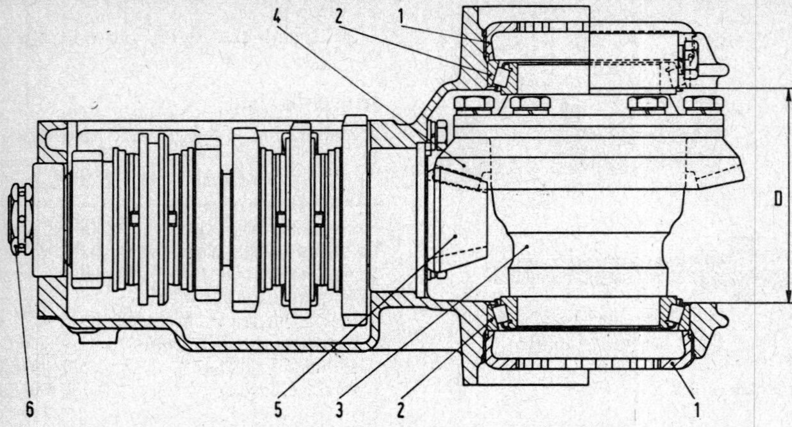

Diagram for checking differential cage bearing preload

1. Bearing adjuster
2. Roller bearings
3. Differential cage
4. Ring gear
5. Drive pinion
6. Drive pinion nut

D Distance between differential carrier caps; tighten bearing adjusters until D increases by .008"-.010" (0.20 to 0.25 mm). (850 Fiat)

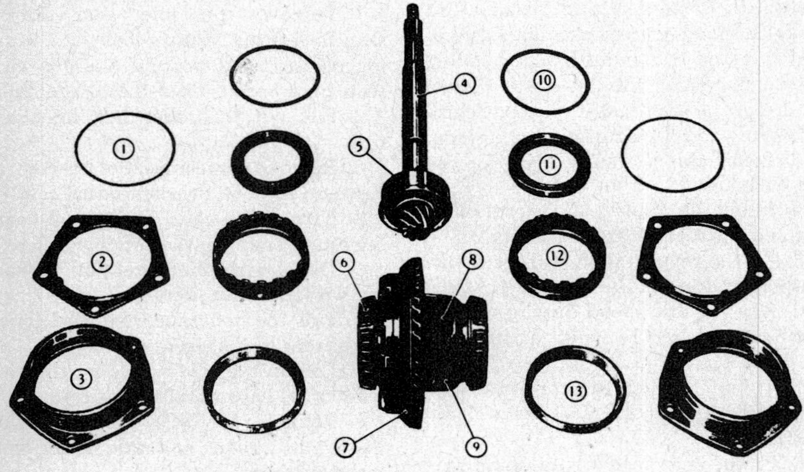

Exploded view of differential and final drive components

1. Gasket for plate
2. Plate securing adjuster 12
3. Roller bearing housing
4. Bevel drive pinion
5. Rear ball bearing for bevel drive pinions
6. Roller bearing inner ring
7. Final drive ring gear
8. Side gear
9. Differential case
10. Bearing housing seal ring
11. Oil seal
12. Roller bearing adjuster
13. Bearing outer ring

ion. By comparing these numbers and the original shim from the pinion, an approximate shim thickness can be determined.

Gather a number of shims of varying thicknesses. Fit the side gears with the thrust rings, idle pinions and idle carrier shaft. Insert the ring gear in the left case half and mate the case halves. The side gears must be adjusted, through the thrust rings, to obtain the proper rotational torque. Check the rotational torque by locking one of the side gears. The torque required to turn the other side gear may not be greater than 3.6 ft lbs. Shims to adjust this value are available in the following sizes: 0.0394 in., 0.0512 in. and 0.0591 in. Install the two roller bearing inner rings. Install this complete assembly in the gearbox-differential case. Install the two bearing housings with seals and roller bearing outer rings. Also install the two oil seals, bearing adjusters and seals. The bearing lockplates should be installed after setting.

Mount a dial indicator and set it at zero. With the adjuster rings slightly in touch with the bearings, tighten one adjuster ring and measure the amount of divarication at the case. Slacken the opposite adjuster ring; the dial indicator must return to zero. Tighten the second adjuster ring again, until a divarication of 0.008–0.010 in. is obtained. Rotate the ring gear through several revolutions to ensure final seating of the bearings. The

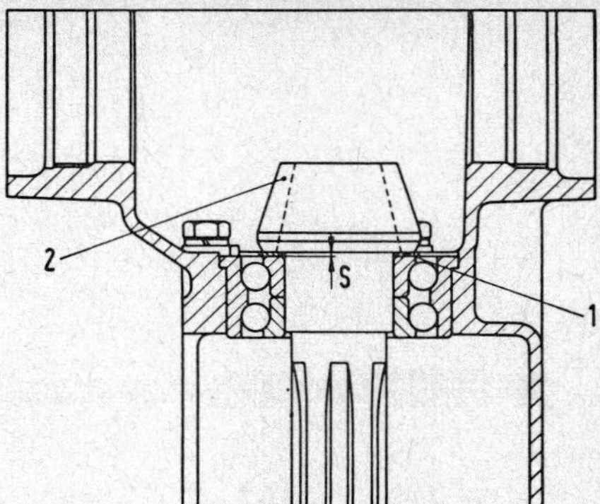

Diagram for fitting drive pinion shim

1. Drive pinion shim
2. Drive pinion
S. Shim thickness

bearings are now preloaded. Mount and zero the dial indicator again and set the backlash to 0.004–0.006 in., by rotating the bearing adjusters. To prevent any alteration of bearing preload, rotate one adjuster ring the same amount as the other, but in an opposite direction.

DRIVE AXLES

Fiat 124 driveshafts are in two parts, a tubular front piece connected to the transmission through a flexible spider coupling and a solid rear piece, connected to the front piece by a universal joint and to the rear axle by a splined sleeve.

Driveshafts

Removal

1. Remove the sleeve of the front shaft from the coupling.
2. Detach the brake hose retaining clip from the cover of the rear shaft and disconnect the hose from the rear brake pipe.
3. Release the brake pipe from the clips.
4. Remove the bolts which secure the rear shaft cover to the differential housing.
5. Disconnect the hand-brake return spring from the central support.
6. Unscrew the four nuts which secure the central pillow block to the underside of the vehicle.
7. Slide the driveshafts toward the front of the car.

Disassembly

1 Remove the spider of the universal joint.

2. Remove the universal joint fork and the snap-ring which holds the bearing dust cover.

3. Slide the rear shaft, complete with bearing, out of the tubular cover.

4. Extract the bearing from the end of the shaft.

5. When the cover has been removed, the sliding sleeve can be removed from the front shaft.

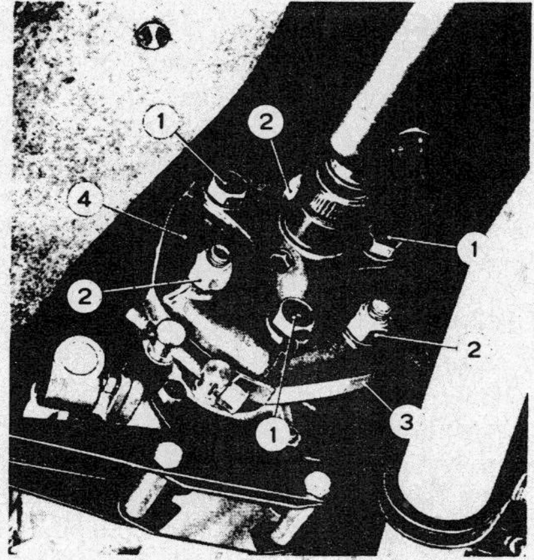

Spider joint connecting driveshaft to transmission.

1. Bolts fixing sliding sleeve on driveshaft to the flexible joint
2. Nuts and bolts fixing transmission sleeve to flexible joint
3. Tool A. 70025
4. Flexible joint

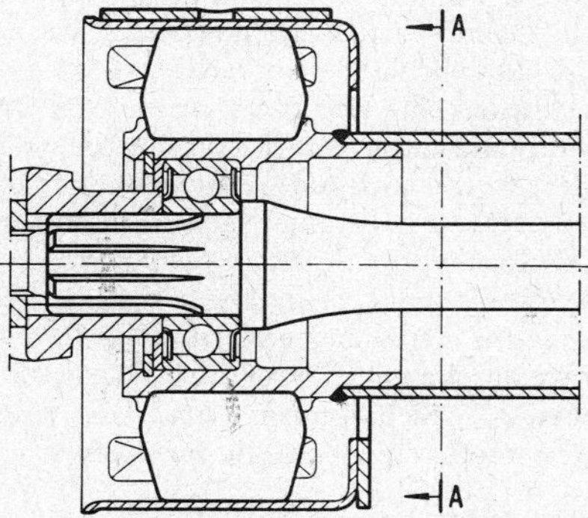

Cross section of central pillow block and driveshaft.

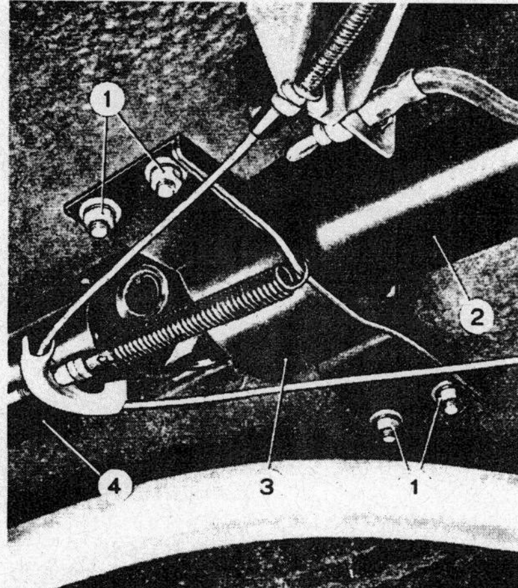

Driveshaft central pillow block

1. Bolts fixing pillow block to body
2. Tubular cover of rear shaft
3. Pillow block housing
4. Front shaft

Drive Axle and Suspension (124)

The rear axle is a semi-floating, hypoid design with the wheels mounted directly on the axle shafts. The axle shafts have integral wheel hubs supported inside by the side gears and outside by the flanges of the axle housing.

Rear Axle

Removal

1. Jack the car up and remove the wheels from the axle shaft hubs.
2. Plug the brake line reservoir outlet with a wooden plug.
3. Remove the brake hose from the pipe.
4. Remove the driveshaft.
5. Disconnect the handbrake cable from both brake calipers.
6. Remove the two trailing arms of the stabilizer bar from the brackets on the axle housing.
7. Remove the brake regulator control rod.
8. Support the axle housing with a hydraulic jack.
9. Remove the upper shock absorber mounting nuts.
10. Remove the trailing arms from the axle housing.
11. Remove the cross-rod.
12. Lower the axle assembly to the ground.

Installation

1. Fit the springs and isolating rings to the seats on the axle housing.
2. Fit the rubber bushings to the upper stems of the shock absorbers.
3. Connect the trailing arms and cross-rod to the axle housing with the nuts finger tight.
4. Extend the shock absorbers and lift the axle with the jack, allowing the upper stems of the shock absorbers to enter the holes in the body.
5. Secure the ends of the shock absorbers from inside the luggage compartment.
6. Connect the brake regulator tie-rod to the mounting on the axle housing.
7. Connect the stabilizer tie-rods to the axle housing, but do not tighten.
8. Fit the driveshaft.
9. Connect the brake hoses to the piping and check the brake fluid level.
10. Bleed the brake system.
11. Fill the axle and loosely fit the wheels.
12. Lower the car and with the car loaded, tighten all rear suspension nuts.

Axle Shafts

Removal

1. Jack up the rear of the car. Remove the wheels. Remove the caliper support bracket assembly without disconnecting the brake fluid lines.
2. Remove the snap-ring which retains the bearing dust cover.
3. Using a slide hammer, remove the axle shaft, complete with snap-ring, dust cover, bearing and bearing retaining collar.
4. Extract the shaft oil seal and O-ring.

NOTE: *Always use a hydraulic press to remove the axle shaft bearing retaining collar.*

Installation

1. Fit the oil seal and O-ring to the housing.
2. Insert the complete axle shaft and fit the snap-ring to the housing.
3. Fit the brake disc to the axle shaft hub with two centering screws.
4. Fit the caliper support bracket and caliper assembly to the axle.
5. Fit the wheel and lower the car to the ground.

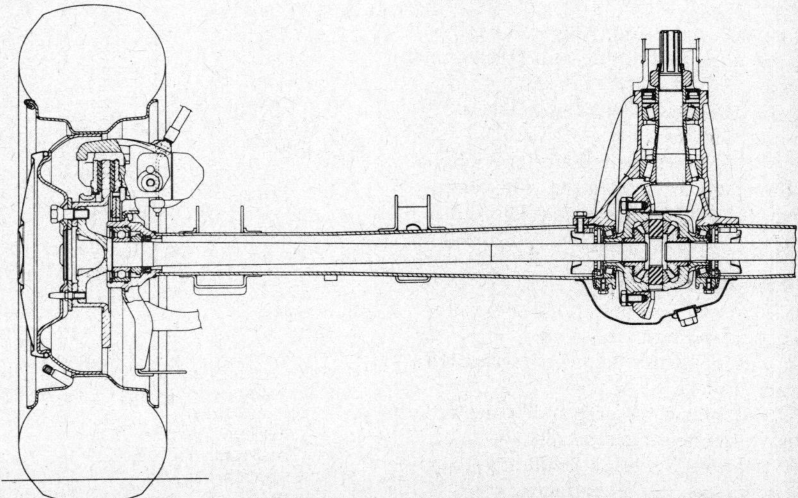

Rear axle assembly, 124 Coupe and Spider

The values of dimensions a, b, c, d, e, f and g are given in the table

Dimensions to be checked	Post-modification[1] in.	Post-modification[1] mm	Pre-modification[1] in.	Pre-modification[1] mm
a	0.63	16	0.82	21
b	2.42	61.5	2.53	64.5
c	0.078	2	0.102	2.6
d	1.22	31	1.35	34.5
e	2.44	62	2.55	65
f	0.393	10	0.314	8
g	0.866	22	1.082	27.5

[1] Modification of rear axle dimensions with vehicles carrying spare parts number 069548 and above.

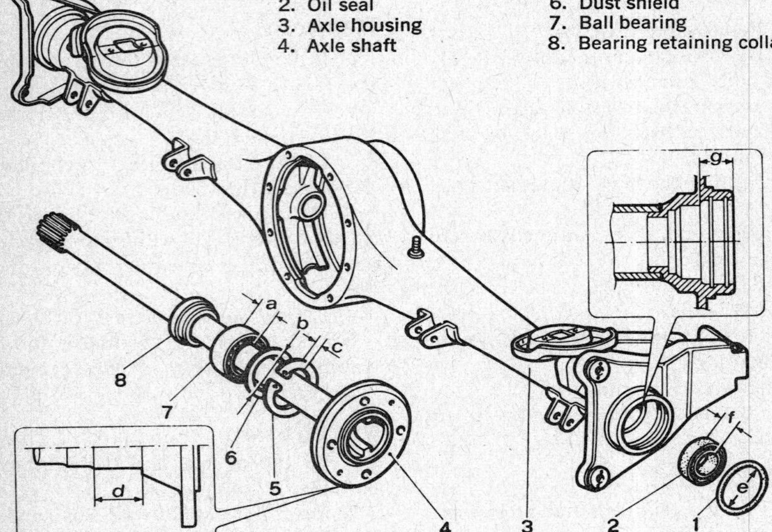

Exploded view of 124 rear axle and axle shaft assembly

Differential

Removal

To remove only the differential, use the following procedure.

1. Unscrew the drain plug in the lower part of the axle housing and drain the gear oil.
2. Jack the rear of the car and remove the rear wheels.
3. Withdraw the axle shafts far enough to disengage them from the side gears.
4. Unbolt and remove the differential from the housing.

Disassembly

1. Remove the bolts and lockplates from the bearing caps.
2. The lockplates hold the bearing adjusters in place.
3. Matchmark the caps and bosses and remove the bearing cap bolts.
4. Remove the caps, retaining rings and roller bearing outer races.
5. Withdraw the differential case from the carrier, complete with gears, ring gear and inner bearing races.
6. Turn the carrier upside down and by holding the pinion, unscrew the pinion nut.
7. Withdraw the pinion, complete with thrust ring, rear roller bearing inner race and collapsible spacer.
8. Remove the oil seal, oil slinger and inner race from the front bearing.
9. Remove the outer race of the rear roller bearing with a drift.
10. Slide the collapsible spacer from the pinion and pull the inner race of the rear roller bearing and thrust washer from the pinion.
11. Remove the inner races of the bearings in which the differential case runs.
12. Remove the ring gear and using a drift, remove the pinion gears shaft.
13. Rotate the side gears and remove these and their thrust washers from the case.

Inspection

Check all gears for damage or wear. Very slight wear damage can be corrected with very fine abrasive paper. Inspect the side gear thrust washers. If the thrust washers are only slightly defective polish them. Be sure that the case and carrier are not cracked.

Assembly

Assemble the side gears and thrust washers in the case. Insert the pinion gears through the opening in the case and engage them with the side gears. Align the holes in the pinion gears with the holes in the case and insert the pinion gears shaft. Check the axial play in each side gear. The play should be from 0–0.039 in. If the side gear play is excessive, replace the thrust washers with thicker ones, to bring the axial play within specifications. Service thrust washers are supplied in the following sizes: 0.076 in., 0.078 in., 0.080 in. and 0.082 in. If the thrust washers were changed, measure the clearance again. If new thrust washers fail to bring the clearance within specifications, the side gears are excessively worn and must be replaced. Fit the ring gear to the case and torque the bolts to 72.0 ft lbs. Fit the inner races of the roller bearings with a driver of proper size.

At this point, assembly of the pinion requires a trial and error method to determine the thickness of the pinion thrust washer, which controls pinion and ring gear mesh, compensating for differences

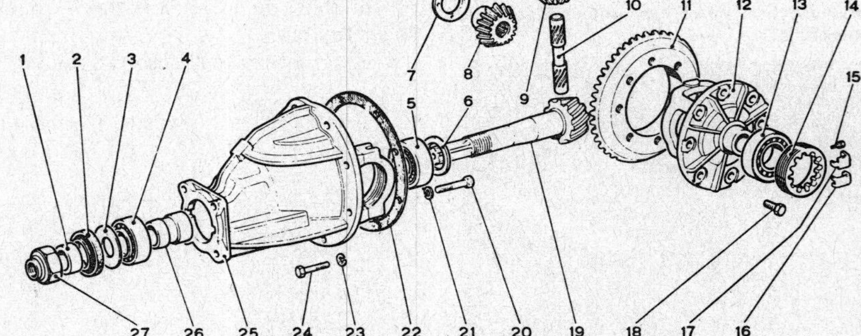

Exploded view of typical Fiat differential assembly

1. Spacer
2. Oil seal
3. Oil slinger
4. Front roller bearing
5. Rear roller bearing
6. Pinion shaft rear roller bearing thrust washer
7. Side gear thrust ring
8. Side gear
9. Pinion gear
10. Pinion gear shaft
11. Ring gear
12. Differential case
13. Differential case roller bearing
14. Bearing adjuster ring
15. Locking plate clip bolt
16. Locking plate
17. Locking plate
18. Bolts fixing ring gear to differential case
19. Bevel pinion
20. Carrier cap bolts
21. Spring washer
22. Gasket
23. Spring washer
24. Differential carrier to axle housing bolt
25. Differential carrier
26. Collapsible spacer
27. Bevel pinion nut

in machining between pinion and carrier. Assemble several thrust washers of varying thicknesses and several collapsible spacers. Pinion bearing thrust washers are in the following thicknesses: 0.100 in., 0.102 in., 0.104 in., 0.106 in., 0.108 in., 0.110 in., 0.112 in., 0.114 in., 0.116 in., 0.118 in., 0.120 in., 0.122 in., 0.124 in., 0.1259 in., 0.1279 in., 0.1299 in. and 0.1311 in.

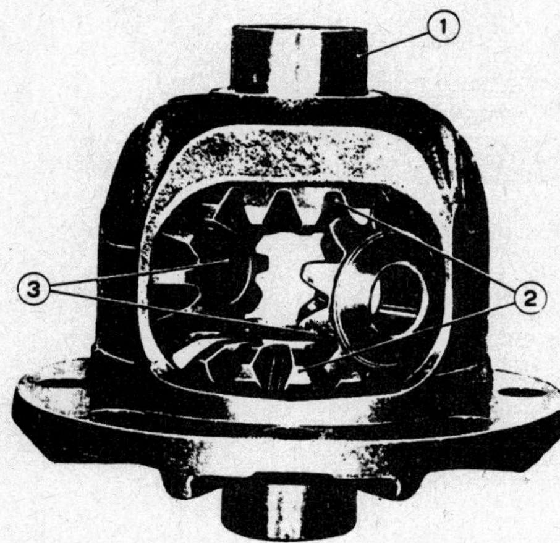

Assembly of side gears in the differential case.

1. Differential case
2. Side gears
3. Pinion gears

Arrange the pinion gears as shown in the figure and push them into place by rolling them on the side gear.

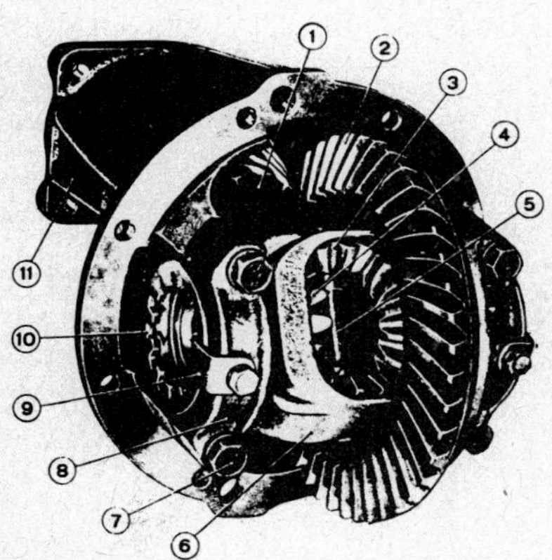

Typical Fiat differential

1. Pinion
2. Ring gear
3. Pinion gear
4. Side gear
5. Pinion gear shaft
6. Differential case
7. Differential case bearing cap screw
8. Differential case bearing cap
9. Ring lockplate
10. Bearing retaining ring
11. Differential housing

If the pinion, ring gear, pinion bearings and differential carrier are not changed, the same collapsible spacer and pinion thrust washer may be re-used. However, if any of those parts are installed new, the thrust washer and collapsible spacer will have to be replaced with new parts.

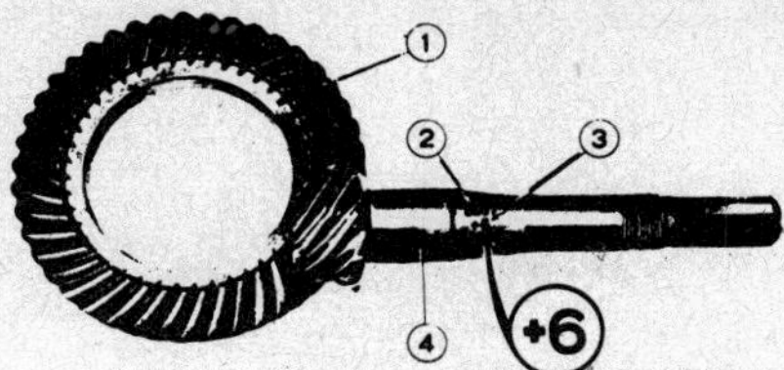

Ring gear and pinion markings

1. Ring gear
2. Serial production and matching number
3. Centesimal value of difference between actual and nominal distance
4. Bevel pinion

By comparing the number stamped on the pinion and ring gear (old or new gear sets), a reasonable determination of thrust washer thickness can be made. The number, stamped on the pinion and preceded by a(+) or (−) sign, is the difference, in hundredths of a millimeter, between the actual fitting clearance and the nominal fitting clearance. Select a thrust washer thought to be of nearly proper size (or as close to the proper size as possible). Assemble the pinion and bearings and insert the pinion assembly in the carrier. Fit the front roller bearing inner race, the oil seal, oil slinger and spacer on the front of the carrier.

The pinion bearings are preloaded in the following manner. Clamp the pinion and torque the pinion nut to 108.5–166.4 ft lbs., constantly checking the rotational torque. The rotational torque of the pinion must be between 1.2–1.5 ft lbs.

NOTE: *If the tightening torque is exceeded, the collapsible spacer will have to be replaced. If the proper rotational torque cannot be obtained, the spacer will have to be removed and replaced with another.*

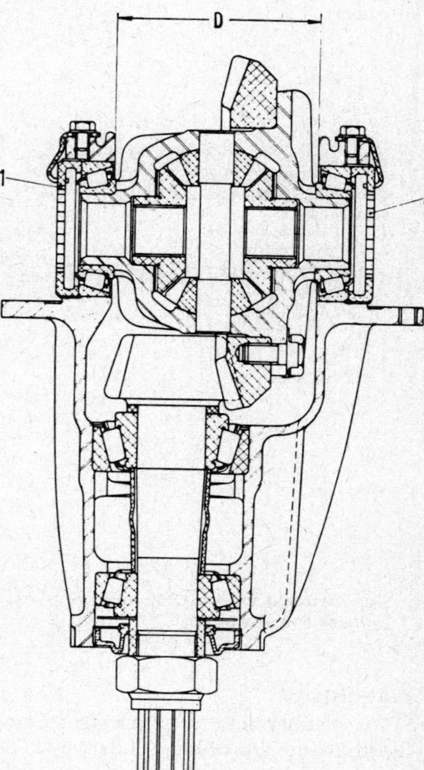

Diagram for fitting pinion

D. Distance between differential case bearing caps: tighten adjusting rings 1. and 2. to increase dimension D

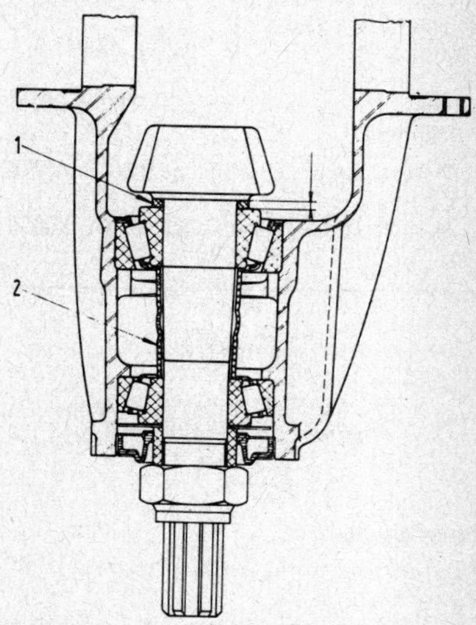

Diagram for checking the differential case bearing preload.

1. Rear bearing thrust ring
2. Collapsible spacer between roller bearings

Fit the differential case into the carrier, complete with bearing outer races. Fit the two bearing retaining and adjusting rings and bring them into light contact with the bearings. Fit the bearing caps and torque the bolts to 36.0 ft lbs. Temporarily adjust the ring gear and pinion backlash to 0.0031–0.0047 in. Alternately, tighten the two bearing adjusting rings the same number of turns, until the differential case bearing cap divergence measures 0.0063–0.0078 in. The ring gear backlash must remain as set.

Backlash

Using a dial gauge, adjust the ring gear backlash to 0.0032–0.0047 in. It is important that if one adjuster ring is turned, the other be turned an equal amount in an opposite direction, ensuring that the preload is not altered.

Coat the ring gear with red lead and check the tooth contact pattern. Depending on the results of this test, the pinion thrust washer may have to be replaced with another of different thickness, either thicker or thinner, depending on the direction in which the pinion must be moved. Bear in mind that if this operation is necessary, the entire process will have to be repeated.

Installation

Installation is the reverse of removal.

Specifications

Pinion nut torque	108.5-166.3 ft. lbs.
Pinion turning torque	1.2-1.5 ft. lbs.
Bearing preload	
Differential cap spread	0.0063-0.0090 in. (increase)[1]
Side gear axial clearance	0-0.0039 in.
Pinion and ring gear backlash	0.0031-0.0047 in.[2]
Oil	
Type	Fiat W 90/M
Quantity	1 pt. 26 oz.

[1] 124 Sport Spyder, Sport Coupe 0.0063-0.0078 in.

[2] 124 Sport Spyder, Sport Coupe 0.0039-0.0059 in.

850 rear suspension in place on vehicle

1. Control arms
2. Coil springs
3. Sway bar
4. Hydraulic brake lines
5. Transmission mounting brackets
6. Flexible joints
7. Handbrake control cable
8. Shock absorbers
9. Axle shafts

REAR SUSPENSION (850)

Removal

1. Jack the car at the rear and set it on stands.
2. Remove a wheel and disconnect a shock absorber at the rear.
3. Tie the axle shaft off from the wheel shaft joint.
4. Disconnect the handbrake control cable from the brake shoe actuating lever.
5. Plug the brake fluid reservoir outlet and detach the brake hose from the brake line.
6. Disconnect the sway bar at the control arm and the transmission mounting bracket.
7. Back out the screws which mount the control arm to the body, at the front and the rear, noting the number of shims.
8. Using a hydraulic jack, lower the rear suspension.
9. Repeat this procedure to lower the other arm.

Disassembly

Disassemble the control arm. This operation should not present any particular difficulty, but the following points should be noted.

After the wheel hub has been removed, remove the ball bearing retainer plate. Withdraw the ball bearing with a slide hammer. Remove the roller bearing cup with a driver.

NOTE: *Whenever the roller bearing has been removed, it must be replaced with a new one.* A driver should be used for removal of control arm bushings. Check the ball and roller bearings for wear. Sliding surfaces of the wheel shaft must show no signs of binding. Always use new spring type oil seals which have been removed.

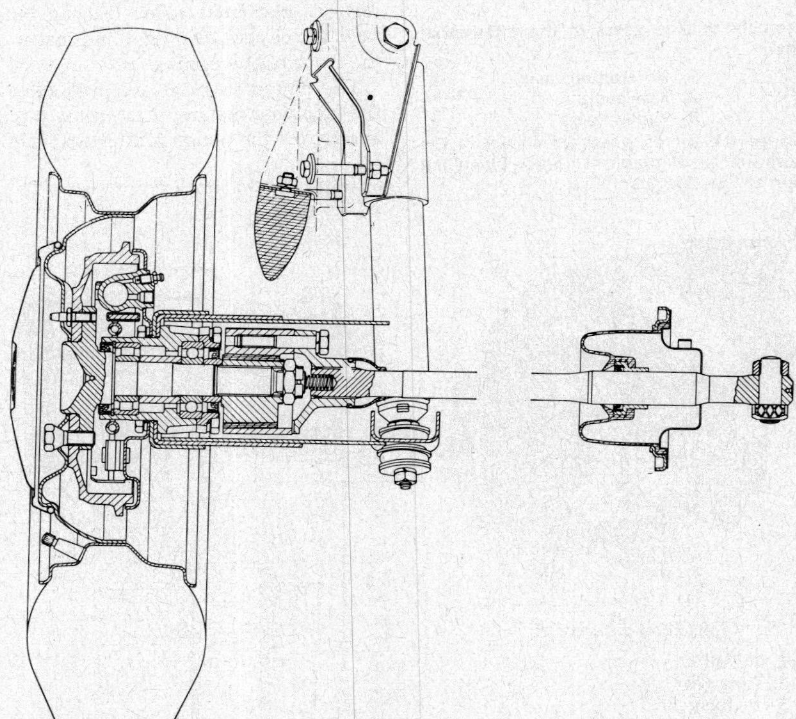

Side-sectional view of 850 rear axle assembly through the wheel, wheel hub, wheel cylinder and axle shaft.

Assembly

To assemble the control arm, reverse the disassembly procedure. Liberally lubricate the bearing cups and bushings with Fiat MR 3 grease and install, using a driver.

Coil Springs

Check to be sure that coil springs are in good condition and show no cracks. Examine the rubber seats and replace these if they are damaged. Coil springs are graded with two colors: yellow paint spot and green paint spot. Coil springs on any one car must show same paint color identification.

Installation

Raise the suspension and set it at the mounting points. Temporarily tighten

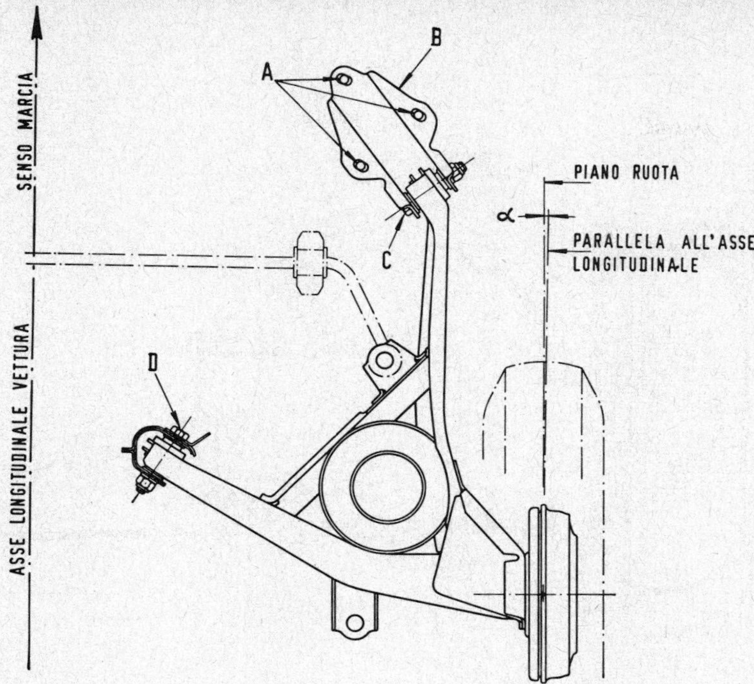

Diagram for setting rear end geometry

A. Screws, front bracket to underbody (recommended torque 28.9 to 36.2 ft. lbs.—4 to 5 kgm.). Tighten these screws after adjusting toe-in with wheel in vertical position—B. Front bracket of control arm—C-D. Screws and nuts, control arm to underbody. These nuts should be drawn up with 65.1 lbs. (9 kgm) of torque with care under full load—Toe in angle, with wheel in vertical position: 0° 12′ ± 6′.
Senso marcia—Director of drive. Asse longitudinale vettura—car centerline. Piano ruota—Wheel plane. Parallela al'asse longitudinale—Parallel to car centerline.

Fastening 850 rear control arm to body

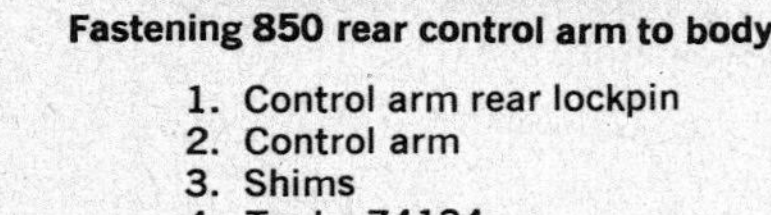

1. Control arm rear lockpin
2. Control arm
3. Shims
4. Tool a.74134

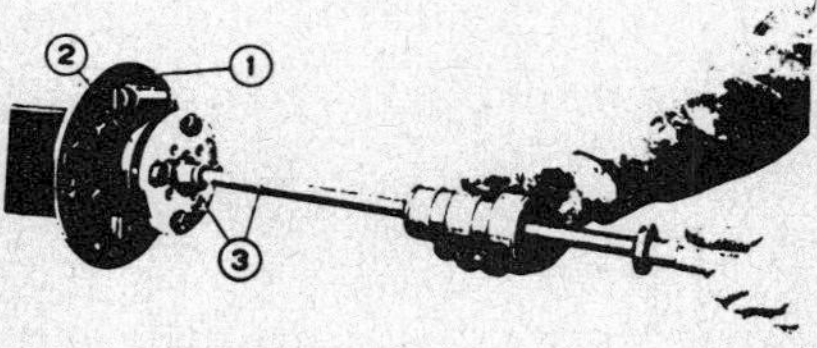

Removing 850 rear wheel hub

1. Brake backing plate
2. Wheel hub
3. Slide hammer for rear wheel hubs

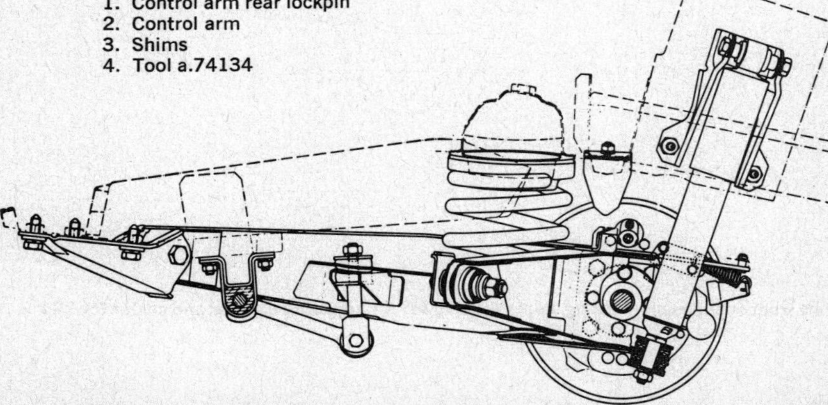

Sectional view of rear suspension across the sway bar mounting

the front mounting screws. Slide the rear end of the control arm into the body bracket. Install the coil spring with rubber seats. Secure the axle shaft to the flexible joint and the shock absorber to the control arm. Insert the shims in the same amount and position as removed, between the "estendblock" and the mounting bracket. Tie up the brake line and handbrake control cable. Remove the plug from the brake fluid reservoir to restore fluid circulation. Install the transmission mounting bracket and sway bar. Fit the wheels and bleed the brakes.

Flexible Joint

Jack the rear of the car and remove the wheel. Remove the axle shaft to flexible joint sleeve screws. Slide the sleeve back on the axle shaft and remove the inner spring. Remove the cotter pin and screw the nut out four complete turns. Attach a slide hammer to the wheel hub and pull the wheel hub part way out. Turn the nut all the way out and replace the flexible joint with a new one. By working the mounting nut, reset the wheel hub to its original position. Torque the nut to 101 ft. lbs. and thread the cotter pin. If the cotter pin does not align with a hole, advance the nut further. Complete the assembly by reversing the disassembly procedures.

FRONT SUSPENSION

124

The front suspension is a wishbone type, with coil springs, hydraulic shock absorbers and stabilizer bar. Upper and lower control arms are connected to the knuckles through ball joints, lubricated for life. The two ball joints are hosed in the control arm and riveted in position. Two lower control arms are connected to the lower crossmembers of the frame.

Ball Joint Inspection

Make sure that the ball joints are perfectly seated in their sockets and that the arms are not loose in them. The whole arm must be changed if the joints are not secure in the arm or if they show signs of wear. The ball joint seals must also be in place, to prevent the entry of water or other matter.

850

The 850's use independent front wheel suspension consisting of a transverse leaf spring secured to the body and kingpins. The leaf spring also acts as a stabilizer. Telescopic, hydraulic shock absorbers are anchored to the body and to the steering knuckle pillar.

Front Wheel Alignment 124

Camber

Camber angle adjustment is made by changing the number of shims under the two bolts that hold the lower control arm to the frame crossmember. Camber is increased by removing shims and reduced by adding shims. Add or remove the same number for each bolt, otherwise caster will be affected.

Caster

Caster angle is increased by moving these shims from the front bolt to the rear and decreased by moving them from the rear bolt to the front.

Toe-in adjustment is made by first loosening the clamp bolts, then turning the sleeves to lengthen or shorten the left- and right-hand tie-rods.

Camber and caster angle and adjustment are made by means of shims installed under the two bolts that hold the control arm to the frame. Camber angle is increased by adding the same number of shims under each bolt and decreased by removing the same number of shims from under each bolt.

Caster is increased by moving shims from the rear bolt to the front bolt and reduced by moving shims from the front bolt to the rear bolt.

Toe-in is adjusted by turning sleeves to lengthen or shorten the left- and right-hand tie-rods.

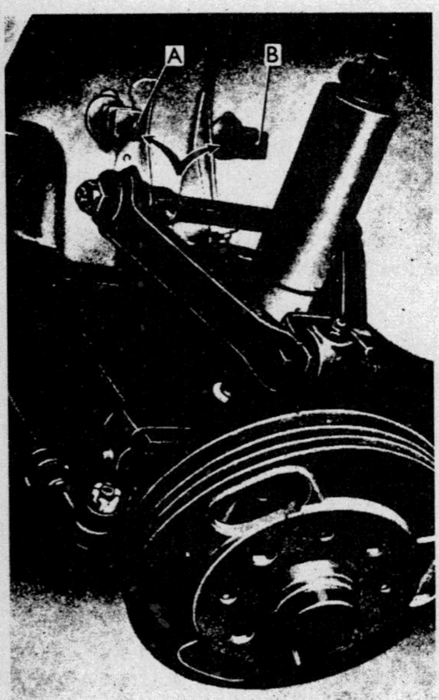

Camber on 850 is increased by adding shims (at arrows) to the wishbone mounting bolts (A and B). Caster is increased by moving shims from rear bolt to front bolt.

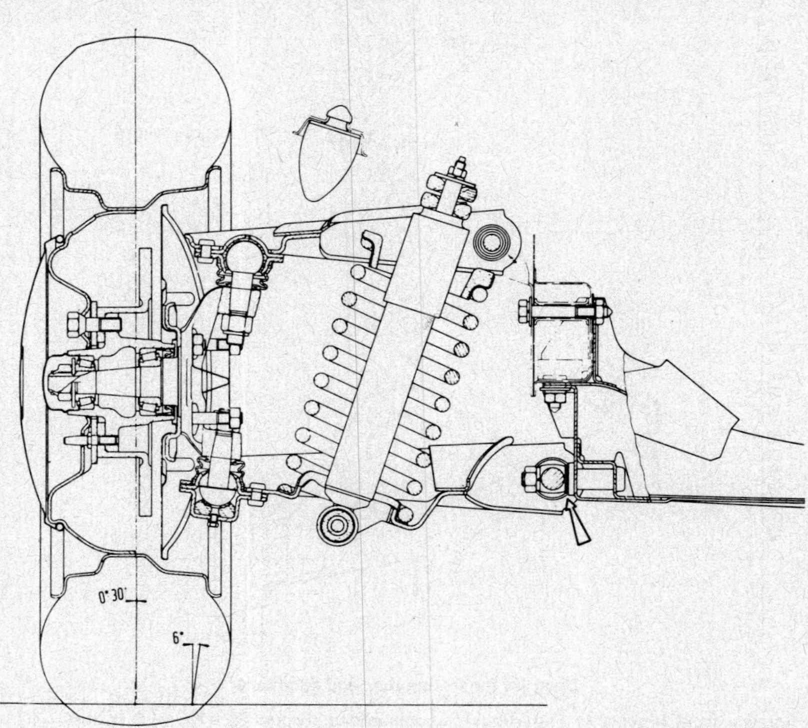

Left front suspension of 124 showing king pin setting and camber angle for loaded car. Arrow points to shims for camber adjustment.

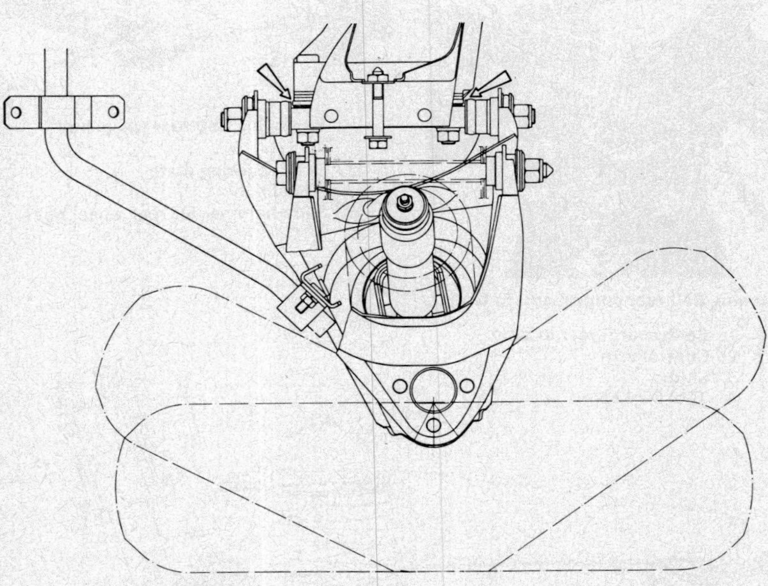

Left front suspension showing shims (at arrows) for adjusting camber and caster for 124

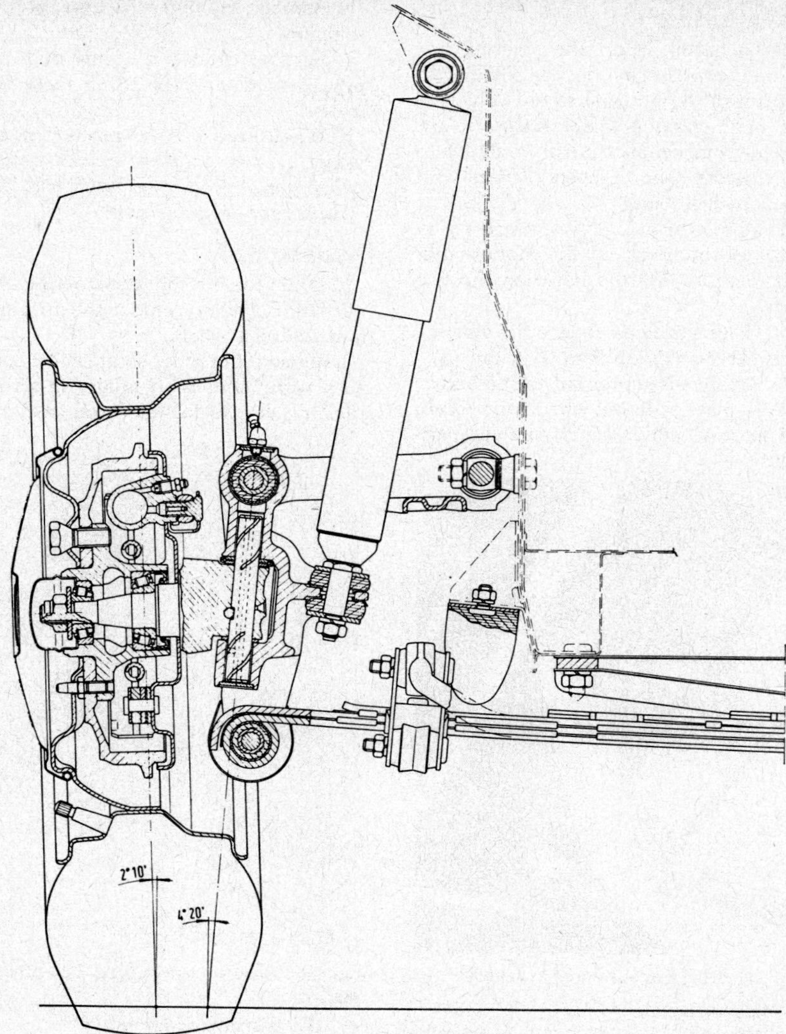

Left front suspension 850

128

The front suspension is an independent type and each wheel assembly must therefore be removed separately.

Removal

1. Slacken the front wheel stud bolts.
2. Slacken the front wheel hub nuts.
3. Place the vehicle on jackstands.
4. Remove the front wheels.
5. Unscrew the nuts which attach the brake caliper to the pillar and secure the caliper to the body.
6. Unscrew the nut which attaches the tie-rod ball joint to the steering arm and then remove the swivel with a puller.
7. Unscrew the nut which attaches the end of the anti-roll bar to the control arm.
8. Detach the control arm from the body.
9. Remove the hub nut.
10. Release the top attachment of the shock absorber by unscrewing the three mounting nuts in the engine compartment.
11. Slide the suspension assembly off the constant-speed joint shaft and fix the axle shaft in such a way as to prevent it from slipping out of the differential.

Installation

1. Attach the anti-roll bar to the body.
2. Take up each completely reassembled control arm and mount the hub on the shaft of the constant-speed joint. At the same time, insert the upper attachment of the shock absorber into the holes provided in the body and secure it with the nuts and the spring washers.
3. Place a flat washer on the shaft of the constant-speed joint and screw up the attachment nut.
4. Grease the rubber bushings in the anti-roll bar-to-control arm joint.
5. Using as many shims as were present on disassembly, reattach the end of the anti-roll bar and its flexible pads to the control arm and reinstall the latter on the body.
6. Attach the tie-rod to the steering arm and tighten the nut to 58 ft lbs.
7. Remount the brake caliper onto the brake disc.

Adjustments

Toe-In

1. Slacken the nut and screw or unscrew the hexagon on the ball pin to obtain the correct degree of toe-in, without moving the steering wheel spokes.
2. Hold the pin in position and lock the nut against the sleeve.

REAR SUSPENSION

128

Adjustments

Camber and Toe-In

1. Raise the vehicle with a pneumatic jack.
2. Compress one end of the leaf spring to shift it from the flexible guide which anchors it to the control arm.

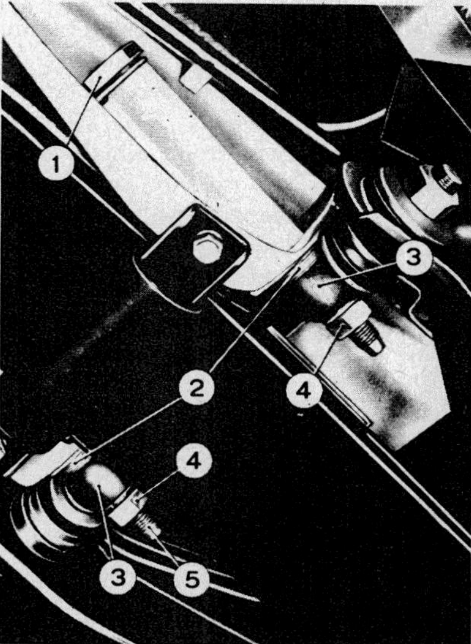

Attachment of left rear control arm to body

1. Screws attaching control arm to body
2. Adjustment shims
3. Control arm pivot
4. Pivot locking nuts
5. Screws attaching control arm to body

3. Remove the guide.
4. Slowly release the spring.
5. Unscrew the nuts which attach the pivot to the body.
6. Partly remove the screw to free the adjustment shims.

7. Carry out the required variation in the number of shims.

8. Reinsert the screw.

9. Carry out this operation on both control arm-to-body screws.

10. Adjust the other wheel if necessary.

11. Reassemble the two flexible guides which anchor the leaf spring to the control arms and tighten the attachment nuts to 22 ft lbs.

NOTE: *To increase the negative camber angle, add an equal number of shims on both screws 1 and 5.*

To decrease the negative camber angle, remove an equal number of shims from both screws 1 and 5.

To increase the toe-in, add shims to the rear screw 5 or remove shims from the front screw 1.

To decrease the toe-in, add shims to the front screw 1 or remove shims from the rear screw 5.

STEERING

128

Removal

1. Disconnect the battery leads.
2. Rest the front of the car on stands.
3. Unscrew the stud bolts and remove the front wheels.
4. Remove the spare wheel.
5. Disconnect the drive pinion from the lower section of the steering column at the universal joint.
6. Using a puller, remove the tie-rods from the steering arms.
7. Remove the screws which attach the top guard in order to facilitate removal of the steering box.
8. Unscrew the steering box from the mounting bracket and remove it from the right side of the vehicle.

Connection of the drive pinion to the steering column lower section with universal joint.

1. Universal joint of lower steering column section
2. Drive pinion
3. Screw and nut

Installation

1. To install, insert the steering box (complete with tie-rods and filled with oil), from the right side of the vehicle.
2. With steering wheel in the straight line position, connect the drive pinion to the steering column lower section, with the universal joints.
3. Mount the assembly on the body by means of the brackets. The rubber cushions must be inserted between the two parts.
4. Connect the tie-rods to the steering arms. Torque the nuts to 58 ft lbs.
5. Attach the top guard to the body.
6. Replace the front wheels and return the spare wheel to the engine compartment.

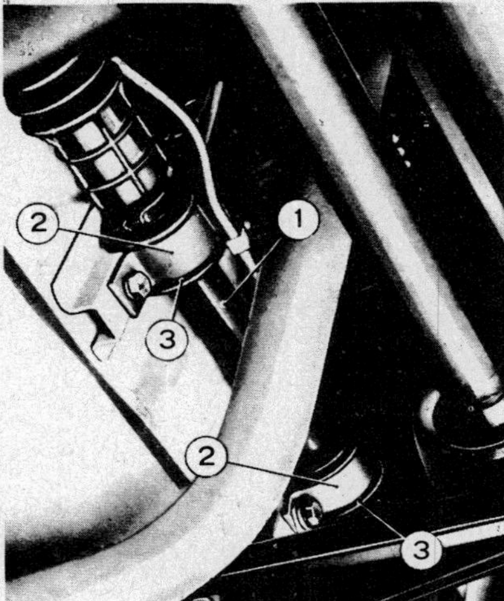

Steering box assembly in vehicle

1. Steering box
2. Steering box to body mounting brackets
3. Rubber cushions

124 Sedan, Coupe and Spyder

Removal

1. Disconnect the battery.
2. Remove horn button and emblem cover.
3. Remove the steering wheel retaining nut and pull the steering wheel from the shaft, using a wheel puller.
4. Remove the turn signal switch half covers and unscrew the retaining collar of the turn signal switch. This is located on the bracket which fixes the steering column to the body.
5. Disconnect the steering column bracket from the ignition switch (threaded ring) and remove the retaining collar of the turn signal switch.
6. Remove the screw which clamps the steering column to the worm shaft and remove the steering column from inside the car.
7. Unscrew the nuts which fix the left-hand steering arm and intermediate arm pins.
8. Remove the pins with an appropriate puller.
9. Remove the steering box from the body by removing the three mounting screws.

NOTE: *Shims can be placed on the steering box bolts to ensure proper alignment. Note the number and placement of such shims.*

Disassembly

1. Drain the oil from the steering box.
2. Using a puller, remove the drop arm from the roller shaft.
3. Remove the roller shaft cover, complete with roller shaft adjusting screw, adjusting disc, lockwasher and locknut.

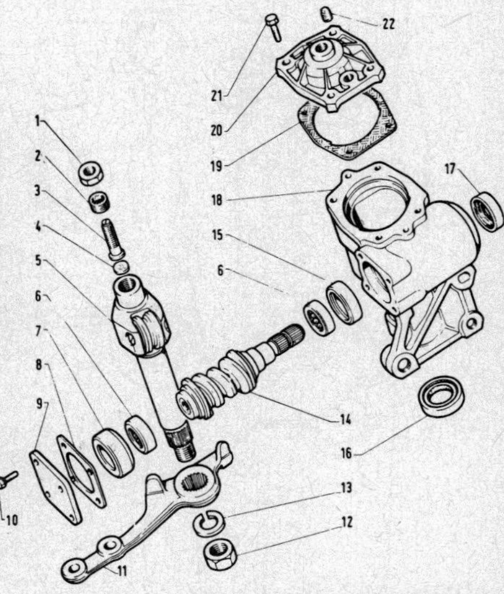

Exploded view of newer type 124 steering gear.

1. Adjusting screw nut
2. Screw ring
3. Adjusting screw
4. Plug
5. Roller shaft
6. Ball bearings
7. Bearing retainer
8. Shims
9. Worm screw thrust cover
10. Cover screws
11. Pitman arm
12. Nut, pitman arm to roller shaft
13. Washer
14. Worm screw
15. Bearing retainer
16. Roller shaft seal
17. Steering column seal
18. Steering gear housing
19. Gasket
20. Steering housing upper cover
21. Upper cover screws
22. Oil filter plug

4. Remove the roller shaft assembly from the steering box.
5. Remove the worm shaft thrust cover and the front bearing adjusting shims.
6. Turn the worm shaft to withdraw the front roller bearing.
7. Use a puller and remove the outer race of the rear roller bearing.
8. Remove the worm and shaft from the steering box along with the inner race of the inner roller bearing.

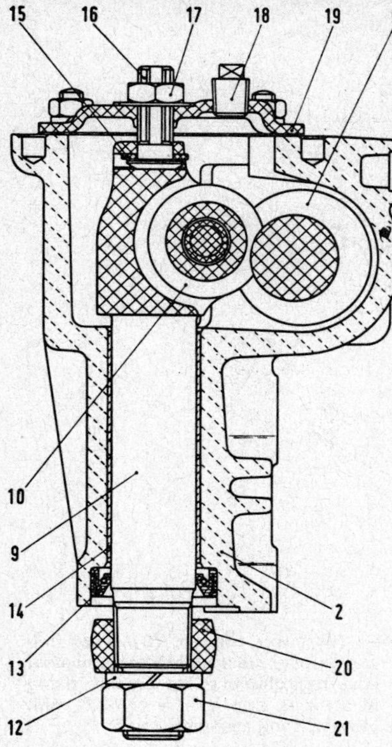

Section through steering box assembly on c/1 of roller shaft.

2. Steering box
5: Worm gear
9. Roller shaft
10. Roller
12. Spring washer under drop arm
13. Roller shaft oil seal
14. Roller shaft bushing
15. Roller shaft adjusting disc
16. Roller shaft adjusting screw
17. Locknut
18. Plug
19. Steering box cover
20. Drop arm
21. Drop arm nut

Fit the steering box cover with roller shaft adjusting screw.

1. Adjusting screw locknut
2. Roller shaft adjusting screw
3. Roller shaft
4. Adjusting screw plate
5. Steering box cover studs
6. Lockwasher

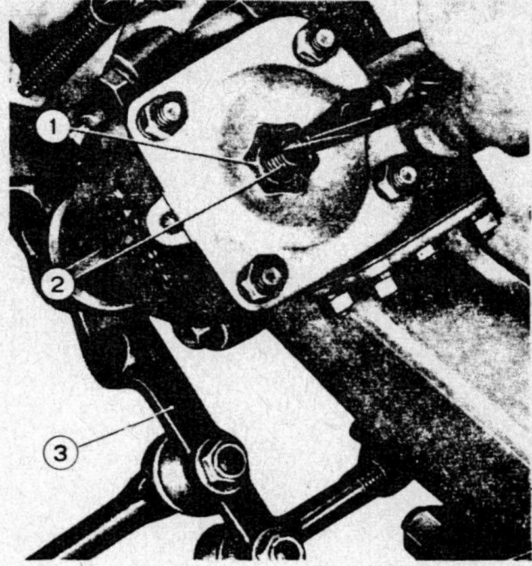

Adjusting worm and roller clearance

1. Lockwasher
2. Adjusting screw
3. Drop arm

9. Withdraw the outer race of the worm shaft rear roller bearing, which will release the shims under the race.

NOTE: *Shims are supplied for service to the worm shaft front and rear roller bearings, in thicknesses from 0.0039–0.0059 in.*

10. Remove the roller shaft oil seal. If the roller shaft bushings are worn, extract these.

Assembly

Check the clearance between bushings and roller shaft. This should be 0.00031–0.00201 in. (0.0039 in. max.). After pressing the bushings into the steering box, they should be reamed to correct diameter (1.1298–1.1306 in.).

1. Drive in the roller shaft bushings.
2. Fit the shims and outer race of the roller shaft rear bearing into the box, using a drift.
3. The same number and placement of shims, found at the time of disassembly, must be used.
4. Fit the inner races of the two roller bearings to the worm and install the worm in the box.
5. Drive the outer race of the front roller bearing into the box and fit the thrust cover.
6. Place shims between the thrust cover and the box as required.
7. Check the rotational torque of the worm shaft, which must be 0.09–0.47 ft lb. If the torque is lower than the specification, reduce the shims; if higher, increase the shims.
8. Fit the roller shaft oil seal.
9. Fit the roller shaft cover with adjusting plate, lockwasher and locknut.
10. Temporarily fit the drop arm to the roller shaft.
11. With the steering box on the bench, the drop arm should be free to rotate through 30° 40' $\pm$1° 40' on either side of the central position.
12. Move the arm in both directions, and check that, through at least 30° in either direction, the clearance between roller and worm is nil.

NOTE: *The clearance adjustment between arm and roller must be made with drop arm in mid-position.*

13. If any clearance is present, eliminate it with the adjusting screw.
14. When the clearance between worm and roller has been adjusted, check the turning torque of the worm shaft, which should now be 0.64–1.22 ft lbs., from the mid position of the drop arm, through a travel of at least 30° right or left. Turning torque should be $\leq$ 50 ft lbs. beyond the angle of 30°, up to the limit of arm travel.
15. During worm and roller adjustment, if the correct mesh does not exist between worm and roller, shims must be inserted to give correct contact.
16. Repeat the adjustment of the worm bearing and the worm and roller.
17. Finally, key the drop arm to the roller shaft, and torque the retaining nut to 173.5 ft lbs.
18. Fill the steering box with a 0.23 qt. of Fiat W 90 oil and fit the plug tightly.

Installation

1. Insert the steering column through the opening in the dashboard.
2. Fit the end of the worm shaft of the steering box to the steering column.

NOTE: *If the car is fitted with an anti-theft key switch, fit the steering shaft so that the keyway is on the left.*

3. Fit the steering box to the body and do not tighten the nuts.
4. Be sure to replace the shims in the proper position.
5. Lock the end of the steering shaft over the splined worm shaft.
6. Replace the supporting bracket to the steering column and connect it to the instrument panel, without tightening the nuts.
7. Connect the left-hand intermediate and side rod pins to the drop arm and secure them with self-locking nuts.
8. Fit the steering wheel temporarily, and turn the wheel several times to steady and settle the assembly.
9. Tighten the steering box mounting nuts.
10. Fit the turn signal switch to the bracket and steering column.
11. Attach the steering column bracket to the instrument panel.
12. Be sure the front wheels are positioned straight ahead, and fit the steering wheel, with spokes horizontal.
13. Stake the nut in place.
14. Connect the turn signal switch and the ignition switch.
15. Fit the two half collars to the turn signal switch and replace the horn button and emblem.

124 Special, Sport Coupe and Sport Spyder

Removal, disassembly, assembly and installation procedures are basically like for the 124 Sedan. During installation, check that no play exists between the bracket and column on the side opposite the bearing on the steering wheel side. Also be sure the universal joints do not bind the steering linkage.

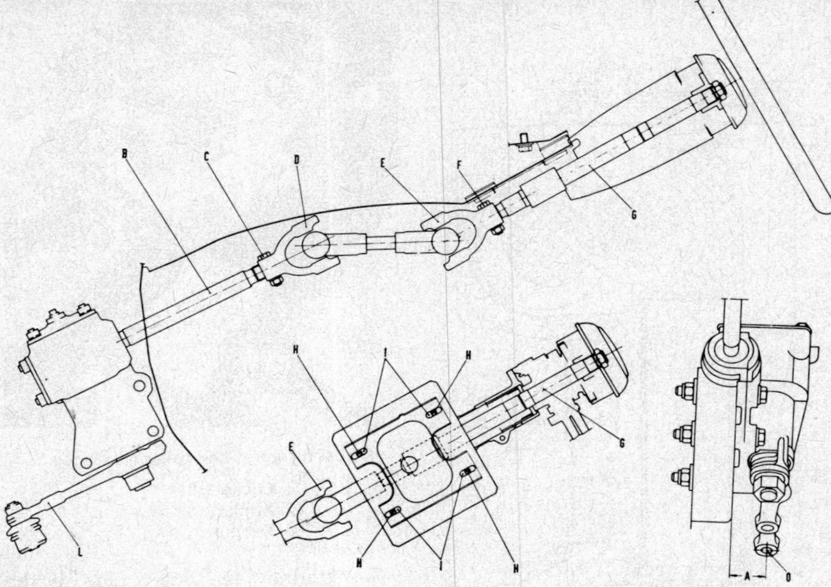

Steering components, Fiat 124 Coupe and Spider. (B) lower column; (C) lower universal joint fork bolt; (D and E) universal joint forks; (F) upper steering column universal joint fork bolt; (G) upper steering column; (H) steering column guide bracket fixing screws; (I) slots; (L) steering arm; (O) center of steering arm eye. A = 42.5 mm. (1.67") approx. This dimension must be respected when fitting assembly to car.

Adjusting worm and sector gear lash (850)

1. Oil filler plug
2. Sector adjusting screw

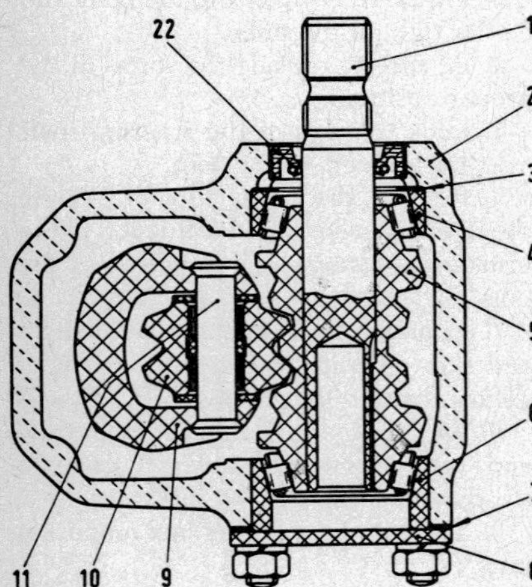

Section through steering box assembly on c/ l of worm shaft.

1. Steering shaft
2. Steering box
3. Worm upper bearing shim
4. Upper roller bearing
5. Worm
6. Lower roller bearing
7. Worm lower bearing shim
8. Worm thrust cover
9. Roller shaft
10. Roller
11. Roller pin

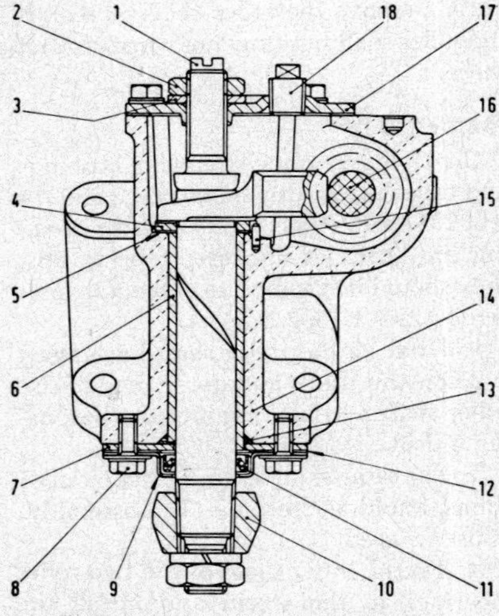

Sectional view of 850 steering gear

1. Sector adjusting screw
2. Locknut
3. Plain washer
4. Thrust washer
5. Shims
6. Eccentric bushing
7. Bushing shim
8. Shim screws
9. Seal cover
10. Pitman arm
11. Oil seal
12. Shim packing
13. Upper oil seal
14. Steering housing
15. Washer (4) location dowel
16. Worm
17. Cover
18. Oil filter plug

850

Removal

1. Pry off the horn button by inserting a screwdriver between the button and wheel hub.
2. Disconnect the horn and remove the steering wheel, using a wheel puller.
3. Working from the luggage compartment, loosen the steering column-to-worm screw.
4. Jack the front of the car up and support it on stands.
5. Disconnect the steering rods from the pitman arm.
6. Remove the mounting nuts and the steering gear.

Disassembly

1. Drain the oil from the steering gear.
2. Using a puller, remove the pitman arm.
3. Remove the worm sector and shaft assembly.
4. Remove the bearing lock and adjusting nut.
5. Slide the worm free, complete with roller bearing cones.
6. Tap out the roller bearing cups and oil seals with a driver.

Assembly

Check the clearance between bushing and sector shaft. The clearance of new parts should be 0–0.0016 in. Wear limit is 0.004 in.

NOTE: *Steering worm and sector are assembled with a touch fit at tooth flank. Adjustment is by turning the eccentric bushing on the worm sector.*

Assembly is the reverse of disassembly, noting the following points. New bushings should always be reamed to obtain specified clearance. Thoroughly wash all components and lubricate them.

Adjustment

This procedure is valid for adjustment after overhaul or as a routine procedure.

1. Disconnect the pitman arm.
2. Back out the screw which retains the shim.
3. Turn the eccentric bushing, through the shim, to move the sector toward the worm.
4. Bushing rotation should allow subsequent insertion of retaining screws in the shim.
5. Should the shim screws already be in the last hole, move the shim one serration on, then secure.
6. If too much play exists at the worm bearings, turn the lower adjuster nut, locking it in place after adjustment.
7. Use a cotter pin to lock the nut.
8. The sector and worm teeth should mesh perfectly.
9. Add or remove shims to move the sector as required. These shims, under the thrust washer, are available in 0.0039 in. thickness.
10. Replace any seal which is damaged.

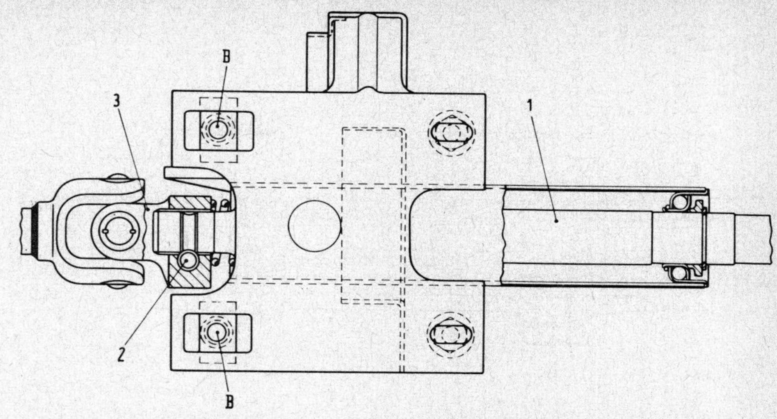

Schematic view of 850 Sp. series (1970-71) collapsible steering column

1. Steering column upper section
2. Attaching screw, yoke to steering column upper section
3. Yoke
B. Attaching screws steering column support to body (upon installation tighten screws until screw heads are twisted off).

124 Sport Series (1971) and

850 Sport Series (1971)

These models are equipped with a collapsible steering column, consisting of three sections, coupled by two universal joints.

NOTE: *When installing this steering column on a car, it is necessary to twist the heads off the stretchbolts.*

BRAKE SYSTEMS

128

Master Cylinder

Removal

1. Remove the spare wheel from the engine compartment.
2. Remove the fluid reservoir cover and plug the outlet to the master cylinder in order to keep the reservoir from draining.
3. Disconnect the reservoir-to-master cylinder tubes.
4. Disconnect the fluid delivery tubing to the front and rear brakes, removing the fastening screws.
5. Remove both nuts and spring washers which secure the master cylinder to the body and remove the master cylinder.

Installation

Installation is the reverse of removal.

Overhaul

1. Disconnect the fluid inlet connector from the cylinder.
2. Remove the boot from its groove in the cylinder body.
3. Back out the set screws and the end plug.
4. Remove from cylinder body the piston return springs, cups, seal rings, and spacers.
5. Check the valve carriers, reaction springs, and rubber seal rings.
6. Inspect the cylinder bore for pits or roughness. If this condition exists, hone the bore to prevent excessive wear of seals or fluid loss.

NOTE: *If the cylinder bore is badly scored or corroded, the cylinder body must be replaced.*

Assembly

Be sure to lubricate all parts with brake fluid.

Assembly is the reverse of disassembly.

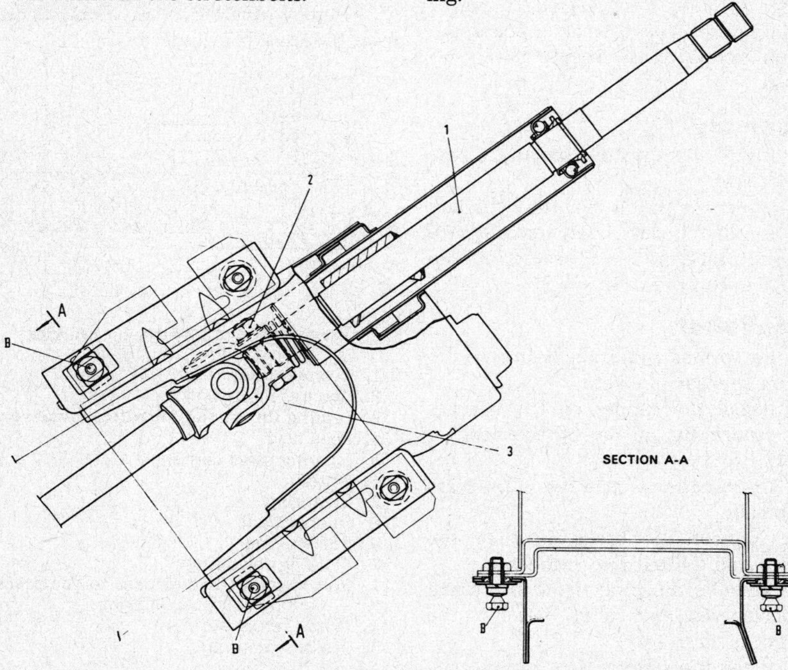

Schematic view of 124 Sp. series (1970-71) collapsible steering column

1. Steering column upper section
2. Screw, fork to steering column section
3. Fork
B. Screws, steering column support to body (to be tightened until screw heads are twisted off).

Front Brakes

Calipers

Removal

1. Place the front of the car on stands and remove the front wheels.

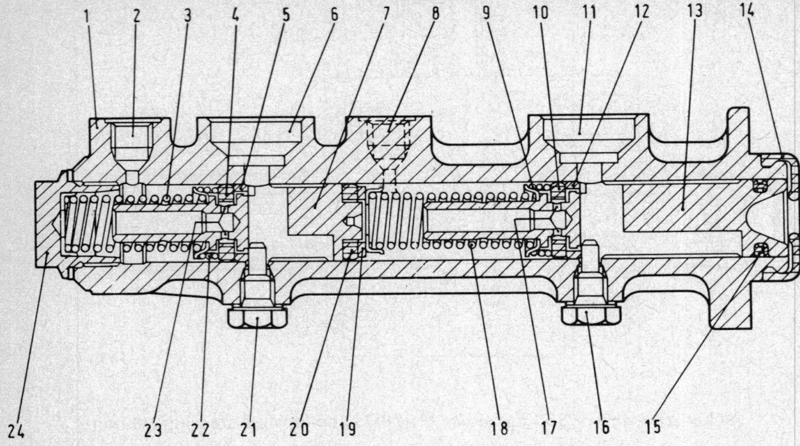

Side section of brake master cylinder

1. Master cylinder body
2. Pressure regulator delivery line connector seat
3. Floating ring carrier return spring
4. Floating ring
5. Spacer
6. Reservoir line connector seat
7. Floating ring carrier
8. Connector seats for front caliper delivery lines
9. Ring pressure spring
10. Floating ring
11. Reservoir line connector seat
12. Spacer
13. Floating ring carrier
14. Dust boot
15. Seal ring
16. Valve carrier stop screw
17. Floating ring compression fluid passage ports
18. Valve carrier return spring
19. Plain washer
20. Seal ring
21. Valve carrier stop screw
22. Ring pressure spring
23. Floating ring compression fluid passage ports
24. End plug

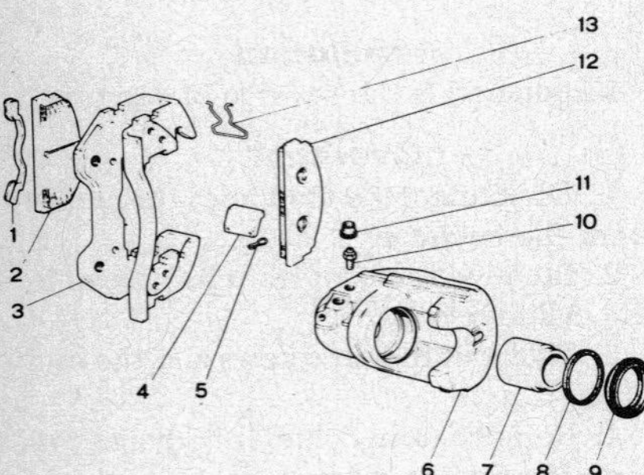

Details of front brake caliper

1. Spring
2. Lining pad
3. Caliper support bracket
4. Caliper locking block
5. Cotter pin
6. Caliper body
7. Piston
8. Seal
9. Piston dust boot
10. Bleeder screw
11. Bleeder screw dust cap
12. Lining pad
13. Caliper spring fastener

2. Plug the outlet ports in the brake fluid reservoir.
3. Disconnect the brake hose from the caliper.
4. Remove the cotter pins from the locking blocks.
5. Remove the caliper blocks.
6. Remove the caliper, brake linings, and springs.

Disassembly

1. Remove the dust cap.
2. Blow the piston out from the caliper cylinder by directing a jet of compressed air into the fluid inlet connector.
3. Remove the seal.
4. Check the piston, as well as the caliper cylinder for signs of scoring or binding. If excessive wear appears, the caliper and piston assembly should be replaced.

Assembly

1. Install the piston seal into the caliper seat.
2. Insert the piston into the cylinder.
3. Install the dust boot, making sure that the boot edge is well seated into the groove cut in the caliper body.

Installation

1. Fit springs and brake linings to the caliper support bracket.
2. Install the caliper on the bracket and secure by means of the locking blocks.
3. Insert cotter pins to retain the locking blocks.
4. Connect the brake hose to the caliper and tighten the connector.
5. Remove the plugs from the brake fluid reservoir and fill the latter to the correct level.
6. Bleed the system.

124

The Fiat 124 model uses a four-wheel disc brake system, while the 850 Spider and Coupe have disc brakes on the front and drum brakes on the rear. The 850 sedan uses drum brakes on all four wheels.

All four disc brakes are self-adjusting and rear brakes are equipped with a regulator, operated by a torsion bar for proper rear wheel trim during braking.

A vacuum servo (power brake) system acts on all four wheels to lessen the required pedal pressure. Maximum runout for brake discs is 0.006 in. (0.15 mm.). To correct for excessive runout, machine the disc. Thickness, however, must be at least 0.374 in. (9.5 mm.). Discs showing damage, deep scoring, or wear exceeding 0.019 in. (0.5 mm.) on either face must be changed.

Friction pads can be inspected for wear from outside the caliper. If damaged, or worn to 0.06 in. (1.5 mm.) (0.12 in., or 3 mm. for the 1600S), replacement is neccessary. When removing reusable pads, mark them to be sure the inside and outside pads are assembled in their proper positions. Make sure that front and rear wheels have pads of the same type as marked by the manufacturer.

Master Cylinder

Removal

1. Remove the reservoir cover and plug the fluid outlet port.
2. Disconnect the pipe between the reservoir and master cylinder.
3. Remove the three way connection from the master cylinder.

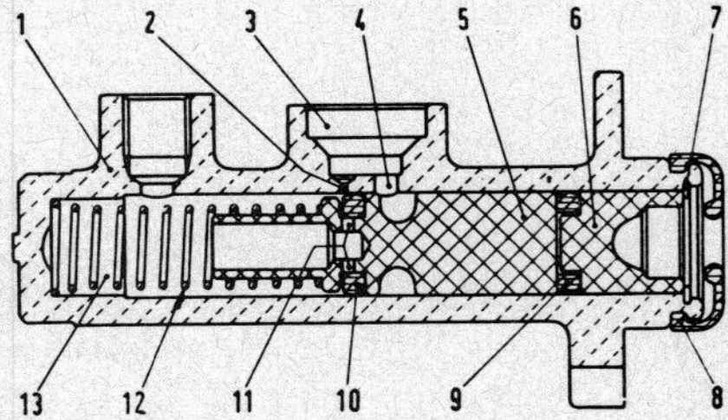

Cross section of 124 master cylinder

1. Cylinder body
2. Compensating port
3. Seating for union of line from reservoir
4. Feed port
5. Floating valve carrier
6. Piston
7. Snap-ring
8. Rubber boot
9. Sealing ring
10. Floating valve ring
11. Port to allow fluid to pass to compress floating valve sealing ring
12. Piston return spring
13. Pressure chamber

4. Unbolt the master cylinder from the firewall.

Disassembly

1. Remove the boot from its groove in the cylinder body.

2. Remove the snap-ring which holds the piston.

3. From the cylinder body, remove the following parts: piston, sealing ring, valve ring carrier, valve ring and piston return spring.

Assembly

1. Inspect the bore of the cylinder and hone any deep irregularities.

2. The honing must be slight, otherwise the bore will be increased, in which case the cylinder body will have to be replaced.

3. Clean all parts thoroughly in brake fluid.

4. Assemble the parts, reversing the disassembly order.

Installation

Installation is the reverse of removal. Do not forget to bleed the brake system.

Front Brakes

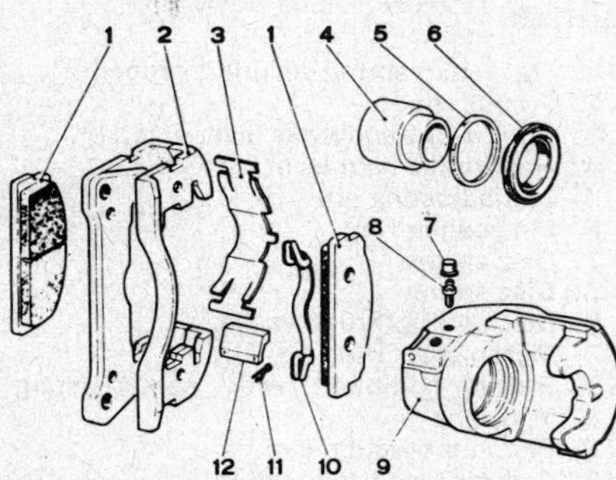

Exploded view of 124 front brake caliper and bracket.

1. Friction pad
2. Caliper bracket
3. Flat radial spring to secure caliper
4. Piston
5. Seal
6. Piston protecting cap
7. Bleed connection protecting cap
8. Bleed connection
9. Caliper body
10. Spring
11. Cotter pin
12. Caliper locking block

Removing disc pads on 124

1. Brake disc
2. Friction pad locking spring
3. Caliper support bracket
4. Friction pad

Caliper Removal

1. Jack the car, put it on stands, and remove the wheels.

2. Plug the outlet port of the brake fluid reservoir.

3. Disconnect the brake hose from the caliper by unscrewing the junction.

4. Remove the cotter pins, which hold the locking blocks in place, and remove the locking blocks.

5. Remove the caliper flat springs, friction pads and springs.

6. Without removing the brake disc from the car, check the brake disc runout.

7. If there are any deep score marks on the disc, be sure these do not exceed 0.-019 in. Past this dimension, discs must be replaced.

Caliper Disassembly

1. Remove the dust boot.

2. Direct a jet of air into the fluid inlet coupling to remove the piston from the caliper cylinder.

3. Remove the seal.

NOTE: *When pistons are removed, piston seals must always be changed.*

4. Wash all parts in hot water and dry with compressed air.

Friction Pad Replacement

Friction pads must be replaced when their thickness is 0.059 in. or less. The caliper must be removed to change pads. There are two types of pads, indentified by an orange or black paint stripe. Only pads of the same class may be used on any one car. When fitting pads, be sure that the inner distance between pads is not less than 0.413 in.

Brake shoe clearance adjustment

A—Adjusting cam nut angle. It must be: 20 degrees for used linings and 25 degrees for new linings

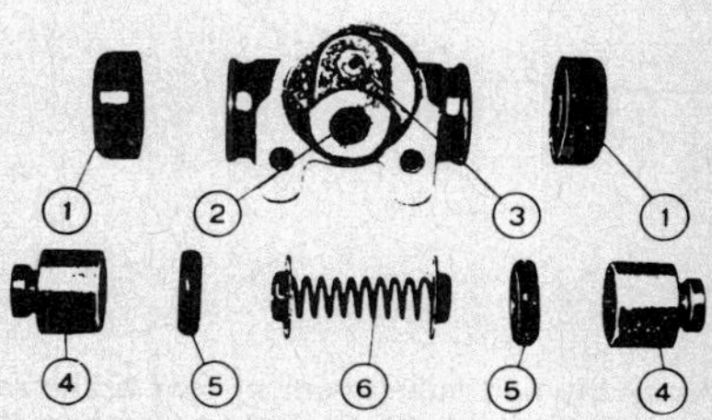

Exploded view of wheel cylinder components.

1. Rubber boots
2. Fluid intake connection
3. Bleeder screw
4. Plunger
5. Valve rings
6. Plunger spring and cups

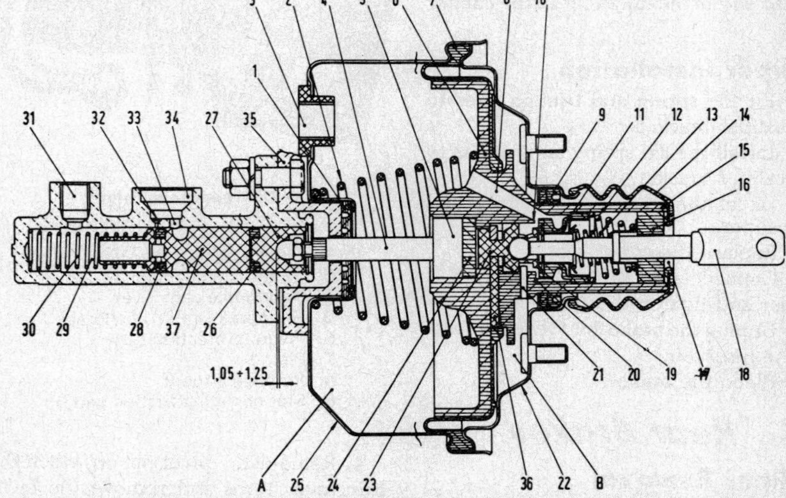

Components of power brake system, 124. (1) front seal; (2) piston return spring; (3) vacuum line union; (4) piston rod; (5) working piston; (6) actuating piston; (7) diaphragm; (8) vacuum duct; (9) rear seal; (10) vacuum port; (11) valve; (12) piston-valve return spring; (13) retaining valve return spring; (14) guide tube rubber boot; (15) actuating piston guide tube; (16) filter element; (17) servo unit air intake; (18) valve control rod; (19) atmospheric pressure passage; (20) vacuum hole; (21) vacuum and air passage; (22) rear body; (23) piston-valve; (24) reaction disc; (25) front body; (26) seal ring; (27) hydraulic piston; (28) floating ring-valve; (29) master cylinder; (30) hydraulic piston return spring; (31) union for connection to 3-way brake distributor; (32) compensating hole; (33) master cylinder inlet port; (34) union for line from reservoir to master cylinder; (35) mounting flange; (36) piston retaining plate; (37) floating ring-valve carrier; (A) front chamber; (B) rear chamber.

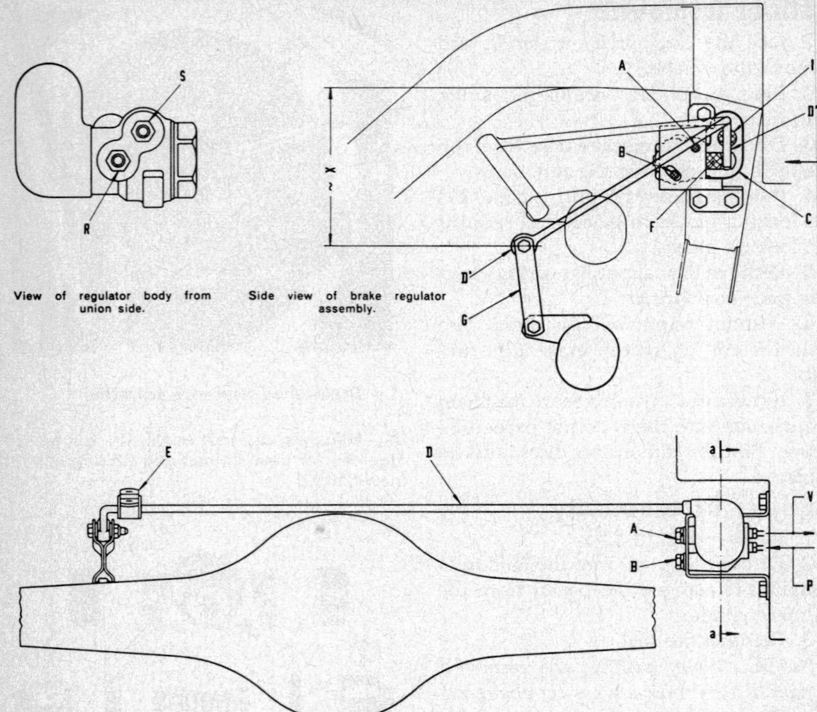

Assembly and adjustment of rear brake regulator, 124. (A and B) regulator mounting screws; (C) boot; (D, D′, D″) torsion bar; (E) torsion bar body mounting; (F) piston; (G) link to bracket on axle; (I) pin; (P) line to master cylinder; (R) union for line from master cylinder; (S) union for line to rear brakes; (V) line to rear brakes.

Caliper Assembly

1. Fit the piston seal to the caliper cylinder.
2. Insert the piston and push it to the far end of the cylinder.
3. Fit the dust boot, making sure that the lip enters the undercut in the caliper body.

Caliper Installation

1. Fit the spring and friction pads to the caliper bracket.
2. Install the flat spring and caliper to the caliper bracket.
3. Insert the locking blocks to retain the caliper.
4. Replace the cotter pins.
5. Connect the brake hose to the caliper and tighten the connection.
6. Unplug the brake fluid reservoir and fill the reservoir.
7. Bleed the brakes.

Rear Brakes

Caliper Removal

Rear caliper removal is the same as front caliper removal.

Caliper Disassembly

1. Remove the dust boot and unscrew the piston from the handbrake plunger.
2. To do this, insert a screwdriver into the slot in the head of the piston.
3. Remove the seal and the handbrake gaiter.

Fiat 124 rear brake caliper

1. Caliper body
2. Bleed connection
3. Gaiter
4. Handbrake cam lever
5. Handbrake cable anchorage
6. Piston protection boot
7. Piston
A. Reference mark
B. Slot engaging friction pad rib

4. Remove the pivot pin on which the cam lever turns and remove the lever along with the plunger seal, disc spring and spring thrust washer.

NOTE: *When the pistons are removed from the caliper, the piston seals must always be changed.*

Caliper Assembly

1. Fit the self-adjusting plunger with seal, spring and thrust washer.
2. Install the handbrake cam lever and fit the pivot pin in the fork of the caliper body.
3. Fit the handbrake lever gaiter.
4. Replace the rubber piston seal in the caliper body.
5. Screw in the piston until it is properly seated and the mark cut in the piston is opposite the bleed connection.

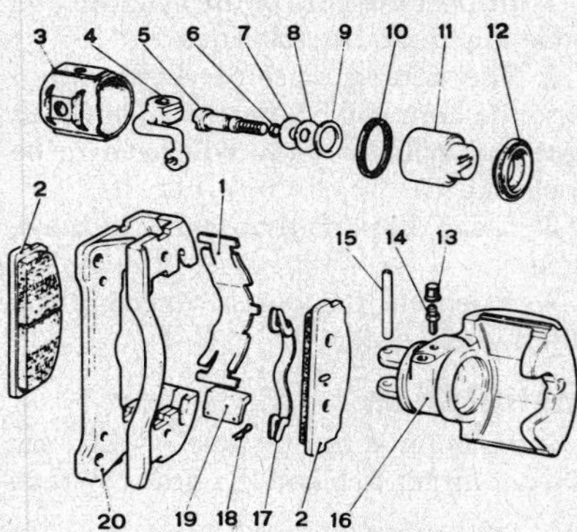

Exploded view of 124 rear brake caliper and bracket.

1. Flat radial spring securing caliper
2. Friction pad
3. Boot over handbrake lever end
4. Handbrake cam lever
5. Self-adjusting pin
6. Pin sealing ring
7. Disc spring
8. Disc spring
9. Disc spring thrust washer
10. Piston seal
11. Piston complete with self-adjusting device
12. Piston protection cap
13. Cap for bleed connection
14. Bleed connection
15. Handbrake cam lever pivot pin
16. Caliper body
17. Spring
18. Cotter pin
19. Caliper locking block
20. Caliper bracket

Friction Pad Replacement

This operation is identical to pad replacement of front brakes.

Caliper Installation

Follow the procedure for front brake caliper installation. Connect the handbrake cable to the cam lever.

Power Brake Booster (124)

Fiat 124's are fitted with a power brake booster operating on all four wheels. It utilizes depression in intake manifold vacuum to increase the normal brake pedal pressure exerted by the driver.

Rear Brake Pressure Regulator

Installation

Before connecting it into the brake line, attach brake regulator to its bracket with two screws , but do not tighten them until a later adjustment is made. Attach torsion bar to body with bracket. Locate end of torsion bar at a distance of 5.78 in. (5.0 in. for the station wagon) from the underside of the body, then lift boot and rotate the regulator on screw until the opposite end of the bar lightly contacts piston projecting from the regulator. Holding the regulator in this position, tighten screws A and B, coat the area of the bar that contacts the piston and pin with grease, and place boot in position.

Attach link to end of torsion bar and to the lug on the axle housing. Complete assembly by connecting brake line from the master cylinder to lower union of regulator, and line which feeds the rear calipers to upper union

Handbrake Adjustment (All Models)

Using the lever, disengage the handbrake cable. Pull the lever up two notches. Unscrew the locknut on the tensioner and turn the adjusting nut until the cable is stretched. Tighten the locknut. The cable is correctly tensioned when the car is held by a movement of the lever through three notches.

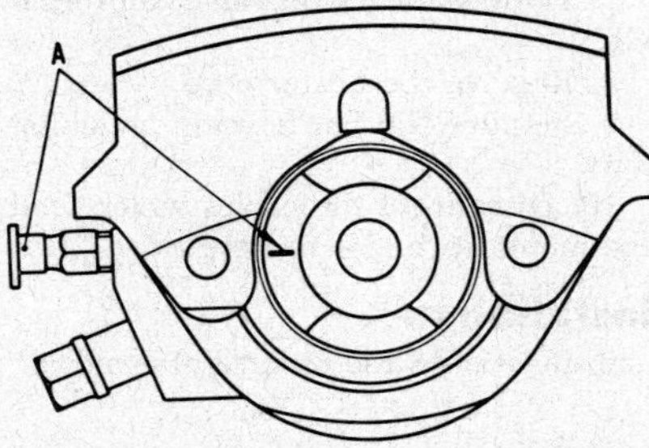

850 disc brake caliper diagram— Mark (A) is to be aligned toward the bleeder screw.

850 Spyder and Coupe, Sport Spyder

These cars employ disc brakes at the front and drum brakes at the rear. The disc brakes require no adjustment, but the friction pads should be replaced when they are worn to a thickness of 0.08 in. (2 mm.) for the 850 and 1100R, and 0.12 in. (3 mm.) for the 1500.

Front Brakes

Pad Replacement

1. Remove the caliper from the mounting brackets.
2. Remove the retaining plates and slide off the pins.
3. Tip the clamps to remove the caliper from the bracket.
4. Replace the pads and push the piston to the bottom of the cylinder.
5. Make sure that the mark on the piston faces the bleeder screw. Replace the caliper.

Brake Calipers

The only service which can be performed to brake calipers is the renewal of seals and pistons. To remove pistons from front calipers, remove the nut and depress the pin at the end. Replace calipers and bleed brakes.

Rear Brakes

Drum Inspection

Jack the car, put it on stands, and remove the rear wheels. Remove the brake drums. Check for scoring or out-of-round.

850 Sedan

The shoes of these drum brakes are self-centering and no manual adjustments are needed to center the shoes with respect to the drum.

To adjust brakes, apply full pedal to center the shoes, then, with the pedal depressed, turn the adjustment cams to full stop. While keeping pedal down, turn cams backward a fraction of a turn at a time until wheel rotates freely with pedal released. If any brake lines have been disconnected, or the pedal operation is spongy, bleed the brake system.

Master Cylinder

Disassembly

1. Remove the master cylinder from the car.
2. Remove the rubber boot from its retaining flange and take out the rod.
3. Remove the boot retaining flange, two gaskets and the plunger stop plate.
4. Remove the following from the master cylinder body: plunger, valve, valve ring carrier, valve ring and return spring.

Assembly

Assembly is the reverse of disassembly.

Wheel Cylinders

Disassembly

Jack the car, put on stands, and remove the wheels and brake drums. Unfasten and remove the rubber boots. The plungers, valve rings and cups on the ends of the reaction spring will be pushed out by the expansion of the spring.

Assembly

Assembly is the reverse of disassembly. Valve rings should be renewed and all parts lubricated before assembly.

Brake Drums

Inspect drums for scoring or an out-of-round condition. Bleed the brake system following any service to the system.

Shoe Clearance Adjustment

Jack the car, put on stands, and push the brake pedal to lock the shoes against the drum. Rotate the adjustment nuts outward (to stop). Rotate them back about 20° and be sure the wheels turn freely.

Bleeding

All Models

1. Fill the reservoir and system with brake fluid.
2. Clean all dirt from the bleeder screws and remove the protective caps.
3. Install a bleeder hose over the fitting in the brake caliper or the wheel cylinder and submerge the other end of the bleeder hose into a clean jar half filled with brake fluid.
4. Loosen the bleeder screw a few turns and have helper press the brake pedal down quickly, allowing it to return slowly.
5. Do this several times until no more air bubbles escape from the rubber hose.
6. Keeping the brake pedal depressed, remove the bleeder hose and tighten the bleeder screw.
7. Clean the bleeder screw and refit the protective cap.
8. Repeat steps 2, 3, 4 and 5 on the other wheels making sure that the reservoir is full after each wheel cylinder is bled.

CHASSIS ELECTRICAL

Windshield Wiper Motor (124)

Removal

The windshield wiper motor is removed from the engine compartment side in the following manner.

1. Unscrew the left-hand spacer nut and remove the left-hand wiper blade and arm.
2. Remove the retaining nuts from the bracket and pull the motor back slightly.
3. Remove the clip connecting the right half-link to the motor and remove the motor.

Installation

Installation is the reverse of removal.

Heater

Removal

1. Drain the engine cooling system and the heater radiator.
2. The lower heater lever must be moved to the right.

3. Loosen the hose clips on the flow and return pipes to the heater.

4. From the engine compartment, remove the rubber seals on the heater pipes.

5. Remove the valve cable from the clip.

6. Disconnect the yellow cable to the fan.

7. Release the spring clips and remove the fan housing.

8. Lower the radiator and remove the air intake shutter control cable.

9. Remove the heater from the car.

Installation

Installation is the reverse of removal. Be sure that the gasket between fan and body is positioned correctly. Run the engine and fill the radiator.

Windshield Wiper Motor (850)

Removal

1. Remove the instrument cluster.

2. Remove the lockrings of the control switches and ornamental plate.

3. Remove the instrument panel lining which is fastened with tight clips.

4. The wiper assembly can be removed through the opening in the instrument panel.

Installation

Installation is the reverse of removal.

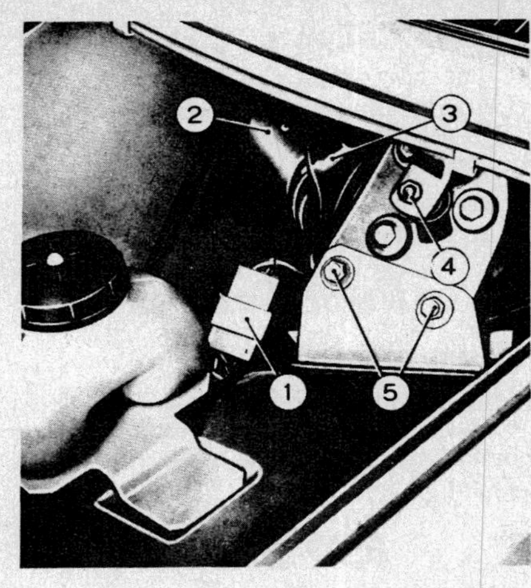

Windshield wiper motor assembly, installed on the car.

1. 4-way blade-contact connector
2. Motor assembly
3. Dust boot
4. Wiper arm actuating lever nut
5. Screws, attaching wiper assembly to mounting bracket

Windshield Wipers 128

Removal

1. Remove the wiper blades and arms.

2. Back out the attaching nuts and remove the wiper blade pivot spacers.

3. Remove the spare wheel.

4. Remove the speedometer cable clip from the body.

5. Remove the screws which attach the wiper assembly to the mounting bracket.

6. Disconnect the connector block and remove the unit completely.

Installation

Installation is the reverse of removal.

Heater Assembly 128

Removal

1. Completely drain the cooling system.

2. Loosen the clips which retain the inlet and outlet hoses.

3. Remove the screw and nut from the air shutter actuating rod.

4. Remove the air conveyor.

5. Slide out the radiator housing spring clips.

6. Withdraw the outside shutter actuating rod.

7. Remove the heater valve control cable.

8. Remove the heater core.

9. Remove the fan housing attaching nuts.

10. Disconnect the cables which feed the motor at the fan switch.

Installation

Installation is the reverse of removal.

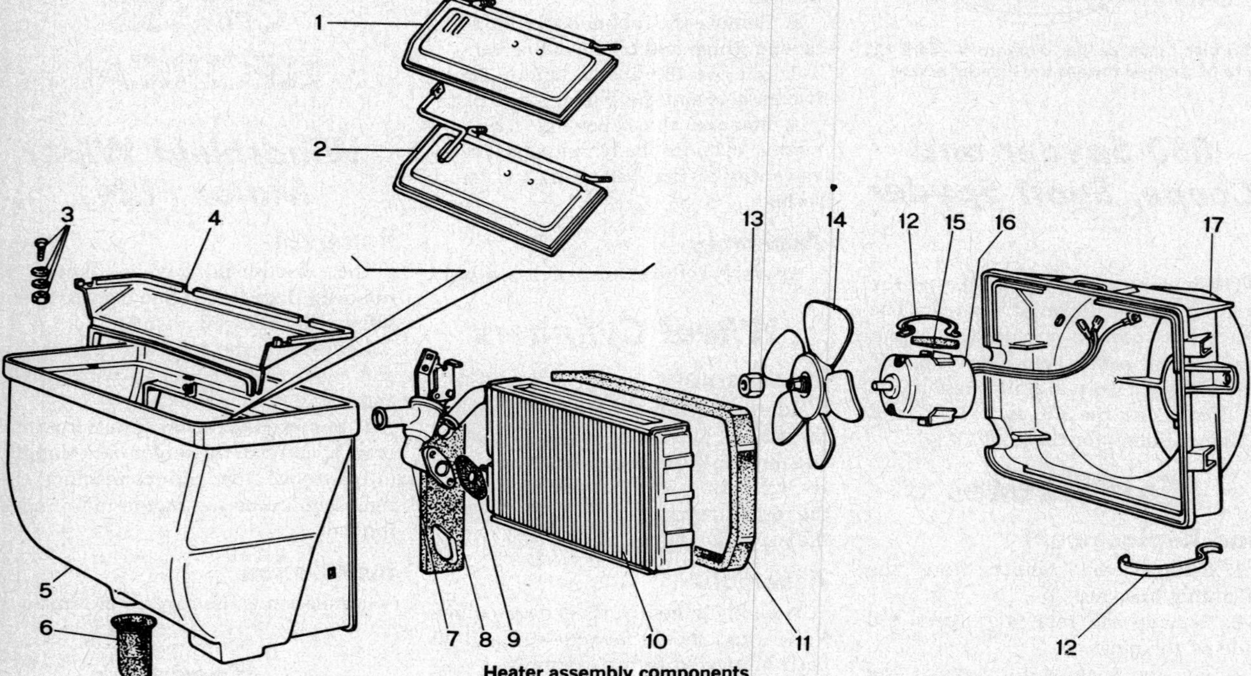

Heater assembly components

1. Upper shutter, for fresh air admission to car interior
2. Lower shutter, for air flow onto radiator (10)
3. Attaching screw, washers and nut
4. Water shield
5. Housing
6. Water drain plug
7. Valve
8. Gasket
9. Gasket
10. Radiator
11. Gasket
12. Spring clips
13. Nut, attaching impeller to motor
14. Impeller
15. Rubber pad
16. Motor
17. Fan housing

HONDA

Index

INTRODUCTION

Honda Motor Company has been selling motorcycles in the United States for over a decade, earning the distinction of number one in sales in the motorcycle world. Until 1971 its automotive sales were limited to the Asian sphere. However this was changed with the introduction of the Honda 600. This two-cylinder "mini" was first marketed on the West Coast and Hawaii, and as 1971 drew to a close, Honda placed 19th in import sales. After Honda's decision to sell its models on a nationwide basis, the 600 rose to 12th in import sales by the middle of 1972.

Both models, the 600 sedan and Z600 coupe, share the same front-wheel drive, air-cooled SOHC engine. Only the sheet metal and styling, in the usual American practice, are changed—with everything done in miniature. Excellent examples of clever design and engineering, the 600's are cheap to operate and maintain.

SERIAL NUMBER IDENTIFICATION

Vehicle and Engine Identification

Year, Model Number & Name	Starting Chassis Serial Number	Starting Engine Number
1971 AN 600, 2dr sedan Z 600, 2dr coupe	1,000,001	1,000,001

Vehicle Identification Number

Z & AN 600

Honda 600 vehicle-identification numbers are mounted on the front edge of the instrument panel, visible from the outside. The first four (Z 600) or five (AN 600) digits indicate the model. The remaining numbers indicate production sequence.

Engine Serial Number

Z & AN 600

The engine serial number is stamped on the crankcase. The first five digits indicate engine-model identification. The remaining numbers refer to production sequence.

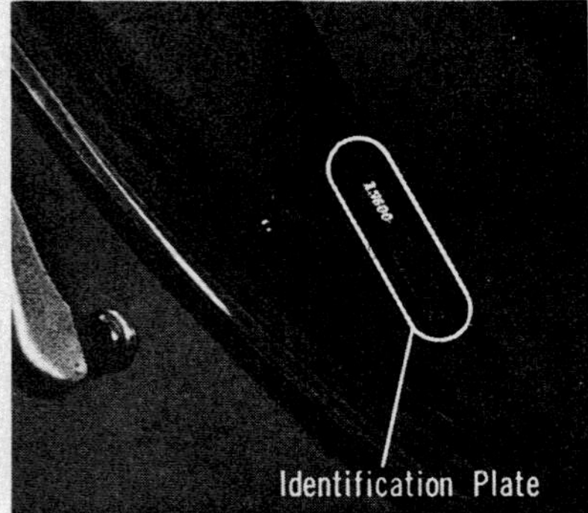

Vehicle Identification Number

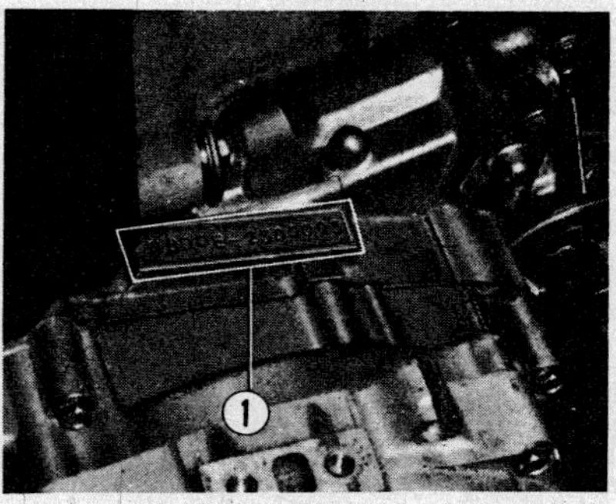

1. Engine number

Engine Serial Number

MODEL IDENTIFICATION

Honda Sedan

GENERAL ENGINE SPECIFICATIONS

Model	Year	Engine (cu in.) Displacement	Carburetor Type	Horsepower @ rpm	Bore x Stroke (in.)	Compression Ratio	Torque @ rpm (ft lbs)
Z & AN 600	1972	36.5 (598.4 cc.)	Keihin	32 @ 6,000	2.91 x 2.74	8.5:1	31.8 @ 4,000

TUNE-UP SPECIFICATIONS

When analyzing compression test results, look for uniformity among cylinders, rather than specific pressures.

Model	Engine Displacement Cu In. (cc)	SPARK PLUGS Type	Gap (in.)	Distributor Point Gap (in.)	Basic Ignition Timing (deg)	Intake Valve Opens (deg)	Fuel Pump Pressure (psi)	Idle Speed (rpm)	VALVE CLEARANCE (in.) In (cold)	Ex (cold)
Z & AN 600	36.5 (598.4 cc)	NGK B-8ES ND W-24ES	0.028-0.032	0.012-0.015	10 BTDC	5 BTDC	2.062	1100-1200	0.004	0.004

CRANKSHAFT AND CONNECTING ROD SPECIFICATIONS

All measurements are given in inches.

Model	Engine Displacement Cu In. (cc)	Main Bearing Journal Dia.	CRANKSHAFT Main Bearing Oil Clearance	Shaft End-Play	Connecting Rod Side Clearance
Z & AN 600	36.5 (598.4 cc)	1.3386-1.3381	0.0003-0.0007	0.0059-0.0118	0.0047-0.0130

PISTON AND RING SPECIFICATIONS

All measurements are given in inches.

Model	Engine Displace. (cu in.)	Piston Clearance	Ring Gap Top Compression	Ring Gap Bottom Compression	Ring Gap Oil Control	Ring Side Clearance Top Compression	Ring Side Clearance Bottom Compression	Ring Side Clearance Oil Control
Z & AN 600	36.5 (598.4 cc)	0.0012	0.008-0.016	0.008-0.016	0.008-0.016	0.0018-0.0030	0.0006-0.0018	0.0006-0.0018

VALVE SPECIFICATIONS

Model	Engine Displacement Cu In. (cc)	Seat Angle (deg)	Face Angle (deg)	Outer Spring Free Length (in.)	Spring Installed Height (in.)	STEM TO GUIDE CLEARANCE (in.) Intake	Exhaust	STEM DIAMETER (in.) Intake	Exhaust
Z & AN 600	36.5 (598.4 cc)	45	45	1.764	1.764	0.0004-0.0016	0.0016-0.0028	0.2591-0.2595	0.2579-0.2583

ALTERNATOR AND REGULATOR SPECIFICATIONS

Model	ALTERNATOR Part No. or Manufacturer	Field Current @ 12 V (amps)	Output (amps) @ 5,000 rpm	REGULATOR Part No. or Manufacturer	Field Relay Yoke Gap (in.)	Field Relay Point Gap (in.)	Field Relay Volts to Close	Regulator Yoke Gap (in.)	Regulator Point Gap (in.)	Regulator Volts @ 5,000 rpm
Z & AN 600	LD 130-03 Hitachi	2	40	Tirril TL 1Z-33 Hitachi	0.008	0.016-0.020	8-10	0.035-0.039	0.016-0.020	13.5-14.5

BRAKE SPECIFICATIONS

All measurements are given in inches.

Model	Master Cylinder Bore	WHEEL CYLINDER OR CALIPER PISTON BORE				BRAKE DISC OR DRUM DIAMETER				New Pad or Lining Thickness
		Front		Rear		Front		Rear		
		Disc	Drum	Disc	Drum	Disc	Drum	Disc	Drum	
Z & AN 600	0.748	1.688	—	—	0.6248	7.17	—	—	7.087-7.126	0.406

— Not Applicable

TORQUE SPECIFICATIONS

All readings are given in ft-lbs.

Model	Engine Displacement Cu In. (cc)	Cylinder Head Bolts	Center Bearing Bolts	Crankcase Retaining Bolts	Crankshaft Pulley Bolts	Exhaust Manifold
Z & AN 600	36.5 (598.4 cc)	10 mm nuts—26.7-31.1 6 mm bolts—7.2-9.0	25.3-28.9	18.1-20.3	18	18.1-20.3

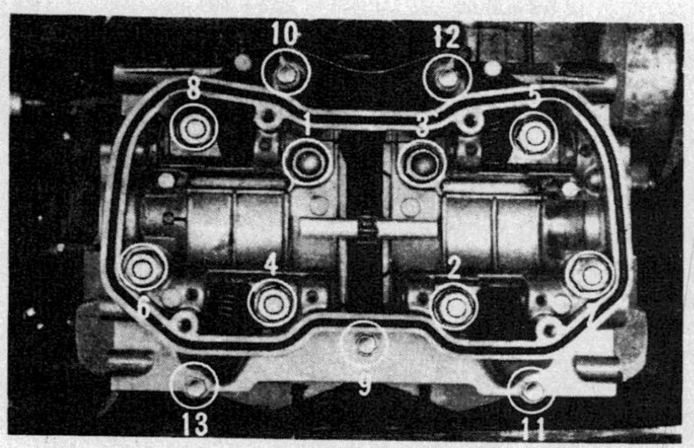

Cylinder Head

Standard Tightening Torque

Unless otherwise specified, the bolts and nuts should be tightened to the torque value listed below.

Bolt/Nut nominal diameter (mm)	Thread pitch (mm)	Torque (ft-lb)
4	0.70	1.45-2.15
5	0.90	3.25-5.05
6	1.00	5.80-8.70
8	1.25	14.5-20.0
9	1.25	22.0-29.0
10	1.25	29.0-39.0
12	1.25	50.5-61.5

Capacities

Model	Engine Displace. Cu In. (cc)	Engine Crankcase (qts)	Gasoline Tank (gals)
Z & AN 600	36.5 (598.4 cc)	3.2	6.9

BATTERY AND STARTER SPECIFICATIONS

Model	Engine Displacement Cu In. (cc)	BATTERY			STARTERS						
		Ampere Hour Capacity	Volts	Terminal Grounded	Lock Test			No-Load Test			Brush Spring Tension (oz)
					Amps	Volts	Torque (ft lbs)	Amps	Volts	RPM	
Z & AN 600	36.5 (598.4 cc)	45	12	Neg	460 or less	6	7.96	Less than 60	12	700 +	28

WHEEL ALIGNMENT

Model	Caster Pref Setting (deg)	Camber Pref Setting (deg)	Toe-In (in.)	Steering Axle Inclination (deg)	WHEEL PIVOT RATIO (deg)	
					Inner Wheel	Outer Wheel
Z & AN 600	1P	½P	0.078	13.6-14.5	35.20	27.55

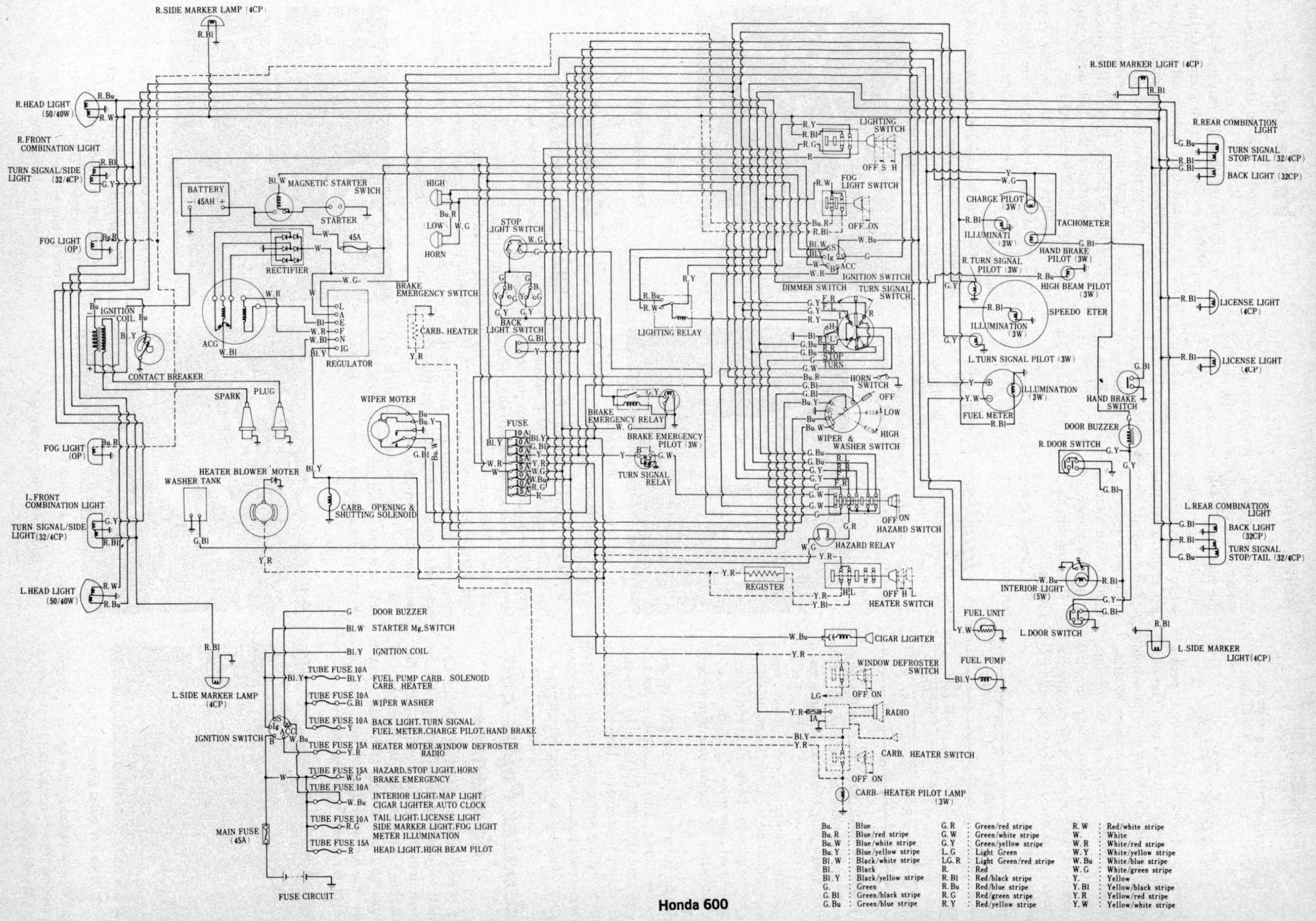
R.SIDE MARKER LAMP (4CP)
R.HEAD LIGHT (50/40W)
R.FRONT COMBINATION LIGHT
TURN SIGNAL/SIDE LIGHT (32/4CP)
FOG LIGHT (OP)
BATTERY 45AH
MAGNETIC STARTER SWICH
STARTER
45A
RECTIFIER
IGNITION COIL
ACG
CONTACT BREAKER
REGULATOR
SPARK PLUG
HIGH
LOW
HORN
BRAKE EMERGENCY SWITCH
CARB. HEATER
WIPER MOTER
HEATER BLOWER MOTER
WASHER TANK
CARB. OPENING & SHUTTING SOLENOID
L.FRONT COMBINATION LIGHT
L.HEAD LIGHT (50/40W)
L.SIDE MARKER LAMP (4CP)
STOP LIGHT SWITCH
BACK LIGHT SWITCH
FUSE
BRAKE EMERGENCY RELAY
BRAKE EMERGENCY PILOT (3W)
TURN SIGNAL RELAY
LIGHTING RELAY
LIGHTING SWITCH
OFF S H
FOG LIGHT SWITCH
OFF ON
IGNITION SWITCH
DIMMER SWITCH
TURN SIGNAL SWITCH
STOP
TURN
HORN SWITCH
WIPER & WASHER SWITCH
OFF
LOW
HIGH
HAZARD SWITCH
HAZARD RELAY
REGISTER
HEATER SWITCH
OFF H L
CHARGE PILOT (3W)
ILLUMINATI (3W)
TACHOMETER
HAND BRAKE PILOT (3W)
R.TURN SIGNAL PILOT (3W)
HIGH BEAM PILOT (3W)
ILLUMINATION (3W)
SPEEDO ETER
L.TURN SIGNAL PILOT (3W)
ILLUMINATION (3W)
FUEL METER
HAND BRAKE SWITCH
DOOR BUZZER
R.DOOR SWITCH
INTERIOR LIGHT (5W)
L.DOOR SWITCH
FUEL UNIT
FUEL PUMP
CIGAR LIGHTER
WINDOW DEFROSTER SWITCH
OFF ON
RADIO
CARB. HEATER SWITCH
OFF ON
CARB. HEATER PILOT LAMP (3W)
R.SIDE MARKER LIGHT (4CP)
R.REAR COMBINATION LIGHT
TURN SIGNAL STOP/TAIL (32/4CP)
BACK LIGHT (32CP)
LICENSE LIGHT (4CP)
LICENSE LIGHT (4CP)
L.REAR COMBINATION LIGHT
BACK LIGHT (32CP)
TURN SIGNAL STOP/TAIL (32/4CP)
L.SIDE MARKER LIGHT (4CP)
G DOOR BUZZER
Bl.W STARTER Mg.SWITCH
Bl.Y IGNITION COIL
TUBE FUSE 10A Bl.Y FUEL PUMP CARB. SOLENOID CARB. HEATER
TUBE FUSE 10A G.Bl WIPER WASHER
TUBE FUSE 10A Y BACK LIGHT, TURN SIGNAL FUEL METER, CHARGE PILOT, HAND BRAKE
TUBE FUSE 15A Y.R HEATER MOTER, WINDOW DEFROSTER RADIO
TUBE FUSE 15A W.G HAZARD, STOP LIGHT, HORN BRAKE EMERGENCY
TUBE FUSE 10A W.Bu INTERIOR LIGHT, MAP LIGHT CIGAR LIGHTER AUTO CLOCK
TUBE FUSE 10A R.G TAIL LIGHT, LICENSE LIGHT SIDE MARKER LIGHT, FOG LIGHT METER ILLUMINATION
TUBE FUSE 15A R HEAD LIGHT, HIGH BEAM PILOT
IGNITION SWITCH
MAIN FUSE (45A)
FUSE CIRCUIT
Bu. : Blue
Bu.R : Blue/red stripe
Bu.W : Blue/white stripe
Bu.Y : Blue/yellow stripe
Bl.W : Black/white stripe
Bl. : Black
Bl.Y : Black/yellow stripe
G. : Green
G.Bl : Green/black stripe
G.Bu : Green/blue stripe
G.R : Green/red stripe
G.W : Green/white stripe
G.Y : Green/yellow stripe
LG : Light Green
LG.R : Light Green/red stripe
R. : Red
R.Bl : Red/black stripe
R.Bu : Red/blue stripe
R.G : Red/green stripe
R.Y : Red/yellow stripe
R.W : Red/white stripe
W. : White
W.R : White/red stripe
W.Y : White/yellow stripe
W.Bu : White/blue stripe
W.G : White/green stripe
Y. : Yellow
Y.Bl : Yellow/black stripe
Y.R : Yellow/red stripe
Y.W : Yellow/white stripe

Honda 600

TUNE-UP PROCEDURES

Spark Plugs

Spark plugs should be chosen according to the type of driving done. The plug with a long insulator nose retains heat enough to burn off oil and combustion deposits under light load conditions. NGK B-8ES spark plugs are original equipment, with other plugs available for various operating conditions. (See the following chart.)

	NGK	ND
Hotter	B-7ES	W-22ES
Standard	B-8ES	W-24ES
Colder	B-9E	—

To ensure peak performance, the plugs should be checked at least every 6,000 miles. Spark plug life is largely governed by operating conditions and varies accordingly. Faulty or excessively worn plugs should be replaced immediately. It is also helpful to check plugs for types of deposit and degree of electrode wear, as an indication of engine operating condition.

Clean dirty plugs with a plug cleaner or wire brush. The plug gap should be readjusted to 0.027–0.032 in. by bending the ground electrode. However, since only two plugs are used at a time, it would probably be just as easy to replace them rather than run on marginal plugs.

Breaker Points and Condenser

1. Check the surfaces of the breaker points for deterioration. If the points are pitted or worn, correct with a point file.

2. For removal or replacement of points and condenser, two lock screws hold the breaker points, and the condenser fits easily with one screw.

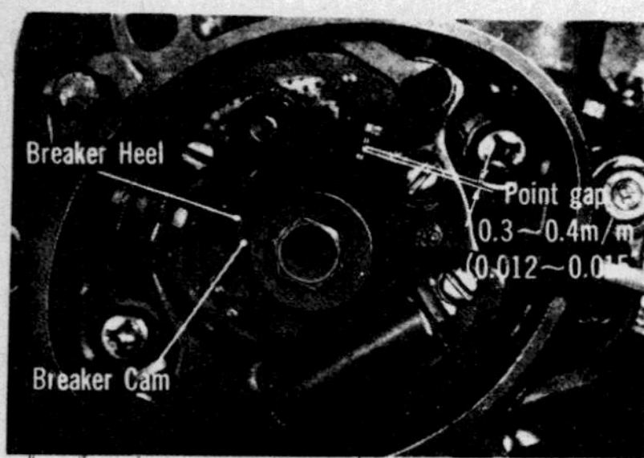

Distributor point gap adjustment

3. When replacing the breaker or condenser be sure to install the insulators, or the part will become grounded.

Adjustment

1. Point gap can be set by first turning the crankshaft pulley until the gap is at its maximum (the point where the heel is at the highest point of the breaker cam).

2. At this position measure the gap with a feeler gauge. The gap should be set at 0.012–0.015 in.

3. To adjust, loosen the two breaker point set screws and move the point assembly with a screwdriver to obtain the proper clearance.

4. Retighten the screws and check the clearance.

5. Check the breaker arm spring for tension.

Ignition Timing

1. Basic timing is set by lining up the "F" mark on the crankshaft pulley with the mark on the flywheel housing cover. When these marks are aligned, the points should start to open.

1. Timing "F" mark
Ignition timing mark

2. Adjust ignition timing after setting the point gap. An easy and inexpensive way is by using a 12-volt lamp connected across the primary wiring to the ground.

3. Turn the crankshaft with the ignition switch on, checking to see if the lamp goes out just when the notch on the flywheel cover is aligned with the "F" mark on the crankshaft pulley.

4. Loosen the vacuum advance lock bolt and move the advancer forward to retard or backward to advance the timing.

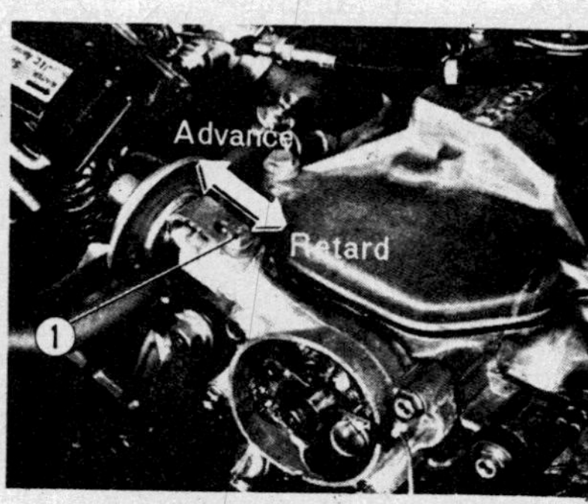

1. Lock bolt
Ignition timing adjustment

Valve Lash

1. Adjust valves when the engine is cold.

2. After removing the camshaft housing cover, rotate the crankshaft until the left intake and right exhaust valve rocker arms are raised the same amount.

3. At this position, check the left exhaust and right intake valve clearances with a feeler gauge. Repeat this procedure to determine the left intake and right exhaust valve clearances.

4. To adjust, loosen the rocker arm lock bolt and turn the rocker arm shaft in to decrease the valve clearance, or out to increase it.

5. Tighten the lock bolt to 25.3–28.6 ft lbs and recheck valve clearances.

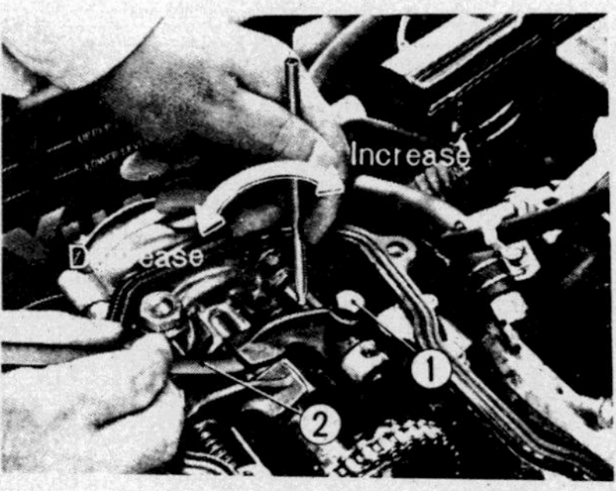

1. Lock bolt
2. Feeler gauge

Valve adjustment

Carburetor

Idle Speed and Mixture

1. To adjust the idle, warm the engine and adjust the throttle stop screw to maintain an idle speed of 1,150 rpm. The idle mixture is controlled by adjusting the idle mixture (pilot) screw within the range of the limiter cap to the position at which the engine idles smoothly.

Carburetor idle and idle mixture adjustment

2. To adjust with the limiter caps removed, set the mixture screw to 1 ¼ turn from closed. Then, turn the screw no more than ⅛ turn in both directions to the position where the engine idles smoothly.

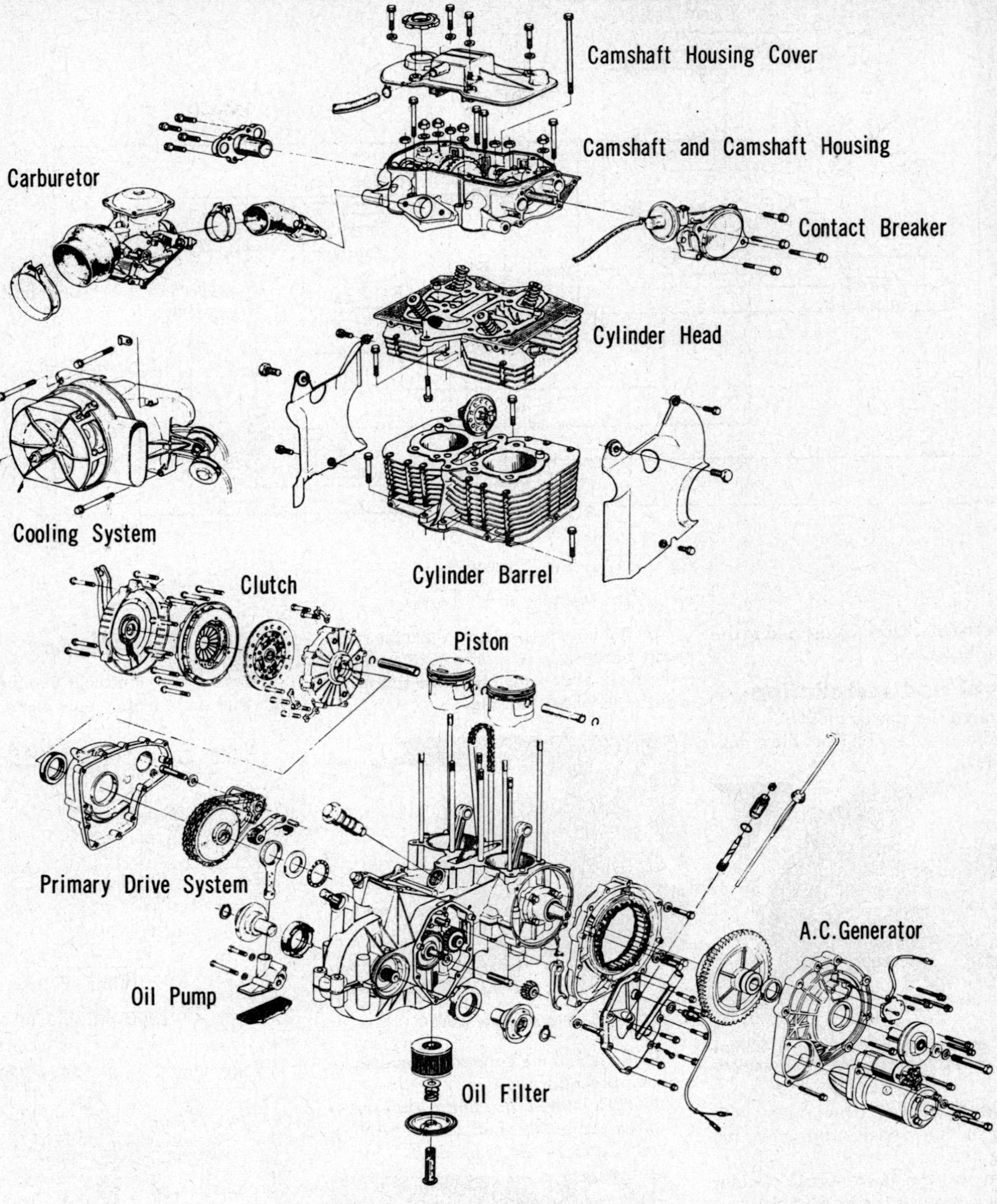
Camshaft Housing Cover
Camshaft and Camshaft Housing
Carburetor
Contact Breaker
Cylinder Head
Cooling System
Clutch
Cylinder Barrel
Piston
Primary Drive System
A.C.Generator
Oil Pump
Oil Filter

Engine disassembly

ENGINE ELECTRICAL

Distributor

Overhaul

To overhaul the distributor, remove the distributor cap, disconnect the vacuum line and primary ignition wire, and remove the advancer assembly bolt, cam, and housing. Replace the gasket on the distributor housing if necessary.

When assembling the spark advance unit, align the groove of the advance and the dowel pin on the camshaft. Reassemble the remaining components, reversing the above procedure. Set the breaker point gap and adjust the ignition timing.

Camshaft Holder
Dowel Pin
Groove

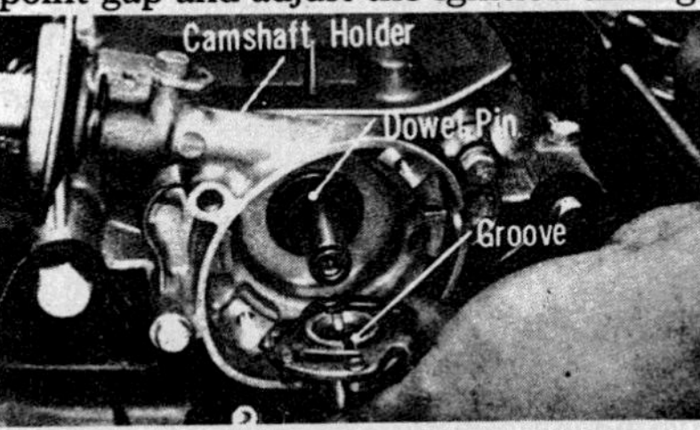

Spark advancer

Alternator

The 600's charging circuit uses an alternator rectfied to DC by a silicone diode. The alternator is installed on the left (battery) side of the engine with the rotor mounted on the front end of the crankshaft.

Removal Precautions

1. After removing the negative (ground) cable from the battery, remove the three white leads and a white and black lead from the rectifier.

2. Separate the white and red striped

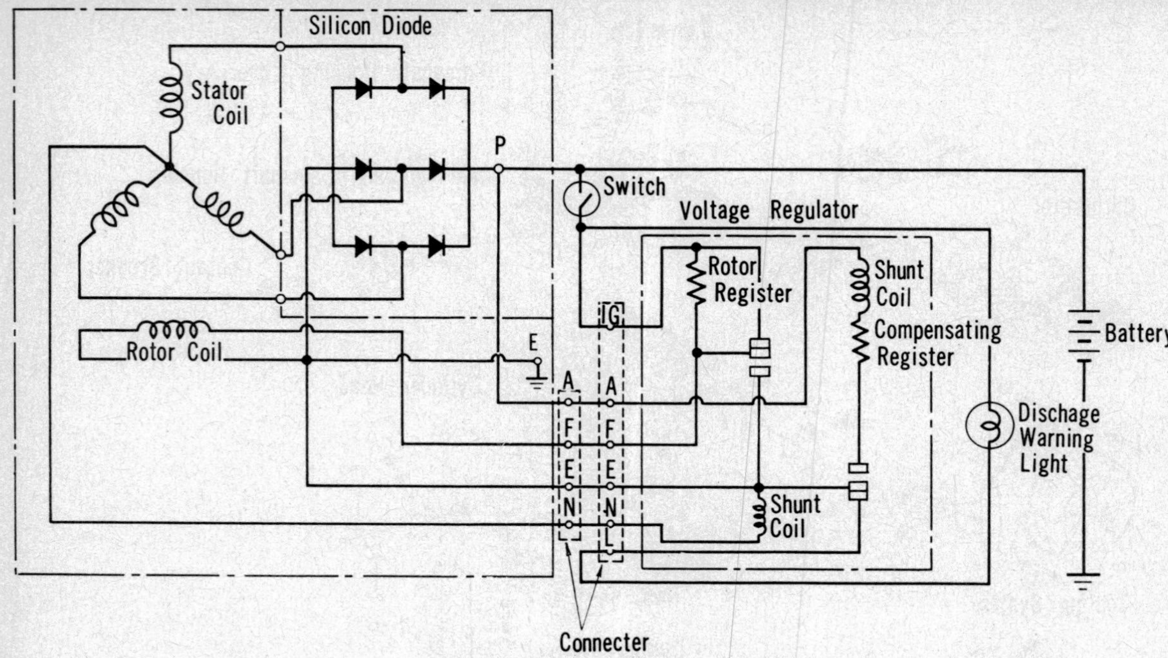

Charging circuit diagram

lead from the black lead connected to the alternator brushes.

Removal and Installation

1. Remove the starter motor.
2. Remove the fan belt from the crankshaft pulley.

Hold the crankshaft pulley with a 22mm (7/8 in.) wrench and remove the retaining bolt.

3. Hold the fan belt drive pulley with a 22 mm (⅞ in.) wrench and remove the retaining bolt.
4. Remove the two brush holder screws and remove the brush holder assembly.
5. Remove the flywheel housing cover bolts and the cover.
6. To remove the generator flywheel-rotor unit, secure the rotor with a flywheel remover and then thread in either a bolt of suitable size or a rotor remover bolt (special tool # 07011-56801). Tap the flywheel-rotor out by hammering lightly upon the head of the flywheel remover. The flywheel-rotor unit is taper fitted in the crankshaft.
7. The generator stator unit is installed in the flywheel housing. Remove the four retaining bolts to separate the flywheel housing from the engine.
8. If it is necessary to replace the stator unit because of a short circuit, remove the three bolts which hold the stator unit to the flywheel housing.

Flywheel removal

9. To install the generator, reverse the above procedure.

NOTE: *When installing the pulley, align the pulley shaft tongue with the end notch of the crankshaft.*

Stator unit retaining bolts and flywheel housing pins.

10. When installing the flywheel housing cover, be sure that the housing has two hollow pins installed.

Regulator

The regulator is attached to the engine sidewall immediately above the battery.

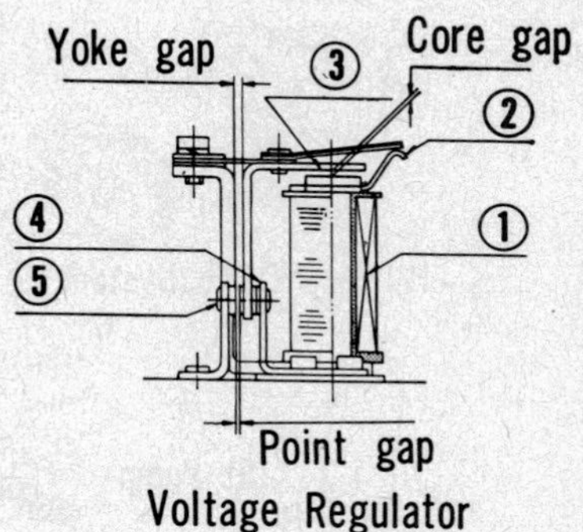

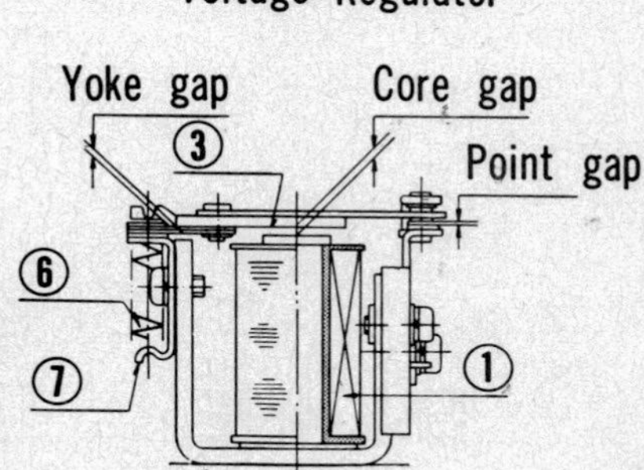

1. Voltage (shunt) coil
2. Adjuster
3. Armature
4. Lower contact
5. Upper contact
6. Spring
7. Hanger

Removal and Installation

1. Remove all regulator terminal lead wires.
2. Remove the right side of the headlight, the regulator retaining bolt and the regulator.

To install, reverse the above procedure.

Gap Adjustment

1. Remove the regulator cap and check the point. If the point is rough, grind it with a fine emery cloth.
2. Check the various gaps and adjust where necessary. Gap adjustment should be performed in the sequence of yoke, core, and point gap.

No-Load Voltage Adjustment

1. Prepare a DC voltmeter-ammeter and connect them according to the illustration.

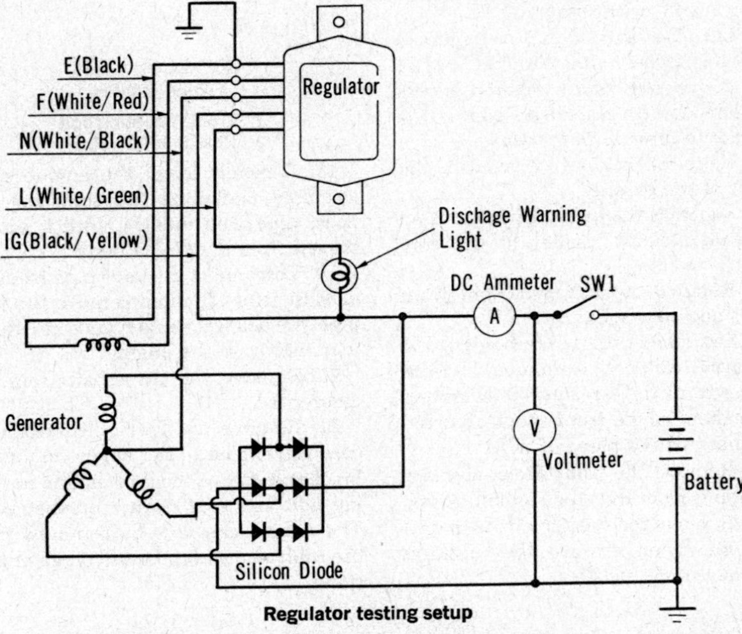

Regulator testing setup

2. When regulating no-load voltage, close the switch SW 1, thereby allowing exciting current to flow from the battery to the generator rotor coil. After generator speed is raised to approximately 800 rpm, set the switch SW 1 to OFF.

NOTE: *In the case of a DC generator, when a regulator is combined with the generator to increase generator speed, voltage rises.* In the case of an AC generator, however, voltage is not generated as prescribed unless the rotor is initially excited with the DC current flowing into the rotor coil from the battery. When speeding up the generator after stopping it once, set switch SW 1 to ON and let current flow from the battery. When voltage is generated, set the switch to OFF and check no-load voltage.

3. Raise generator speed to the rated value of 5,000 rpm and regulate no-load voltage with the regulator.
4. If no-load voltage is lower than the rated voltage (13.5 V), bend the armature spring adjuster upward to obtain a middle reading of 14.0 V. If the voltage is higher than the rated voltage (14.5 V), lower the adjuster to obtain a 14.0 V reading.
5. Generator voltage, after completing the adjustment, is shown in figure 26. When the generator operation is changed from low speed (with the lower contact actuated) to high speed (with the upper contact actuated), there is a voltage fluctuation of approximately +0.5 V, which is a normal rise.
6. If the voltage change exceeds 0.5 V, or if there is a voltage drop when the generator operation is changed to high speed, inspect the core gap again. If the gap is too large, voltage rises, and if too small, voltage drops.

Adjusting Relay Cut-In Voltage

1. When adjusting the cut-in voltage of the discharge warning relay, raise generator speed as prescribed in Steps 2 and 3 above.
2. Check cut-in voltage. Operating voltage should be 8–10 V at P terminal.

Relay Cut-in Voltage

Operating Voltage	Tensile Force of Coil Spring	Adjustment
High	Strong	Raise Hanger
Low	Weak	Lower Hanger

Starter

The starter motor for the Honda 600 consists primarily of a magnetic switch, motor, and pinion. The magnetic switch engages and disengages the pinion through the shift lever by moving the plunger.

Removal and Disassembly

1. To remove the starter from the flywheel cover, disconnect the wiring and the two retaining bolts.
2. Remove the three bolts which hold the magnetic switch, and take the switch and the return spring from the starter motor.
3. Detach the rear cover, exposing the four carbon brushes and the brush holder. Remove the brushes and the brush holder.

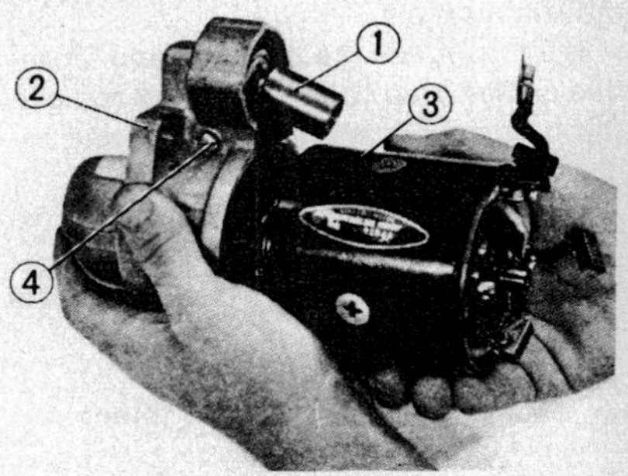

Starter motor case disassembly

1. Plunger
2. Case assembly
3. Yoke assembly
4. Shift lever pin

4. Remove the yoke from the case.
5. Remove the shift lever pin to free the plunger from the shift lever.
6. Pull out the armature and remove it from the shift lever.
7. The armature can be disassembled according to the illustration.

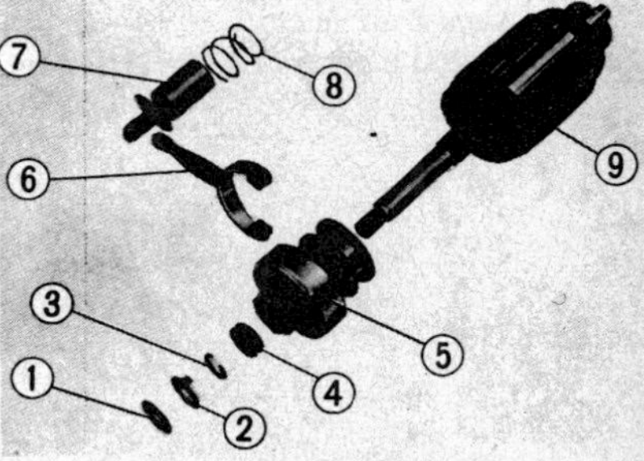

Armature—exploded view

1. Thrust washer (A)
2. Pinion stopper washer
3. Pinion stopper clip
4. Pinion stopper
5. Pinion assembly
6. Shift lever
7. Plunger
8. Plunger return spring
9. Armature unit

After disassembly be sure to check:

1. The armature for shorting, grounding, and physical condition;

2. the brushes, brush spring, and brush motion, cleaning or replacing wherever necessary;

3. the pinion for worn and damaged parts. The overrunning clutch cannot be disassembled.

Installation

For reassembly and installation, reverse the above procedures.

ENGINE MECHANICAL

Engine Removal and Installation

1. Drain the crankcase oil by removing the drain plug.

2. Disconnect the positive and negative cables from the battery and remove the battery. Disconnect the positive cable from the main fuse.

3. Disconnect the following control cables and wiring from the engine:
 a. Throttle and choke control cables
 b. Tachometer drive cable
 c. Engine ground wire
 d. Ignition primary wire (blue)
 e. High tension cables
 f. Back-up switch wires

4. Disconnect the breather tube from the camshaft housing cover.

5. Disconnect the fuel line and vacuum advance tube from the carburetor. Disconnect the fuel solenoid. Remove the air cleaner and the carburetor/intake manifold assembly from the engine.

6. Disconnect the following ducts:
 a. Hot air duct
 b. Heater duct
 c. Heater ducts
 d. Exhaust air duct

7. Remove the heater blower from the engine compartment.

8. Separate the speedometer cable and clutch control cable from the engine. Disconnect the starter solenoid and generator wiring.

9. Using a hammer and punch, remove the gear shift rod pin. Separate the gear shift column from the gear shift rod.

10. Push the gear shift rod in to prevent it from touching the floor board when the engine is removed.

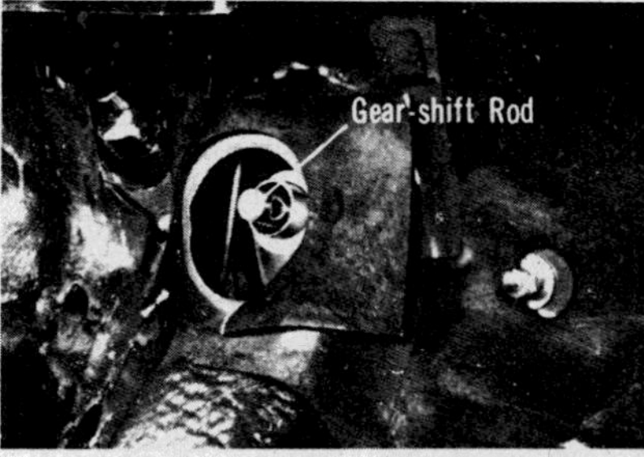

Push gearshift rod in to clear the floorboard

11. Jack up the front end of the Honda and support it with stands.

NOTE: *The body should be raised so that the center under pan is at least 34 in. above the floor. Wooden blocks should also be placed on top of the stands to prevent body damage.*

12. Raise the jack until it supports the weight of the engine.

13. Separate the exhaust muffler from the main exhaust muffler at the connecter.

14. Remove the left and right front wheels and splashguards.

15. Disconnect the brake hoses at the front brake calipers, or remove the front calipers from the steering knuckles and attach them to the front shock absorber assemblies with a piece of wire.

16. Remove the front shock absorber assemblies from the steering knuckles.

17. Remove the subframe rear mounting bolts. Then remove the subframe front mounting bolts.

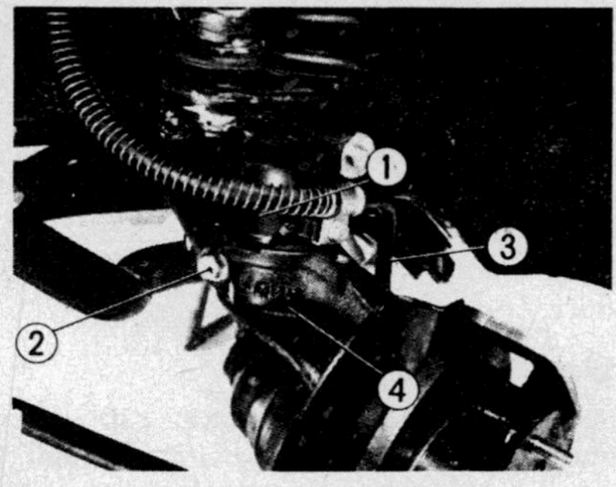

Brakeline connections

1. Front shock assembly
2. Front strut lock bolt
3. Brake hose
4. Knuckle

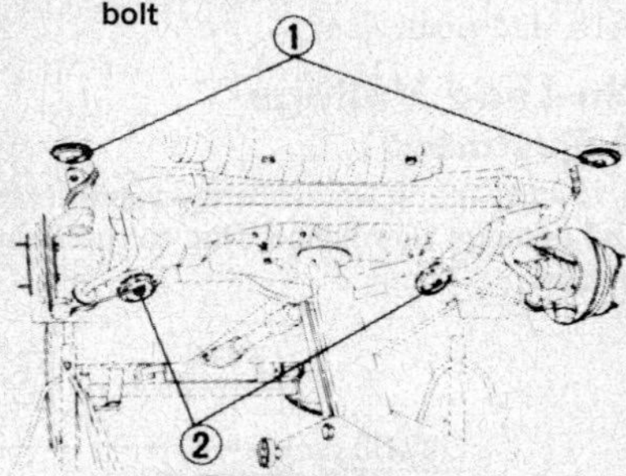

Engine mounts

1. Front mounting bolt
2. Rear mounting bolt

18. Carefully lower the engine as an assembly, including the subframe, exhaust pipe, and muffler, until it can be moved from under the body.

19. Disconnect the joint pipe from the exhaust joint pipe and remove the joint pipe, the heat exchanger, and the exhaust manifold from the engine.

20. Remove the driveshaft from the differential.

21. Remove the four bolts which secure the engine to the engine mounting bracket. Remove the rear engine mounting bolt and rear engine bracket bolts. The engine can now be removed from the subframe and mounted on an engine stand.

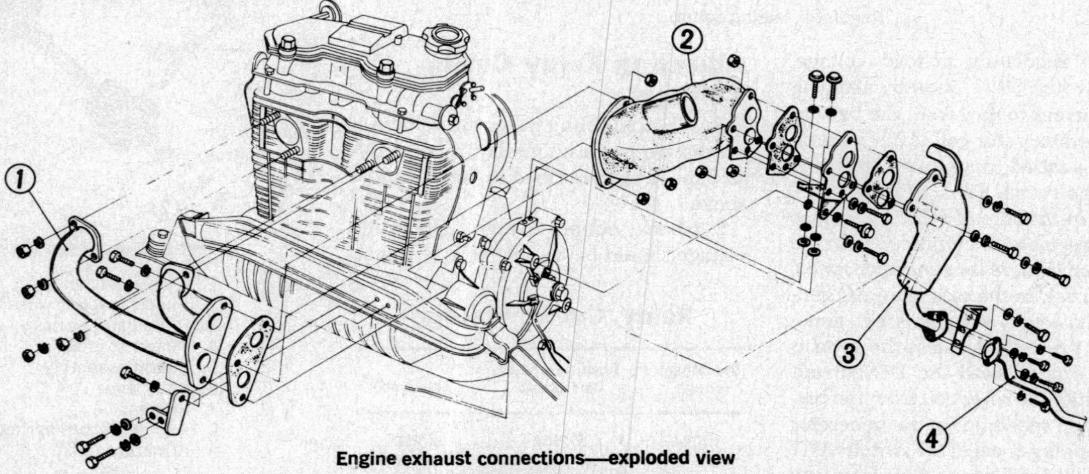

Engine exhaust connections—exploded view

1. Exhaust manifold
2. Heat exchanger
3. Joint pipe (A)
4. Exhaust joint pipe

Engine cable and hose connections

1. Main fuse
2. Speedometer cable
3. Exhaust air duct
4. High tension cable
5. Ignition primary wire
6. Engine ground
7. Heater duct B.
8. Heater duct
9. Hot air duct
10. Clutch control cable
11. Choke control cable
12. Throttle control cable
13. Heater duct A.
14. Heater blower motor
15. Tachometer cable

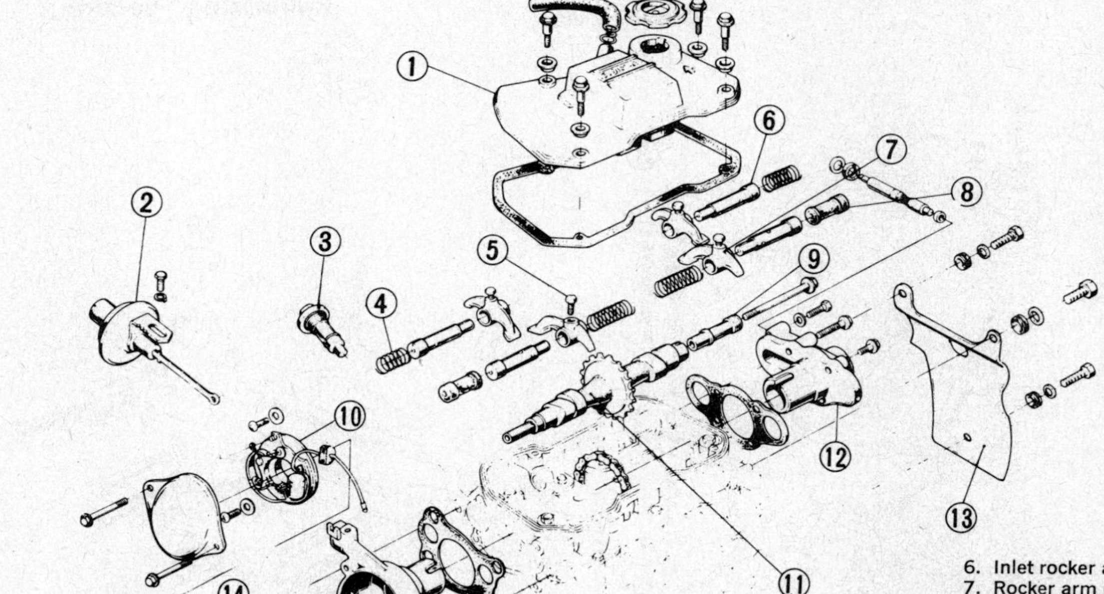

1. Camshaft housing cover
2. Vacuum spark advancer assembly
3. Cam chain tensioner
4. Inlet rocker arm spring
5. Rocker arm lock bolt
6. Inlet rocker arm shaft
7. Rocker arm (L)
8. Exhaust rocker arm shaft spacer
9. Tachometer pinion
10. Contact breaker assembly
11. Camshaft
12. Camshaft holder (L)
13. Engine shroud assembly (L)
14. Mechanical spark advancer assembly
15. Camshaft holder (R)
16. Engine shroud assembly (R)

Upper engine disassembly

22. To install the engine, reverse the removal procedure, paying careful attention to the following:

a. When installing the knuckle to the front shock absorber assembly, spread the knuckle by inserting a screwdriver into the knuckle slot.

b. Raise the engine and subframe assembly about half way into position and align the tabs on the front suspension mainshafts with the slots in the knuckles.

Front shock absorber removal

1. Front shock assembly
2. Aligning groove
3. Knuckle

c. Check to see that the gear shift rod is not interfering with the car body.

23. After mounting the engine, the following items should be checked:

a. Bleed the air from the brake system

b. Carburetor idle adjustment

c. Ignition timing

d. Clutch adjustment

e. Front suspension alignment (toe-in)

24. When tightening the engine mounting bolts and nuts, follow the torque specifications listed.

Cylinder Head

Removal and Installation

1. Disconnect the positive and negative cables from the battery and remove the battery.

2. Disconnect the following cables and wiring from the engine:

a. Tachometer drive cable

b. Engine ground strap

c. Ignition primary wire (blue)

d. High tension cables

e. Fuel solenoid wiring.

3. Disconnect the breather tube from the camshaft housing cover.

4. Disconnect the vacuum booster hose at the intake manifold.

5. Remove the throttle and choke cable clip.

6. Disconnect the fuel line at the carburetor.

7. Remove the intake manifold, carburetor, and air cleaner as a complete unit.

8. Disconnect the following ducts:

a. Hot air duct

b. Heater duct

c. Exhaust air duct

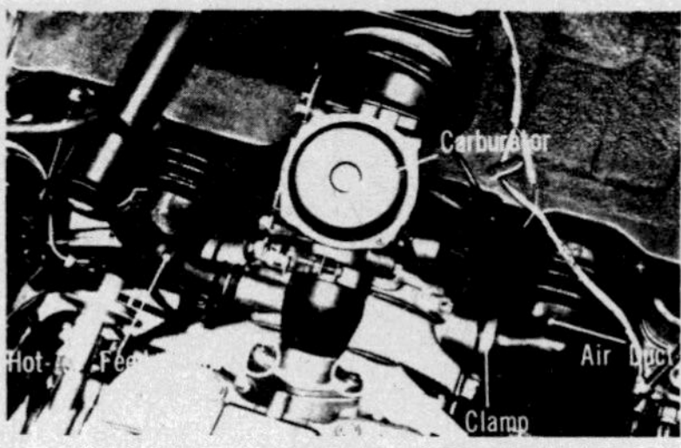

Intake manifold removal

9. Remove the front bumper guard, right and left front combination lights, and the front grill.

10. Remove the exhaust manifold.

11. Remove the camshaft (see "Camshaft Removal").

12. Remove the 6 mm bolts which hold the camshaft housing, and the 10 mm nuts, reversing the installation order.

13. Remove the 6 mm cylinder head bolts located below the intake manifold and remove the cylinder head.

14. To reassemble, reverse the removal procedure. Be certain that four hollow pins (two on each side) are provided for proper alignment of the cylinder head and the camshaft housing. Tighten, in proper order, the cylinder head and camshaft housing nuts and bolts according to torque specifications.

Overhaul (See "Engine Rebuilding" section).

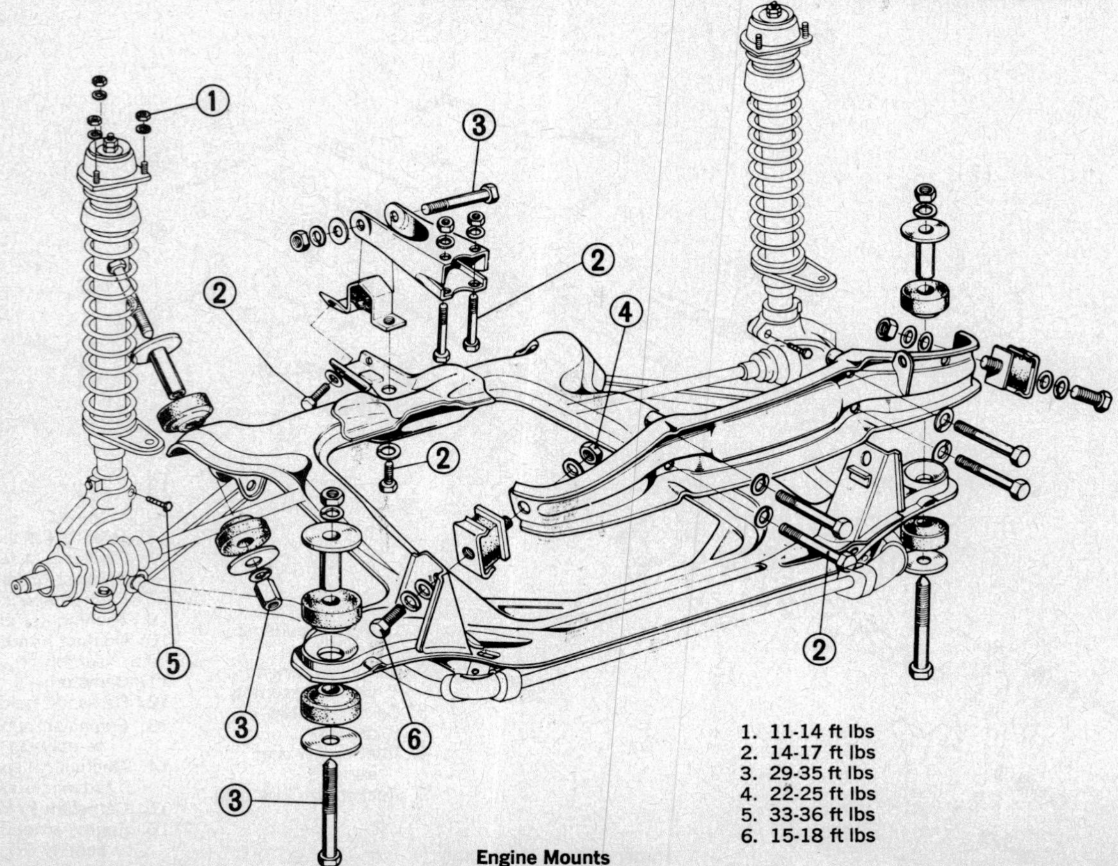

Engine Mounts

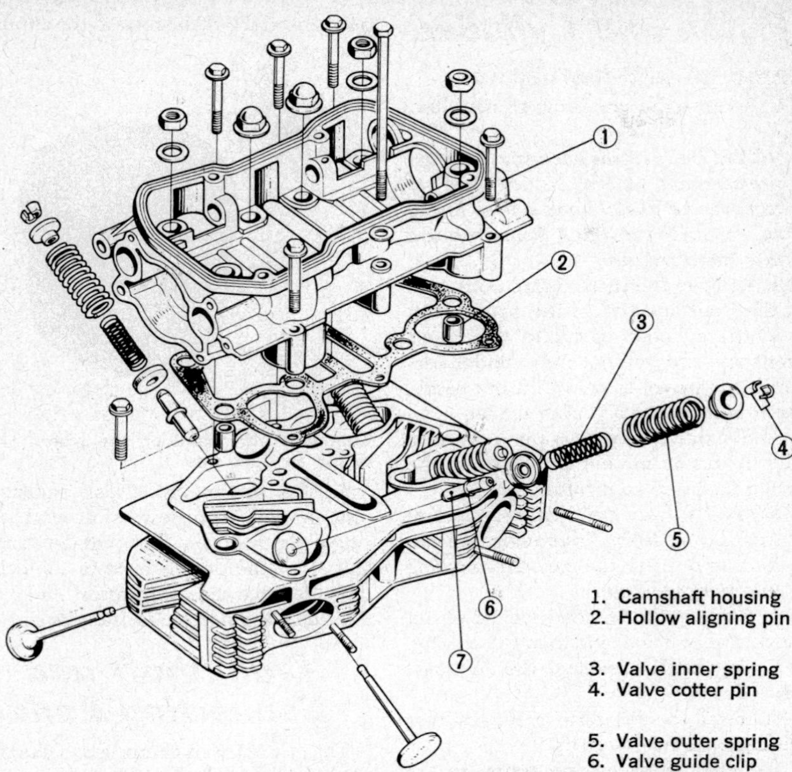

Camshaft housing and cylinder head

Camshaft

Removal and Installation

1. Remove the left and right engine shrouds and the cooling fan housing.

2. Loosen and remove the camshaft chain tensioner. The chain tensioner is an automatic hydraulic mechanism designed to apply a constant pressure on the cam chain. The chain tensioner can be removed after the carburetor and cooling fan housing are removed. To remove the chain tensioner, use a socket wrench only. If the part is tight, use a plastic hammer and gently tap the top of the tensioner. The shock will free the part easily.

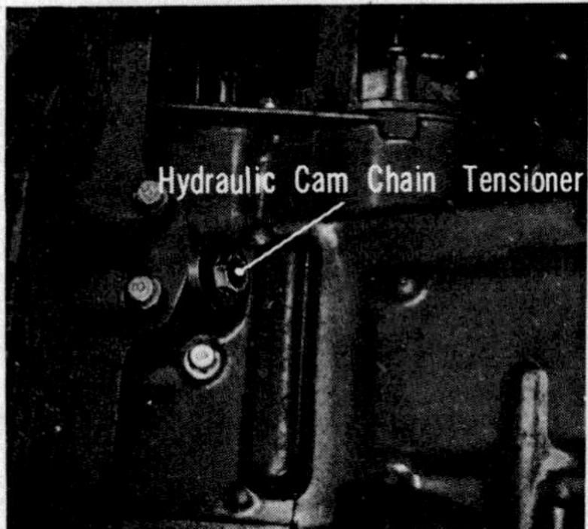

Chain tensioner

3. Remove the camshaft housing cover.

4. Turn the camshaft to the position where the right cam lobes do not push the rocker arms up. The notch on the flywheel pulley will be aligned with the "T" on the flywheel housing cover (top dead center for the compression stroke).

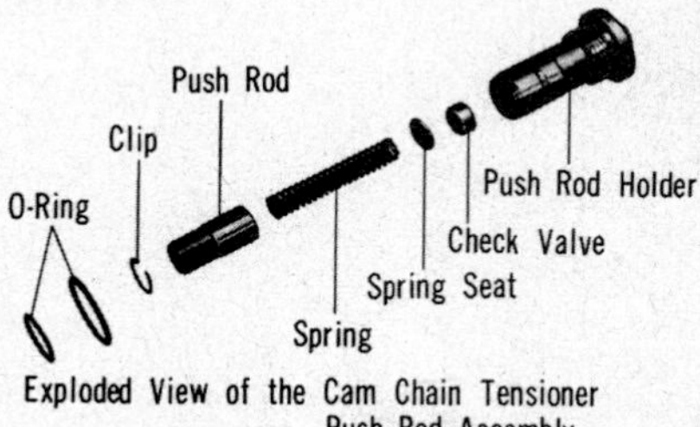

Exploded view of chain tensioner

5. Remove the bolt which secures the mechanical spark advancer to the camshaft and then remove the right camshaft holder. When removing the right camshaft holder, exercise care to prevent the inlet rocker shaft springs from jumping out.

6. Rotate the camshaft until the left cam lobes do not push the rocker arm up and then remove the left camshaft holder.

7. Remove the rocker arm shafts and the rocker arms.

8. Remove the tachometer pinion from the camshaft.

9. Remove the cam chain from the sprocket and pull out the camshaft by first pushing it to the right until it clears the housing on the left and then lifting it up and out to the left.

10. To install the camshaft, reverse the removal procedure. The following items must be carefully checked when installing the camshaft:

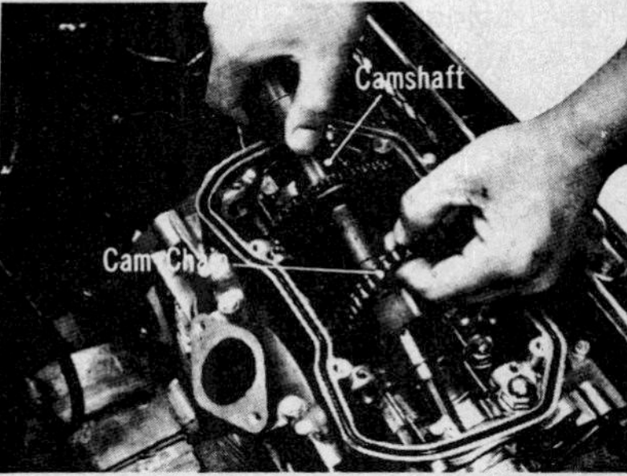

Push the camshaft to the right until it clears the housing on the left.

a. To install the cam chain, turn the crankshaft in its normal rotating direction and align the notch on the flywheel pulley with the "T" on the flywheel housing cover. Align the camshaft so that the horizontal mark on the sprocket is at the top and parallel to the top face of the camshaft housing.

Align the cam so that the horizontal mark on the sprocket is at the top and parallel to the top face of the cam housing.

b. Each rocker arm is marked either "R" or "L", for right and left. Install the right side rocker arms and camshaft holder first. Install the rocker arm shafts with the mark up. This will give the largest valve clearance and will facilitate installation of the camshaft holder.

Install the rocker arm shafts with the mark up.

1. Punch mark

c. Turn the crankshaft and align the "T" mark on the flywheel pulley with the mark on the flywheel housing cover so that the right side piston is at top dead center, on the compression stroke, for installation of the right camshaft holder.

d. After installing the right camshaft holder, turn the crankshaft 360° to again align the notch on the housing with the "T" on the pulley. Fit the left camshaft holder at an angle of 90° to the normal position and install the rocker arms and shafts.

Install the left cam holder 90 degrees to the normal position to install rocker arms and shafts.

e. Check valve timing before adjusting the valve clearances. The camshaft notch should be centered in the left cam holder notch when the "T" mark is aligned with the mark on the flywheel housing cover.

Piston and Cylinder

Removal and Installation

1. Remove the cam chain guide roller.

NOTE: *If the repair necessitates piston replacement, there is no need to remove the chain: hook a wire to the cam chain to prevent it from dropping into the crankcase.*

2. Remove the three 6 mm bolts (one in the front and two in the rear) which hold the cylinder barrel to the upper crankcase and pull out the cylinder barrel. If the barrel does not lift out easily, tap it lightly with a rubber mallet.
3. Remove the piston pin retainers, pull the piston pin out and separate the piston from the connecting rod.

   NOTE: *Cover the upper crankcase with a rag, before removing the pistons, to prevent the parts from falling into the crankcase.*
4. Remove the first and second piston rings (compression) and then the oil ring.
5. To install, reverse the removal procedure.
6. Install the piston rings. Be sure that the lettered side faces up.
7. When attaching the piston to the connecting rod, the "IN" mark on the piston head should be toward the air inlet side.

Turn the "IN" mark on the piston head to the air inlet side.

8. After placing piston seats under the pistons and compressors around the rings, gently lower the cylinder barrel and allow the pistons to fit in the cylinders. Remove the compressors and seats after all the rings are in the cylinder.

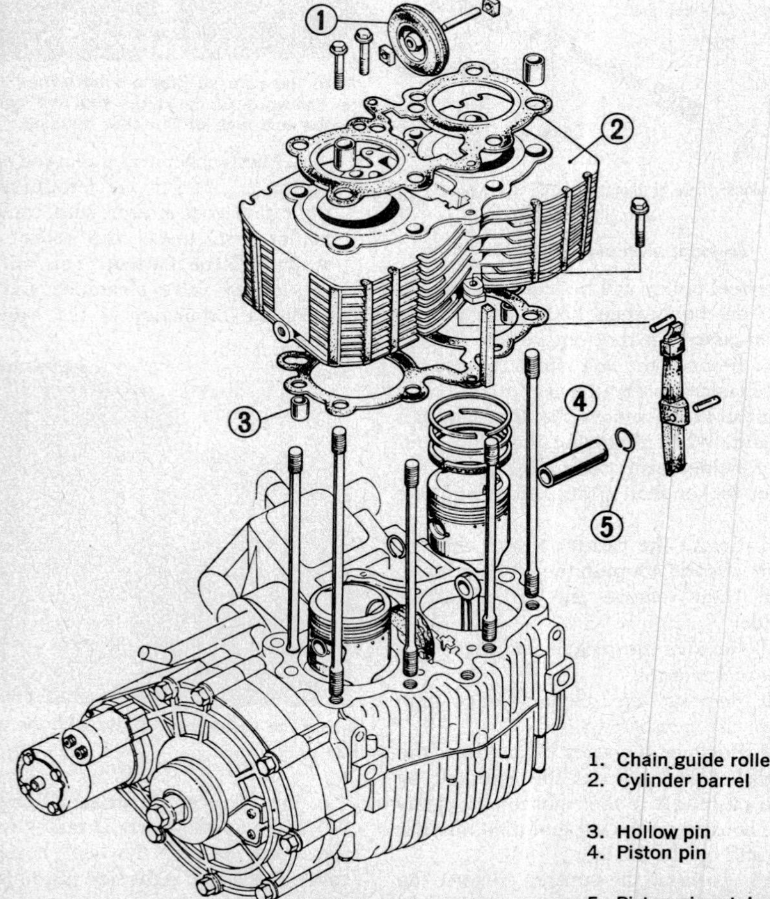

1. Chain guide roller
2. Cylinder barrel
3. Hollow pin
4. Piston pin
5. Piston pin retainer

Piston and cylinder removal

Crankshaft and Connecting Rods

The crankshaft is composed of five precisely machined parts that are press-assembled into an integral unit. It is supported at four points on needle roller bearings for high speed, noiseless operation. The connecting rods are likewise integral with the crankshaft assembly by means of roller bearings.

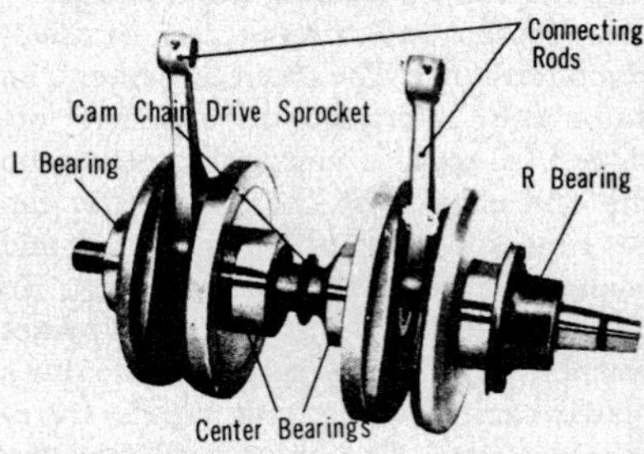

Crankshaft and connecting rod assembly

Removal and Installation

1. Remove the camshaft.
2. Remove the camshaft housing and cylinder head.
3. Remove the cylinder barrel and pistons.
4. Remove the generator.
5. Remove the bolt in the upper crankcase located to the left of the cam chain tensioner.
6. Remove the four bolts which hold the right main roller bearing retainer.
7. Remove the crankcase right side cover.
8. Disassemble the clutch. (See the "Clutch" section)
9. Remove the crankcase left side cover and primary drive assembly, including the oil pump. (See "Primary Drive" section)

Remove the upper crankcase bolt located next to the cam chain tensioner.

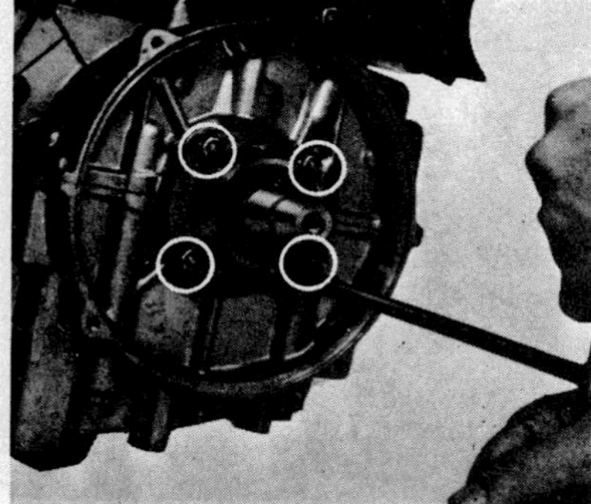

Remove the four bolts which attach the right main bearing holder.

10. Turn the engine upside down and remove the ten 6 mm bolts and eight 8 mm bolts. Separate the lower crankcase from the upper crankcase. Tap the case lightly with a wooden hammer to facilitate removal.

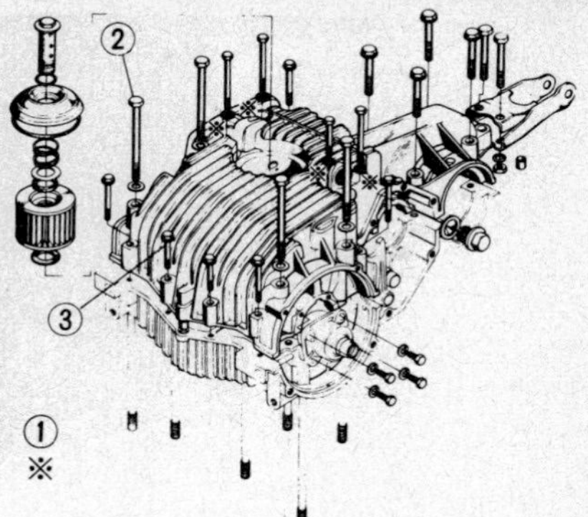

Lower crankcase disassembly

1. Flat washer
2. 8mm bolt
3. 6mm bolt

11. Remove the center bearing holder and pull the crankshaft out of the upper crankcase with the right and left main roller bearing retainer holders, and the cam chain, still attached.

12. Assemble the cam chain on the crankshaft before mounting the crankshaft on the upper crankcase.

13. The alignment of the crankshaft on the crankcase is performed by three dowel pins. Two of the pins fit into recesses on the crankcase mating surface and one fits in at the top of the center main bearing holder.

14. The oil holes in the center bearing should be aligned with the grooves in the crankcase. Be sure that the cam chain is properly seated on the sprocket before tightening the center bearing retainer holder.

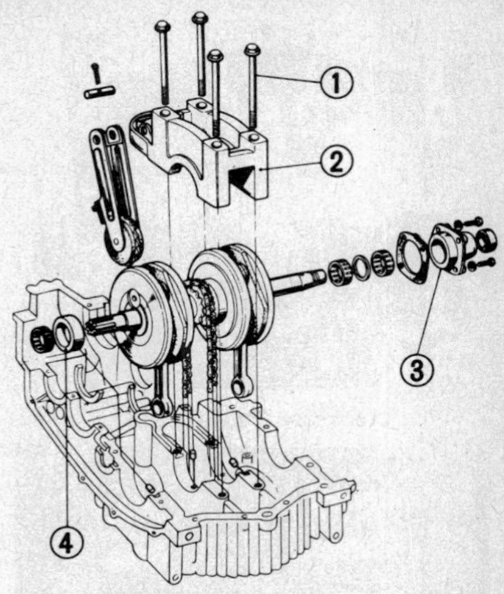

Crankshaft removal

1. Center bearing holder bolts
2. Center bearing holder
3. Main bearing retainer holder (right)
4. Main bearing retainer holder (left)

15. There are no dowel pins in the right bearing retainer holder to position the bearing. The oil return hole must be toward the top of the engine, or in the UP position, when the crankshaft is being mounted (see figure).

16. Use flat washers for five of the 6 mm mounting bolts (the bolts shown in the figure and the mounting bolt next to the cam chain tensioner).

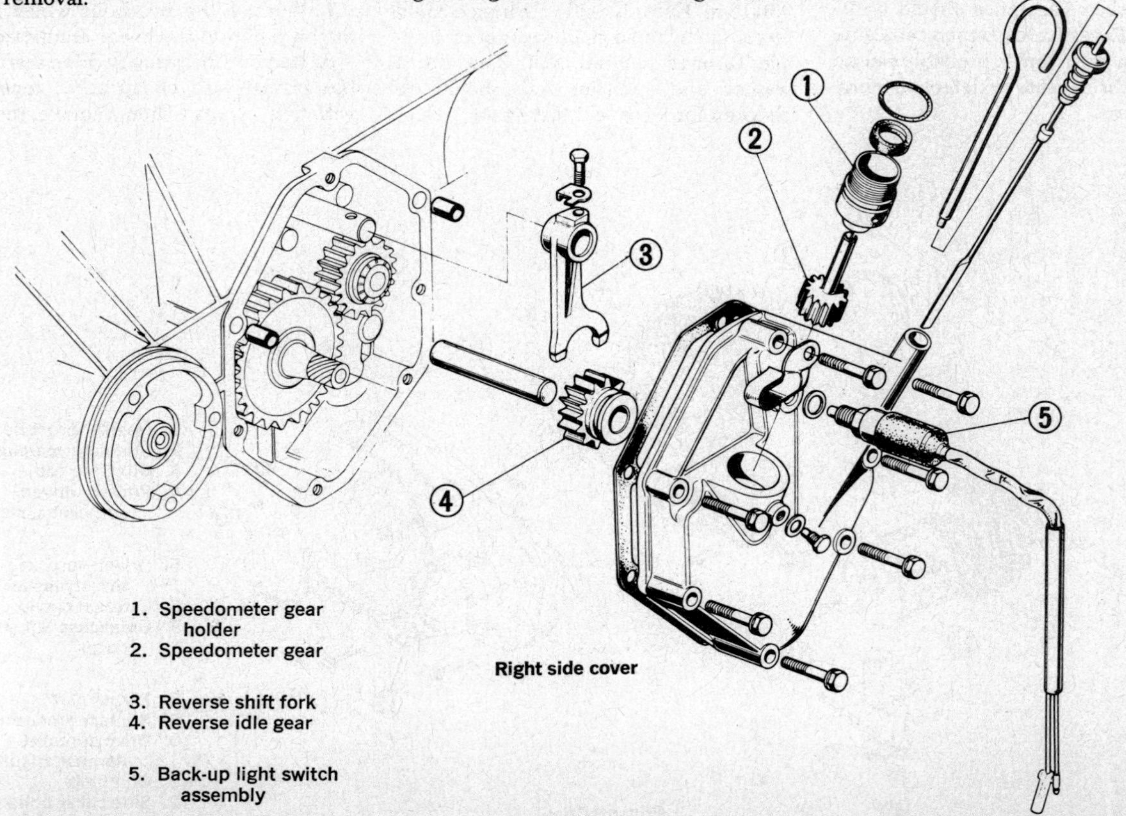

Right side cover

1. Speedometer gear holder
2. Speedometer gear
3. Reverse shift fork
4. Reverse idle gear
5. Back-up light switch assembly

Crankcase installing pins

The right bearing holder oil return hole should be pointed up.

1. Dowel pins
2. Right bearing oil return hole

The oil holes in the center bearing should be aligned with the grooves in the crankcase.

Check the clearance of the primary drive sprocket (0-0.0078 in.).

Check the side clearance of the primary driven sprocket.

Primary Drive

Removal and Installation

1. Remove the clutch assembly.
2. Remove the left side cover.
3. Check the clearance of the primary drive sprocket. Clearance should be 0–0.0078 in. Excessive clearance can cause faster chain wear, and is probably caused by a worn thrust plate or defective vibration dampers.
4. Check the side clearance of the primary driven sprocket with two feeler gauges. Side clearance should be 0.0039–0.0118 in. Excessive side clearance could be caused by rapid chain wear or oil leakage through the oil seal. The thrust washer and sprocket hub should be checked for wear and distortion.
5. Remove the drive sprocket mounting bolt and drive chain tensioner.
6. Remove the circlip and thrust washer from the driven sprocket.
7. Remove the two bolts which hold the oil pump to the lower crankcase.
8. Remove the primary drive shaft and the primary driven sprocket together with the chains. Then remove the oil

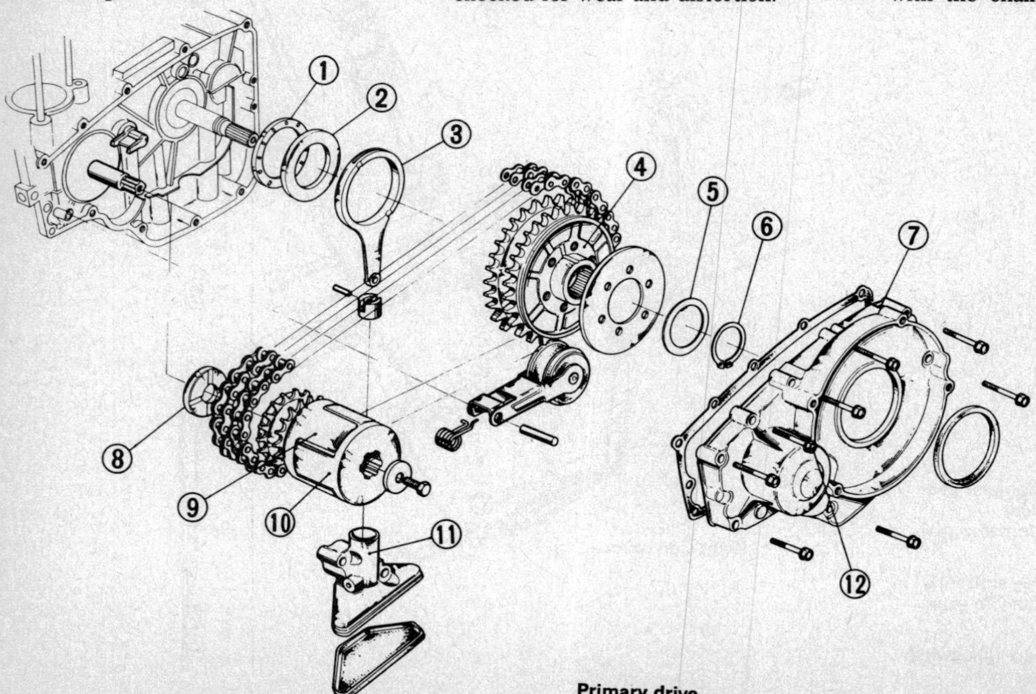

1. Needle thrust bearing
2. Clutch thrust plate
3. Oil pump rod
4. Primary driven sprocket assembly
5. Driven sprocket thrust washer
6. External circlip
7. Crankcase left side cover
8. Thrust plate
9. Primary drive shaft
10. Drive sprocket damper adapter
11. Oil pump
12. Side cover bolts

Primary drive

pump as an assembly.

9. Remove the thrust washer and the needle thrust bearing from the mainshaft.

10. The primary drive sprocket vibration dampers can be removed if the drive sprocket damper adapter is removed from the primary drive shaft.

Removing the primary drive vibration dampers.

11. To assemble and install the primary drive, reverse the removal proceedures. The following items must be carefully checked during installation:

a. Install the drive sprocket damper adapter onto the primary drive shaft with the alignment marks in proper position.

Install the damper adapter to the primary drive shaft with the alignment marks in the proper position.

b. Install the primary driven sprocket dampers with the "Y", embossed on the end face of the dampers, facing out (clutch side).

Install the primary driven dampers with the "Y" on the ends facing out.

c. After installing the driven sprocket dampers, fit the other driven sprocket so that the aligning marks on the sprockets are 180° apart. The teeth on the two primary driven sprockets will be displaced half pitch when the sprockets are assembled properly.

Fit the driven sprockets so the aligning marks are 180 degrees apart.

When assembled properly, the teeth on the driven sprockets will be displaced half-pitch.

1. Teeth at half-pitch

Install the set plate onto the driven sprocket hub with the chamfered side facing the hub.

d. Having made sure that the set plate is not distorted nor worn excessively, install it on the driven sprocket hub with the chamfered side facing the sprocket hub.

e. Mount the needle thrust bearing onto the main shaft bearing and install the oil pump assembly with the clutch thrust plate. Then install the primary drive shaft and primary driven sprocket, together with the chains, as an assembly. Install the primary drive chain tensioner and the left side cover. Before tightening the left crankcase side cover bolts, apply thread lock cement.

Intake Manifold

The intake manifold consists of a single short tube leading from the carburetor to the engine. It is attached to the engine by two bolts, and to the carburetor with a single clamp.

Exhaust System

The exhaust system of the Honda 600 consists of a small manifold connected to a heat exchanger which is, in turn, attached to a series of exhaust pipes and mufflers. Disassemble and install as shown in the figures. Be sure, when assembling, to tighten the bolts to the specified torque and to always use new gaskets.

ENGINE LUBRICATION

The engine oil is contained in the lower crankcase, which is provided with cooling fins. The transmission and differential are also lubricated by the engine oil. The

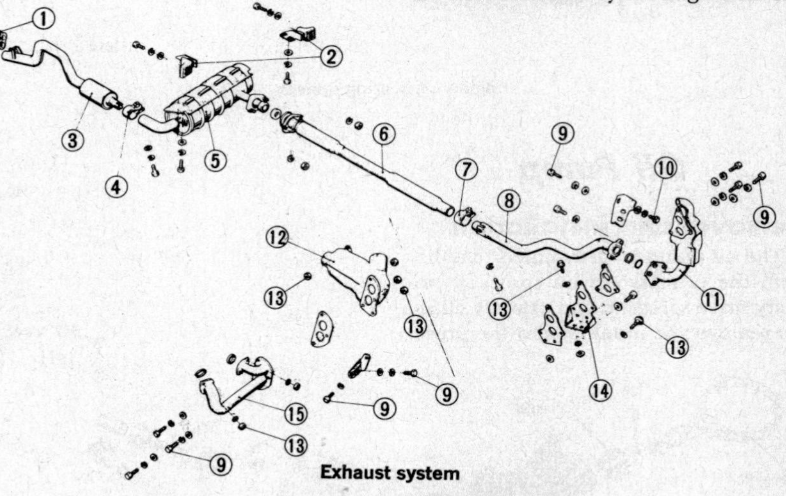

Exhaust system

1. Tail pipe mounting cushion
2. Tail pipe mounting bracket
3. Tail pipe
4. Tail pipe clamp
5. Main exhaust muffler
6. Exhaust pipe/muffler (A)
7. Exhaust pipe clamp
8. Exhaust joint pipe
9. Tighten to 17.4-20.2 ft lbs.
10. Tighten to 28.9-34.7 ft lbs
11. Joint pipe (A)
12. Heat exchanger
13. Tighten to 14.5-17.4 ft lbs
14. Exchanger stay
15. Exhaust manifold

lubricant is pressurized by a plunger-type oil pump.

The lubricating system is branched into two main routes. One route supplies oil to the oil nozzle which lubricates the primary chains; the other route is further divided to lubricate the crankshaft and cylinder head area.

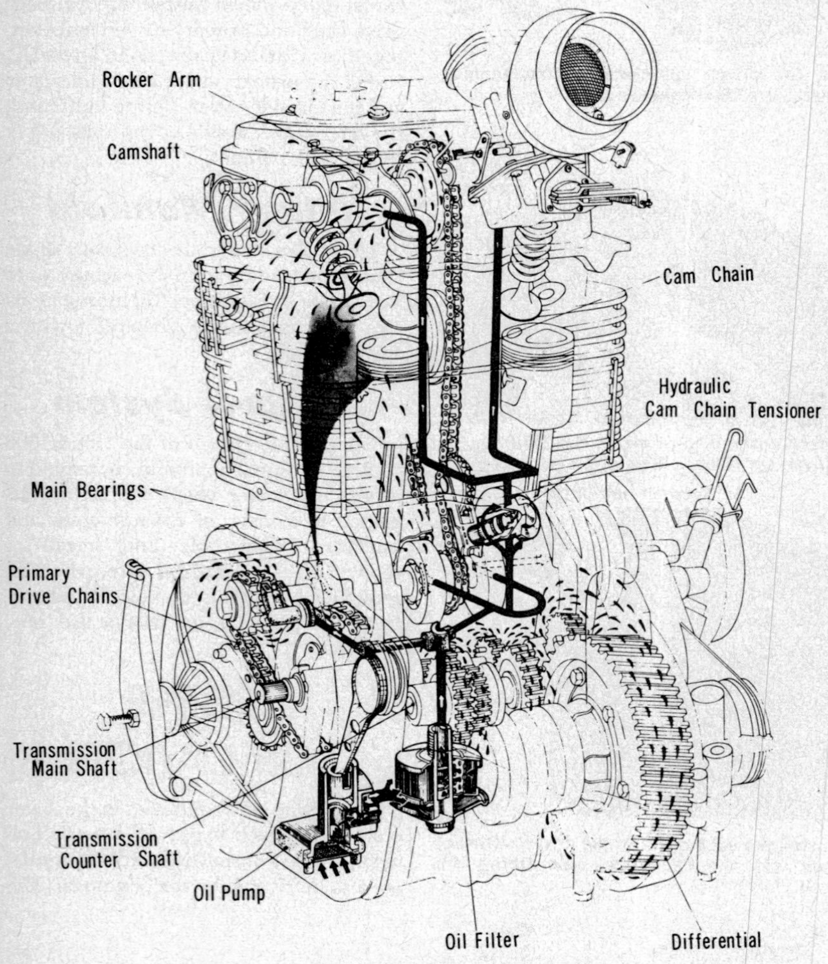

Engine lubricating system

Oil Pump

Removal and Installation

The oil pump is dismounted together with the primary driven sprocket, primary drive sprocket, and primary chain. To remove and install, follow the procedures given for the primary drive. Be sure to clean the strainer and check the remaining parts, including the needle thrust bearing, for wear—replacing where necessary. When reassembling, use iron washers with the oil pump installing bolts.

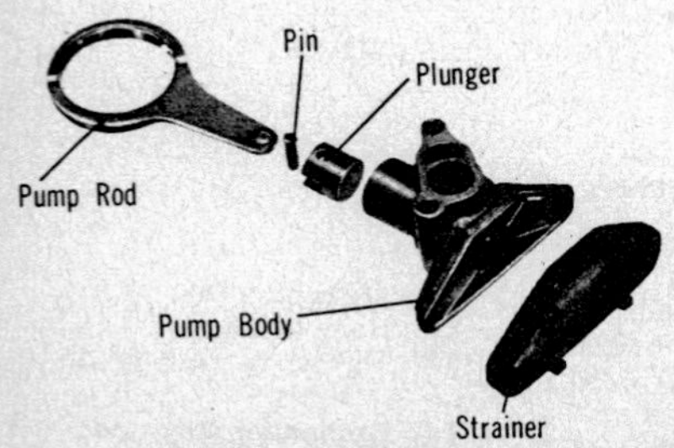

Oil pump assembly

ENGINE COOLING

The engine is cooled by forced air and is designed to use the hot air for compartment heating during cold weather. The engine cooling equipment consists of a cooling fan, drive mechanism, fan belt and pulleys, the cooling fan housing, heater drum, and the fan shrouds around the cylinder head and cylinders. The cooling air is taken from the front of the engine and guided around the cylinder head and cylinders by the fan shrouds and then driven out of the fan housing by the cooling fan.

Removal and Installation

1. Loosen the belt tension pulley and remove the cooling fan drive belt from the fan belt drive pulley.
2. Remove the cooling fan housing.
3. Remove the fan belt drive pulley.
4. Remove the cooling fan housing.
5. The cooling fan pulley is press-fitted to the cooling fan shaft. Remove the pulley with a hydraulic press. The fan housing ribs may be damaged if removal is attempted by hammering.

To install the cooling system, reverse the removal procedure. Be sure to use a hydraulic press for installing the fan pulley. Reassembly will be easier if the fan drive belt is fitted to the cooling fan pulley in advance, and then to the fan belt drive pulley.

EMISSION CONTROLS

The Honda 600 emission control system consists of a sealed crankcase ventilator. Blow-by gas is led from the top of the camshaft housing cover into the air

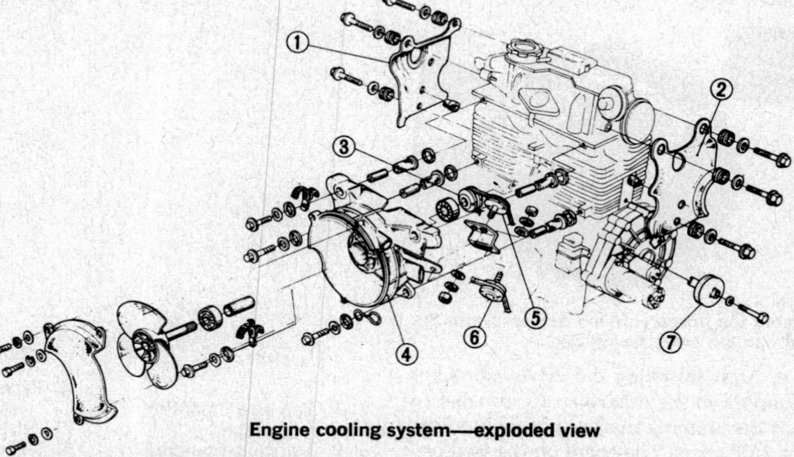

Engine cooling system—exploded view

1. Engine shroud assembly (L)
2. Engine shroud assembly (R)
3. Cooling fan pulley
4. Cooling fan housing
5. Idle pulley
6. Belt tension pulley
7. Fan belt drive pulley

cleaner case through a breather tube and is not discharged into the atmosphere. The blow-by gas and the oil vapor are condensed in the chamber of the air cleaner case and separated into liquid and gas. The harmful gas is sucked into the intake manifold through the air cleaner element, while the liquid settles into the chamber of the air cleaner case.

Engine breather tube

1. Sealed crankcase ventilation—breather tube

Inspection and Maintenance

1. Remove the breather tube at both ends and check for any clogging or damage.

2. Remove the rubber drain plug from the air cleaner case and drain any accumulation of oil.

FUEL SYSTEM

Electric Fuel Pump

Removal and Installation

1. Remove the rear seat cushion, followed by the pump inspection lid.

2. Disconnect the fuel feed from the pump and filter.

3. Remove the two mounting bolts from the fuel pump and separate the pump from the body.

To install, reverse the removal procedure.

Testing and Adjusting

1. Measure the pump terminal voltage. Turn on the engine key switch. Connect a DC voltmeter across the positive (+) terminal of the pump and the body. If 12V is not indicated, check the terminal voltage of the battery or look for open wiring in the harness.

2. Check the resistance of the pump coil. Disconnect the connector at the positive (+) terminal and measure with an ohmmeter between the positive (+) terminal and ground. A reading of 5 ohms is satisfactory.

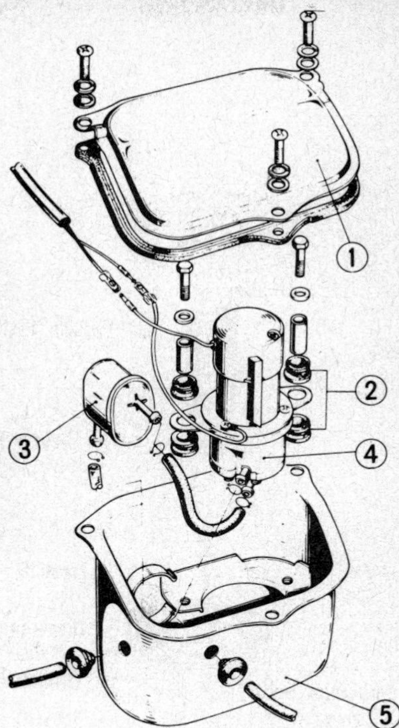

Fuel pump assembly—exploded view

1. Fuel pump lid
2. Fuel pump mounting cushion
3. Fuel filter assembly
4. Fuel pump assembly
5. Fuel pump container

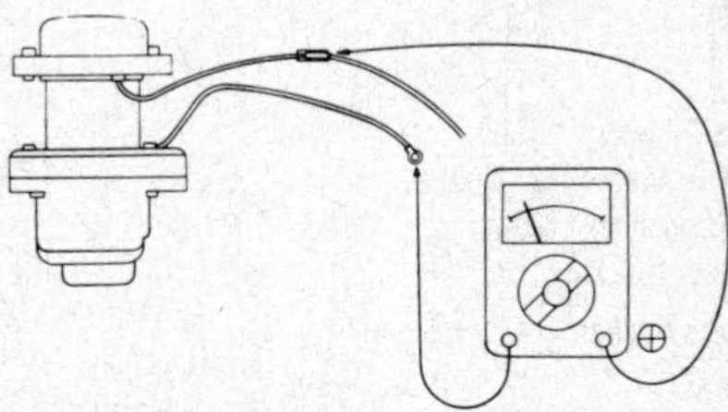

To measure the pump terminal voltage, connect a DC voltmeter across the positive (+) terminal of the pump and the body.

Pump Discharge Test

Simple Test Procedure

1. Disconnect the fuel line from the carburetor and place the end in a container.

2. Turn on the engine switch and check the fuel flow.

3. If the flow is extremely low, check for clogging in the fuel filter.

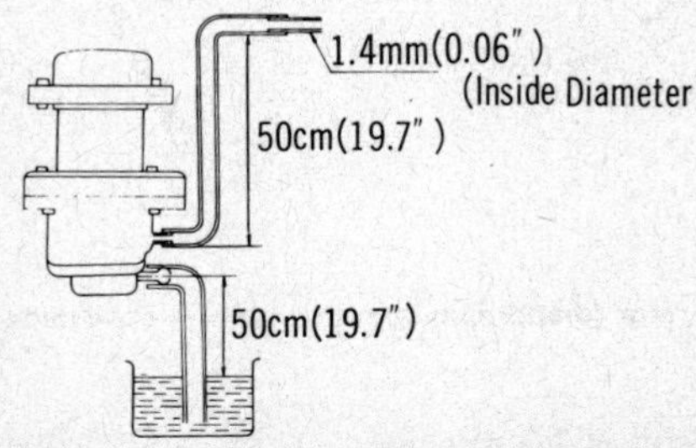

Pump discharge test—precision test procedure.

4. Replace the pump if there is no operating noise.

Precision Test Procedure

1. Separate the pump body and the filter.

2. Fit vinyl tubes, with an inside diameter of 0.236 in., to the intake and outlet. Extend the tube 20 in. below the intake, and the same amount above the outlet.

3. Turn on the switch.

4. The fuel flow should be more than 30.5 cu in./min.

5. For more precise measurement, reduce the inside diameter of the outlet to 0.055 in. The flow should exceed 15.2 cu in./min. at this time, and the discharge pressure should be 2.1 psi.

6. If no pump body trouble is found, check the contact of the ground cable secured by the mounting bolt. A loose or corroded ground will cause pump failure even if the pump is in good condition.

NOTE: *Do not disassemble the electromagnetic components.*

Carburetor

Early Honda 600's came with carburetors containing a diaphragm-operated piston. The diaphragm was a weak point as it would wear and split, letting the piston drop. Subsequent carburetor models are operated with a vacuum piston.

Removal and Installation

1. Remove the fuel line, choke and throttle control cables, and fuel solenoid valve wires.

2. Remove the intake manifold clamp and the carburetor assembly.

3. To install, reverse the removal procedure.

Overhaul

All Types

Efficient carburetion depends greatly on careful cleaning and inspection during overhaul since dirt, gum, water, or varnish in or on the carburetor parts are often responsible for poor performance.

Overhaul your carburetor in a clean, dust-free area. Carefully disassemble the carburetor, referring often to the exploded views. Keep all similar and look-alike parts segregated during disassembly and cleaning to avoid accidental interchange during assembly. Make a note of all jet sizes.

When the carburetor is disassembled, wash all parts (except diaphragms, electric choke units, pump plunger, and any other plastic, leather, fiber, or rubber parts) in clean carburetor solvent. Do not leave parts in the solvent any longer than is necessary to sufficiently loosen the deposits. Excessive cleaning may remove the special finish from the float bowl and choke valve bodies, leaving these parts unfit for service. Rinse all parts in clean

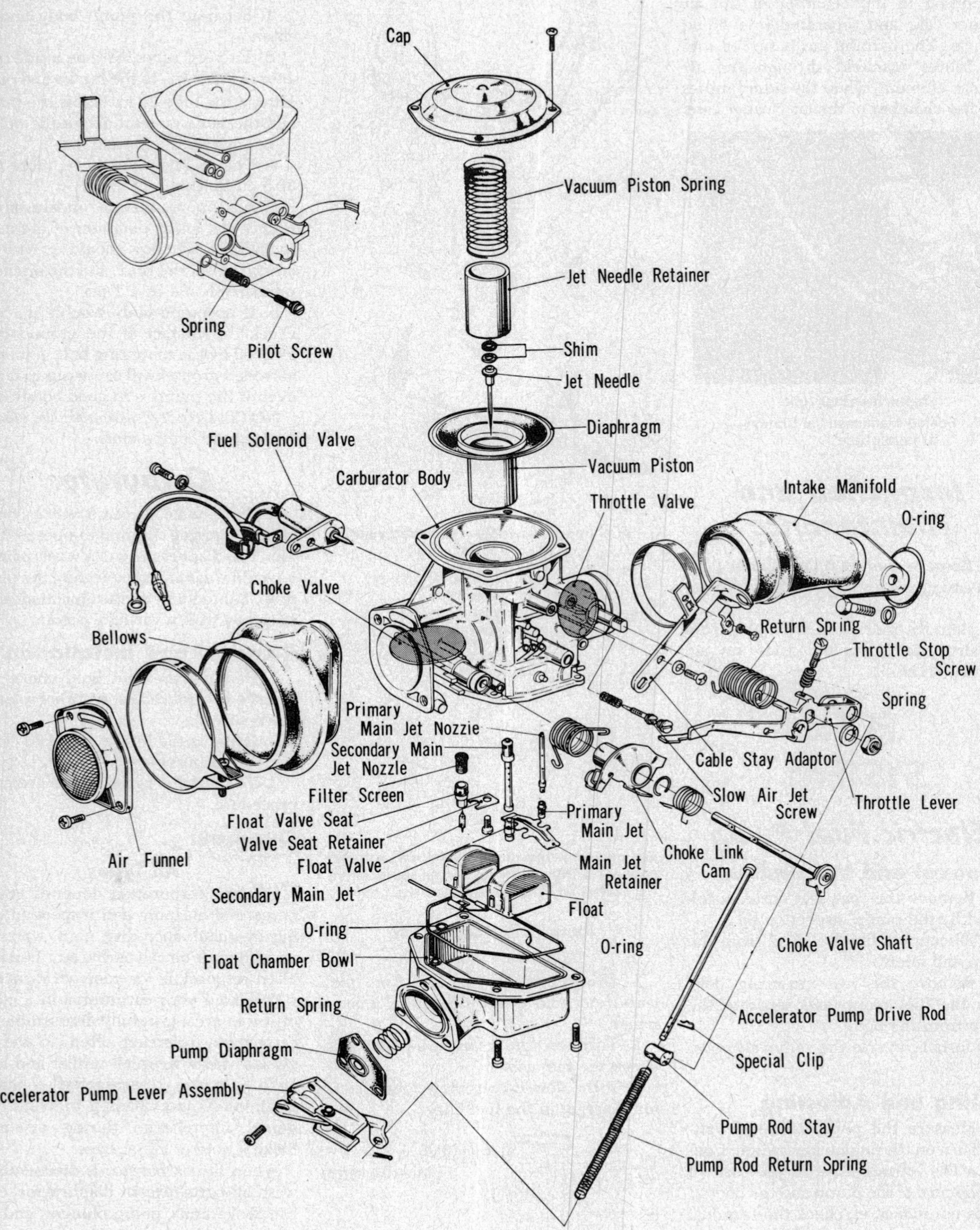

Carburetor (diaphragm-operated type)—exploded view

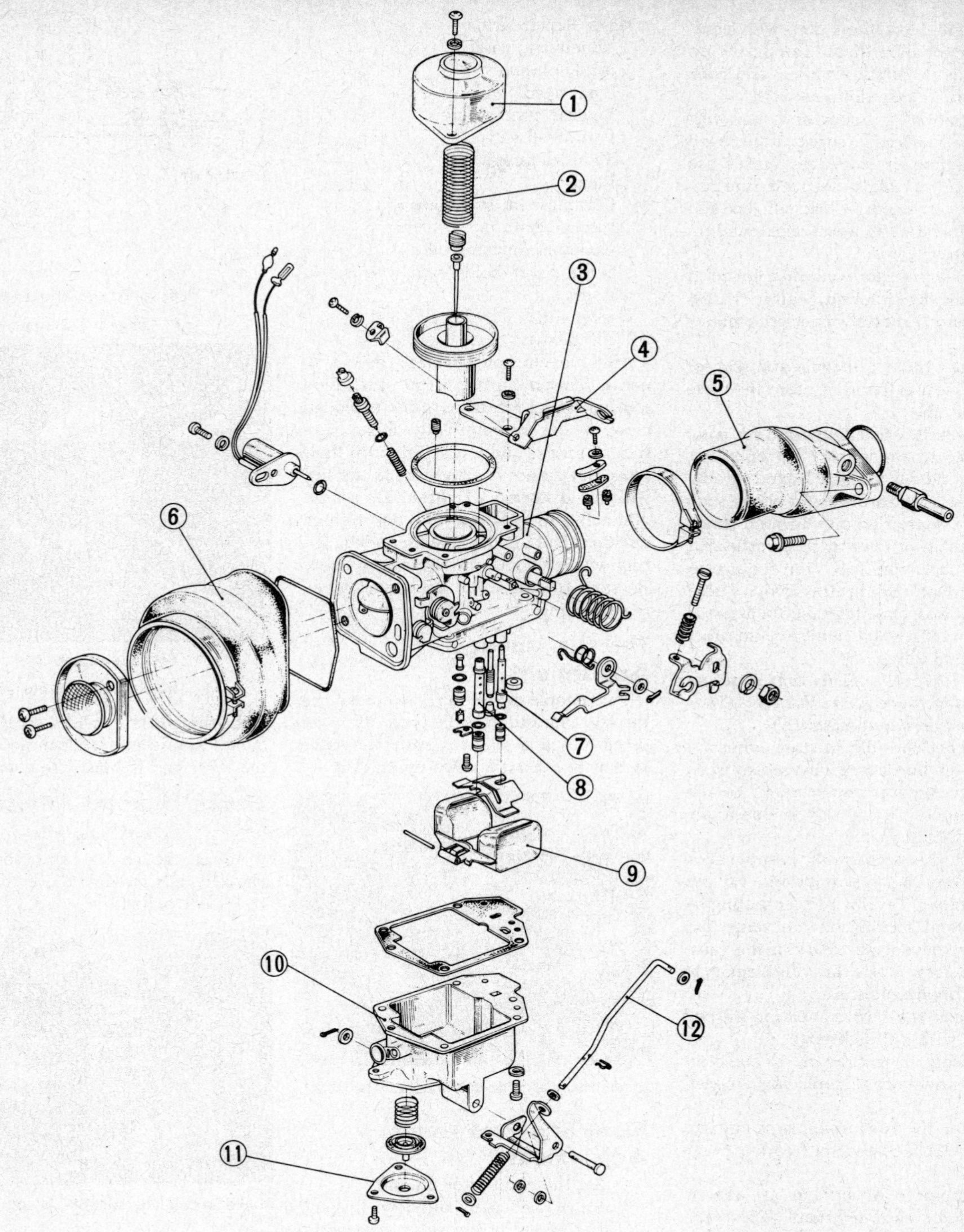

Carburetor (vacuum-piston type)—exploded view

1. Carburetor cap
2. Vacuum piston spring
3. Carburetor body
4. Plate (A) stay
5. Intake manifold
6. Air cleaner-to-carburetor bellows
7. Primary main jet nozzle
8. Needle jet
9. Carburetor float
10. Float chamber body
11. Accelerator pump cover
12. Accelerator pump drive rod

solvent and blow them dry with compressed air or allow them to air dry. Wipe clean all cork, plastic, leather, and fiber parts with a clean, lint-free cloth.

Blow out all passages and jets with compressed air and be sure that there are no restrictions or blockages. Never use wire or similar tools to clean jets, fuel passages, or air bleeds. Clean all jets and valves separately to avoid accidental interchange.

Check all parts for wear or damage. If wear or damage is found, replace the defective parts. Especially check the following:

1. Check the float needle and seat for wear. If wear is found, replace the complete assembly.
2. Check the float hinge pin for wear and the float(s) for dents or distortion. Replace the float if fuel has leaked into it.
3. Check the throttle and choke shaft bores for wear or an out-of-round condition. Damage or wear to the throttle arm, shaft, or shaft bore will often require replacement of the throttle body. These parts require a close tolerance of fit; wear may allow air leakage, which could affect starting and idling.

NOTE: *Throttle shafts and bushings are not included in overhaul kits. They can be purchased separately.*

4. Inspect the idle mixture adjusting needles for burrs or grooves. Any such condition requires replacement of the needle, since you will not be able to obtain a satisfactory idle.
5. Test the accelerator pump check valves. They should pass air one way but not the other. Test for proper seating by blowing and sucking on the valve. Replace the valve if necessary. If the valve is satisfactory, wash the valve again to remove breath moisture.
6. Check the bowl cover for warped surfaces with a straightedge.
7. Closely inspect the valves and seats for wear and damage, replacing as necessary.
8. After the carburetor is assembled, check the choke valve for freedom of operation.

Carburetor overhaul kits are recommended for each overhaul. These kits contain all gaskets and new parts to replace those that deteriorate most rapidly. Failure to replace all parts supplied with the kit (especially gaskets) can result in poor performance later.

Some carburetor manufacturers supply overhaul kits of three basic types: minor repair; major repair; and gasket kits. Basically, they contain the following:

Minor Repair Kits:
- All gaskets
- Float needle valve
- Volume control screw
- All diaphragms
- Spring for the pump diaphragm

Major Repair Kits:
- All jets and gaskets
- All diaphragms
- Float needle valve
- Volume control screw
- Pump ball valve
- Main jet carrier
- Float
- Complete intermediate rod
- Intermediate pump lever
- Complete injector tube
- Some cover hold-down screws and washers

Gasket Kits:
- All gaskets

After cleaning and checking all components, reassemble the carburetor, using new parts and referring to the exploded view. When reassembling, make sure that all screws and jets are tight in their seats, but do not overtighten, as the tips will be distorted. Tighten all screws gradually, in rotation. Do not tighten needle valves into their seats; uneven jetting will result. Always use new gaskets. Be sure to adjust the float level when reassembling.

Throttle Linkage Adjustment

Two people are required to make the throttle adjustment. Depress the gas pedal fully and adjust the throttle cable so that the throttle valve opens fully.

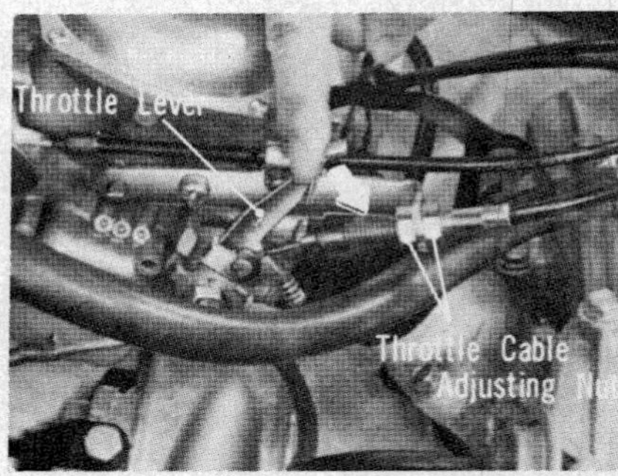

Use the throttle cable nut to adjust the throttle

Float and Fuel Level Adjustment

1. Set the carburetor on end.
2. Move the float up and down by hand so that the end of the valve comes into slight contact with the float arm, or there is approximately a 0.004 in. clearance between them.
3. Measure the float height. The float height should be 0.807 in. $\pm$ 0.002 in.

Fast Idle Adjustment

1. Open the choke valve completely.
2. Close the throttle valve fully by loosening the throttle stop screw.
3. After the engine has reached normal operating temperature, pull the choke knob out. The engine should idle at 4,000 rpm.
4. To adjust the fast idle, bend the tip of the throttle lever with a screwdriver to obtain the necessary clearance between the lever and the fast idle cam.

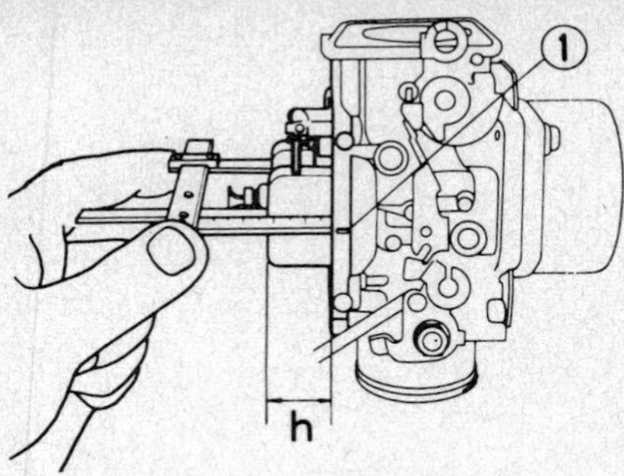

Measuring float adjustment

1. Gauge match mark

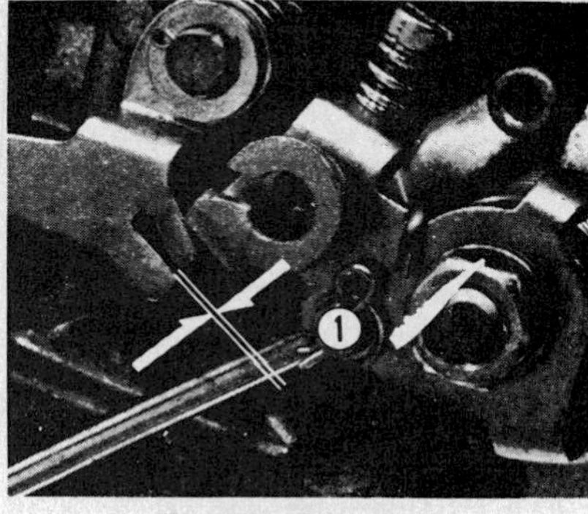

Fast idle adjustment

1. The point to be adjusted

Choke Linkage Adjustment

Diaphragm Model

Adjust the choke cable so that the choke is fully open when the choke control is not pulled.

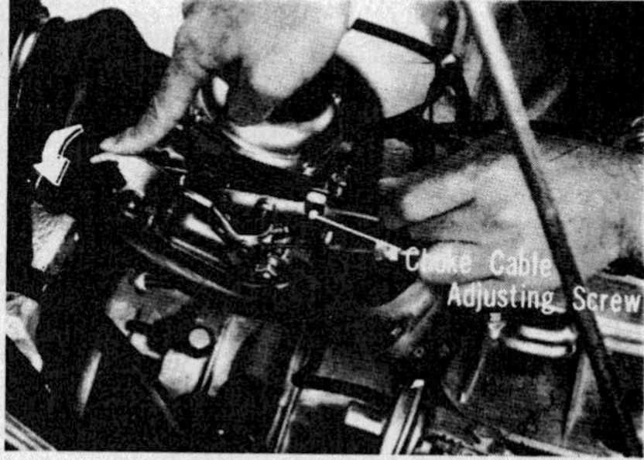

Choke linkage adjustment—diaphragm model

Vacuum Piston Model

To adjust the choke, position the relief spring, according to figure 80, to adjust the spring tension.

Accelerator Pump Adjustment

1. Turn the idle stop screw out until the screw no longer contacts the throttle stop plate (throttle butterfly completely closed).
2. Measure the clearance between the rocker arm and pump cover with a thickness gauge This clearance corresponds to the pump stroke.

Choke adjustment—vacuum piston model

1. Extreme cold conditions
2. Standard
3. Relief spring

Accelerator pump—rocker arm-pump cover clearance

1. Stroke
2. Rocker arm

3. Relocate the clip along the pump rod to adjust the pump stroke to 0.010–0.018 in. Lower the clip to increase the pump stroke; raise the clip to decrease the pump stroke.

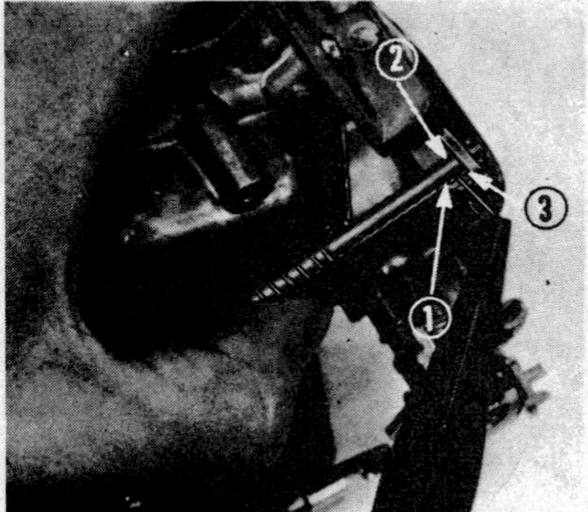

Pump adjusting clip—diaphragm model

1. High stroke
2. Standard
3. Low stroke

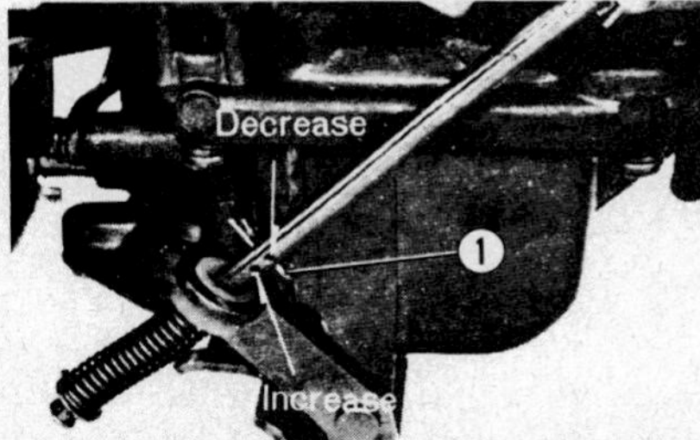

Pump adjusting clip—vacuum piston model

1. Pump adjusting clip

4. When the specified stroke cannot be obtained by repositioning the clip, readjust the stroke by bending the end of the rocker arm.

MANUAL TRANSMISSION

Removal and Installation

1. Remove the crankcase right side cover. Unbend the lockwasher and remove the bolt in preparation to removing the reverse gear shift fork.

2. Remove the reverse gear shift fork together with the reverse gear from the reverse gear shift fork shaft.

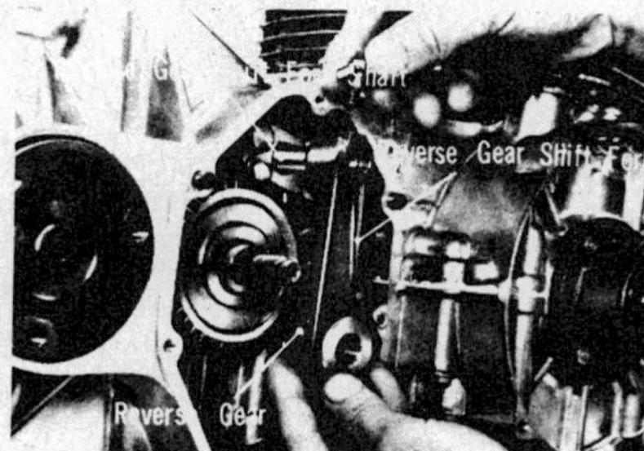

Remove the reverse gear shift fork and reverse gear

3. Separate the lower crankcase from the upper crankcase.

4. Remove the main shaft assembly from the upper crankcase.

5. Remove the external circlip from the main shaft. Remove the remaining clips, retainers, bearings, and gears in the order specified in the the figure.

6. Separate the countershaft from the upper crankcase.

7. Unfasten the needle bearing retainer set ring. Remove the remaining countershaft parts in the order given in the figure.

NOTE: *The countershaft reverse gear is press fitted to the countershaft.*

No attempt should be made to disassemble the reverse gear and ball bearing from the countershaft.

To install, reverse the removal procedure. Be careful to note the following items:

a. When installing the synchronizer hub and sleeve, note that two adjacent notches on the hub are deeper than the others at three places; on the sleeve, two adjacent teeth are higher than the others at three places. Install the hub and sleeve so that these sets of teeth are matched. Make sure that the index mark punched on the sleeve is positioned in the center of any three notches in the hub.

b. When installing the mainshaft and countershaft in the upper crankcase, align the holes on the needle bearing retainer with the set ring protrusions.

Constant Mesh Transmission

Early Honda 600's were equipped with a constant-mesh, four speed transmission. Each gear on the mainshaft and countershaft rotates independently of the shaft and is in constant mesh with its matching gears. The power is transmitted and controlled by shifting the shift gears, which are slide fitted on the shafts.

Overhaul

1. Measure the clearance between the needle roller bearing and the mainshaft top gear, and between the needle roller bearing and countershaft low gear.

The countershaft side clearance should be 0.0079–0.0197 in. The mainshaft side clearance should be 0.0139–0.0256 in. If side clearances are beyond serviceable limits, adjust by replacing the thrust plate on the mainshaft and countershaft.

2. Measure the side clearance of the mainshaft third gear, using a thickness (feeler) gauge.

The standard tolerance should be 0.-0039–0.0157 in.

4. Measure the radial clearance of the mainshaft top and third gears, and of the countershaft low and second gears, by determining the difference between the shaft diameter and the inside diameter for the respective gear.

The gear radial tolerance on every gear should be 0.008–0.0024 in.

5. Check the clearance between the shaft serration and the shift gear by turn-

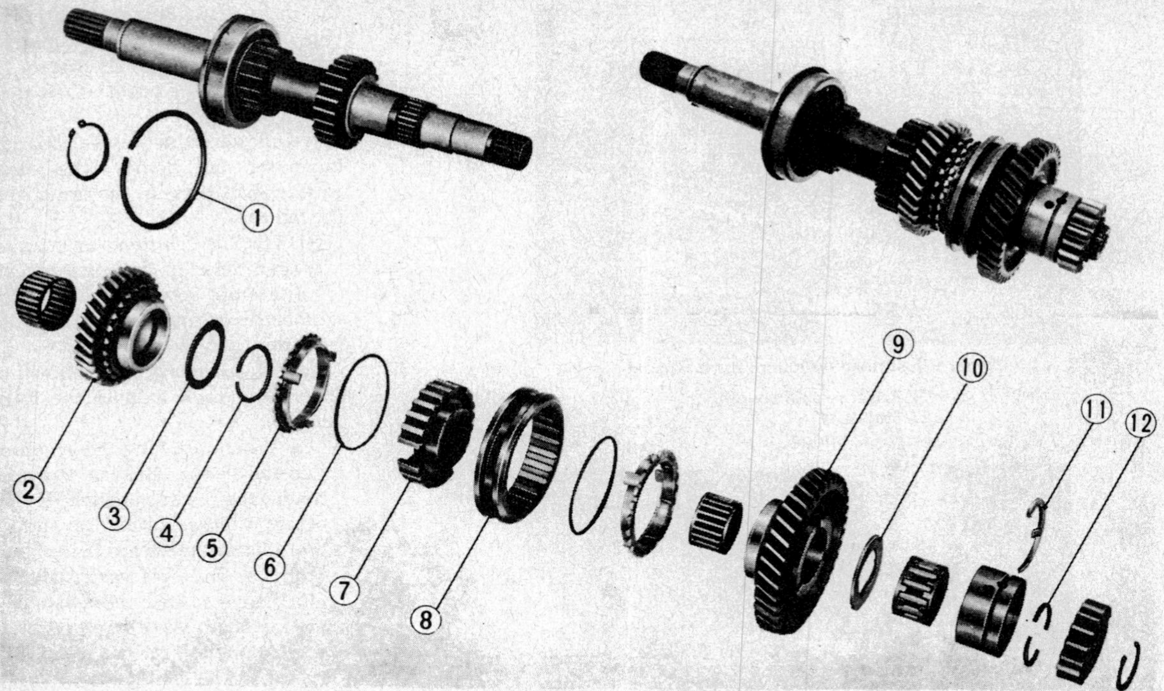

Transmission—mainshaft assembly

1. Set ring (62 mm)
2. Third/top gear
3. Thrust plate
4. Set ring (25 mm)
5. Blocking ring
6. Synchronizer spring
7. Synchronizer hub
8. Synchronizer sleeve
9. Mainshaft top gear
10. Thrust plate
11. Bearing retainer set ring (36 mm)
12. Reverse stopping ring

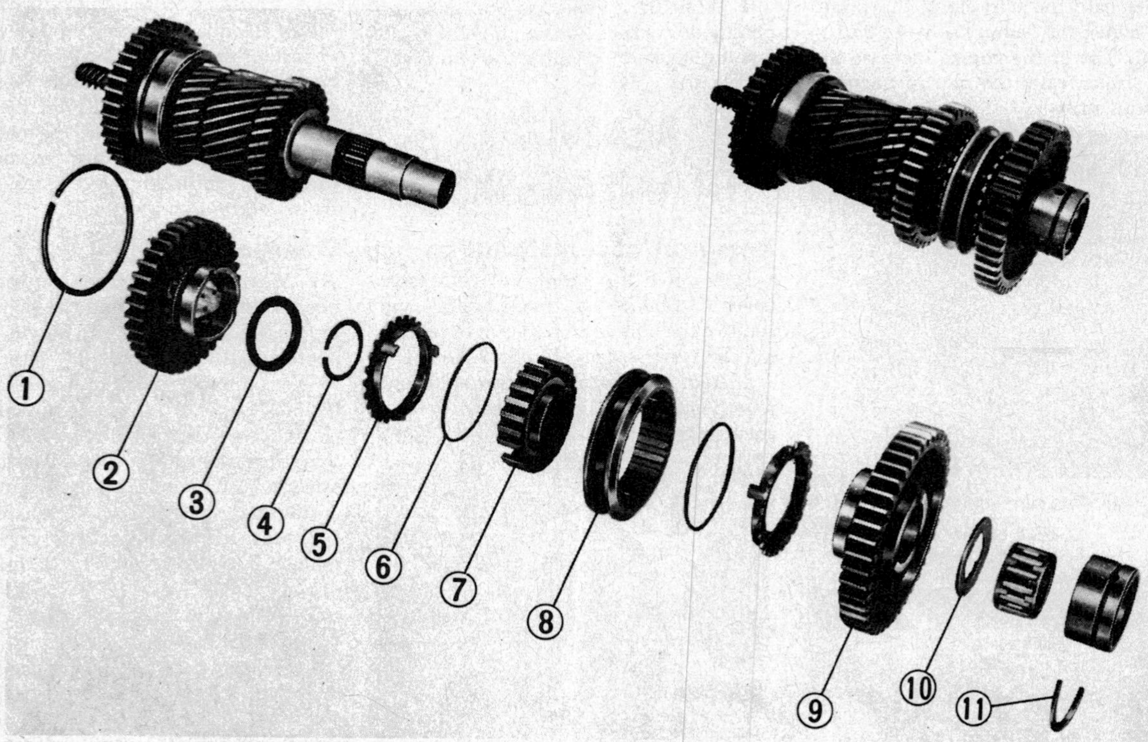

Transmission—countershaft assembly

1. Set ring (62 mm)
2. Countershaft second gear
3. Thrust plate
4. Set ring (25 mm)
5. Blocking ring
6. Synchronizer spring
7. Synchronizer hub
8. Synchronizer sleeve
9. Countershaft low gear
10. Thrust plate (C)
11. Bearing retainer set ring

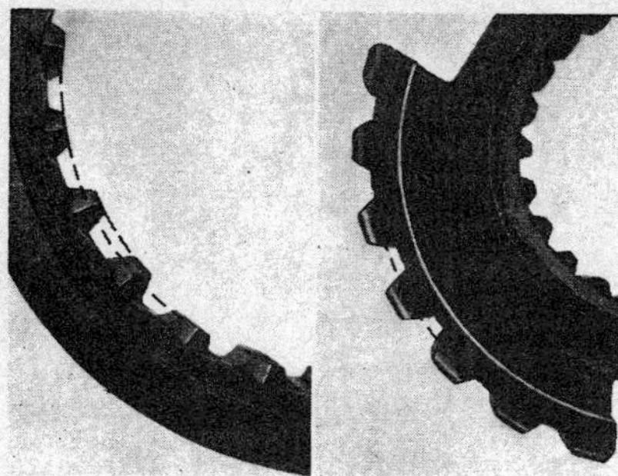

Note that two adjacent notches (on hub) and two adjacent teeth (on sleeve) are made for alignment.

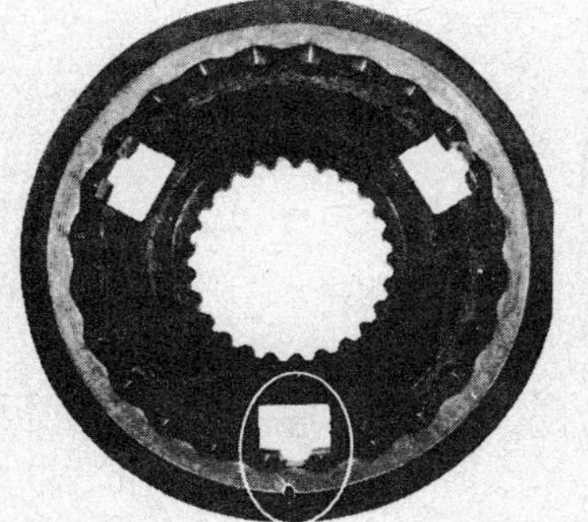

Position the index mark, punched on the sleeve, in the center of any three notches on the hub.

Align the holes in the needle bearing retainer with the protrusions on the set rings

Measuring roller bearing/top gear clearance on the main shaft Repeat for roller bearing/ low gear clearance on the countershaft

ing the gear on the shaft and determining if the clearance is excessive.

6. Measure the right and left bearing side clearances of both the mainshaft and countershaft.

The main and countershaft bearing side clearance should be 0.0012–0.0019 in.

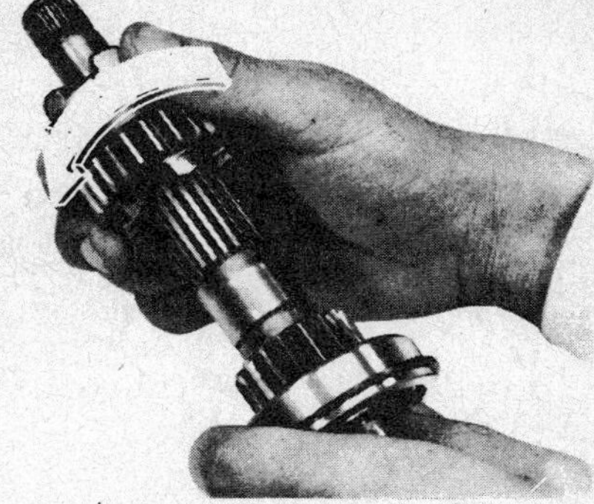

Check shaft serration/shift gear clearance by turning the gear on the shaft

Measure the wear to the low/second shift fork and the third/top shift fork.

7. Measure the wear to the low/-second shift fork and the third/top shift fork.

The standard tolerance should be 0.-2264–0.2303 in. Also check the clearance between the shift fork fingers and the synchronizer sleeve. Standard clearance is 0.0039–0.0118 in.

8. Determine the amount of backlash in the transmission gears by fixing one side of the gear pair and locking the mating gear.

The backlash should be 0.0025–0.0050 in.

Gear Shift Mechanism

Shift Forks and Shafts

Removal and Installation

1. Remove the reverse shift fork. Remove the fork shaft setting bolts.
2. Remove the guide plate and take the steel balls out.
3. Remove the respective shift fork shafts from the guide plate side.
4. Remove the fork shaft interlock pin from the reverse shift fork shaft.

To install, reverse the removal procedure. Carefully check the following items when installing:

a. Install the fork shaft interlock pin and steel balls securely to prevent improper engagement of the gears. These parts must be cleaned prior to assembly.

b. The guide plate holds the pin and balls. Place the plate in position and see if the bolt holes line up. If the bolt holes are not aligned, rotate the plate 180° and install and tighten the bolts.

c. Replace the lock washers with new ones during installation.

Gear Shift Plates

Removal and Installation

1. Remove the ball spring retaining bolt from the gear shift rod and take the spring and steel ball out.
2. Separate the gear shift rod from the gear shift arm and take them out of the case.
3. Remove the ball spring retaining bolt from the reverse gear restricting pin and take the spring and steel ball out.
4. Remove the reverse pin spring seat and remove the reverse gear restricting pin.
5. Remove the four 6 mm bolts, the gear shift plates, and the gear shift guide plates from the crankcase.
6. Remove the retaining screws and the reverse select lever pivot bolt from the guide plates and separate the gear shift guide plates from the gear shift plates.

To assemble and install, reverse the removal procedure. Be careful not to interchange the ball spring retaining bolts and springs, since the bolts and springs for the gear shift rod and for the reverse gear restricting pin are different lengths.

Be sure to measure the amount of wear to the third/top shift plate, the low/-second shift plate, and the gear shift on the reverse shift plate. The standard tolerance is 0.284–0.287 in.

Gear Shifter

Disassemble and install according to the illustration.

Maintenance and Adjustment

1. When assembling, lightly grease the return spring and universal joint where the shift rod and lever join.
2. To adjust the shift lever, set the lever into first or third gear. The lever should be 2.0–2.8 inches from the edge of the knob to the edge of the dash. The shift lever can be adjusted to the driver's convenience. To lower the shift lever, move the bracket to the rear.
3. To check for play in the shift lever, set the shifter into neutral and make sure the stroke is from 2.0 to 2.4 inches when the shifter is moved lightly to the left. If the stroke is too large, a worn joint is the cause. If this is the case, replace the shift lever (adjustment is impossible).

CLUTCH

The clutch is a dry, single-disc type, using a diaphragm spring. Engine power

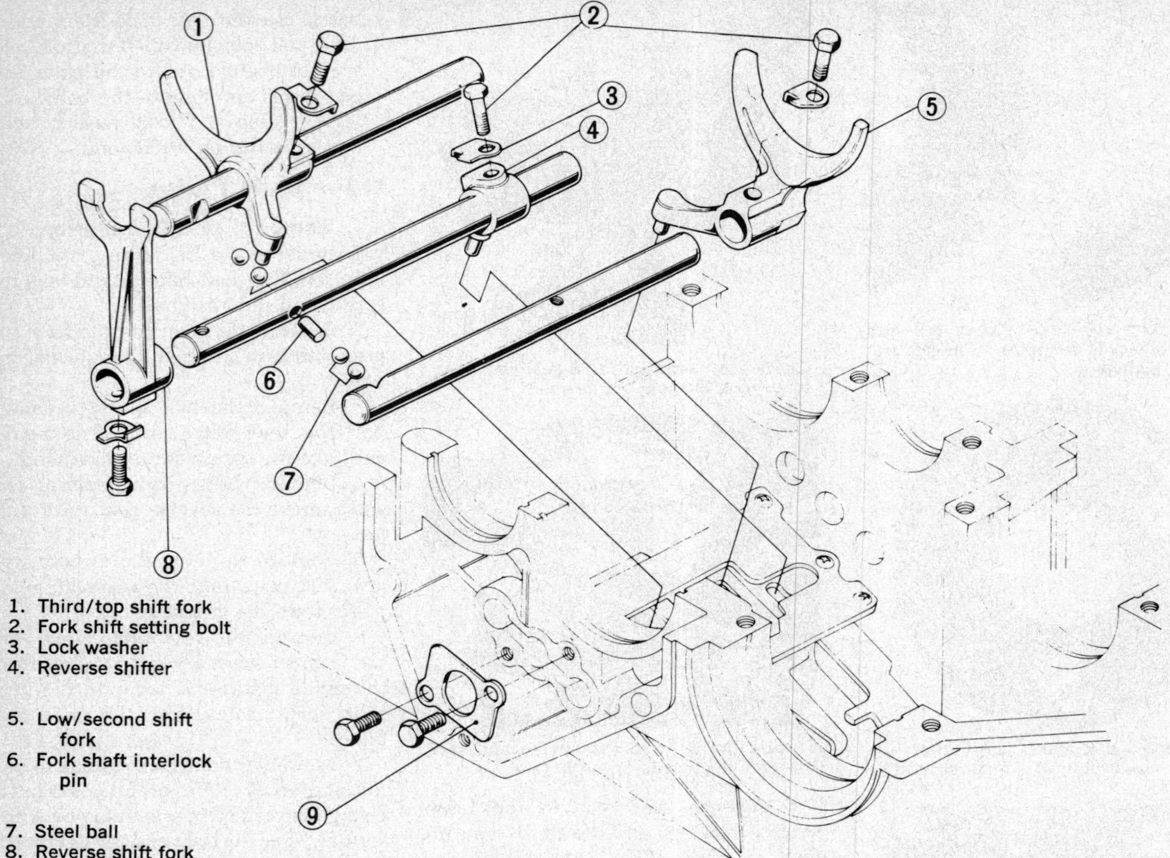

1. Third/top shift fork
2. Fork shift setting bolt
3. Lock washer
4. Reverse shifter
5. Low/second shift fork
6. Fork shaft interlock pin
7. Steel ball
8. Reverse shift fork
9. Guide plate

Shift forks—exploded view

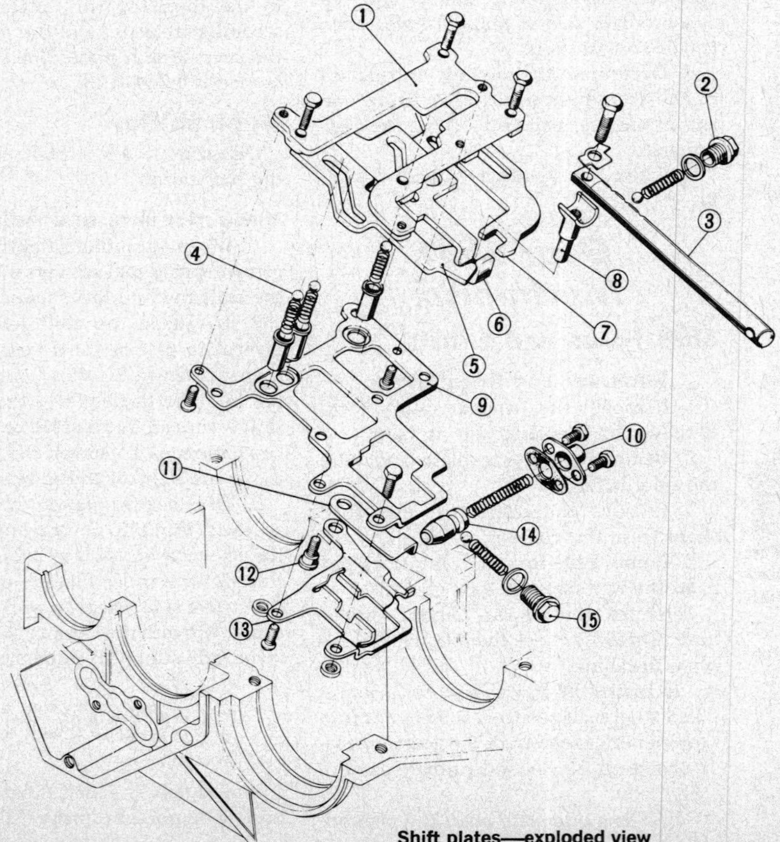

1. Gear shift plate cover
2. Ball spring retaining bolt
3. Gear shift rod
4. Steel ball
5. Third/top shift plate
6. Low/second shift plate
7. Reverse shift plate
8. Gear shift arm
9. Gear shift guide lower plate
10. Reverse pin spring seat
11. Reverse select lever
12. Reverse select lever pivot bolt
13. Gear shift guide upper plate
14. Reverse gear restricting pin
15. Ball spring retaining bolt

Shift plates—exploded view

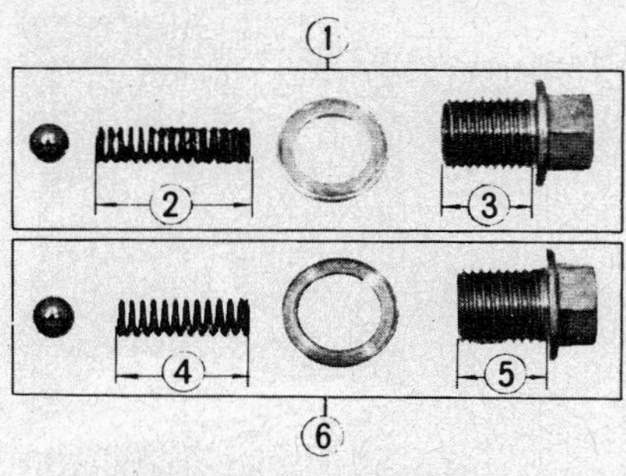

Linkage bolts and springs

1. For gear shift rod
2. 1.318 in.
3. 1.043 in.
4. 1.102 in.
5. 0.925 in.
6. For reverse gear restricting pin

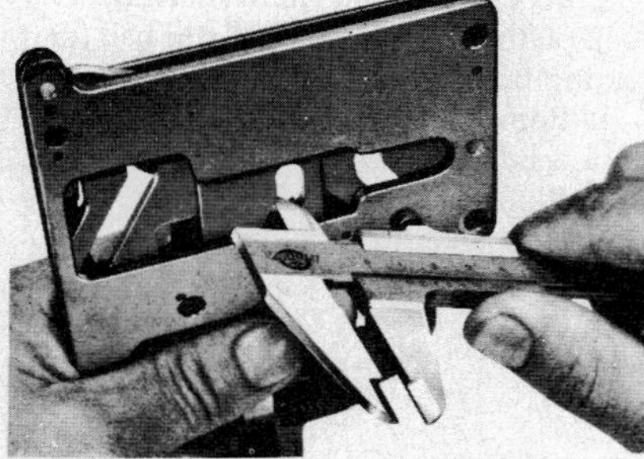

Measure the wear on all of the shift plates

is transmitted from the crankshaft, via the primary drive chains, to rotate the clutch drum and pressure disc assembly, bolted to the primary driven sprocket.

Removal and Installation

1. Remove the heater blower unit from the engine compartment.
2. Remove the joint pipe assembly.
3. Remove the two bottom side bolts from the heat exchanger stay.
4. Remove the adjusting bolt on the clutch release lever and remove the clutch control cable from the release lever and from the clutch housing.
5. Remove the clutch housing retaining bolts and remove the housing from the left side cover.
6. Remove the pressure disc assembly from the clutch drum.
7. Remove the clutch friction disc from the mainshaft.

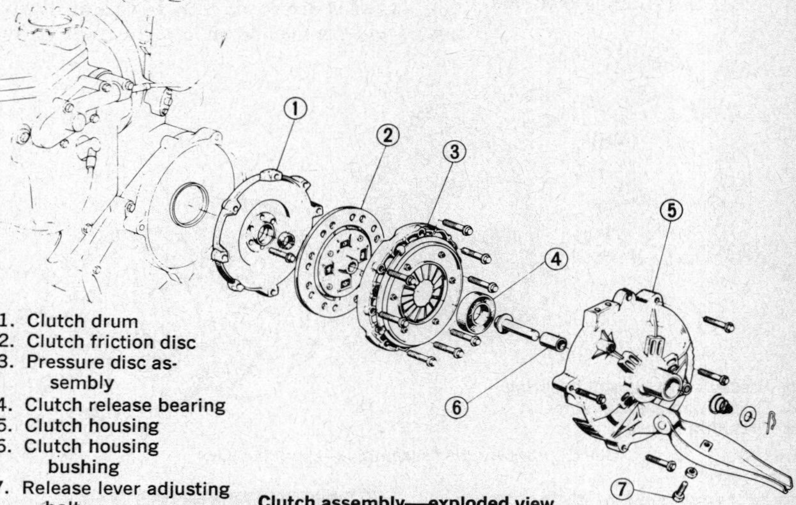

1. Clutch drum
2. Clutch friction disc
3. Pressure disc assembly
4. Clutch release bearing
5. Clutch housing
6. Clutch housing bushing
7. Release lever adjusting bolt

Clutch assembly—exploded view

1. Lever stay pivot collar
2. Pivot pin side bushing
3. Pivot pin bushing
4. Shift rod bracket
5. Shift lever
6. Shift lever bushing
7. Shift lever pin
8. Gear shift rod joint pin
9. Gear shift lever
10. Shift lever pin
11. Gear shift rod
12. Return spring

Gear shifter—exploded view

8. Remove the clutch drum.
9. Remove the cotter pin at the end of the clutch release rod and remove the clutch release bearing from the clutch housing. The clutch release bearing and rod can be separated by tapping the rod with a pin punch lightly. When driving the rod into the clutch release bearing, install the rod so that the side of the bearing, on which the outer race protrudes beyond the face of the inner race, faces the clutch diaphragm spring.
10. To disassemble the pressure disc, remove the four retaining springs and remove the nuts which retain the diaphragm setting plate.

To reassemble and install, reverse the removal procedure. Be sure to observe the following:

a. When installing the pressure disc to the clutch disc, align the punch marks.

b. When installing the clutch drum, do not damage the oil seal nor fold the seal lip.

c. Before the final tightening of the clutch housing, align the heat exchanger stay with all bolts in place. Tighten the clutch housing bolts and then remove the bolts necessary to install the joint pipe assembly.

d. Apply thread lock to the clutch drum retaining bolts when installing.

Shift lever should be 2.0-2.8 in. from the edge of the knob to the edge of the dash.

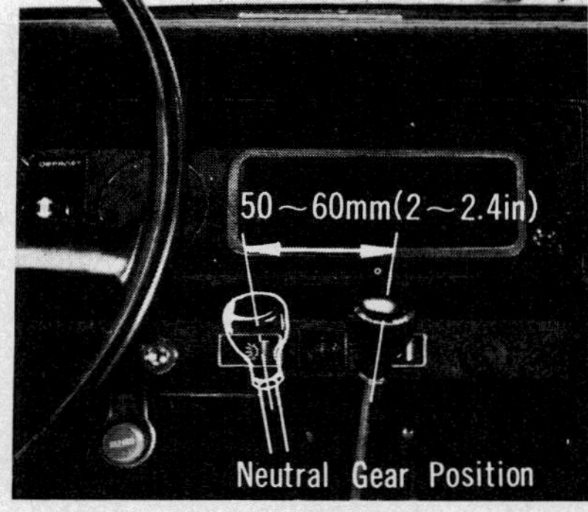

The stroke of the shift lever play should be 2.0-2.4 in.

Pedal Height Adjustment

Clutch pedal height adjustment should be made before pedal lash adjustment.

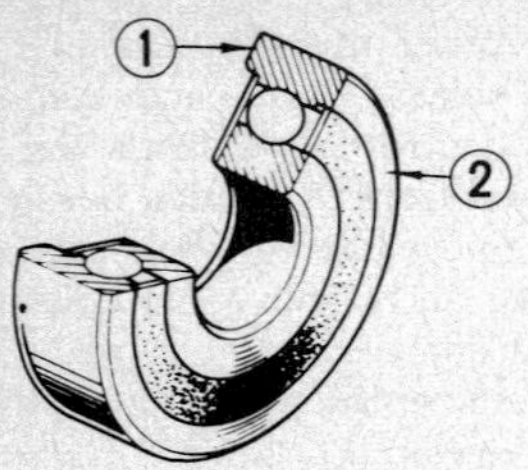

Clutch throw-out bearing

1. Diaphragm spring side
2. Release bearing shaft side

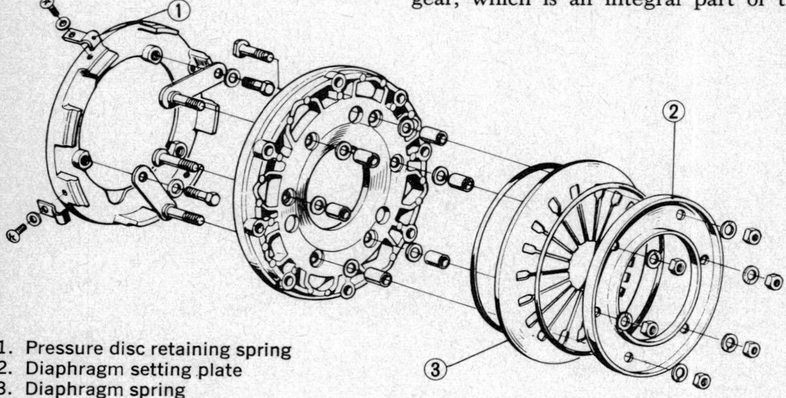

1. Pressure disc retaining spring
2. Diaphragm setting plate
3. Diaphragm spring

Clutch pressure disc assembly—exploded view

Align the punch marks on the clutch and pressure discs.

After loosening the lock nut, move the adjusting bolt in or out to adjust the pedal height. Adjust the pedal to match the brake pedal height.

Clutch pedal height adjustment

Free-Play Adjustment

Check the clutch release lever for play at the tip of the lever. The specified play is 0.08–0.12 in. Adjust the pedal free-play by means of the adjusting bolt. Check the clutch cable for movement and damage at the release lever end and at the clutch pedal end.

DRIVE AXLES

The differential is housed in the crankcase housing, behind the transmission, and is driven directly by the final drive gear, which is an integral part of the transmission countershaft. By this arrangement, the differential, along with the transmission, is lubricated by the engine oil. The principal gears used in the differential are a helical type.

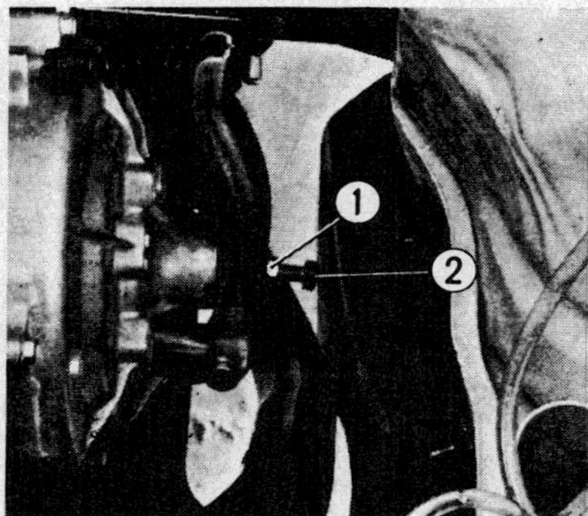

Clutch free-play adjustment

1. Lock nut
2. Adjusting bolt

Driveshaft

The front drive shaft assembly consists of an axle shaft and a drive-shaft with two universal joints.

A constant velocity ball joint is used for both universal joints, which are factory-packed with special grease and enclosed in sealed rubber boots. The outer ball joint cannot be disassembled except for removal of the boot.

Removal and Disassembly

1. Remove the front wheel.

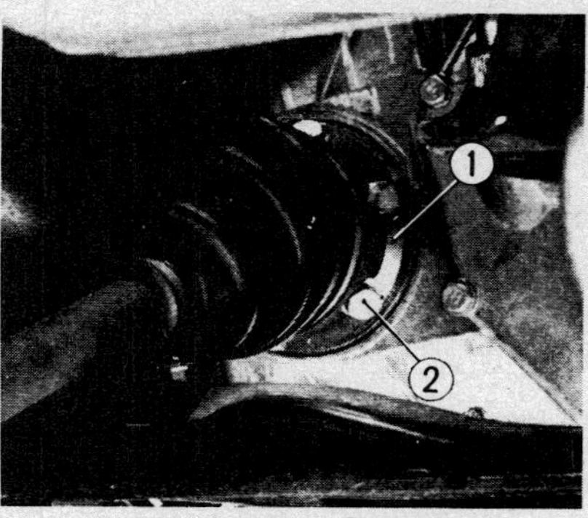

Straighten the joint lock plate tabs and remove the ball joint set bolts.

1. Joint lock plate
2. Ball joint setting bolt

2. Straighten the joint setting bolt lock-plate tabs and remove the ball joint setting bolts.
3. Remove the front brake caliper as an assembly.
4. Remove the front hub and brake disc as an assembly.

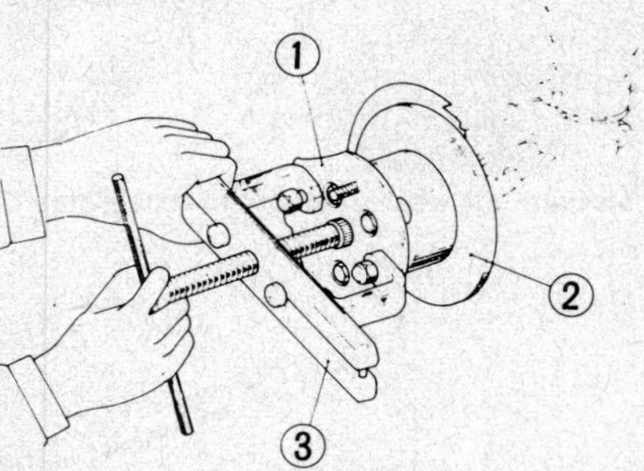

Remove the front hub and front brake disc as an assembly.

1. Front hub
2. Front brake disc
3. Brake drum puller

5. Remove the front brake mudguard.
6. Install the drive-shaft replacer (special tool # 07045-56805) with the replacer flange (tool #07045-56810) bolted to the knuckle, and the attachment (tool #07045-56820) set to the axle shaft, as shown. Tighten the center bolt of the replacer with a socket wrench. Then separate the drive shaft from the knuckle.

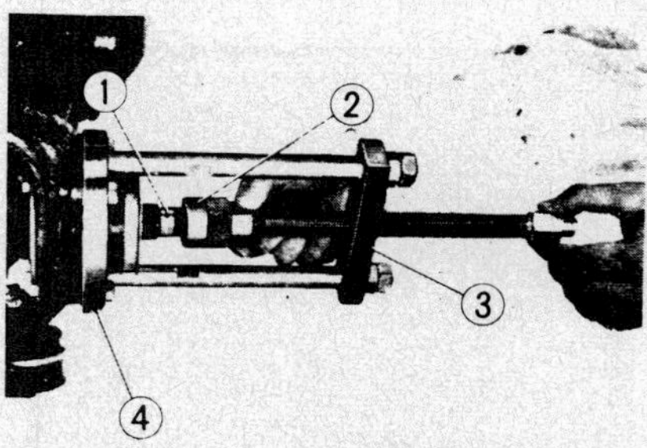

Separate the drive shaft from the knuckle

1. Axle shaft
2. Attachment
3. Drive shaft remover
4. Flange

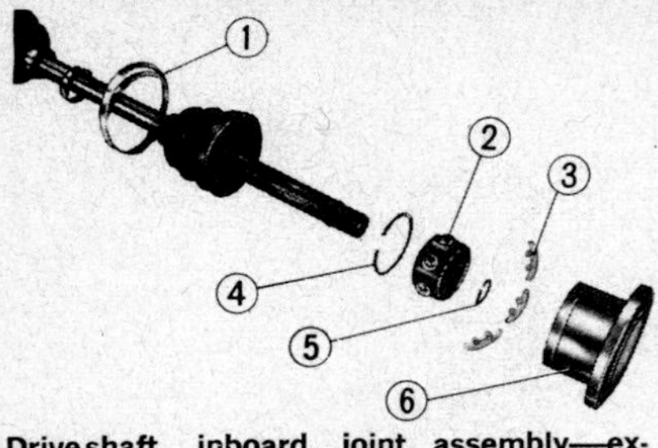

Driveshaft inboard joint assembly—exploded view.
1. Band
2. Inner Retainer
3. Joint setting bolt lock plate
4. Ring
5. External circlip
6. Inboard joint

7. To disassemble the ball joint:

a. Remove the boot band.

b. Remove the stop ring with a screwdriver.

c. Remove the external circlip

The inboard joint and inner retainer can now be removed.

Overhaul and Installation

To assemble and install the drive-shaft, reverse the removal procedure. The following items must be carefully checked when the driveshaft is reassembled.

a. Wash all the parts prior to assembly and check them for damage and excessive wear. Replace the boots if they are broken or cracked.

b. Fit the boot to the drive-shaft and set the inner retainer on the drive shaft with a circlip.

c. Fill the joint flange with the recommended lubricant. Insert the joint flange and secure it with the internal stop-ring.

d. Install the boot band with a band fastener (special tool #07043-55101) and stake it at two places with a punch fitted to the fastener. Then cut off the end of the band leaving about 0.39 in. and bend it so that it covers the staked portion.

e. To install the drive-shaft assembly, reverse the removal procedure using the drive shaft replacer. Tighten the drive shaft bolts to a specified torque of 20.3–23.1 ft lbs.

NOTE: *If the front hub is loose on the spindle, replace the hub or driveshaft with a new one.*

REAR SUSPENSION

Shock Absorber

Removal and Installation

1. Separate the rear shock absorber from the leaf spring retaining plate.

2. Remove the rear seat back and disconnect the rear shock absorber from the rear wheel housing.

To install, reverse the removal procedure.

Leaf Springs-Axle Beam

1. Remove the rear brakes. (See the "Brake" section.)

2. Disconnect the brake hose and parking brake cable B from the rear axle beam.

3. Remove the retaining bolts at the front and rear of the rear leaf spring and remove the axle beam and rear leaf spring as an assembly.

4. The rear axle beam and rear leaf springs can be separated after the leaf spring retaining U-bolts are removed.

To install, reverse the removal procedure. Measure the body height after installing the rear leaf springs and adjust the locations of the spring shackles if there is any lateral lean.

Upon completion of the installation, check the rear suspension for misalignment of front and rear wheel tread. Drive the car over a wet section of pavement. Then drive in a straight line on dry pavement and stop. The rear tire imprint should appear an equal distance slightly inside the front tire tracks.

FRONT SUSPENSION

Front Strut

Removal and Installation

1. Remove the wheels and brakes.

2. Separate the tie rods from the knuckle rods with a tie rod ball joint puller (or special tool #07092-55103).

3. Separate the front suspension ball joint from the knuckle with the ball joint puller.

4. Remove the front stabilizer bar from the subframe.

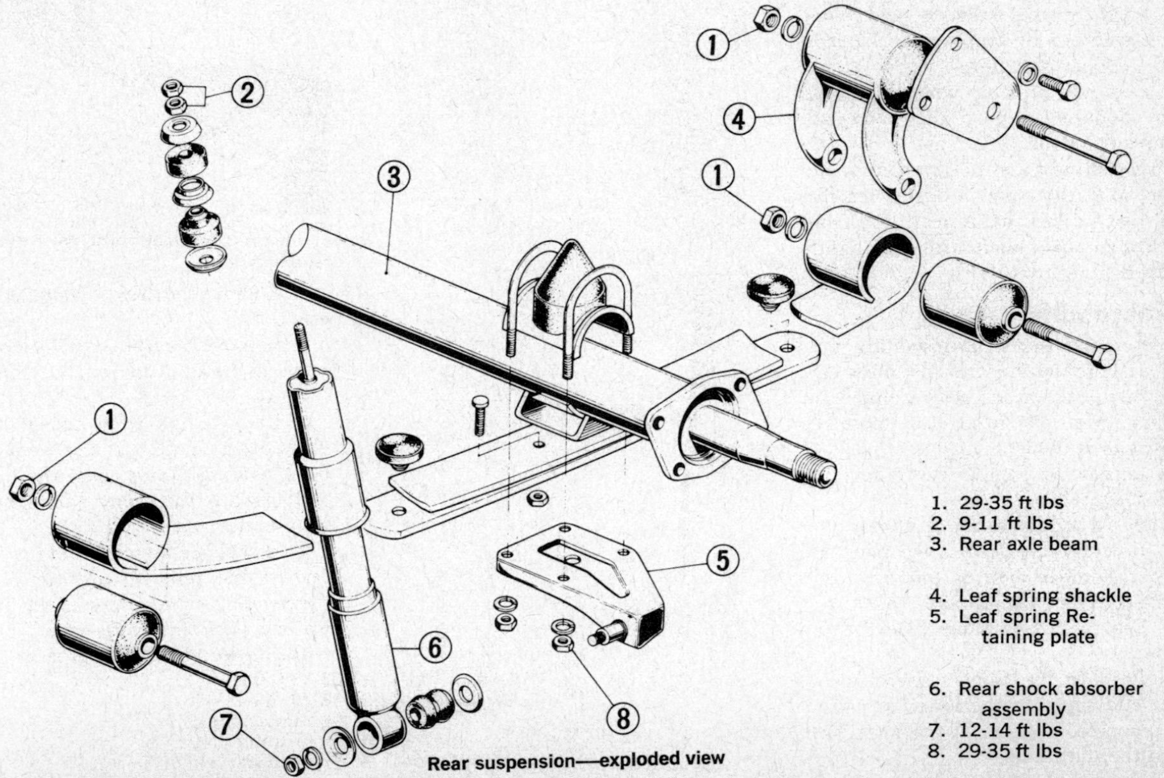

Rear suspension—exploded view

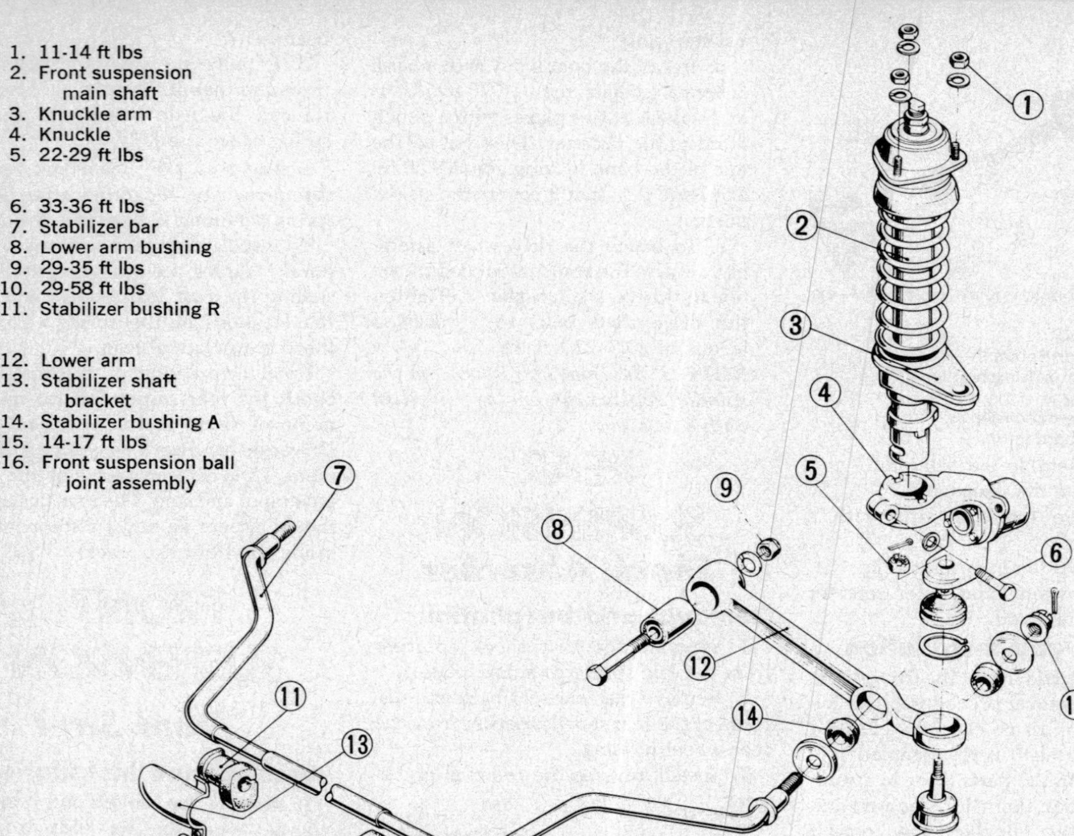

Front suspension—exploded view

5. Remove the front strut lock bolts.

6. Separate the knuckle and front shock absorber by tapping the knuckle with a copper hammer.

7. Remove the nuts which hold the strut mounting cap to the body and remove the strut.

To install, reverse the removal procedure. To fit the knuckle during installation, place a jack underneath the front suspension main shaft arm and lightly compress the front shock.

Disassembly

1. Remove the strut mounting nuts and washers and the strut mounting cap.

2. Install the front strut compressor and compress the front strut gradually and remove the cotter ring.

3. Loosen the handle and remove the strut unit.

Knuckle and Lower Arm Removal

1. Remove the front brake pads and caliper. Remove the front hub and front brake disc. (See the "Brake" section)

2. Separate the stabilizer from the subframe.

3. Remove the front suspension ball joint and separate the lower arm from the knuckle. Disconnect the lower arm from the subframe.

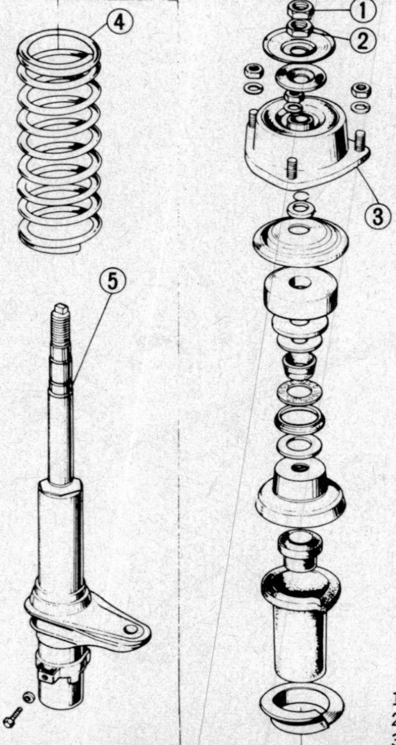

Front strut assembly—exploded view

1. 33-36 ft lbs
2. 18-22 ft lbs
3. Strut mounting cap
4. Front spring
5. Front suspension mainshaft

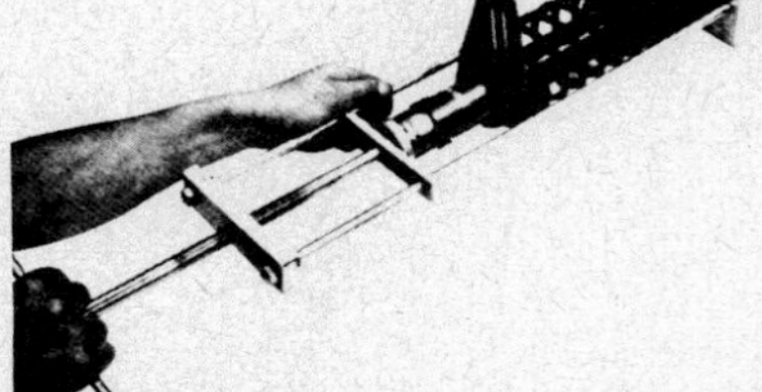

Compress the front strut to remove the retaining ring.

4. Remove the driveshaft ball joint setting bolts.

5. Remove the front strut lock bolt and separate the knuckle from the front strut.

6. Remove the front wheel bearing dust cover, bearing dust seal cover, and front bearing O-ring from the knuckle, and remove the front wheel bearings from both sides.

To install the knuckle and lower arm, reverse the removal procedure. Apply the recommended grease to the dust seal lip and pack the front wheel bearings with the recommended grease.

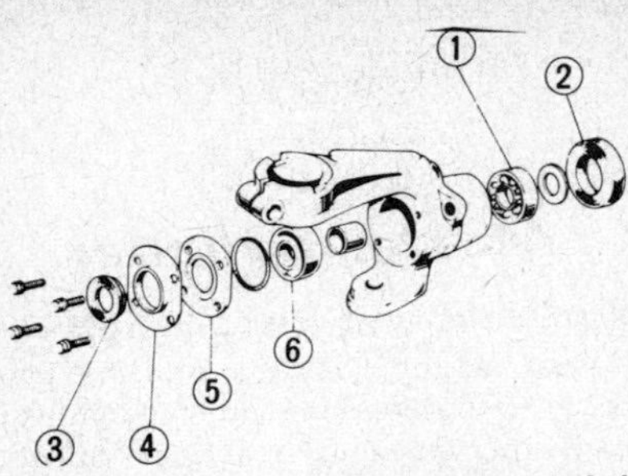

Knuckle/front bearing assembly—exploded view.

1. Front wheel bearing
2. Disc brake dust seal
3. Front wheel bearing dust seal
4. Bearing dust seal cover
5. Front wheel bearing cover
6. Front wheel bearing

Adjustments

Toe-Out

Toe-out is the difference of the distance between the forward extremes of the front tires and the distance between the rearward extremes of the front tires. Toe-out is 0.078 in. for Honda. Toe-out can be adjusted by loosening the lock-nuts at each of the tie rods and then turning the tie rods in an opposite direction from each other, in equal amounts.

Rotate the tie-rods to adjust toe-out

Caster and Camber

Caster and camber cannot be adjusted on the Honda 600. If there is incorrect caster and camber, replace the defective parts.

STEERING

The steering assembly is a rack and pinion type. The steering column is divided with two universal joints and is bent. The steering gear box is located on the firewall and is positioned horizontally with four bolts. The pinion gear is connected to the steering column with serration and is secured with calmp bolts. Thrust applied to the pinion gear is received by the U-shaped thrust plate fitted to the groove near the pinion gear head, and end play of the pinion gear is adjusted by the pinion adjusting bolt.

Steering Wheel

Removal and Installation

1. Pull the safety pad (horn button) off and remove the retaining nut.
2. Disconnect the ground wire from the horn switch and remove the switch.
3. Remove the wheel with a conventional steering wheel puller and pull the cam spring and washers from the steering shaft.
4. To install the steering wheel, reverse the removal procedure. Be sure to apply a thin coat of grease to the engine side of the steering wheel mounting plate.

Turn Signal and Steering Column

Removal and Installation

1. After removing the steering wheel, unfasten the four bolts which hold the steering column to the instrument panel.
2. Remove the bolts at each end of the universal joint assembly and separate the assembly from the steering shaft.
3. After removing the housing sections from the column, loosen the screws which hold the turn signal unit to the column. Removal of the unit can be accomplished by first tapping the head of the screws.
4. Pull the steering shaft out of the column and remove the bushings at the top and bottom of the column. Replace the bushings with new ones.

NOTE: *Be sure to release the steering lock and leave the key in when disassembling the steering column.*

5. The ignition lock switch is clamped to the steering column and held by a single lock bolt.
6. To assemble the steering column, reverse the removal procedure being careful to position the key nut which wedges the turn signal switch in place.

Steering Gear

Removal and Installation

1. Remove the heater blower unit, carburetor, and fan housing.
2. Remove the nuts at the end of the tie-rods and separate the tie-rods from the knuckle arms with a ball joint puller.
3. Disconnect the pinion from the

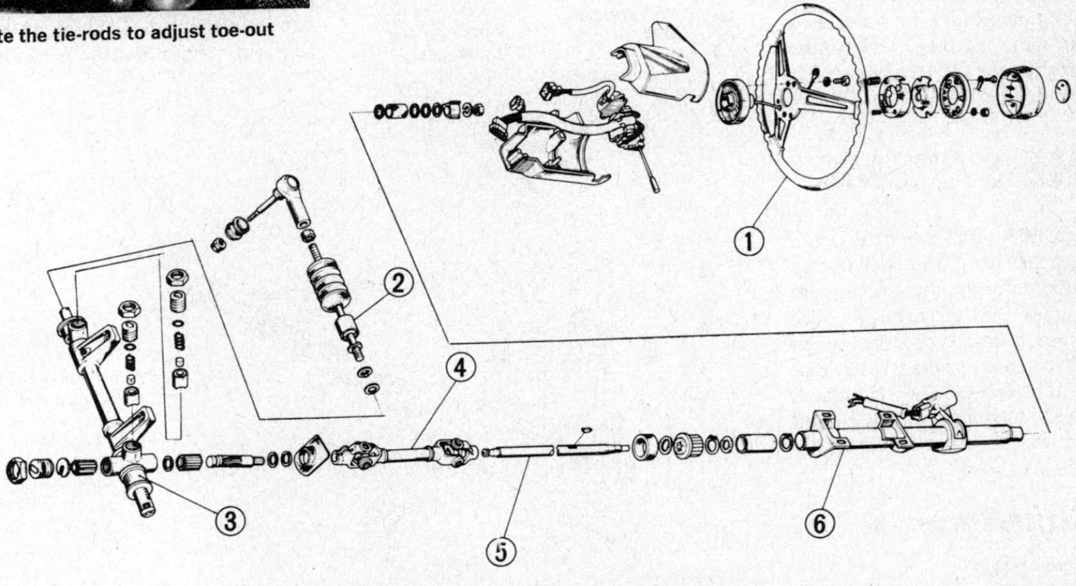

Steering assembly—exploded view

1. Steering wheel
2. Rack end assmebly
3. Steering gear box
4. Universal joint assembly
5. Steering shaft
6. Steering column

joint assembly.

4. Remove the gear box bolts from the engine side and the two interior bolts holding the steering gear box, and remove the gear box unit.

5. To remove the rack end assembly, first straighten the tie-rod lock washer and then turn the tie-rod with a wrench, separating the tie-rod from the steering rack.

6. Remove the left and right rack guides. Turn the pinion clockwise and pull out the rack.

7. To remove the steering pinion, loosen the pinion washer nut and remove the washer bolt. Push the pinion down and remove the thrust washer. The pinion can now be pulled out.

8. When installing, be sure to grease the moving parts, replace the tie-rod washers and cotter pins, and perform the proper adjustments.

Adjustments

1. Shake the rack end ball joint, checking for wear. A loose ball joint could cause a rattling noise from the steering gear box.

2. With a spring scale, measure the force required to move the tie-rod. The standard range is 0.5–3.3 lbs. Another simple way of checking the force is to hold the rack in a horizontal position. If the steering rack end does not lower by its own weight, the condition is satisfactory.

A rattling noise may develop if the rack gear bushing is worn excessively. If the play is more than 0.002 in., replacement of parts is necessary.

First, adjust the rack guide farthest from the pinion. Tighten the adjusting bolt until it stops and then back off the bolt about 20 degrees. Secure the bolt with the lock nut. Adjust the other rack guide in the same manner. The proper tightening torque for the lock nuts is 14.-5–18.1 ft lbs.

BRAKE SYSTEMS

The Honda 600 utilizes a dual brake system where the front and rear brakes function independently and one system remains in operation if the other one fails. A leading/trailing type drum brake is used for the rear brakes, with disc brakes for the front. The Honda is equipped with a brake warning light which is activated when a defect in the brake system occurs.

Adjustments

Pedal Free-Play

Measure the distance from the floor (with the carpet removed) to the brake pedal. Then disconnect the return spring and again measure the distance from the floor to the brake pedal. The difference in the two measurements is the pedal free-play. The specified free-play is 0.04–0.34 in. Free-play adjustment is made by loosening the lock nut on the brake light switch and rotating the switch body until the specified clearance is obtained.

Brake Performance

If braking difficulties are experienced:

a. Check and adjust tire pressure

b. Check the front pads for wear and check the movement of the calipers

c. Check the drums for wear and adjust the linings,

Parking Brake

The rear wheels should be locked when the parking brake lever is pulled one to five notches. Adjustment should be made by turning the adjusting nut located at the rear axle shaft.

Rods and Cables

Check the cables for wear and damage and check the cable guide and equalizer-/adjusting nut for looseness. Also check the equalizer cable, where it contacts the equalizer, for any signs of wear. Apply grease between the equalizer and cable if necessary.

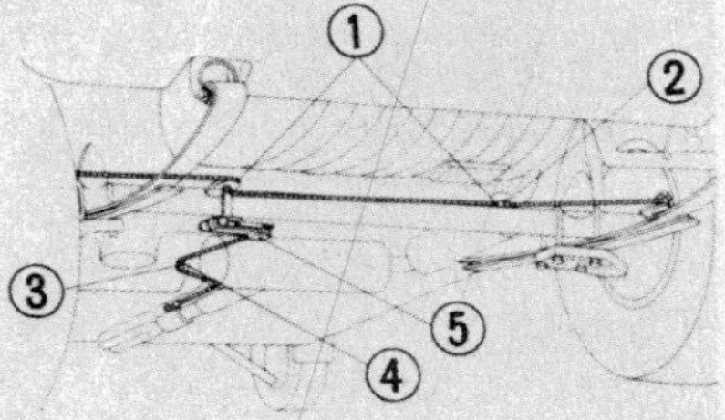

Parking brake cable lubrication

1. Apply grease
2. Guide
3. Guide
4. Apply grease
5. Equalizer

HYDRAULIC SYSTEM

Master Cylinder

Removal and Installation

Dual master cylinders, utilizing two brake circuits working independently of each other for the front and rear brakes, are installed on the Honda 600.

Before removing the master cylinder, cover the body surfaces with fender covers and rags to prevent damage to painted surfaces by brake fluid.

1. Disconnect the brake pedal and the master cylinder push rod by removing the lock pin.

2. Remove the warning switch wires, the brake fluid tube, and the brake pipe from the master cylinder. Remove the two mounting bolts and remove the master cylinder as an assembly.

3. To extract the primary and secondary pistons, remove the internal circlip and two stopper bolts.

4. Remove the brake pipe joints and check valves, bleeder valves, brake fluid tube connectors, and low brake fluid warning switches.

To install, reverse the removal procedure, being sure to apply brake fluid to the piston and inside surfaces of the cylinder. Insert the check valve seat and piston into the cylinder, and then fit the push rod bump plate, securing it with the circlip. Connect the push rod to the brake pedal before installing the master cylinder.

Overhaul

Wash all disassembled parts in brake fluid. Dry the parts with compressed air and store them in a watertight container to avoid contamination. Inspect the pis-

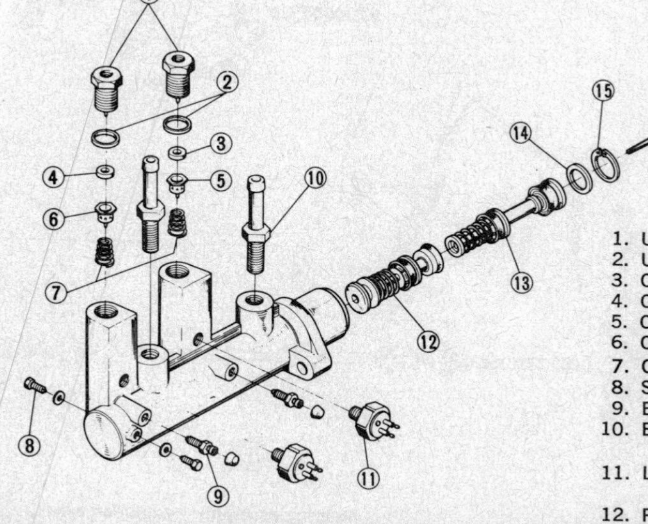

Brake master cylinder—exploded view

1. Union cap assembly
2. Union cap gasket
3. Check valve washer
4. Check valve seat
5. Check valve (rear)
6. Check valve (front)
7. Check valve spring
8. Stopper bolt
9. Bleed valve
10. Brake fluid tube connector
11. Low brake fluid warning switch
12. Primary piston
13. Secondary piston
14. Pushrod bump plate
15. Pushrod

ton and check valves for damage and the cylinder bore for smoothness, replacing where necessary. When reassembling, measure the clearance between the piston and cylinder bore with a feeler gauge. The standard clearance is 0.00079–0.00413 in.

Bleeding

When it is necessary to flush the brake hydraulic system because of parts replacement or fluid contamination, the following procedure should be observed:

1. Begin the fluid change at the wheel farthest from the master cylinder.
2. Loosen the wheel cylinder bleeder screw. Drain the brake fluid by pumping the brake pedal. Pump the pedal until all of the old fluid has been pumped out and replaced by new fluid.
3. The flushing procedure should be performed in the following sequence:
   a. Bleed the left rear brake
   b. Bleed the right front brake
   c. Bleed the left front brake
4. Bleed the back of the master cylinder before the front, through the two bleed valves. Fasten one end of a plastic tube onto the bleed valve and immerse the other end in a clear jar filled with brake fluid. When air bubbles cease to emerge from the end of the tubing, the bleeding is completed. Be sure to keep the fluid reservoir filled at all times during the bleeding process so air does not enter the system.

FRONT DISC BRAKES

Disc Brake Pads

Removal and Installation

1. After removing the wheel, remove the pad retaining clip which is fitted in the holes of the pad retaining pins.
2. Remove the two retaining pins and fitting springs with pliers. When removing them, care must be taken to prevent the springs from flying apart.
3. The front brake pad can be removed, together with the shim, after removing the springs and pins. If the pads are difficult to remove, open the bleeder valve and move the caliper in the direction of the piston. The pads will become loose and can be easily removed.

NOTE: *After the pads are removed, the brake pedal must not be touched.*

The disc pads should be replaced when approximately 0.8 in. lining thickness remains.

To provide space for installing the pad, loosen the bleed valve and push the inner piston back into the cylinder. Also push back the outer piston by applying pressure to the caliper. After providing space for the pads, close the bleed valve and insert the pad. Insert a shim behind each pad with the arrow on the shim pointing up. Incorrect installation of the shims can cause squeaking brakes.

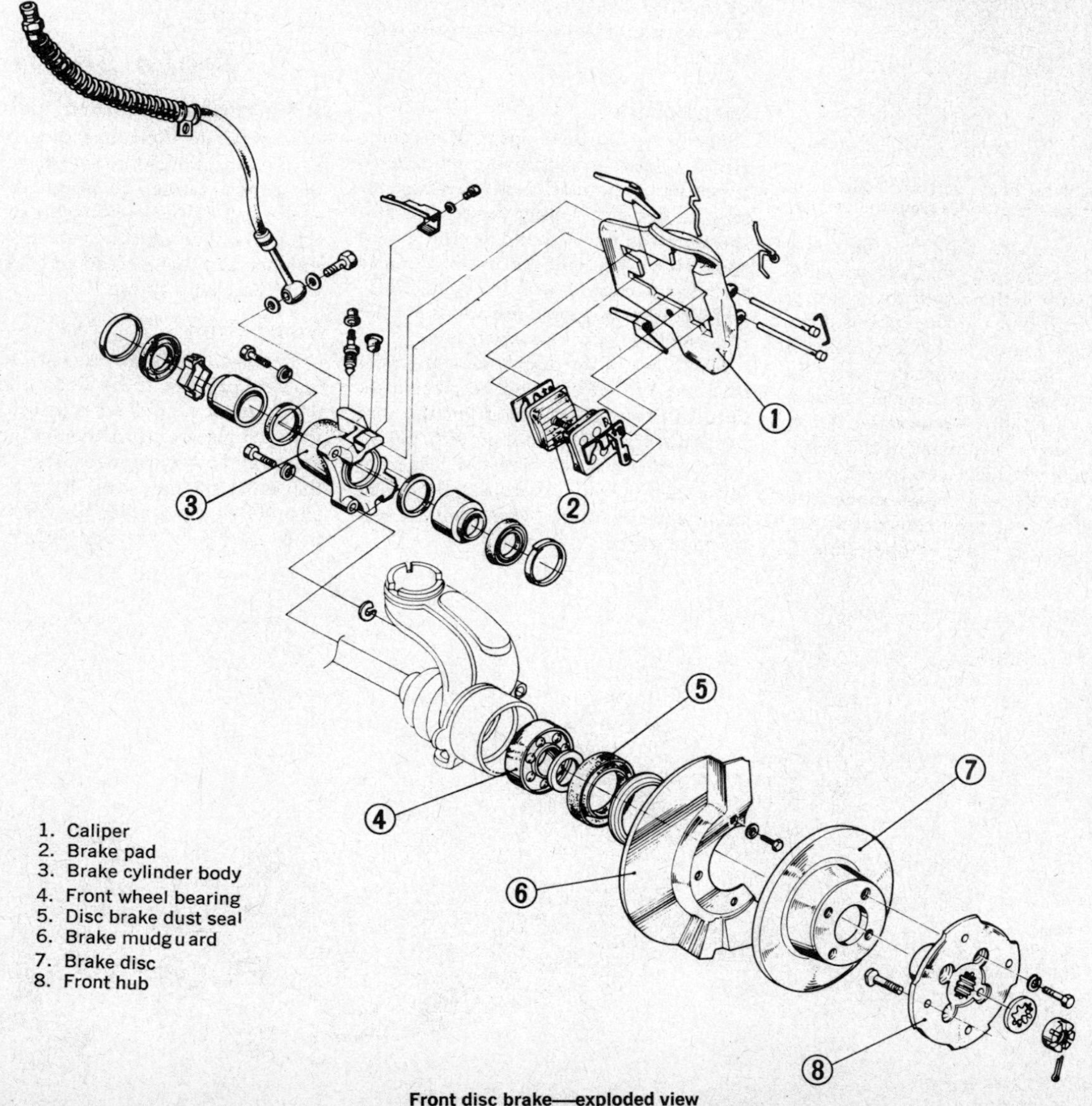

Front disc brake—exploded view

Disc Brake Calipers

1. The caliper housing is mounted to the knuckle with two 10 mm bolts located behind the cylinder.

2. Remove the brake hose and then the caliper. Remove the brake pads from the caliper.

3. Tap the cylinder body lightly with a plastic hammer (where the 10 mm mounting bolts were located) to remove the cylinder. Exercise extreme care to avoid damaging the cylinder body. If only the cylinder body moves, without the outer piston, a gentle tap on the piston should loosen it. Remove the bias ring and the two yoke springs from the caliper.

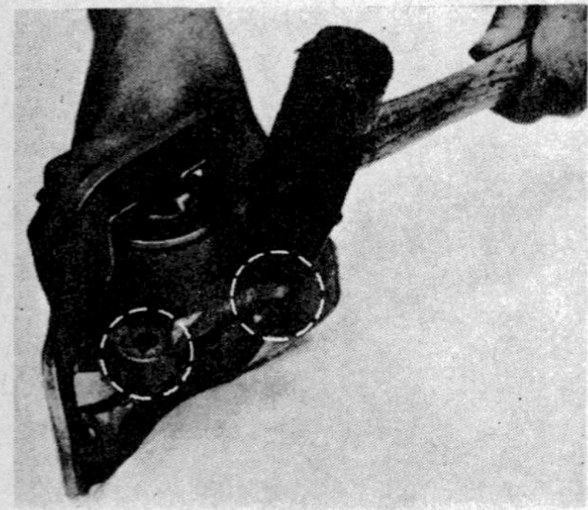

Tap the cylinder body with a plastic hammer to remove the cylinder from the caliper.

4. To dismantle the cylinder, first remove the retaining rings at both ends of the cylinder with a screwdriver, being careful not to damage the rubber boot. Both pistons (inner and outer) can be removed from the cylinder body by pushing through from one end with a wooden rod. Finally, remove the piston seals, installed on the inside of the cylinder at both ends, with a screwdriver.

5. To install and reassemble the caliper unit, reverse the removal procedures. Inspect the caliper operation. If lining wear differs extremely between inner and outer pads, the caliper may be unable to move properly due to rust and dust on the sliding surfaces. Clean the sliding part of the caliper and apply brake grease. Measure the amount of force required to slide the caliper from the neutral position with a spring scale. The standard force is 55 lbs.

Brake Disc

Removal and Installation

1. Remove the wheel and caliper assembly.

2. Remove the center spindle nut and extract the hub using a wheel puller. Pull the brake disc off after the hub.

To install, reverse the removal procedure. Check the wheel bearings, after installing the hub, for excessive play and replace if necessary. Measure the total lateral runout of the disc by turning slowly. Do not push the disc in the axial direction as this will give a false reading. The maximum permissible runout is 0.004 in.

Inspection

The brake disc develops circular scores after long or even short usage when there is frequent braking. Excessive scoring not only causes a squealing brake, but also shortens the service life of the brake pads. However, light scoring of the disc surface, not exceeding 0.015 in. in depth, will result from normal use and is not detrimental to brake operation.

Machining of the disc, having an initial thickness of 0.378 in., will result in a reduced thickness. Do not grind the disc beyond the serviceable limit of 0.299 in.

Refer to the illustrations for disassembly of the front wheel bearings. Be sure to pack the bearings with the recommended grease

REAR DRUM BRAKES

Brake Drums

Removal and Installation

1. After removing the rear wheel, remove the rear wheel bearing cap and the castellated nut.

2. Remove the rear brake drum with a puller (or special tool #7009-57906).

To install, reverse the removal procedure.

Inspection

Check the drum for cracks and the inner surface of the shoe for excessive wear and damage. Permissible play of the drum inner circumference is less than 0.002 in. with respect to the center of the shaft. Deviation from true should be less than 0.0004 in. A larger deformity can result in brake squealing which requires grinding within the permissible depth of up to 0.020 in.

Brake Shoes

Removal and Installation

To separate the brake shoe from the back plate, unhook the return spring and the clamp spring. To install the brake shoes, first fit the parking brake arm to the brake shoes. Fit the return spring to the shoe and then extend and fit the shoe with the clamp spring.

Inspection

Measure the thickness of the shoe lining with calipers. If the lining is less than 0.055 in., it should be replaced. If the shoe is replaced, check the new lining for cracks and other damage. Make sure that the lining surface is free from grease or oil and that the contact faces on the back plate are free of rust and dirt. When in-

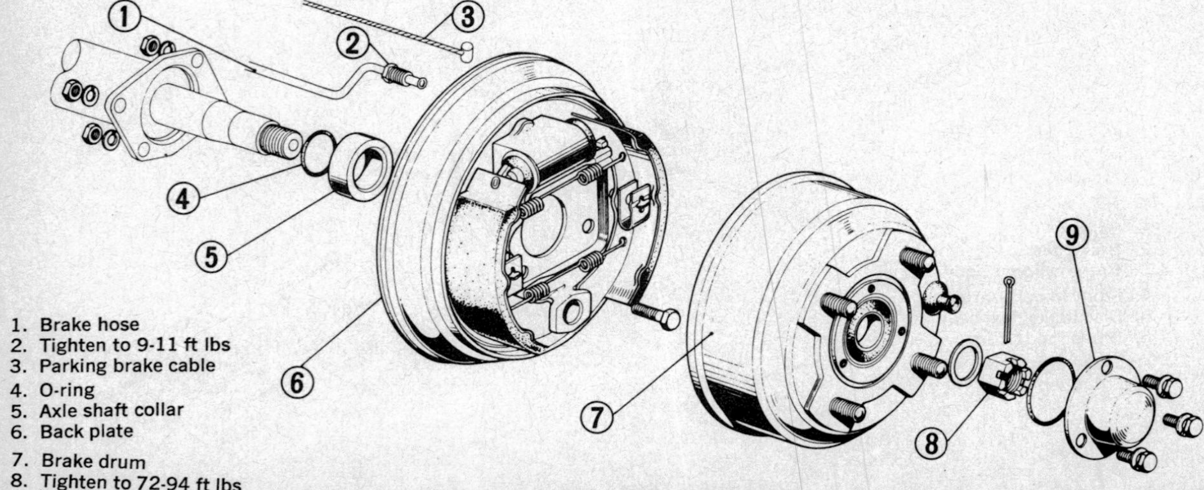

Rear drum brake—exploded view

Rear brake shoe assembly

1. Parking brake arm
2. Shoe return spring
3. Clamp spring

stalling the brake shoes, apply a light coating of grease to the contact faces, and make sure that the position of the shoes is correct.

Wheel Cylinders

Removal and Installation

After removing the brake shoes and the backplate, remove the two retaining nuts (on the rear side of the back plate) which hold the wheel cylinder. To install, reverse the removal procedure.

Rear wheel cylinder

1. Wheel cylinder dust seal
2. Rear cylinder body
3. Wheel cylinder pistons

Inspection and Overhaul

Remove the wheel cylinder dust seals from the grooves to permit the removal of the cylinder pistons.

Wash all parts in brake fluid and check the cylinder bore and pistons for scratches or other damage, replacing where necessary. Check the clearance between the piston and the cylinder bore by taking the difference between the piston diameter and the bore diameter. The standard value of clearance is 0.0008–0.004 in. When fitting the wheel cylinder to the back plate, be sure to apply a light coat of grease to the contact surface.

PARKING BRAKE

The parking brake is a mechanical type which applies braking force to the rear wheels, through the rear brake shoes. The cable, which is attached to the tail end of the parking brake lever, extends to the equalizer and to the right and left rear brakes. When the lever is pulled, the cable becomes taut, pulling both the right and left parking brake arms fitted to the brake shoes.

Cable

Removal and Installation

1. Remove the adjusting nut from the equalizer mounted on the rear axle and separate the cable from the equalizer.
2. Set the parking brake to a fully released position and remove the cotter pin from the side of the brake lever.
3. After removing the cotter pin, pull out the pin which connects the cable and the lever.
4. Detach the cable from the guides at the front and right side of the fuel tank and remove the cable.
5. To install, reverse the removal procedure, making sure that grease is applied to the cable and the guides.

CHASSIS ELECTRICAL

Heater Blower

The Honda 600 utilizes an exhaust type of heater where air, heated by the exhaust system, is fed by a blower into the interior of the car. Air is introduced through hood vents and forced through the heat exchanger by the blower before entering the car. The blower is connected to the engine compartment by two bolts and can be easily removed after disconnecting the two heater ducts.

Radio

The radio is located in the center of the instrument panel, immediately below the center air outlet. It is mounted on a supporting bracket and held in place with mounting nuts located behind the control knobs.

1. When removing the radio from the instrument panel, be sure to disconnect the battery ground cable, and the antenna and speaker connectors from the radio.

Windshield Wiper Motor

Windshield wiper motor—connecting apparatus.

The wiper motor is connected to the engine compartment wall, beneath the center of the front windshield. The motor is connected to the wipers through a connecting link held by a cotter pin, and is held to the bulkhead by four bolts. When installing the motor, be sure to color-match the motor leads properly when rewiring.

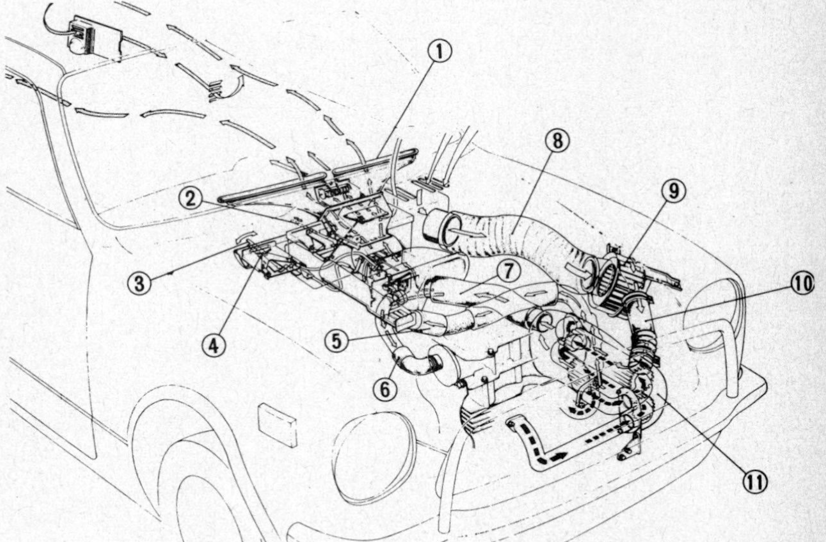

Heater assembly

1. Defroster upper nozzle
2. Fresh air control lever
3. Heater control lever
4. Defroster control lever
5. Hot air duct
6. Exhaust air duct
7. Heater duct
8. Heater duct B
9. Heater blower
10. Heater duct A
11. Heat exchanger

Instrument Cluster

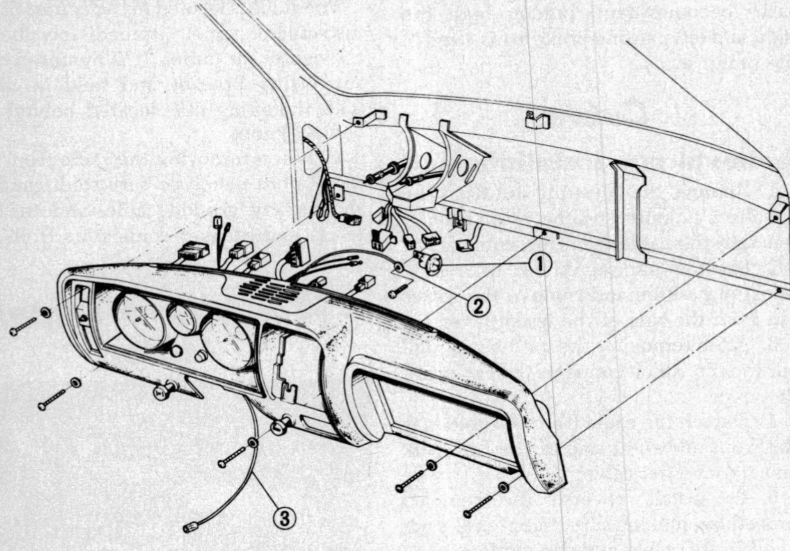

Instrument panel removal—exploded view

1. Ignition key removal warning buzzer
2. Ground wire
3. Parking brake switch wire

Removal and Installation

1. To remove the instrument cluster panel, pull out the center panel/radio unit, held by the two radio mounting nuts. Remove the choke cable assembly.

2. Remove the steering column retaining bolts and lower the column and the wheel to the floor.

3. Remove the panel retaining screws and pull out the panel. Disconnect the speedometer and tachometer cables and the wire harness at the couplers. Disconnect the wire harness from the light switch, brake warning light, turn signal pilot, hi-beam pilot, and fuel gauge.

4. Remove the respective meters from their mounts.

To install and assemble the instrument cluster panel, reverse the removal procedure.

Fuse Box

Location

The fuse box is located on the right side of the passenger compartment, underneath the glove compartment.

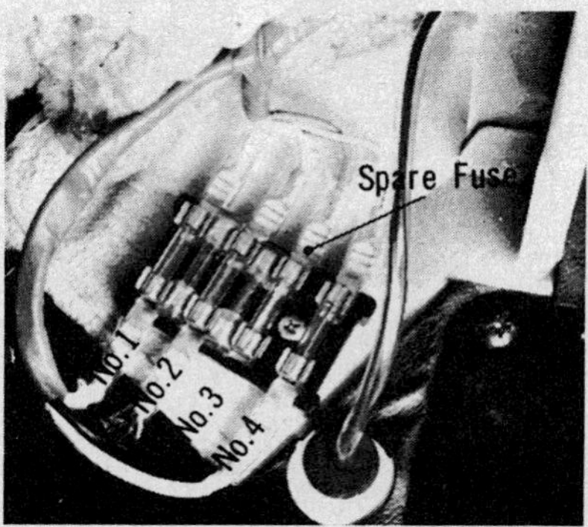

Fuse box

Fuse Box Specifications

No. 1	15A Heater Blower Motor
No. 2	15A Back-up Lights Turn Signal Lights Wiper Motor Fuel Gauge
No. 3	20A Side Marker Lights Tail Lights License Light Stop Lights Headlights
No. 4	20A Horn Cigarette Lighter Interior Light Radio Hazard Warning Light

MAZDA

Index

INTRODUCTION

Toyo Kogyo Co., Ltd., Mazda's parent company, began manufacturing cork products over fifty years ago. In 1927, the company expanded into the machinery and tool business; by 1930 they were producing motorcycles under the Mazda name.

Their first three-wheeled trucks appeared in 1931. The first prototype automobile was built in 1940, but it was not until 1960 that the first Mazda R-360 coupe was sold.

In the interim, Toyo Kogyo produced light three-wheeled trucks, reaching, in 1957, a peak annual production of 20,000 units.

Shortly after automobile production began in 1960, Toyo Kogyo obtained a license from NSU-Wankel to develop and produce the rotary engine.

The first prototype car powered by this engine, the Mazda 110S—a two passenger sports car—appeared in August 1963. The car did not go on sale until it had been thoroughly tested. The first units were offered for sale in May 1967. The 110S was soon joined by smaller, cheaper model which put the rotary engine within the reach of the average consumer.

In 1970, Toyo Kogyo began exporting its Mazda cars (both rotary engined and conventional) to the United States. At first they were available only in the Pacific Northwest, but they have rapidly expanded their market to include almost all of the U.S.

Led by the success of the unique rotary engine powered automobile, Mazda has rapidly climbed into the "top ten" in imported car sales in this country.

SERIAL NUMBER IDENTIFICATION

Vehicle

RX-3

The serial number on RX-3 models is on a plate located on the driver's side windshield pillar and is visible through the glass.

A vehicle identification number (VIN) plate, bearing the serial number and other data, is attached to the cowl.

The serial number consists of a series identification number (see chart), followed by a six-digit production number.

RX-2

The VIN plate location and composition of the serial number for RX-2 models is the same as for RX-3 models, above. The only difference between models is the location of the RX-2 serial number plate: it is attached to the upper left-hand side of the instrument panel and is visible through the windshield. See the chart for proper model identification.

Engine

RX-3 and RX-2

The engine number is located on a plate which is attached to the 12A rotary engine housing, just behind the upper distributor. The 12A engine is used on both models.

The engine number consists of an identification number (see chart), followed by a six-digit production number.

Engine Identification Codes

Model	TRANSMISSION Manual	Automatic
RX-3	12AH	12AQ
RX-2	12AJ	12AT

MODEL IDENTIFICATION

Year	Model	Body Type	Code
1971	RX-2	Sedan	—
	RX-2	Coupe	—
1972	RX-3	Sedan	S124 BL
	RX-3	Coupe	M124 B6
	RX-3	Wagon	S124 WL
	RX-2	Sedan	SN1224A-S
	RX-2	Coupe	SN122A-SCA
1973	RX-3	Sedan	2RS 124A
	RX-3	Coupe	2RS 124A
	RX-3	Wagon	2RS 124W
	RX-2	Sedan	2RS 122A
	RX-2	Coupe	2RS 122A

MODEL IDENTIFICATION

1972-73 RX-3

1971-73 RX-2

TUNE-UP SPECIFICATIONS

Year	Model	Spark Plugs Type	Spark Plugs Gap	Distributors (both) Point Gap (in.)	Distributors (both) Point Dwell (deg)	Ignition Timing (deg) Leading Normal	Ignition Timing (deg) Leading Retarded	Ignition Timing (deg) Trailing Normal	Idle Speed (rpm) MT	Idle Speed (rpm) AT
1971-73	All	①	0.031-0.035	0.018	58 ± 3	TDC	10A	10A	900	750②

① See chart in text for manufacturer's recommendation for proper spark plug make and type
② Transmission in drive (D)
TDC Top dead center
A After top dead center
B Before top dead center
MT Manual transmission
AT Automatic transmission
deg degrees

GENERAL ENGINE SPECIFICATIONS

Model	Engine Displacement Cu In. (cc)	Carburetor Type	Net Horsepower @ rpm	Net Torque @ rpm	Rotor Displacement (Cu In.)	Compression Ratio	Oil Pressure @ rpm (psi)
RX-3	70 (1,146)	4-bbl	90 @ 6,000	96 @ 4,000	35	9.4:1	71.1 @ 3,000
RX-2	70 (1,146)	4-bbl	97 @ 6,500	98 @ 4,000	35	9.4:1	71.1 @ 3,000

ECCENTRIC SHAFT SPECIFICATIONS

All measurements are given in inches.

Model	Journal Diameter Main Bearing	Journal Diameter Rotor Bearing	Oil Clearance Main Bearing	Oil Clearance Rotor Bearing	Eccentric Shaft End-Play Normal	Eccentric Shaft End-Play Limit	Shaft Runout
RX-3 and RX-2	1.6929	2.9134	0.0016-0.0028	0.0020-0.0035①	0.0016-0.0028	0.0035	0.0008

① 1972-73 models—0.0016-0.0031

ROTOR AND HOUSING SPECIFICATIONS

All measurements are given in inches.

Model	Rotor: Side Clearance	Rotor: Standard Protrusion of Land	Rotor: Limit of Protrusion of Land	Housings: Front and Rear Distortion Limit	Housings: Front and Rear Wear Limit	Housings: Rotor Width	Housings: Rotor Distortion Limit	Housings: Intermediate Distortion Limit	Housings: Intermediate Wear Limit
RX-3 and RX-2	0.0051-0.0067	0.004-0.006	0.003	0.002	0.004	2.7539	0.002	0.002	0.004

SEAL CLEARANCES

All measurements are given in inches.

Model	Apex Seals To Side Housing Normal	Apex Seals To Side Housing Limit	Apex Seals To Rotor Groove Normal	Apex Seals To Rotor Groove Limit	Corner Seal to Rotor Groove Normal	Corner Seal to Rotor Groove Limit	Side Seal To Rotor Groove Normal	Side Seal To Rotor Groove Limit	Side Seal To Corner Seal Normal	Side Seal To Corner Seal Limit
RX-3 and RX-2	0.0020-0.0028①	0.0039	0.0014-0.0029	0.0039	0.0008-0.0019	0.0031	0.0016-0.0028	0.0039	0.002-0.006	0.016

① Arctic Specifications—0.0004-0.0020

SEAL SPECIFICATIONS

All measurements are given in inches.

Model	APEX SEAL Normal Height	APEX SEAL Height Limit	Corner Seal Width	SIDE SEAL Thickness	SIDE SEAL Width	OIL SEAL CONTACT WIDTH OF LIP Normal	OIL SEAL CONTACT WIDTH OF LIP Limit
RX-3 and RX-2	0.03937	0.03150	0.2756	0.0394	0.1378	0.008	0.031

TORQUE SPECIFICATIONS

Engine Displacement Cu In. (cc)	Front Cover	Bearing Housing	Rear Stationary Gear	Eccentric Shaft Pulley Bolt	Flywheel to Eccentric Shaft Nut	MANIFOLDS Intake	MANIFOLDS Exhaust	Oil Pan	Tension Bolts
70 (1,156)	15	15	15	45	350	15	30	7	20

TORQUE SEQUENCES

Tension bolt loosening sequence
(© Toyo Kogyo Co., Ltd.)

Tension bolt tightening sequence
(© Toyo Kogyo Co., Ltd.)

CAPACITIES

Year	Model	Engine Displacement Cu In. (cc)	ENGINE OIL PAN (qts) With Filter	ENGINE OIL PAN (qts) Without Filter	TRANSMISSION (pts) Manual 4-spd	TRANSMISSION (pts) Automatic	Drive Axle (pts)	Gasoline Tank (gals)	Cooling System (qts)
1972-73	RX-3	70 (1156)	5.50	4.45	3.20	11.62	3.00	15.6①	8.45
1971-72	RX-2	70 (1156)	5.80	4.65	3.20	11.62	2.60	16.9	8.45

① Station Wagon 14.3

BRAKE SPECIFICATIONS

All measurements given in inches.

Model	Master Cylinder Bore	WHEEL CYLINDER CALIPER BORE Front (Disc)	WHEEL CYLINDER CALIPER BORE Rear (Drum)	BRAKE DISC OR DRUM DIAMETER Front (Disc)	BRAKE DISC OR DRUM DIAMETER Rear (Drum)	New Pad or Lining Thickness
RX-3	0.875	2.125	0.750	9.055	7.874	0.559
RX-2	0.875	2.125	0.812	9.055	7.874	0.559

WHEEL ALIGNMENT

Model	CASTER Range (deg)	CASTER Pref Setting (deg)	CAMBER Range (deg)	CAMBER Pref Setting (deg)	Toe-in (in.)	Steering Axis Inclination
RX-3	$1\frac{1}{2}$P-2P	$1\frac{1}{4}$P	$1\frac{1}{4}$N-$1\frac{3}{4}$P	$\frac{3}{4}$P	0-0.24	$8\frac{3}{4}$P
RX-2	$\frac{1}{4}$P-$1\frac{3}{4}$P	1P	$\frac{1}{2}$N-$1\frac{1}{2}$P	$\frac{1}{2}$P	0-0.24	$8\frac{3}{4}$P

Pref Preferred
deg degrees
P Positive
N Negative

BATTERY AND STARTER SPECIFICATIONS

		BATTERY			STARTERS						
					Lock Test			No-Load Test			
Year	Model	Amp Hour Capy.	Volts	Term. Grnd.	Amps	Volts	Torque (ft lbs)	Amps	Volts	RPM	Brush Spring Tension (oz.)
1971	RX-2	60	12	Neg	60	6	19.5	70	12	3,600	40.0
1972-73	RX-2 and RX-3 w/MT	70	12	Neg	60	6	19.5	70	12	3,600	56.3
1972-73	RX-2 and RX-3 w/AT	70	12	Neg	60	4	43.5	100	12	5,400	56.3

MT Manual transmission
AT Automatic transmission
Neg Negative

ALTERNATOR AND REGULATOR SPECIFICATIONS

		ALTERNATOR			REGULATOR				
Year	Model	Manu-facturer	Field current @ 14 V	Output (amps)	Manu-facturer	Air Gap (in.)	Point Gap (in.)	Back Gap (in.)	Volts @ 75°
1971-73	RX-2 and RX-3	—	32	40	—	0.028-0.043	0.012-0.016	0.028-0.043	14

WIRING DIAGRAMS

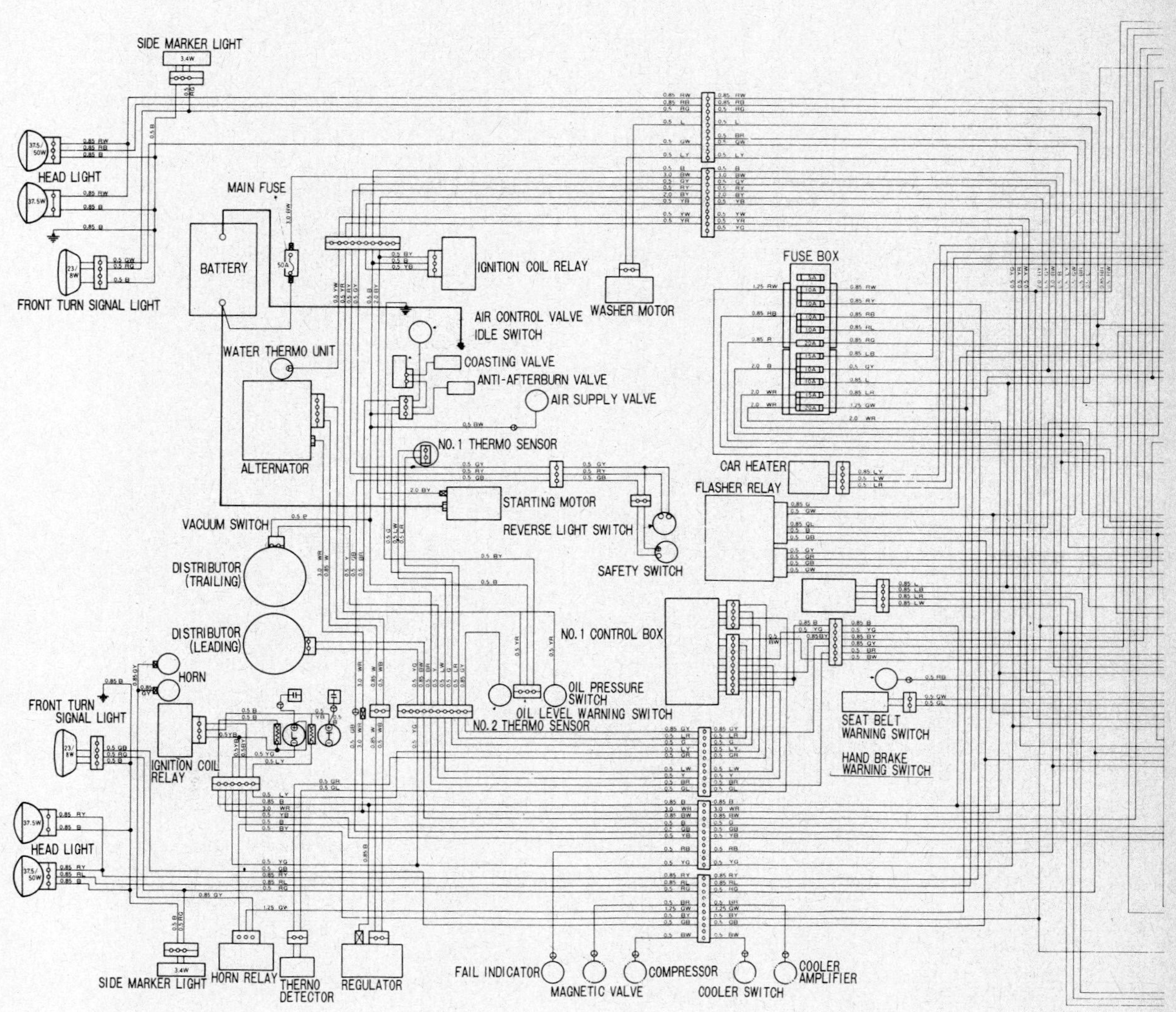

RX-3 (© Toyo Kogyo Co., Ltd.)

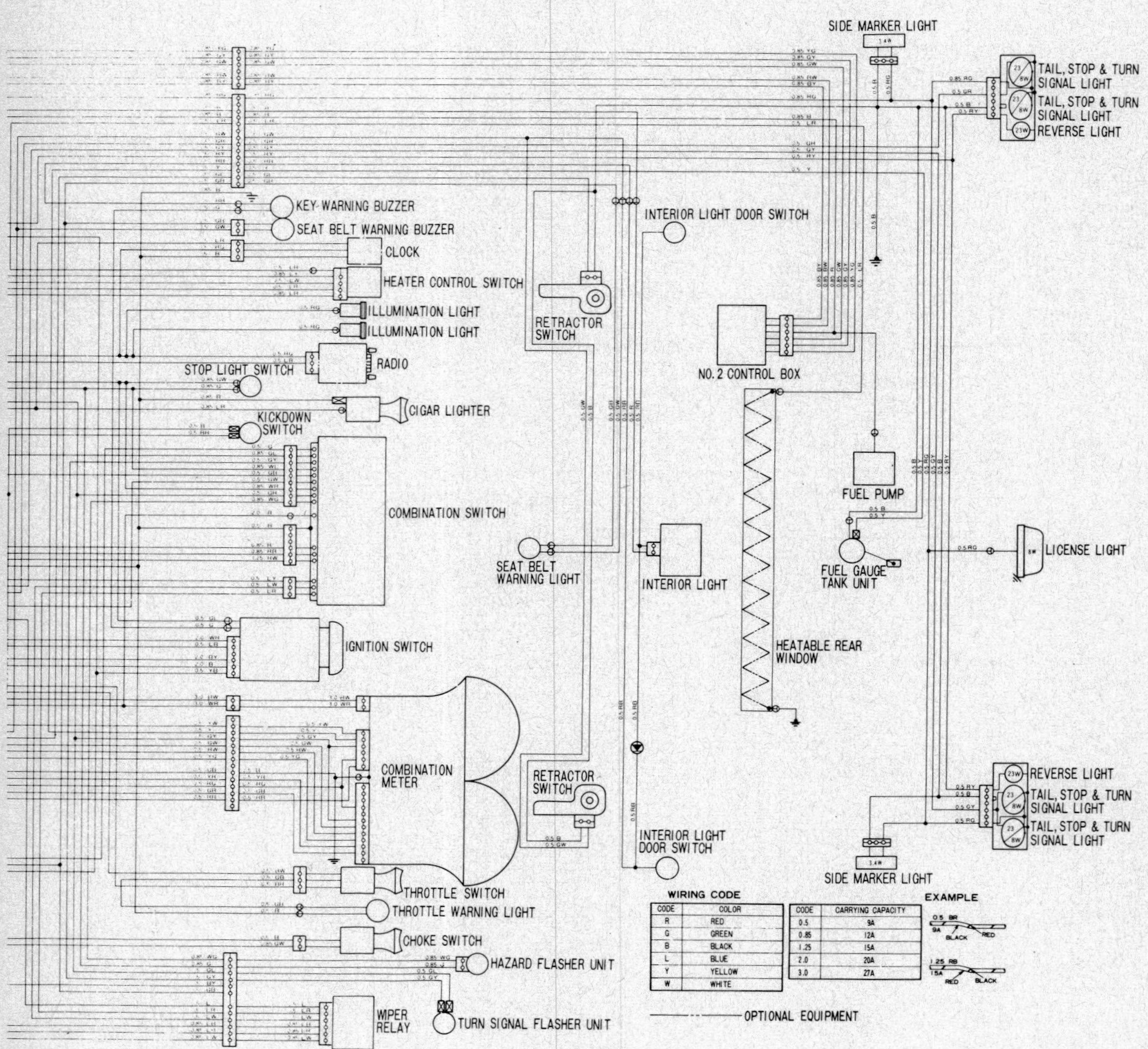

CODE	COLOR
R	RED
G	GREEN
B	BLACK
L	BLUE
Y	YELLOW
W	WHITE

CODE	CARRYING CAPACITY
0.5	9A
0.85	12A
1.25	15A
2.0	20A
3.0	27A

RX-3 (© Toyo Kogyo Co., Ltd.)

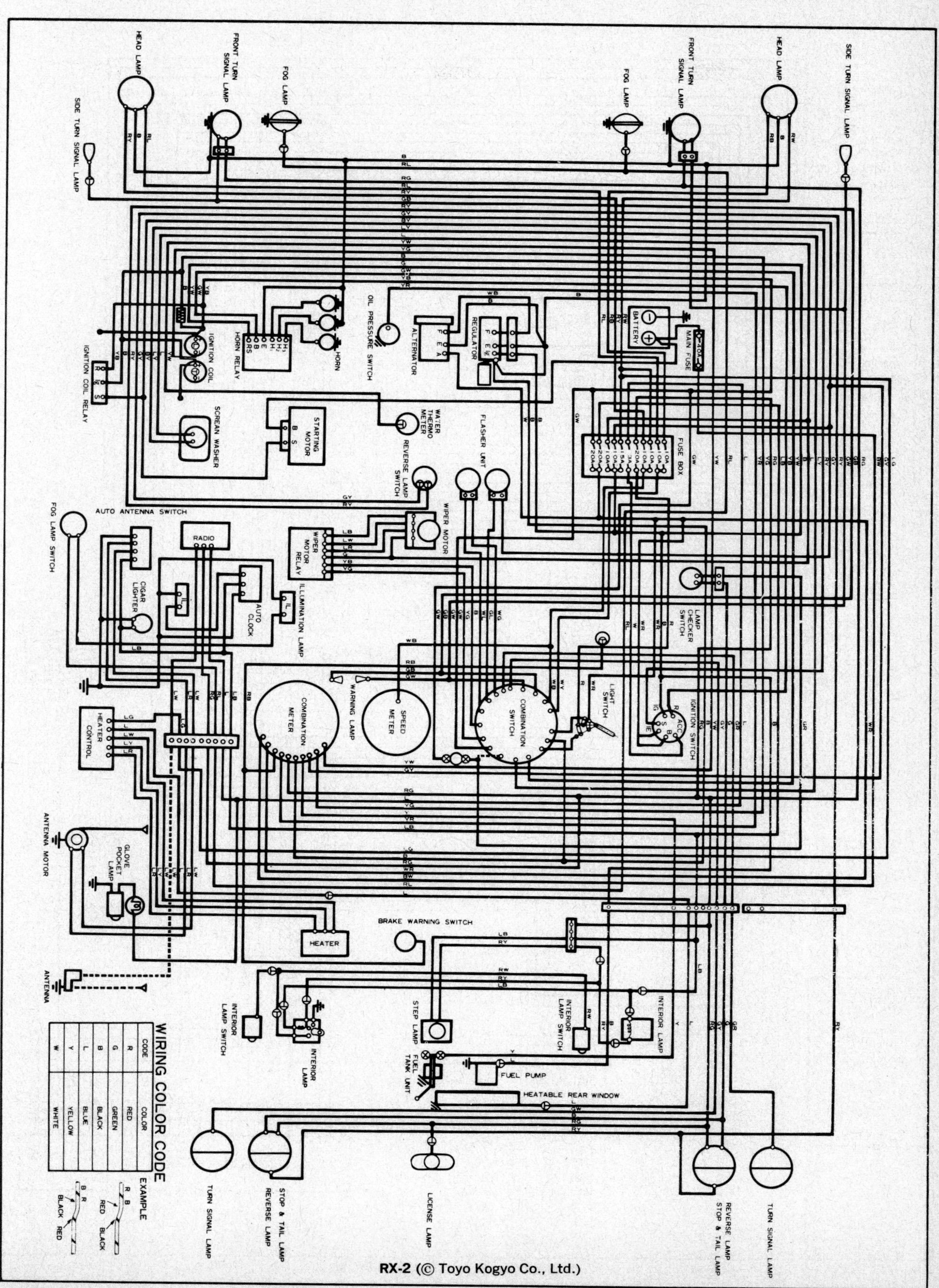

RX-2 (© Toyo Kogyo Co., Ltd.)

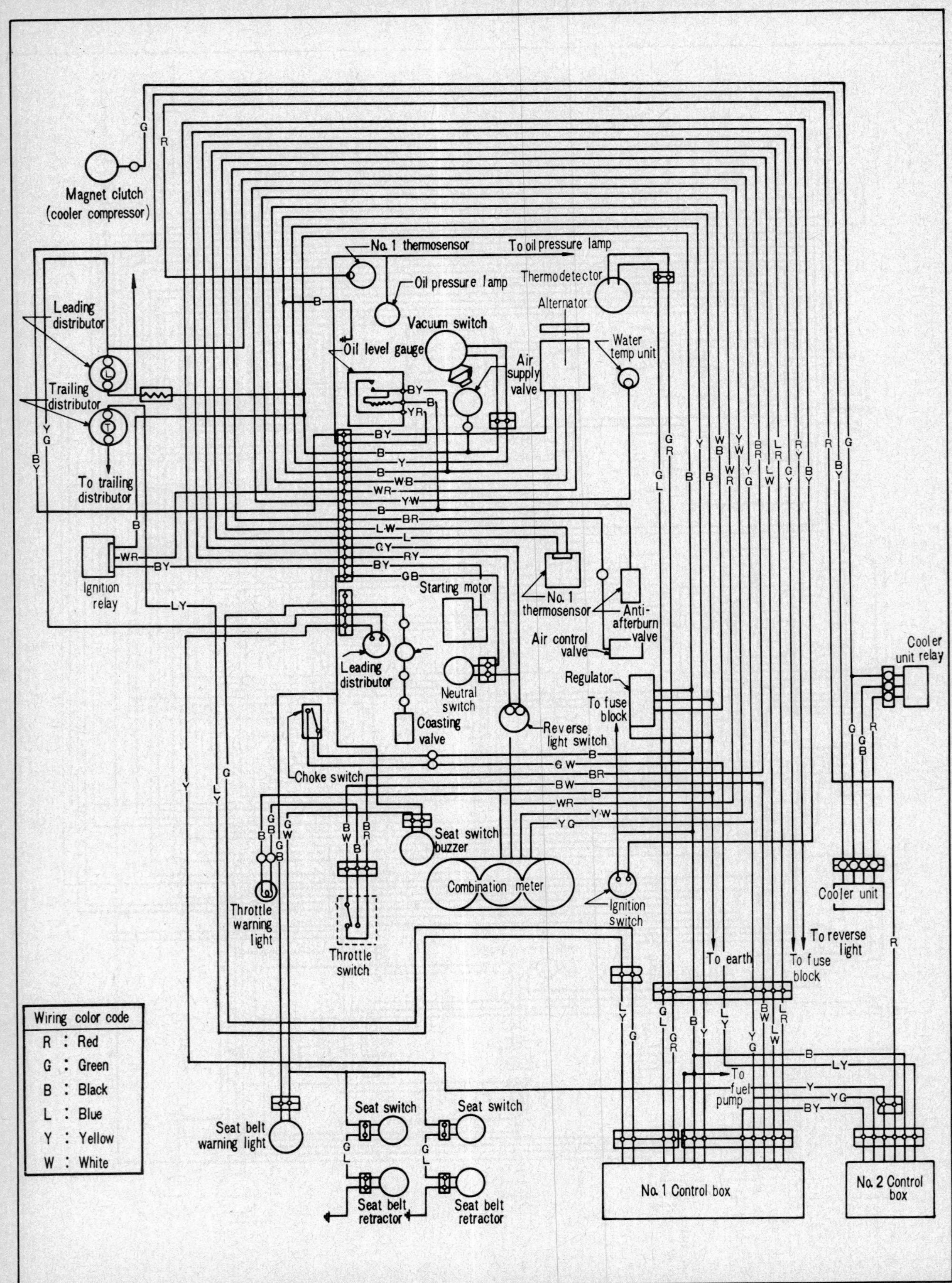

RX-2 emission control system (© Toyo Kogyo Co., Ltd.)

TUNE-UP PROCEDURES

Spark Plugs

The spark plugs should be checked and adjusted every 4,000 miles or 4 months. New plugs should be installed every 12,000 miles or 12 months.

The Mazda rotary engine has four spark plugs. Each of the two combustion chambers uses two plugs. The leading bottom spark plug fires first, igniting the fuel/air mixture, as in conventional engines; the trailing top plug fires a short time afterward (10° later), igniting any unburned mixture. This aids in more complete combustion in the long narrow chamber, which helps to reduce exhaust emissions of unburned fuel.

The spark plugs are specially constructed and designed for use only in the Mazda rotary engine. They are available from the manufacturers listed below, in two heat ranges.

Spark Plug Usage*

Maker	PART NUMBER Standard	Cold
NKG	B-7EM or B-7EJ	B-8EM or B-8EJ
Nippondenso	W-22EA	W-25EA
Champion	N-80B	N-78B

*Manufacturer's recommendation

CAUTION: *The above listed spark plugs are specified for use by Toyo Kogyo, Co., Ltd. Use these plugs only, do not substitute a different type of plug.*

Check the spark plugs at 4,000 mile intervals in the following manner:

1. Remove the wire from one of the plugs. Use a spark plug wrench with a rubber insulator to remove the plug.

NOTE: *Both the distributor and the engine housing are marked to aid in identification of the spark plug and distributor connections. However, to avoid confusion, it is easier to remove one plug at a time.*

2. Check each plug for badly worn electrodes, black deposits, fouling, or cracked porcelain.
3. Clean the plug with a wire brush, if it is dirty.
4. Replace any plug which has a badly worn or burned electrode.
5. Measure the electrode gap with a wire gauge.

NOTE: *Do not use a flat gauge; an inaccurate reading will be obtained.*

6. Adjust the gap so that it falls between 0.031–0.035 in. Replace any plug which has a measured gap of 0.043 in. or more.

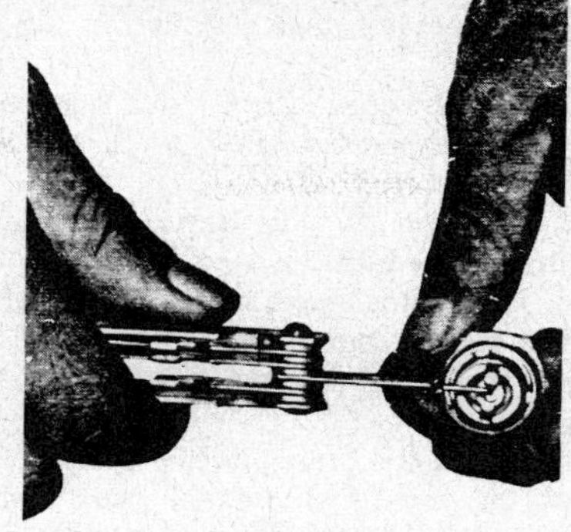

Checking the electrode gap; note dual electrodes
(© Toyo Kogyo Co., Ltd.)

7. If the electrode shows signs of burning white or if the electrodes are burning rapidly, replace the plugs with cold range plugs.

NOTE: *When replacing spark plugs be sure all plugs are of the same manufacture and heat range. It is a good idea to replace plugs in sets of four, if possible.*

8. Replace the spark plug and torque it to 10 ft lbs.
9. Repeat steps 1–9 for each plug.

Breaker Points

Mazda RX-2 and RX-3 models are equipped with two distributors. One distributor operates the leading set of plugs and the other the trailing set. When checking or replacing points, remember to service both distributors.

Adjustment

The points should be checked and adjusted every 4,000 miles.

To check the point gap and adjust it, proceed in the following manner:

1. Unfasten the clips and remove the cap from one of the distributors. Leave the leads attached to the cap.
2. Remove the rotor from the distributor.
3. Clean the points with a point file, if they are pitted. If they are badly pitted or burned, replace them, as detailed in the section below.
4. Rotate the engine by using a remote starter switch, or have someone inside the car operate the ignition key, until the rubbing block is at the top of the cam.
5. Check the point gap with a feeler gauge. The gap should be 0.018 in.
6. Adjust the point gap with a screwdriver.

NOTE: *The leading distributor on 1972–73 Mazda's has two sets of points.*

7. After completing adjustment, install the rotor and cap on the distributor.

Repeat steps 1–7 for the other distributor.

Removal and Installation

New points should be installed every 12,000 miles or once a year.

1. Repeat steps 1 and 2 of the adjustment procedure.
2. Unfasten the two screws which secure the point set and remove it.
3. Install the new set of points and fasten it with the two screws.

NOTE: *The leading distributor on 1972–73 models has two sets of points.*

4. Adjust the point gap as detailed above and the dwell as detailed below.
5. Install the rotor and the cap on the distributor.
6. Repeat the procedure for the other distributor.

Condenser

The condenser should be replaced every time the points are replaced, i.e., every 12,000 miles.

If the condenser is suspect, the easiest way to check it is by replacing it with a new one. The condenser capacity is 0.27 mfd. To replace the condenser, perform the following steps:

1. Remove the distributor cap. Leave the wires connected. Withdraw the rotor.
2. Loosen the condenser lead retaining screw from inside the distributor and unfasten the clip.
3. Unfasten the condenser retaining screw which is located on the outside of the distributor housing.

NOTE: *The smaller condenser, mounted next to the ignition condenser, is for radio noise suppression. It need only be replaced if a clicking sound is heard over the radio.*

4. Remove the condenser.

Install the new condenser in the reverse order of removal.

Dwell Angle

Make separate checks of dwell angle for each distributor, in the following manner:

1. Disconnect the vacuum line from the distributor and plug it with a pencil or a golf tee.
2. Connect the dwell meter in accordance with its manufacturer's instructions.
3. Run the engine at idle, after it has been allowed to warm up.
4. Observe the dwell meter reading. It should be between 55 and 61 degrees (58 degrees is normal).
5. If it is not within specifications, adjust the contact point gap as outlined above.

NOTE: *If dwell angle is above the specified amount, the point gap is too small; if it is below, the gap is too large.*

6. If both the dwell angle and the contact point gap cannot be brought to within specifications, check for one or more of the following:
   a. Worn distributor cam
   b. Worn rubbing block
   c. Bent movable contact arm

Replace any of the parts, if necessary.

7. When the dwell angle check is completed, disconnect the meter and reconnect the vacuum line.

Ignition Timing

Normal Timing

As in other tune-up procedures involving the ignition system, both distributors must be adjusted separately. Begin with the *leading* distributor when checking timing:

1. Connect a timing light to the leading distributor spark plug cable which runs to the number one (front) rotor. Check the manufacturer's instructions for specific hook-up details.
2. Start the engine and run it at idle speed.
3. Loosen the distributor locknuts so that the distributor can be rotated.
4. Aim the timing light at the timing indicator pin in the front housing.
5. The *yellow* mark (TDC) should align with the pin on the housing.
6. If it does not, rotate the distributor until it aligns.
7. Tighten the locknuts and recheck the timing.

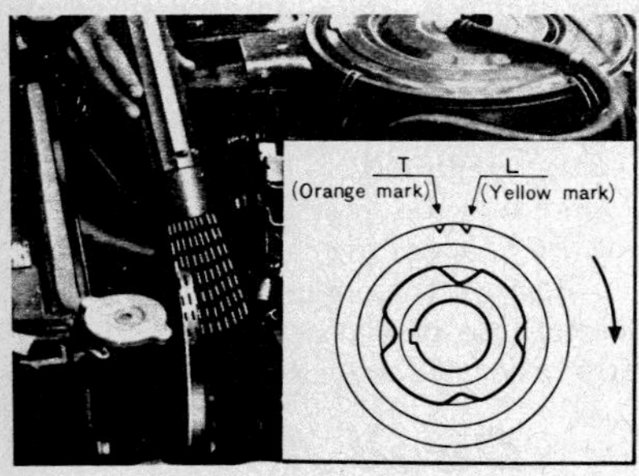

Ignition timing marks
(© Toyo Kogyo Co., Ltd.)

The ignition timing for the trailing distributor is checked and adjusted in the same manner, except that the timing light lead should be connected to the trailing distributor spark plug cable which runs to the number one rotor.

When the timing light is pointed at the eccentric shaft pulley, the *orange* mark (10°ATDC) should align with the timing pointer.

When the adjustment of normal timing has been completed for both distributors on 1972–73 models, proceed with the next section.

Retarded Timing

On 1972–73 Mazda RX-2 and RX-3 models, the leading distributor is equipped with dual points. One set of points is for normal ignition system operation, and the other is used for retarded operation during engine warm-up. To test and adjust retarded timing proceed in the following manner:

1. Disconnect both of the thermosensor connections. See "Emission Controls".

   NOTE: *Disconnect the No.2 thermosensor connection only on cars with manual transmissions*

2. Unfasten the idle and/or vacuum switch connections.
3. Detach the choke switch connector.
4. Connect the timing light to the number one (front) rotor, leading spark plug cable.
5. Check the timing at 900 rpm, (750 rpm in Drive—automatic) with the strobe, as above. The pointer should align with the *orange* mark on the timing pulley (10°ATDC ± 2°).

If the retarded timing setting is incorrect, adjust in the following manner:

1. Turn the engine off.
2. Unfasten the clips and remove the distributor cap. Withdraw the rotor.
3. Loosen the adjusting screws and move the point set base to correct the retarded timing setting.

   NOTE: *Do not rotate the distributor housing.*

4. Assemble the distributor and check the retarded timing again with the strobe.
5. When the timing is satisfactory, disconnect the timing light and connect all of the leads.

   NOTE: *If the timing cannot be brought to specification, check the components of the "air flow control system". See "Emission Controls".*

Ignition Coils

Each one of the igntion systems has its own coil. The leading system coil has an *external* ballast resistor, while the trailing system ignition coil has an *internal* resistor. Check the coils in the following manner:

1. Check for signs of external oil leakage around the coils. Replace either coil if it is leaking.
2. Remove the positive (+) and negative (−) leads from each of the coils.
3. Check the primary resistance with an ohmmeter:
   a. Leading coil resistance:
   RX-2: HP5-13J—1.35 ohms
   RX-3: HP5-13J—1.35 ohms
   b. Trailing coil:
   RX-2: HP5-10F—3.09 ohms
   RX-3: HP5-13E—1.60 ohms

   Replace either one of the coils if it is not up to specifications.

4. When checking is completed, reconnect the leads to the coils, being careful to connect the proper leads to the proper coils.

Compression

Because of the unusual shape of the combustion chamber, the lack of valves and because there are three chambers for each rotor, a normal gauge is useless for the measurement of rotary engine compression.

Mazda makes a special recording compression tester which produces a separate graph for each of the three chambers.

This is a fairly expensive piece of equipment and not one that most mechanics are likely to have around. If low compression is suspected, your best bet is to check with your local Mazda dealer, who does have this instrument.

Carburetor

NOTE: *For further carburetor adjustments, see the "Fuel System" section below.*

Idle Speed and Mixture

1. Start the engine and allow it to warm up. Remove the air cleaner assembly.
2. Operate the secondary throttle valve. Be sure that it returns fully.
3. Connect a tachometer to the engine in accordance with its manufacturer's instructions, or if none is available, have someone sit in the car and watch the tachometer on the instrument panel.
4. Adjust the mixture by seating the mixture control screw lightly and then unscrew it four to five turns.
5. Turn the idle screw until the specified idle speed obtained; it may be necessary to turn the mixture control screw slightly, as well.

   CAUTION: *The carburetor is equipped with an idle limiter screw as an aid in controling emissions; do not attempt to defeat its purpose by adjusting it.*

6. Remove the tachometer (if used) and install the air cleaner once idle adjustments are completed.

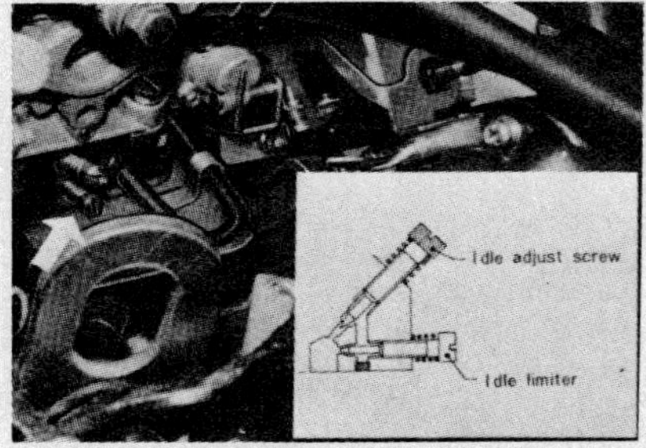

The idle adjustment screw (upper arrow) and the idle limiter screw (lower arrow)
(© Toyo Kogyo Co., Ltd.)

ENGINE ELECTRICAL

Distributors

Removal and Installation

The removal procedure for both the

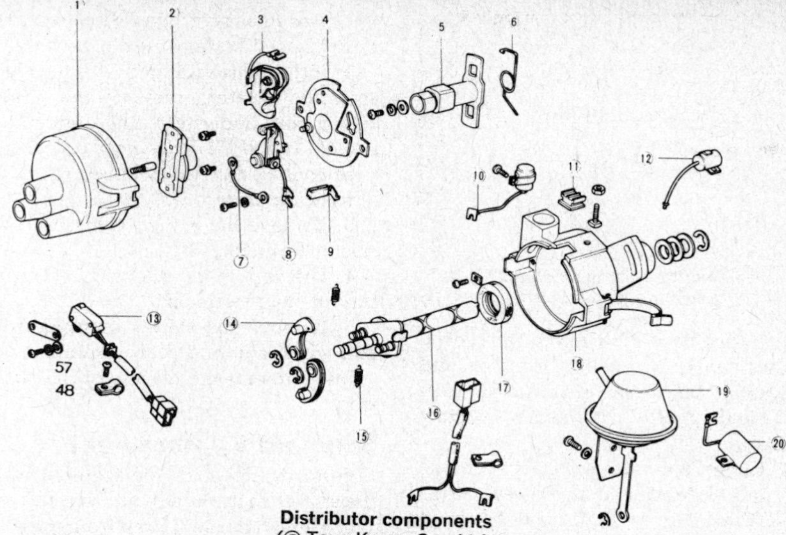

Distributor components
(© Toyo Kogyo Co., Ltd.)

1. Cap
2. Rotor
3. Point set
4. Breaker plate
5. Cam
6. Spring
7. Ground wire
8. Point set
9. Felt
10. Ignition condenser
11. Terminal
12. Radio supression condenser
13. Vacuum switch—trailing distributor only
14. Governor
15. Governor spring
16. Shaft
17. Oil seal
18. Distributor housing
19. Vacuum advance unit
20. Ignition condenser

leading and the trailing distributors is the same. To remove either or both of them, proceed in the following manner:

NOTE: *It is a good idea to remove and install the distributors separately to avoid confusion.*

1. Disconnect the vacuum advance line at the distributor.
2. Unfasten the vacuum advance switch connector (trailing distributor).
3. Disconnect the primary wire at the coil.
4. Note the letters and numbers identifying them, and remove the spark plug cables.
5. Matchmark the distributor housing and sockets. Also, matchmark the position of the rotor, relative to the distributor housing. These marks are an aid when installing the distributor in a properly timed engine.
6. Remove the distributor clamping screw and carefully lift the distributor out of its socket.

NOTE: *Try to avoid rotating the engine while the distributors are removed. Unnecessary rotation of the engine under these conditions only means more work.*

If the engine has not been rotated with either of the distributors removed, their installation is performed in the reverse order of removal. Use the matchmarks made during removal to correctly position the distributors in their sockets.

NOTE: *If both distributors were removed at the same time, use care to see that they are returned to their proper sockets. Both the distributors and the front cover are marked to aid in correct installation.*

Once the distributors are installed, adjust the point gap, dwell angle, and timing, as detailed above.

If the engine was rotated or otherwise disturbed after either distributor was removed, installation is performed in the following manner:

1. Turn the engine until the white mark on the eccentric shaft pulley is aligned with the pointer on the front cover. This will always be top dead center (TDC) of the number one rotor's compression cycle, because each rotor makes only 1/3 of a turn for each full rotation of the eccentric shaft.

NOTE: *TDC cannot be found by feeling for compression at the number one spark plug hole, as in a conventional piston engine.*

2. Align the marks that are stamped on each distributor housing and driven gear.

3. Install either distributor so that the key on the end of its drive engages with the slot in the socket.

NOTE: *If both of the distributors were removed at the same time, be careful not to mix their parts or confuse them upon installation. Both the distributors and the front housing are marked with a "T" or an "L"; insert the distributor which has the same letter as the housing, into its proper socket.*

4. Rotate each distributor slightly until its points just start to open and then tighten its locknut.
5. Check the point gap (see above) and install the cap.
6. Carefully connect all of the vacuum lines and the wires to the proper distributor.

Align the distributor identification marks prior to installation
(© Toyo Kogyo Co., Ltd.)

NOTE: *Spark plug position and leads are marked, as is each distributor cap, to aid installation.*

7. Check and adjust the dwell angle and ignition timing, using the procedures oulined above.
8. Connect the vacuum advance lines to the distributors.

Firing Order

The firing order for the Mazda rotary engine is 1–2, with the trailing spark plugs firing ten degrees after the leading.

Alternator

Alternator Service Precautions

Because of the nature of alternator design, special care must be taken when servicing the charging system.

1. Battery polarity should be checked before making any connections such as jumper cables or battery charger leads. Reversed battery connections will damage the diode rectifiers.
2. The battery must never be disconnected while the alternator is running because the regulator will be ruined.
3. Always disconnect the battery ground cable before replacing the alternator.
4. Do not attempt to polarize an alternator.
5. Do not short across or ground any alternator terminals.
6. Always disconnect the battery ground cable before removing the alternator output cable whether the engine is running or not.
7. If electric arc welding equipment is to be used on the car, first disconnect the battery and alternator cables. Never operate the car with the electric arc welding equipment attached.
8. If the battery is to be "quick charged", disconnect the positive cable from the battery.

Removal and Installation

1. Disconnect the battery ground cable at the negative (−) terminal.
2. Disconnect all of the leads from the alternator.
3. Remove the alternator adjusting link bolt. Do not remove the adjusting link.
4. Remove the alternator securing nuts and bolts. Withdraw the drivebelt and remove the alternator.

Installation is performed in the reverse order of removal. Adjust the drivebelt tension as detailed below.

Belt Tension Adjustment

1. Check the drivebelt tension by applying about 22 lbs of thumb pressure to the belt, midway between the eccentric shaft and alternator pulleys. The belt should deflect to the following specifications:

Old belt—0.59–0.67 in.
New belt—0.47–0.55 in.

2. If belt deflection is not within specifications, loosen but do not remove the bolt on the adjusting link.
3. Push the alternator in the direction required to obtain proper belt deflection.

CAUTION: *Do not pry or pound the alternator housing.*

4. Tighten the adjusting link bolt to 20 ft lbs.

Regulator

Removal and Installation

1. Disconnect the battery ground cable at the negative (−) battery terminal.
2. Disconnect the wiring from the regulator.
3. Remove the regulator mounting screws.
4. Remove the regulator.

Installation is performed in the reverse order of removal.

Voltage Adjustments

1. Remove the cover from the regulator.
2. Check the air gap, the point gap, and the back gap with a feeler gauge (see illustration).

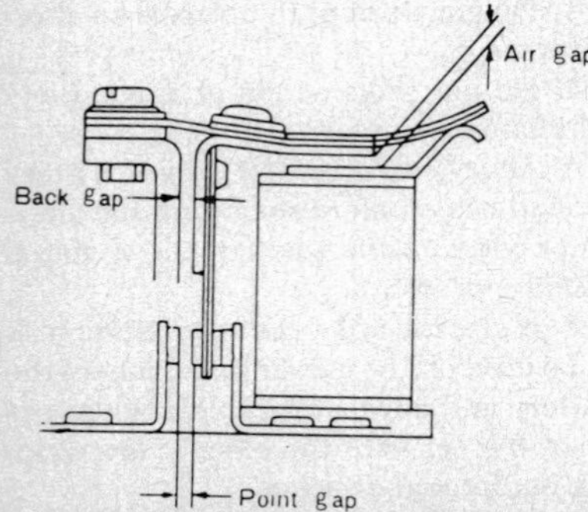

Regulator mechanical adjustments
(© Toyo Kogyo Co., Ltd.)

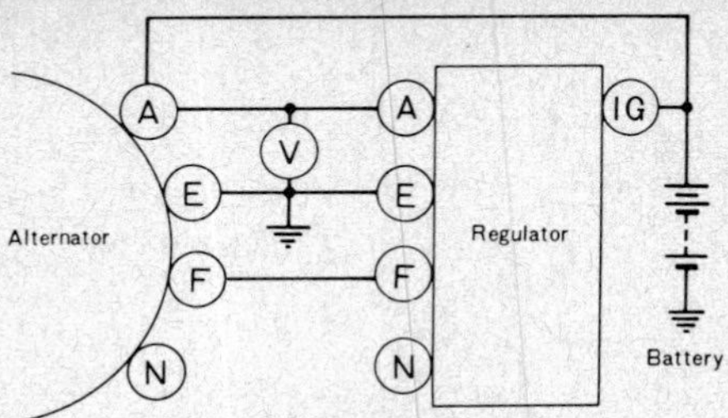

Testing the voltage regulator
(© Toyo Kogyo Co., Ltd.)

3. If they do not fall within the specifications given in the "Alternator and Regulator" chart above, adjust the gaps by bending the stationary contact bracket.
4. Connect a voltmeter between the "A" and "E" terminal of the regulator.

NOTE: *Be sure that the car's battery is fully charged before proceeding with this test.*

5. Start the engine and run it at 2,000 rpm (4,000 alternator rpm). The voltmeter reading should be 13.5–14.5 V.
6. Stop the engine.
7. Bend the upper plate *down* to decrease the voltage setting or *up* to increase the setting, as required.
8. If the regulator cannot be brought within specifications, replace it.
9. When the test is completed, disconnect the voltmeter and replace the regulator cover.

Starter

Removal and Installation

NOTE: *There are two possible locations for the starter motor; one is on the lower right-hand side of the engine and the other is on the upper right-hand side.*

1. Remove the ground cable from the negative (−) battery terminal.
2. If the car is equipped with the lower mounted starter, remove the gravel shield from underneath the engine.

CAUTION: *Be extremely careful not to contact the hot exhaust pipe while working underneath the car.*

3. Remove the battery cable from the starter terminal.
4. Disconnect the solenoid leads from the solenoid terminals.
5. Remove the starter securing bolts and withdraw the starter assembly.

Installation is the reverse of the above steps.

Solenoid Replacement

Perform solenoid replacement with the starter motor removed from the car.

1. Detach the field strap from the solenoid terminals.
2. Remove the solenoid securing screws.
3. Withdraw the solenoid spring and washers from the starter drive housing.

Solenoid installation is performed in the reverse order of removal.

Starter Drive Replacement

1. Perform the solenoid removal procedure as above.
2. Remove the plunger from the drive engagement fork.
3. Unfasten the nuts from the thru-bolts.

NOTE: *Unless further disassembly of the starter is desired, do not remove the thru-bolts.*

4. Remove the drive housing from the front of the starter.
5. Remove the engagement fork, spring, and spring seat.

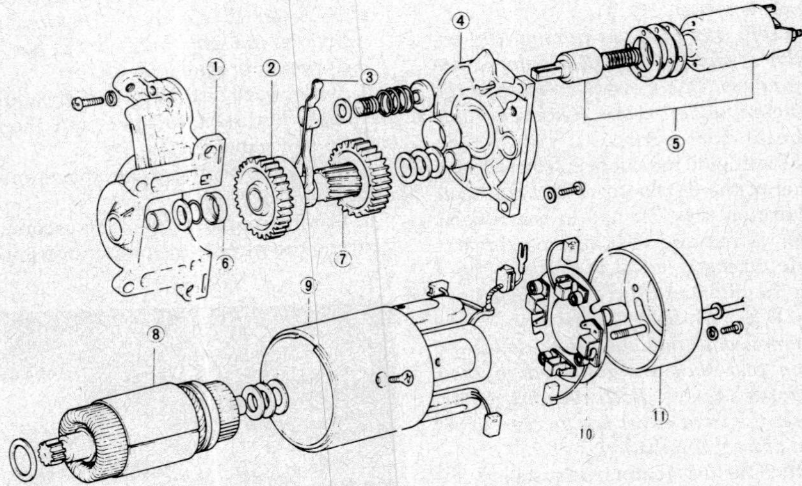

Starter components
(© Toyo Kogyo Co., Ltd.)

1. Front housing
2. Overruning clutch
3. Engagement fork
4. Center frame
5. Solenoid
6. Stop
7. Idler gear
8. Armature
9. Field coil
10. Brush holder
11. End frame

How the rotary engine works.

1. Intake.
Fuel/air mixture is drawn into combustion chamber by revolving rotor through intake port (upper left). No valves or valve-operating mechanism needed.

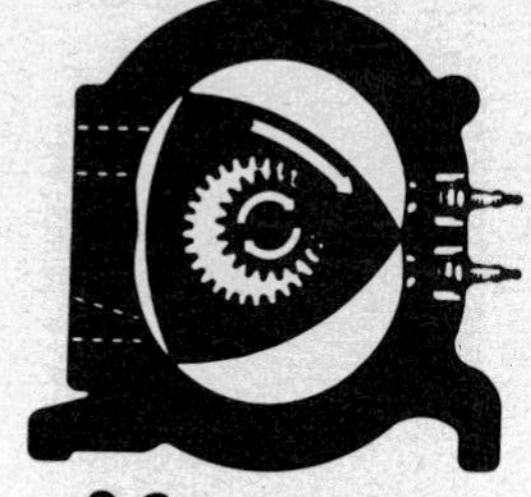

2. Compression.
As rotor continues revolving, it reduces space in chamber containing fuel and air. This compresses mixture.

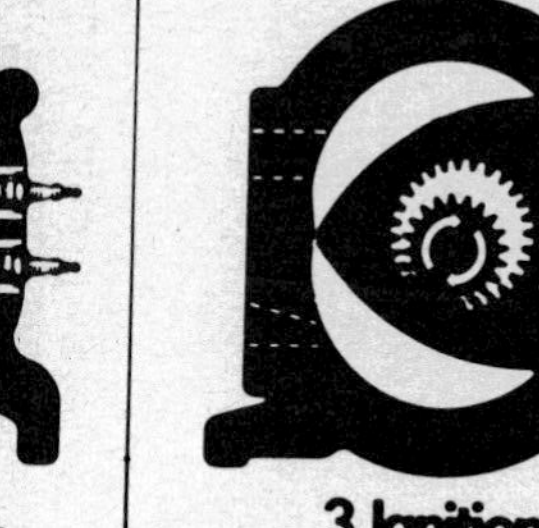

3. Ignition.
Fuel/air mixture now fully compressed. Leading sparkplug fires. A split-second later, following plug fires to assure complete combustion.

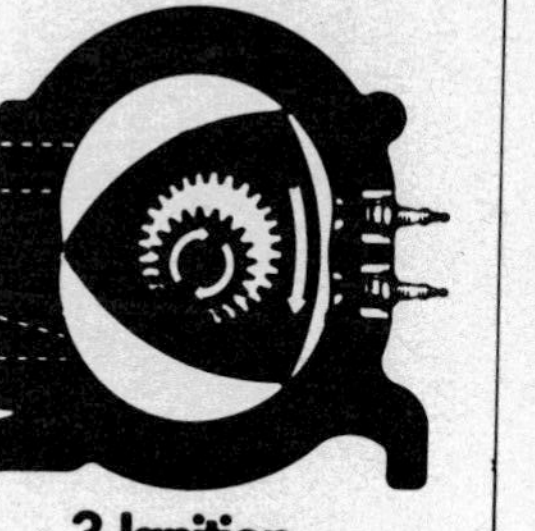

4. Exhaust.
Exploding mixture drives rotor, providing power. Rotor then expels gases through exhaust port.

How your piston engine works.

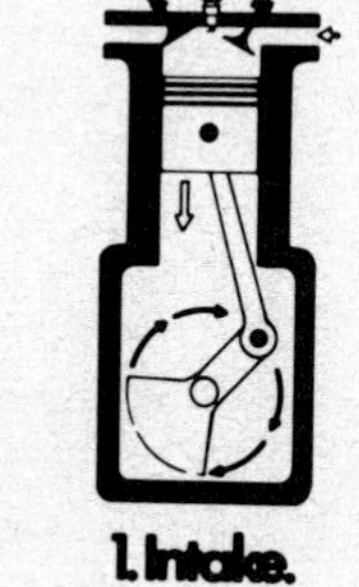

1. Intake.

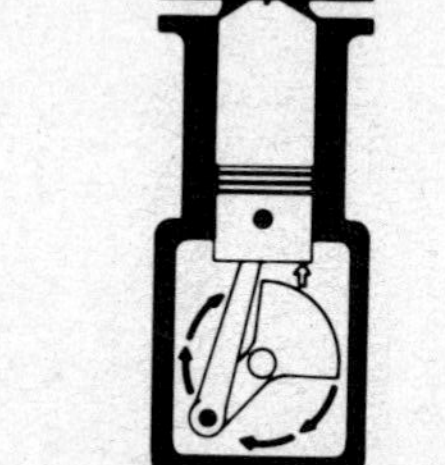

2. Compression.

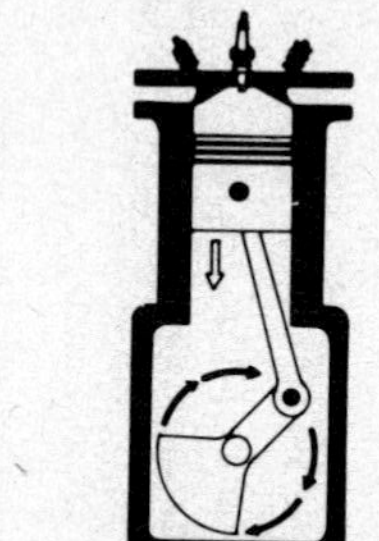

3. Ignition.

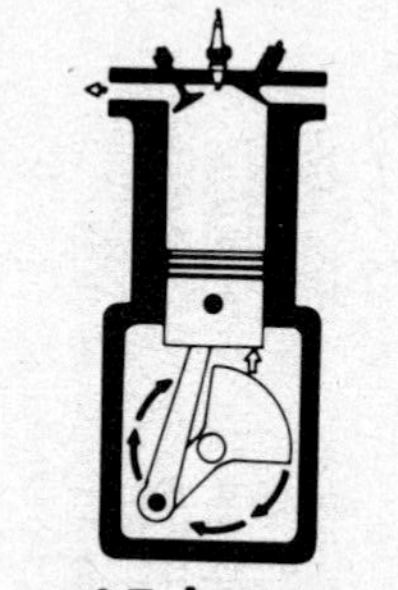

4. Exhaust.

Mazda's rotary engine licensed by NSU-WANKEL.

6. Withdraw the over-running clutch from the armature shaft.

Assembly is performed in the reverse order of disassembly. Check the clearance between the pinion and the stop collar with the solenoid closed. It should be 0.0012–0.0060 in.

ENGINE MECHANICAL

NOTE: *Because of the unique design of the Mazda rotary engine, some procedures require the use of special factory tools. The text notes where these tools are necessary. If the tools are not available, the job should not be undertaken.*

Design

The Mazda rotary engine replaces conventional pistons with three-cornered rotors which have rounded sides. The rotors are mounted on a shaft which has eccentrics rather than crank throws.

The chamber which the rotor travels in is roughly oval-shaped, but with the sides of the oval bowed in slightly. The technical name for this shape is a two-lobe epitrochoid.

As the rotor travels its path in the chamber, it performs the same four functions as the piston in a traditional piston engine:

1. Intake
2. Compression
3. Igntion
4. Exhaust

But all four functions in a rotary engine are happening concurrently, rather than in four separate stages.

Ignition of the compressed fuel/air mixture occurs each time a side of the rotor passes the spark plugs. Since the rotor has three sides, there are three complete power impulses for each complete revolution of the rotor.

As it moves, the rotor exerts pressure on the cam of the eccentric shaft, causing the shaft to turn.

Because there are three power pulses for every revolution of the rotor, the eccentric shaft must make three complete revolutions for every one of the rotor. To maintain this ratio, the rotor has an internal gear that meshes with a fixed gear in a three-to-one ratio. If it were not for this gear arrangement, the rotor would spin freely and timing would be lost.

The Mazda rotary engine has two rotors mounted 60 degrees out of phase. This produces six power impulses for each complete revolution of both rotors and two power impulses for each revolution of the eccentric shaft.

Because of the number of power impulses for each revolution of the rotor, and because all four functions are concurrent, the rotary engine is able to produce a much greater amount of power for its size and weight than a comparable reciprocating piston engine.

Instead of using valves to control the intake and exhaust operations, the rotor uncovers and covers ports on the wall of the chamber as it turns. Thus, a complex valve train is unnecessary. The resulting elimination of parts further reduces the size and weight of the engine, as well as eliminating a major source of mechanical problems.

Spring-loaded carbon seals are used to prevent loss of compression around the rotor apexes and cast iron seals are used to prevent loss of compression around the side faces of the rotor. These seals are equivalent to compression rings on a conventional piston but must be more durable because of the high rotor rpm to which they are exposed.

Oil is controlled by means of circular seals mounted in two grooves on the side face of the rotor. These oil seals function to keep oil out of the combustion chamber and gasoline out of the crankcase, in a similar manner to the oil control ring on a piston.

The rotor housing is made of aluminum and the surfaces of the chamber are chrome plated for durability and the prevention of wear damage.

Engine Removal and Installation

CAUTION: *Be sure that the engine has completely cooled before attempting to remove it.*

1. Scribe matchmarks on the hood and hinges. Remove the hood from the hinges.
2. Working from underneath the car, remove the gravel shield; then drain the cooling system and the engine oil.
3. Disconnect the cable from the negative (−) battery terminal.
4. Remove the air cleaner, its bracket, and its attendant hoses.
5. Detach the accelerator cable, choke cable, and fuel lines from the carburetor.
6. Remove the nuts which secure the thermostat housing. Disconnect the ground cable from the housing and install the housing again after the cable is removed.
7. Disconnect the power brake vacuum line from the intake manifold.
8. Remove the fan shroud securing bolts and then the shroud itself.
9. Remove the bolts which secure the fan clutch to the eccentric shaft pulley. Withdraw the fan and clutch as a single unit.

NOTE: *Keep the fan clutch in an upright position, so that its fluid does not leak out.*

10. Unfasten the clamps and remove both of the radiator hoses.
11. Note their respective positions and remove the spark plug cables. Disconnect the primary leads from the distributors and remove both of the distributor caps.
12. Detach all of the leads from the alternator, the water temperature sender, the oil pressure sender, and the starter motor.
13. Disconnect all of the wiring from the emission control system components. See "Emission Controls," below.
14. Detach the heater hoses at the engine.
15. Detach the oil lines from the front and the rear of the engine.
16. Disconnect the battery cable from the positive (+) battery terminal and from the engine.
17. Unfasten the nuts which secure the clutch slave cylinder and tie the cylinder up out of the way.

NOTE: *Do not remove the hydraulic line from the slave cylinder.*

18. Remove the exhaust pipe and the thermal reactor.

CAUTION: *Be sure that the thermal reactor has completely cooled; severe burns could result if it has not.*

19. Evenly and in two or three stages, remove the nuts and bolts which secure the clutch housing to the engine.
20. Support the transmission with a jack.
21. Remove the nuts from each of the engine mounts.
22. Attach a lifting sling to the lifting bracket on the rear of the engine housing.
23. Use a hoist to take up the slack on the sling.

CAUTION: *Be sure that the hoist is secure to prevent possible personal injury or damage to the engine.*

24. Pull the engine forward until it clears the transmission input shaft. Lift the engine straight up and out of the car.

NOTE: *Be careful not to damage any of the components which remain in the car.*

25. Remove the heat stove from the exhaust manifold.
26. Remove the thermal reactor as outlined below.
27. Mount the engine on a work stand.

NOTE: *A special three part work stand, designed for the rotary engine, is manufactured by Mazda.*

Engine installation is performed in the reverse order of removal. Remember to fill up all of the fluids to specification and to adjust the ignition to specification, once installation is completed.

Rotary Engine Overhaul

Disassembly

Engine disassembly should be performed in the following order, after it has been removed from the automobile and placed on a workstand:

1. Remove all of the components of the emission control system. See "Emission Controls," below.
2. Detach the metering oil pump linkage, oil lines, and vacuum sensing lines from the carburetor.
3. Remove the intake manifold securing nuts, evenly and in several stages.
4. Remove the intake manifold assembly complete with the carburetor.
5. Remove the alternator adjusting link bolt but do not remove the adjusting link itself.
6. Unfasten the alternator attaching bolts, then remove the alternator and its drive belt.
7. Remove the pulley from the water pump.
8. Unfasten the five nuts and two bolts which secure the water pump and remove the pump.
9. Remove the clamping nuts from both of the distributors and withdraw the distributors from their sockets.
10. Mark the distributor sockets for identification during assembly. Remove the nuts and withdraw the distributor sockets from the front housing.
11. Attach a brake to keep the ring gear from turning (Mazda part number 49 0820 060A).
12. Unfasten the eccentric shaft pulley bolt. Remove the pulley and the key from the eccentric shaft.
13. Unfasten the clutch cover attachment bolts.
14. Remove the clutch assembly from the flywheel.
15. Straighten the tabs on the flywheel nut lockwasher.
16. Remove the flywheel nut with a large wrench.

CAUTION: *Do not use locking pliers or a hammer and chisel to remove the flywheel nut.*

17. Remove the flywheel with a puller.
18. Invert the engine on the workstand.
19. Remove the oil pan bolts and take the oil pan off of the engine, complete with its gasket.
20. Remove the oil strainer bolts, the oil strainer, and its gasket.
21. Mark the front and rear rotor housings, which are identical in appearance, so that they will not be confused upon assembly.
22. With the front of the engine facing upward in the stand, unfasten the front engine mount nuts and remove the mounts.

Mark the front and rear rotor housings to prevent confusion during assembly (© Toyo Kogyo Co., Ltd.)

23. Remove the front engine cover securing bolts. Lift off the cover and its gasket.
24. Withdraw the O-ring from the passage on the front of the housing.
25. On 1972–73 models, remove the oil pump drive chain and related components in the following manner:
    a. Slide the oil slinger, spacer, and distributor drive gear off of the eccentric shaft.
    b. Remove the chain tensioner nuts and the chain tensioner.
    c. Remove the locknut and washer from the oil pump sprocket.
    d. Simultaneously slide the sprockets off of the eccentric shaft and oil pump driveshaft, complete with the chain.
    e. Remove the key from the eccentric shaft.
26. Slide the oil pump drive gear (1971 models), balancing weight, thrust washer, and the first needle bearing off of the eccentric shaft.
27. Unfasten the bearing housing securing bolts.
28. Remove the bearing housing, second needle bearing, spacer, and thrust washer.
29. Turn the engine in the workstand so that the top side of it is facing upward.
30. Loosen the engine housing tension bolts in the order illustrated under "Torque Sequences".

CAUTION: *Loosen the bolts evenly and in two or three stages.*

31. With the front of the engine facing up, lift the front housing off of the eccentric shaft.
32. Remove any side seals which are sticking to the surface of the front housing and place them in their original position on the rotor.
33. Remove the rotor seals and related components in the following order, after noting their original positions, so that they will not be confused during assembly:
    a. Corner seals—3
    b. Corner seal springs—3
    c. Side seals—6
    d. Side seal springs—6

Remove any side seals adhering to the front housing surfaces

NOTE: *Each seal has its own installation mark next to its groove on the rotor. Mazda has a special seal tray (part no. 49 0813 250) which uses the same marks on it, so that the seals will not be confused during storage and assembly.*

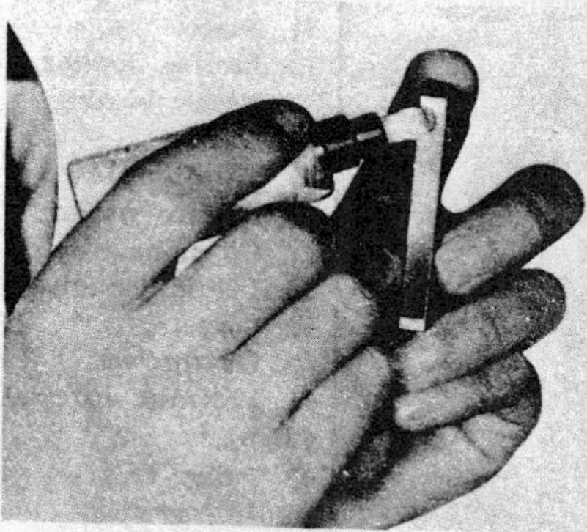

Use a felt-tipped pen to mark the bottom of each apex seal (© Toyo Kogyo Co., Ltd.)

34. Remove the oil seals and O-rings from the grooves in the rotor face.
35. Hold the front rotor housing down while threading a nut and bolt of the proper *metric* size into each of the hollow dowels on the engine housing.
36. Remove the dowels by holding the bolt with wrench while tightening the nut. Once the dowel contacts the nut, back off on the nut and insert a spacer between the nut and the housing. Continue tightening the nut and inserting spacers until each dowel is out of the housing.
37. Lift the front housing away from the rotor.

CAUTION: *When lifting the housing off of the rotor, be careful that the apex seals do not fall off. If they strike a hard surface, they will shatter.*

38. Remove the air injection nozzles, the O-rings, and the rubber seals from the front housing.
39. Remove the apex seals and their springs from the front rotor. When removing each seal, place an identification mark on its *bottom,* with a felt tipped pen, so that it can be installed in the proper location and direction. If some of

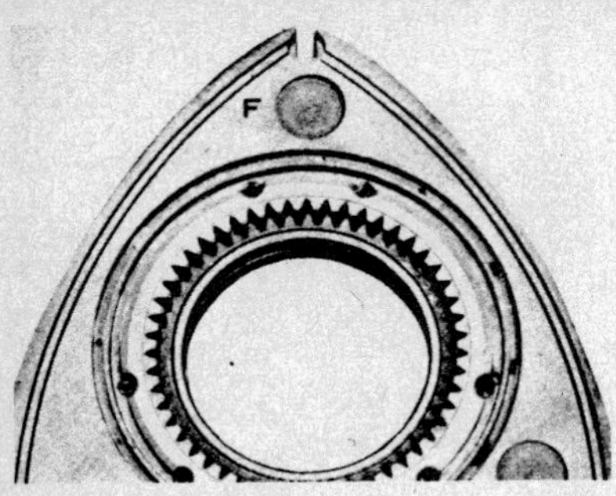

The front rotor is marked with an "F" on its internal gear side; The rear rotor is marked with an "R" in a similar manner. (© Toyo Kogyo Co., Ltd.)

the seals have come off, be sure to note their proper location.

CAUTION: *When marking the seal, do not use a punch or scratch the surface of the seal.*

40. Remove the front rotor from the eccentric shaft and place it face down on a clean, soft cloth.

NOTE: *The internal gear side of the front rotor is marked with an "F" to ensure installation in the proper rotor housing.*

41. Remove the seals and springs from the rear side of the rotor in the same manner as detailed for the front side in step 38.

42. Hold the intermediate housing down and remove the hollow dowels, as outlined for the front rotor housing in steps 35–36.

43. Lift the intermediate housing off of the eccentric shaft by sliding it beyond the front rotor journal while pushing up on the shaft. Be careful not to damage the eccentric shaft.

44. Withdraw the eccentric shaft.

45. Repeat steps 35–41 to remove the rear rotor housing and rotor.

NOTE: *The internal gear side of the rear rotor is marked with an "R" to ensure installation in the proper rotor housing.*

Inspection and Replacement

Front Housing

1. Check the housing for signs of gas or water leakage.

2. Remove the carbon deposits from the front housing with extra fine emery cloth.

NOTE: *If a carbon scraper must be used, be careful not to damage the mating surfaces of the housing.*

3. Remove any of the old sealer which is adhering to the housing, using a brush or a cloth soaked in Ke-tone®.

4. Check for distortion by placing a sraightedge on the surface of the housing. Measure the clearance between the straightedge and the housing with a feeler gauge. If the clearance is greater than 0.002 in. at any point, replace the housing.

5. Use a dial indicator to check for wear on the rotor contact surfaces of the housing. If the wear is greater than 0.004 in., replace the housing.

NOTE: *The wear at either end of the minor axis is greater than at any other point on the housing. However, this is normal and should be no cause for concern.*

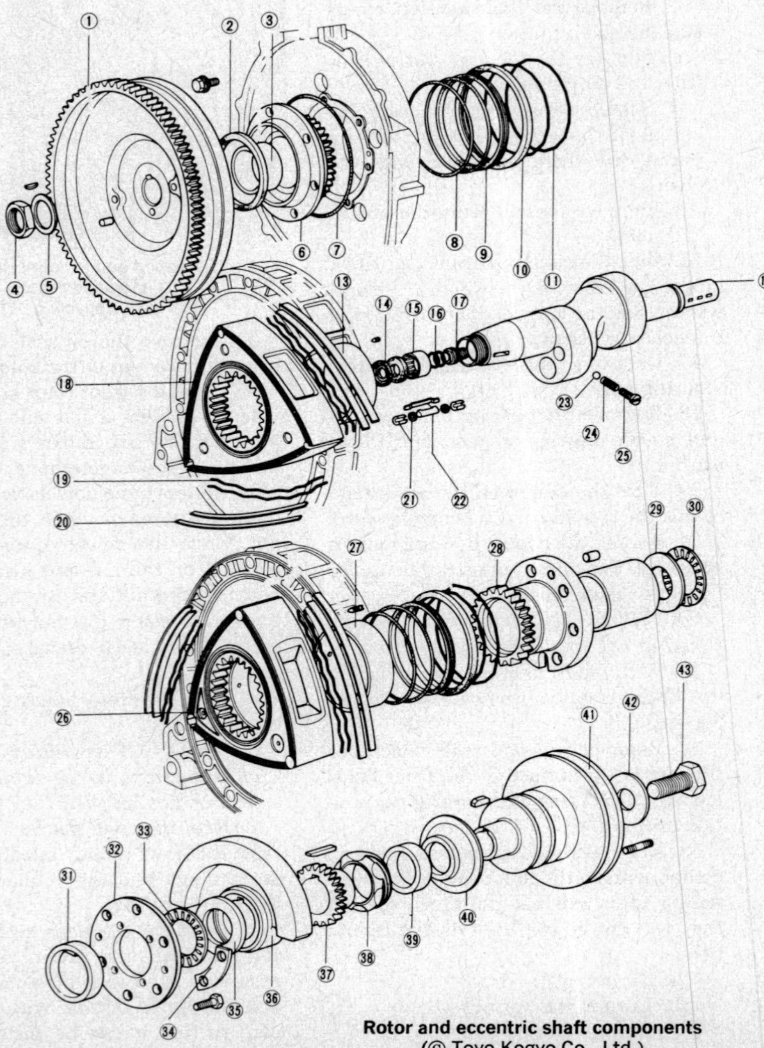

1. Flywheel
2. Oil seal
3. Main bearing
4. Locknut
5. Washer
6. Rear stationary gear
7. O-ring
8. Oil seal O-ring
9. Oil seal
10. Oil seal
11. Oil seal spring
12. Eccentric shaft
13. Rotor bearing
14. Grease seal
15. Needle bearing
16. O-ring
17. Blind plug
18. Front rotor
19. Side seal spring
20. Side seal
21. Corner seal and spring
22. Apex seal and spring
23. Ball
24. Spring
25. Oil nozzle
26. Rear rotor
27. Rotor bearing
28. Front stationary gear
29. Thrust washer
30. Thrust bearing
31. Spacer
32. Bearing housing
33. Needle bearing
34. Washer
35. Thrust plate
36. Balance weight
37. Oil pump drive sprocket (1972-73) or gear (1971)
38. Distributor drive gear
39. Spacer
40. Oil slinger
41. Eccentric shaft pulley
42. Washer
43. Pulley bolt

Rotor and eccentric shaft components (© Toyo Kogyo Co., Ltd.)

Measure the housing distortion along the axes indicated
(© Toyo Kogyo Co., Ltd.)

Measuring housing wear with a dial indicator
(© Toyo Kogyo Co., Ltd.)

Front Stationary Gear and Main Bearing

1. Examine the teeth of the stationary gear for wear or damage.

2. Be sure that the main bearing shows no signs of excessive wear, scoring, or flaking.

3. Check the main bearing-to-eccentric journal clearance by measuring the journal with a vernier caliper and the bearing with a pair of inside calipers.

The clearance should be between 0.0018–0.0028 in. and the wear limit is 0.0039 in. Replace either the main bearing or the eccentric shaft if it is greater than this. If the main bearing is to be replaced, proceed as detailed in the following section.

Main Bearing Replacement

1. Unfasten the securing bolts, if used. Drive the stationary gear and main bearing assembly out of the housing with a brass drift.

2. Press the main bearing out of the stationary gear.

3. Press a new main bearing into the stationary gear so that it is in the same position that the old bearing was.

4. Align the slot in the stationary gear flange with the dowel pin in the housing and press the gear into place. Install the securing bolts, if required.

NOTE: *To aid in stationary gear and main bearing removal and installation, Mazda manufactures a special tool, part number 49 0813 235.*

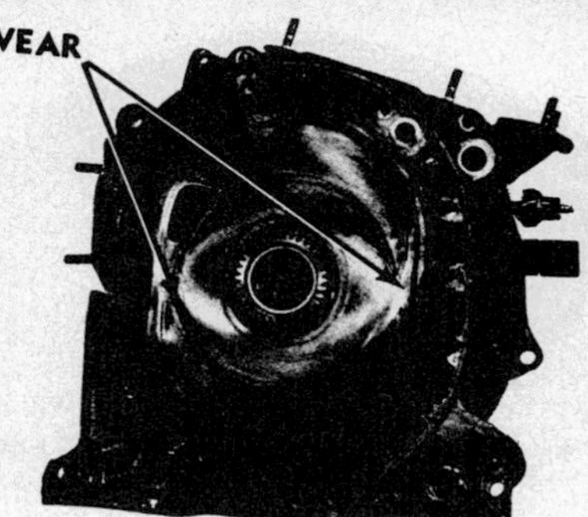

Most of the front and rear housing wear occurs at the ends of the minor axis, as indicated.

Align the slot in the stationary gear flange with the pin in the housing (arrow)
(© Toyo Kogyo Co., Ltd.)

Intermediate and Rear Housings

Inspection of the intermediate and rear housings is carried out in the same manner as detailed for the front housing. Replacement of the rear main bearing and stationary gear (mounted on the rear housing) is given below.

Rear Stationary Gear and Main Bearing

Inspect the rear stationary gear and main bearing in a similar manner to the front. In addition, examine the O-ring, which is located in the stationary gear, for signs of wear or damage. Replace the O-ring, if necessary.

If required, replace the stationary gear in the following manner:

1. Remove the rear stationary gear securing bolts.

2. Drive the stationary gear out of the rear housing with a brass drift.

3. Apply a light coating of grease to a new O-ring and fit it into the groove on the stationary gear.

4. Apply sealer to the flange of the stationary gear.

5. Install the stationary gear on the housing so that the slot on its flange aligns with the pin on the rear housing.

CAUTION: *Use care not to damage the O-ring during installation.*

6. Tighten the stationary gear bolts evenly, and in several stages, to 15 ft lbs.

Position the O-ring in the groove on the stationary gear (arrow)
(© Toyo Kogyo Co., Ltd.)

Rotor Housings

1. Examine the inner margin of both housings for signs of gas or water leakage.

2. Wipe the inner surface of each housing with a clean cloth to remove the carbon deposits.

NOTE: *If the carbon deposits are stubborn, soak the cloth in a solution of Ke-tone. Do not scrape or sand the chrome*

Measure the rotor housing distortion along the axes indicated
(© Toyo Kogyo Co., Ltd.)

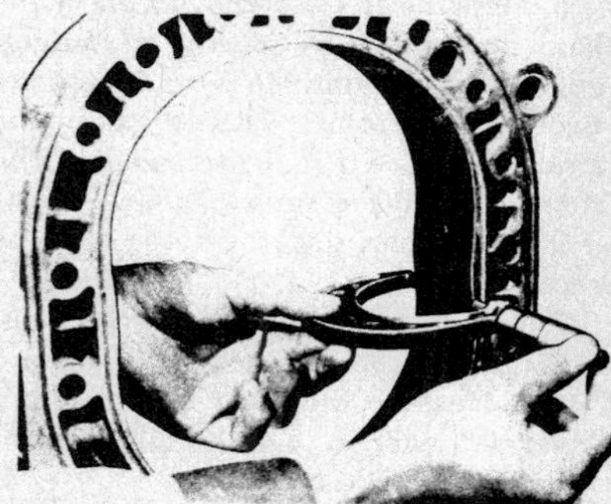

Check the rotor housing width at eight points near the trochoid surface
(© Toyo Kogyo Co., Ltd.)

plated surfaces of the rotor chamber.

3. Clean all of the rust deposits out of the cooling passages of each rotor housing.

4. Remove the old sealer with a cloth soaked in Ke-tone.

5. Examine the chromium plated inner surfaces for scoring, flaking, or other signs of damage. If any are present, the housing must be replaced.

6. Check the rotor housings for distortion by placing a straightedge on the axes.

7. Measure the clearance between the straightedge and the housing with a feeler gauge. If the gap exceeds 0.002 in., replace the rotor housing.

8. Check the widths of both rotor housings, at a minimum of eight points near the trochoid surfaces of each housing, using a vernier caliper.

If the difference between the maximum and minimum values obtained is greater than 0.0031 in., replace the housing. A housing in this condition will be prone to gas and coolant leakage.

NOTE: *Standard rotor housing width is 2.7559 in.*

Rotors

1. Check the rotor for signs of blow-by around the side and corner seal areas.

2. The color of the carbon deposits on the rotor should be brown, just as in a piston engine.

NOTE: *Usually the carbon deposits on the leading side of the rotor are brown, while those on the trailing side tend toward black, as viewed from the direction of rotation.*

3. Remove the carbon on the rotor with a scraper or extra fine emery paper. Use the scraper carefully, when doing the seal grooves, so that no damage is done to them.

4. After removing the carbon, wash the rotor in solvent and blow it dry with compressed air.

5. Examine the internal gear for cracks or damaged teeth.

NOTE: *If the internal gear is damaged, the rotor and gear must be replaced as a single assembly.*

6. With the oil seal removed, check the land protrusions by placing a straightedge over the lands. Measure the gap between the rotor surface and the straightedge with a feeler gauge. The standard specification is 0.004–0.006 in.; if it is less than this, the rotor must be replaced.

7. Check the gaps between the housings and the rotor on both of its sides:

a. Measure the rotor width with a vernier caliper. The standard rotor width is 2.7500 in.

b. Compare the rotor width against the width of the rotor housing which was measured above. The standard rotor housing width is 2.7559 in.

c. Replace the rotor, if the difference between the two measurements is not within 0.0051–0.0067 in.

8. Check the rotor bearing for flaking, wearing, or scoring and proceed as indicated in the next section, if any of these are present.

The rotors are classified into five lettered grades, according to their weight. A letter between A and E is stamped on the internal gear side of the rotor. If it becomes necessary to replace a rotor, use one marked with a "C" because this is the standard replacement rotor, and it can be used in most balancing combinations.

Normal shading of carbon deposits on rotor
(© Toyo Kogyo Co., Ltd.)

Measure the rotor width at the point indicated
(© Toyo Kogyo Co., Ltd.)

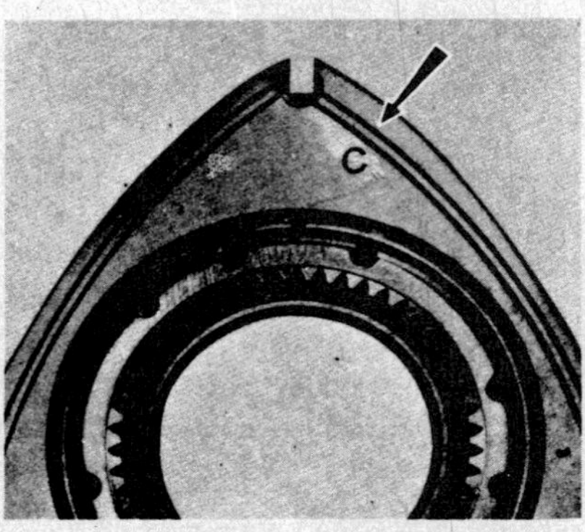

Weight classification letter placement (arrow)
(© Toyo Kogyo Co., Ltd.)

Rotor Bearing Replacement

CAUTION: *The use of the special service tools, as indicated in the text, is mandatory, if damage to the rotor is to be avoided.*

Check the clearance between the rotor bearing and the rotor journal on the eccentric shaft. Meausre the inner diameter of the rotor bearing and the outer diameter of the journal; the standard clearance is 0.0016–0.0031 in. The wear limit is 0.0039 in.; replace the bearing if it exceeds this.

To replace the bearing, proceed in the following manner:

1. Install the bearing expander (Mazda part number 49 0813 245) in the rotor bearing. If the expander is not used, bearing deformation will result when the holes are drilled.

Insert the special bearing expander into the rotor
(© Toyo Kogyo Co., Ltd.)

Installing a new rotor bearing
(© Toyo Kogyo Co., Ltd.)

2. Drill a 0.14 in. diameter hole, roughly 0.028 in. deep, into each of the lockscrews which secure the bearings to the rotor. Use a #28 drill.

3. Remove the bearing expander.

4. Support the rotor so that the internal gear is facing upward.

5. Using the rotor bearing remover (Mazda part number 49 0813 240), less the adaptor ring, press the bearing out of the rotor.

CAUTION: *Be extremely careful not to damage the internal gear. It cannot be replaced separately from the rotor.*

6. If the bore in which the bearing is installed is damaged, dress it with emery paper and blow it clean with compressed air.

7. With the rotor internal gear facing upward, press-fit a new bearing into the bore. Use the bearing replacer with the adaptor screws removed.

NOTE: *Be sure that the oil hole in the bearing is aligned with the hole in the apex side of the rotor. Once the bearing is installed, it should be flush with the rotor boss.*

8. Insert the rotor bearing expander into the new bearing, as in step 1.

9. Drill 0.14 in. holes, about 0.28 in. deep, within 0.28 in. of the original lockscrew holes (either to the left or right of them) with a #28 drill. The center of the holes must be 0.02 in. from the rotor bore.

NOTE: *The new holes should all be in the same direction from the original holes; e.g., if the first hole is drilled to the left of the original hole, drill the remaining holes to the left of the other lockscrew holes.*

10. Thread the holes with an M4, P-0.70 mm metric tap.

11. Install the bearing lockscrews and stake them with a punch so that they cannot work loose.

12. Wash the rotor and blow it dry with compressed air.

Oil Seal Inspection

NOTE: *Inspect the oil seal while it is mounted in the rotor.*

1. Examine the oil seal for signs of wear or damage.

2. Measure the width of the oil seal lip. If it is greater than 0.031 in., replace the oil seal.

3. Measure the protrusion of the oil seal; it should be greater than 0.020 in. Replace the seal, as detailed below, if it is not.

Oil Seal Replacement

NOTE: *Replace the rubber O-ring in the oil seal as a normal part of engine overhaul.*

1. Pry the seal out gently by inserting a screwdriver into the slots on the rotor.

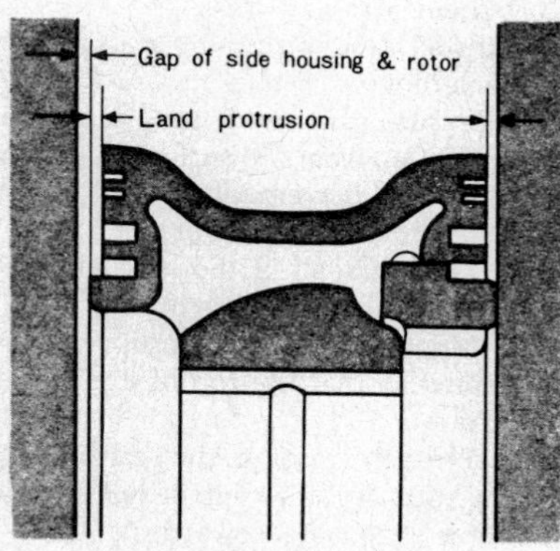

Oil seal protrusion
(© Toyo Kogyo Co., Ltd.)

Do not remove the seal by prying it at only one point; seal deformation will result.

CAUTION: *Be careful not to deform the lip of the oil seal if it is to be reinstalled.*

2. Fit both of the oil seal springs into their respective grooves so that their ends are facing upward and their gaps are opposite each other on the rotor.

3. Insert a new rubber O-ring into each of the oil seals.

NOTE: *Before installing the O-rings into the oil seals, fit each of the seals into its proper groove on the rotor. Check to see that all of the seals move smoothly and freely.*

4. Coat the oil seal groove and the oil seal with engine oil.

5. Gently press the oil seal into the groove with your fingers. Be careful not to distort the seal.

NOTE: *Be sure that the white mark is on the bottom side of each seal when it is installed.*

6. Repeat the installation procedure for the oil seals on both sides of each rotor.

Apex Seals

CAUTION: *Although the apex seals are extremely durable when in service, they are easily broken when they are being handled. Be careful never to drop them.*

1. Remove the carbon deposits from the apex seals and their springs. Do not use emery cloth on the seals as it will damage their finish.

2. Wash the seals and the springs in cleaning solution.

3. Check the apex seals for cracks and other signs of wear or damage.

4. Test the seal springs for weakness.

5. Use a micrometer to check the seal height. Replace any seal if its height is less than 0.3150 in.

6. With a feeler gauge, check the side clearance between the apex seal and the groove in the rotor. Insert the gauge until its tip contacts the bottom of the groove. If the gap is greater than 0.004 in., replace the seal.

7. Check the gap between the apex seals and the side housing in the following manner:

a. Use a vernier caliper to measure the length of each apex seal.

b. Compare this measurement to the *minimum* figure obtained when the rotor housing width was being measured.

c. If the difference is more than 0.0059 in., replace the seal.

d. If, on the other hand, the seal is too long, sand the ends of the seal with emery cloth until the proper length is reached.

CAUTION: *Do not use the emery cloth on the faces of the seal.*

Side Seals

1. Remove the carbon deposits from the side seals and their springs with a carbon scraper.

2. Check the side seals for cracks or wear. Replace any seals found defective.

3. Check the clearance between the side seals and their grooves with a feeler gauge. Replace any side seals with a clearance of more than 0.0039 in. The standard clearance is 0.002–0.003 in.

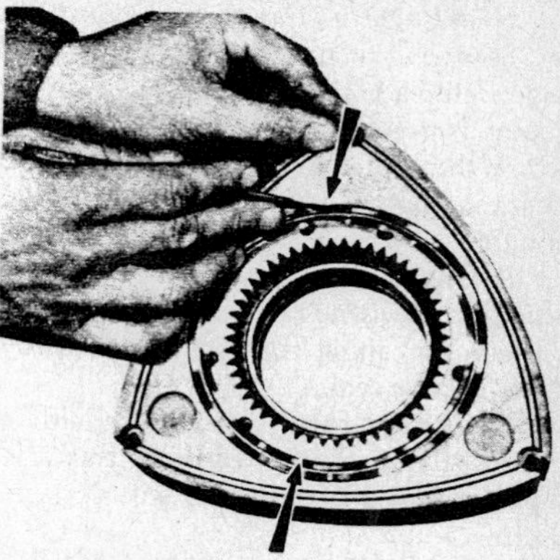

Position the oil seal spring gaps at arrows
(© Toyo Kogyo Co., Ltd.)

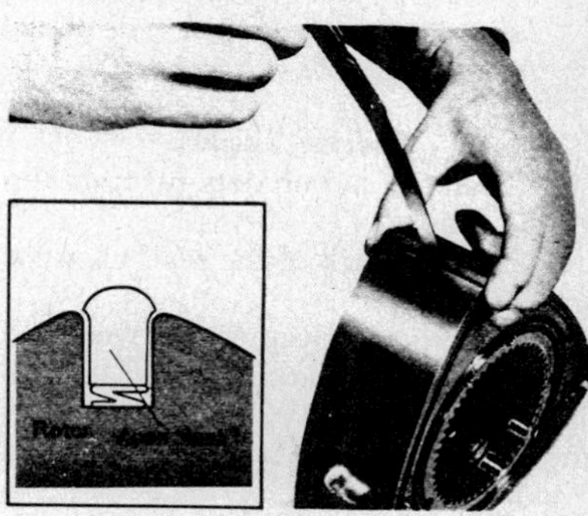

Check the gap between the apex seal and groove with a feeler gauge
(© Toyo Kogyo Co., Ltd.)

Apex seal-to-side seal housing gap
(© Toyo Kogyo Co., Ltd.)

4. Check the clearance between the side seals and the corner seals with both installed in the rotor.

a. Insert a feeler gauge between the end of the side seal and the corner seal.

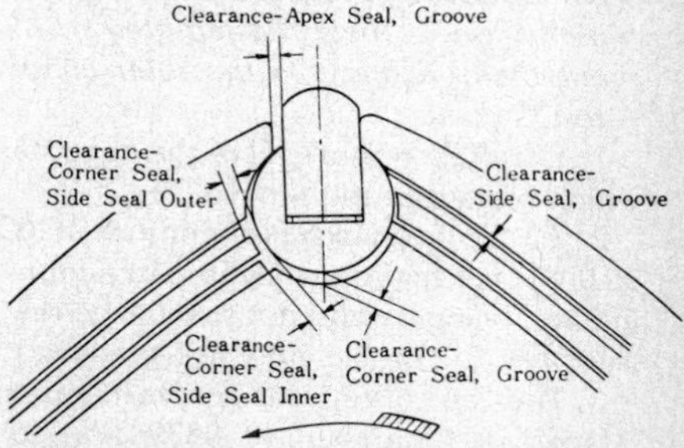

Check the clearance of the seals at the points indicated
(© Toyo Kogyo Co., Ltd.)

NOTE: *Insert the gauge against the direction of the rotor's rotation.*

b. Replace the side seal if the clearance is greater than 0.016 in.

5. If the side seal is replaced, adjust the clearance between it and the corner seal as follows:

a. File the side seal on its reverse side, in the same rotational direction of the rotor, along the outline made by the corner seal.

b. The clearance obtained should be 0.002–0.006 in. If it exceeds this, the performance of the seals will deteriorate.

CAUTION: *There are four different types of side seals, depending upon location. Do not mix the seals up and be sure to use the proper type of seal for replacement.*

Corner Seals

1. Clean the carbon deposits from the corner seals.
2. Examine each of the seals for wear or damage.
3. Measure the clearance between the corner seal and its groove. The clearance should be 0.0008–0.0019 in. The wear limit of the gap is 0.0031 in.
4. If the wear between the corner seal and the groove is uneven, check the clearance with the special "bar limit gauge" (Mazda part number 49 0839 165). The gauge has a "go" end and a "no go" end. Use the gauge in the following manner:

a. If neither end of the gauge goes into the groove, the clearance is within specifications.

b. If the "go" end of the gauge fits into the groove, but the "no go" end does not, replace the corner seal with one that is 0.0012 in. oversize.

c. If both ends of the gauge fit into the groove, then the groove must be reamed out as detailed below. Replace the corner seal with one which is 0.0072 in. oversize, after reaming.

NOTE: *Take the measurement of the groove in the direction of maximum wear,i.e. that of rotation.*

Corner Seal Groove Reaming

NOTE: *This procedure requires the use of special tools; if attempted without them, damage to the rotor could result.*

1. Carefully remove all of the deposits which remain in the groove.
2. Fit the jig (Mazda part number 2113 99 900) over the rotor. Tighten its adjusting bar, being careful not to damage the rotor bearing or the apex seal grooves.
3. Use the corner seal groove reamer (Mazda part number 49 0839 170) to ream the groove.
4. Rotate the reamer at least 20 times, while applying engine oil as a coolant.

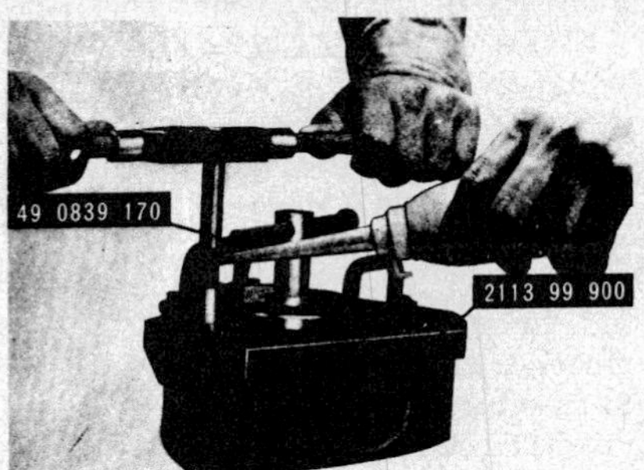

Reaming the corner seal groove
(© Toyo Kogyo Co., Ltd.)

NOTE: *If engine oil is not used, it will be impossible to obtain the proper groove surfacing.*

5. Remove the reamer and the jig.
6. Repeat steps 1–5 for each of the corner seal grooves.
7. Clean the rotor completely and check it for any signs of damage.
8. Fit a 0.0079 in. oversize corner seal into the groove and check its clearance. Clearance should be 0.0008–0.0019 in.

Seal Springs

Check the seal springs for damage or weakness. Be exceptionally careful when checking the spring areas which contact either the rotor or the seal.

Eccentric Shaft

1. Wash the eccentric shaft in solvent and blow the oil passages dry with compressed air.
2. Check the shaft for wear, cracks, or other signs of damage. Make sure that none of the oil passages are clogged.
3. Measure the shaft journals with a vernier caliper. The standard specifications are:

Main journals—1.6929 in.

Rotor journals—2.9134 in.

Replace the shaft if any of its journals shows excessive wear.

4. Check eccentric shaft runout by placing the shaft on V-blocks and using a dial indicator as shown. Rotate the shaft slowly and note the dial indicator reading. If runout is more than 0.0008 in., replace the eccentric shaft.
5. Check the blind plug at the end of the shaft. If it is loose or leaking, remove it with an allen wrench and replace the O-ring.
6. Check the operation of the needle roller bearing for smoothness by inserting a mainshaft into the bearing and rotating it. Examine the bearing for signs of wear or damage.
7. Replace the bearing, if necessary, with the special bearing replacer (Mazda part numbers 49 0823 073 and 49 0823 072).

Engine Assembly

1. Place the rear rotor on a rubber pad or a clean, thick cloth.
2. Install the oil seals on both sides of the rotor, if you have not already done so. Follow the procedure outlined in the appropriate section under "Inspection and Replacement", below.
3. Place the rear rotor, still using the pad or cloth, so that its internal gear is facing upward.

NOTE: *When installing the various seals, consult the marks made during engine disassembly in order to ensure installation of the seals in their proper location.*

4. Place each of the apex seals into their respective grooves, without fitting the springs.
5. Place each of the corner seal springs, followed by the corner seals, into the grooves on the rotor. Lubricate them with engine oil.
6. Check to see that the upper surface of the corner seal is 0.05–0.06 in. higher than the rotor. The corner seal should also move freely when finger pressure is applied to it.
7. Place the side seal springs into their grooves with both ends facing upward. Coat them with engine oil.
8. Install each of the side seals into its proper groove.
9. Be sure that each seal protrudes about 0.04 in. from the surface of the rotor. Test free movement of the seals by pressing them with your finger.
10. Lubricate all of the seals and the internal gear with engine oil.
11. Mount the rear housing in the workstand so that the top of it is facing upward.
12. Place the rotor on the rear housing so that both its rotor contact surface and the rotor are facing upward.

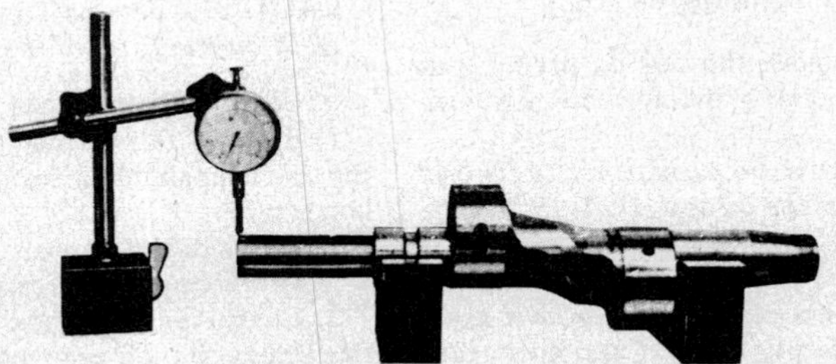

Position the dial indicator as shown, in order to measure shaft runout
(© Toyo Kogyo Co., Ltd.)

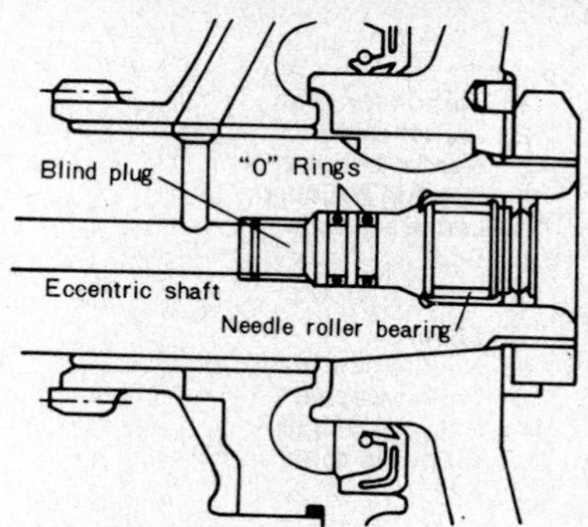

Eccentric shaft blind plug assembly
(© Toyo Kogyo Co., Ltd.)

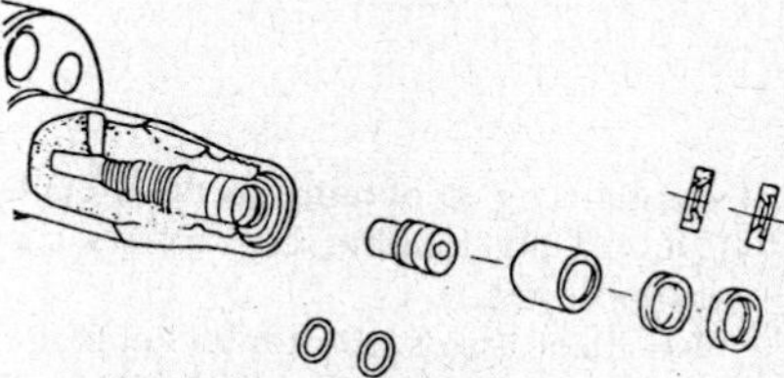

Needle bearing components

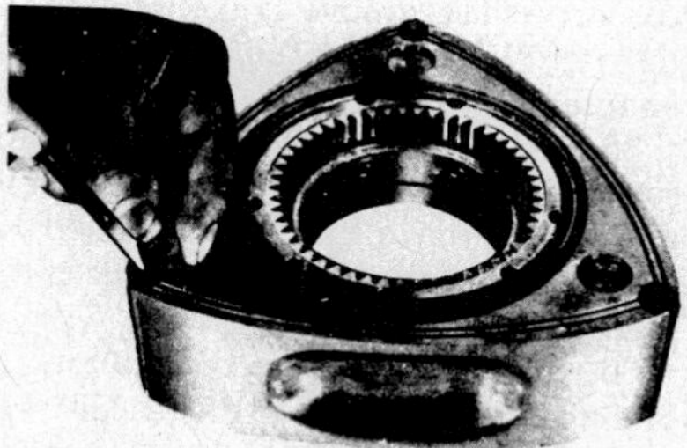

Corner seal installation
(© Toyo Kogyo Co., Ltd.)

The rear rotor must be positioned as shown during engine assembly
(© Toyo Kogyo Co., Ltd.)

CAUTION: *Be sure that none of the seals falls off while the rotor is being moved.*

13. Mesh the rotor internal gear with the stationary gear on the housing, so that the apexes of the rotor are positioned as illustrated.

NOTE: *When positioning the rotor, be sure that none of the corner seals drops into the ports.*

14. Remove the three apex seals from the rotor and place them so that they are near their proper installation positions,

15. Lubricate the eccentric shaft rear rotor and main bearing journals with engine oil.

16. Insert the eccentric shaft into the rotor and rear housing using care not to damage any of the bearings or journals.

17. Fit the air injection nozzles into place. Apply sealer to the back of the rear rotor housing.

NOTE: *Use care not to get any sealer into the water or oil passages of the rear housing.*

18. Apply a small amount of rubber lubricant on new O-rings and rubber seals, then install them into the rear side of the rotor housing.

19. Invert the rear rotor housing. Fit it over the rotor and then onto the rear housing. Be sure that none of the O-rings or rubber seals falls out of the housing.

20. Coat the hollow dowels with engine oil. Fit the dowels through the holes in the rotor housing and into the holes on the rear housing.

21. Install the apex seals, complete with springs, in the proper position and in the proper direction within the rotor.

22. Position the corner and side seals, with their springs, in the proper grooves. Be sure that they are facing in the correct direction.

23. Lightly lubricate the rotor and the rotor contact surface of the rear housing with engine oil.

24. Apply sealer to the O-rings and rubber seals. Install them on the intermediate housing, in a similar manner to that outlined in steps 17–18 above.

25. Hold the back end of the eccentric shaft up so that the front end of the rear rotor journal does not extend beyond the front side of the rotor bearing.

26. Fit the intermediate housing onto the rear rotor housing, while holding the eccentric shaft, as explained in the step above.

27. Install the front rotor and rotor housing in the same manner outlined for the rear rotor and housing in steps 1–23.

NOTE: *The proper relationship between the timing of the front and rear rotors will be obtained when the front rotor is placed over the rotor journal on the eccentric shaft, and positioned as the rear rotor is in step 13.*

28. Apply engine oil to the front housing stationary gear and main bearing. Place the front housing over the front rotor housing. If necessary, turn the front rotor slightly to engage its internal gear with the front housing stationary gear.

29. Install the tension bolts in the following manner:

a. Fit each bolt through the housings and turn it two or three times.

b. Rotate the engine in the stand so that its top is facing upward.

c. Tighten the bolts evenly and in two or three stages. Use the sequence illustrated below and the torque figure listed in the torque specifications chart.

CAUTION: *Do not tighten the bolts one at a time.*

d. Rotate the eccentric shaft so that it operates lightly and smoothly.

30. Coat the rear oil seal with engine oil. Apply Loctite® to the threads on the eccentric shaft through the key.

31. Install the flywheel on the rear of the eccentric shaft with its keyway over the key on the shaft.

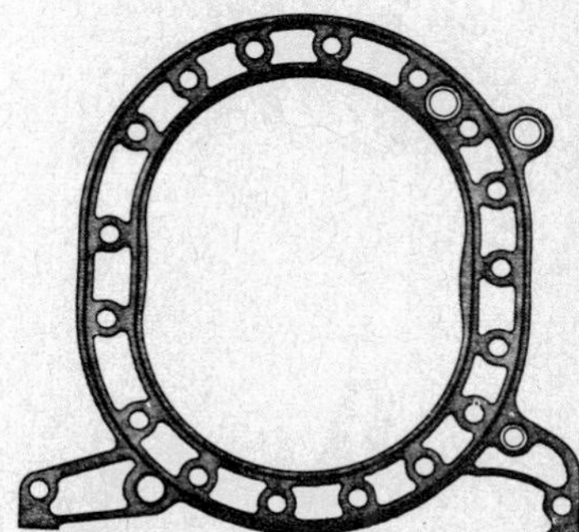

Apply sealer to the grey shadowed areas of the rotor housing
(© Toyo Kogyo Co., Ltd.)

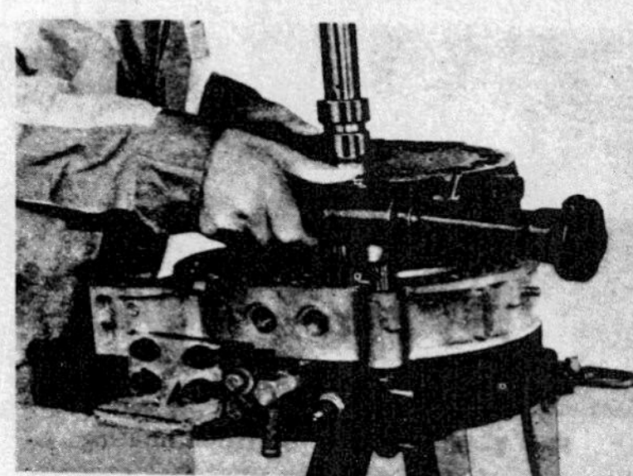

Intermediate housing installation
(© Toyo Kogyo Co., Ltd.)

32. Coat both sides of the flywheel lockwasher with sealer, then fit the washer on the eccentric shaft.

33. Finger tighten the flywheel locknut. Use a brake on the flywheel to keep it from rotating while tightening the nut on the flywheel to 350 ft lbs.

34. Turn the engine on the workstand so that its front end is facing up.

35. Slip the thrust plate, spacer, and the rear needle bearing over the front of the eccentric shaft. Lubricate the parts which were just installed with engine oil.

36. Install the bearing housing, tighten its securing bolts, and bend the lockwasher tabs upward.

37. Fit the front needle bearing and thrust washer on the shaft, then coat them with engine oil. Install the balance weight and the oil pump drive gear on the shaft.

38. On 1972–73 models, fit the oil pump drive chain over both of the sprockets. Install the sprocket and chain assembly over the eccentric and oil pump shafts simultaneously. Place the key on the eccentric shaft.

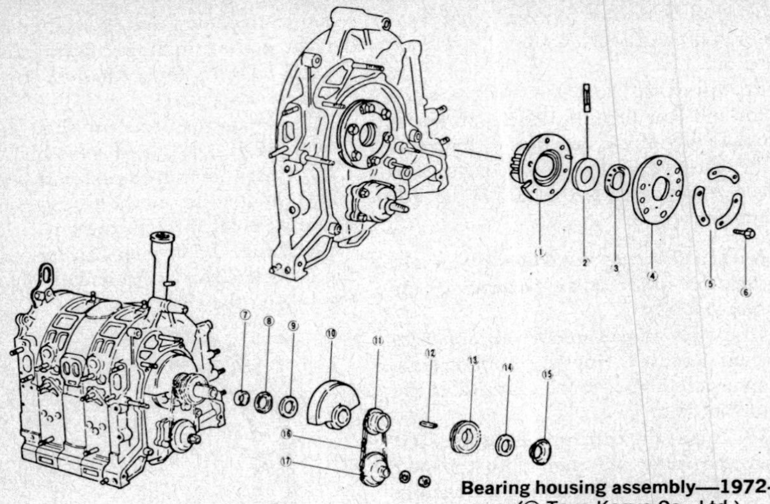

Bearing housing assembly—1972-73
(© Toyo Kogyo Co., Ltd.)

Use a dial indicator attached to the flywheel to measure eccentric shaft end-play
(© Toyo Kogyo Co., Ltd.)

Installing oil pump
(© Toyo Kogyo Co., Ltd.)

NOTE: *Be sure that both of the sprockets are engaged by the chain before installing them over the shafts.*

39. Slip the distributor drive gear, the spacer, and the oil slinger over the eccentric shaft.

40. Align the keyway on the eccentric shaft pulley with the key on the shaft and install the pulley. Tighten the pulley securing bolt to 47 ft lbs while holding the flywheel with the brake.

41. Check eccentric shaft end-play in the following manner:

a. Attach a dial indicator to the flywheel. Move the flywheel forward and backward.

b. Note the reading on the dial indicator; it should be 0.0016–0.0018 in.

c. If the end-play is not within specifications, adjust it by replacing the front spacer. Spacers come in four sizes, ranging from 0.3151–0.3181 in.

d. Check the end-play again and, if it is now within specifications, proceed with the next step.

42. Remove the pulley from the front of the eccentric shaft. Tighten the oil pump drive sprocket nut and bend the locktabs on the lockwasher.

43. Fit a new O-ring over the front cover oil passage.

44. Install the chain tensioner and tighten its securing bolts.

45. Position the front cover gasket and the front cover on the front housing, then secure the front cover with its attachment bolts.

46. Install the eccentric shaft pulley again. Tighten its bolt to 47 ft lbs.

47. Use a spare mainshaft or an arbor to hold the clutch disc in place.

48. Install the clutch cover and pressure plate assembly over the flywheel.

NOTE: *Align the O-mark on the clutch cover with the hole in the flywheel.*

49. Tighten the clutch cover bolts to 15 ft lbs while holding the ring gear with a brake. Install the self tapping bolt into the reamed hole.

50. With the bottom of the engine pointing upward in the workstand, cut the excess front cover gasket at the oil pan mounting flange.

51. Install the oil strainer gasket and the strainer. Bolt them to the front housing.

52. Apply sealer to the oil pan and housing mounting flanges. Install the oil pan and gasket. Tighten the bolts evenly, and in several stages, to 7 ft lbs.

53. Align the white mark on the eccentric shaft pulley with the pointer on the front housing to obtain top dead center (TDC) of the number one rotor's compression cycle.

54. Place the distributor socket gaskets on the housing. Install the trailing distributor socket into the housing so that the driveshaft groove is inclined 34° to the right of the longitudinal axis of the engine.

55. Install the leading distributor socket in a similar manner, except that its driveshaft groove should be inclined 17° to the right of the longitudinal axis of the engine.

56. Install both of the distributors, as outlined under "Engine Electrical".

57. Install the water pump as detailed under "Cooling System".

58. Bolt the engine mounts onto the front housing.

59. Perform alternator installation and drivebelt tension adjustments as detailed under "Engine Electrical".

60. Position the intake manifold/carburetor assembly and gaskets onto the engine. Tighten the manifold securing nuts evenly, working in two or three stages, to the specifications in the "Torque Specifications" chart.

NOTE: *Start from the inside and work out when tightening the bolts.*

61. Attach the oil lines, the vacuum lines, and the metering oil pump linkage to the carburetor.

62. Remove the engine from the workstand.

Position the slots in the distributor drive as shown
(© Toyo Kogyo Co., Ltd.)

63. Install the gaskets and the the thermal reactor on the engine. Tighten its securing nuts evenly, working in two or three stages, to the specifications in the "Torque Specifications" chart.

64. Place the heat stove over the thermal reactor and secure it with its mounting nuts.

65. Install the components of the emission control system, as detailed in "Emission Controls".

66. Install the engine in the car.

Intake Manifold

Removal and Installation

To remove the intake manifold and carburetor assembly with the engine remaining in the automobile, proceed in the following manner:

1. Perform steps 2,3,4,5,7, and 13 of "Engine Removal and Installation", above. Do not remove the engine.
2. Then perform steps 1,2,3, and 4 of "Engine Disassembly", above.

Install the intake manifold and carburetor assembly in the reverse order of removal. Tighten the manifold securing nuts, working from the inside out, and in two or three stages, to the torque specifications found in the "Torque Specifications" chart.

Thermal Reactor

Removal and Installation

CAUTION: *The thermal reactor operates at extremely high temperatures. Allow the engine to cool completely before attempting to remove it.*

To remove the thermal reactor, which replaces the exhaust manifold, proceed in the following manner:

1. Remove the air cleaner assembly from the carburetor.
2. Unbolt and remove the air injection pump, as outlined in "Emission Controls".
3. Remove the intake manifold assembly, complete with carburetor. See the section above.
4. Remove. the heat stove from the thermal reactor.
5. Unfasten the thermal reactor securing nuts, including those on the exhaust pipe flange.

NOTE: *The bottom nut is difficult to reach. Mazda makes a special wrench (part number 49 213 001) to remove it. If the wrench is unavailable, a flexible drive metric socket wrench may be substituted.*

6. Lift the thermal reactor away from the engine.

Installation of the thermal reactor is performed in the reverse order of removal.

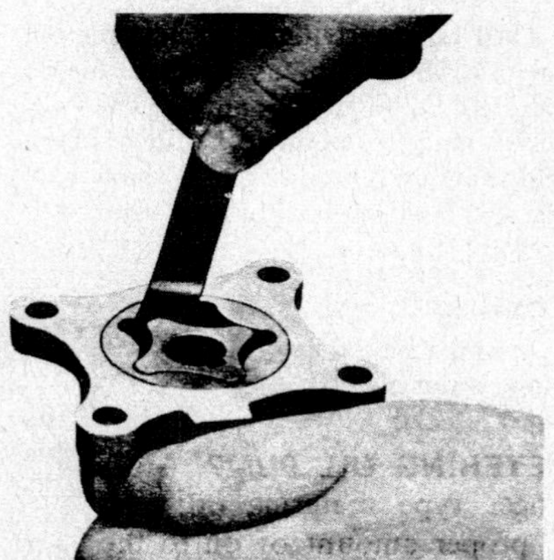

Measure the clearance between the rotors with a feeler gauge
(© Toyo Kogyo Co., Ltd.)

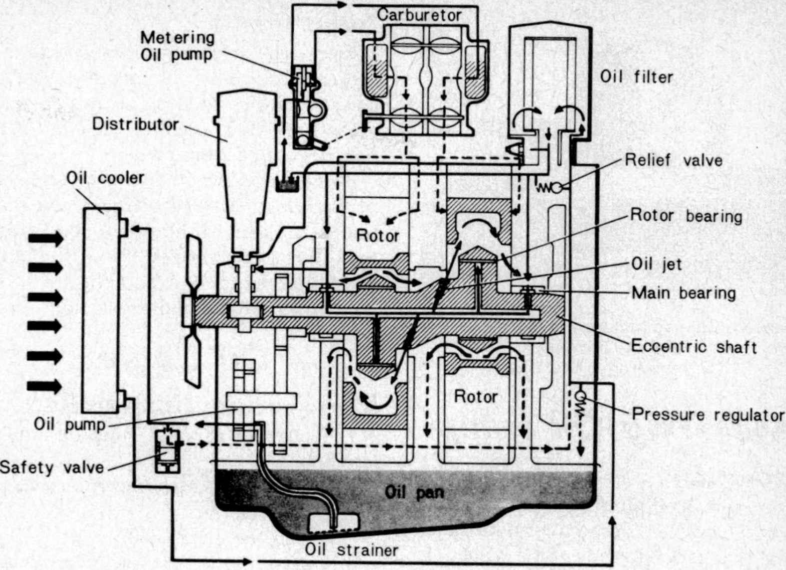

Lubrication circuits—1972-73 illustrated
(© Toyo Kogyo Co., Ltd.)

ENGINE LUBRICATION

A conventional oil pump, which is either gear (1971) or chain (1972–73) driven, circulates oil through the rotary engine. A full-flow filter is mounted on the top of the rear housing and an oil cooler is used to reduce the temperature of the engine oil.

An unusual feature of the rotary engine lubrication system is a metering oil pump which injects oil into the float chamber of the carburetor. Once there, it is mixed with the fuel which is to be burned, thus providing extra lubrication for the seals. The metering oil pump is designed to work only when the engine is working under a load.

Oil Pan

Removal and Installation

1. Raise the front of the car and support it with jackstands.

CAUTION: *Be sure that the car is supported securely.*

2. Remove the drain plug and drain the engine oil.
3. Remove the nuts and bolts which secure the gravel shield and withdraw it from underneath the car.
4. Unfasten the retaining bolts and remove the oil pan with its gasket.

Oil pan installation is performed in the reverse order of removal. Coat both the oil pan flange and its mounting flange with sealer, prior to assembly.

Oil Pump

Removal and Installation

Oil pump removal and installation is contained in the engine overhaul section above. Perform only those steps needed to remove the oil pump.

Checking Clearances

1. Separate the halves of the oil pump housing.
2. Measure the clearance between the lobes of the rotors with a feeler gauge. The clearance should be 0.0004–0.0035 in. Replace both of the rotors if the clearance exceeds 0.006 in.
3. Check the clearance between the outer rotor and the housing with a feeler gauge. The clearance should be 0.008–0.010 in. If the clearance is greater than 0.012 in., replace both of the rotors.
4. Place a straightedge across the pump housing. Measure the gap between the straightedge and the housing with a feeler gauge. The gap should be 0.001–0.005 in. If the gap exceeds 0.012 in., replace the rotors or the pump housing.

Measure the gap between the straightedge and the housing
(© Toyo Kogyo Co., Ltd.)

Metering Oil Pump

Operation

A metering oil pump, mounted on the top of the engine, is used to provide additional lubrication to the engine when it is operating under a load. The pump provides oil to the carburetor, where it is mixed in the float chamber with the fuel to be burned.

The metering pump is a plunger type and is controlled by throttle opening. A cam arrangement, connected to the carburetor throttle lever, operates a plunger. The plunger, in turn, acts on a differential plunger, the stroke of which determines the amount of oil flow.

When the throttle opening is small, the amount of the plunger stroke is small; as the throttle opening increases, so does the amount of the plunger stroke.

Testing

1. At the carburetor, disconnect the oil lines which run from the metering oil pump to the carburetor.

2. Use a container which has a scale calibrated in cubic centimeters (cc) on its side to catch the pump discharge from the oil lines.

NOTE: *Such a container is available from a scientific equipment supply house.*

3. Run the engine at 2,000 rpm for six minutes.

4. At the end of this time, 2.4–2.9cc should be collected in the container. If not, adjust the pump as explained below.

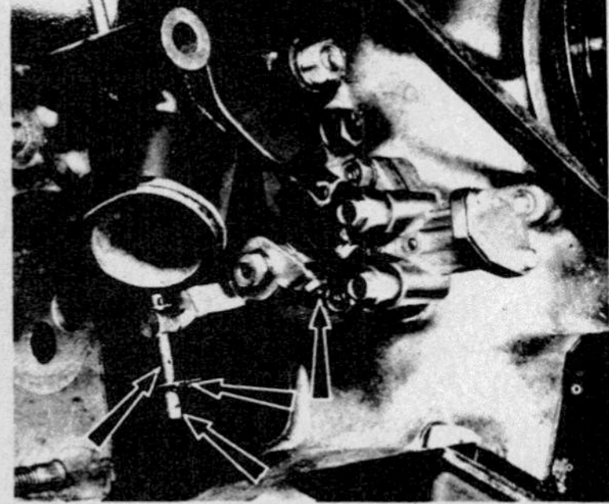

Arrow indicates the metering oil pump adjusting screw
(© Toyo Kogyo Co., Ltd.)

Adjustments

Rotate the adjusting screw on the metering oil pump to obtain the proper oil flow. Clockwise rotation of the screw *increases* the flow; counterclockwise rotation *decreases* the oil flow.

If necessary, the oil discharge rate may be further adjusted by changing the position of the cam in the pump connecting rod. The shorter the rod throw, the more oil will be pumped. Adjust the throw by means of the three holes provided.

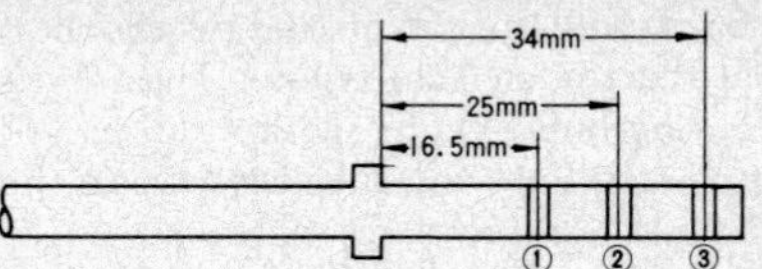

Connecting rod adjusting holes
(© Toyo Kogyo Co., Ltd.)

Oil Cooler

Removal and Installation

1. Raise the car and support it with jackstands.

CAUTION: *Be sure that the car is securely supported.*

2. Drain the engine oil.

3. Unfasten the screws which retain the gravel shield and remove the shield.

4. Unfasten the oil lines from the oil cooler.

5. Unfasten the nuts which secure the oil cooler to the radiator.

6. Remove the oil cooler.

Examine the oil cooler for signs of leakage. Solder any leaks found. Blow the cooler fins clean with compressed air.

Installation is performed in the reverse order of removal.

ENGINE COOLING

Radiator

Removal and Installation

CAUTION: *Perform this operation when the engine has cooled completely.*

1. Drain the engine coolant into a large, clean container so that it may be reused.

2. Remove the nuts and bolts which attach the shroud to the radiator. Withdraw the shroud.

3. Remove the upper, lower, and expansion tank hoses from the radiator.

4. Unfasten the bolts which attach the radiator to its mounting bracket. Remove the oil cooler nuts and bolts.

5. Withdraw the radiator from the car.

Install the radiator in the reverse order of removal.

Water Pump

Removal and Installation

1. Drain the engine coolant into a large, clean container for reuse.

2. Remove the air cleaner assembly from the carburetor.

3. Loosen, but do not remove, the water pump pulley securing bolts.

4. Loosen the alternator adjusting link bolts and remove the drivebelt.

5. Unfasten the water pump pulley bolts and remove the pulley.

6. Unfasten the pump bolts from the front cover and withdraw the pump.

7. Separate the pump body from the casing, after removing the bolts.

Installation is performed in the reverse order of removal.

Thermostat

Removal and Installation

1. Drain the engine coolant into a large, clean container for reuse.

2. Remove the nuts which secure the thermostat housing to the water pump.

3. Lift out the thermostat.

Thermostat installation is performed in the reverse order of removal.

CAUTION: *The thermostat is equipped with a plunger which covers and uncovers a by-pass hole at its bottom. Because of this unusual construction, only the specified Mazda thermostat should be used for replacement. A standard thermostat will cause the engine to overheat.*

EMISSION CONTROLS

Positive Crankcase Ventilation (PCV) System

The positive crankcase ventilation valve (PCV) is located on the intake manifold below the carburetor. The PCV valve, which is operated by intake manifold vacuum, is used to meter the flow of air and fuel vapors through the rotor housing.

Testing

1. Make sure that the air cleaner element is not clogged.

2. Connect a vacuum gauge into the line which runs between the PCV valve and the oil filler tube, by means of a T-connector.

3. Increase the engine speed to 2,500–3,000 rpm. The vacuum reading should be below 2.4 in. Hg. If it is not, replace the PCV valve.

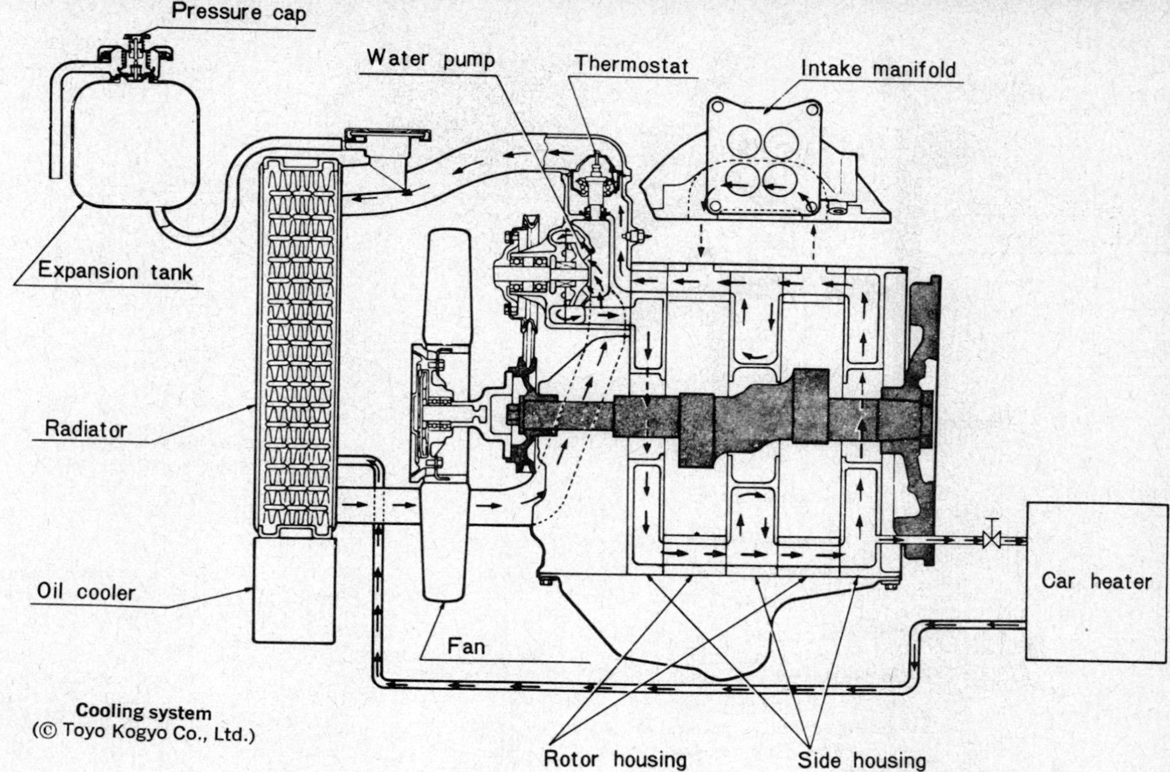

Cooling system
(© Toyo Kogyo Co., Ltd.)

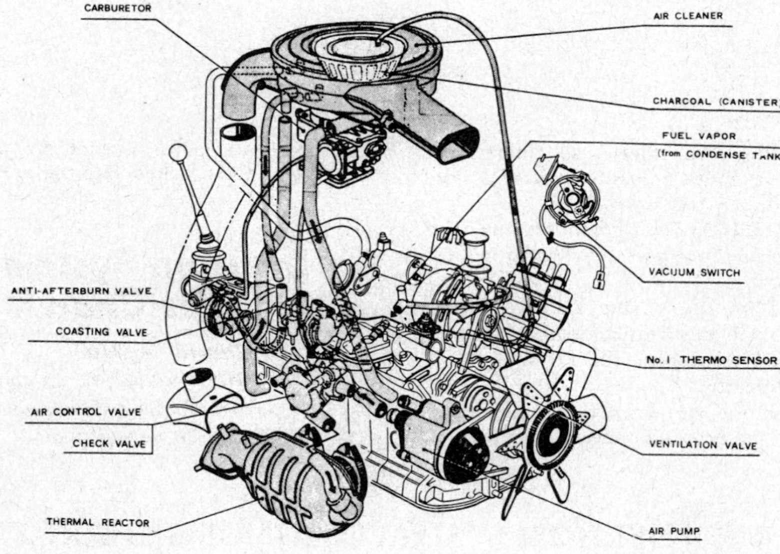

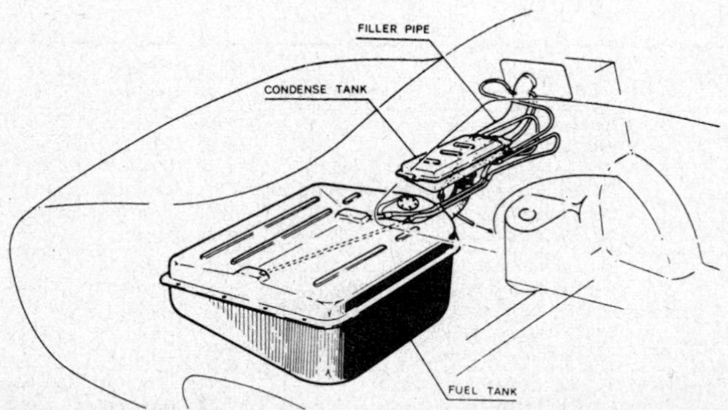

Components of the emission control system—1972 (other years are similar)
(© Toyo Kogyo Co., Ltd.)

PCV Valve Removal and Installation

1. Remove the air cleaner assembly.
2. Remove the fuel return valve from the carburetor.
3. Unfasten the distributor vacuum lines at the carburetor.
4. Disconnect the hose from the PCV valve.
5. Use a flexible drive metric socket wrench to remove the valve from the intake manifold.

NOTE: *If a flexible drive metric socket wrench is not available, the intake manifold must be removed in order to gain access to the PCV valve.*

Installation of a new PCV valve is performed in the reverse order of removal.

Air Injection System

The air injection system used on the Mazda rotary engine differs from one used on a conventional piston engine in two respects:

1. Air is supplied not only to burn the gases in the exhaust ports, it is also used to cool the thermal reactor.
2. A three-way "air control valve" is used in place of the conventional anti-backfire and diverter valves. It contains an air cut-out valve, a relief valve, and a safety valve.

Air is supplied to the system by a normal vane-type air pump. The air flows from the pump to the air control valve where it is routed to the air injection nozzles, to cool the thermal reactor or, in

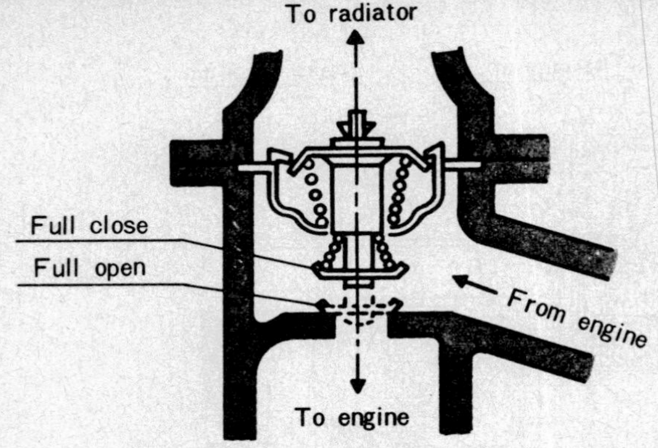

Thermostat installation and by-pass circuit
(© Toyo Kogyo Co., Ltd.)

Vacuum gauge
Ventilation valve

Testing the PCV valve
(© Toyo Kogyo Co., Ltd.)

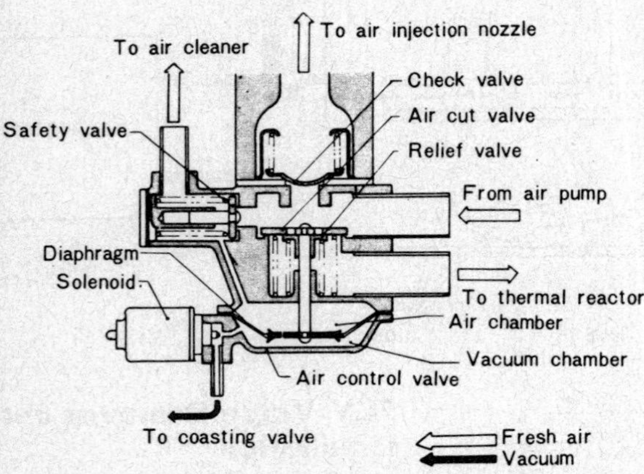

Cross-section of the air control valve
(© Toyo Kogyo Co., Ltd.)

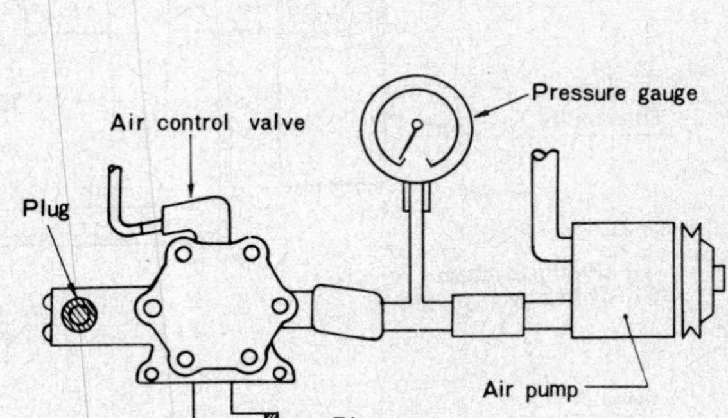

Testing the air pump
(© Toyo Kogyo Co., Ltd.)

case of a system malfunction, to the air cleaner. A check valve, located beneath the air control valve seat, prevents the back-flow of hot exhaust gases into the air injection system, in case of loss of air pressure.

Air injection nozzles are used to feed air into the exhaust ports, just as in a conventional piston engine.

Component Testing

Air Pump

1. Check the air pump drive belt tension by applying 22 lbs of pressure halfway between the water pump and air pump pulleys. The belt should deflect 0.-28–0.35 in. Adjust the belt, if necessary, or replace it if it is cracked or worn.
2. Turn the pump by hand. If it has seized, the drive belt will slip producing noise.

NOTE: *Disregard any chirping, squealing, or rolling sounds coming from inside of the pump; these are normal when it is being turned by hand.*

3. Check the hoses and connections for leaks. Hissing or a blast of air is indicative of a leak. Soapy water, applied around the area in question, is a good method for detecting leaks.
4. Connect a pressure gauge between the air pump and the air control valve with a T-fitting.
5. Plug the other hose connections (outlets) on the air control valve, as illustrated.

CAUTION: *Be careful not to touch the thermal reactor; severe burns will result.*

6. With the engine at normal idle speed, the pressure gauge should read 0.-93–0.75 psi. Replace the air pump if it is less than this.
7. If the air pump is not defective, leave the pressure gauge connected but unplug the two connections at the air control valve and proceed with the next test.

Air Injection System Diagnosis Chart

Air Control Valve

CAUTION: *When testing the air control valve, avoid touching the thermal reactor as severe burns will result.*

AIR INJECTION SYSTEM DIAGNOSIS CHART

Problem	*Cause*	*Cure*
1. Noisy drive belt	1a Loose belt 1b Seized pump	1a Tighten belt 1b Replace
2. Noisy pump	2a Leaking hose 2b Loose hose 2c Hose contacting other parts 2d Diverter or check valve failure 2e Pump mounting loose 2g Defective pump	2a Trace and fix leak 2b Tighten hose clamp 2c Reposition hose 2d Replace 2e Tighten securing bolts 2g Replace
3. No air supply	3a Loose belt 3b Leak in hose or at fitting 3c Defective anti-backfire valve 3d Defective check valve 3e Defective pump	3a Tighten belt 3b Trace and fix leak 3c Replace 3d Replace 3e Replace
4. Exhaust backfire	4a Vacuum or air leaks 4b Defective anti-backfire valve 4c Sticking choke 4d Choke setting rich	4a Trace and fix leak 4b Replace 4c Service choke 4d Adjust choke

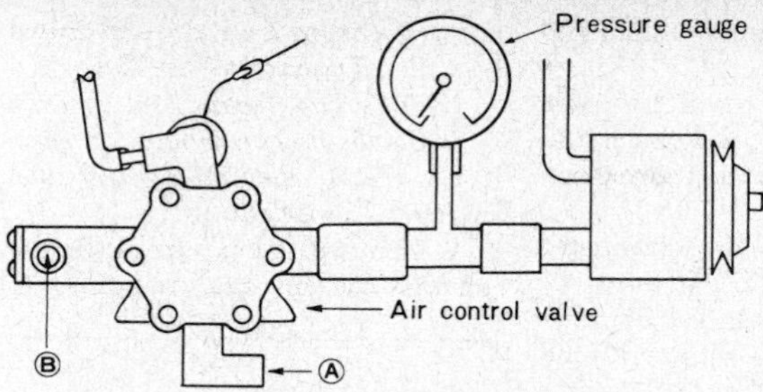

Testing the air control valve
(© Toyo Kogyo Co., Ltd.)

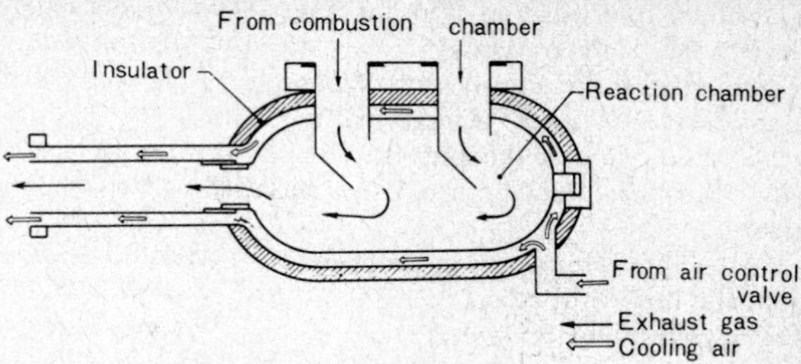

Thermal reactor cooling circuit
(© Toyo Kogyo Co., Ltd.)

1. Test the air control valve solenoid as follows:
   a. Turn the ignition switch off and on. A click should be heard coming from the solenoid. If no sound is audible, check the solenoid wiring.
   b. If no defect is found in the solenoid wiring, connect the solenoid directly to the car's battery. If the solenoid still does not click, it is defective and must be replaced. If the solenoid is functioning, then check the components of the air flow control system, below.
2. Start the engine and run it at idle speed. The pressure gauge should still read 0.37–0.75 psi. No air should leak from the two oulets which were unplugged.
3. Increase the engine speed to 3,500 rpm (3,000—automatic transmission). The pressure gauge should now read 2.-0–2.8 psi and the two outlets still should not be leaking air.
4. Return the engine to idle.
5. Disconnect the solenoid wiring. Air should now flow from the outlet marked "A" in the illustration, but not from the outlet marked "B". The pressure gauge reading should remain the same as in step 2.
6. Reconnect the solenoid.
7. If the relief valve is faulty, air sent from the air pump will flow into the cooling passages of the thermal reactor when the engine is at idle speed.
8. If the safety valve is faulty, air will flow into the air cleaner when the engine is idling.
9. Replace the air control valve if it fails to pass any one of the above tests. Remember to disconnect the pressure gauge.

Check Valve

1. Remove the check valve as detailed below.

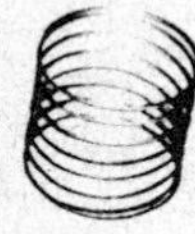

Components of the check valve
(© Toyo Kogyo Co., Ltd.)

2. Depress the valve plate to see if it will seat properly.
3. Measure the free length of the valve spring; it should be 1.22 in.
4. Measure the installed length of the spring: it should be 0.68 in.

NOTE: *The free length of the check valve spring should be 0.75 in. on models with automatic transmissions.*

Replace the check valve if it is not up to specifications.

Component Removal and Installation

Air Pump

1. Remove the air cleaner assembly from the carburetor.
2. Loosen, but do not remove, the adjusting link bolt.
3. Push the pump toward the engine to slacken belt tension and remove the drive belt.
4. Disconnect the air supply hoses from the pump.
5. Unfasten the pump securing bolts and remove the pump.

CAUTION: *Do not pry on the air pump housing during removal and do not clamp the housing in a vise once the pump has been removed. Any type of heavy pressure applied to the housing will cause it to distort.*

Installation is performed in the reverse order of removal. Adjust the belt tension by moving the air pump to the specification given in the "Testing" section, above.

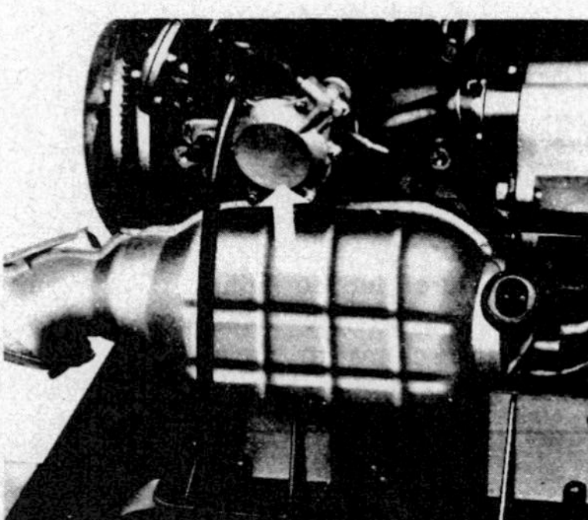
Arrow indicates position of the air control valve
(© Toyo Kogyo Co., Ltd.)

Air Control Valve

CAUTION: *Remove the air control valve only after the thermal reactor has cooled sufficiently to prevent the danger of a serious burn.*

1. Remove the air cleaner assembly.
2. Unfasten the leads from the air control valve solenoid.
3. Disconnect the air hoses from the valve.
4. Loosen the screws which secure the air control valve and remove the valve.

Valve installation is performed in the reverse order of removal.

Check Valve

1. Perform the air control valve removal procedure, detailed above. Be sure to pay attention to the **CAUTION.**
2. Remove the check valve seat.
3. Withdraw the valve plate and spring.

Install the check valve in the reverse order of removal.

Air Injection Nozzle

1. Remove the gravel shield from underneath the car.
2. Perform the oil pan removal procedure, as detailed in "Engine Lubrication", above.
3. Unbolt the air injection nozzles from both of the rotor housings.

Nozzle installation is performed in the reverse order of removal.

Thermal Reactor

A thermal reactor is used in place of a conventional exhaust manifold. It is used to oxidize unburned hydrocarbons and carbon monoxide before they can be released into the atmosphere.

If the engine speed exceeds 4,000 rpm, or if the car is decelerating, the air control valve diverts air into passages in the thermal reactor housing in order to cool the reactor.

A one-way valve prevents hot exhaust gases from flowing back into the air injection system. The valve is located at the reactor air intake.

Inspection

CAUTION: *Perform thermal reactor inspection only after the reactor has cooled sufficiently to prevent severe burns.*

1. Examine the reactor housing for cracks or other signs of damage.

2. Remove the air supply hose from the one-way valve. Insert a screwdriver into the valve and test the butterfly for smooth operation. Replace the valve if necessary.

3. If the valve is functioning properly, connect the hose to it again.

NOTE: *Remember to check the components of the air injection system which are related to the thermal reactor.*

Removal and Installation

Thermal reactor removal and installation procedures are given in the "Engine Mechanical" section, above.

Air Flow Control System

1971 RX-2 Models

The air flow control system, used on the 1971 RX-2 sedans and coupes, consists of a thermosensor, thermodetector, vacuum switch, and a control box.

The system determines when the trailing distributor should be used, depending upon engine temperature and speed (rpm).

The air flow control system also operates the solenoid on the air flow control valve (see above).

When the engine is cold, the thermosensor sends a signal to the control box which, in turn, activates the trailing distributor. The thermodetector is used to keep the thermosensor from being influenced by ambient temperatures. This ensures easier cold starting and better driveability.

The trailing distributor is also activated by the vacuum switch when the engine is at normal idle or full-throttle operation. Under all other operating conditions, the trailing distributor does not function.

1972–73 All Models

In addition to the components listed above, for the 1971 models, the air flow control system for 1972–73 adds an extra thermosensor and control box. A choke control switch is added, as well.

The additional control box, choke switch, and thermosensor are used to retard the timing of the leading distributor 10° when the engine is cold. The timing is retarded by means of an additional set of points in the leading distributor, which has no vacuum advance.

Component Testing

No. 1 Thermosensor—All Models

NOTE: *Begin this test procedure with the engine cold.*

1. Remove the air cleaner.

2. Examine the No. 1 thermosensor, which is located next to the thermostat housing, for leakage around the boot and for signs of wax leakage.

3. Disconnect the multiconnector from the thermosensor and place the prods of an ohmmeter on the thermosensor terminals.

a. On 1971 models the ohmmeter should read less than 200 k-ohms.

b. On 1972–73 models, the ohmmeter should read over 7 k-ohms with the engine cold and less than 2.3 k-ohms after the engine has been warmed up.

4. Replace the thermosensor with a new one, if the reading on the ohmmeter is not within specifications.

5. If the No. 1 thermosensor is functioning properly, proceed with the appropriate test for the thermodetector below.

Thermodetector—1971

1. Unfasten the thermodetector connections.

2. Connect the test prods of an ohmmeter to the leads coming out of the thermodetector.

3. If the ohmmeter reading is below 200 k-ohms, the thermodetector is functioning satisfactorily.

4. Replace the thermodetector if it is defective and proceed with the vacuum switch if it is not.

Themodetector—1972–73

The test procedure is the same as that for the 1971 models, above. However, use the following chart to determine the correct ohmmeter reading for the ambient temperature at the time of the test:

Ambient Temperature (°F)	Resistance (k-ohms ± 5%)
−4	10.0
+32	3.0
+68	1.2
+105	0.5

Vacuum Switch—Manual Transmission Only

NOTE: *The vacuum switch is located in the leading distributor on 1971 models and in the trailing distributor on 1972–73 models.*

1. Remove the cap from the distributor that contains the vacuum switch.

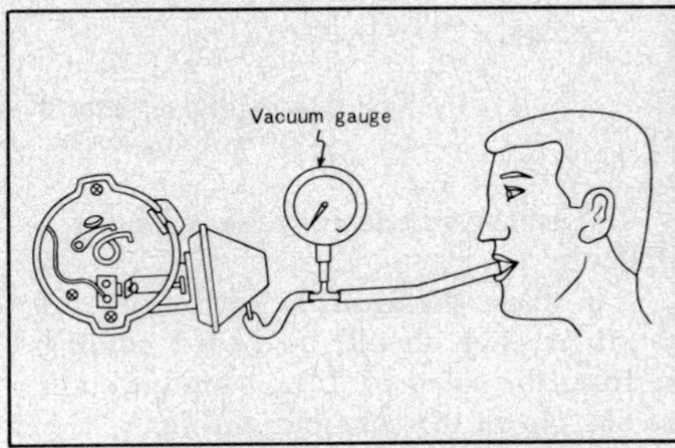

Testing the vacuum switch
(© Toyo Kogyo Co., Ltd.)

2. Disconnect the vacuum lines from the same distributor's vacuum advance unit. Connect a vacuum gauge in its place, by means of a T-fitting.

3. Suck on the free end of the hose coming from the vacuum gauge. When the vacuum gauge reading is about 7 in. Hg, the vacuum switch should be heard to click from ON to OFF.

4. Reduce the vacuum level to 3–5 in. Hg, the vacuum switch should be heard to click ON.

5. Replace the distributor cap and remove the vacuum switch connector from the No. 1 thermosensor.

6. Connect a timing light to the *trailing* distributor, regardless of which distributor contains the vacuum switch.

7. The timing light should go off, i.e., the switch should go off, at 1,900±300 rpm.

8. Check all of the vacuum lines and connections for leaks. If none are found, and the vacuum switch is not working properly, replace it. If the vacuum switch is not defective, proceed with the test for the No. 1 control box.

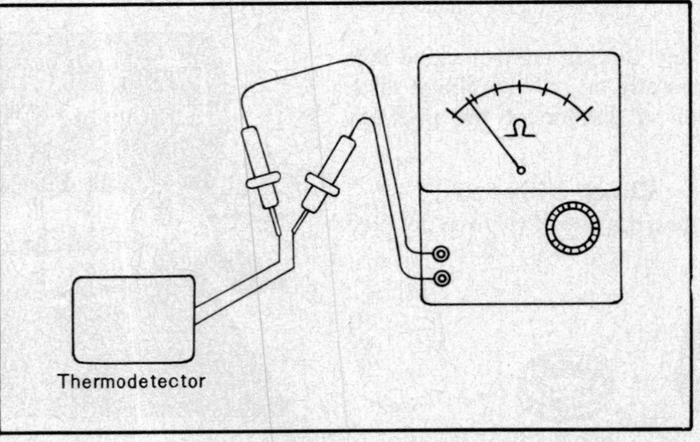

Testing the thermodetector
(© Toyo Kogyo Co., Ltd.)

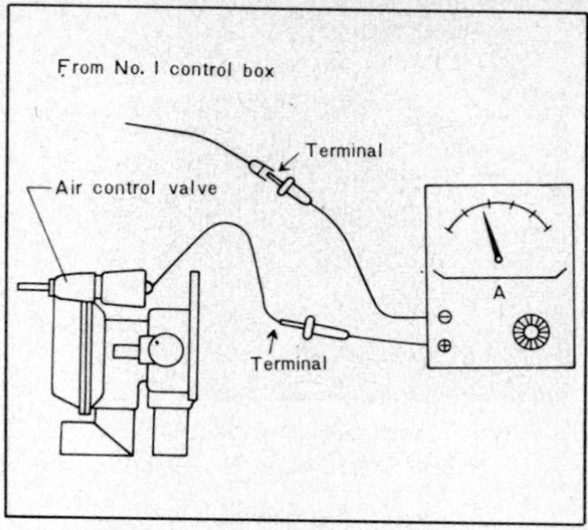

Testing the No. 1 control box
(© Toyo Kogyo Co., Ltd.)

NOTE: *If the control box is to be tested, leave the timing light connected to the trailing distributor.*

No. 1 Control Box—All Models

NOTE: *If all of the other components of the air flow control system are functioning properly and the system wiring and vacuum lines are in good condition, then the fault probably lies in the No.1 control box. Perform the following tests to verify this.*

1. Disconnect the No. 1 thermosensor. On 1973 models, disconnect the vacuum switch (manual transmission) and the idle switch multiconnectors.

2. Start the engine and run it to the speeds specified below. The timing light should come on in these speed ranges:

Manual Transmission—3,800–4,200rpm

Automatic Transmission—4,600–5,200rpm

NOTE: *These speeds should be held for an instant only.*

3. Connect an ammeter to the air control valve solenoid leads and to ground.

a. Current should flow when the engine speed is between 900–4,000±200 rpm (manual) or 750–5,200 (automatic).

b. Current flow should cease above 4,200 rpm (manual) or 5,200 rpm (automatic).

4. On 1971 models which are equipped with an anti-afterburn valve solenoid, repeat step 3 on this solenoid to test its operation.

5. Short together the pins of the No. 1 thermosensor multiconnector with a jumper wire. Connect the timing light to the trailing distributor, if it is not already in place.

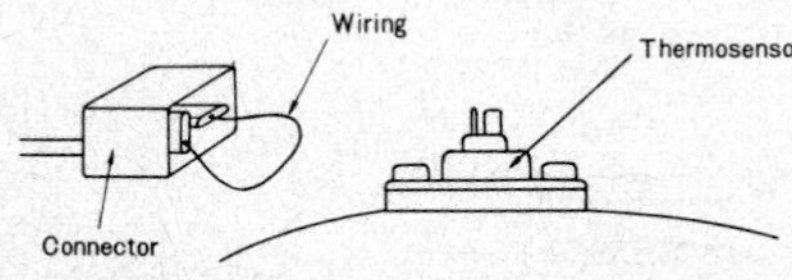

Short the pins of the No. 1 thermosensor multiconnector with a jumper wire
(© Toyo Kogyo Co., Ltd.)

a. The timing light should go on when the engine is below 4,200 rpm (manual) or below 5,200 rpm (automatic).

b. On automatic transmission equipped models, connect an ammeter to the air control valve solenoid. Current should flow to the solenoid when the engine speed is below 3,400±200 rpm and should cease flowing above this speed.

6. Remove the jumper wire from the multiconnector and reconnect the No. 1 thermosensor. Reconnect the vacuum switch if it was disconnected.

7. Connect the prods of the ammeter to the coasting valve solenoid terminals.

NOTE: *For a further description of coasting valve operation, see "Deceleration Control Systems", below.*

8. No current should flow to the solenoid with the engine at idle. Increase the engine speed; current should begin flowing between 1,250 and 1,550 rpm. Decrease engine speed; current should cease flowing between 1,300 and 1,100 rpm (1,400rpm—automatic transmission).

If the No. 1 control box proves to be defective, replace it. Remember to disconnect all of the test equipment and reconnect the system components when the tests are completed.

No. 2 Thermosensor—1972–73 Manual

NOTE: *Begin this test with the engine cold.*

1. Check the terminal of the No. 2 thermosensor, which protrudes from the oil pan, for breakage.

2. Connect one ohmmeter prod to the terminal of the thermosensor and ground the other prod.

3. Take two ohmmeter readings:

a. With the air and water temperature below 86°F, the ohmmeter should register less than 5 k-ohms.

b. With the engine warmed up (water temperature above 158°F) the ohmmeter should register under 2 k-ohms.

If the thermosensor is defective, replace it; if not go on to the next test.

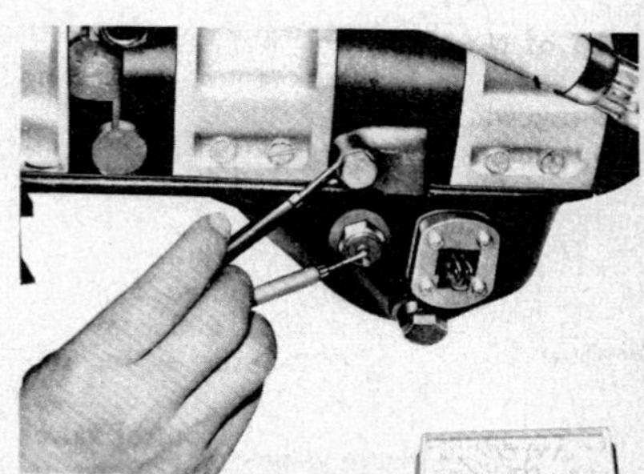

Testing the No. 2 thermosensor
(© Toyo Kogyo Co., Ltd.)

Arrow indicates position of the No. 1 thermosensor
(© Toyo Kogyo Co., Ltd.)

No.2 Control Box—1972–73

1. Disconnect both of the thermosensors.

NOTE: *Only manual transmission equipped models have a No. 2 thermosensor.*

2. Unfasten the trailing vacuum switch connection (manual transmission only).

3. Connect a timing light to the leading distributor.

4. Start the engine and increase its speed, without placing a load on it, to 2,000–2,500 rpm.

5. Pull the choke switch, which is located underneath the dashboard, out about 0.2–0.04 in. or 0.8–1.0 in. on automatic models. The engine speed should decrease by 200–300 rpm. If it does not, then test the choke switch to be sure that it's functioning correctly.

6. Disconnect the leading distributor at its negative (−) terminal so that only its retarded side is receiving power.

7. Start the engine and run it at idle.

8. Aim the timing light at the pointer on the front cover. The orange timing mark (10°ATDC) on the pulley should be seen to align with the pointer.

NOTE: *Be sure that the ignition timing is adjusted correctly before replacing the No. 2 control box with a new one.*

Replace the No. 2 control box if it is defective. When finished, remove the test equipment and reconnect all of those components that were disconnected for this test.

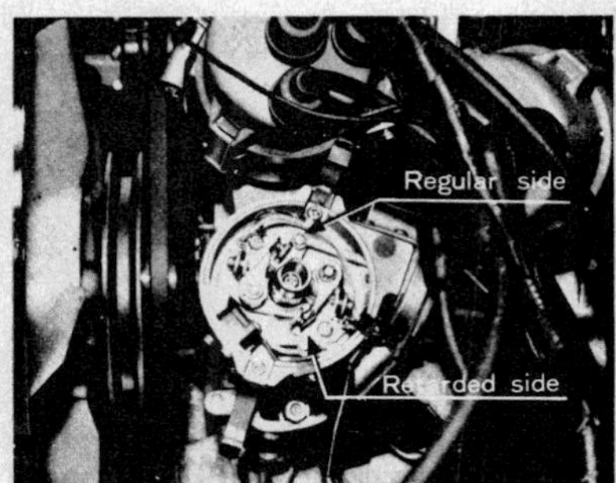

Dual-point leading distributor
(© Toyo Kogyo Co., Ltd.)

Component Removal and Installation

No. 1 Thermosensor

1. Remove the air cleaner assembly.
2. If necessary, remove the starter motor as detailed under "Engine Electrical".
3. Unplug the thermosensor multiconnector.
4. Withdraw the boot from the thermosensor.
5. Unfasten its securing nuts and remove the thermosensor.

Installation is performed in the reverse order of removal.

No. 1 Control Box

CAUTION: *Be sure that the ignition is turned off to prevent damage to the control box.*

1. Open the luggage compartment.
2. Unfasten its screws and remove the panel from the back of the compartment.
3. Unfasten the control box multiconnector.
4. Loosen the control box securing nuts and remove the box.

Installation of the control box is performed in the reverse order of removal.

No. 2 Thermosensor

1. Drain the engine oil into a large, clean container for reuse.
2. Unfasten the connector from the No. 2 thermosensor.
3. Unscrew the thermosensor from the oil pan.

Installation is performed in the reverse order of removal.

No. 2 Control Box

The No. 2 control box is located in the luggage compartment next to the No. 1 control box. Its removal and installation are performed in the same manner as for the No. 1 control box (see above).

Both control boxes are located behind the luggage compartment trim panel
(© Toyo Kogyo Co., Ltd.)

Other Components

Any of the other components used in the air flow control system are removed by unfastening their multiconnectors and removing the screws which secure them.

Deceleration Control System

The deceleration control system uses an anti-afterburn valve, a coasting valve, and an air supply valve. In addition, either a throttle positioner (1971) or an idle sensing switch (1972–73) is fitted to the carburetor. The No. 1 control box is shared with the air flow control system.

The anti-afterburn valve, which is located on the intake manifold, is used to supply fresh air to the manifold during deceleration or when the engine is shut off, in order to prevent afterburning.

A coasting valve, which functions in a similar manner, is used to prevent an overly rich mixture during deceleration. The coasting valve also vents the vacuum chamber of the air control valve during deceleration. The valve is operated by a solenoid which is controlled by the No. 1 control box and, on 1972–73 models, the idle sensing switch.

Thermodetector location
(© Toyo Kogyo Co., Ltd.)

1971 models have a throttle positioner to keep idle speed at about 950 rpm during deceleration.

1972–73 models do not have a throttle positioner; they have an idle sensing switch attached to the carburetor in its place. When the throttle closes, its linkage contacts a plunger on the switch which completes the circuit from the No. 1 control box to the coasting valve thus causing the coasting valve to operate. On automatic transmission equipped models, it also determines trailing distributor operation.

A solenoid-operated air supply valve opens when the ignition is shut off to prevent the engine from dieseling (running on).

Component Testing

Anti-Afterburn Valve—All Models

1. Remove the air cleaner assembly.
2. Remove the hose from the air intake on the anti-afterburn valve.
3. With the engine idling, place your hand over the air intake. If a strong suction is felt, the valve is defective and should be replaced.

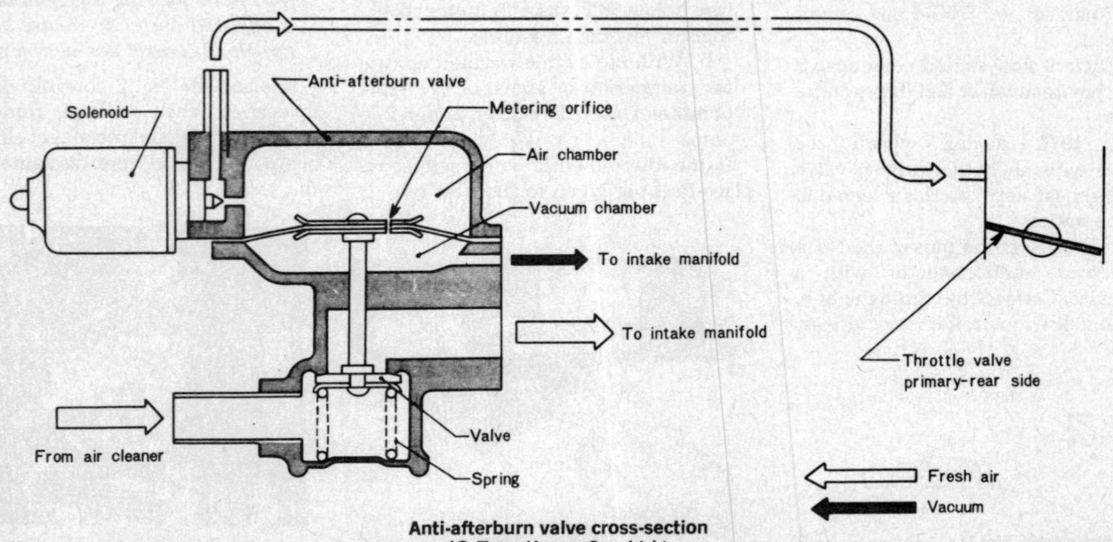

Anti-afterburn valve cross-section
(© Toyo Kogyo Co., Ltd.)

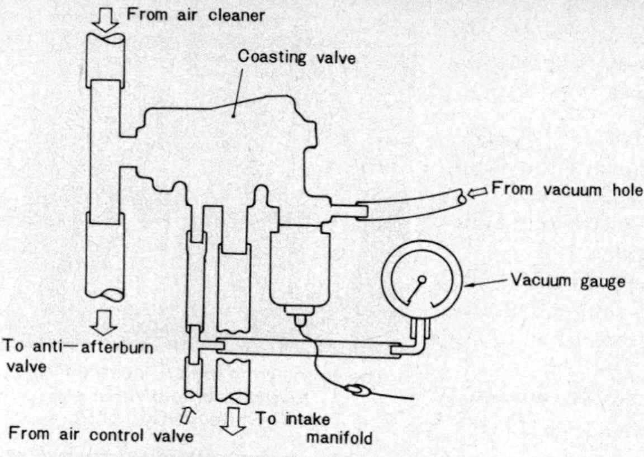

Testing the coasting valve
(© Toyo Kogyo Co., Ltd.)

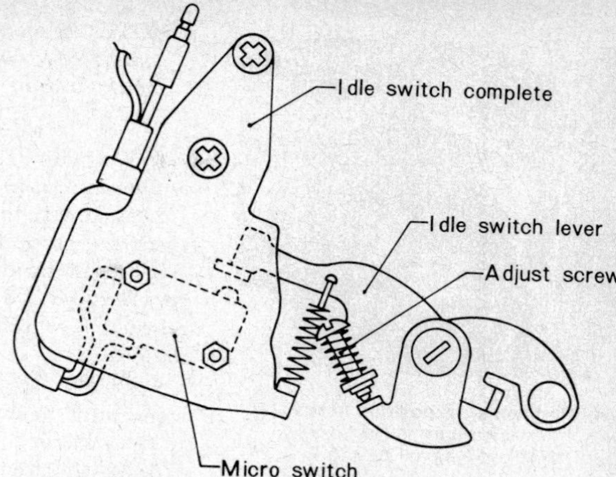

1972 idle switch—1973 uses a multiconnector
(© Toyo Kogyo Co., Ltd.)

4. Increase the engine speed to 3,500–3,800 rpm. Release the throttle and allow it to snap shut. Air should be drawn in through the valve air intake for no longer than one second.

5. Keep the engine idling and disconnect the anti-afterburn valve solenoid wiring. Air should flow into the air intake while the solenoid is disconnected.

If the anti-afterburn valve fails to function properly, replace it with a new one. Remember to connect the air supply hose and the solenoid wiring after completing the test.

Coasting Valve—All Models

1. Install a vacuum gauge in the line which runs from the coasting valve to the air control valve, by means of a T-fitting.
2. Start the engine and allow it to warm up.
3. With the engine at idle, the vacuum gauge should read at least 16 in. Hg.
4. Increase the engine speed to 2,500 rpm. Release the throttle valve so that it snaps shut. The vacuum reading should momentarily be 0–1 in. Hg and then return to 16 in. Hg when the engine speed drops below 1,300–1,100 rpm (manual) or 1,450–1,350 (automatic).

If the vacuum readings are within specifications, the vacuum valve is functioning correctly. If they are not, proceed with the rest of the test.

5. Check the circuit from the No. 1 control box to the coasting valve, as detailed in steps 8–9 of the no. 1 control box test procedure above.
6. Check the operation of the solenoid by connecting it directly to the car battery. If it fails to click on and off, it is defective and must be replaced.
7. Examine the vacuum lines to see that they are not clogged or leaking.
8. Inspect the passage which runs between the air intake and the vacuum chamber of the coasting valve to be sure that it is not clogged.
9. Check the idle mixture; if it is not adjusted properly, it can affect valve operation.

If all of the checks above are positive, and the vacuum readings are incorrect, the valve is defective and must be replaced.

Throttle Positioner—1971

1. Remove the air supply hose from the coasting valve and plug its intake.
2. Start the engine and increase its speed to 2,000 rpm.
3. Connect the solenoid on the coasting valve directly to the car's battery.
4. Release the throttle so that it snaps shut. The idle speed should not go lower than 950 rpm ($\pm$50 rpm). If it fails to do so, adjust the throttle positioner as outlined below.

Idle Switch—1972–73

1. Unfasten the idle switch leads.
2. Connect a test meter to the switch terminals.
3. With the engine at idle, the meter should indicate a completed circuit.
4. Depress the plunger on the idle switch; the circuit should be broken (no meter reading).

If the idle switch is not functioning properly, replace it with a new one.

Air Supply Valve—1971–72

1. Remove the hose from the air supply valve air intake.
2. Start the engine and allow it to run at idle.
3. Block the air intake with your finger. The idle speed should be reduced by no more than 30 rpm.
4. Disconnect the air supply valve solenoid wiring. A large volume of air should be drawn into the air intake.

If the switch fails to function as outlined above, replace it with a new one.

Component Removal and Installation

Anti-Afterburn Valve

1. Remove the air cleaner assembly.
2. Disconnect the air hoses and vacuum lines from the valve.
3. Unfasten the solenoid wiring.
4. Remove the securing nuts and withdraw the valve.

Installation is performed in the reverse order of removal.

Coasting Valve

The coasting valve is removed and installed in the same manner as the anti-afterburn valve.

Idle Switch

1. Remove the coasting valve. See the section above.
2. Remove the carburetor as detailed elsewhere, in this section.
3. Disconnect the wiring from the switch.

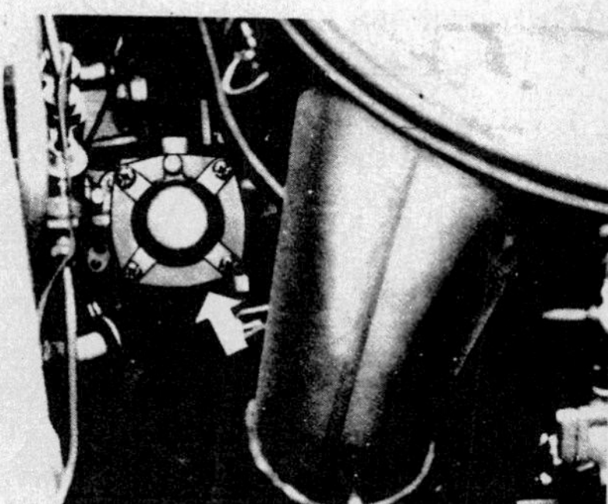

Arrow shows air valve location—1971-72
(© Toyo Kogyo Co., Ltd.)

Arrow indicates the position of the anti-afterburn valve
(© Toyo Kogyo Co., Ltd.)

Arrow indicates the position of the coasting valve
(© Toyo Kogyo Co., Ltd.)

4. Unfasten the securing screws and remove the switch.

Installation is performed in the reverse order of removal. After installing the switch, adjust it as outlined under "Adjustments", below.

Air Supply Valve

1. Remove the air cleaner and the hot air duct.
2. Disconnect the air hose, the vacuum lines, and the solenoid wiring from the valve.
3. Unfasten the screws which secure the valve and remove it.

Air supply valve installation is performed in the reverse order of removal.

Adjustments

Throttle Positioner

1. Disconnect the wiring from the coasting valve solenoid and connect the solenoid directly to the car battery.
2. Loosen the locknut on the solenoid adjuster.
3. Rotate the adjuster until an idle speed of 950±50 rpm is obtained after releasing the throttle from an engine speed of 2,000 rpm.
4. Tighten the locknut carefully once the proper idle speed has been obtained.
5. Disconnect the coasting valve solenoid from the battery and reconnect it as found.

NOTE: *As soon as the solenoid is disconnected from the battery, idle speed should drop to 800 rpm.*

Idle Switch

1. Warm up the engine until the water temperature is at least 159°F.
2. Make sure that the mixture and idle speed are properly adjusted.
3. Adjust the idle speed to 1,075–1,100 rpm (1,200–1,300 rpm—automatic transmission) by rotating the throttle adjusting screw.
4. Rotate the idle switch adjusting screw until the switch changes from OFF to ON position.
5. Slowly turn the idle switch adjusting screw back to the point where the switch just changes from ON to OFF.
6. Turn the throttle screw back so that the engine returns to idle.

NOTE: *Be sure that the idle switch goes on when the idle speed is still above 1,000 rpm.*

Evaporative Emission Control System

The vapors rising from the gasoline in the fuel tank are vented into a separate condensing tank which is located in the luggage compartment. There they condense and return to the fuel tank in liquid form when the engine is not running.

When the engine is running, the fuel vapors are sucked directly into the engine through the PCV valve and are burned along with the air/fuel mixture.

Any additional fuel vapors which are not handled by the condensing tank are stored in a charcoal cannister (1971) or filter which is incorporated into the air cleaner (1972–73). When the engine is running, the charcoal is purged of its stored fuel vapor.

On 1971 and 1973 models, a check valve vents the fuel vapor into the atmosphere if pressure in the fuel tank becomes excessive. The check valve is located in the luggage compartment, next to the condensing tank.

The condensing tank is located in the luggage compartment
(© Toyo Kogyo Co., Ltd.)

Evaporative emission control system—1972
(© Toyo Kogyo Co., Ltd.)

System Testing

There are several things to check for if a malfunction of the evaporative emission control system is suspected.

1. Leaks may be traced by using an infrared hydrocarbon tester. Run the test probe along the lines and connections. The meter will indicate the presence of a leak by a high hydrocarbon (HC) reading. This method is much more accurate than a visual inspection which would indicate only the presence of a leak large enough to pass liquid.
2. Leaks may be caused by any of the following, so always check these areas when looking for them:
   a. Defective or worn lines;
   b. Disconnected or pinched lines;
   c. Improperly routed lines;
   d. A defective check valve.

   NOTE: *If it becomes necessary to replace any of the lines used in the evaporative emission control system, use only those hoses which are fuel resistant or are marked "EVAP."*
3. If the fuel tank has collapsed, it may be the fault of clogged or pinched vent lines, a defective vapor separator, or a plugged or incorrect fuel filler cap.

FUEL SYSTEM

Electric Fuel Pump

Location and Type

The electric fuel pump is located in the luggage compartment of the RX-2/RX-3 coupes and sedans. On RX-3 station wagons, it is located behind the left-hand trim panel in the luggage compartment.

Removal and Installation

Sedans and Coupes

1. Open the luggage compartment lid.
2. Remove the rear inside trim panel, after unfastening its two securing screws.
3. Disconnect the wiring and the fuel lines from the pump.
4. Unfasten the nuts and bolts which secure the pump assembly. Remove the pump.

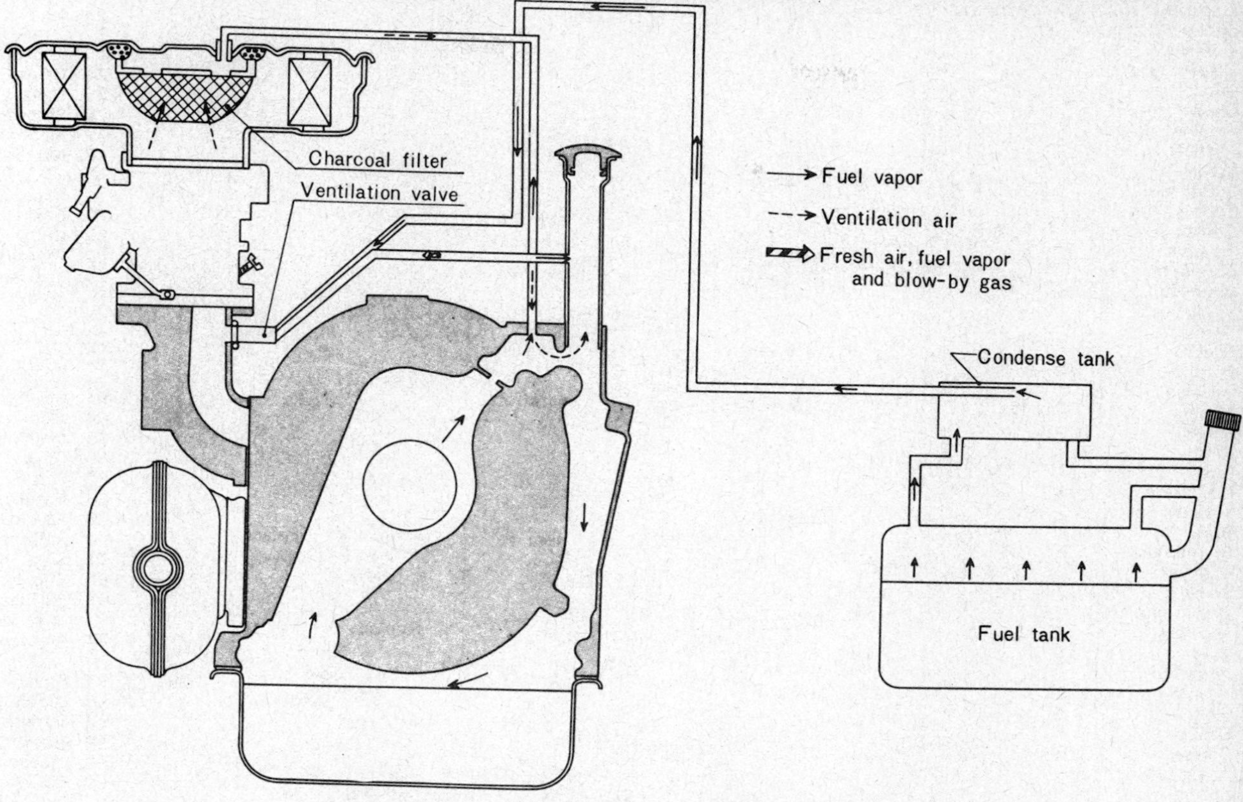

Fuel pump location all sedans and coupes (© Toyo Kogyo Co., Ltd.)

Fuel pump location on the RX-3 wagon (© Toyo Kogyo Co., Ltd.)

Installation is performed in the reverse order of installation.

Station Wagon

1. Remove the left-hand cargo compartment trim panel.
2. Disconnect the wiring and fuel lines from the pump.
3. Unfasten the nuts which secure the pump and remove the pump.

Installation is performed in the reverse order of removal.

Carburetor

Removal and Installation

1. Remove the air cleaner assembly complete with its hoses and mounting bracket.
2. Detach the choke and accelerator cables from the carburetor.
3. Disconnect the fuel and vacuum lines from the carburetor.
4. Remove the oil line which runs to the metering oil pump, at the carburetor.
5. Unfasten the idle sensor switch wiring, if so equipped.
6. Remove the carburetor attaching nuts and/or bolts, gasket or heat insulator, and remove the carburetor.

Installation is performed in the reverse order of removal. Use a new gasket. Fill the float bowl with gasoline to aid in engine starting.

Overhaul

Efficient carburetion depends greatly on careful cleaning and inspection during overhaul since dirt, gum, water, or varnish in or on the carburetor parts are often responsible for poor performance.

Overhaul your carburetor in a clean, dust-free area. Carefully disassemble the carburetor, referring often to the exploded views. Keep all similar and look-alike parts segregated during disassembly and cleaning to avoid accidental interchange during assembly. Make a note of all jet sizes.

When the carburetor is disassembled, wash all parts (except diaphragms, electric choke units, pump plunger, and any other plastic, leather, fiber, or rubber parts) in clean carburetor solvent. Do not leave parts in the solvent any longer than is necessary to sufficiently loosen the deposits. Excessive cleaning may remove the special finish from the float bowl and choke valve bodies, leaving these parts unfit for service. Rinse all parts in clean solvent and blow them dry with compressed air or allow them to air dry. Wipe clean all cork, plastic, leather, and fiber parts with a clean, lint-free cloth.

Blow out all passages and jets with compressed air and be sure that there are no restrictions or blockages. Never use wire or similar tools to clean jets, fuel passages, or air bleeds. Clean all jets and valves separately to avoid accidental interchange.

Check all parts for wear or damage. If wear or damage is found, replace the defective parts. Especially check the following:

1. Check the float needle and seat for wear. If wear is found, replace the complete assembly.
2. Check the float hinge pin for wear and the float(s) for dents or distortion. Replace the float if fuel has leaked into it.
3. Check the throttle and choke shaft bores for wear or an out-of-round condition. Damage or wear to the throttle arm, shaft, or shaft bore will often require replacement of the throttle body. These parts require a close tolerance of fit; wear may allow air leakage, which could affect starting and idling.

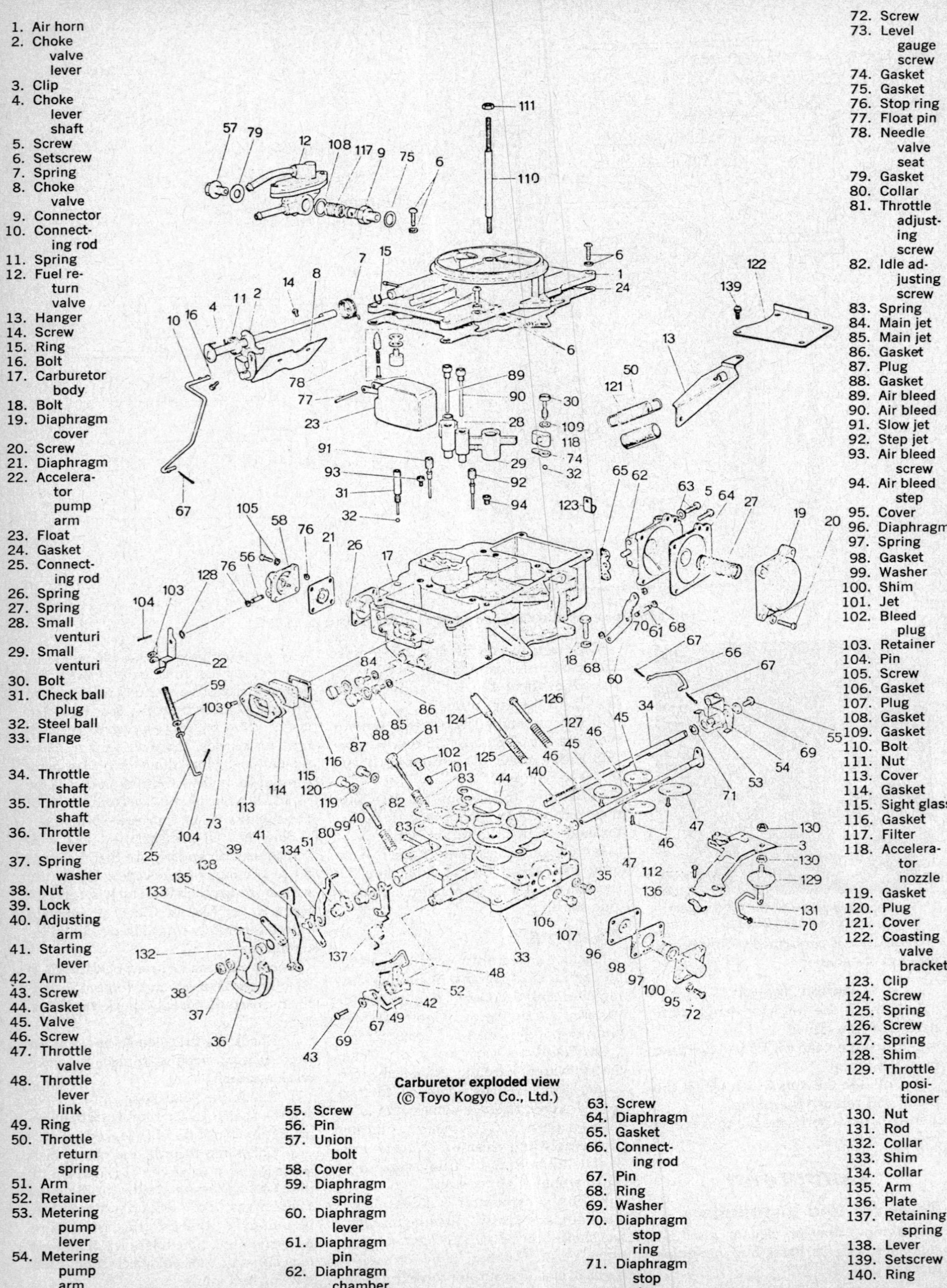

Carburetor exploded view
(© Toyo Kogyo Co., Ltd.)

1. Air horn
2. Choke valve lever
3. Clip
4. Choke lever shaft
5. Screw
6. Setscrew
7. Spring
8. Choke valve
9. Connector
10. Connecting rod
11. Spring
12. Fuel return valve
13. Hanger
14. Screw
15. Ring
16. Bolt
17. Carburetor body
18. Bolt
19. Diaphragm cover
20. Screw
21. Diaphragm
22. Accelerator pump arm
23. Float
24. Gasket
25. Connecting rod
26. Spring
27. Spring
28. Small venturi
29. Small venturi
30. Bolt
31. Check ball plug
32. Steel ball
33. Flange
34. Throttle shaft
35. Throttle shaft
36. Throttle lever
37. Spring washer
38. Nut
39. Lock
40. Adjusting arm
41. Starting lever
42. Arm
43. Screw
44. Gasket
45. Valve
46. Screw
47. Throttle valve
48. Throttle lever link
49. Ring
50. Throttle return spring
51. Arm
52. Retainer
53. Metering pump lever
54. Metering pump arm
55. Screw
56. Pin
57. Union bolt
58. Cover
59. Diaphragm spring
60. Diaphragm lever
61. Diaphragm pin
62. Diaphragm chamber
63. Screw
64. Diaphragm
65. Gasket
66. Connecting rod
67. Pin
68. Ring
69. Washer
70. Diaphragm stop ring
71. Diaphragm stop ring
72. Screw
73. Level gauge screw
74. Gasket
75. Gasket
76. Stop ring
77. Float pin
78. Needle valve seat
79. Gasket
80. Collar
81. Throttle adjusting screw
82. Idle adjusting screw
83. Spring
84. Main jet
85. Main jet
86. Gasket
87. Plug
88. Gasket
89. Air bleed
90. Air bleed
91. Slow jet
92. Step jet
93. Air bleed screw
94. Air bleed step
95. Cover
96. Diaphragm
97. Spring
98. Gasket
99. Washer
100. Shim
101. Jet
102. Bleed plug
103. Retainer
104. Pin
105. Screw
106. Gasket
107. Plug
108. Gasket
109. Gasket
110. Bolt
111. Nut
113. Cover
114. Gasket
115. Sight glass
116. Gasket
117. Filter
118. Accelerator nozzle
119. Gasket
120. Plug
121. Cover
122. Coasting valve bracket
123. Clip
124. Screw
125. Spring
126. Screw
127. Spring
128. Shim
129. Throttle positioner
130. Nut
131. Rod
132. Collar
133. Shim
134. Collar
135. Arm
136. Plate
137. Retaining spring
138. Lever
139. Setscrew
140. Ring

NOTE: *Throttle shafts and bushings are not included in overhaul kits. They can be purchased separately.*

4. Inspect the idle mixture adjusting needles for burrs or grooves. Any such condition requires replacement of the needle, since you will not be able to obtain a satisfactory idle.

5. Test the accelerator pump check valves. They should pass air one way but not the other. Test for proper seating by blowing and sucking on the valve. Replace the valve if necessary. If the valve is satisfactory, wash the valve again to remove breath moisture.

6. Check the bowl cover for warped surfaces with a straightedge.

7. Closely inspect the valves and seats for wear and damage, replacing as necessary.

8. After the carburetor is assembled, check the choke valve for freedom of operation.

Carburetor overhaul kits are recommended for each overhaul. These kits contain all gaskets and new parts to replace those that deteriorate most rapidly. Failure to replace all parts supplied with the kit (especially gaskets) can result in poor performance later.

Some carburetor manufacturers supply overhaul kits of three basic types: minor repair; major repair; and gasket kits. Basically, they contain the following:

Minor Repair Kits:
- All gaskets
- Float needle valve
- Volume control screw
- All diaphragms
- Spring for the pump diaphragm

Major Repair Kits:
- All jets and gaskets
- All diaphragms
- Float needle valve
- Volume control screw
- Pump ball valve
- Main jet carrier
- Float
- Complete intermediate rod
- Intermediate pump lever
- Complete injector tube
- Some cover hold-down screws and washers

Gasket Kits:
- All gaskets

(1) is the float seat lip and "A" is the distance to be measured with float in the raised position
(© Toyo Kogyo Co., Ltd.)

After cleaning and checking all components, reassemble the carburetor, using new parts and referring to the exploded view. When reassembling, make sure that all screws and jets are tight in their seats, but do not overtighten, as the tips will be distorted. Tighten all screws gradually, in rotation. Do not tighten needle valves into their seats; uneven jetting will result. Always use new gaskets. Be sure to adjust the float level when reassembling.

Float and Fuel Level Adjustments

1971 Models

1. Adjust the amount of fuel coming through the needle valve by bending the float stop so that the distance between the lowest part of the float and the lower air horn face is 2.1–2.2 in.

2. Invert the air horn and lower the float so that the float seat lip is just contacting the needle valve.

3. Adjust the fuel level by adding or subtracting washers at the fuel intake so that the distance between the upper face of the float and the lower face of the air horn is 1.8–1.9 in.

1972–73 Models

1. Perform steps 1–2 of the 1971 procedure, above.

2. Measure the clearance between the float and the surface of the air horn gasket; it should be 0.22 in.

3. Bend the float seat lip in order to adjust the float setting.

Fast Idle Adjustment

1. With the choke valve fully closed, measure the clearance between the primary throttle valve and bore using a wire gauge.

Float lowered—1972-73
(© Toyo Kogyo Co., Ltd.)

2. Compare this measurement with the specifications given in the chart at the end of this section.

3. Bend the fast idle lever if adjustment of the clearance is required.

4. Test the choke valve to make sure that it operates freely.

5. Open the choke valve all the way. The throttle valve should be opened less than one degree, when measured with a protractor.

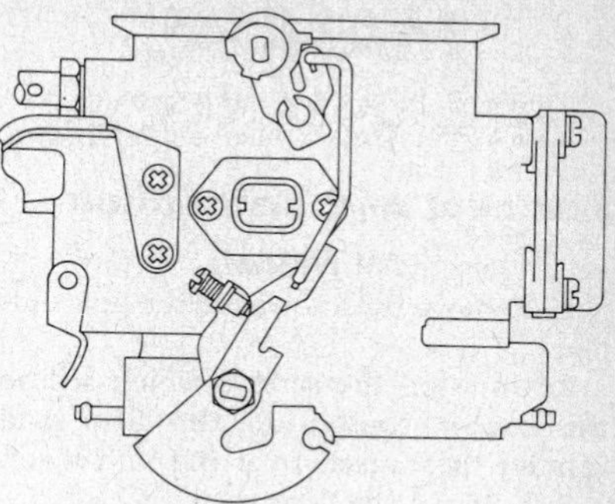

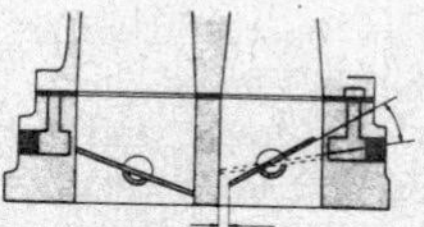

Fast idle adjustments: measure the angle "A" and clearance "B"
(© Toyo Kogyo Co., Ltd.)

Arrow indicates pump adjustment
(© Toyo Kogyo Co., Ltd.)

6. Close the choke valve to an angle of 35°. The throttle valve should just begin to open at this point.

7. Start the engine and run it at idle. The choke diaphragm rod should be pulled all the way out. If it is not, check for a clogged or an improperly connected vacuum line.

Year	Throttle Valve Clearance (in.)
1971	0.047
1972-73 (M/T)	0.045
1973 (A/T)	0.055

Accelerator Pump Adjustment

1. Remove the air cleaner assembly.

2. Move the primary throttle valve and check pump discharge.

3. If there is no discharge, check for a clogged pump nozzle or a binding pump lever.

4. If it is binding, dress the sliding surface of the lever with sandpaper and lubricate it with oil.

5. If pump discharge is still unsatisfactory, adjust the pump lever by selecting one of the two other adjusting holes in the connecting rod.

MANUAL TRANSMISSION

Removal and Installation

All Models

1. Remove the knob from the gearshift lever.
2. Unfasten the screws which secure the center console to the floor and remove the console over the shift lever.
3. Remove the floor mat.
4. Unfasten the screws which attach the shift lever boot and withdraw the boot over the shift lever.
5. Unbolt the cover and remove it from the gearshift lever retainer.
6. Pull the gearshift lever, complete with its shims and bushings, straight up and out of its retainer.
7. Detach the ground lead from the negative (−) battery terminal.
8. Unfasten the nuts which secure the clutch release cylinder and tie the cylinder up out of the way. Do not disconnect the hydraulic line from the clutch release cylinder.
9. Detach the back-up light switch multiconnector which is located near the clutch release cylinder.
10. Raise the car and support it with jackstands.

CAUTION: *Be sure that the car is securely supported.*

11. Unscrew the transmission drain plug and drain the oil. Wipe the drain plug clean and install it.
12. Remove the driveshaft, as described below, and plug up the transmission extension housing.

NOTE: *An old U-joint yoke makes an excellent plug. Or, lacking this, secure a plastic bag over the opening with rubber bands.*

13. Detach the exhaust pipe from the thermal reactor flange.

CAUTION: *Be sure that the reactor and exhaust pipe have cooled sufficiently to prevent severe burns.*

14. Unfasten the speedometer cable from the extension housing.
15. Detach the starter motor wiring. Remove its securing nuts and bolts and withdraw the starter motor.
16. Support the transmission with a block of wood mounted on a jack.
17. Remove the nuts which attach the transmission support to the frame members.
18. Evenly, and in several stages, remove the bolts which retain the bell housing on the engine.
19. Carefully slide the transmission assembly rearward until the input shaft has cleared the clutch disc.
20. Gently lower the transmission from the car.

Transmission installation is performed in the reverse order of removal. Align the clutch plate with an arbor or an old input shaft. Adjust the clutch and shift linkage as detailed elsewhere. Refill the transmission with gear oil:

Below 0°F—SAE EP 80
Above 0°F—SAE EP 90

Overhaul

Disassembly

1. Remove the clutch throwout bearing, spring, and fork.
2. Unfasten the bolts which secure the bellhousing to the transmission case. Remove the bellhousing assembly.
3. Remove the shift lever tower from the extension housing.
4. Withdraw the spring seat and spring from the end of the intermediate lever.
5. Unfasten the nuts which secure the extension housing to the transmission case. Slide the extension housing off of the mainshaft.

NOTE: *Turn the intermediate lever end as far to the left as it will go, while sliding the extension housing off.*

6. Remove the spring cap bolt, the spring, and contact piece from the extension housing.
7. Remove the intermediate lever assembly from the extension housing.
8. Remove its setscrew and then the speedometer driven gear from the extension housing.
9. Remove the bottom cover and the two upper covers from the transmission case.
10. Remove the shift fork rod lockballs and springs; then remove the interlock pins.
11. Unfasten the shift fork retaining bolts. Remove the shift forks along with the reverse idler gear from the transmission case.
12. Slide the speedometer drive gear off of the mainshaft and remove the lock-

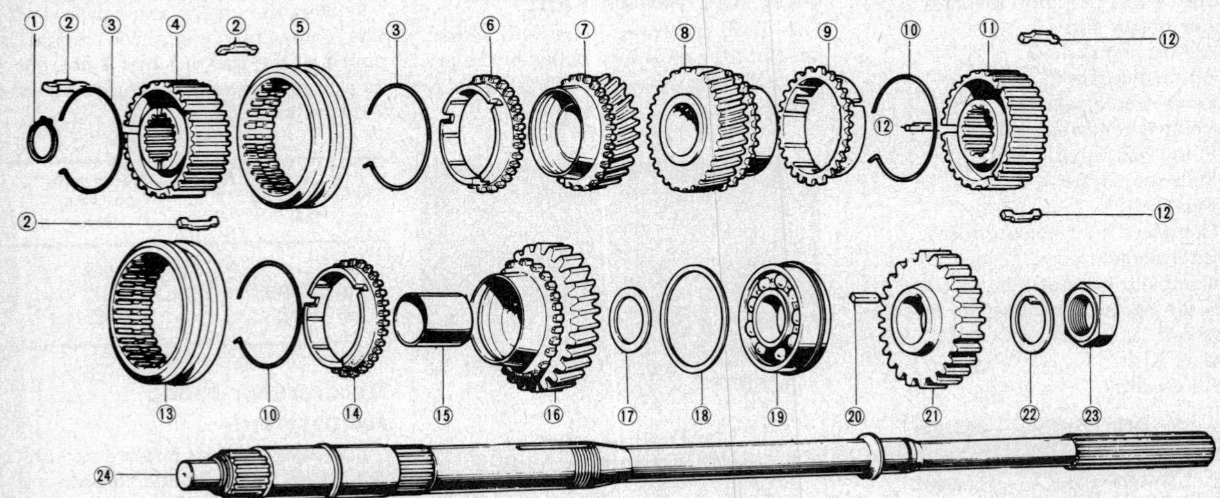

Mainshaft assembly
(© Toyo Kogyo Co., Ltd.)

1. Snap-ring
2. Key
3. Spring
4. First and second clutch hub
5. Clutch hub sleeve
6. Third gear synchronizer ring
7. Third gear
8. Second gear
9. Second gear synchronizer ring
10. Spring
11. Third and fourth clutch hub
12. Key
13. Third and fourth clutch hub sleeve
14. Low synchronizer ring
15. Low gear sleeve
16. Low gear
17. Thrust washer
18. Adjusting shim
19. Ball bearing
20. Key
21. Reverse gear
22. Lockwasher
23. Locknut
24. Mainshaft

ball, after first withdrawing the snap-ring at the rear of the speedometer drive gear.

13. Check the synchronizer key clearance in the following manner:

a. Shift the transmission into third gear.

b. Use a feeler gauge to check the clearance between the synchronizer key and the opposite edge of the synchronizer ring. The clearance should be 0.0295–0.0787 in.

c. If the measurement is greater than 0.0787 in., use a thicker thrust washer between first gear and the mainshaft bearing. Selective fit thrust washers are available in three sizes, ranging from 0.0984 to 0.1387 in.

14. Hold the mainshaft to prevent it from turning.

CAUTION: *Be careful when holding the mainshaft not to bend it or damage its surface.*

15. Unfasten the reverse gear locknut. Remove the lockwasher, reverse gear, and the key.

16. Remove the snap-ring from the counter gear and remove the reverse countergear.

17. Remove the bearing retainer and reverse idler gear shaft.

18. Use a bearing puller to remove the ball bearing on the mainshaft and the roller bearing on the countershaft.

19. Remove the snap-rings from the ball bearings on the front side of the transmission case. Then, using the puller, remove the bearings from the input gear and the countergear.

20. Withdraw the input gear, the countergear, and the mainshaft assembly from the case.

21. Remove these parts from the mainshaft in the following order:

a. Thrust washer
b. First gear and sleeve assembly
c. Synchronizer ring
d. First/second gear clutch hub
e. Synchronizer ring
f. Second gear

22. Remove the snap-ring on the front end of the mainshaft; then remove these parts in the following order:

a. Third/fourth clutch hub
b. Synchronizer ring
c. Third gear

Inspection

Clean the transmission case thoroughly with solvent and blow it dry with compressed air. Inspect the case for cracks or other signs of damage.

Inspect all of the bearings for wear or roughness.

Examine each of the gears. Replace any gears that have chipped or missing teeth, or gears that show signs of excessive wear.

Check the operation of the synchronizers. Replace any which are worn or damaged.

Place the mainshaft on V-blocks, and measure its runout with a dial indicator. If runout exceeds 0.0012 in., replace the mainshaft.

Assembly

1. Assemble the first/second and the third/fourth clutch hubs, with their sleeves. Be careful not to mix up any of the components of the two assemblies.

2. Install the following items, working from the rear side of the mainshaft, in the order listed:

a. Second gear
b. Synchronizer ring
c. First/second clutch hub
d. Synchronizer ring
e. First gear sleeve
f. First gear
g. Thrust washer

3. Working from the front side of the mainshaft, install these items in the following order:

a. Third gear
b. Synchronizer ring
c. Third/fourth clutch hub
d. Snap-ring

4. Install the needle roller bearing and the synchronizer ring on the input shaft.

5. Temporarily place the input shaft/mainshaft assembly into the transmission case without using the ball bearings.

6. Fit the first/second and third/fourth shift forks into their respective grooves on the clutch sleeves.

7. Place the countergear assembly in the transmission case.

8. Install the needle roller bearing on the rear side of the countershaft. Install the roller bearing, using the same number of adjustment shims, as were removed, on the front of the countershaft. Fit its snap-ring in place.

9. Install the roller bearings, shims, and snap-rings on the input shaft and on the mainshaft in the same order as outlined in step 8.

10. Fit the reverse gear and snap-ring onto the countershaft.

11. Install the bearing retainer and the reverse idler gearshaft in the transmission case. Torque the bearing retainer bolts to 7 ft lbs.

12. Install the reverse gear and key on the mainshaft.

13. Hold the mainshaft to keep it from turning. Install its lockwasher and locknut. Tighten the lockwasher to 170 ft lbs and then bend up the tabs on the lockwasher.

14. Fit the first/second shift rod into the transmission case and lock it to the first/second shift fork with its set screw.

15. Place the shift rod in Neutral and insert the interlock pin.

16. Install the third/fourth shift rod and interlock pin in the same manner detailed in steps 14 and 15.

17. Install the reverse shift rod and reverse idler gear in the case.

18. Place the shift lockballs and springs into the grooves on the shift rods and install the spring caps.

19. Install the bottom cover and the top covers on the transmission case.

20. Use the lockball to hold the speedometer drive gear on the mainshaft and retain it with the snap-ring.

21. Carefully drive the oil seal into the rear side of the extension housing.

22. Insert the intermediate lever into the extension housing. Install the end onto it and secure it with the setbolt.

23. Fit the contact piece and spring into the extension housing. Secure them with the spring cap bolt.

24. Screw the back-up light switch into the extension housing.

25. Install the speedometer driven gear assembly into the housing, then secure them with the lockplate.

26. Place the gasket on the rear of the transmission case. Bolt the extension housing to the case.

NOTE: *Turn the intermediate lever end as far to the left as it will go, while performing step 26.*

27. Check the operation of the intermediate lever for smoothness.

28. Insert the selector lever interlock over the return spring and install both into the shift tower.

29. Install the lockball and spring so that they align with the groove on the interlock. Screw the spring cap in place and the setscrew into the tower.

30. Install the spring and seat in the intermediate lever end.

31. Place the shift tower gasket on the extension housing and bolt the tower in place.

32. Place a gasket on the front of the transmission case. Install the bellhousing over the gasket.

33. Fit the throwout bearing, spring, and fork into the bellhousing.

34. Remove the transmission from the workstand and install it in the car.

Shift Lever Adjustment

The shift lever may be adjusted during transmission installation by means of the adjusting shims on the three bolts between the cover plate and the packing. The force required to move the shift knob should be 4.4–8.8 lbs.

CLUTCH

Removal and Installation

1. Remove the transmission as detailed above.

2. Attach a brake to the flywheel.

3. Install a clutch arbor to hold the clutch in place. An old input shaft makes an excellent arbor.

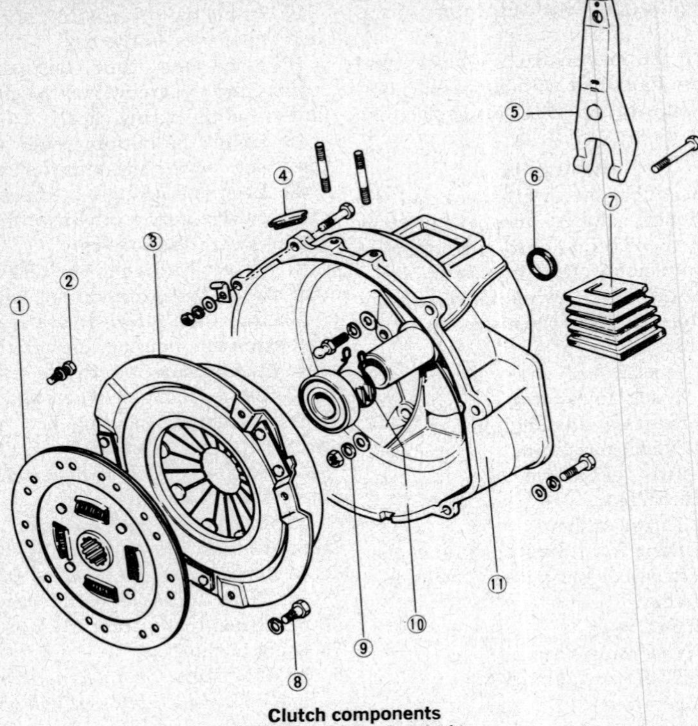

Clutch components
(© Toyo Kogyo Co., Ltd.)

1. Clutch disc
2. Bolt
3. Clutch cover and pressure plate assembly
4. Service hole cover
5. Release fork
6. Oil seal
7. Dust boot
8. Reamer bolt
9. Release bearing
10. Spring
11. Clutch housing

4. Unfasten the bolts which secure the clutch cover, one turn at a time in sequence, until the clutch spring tension is released. Remove the bolts evenly.

5. Remove the clutch disc.

CAUTION: *Be careful not to get grease or oil on the surface of the clutch disc.*

6. Unfasten the nut which secures the flywheel to the eccentric shaft, using a suitably large wrench.

7. Remove the flywheel with a puller.

8. Unhook the return spring from the throwout bearing and remove the bearing.

9. Pull out the release fork until the retaining spring frees itself from the ball stud. Withdraw the fork from the housing.

Clutch installation is performed in the following order:

1. Clean the flywheel and pressure plate surfaces with fine sandpaper. Be sure that there is no oil or grease on them. Grease the eccentric shaft needle bearing.

2. Apply Loctite® on the eccentric shaft threads. Install the flywheel with its keyway over the key on the eccentric shaft.

3. Apply sealer to both sides of the flywheel lockwasher and position the lockwasher on the eccentric shaft.

4. Install the flywheel locknut and tighten it to 350 ft lbs; then bend the tabs of the lockwasher up around it.

5. Use an arbor to center the clutch disc during installation. Install the clutch disc with the long end of its hub facing the transmission.

NOTE: *Use an old input shaft to center the clutch disc, if an arbor is not available.*

6. Align the O-mark on the clutch cover with the reamed hole or the O-mark on the flywheel.

7. Tighten the clutch cover bolts evenly, and in two or three stages, to 13–20 ft lbs.

CAUTION: *Do not tighten the bolts one at a time.*

8. Grease the pivot pin. Insert the release fork through its boot so that its retaining spring contacts the pivot pin.

9. Lightly grease the face of the throwout bearing and its clutch housing retainer.

10. Install the throwout bearing and return spring. Check the operation of the release fork and throwout bearing for smoothness.

11. Install the transmission.

Pedal Height Adjustment

1. Loosen the locknut on the adjusting bolt.

2. Turn the adjusting bolt until the clearance between the pedal pad and the

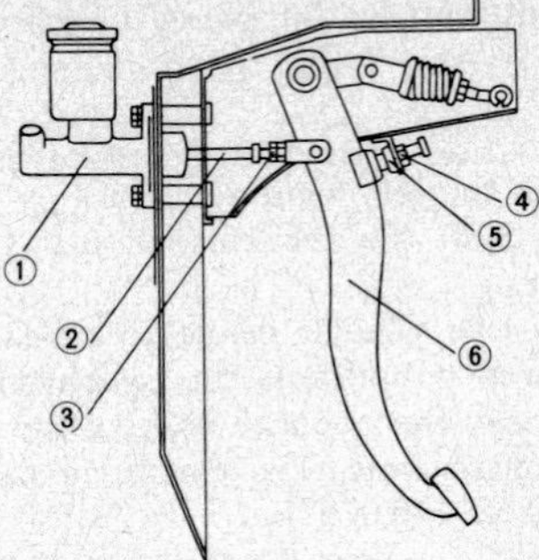

Clutch pedal height adjustment
(© Toyo Kogyo Co., Ltd.)

1. Master cylinder
2. Rod
3. Locknut
4. Adjusting bolt
5. Locknut
6. Clutch pedal

floormat is 7.28 in.

3. Carefully tighten the locknut.

Pedal Free-Play Adjustment

1. Loosen the locknut on the master cylinder pushrod.

2. Rotate the pushrod until the clutch pedal has a travel of 0.8–1.2 in. before clutch disengagement.

3. Carefully tighten the locknut.

Release Fork Free-Play Adjustment

1. Unfasten the return spring from the release fork.

2. Loosen the locknut on the release rod.

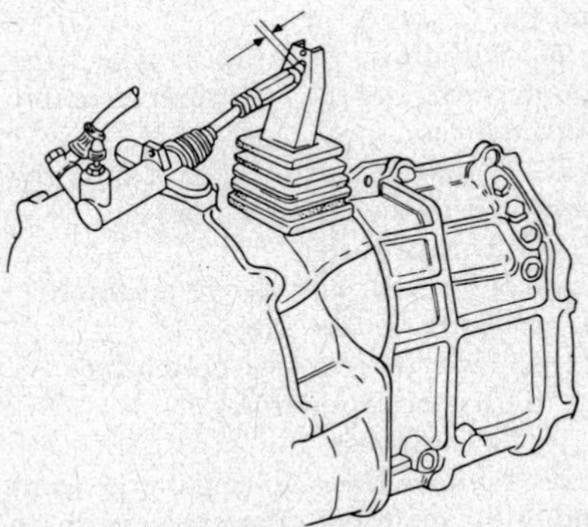

Release fork free-play is measured at arrows
(© Toyo Kogyo Co., Ltd.)

3. Turn the adjusting nut on the release rod until the proper release fork free-play is obtained:

RX-3—0.12–0.16 in.
RX-2—0.16–0.20 in.

4. Carefully tighten the locknut and hook the return spring back on the release fork.

Clutch Master Cylinder

Removal and Installation

1. Unfasten the hydraulic line from the master cylinder outlet.

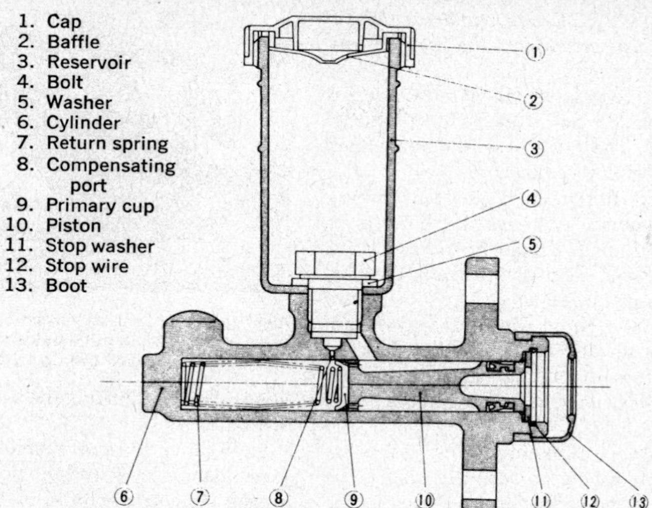

Cutaway view of the master cylinder
(© Toyo Kogyo Co., Ltd.)

CAUTION: *Use care not to drip any hydraulic fluid on the car's painted surfaces, as it is an excellent paint remover.*

2. Remove the nuts which secure the master cylinder assembly to the firewall.
3. Withdraw the master cylinder straight out and away from the firewall.

Installation is performed in the reverse order of removal. Bleed the hydraulic system as detailed below.

Overhaul

1. Thoroughly clean the outside of the master cylinder.
2. Drain the hydraulic fluid from the cylinder. Unbolt the reservoir from the cylinder body.
3. Remove the boot from the cylinder.
4. Release the wire piston stop with a screwdriver and withdraw the stop washer.
5. Withdraw the piston, piston cups, and return spring from the cylinder bore.
6. Wash all of the parts in clean hydraulic (brake) fluid.
7. Examine the piston cups. If they are damaged, softened, or swollen, replace them with new ones.
8. Check the piston and bore for scoring or roughness.
9. Use a wire gauge to check the clearance between the piston and its bore. Replace either the piston or the cylinder if the clearance is greater than 0.006 in.
10. Be sure that the compensating port in the cylinder is not clogged.

Assembly of the master cylinder is performed in the following order:

1. Dip the piston and cups in clean hydraulic (brake) fluid.
2. Bolt the reservoir up to the cylinder body.
3. Fit the return spring into the cylinder.
4. Insert the primary cup in the bore so that its flat side is facing the piston.
5. Place the secondary cup on the piston and insert them in the cylinder bore.
6. Install the stop washer and the wire piston stop.
7. Fill the reservoir half-full of hydraulic fluid. Operate the piston with a screwdriver until fluid spurts out of the cylinder outlet.
8. Fit the boot on the cylinder.

Clutch Release Cylinder

Removal and Installation

1. Unscrew the hydraulic line from the release cylinder.
2. Unhook the release fork return spring from the cylinder.
3. Unfasten the nuts which secure the release cylinder to the transmission.

Installation is performed in the reverse order of removal. Bleed the hydraulic system, as detailed below, and adjust the release fork free-play, as detailed above.

Overhaul

Consult the master cylinder overhaul section above for release cylinder overhaul procedures.

System Bleeding

1. Remove the rubber cap from the bleeder screw on the release cylinder.
2. Place a bleeder tube over the end of the bleeder screw.
3. Submerge the other end of the tube in a jar half-filled with hydraulic (brake) fluid.
4. Depress the clutch pedal fully and allow it to return slowly.
5. Keep repeating step 4, while watching the hydraulic fluid in the jar. As soon as the air bubbles disappear, close the bleeder screw.

NOTE: *During the bleeding procedure the reservoir must be kept at least half-full.*

6. Remove the tube and refit the rubber cap. Fill the reservoir with hydraulic fluid.

AUTOMATIC TRANSMISSION

Removal and Installation

1. Remove the ground cable from the negative battery terminal.
2. Jack up the car and support it with jackstands.

CAUTION: *Be sure that the car is securely supported.*

3. Remove the heat shroud. Unfasten the exhaust pipe bracket on the right-hand side of the torque converter housing.
4. Unfasten the bolts which secure the exhaust pipe to the rear side of the front

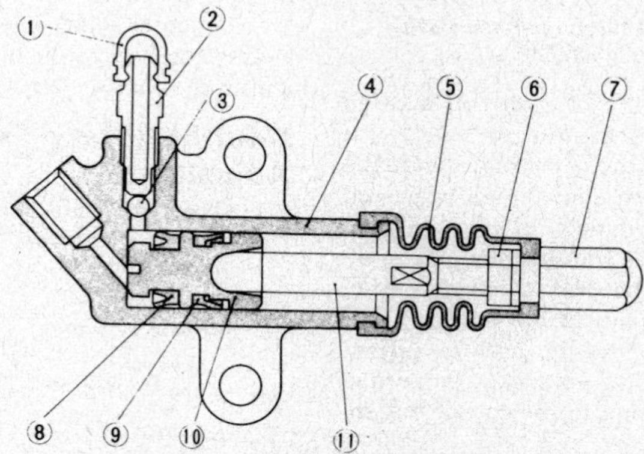

Cutaway view of the release cylinder
(© Toyo Kogyo Co., Ltd.)

1. Cap
2. Bleeder screw
3. Valve
4. Cylinder
5. Boot
6. Lock nut
7. Adjusting nut
8. Primary cup
9. Secondary cup
10. Piston
11. Push rod

muffler. Detach the exhaust pipe.

CAUTION: *The exhaust system on rotary engine-equipped Mazda's gets considerably hotter than a conventional system; be sure to allow enough time for it to cool before performing steps 3–4.*

5. Unfasten the four bolts from the driveshaft flange and withdraw the driveshaft from the extension housing. Plug up the hole in the extension housing so that fluid does not leak out.
6. Detach the speedometer cable at the extension housing.
7. Remove the control rod.
8. Unfasten the vacuum lines from the vacuum modulator.
9. Unfasten the multiconnector from the downshift solenoid and the neutral safety switch. Remove the wires from the bracket.
10. Disconnect the lines which run to the oil cooler on the left-hand side of the transmission.
11. Attach a brake to the ring gear.
12. Remove the starter motor. See the appropriate section under "Engine Electrical" for details.
13. Matchmark the torque converter and the flex-plate.
14. Working through the starter motor mounting hole, unfasten the four bolts which secure the torque converter to the flex-plate.

Loosening the torque converter bolts
(© Toyo Kogyo Co., Ltd.)

15. Support the transmission with an automatic transmission jack.
16. Unfasten the nuts which secure the transmission support member and remove the member.
17. Lower the transmission jack to increase the gap between the transmission and the underbody of the car.
18. Unfasten evenly, and in several stages, the bolts which secure the torque converter housing to the top of the engine.
19. Raise the transmission so that it is level again.
20. Use a screwdriver to carefully apply pressure between the torque converter and the flex-plate.
21. Slide the transmission rearward and lower it from the car.

CAUTION: *Do not rest the weight of the transmission on the torque converter splines.*

Automatic transmission installation is performed in almost the reverse order of removal. There are several points which should be noted, however:

1. Before installing the transmission, use a dial indicator to measure flex-plate runout. Runout should be around 0.012 in. If runout exceeds 0.020 in., the flex-plate must be replaced.
2. Hand-tighten the four torque converter installation bolts and then lock the flex-plate with a brake. Next, tighten the four bolts evenly, and in several stages, to 29–36 ft lbs.
3. After completing transmission installation, rotate the eccentric shaft to be sure that there is no interference in the transmission.
4. Fill the transmission with Dexron® transmission fluid. Converter capacity is 5.7 qts.

NOTE: *Do not use "type-F" automatic transmission fluid or gear oil in the transmission.*

5. Check and adjust the following items, after completing installation:
   a. Shift linkage
   b. Neutral safety switch
   c. Engine idle speed
   d. Kickdown switch and downshift solenoid
6. Check the fluid level again and road test the car.

Shift Linkage Adjustment

1. Unfasten the T-joint on the intermediate lever.
2. Place the range selector lever, which is mounted on the side of the transmission case, in Neutral (N); i.e., so that the slot in the selector shaft is pointing straight up and down.
3. Adjust the console-mounted gear selector lever by turning the T-joint until it indicates Neutral (N).
4. Reconnect the T-joint. Check the gear selector operation in all other ranges and to see that the linkage has no slack.

Neutral Safety Switch Adjustment

1. Check the shift linkage, as detailed

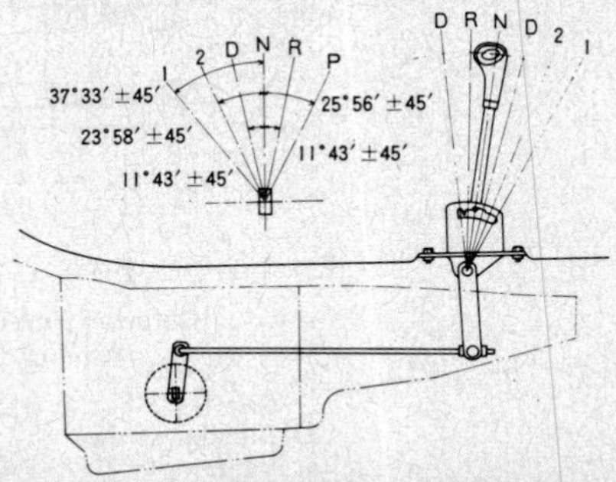

Transmission linkage adjustment
(© Toyo Kogyo Co., Ltd.)

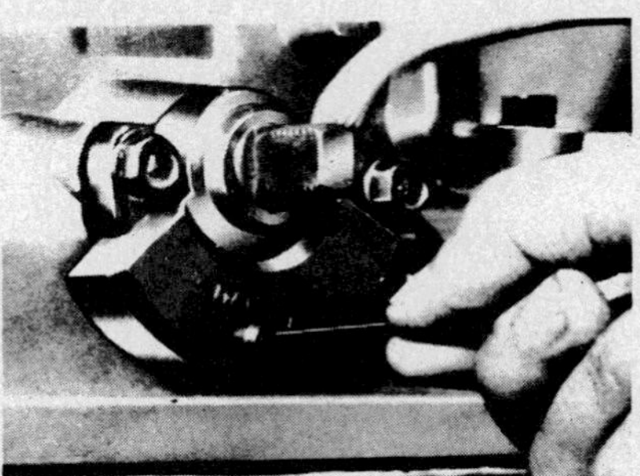

Align the neutral safety switch by inserting a drill through the holes on it
(© Toyo Kogyo Co., Ltd.)

above, before adjusting the neutral safety switch.

2. Remove the nut which secures the gear selector lever and the neutral safety switch attaching bolts.
3. Unfasten the screw which is located underneath the switch body.
4. Place the selector shaft in Neutral by using the gear selector lever.

NOTE: *If the linkage is adjusted properly, the slot in the selector shaft should be vertical.*

5. Move the switch body so that the screw hole in the case aligns with the hole in the internal rotor.
6. Check their alignment by inserting an 0.009 in. diameter pin or a No. 53 drill through the holes.
7. Once the proper alignment is obtained, tighten the switch mounting bolts. Remove the pin or drill and insert the screw back into the hole.
8. Tighten the nut which secures the gearshift selector lever.
9. Check the operation of the neutral safety switch again. If it still is not operating properly, i.e., the car starts in positions other than P (Park) or N (Neutral) or the back-up lights come on in gears other than R (Reverse), replace the switch.

Kickdown Switch and Downshift Solenoid Adjustment

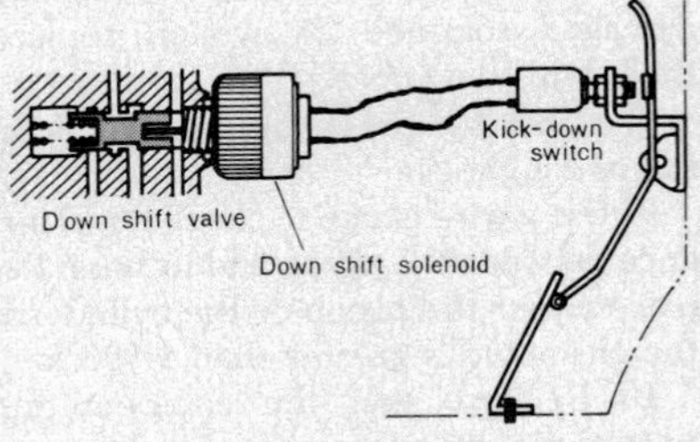

Kickdown switch and downshift solenoid circuit
(© Toyo Kogyo Co., Ltd.)

1. Check the accelerator linkage for smooth operation.
2. Turn the ignition on but do not start the engine.
3. Depress the accelerator pedal fully to the floor. As the pedal nears the end of

its travel, a light "click" should be heard from the downshift solenoid.

4. If the kickdown switch operates too soon, loosen the locknut on the switch shaft. Adjust the shaft so that the accelerator linkage makes contact with it when the pedal is depressed 7/8–15/16 of the way to the floor. Tighten the locknut.

5. If no noise comes from the solenoid at all, then check the wiring for the solenoid and the switch.

6. If the wiring is in good condition, then remove the wire from the solenoid and connect it to a 12V power source. If the solenoid does not click when connected, it is defective and should be replaced.

NOTE: *When the solenoid is removed, about two pints of transmission fluid will leak out; have a container ready to catch it. Remember to add more fluid to the transmission after installing the new solenoid.*

DRIVE AXLES

Driveshaft and U-Joints

Removal and Installation

RX-3 Models

1. Raise the rear end of the car and support it using jackstands.

CAUTION: *Be sure that the car is securely supported. Remember, you will be working underneath it.*

2. Matchmark the flanges on the driveshaft and pinion so that they may be installed in their original position.

3. Remove the four bolts which secure the driveshaft to the pinion flange.

4. Lower the back end of the driveshaft and slide the front end out of the transmission.

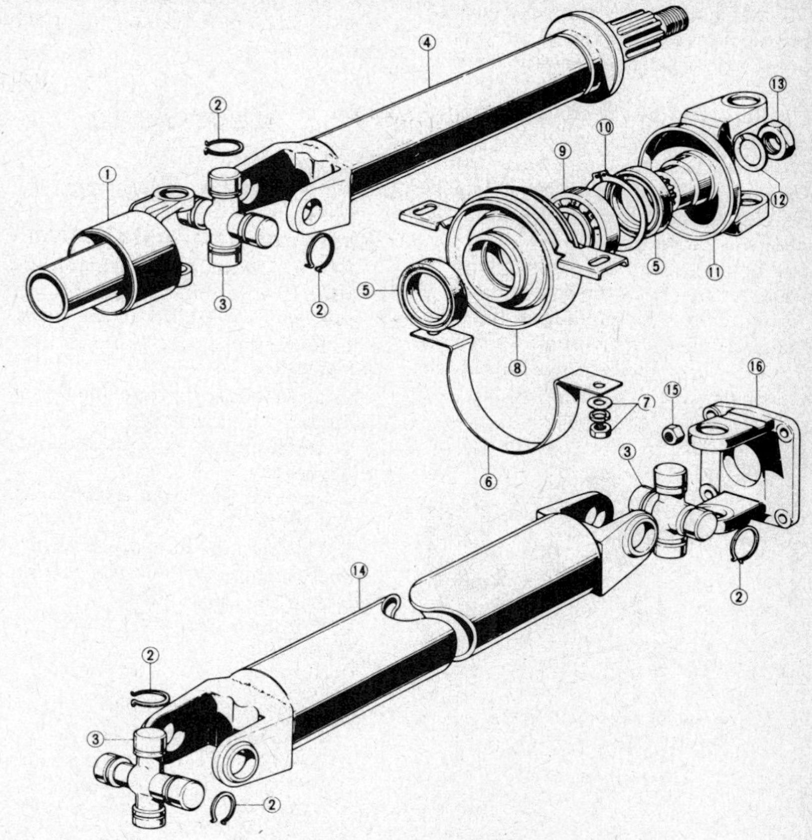

Components of the RX-2 driveshaft
(© Toyo Kogyo Co., Ltd.)

1. Sliding yoke
2. Snap ring
3. Universal joint
4. Propeller shaft
5. Oil seal
6. Protector
7. Nut and washer
8. Center bearing support
9. Ball bearing
10. Snap-ring
11. Yoke
12. Washer
13. Nut
14. Propeller shaft
15. Nut
16. Universal joint yoke

5. Plug up the hole in the transmission to prevent it from leaking.

NOTE: *Use an old U-joint yoke; or, if none is available, place a plastic bag, secured with rubber bands, over the hole.*

Driveshaft installation is performed in the reverse order of removal. Tighten the driveshaft-to-pinion flange bolts to 22 ft lbs.

RX-2 Models

The driveshaft used on RX-2 models is removed in a manner similar to that outlined for RX-3 models above. The only difference in the removal procedure is that the center bearing must be unbolted prior to driveshaft removal. Remove the driveshaft and the center bearing as a single unit.

NOTE: *Do not remove the oil seals and the center bearing from the support unless they are defective.*

Installation is performed in the reverse order of removal. Tighten the center bearing support bolts to 14–21 ft lbs and the driveshaft-to-pinion flange bolts to 25–27 ft lbs.

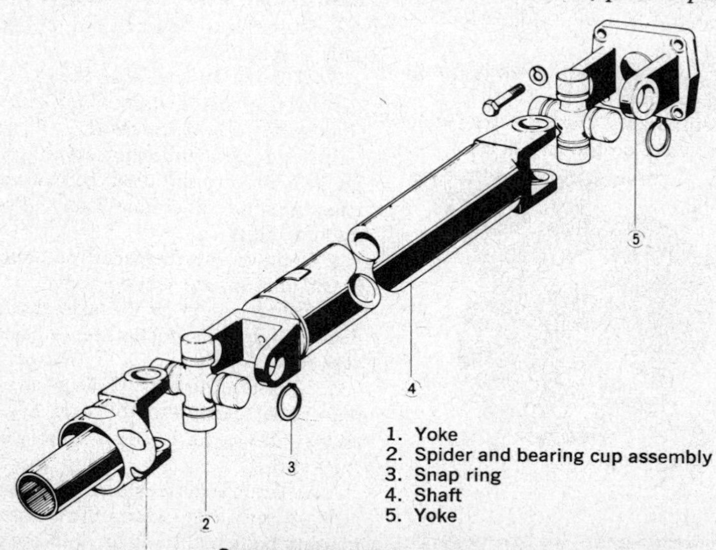

1. Yoke
2. Spider and bearing cup assembly
3. Snap ring
4. Shaft
5. Yoke

Components of the RX-3 driveshaft
(© Toyo Kogyo Co., Ltd.)

U-Joint Overhaul

Perform this procedure with the driveshaft removed from the car.

1. Matchmark both the yoke and the driveshaft so that they can be returned to their original balancing position during assembly.

2. Remove the bearing snap-rings from the yoke.

3. Use a hammer and a brass drift to drive *in* one of the bearing cups. Remove the cup which is protruding from the other side of the yoke.

4. Remove the other bearing cups by pressing them from the spider.

5. Withdraw the spider from the yoke. Examine the spider journals for rusting or wear. Check the bearings for smoothness or pitting.

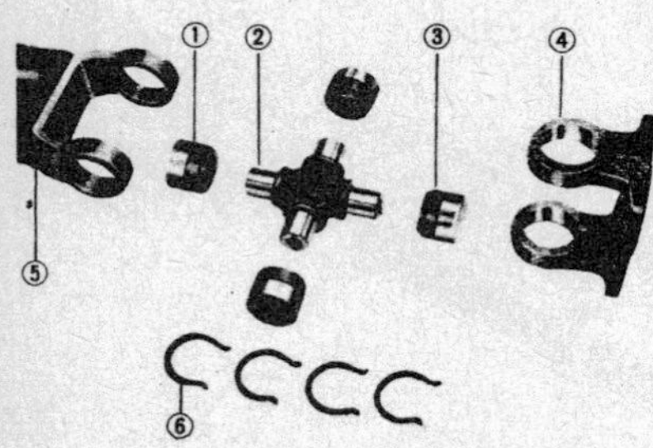

Components of the U-joint
(©Toyo Kogyo Co., Ltd.)

1. Roller bearing (cup)
2. Spider
3. Oil seal
4. Yoke
5. Driveshaft
6. Snap-ring

Measure the spider diameter. The standard diameter is 0.5795 in. If the spider wear exceeds 0.0040 in. on RX-2 models or 0.0079 in. on RX-3 models, replace the spider.

NOTE: *The spider and bearing are replaced as a complete assembly only.*

Check the seals and rollers for wear or damage.

Assembly of the U-joint is performed in the following order:

1. Pack the bearing cups with grease.
2. Fit the rollers into the cups and install the dust seals.
3. Place the spider in the yoke and then fit one of the bearing cups into its bore in the yoke.
4. Press the bearing cup home, while guiding the spider into it so that a snap-ring can be installed.
5. Press-fit the other bearings into the yoke.
6. Select a snap-ring to obtain minimum end-play of the spider. Use snap-rings of the same thickness on both sides to center the spider.

NOTE: *Selective fit snap-rings are available in sizes ranging from 0.048 to 0.054 in.*

7. Install the spider/yoke assembly and bearings to the driveshaft in the same manner as the spider was assembled to the yoke.
8. Test the operation of the U-joint assembly. The spider should move freely with no binding.

Rear Axle

Axle Shafts

Removal and Installation

NOTE: *The left and the right rear axle shafts are not interchangeable, as the left shaft is shorter than the right.*

1. Remove the wheel disc and loosen the lug nuts.
2. Raise the rear of the car and support the axle with jackstands.
3. Unfasten the lug nuts and remove the wheel.
4. Remove the brake assembly as detailed below.
5. Unfasten the nuts which secure the brake backing plate and the bearing retainer to the axle housing.
6. Withdraw the axle shaft with a puller.

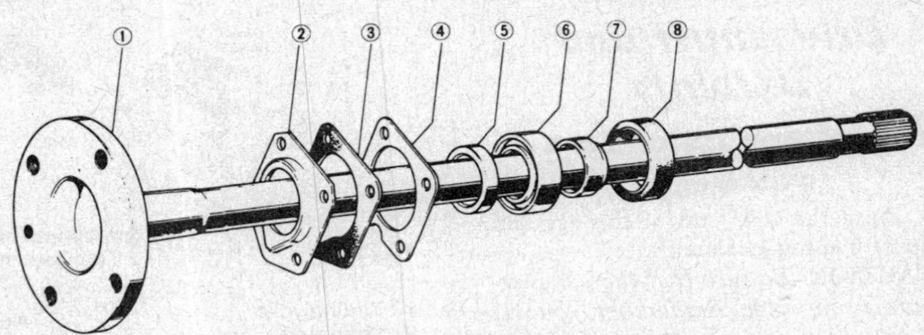

Components of the axle shaft assembly
(© Toyo Kogyo Co., Ltd.)

1. Rear axle shaft
2. Bearing retainer
3. Gasket
4. Shim
5. Spacer
6. Bearing
7. Bearing collar
8. Oil seal

Axle shaft installation is performed in the following order:

1. Apply grease to the oil seal lips and then insert the oil seal into the axle housing.
2. Check the axle shaft end-play in the following manner:
   a. Temporarily install the brake backing plate on the axle shaft.

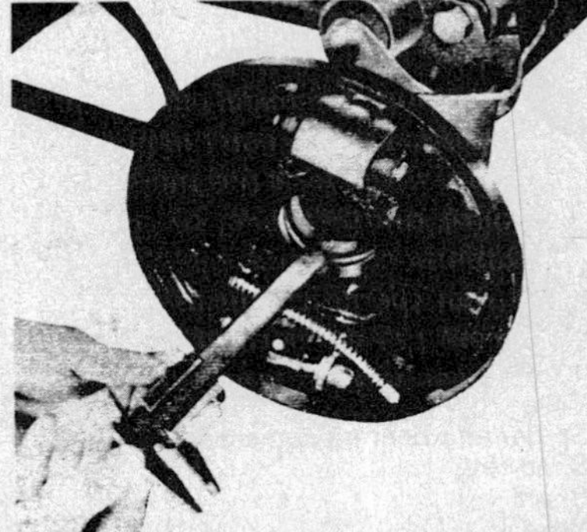

Measure the depth of the bearing seat
(© Toyo Kogyo Co., Ltd.)

   b. Measure the depth of the bearing seat and then measure the width of the bearing outer race.
   c. The difference between the two measurements is equal to the overall thickness of the adjusting shims required. Shims are available in thicknesses of 0.004 and 0.016 in.

NOTE: *The maximum permissible end-play is 0.004 in.*

3. Remove the backing plate and apply sealer to the rear axle surfaces which contact it. Install the backing plate again.
4. Install the rear axle shaft, bearing retainer, gasket, and shims through the backing plate and into the axle housing. Coat the shims with a small amount of sealer first.
5. Engage the splines on the differential side gear with those on the end of the axle shaft.
6. Install the brake assembly and adjust it.
7. Install the wheel and lower the car.

Differential

Removal and Installation

1. Raise the automobile and support it with jackstands.

CAUTION: *Be sure that the car is securely supported. Remember, you will be working underneath it.*

2. Remove the drain (lower) plug from the axle housing and drain the lubricant into a suitable container, Clean and reinstall the plug.
3. Remove the driveshaft as detailed in the appropriate section above.
4. Remove both of the axle shafts as detailed in the section immediately above.
5. Unfasten the nuts which secure the differential carrier to the axle housing and withdraw the carrier assembly from the housing.

Installation is performed in the reverse order of removal. Tighten the carrier-to-housing bolts to 14.5 ft lbs. Fill the axle housing to the level just below the filler

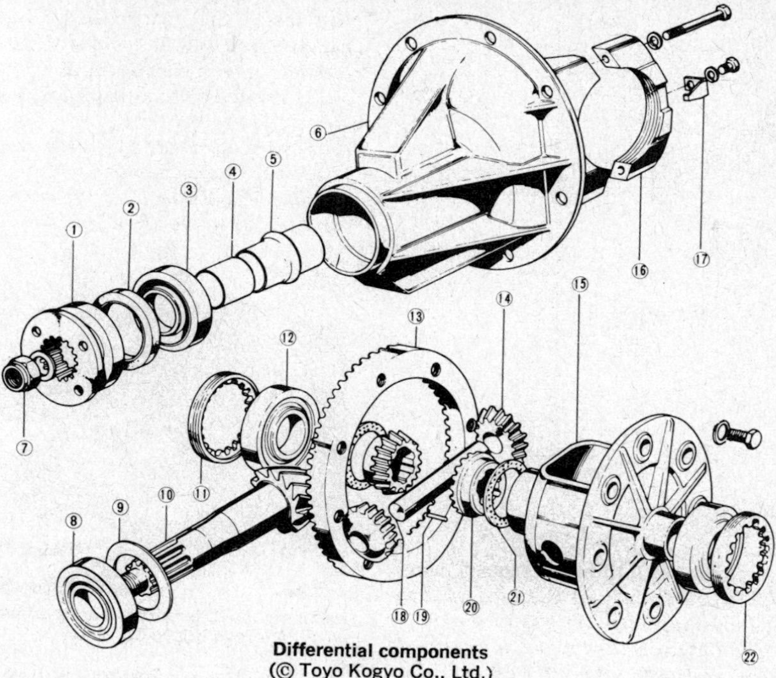

Differential components
(© Toyo Kogyo Co., Ltd.)

1. Pinion flange
2. Pinion oil seal
3. Pinion front bearing
4. Pinion bearing collar
5. Collapsible pinion bearing spacer
6. Carrier
7. Pinion nut
8. Pinion rear bearing
9. Adjusting washer (Adjusting spacer)
10. Drive pinion
11. Pinion side adjusting nut
12. Side bearing
13. Ring gear
14. Pinion gear
15. Differential gear case
16. Bearing cap
17. Adjusting nut lock
18. Pinion shaft
19. Pinion shaft lock pin
20. Side gear
21. Thrust washer
22. Ring gear side adjusting nut

plug with one of the following:
Above 0°F—HP SAE 90
Below 0°F—HP SAE 80

Overhaul

Disassembly

1. Mount the carrier on a workstand.
2. Apply identification marks to the carrier, bearing caps, and adjuster, to aid in installation.
3. Unfasten the bolts which secure adjusting nut lockplates and then remove the lockplates.
4. Loosen, but do not remove, the bearing cap securing nuts and then back off on the adjuster, just enough to remove bearing preload.
5. Remove the differential assembly, complete with the outer bearing races.

CAUTION: *Be sure that each bearing outer race remains with its bearing.*

6. Remove the differential bearings from the gear case with a puller.

NOTE: *Use care not to mix up the bearings when setting them aside.*

7. unfasten the bolts which secure the ring gear to the gear case and remove their washers. Separate the ring gear from the case.
8. Straighten out the punched portion of the gear case, then drive the pinion gear shaft locking pin out of the case with a brass drift.
9. Withdraw the pinion gear shaft.
10. Rotate each of the pinion (spider) gears 90° and remove them, complete with thrust washers.
11. Remove the side gears and thrust washers.
12. Hold the pinion flange by screwing two bolts into it and grabbing them with a spanner or a pipewrench. Remove the pinion nut.
13. Remove the pinion from the carrier.

NOTE: *If the pinion is difficult to remove, tap it with a plastic hammer while guiding it out by hand.*

14. Remove the collar, if so equipped, and the collapsible spacer from the pinion.
15. Press out the rear bearing and remove the adjustable shim. Save the shim for later reference.
16. Withdraw the oil seal and the front bearing from the carrier.
17. If necessary, the pinion bearing outer races can be driven out with a brass drift placed in the slots which are provided for this purpose.

NOTE: *Do not remove the outer races unless they are worn or damaged. If they are replaced, the bearing cones must be replaced as well.*

Inspection

1. Check all of the gears for chipping, broken teeth, wear, or other signs of damage. Replace any gears, as required.
2. Examine the carrier and pinion flange for cracks, wear, and other signs of damage. Replace these parts as necessary.
3. Check the clearance between the splines on the side gears and the rear axle shafts. If it is greater than 0.012 in., replace either the side gears or the axle shafts.
4. Inspect the oil seal for wear and/or damage; replace it if either are present.

Assembly and Adjustment

NOTE: *Start out with a handful of collapsible spacers and different sizes of pinion adjusting shims.*

1. If the old pinion/ring gear assembly and rear bearing are being used, replace the shim with a new one of the same size (identification marking) as was removed. Use a new collapsible spacer.
2. If a new pinion/ring gear assembly or rear bearing is being used, determine the correct adjustment shim size in the following manner:

a. Look at the identification markings on the old pinion and shim which were removed. Record their markings.

NOTE: *Pinion markings are given in plus (+) or minus (−) millimeter measurements while the shim has a numbered identification code. Consult the chart below for proper shim identification.*

Marking	Thickness (mm)	Marking	Thickness (mm)
08	3.08	29	3.29
11	3.11	32	3.32
14	3.14	35	3.35
17	3.17	38	3.38
20	3.20	41	3.41
23	3.23	44	3.44
26	3.26	47	3.47

b. Look at the identification measurement stamped on the new pinion and note its value.

c. Calculate the difference between the measurements of the new and old pinions by adding or subtracting, as necessary.

d. If the value on the new pinion is *less* than the value on the old, *add* the difference to the thickness of the old shim (in millimeters). Use a new shim of the total thickness.

e. If the value on the new pinion is *greater* than the value on the old, *subtract* the difference from the thickness of the old shim (in millimeters). Use a new shim having a thickness of the difference.

f. If the rear pinion bearing was replaced, measure the difference (in millimeters) between the new and the old

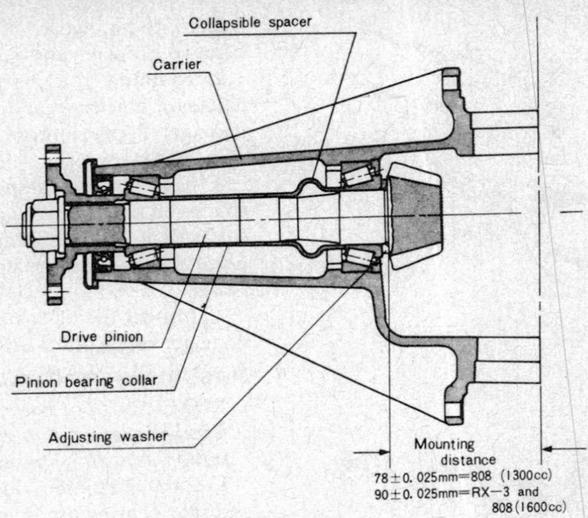

Proper pinion positioning
(© Toyo Kogyo Co., Ltd.)

bearing. Add or subtract the difference between the two bearings from the size of the adjusting shim.

g. Select the proper size adjusting shim, as determined in the steps above, from one of the following:

3. Position the adjusting shim, of the size as determined in steps 1 or 2, and install the rear pinion bearing on the pinion.

4. If they were removed, install the pinion bearing outer races in the carrier. Be sure that they are properly seated.

5. Place the pinion assembly through the collapsible spacer and into the carrier.

NOTE: *Use a new collapsible spacer.*

6. Position the front bearing on the pinion. Hold the pinion as far forward as it will go and drive the front bearing on to the pinion until it is fully seated.

7. Coat the lips of the pinion oil seal with grease and fit the seal into the carrier.

8. Tap the pinion flange home on the pinion with a rubber mallet.

9. Install the pinion washer and nut but do not tighten the nut.

10. With the nut still loose, i.e., with no preload on the pinion, check the amount of force required to turn the pinion with a torque wrench that is calibrated in inch pounds; this will measure the amount of drag produced by the oil seal.

11. Install two bolts on the pinion flange and hold it with a spanner or pipe wrench to keep it from rotating. Tighten the pinion nut to 94 ft lbs.

CAUTION: *Use care not to over-tighten the pinion, as the spacer will collapse and have to be replaced.*

12. Release the pinion flange and measure the amount of preload obtained using the inch/pound torque wrench.

13. Continue tightening the pinion nut, if necessary, a little at a time. Check the preload after each small amount of tightening, until the final preload figure of 7.8–12.2 ft lbs plus the oil seal drag measured in step 10, is obtained.

CAUTION: *If the preload is exceeded, the collapsible spacer will be compressed too much. A new spacer will have to be installed and the bearing preload adjusted all over again. Proper preload cannot be obtained by simply backing off on the nut.*

14. Install thrust washers on both of the side gears and fit the gears into the case.

15. Fit the two pinion (spider) gears into the case, through the opening, so that they are exactly 180° apart.

16. Turn the gears through 90° so that the pinion shaft holes in the case align with the holes in the pinion gears.

17. Insert the pinion gear shaft into the holes in the case and through the holes in the pinion gears.

NOTE: *Align the pinion shaft so that the lockpin holes in it align with the holes in the case.*

18. Check the backlash between the side gears and the pinion gears with a dial indicator. The backlash between the gear teeth should be 0–0.004 in. If backlash exceeds 0.008 in., adjust it to specifications by selecting one of the following side gear thrust washers:

Marking	Thickness (in.)
0	0.0787
1	0.0827
2	0.0866

NOTE: Use the same thickness thrust washers for both side gears.

19. Install and stake the lockpin onto the pinion shaft.

20. Bolt the ring gear up to the gear case. Torque the bolts evenly, and in sequence, to 40–47 ft lbs. Lock the bolts in place with their lockplates.

21. Install the gear bearings in the gear case hub and fit each of the outer races into its respective bearing.

22. Place the differential gearset in the carrier.

NOTE: *Be sure that the marks used for backlash adjustment, which are stamped on the faces of the ring gear and pinion teeth, are aligned.*

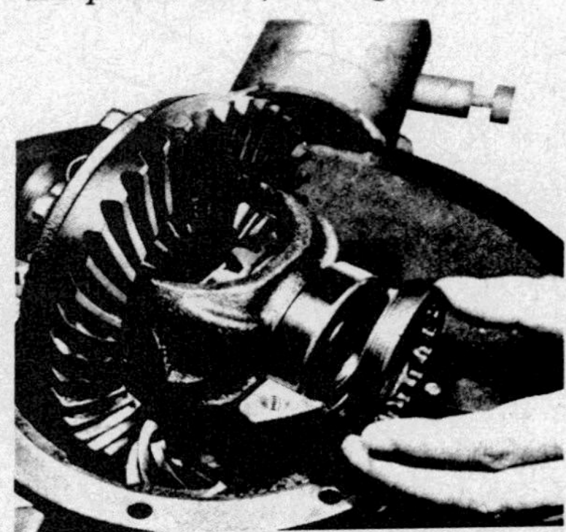

Installing the differential bearing adjuster
(© Toyo Kogyo Co., Ltd.)

23. Install the adjusters on their respective sides by consulting the identification marks made during their removal.

24. Install the bearing cups properly by consulting the identification marks made on them during removal.

25. Rotate the adjusters until the bearings are properly positioned in their outer races and their end-play is eliminated.

26. Finger tighten one of the bearing cap bolts on each bearing.

27. Attach a dial indicator to the flange on the carrier so that its plunger comes into contact with the ring gear at right angles to its teeth.

28. Check the backlash between the pinion and the ring gear teeth:

a. If backlash is *more* than specified, loosen the adjusting nut on the pinion side one notch and tighten the ring gear adjusting nut one notch.

b. If the backlash is *less* than specified, loosen the adjusting nut on the ring gear side one notch and tighten the pinion adjusting nut one notch.

c. Repeat the procedure until the specified backlash of 0.0067–0.0075 in. is obtained.

29. Tighten the adjusting nut on the differential bearings to obtain proper preload. Proper preload is determined when the distance between the pilot sections of the bearing caps is 7.3033 in. Measure the distance with a vernier caliper.

NOTE: *Be careful not to disturb the backlash between the pinion and the ring gear teeth while adjusting the bearing preload.*

30. Tighten the bearing cap securing bolts to 30 ft lbs. Install the lockplate on

the bearing adjuster so that they cannot loosen.

31. Coat both sides of about six to eight ring gear teeth with red lead. Move the ring gear back and forth several times and then examine the contact pattern made. Compare it to the illustrations below. Adjust the preload or backlash, as required to obtain proper tooth contact.

32. Install the carrier in the axle housing, as outlined above.

Ring Gear Contact Patterns

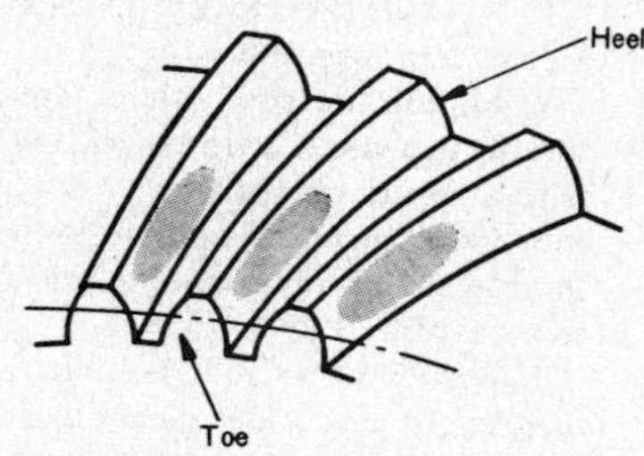

Correct contact pattern
(© Toyo Kogyo Co., Ltd.)

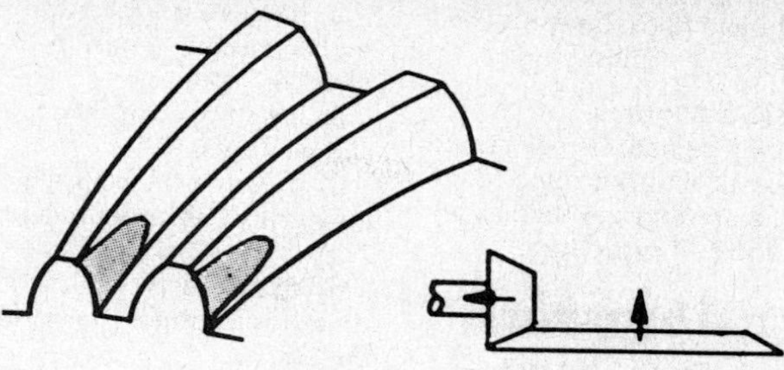

Too much toe contact
(© Toyo Kogyo Co., Ltd.)

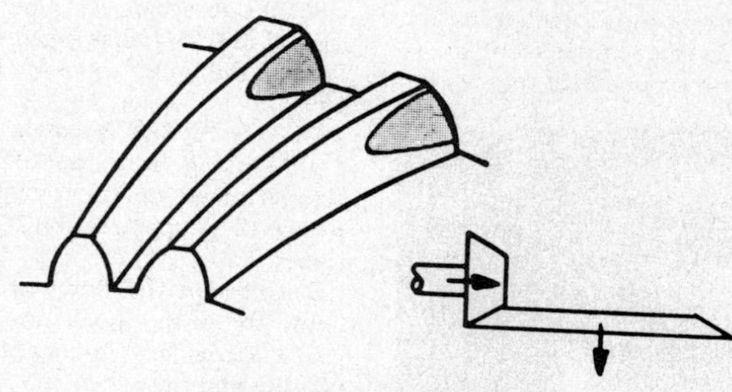

Too much heel contact
(© Toyo Kogyo Co., Ltd.)

REAR SUSPENSION

Springs

Removal and Installation

RX-3 Models

1. Remove the wheel disc and loosen the lug nuts.
2. Raise the back end of the car and support it with jackstands.

CAUTION: *Be sure that the car is securely supported.*

3. Remove the lug nuts and the wheel.
4. Support the rear axle housing with jackstands.
5. Unfasten the nuts which secure the U-bolts. Withdraw the U-bolt seat, rubber pad, plate, and the U-bolt itself.
6. Unfasten the two bolts and the nut that secure the spring pin to the front end of the rear spring.
7. Pry the spring pin out with a large, flat screwdriver inserted between the spring pin and its body bracket.
8. Unfasten the nuts and the bolts which attach the rear shackle to the car's body.
9. Withdraw the rear spring assembly, complete with its shackle.
10. Remove the shackle assembly from the end of the spring.
11. Pull the rubber bushings out from both ends of the spring.

Rear spring installation is performed in the reverse order of removal. When installing the rubber bushings, do not lubricate them. Tighten the U-bolt securing

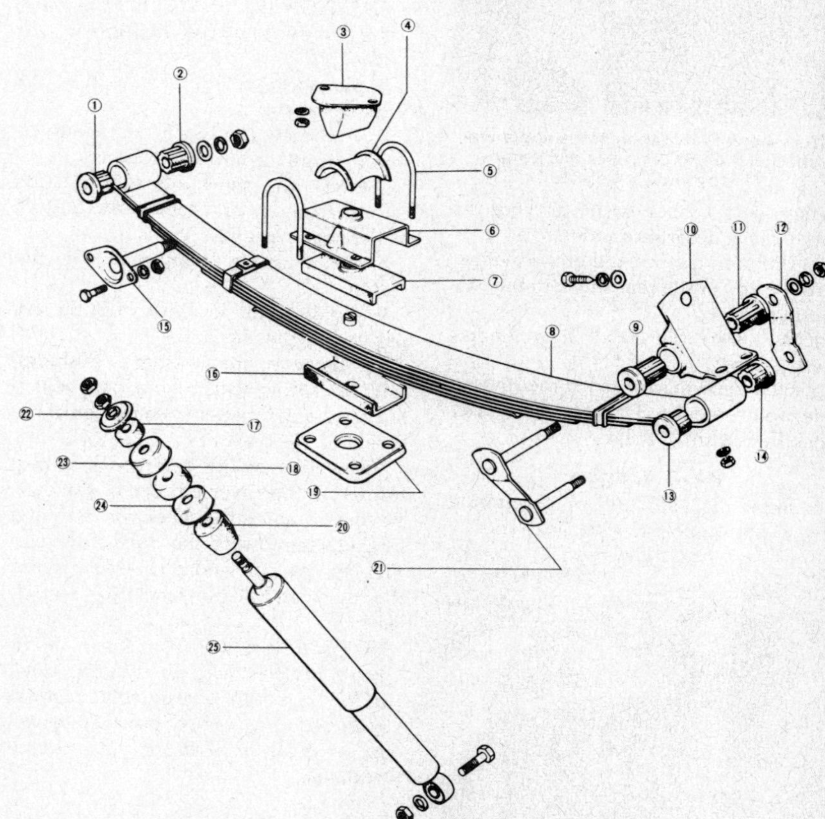

RX-3 sedan and coupe rear suspension—wagon similar
(© Toyo Kogyo Co., Ltd.)

1. Bushing
2. Bushing
3. Bound stopper
4. U-bolt seat
5. U-bolt
6. Plate
7. Rubber pad
8. Rear spring
9. Bushing
10. Shackle hanger
11. Bushing
12. Shackle plate
13. Bushing
14. Bushing
15. Spring pin
16. Rubber pad
17. Bushing
18. Bushing
19. Spring clamp
20. Damper stopper
21. Shackle
22. Washer
23. Holder
24. Damper stopper casing
25. Rear shock absorber

nuts to 30 ft lbs and both the spring and the shackle pins to 14 ft lbs.

RX-2 Models

Rear coil spring removal is performed as part of the shock absorber removal operation. See the appropriate section below for the combined procedure.

Shock Absorbers

Removal and Installation

RX-3 Coupes and Sedans

1. Remove the trim panel from the rear of the luggage compartment.
2. Unfasten the nuts, then remove the

Arrow shows the location of the upper rear shock nut on RX-3 coupes and sedans (© Toyo Kogyo Co., Ltd.)

washers and rubber bushings from the upper shock absorber mounts.

3. Unfasten the nut and bolt which secure the end of the rear shock to the axle housing.
4. Withdraw the shock from underneath the car.

Installation is performed in the reverse order of removal. Tighten the upper shock mount to 15 ft lbs.

RX-3 Wagon

1. Raise the back end of the station wagon and support it with jackstands.

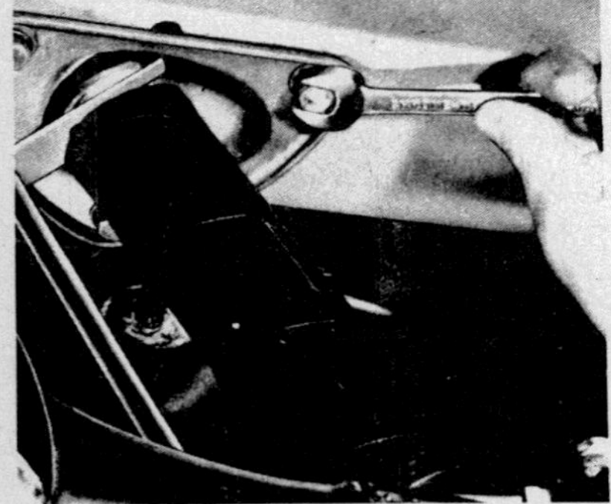

Removing the rear shock upper mounting bracket on RX-3 wagons (© Toyo Kogyo Co., Ltd.)

CAUTION: *Be sure that the car is securely supported. Remember, you will be working underneath it.*

2. Remove the locknuts, washers, and rubber bushings from the bottom shock absorber mount.
3. Install a compressor on the shock and compress it.
4. Unfasten the bolts which secure the upper shock absorber mount to the body.
5. Withdraw the shock, with the compressor still attached, from underneath the car.
6. Slowly remove the compressor from the shock.

Shock absorber installation is performed in the reverse order of removal. Tighten the upper shock mount to 15 ft lbs.

RX-2 Models

1. Working from inside the luggage compartment, unfasten the nuts which secure the upper end of the shock absorber.
2. Unfasten the nut and bolt at the lower end of the shock absorber.
3. Place a jack underneath the axle housing and raise the car.
4. Place jackstands underneath the frame side rails.

CAUTION: *Be sure that the jackstands are properly placed under the side rails.*

5. Slowly lower the jack to take the load off the springs.
6. Withdraw the shock/coil spring assembly from underneath the car.
7. Mark the shock for identification during assembly and secure the bottom of the shock in a vise.
8. Fit a spring compressor on the spring.
9. Unfasten the locknuts from the upper end of the shock.
10. Remove the washers, bushings, setplate, spring seat, rubber pad, adjusting plate, and bumper from the top of the shock.

Installation of the rear shock is performed in the reverse order of removal. Be sure to mount the shock with its stone guard facing toward the front of the car. Tighten the bolt and nut which secure the lower end of the shock, to 72–87 ft lbs.

NOTE: *If a new coil spring is being fitted, match it with an adjusting plate of the correct thickness to obtain equal road clearance on both sides. There are three different sizes of coil springs available.*

FRONT SUSPENSION

McPherson Struts

Removal and Installation

1. Remove the wheel disc (if so equipped) and loosen the lug nuts.
2. Raise the front of the vehicle and support it with jackstands. Do not jack or support it by any of the front suspension members.

CAUTION: *Be sure that the car is securely supported.*

3. Remove the wheel. Unfasten the three nuts which secure the upper shock mount to the top of the wheel arch.
4. Remove the brake caliper and disc as detailed below.
5. Unfasten the two bolts that secure the lower end of the shock to the steering knuckle arm.
6. Remove the shock and coil spring as a complete assembly.
7. Mount the strut (shock/spring) assembly in a vise. Compress the coil spring with a spring compressor.
8. Hold the upper end of the shock piston rod with a pipe wrench and remove the locknut.
9. Remove the following parts from the top of the shock absorber in the order listed:
   a. Rubber mount
   b. Bearing
   c. Rubber seat
   d. Adjusting plate(s)
   e. Sealing ring
   f. Dust boot
   g. Coil spring
   h. Lower seat

   CAUTION: *When removing the spring compressor from the coil spring, do so gradually so that spring tension is not released all at once.*

Installation of the McPherson strut is performed in the reverse order of removal. Tighten the nut on the top of the piston rod to 10 ft lbs.

NOTE: *If a new coil spring is being fitted, match it with an adjusting plate of the correct thickness to obtain equal road clearance on both sides. Do not use more than two adjusting plates on a side.*

Control Arm

Removal and Installation

1. Perform the first two steps of the McPherson strut removal procedure.
2. Remove the cotter pin and nut, which secure the tie-rod end, from the knuckle arm; then use a puller to separate them.
3. Unfasten the bolts which secure the lower end of the shock absorber to the knuckle arm.
4. Remove the nut, then withdraw the rubber bushing and washer which secure the stabilizer bar to the control arm.
5. Unfasten the nut and bolt which secure the control arm to the frame member.
6. Push outward on the strut assembly while removing the end of the control arm from the frame member.

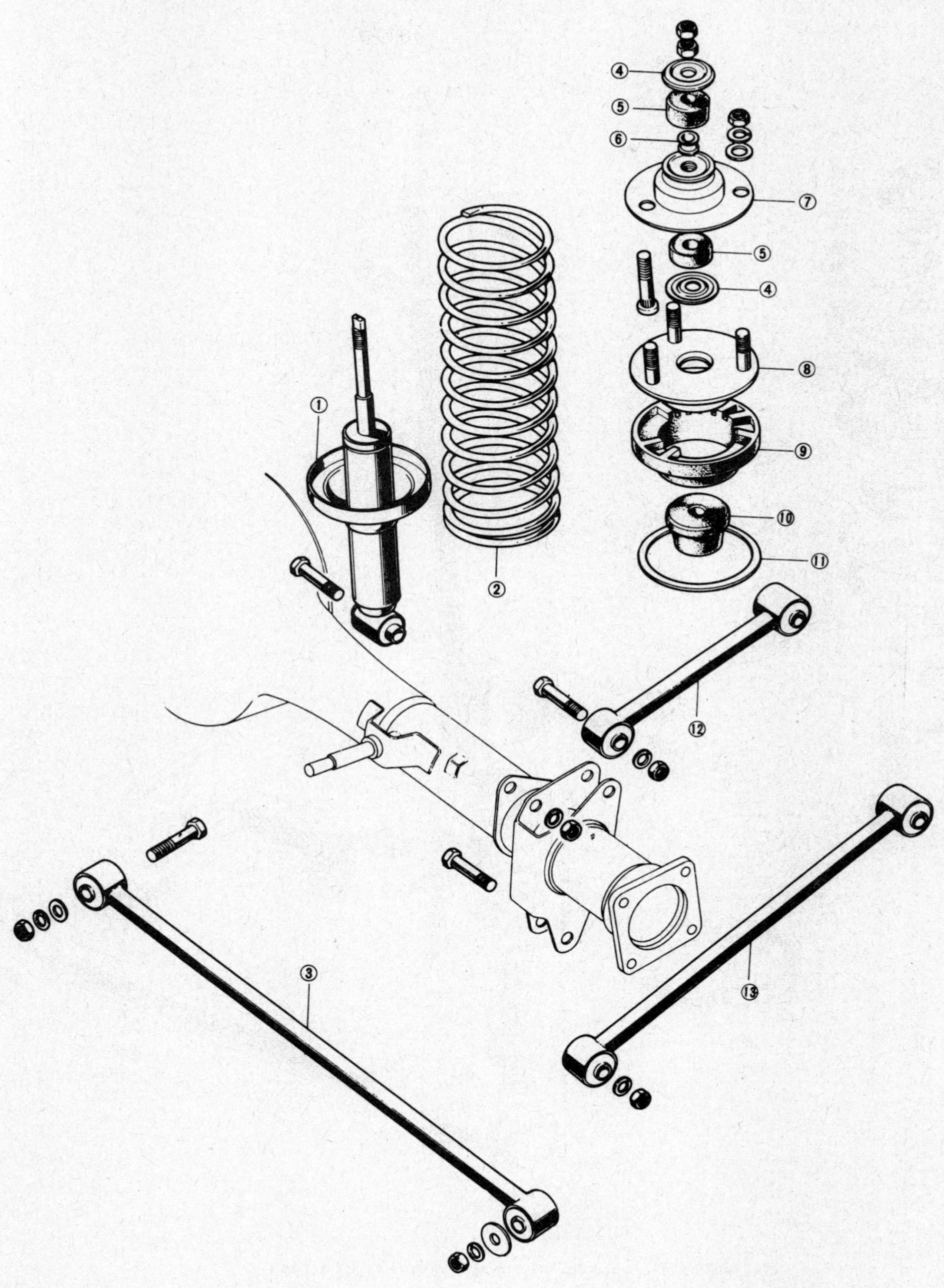

RX-2 rear suspension assembly (© Toyo Kogyo Co., Ltd.)

1. Shock absorber
2. Coil spring
3. Lateral rod
4. Retainer
5. Rubber insulator
6. Gromet
7. Set plate
8. Spring seat (upper)
9. Rubber seat
10. Bound stopper
11. Adjusting plate
12. Upper link
13. Lower link

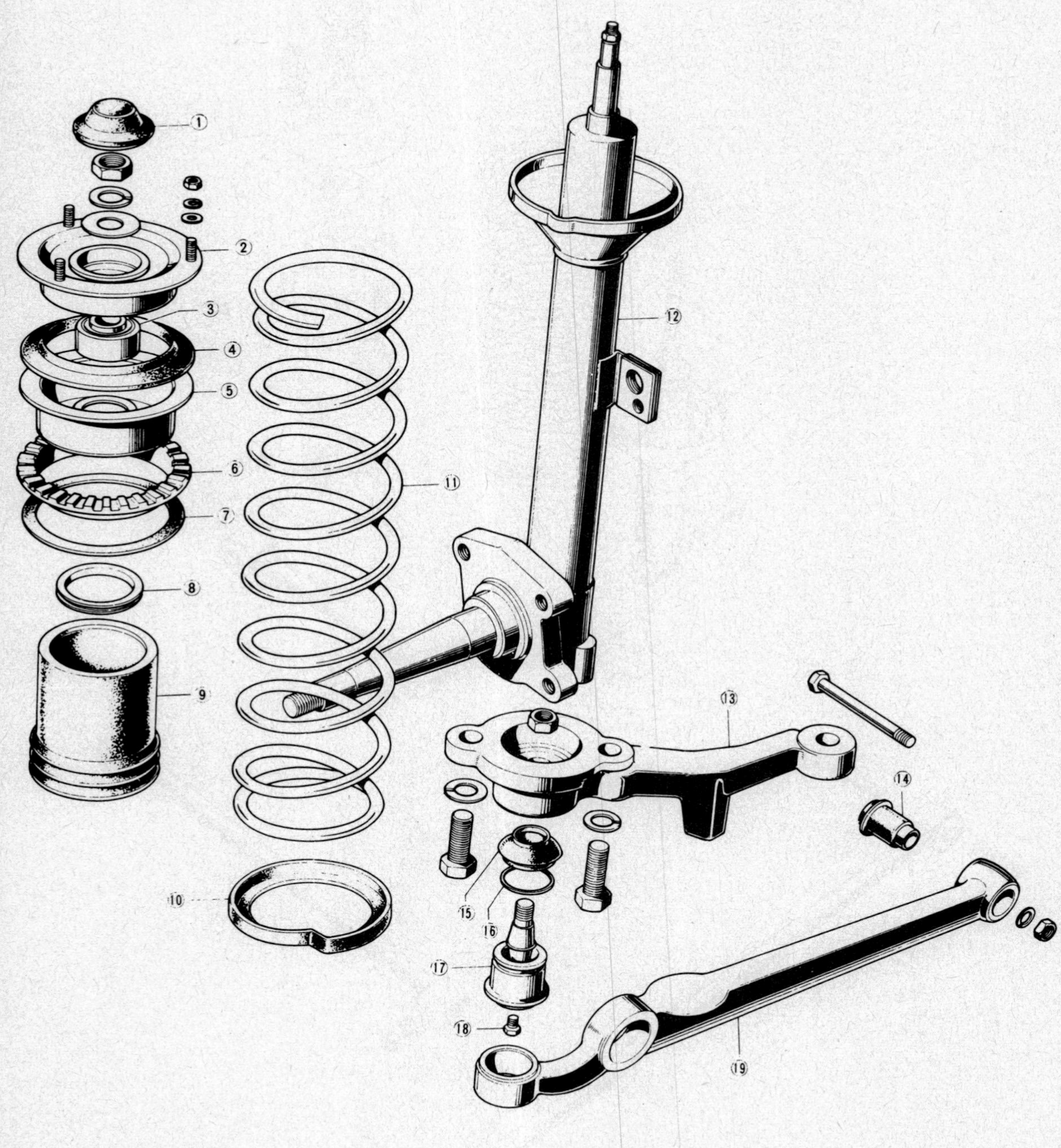

McPherson strut front suspension (© Toyo Kogyo Co., Ltd.)

1. Cap
2. Rubber mounting
3. Bearing
4. Seal
5. Spring seat (upper)
6. Rubber seat (upper)
7. Adjusting plate
8. Dust seal ring
9. Boot
10. Rubber seat (lower)
11. Coil springs
12. Front shock absorber assembly
13. Knuckle arm
14. Rubber bushing
15. Dust seal
16. Setring
17. Ball joint
18. Plug
19. Arm

Removing the control arm
(© Toyo Kogyo Co., Ltd.)

7. Remove the control arm and steering knuckle arm as an assembly.

8. Install the assembly in a vise. Remove its cotter pin and unfasten the ball joint nut; then separate the knuckle arm from the control arm with a puller.

Installation of the control arm is performed in the reverse order of its removal. Torque the control arm-to-crossmember nut and bolt to 34 ft lbs on the RX-3, and 51–65 ft lbs on the RX-2.

Ball Joints

Inspection

1. Perform steps 1–5 of the control arm removal procedure.

2. Check the ball joint dust boot condition. Replace the boot if it will allow water or dirt to enter the ball joint assembly.

3. Check the amount of pressure required to turn the ball stud, by hooking a pull scale into the tie-rod hole in the knuckle arm. Pull the spring scale until the arm just begins to turn; this should require 13–24 ft lbs.

4. Replace the ball joint, as detailed in the following section, if it is not up to specification.

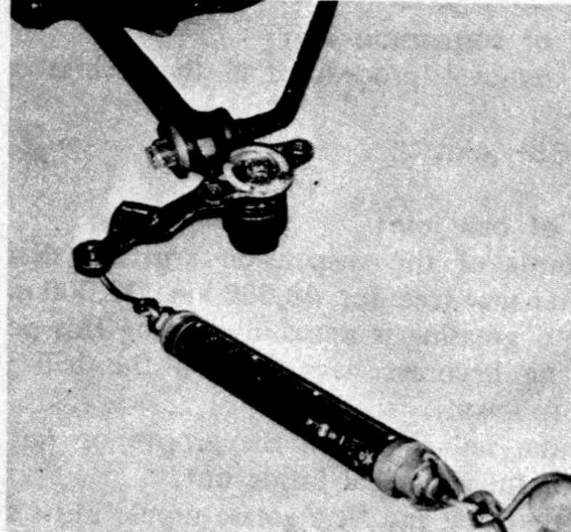
Checking the ball stud rotational torque with a spring scale
(© Toyo Kogyo Co., Ltd.)

Removal and Installation

1. Complete the control arm removal procedure, as detailed above.

2. Remove the set-ring and the dust boot from the ball joint.

3. Clean the ball joint and control arm assembly.

4. Press the ball joint out of the control arm.

Installation of a new ball joint is performed in the following order:

1. Clean the ball joint mounting bore and coat it with kerosene.

2. Press the ball joint into the control arm.

NOTE: *If the pressure required to press the new ball joint into place is less than 3,300 lbs, the bore is worn and the control arm must be replaced.*

3. Attach the ball joint/control arm assembly to the steering knuckle. Tighten the nut to 60 ft lbs and insert the cotter pin.

4. Install the control arm in the car, as detailed above.

Front End Alignment

Caster and Camber

Caster and camber are preset by the manufacturer. They require adjustment only if the suspension and steering linkage components are damaged. In this case, adjustment is accomplished by replacing the damaged part.

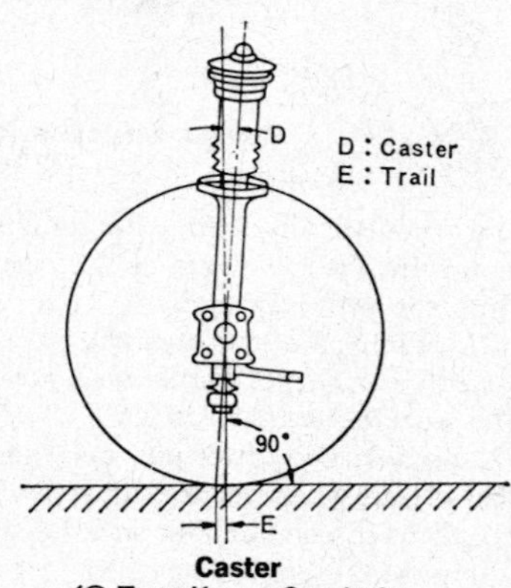

Caster
(© Toyo Kogyo Co., Ltd.)

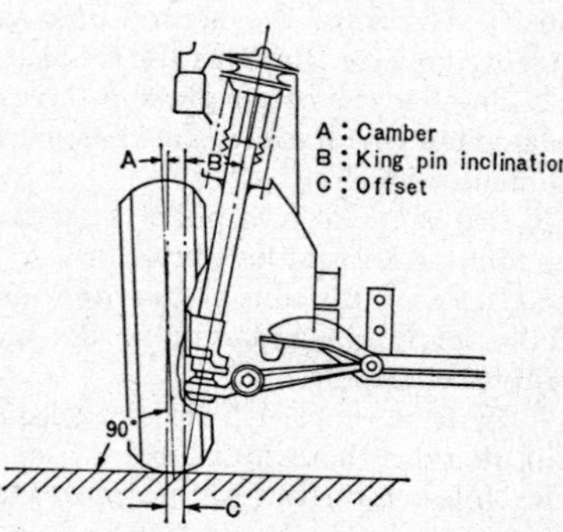

Camber
(© Toyo Kogyo Co., Ltd.)

To check caster and camber, use an alignment checking machine by following its manufacturer's instructions. Compare the results obtained against the specifications in the "Wheel Alignment Specifications" chart.

Toe-In Adjustment

Toe-in is the difference in the distance between the front wheels, as measured at both the front and the rear of the front tire.

1. Raise the front of the car so that its front wheels are just clear of the ground.

2. Use a scribing block to mark a line at the center of each tire tread while rotating the wheels by hand.

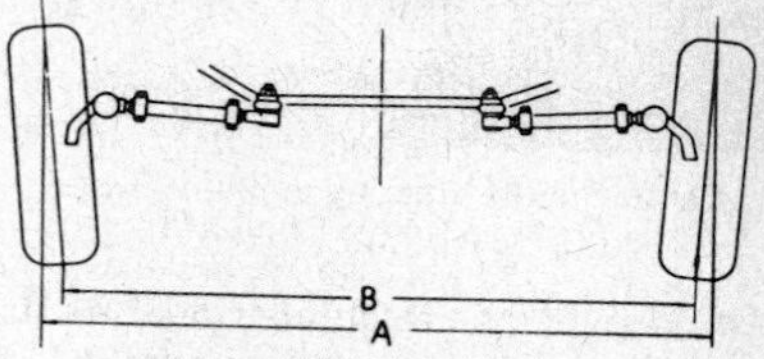

Measuring toe-in
(© Toyo Kogyo Co., Ltd.)

3. Measure the distance between the marked lines at both their front and rear.

NOTE: *Take both measurements at equal distances from the ground.*

4. The toe-in is equal to the difference between the front and rear measurements. This difference should equal 0–0.24 in. for both models.

5. To adjust the toe-in, loosen the tie-rod locknuts and turn both tie-rods an equal amount, until the proper specification is obtained.

STEERING

Steering Wheel

Removal and Installation

1. Remove the screws which secure the crash pad/horn button assembly to the steering wheel. Remove the assembly.

2. Punch matchmarks on the steering wheel and steering shaft.

3. Unfasten the steering wheel hub nut and remove the steering wheel with a puller.

CAUTION: *The steering column is collapsible; pounding on it or applying excessive pressure to it may cause it to deform, in which case, the entire column will have to be replaced.*

Installation of the steering wheel is performed in the reverse order of removal. Tighten the steering wheel nut to 25 ft lbs.

Combination (Turn Signal) Switch Replacement

1. Disconnect the ground cable from the battery.

2. Remove the steering wheel, as detailed above.

3. Unfasten the left-hand column shroud securing screws and remove the shroud.

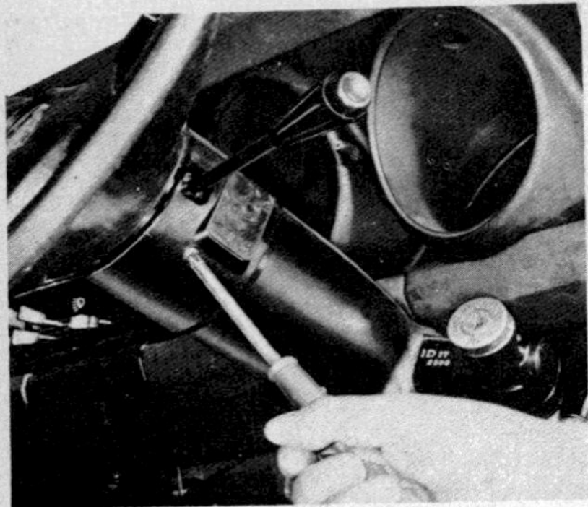

Removing the steering column shroud (© Toyo Kogyo Co., Ltd.)

4. Remove the retaining ring from the combination (turn signal) switch.

5. Withdraw the switch over the steering column, after unfastening its multiconnector from underneath the dash panel.

Installation is performed in the reverse order of removal.

Ignition Lock/Switch Assembly

Removal and Installation

1. Disconnect the ground cable from the battery.
2. Remove the light switch knob.
3. Remove the left and right steering column shrouds by unfastening their retaining screws.
4. Disconnect the multiconnector from the switch assembly.
5. Use a file or a hacksaw to make slots in the switch securing bolts. Remove the bolts with a screwdriver.

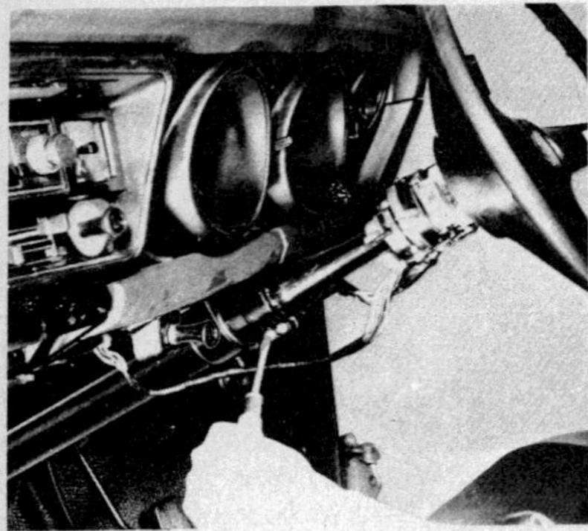

Cut slots in the switch securing bolts and remove them with a screwdriver (© Toyo Kogyo Co., Ltd.)

6. Withdraw the switch assembly.

To install the switch, follow the removal procedure in reverse order. After tightening the switch securing bolts, break their heads off, in order to make the switch difficult for a thief to remove.

Steering Linkage

Removal and Installation

1. Turn the steering wheel so that the front wheels are pointing straight ahead. Then raise the front end of the car and support it with jackstands.

CAUTION: *Be sure that the car is securely supported. Remember, you will be working underneath it.*

2. Remove the cotter pins and the castellated nuts which secure the ends of the tie-rods to the center link and the steering knuckle.
3. Use a ball joint puller to disconnect the tie-rods from the center link and steering knuckle. Remove the tie-rods.
4. Remove the cotter pin and the castellated nut which secure the idler arm to the center link.
5. Use the ball joint puller to detach the idler arm from the center link.
6. Unfasten the nuts at the other end of the idler arm and remove the arm from its bracket.
7. Perform steps 4–5 for the pitman arm. Remove the center link.
8. Unfasten the nut which secures the pitman arm to the sector shaft and use a puller to separate them.

Installation is performed in the reverse order of removal. Align the marks on the pitman arm and the sector shaft to ensure proper steering linkage alignment. Torque the removed nuts and bolts to the specifications given at the end of this section. Check and adjust the toe-in, as outlined above.

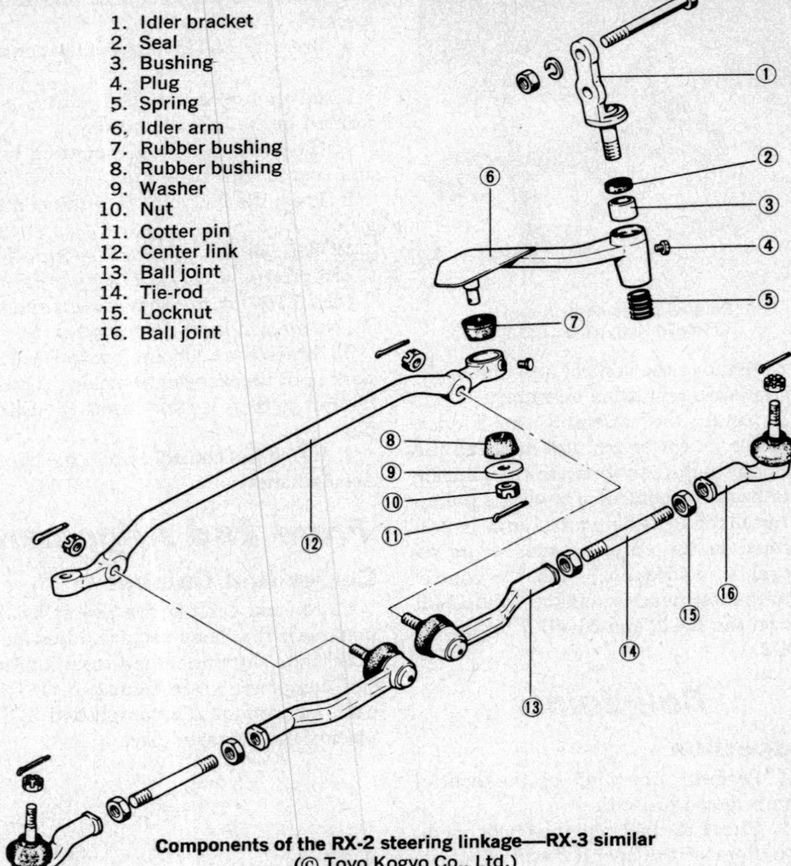

Components of the RX-2 steering linkage—RX-3 similar (© Toyo Kogyo Co., Ltd.)

Steering Linkage Torque Specifications

Part	Torque (ft lbs)
Pitman arm	94-123
Idler arm spindle	36-58
Idler arm bracket	33-41
Ball studs—tie-rods/center link	18-25
Tie-rod locknuts	51-58
Idler arm-to-center link	22-25

BRAKE SYSTEMS

Adjustments

Front Discs

The front disc brakes are self-adjusting by design. As the brake pads and discs wear, fluid pressure compensates for the amount of wear. Because this action causes the fluid level to go down, the level should be checked and replenished as often as is necessary.

Rear Brake Drums

1. Block the front wheels, raise the car, and support it with jackstands.

CAUTION: *Be sure that the car is securely supported. Remember, you will be working underneath it.*

2. Release the parking brake completely.

3. Remove the adjusting hole plugs from the backing plate.

4. Engage the adjuster with a screwdriver. Turn the adjuster in the direction of the arrow stamped on the backing plate until the brake shoes are fully expanded, i.e., the wheel will not turn.

5. Pump the brake pedal several times to be sure that the brake shoe contacts the drum evenly.

NOTE: *If the wheel turns after you remove your foot from the brake pedal, continue turning the adjuster until the wheel will no longer rotate.*

6. Back off on the adjuster about five notches. The wheel should rotate freely, without dragging. If it does not, turn the adjuster an additional notch.

7. Pump the brake pedal several times and check wheel rotation again.

8. Fit the plug into the adjusting hole and then repeat the adjusting procedure for the three other rear brake shoes.

Brake Pedal

1. Detach the wiring from the brake light switch terminals.

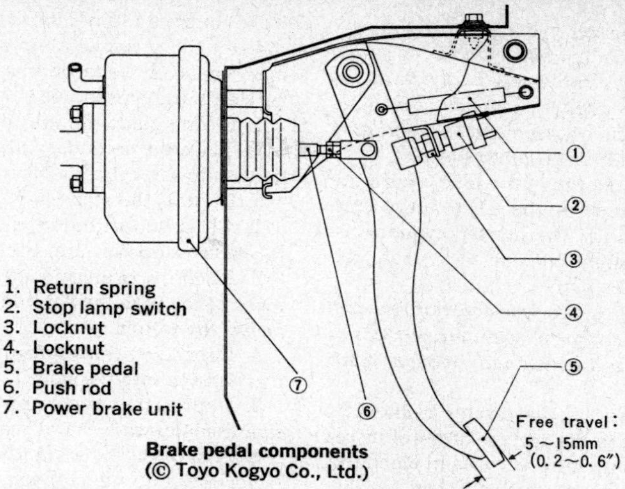

1. Return spring
2. Stop lamp switch
3. Locknut
4. Locknut
5. Brake pedal
6. Push rod
7. Power brake unit

Brake pedal components
(© Toyo Kogyo Co., Ltd.)

2. Loosen the locknut on the switch.

3. Turn the switch until the distance between the pedal and the floor is 7.3 in.

4. Tighten the locknut on switch.

5. Loosen the locknut located on the push rod.

6. Rotate the pushrod, until a pedal free travel of 0.2–0.6 in. is obtained.

7. Tighten the pushrod locknut.

HYDRAULIC SYSTEM

Master Cylinder

Removal and Installation

1. Detach all of the hydraulic lines

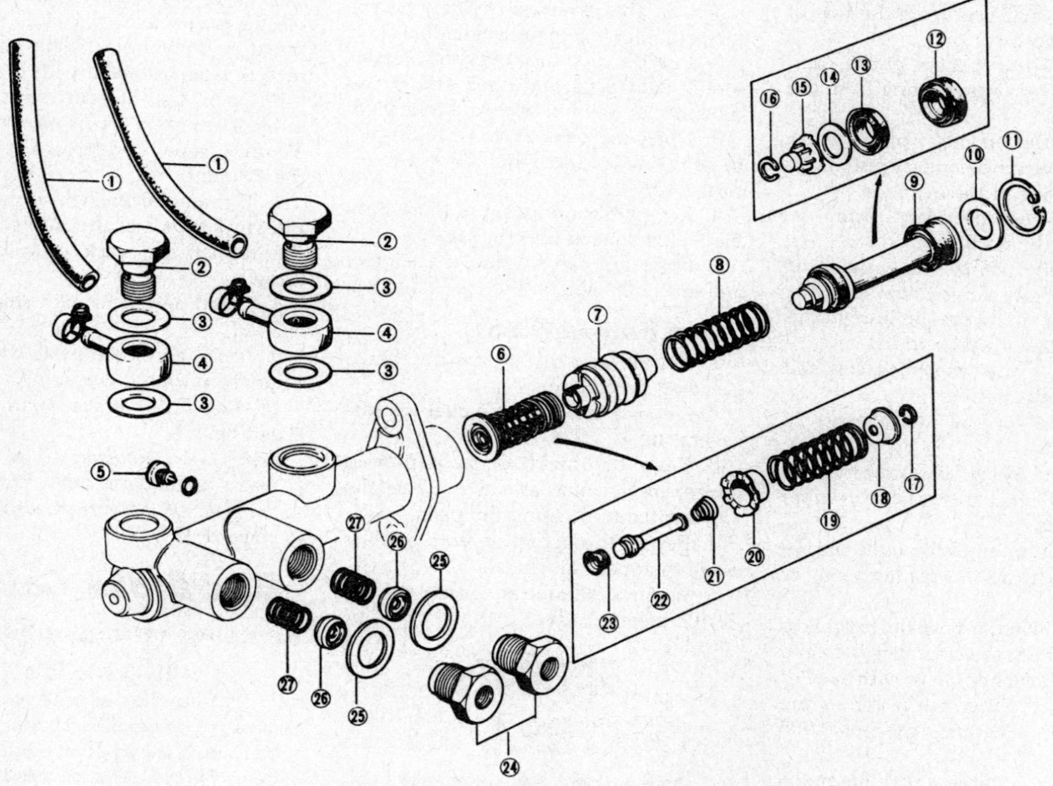

Components of the master cylinder
(© Toyo Kogyo Co., Ltd.)

1. Hydraulic line
2. Connector bolt
3. Washer
4. Union
5. Stop bolt
6. Valve and spring
7. Secondary piston
8. Return spring
9. Primary piston
10. Washer
11. Retaining ring
12. Secondary cup
13. Primary cup
14. Spacer
15. Spring seat
16. Stop ring
17. Stop ring
18. Spring seat
19. Return spring
20. Valve case
21. Spring
22. Valve rod
23. Valve
24. Outlet fitting
25. Washer
26. Check valve
27. Spring

from the master cylinder.

NOTE: *On models which have a fluid reservoir located separately from the master cylinder, remove the lines which run between the two and plug the lines to prevent leakage.*

2. Unfasten the nuts which secure the master cylinder to the power brake unit.
3. Withdraw the master cylinder assembly straight out and away from the power brake unit.

CAUTION: *Be careful not to spill brake fluid on the painted surfaces of the car, as it makes and excellent paint remover.*

Installation of the master cylinder is performed in the reverse order of its removal. Fill up its reservoir and bleed the brake system, as detailed below.

Overhaul

1. Clean the outside of the master cylinder and drain any brake fluid remaining in it.
2. Remove the fluid reservoir from the top of the cylinder, if so equipped.
3. Remove the boot from the rear of the cylinder.
4. Depress the primary piston and withdraw the snap-ring from the rear of the cylinder bore.
5. Withdraw the washers, piston, cups, spacer, seat, and return spring from the cylinder bore.
6. Depress the secondary piston with a rod and remove the secondary piston bolt from the outside of the cylinder.
7. Remove the secondary piston assembly from the bore.

NOTE: *Blow out the assembly with compressed air, if necessary.*

8. Unfasten the hydraulic line fittings from the master cylinder outlet.
9. Withdraw the check valves and springs from the outlets.
10. Wash all of the components in clean brake fluid.

CAUTION: *Never use kerosene or gasoline to clean the master cylinder components.*

Examine all of the piston cups and replace any that are worn, damaged, or swollen.

Check the cylinder bore for roughness or scoring. Check the clearance between the piston and cylinder bore with a feeler gauge. Replace either the piston or the cylinder if the clearance exceeds 0.006 in.

Blow the dirt and the remaining brake fluid out of the cylinder with compressed air.

Master cylinder assembly is performed in the following order:

1. Dip all of the components, except for the cylinder, in clean brake fluid.
2. Install the check valve assemblies in the master cylinder outlets.
3. Insert the return spring and the valve components into the cylinder bore.
4. Fit the secondary cup and the primary cup over the secondary piston. The flat side of the cups should face the piston.
5. Fit the guide pin into the stop-bolt hole. Place the secondary piston components into the cylinder bore.
6. Depress the secondary piston as far as it will go and withdraw the guide pin. Screw the stop bolt into the hole.
7. Place the primary cups on the primary piston with the flat side of the cups facing the piston.
8. Insert the return spring and the primary piston into the bore.
9. Depress the primary piston, then install the stop-washer and snap-ring.

NOTE: *Be sure that the piston cups do not cover up the compensating ports.*

10. Install the dust boot on the end of the cylinder.

Bleeding

Disc Brakes (Front)

NOTE: *Keep the master cylinder reservoir at least ¾ full during the bleeding operation.*

1. Remove the cap from the bleeder screw on that wheel cylinder which is furthest from the master cylinder.
2. Install a vinyl tube over the bleeder screw. Submerge the other end of the tube in a jar half-full of clean brake fluid.
3. Open the bleeder valve. Fully depress the brake pedal and allow it to return slowly.
4. Repeat this operation until air bubbles cease flowing into the jar.
5. Close the valve, remove the tube, and install the cap on the bleeder valve.

Drum Brakes (Rear)

1. Repeat steps 1–2 of the disc brake bleeding procedure.
2. Depress the brake pedal rapidly several times.
3. Keep the brake pedal depressed and open the bleeder valve. Close the valve without releasing the pedal.
4. Repeat this operation until bubbles cease to appear in the jar.
5. Remove the tube and install the cap on the bleeder valve.

FRONT DISC BRAKES

Disc Brake Pads

Removal and Installation

All Models

1. Raise the front of the car and support it with jackstands.

CAUTION: *Be sure that the car is securely supported.*

2. Remove the hub cap and the wheel.

3a. On RX-3 models, unfasten the retainer and withdraw the locating pins.

3b. On RX-2 models, remove the scuring clips, the stop plates, the caliper assembly, and the anti-rattle spring.

CAUTION: *Do not disconnect the hydraulic line from the caliper when only pad removal is being performed.*

4. Remove the return spring and withdraw the pad.

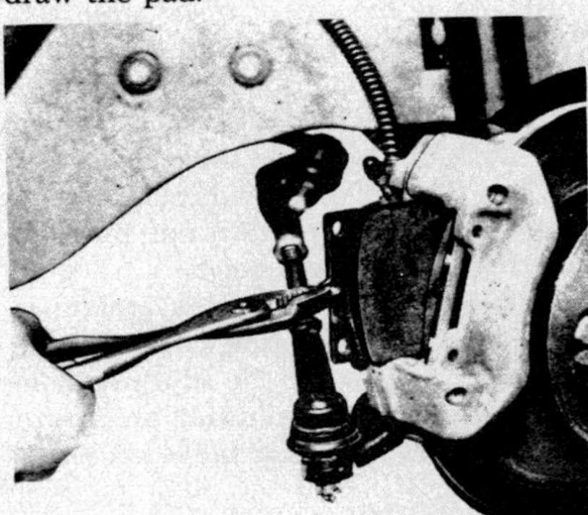

Removing the brake pad on RX-3 models (© Toyo Kogyo Co., Ltd.)

5. Take the rubber cap off of the bleeder screw and fit a vinyl tube over the screw. Submerge the other end of the tube in a jar half-filled with brake fluid.
6. Open the bleeder screw. Use a screwdriver with its blade wrapped in electrical tape, to depress the piston in the cylinder.
7. Tighten the bleeder screw. Remove the vinyl tube and the screwdriver. Fit the rubber cap back on the bleeder screw.
8. Install new pads with shims in the caliper.
9. Install all of the parts which were removed during disassembly.
10. Bleed the brake system, as outlined below.

CAUTION: *Replace all of the front brake pads at the same time. Do not use pads of different materials for replacement.*

Disc Brake Calipers

Removal and Installation

RX-3 Models

1. Perform the disc brake pad removal procedure, as detailed above.
2. Detach the hydraulic line from the caliper. Plug the end of the line to prevent the entrance of dirt or the loss of fluid.
3. Unfasten the bolts which secure the caliper to the support and remove the caliper.

Follow the caliper removal procedure in reverse order for installation. Bleed the hydraulic system after completing installation.

RX-2 Models

Perform steps 1–3 of the disc brake pad removal procedure, as outlined above. In addition, disconnect and plug the hydraulic line at the caliper.

Caliper installation is performed in the reverse order of removal. Bleed the hydraulic system after completing installation.

Overhaul

All Models

1. Thoroughly clean the outside of the caliper.
2. Remove the dust boot retainer and the boot.
3. Place a piece of hardwood in front of the piston.
4. Gradually apply compressed air through the hydraulic line fitting and withdraw the piston.

NOTE: *If the piston is frozen and cannot be removed from the caliper, tap lightly around it while air pressure is being applied.*

5. Withdraw the piston and seal from the caliper bore.
6. If necessary, remove the bleeder screw.
7. Wash all of the parts in clean brake fluid. Dry them off with compressed air.

CAUTION: *Do not wash the parts in kerosene or gasoline.*

Examine the caliper bore and piston for scores, scratches, or rust. Replace either part as required. Minor scratches, rust, or scoring can be corrected by dressing with crocus cloth.

NOTE: *Discard the old piston seal and dust boot. Replace them with new ones.*

Apply clean brake fluid to the piston and bore. Assemble the caliper in the reverse order of disassembly. Install it on the car and bleed the brake system.

Brake Disc

Removal and Installation

1. Remove the caliper assembly, as detailed in the appropriate section above.

NOTE: *It is unnecessary to completely remove the caliper from the car. Leave the hydraulic line wired to it and wire the caliper to the underbody of the car so that it is out of the way.*

2. Check disc runout, as detailed below, before removing it from the car.
3. Withdraw the cotter pin, nut-lock, adjusting nut, and washer from the spindle.
4. Take the thrust washer and outer bearing off of the hub.
5. Pull the brake disc/wheel hub assembly off of the spindle.
6. Unbolt and separate the brake disc from the hub after matchmarking them for proper installation.

CAUTION: *Do not drive the disc off of the hub.*

Installation of the disc and hub is performed in the reverse order of removal. Adjust the bearing preload, as detailed below.

Inspection

1. With a dial indicator, measure the lateral runout of the disc while the disc is still installed on the spindle.

NOTE: *Be sure that the wheel bearings are adjusted properly before checking runout.*

2. If runout exceeds more than 0.003 in., replace or resurface the disc.
3. Inspect the surface of the disc for scores or pits and resurface it, if necessary.
4. If the disc is resurfaced, its thickness should be no less than the following:

RX-3—0.394 in.
RX-2—0.433 in.

Wheel Bearings

Removal and Installation

1. Remove the brake disc/hub assembly and separate them, as detailed above.
2. Drive the seal out and then remove the inner bearing from the hub.
3. Drive the outer bearing races out with a brass drift applied to the slots provided for this purpose.
4. Clean the inner and outer bearings, completely.

CAUTION: *Do not use compressed air to spin the bearings dry.*

5. Clean the spindle and the hub cavity with solvent.

Installation is performed in the reverse order of removal. However, the following points should be noted:

1. Repack the bearings and the hub cavity with lithium grease.

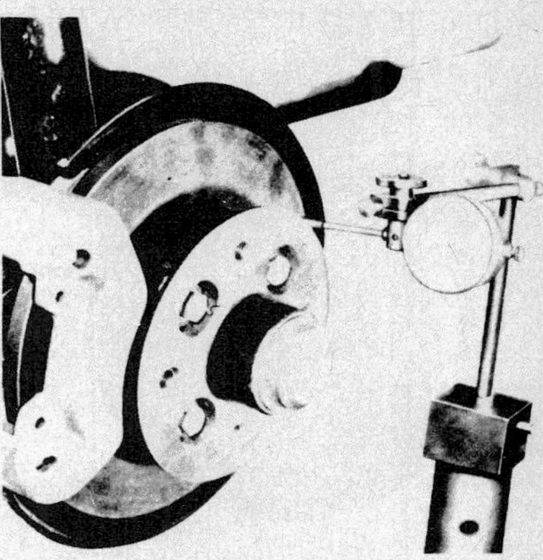

Checking the front brake disc runout (© Toyo Kogyo Co., Ltd.)

CAUTION: *Do not over pack them.*

2. Install the wheel hub-to-brake disc bolts to 36 ft lbs torque.
3. Adjust the bearing preload, as described below.

Preload Adjustment

NOTE: *This operation is performed with the wheel, grease cap, nut lock, and cotter pin removed.*

1. To seat the bearings, rotate the hub/disc assembly while tightening the adjusting nut.
2. Back off on the adjusting nut about 1/6 of a turn.
3. Hook a spring scale in one of the bolt holes on the hub.
4. Pull the spring scale squarely, until the hub just begins to rotate. The scale reading should be 0.9–2.2 lbs. Tighten the adjusting nut until the proper spring scale reading is obtained.
5. Place the castellated nut lock over the adjusting nut. Align one of the slots on the nut-lock with the hole in the spindle and fit the cotter pin into place.

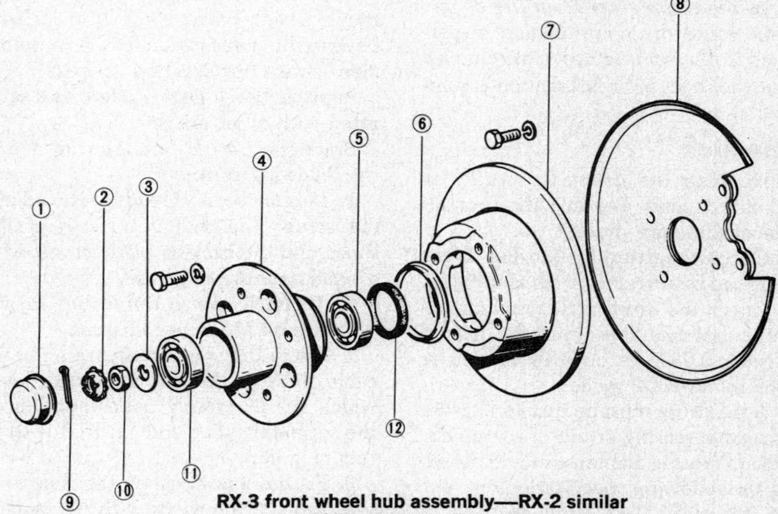

RX-3 front wheel hub assembly—RX-2 similar (© Toyo Kogyo Co., Ltd.)

1. Grease cap
2. Nut lock
3. Flat washer
4. Hub
5. Inner bearing
6. Dust ring
7. Brake disc
8. Backing plate
9. Cotter pin
10. Adjusting nut
11. Outer bearing
12. Grease seal

Checking front wheel bearing preload
(© Toyo Kogyo Co., Ltd.)

Shoe return spring removal
(© Toyo Kogyo Co., Ltd.)

REAR DRUM BRAKES

Brake Drums

Removal and Installation

1. Remove the wheel disc and loosen the lug nuts.
2. Raise the rear of the car and support it with jackstands.

CAUTION: *Be sure that the car is securely supported. Remember, you will be working underneath it.*

3. Remove the lug nuts and the rear wheel.
4. Be sure that the packing brake is fully released.
5. Remove the bolts which secure the drum to the rear axle shaft flange.
6. Pull the brake drum off of the flange.

NOTE: *If the drum will not come off easily, screw the drum securing bolts into the two tapped holes in the drum. Tighten the bolts evenly in order to force the drum away from the flange.*

Rear brake drum installation is performed in the reverse order of removal. Adjust the shoes after installation is completed.

Inspection

1. Examine the drum for cracks or overheating spots. Replace the drum if either of these are present.
2. Check the drum for scoring. Light scoring can be corrected with sandpaper.
3. Check the drum with a dial indicator for out-of-roundness; turn the drum if it exceeds 0.0393 in. on RX-3 models or 0.0059 in. on RX-2 models.
4. If the drum must be turned because of excessive scoring or out-of-roundness, the drum's inside diameter should not exceed the following specifications:

RX-3 models—7.8347 inches
RX-2 models—7.9135 inches

NOTE: *If one drum is turned, the opposite drum should also be turned to the same size.*

Brake Shoes

Removal and Installation

1. Perform the brake drum removal procedure, as detailed above.
2. Remove the return springs from the upper side of the shoe with a brake spring removal tool.
3. Remove the return springs from the lower side of the shoes in the same manner, as in step 2.
4. Remove the shoe retaining spring:
   a. On RX-3 models, by removing the retaining pin with pliers.
   b. On RX-2 models, by compressing the retaining spring while turning the pin 90°.
5. Withdraw the primary shoes and the parking brake link.
6. Disengage the parking brake lever from the secondary shoes by unfastening its retaining clip.
7. Remove the secondary shoe.

CAUTION: *Be careful not to get oil or grease on the lining material.*

Inspect the linings; replace them if they are badly burned or if worn 0.039 in. beyond the specification for a new lining. (See "Brake Specification" chart)

Replace the linings if they are saturated with oil or grease.

Brake shoe installation is performed in the following manner:

1. Lubricate the threads of the adjusting screw, the sliding surfaces of the shoes, and the backing plate flanges with a small quantity of grease.

CAUTION: *Be careful not to get grease on the lining surfaces.*

2. Install the eye of the parking brake cable through the parking brake lever which has previously been installed on the secondary shoe and secured with its retaining clip.
3. Fit the link between the shoes.
4. Engage the shoes with the slots in the anchor (adjusting screw) and the wheel cylinder.
5. Fasten the shoes to the backing plate with the retaining springs and pins.
6. Install the shoe return springs with the tool used during removal.
7. Install the drums and adjust the shoes, as detailed elsewhere.

NOTE: *If a slight amount of grease has gotten on the shoes during installation, it may be removed by light sanding.*

Wheel Cylinders

Removal and Installation

1. Remove the brake drums and shoes, as detailed above.
2. Disconnect the hydraulic line from the wheel cylinder by unfastening the nut on the rear of the backing plate.
3. Plug the line to prevent dirt from entering the system or brake fluid from leaking out.
4. Unfasten the nuts which secure the wheel cylinder to the backing plate and remove the cylinder.

Installation of the wheel cylinder is performed in the reverse order of removal. Bleed the hydraulic system and adjust the brake shoes after installation is completed.

Overhaul

1. Remove the boots at either end of the wheel cylinder.
2. Withdraw the pistons, piston cups, push rods, and return spring.
3. Wash all of the components in clean brake fluid.

CAUTION: *Never use kerosene or gasoline to clean wheel cylinder components.*

Check the cylinder bore and piston for roughness or scoring. Use a wheel cylinder hone, if necessary.

Measure the clearance between the cylinder and the piston with a feeler gauge. If the clearance is greater than 0.006 in., replace either the piston or the cylinder.

Examine the piston cups for wear, softening, or swelling; replace them if necessary.

Assembly is performed as follows:

1. Apply clean brake fluid to the cylin-

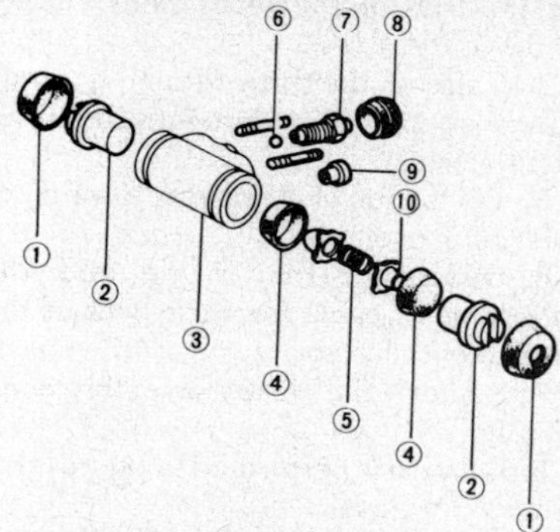

Rear wheel cylinder components
(© Toyo Kogyo Co., Ltd.)

1. Boot
2. Piston
3. Cylinder body
4. Piston cup
5. Return spring
6. Steel ball
7. Bleeder screw
8. Bleeder screw cap
9. Hydraulic line seat
10. Push rod

der bore, pistons, and cups.

2. Fit the steel ball into the bleed hole and install the screw, if removed.

3. Insert the parts into the cylinder bore in the reverse order of removal.

NOTE: *Install the piston cups so that their flat side is facing outward.*

4. Fit the boots over both ends of the cylinder.

PARKING BRAKE

Adjustment

1. Adjust the rear brake shoes, as outlined above.

2. Adjust the front cable with the nut located at the rear of the parking brake. The handle should require 3–7 notches for RX-3 models, and 2–3 notches for RX-2 models to apply the parking brake.

3. Operate the parking brake several times; check to see that the rear wheels do not drag when it is fully released.

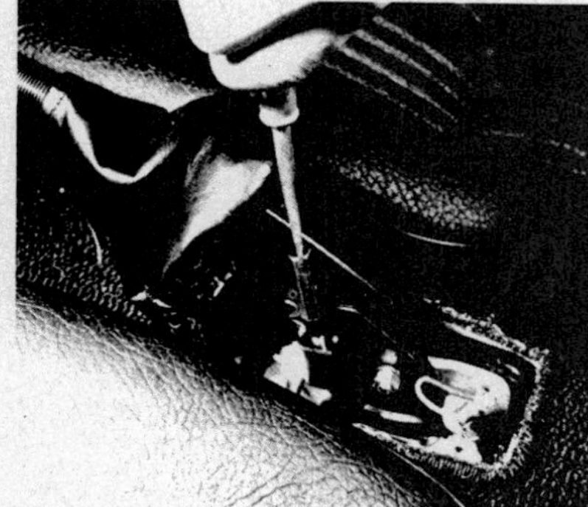

Adjusting the parking brake
(© Toyo Kogyo Co., Ltd.)

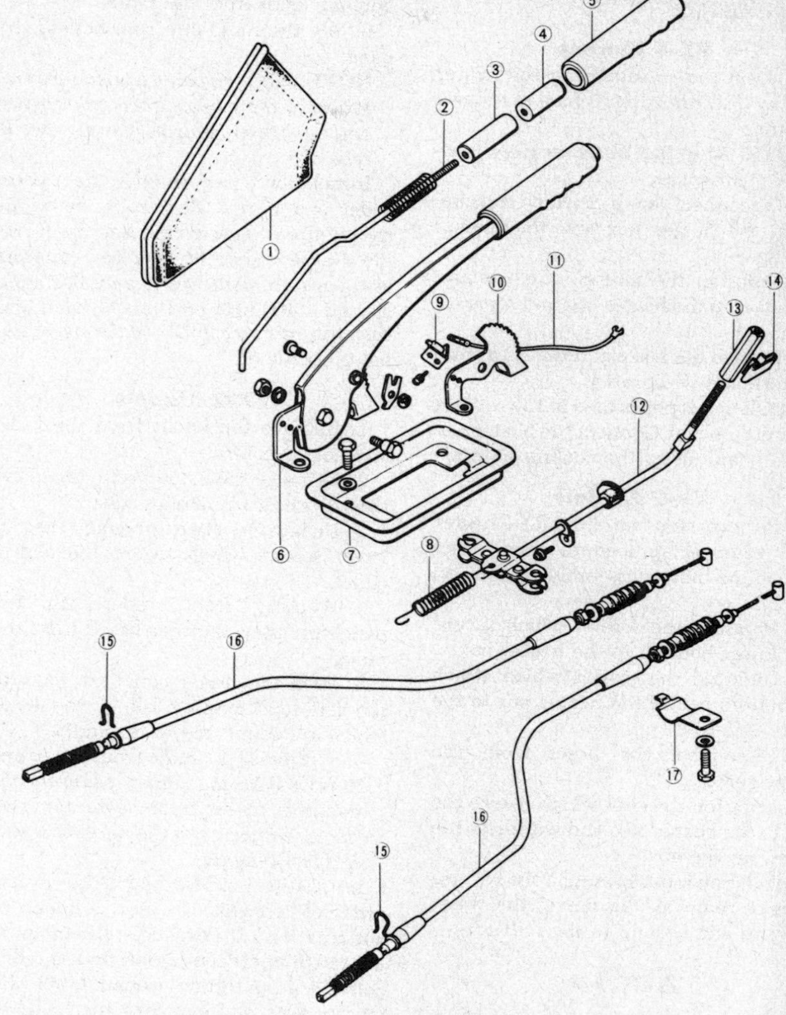

RX-3 parking brake components—RX-2 similar
(© Toyo Kogyo Co., Ltd.)

1. Boot
2. Release rod
3. Spacer
4. Button
5. Cap
6. Parking brake lever
7. Plate
8. Return spring
9. Parking lamp switch
10. Sector
11. Parking lamp switch wire
12. Front cable
13. Adjusting nut
14. Clip
15. Clip
16. Rear cable
17. Cable clip

CHASSIS ELECTRICAL

Heater Blower

Removal and Installation

NOTE: *On models equipped with dealer installed air conditioning, blower access may be slightly more difficult.*

All Models

The heater blower is located underneath of the dash panel, inside of the passenger compartment. On RX-3 models the blower is located next to the heater box and connected to it by a duct. On RX-2 models, it is attached directly to the heater box and therefore no connecting duct is used.

Remove the heater blower/motor assembly in the following order:

1. Disconnect the blower motor multi-connector.

2. Unfasten the three screws which fasten the blower/motor assembly to the housing.

3. Withdraw the assembly.

Installation is performed in the reverse order of removal.

Heater Core

Removal and Installation

NOTE: *On models equipped with dealer installed air conditioning,* *heater core access may be slightly more difficult.*

RX-3 Models

1. Drain the coolant from the heater core, by disconnecting its hose at the water pump.

NOTE: *Save the water in clean container for reuse.*

2. Disconnect the duct which runs between the heater box and the blower housing.
3. Unfasten the screws which secure the halves of the heater box and separate them.
4. Detach the hoses and the clips from the core and withdraw it.

Installation is performed in the reverse order of removal. Connect the heater water hose and fill up the cooling system.

RX-2 Models

1. Perform step one of the RX-3 heater core removal procedure and then remove the blower assembly, as detailed above.
2. Unfasten the screws which secure the blower housing to the heater box.
3. Unfasten the screws which attach the bottom half of the heater box to the top.
4. Disconnect the hoses from the heater core.
5. Unfasten the clips which secure the core to the heater box, and withdraw the core from the box.

Installation is performed in the reverse order of removal. Reconnect the water hose and add coolant to the radiator.

Radio

Removal and Installation

CAUTION: *Never operate the radio with the speaker disconnected or with the speaker leads shorted together. Damage to the output transistors will result. Always replace the speaker with one of the same impedance (ohms) as was removed.*

RX-3 Models

1. Unfasten the two upper and the two lower screws which secure the center panel to the dashboard.
2. Remove the ashtray.
3. Remove the knobs from both the radio and the heater controls.
4. Tip the center panel forward.
5. Disconnect the power, speaker, and antenna leads from the radio.
6. Slip the radio out from behind the panel.

NOTE: *With the panel tipped forward, access to the gauges, their pilot lights, and the heater controls may also be obtained.*

Installation is performed in the reverse order of removal. Remember to adjust the trimmer screw (condenser) on the radio if a new antenna or a new antenna lead has been used. Select a weak station around 1,400 kHz on the AM band and turn the trimmer until the strongest signal is obtained.

RX-2 Models

1. Remove the knobs from the radio and heater controls.
2. Remove the knob from the hand throttle and its retaining collar.
3. Unfasten the two upper and the two lower screws which secure the center panel.
4. Working from underneath the panel, unfasten the rear brace from the radio.
5. Pivot the center panel sideways (to the left) and remove all of the leads which are connected to the radio.
6. Withdraw the radio from the panel.

NOTE: *With the center panel turned sideways, access to the heater controls, clock, switches, and the pilot light may also be obtained.*

Installation is performed in the reverse order of removal. If a new antenna or antenna lead is installed, remember to adjust trimmer (condenser) on the radio. Select a weak station around 1,400 kHz on the AM band and turn the trimmer screw until the strongest signal is obtained.

Instrument Cluster

Removal and Installation

RX-3 Models

1. Disconnect the ground cable from the negative (−) battery terminal.
2. Pull the knob off of the steering column-mounted headlight switch. Remove the screws fastening the halves of the steering column shroud and separate the halves.
3. Open the left-hand (driver's side) door, to gain access to the screw located on the side of the instrument cluster. Remove the screw.
4. Unfasten the three retaining screws which are located underneath the insrument cluster.
5. Tip the top of the cluster toward the steering wheel.
6. Disconnect the wiring and the speedometer cable from the back of the instrument cluster.
7. Remove the cluster assembly completely.

Installation is performed in the reverse order of removal.

RX-2 Models

1. Disconnect the ground cable from the negative terminal (−) of the battery.
2. Unfasten the screws which hold the halves of the steering column shroud together and pull off the headlight switch knob. Separate the halves of the shroud.
3. Working from underneath the instrument cluster, disconnect the speedometer cable.
4. Unfasten the two upper and the two lower screws which secure the instrument cluster.
5. Tip the top of the cluster toward the steering wheel.
6. Disconnect each component by unfastening its electrical connector.
7. Lift the cluster away from the dash panel.

Installation is performed in the reverse order of removal.

Fuses

Fuse Box Location

The fuses boxes on both the RX-3 and the RX-2 models are located underneath the right-hand (passenger's) side of the dash.

On the RX-3 models, the box is located just above the lower parcel shelf, and uses a back-hinged cover.

On RX-2 models, the box is located underneath the leading edge of the dash and is equipped with a sliding cover.

Both of the covers have the location, amperage, and the circuit protected by each individual fuse, stamped on them.

The cable running from the positive side of the battery is equipped with a fusible link on both models.

CAUTION: *Do not replace the fusible link with a regular wire if it burns out. If it must be replaced, use the proper Mazda part.*

MERCEDES-BENZ

Index

INTRODUCTION

This section is intended to serve as a guide to the tune-up and repair of all 1968–73 Mercedes-Benz cars, except the 600.

Some illustrations in this book have small numbers which identify various components shown in the illustration. Not all of the components shown in a given illustration are relevant. For this reason, only those components that are relative to the procedure are identified.

Development

The history of Mercedes-Benz automobiles is steeped in a tradition of engineering excellence and performance and Mercedes-Benz cars have no peer for quality, craftsmanship, durability, and engineering safety.

While the name Mercedes-Benz is familiar to most Americans, few are aware that the founders of Mercedes-Benz share credit for inventing the automobile. Two mechanical engineers, Gottlieb Daimler and Karl Benz, brought their revolutionary machines to life in 1886, 22 years before Henry Ford's Model T.

In addition to pioneering such technical advances as fuel injected engines and the first diesel powered car, Mercedes-Benz has played a prominent role in racing. No other car manufacturer can match Mercedes' record of over 4000 competition victories: a long string stretching back to history's first auto race from Paris to Rouen in 1894. In the pursuit of land speed records, Mercedes-Benz has been equally successful. The legendary Blitzen Benz was the world's fastest automobile from 1911 to 1924; and a 1938 Mercedes-Benz record of 271.5 mph still stands as the highest speed ever recorded on a highway.

In 1968, Mercedes-Benz introduced the "New Generation" of Mercedes-Benz cars. These new sedans, the 220D/8, 220/8, 230/8 and the 250/8, share the same new body style and represent a nine year advance in automotive design (the preceding models were first introduced in 1959). The new bodies featured a sharply sloping hood with decreased frontal area, to insure a smoother flow of air over the car, greater glass area and a squared off rear deck. These new features combine to give the cars a look that is clean and simple, and at the same time, classic. The smaller sedans were followed by the 280 series and the 300 series, all the way up to the 300SEL 6.3 in 1970. All bodies share the same basic concept of clean and timeless styling. Such features as independent suspension and four wheel disc brakes are notable safety features of Mercedes-Benz cars.

The 350 SLC (450SLC in 1973) marks an important change in the coupe design philosophy of Mercedes-Benz. Previous coupe designs were derived from the contemporary sedan models but the 350 and 450SLC models are based on the 350SL coupe/roadster, resulting in a vehicle which combines sports car performance with luxurious looks and comfort. The 350 and 450SLC replace the coupe and convertible models which were built until 1971. The most recent version was the 280SE 3.5 which had been introduced in 1961 as the 220SE coupe and convertible. The introduction of the 350 and 450SL and SLC models marks the end of four and five seater convertible production by Mercedes-Benz.

Coverage

Mercedes-Benz cars are covered herein from the introduction of the 1968 Phase II models through all 1973 models, except the 600. It is recognized that few if any 600 owners are interested in doing their own work and that a Mercedes-Benz dealer can provide the best service for this model. In general, however, the engine and transmission are identical to the ones used in the 300SEL 6.3 with minor modifications. For a complete list of cars covered, consult the Engine/Vehicle Identification Chart.

MODEL IDENTIFICATION

Since the Mercedes-Benz design is in continuous development and evolution, the newest developments are put into production as soon as they become available. Therefore, while it is true that arbitrary cut-off chassis numbers are chosen each year to designate the onset of the "new" model year, it does not necessarily mean that a 1968 car is radically different from a 1969 model. Especially, it does not mean that an "old" 1968 is now obsolete.

All this is great for the owner, but it presents a problem when ordering parts. The solution is found in the comprehensive Daimler-Benz identification plates, found in various places, but usually under the hood and on the door posts. Consulting the illustration pertaining to your model (220/8, 250C etc.), find the locations of the chassis number plate, type plate and engine plate. With these numbers, plus the engine and other subsystem serial numbers, one is armed with all the information he needs to identify his car.

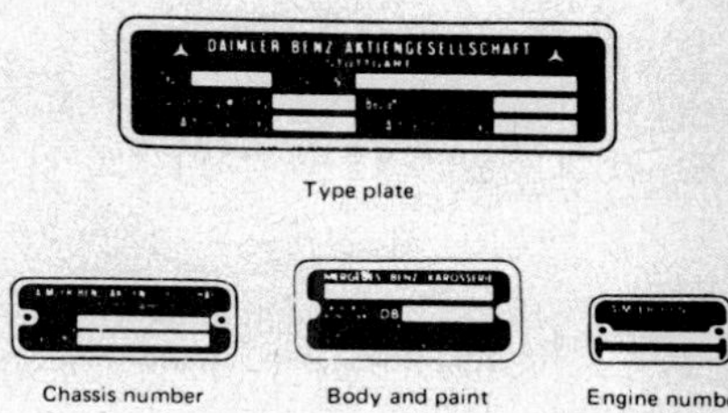

Identification plates

1. Type plate
2. Chassis number plate
3. Body and paint number plate
4. Engine number plate

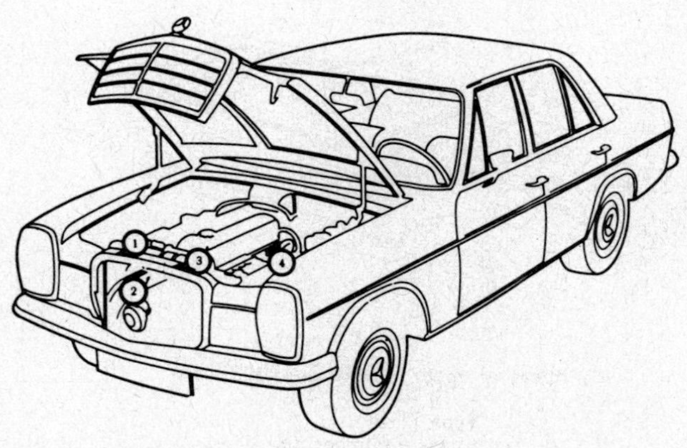

Identification plate locations—sedans (early /8 series).

Identification plate locations—sedans (1971).

1. Certification plate
2. Chassis number
3. Body number and paintwork number
4. Engine number

Identification plate locations—280SL (1971).

1. Certification plate
2. Chassis number
3. Body number and Paintwork number
4. Engine number

Identification plate locations—sedans (1972-73).

1. Vehicle name plate with safety certification
2. Chassis number (left front door past and front stiffening)
3. Body number and paintwork number
4. Engine number on engine-block, rear
5. Emission control information

Identification plate locations—350SL, 450SL and 450SLC (1972-73).

1. Vehicle name plate with safety certification
2. Chassis number (left front door post and front stiffening)
3. Body number and paintwork number
4. Engine number on rear of engine block
5. Emission control information

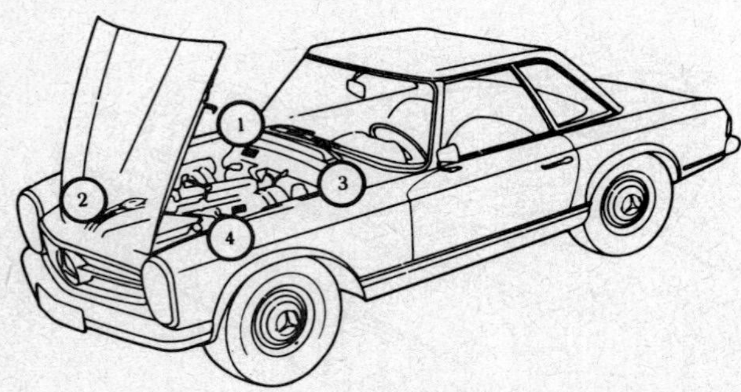

Identification plate locations—280SL (to 1970).

1. Type plate
2. Chassis number (stamped on frame)
3. Body and paint number plate
4. Engine number plate

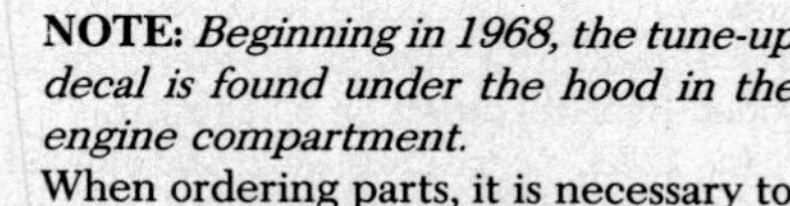

NOTE: *Beginning in 1968, the tune-up decal is found under the hood in the engine compartment.*

When ordering parts, it is necessary to give the complete chassis number, plus the numbers of the concerned area. For example, when ordering pistons or a distributor cap you must give the engine number as well as chassis number. If you are ordering front suspension components, give the front axle number.

The model/engine identification chart gives a picture of the model/engine/-chassis combinations that have been imported to the United States since 1968. Some models were in production much earlier and are included because of popularity.

All models that are now out of

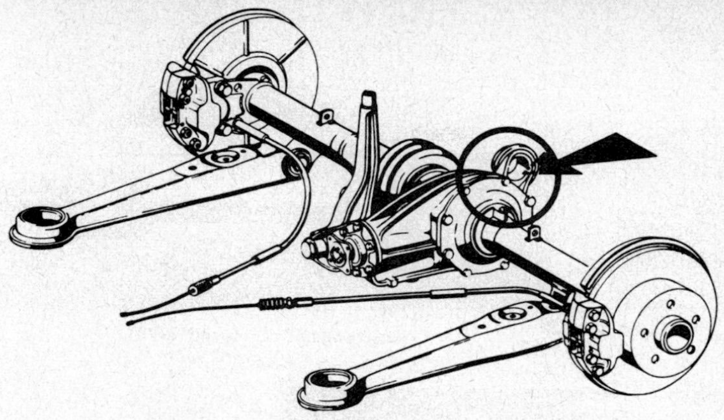

Rear suspension identification number location.

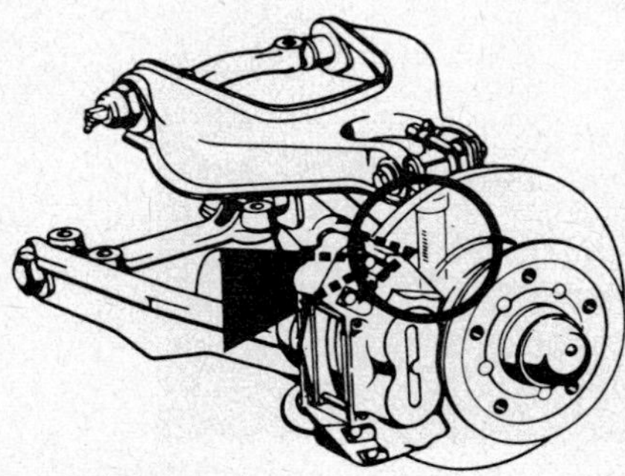

Front suspension identification number location.

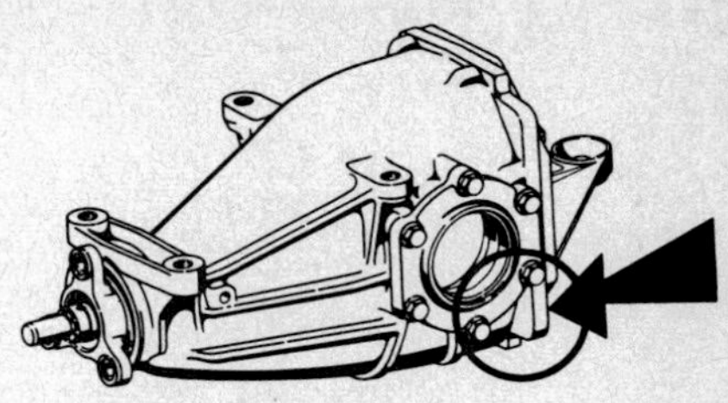

Differential identification number location

production, are shown along with their starting and ending chassis numbers. This is especially useful where the same designation has been carried over to a different vehicle.

An example of this is the 230. While the 230 is now out of production and the 230/8 has taken its place, the two have the same designation on the trunk lid. (The "/8" does not appear.) The chassis number immediately indicates whether you have a "new" 230, although the more modern styling should be a clue.

It should be noted that the center number (10 or 12) in the chassis number indicates the type transmission. A "10" indicates that the car is equipped with a manual transmission, while a "12" indicates an automatic. These numbers, of course, will vary with individual transmission options for individual cars.

MODEL IDENTIFICATION

220/8 and 220D/8

250/8 sedan

230/B sedan

250C (coupe)

280S/8, 280SE/8, 280SEL/8, 300SEL/8

280 sedan (introduced 1973)

280SL/8

300SEL/8 6.3 (same as 300SEL/8 except for rear 6.3 badge).

350SL (introduced 1972)

450SLC (introduced 1973)

ENGINE/VEHICLE IDENTIFICATION

Model	Chassis Type	Engine Model	Engine Type	Engine Description (Fuel, Fuel Delivery, Valve Gear, Displacement)	Production Years
220D/8	115.110	OM615	615.912	Diesel (2197 cc)	1968-73
220/8	115.110	M115	115.920	Gas, Carb., OHC, (2197 cc)	1968-73
230/8	114.015	M180	180.954	Gas, Carb., OHC, (2292 cc)	1968-69
250/8	114.010	M114	114.920	Gas, Carb., OHC, (2496 cc)	1968-70
250/8	114.011	M130V	130.923	Gas, Carb., OHC, (2778 cc)	1971-72
250C	114.023	M130V	130.923	Gas, Carb., OHC, (2778 cc)	1970-72
280S/8	108.016	M130V	130.920	Gas, Carb., OHC, (2778 cc)	1968-71
(sedan)		M130E	130.980	Gas, Fuel Inj., OHC, (2778 cc)	1968-72
280SE/8	111.024 (cvt)	M130E	130.980	Gas, Fuel Inj., OHC, (2778 cc)	1968-72
(cpe/cvt)	111.025 (cpe)	M130E	130.980	Gas, Fuel Inj., OHC, (2778 cc)	1968-72
280SEL/8	108.019	M130E	130.980	Gas, Fuel Inj., OHC, (2778 cc)	1968-71
280SE 3.5	111.024 (cvt)	M116	116.980	Gas, Fuel Inj., OHC, (3499 cc)	1971
(cpe/cvt)	111.025 (cpe)	M116	116.980	Gas, Fuel Inj., OHC, (3499 cc)	1971
280SE 4.5	108.067	M117	117.984	Gas, Fuel Inj., OHC, (4520 cc)	1972-73
280SEL 4.5	108.068	M117	117.984	Gas, Fuel Inj., OHC, (4520 cc)	1972-73
280	114.060	M110	110.921	Gas, Carb., DOHC, (2746 cc)	1973
280C	114.073	M110	110.921	Gas, Carb., DOHC, (2746 cc)	1973
280SL/8	113.044	M130E	130.983	Gas, Fuel Inj., OHC, (2778 cc)	1968-71
(roadster)					
300SEL/8	109.016	M130E	130.981	Gas, Fuel Inj., OHC, (2778 cc)	1968-70
300SEL 3.5	109.056	M116	116.981	Gas, Fuel Inj., OHC, (3499 cc)	1970-71
300SEL 4.5	109.057	M117	117.981	Gas, Fuel Inj., OHC, (4520 cc)	1972-73
300SEL 6.3	109.018	M100	100.981	Gas, Fuel Inj., OHC, (6332 cc)	1970-71
350SL	107.044	M117	117.982	Gas, Fuel Inj., OHC, (4520 cc)	1972
450SL	107.044	M117	117.982	Gas, Fuel Inj., OHC, (4520 cc)	1973
450SLC	107.044	M117	117.982	Gas, Fuel Inj., OHC, (4520 cc)	1973

cvt convertible
cpe coupe

OUT OF PRODUCTION MODELS

Model	Starting Serial No.	Ending Serial No.	Model	Starting Serial No.	Ending Serial No.
190c	110.010—10—000001	110.010—10—130557	250SE/C (coupe)	111.021—10—082991	111.021—10—089205
200	110.010—10—130558	110.010—10—200761			
190Dc	110.110—10—000001	110.110—10—225647	250SE/C (convt.)	111.023—10—082991	111.023—10—089205
200D	110.110—10—225648	110.110—10—387263			
230	110.011—10—000001	110.011—10—040258	300SE (sedan)	112.014—10—000001	112.014—10—005137
220b	111.010—10—000001	111.010—10—069692			
220Sb	111.012—10—000001	111.012—10—161126	300SE (long wb)	112.015—10—000001	112.015—10—005137
230S	111.010—10—069693	111.010—10—110798			
250S	108.012—10—000001	③	300SE (coupe)①	112.021—10—000001	112.021—10—005137
220SEb	111.014—10—000001	111.014—10—082687			
250SE	108.014—10—000001	108.014—10—055181	300SE (convt.)①	112.023—10—000001	112.023—10—005137
230SL	113.042—10—000001	113.042—10—019832			
250SL	113.043—10—000001	113.043—10—005196	300SEb	108.015—10—000001	108.015—10—002737
220SEb/C (coupe)	111.021—10—000001	111.021—10—082990	300SEL	109.015—10—000001	109.015—10—002369
			300SE (coupe)②	112.021—10—005138	112.021—10—009875
220SEb/C (convt.)	111.023—10—000001	111.023—10—082990	300SE (convt.)②	112.023—10—005138	112.023—10—009875

① To August, 1965.
② From August, 1965.
③ Still in production, but not imported after 1968.
wb wheelbase
convt. convertible

Transmission Identification

Since 1968, Mercedes-Benz cars for the U.S. market have been equipped with either a 4-speed manual transmission or with a fully automatic 3 or 4-speed unit. Manual transmissions are one of two types, either a side cover or a top cover unit.

Serial numbers on the side cover unit are located on a pad on the side cover of the transmission (left side).

Serial numbers on the top cover unit are stamped on the inside of the bellhousing at the bottom. The transmission must be removed to view these.

Automatic transmission serial numbers are located on a metal plate which is attached to the driver's side of the transmission.

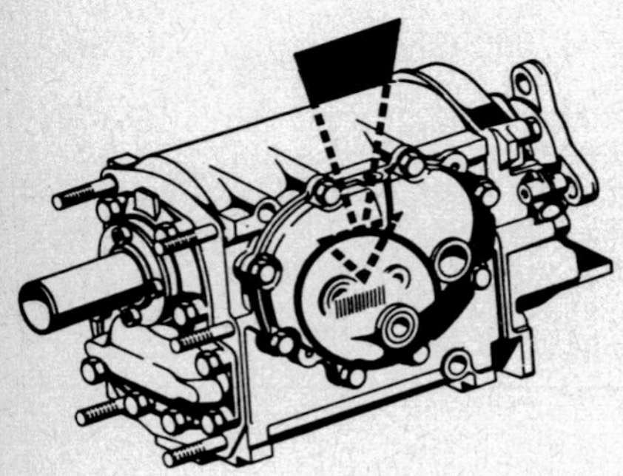

Transmission identification number—side cover transmission.

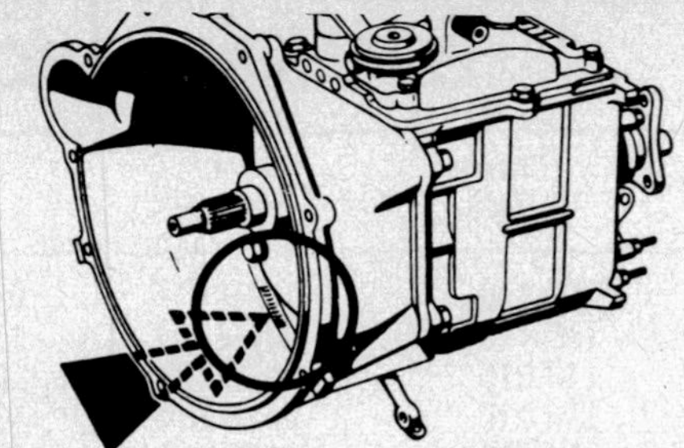

Transmission identification number—top cover transmission.

AUTOMATIC TRANSMISSION APPLICATIONS

Transmission Type	Model Application
K4A 025 2 planetary gearset	280S/8, 280SE/8, 280SEL/8, 300SEL/8 (all to May, 1969) and 280S1/8
K4C 025 3 planetary gearset	220D/8, 220/8, 230/8, 250/8, 250C, 280S/8 (from May, 1969), 280SE/8 (from May, 1969), 280SEL/8 from May, 1969), 300SEL/8 (from May, 1969), 280, 280C
K4B 050 3 planetary gearset	300SEL 6.3
K4A 040 3 planetary gearset (flat oil pan)	280SE 3.5, 300SEL 3.5
K4A 040 3 planetary gearset (deep oil pan)	280SE 3.5, 300SEL 3.5
W3A 040 torque converter	280SE 4.5, 280SEL 4.5, 300SEL 4.5, 350SL, 450SL, 450SLC

TRANSMISSION APPLICATIONS

Model	Vehicle Type	TRANSMISSION Manual	TRANSMISSION Automatic
220D/8	115.110	G76/18	K4C 025
220/8	115.110	G76/18	K4C 025
230/8	114.015	G76/18	K4C 025
250/8	114.010	G76/18	K4C 025
250/8 (1971-72)	114.011	G76/18	K4C 025
250C	114.023	G76/18	K4C 025
280S/8	108.016	G72①	K4C 025②
280SE/8 (sedan)	108.018	G72①	K4C 025②
280SE/8 (cpe-cvt)	111.024-111.025	—	K4C 025②
280SEL/8	108.019	—	K4C 025②
280SE 3.5 (cpe-cvt)	111.024-111.025	—	K4A 040
280SE 4.5	108.067	—	W34 040
280SEL 4.5	108.068	—	W34 040
280	114.060	—	K4C 025
280C	114.073	—	K4C 025
280SL/8	113.044	G72	K4A 025
300SEL/8	109.016	G72①	K4C 025②
300SEL 3.5	109.056	G76/27A	K4A 040
300SEL 4.5	109.057	—	W3A 040
300SEL 6.3	109.018	—	W3A 040
350SL	107.044	—	K4B 040
450SL	107.044	—	W3A 040
450SLC	107.044	—	W3A 040

① Until May, 1969; from May, 1969, transmission G76/27 is installed
② From May, 1969; until May, 1969, transmission K4A 025 is installed
— Not applicable

AUTOMATIC TRANSMISSION FLUIDS

Transmission Type	Model Application	Type A Suffix A	Type B Dexron B
K4A 025 2 planetary gearset	280S/8, 280SE/8, 280SEL/8, 300SEL/8 (all to May, 1969) and 280S1/8	X	
K4C 025 3 planetary gearset	220D/8, 220/8, 230/8, 250/8, 250C, 280S/8 (from May, 1969), 280SE/8 (from May, 1969), 280SEL/8 (from May, 1969), 300SEL/8 from May, 1969), 280, 280C		X
K4B 050 3 planetary gearset	300SEL 6.3		X
K4A 040 3 planetary gearset (flat oil pan)	280SE 3.5, 300SEL 3.5		X
K4A 040 3 planetary gearset (deep oil pan)	280SE 3.5, 300SEL 3.5		X
W3A 040 torque converter	280SE 4.5, 280SEL 4.5, 300SEL 4.5, 350SL, 450SL, 450SLC		X

Recommended Diesel Engine Oils

While there are many high quality diesel engine oils, the following are particularly suitable for the 220D/8. These provide the greatest engine life and best serivce.

Castrol (HD)
Esso Engine Oil (HD)
Valvoline Super HP HDM
Veedol High Detergency HD900

Approved Special Lubricants

Rear Axle

The following lubricants are recommended for standard type rear axles which are NOT equipped with limited slip differentials. In the event that the specified lubricants are not available use a good quality SAE 90 hypoid gear lubricant. All of the following lubricants are SAE 90 hypoid lubricants.

Amalie Multi-purpose Lube
Caltex Multi-purpose Thuban EP 90
Castrol Hypoid B
Castrol Hypoid ELH
Chevron (RPM) Universal Gear Lubricant
Esso Gear Oil GX 90
Gulf Multi-purpose Gear Lubricant
Kendall Three Star Gear Lube
Pennzoil Gear Lubricant 4080 MP/4090 MP
Shell HD 90
Sinclair Extra Duty Gear Lube
Sunoco Multi-purpose Gear Lubricant (MPGL5)
Texaco Multigear Lube EP
Valvoline Gear Lubricant 18MD
Veedol Multigear HD

For vehicles equipped with LIMITED SLIP DIFFERENTIALS, Mercedes-Benz recommends that Veedol Multigen Limited Slip Special lubricant be used for the best results.

Automatic Level Control

Mercedes-Benz recommends that only the following fluids be used in the automatic level control unit:

Aral 1010
Gasolin 1010
Shell Tellus T 17
Shell Aero Fluid 4

Recommended Chassis Greases

Caltex Marfak 1
Esso
Mobilgrease No. 4
Texaco Marfak 1
Valvoline
Veedol VC

MAINTENANCE INTERVALS

All figures in Thousands of Miles

Model	Automatic Trans. Fluid: Check & Refill	Automatic Trans. Fluid: Change	Engine Oil: Check* & Refill	Engine Oil: ** Change	Oil Filter Change	Oil Bath Air Filter Change	Paper Ele. Air Filter: Clean	Paper Ele. Air Filter: Change	Inj. Pump Oil Check	Chassis Lube	Man. Trans. Oil Change	Power Steer. Fluid Refill	Man. Steer. Oil Refill	Rear Axle Oil Change	Level Control Fluid Refill	Brake Fluid Refill	Wheel Bearings Repack
1968-71																	
220D/8	3	12	3	3	3	3	—	—	12	3	12	3	12	12	3	3	12
220/8	3	30	3	6	6	—	16	80	—	3①	12	3	12	12	3	3	12
230/8	3	12	3	6	6	—	16	80	—	3①	12	3	12	12	3	3	12
250/8	3	12	3	6	6	—	16	80	—	3①	12	3	12	12	3	3	12
250/C	3	12	3	6	6	—	16	80	—	3①	12	3	12	12	3	3	12
280S/8	3	12	3	6	6	—	16	80	—	3①	12	3	12	12	3	3	12
280SE/8 280SEL/8	3	12	3	6	6	—	16	80	—	3①	12	3	12	12	3	3	12
280SE 3.5	3	12	3	6	6	—	16	80	—	3①	12	3	12	12	3	3	12
280SL/8	3	12	3	6	6	—	16	80	—	3①	12	3	12	12	3	3	12
300SEL/8	3	12	3	6	6	—	16	80	—	3①	12	3	—	12	3	3	12
300SFL 3.5	3	12	3	6	6	—	16	80	—	3①	12	3	—	12	3	3	12
300SEL 6.3	3	12	3	6	6	—	16	80	—	3①	12	3	—	12	3	3	12②
1972-73																	
220D/8	10	30	*	3	3	10	—	—	10	5	10	10	10	10	10	10	30
220/8	10	30	*	5	5	—	10③	30③	—	5	10	10	10	10	10	10	30
250C, 250/8	10	30	*	5	5	—	10③	30③	—	5	10	10	10	10	10	10	30
280SE/8 280SEL/8	10	30	*	5	5	—	10③	30③	10	5	10	10	10	10	—	10	30
280SE 4.5 280SEL 4.5	10	30	*	5	5	—	10③	30③	10	5	10	10	10	10	—	10	30
280, 280C	10	30	*	5	5	—	10③	30③	—	5	10	10	10	10	—	10	30
300SEL 4.5	10	30	*	5	5	—	10③	30③	—	5	10	10	10	10	—	10	30
350SL	10	30	*	5	5	—	10③	30③	10	5	10	10	10	10	10	10	30
450SL, SLC	10	30	*	5	5	—	10③	30③	10	5	10	10	10	10	10	10	30

① Every 1500 miles or every month under adverse conditions; at least every 2 months regardless.

* For safety, the engine oil should be checked at each fuel stop.

** Cut the prescribed interval in half, if the car is operated in extremely dusty areas or is driven at sustained high speeds. Change transmission oil filter every 30,000 miles.

— Not applicable

② Also every spring and fall

③ In severe dust conditions, renew every 10,000 milies
Check oil level every 3,000 miles, overhaul air filter more frequently in severe dust conditions.

GENERAL GASOLINE ENGINE SPECIFICATIONS

Year Model	Engine Model	Engine Displacement (cc)	Carburetor Type	Horsepower @ rpm (SAE)	Torque @ rpm (ft lbs) (SAE)	Bore x Stroke (mm)	Compression Ratio	Firing Order
220/8	M115	2197	2 Solex 36/40 PDSI	116 @ 5200	142 @ 3000	87.00 x 92.40	9.0:1	1 3 4 2
230/8	M180	2292	2 Zenith 35/40 INAT	135 @ 5600	145 @ 3800	81.75 x 72.80	9.0:1	1 5 3 6 2 4
250/8	M114	2496	2 Zenith 35/40 INAT	146 @ 5600	161 @ 3800	82.00 x 78.80	9.0:1	1 5 3 6 2 4
250/8, 250C	M130V	2778	2 Zenith 35/40 INAT	157 @ 5400	181 @ 3100	86.50 x 78.80	9.0:1	1 5 3 6 2 4
280S/8 280SEL/8	M130E	2778	Fuel Injection	180 @ 5750	193 @ 4500	86.50 x 78.80	9.5:1	1 5 3 6 2 4
280SE 3.5 300SEL 3.5	M116	3499	Fuel Injection	230 @ 5000	232 @ 4200	92.00 x 65.8	9.5:1	1 5 4 8 6 3 7 2
280SE 4.5 280SEL 4.5 300SEL 4.5	M117	4520	Fuel Injection	230 @ 5000	232 @ 4200	92.00 x 85.00	8.0:1	1 5 4 8 6 3 7 2
280, 280C (1973)	M110	2746	Solex 4-bbl	N.A.①	N.A.①	86.00 x 78.80	8.0:1	1 5 3 6 2 4
280SL/8	M130E	2778	Fuel Injection	180 @ 5750	193 @ 4500	86.50 x 78.80	9.5:1	1 5 3 6 2 4
300SEL/8	M130E	2778	Fuel Injection	180 @ 5750	193 @ 4500	86.50 x 78.80	9.5:1	1 5 3 6 2 4
300SEL 6.3	M100	6332	Fuel Injection	300 @ 4100	434 @ 3000	103.00 x 95.00	9.0:1	1 5 4 8 6 3 7 2
350SL, 450SL, 450SLC	M117	4520	Fuel Injection	230 @ 5000	232 @ 4200	92.00 x 85.00	8.0:1	1 5 4 8 6 3 7 2

① Maximum RPM—6500

GENERAL DIESEL ENGINE SPECIFICATIONS

Car Model	Engine Model	Engine Displace. (cc)	Carburetor Type	Horsepower @ rpm (SAE)	Torque @ rpm (ft lbs) (SAE)	Bore x Stroke (mm)	Compression Ratio	Firing Order
220D/8	OM615	2197	Fuel Injection	65 @ 4200	65 @ 4200	87 x 92.4	21:1	1 3 4 2

GASOLINE ENGINE TUNE-UP SPECIFICATIONS

When analyzing compression results, look for uniformity among cylinders rather than specific pressures.

Car Model	Engine Type	SPARK PLUGS Type	SPARK PLUGS Gap (in.)	Distributor Point Dwell (deg)	Ignition Timing	Intake Valve Opens (deg)	Fuel Pump Pressure (psi) @ Idle	Idle Speed (rpm)	VALVE CLEARANCE (in.) ▲ In (cold)	VALVE CLEARANCE (in.) ▲ Ex (cold)
220/8	115.920	①	①	50 ± 2	②	11B	2-3	750-850	0.003	0.008
230/8	180.954	①	①	38 + 3 − 1	②	11B	2-3	800-900	0.003	0.007
250/8	114.920	①	①	38 + 3 − 1	②	11B	2-3	800-900	0.003	0.007
250/8 (1971-72)	130.920	①	①	40 ± 1	②	11B	2-3	800-900	0.003	0.007
250C	130.920	①	①	40 ± 1	②	11B	2-3	800-900	0.003	0.007
280S/8	130.920	①	①	40 ± 1	②	11B	2-3	800-900	0.003	0.007
280SE/8, 280SEL/8	130.980	①	①	40 ± 1	②	11B	30③	④	0.003	0.007
280SE 3.5	116.980	①	①	30 ± 1	②	27B	30③	750-800	0.003	0.007
280SE 4.5 280SEL 4.5	117.984	①	①	32 ± 2	②	27B	30③	700-800	0.003	0.007
280,280C (1973)	110.921	①	①	42 ± 1	②	11A	3.5-5.0	750-900	0.004	0.008
280SL/8	130.983	①	①	40 ± 1	②	11B	30③	④	0.003	0.007
300SEL/8	130.981	①	①	40 ± 1	②	11B	30③	④	0.003	0.007
300SEL 3.5	116.981	①	①	30 ± 1	②	27B	30③	750-800	0.003	0.007
300SEL 4.5	117.981	①	①	32 ± 1	②	27B	30③	700-800	0.003	0.007
300SEL 6.3	100.981	①	①	36 ± 2⑤	②	⑥	30③	560-600	0.004	0.008
350SL	116.982	①	①	32 ± 2	②	27B	30③	700-800	0.003	0.007
450SL, 450SLC	117.982	①	①	32 ± 2	②	27B	30③	700-800	0.003	0.007

CAUTION: If the specifications listed above differ from those on the tune-up decal in the engine compartment, use those listed on the tune-up decal.

NOTES:
1. On transistor ignitions, only a transistorized dwell meter can be used. Transistor ignitions are recognizable by the "Blue" ignition coil, 2 series resistors and the transistor switchgear.
2. On dual point distributors, check each set separately by inserting an insulator between each set in turn. Dwell values given are total both sets.
3. To counteract wear of the fiber contact block, adjust the dwell to the lower end of the range.

① See the spark plug chart for recommendations.
A ATDC
B BTDC
▲ On all engines with intake valve clearance of .003 in., it is better to set the values at .003 in. "loose" (closer to 0.004 in.).

② See "Ignition Timing Specifications"
③ Injection pump pressure
④ 1968-69—700-800; 1970-71—750-850; 1972-73—700-850.
⑤ Total dwell
⑥ Left bank—5B; Right bank—7B

SPARK PLUGS RECOMMENDATIONS*

All measurements in inches

Car Model	Engine	1968 Type	1968 Gap	1969 Type	1969 Gap	1970 Type	1970 Gap	1971 Type	1971 Gap	1972 Type	1972 Gap	1973 Type	1973 Gap
220/8	115.920	N8Y	0.024	N8Y	0.024	N8Y	0.024	N8Y	0.024	N9Y	0.024	N9Y	0.024
230/8	180.954	N8Y	0.024	N8Y	0.024	—	—	—	—	—	—	—	—
250/8	114.920	N8Y	0.024	N8Y	0.024	N9Y	0.024	—	—	—	—	—	—
250/8 (1971-72)	130.923	—	—	—	—	—	—	N8Y	0.024	N8Y	0.024	—	—
250C	130.923	—	—	—	—	—	—	N8Y	0.024	N8Y	0.024	—	—
280S/8	130.920	N8Y	0.024	N8Y	0.024	N8Y	0.024	N8Y	0.024	N8Y	0.024	—	—
280SE/8 280SEL/8	130.980	N7Y	0.024	N7Y	0.024	N7Y	0.024	N7Y	0.024	N7Y	0.024	—	—
280SE 3.5	116.980	—	—	—	—	—	—	N12Y	0.024	N12Y	0.024	—	—
280SE 4.5 280SEL 4.5	117.984	—	—	—	—	—	—	—	—	N12Y	0.024	—	—
280, 280C	110.921	—	—	—	—	—	—	—	—	—	—	N9Y	0.024
280SL/8	130.983	N7Y	0.024	N7Y	0.024	N7Y	0.024	N7Y	0.024	—	—	—	—
300SEL/8	130.981	N7Y	0.024	N7Y	0.024	—	—	—	—	—	—	—	—
300SEL 3.5	116.981	—	—	—	—	N12Y	0.024	N12Y	0.024	—	—	—	—
300SEL 4.5	117.981	—	—	—	—	—	—	—	—	N12Y	0.024	N12Y	0.024
300SEL 6.3	100.981	—	—	—	—	N12Y	0.024	N12Y	0.024	—	—	—	—
350SL	117.982	—	—	—	—	—	—	—	—	N12Y	0.024	—	—
450SL, 450SLC	117.982	—	—	—	—	—	—	—	—	—	—	N12Y	0.024

* All recommended plugs are Champion

— Not applicable

IDLE SPEED EXHAUST GAS VALVES (1968-72)

(% CO at Idle)

NOTE: For Gasoline Engines Only

Model Year Engine	1968/69 Speed rpm	1968/69 Exhaust Gas Value % CO	1970/71 Speed rpm	1970/71 Exhaust Gas Value % CO	1972 Speed rpm	1972 Exhaust Gas Value % CO
114	800-900	1.0-1.5	800-900	1.5-3.5	—	—
115	850-950	2.0-2.5	800-850	3.0-4.0	750-850	2.0-3.5
130.920	800-900	1.0-1.5	800-900	1.0-1.5	—	—
130.923	800-900	1.0-1.5	800-900	1.0-1.5	800-900	1.0-1.5
180.954	800-900	1.5-2.5	—	—	—	—
100	560-600	3.5-5.5	560-600	3.5-5.0	560-620	1.0-4.0
116	—	—	750-800	1.0-2.0	—	—
117	—	—	—	—	700-800	0.5-2.0

— Not applicable

NOTE: If the values on the tune-up decal in the engine compartment, differ from those listed above, use the values on the tune-up decal.

IGNITION TIMING SPECIFICATIONS

Car Model	Engine Type	IGNITION TIMING 1968-69 @ 4500 rpm w/o vacuum	1970-71 @ 800 rpm w/vacuum	1972 @ 800 rpm w/vacuum	1973 @ 800 rpm w/vacuum
220/8	115.920	43B	5A	5A	10B
230/8	180.954	37B	—	—	—
250/8	114.920	37B	4A	—	—
250/8 (1971-72)	130.923	—	4A	4A	—
250C	130.923	—	4A	4A	—
280S/8	130.920	37B	4A	—	—
280SE/8, 280SEL/8	130.980	30B	8A	6A	—
280SE 3.5	116.980	—	—	—	—
280SE 4.5, 280SEL 4.5	117.984	—	—	5A	5A
280, 280C	110.921	30B	8A	—	4A
280SL/8	130.983	30B	8A	—	—
300SEL/8	130.981	—	6A	—	—
300SEL 3.5	116.981	—	—	—	—
300SEL 4.5	117.981	26B @ 3000	32B @ 3000	5A	5A
300SEL 6.3	100.981	—	6A	—	—
350SL	117.982	—	—	5A	—
450SL, 450SLC	117.982	—	—	—	5A

— Not Applicable
B BTDC
A ATDC
w/ with (vacuum connected)
w/o without (vacuum disconnected)

CAUTION: Do not run the engine at high RPM speeds (3000-4500) for more than an instant. Severe engine damage can result.

DIESEL TUNE-UP SPECIFICATIONS

Model	VALVE CLEARANCE (cold) ① Intake (in.)	Exhaust (in.)	Intake valve opens (deg)	Injection pump setting (deg)	INJECTION NOZZLE PRESSURE (psi) New	Used	Idle speed (rpm) ③	Cranking compression pressure (psi)
220D/8	0.004②	0.016	12.5B	24B	1564-1706	1422-1706	750-800	284-327

① Hot: Intake—0.008 in. Exhaust—0.018 in.
② In cold weather (below 5° F.), increase to 0.006 in. cold.
③ Manual transmission in Neutral; Automatic in Drive.
B Before Top Dead Center

FIRING ORDERS

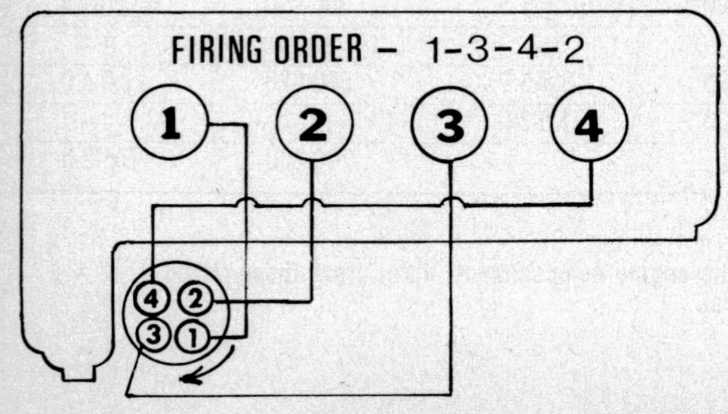

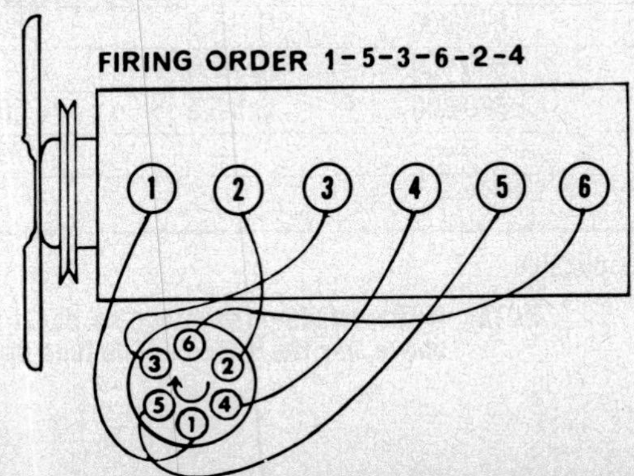

6 cylinder engines (except 280 and 280C)

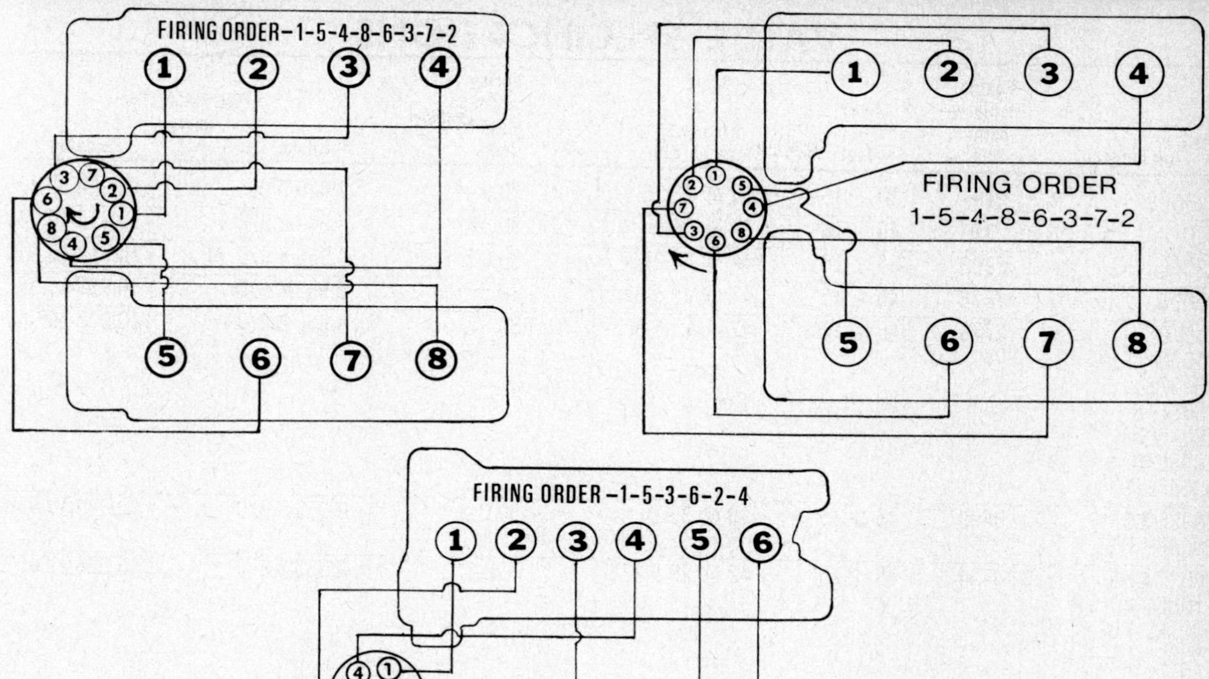

CRANKSHAFT AND CONNECTING ROD SPECIFICATIONS

All measurements are given in millimeters

Car Model	Engine Displace. (cc)	Engine Model	CRANKSHAFT Main Brg. Journal Dia.	Main Brg. Oil Clearance	Shaft End-Play	Thrust on No.	CONNECTING ROD Journal Diameter	Oil Clearance	Side Clearance
220/8 220D/B	2197 2197	M115 OM615	69.965- 69.965	0.045- 0.065	0.100- 0.240	①	51.955- 51.965	0.035- 0.055	0.110- 0.260
230/8	2292	M180	59.955- 59.965	0.045- 0.065	0.100- 0.250	①	47.955- 47.965	0.035- 0.055	0.110- 0.260
250/8	2496	M114	59.955- 59.965	0.045- 0.065	0.100- 0.240	①	47.955- 47.965	0.035- 0.055	0.110- 0.260
250/8 250/C 280S/8 280SEL/8 280SE/8 280SL/8 300SEL/8	2778	M130	59.955- 59.965	0.045- 0.065	0.100- 0.240	①	47.965 47.955-	0.055 0.035-	0.260 0.110-
280SE 3.5 300SEL 3.5	3499 3499	M116	63.955- 63.965	0.035- 0.075	0.100- 0.240	①	51.955- 51.965	0.035- 0.065	0.220- 0.380
280SE 4.5 280SEL 4.5 300SEL 4.5 350SL 450SL 450SLC	4520	M117	63.955- 63.965	0.035- 0.075	0.100- 0.240	①	51.955- 51.965	0.035- 0.065	0.220- 0.380
300SEL 6.3	6332	M100	69.945- 69.965	0.045- 0.065	0.100- 0.240	①	54.940- 54.600	0.045- 0.065	0.220- 0.359
28C 280C	2746	M110	N.A.	N.A.	N.A.	①	N.A.	N.A.	N.A.

N.A. Not Available
① Center main on 5 main bearing engines; rear main on 7 main bearing engines.

VALVE SPECIFICATIONS

Car Model	Engine Displacement (cc)	Seat Angle (deg)	Spring Test Pressure (mm @ KP)	Spring Installed Height (mm)	STEM DIAMETER (mm) Intake	Exhaust
220D/8	2197	30 + 15′	38.4 @ 23-26.4	29.9	9.920-9.905	9.918-9.940
220/8	2197	45 + 15′	39 @ 36①	30.0①	8.948-8.970	10.918-10.940
230/8	2292	45 + 15′	40 @ 24-27①	30.0①	8.955-8.970	10.918-10.940
250/8	2496	45 + 15′	42 @ 29.5-32.5①	30.5①	8.955-8.970	10.918-10.940
250/8 250/C 280S/8 280SE/8 280SEL/8 280SL/8 300SEL/8	2778	45 + 15′	42 @ 29.5-32.5①	30.5①	8.955-8.970	10.918-10.940
280SE 3.5 300SEL 3.5	3499	45 + 15′	39 @ 36①	30.0①	8.955-8.970	10.928-10.950
280SE 4.5 280SEL 4.5 300SEL 4.5 350SL 450SL 450SLC	4520	45 + 15′	42 @ 29.5-32.5①	30.5①	8.955-8.970	10.928-10.950
280 280C	2746	45 + 15′	N.A.	N.A.	N.A.	N.A.
300SEL 6.3	6332	45 + 15′	44.5 @ 42.3	35.4	8.948-8.970	11.932-11.950

① Outer spring—The spring should be installed so that the close coils are in contact with the cylinder head

VALVE TIMING SPECIFICATIONS

Model	Camshaft Code Number	INTAKE VALVE Opens BTDC	Closes ABDC	EXHAUST VALVE Opens BBDC	Closes ATDC
220/8	61	11	47	48	16
220D/8	18	12.5	41.5	45	9
230/8 250/8 280S/8 280SE/8 280SEL/8	0835	11	47	48	16
280SE/8 300SEL/8	0935	12	56	53	21
280SE 3.5 300SEL 3.5	46/47①	22	50	45	17
280SE 3.5 300SEL 3.5 280SE 4.5 280SEL 4.5 300SEL 4.5	52/53①	27	43	61	13
350SL 450SL 450SLC	48/49①	22	48	47	17
300SEL 6.3	L-16 R-17	L-5 R-7	L-50 R-48	L-40 R-42	L-15.5 R-13.5
280 280C	30/33②	11	15	22	14

① Camshafts with identification number 46, 48, or 52 are for the left bank of cylinders (5-8). Camshafts with identification code number 47, 49 or 53 are for the right bank of cylinders (1-4).

② Code number 30 for exhaust camshaft
Code number 33 for intake camshaft

L Left
R Right
BTDC Before Top Dead Center
ABDC After Bottom Dead Center
BBDC Before Bottom Dead Center

TORQUE SPECIFICATIONS

All readings in ft lbs

Car Model	Engine Model	Cylinder Head Bolts ②	Rod Bearing Bolts	Main Bearing Bolts	Crankshaft Pulley Bolt	Flywheel To Crankshaft Bolts	Cam Sprocket Bolt(s)	Exhaust Manifold Bolts
220/8	OM615	65	①	65	151-158	①	18	18-21
220/8 230/8 250/8	M180 M114 M115	58	①	58③	151-158	①	18	18-21
250/8 280S/8 280SE/8 280SEL/8 280SL/8 300SEL/	M130	72	①	58	151-158	①	18	18-21
280SE 3.5 300SEL 3.5 280SE 4.5 280SEL 4.5 300SE 4.5 350SL 450SL 450SLC	M116 M117	36	①	④	180-194	①	36	18-21
300SEL 6.3	M100	58	①	58	290	①	30-33	18-21
280 280C	M110	58	①	58	206-226	①	58	N.A.

① See text
② With cold engine; cylinder head bolts should be tightened in at least 3 stages
③ 65 on M115 engines
④ M 10 bolts—37 ft lbs
M 12 bolts—72 ft lbs
N.A. Not available

TORQUE SEQUENCES

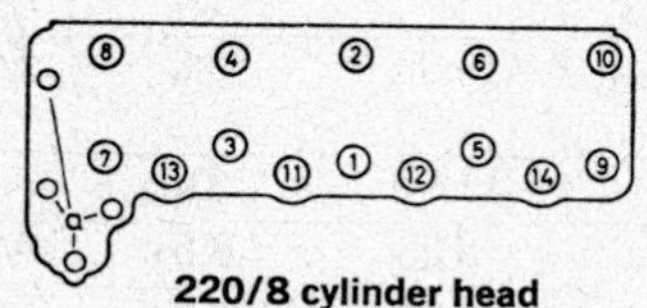

220/8 cylinder head

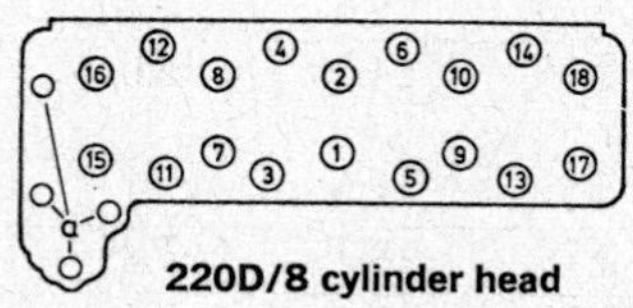

220D/8 cylinder head

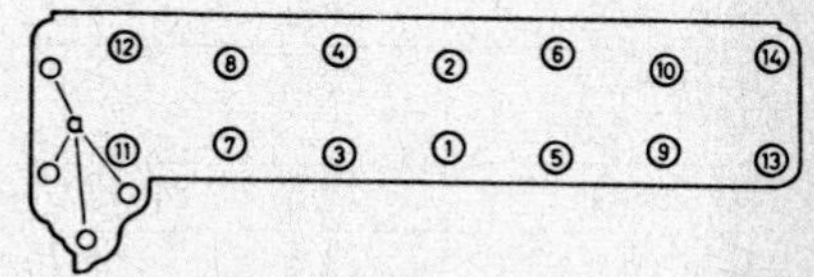

Cylinder head—230/8, 250/8, 250C, 280S/8, 280SE/8, 280SEL/8, 280SL/8, 300SEL/8.

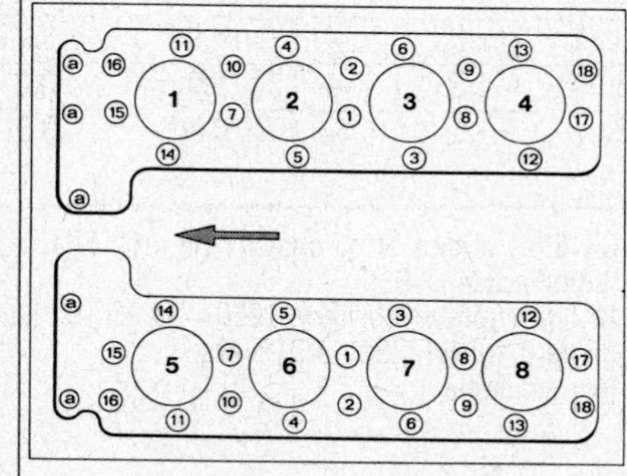

Cylinder heads—3.5 and 4.5 V-8's

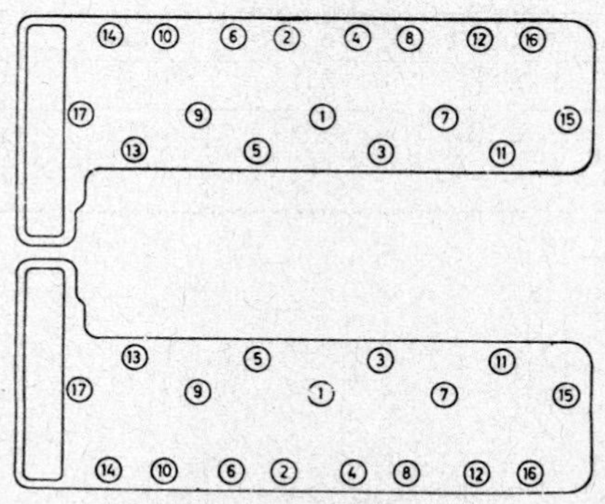

300SEL 6.3 cylinder heads

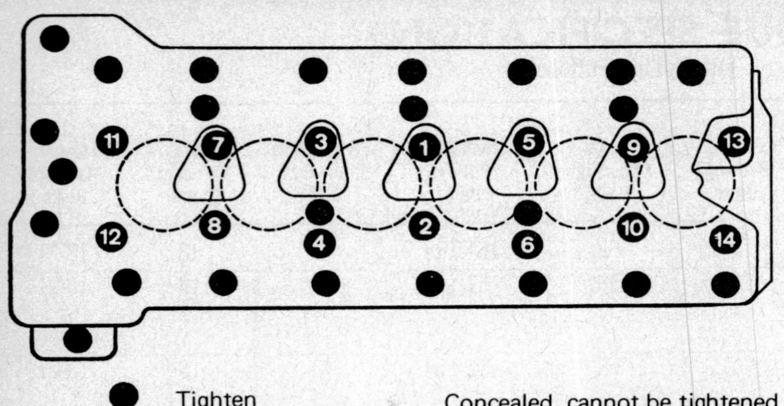

Tighten Concealed, cannot be tightened

280 and 280C cylinder head

Main bearing cap torque sequence—3.5 and 4.5 V-8's.

CAPACITIES

Model	Fuel Tank (gals)	CRANKCASE (qts) Max	Min	Radiator (qts)	Rear Axle (pts)	Oil Filter (pts)	TRANSMISSION (pts) Manual	Automatic	Power Steering (pts)	Manual Steering (pts)
220D/8	17.25	4.25⑦	2.5	11.25	2.5	2.0	3.0	9.75①	3.0	5/8
220/8	17.25	4.25	2.5	11.0	2.5	1.0	3.5	8.75②	3.0	5/8
230/8	17.25	5.75⑧	3.75	11.0	2.5	1.0	3.5	9.75①	3.0	5/8
250/8	17.25	5.75⑧	3.75	10.5	2.5	1.0	3.5	9.75①	3.0	5/8
250/8 (1971-72)	17.25	5.75⑧	3.75	11.0	2.5	1.0	3.5	9.75①	3.0	5/8
250C	21.5	5.75⑧	3.75	11.0	2.5	1.0	3.5	9.75①	3.0	5/8
280S/8	21.5	5.75⑧	3.75	11.0	5.25	1.0	3.0	8.0③	3.0	5/8
280SE/8 280SEL/8	21.5	5.75⑧	3.75	11.25	5.25	1.0	3.0	8.0③	3.0	5/8
280SE 3.5	24.5	7.0	4.75	14.0	5.25	1.5	3.5	⑨	3.0	5/8
280SE 4.5 280SEL 4.5	25.0	8.0	6.0	14.75	6.0	1.5	—	19.0⑤	3.0	5/8
280, 280C	19.5	7.0	5.5	11.5	2.1	1.5	—	11.6⑥	3.0	—
280SL/8	21.5	5.75⑧	3.75	13.25	5.25	1.0	3.0	8.0③	3.0	5/8
300SEL/8	21.5	5.75⑧	3.75	11.0	5.25	1.0	3.0	8.0③	3.0	5/8
300SEL 3.5	24.5	7.0	4.75	14.0	5.25	1.5	3.5	⑨	3.0	—
300SEL 4.5	25.0	8.0	6.0	14.75	6.0	1.5	—	19.0⑤	3.0	—
300SEL 6.3	27.75	6.75	5.25	19.0	5.25	2.0	—	16.5④	3.25	5/8
350SL	27.5	8.0	6.0	16.0	3.0	1.5	—	19.0⑤	3.0	—
450SL 450SLC	27.5	8.0	6.0	16.0	3.0	1.5	—	19.0⑤	3.0	—

① Initial filling—11.5
② Initial filling—11.75
③ Initial filling—10.0
④ Initial filling—18.5
⑤ Initial filling—17.0
⑥ Initial filling—9.5
⑦ Oil filter added after chassis no. 052 894; add 1 pt extra
⑧ Wil oil cooler—6.25
⑨ 13.5 pts (since February, 1970—14.25 pts, due to modified oil pan); Initial filling—11.5 pts.
— Not available

CARBURETOR SPECIFICATIONS

Car Model	Carburetor	Main Jet	Air Correction Jet	Emulsion Tube	Idle Jet	Idle Air Bleed	Float Adjustment	Choke Gap	Fast Idle Speed	Automatic Choke Cover Setting
220/8	2-Solex 36-40 PDSI						15-17	N.A.	N.A.	N.A.
	Primary	137.5	80	0.5	62.5	1.6				
	Secondary	—	—	—	—	—				
230/8	2-Zenith 35/40 INAT						21-23	N.A.	2400-2600	Index
	Primary	x 115	100	4S	45	1.3				
	Secondary	x 120	130	4N	—	—				
250/8	2-Zenith 35/40 INAT						21-23	2.0-2.3	2500-2700①	Index②
	Primary	x 115	100	4S	45	1.3				
	Secondary	x 125	120	4N	—	—				
250C 280S/8	2-Zenith 35-40 INAT						21-23	2.0-2.2	2500-2700③	Index
	Primary	x 115	90	4S	45	1.3				
	Secondary	x 125	110	4N	—	—				
280 280	1-Solex 4 A 1						N.A.	1.5	2400-2600	Index
	Primary	x 97.5	N.A.	N.A.	N.A.	110				
	Secondary	—	—	N.A.	N.A.	—				

① Front carburetor only. On rear carburetor, 1400 rpm if adjusting screw is provided

② After 3000 miles, the cover should be set approx 5 mm against the direction of the arrow

③ On vehicles after 1970, the vacuum hose at the carburetor must be disconnected and plugged to check fast idle

— Not Applicable

N.A. Not Available at the time of publication

CARBURETOR ALTITUDE ADJUSTMENT

Carburetors equipped with standard jets supply too rich a mixture at high altitudes. To avoid this, larger air correction jets are installed. The principle in altitude adjustment is to choose the largest possible air correction jet that will give a minimum of performance loss. If the jet is too large or the jet chosen for altitude adjustment is regularly used at full load at normal altitudes, there is a good possibility that the engine will overheat because of too lean a mixture. The following chart gives the recommended air correction jets for various altitudes.

Model	Carburetor(s)	3300-5000	5000-8300	8300-11,500	Above 11,500
220/8	Solex 36-40 PDSI				
	Primary	90	110	115	130
230/8	Zenith 35/40 INAT				
	Primary	120	140	160	180
	Secondary	150	170	190	190
250/8	Zenith 35/40 INAT				
	Primary	120	140	160	180
	Secondary	140	160	180	180
280S/8 250C	Zenith 35/40 INAT			160	180
	Primary	120	140	170	190
	Secondary	130	150		

CARBURETOR SPECIFICATIONS

Type	220/8
Carburetor designation	Stromberg 175 CDT
Main metering needle	RA
Main metering jet	100
Float needle valve	2.25
Float adjustment	15-17
Fast idle speed with warm engine	3300-3600
Automatic choke cover adjustment	Index
Oil damper air piston	Engine oil①

① During extended periods of cold weather below freezing Automatic Transmission Fluid (ATF).

WHEEL ALIGNMENT SPECIFICATIONS

Car Model	FRONT WHEELS Camber (deg)	Caster (deg) Mech. Steer.	Caster (deg) Power Steer.	Toe-in (mm)	REAR WHEELS Camber (deg)	REAR WHEELS Toe-in (mm)
220D/8	0°15′ $^{+10′}_{-20′}$	2°40′ ± 20′	3°40′ ± 20′	2-4	See Chart 1	See Chart 2
220/8	0°15′ $^{+10′}_{-20′}$	2°40′ ± 20′	3°40′ ± 20′	2-4	See Chart 1	See Chart 2
230/8	0°15′ $^{+10′}_{-20′}$	2°40′ ± 20′	3°40′ ± 20′	2-4	See Chart 1	See Chart 2
250/	0°15′ $^{+10′}_{-20′}$	2°40′ ± 20′	3°40′ ± 20′	2-4	See Chart 1	See Chart 2
250C	0°15′ $^{+10′}_{-20′}$	2°40′ ± 20′	3°40′ ± 20′	2-4	See Chart 1	See Chart 2
280S/8	0°30′ − 20′	3°30′ ± 15′	4° ± 15′	1-3	0° ± 30′	0 ± 2
280SE/8	0°30′ − 20′	3°30′ ± 15′	4° ± 15′	1-3	0° ± 30′	0 ± 2
280SEL/8	0°30′ − 20′	3°30′ ± 15′	4° ± 15′	1-3	0° ± 30′	0 ± 2
280SE 3.5	0°30′ − 20′	3°30′ ± 15′	4° ± 15′	1-3	0° ± 30′	0 ± 2
280SE 4.5	0°30′ − 20′	3°30′ ± 15′	4° ± 15′	1-3	0° ± 30′	0 ± 2
280SEL 4.5	0°30′ − 20′	3°30′ ± 15′	4° ± 15′	1-3	0° ± 30′	0 ± 2
280, 280C	0°15′ $^{+10′}_{-20′}$	—	3°40′ ± 15′	1-3	See Chart 1	0 ± 2
280SL/8	0°10′ + 20′	3°30′ ± 15′	4° ± 15′	1-3	+1°45′ ± 30′	0 ± 2
300SEL/8	0°20′ − 20′	—	4° ± 15′	1-3	−0°45′ ± 15′	0 ± 2
300SEL 3.5	0°20′ − 20′	—	4° ± 15′	1-3	−0°45′ ± 15′	0 ± 2
300SEL 4.5	0°20′ − 20′	—	4° ± 15′	1-3	−0°45′ ± 15′	0 ± 2
300SEL 6.3	0°20′ − 20′	—	6° ± 15′	1-3	−0°45′ ± 1°	0 ± 2
350SL 450SL 450SLC	0° $^{\pm 10′}_{-20′}$	—	3°40′ ± 20′	1-3	See Chart 1	See Chart 2

Wheel Alignment Chart 1

Control Arm Position (mm)	Corresponds to Rear Wheel Camber on: 220D/8, 220/8, 230/8, 250/8, 250C	350SL, 450SL, 450SLC
+ 80	+ 2°30′ ± 30′	—
+ 75	+ 2°15′ ± 30′	—
+ 70	+ 2° ± 30′	—
+ 65	+ 1°45′ ± 30′	—
+ 60	+ 1°30′ ± 30′	—
+ 55	+ 1°15′ ± 30′	—
+ 50	+ 1° ± 30′	+ 0°50′ ± 30′
+ 45	+ 0°45′ ± 30′	+ 0°35′ ± 30′
+ 40	+0°30′ ± 30′	+ 0°20′ ± 30′
+ 35	+ 0°15′ ± 30′	+ 0°05′ ± 30′
+ 30	0° ± 30′	− 0°10′ ± 30′
+ 25	− 0°15′ ± 30′	− 0°25′ ± 30′
+ 20	− 0°30′ ± 30′	− 0°40′ ± 30′
+ 15	−0°45′ ± 30′	− 0°55′ ± 30′
+ 10	− 1° ± 30′	− 1°10′ ± 30′
+ 5	− 1°15′ ± 30′	− 1°25′ ± 30′
0	− 1°30′ ± 30′	− 1°40′ ± 30′
− 5	− 1°45′ ± 30′	− 1°55′ ± 30′
− 10	− 2° ± 30′	− 2°10′ ± 30′
− 15	− 2°15′ ± 30′	− 2°25′ ± 30′
− 20	− 2°30′ ± 30′	− 2°40′ ± 30′

Wheel Alignment Chart 2

220D/8, 220/8, 230/8, 250/8, 250C, 350SL, 450SL, 450SLC

Rear Wheel Control Arm Position (mm)	Corresponds to Rear Wheel Toe-in of:
0 to + 35 mm	1 $^{+2}_{-1}$ mm or 0°10′ $^{+20′}_{-10′}$
+ 35 to + 50 mm	1.5 $^{+2}_{-1}$ mm or 0°15′ $^{+20′}_{-10′}$
+ 50 to + 60 mm	2 $^{+2}_{-1}$ mm or 0°20′ $^{+20′}_{-10′}$
+ 60 to + 70 mm	2.5 $^{+2}_{-1}$ mm or 0°25′ $^{+20′}_{-10′}$
+ 70 to + 80 mm	3.0 $^{+2}_{-1}$ mm or 0°30′ $^{+20′}_{-10′}$

BATTERY AND STARTER SPECIFICATIONS

Engine Model ▲	BATTERY Amp. Hour Capy.	Volts	Term. Grnd.	STARTERS Bosch Designation	Load Test Amps.	Load Test Volts	Load Test RPM	No-Load Test Amps.	No-Load Test Volts	No-Load Test RPM
OM615	88	12	Neg	IF 12V 2.5 PS	650-750	9.0	1000-1200	80-95	12	7500-8500
M115 M130 M180	55	12	Neg	EF (R) 12V 0.8 PS	165-200	9.0	1100-1450	35-45	12	6400-7900
M114① M115② M116 M117 M130① M180①	66	12	Neg	GF 12V 1.4 PS	290-330	9.0	1600-1800	50-70	12	9000-11000
M100	66	12	Neg	IB (R) 12V 2.5 PS	300-360	9.0	1150-1450	50-70	12	6400-8100
M110	N.A.	12	Neg	N.A.	N.A.	N.A.	N.A.	N.A.	N.A.	N.A.

▲ Consult the Engine/Vehicle Identification chart for specific engine models used in your vehicle
① From August, 1968
② From May, 1968
N.A. Not Available

DISC BRAKE SPECIFICATIONS

Model	Master Cylinder Bore (in.)	CALIPER PISTON BORE (mm) Front	Rear	BRAKE DISC DIAMETER (mm) Front	Rear	New Pad Lining Thickness	Brake Disc Run-Out (in.)
220D/8 230/8 250/8 250C 280 280C	15/16	56.940-56.970	39.950-39.975	273 ± 0.2 ②	279 ± 0.2	①	0.0047 (max)
1st Version 280S/8 280SE/8 280SL/8 300SEL/8 300SEL 6.3	15/16	56.986-57.036	41.986-42.029	273 ± 0.2	279 ± 0.2	①	0.0047 (max)
2nd Version 280S/8 280SE/8 280SEL/8 300SEL/8 300SEL 6.3 280SE 3.5 300SEL 3.5 280SEL 4.5 280SE 4.5 300SEL 4.5	15/16	56.986-57.036	34.986-35.027	273 ± 0.2	279 ± 0.2	①	0.0047 (max)
350SL 450SL 450SLC	15/16	56.986-57.036	37.986-38.027	273 ± 0.2	279 ± 0.2	①	0.0047 (max)

① Brake pad without backing plate: 10 mm (0.394 in.)
Brake pad with backing plate: 15 mm (0.581 in.)
② 280 and 280C—278 ± 0.2 mm

LIGHT BULB SPECIFICATIONS

All Models Except 350SL, 450SL and 450SLC

Bulb	Wattage
High and low beams	Sealed beam
Fog lights	35
Turn signal indicators	21
Stop lights	21
Back-up lights	21①
License plate	5
Tail lights	5
Parking lights	5
Side markers	4
Interior lights	10
Instrument lights	3
Indicator lights	3

① Before 1970, 15 watts

LIGHT BULB SPECIFICATIONS

350SL, 450SL and 450SLC

Bulb	Wattage
High and low beams	Sealed beams
Fog lights	Halogen H3
Rear Turn signals	21
Stop lights	21
Back-up lights	21
License plate light	5
Rear Tail lights	5
Front parking and Turn signals	12
Front side markers	4
Rear side markers	5

FUSES

220D/8, 220/8, 230/8, 250/8 and 250C

Fuse No.	Amp.	Protected Circuits
1	8	Courtesy lights, clearance lights, clock and turn signals
2	25	Windshield wipers, windshield washers, horns and cigarette lighter
3	8	Automatic transmission or optional equipment
4	8	Hazard warning flashers, choke control or automatic choke
5	8	Back-up lights, fuel gauge, fuel reserve gauge, brake warning lights
6	8	Stop lights and heater blower
7	8	Right tail light, right parking light, right license plate light (230/8 and 250/8), instrument lights, trunk light
8	8	Left tail light, left parking light, left license plate light (230/8 and 250/8), instrument lights and license plate light (220D/8, 220/8)
9	8	Right high beam and high beam indicator light
10	8	Left high beam
11	8	Right low beam
12	8	Left low beam
*	25	Electric sunroof
*	16	Rear window defroster
*	16 (2)	Electric windows
*	16	Air conditioner coolant blower
*	8	Air conditioner heater blower
*	8	Automatic aerial
*	2	Radio

NOTE: The ignition is not fused and the radio has a separate fuse which is used when the ignition is in the 1 or 2 position.

* These fuses are located in separate fuse boxes.

FUSES

300SEL/8, 280SE 3.5, 280SE 4.5, 280SEL 4.5, 300SEL 3.5, 300SEL 4.5, and 300SEL 6.3

Fuse No.	Amp.	Protected Circuits
1	8	Courtesy lights, parking lights, clock, headlight flashers, glove compartment light, fusebox light, trunk light, window relay, hazard flashers
2	25	Windshield wipers, windshield washers, cigarette lighter
3	8	Control for automatic transmission (300SEL/8)
4	8	Fuel pump relay (e.5 and 3.5 models)
5	8	Turn signals, brake lights, back-up lights, fuel gauge, fuel reserve gauge, brake warning lights, air suspension warning light, automatic transmission solenoid (300SEL/8) and tachometer (300SEL 6.3)
6	25	Automatic choke, heater blower
7	8	Right tail light, right parking light, right license plate light, instrument lights
8	8	Left tail light, left parking light, left license plate light, fog lights
9	8	Right high beams, high beam indicator light
10	8	Left high beam
11	8	Right low beam
12	8	Left low beam
*	25	Electric sunroof
*	16	Rear window defroster
*	25 (4)	Electric windows

NOTE: The ignition is not fused and the radio is equipped with another fuse which is used when the ignition is in position 1 or 2.

* Separate fuse boxes located in the engine compartment.

FUSES

280S/8

Fuse No.	Amp.	Protected Circuits
1	8	Courtesy lights, parking light, clock, headlight, flasher, glove compartment light, fusebox light, trunk light and hazard warning flashers
2	25	Windshield wipers, windshield washers, horns, and cigarette lighter
3	8	Automatic transmission control (optional)
4	8	Turn signals, automatic choke
5	8	Back-up lights, fuel gauge, fuel reserve gauge, brake warning lights
6	8	Brake lights, heater blower
7	8	Right tail light, right parking light, instrument lights
8	8	Left tail light, left parking light, license plate light, and fog lights
9	8	Right high beam and high beam indicator light
10	8	Left high beam
11	8	Right low beam
12	8	Left low beam
*	2	Radio
*	25	Electric sunroof
*	16	Rear window defroster
*	25 (4)	Electric windows

NOTE: The ignition is not fused and the radio is also protected by another fuse which is used when the ignition key is in position 1 or 2.

* Separate fuse boxes located in the engine compartment

FUSES

280SE/, 280SEL/8

Fuse No.	Amp.	Protected Circuits
1	8	Courtesy lights, parking lights, clock, flashers, glove compartment light, fusebox light, and trunk light.
2	25	Windshield wipers, windshield washers, horns, and cigarette lighter
3	8	Control for automatic transmission (optional)
4	8	Fuel pump
5	8	Turn signals, brake lights, back-up lights, fuel gauge, fuel reserve gauge, brake warning lights, automatic transmission solenoid
6	25	Automatic choke, heater blower
7	8	Right tail light, right parking light, instrument lights
8	8	Left tail light, left parking light, license plate lights, fog lights
9	8	Right high beam and high beam indicator light
10	8	Left high beam
11	8	Right low beam
12	8	Left low beam
*	25	Electric sunroof
*	16	Rear window defroster
*	25 (4)	Electric windows

NOTE: The ignition is not fused. The radio also has a 2 amp fuse which is used when the ignition is in position 1 or 2.

* Separate fuse boxes in the engine compartment.

FUSES

280 and 280C

Fuse No.	Amp.	Protected Circuits
1	8	Clock, trunk light, glove compartment light, courtesy lights, hazard warning flashers, and automatic antenna (optional)
2	16	Windshield wipers, horns and auxiliary horns, cigarette lighter
3	8	Idle cut-off switch, automatic choke, brake lights, back-up lights, instrument lights, seat belt warning system, emission control system
4	8	Turn signals, automatic transmission
5	—	Open
6	8	Heater blower
7	8	Right tail light, right parking light, license plate light, instrument lights, side marker lights, transmission shift quadrant indicator light
8	8	Left tail light, left parking light
9	8	Right high beams, high beam indicator light
10	8	Left high beam
11	8	Right low beam
12	16	Left low beam, fog lights
*	16	Air conditioning
*	16	Auxiliary electric fan
*	16	Rear window defroster
*	16	Electric sunroof
	16 (2)	Electric windows
*	2 ①	Radio

— Not applicable

① Glass fuse

FUSES
280SL

Fuse No.	Amp.	Protected Circuits
1	8	Courtesy lights, parking lights, clock, flashers, glove compartment light, fusebox light, and trunk light.
2	25	Windshield wipers, windshield washers, horns, and cigarette lighter
3	8	Control for automatic transmission (optional)
4	8	Fuel pump
5	8	Turn signals, brake lights, back-up lights, fuel gauge, fuel reserve gauge, brake warning lights, automatic transmission solenoid
6	25	Automatic choke, heater blower, starting valve
7	8	Right tail light, right parking light, instrument lights
8	8	Left tail light, left parking light, license plate lights, fog lights
9	8	Right high beam and high beam indicator light
10	8	Left high beam
11	8	Right low beam
12	8	Left low beam
*	25	Electric sunroof
*	16	Rear window defroster
*	25 (4)	Electric windows

NOTE: The ignition is not fused. The radio also has a 2 amp fuse which is used when the ignition is in position 1 and 2.

* Separate fuse boxes in the engine compartment

FUSES
350SL, 450SL and 450SLC

Fuse No.	Amp.	Protected Circuits
1	8	Automatic antenna
2	8	Clock, warning flashers, trunk and glove compartment light, courtesy lights, and parking lights
3	2	Radio
4	8	Headlight flasher
5	25	Windshield wipers and washers
6	8	Side marker lights
7	8	Heater blower and air conditioner
8	8	Turn signals, back-up light, and instrument cluster lights
9	8	Air conditioning blower
10	8	Stop lights and automatic choke
11	25	Rear window defroster
12	8	Automatic transmission
13	8	Right clearance lights, right tail light, right parking light, license plate light, and instrument panel lights
14	8	Fuel pump
15	8	Halogen fog lights, fog tail lights
16	8	Left clearance light, left tail light, left parking light
17	8	Left low beam, high beam indicator
18	8	Left high beam
19	8	Right low beam
20	8	Right high beam

WIRING DIAGRAMS

NOTE: Wiring diagrams are not designated by year. Because of this, minor differences may exist on late model cars.

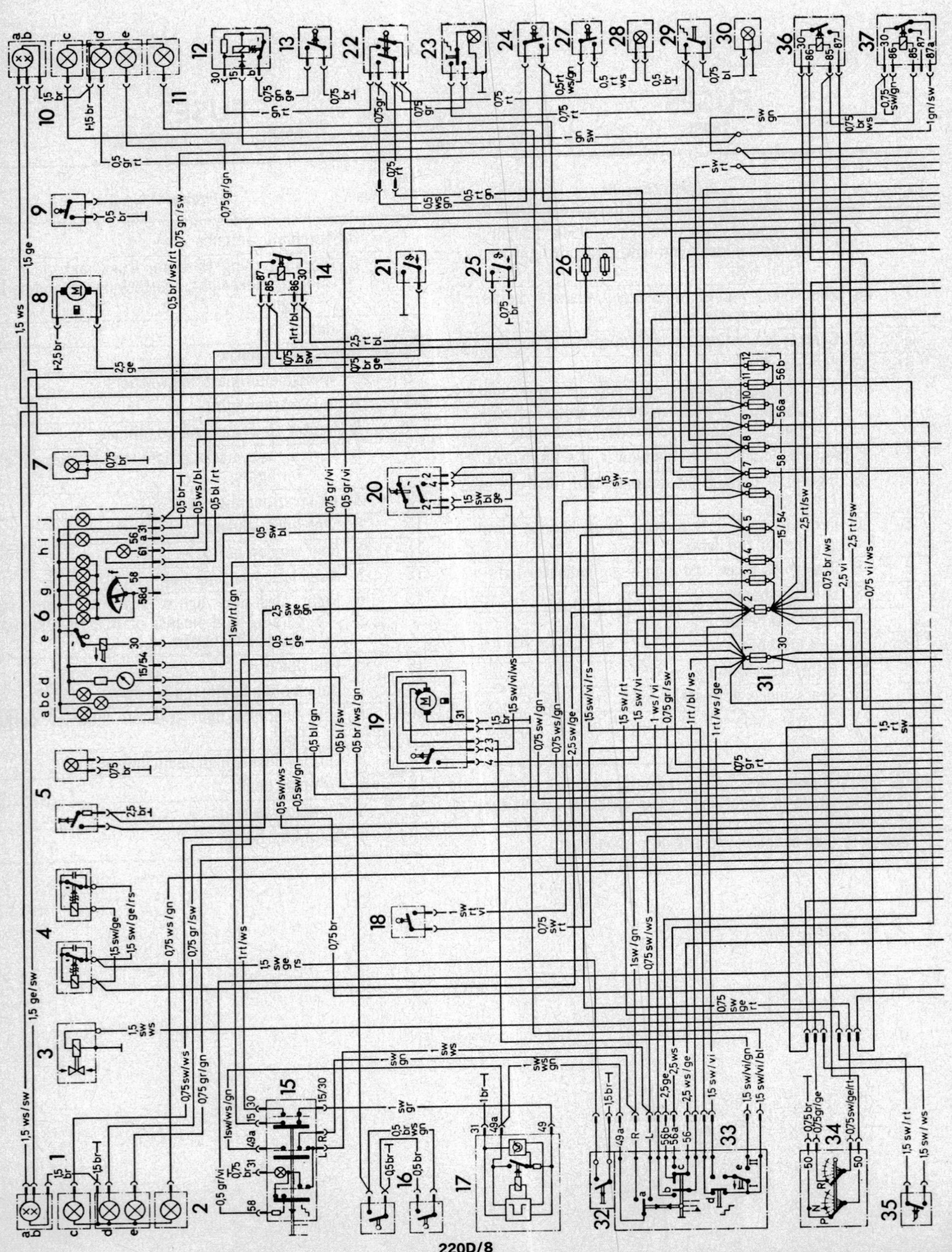

220D/8

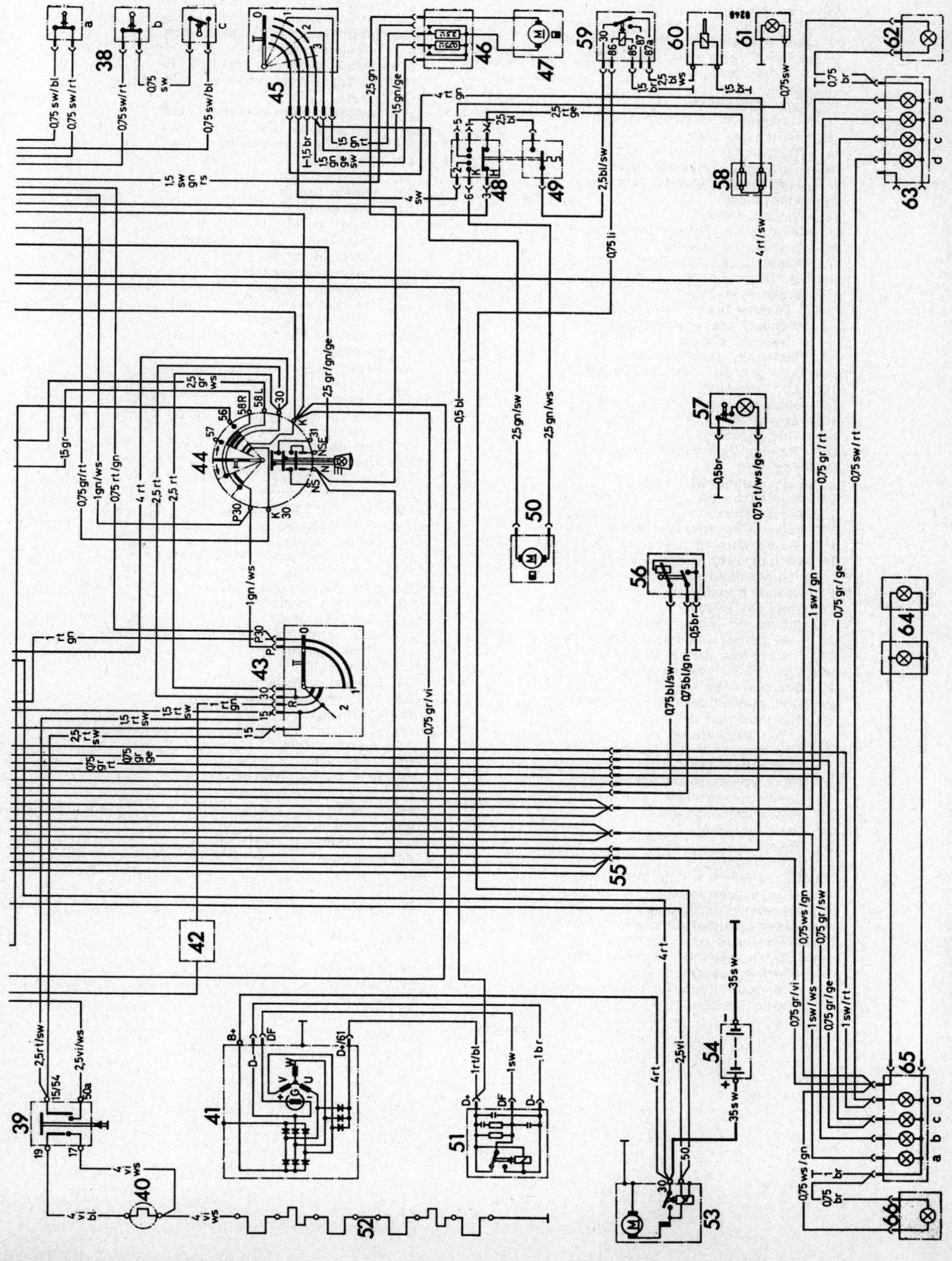

1. Light assembly, left
(a)—High beam
(b)—Low beam
(c)—Turn signal
(d)—Parking light/Side light
(e)—Fog light
2. Side marker light, left
3. Solenoid valve on automatic transmission
4. Horn
5. Cigar lighter with ashtray illumination
6. Instrument cluster
(a)—Turn signal indicator, left
(b)—Turn signal indicator, right
(c)—Fuel reserve warning light
(d)—Fuel gauge
(e)—Electric clock
(f)—Instrument lighting rheostat
(g)—Instrument lighting
(h)—Charging indicator light
(i) High beam indicator light
(j)—Brake fluid level/ parking brake warning light
7. Warning light for safety belt warning system
8. Electrically operated fan
9. Parking brake warning light switch
10. Light assembly, right
(a)—High beam
(b)—Low beam
(c)—Turn signal
(d)—Parking light/Side light
(e)—Fog light
11. Side marker light, right
12. Warning buzzer
13. Buzzer switch
14. Relay of electrically operated fan
15. Hazard warning flasher switch
16. Warning light switch, brake fluid level
17. Flasher transmitter
18. Stoplight switch
19. Windshield wiper motor
20. Foot pump, windshield washer
21. Temperature switch 212° F
22. Door contact switch, left, front
23. Courtesy light
24. Door contact switch, right front
25. Thermostatic switch (air conditioner)
26. Fuse box, houses 2 fuses (auxiliary fan)
27. Glove compartment light switch
28. Glove compartment light
29. Rear roof light switch
30. Rear roof light
31. Fuses
32. Horn ring
33. Combination switch
(a)—Turn signal switch
(b)—Headlight flasher switch
(c)—Hand-operated dimmer switch
(d)—Windshield wiper switch
(e)—Switch windshield wiper speed
34. Starting lock switch and back-up light switch (automatic transmission)
35. Kickdown switch (automatic transmission)
36. Starter relay (automatic transmission)
37. Relay warning system (automatic transmission)
38. Control switches for safety belt warning system
(a)—switch in driver's seat belt reel
(b)—switch in front passenger seat belt reel
(c)—switch in front passenger seat
39. Glow plug switch
40. Glow plug control lamp
41. Alternator
42. Lead for radio
43. Ignition switch
44. Light switch
45. Blower switch
46. Blower motor series resistor
47. Blower motor (heater)
48. Change-over switch, cooling—heating
49. Thermostat and control switch (air conditioner)
50. Blower motor (air conditioner)
51. Regulator
52. Glow plugs and series resistor
53. Starter
54. Battery
55. Plug connection for tail light wiring harness
56. Fuel gauge sending unit
57. Trunk light
58. Fuse box, houses 2 fuses (air conditioner)
59. Relay (air conditioning compressor)
60. Electro-magnetic clutch air conditioning compressor
61. Indicator light (air conditioner)
62. Side marker light, right
63. Tail light assembly right side
(a)—Turn signal
(b)—Tail light/side light
(c)—Back-up light
(d)—Stop light
64. License plate light
65. Tail light assembly, left side
(a)—Turn signal
(b)—Tail light/Side light
(c)—Back-up light
(d)—Stop light
66. Side marker light, left

ws white
gn green
br brown
ge yellow
gr gray
rs pink
bl blue
rt red
sw black
el ivory
nf neutral
vi violet
li lilac

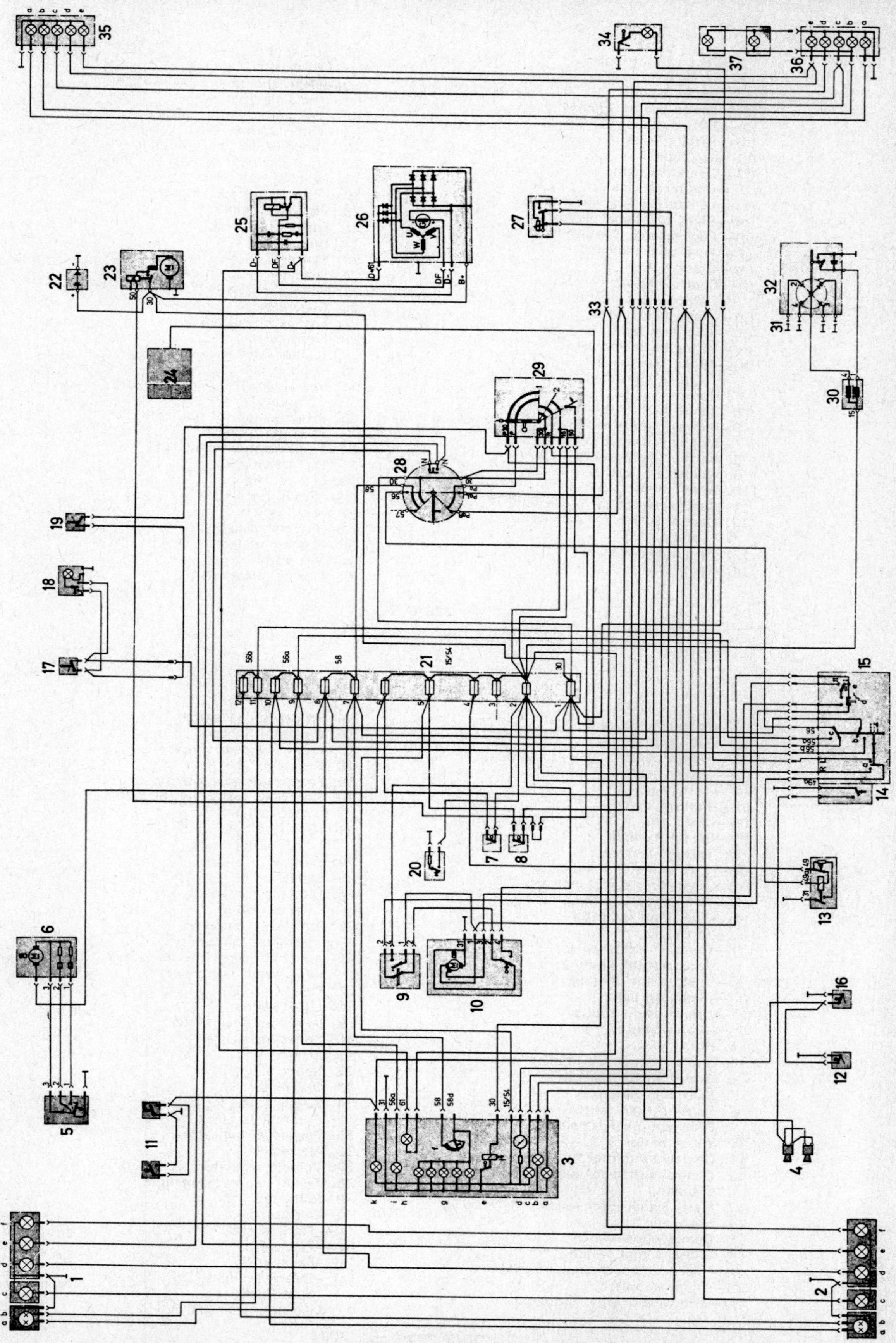

1. Right lighting unit
2. Left lighting unit
(a)—Upper beam
(b)—Lower beam
(c)—Turn signal light
(d)—Parking light
(e)—Fog light
(f)—Clearance light
3. Instrument cluster
(a)—Left turn signal indicator
(b)—Right turnsignal indicator
(c)—Fuel reserve warning light
(d)—Fuel level indicator
(e)—Clock
(f)—Control resistance for instrument lighting
(g)—Instrument lights
(h)—Charging light
(i)—Upper beam indicator
(k)—Brake control Choke control indicator
4. Horn
5. Blower switch (air intake)
6. Blower motor (air intake)
7. Stoplight switch
8. Back-up light switch
9. Windshield washer
10. Wiper motor
11. Control switch for brake fluid
12. Control switch for parking brake
13. Turn signal flasher
14. Horn ring
15. Combination switch
(a)—Flash signal switch
(b)—Flash approach signal switch
(c)—Hand dimmer
(d)—Windshield wiper switch
(e)—Wiper speed switch
16. Choke cable control switch
17. Front left door contact
18. Reading light
19. Front right door contact
20. Cigarette lighter
21. Fuses
22. Battery
23. Starter
24. Lead for optional extra (radio)
25. Voltage regulator
26. Generator
27. Fuel level indicator
28. Light switch
29. Ignition starter switch
30. Ignition coil
31. Spark plugs
32. Distributor
33. Sleeve union for tail light wiring harness
34. Trunk compartment light
35. Right tail light
36. Left tail light
(a)—Flash signal
(b)—Tail light
(c)—Reversing light
(d)—Clearance light
(e)—Stoplight
37. License plate light

220/8

1. Right lighting unit
2. Left lighting unit
(a)—Upper beam
(b)—Lower beam
(c)—Turn signal
(d)—Parking light
(e)—Fog light
(f)—Clearance light
3. Instrument cluster
(a)—Left turn signal indicator
(b)—Right turn signal indicator
(c)—Fuel reserve warning light
(d)—Fuel level indicator
(e)—Clock
(f)—Control resistance for instrument lighting
(g)—Instrument lighting
(h)—Charging light
(i)—Upper beam control
(k)—Brake control
4. Horn
5. Blower switch (air intake)
6. Blower motor (air intake)
7. Stop light switch
8. Back-up light switch
9. Foot pump windshield washer
10. Wiper motor
11. Control switch for brake fluid
12. Control switch for parking brake
13. Flash signal mechanism
14. Horn ring
15. Combination switch
(a)—Flash signal switch
(b)—Flash approach signal switch
(c)—Dimmer switch
(d)—Windshield wiper switch
(e)—Wiper speed switch
16. Cigarette lighter
17. Front left door contact
18. Reading light
19. Front right door contact
20. Roof-light switch (on Model 250 only)
21. Rear roof light (on Model 250 only)
22. Battery
23. Starter
24. Lead for optional extra (radio)
25. Automatic choke on rear carburetor
26. Automatic start mechanism on front carburetor
27. Fuses
28. Light switch
29. Ignition-starter switch
30. Series resistance
31. Ignition coil
32. Spark plugs
33. Distributor
34. Sleeve union for tail light wiring harness
35. Fuel level indicator
36. Alternator
37. Voltage regulator
38. Trunk compartment light
39. Right tail light
40. Left tail light
(a)—Flash signal
(b)—Tail light
(c)—Back-up light
(d)—Clearance light
(e)—Stop light
41. License plate light

230/8, 250/8 and 250C

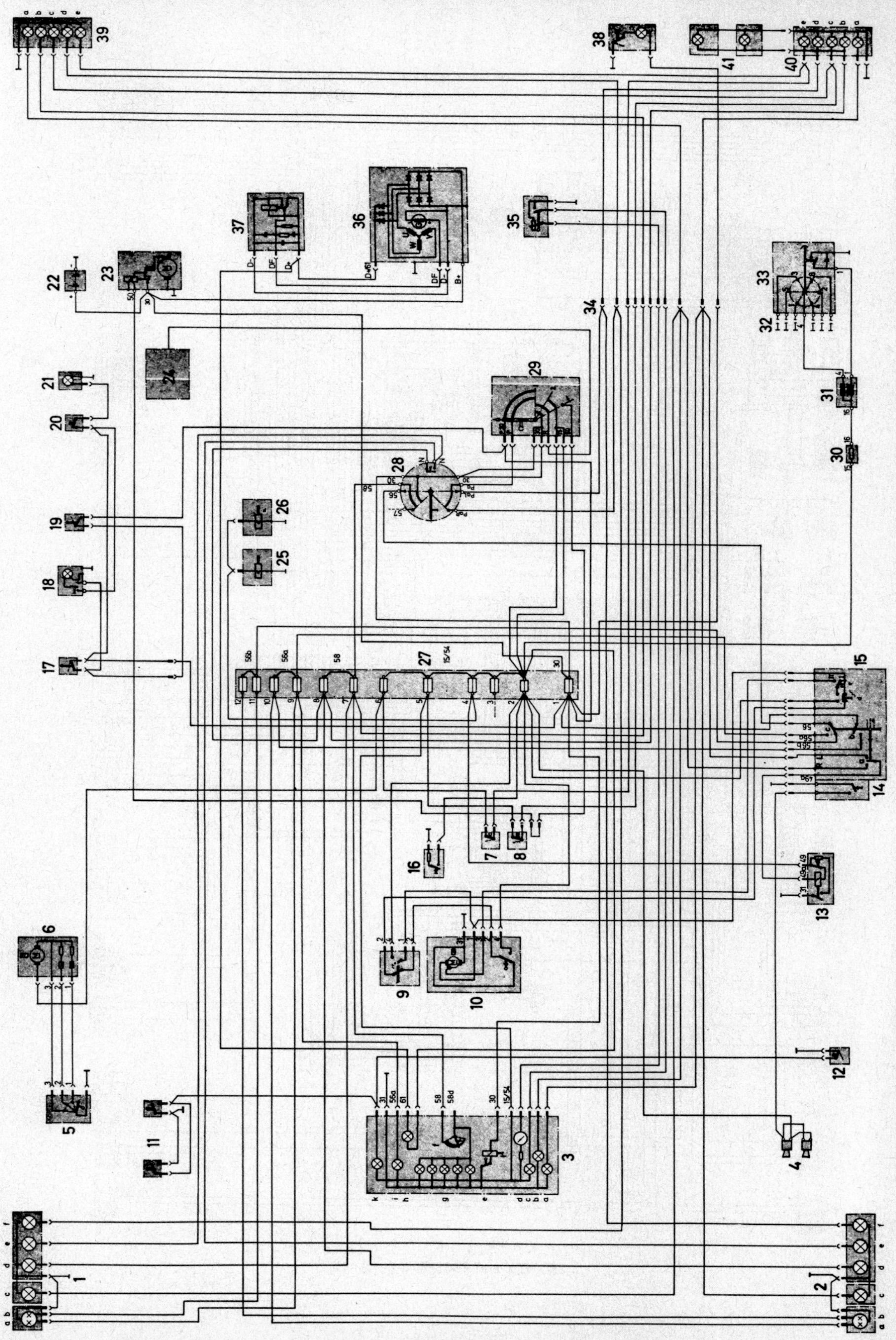

230/8, 250/8 and 250C

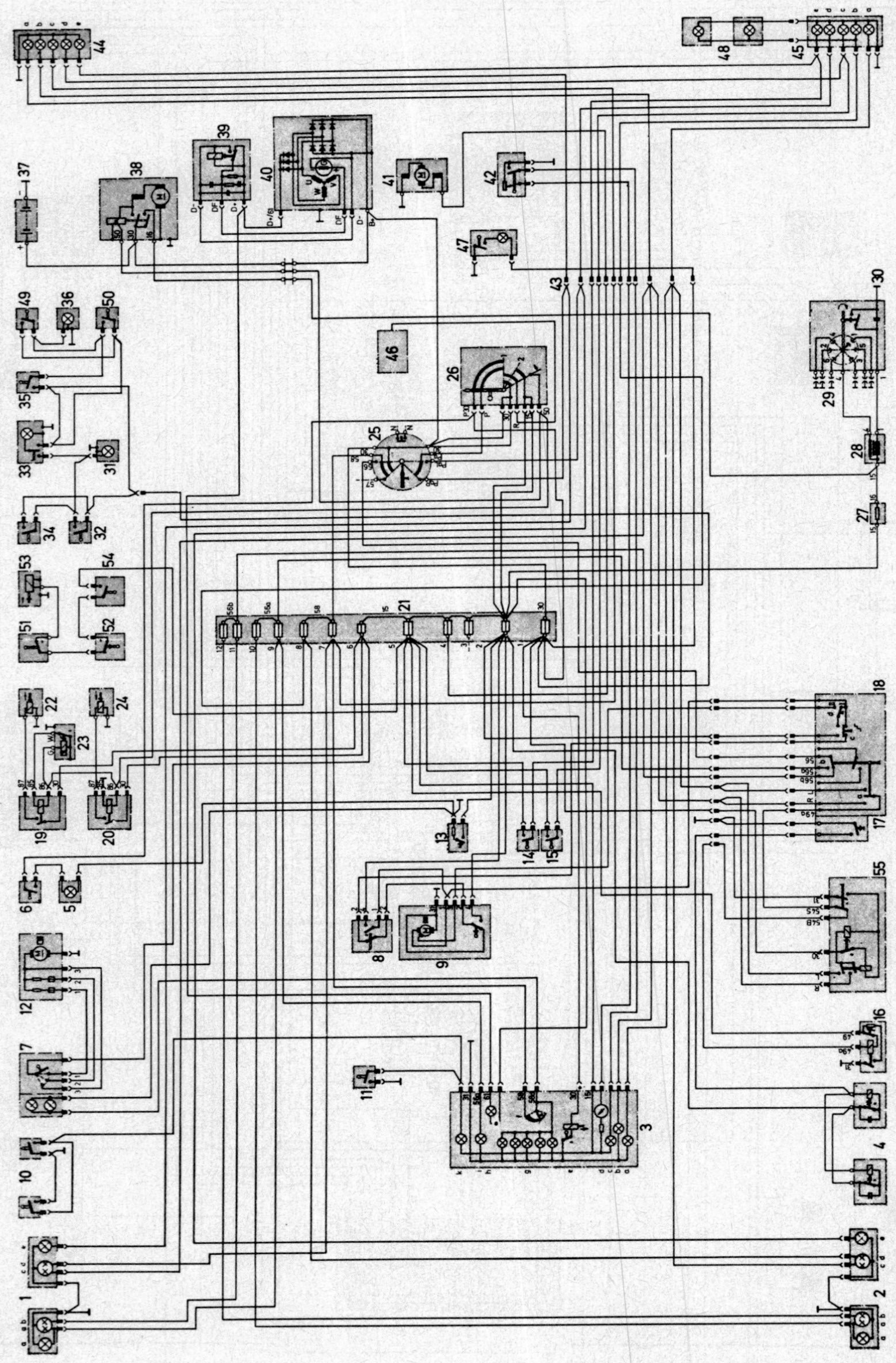

280SE/8 and 280SEL/8 (sedans)

1. Light assembly (right side)
2. Light assembly (left side)
(a)—High beam
(b)—Low beam
(c)—Turn signal light
(d)—Parking light
(e)—Side light
3. Instrument cluster
(a)—Turn signal light indicator, left
(b)—Turn signal indicator, right
(c)—Low fuel level warning light
(d)—Fuel gauge
(e)—Clock
(f)—Instrument illumination rheostat
(g)—Instrument illumination
(h)—Generator (alternator) charge warning light
(i)—High beam indicator
(k)—Parking brake and brake fluid level warning light
4. Dual horn system
5. Glove compartment light
6. Switch for glove compartment light
7. Heater blower switch
8. Windshield washer foot pump
9. Wiper motor
10. Brake fluid level warning light control element
11. Parking brake warning light control element
12. Heater blower motor
13. Cigarette lighter
14. Stop light switch
15. Back up light switch
16. Sending unit for turn signal light
17. Horn ring
18. Combination switch
(a)—Turn signal light switch
(b)—Headlight dimmer switch
(c)—Windshield wiper switch
(d)—Windshield wiper speed control switch
19. Relay for starter valve
20. Relay for mixture control
21. Fuses
22. Magneto for starter valve
23. Thermo time switch
24. Magneto for mixture control
25. Headlight switch
26. Ignition starter switch
27. Series resistance
28. Ignition coil
29. Spark plugs
30. Distributor
31. Entrance light
32. Courtesy light switch, left front door
33. Reading light
34. Couresty light switch, right front door
35. Switch for dome light
36. Dome light, rear
37. Battery
38. Starter
39. Voltage regulator
40. Alternator
41. Fuel pump
42. Fuel gauge sending unit
43. Rear light unit wiring harness connecting plug
44. Rear light unit (right side)
45. Rear light unit (left side)
(a)—Turn signal light
(b)—Tail light
(c)—Back up light
(d)—Side light
(e)—Stop light
46. Spare wire for extras (radio)
47. Trunk light
48. License plate light
49. Door contact, rear, right
50. Door contact, rear, left
51. Switch, accelerator pedal shaft
52. Switch, clutch pedal
53. Solenoid, injection pump
54. Switch, gear-shift position (in 3rd and 4th gear closed)

(51–54: for exhaust emission control system)

55. Hazard warning light transmitter

280SE/8 and 280SEL/8 (sedans)

1. Light assembly (right side)
2. Light assembly (left side)
(a)—High beam
(b)—Low beam
(c)—Turn signal light
(d)—Parking light
(e)—Side light
3. Instrument cluster
(a)—Turn signal light indicator, left
(b)—Turn signal light indicator, right
(c)—Low fuel level warning light
(d)—Fuel gauge
(e)—Instrument illumination
(f)—Instrument illumination rheostat
(g)—Generator (alternator) charge warning light
(h)—High beam indicator
(i)—Parking brake and brake fluid level warning light
4. Horn system
5. Glove compartment light
6. Switch for glove compartment lighter
7. Heater blower switch
8. Windshield washer foot pump
9 Wiper motor
10. Brake fluid level warning light control element
11. Parking brake warning light control element
12. Heater blower motor
13. Cigarette lighter
14. Stop light switch
15. Back-up light switch
16. Sending unit for turn signal light
17. Horn ring
18. Combination switch
(a)—Turn signal light switch
(b)—Headlight dimmer switch
(c)—Windshield wiper switch
(d)—Windshield wiper speed control switch
19. Relay for starter valve
20. Relay for mixture control
21. Fuses
22. Magneto for starter valve
23. Thermo time switch
24. Magneto for mixture control
25. Headlight switch
26. Ignition starter switch
27. Series resistance
28. Ignition coil
29. Spark plugs
30. Distributor
31. Courtesy light
32. Courtesy light switch, left door
33. Reading light
34. Courtesy light switch, right door
35. Switch for dome light, rear
36. Dome light, rear
37. Battery
38. Starter
39. Voltage regulator
40. Alternator
41. Fuel pump
42. Fuel gauge sending unit
43. Rear light unit wiring harness connecting plug
44. Rear light unit (right side)
45. Rear light unit (left side)
(a)—Turn signal light
(b)—Tail light
(c)—Back-up light
(d)—Side light
(e)—Stop light
46. Spare wire for extras (radio)
47. Trunk light
48. Clock
49. Speedometer light
50. Tachometer
(a)—Tachometer light
(b)—Electric indicating system
51. License plate light
52. Automatic antenna (optional)
53. Switch, 3rd gear
54. Switch, 4th gear
55. Switch, clutch pedal
56. Switch, accelerator pedal shaft

(53–56: for exhaust emission control system)

57. Magneto
58. Hazard warning light transmitter

280SE/8 (coupe and convertible)

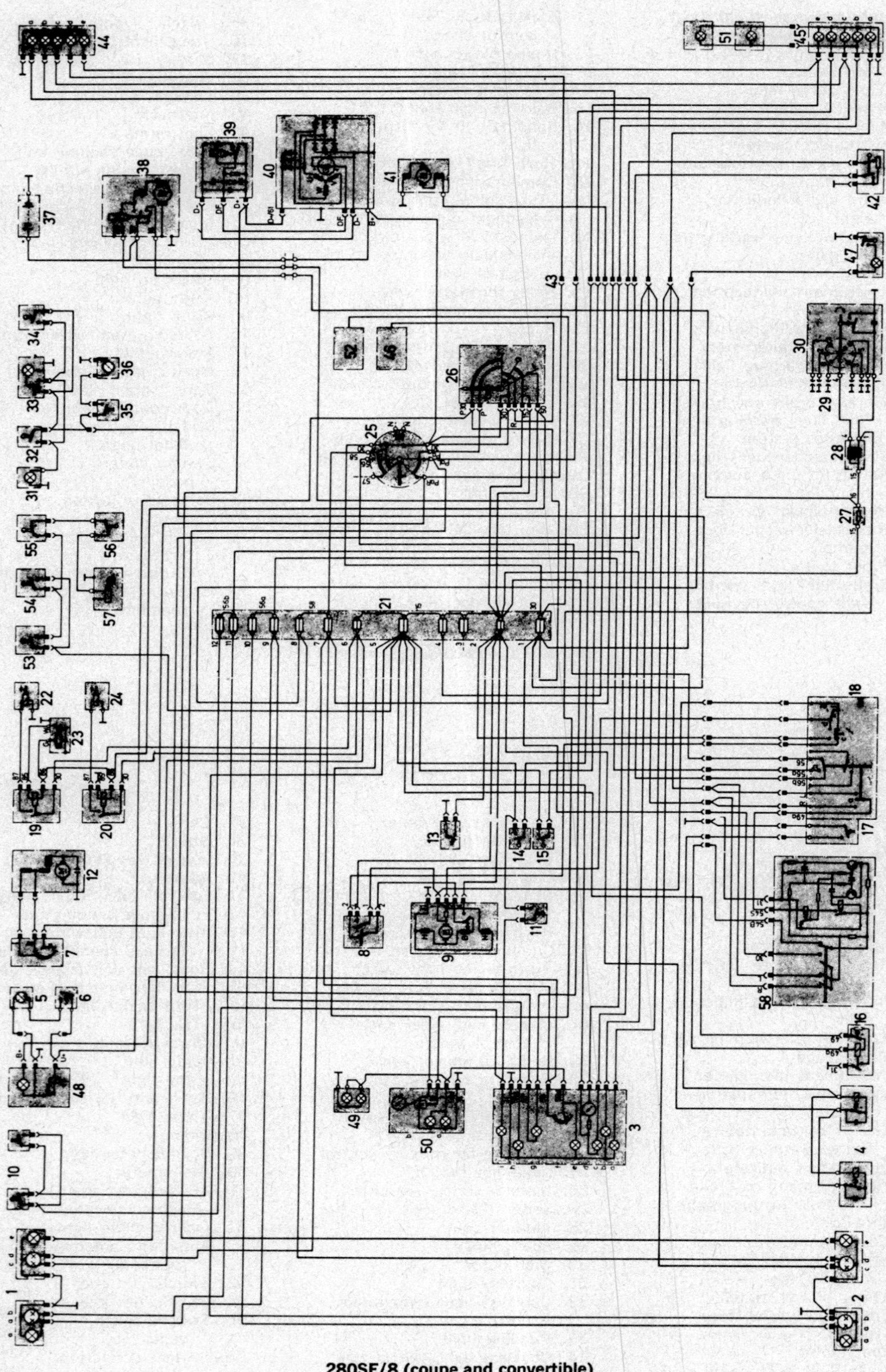

280SE/8 (coupe and convertible)

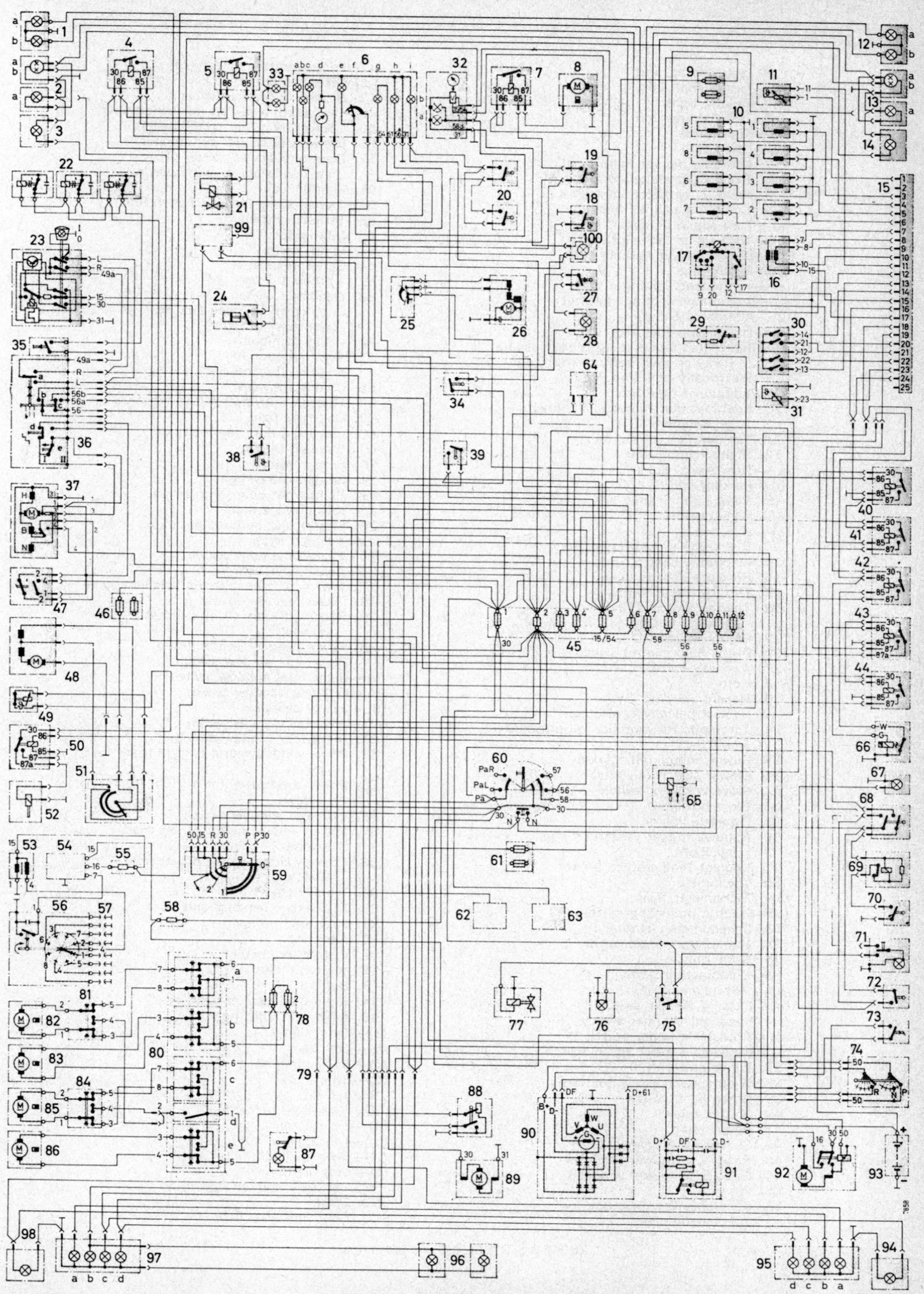

280SE 3.5, 280SE 4.5 and 280SEL 4.5

1. Left lighting unit
(a)—Turn signal light
(b)—Parking light
2. Left lighting unit
(a)—High beam
(b)—Low beam
3. Left side marker light, front
4. Relay 2, emission control
5. Relay 1, emission control
6. Combination instrument
(a)—Turn signal indicator, left
(b)—Turn signal indicator, right
(c)—Low fuel level warning light
(d)—Fuel gauge
(e)—Instrument lighting
(f)—Instrument lighting rheostat
(g)—Alternator charge
(h)—High beam indicator
(i)—Brake fluid and parking brake indicator
7. Relay of electrically operated fan
8. Electrically operated fan
9. Additional fuse box
10. Fuel injection valves with marks for cylinders
11. Temperature sensor (air)
12. Right lighting unit
(a)—Turn signal light
(b)—Parking light
13. Right lighting unit
(a)—High beam
(b)—Low beam
14. Right side marker light, front
15. Electronic control unit
16. Pressure sensor (air)
17. Throttle valve switch
18. Thermo switch 212° F (electric fan)
19. Safety switch
20. Brake fluid control switch
21. Two-way valve
22. Horn
23. Hazard warning flasher (electronically controlled)
24. Automatic transmission oil pressure switch
25. Blower motor (air intake)
26. Blower switch (air intake)
27. Glove box light switch
28. Glove box light
29. Cigarette lighter
30. Impulse trigger (electronic fuel injection)
31. Coolant temperature sensor
32. Tachometer
(a)—Tachometer light
(b)—Electric indicating system
33. Speedometer lighting
34. Handbrake control switch
35. Horn ring
36. Combination switch
(a)—Turn signal switch
(b)—Passing flasher switch
(c)—Headlight dimmer switch
(d)—Windshield wiper switch
(e)—Windshield wiper speed switch
37. Wiper motor
38. Thermo switch (electric fan)
39. Brake light switch
40. Master relay
41. Pump relay
42. Starter valve relay
43. Relay 2 for power windows
44. Relay 1 for power windows
45. Fuses
46. Supplementary fuse box for air conditioner
47. Foot-operated windshield washer pump
48. Blower (air conditioner)
49. Temperature switch (air conditioner)
50. Control relay (air conditioner)
51. Blower switch (air conditioner)
52. Electro-magnetic clutch of air conditioning compressor
53. Ignition coil
54. Transitorized ignition switch unit
55. Series resistance
56. Distributor
57. Spark plugs
58. Series resistance
59. Ignition switch
60. Headlight switch
61. Supplementary fuse box for side marker lights
62. Radio (optional)
63. Aerial (optional)
64. Adapter (tachometer)
65. Cold start valve
66. Thermo time switch
67. Courtesy light
68. Left front door jamb switch
69. Warning buzzer
70. Buzzer switch
71. Front reading light
72. Right front door jamb switch
73. Kick-down switch
74. Starter lock-out and back-up light switch
75. Rear dome light switch
76. Rear dome light
77. Automatic transmission solenoid valve
78. Power window fuses
79. Rear light unit wiring harness connector
80. Power window switch group
(a)—Right rear window switch
(b)—Right front window switch
(c)—Left rear window switch
(d)—Safety switch
(e)—Left front window switch
81. Right rear window switch
82. Power window motor of right rear window
83. Power window motor of right front window
84. Left rear window switch
85. Power window motor of left rear window
86. Power window motor of left front window
87. Trunk light
88. Fuel gauge sending unit
89. Fuel feed pump
90. Alternator
91. Voltage regulator
92. Starter motor
93. Battery
94. Right side marker light, rear
95. Rear light unit, right
(a)—Turn signal
(b)—Tail light
(c)—Back-up light
(d)—Stop ligth
96. License plate light
97. Rear light unit, left
(a)—Turn signal
(b)—Tail light
(c)—Back-up light
(d)—Stop light
98. Left side marker light, rear
99. Clock
100. Shift indicator light

280SE 3.5, 280SE 4.5 and 280SEL 4.5

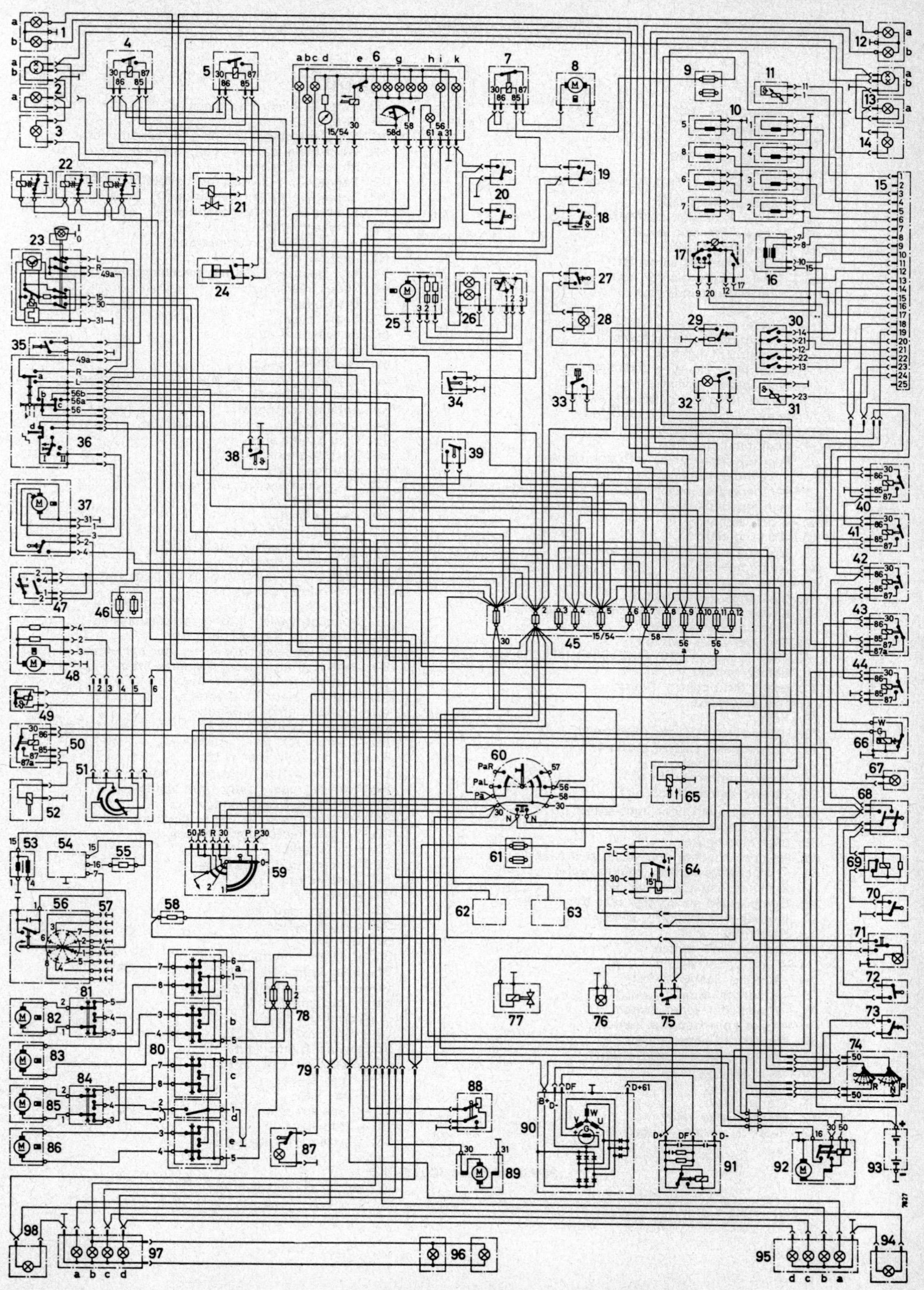

300SEL 3.5 and 300SEL 4.5

1. Lighting unit, left
(a)—Turn signal
(b)—Parking light
2. Lighting unit, left
(a)—High beam
(b)—Low beam
3. Clearance light, left
4. Relay 2, emission control
5. Relay 1, emission control
6. Instrument cluster
(a)—Turn signal indicator, left
(b)—Turn signal indicator, right
(c)—Fuel reserve indicator
(d)—Fuel gage
(e)—Clock
(f)—Instrument lighting rheostat
(g)—Instrument lighting
(h)—Alternator charging indicator
(i)—High beam indicator
(k)—Brake fluid and parking brake indicator
7 Relay, electrically operated fan
8. Electrically operated fan
9. Additional fuse box
10. Fuel injection valves with appropriate cylinder designation
11. Temperature sensor (air)
12. Lighting unit, right
(a)—Turn signal
(b)—Parking light
13. Lighting unit, right
(a)—High beam
(b)—Low beam
14. Clearance light, right
15. Electronic control unit, multiple plug
16. Pressure sensor (air)
17. Throttle valve switch
18. Thermo switch 100° C (212° F), Electric fan
19. Safety switch
20. Brake fluid control switch
21. Two-way valve
22. Horn
23. Hazard warning light (electronic)
24. Oil pressure switch, automatic transmission
25. Blower motor (fresh air)
26. Blower switch (fresh air)
27. Glove compartment light switch
28. Glove compartment light
29. Cigarette lighter
30. Impulse sending unit (contact breaker)
31. Temperature sensor, cooling water
32. Air suspension warning light
33. Compressed air control switch
34. Parking brake control switch
35. Horn ring
36. Combination switch
(a)—Turn signal switch
(b)—Passing flasher switch
(c)—Headlight dimmer switch
(d)—Windshield wiper switch
(e)—Wiper speed control switch
37. Windshield wiper motor
38. Thermo switch (electric fan)
39. Stop light switch
40. Master relay
41. Pump relay
42. Starter valve relay
43. Relay 2, electric window
44. Relay 1, electric window
45. Fuses
46. Supplementary fuse box, air conditioner
47. Windshield washer pump, foot-operated
48. Blower (air conditioner)
49. Temperature switch (air conditioner)
50. Control relay (air conditioner)
51. Blower switch (air conditioner)
52. Electro-magnetic clutch, air conditioning compressor
53. Ignition coil
54. Transistorized ignition switching unit
55. Series resistance
56. Distributor
57. Spark plugs
58. Series resistance
59. Ignition switch
60. Headlight switch
61. Supplementary fuse box, clearance lights
62. Radio (optional)
63. Antenna (optional)
64. Delay switch, front reading light
65. Cold start valve
66. Thermo-time switch
67. Courtesy light
68. Door jamb switch, left front
69. Warning buzzer
70. Buzzer switch
71. Reading light, front
72. Door jamb switch, right front
73. Kick-down switch
74. Starter lock-out and back-up light switch
75. Dome light switch, rear
76. Dome light, rear
77. Solenoid valve, automatic transmission
78. Fuses, electric window lifter
79. Wiring harness connector, rear light unit
80. Switch group, electric window lifter
(a)—Switch, right rear window
(b)—Switch, right front window
(c)—Switch, left rear window
(d)—Safety switch
(e)—Switch, left front window
81. Switch, right rear window
82. Window motor, right rear window
83. Window motor, right front window
84. Switch, left rear window
85. Window motor, left rear window
86. Window motor, left front window
87. Trunk light
88. Sending unit, fuel gage
89. Fuel pump
90. Alternator
91. Voltage regulator
92. Starter motor
93. Battery
94. Clearance light, right
95. Rear light unit, right
(a)—Turn signal
(b)—Tail light
(c)—Back-up light
(d)—Stop light
96. License plate light
97. Rear light unit, left
(a)—Turn signal
(b)—Tail light
(c)—Back-up light
(d)—Stop light
98. Clearance light, left

300SEL 3.5 and 300SEL 4.5

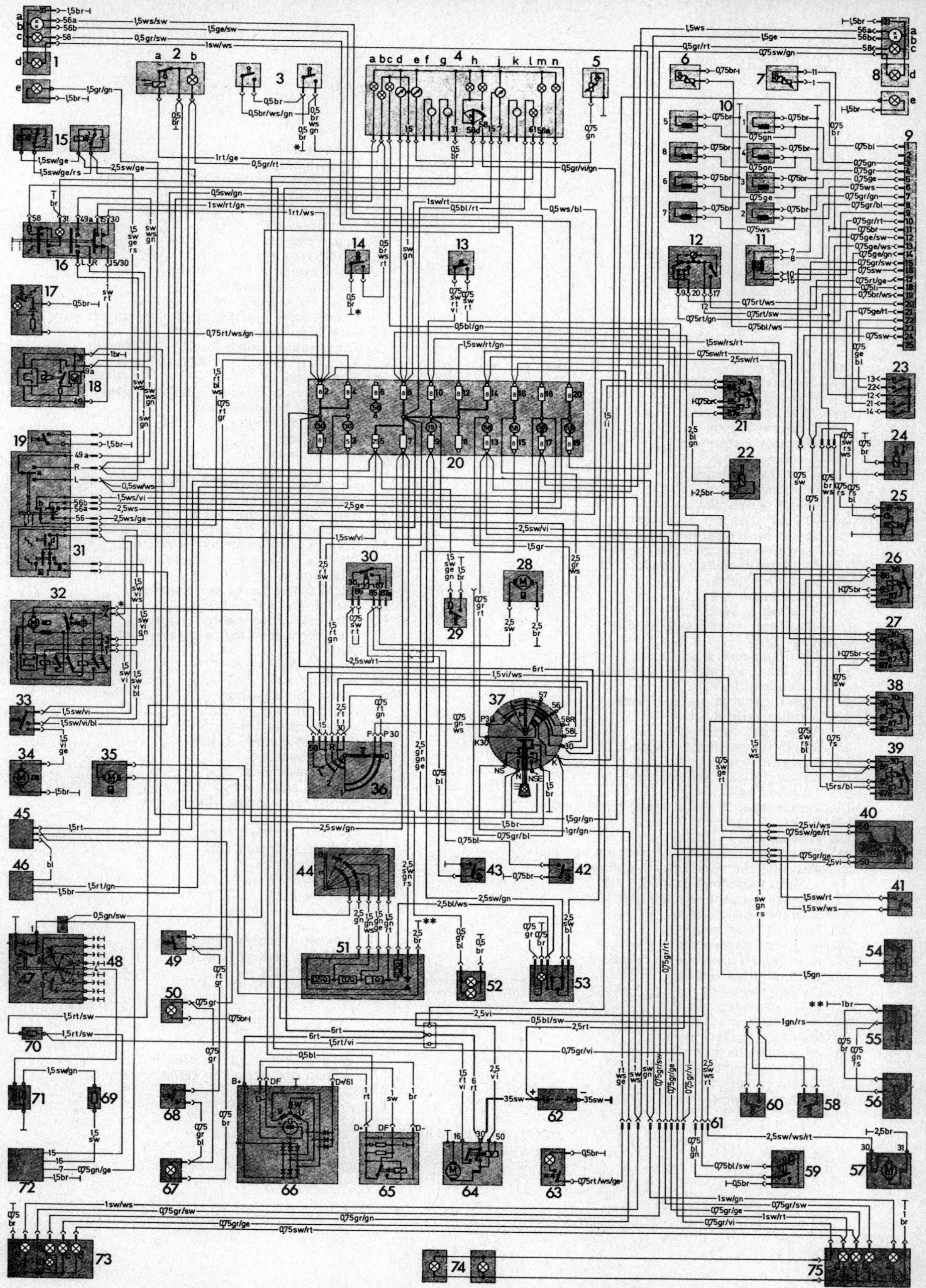

350,SL, 450SL and 450SLC

1. Light unit left
(a)—High beam
(b)—Low beam (dimmer)
(c)—Clearance light/parking light
(d)—Blinker (flasher) light
(e)—Fog light
2. Electric clock
(a)—Function
(b)—Illumination
3. Control switch for brake fluid
4. Instrument cluster
(a)—Blinker (flasher) pilot left
(b)—Service and parking brake pilot
(c)—Fuel reserve warning light
(d)—Fuel gage
(e)—Temperature indicator
(f)—Pilot light not used
(g)—Pilot light not used
(h)—Instrument light
(i)—Rheostat instrument light
(j)—Tachometer
(k)—Pilot light not used
(l)—Charging control
(m)—High beam pilot
(n)—Blinker (flasher) pilot right
5. Sender for temperature indicator
6. Temperature sensor cooling water
7. Temperature sensor induction air
8. Light unit right
(a)—High beam
(b)—Low beam (dimmer)
(c)—Clearance light/parking light
(e)—Fog light
9. Electronic control unit multi-point connector
10. Fuel injection valves with cylinder designation
11. Intake manifold pressure sensor
12. Throttle valve switch
13. Brake light switch
14. Switch for parking brake pilot
15. Dual-tone horn
16. Warning blinker (flasher) switch
17. Glovebox light
18. Direction signal and warning blinker relay
19. Horn
20. Fusebox
21. Changeover relay air-conditioning optional
22. Magnetic clutch refrigerant compressor air-conditioning optional
23. Impulse trigger in ignition distributor
24. Starting valve
25. Thermal time switch
26. Relay for starting motor
27. Main relay for electronic injection
28. Electronic fan optional
29. Cigarette lighter
30. Relay for electric fan
31. Instrument cluster
(a)—Blinker (flasher) switch
(b)—Headlight flasher switch
(c)—Manual dimmer switch
(d)—Wiper switch
(e)—Switch for wiper speed
(I)—Slow wiping
(II)—Fast wiping
(III)—Intermittent wiping
32. Wiper motor
33. Switch for electric washer pump
34. Electric washer pump
35. Fan motor
36. Ignition starter switch
37. Light switch
38. Relay for fuel pump
39. Relay for starting value
40. Starter locking and back-up light switch
41. Kick-down switch (optional)
42. Temperature switch for 65° C (optional)
43. Temperature switch 100°C optional
44. Blower switch
45. Leads for optional automatic antenna
46. Leads for optional radio
47. Ignition distributor
48. Spark plugs
49. Door contact switch right
50. Entrance light right
51. Series resistance blower motor
52. Lights for heater controls
53. Temperature controller air-conditioning optional
54. Solenoid valve for automatic transmission
55. Three-way valve for heater controls
56. Three-way valve for heater controls
57. Fuel pump
58. Micro switch for heater controls
59. Transmitter for fuel gauge
60. Micro switch for heater controls
61. Plug connection for tail light wiring harness
62. Battery
63. Trunk light
64. Starting motor
65. Alternator regulator
66. Alternator
67. Left courtesy light
68. Door contact switch left
70. Series resistance
69. Series resistance
71. Ignition coil
72. Switch for transistor ignition
73. Tail light left
(a)—Blinker (flasher) light
(b)—Tail and parking light
(c)—Back-up light
(d)—Stop light
e)—Fog tail light
74. License plate light
75. Tail light right
(a)—Blinker (flasher) light
(b)—Tail and parking light
(c)—Back-up light
(d)—Stop light

* Ground connection on wiper motor
** Ground connection on series resistance blower motor

350,SL, 450SL and 450SLC

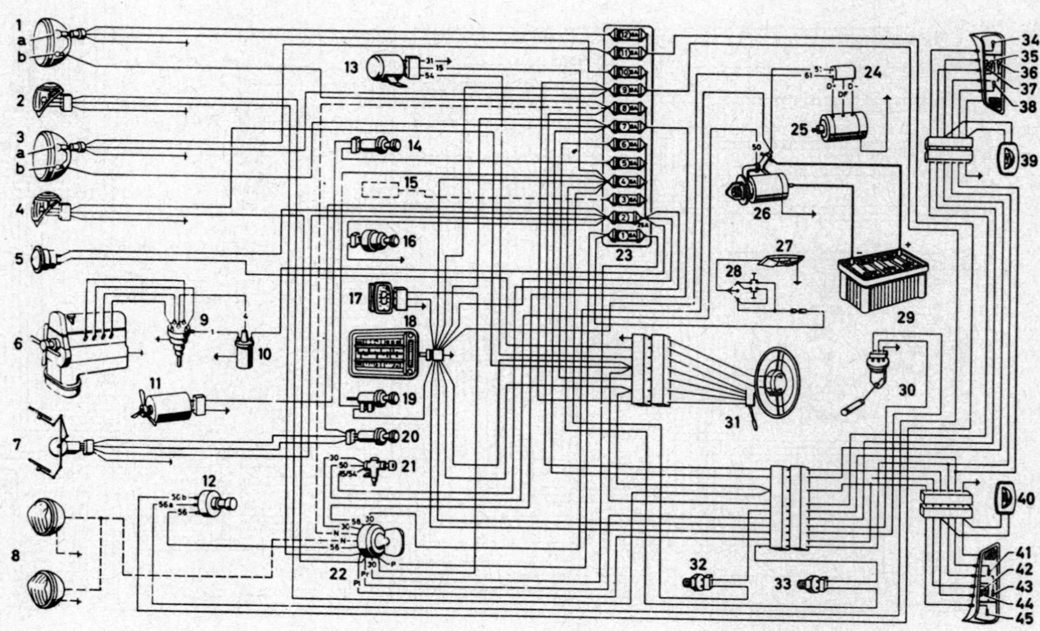

1a. Headlight left, upper beam and lower beam
1b. Headlight left, parking light
2. Clearance and flash signal lights left
3a. Headlight right, upper beam and lower beam
3b. Headlight right, parking light
4. Clearance and flash signal lights right
5. Horn
6. Engine
7. Windshield wiper
8. Fog light (optional extra)
9. Distributor
10. Ignition coil
11. Heater blower motor
12. Foot dimmer switch
13. Flash signal mechanism
14. Heater blower switch
15. Free for optional extra
16. Cigar lighter
17. Clock
18. Instrument cluster
19. Choke control
20. Windshield wiper switch
21. Ignition starter switch
22. Light switch with additional positions for clearance light and pull switch for fog lights
23. Fuses
24. Regulator
25. Generator
26. Starter
27. Reading light
28. Door contact switch
29. Battery
30. Fuel level indicator
31. Flash signal switch with upper beam flash signal switch
32. Stop light switch
33. Reversing light switch
34. Flash signal right
35. Clearance light right
36. Reversing light right
37. Tail light right
38. Stop light right
39. License plate light right
40. License plate light left
41. Stop light left
42. Tail light left
43. Reversing light left
44. Clearance light left
45. Flash signal left

Wiring diagram—190c.

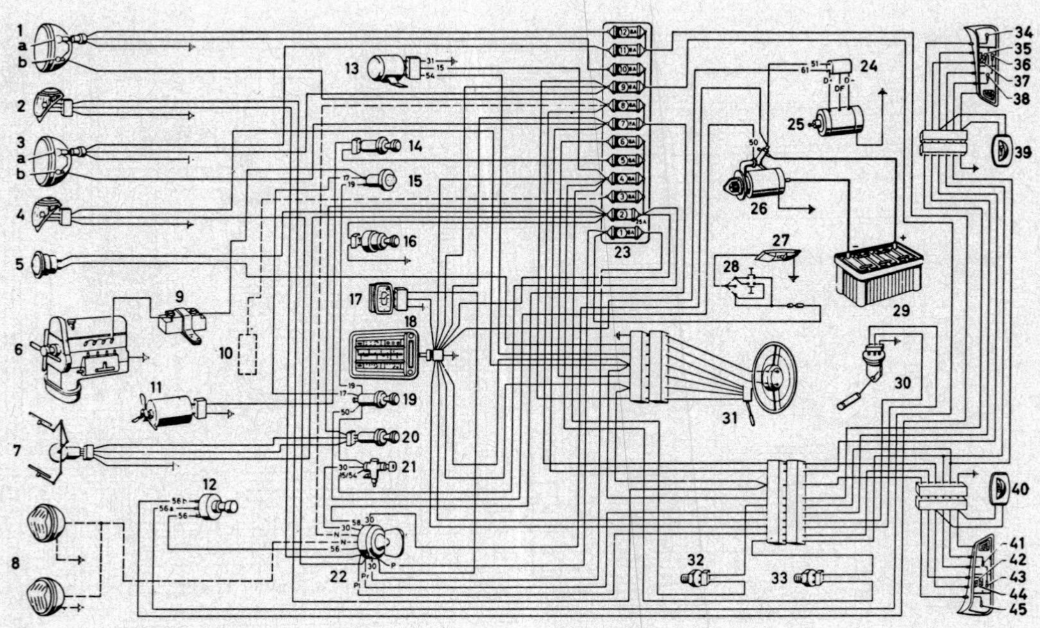

1a. Headlight left, upper beam and lower beam
1b. Headlight left, parking light
2. Clearance and flash signal lights left
3a. Headlight right, upper beam and lower beam
3b. Headlight right, parking light
4. Clearance and flash signal lights right
5. Horn
6. Engine
7. Windshield wiper
8. Fog light (optional extra)
9. Glow plug resistance
10. Free for optional extra
11. Heater blower motor
12. Foot dimmer switch
13. Flash signal mechanism
14. Heater blower switch
15. Glow plug indicator resistor
16. Cigar lighter
17. Clock
18. Instrument cluster
19. Glow plug starter switch
20. Windshield wiper switch
21. Steering lock
22. Light switch with additional positions for clearance light and pull switch for fog lights
23. Fuses
24. Regulator
25. Generator
26. Starter
27. Reading light
28. Door contact switch
29. Battery
30. Fuel level indicator
31. Flash signal switch with upper beam flash signal switch
32. Stop light switch
33. Reversing light switch
34. Flash signal right
35. Clearance light right
36. Reversing light right
37. Tail light right
38. Stop light right
39. License plate light right
40. License plate light left
41. Stop light left
42. Tail light left
43. Reversing light left
44. Clearance light left
45. Flash signal left

Wiring diagram—190Dc.

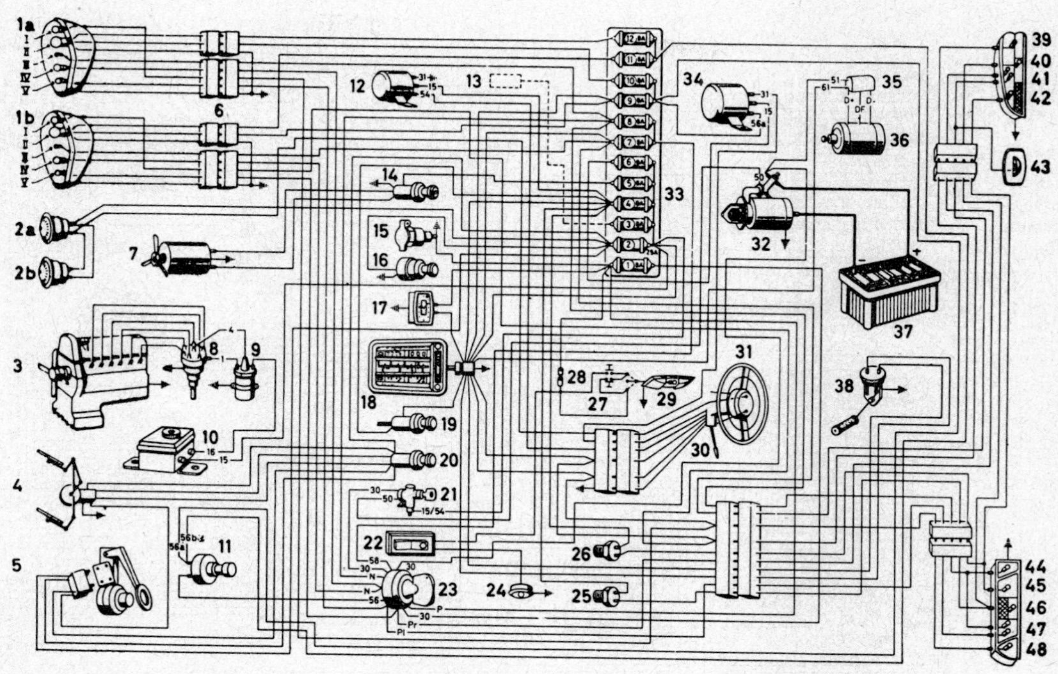

1a. Lighting unit left
 I. Flash signal light
 II. Upper beam and lower beam
 III. Parking light
 IV. Fog light
 V. Clearance light
1b. Lighting unit right
 I. Flash signal light
 II. Upper beam and lower beam
 III. Parking light
 IV. Fog light
 V. Clearance light
2a. Horn right
2b. Horn left
3. Engine
4. Windshield wiper, two-stage
5. Foot pump with switch for windshield washer
6. Plug connections
7. Heater blower motor
8. Distributor
9. Ignition coil
10. Series resistance
11. Foot dimmer switch
12. Flash signal mechanism
13. Automatic clutch (optional)
14. Heater blower switch
15. Socket
16. Cigar lighter
17. Clock
18. Instrument cluster
19. Choke control
20. Windshield wiper switch
21. Ignition starter switch
22. Roof light switch (220 Sb)
23. Rotary light switch with positions for clearance light left and right and pull switch for fog lights
24. Roof light
25. Reversing light switch
26. Stop light switch
27. Door contact switch
28. Plug connections
29. Reading light
30. Flash signal switch and upper beam signal switch
31. Steering wheel with horn ring
32. Starter
33. Fuses
34. Upper beam flash mechanism
35. Regulator
36. Generator
37. Battery
38. Fuel level indicator
39. Flash signal right
40. Reversing light right
41. Clearance light and tail light right
42. Stop light right
43. License plate light right
44. License plate light left
45. Stop light left
46. Reversing light left
47. Tail and clearance light left
48. Flash signal left

Wiring diagram—220b, 220Sb (first version).

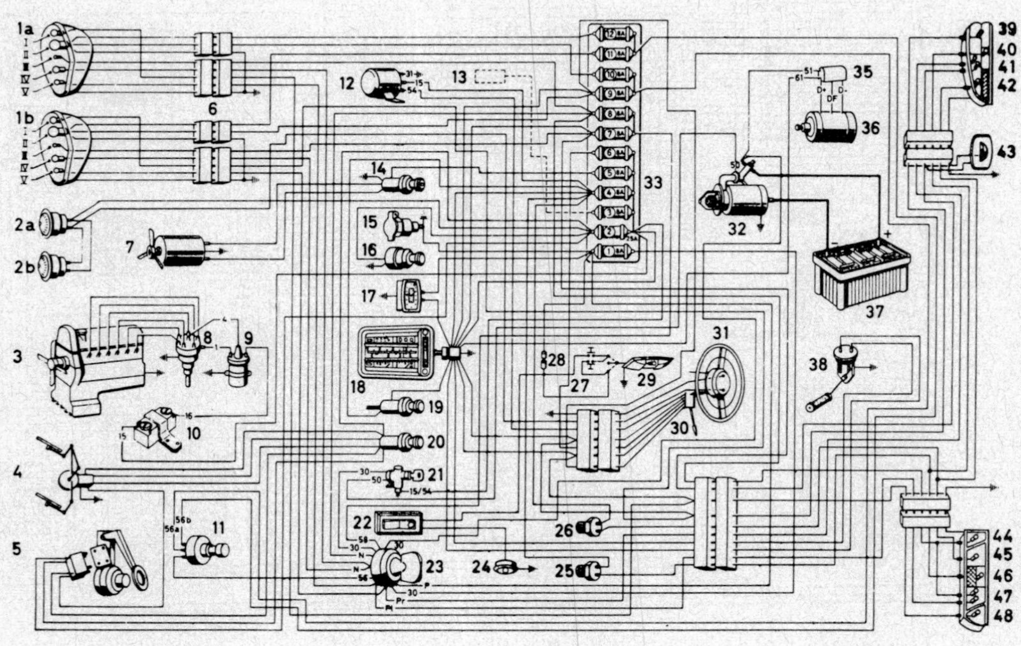

1a. Lighting unit left
  I. Flash signal light
  II. Upper beam and lower beam
  III. Parking light
  IV. Fog light
  V. Clearance light
1b. Lighting unit right
  I. Flash signal light
  II. Upper beam and lower beam
  III. Parking light
  IV. Fog light
  V. Clearance light
2a. Horn right
2b. Horn left
3. Engine
4. Windshield wiper (two-stage in 220 S)
5. Foot pump for windshield washer with switch for windshield wiper
6. Plug connections
7. Heater blower motor
8. Distributor
9. Ignition coil
10. Series resistance
11. Foot dimmer switch
12. Flash signal mechanism
13. Free for optional extra
14. Heater blower switch
15. Socket
16. Cigar lighter
17. Clock
18. Instrument cluster
19. Choke control
20. Windshield wiper switch
21. Steering lock
22. Roof light switch (only Model 220 S)
23. Light switch with additional positions for clearance light and pull switch for fog lights
24. Roof light (only Model 220 S)
25. Reversing light switch
26. Stop light switch
27. Door contact switch
28. Plug connection
29. Reading light
30. Flash signal switch and upper beam flash signal switch
31. Steering wheel with horn ring
32. Starter 12 volts
33. Fuses
35. Regulator
36. Generator 12 volts
37. Battery 12 volts
38. Fuel level indicator

Arrangement Model 220:
39. Flash signal right
40. Reversing light right
41. Clearance light and tail light right
42. Stop light right
43. License plate light right

Arrangement Model 220 S:
44. License plate light left
45. Stop light left
46. Reversing light left
47. Tail and clearance light left
48. Flash signal left

Wiring diagram—220b, 220Sb (second version).

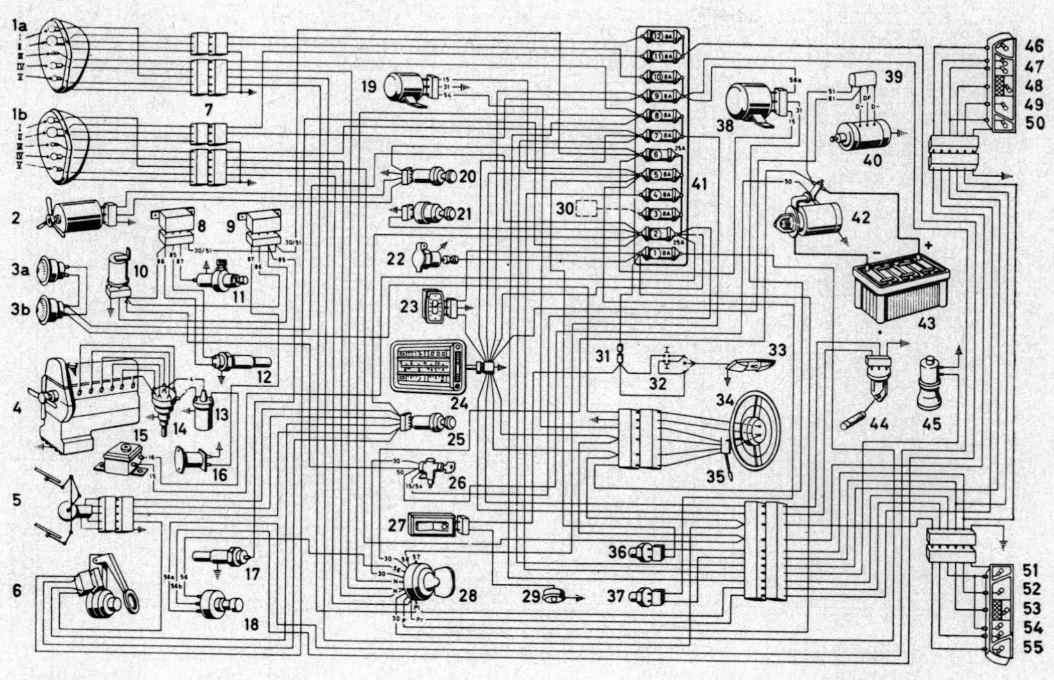

1a. Lighting unit left
I. Flash signal light
II. Upper beam and lower beam
III. Parking light
IV. Fog light
V. Clearance light
1b. Lighting unit right
I. Flash signal light
II. Upper beam and lower beam
III. Parking light
IV. Fog light
V. Clearance light
2. Heater blower motor
3a. Horn right
3b. Horn left
4. Spark plugs (engine)
5. Windshield wiper
6. Foot pump and switch for windshield washer
7. Plug connection
8. Relay for electromagnetic starting valve
9. Relay for automatic starter aid
10. Time switch
11. Electro-magnetic starting valve
12. Thermo time switch
13. Ignition coil
14. Distributor
15. Series resistance for ignition coil
16. Magnet for mixture control
17. Thermo switch
18. Foot dimmer switch
19. Flash signal mechanism
20. Switch for heater blower motor
21. Cigar lighter
22. Socket
23. Electric clock
24. Instrument cluster
25. Windshield wiper switch
26. Steering lock
27. Roof light switch
28. Rotary light switch
29. Roof light
30. Free for optional extra
31. Plug connection
32. Door contact switch left and right
33. Reading light
34. Steering wheel with horn ring
35. Flash signal switch and upper beam flash signal switch
36. Stop light switch
37. Reversing light switch
38. Beam flash signal
39. Regulator (Lima)
40. Generator
41. Fuses
42. Starter
43. Battery
44. Fuel level indicator
45. Electric fuel feed pump
46. Flash signal right
47. Tail light and clearance light right
48. Reversing light right
49. Stop light right
50. License plate light right
51. Licnse plate light left
52. Stop light left
53. Reversing light left
54. Tail light and clearance light left
55. Flash signal left

Wiring diagram—220b, 220Sb (first version).

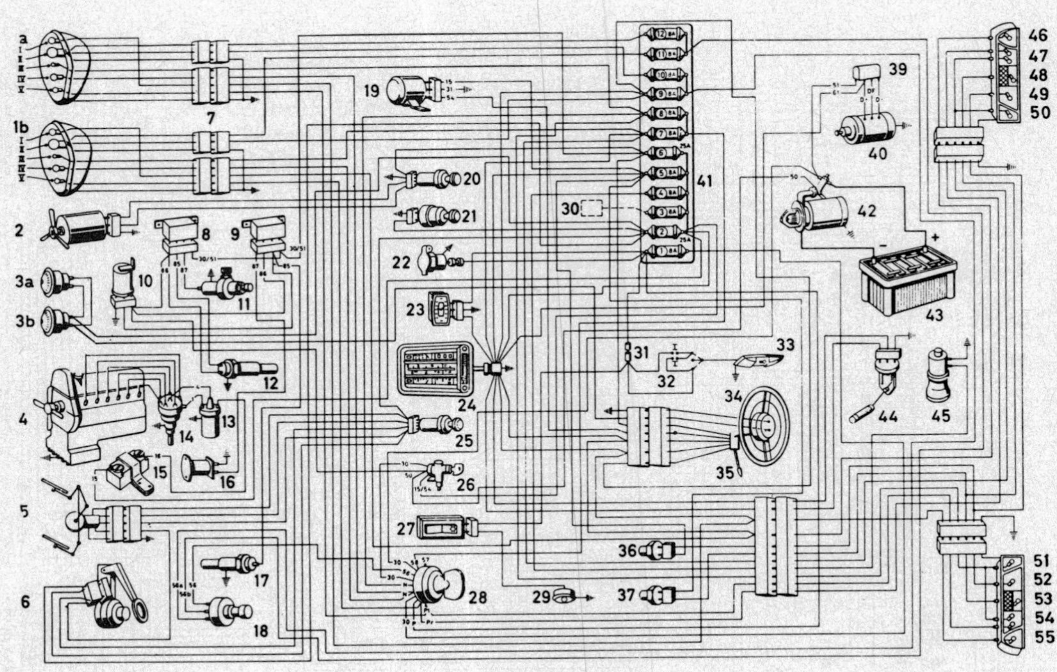

1a. Lighting unit left
 I. Flash signal light
 II. Upper beam and lower beam
 III. Parking light
 IV. Fog light
 V. Clearance light
1b. Lighting unit right
 I. Flash signal light
 II. Upper beam and lower beam
 III. Parking light
 IV. Fog light
 V. Clearance light
2. Heater blower motor
3a. Horn right
3b. Horn left
4. Spark plugs (engine)
5. Windshield wiper, two-stage
6. Foot pump and switch for windshield washer
7. Plug connection
8. Relay for electromagnetic starting valve
9. Relay for automatic starter aid
10. Time switch (delay switch)
11. Electromagnetic starting valve
12. Thermo time switch
13. Ignition coil
14. Distributor
15. Series resistance for ignition coil
16. Magnet for mixture control
17. Thermo switch
18. Foot dimmer switch
19. Flash signal mechanism
20. Switch for heater blower motor
21. Cigar lighter
22. Socket
23. Electric clock
24. Instrument cluster
25. Windshield wiper switch
26. Steering lock
27. Roof light switch
28. Rotary light switch
29. Roof light
30. Free for optional extra
31. Plug connection
32. Door contact switch left and right
33. Reading light
34. Steering wheel with horn ring
35. Flash signal switch and upper beam flash signal switch
36. Stop light switch
37. Reversing light switch
39. Regulator (Lima)
40. Generator
41. Fuses
42. Starter
43. Battery
44. Fuel level indicator
45. Electric fuel feed pump
46. Flash signal right
47. Tail light and clearance light right
48. Reversing light right
49. Stop light right
50. License plate light right
51. License plate light left
52. Stop light left
53. Reversing light left
54. Tail light and clearance light left
55. Flash signal left

Wiring diagram—220SEb sedan (second version).

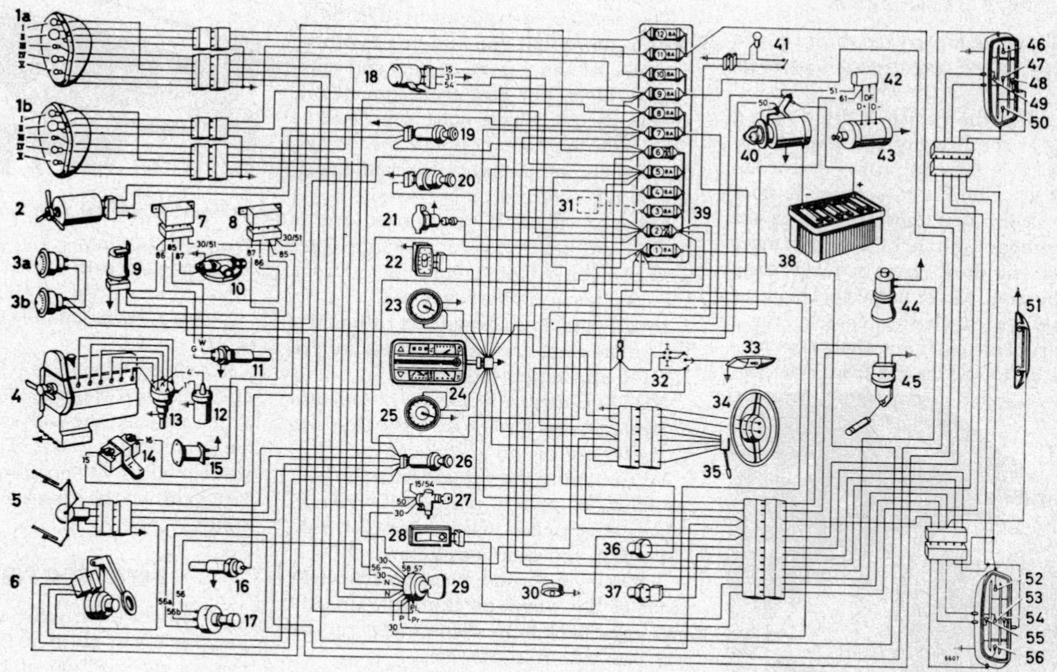

1a. Lighting unit left
  I. Flash signal light
  II. Upper beam and lower beam
  III. Parking light
  IV. Fog light
  V. Clearance light
1b. Lighting unit right
  I. Flash signal light
  II. Upper beam and lower beam
  III. Parking light
  IV. Fog light
  V. Clearance light
2. Heater blower motor
3a. Horn right
3b. Horn left
4. Spark plugs (engine)
5. Windshield wiper, two-stage
6. Foot pump for windshield washer with switch for windshield wiper
7. Relay for electromagnetic starting valve
8. Relay for automatic starter aid
9. Time switch for automatic starter aid
10. Electromagnetic starting valve
11. Thermo time switch (for para 10)
12. Ignition coil
13. Distributor
14. Series resistance for ignition coil
15. Solenoid switch for mixture control
16. Thermo switch (for para 15)
17. Foot dimmer switch
18. Flash signal mechanism
19. Blower switch with pilot light
20. Cigar lighter
21. Socket
22. Electric clock
23. Speedometer
24. Instrument cluster
25. Revolution counter
26. Windshield wiper switch
27. Steering lock
28. Roof light switch
29. Rotary light switch
30. Roof light
31. Optional extra
32. Door contact switch left and right
33. Reading light
34. Steering wheel with horn ring
35. Flash signal switch and upper beam flash signal switch
36. Reversing light switch
38. Battery
39. Fuses
40. Starter
41. Glove compartment light
42. Regulator (generator)
43. Generator
44. Electric fuel feed pump
45. Fuel level indicator
46. Flash signal right
47. Tail light right
48. Reversing light right
49. Clearance light right
50. Stop light right
51. License plate light
52. Stop light left
53. Tail light left
54. Reversing light left
55. Clearance light left
56. Flash signal left

Wiring diagram—220SEb Coupe.

Towing

All Models

CAUTION: *If, for any reason, a vehicle must be towed, great care should be used.*

For towing, the vehicle is fitted with a tow ring at the front of the chassis side member. A similar ring is provided at the rear for attaching a tow rope. It goes without saying that these tow rings are for emergency use and for short distances only. A strong, flexible woven fabric strap should be used. Never use a steel cable or rope. Always check the vehicle for a plate or sticker specifying that the vehicle only be towed on the front wheels.

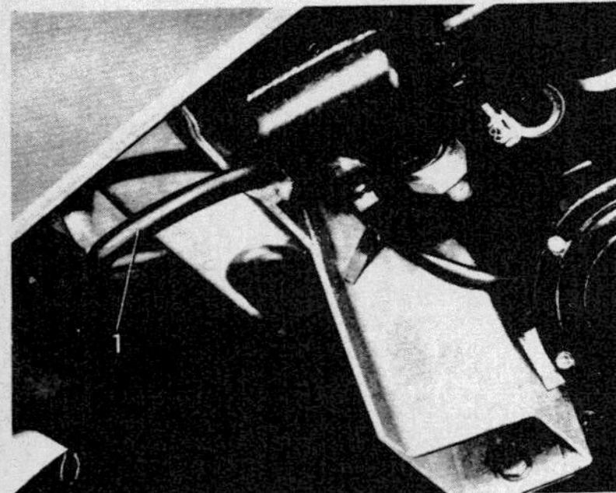

Front towing eye

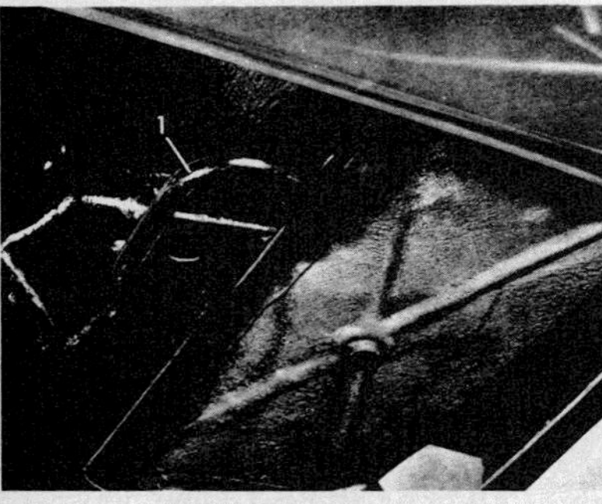

Rear towing eye

Vehicles equipped with manual transmissions should be towed in Neutral and vehicles with automatic transmissions should be towed with the selector lever in N. The towing speed should never exceed 30 miles per hour.

CAUTION: *On vehicles with a damaged front end section, the driveshaft must be disconnected to ensure that cooling water does not enter the transmission fluid or that the transmission is no longer lubricated due to an interrupted oil circuit.*

Jacking and Hoisting

The bumper jack supplied with the car should never be used for any service operation other than tire changing. NEVER get under the car while it is supported by a bumper jack. If the jack should slip or tip over, as bumper jacks often do, it would be exceedingly difficult to raise the car while pinned underneath. Always block the wheels when changing tires.

The service operations in this book often require that one end or the other, or both, of the car be raised and supported safely. The best arrangement is a grease pit or a vehicle hoist. The illustrations show the contact points for various types of lift equipment. A hydraulic floor jack is also referred to.

Drive-on trestles, or ramps, are a handy and safe way to raise the car. These can be bought or constructed from suitable heavy timbers or steel.

In any case, it is always best to spend a little extra time to make sure that the car is lifted and supported safely.

NOTE: *Concrete blocks are not recommended, since they may break if the load is not evenly distributed.*

When raising the vehicle with the jack supplied, be sure to position the chocks which are supplied in the vehicle's trunk.

Position the chocks as follows:

1. On level ground, place one chock in front of the wheel on the opposite side and one chock behind the wheel on the opposite side from the jack.
2. On a grade, place one chock behind the front and rear wheels on the opposite side from the jack.
3. On vehicles with manual transmission, place the transmission in low gear. On vehicles with automatic transmissions, place the selector lever in Park.
4. Always be sure to set the parking brake firmly.

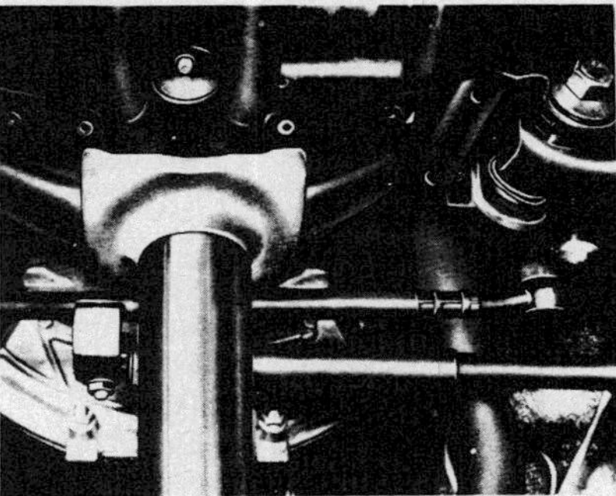

Jacking the front of the vehicle with a pit or floor jack.

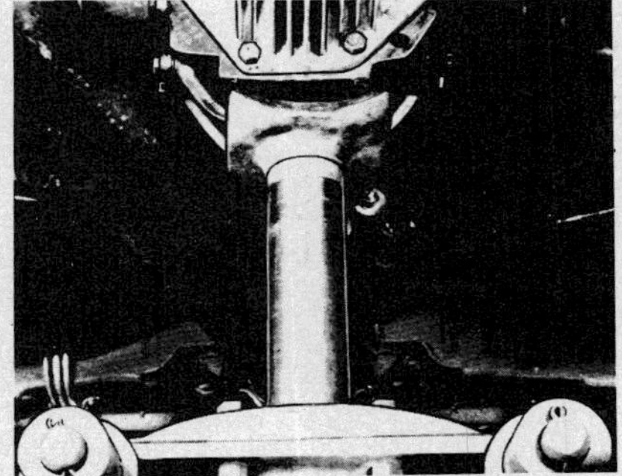

Jacking the rear of the vehicle with a pit or floor jack.

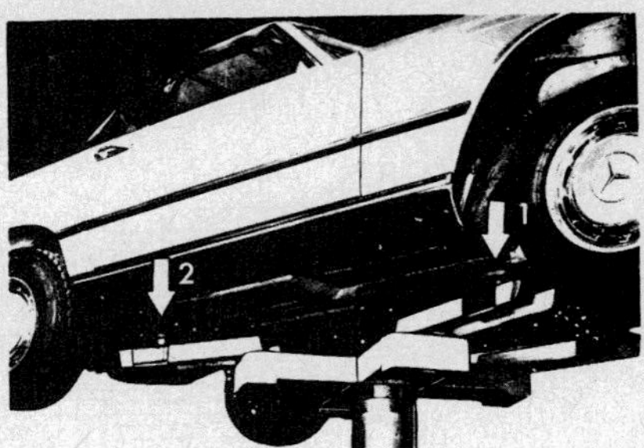

Jacking the vehicle with a cross-head jack

1. Inner frame side member
2. Rear axle carrier

5. Always position the vehicle jack vertically.

In a shop, the vehicle is best lifted with a pit jack or cross-head jack. To lift the car with a pit jack, the jack should be under the front and rear axle. This also applies to floor jacks. When using a cross-head jack, position the lifting platforms as illustrated.

Tire Rotation

To obtain even wear and the longest possible life of all tires, it is advisable to change the position of the wheels and tires periodically (summer tires—every 3000 miles and winter tires—every 1500 miles). With radial snow tires it is important to rotate the tires to prevent loss of normal handling. It is of equal importance to adjust the tire pressure to specifications after this operation.

The tires should only be rotated front to rear and on the same side. The driving direction of the tire should remain constant.

Tire Pressure

A table located in the tank filler flap lists the tire pressures for various tire designs, as well as conditions. The tire pressures quoted for light loads are minimum and afford the greatest driving comfort. Higher tire pressures intended for heavier loads are permissible for lightly loaded vehicles and will increase the handling ability, although the suspension will become slightly harder.

Since the tire temperature and pressure will increase with vehicel speed, the tire pressure should be adjusted only on cold tires. Tire pressure on hot tires should only be corrected if the pressure has dropped below that listed in the table and the operating conditions are taken into consideration.

Wheels

There are several precautions which should be observed when tightening the

Torque sequence for light alloy and steel disc wheels.

spherical collar bolts on disc wheels.

1. Be sure that the correct tightening sequence is followed.
2. The correct torque for the spherical collar bolts is 72 ft lbs.
3. Only the spherical collar bolts should be used for the disc wheels (light alloy and steel wheels).

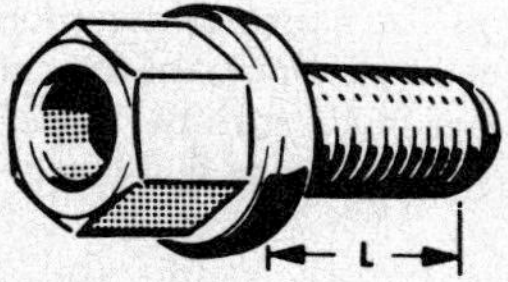

Spherical collar bolts for steel disc wheels. L = approx. 0.8 in.

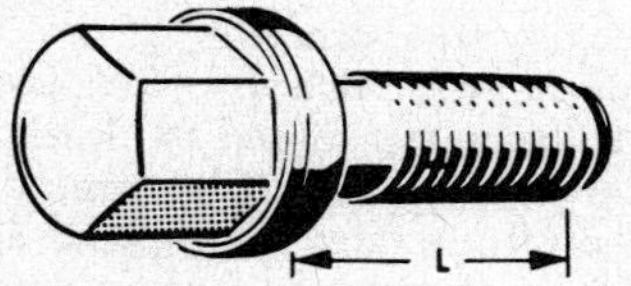

Spherical collar bolts for light alloy wheels. L = approx. 1.2 in.

4. Do not use an air gun to tighten the spherical collar bolts. These should only be tightened with a torque wrench.
5. The tightening torque is for cold wheels. If the wheels are tightened when warm, be sure that they are not tightened to the full torque. As soon as the wheels have cooled, torque them to the correct specification.

TUNE-UP PROCEDURES

The extent of an engine tune-up is usually determined by the length of time since the previous service, although the type of driving and the general mechanical condition of the engine must be considered. Specific maintenance should also be performed at regular intervals, depending on operating conditions. The troubleshooting section of this manual is general in nature, yet specific enough to locate the problem. Service usually comprises two areas: diagnosis and repair. While the apparent cause of trouble, in many cases, is worn or damaged parts, performance problems are less obvious. The first job is to locate the problem and cause. Once the problem has been isolated, refer to the appropriate section for repair, removal or adjustment procedures.

It is advisable to read the entire chapter before beginning a tune-up, although those who are more familiar with tune-up procedures may wish to go directly to the instructions.

Spark Plugs

Spark plugs should be checked frequently (approximately 5000 miles) depending on use. Mercedes-Benz recommends that the spark plugs be renewed at least every 10,000 miles; if heavily leaded fuels are used, they should be replaced every 5000 miles. All the recommendations are based on the ambient conditions as well as driving conditions. If the car is driven at high speeds constantly, the plugs will probably not need as much attention as those used for constant stop-and-start driving.

The electrode end of the plug (the end with the threads) is a good indicator of the internal condition of your engine. If a spark plug has fouled and caused the engine to misfire, the problem will have to be found and corrected. Often, by "reading" the spark plugs, they will lead you to the cause of the problem. Spark plug conditions and probable causes are listed in the "Troubleshooting" section of this book. It is a good idea to pull the plugs once in a while just to get an idea of the internal condition of the engine.

NOTE: *A small amount of light tan-colored deposits on the electrode end of the spark plug is quite normal. These plugs need not be replaced, unless they are severely worn.*

It is generally advisable to use the factory recommended spark plug, although in cases of extremely hard use (e.g., driving cross country in August), going to the next cooler heat range is all right. The same is true if most driving is done in the city or over short distances, go to the next hotter range spark plug to eliminate spark plug fouling.

NOTE: *Some Mercedes-Benz automobiles are equipped with platinum spark plugs. These spark plugs must be regapped more carefully than "normal" types, and, while their lifespan may be longer, they are also subject to the "once only" regapping rule.*

To regap a platinum plug, the body electrode is bent slightly forward by light strokes applied at the arrowed portion of its outer casing. If in doubt concerning spark plug substitution, consult a Mercedes-Benz dealer.

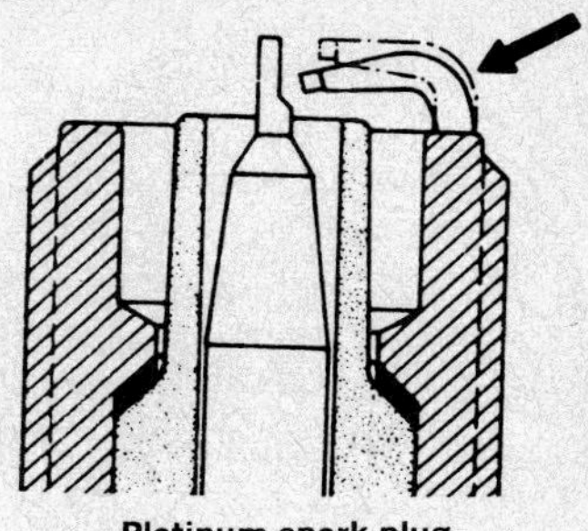

Platinum spark plug

Spark plugs should be gapped even when new plugs are installed and when they are checked periodically.

To gap the spark plugs, remove each one in turn and measure the gap with a round feeler gauge of the appropriate thickness. Prior to removing the plugs, blow dirt away with compressed air. This is especially necessary on 280 and 280C engines. Insert the round feeler gauge between the center and side electrode. To adjust the gap, bend the side electrode with the tool on the end of the feeler gauge until the specified gap is obtained.

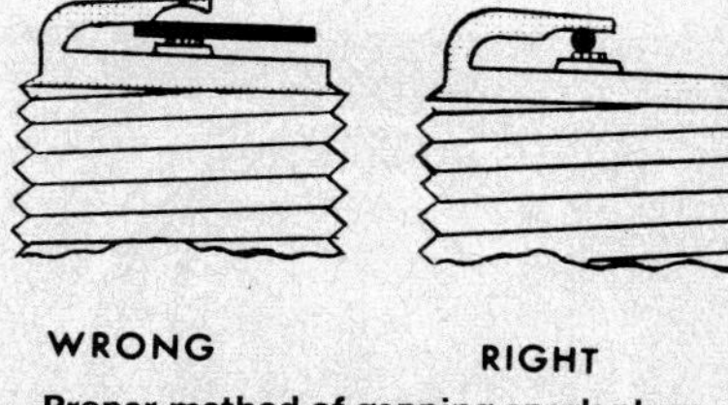

Proper method of gapping spark plugs

When installing the plugs, insert the plugs into the engine and tighten them finger-tight. Be sure that the plugs are not cross-threaded. If the plugs use metal gaskets, new gaskets should be installed each time the plugs are removed and installed.

Tighten the spark plugs to 18–21 ft lbs and install the spark plug wires on their respective plugs. Be sure that each wire is firmly connected.

While you are about the task of checking the spark plugs, the spark plug wires should also be checked. Any wires that are cracked or brittle should be replaced. Bend the wires into a loop to check for cracks.

Breaker Points and Condenser

Replacement

1. Raise the hood and remove the rubber or plastic cover from the distributor.
2. Release the clips on the side of the distributor cap and remove the cap. Lay it aside.
3. Remove the rotor and plate from the distributor shaft.
4. Remove the distributor contact holder by removing the screw or screws.

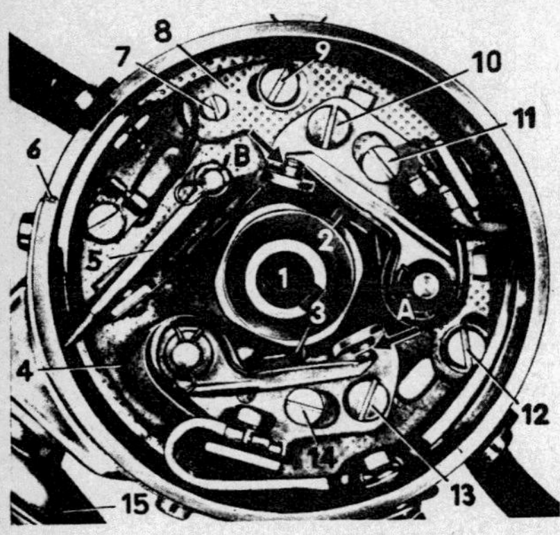

Distributor with two sets of points (300-SEL 6.3).

(a)—Contact breaker set (open)
(b)—Contact breaker set (closed)
1. Distributor cam
2,3. Slide piece
4. Base plate
5. Pull rod for vacuum adjustment
6. Cylinder 1 marking
7. Adjusting cam
8. Intermediate plate
9,12. Attaching screw
10,13. Attaching screw for contact breakers
11,14. Adjusting screw
15. Vacuum diaphragm

Distributor used on 3.5 and 4.5 V-8 engines.

Some models also have a snap-ring on the bearing contact lever, which must also be removed. Pry the wire from the connecting terminal or loosen the screw at the terminal and remove the wire from the connecting terminal.

5. On models with 2 sets of points, remove the snap-rings from the bearing pins and unscrew the setscrews and screw at the connecting terminal. Pull both contact sets off the bearing pins and remove the wire from the connector.

6. Disconnect the condenser wire and remove the condenser from its bracket.

7. Before installing new points, clean the contact surfaces by squeezing them against a clean matchbook cover. This will remove any film or condensate.

8. Lightly coat the slide piece of the contact breaker with high temperature multipurpose grease.

9. On vehicles manufactured prior to January, 1970, add about 2 drops of oil to the felt pad on the shaft and, if installed, to the distributor oiler. On vehicles made

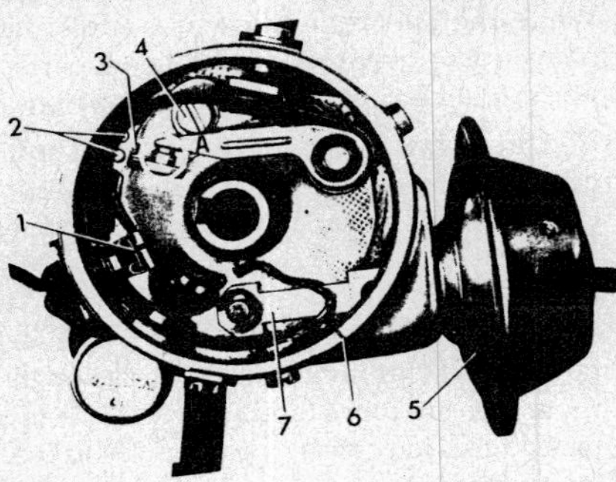

Distributor used on 4, 6 and early 8 cylinder engines.

(a)—Contact breaker pair (contact closed)

1. Connecting terminal from low-voltage to ignition coil and to cable from breaker arm
2. Bosses on contact breaker plate
3. Contact holder with adjusting slot
4. Screw for contact holder
5. Vacuum box with diaphragm
6. Notch on distributor housing rim of distributor for cylinder no. 1
7. Pull rod for vacuum control

after January, 1970, the felt pad no longer requires lubrication.

10. Check to be sure that the contacts are parallel and at the same level with each other when closed. Misalignment can be corrected by bending the fixed contact support. Never bend the movable contact support.

11. On distributors with 2 sets of points, clean the connecting cable and insulating plate.

12. Install a new condenser and connect the wire.

13. Install a new contact set or sets into the distributor.

14. Install the hold-down screw(s) and/or the snap-rings on the bearing pins of the contact plate.

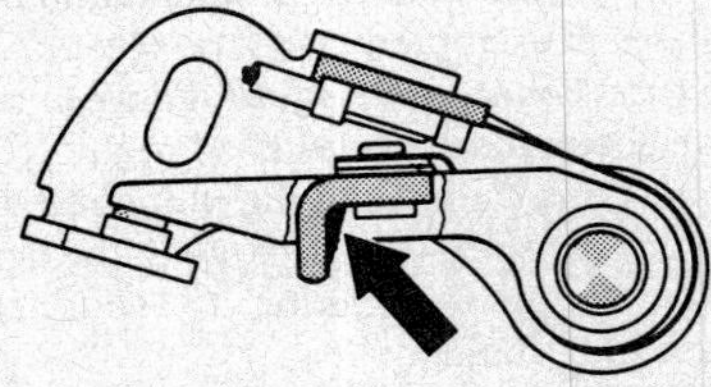

Slide piece of the contact breaker

LATERAL MISALIGNMENT

PROPER LATERAL ALIGNMENT

CORRECT LATERAL MISALIGNMENT BY BENDING FIXED CONTACT SUPPORT <u>NEVER BEND BREAKER LEVER</u>

Proper point alignment

15. Connect the wire to the terminal and tighten the nut, if necessary.

16. Install the plate and rotor on the shaft.

17. Install the cap and secure it in place with the clips.

18. Check the dwell angle and ignition timing. Adjust if necessary.

Dwell Angle

Adjust

When setting ignition contact points, it is advisable to observe the following general rules:

1. If the points are old, they should not be adjusted using a feeler gauge. The gauge will not give an accurate reading on a pitted surface.

2. Never file the points—this removes their protective coating and results in rapid pitting.

3. When using a feeler gauge to set new points, be certain that the points are fully open. The fiber rubbing block must rest on the highest point of the cam lobe.

4. Always make sure the feeler gauge is free of oil or grease before setting points.

5. Make sure the points are properly aligned and that the feeler gauge is not tilted. If points are misaligned, bend the fixed contact support only, never the movable breaker arm.

A dwell meter virtually eliminates errors in point gap caused bv distributor cam lobes being unequally worn, or human error. In any case, point dwell should be checked as soon as possible after setting with a feeler gauge, because it is a far more accurate check of point operation under normal operating conditions.

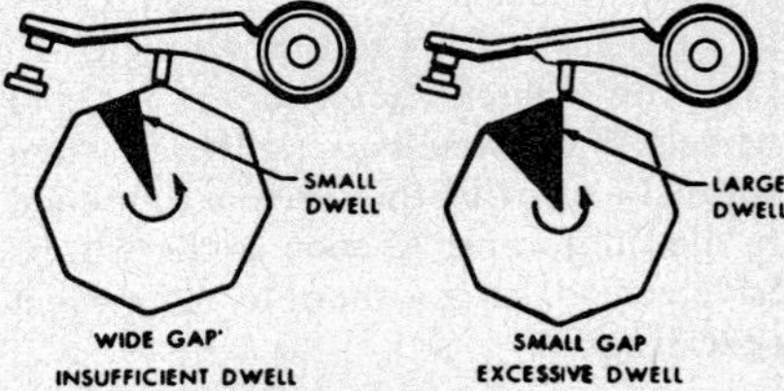

Dwell as a function of point gap

Because the fiber block wears down gradually in service, it is good practice to set the dwell on the low side of any dwell range (smaller number of degrees) given in specifications. As the block wears, the dwell becomes greater (toward the center of the range) and point life is increased between adjustments.

All Models Except 220D and 300SEL 6.3

Normal Method

1. The dwell angle should be measured at idle speed.

2. Raise the hood and connect a dwell meter and tachometer.

3. Start the engine and allow it to reach normal idle speed. Read the dwell angle from the meter on the appropriate scale.

4. If the dwell varies by 5 or more degrees from the specifications, the points should be replaced.

NOTE: *On normal coil ignitions, the dwell angle should not be adjusted on worn contact points. It is also possible that a given dwell meter will not work satisfactorily on transistor ignitions. This depends on the construction of the individual meter used.*

5. If the dwell angle is not according to specifications, remove the distributor cap and adjust the dwell angle. Reduce the point gap if the dwell angle is too small, or increase the contact point gap if the dwell angle is too large.

6. To actually adjust the point gap, loosen the hold-down screw and insert a screwdriver between the lugs on the breaker plate and move the plate to the desired location. Tighten the hold-down screw. On some models it is possible to adjust the point gap by means of the eccentric screw provided for this purpose in the breaker plate.

7. Recheck the dwell angle and adjust the gap again if it is still not satisfactory. Repeat the process until the dwell angle is as specified.

Alternative Method

As an alternative in the absence of a dwell meter, or to set the point gap initially, a feeler gauge may be used, but this method is far less accurate.

1. Remove the distributor cap.
2. Turn the distributor shaft until the contact breaker arm is on the exact highest point of the cam lobe.
3. Insert a clean (non-greasy) feeler blade, of the specified thickness, between the contact faces of the points.
4. Adjust the gap as detailed above in Step 6.
5. Run the engine for a few seconds and recheck the adjustment to be sure.

300SEL 6.3

To check the dwell on this distributor, each set must be checked separately. Block off each set in turn with an insulating block. Dwell angle is checked with the center coil wire disconnected and at cranking speed.

1. Connect a dwell meter.
2. Crank the engine and read the dwell from the appropriate scale on the meter.
3. If the total dwell is below specifications, replace the point sets.
4. To adjust the point gap, remove the cap and loosen the setscrews in the plate. The setscrews are located immediately behind the contact point faces.
5. Turn the eccentric screw until a gap of 0.012–0.016 in. is obtained on EACH set of points. This setting can be made with a feeler gauge.
6. Tighten the setscrews and recheck the dwell angles, both individually and totally.

Ignition Timing

Adjust

Setting the ignition timing is basically the same for each model. Generally, it is best set with a timing light. The simple 12-volt test light should not be considered a substitute for a timing light. Test lights are generally useful only for finding approximate settings after the distributor has been removed.

Before setting the ignition timing, be sure that the point gap (dwell angle) is set to the proper specifications since this will influence the timing, while timing will have no influence on the dwell angle.

Before attempting to set the timing, read the "Ignition Timing Specifications" chart carefully and determine at what speed the timing should be set and whether the vacuum should be connected or disconnected and plugged.

CAUTION: *On those engines which require that the timing be set at 3000 or 4500 rpm, run the engine at that speed for only an instant. Running the engine for any longer than an instant at high rpm is extremely dangerous and could result in engine damage.*

It is a good idea to paint the appropriate timing mark with dayglow or white paint to make it quickly and easily visible.

Be sure that all wires, hands, and arms are out of the way of the fan. Do not wear any loose clothing when reaching anywhere near the fan.

On engines with transistorized coil ignition, the timing light may or may not work depending on the construction of the light. If in doubt, consult a Mercedes-Benz dealer.

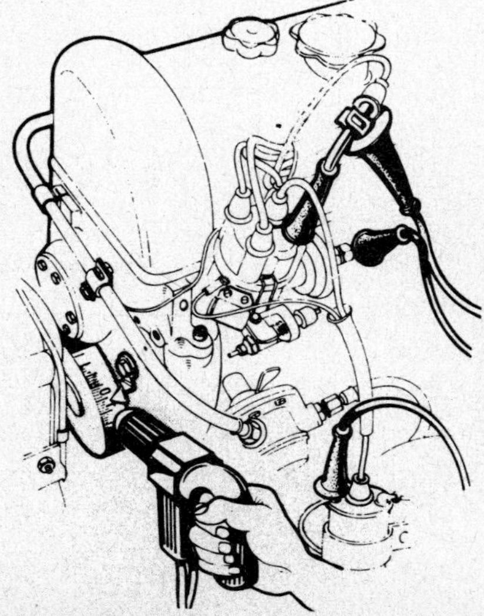

Checking ignition timing with a timing light

All Engines (Except 300SEL 6.3)

1. Raise the hood and connect a tachometer.
2. Connect a timing light as specified by the manufacturer.
3. Disconnect and plug the vacuum line(s) (a golf tee usually works well) if necessary. See "Ignition Timing Specifications". In addition, on 1970 and later 280S/8 models, the cable plug on the temperature switch in the thermostat housing must also be disconnected to eliminate the possibility of the engine switching from retard to advance while adjusting the timing.
4. On carbureted 280 and 280C engines, be sure to disconnect both vacuum lines and plug these.

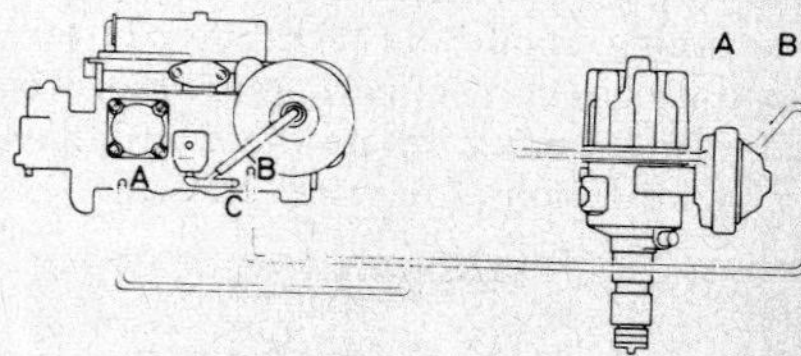

Vacuum connections on 280 and 280C engine.

(a)—Vacuum connection (retard) (white)
(b)—Vacuum connection (advance) (red)
(c)—Vacuum connection to vacuum governor and fuel return valve

5. Run the engine at the specified speed (SEE PREVIOUS **CAUTION**) and read the firing point on the balancing plate or vibration damper while shining the light on it.

NOTE: *The balancer on some 6-cylinder engines has 2 timing scales. The front degree scale (in driving direction) is for use with the old (9 mm wide) pointer. The rear scale (in driving direction) is for use with the new (triangular) pointer. If in doubt as to which scale to use, rotate the crankshaft (in the direction of rotation only) until the distributor rotor is aligned with the notch on the distributor housing (No. 1 cylinder). In this position, the timing pointer should be at TDC on the proper timing scale.*

Old 6 cylinder timing pointer (9 mm wide)

1. TDC mark and degree scale
2. Pointer (9 mm wide)

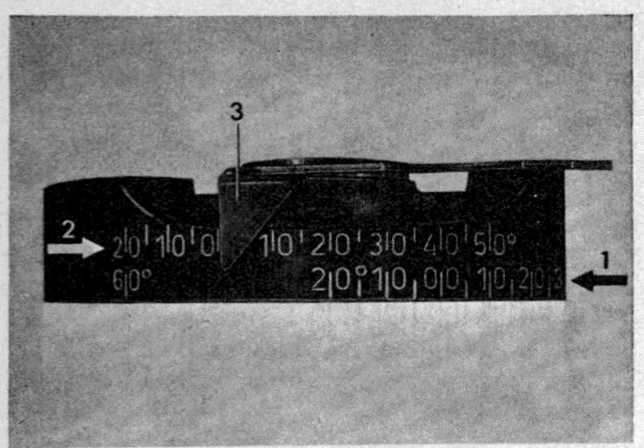

New 6 cylinder timing pointer (triangular)

1. Front degree scale
2. Rear degree scale
3. Triangular pointer

6. The ignition timing can be adjusted by loosening the distributor clamp bolt and rotating the distributor. To advance the timing, rotate the distributor in the opposite direction of normal rotation. To retard the timing, rotate the distributor in the direction of normal rotation.

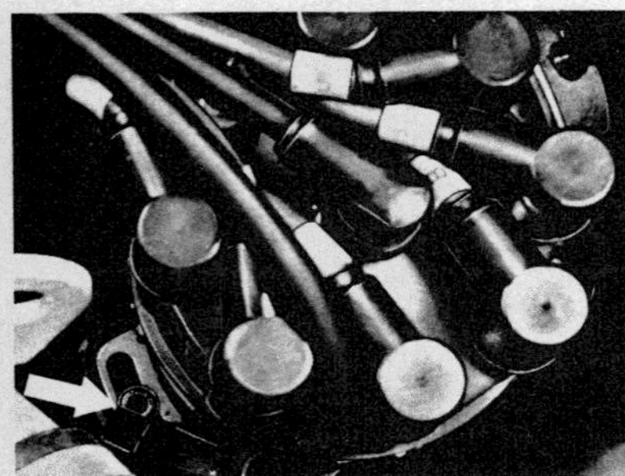

Distributor clamp bolt (arrow)

CAUTION: *When setting the timing at high rpm (3000–4500) do not try to adjust the timing while the engine is running. Run the engine to the specified rpm (for an instant) and read the timing on the scale. Shut the engine off and adjust the timing by rotating the distributor in the proper direction slightly. Repeat the process of adjusting the timing slightly and reading the timing on the scale until the timing is adjusted correctly.*

7. On 1970 and later 280S/8 models, install the temperature switch cable plug after the timing is set satisfactorily. Check the operation of the changeover switch by connecting the temperature switch on the thermostat housing to ground. The speed should increase from approximately 800 rpm to approximately 1300–1500 rpm.

8. Once the timing has been adjusted, recheck the timing once more to be sure that it has not been disturbed.

9. Remove the timing light and tachometer and connect any wires that were removed.

10. If applicable, unplug and connect the vacuum line(s).

300SEL 6.3

All of the preceding information applies to the 300SEL 6.3 in addition to the following steps.

1. Disconnect and plug the vacuum line. Connect a timing light and tachometer to No. 1 cylinder and observe the timing mark at the specified rpm. Before doing this, carefully read the two preceding CAUTIONs.

2. If necessary, adjust the timing in the manner described in the preceding instruction.

3. Because of the dual point distributor, it is also necessary to check the timing on No. 5 cylinder.

4. The values obtained should be the same as those for No. 1 cylinder.

5. If not, reset the point gaps (they must set equally) and recheck the dwell on both sets of points. It may be necessary to reset the timing after altering the dwell angle.

NOTE: *This engine is best set on a test stand by a dealer because the points must be perfectly synchronized for the engine to operate perfectly.*

6. Remove the timing light and unplug and reconnect the vacuum line.

Valve Clearance

Adjust

The valve clearance of all gasoline engines should be checked and, if necessary, adjusted when the engine is cold.

Carbureted Engines (Except 280, 280C)

The valve clearance is measured between the sliding surface of the rocker arm and the heel of the camshaft lobe. The highest point of the camshaft lobe should be at a 90° angle to the sliding surface of the rocker arm.

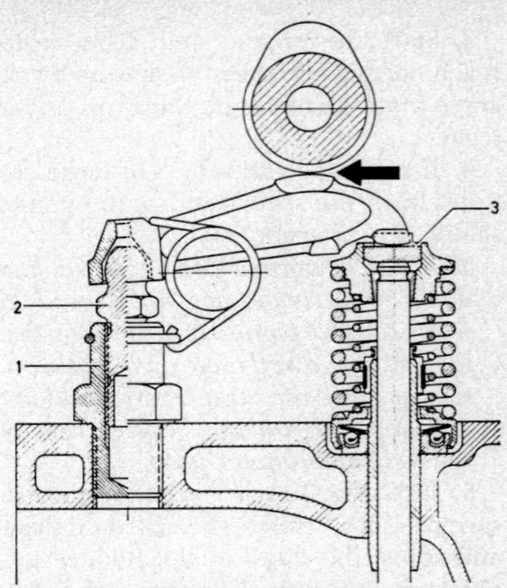

Measure the valve clearance between the surface of the rocker arm and the heel of the camshaft lobe (carbureted engines except for 280, 280C).

1. Threaded bushing
2. Adjusting screw
3. Pressure piece

1. Remove the air vent hose from the valve cover. Remove the spark plugs.

2. Remove the valve cover and gasket. On 230/8 and 250/8 engines, remove the air cleaner also.

3. Note the position of the intake and exhaust valves.

4. Rotate the crankshaft, by means of a socket wrench on the crankshaft pulley bolt, until the heel of the camshaft lobe is perpendicular to the sliding surface of the rocker arm.

NOTE: *Do not rotate the engine using the camshaft sprocket bolt. The strain will distort the timing chain tensioner rail. Always rotate the engine in the direction of normal rotation only.*

5. Some models have holes in the vibration damper plate to assist in crank-

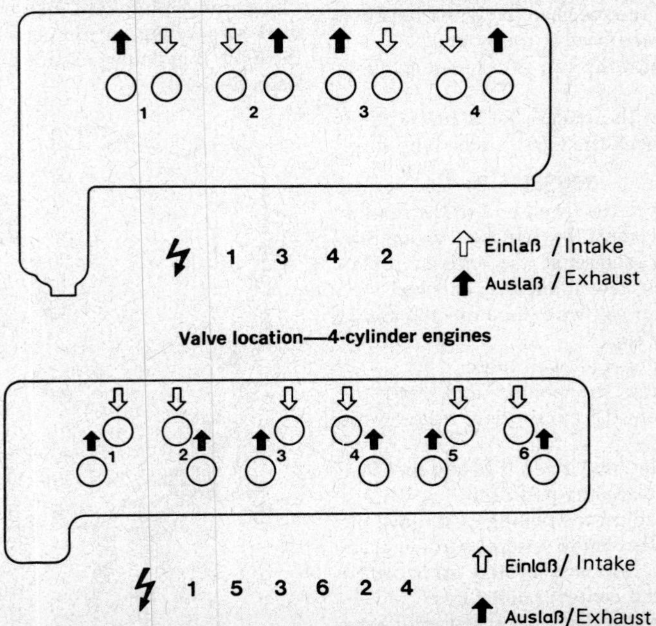

Valve location—4-cylinder engines

Valve location—6 cylinder engines

shaft rotation. In this case, a screwdriver can be used to carefully rotate the crankshaft.

6. To measure the valve clearance, insert a feeler blade of the specified thickness between the heel of the camshaft lobe and the sliding surface of the rocker arm. The clearance is correct if the blade can be inserted and withdrawn with a very slight drag.

7. If adjustment is necessary, it can be done by turning the ball pin head at the hex collar. If the clearance is too small, increase it by turning the ball pin head in. If the clearance is too large, decrease it by turning the ball pin head out.

NOTE: *This adjustment is ideally made with a special adaptor and a torque wrench. The shape of the adaptor is dictated by the need for accurate torque readings and, by using it, the torque wrench can be directly aligned with the ball pin head.*

Adjusting the valve clearance

(a)—Position of cam when adjusting valve clearance
1. Feeler gauge strip
2. Valve clearance wrench
3. Torque wrench

8. When the ball pin head is turned, the adjusting torque should be 14.4–25.0 ft lbs. If the torque is less than 14.4 ft lbs, the ball pin head will vibrate and the clearance will not remain as set. If the valve clearance is too small, and the ball pin head cannot be screwed in far enough to correct it, a thinner pressure piece should be installed in the spring retainer. The standard thickness of the pressure piece is 0.177 in. Pressure pieces are available in thicknesses of 0.137 in., and 0.0985 in. To replace the pressure piece, the rocker arm must be removed.

9. After all the valves have been checked and adjusted in the manner described above, install the valve cover. Be sure that the gasket is seated properly. It is best to use a new gasket whenever the valve cover is removed.

10. Install the spark plugs.

11. Reconnect the air vent line to the valve cover and install the air cleaner, if removed.

12. Run the engine and check for leaks at the rocker arm cover.

Fuel Injected Engines (6-Cylinder, V-8)

The valve clearance is measured between the sliding surface of the rocker arm and the heel of the camshaft lobe. The highest point of the camshaft lobe should be at a 90° angle to the sliding surface of the rocker arm.

1. Loosen the venting line and remove the regulating linkage. Remove the valve cover.

2. On V-8 engines, disconnect the cable from the ignition coil.

3. On models with the 3.5 liter engine, remove the plastic cover from around the crankshaft pulley.

4. Identify all of the valves, as intake or exhaust.

5. Beginning with No. 1 cylinder, crank the engine with the starter to position the heel of the camshaft approximately over the sliding surface of the rocker arm.

6. Rotate the crankshaft by means of a a socket wrench on the crankshaft pulley bolt until the heel of the camshaft lobe is perpendicular to the sliding surface of the rocker arm.

NOTE: *Do not rotate the engine using the camshaft sprocket bolt. The strain will distort the timing chain tensioner rail. Always rotate the engine in the direction of normal rotation only.*

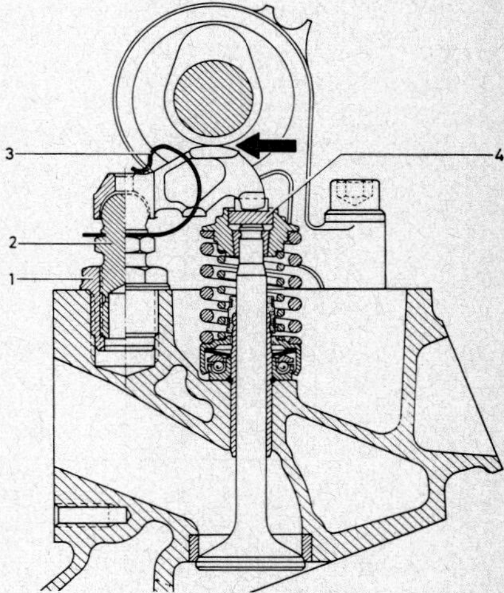

Valve clearance measurement on V-8 engines (the 6-cylinder fuel injected engines are measured in the same manner as the 6-cylinder carbureted engines).

1. Threaded bushing
2. Adjuster
3. Spring
4. Pressure piece

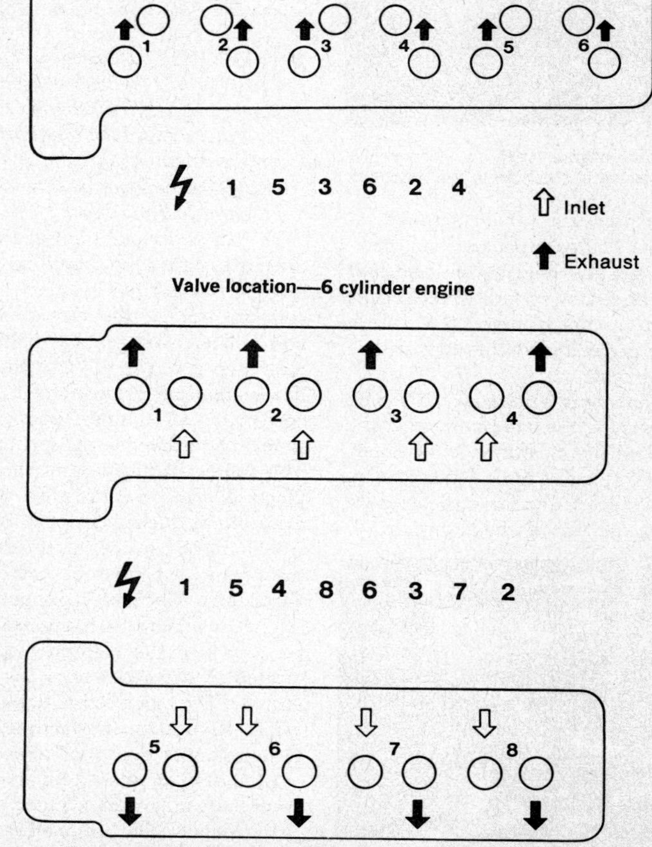

Valve location—6 cylinder engine

Valve location—3.5 and 4.5 V-8 engines

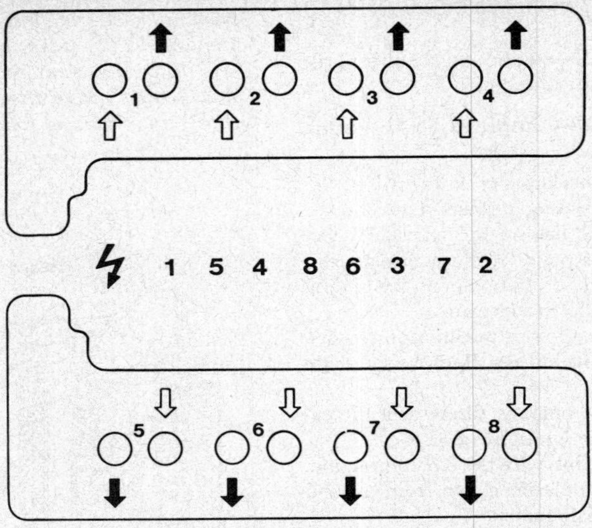

Valve location—6.3 V-8

7. Some models have holes in the vibration damper plate to assist in crankshaft rotation. In this case, a screwdriver can be used to carefully rotate the crankshaft.

Turning the engine with a screwdriver (arrow) inserted in the hole in the balancer.

8. To measure the valve clearance, insert a feeler blade of the specified thickness between the heel of the camshaft lobe and the sliding surface of the rocker arm. The clearance is correct if the blade can be inserted and withdrawn with a very slight drag.

9. If adjustment is necessary, it can be done by turning the ball pin head at the hex collar. If the clearance is too small, increase it by turning the ball pin head in. If the clearance is too large, decrease it by turning the ball pin head out.

Adjusting the valves on 3.5 and 4.5 V-8 engines with feeler blade arrow.

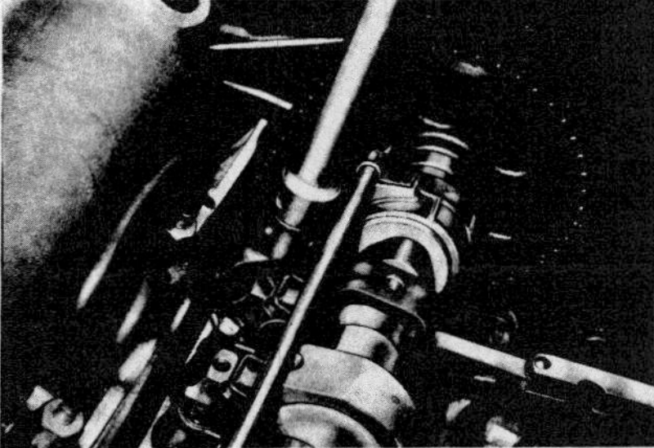
Adjusting the valves on the 6.3 V-8 engine

NOTE: *This adjustment is ideally made with a special adaptor and a torque wrench. The shape of the adaptor is dictated by the need for accurate torque readings and, by using it, the torque wrench can be directly aligned with the ball pin head.*

10. When the ball pin head is turned, the adjusting torque should be 14.4–28.8 ft lbs. If the torque is lower, either the adjusting screw, the threaded bolt, or both will have to be replaced. If the valve clearance is too small, and the ball pin head cannot be screwed in far enough to correct it, a thinner pressure piece should be installed in the spring retainer. The standard thickness of the pressure piece is 0.177 in. Pressure pieces are available in thicknesses of 0.137 in., and 0.0985 in. To replace the pressure piece, the rocker arm must be removed. (See the Engine Mechanical Section.)

11. On 3.5 liter V-8 engines, check to be sure that the clamping springs are located in the recesses of the adjusting screws. This should be done after all valves have been satisfactorily adjusted in the manner described above.

12. Install the plastic cover around the crankshaft pulley on 3.5 liter engines.

13. Install the regulating linkage, valve cover gasket, and valve cover. Be sure the gasket is seated properly.

14. Connect the cable to the coil and the venting line. Run the engine and check for leaks at the valve cover.

280 and 280C (Carbureted)

The valve clearance is measured between the sliding surface of the rocker arm and the heel of the camshaft lobe. The highest point of the camshaft lobe should be at a 90° angle to the sliding surface of the rocker arm.

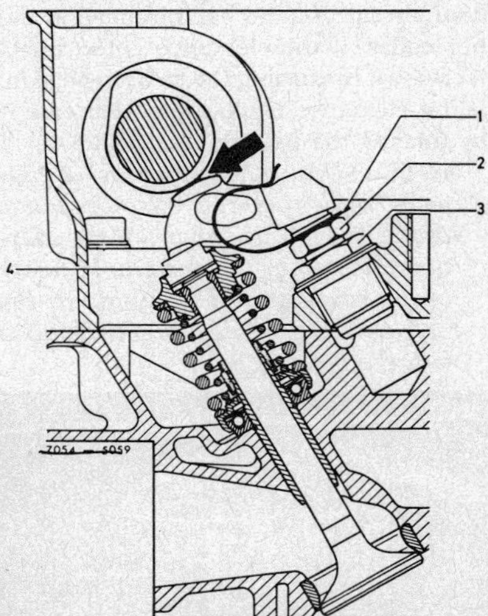

Check the valve clearance between the sliding surface of the rocker arm and the heel of the camshaft lobe on 280 and 280C engines.

1. Tension spring
2. Adjusting screw
3. Threaded bushing
4. Pressure piece

1. Loosen the venting line and remove the valve cover.

2. Remove the tension springs and rubber gaskets.

3. Identify all of the valves as to intake or exhaust.

Removing the tension springs

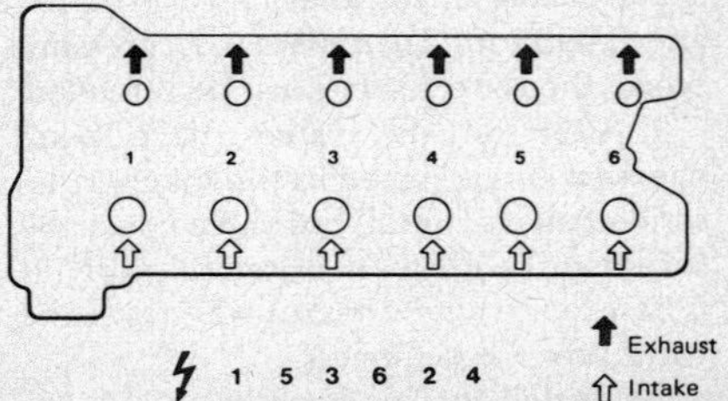

Valve locations—280 and 280C engine

4. Beginning with No. 1 cylinder, crank the engine with the starter to position the heel of the camshaft lobe approximately over the sliding surface of the rocker arm.

5. Rotate the crankshaft, by means of a socket wrench on the crankshaft pulley, until the heel of the camshaft lobe is perpendicular to the sliding surface of the rocker arm.

NOTE: *Do not rotate the engine using the camshaft sprocket bolt. The strain will distort the timing chain tensioner rail. Always rotate the engine in the direction of normal rotation only.*

6. To measure the valve clearance, insert a feeler blade of the specified thickness between the heel of the camshaft lobe and the sliding surface of the rocker arm. The clearance is correct if the blade can be inserted and withdrawn with a very slight drag.

7. If adjustment is necessary, it can be done by turning the ball pin head at the hex collar. If the clearance is too small, increase it by turning the ball pin head in. If the clearance is too large, decrease it by turning the ball pin head out.

Adjusting the valve clearance on the 280 and 280C engine.

NOTE: *This adjustment is ideally made with a special adaptor and a torque wrench. The shape of the adaptor is dictated by the need for accurate torque readings and, by using it, the torque wrench can be directly aligned with the ball pin head.*

8. When the ball pin head is turned the adjusting torque should be 14.4–28.8 ft lbs. If the torque is lower, either the adjusting screw, the threaded bolt, or both will have to be replaced. If the valve clearance is too small, and the ball pin head cannot be screwed in far enough to correct it, a thinner pressure piece should be installed in the spring retainer. The standard thickness of the pressure piece is 0.177 in. Pressure pieces are available in thicknesses of 0.137 in., and 0.0985 in. To replace the pressure piece, the rocker arm must be removed.

9. After all the valves have been adjusted as described above, push the tension springs into the grooves on the adjusting screws.

10. Check and, if necessary, replace the rubber gaskets before installing the valve cover.

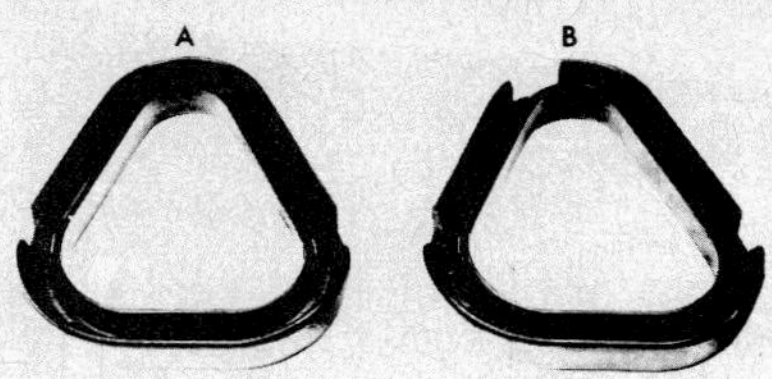

Two versions of rubber gaskets

(a)—Spark plug holes 1, 3 and 5
(b)—Spark plug holes 2 and 4

CAUTION: *Two types of rubber gaskets are used.*

11. Install the valve cover gasket and valve cover. Be sure that the gasket is seated properly to prevent leaks. If necessary, install a new valve cover gasket.

12. Connect the cable to the coil and connect the venting line to the valve cover.

13. Run the engine and check for leaks at the valve cover.

Idle Speed

Carbureted Engines

The adjustments given here are intended to include only those which would be performed in the course of a normal tune-up, after the spark plugs, dwell angle, and ignition timing have been adjusted. Obviously, there are other adjustments which can and should be made for various reasons. These can be found under "Emission Controls and Fuel Systems". The following chart gives the applications of various carburetors.

NOTE: *Idle speed and fuel mixture are best set with a CO meter to comply with federal emission regulations. Follow the instructions that are packaged with the meter.*

Carburetor Applications

Model	Year	Carburetor
220/8	1968-70	2 Solex 36-40 PDSI
220/8	1970-73	1 Stromberg 175 CDT
230/8 250/8 250C 280/8	1968-69 1968-70 1970-72 1968-71	2 Zenith 35/40 INAT
280 280C	1973 1973	1 Solex 4A1

Solex 36–40 PDSI

1. Start the engine and allow it to warm to normal operating temperature.

2. Detach the throttle actuating pushrods from the front and rear carburetor and detach the short horizontal pushrod from the front carburetor.

3. Adjust the pushrod (between the carburetors) to the distance between the pivot pins on the angle relay lever.

4. Be sure that the throttle valve shafts move freely.

5. Connect a tachometer to the engine and adjust the idle speed, using the idle adjustment screws.

6. Synchronize the two carburetors. See "Synchronizing Multiple Carburetor Installations," which follows in this section.

7. Set the mixture adjustment screws for maximum rpm and even running of the engine. As an alternative, set them to maximum vacuum with a gauge.

8. Set the pushrod at the front carburetor to the point where the angle relay lever is approximately 0.040 in. away from the stop casting on the manifold. Install the rear pushrod so that there is no binding.

9. Adjust the length of the horizontal pushrod on the front carburetor to meet the conditions in step 8. The length of the rod can be varied by the adjusting screw in the middle of the pushrod.

On cars with manual transmission, adjust the length of the pushrod until the roller nestles comfortably in the end of the slot of the quadrant lever.

On cars with automatic transmission, run the engine in Neutral and screw in the control rod until the rod can be installed (while completely expanded) with the throttle valve lever against the idle stop.

10. Install the air cleaner on the carburetor and readjust the engine for optimum rpm.

11. On cars with automatic transmissions, adjust the vacuum regulator by backing out the hex bolt until there is approximately 0.040 in. clearance between the hex bolt and the angle relay lever. Before performing this adjustment, however, note the following conditions:

a. On cars equipped with EITHER air conditioning or automatic transmis-

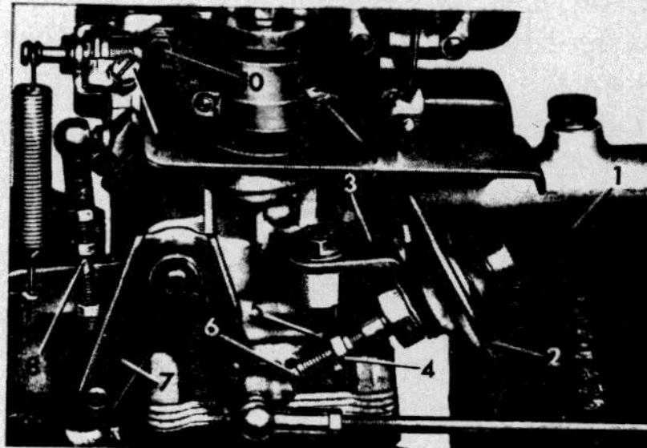

Vacuum regulator adjustment—Solex 36-40 PDSI carburetor.

1. Vacuum hose
2. Closing damper
3. Bracket
4. Locknut
5. Stop
6. Hexagon bolt
7. Angle relay lever
8. Pushrod
9. Starter adjustment screw
10. Idle adjustment screw
11. Mixture adjustment screw

2 Solex 36-40 PDSI carburetors

1. Pushrod
2. Angle relay lever
3. Pivot pin
4. Pushrod
5. Throttle lever
6. Idle adjustment screw
7. Starter, adjustment screw
8. Idle fuel adjustment screw
9. Starter link rod
10. Fuel return valve
11. Flat spring
12. Adjustment screw for fuel return valve
13. Angle relay lever stop
14. Adjusting ring
15. Pushrod
16. Angle relay lever
17. Quadrant lever
18. Roller

sion, place the car in Drive or switch on the air conditioning (as applicable) and adjust the hex bolt of the closing damper until the specified idle speed is obtained. Adjust the stopnut until the nut rests against the stop.

b. On cars with EITHER automatic transmission and power steering, automatic transmission and air conditioning, OR air conditioning and power steering, put the car in gear or switch on the air conditioning (as applicable). Adjust the hex bolt to the specified idle speed. Set the stopnut at a point 0.080 in. from the stop. After cutting in the second unit (by putting on the power steering to full lock) the specified idle speed should not vary much with the stopnut against the stop.

c. On vehicles equipped with air conditioning, power steering, and automatic transmission (and all of them operating), it does not matter if the idle speed falls below specifications, as long as the smoothness of the engine is not affected.

Stromberg 175 CDT

1. Turn off the heater and run the vehicle to normal operating temperature. Remove the air intake and air cleaner from cars equipped with air conditioning.

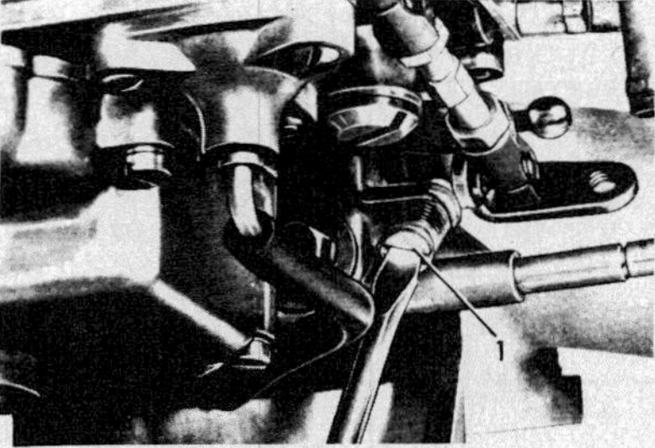

Adjust the idle speed on Stromberg 175 CDT carburetors with the idle speed adjusting screw (1).

Adjust the fuel mixture on Stromberg 175 CDT carburetors with the fuel mixture screw (4).

1. Idle speed adjusting screw
2. Holding screw
3. Stop nut
4. Fuel control screw (idle speed shut-off valve)

2. Disconnect the control rod on the carburetor.

3. Check the throttle valve for ease of operation.

4. Connect a tachometer and adjust the idle speed to specifications with the idle speed adjusting screw.

5. See whether the idle speed stop is resting against the throttle valve lever and not against the vacuum governor. Set the vacuum governor back if required.

6. If an exhaust gas analyzer (CO meter) is available, check the exhaust gas for percentage of CO.

7. If required, adjust the gas rating by means of the fuel mixture screw. Loosen the locknut while simultaneously holding the nozzle screw and turning the fuel shut-off valve. Accelerate a brief instant after each adjustment of the idle speed and fuel control screw, to stabilize the mixture.

8. Check the idle speed again and adjust with the idle speed adjusting screw, if required.

9. Adjust the control linkage as follows:

a. On vehicles with manual transmission, attach the control rod and adjust it so that the roller rests in the gate lever without binding. The control lever is equipped with right and left-hand threads.

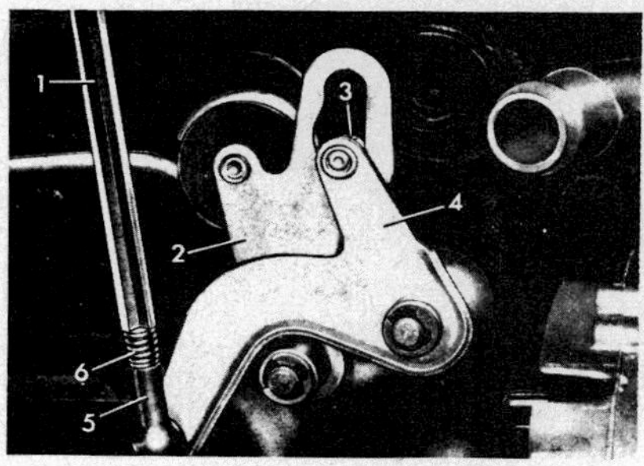

Adjusting the Stromberg 175 CDT control linkage on manual transmission vehicles.

1. Control rod
2. Gate lever
3. Roller
4. Bellcrank
5. Ball joint
6. Compression spring

Adjusting the Stromberg 175 CDT control linkage on automatic transmission vehicles.

7. Pull rod
8. Ball socket
9. Intermediate lever
10. Control rod
11. Ball socket
12. Control rod

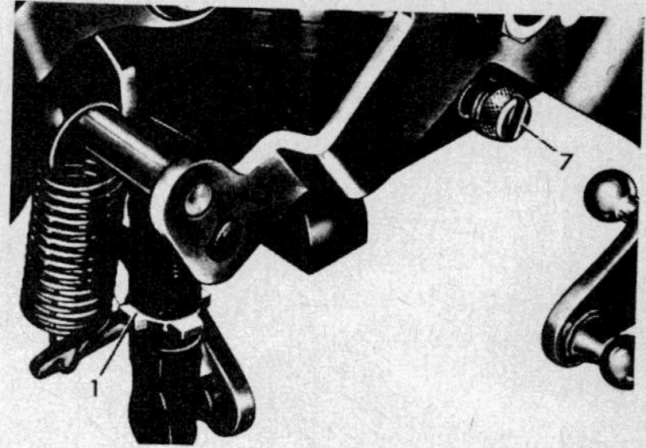

Adjusting screws on Zenith 35/40 INAT carburetors.

1. Idling speed adjusting screw
2. Mixture adjusting screw

b. On vehicles with automatic transmission, run the engine at idle speed. Set the control rod so that it can be attached with no binding.

Zenith 35/40 INAT

1. Run the engine to normal operating temperature.

2. Remove the air cleaner and, on 1970 models, remove the cable plug from the temperature switch on the thermostat housing.

3. Disconnect the connecting rod and regulating rod.

4. Check the throttle levers for ease of operation.

5. Be sure that both throttle valve levers are resting against the idle speed stop. Turn back the adjusting screw on vehicles with a vacuum regulator.

6. Connect a tachometer and adjust the idle speed to specifications with the idle adjusting screws.

7. Synchronize both carburetors. See "Synchronizing Multiple Carburetor Installations" which follows in this section.

8. Adjust the mixture regulating screws with a CO meter (if available) to the specified figure. If no CO meter is available, adjust the regulating screws to maximum engine rpm or to maximum vacuum.

NOTE: *Since 1970, the adjustment of the mixture screws is restricted.*

9. Check the idle and synchronization again.

10. Attach the connecting rod so that it does not bind; check it with a synchronization tester to be sure that both carburetors are opening simultaneously. Raise the actuating lever of the front carburetor to obtain a speed of approximately 1200–1500 rpm. Check the synchronization of both carburetors and adjust the connecting rod if necessary.

11. Adjust the regulating rod as follows:

a. On cars with manual transmission, adjust the regulating rod so that the roller in the cam lever rests against the end stop with no binding.

Zenith 35/40 INAT dual installation

1. Idle adjustment screw
2. Throttle valve lever
3. Test joint
4. Pump lever
5. Idle stop screw
6. Float chamber vent valve
7. Idle mixture adjustment screw
8. Actuating lever
9. Hexagon bolt
10. Adjustment nut
11. Connecting rod
12. Adjustment screw
13. Return valve lever
14. Fuel return valve
15. Nut
16. Control rod
17. Lever
18. Lever
19. Adjustment screw

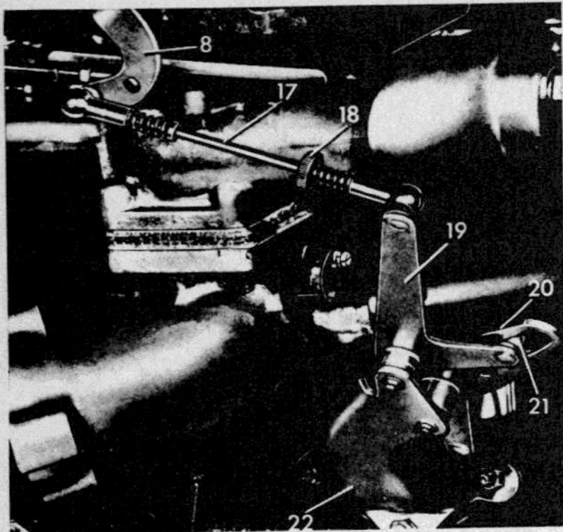

Regulating rod adjustment on manual transmission vehicles.

8. Actuating lever
17. Regulating rod
18. Adjusting nut
19. Bellcrank
20. Cam lever
21. Roller
22. Bearing bracket

b. On vehicles with automatic transmissions, disconnect the pull rod on the adjusting lever and push the pull rod to the idling position of the transmission. Loosen the clamp screw on the intermediate lever and turn the adjusting lever toward the intermediate lever until the ball socket of the pull rod can be pushed onto the ball socket of the adjusting lever with no binding. Adjust the regulating rod so that with the engine running, the regulating rod can be connected without binding (when fully extended). The actuating lever should rest against the idle speed stop screw.

12. Install the air cleaner and check the idle speed and CO content of the exhaust.

13. Reconnect the cable plug to the temperature switch on the thermostat housing.

Solex 4 A 1

1. The idle speed adjustment on this carburetor is made with the air cleaner installed and the crankcase breather connected.

Solex 4A 1 carburetor linkage

61. Adjusting nut
62. Locknut
63. Adjusting screw (vacuum governor)
68. Idling speed adjusting screw
119. Guide lever
120. Angle lever
130. Regulating rod
140. Slide rod
144. Connecting rod

2. Warm the engine to normal operating temperature. Do not adjust the idle after the engine has been driven very far because the engine will be too hot.

3. Disconnect the regulating rod on the carburetor.

4. Check the throttle valve shaft for binding.

5. Adjust the idle speed to specifications with the idle speed adjusting screw. This should be done with a tachometer installed. Be sure that the idle speed stop is on the throttle valve lever and not on the vacuum governor. Loosen the spring of the vacuum governor, if necessary, by altering the setting of the adjusting nut.

Solex 4A 1 idle speed adjustment

61. Adjusting nut
68. Idling speed adjusting screw
130. Regulating rod

6. If a CO meter is available, check the CO content of the exhaust gas. Follow the manufacturer's directions. If necessary, turn both mixture control screws to the right against the stop. Turn both screws simultaneously to the left until the CO percentage is within specifications. Turning the screws out will give a richer mixture and turning the screws in will give a leaner mixture.

Solex 4A 1 mixture control screws (arrows).

7. Check the idle speed once again until both the idle speed and CO percentage of the exhaust gas are as specified.

Balancing Multiple Carburetor Installations

Carburetor synchronization is greatly simplified by use of one of the various devices made for the purpose. A Moto Meter® unit is illustrated, but a similar device is readily available in this country under the name Uni-Syn®.

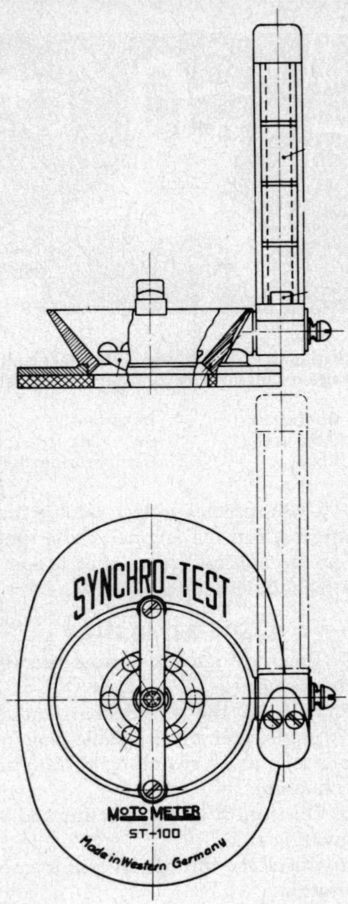

Synchronizer for dual carburetor installations.

To use this unit, warm up the engine, then remove the air cleaner and disconnect the linkage between the carburetors. Adjust the idle speed as previously described, then place the synchronizing device on the air venturi of one of the carburetors. Adjust the air intake on the measuring unit until the ball float is somewhere in the center of the tube. Now simply transfer the unit to the other carburetor and note how far the ball rises. Adjust carburetors until the ball rises equally for both.

NOTE: *A grease pencil is handy for marking the ball position in the tube. The tube must be vertical to allow free movement of the ball.*

Fuel Injected Engines

Mercedes-Benz passenger cars use two types of fuel injection. All U.S.A. version passenger cars with 6-cylinder engines and the 300SEL 6.3 use mechanical injection units. All U.S.A. cars with either the 3.5 or the 4.5 liter engine use electronically controlled injection units.

The injection pump and its attendant linkage can only be accurately tested and adjusted using special test equipment and tools which are not readily available. For this reason it is recommended that all but the simplest service operations concerning the fuel injection system be referred to a Mercedes-Benz dealer. Even when adjusting idle speed on fuel-injected engines, be very careful. The system is extremely sensitive.

Mechanical Fuel Injection

1. Run the engine until it has warmed to normal operating temperature. Do not adjust the idle speed when the engine is extremely hot.

2. Check to be sure that the throttle valve is closing completely without binding.

3. Under firm pressure, the throttle valve should exert a slight pressure on the idle speed stop screw without binding. If necessary, adjust this with the stop screw.

4. Be sure that the regulating levers on the injection pump and the venturi control unit are seated against the idle speed stops.

5. Connect a tachometer and adjust the idle speed to specifications by turning the idle speed air screw.

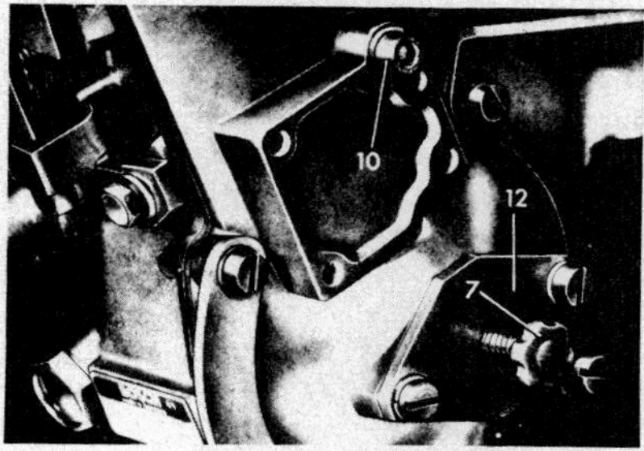

Idle speed air adjustment on mechanical fuel injection.

7. Idling speed adjusting screw
10. Closing screw—full load adjustment
12. Closing flange partial load adjustment

NOTE: *It must be emphasized that adjustments of this nature are extremely critical in light of emission control regulations. For best results it is necessary to use a CO meter. See the specifications or the tune-up decal for CO percentages.*

6. If the emission valves must be adjusted, stop the engine. Turn the idle speed adjusting screw (on the pump) to the left if the mixture is too rich, or to the right if the mixture is too lean. Note that the pump idle screw is turned from notch to notch. It should not be turned more than three notches in either direction.

7. Start the engine and check the idle speed; readjust with the idle speed air screw if necessary. Repeat this procedure until the idle speed and emissions content are satisfactory.

8. If no CO meter is available, idle speed can be adjusted as follows:

a. Connect a vacuum gauge to the vacuum pressure test connection on the venturi control unit.

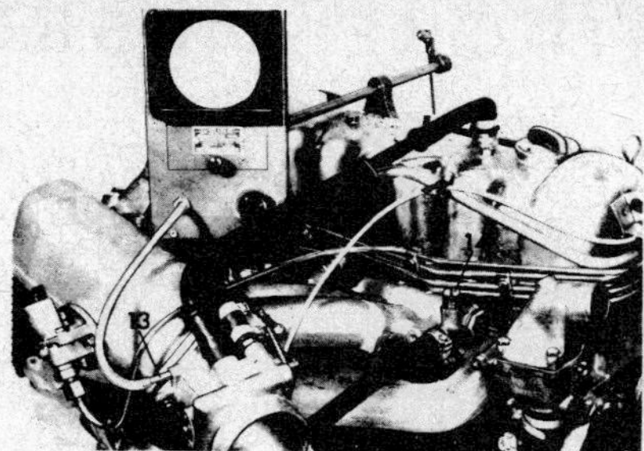

Idle speed adjustment on mechanical fuel injection.

13. Test connection
14. Idling speed air screw

b. Open the idle speed air screw slightly until the vacuum falls off. Close the idle speed air screw until the vacuum falls off again. From this point, adjust the idle speed air screw until maximum rpm is obtained.

c. Read the idle speed on a tachometer. If the speed is too high, the mixture is too rich. If the speed is too low, the mixture is too lean.

d. Adjust the mixture as required on the idle speed adjusting screw on the injection pump. Note that the adjusting screw is adjusted from notch to notch. It should not be adjusted more than three notches in either direction.

e. Repeat the adjustment of the idle speed air screw and, if necessary, the idle speed adjusting screw on the injection pump.

Electronic Fuel Injection

1. Run the engine to normal operating temperature. The idle speed should not be adjusted when the engine is extremely hot.

2. Remove the air cleaner.

3. Disconnect the connecting rod from the valve connection and check to be sure that the throttle valve closes completely without binding.

4. Re-attach the connecting rod so that it does not bind.

5. Connect a tachometer and adjust the idle speed to specifications with the idle speed air screw.

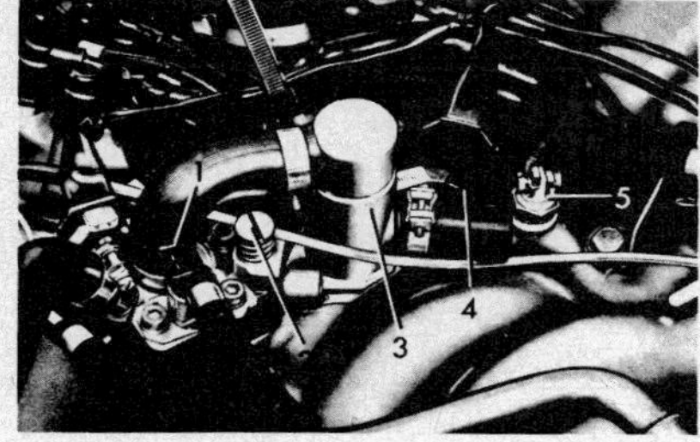

Idle speed adjustment on electronic fuel injection.

1. Starting valve
2. Idling speed air screw
3. Supplementary air valve
4. Water temperature sensor
5. Thermal time switch

6. Check the exhaust gas content with a CO meter. If necessary, adjust the CO content with the adjusting screw on the control unit. Turning the screw clockwise will give a richer mixture while turning the screw counterclockwise will give a leaner mixture.

Fuel mixture adjustment (arrow) on electronic fuel injection control box.

7. The control unit can be reached after removing the inner lining below the glovebox.

8. Check and, if necessary, readjust the idle speed.

9. Install the air cleaner. Check the idle speed and exhaust emissions values and readjust if necessary.

10. Remove the tachometer.

Diesel Engine Tune-Up and Troubleshooting

The diesel and gasoline engines used by Mercedes-Benz differ essentially in only one way—how the fuel is ignited. Both types are four cycle engines; that is, their operating cycles consist of (1) an intake stroke, whereby air (or air-fuel mixture) is pulled into the combustion chamber, (2) a compression stroke, during which the air (or air-fuel mixture) is compressed and heated, (3) a power stroke, caused by the burning (ignition) of the injected fuel and air mixture, and (4) an exhaust stroke, which literally pushes the burned and unburned gases out of the engine.

A diesel engine does not have an ignition system as such, although there are glow plugs for starting. To ignite its fuel-air mixture, the diesel depends on the heating effect of compression pressure. If the pressure is high enough, through high compression ratios and combustion chamber design, the fuel-air mixture will ignite of its own accord.

The diesel, having no ignition system, is simplified to an extent, although the timed fuel injection required may offset this to a degree. Advantages lie in increased fuel economy using lower grades of fuel, along with long life due to rugged construction.

FOUR STROKE DIESEL CYCLE

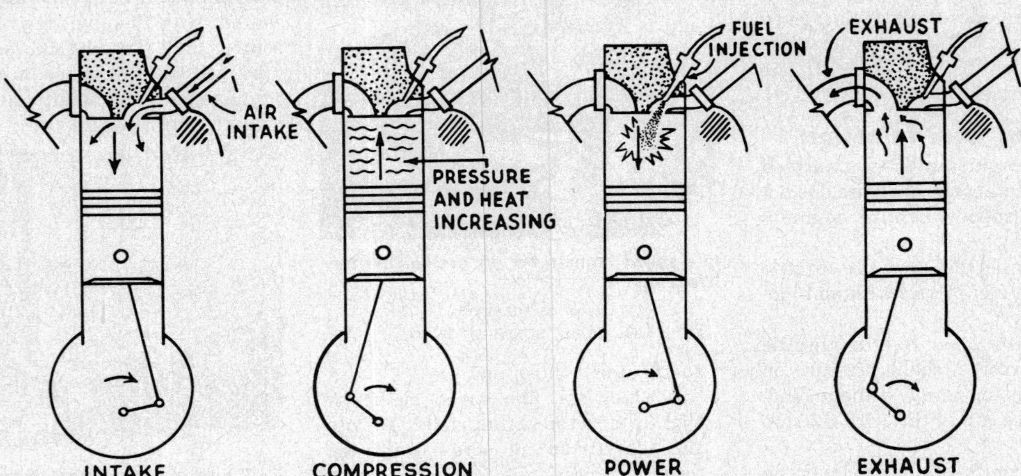

Troubleshooting a Non-Starting Engine

Any discussion of diesel engine troubleshooting must involve fuel injection, since most poor running conditions stem from a malfunction in this system.

The fuel feed pump, driven by the injection pump, acts the same as the fuel pump of any gasoline engine, pumping fuel from the tank to the engine. The fuel passes through two fuel filters, the transparent prefilter and the larger main filter. From there it goes into the suction chamber of the injection pump, in which a constant fuel pressure is maintained by the overflow valve. At a *minimum* pressure of 11.8 psi, surplus fuel flows back into the fuel tank via this valve. The fuel pump has a pumping capacity much greater than is necessary in order to keep the chamber always full of bubble-free fuel.

The injection pump plungers force the fuel from the suction chamber through the pump pressure valves into the injection lines—thence to the injection nozzles, at a spray pressure of 1564–1706 psi. The spray must pass through the prechamber before reaching the main combustion chamber. Surplus fuel at the injectors is passed through leakage lines into the fuel tank.

The fuel volume is influenced by the accelerator pedal position, engine load and speed, and controlled by the pneu-

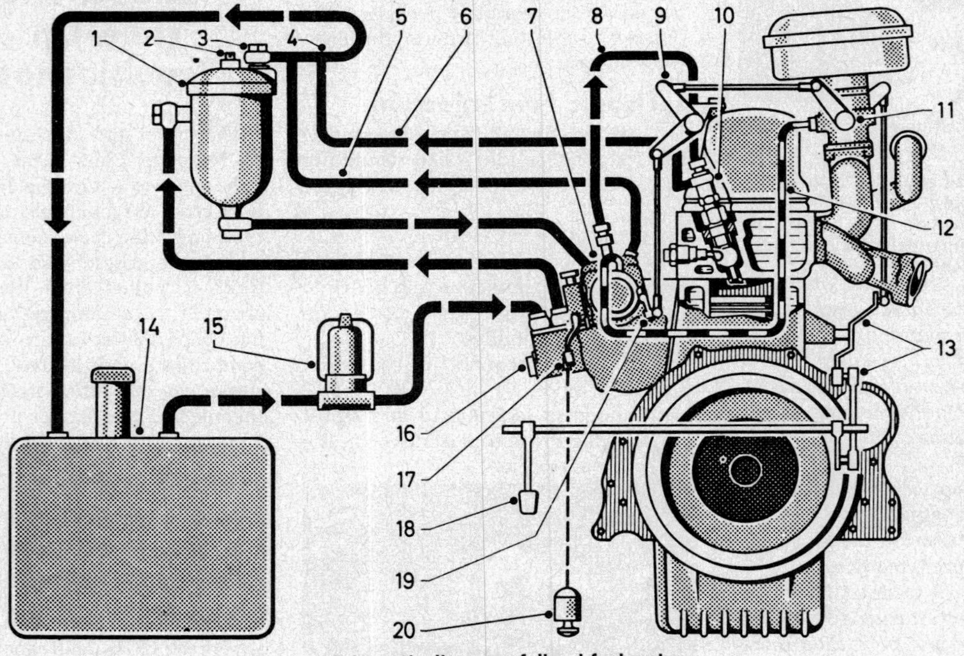

Schematic diagram of diesel fuel system

1. Main fuel filter
2. Vent screw
3. Hollow screw with throttle screw
4. Fuel return line
5. Overflow line
6. Injection nozzle leakage line
7. Injection pump
8. Pressure line from injection pump to injection nozzle
9. Angular lever for auxiliary mechanical control
0. Injection nozzle
11. Venturi control unit
12. Vacuum line with throttle screw
13. Linkage and lever for accelerator pedal control
14. Fuel tank
15. Fuel prefilter
16. Fuel feed pump with hand pump
17. Adjusting lever
18. Accelerator pedal
19. Lever for auxiliary mechanical control
20. Heater plug starting switch with starting and stopping cable

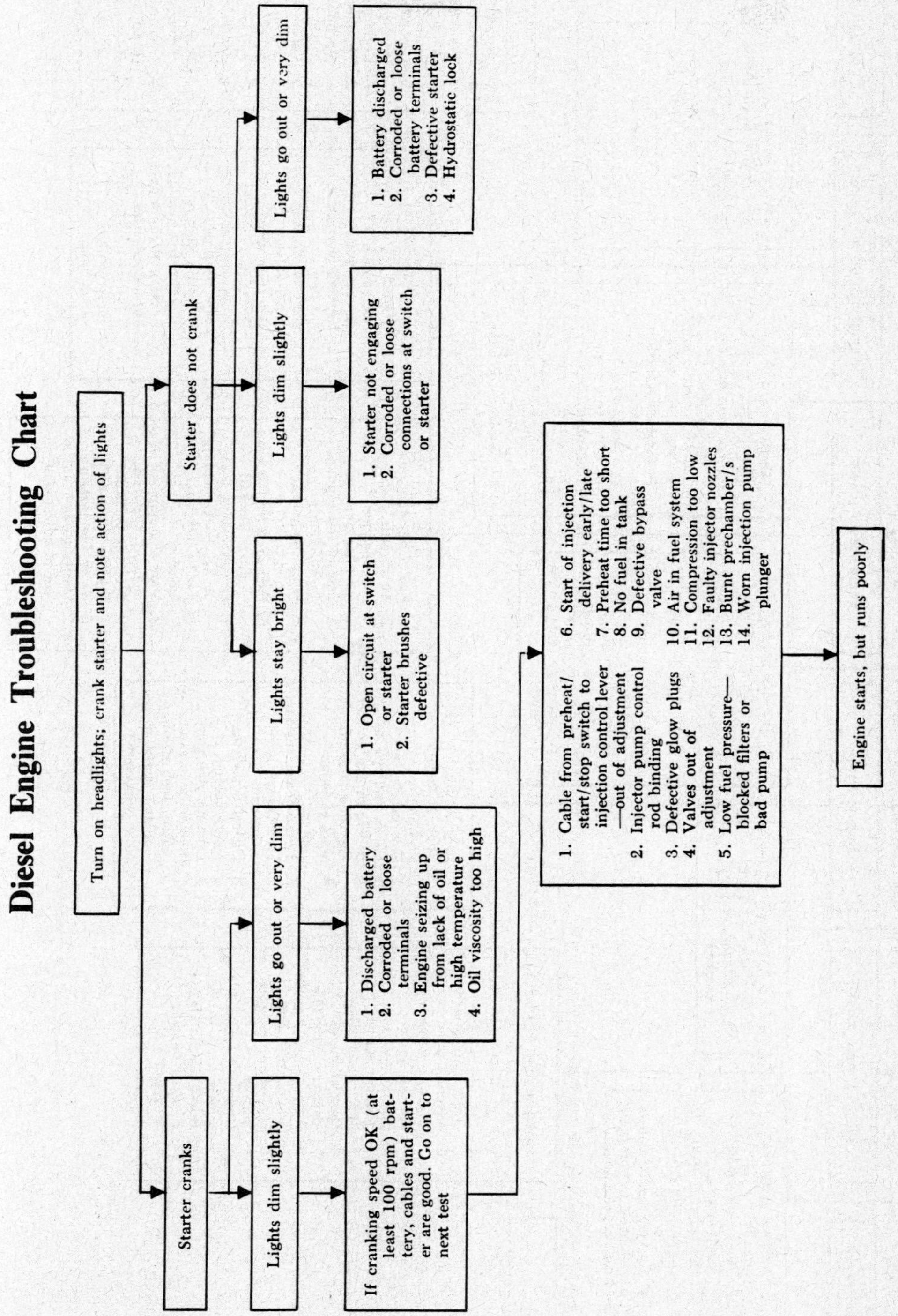

Diesel Engine Troubleshooting Chart

Turn on headlights; crank starter and note action of lights

- **Starter cranks**
  - **Lights dim slightly** → If cranking speed OK (at least 100 rpm) battery, cables and starter are good. Go on to next test
  - **Lights go out or very dim** →
    1. Discharged battery
    2. Corroded or loose terminals
    3. Engine seizing up from lack of oil or high temperature
    4. Oil viscosity too high
- **Starter does not crank**
  - **Lights stay bright** →
    1. Open circuit at switch or starter
    2. Starter brushes defective
  - **Lights dim slightly** →
    1. Starter not engaging
    2. Corroded or loose connections at switch or starter
  - **Lights go out or very dim** →
    1. Battery discharged
    2. Corroded or loose battery terminals
    3. Defective starter
    4. Hydrostatic lock

Next test (from "If cranking speed OK…"):

1. Cable from preheat/start/stop switch to injection control lever—out of adjustment
2. Injector pump control rod binding
3. Defective glow plugs
4. Valves out of adjustment
5. Low fuel pressure—blocked filters or bad pump
6. Start of injection delivery early/late
7. Preheat time too short
8. No fuel in tank
9. Defective bypass valve
10. Air in fuel system
11. Compression too low
12. Faulty injector nozzles
13. Burnt prechamber/s
14. Worn injection pump plunger

→ **Engine starts, but runs poorly**

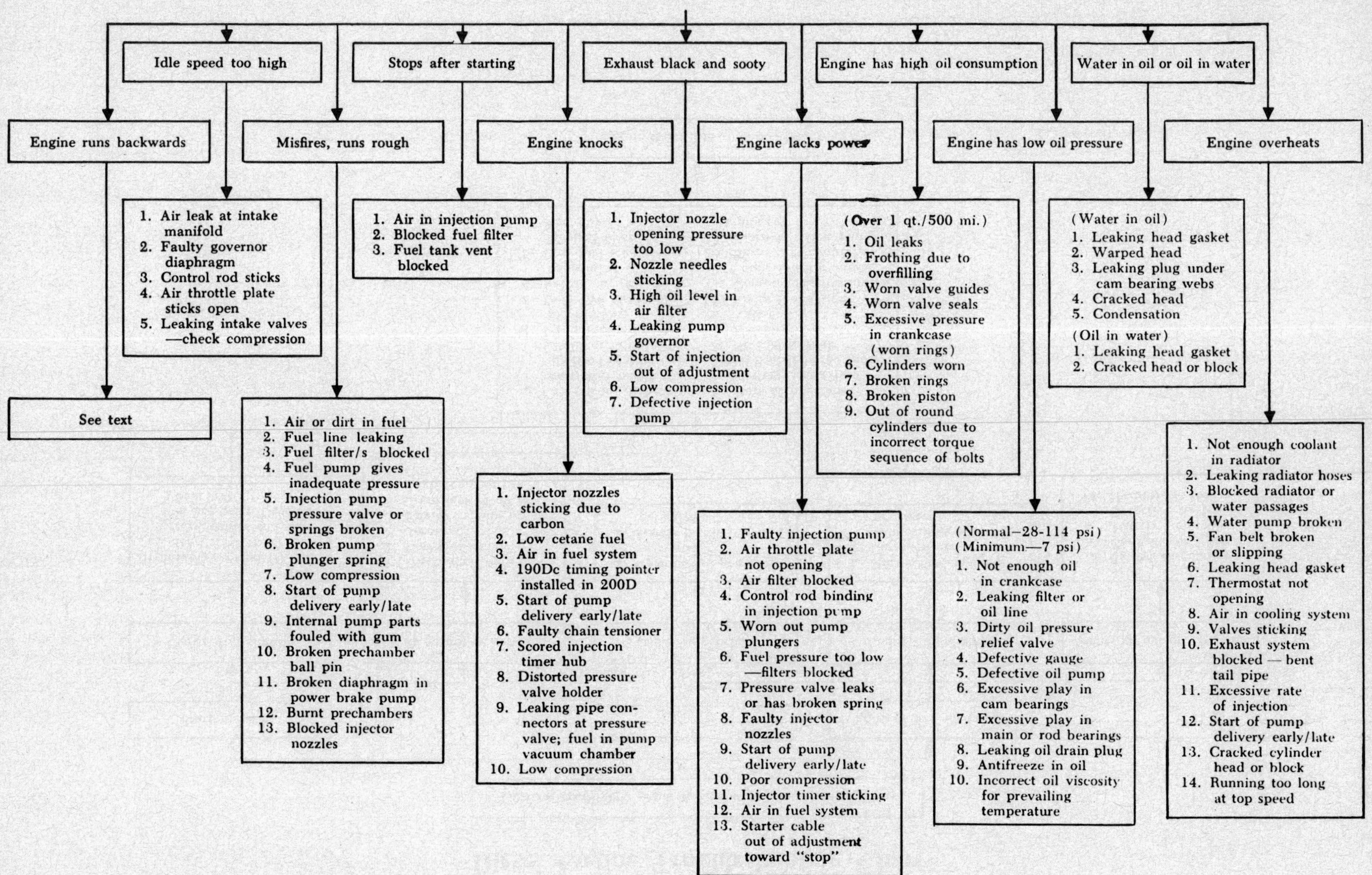
Engine runs backwards
See text
Idle speed too high
1. Air leak at intake manifold
2. Faulty governor diaphragm
3. Control rod sticks
4. Air throttle plate sticks open
5. Leaking intake valves —check compression
Misfires, runs rough
1. Air or dirt in fuel
2. Fuel line leaking
3. Fuel filter/s blocked
4. Fuel pump gives inadequate pressure
5. Injection pump pressure valve or springs broken
6. Broken pump plunger spring
7. Low compression
8. Start of pump delivery early/late
9. Internal pump parts fouled with gum
10. Broken prechamber ball pin
11. Broken diaphragm in power brake pump
12. Burnt prechambers
13. Blocked injector nozzles
Stops after starting
1. Air in injection pump
2. Blocked fuel filter
3. Fuel tank vent blocked
Engine knocks
1. Injector nozzles sticking due to carbon
2. Low cetane fuel
3. Air in fuel system
4. 190Dc timing pointer installed in 200D
5. Start of pump delivery early/late
6. Faulty chain tensioner
7. Scored injection timer hub
8. Distorted pressure valve holder
9. Leaking pipe connectors at pressure valve; fuel in pump vacuum chamber
10. Low compression
Exhaust black and sooty
1. Injector nozzle opening pressure too low
2. Nozzle needles sticking
3. High oil level in air filter
4. Leaking pump governor
5. Start of injection out of adjustment
6. Low compression
7. Defective injection pump
Engine lacks power
1. Faulty injection pump
2. Air throttle plate not opening
3. Air filter blocked
4. Control rod binding in injection pump
5. Worn out pump plungers
6. Fuel pressure too low —filters blocked
7. Pressure valve leaks or has broken spring
8. Faulty injector nozzles
9. Start of pump delivery early/late
10. Poor compression
11. Injector timer sticking
12. Air in fuel system
13. Starter cable out of adjustment toward "stop"
Engine has high oil consumption
(Over 1 qt./500 mi.)
1. Oil leaks
2. Frothing due to overfilling
3. Worn valve guides
4. Worn valve seals
5. Excessive pressure in crankcase (worn rings)
6. Cylinders worn
7. Broken rings
8. Broken piston
9. Out of round cylinders due to incorrect torque sequence of bolts
Engine has low oil pressure
(Normal—28-114 psi)
(Minimum—7 psi)
1. Not enough oil in crankcase
2. Leaking filter or oil line
3. Dirty oil pressure relief valve
4. Defective gauge
5. Defective oil pump
6. Excessive play in cam bearings
7. Excessive play in main or rod bearings
8. Leaking oil drain plug
9. Antifreeze in oil
10. Incorrect oil viscosity for prevailing temperature
Water in oil or oil in water
(Water in oil)
1. Leaking head gasket
2. Warped head
3. Leaking plug under cam bearing webs
4. Cracked head
5. Condensation
(Oil in water)
1. Leaking head gasket
2. Cracked head or block
Engine overheats
1. Not enough coolant in radiator
2. Leaking radiator hoses
3. Blocked radiator or water passages
4. Water pump broken
5. Fan belt broken or slipping
6. Leaking head gasket
7. Thermostat not opening
8. Air in cooling system
9. Valves sticking
10. Exhaust system blocked — bent tail pipe
11. Excessive rate of injection
12. Start of pump delivery early/late
13. Cracked cylinder head or block
14. Running too long at top speed

matic governor on the rear of the injection pump.

If the engine will not start, as usually happens in cold weather with a poorly maintained car, try turning the idle speed adjuster knob all the way counterclockwise, pre-glow for a full minute, push the clutch all the way in, and the accelerator pedal halfway down. Then try to start the engine. If the engine does not start after 10–15 seconds, pre-glow again and repeat the procedure. If the engine fires a few times but just won't catch, hold the starter on for a longer period.

This assumes, of course, that the starter motor turns the engine over at all. The most common cause of the starter not working, or working sluggishly, is a low battery, sometimes in combination with "summer" oil. The diesel, having such a high compression ratio (21:1) is difficult to turn over with high viscosity oil working against it.

If, after checking the battery, starter, cables, and oil, the engine still will not start, a check of one, or all, of the following areas is in order:

1. Cable from pre-glow/start-stop switch to injection control lever.
2. Injection pump control rod.
3. Compression pressure (including valve adjustment).
4. Glow plugs.
5. Fuel pressure.
6. Start of injection pump delivery.

Starting cable adjustment

1. Adjusting lever (starting and stopping cable lever)
2. Eye with rubber molding of starting and stopping cable
3. Angle bracket
4. Coil spring

Cable

1. To adjust the cable, first disconnect the ground cable from the negative battery post. Push the control knob all the way in to the STOP position. In this position, the adjusting lever on the injection pump will be pushed completely forward.

2. Next, pull the knob to the START position. In this position, the pin of the adjusting lever should rest against the end of the eye.

3. Now release the knob. The adjusting lever should return to the DRIVING position. In both this and the pre-glow position, the adjusting lever pin must clear the eye end by at least 0.080 in. If not, adjust the cable by loosening the bolt and moving the coil spring outer housing with relation to the angle bracket. Also, make sure the adjusting lever is firmly attached to the pump shaft by tightening the clamp screw.

4. Check the cable and adjusting lever for free movement and make sure that the lever is pulled all the way back when the knob is pulled to the starting position.

5. Reconnect the battery cable and try to start the engine.

NOTE: *If both the start and stop positions cannot be adjusted properly, it is best to sacrifice a little starting delivery to gain a full stop position on the lever.*

Control Rod

The control rod runs through the center of the injection pump, one end protruding from the end housing, covered with a protective cap. If this rod is binding in the stop position, no fuel is delivered to the injectors and the engine will not start. Remove the end cap and check the rod for binding.

Compression

The section on compression testing found in the "Tune-Up" charts applies to diesel engines as well. The only difference in testing is that the glow plugs instead of the spark plugs are removed for the test. Individual cylinder pressures should not vary more than 45 psi.

Don't forget, valve clearances set too close will result in poor compression readings for the diesel, also.

Some engines have a valve rotator installed. If this rotator fails, compression will be low. Usually, the replacement of the rotator will bring compression back up to normal.

Testing glow plugs

Glow Plugs

The glow plugs provide a means for ignition during starting and perform the same function as normal spark plugs, although they do so in a different manner.

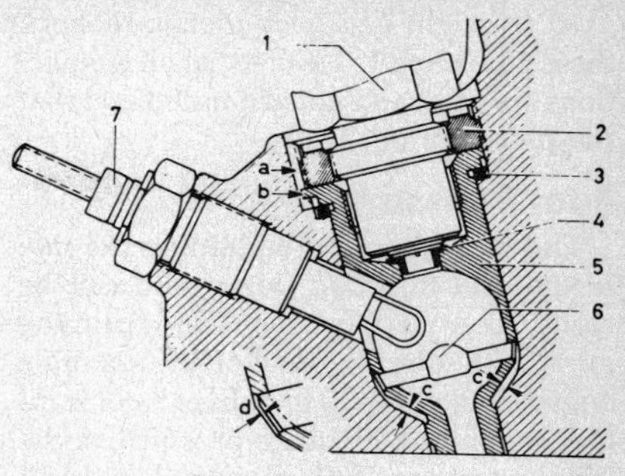

Glow plug and prechamber

(a)—Groove in cylinder head
(b)—Lug securing prechamber
(c)—Distance between prechamber and cylinder head
(d)—Max. permissible measure of a retracted ball pin with respect to the outer dia. of the prechamber (.020")
1. Nozzle holder
2. Threaded ring
3. Seal ring between prechamber and cylinder head
4. Seal ring between prechamber and nozzle holder (nozzle plate)
5. Prechamber (ball pin version)
6. Ball pin in the prechamber
7. Glow plug

The light on the dashboard which indicates when the glow plugs are hot enough to fire can also serve as a troubleshooting aid. If the light does not glow, it usually indicates a faulty plug.

1. Test the plugs by having an assistant hold the starting knob in the preheat position while shorting the plugs to ground, in turn, with a screwdriver. Each plug should produce a spark if working properly. While bridging the connections, the light on the dashboard should light.

2. If, after disconnecting the ground lead of the preheating system, the light still stays lit, a short circuit in the system is indicated. This is usually caused by a carbon-fouled plug electrode or by a lead touching the cylinder head. Check the leads first.

3. If they seem satisfactory pull the knob to the preheat position and disconnect one plug power lead at a time, starting from the ground end, until the light goes out, indicating the faulty plug.

4. Glow plugs can be cleaned, but it is better to replace them if they are badly fouled.

5. To remove the plugs, loosen the cable, if this has not been done already, by removing the knurled nut.

6. Unscrew the other nuts and remove the insulators and the bus bars.

7. Using a 21 mm socket, unscrew and remove the glow plugs.

8. Before installing new plugs, clean the ducts and prechamber bores with a stiff bristle brush or a small scraper. The ball pin in the prechamber is easy to break, so don't go much deeper than 2 in. into the plug hole.

9. Crank the engine a few times to blow out any carbon particles loosened by the scraping, then insert the plugs. Do not exceed 35 ft lbs torque.

10. It might be a good idea to recheck these new plugs to ensure that all connections are tight and not grounded and that the plugs are not faulty.

Fuel Pressure

The fuel pump is mounted on the side of the fuel injection pump and can be easily identified by the hand priming pump. Its job, like that of the gasoline engine fuel pump, is to deliver a constant fuel volume, at adequate pressure, to the injection pump. With the diesel engine it is extremely important that the fuel is airfree, without bubbles. A fuel bypass valve is located in the injection pump to maintain constant fuel pressure for the engine load. This valve opens at a pressure of 14.7–22 psi, sending excess fuel back into the supply system.

Pressure valve components

1. Pipe joint
2. Rubber sealing ring
3. Coil spring
4. Sealing ring
5. Pressure valve plate with pressure valve

As with most things mechanical, accurate testing is possible only with the proper instruments. A general check of fuel pressure can be made, however, if one assumes that the bypass valve is functioning properly.

1. Disconnect the return line at the fitting and hold the line over an open coffee can.

2. Start the engine and watch the line. If fuel comes out, it can be assumed that the fuel pressure is sufficient, as a pressure of at least 14.7 psi is required to open a good bypass valve.

3. It is also a good practice to check the discharge line from the fuel filter, as a blocked filter will deliver no fuel.

4. Check the tank before assuming the worst about a fuel pump. Gauges have been known to be wrong. It may be a good idea to disconnect the input line from the fuel tank and blow back through it with low-pressure compressed air. A line free of debris will allow the air to bubble in the tank.

CAUTION: *High pressure air will blow out the fuel tank filter.*

5. Defective fuel pumps should be replaced, as it is not really feasible to rebuild them without the proper tools.

6. To check the pump, unscrew the hand pump and remove the suction valve. Unscrew the plug which covers the pressure valve and remove the valve. Worn valve seats can be reground sometimes, but it is better to replace them.

7. To check the plunger, remove the plug and pull the plunger and spring. If it is badly scored or worn, the pump must be replaced. If the pump is only clogged with gum, it is possible to clean it with lacquer thinner or carbon tetrachloride but a new rubber O-ring should be used on the hand pump during reassembly.

Start of Injection Pump Delivery

As the piston comes up on the compression stroke, there is a delay caused by the fuel having to come from the pump to the injector nozzle. For example, if injection takes place too early, temperatures may not yet be high enough for ignition (piston has not come up far enough to compress the air). To compensate for this lag, the injection pump begins to deliver fuel to the nozzle 24° before top dead center (BTDC) is reached for the 220 D/8.

1. To check the start of delivery, remove the negative battery cable and set the piston of No. 1 cylinder at top dead center by lining up the TDC mark on the crankshaft pulley with the pointer. If TDC is achieved, both intake and exhaust valves of No. 1 cylinder will be closed (springs not compressed).

2. This can be checked by removing the camshaft cover and observing the relationship of the rockers to the valve stems.

3. Using a wrench on the crankshaft pulley nut (never use the camshaft pulley nut, as the timing chain rails will be damaged), turn the engine over 1¾ turns, in the normal direction of rotation.

4. Unscrew the injection line at the pipe union of the first pump cylinder. Remove the pipe union, rubber O-ring, spring, and the pressure valve. Replace the union and screw on an overflow pipe.

5. Detach the starting cable from the lever at the injection pump and make sure that the lever is in the full delivery position. If this is not done, the test may be inaccurate.

Measuring the start of pump delivery

1. Adjustment lever of injection pump
2. Hand-operated fuel pump
3. Jaws for locking two pipe unions
4. Tachometer drive
5. Overflow pipe
6. Bleed screw
7. Fuel container
8. Fuel return lines

6. Either connect an auxilliary fuel container to the injection pump or fill the main fuel filter by operating the hand pump and cranking the bleed screw to ensure that the fuel is air-free.

7. With the wrench on the crankshaft pulley, turn the engine over slowly in the normal direction of rotation until the fuel stream from the overflow pipe stops dripping.

NOTE: *Another drop may follow 10–15 seconds later, but this is normal.*

8. At this point, the pump piston covers the intake core in the pump cylinder and the start of delivery point has been reached. The crankshaft pointer should read 24° BTDC, for 220 D/8 models.

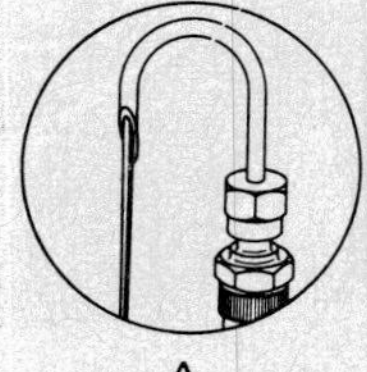
A

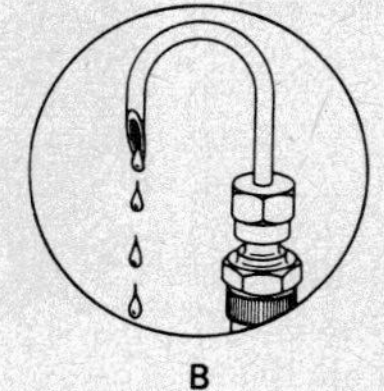
B

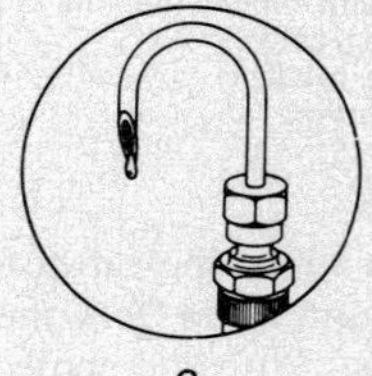
C

Overflow pipe during test

(a)—Solid fuel stream
(b)—Fuel begins to drip
(c)—One drop follows 10-15 seconds later

9. Repeat the test by continuing to turn the crankshaft in the direction of rotation—two turns. At the end of the second revolution, the fuel should cease dripping again at the proper point.

10. To adjust the start of delivery, loosen the bolts of the front flange and rotate the pump toward the engine to begin delivery earlier, or away from the engine to delay delivery. It may be necessary to disconnect the injector tubes so that the pump will be free enough to rotate.

11. Remove all test equipment and reassemble, using a new seal in the pressure valve assembly. The pressure valve assembly pipe union must be tightened to exactly 25 ft lbs with the threads coated with petroleum jelly.

12. Bleed the fuel system by opening the bleed screw and pumping the hand pump to evacuate any air.

13. Re-attach the starting cable and adjust as previously detailed.

Troubleshooting a Poorly Running Engine

A careful study of the troubleshooting chart will reveal most of the symptoms of poor running associated with diesel engines of this type, along with their probable causes. You will also note that many items are found in more than one column because the breakdown or malfunctioning of one component part could cause any number of problems, depending on whether other components are involved in this breakdown. For instance, a blocked fuel filter could cause the engine to stop immediately after starting, cause it to misfire or run badly, or even not start at all.

Many of the problems listed have been covered elsewhere. Compression testing, for example, is explained, as are the causes of poor compression. Many of the other items have obvious corrective measures.

In order to eliminate repetition, the most common testing and repair procedures follow in no particular order or sequence. Simply consult the troubleshooting chart and find the associated test.

Engine Runs Backward

Under the proper conditions the diesel engine can run backward (although poorly) accompanied by smoke issuing from the air cleaner. This is not a common condition but one that can be damaging to the engine.

For example, if reverse gear is accidentally engaged while coasting forward, or if the engine stalls under load and restarts itself, the engine can run backward. To stop it, engage a gear and let out the clutch suddenly, or block the exhaust pipe with a rag. This can also happen if an attempt is made to start the engine without preheating. If the switch is moved from the start to the preheat position, the beginning of preheat may coincide with engine revolutions, causing extremely early ignition. If this happens, the air filter will quickly catch fire and the engine can seize due to lack of oil, so quick action is necessary.

Since 1962, diesel engines have had a check throttle valve installed to prevent this situation, so a check of that valve will usually isolate the problem. Lubricate the valve every 5,000 miles with engine oil.

Engine Stops After Starting

This can be caused by a blocked fuel tank, fuel filter, or an air-locked injection pump. Remove the tank filler cap and try starting the engine. Remove the fuel line to the injection pump and crank the engine. Check the fuel volume. Bleed the fuel system.

Idle Speed Too High

Air leaks at the intake manifold can be located by squirting some soapy water at any suspected joints, with the engine running. The solution will be sucked in or bubble if a leak exists.

The injection pump governor diaphragm cannot be checked accurately unless the pump is placed on a test stand. It is possible, however, to determine roughly whether or not the governor is operating. First, with the engine idling, squirt a soapy water solution over the intake manifold, vacuum line, governor housing, and air venturi housing joints to check for leakage. An old squirt type oil can works well to avoid soaking the engine.

1. Remove the starting cable from the control lever of the injection pump and remove the sleeve over the control rod.

2. Unscrew the vacuum line and actuate the control lever, making sure the control rod goes to its full stop position, while holding your thumb over the fitting.

Checking the vacuum cleaner

1. Vacuum union
2. Control lever
3. Protector sleeve over control rod

3. Release the control lever and observe the control rod. If the diaphragm of the pump governor is functioning, the control rod will move slightly, but will be restrained by vacuum produced in the housing. Removing your thumb should allow the control rod to move. If this test indicates the diaphragm to be faulty, remove the four bolts and take out the diaphragm for inspection.

4. It is possible, although not the best procedure, to replace the diaphragm with the injection pump in place, but care must be taken in assembly. For example, it is easy to lose the compensator mechanism components. It is also necessary to use a dial indicator to measure the maximum compensator travel.

5. To measure this travel, obtain a pin 6 mm in diameter (approximately 0.235 in.) and insert it through the sleeve of the old diaphragm and compensator pin. Place the assembly on a large socket for stability. Set up the gauge as illustrated, with the prod tip on the end of the compensator pin, slightly preloaded. Press down on the prod and measure existing travel (maximum travel is 0.043–0.105 in.)

Checking the diaphragm

1. Prod of dial indicator
2. Sleeve of diaphragm
3. Piece of tubing
4. Pin, 6 mm. in diameter
5. Compensator pin

6. Disassemble the old diaphragm and insert the shims into the new one. Now measure maximum travel of the diaphragm. The difference in readings should not exceed 0.0024 in. Shims are available to make corrections.

Uneven Running, Metallic Noise, Blue Smoke

The usual cause of this condition is a broken ball pin in the prechamber, a jammed injection nozzle, or a leaky vacuum pump system.

With the car stationary, rev the engine a few times and note the exhaust. If intermittent clouds of black smoke are emitted, it indicates one or more of the injection nozzles is faulty.

1. To determine which nozzle is malfunctioning, allow the engine to idle.

2. Loosen the cap nuts of each injection tube, one at a time, about ½ turn, then retighten. If there is no change in the rough idle, it indicates a faulty nozzle. A good nozzle will be indicated by a further roughening of the idle when the cap nut is unscrewed.

3. To remove the nozzle, take off the cap nut and unscrew the nut that holds the banjo fitting.

4. Remove the bolt and the overflow line.

5. Then, unscrew the nozzle assembly and seal.

6. Examine the prechamber for carbon deposits and clean it if necessary.

7. To disassemble the nozzle holder, remove the cap nut with a 27 mm box wrench, then pull out the nozzle assembly and jet needle.

8. Remove the nozzle element, thrust pin, and spring from the nozzle holder. It is very easy to crush or distort the nozzle holder, therefore do *not* clamp it in a vise to disassemble. Individual nozzle components are run-in together and never should be interchanged.

9. Nozzle testing requires special equipment capable of producing accurately measured pressure while allowing observation of the spray pattern. Since this equipment is not readily available and jury-rigged setups do not produce good results, it is recommended that the dealer do any nozzle testing.

10. In any case, malfunctioning nozzles are usually only fouled and, if care is exercised, they can be hand-cleaned.

11. Brush any carbon away using a brass-bristle brush or a piece of kerosene-soaked wood. Never use a steel scraper, because any burrs will ruin the injector. Using a sharpened brass rod, scrape any deposits from the grooves and orifices, then soak in solvent and blow out with compressed air.

12. Examine for burrs or scratches and out-of-round injection holes, then make sure that the jet needle moves freely in the nozzle.

13. Immerse the assembly in diesel fuel and pull the jet needle about one-third out of the nozzle, then release it. The jet should fall of its own weight.

14. In emergency situations only, burrs keeping the jet from sliding may be removed by lapping with fine valve grinding compound. Damaged seating surfaces, however, usually will not be restored by lapping. It is best to replace such damaged units.

15. Assemble the unit carefully, checking the illustrations for correct parts assembly. Any dirt will prevent free operation of the jet.

16. When tightening the cap nut, do not exceed 50 ft lbs—excessive torque may distort the nozzle and cause the jet needle to bind.

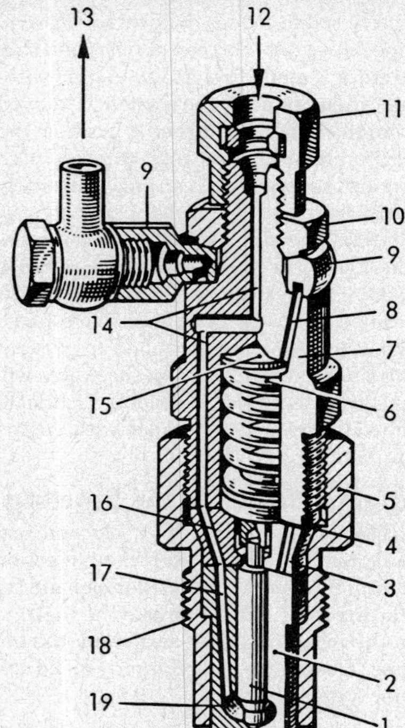

Nozzle holder injection assembly

1. Jet needle
2. Nozzle assembly
3. Nozzle element
4. Thrust pin
5. Cap nut for fixing injection nozzle
6. Compression spring
7. Nozzle holder
8. Drain hole in the nozzle holder
9. Through-way jointing piece with annular canal for leak-off oil union
10. Hexagon nut for fixing the through-way jointing piece
11. Cap nut for fixing the injection pipe
12. Fuel feed
13. Leak-off drain back to fuel tank
14. Pressure canal in the nozzle holder
15. Special washers belonging to compression spring (machined steel disks)
16. Annular groove and feed bores in nozzle element
17. Annular groove and pressure canal in nozzle assembly
18. Mounting thread
19. Pressure chamber in nozzle assembly

CAUTION: *Always use new seals when reassembling and installing injectors and never try to stop leaks by overtightening connections.*

Uneven Running, Droning Noise, Very Heavy Blue Smoke

This condition is usually caused by a cracked diaphragm in the power brake vacuum pump. Engine oil is sucked through the crack into the vacuum hose, then into the intake manifold. The result can be burned prechambers if not corrected in time, as well as general carbon build-up in the combustion chamber.

1. Remove the hose from the vacuum pump to the intake manifold. If it is filled with oil, the prechambers must be examined for damage. If the prechamber is scorched badly or burnt away, it must be replaced. Unfortunately, special tools are required for this job. In light of the difficulty sometimes encountered in removal even *with* the special tools, it is almost certain that any substitute will not work and may even damage the cylinder head. Leave this job to the dealer and confine activity to general scraping and cleaning of the chamber. This usually will be sufficient if the condition was caught in time. To alleviate the cause of the problem, the vacuum pump diaphragm must be replaced.

2. To check the diaphragm, detach the vacuum hose between the pump and the power brake and, using a T-fitting connector, connect a vacuum gauge into the line. With the engine running at 2,000 rpm, the gauge should show a little over 21 in. Hg. (vacuum) after about 10 seconds.

Engine Knocks

"Knocking" of the engine falls into four general categories:

1. Knocking during idling.
2. Knocking under partial load at low speed.
3. Knocking under partial load at high speed.
4. Hard knocking, engine shaking on mounts.

Unless the noise has some mechanical cause, for instance, worn connecting rod bearings, diesel knock can be considered harmless to everything but the driver's ears.

Knocking During Idling

This is a normal condition with diesel engines and nothing really can be done about it. Injection nozzle replacement, although often done, is not a guarantee that the noise will stop. In fact, the new clean nozzles will often make the noise more pronounced.

Knocking at Partial Load at Low Speed

This usually occurs with a cold engine and becomes less as the engine heats up. The most common cause of this is use of diesel fuel with too low a cetane rating (equivalent to "octane" for gasoline). Try mixing about a quart of engine oil with each tank of fuel or change fuel brands.

Often air in the fuel system will cause this problem as well. Check all fuel lines and hoses, from the tank all the way up. The fuel filter and hand pump can also develop leaks. Bleed the fuel system, as described previously in this section, and check the fuel pump vacuum (idle speed=6–12 in. Hg.) and pressure (open pressure of relief valve at idle=11–21 psi).

Knocking at Partial Load at Higher Speeds

This type of knocking usually happens in third gear traveling at 30–45 mph. It can be distinguished by the fact that it gets louder as the engine heats up.

This is often caused by a faulty timing chain tensioner. When the chain loses tension it vibrates, causing a rattle. In addition, the injection timer hub can be scored to such a degree that injection timing is retarded.

1. To accurately check the chain tensioner requires special test equipment. However, if the tensioner is bad enough to cause chain rattle, it will suffice to remove it, clamp it down, fill it with oil and bleed it, then push down slowly.
2. If the tensioner is good, it will require quite high pressure to compress and will compress very slowly.
3. To remove the tensioner, first take off the camshaft cover and drain the radiator to a level below the thermostat housing.
4. Remove the housing and the idler pulley bracket. The tensioner now can be easily removed.
5. Check the tensioner and, if necessary, replace it. Parts are available separately, but the pressure pin and housing must be replaced together for proper operation.
6. To bleed the tensioner after installation, fill the oil case in the cylinder head with engine oil and, using a screwdriver, push the tension sprocket bearing as far as it will go.

Bleeding the timing chain tensioner

7. Slowly release the tensioner, making sure the oil case is filled with oil at all times.
8. Repeat the procedure until no air bubbles appear and there is no free-play on the tensioner.

The injection timer can be removed and checked in the following manner:

1. Remove the radiator.
2. Detach the vacuum and pressure hoses from the vacuum pump. Remove the vacuum pump.
3. Remove the cover screws and cover. Remove the hex nut and washer from the shaft.
4. Remove the camshaft cover.
5. Remove the hex screw and holder.
6. Remove the camshaft sprocket bolt.
7. Turn the crankshaft, using a wrench on the pulley nut, in the direction of rotation until the TDC mark coincides with the pointer.
8. Matchmark the position of the chain with the injection timer. (Use paint dots.)
9. Matchmark the position of the chain on the camshaft sprocket.
10. Remove the chain tensioner.
11. Remove the screw and the inner and outer sliding rails.
12. Pull the camshaft sprocket, making sure the thrust washers are not lost.
13. Unscrew the locking screw and pull the upper guide rail pivot pin.
14. Using a strip of sheet metal or cardboard between the chain and the gear teeth, remove the chain from the intermediate sprocket.
15. Pry off the injection timer, being careful not to turn over the engine or camshaft.
16. Inspect the timer. If badly scored or broken internally, replace it, remembering to transfer matchmarks from the old timer.
17. When reassembling, follow the removal procedure in reverse, being careful to align or stiffwire the matchmarks. A bent piece of brazing rod will hold the guide rail in place while inserting the pivot pin. Don't forget to bleed the chain tensioner.

Hard Knocking and Shaking of Engine

The main cause of this is a sticking injector nozzle. These can be tested as described earlier in this section, as well as the pressure valve holders, another cause of the problem.

Leaks between the pipe connectors and pressure valve holders can cause fuel to leak into the governor vacuum chamber. Replacement of the seals will stop the problem, but the fuel must be drained from the vacuum chamber. Unscrew the oil level plug and loosen the governor housing bolts. Drain the fuel by pulling the housing away.

Injection Pump

In many cases of poor running, the injection pump itself is at fault. Fuel that is extremely gritty will cause wear of the pump plungers and plunger springs can break in service. Accurate testing of the pump must be carried out on a test stand. Aside from testing the governor vacuum and control rod, little else other than visual inspection for broken or worn parts can be accomplished.

1. To remove the pump for service, unscrew all the injection lines, the vacuum line and fuel lines.
2. Plug the lines, then detach the connecting rod for the auxiliary mechanical control and the starting cable at the adjusting lever.
3. Turn the crankshaft, in the normal direction of rotation, to align the 45° BTDC mark with the pointer (No. 1 piston on compression stroke).
4. Matchmark the pump and flange.
5. Unscrew the nut at the bell-shaped support, then the front flange hold-down nuts. Pull the pump from the crankcase, then remove the coupling sleeve from the pump drive collar or driveshaft. New pumps do not come with the splined drive collar, therefore the old one must be removed if the pump is to be exchanged.
6. Using a puller, carefully remove the collar and woodruff key.
7. To install the pump, be sure that the crankshaft has not moved from the 45° BTDC position, then insert the Woodruff key into its groove in the driveshaft, making sure the shaft is dirt free.
8. Install the drive collar and hex nut, using a pair of pliers wrapped in tape to hold the collar while tightening the nut. It is extremely important that the splines are not damaged in any way during this operation.
9. Try sliding the coupling sleeve onto the drive collar. If it slides on easily, it can be pressed onto the driveshaft. Remove the oil overflow pipe plug at the rear of the injection pump and adjust start of delivery position by aligning the marks. Apply light finger pressure to the follower in a direction opposite normal direction of rotation (left). This pressure should cause the drive collar to jump two teeth.
10. Grease the paper gaskets with petroleum jelly and install them to side of crankcase, then install pump, finger-tightening the bolts in the slotted holes.
11. Turn the crankshaft in the direction of rotation to 24° BTDC and check the start of delivery, as outlined previously.

Diesel Engine Tune-Up

Some of the tune-up procedures have been covered in the "Diesel Engine Troubleshooting" section. For those who are not having any problems and wish to tune their engines as part of normal maintenance procedure, these tune-up jobs are listed below. (Starred items have been covered previously.)

1. Adjust idle speed.

*2. Check pneumatic governor for leakage.

3. Adjust idle control cable.
4. Adjust additional mechanical control (Stupser).

5. Adjust no-load maximum speed (governor).
6. Adjust full-load maximum speed (governor).
7. Adjust for minimum exhaust smoke.
8. Adjust valves.
*9. Check start of delivery.
*10. Check glow plugs and prechamber.
*11. Check and adjust start/stop cable.

While not a regular tune-up procedure, checking and adjustment of valve timing should be done, as it can affect performance to a considerable degree. It is also a good practice to check this if the chain tensioner has been removed or replaced to rectify a noise condition.

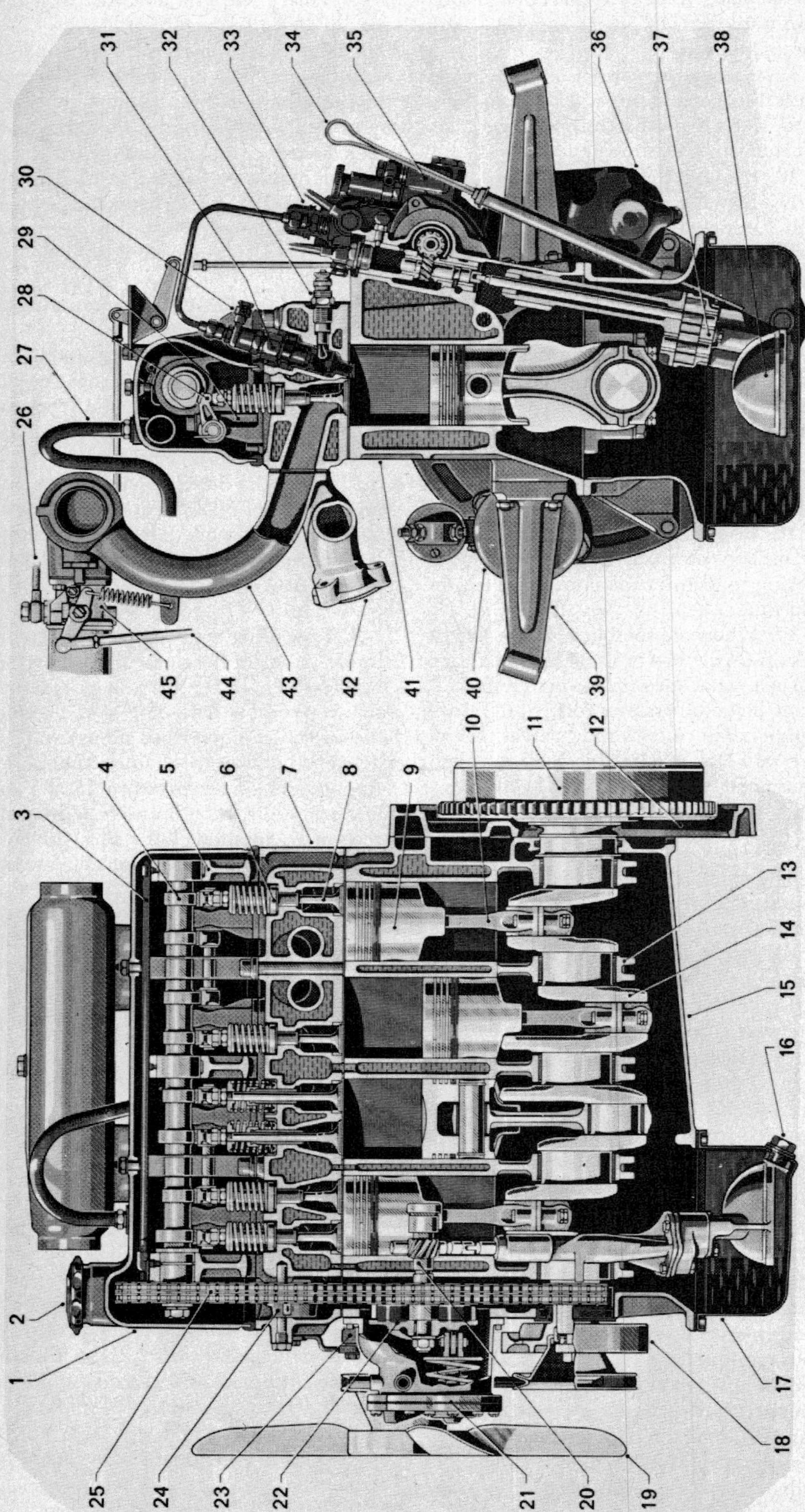

1. Magnetic fan coupling
2. Retaining plate (for pulley)
3. Sprocket wheel (for injection pump)
4. Fuel pressure lines
5. Double roller chain
6. Camshaft bearing
7. Oil filler neck
8. Intake valve
9. Exhaust valve
10. Oil pipe (camshaft lubrication)
11. Rocker arm
12. Control shaft
13. Camshaft
14. Rocker arm support
15. Breather pipe
16. Anti-interference plug
17. Cooling water connection (to control valve)
18. Cylinder head cover
19. Suction pipe
20. Mixture controller
21. Idling control
22. Cooling water control
23. Injection valve
24. Ignition distributor
25. Vacuum control
26. Cooling water thermostat
27. Pressure cell
28. Oil dipstick
29. Injection pump
30. Spark plug
31. Piston
32. Oil line (to oil cooler)
33. Fuel filter
34. Oil pump
35. Oil sump
36. Suction strainer
37. Engine bracket
38. Water pump
39. Exhaust manifold
40. Fuel line (starting valve)
41. Vacuum line (to ignition distributor)
42. Hot air pipe (injection pump starting valve)
43. Oil cooler
44. Flywheel
45. Crankshaft
46. Connecting rod
47. Crankshaft bearing cover
48. Oil drain plug
49. Vibration damper
50. Fan

Longitudinal and cross-section—300SE engine (M 189).

Idle Speed Adjustment

1. To adjust idle speed, start the engine and allow it to come to normal operating temperature.

2. Turn the idle control knob on the dashboard to the extreme right to get enough slack in the cable. It may be necessary to readjust the cable bracket to get the required free-play.

3. Since there is no electronic ignition system, a mechanical tachometer take-off drive is provided. (If such a tachometer is not available, adjust the idle speed by ear to about 700–800 rpm, manual transmission in Neutral and automatic in Drive, with the parking brake on fully and the wheels chocked.) The ammeter light will go out when sufficient speed is reached.

4. To adjust the idle speed, turn the idle screw on the air intake in or out. If the vacuum line is leaking, the idle speed will not drop when the screw is turned, so make sure both the line connections and the pneumatic governor are good before proceeding.

Air venturi and linkage

1. Full-load stop screw
2. Front control valve
3. Connecting rod from front control valve lever to angle lever for injection pump butt bolt operation
4. Idle stop screw
5. Vacuum line to injection pump
6. Check valve lever with stop for automatic opening and rubber damping (in this position the check valve is open)
7. Follower on rear control valve lever for automatic opening of check valve
8. Rear control valve lever
9. Connecting rod (approx. 250 mm. long) to reversing lever, pushrod, control shaft, pedal lever, foot-plate
10. Power brake line to vacuum pump

5. Drain any fuel that might have leaked into the governor housing by unscrewing the oil level plug and loosening the governor housing bolts.

Idle Control Cable

1. Turn the idle control knob on the dashboard to the extreme right and adjust the cable to provide 0.004–0.008 in. clearance between the adjusting ring and the relay lever. The cable must be checked for binding as well and lubricated if necessary.

Additional Mechanical Control

1. This control mechanism helps to eliminate idle speed variations, i.e., "hunting".

2. With the idle speed properly adjusted, detach the connecting rods and measure their length, center to center between ball sockets.

Connecting rod No. 2—310 mm (12.1 in.)

Connecting rod No. 6—205 mm (8.1 in.)

Connecting rod No. 9—250 mm (9.8 in.)

With the rods adjusted, detach connecting rod No. 6 from the relay lever and push it down until it rests against the idle stop. In this position, clearance between the ball socket and head should be 0.04 in. If it requires more than 0.04 in. lift to reattach the connecting rod, unscrew the ball socket.

Maximum Speed Adjustment, No-Load Conditions

This adjustment must be made using a tachometer. The purpose of this adjustment is to limit the maximum engine revolutions so that the engine will never exceed its design speed in service.

1. First, warm up the engine and press the accelerator to the floor.

CAUTION: *Under no circumstances should the engine be revved to 5,000 rpm for more than an instant (split-second). Running the engine for any longer than a split-second at high no-load rpm is extremely dangerous and could result in engine damage.* The full-load stop at the air venturi should be contacted by the linkage and the engine speed should not exceed 5,000 rpm.

2. The speed can be adjusted by turning the full-load stop screw.

3. If the throttle plate is already all the way open and the speed is not up to par, the injection pump control spring tension may be increased by shimming. A 0.004 in. shim will usually increase the engine speed by about 120–150 rpm, depending on the original tension of the spring.

CAUTION: *At first glance, this appears to be an easy way to increase the engine speed range, thus the power output. Unfortunately, the power output decreases sharply above 5,000 rpm, and the reliability of the engine suffers as well, to the point of almost certain bearing failure or crankshaft destruction.*

Maximum Speed at Full-Load

If all aspects of engine and chassis performance have been checked and/or adjusted to produce optimum power and the car will not reach its maximum speed, the full-load stop screw can be adjusted further, or the injection pump control spring tension can be increased slightly. However, under no circumstances should the engine speed under no-load conditions be allowed to go over 5,000 rpm. If no-load engine speed is satisfactory check the speedometer for accuracy, using a stopwatch and a turnpike measured mile.

NOTE: *The best full-load engine speed is 4,350 rpm.*

Model	*Max. speed in second gear (mph)*	*Max. speed in third gear (mph)*	*Top speed (mph*)*
190 Dc	34	54	77
200 D	34	54	80
220 D/8	35	57	83

*Depends on transmission power drain.
NOTE: The best full-load engine speed is 4,350 rpm.

Exhaust Smoke Emission

If the emission of black exhaust smoke seems excessive, test in the following manner: make all engine checks and adjustments and, with the engine fully tuned, road test the car on a slight grade.

1. Accelerate in third gear from about 15 mph to the third-gear shift point mark on the speedometer. Have a passenger watch the exhaust smoke while doing this. If the smoke remains black and can be seen extending three or four feet behind, the maximum fuel delivery rate is too high.

2. Adjust by screwing in the full-load stop screw on the *injection pump governor* about ¼ turn. Repeat the road test and adjust in small increments until the smoke disappears.

CAUTION: *Do not exceed ½ turn total.*

3. If the smoke level is still objectionable, the full-load stop screw on the *air venturi* can be adjusted to reduce maximum speed slightly, or the injection pump start of delivery can be retarded 2°.

Valve Adjustment

Valve adjustment for diesel engines is basically the same as that given for 220/8 gasoline engines. On the diesel, however, the feeler gauge must be inserted between the rocker arm and the cap nut.

1. Remove the camshaft cover and turn the engine, using a wrench on the crankshaft pulley nut (22 mm), until the TDC mark and the pointer are aligned.

2. This job can be accomplished easily if someone helps. First, a wrench must be placed on the valve spring retainer hex nut.

3. The hex nut then must be loosened with another open end wrench (bent to fit) while the cap nut is held with another wrench.

4. Turn the cap nut to adjust, then tighten the locknut and recheck. Go on to the other cylinders turning the crankshaft to TDC position for each adjustment.

Adjusting the valves

6. Rocker arm pad.
7. Cap nut
8. Locknut
14. Holding wrench
15. Feeler Blade
16. Adjusting wrench

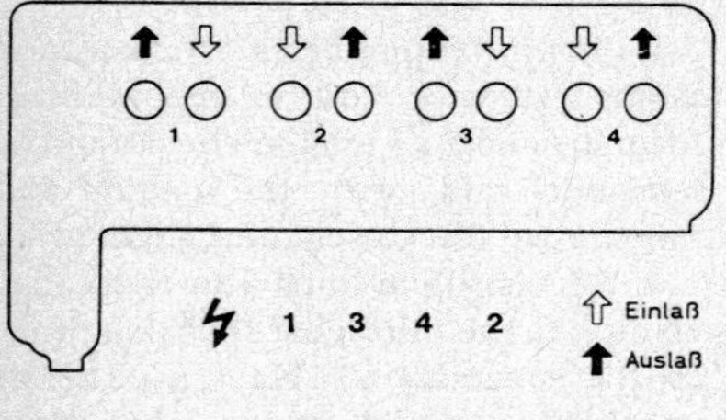

Valve locations—Diesel engines

ENGINE ELECTRICAL

Distributor

Removal and Installation

The removal and installation procedures for all distributors on Mercedes-Benz vehicles are basically similar. However, certain minor differences may exist from model to model.

1. The distributor is usually located on the front of the engine.
2. Remove the dust cover, distributor cap, cable plug connections, and vacuum line.
3. Rotating the engine in the normal direction, crank it around until the markings on the distributor rotor and distributor housing are aligned.
4. The engine can be cranked with a socket wrench on the balancer bolt or with a screwdriver inserted in the balancer.
5. Matchmark the distributor body and the engine so that the distributor can be returned to its original position. White paint can be used for this purpose.
6. Remove the distributor hold-down bolt and withdraw the distributor from the engine.

NOTE: *Do not crank the engine while the distributor is removed.*

7. To install the distributor, reverse the removal instructions. Insert the distributor so that the matchmarks on the distributor and engine are aligned.
8. Tighten the clamp bolt and check the dwell angle and ignition timing.

Alternator

All Mercedes-Benz cars imported into the United States since 1968 use 12 volt alternators, sometimes in conjunction with the transistor ignition system.

Alternator Precautions

Some precautions that should be taken into consideration when working on this, or any other, AC charging system are as follows:

1. Never switch battery polarity.
2. When installing a battery, always connect the grounded terminal first.
3. Never disconnect the battery while the engine is running.
4. If the molded connector is disconnected from the alternator, do not ground the hot wire.
5. Never run the alternator with the main output cable disconnected.
6. Never electric weld around the car without disconnecting the alternator.
7. Never apply any voltage in excess of battery voltage during testing.
8. Never "jump" a battery for starting purposes with more than 12 volts.

Removal and Installation

Viewing the engine from the front, the alternator is located on the left or right-hand side, usually down low. Because of the location, it is generally easier to remove the alternator from below the vehicle. The following is a general procedure for all models.

1. Locate the alternator and disconnect and tag all wires.
2. Loosen the adjusting (pivot) bolt or the adjusting mechanism and swing the alternator in toward the engine.
3. Remove the drive belt from the alternator pulley.
4. The alternator can now be removed from its mounting bracket or the bracket and alternator can be removed from the engine.
5. Installation is the reverse of removal.
6. Re-tension all of the drive belts that were loosened.

Belt Tension Adjustment

All alternator drive belts should be tensioned to approximately ½ in. deflection under thumb pressure at the middle of its longest span.

All Vehicles Except 6-Cylinder Engines with 55 Amp. Alternator and Double Groove Pulley

1. Loosen the counternut and the attaching bolt.

Adjusting the alternator belt tension—all models except 6 cylinder engines with 55 amp. alternator and double groove pulley.

1. Locknut
2. Pivot bolt
3. Adjusting nut

2. Adjust the drive belt tension with the tensioning nut.
3. Tighten the attaching bolt and counternut.

NOTE: *Observe the following when tensioning new drive belts on vehicles equipped with 55 amp. alternators. The 2 drive belts are of different lengths; one encircles the crankshaft, alternator and water pump pulleys, while the shorter one encircles the water pump and alternator only. Tighten the longer belt first as previously detailed. After a brief period of operation, the long V-belt will stretch. After this occurs, the short drive belt should be tensioned, followed by the longer belt.*

6-Cylinder Engines with 55 Amp. Alternator and Double Groove Pulley

1. Loosen the attaching bolt.

Adjusting alternator belt tension—6 cylinder engines with 55 amp alternator and double groove pulley.

1. Adjusting bolt
2. Outer attaching bolt
3. Inner attaching bolt

2. Using a lever, pry the alternator outward. If equipped with air conditioning, this may be easier from underneath the vehicle.
3. Tighten the attaching bolts.

Starter

All Mercedes-Benz passenger cars are equipped with 12-volt Bosch electric starters of various rated outputs. The starter motor is actually nothing but a simple series-wound electric motor of high torque output, fitted with a drive pinion and a device to mesh the pinion with the flywheel ring gear. The carrier, which is connected to the pinion through the overrunning clutch, runs in splines machined in the armature shaft. When the armature rotates, these splines force the pinion into mesh. When the engine starts, the overrunning (one-way) clutch releases the pinion and the unit disengages. The starter is actuated and the pinion engaged by an electric solenoid mounted on top of the starter motor.

When removing the starter, note the exact positions of all wires and washers since they should be installed in their original locations. Also, on some models it may be necessary to position the front wheels to the left or right to provide working clearance.

Removal and Installation

1. Remove all wires from the starter and tag them for location.
2. Disconnect the battery cable.
3. Unbolt the starter from the bell housing and remove the ground cable.
4. Remove the starter from underneath the car.
5. Installation is the reverse of removal. Be sure to replace all wires and washers in their original locations.

Starter installed (typical installation)

1. Terminal 30
2. Terminal 50
3. Solenoid
4. Hex head screw
5. Hex nut
6. Exhaust manifold
7. Hex nut
8. Holding bracket
9. Holding bracket

Battery

The battery is located in the engine compartment and can be easily removed by disconnecting the battery cables and removing the hold-down clamp.

ENGINE MECHANICAL

Mercedes-Benz has used a variety of different engines since 1968. All engines are of overhead valve design, operating the valves through individual rocker arms. The smallest of the engines is the 2197 cc gasoline engine installed in the 220/8. A diesel engine of the same displacement is also available in the 220D/8. Six-cylinder, OHC cam engines are available in displacements from 2292 to 2778 cc's. The exception to the six-cylinder engine family is the DOHC engine installed in the 280 and 280C. All larger sedans (280 and 300 series cars 1970 and later) use either a 3.5, 4.5, or 6.3 liter V-8. The 6.3 liter engine is used exclusively in the 300SEL 6.3 and the 600 series (which is not covered in this book). All V-8's are OHC models with one camshaft per head.

NOTE: *Care should be taken when working on Mercedes-Benz engines since there are many aluminum parts which can be damaged if carelessly handled.*

CAUTION: *Before attempting any service on a Mercedes-Benz engine with mechanical fuel injection, read each procedure carefully. The mechanical fuel injection is very sensitive. Anytime the linkage is disconnected, the possibility exists that it will have to be readjusted. This is a complicated procedure requiring very special instruments and should not be attempted by anyone*

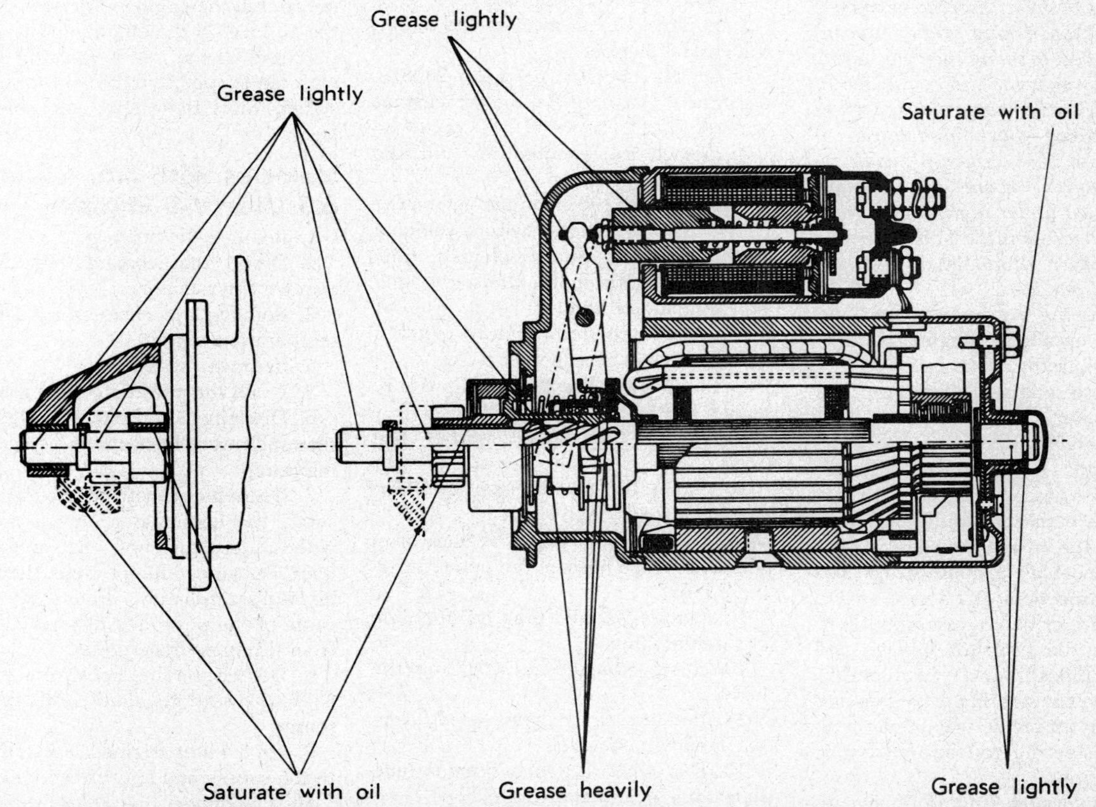

Starter motor lubricaion points

other than a trained Mercedes-Benz mechanic. It is possible, however, to disconnect and reassemble the linkage without disturbing the adjustment, providing that great care is taken throughout the procedure and that components are match marked whenever possible. It should be pointed out however, that there is no guarantee of satisfactory adjustment once the linkage has been disturbed.

Engine Removal and Installation

NOTE: *In all cases, Mercedes-Benz engines and transmissions are removed as a unit.*

220/8, 220D/8, 230/8, 250/8

1. First, remove the hood, then drain the cooling system and disconnect the battery. While not strictly necessary, it is better to remove the battery completely to prevent breakage by the engine as it is lifted out.
2. Remove the fan shroud, radiator, and disconnect all heater hoses and oil cooler lines.
3. Remove the air cleaner and all fuel, vacuum and oil hoses (e.g., power steering and power brakes). Plug all openings to keep out dirt.

CAUTION: *Air conditioner lines should not be indiscriminately disconnected without taking proper precautions. It is best to swing the compressor out of the way while still connected to its hoses. Never do any welding around the compressor—heat may cause an explosion. Also, the refrigerant, while inert at normal room temperature, breaks down under high temperature into hydrogen fluoride and phosgene (among other products), which are highly poisonous.*

4. Remove the viscous coupling and fan and, on applicable engines, disconnect the carburetor choke cable.
5. On diesel engines, disconnect the idle control and starting cables.
6. On all engines, disconnect the accelerator linkage.
7. On six-cylinder engines with a three-groove crankshaft pulley, remove the heater pipe on the firewall.
8. Disconnect all ground straps and electrical connections. It is a good idea to tag each wire for easy reassembly.
9. Detach the gearshift linkage and the exhaust pipes from the manifolds.
10. Loosen the steering relay arm and pull it down out of the way, along with the center steering rod and hydraulic steering damper.
11. The hydraulic engine shock absorber should be removed.
12. Remove the hydraulic line from the clutch housing and the oil line connectors from the automatic transmission.
13. Unbolt the clutch slave cylinder from the bellhousing after removing the return spring.
14. Remove the exhaust pipe bracket attached to the transmission and place a wood-padded jack under the bellhousing, or place a cable sling under the oil pan, to support the engine.
15. Mark the position of the rear engine support and unbolt the two outer bolts, then remove the top bolt at the transmission and pull the support out.
16. Disconnect the speedometer cable and the front driveshaft U-joint. Push the driveshaft back and wire it out of the way.
17. Unbolt the engine mounts on both sides and, on four-cylinder engines, the front limit stop.
18. Unbolt the power steering fluid reservoir and swing it out of the way; then, using a chain hoist and cable, lift the engine and transmission upward and outward. An angle of about 45° will allow the car to be pushed backward while the engine is coming up.
19. Reverse the procedure to install, making sure to bleed the hydraulic clutch, power steering, power brakes and fuel system.

280S/8, 280SE/8, 280SEL/8, 280SL/8, and 300SEL/8

1. Remove the engine hood.
2. Remove the air cleaner and loosen the engine damper.
3. On all models except the 280S/8, disconnect the hose for the air cleaner and idle speed line.
4. Detach the vacuum line for the brakes.
5. Loosen the cable connections on the cold start valve, idle switch, solenoid switch, injection pump solenoid, time switch, automatic choke, alternator, ignition coil, and oil sender.
6. Unscrew the temperature switch.
7. Disconnect the heater hoses.
8. Remove the line to the oil pressure gauge.
9. Lay the windshield washer bag aside.
10. Drain the power steering reservoir.
11. Unscrew and plug the high pressure and return lines on the power steering pump.
12. Disconnect and plug the fuel line at the fuel filter.
13. Remove the ground strap from the body.
14. Remove the exhaust pipes from the exhaust manifolds.
15. Disconnect the speedometer shaft, shift linkage, and control linkage.
16. Remove the bracket from the exhaust pipe support on the transmission, loosen the clamp, and push the holder down.
17. Support the transmission with a jack.
18. Disconnect the driveshaft and slide it toward the rear of the car.
19. Mark the position of the rear engine support and remove it.

Rear engine mount removal—280S/8, 280SE/8, 280SEL/8, 280SL/8, and 300-SEL/8.
1. Rear engine carrier
2. Engine mount
3. Exhaust pipe support (automatic transmission)

20. Remove the splash shield.
21. Loosen the front engine mounting bolts.
22. Connect a hoist to the engine and take up all the slack.
23. Remove the front engine mount bolts and remove the engine and transmssion by pulling it out at a 45° angle.
24. Installation is the reverse of removal. Fill the engine with water, check the oil level in the engine and transmission, and fill the power steering system with the proper fluid. Bleed the steering system. Start the engine and check for leaks.

Vehicles with 3.5, 4.5, and 6.3 Liter V-8 Engines

1. Remove the hood.
2. Drain the cooling system and remove the radiator.
3. Remove the cable plug from the temperature switch.
4. Remove the battery.
5. Drain the power steering reservoir.
6. Disconnect and plug the high pressure and return lines on the power steering pump.
7. On vehicles with air conditioning, swing the compressor out of the way without disconnecting the pressurized lines. The air conditioner lines should not be indiscriminately disconnected because of the possibility of physical harm from the pressurized gases.
8. Detach the fuel lines from the fuel filter, pressure regulator, and pressure sensor.
9. On 3.5 liter engines, loosen the line to the supply and anti-freeze tanks.
10. Disconnect the cables from the ignition coil and transistor ignition switchbox.

11. Disconnect the brake vacuum lines.

12. Detach the cable connections for the following:

a. venturi control unit
b. temperature sensor
c. distributor
d. temperature switch
e. cold starting valve

13. Remove the regulating shaft by pushing it in the direction of the firewall.

14. Disconnect the thrust and pull-rods.

15. Disconnect the heater lines.

16. Detach the lines to the oil pressure and temperature gauges.

17. Remove the ground strap from the vehicle.

18. Detach the cables from the alternator, terminal bridge, and battery. Remove the battery.

19. Position a lifting sling on the engine and take up the slack in the chain.

20. Remove the left-hand engine mount and loosen the hex nut on the right-hand mount.

21. Remove the exhaust system. Remove the connecting rod chain on the rear level control valve and loosen the torsion bar slightly. Raise the vehicle slightly at the rear and remove the exhaust system in a rearward direction.

22. Disconnect the handbrake cable.

23. Remove the shield plate from the transmission tunnel.

24. Loosen the driveshaft intermediate bearing and the driveshaft slide.

Supporting the transmission—3.5 and 4.5 V-8's.

1. U-Joint flange
2. Front driveshaft
3. Hex bolt
4. U-Joint plate
5. Wooden block

25. Support the transmission with a jack.

26. Mark the installation of the crossmember and remove it.

27. Unbolt the front U-joint flange on the transmission and push it back.

28. Disconnect the speedometer shaft, shift rod, control pressure rod, regulating linkage (on automatic transmissions), kickdown switch cable, starter lockout switch cable, and the cable for the backup light switch.

29. On manual transmissions, loosen the hydraulic clutch lines.

30. Remove the front engine mounting bolt and remove the engine at approximately a 45° angle.

31. Installation is the reverse of removal. Lower the engine until it is behind the front axle carrier. Place a jack under the transmission and lower the engine into its compartment. While lowering the engine, install the right-hand shock mount.

Fill the engine with all required fluids and start the engine. Check for leaks.

280 and 280C

1. Scribe alignment marks on the hood hinges and remove the hood. Drain the coolant from the radiator and block.

2. Remove the radiator.

3. Disconnect the lines from the vacuum pump.

4. On vehicles with air conditioning, remove the compressor and place it aside.

CAUTION: *Do not remove the refrigerant lines from the compressor. Physical harm could result.*

5. Disconnect and tag all electrical connections from the engine.

6. Disconnect all coolant and vacuum lines from the engine.

7. Disconnect and plug the pressure oil lines from the power steering pump after draining the pump reservoir.

8. Remove the accelerator linkage control rod by pulling off the lock-ring and pushing the shaft in the direction of the firewall.

9. Loosen and remove the exhaust pipes from the manifold and transmission supports.

10. Disconnect the transmission linkage and all other connections.

11. Loosen the front right (driving direction) shock absorber from the front axle carrier.

12. Remove the left-hand engine shock absorber from the engine mount.

13. Attach a lifting device to the engine and tension the cables.

14. Unbolt the engine and transmission mounts and remove the engine at a 45° angle.

15. Installation is the reverse of removal. Be sure to check all fluids and fill or top up as necessary. Check all adjustments on the engine.

Cylinder Head

Removal and Installation

4 and 6-Cylinder Engines (Except 280, 280C)

While cylinder head removal and installation may seem fairly straightforward, some precautions must be observed to ensure that valve timing is not disturbed.

1. Drain the radiator and remove all hoses and wires.

2. Remove the camshaft cover and associated throttle linkage, then press out the spring clamp from the notch in the rocker arm.

3. Push the clamp outward over the ball cap of the rocker, then depress the valve with a large screwdriver, and lift the rocker arm out of the ball pin head.

4. Remove the rocker arm supports and the camshaft sprocket nut.

5. On diesels, the rockers and their supports must be removed together.

6. Using a suitable puller, remove the camshaft sprocket after having first marked the chain, sprocket, and cam for ease in assembly.

7. Remove the sprocket and chain and wire it out of the way.

CAUTION: *Make sure the chain is securely wired so that it will not slide down into the engine.*

8. Unbolt the manifolds and exhaust header pipe and push them out of the way.

Engine removal—280 and 280C. Insets show lift attaching points.

9. Loosen the cylinder head hold-down bolts in the reverse order of that shown in torque diagrams for each model. It is good practice to loosen each bolt a little at a time, working around the head, until all are free. This prevents unequal stresses on the metal.

10. Reach into the engine compartment and gradually work the head loose from each end by rocking it. Never, under any circumstances, use a screwdriver between the head and block to pry, as the head will be scarred badly and may be ruined.

11. Installation is the reverse of removal.

3.5 and 4.5 Liter V-8 Engines

1. Drain the cooling system.
2. Remove the battery.
3. Remove the air cleaner.
4. Pull the cable plug from the temperature sensor.
5. Detach the vacuum hose from the venturi control unit.
6. Remove the following electrical connections:
   a. injection valves
   b. distributor
   c. venturi control unit
   d. temperature sensor and temperature switch
   e. starting valve
   f. temperature switch for the auxilliary fan.
7. Loosen the ring line on the fuel distributor.

The fuel feed system must be disconnected to remove the cylinder heads on 3.5 and 4.5 V-8's.

1. Injection valve holding screws
2. Pressure regulator
   Arrows—disconnect ring line at arrows
3. Ring line
   Arrows—disconnect ring line at arrows

8. Loosen the screws on the injection valves and pressure regulator. Remove the ring line with the injection valves and pressure regulator.

9. Plug the holes for the injection valves in the cylinder head.

10. Remove the regulating shaft by disconnecting the pull-rod and the thrust rod.

11. Remove the ignition cable plug.

12. Loosen the heating connection on the intake manifold.

13. Loosen the vacuum connection for the central lock at the transmission.

14. Remove the oil filler tube from the right-hand cylinder head and remove the temperature connector.

15. Remove the oil pressure gauge line from the left-hand cylinder head.

16. Loosen the coolant connection on the intake manifold.

17. Remove the intake manifold.

18. Loosen the alternator belt and remove the alternator and mounting bracket.

19. Remove the electrical connections from the distributor and electronic ignition switchgear.

20. Drain some fluid from the power steering reservoir and disconnect and plug the return hose and high pressure supply line.

21. Disconnect the exhaust system.

22. Loosen the right-hand holder for the engine damper.

23. Remove the right-hand chain tensioner.

24. Matchmark the camshaft, camshaft sprocket, and chain. Remove the camshaft sprocket and chain after removing the cylinder head cover. Be sure to hang the chain and sprocket to prevent it from falling into the timing chain case.

25. Remove the upper slide rail.

26. Unscrew the cylinder head bolts. This should be done with a cold engine. Unscrew the bolts in the reverse order of the illustrated torque sequences. Unscrew all the bolts a little at a time and proceed in this manner until all the bolts have been removed.

The bottom row of camshaft support bolts (arrows) must be removed on 3.5 and 4.5 V-8's to remove the heads.

27. Remove the cylinder head. Do not pry on the cylinder head.

28. Remove the cylinder head gasket.

29. Clean the cylinder head and cylinder block joint faces.

30. To install, position the cylinder head gasket.

31. Do not confuse the cylinder head gaskets. The left-hand head has two attaching holes in the timing chain cover while the right-hand head has three.

32. Install the cylinder head and torque the bolts according to the illustrated torque sequence.

33. Further installation is the reverse of removal. Check the valve clearance and fill the engine with oil. Top up the power steering and bleed the power steering.

34. Run the engine and check for leaks.

300SEL 6.3

1. Drain the cooling system.
2. Remove the spark plug wires and lay these aside.
3. From the left-hand cylinder head, disconnect or remove the following:
   a. ignition coil
   b. distributor
   c. idling throttle switch on the venturi control unit
4. Remove the left-hand ignition coil from its holder.
5. Remove the crankcase breather line from the rocker arm cover.
6. Loosen the right-hand crankcase breather line on the venturi control unit and unscrew the vacuum line from the control unit.
7. Remove the right-hand longitudinal regulating shaft and bearing bracket together with the engine regulating shaft.
8. Disconnect the right-hand venturi control unit heater, heated water intake line, and water return line.
9. Disconnect the intake scoop between the intake line and the air cleaner.
10. Remove the right-hand air line from between the air cleaner and injection pump.
11. Disconnect the fuel line, air line, and electric connection from the starting valve.
12. Remove the three rubber hoses between the intake manifolds.
13. Remove the left-hand hose from the heated water return line. Pull the hose from the heating water return line and loosen the holder. Pry the return line from the stud with a screwdriver.
14. Slacken the V-belt on the air conditioning compressor and remove the compressor and bracket from the cylinder head.

NOTE: *Do not disconnect the lines from the compressor.*

15. Drain th power steering reservoir and slacken the drive belt. Remove the oil pressure line and return line. Plug these lines. Remove the pump from its mounting.
16. Remove the left-hand brake unit so that the rear outside cylinder head bolt is accessible.
17. From the right-hand head, disconnect the temperature sensor and the wires from the time delay and heat switch.
18. Detach the left-hand oil pressure gauge line at the connection.
19. Disconnect the heating water intake pipe.
20. Loosen the right-hand engine damper.
21. Disconnect the exhaust manifold.
22. Remove the rocker arm cover.

Top view of the 6.3 V-8 for cylinder head(s) removal

1. Oil pressure gauge line connection
2. Heating water return flow pipe
3. Starting valve
4. Fuel line
5. Rubber hose
6. Crankcase breather
7. Rubber hose
8. Engine regulating shaft
9. Bearing bracket
10. Vacuum connection
11. Vacuum line
12. Heating water intake pipe
13. Fuel diaphragm damper
14. Air line

23. Remove the clip for the cylinder head cover.

24. Rotate the engine with a socket wrench on the crankshaft pulley and place it at TDC. Rotate the engine in the direction of normal rotation only.

25. Remove the right-hand chain tensioner.

26. Matchmark the camshaft sprocket, camshaft, and chain. Unbolt and remove the camshaft sprocket. The timing gears and chains should be suspended so that the chains remain on the gears.

27. Loosen the cylinder head bolts in small increments, using the reverse order of the tightening sequence.

NOTE: *The bottom row of camshaft bearing bolts are cylinder head bolts and must also be loosened.*

CAUTION: *Do not attempt cylinder head removal on a warm engine. Cylinder head warpage may result.*

28. Remove the cylinder head. Do not pry on the cylinder head. It may be loosened by tapping with a rubber mallet.

29. Remove the cylinder head gasket and clean the mating surfaces of the block and cylinder head.

30. To install, position a new cylinder head gasket.

31. Tighten the cylinder head bolts according to the bolt tightening sequence.

32. Further installation is the reverse of removal.

33. Check the valve clearance and fill the engine with oil if necessary. Top up the power steering reservoir and bleed the system. Fill the cooling system.

34. Run the engine until warm and check for leaks.

280, 280C

1. Completely drain the cooling system.
2. Remove the air filter.
3. Remove the radiator.
4. Remove the rocker arm cover.
5. Remove the battery. Remove the idler pulley and the holding bracket for the compressor.
6. Remove the compressor and bracket and lay them aside without disconnecting any of the lines.

CAUTION: *Disconnecting any of the refrigerant lines could result in physical harm.*

7. Unbolt the cover from the camshaft housing.
8. Disconnect the heated water line from the carburetor, the vacuum line on the starter housing, and the distributor vacuum line.
9. Disconnect all electrical connections, water lines, fuel lines, and vacuum lines which are connected to the cylinder head. Tag these for reassembly.
10. Remove the regulating linkage shaft.
11. Remove the EGR line between the exhaust return valve and the exhaust pipe.
12. Disconnect and plug the oil return line at the cylinder head.
13. At the thermostat housing, loosen the hose which passes between the thermostat housing and the water pump. Unscrew the bypass line on the water pump.
14. Loosen the oil dipstick tube from the clamp and bend it slightly sideward.
15. Unbolt the exhaust pipes from the exhaust manifolds and from the bracket on the transmission.
16. Force the tension springs out of the rocker arm with a screwdriver.
17. Remove all of the rocker arms.
18. Crank the engine to TDC. This can be done with a socket wrench on the crankshaft pulley bolt. The marks on the camshaft's sprockets and bearing housings must be aligned.

The marks on the camshafts and bearing housings must be aligned when the 280 and 290C engines is at TDC.

19. Hold the camshafts and remove the bolts which hold each camshaft gear to the camshaft.

20. Remove the upper slide rail. Knock out the bearing bolts with a puller.

21. Remove the chain tensioner.

22. Push both camshafts toward the rear and remove the camshafts' sprockets.

23. Remove the spacer sleeves on both camshafts. The sleeves are located in front of the camshaft bearings.

24. Remove the guide wheel by unscrewing the plug and removing the bearing bolt.

25. Lift off the timing chain and suspend the chain from the hood with a piece of wire. Pull out the guide gear.

26. Remove the slide rail in the cylinder head by removing the bearing pin with a puller.

27. Loosen the cylinder head bolts in small increments, using the reverse order of the tightening sequence. This should be done on a cold engine to prevent the possibility of head warpage.

28. Pull out the two bolts in the chain case with a magnet. Be careful not to drop the washers.

29. Pull up on the timing chain and force the tensioning rail toward the center of the engine.

30. Lift the cylinder head up in a vertical direction.

NOTE: *Mercedes-Benz recommends two men for this job.*

31. Remove the cylinder head gasket and clean the joint faces of the block and head.

32. To install, cut 2 pieces of wood ½ in. x 1 ½ in. x 9 ½ in. Lay one piece between cylinders 1 and 2 in the upright position and the other flat between cylinders 5 and 6.

33. Install the cylinder head in an inclined position so that the timing chain and tensioning rail can be inserted.

34. Lift the cylinder head at the front and remove the front piece of wood toward the exhaust side. Carefully lower the cylinder head until the bolt holes align.

35. Lift the head at the rear so that the board can be removed toward the exhaust side. Carefully lower the cylinder head until all of the bolt holes align.

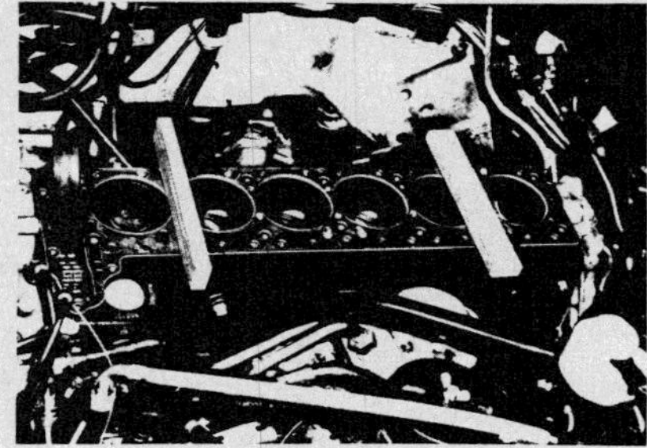

Fabricated tools for installing the cylinder head on 280 and 280C engine.

36. Tighten the cylinder head bolts in gradual steps until they are fully tightened. Follow the torque sequence illustrated.

37. Check to be sure that both camshafts rotate freely after the bolts are tight.

38. The remainder of installation is the reverse of removal. Be sure that the spacer for the camshaft gear, with the engaging lugs for the vacuum pump drive gear, is installed on the exhaust side. Also, the washers for the bolts attaching the camshaft gears to the camshafts must be installed with the domed side against the head of the bolt.

39. Note that the attaching bolt for the exhaust camshaft gear is 0.2 in. shorter.

40. Be sure to adjust the valve clearance and fill the cooling system. Run the engine and check for leaks.

Overhaul

Overhaul procedures for cylinder heads are contained in the "Engine Rebuilding" section of this book. Consult this section for detailed overhaul procedures.

Valve Guides

Removal and Installation

All Models

1. Remove the cylinder head.

2. Clean the valve guide with a brush, knocking away all loose carbon and oil deposits.

3. Knock out the old valve guide with a drift.

4. Check the bore in the cylinder head and clean up any rough spots. Use a reamer for this purpose. If necessary, the valve guide bore can be reamed for oversize valve guides.

5. Clean the basic bores for the valve guides.

6. Heat the cylinder head in water to approximately 176–194° F.

7. If possible cool the valve guides slightly.

8. Drive the valve guides into the bores with a drift. Coat the bores in the cylinder head with wax prior to installation and be sure that the circlip rests against the cylinder head.

9. Let the head cool and try to knock the valve guide out with light hammer blows and a plastic drift. If the guide can be knocked out, try another guide with a tighter fit.

10. Install the cylinder head.

Rocker Arms

Removal and Installation

Diesel Engines

Rocker arms on diesel engines can only be removed as a unit with the respective rocker arm blocks.

1. Detach the connecting rod for the venturi control unit from the bearing bracket lever and remove the bearing bracket from the rocker arm cover.

2. Remove the air vent line from the rocker arm cover and remove the rocker arm cover.

3. Remove the stretchbolts from the rocker arm blocks and remove the blocks with the rocker arms. Turn the crankshaft in each case so that the camshaft does not put any load on the rocker arms.

NOTE: *Turn the crankshaft with a socket wrench on the crankshaft pulley bolt. Do not rotate the engine by turning the camshaft sprocket.*

4. Before installing the rocker arms, check the sliding surfaces of the ball cup and rocker arms. Replace any defective parts.

5. To install, assemble the rocker arm blocks and insert new stretchbolts.

6. Tighten the stretchbolts. In each case, position the camshaft so that there is no load on the rocker arms. See the previous **NOTE.**

7. Check to be sure that the tension clamps have engaged with the notches of the rocker arm blocks.

8. Adjust the valve clearance.

9. Reinstall the rocker arm cover, air vent line, and bearing bracket for the reverse lever. Attach the connecting rod for the venturi control unit to the reversing lever.

10. Make sure that during acceleration, the control cable can move freely without binding.

11. Start the engine and check the rocker arm cover for leaks.

Gasoline Engines

Before removing the rocker arm(s), be sure that they are identified by their position relative to the camshaft lobe. They should be installed in the same place as they were before assembly.

1. Remove the rocker arm cover or covers.

2. Force the clamping spring out of the notch in the top of the rocker arm. Slide it in an outward direction across the ball socket of the rocker arm.

NOTE: *Turn the engine over each*

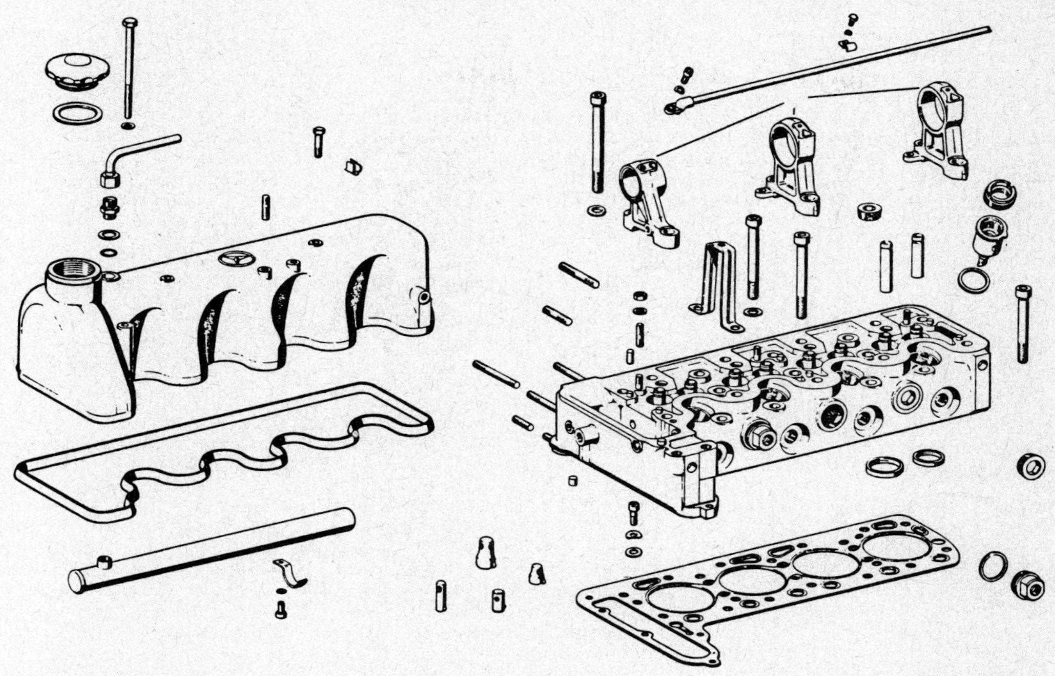

Diesel engine cylinder head

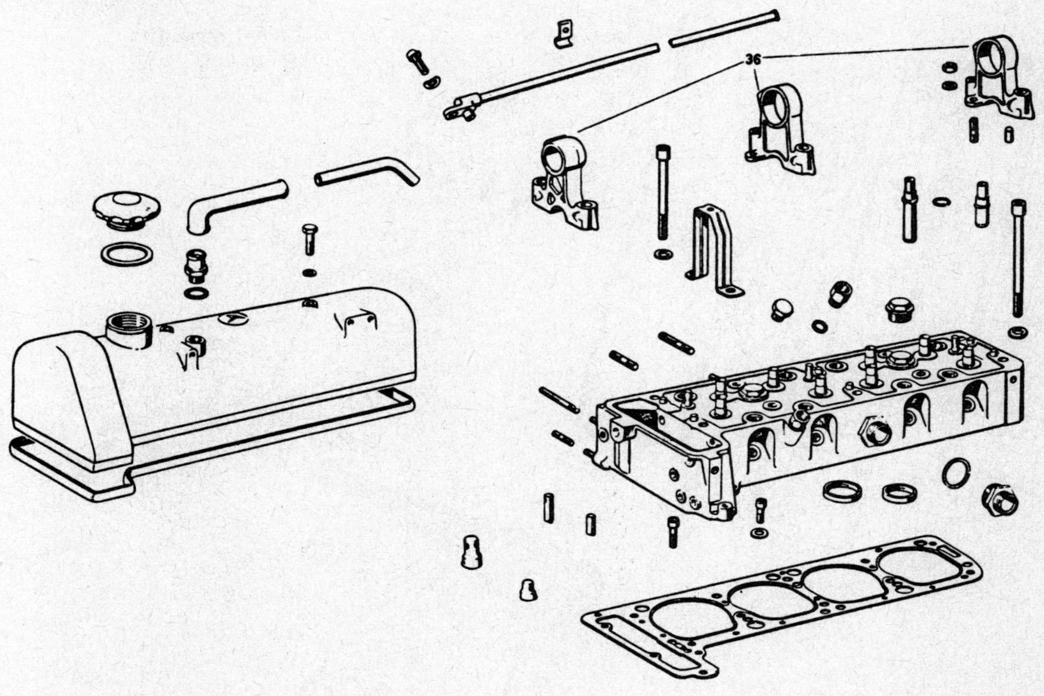

4-cylinder head

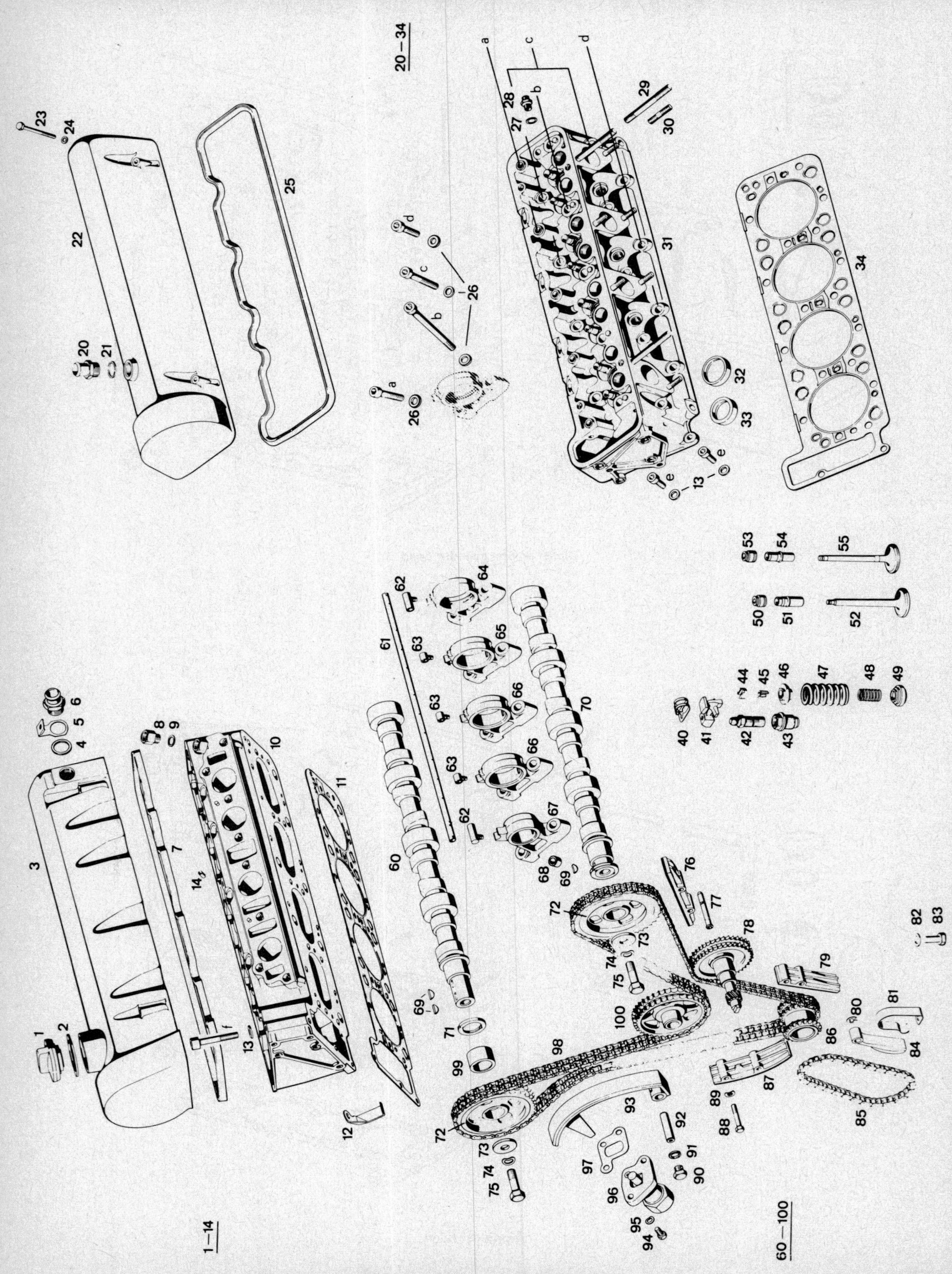

V-8 engine cylinder head (3.5 and 4.5 shown)

Cylinder head right 1-14

1. Filler plug
2. Sealing ring
3. Cylinder head cover
4. Sealing ring
5. Holder for cable to injection valves
6. Connection
7. Valve cover gasket
8. Connection to temperature sensor
9. Sealing ring
10. Cylinder head
11. Cylinder head gasket
12. Cable holder
13. 5 Washers
14. Hollow dowel pins

Cylinder head left 20-34 . . . .

20. Connection
21. Sealing ring
22. Cylinder head cover
23. 8 Screws
24. 8 Sealing rings
25. Cylinder head cover gasket
26. 36 Washers
27. Sealing ring
28. Screw connection oil pressure gauge
29. 3 Studs
30. 13 Studs
31. Cylinder head
32. Valve seat ring—intake
33. Valve seat ring—exhaust
34. Cylinder head gasket

Cylinder head bolts

(a)—10 M 10 x 50chrauben)
(camshaft bearing fastening bolts)
(b)—10 M 10 x 155
(c)—18 M 10 x 80
(d)—8 M 10 x 55
(e)—4 M 8 x 30
(f)—1 M 8 x 70

Valve arrangement 40-55

40. Tensioning spring
41. Rocker arm
42. Adjusting screw
43. Threaded bushing
44. Thrust piece
45. Valve cone piece
46. Valve spring retainer
47. Outer valve spring
48. Inner valve spring
49. Rotator
50. Intake valve seal
51. Exhaust valve guide
52. Intake valve
53. Exhaust valve seal
54. Exhaust valve guide
55. Exhaust valve

Engine timing 60-100

60. Camshaft-right
61. Oil pipe (external lubrication) } Oil pipe to camshaft bearing
62. Connecting piece
63. Connecting piece
64. Camshaft bearing-flywheel end
65. Camshaft bearing 4
66. Camshaft bearing 2 and 3
67. Camshaft bearing-cranking end
68. 5 Hollow dowel pins
69. Spring washer
70. Camshaft-left
71. Compensating washer
72. Camshaft gear
73. Washer-camshaft gear
74. Spring washer
75. Bolt
76. 3 Slide rails
77. 6 Bearing bolts
78. Drive gear ignition distributor
79. Guide rail
80. Lockwasher
81. Spring—chain tensioner, oil pump
82. Washer
83. Screw
84. Clamp
85. Single roller chain (oil pump drive)
86. Crankshaft gear
87. Slide rail
88. 4 Screws
89. 4 Spring washers
90. Plug
91. Sealing ring
92. Bearing bolt
93. Tensioning lever
94. 2 Bolts
95. 2 Spring washers
96. Chain tensioner
97. Gasket
98. Double roller chain
99. Spacer ring
100. Idler gear

V-8 engine cylinder head (3.5 and 4.5 shown)

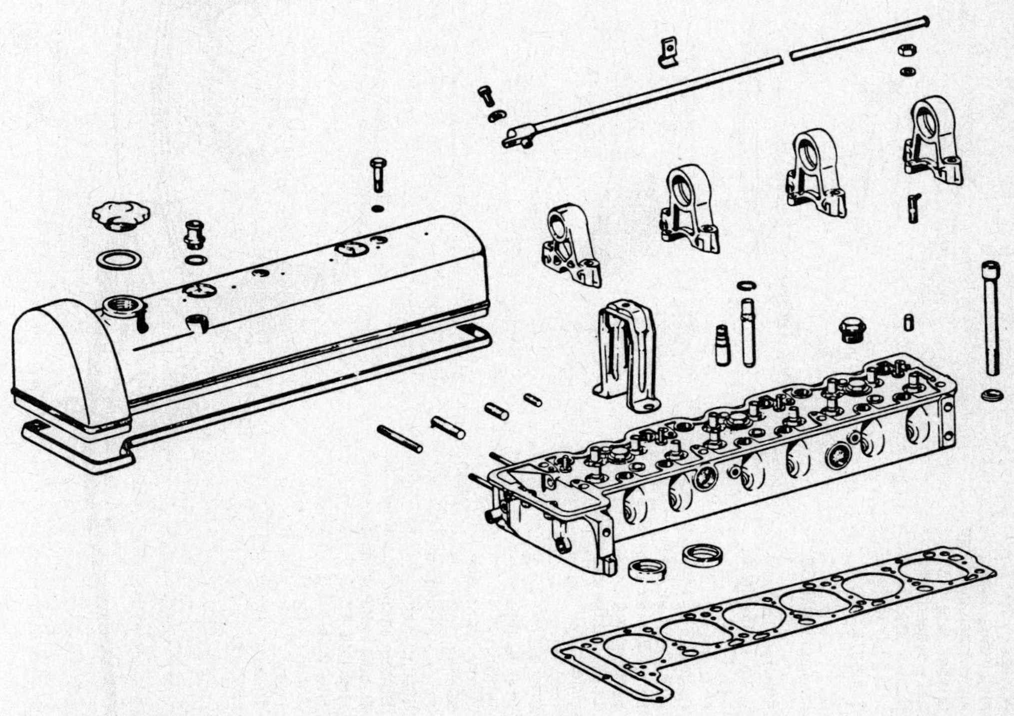

6-cylinder head (except 280 and 280C)

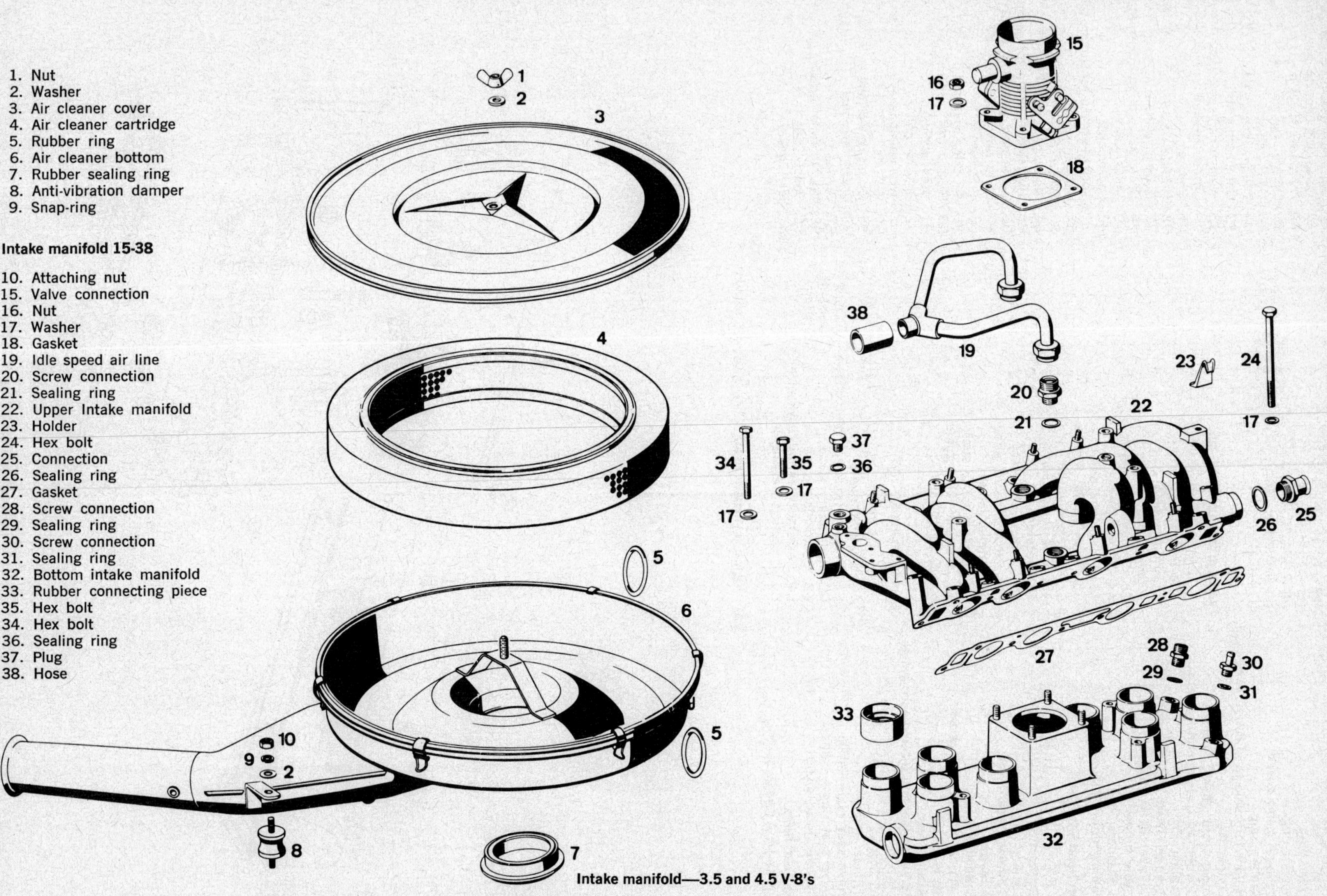

1. Nut
2. Washer
3. Air cleaner cover
4. Air cleaner cartridge
5. Rubber ring
6. Air cleaner bottom
7. Rubber sealing ring
8. Anti-vibration damper
9. Snap-ring

Intake manifold 15-38

10. Attaching nut
15. Valve connection
16. Nut
17. Washer
18. Gasket
19. Idle speed air line
20. Screw connection
21. Sealing ring
22. Upper Intake manifold
23. Holder
24. Hex bolt
25. Connection
26. Sealing ring
27. Gasket
28. Screw connection
29. Sealing ring
30. Screw connection
31. Sealing ring
32. Bottom intake manifold
33. Rubber connecting piece
35. Hex bolt
34. Hex bolt
36. Sealing ring
37. Plug
38. Hose

Intake manifold—3.5 and 4.5 V-8's

time to relieve any load from the rocker arm.

3. On 3.5 and 4.5 models, the clamping spring must be forced from the adjusting screw with a screwdriver.

4. Force the valve down to remove load from the rocker arm.

5. Lift the rocker arm from the ball pin and remove the rocker arm.

6. To install the rocker arm(s), force the rocker arm down until the rocker arm and its ball socket can be installed in the top of the ball pin.

7. Install the rocker arms.

8. Slide the clamping spring across the ball socket of the rocker arm until it rests in the notch of the rocker arm.

9. On 3.5 and 4.5 models, engage the clamping spring into the recess of the adjusting screw.

10. Check and, if necessary, adjust the valve clearance.

11. After completion of the adjustment, check to be sure that the clamping springs are correctly seated.

12. Install the rocker arm cover and connect any hoses or lines that were disconnected.

13. Run the engine and check for leaks at the rocker arm cover.

Intake Manifold

Removal and Installation

350SL, 450SL and 450SLC

1. Partially drain the coolant.
2. Remove the air cleaner.
3. Disconnect the regulating linkage and remove the longitudinal regulating shaft.
4. Pull off all cable plug connections.
5. Disconnect and plug the fuel lines on the pressure regulator and starting valve.
6. Unscrew the nuts on the injection valves and set the injection valves aside.
7. Remove the sixteen attaching bolts from the intake manifold.
8. Loosen the hose clip on the thermostat housing hose and disconnect the hose.
9. Remove the intake manifold. If a portion of the manifold must be replaced, disassemble the intake manifold. Replace the rubber connections during reassembly.
10. Intake manifold installation is the reverse of removal. Replace all seals and gaskets. Adjust the linkage and idle speed.

Exhaust Manifold

Removal and Installation

350SL, 450SL and 450SLC

1. Unbolt the exhaust pipes from the manifolds.
2. Disconnect the rubber mounting ring from the exhaust system.
3. Loosen the shield plate on the exhaust manifold.
4. When removing the left-hand exhaust manifold, remove the shield plate for the engine mount together with the engine damper.
5. Unbolt the manifold from the engine.
6. Pull the manifolds off the mounting studs by turning the left-hand exhaust manifold forward and down and removing it upward. Remove the right-hand manifold downward and toward the rear.
7. Installation is the reverse of removal. Replace all gaskets and nuts. Mount the flanged gaskets between the exhaust manifold and the cylinder head with their flat sides toward the exhaust manifold.
8. Tighten all nuts evenly and to the specified torque. Run the engine and check for a tight fit.

Engine Disassembly

All Models

NOTE: *This procedure is general and intended to apply to all Mercedes-Benz engines. It is suggested, however, that you be entirely familiar with Mercedes-Benz engines and be equipped with the numerous special tools before attempting an engine rebuild. If at all in doubt concerning any procedure, refer the job to a qualified dealer. While this may be more expensive, it will probably produce better results in the end. If you attempt the rebuild yourself, refer often to the "Engine Rebuilding" section, and read the procedure carefully before beginning.*

1. Remove the engine and support it on an engine stand or other suitable support.
2. Set the engine at TDC and matchmark the timing chain and timing gear (s). Remove the cylinder head(s) and gasket(s).
3. Remove the oil pan bolts and the pan and, on most models, the lower crankcase section.
4. Remove the oil pump.
5. Matchmark the connecting rod bearing caps to identify the proper cylinder for reassembly. Matchmark the sides of the connecting rod and side of the bearing cap for proper alignment. Pistons should bear an arrow indicating the front. If not, mark the front of the piston with an arrow using a magic marker. Also identify pistons as to cylinder so they may be replaced in their original location.
6. Remove the connecting rod nuts, bearing caps, and lower bearing shells.
7. Place small pieces of plastic tubing on the rod bolts to prevent crankshaft damage.
8. Inspect the crankshaft journals for nicks and roughness and measure diameters.
9. Turn the engine over and ream the ridge from the top of the cylinders to remove all carbon deposits.
10. Using a hammer handle or other piece of hardwood, gently tap the pistons and rods out from the bottom.
11. The cylinder bores can be inspected at this time for taper and general wear.

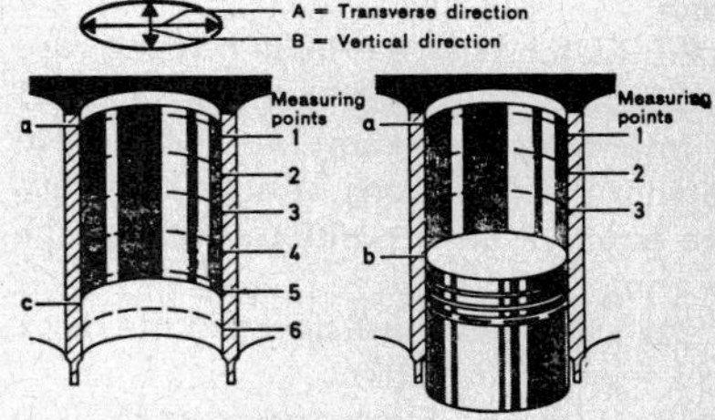

Cylinder bore gauging points

12. Check the pistons for proper size and inspect the ring grooves. If any rings are cracked, it is almost certain that the grooves are no longer true, because broken rings work up and down. It is best to replace any such worn pistons.
13. The pistons, pins and connecting rods are marked with a color dot assembly code. Only parts having the same color may be used together.
14. If the cylinders are bored, make sure the machinist has the pistons beforehand-cylinder bore sizes are nominal, and the pistons must be individually fitted to the block. Maximum piston weight deviation in any one engine is 4 grams.
15. The flywheel and crankshaft are balanced together as a unit. Matchmark the location of the flywheel relative to the crankshaft, then remove the flywheel. Stretch bolts are used on some newer flywheels and can be identified by their "hourglass" shape. Once used, they should be discarded and replaced at assembly.
16. Remove the water pump, alternator, and fuel pump, if not done previously.

Clamping the vibration damper on 6.3 engines.

17. Unbolt and remove the vibration damper and crankshaft pulley. On certain models, especially 300SEL 6.3, it is necessary to clamp the vibration damper with C-clamps before removing the bolts. Otherwise, the vibration damper will come apart.

18. Remove the timing chain tensioner and chain cover.

19. Matchmark the position of the timing chain on the timing gear of the crankshaft.

20. Matchmark the main bearing caps for number and position in the block. It is important that they are installed in their original positions. Most bearing caps are numbered for position. Remove the bearing caps.

21. Lift the crankshaft out of the block in a forward direction.

22. With the block completely disassembled, inspect the water passages and bearing webs for cracks. If the water passages are plugged with rust, they can be cleaned out by boiling the block at a radiator shop.

CAUTION: *Aluminum parts must not be boiled out-they will be eroded by chemicals.*

23. Measure piston ring end gap by sliding a new ring into the bore and measuring. Measure the gap at top, bottom, and midpoint of piston travel and correct by filing or grinding the ring ends.

24. To check bearing clearances, use Plastigage® inserted between the bearing and the crankshaft journal. Blow out all crankshaft oil passages before measuring; torque the bolts to specification. Plastigage® is a thin plastic strip that is crushed by the bearing and cap and spreads out an amount in proportion to clearance. After torquing the bearing cap, remove the cap and compare the width of the Plastigage® with the scale.

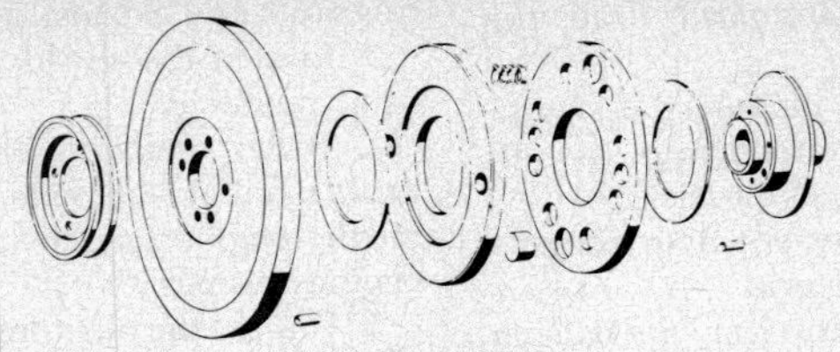

300SEL 6.3 vibration damper

NOTE: *Do not rotate the crankshaft. Bearing shells of various thicknesses are available, and should be used to correct clearance; it may be necessary to machine the crankshaft journals undersize to obtain the proper oil clearance.*

CAUTION: *Use of shim stock between bearings and caps to decrease clearance is not a good practice.*

25. Check crankshaft end-play using a feeler gauge.

26. When installing new piston rings, ring grooves must be cleaned out, preferably using a special groove cleaner, although a broken ring will work as well. After installing the rings, check ring side clearance.

Engine Assembly

All Models

1. Assemble the engine using all new gaskets and seals and make sure all parts are properly lubricated. Bearing shells and cylinder walls must be lubricated with engine oil before assembly. Make sure no metal chips remain in the cylinder bores or crankcase.

2. To install pistons and rods, turn the engine right side up and insert the rods into the cylinders. Clamp the rings to the piston, with their gaps equally spaced around the circumference, using a piston ring compressor. Gently tap the piston into the bore, using a hammer handle or similar hard wood, making sure the rings clear the edge.

3. Torque the rod and main caps to specification and try to turn the crankshaft by hand. It should turn with moderate resistance, not spin freely or be locked up.

4. Disassemble the oil pump and check the gear backlash. Place a straightedge on the cover and check for warpage. Deep scoring on the cover usually indicates that metal or dirt particles have been circulating through the oil system. Covers can be machined, but it is best to replace them if damaged.

5. Install the oil pump.

6. Install the oil pan and lower crankcase and tighten the bolts evenly all

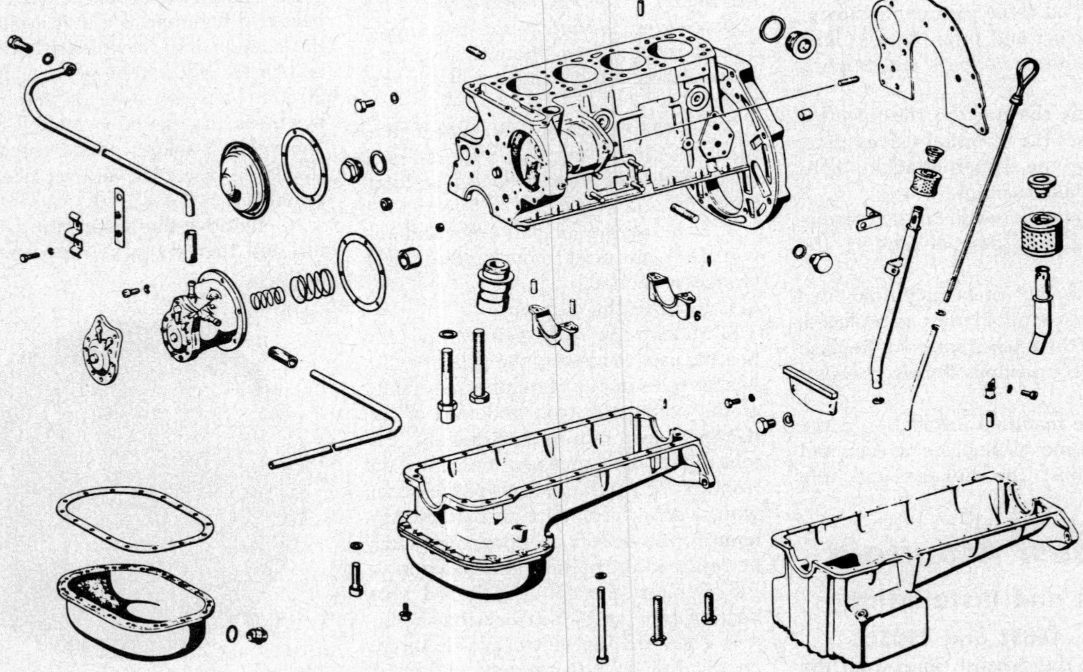

4-cylinder Diesel engine cylinder block compoents.

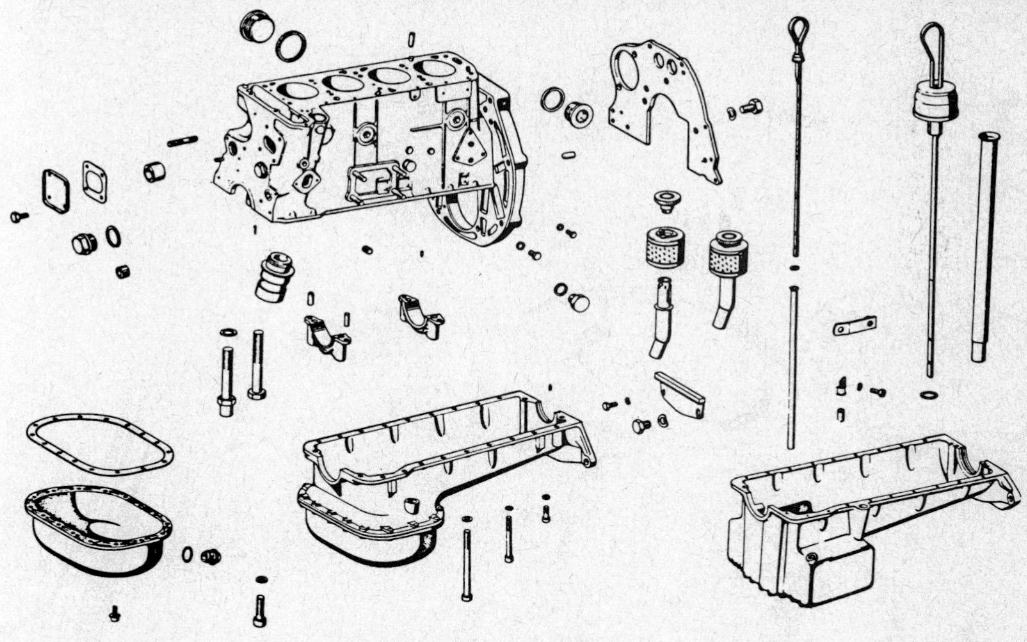

4-cylinder gasoline engine cylinder block components.

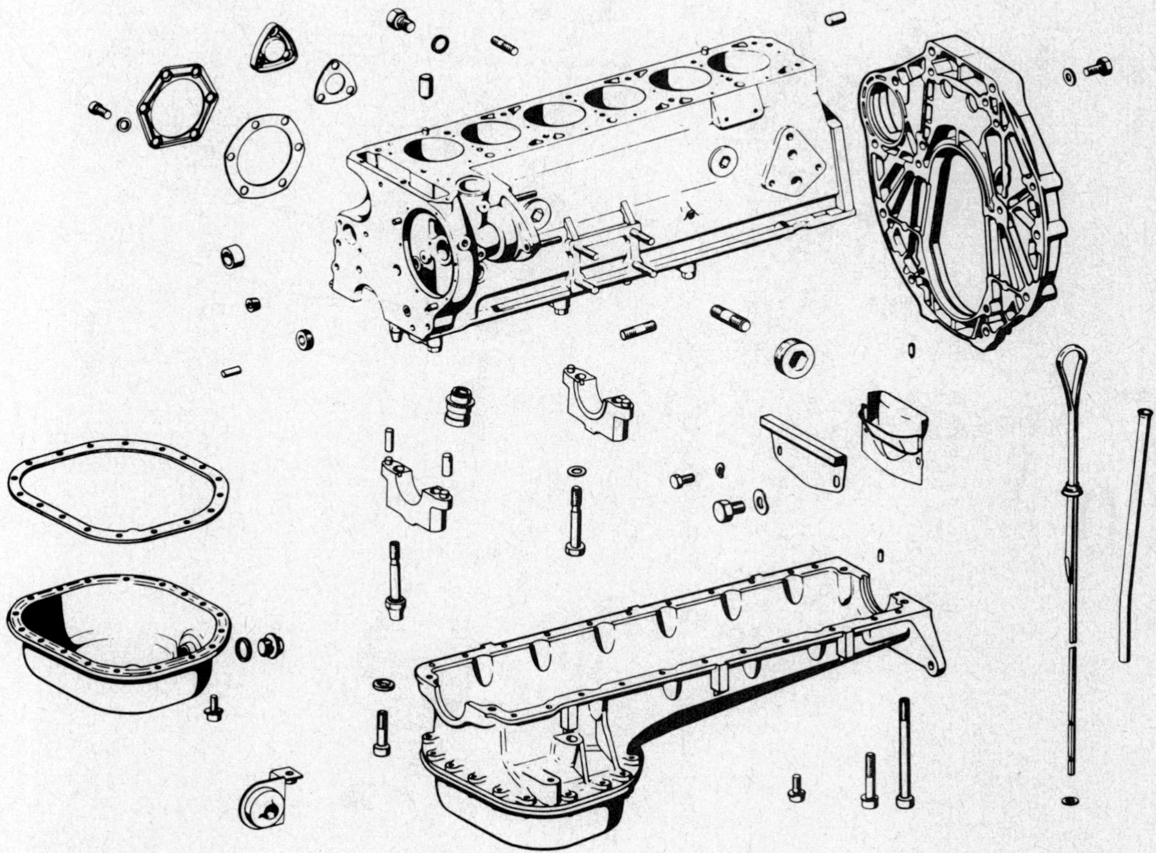

6-cylinder engine block components

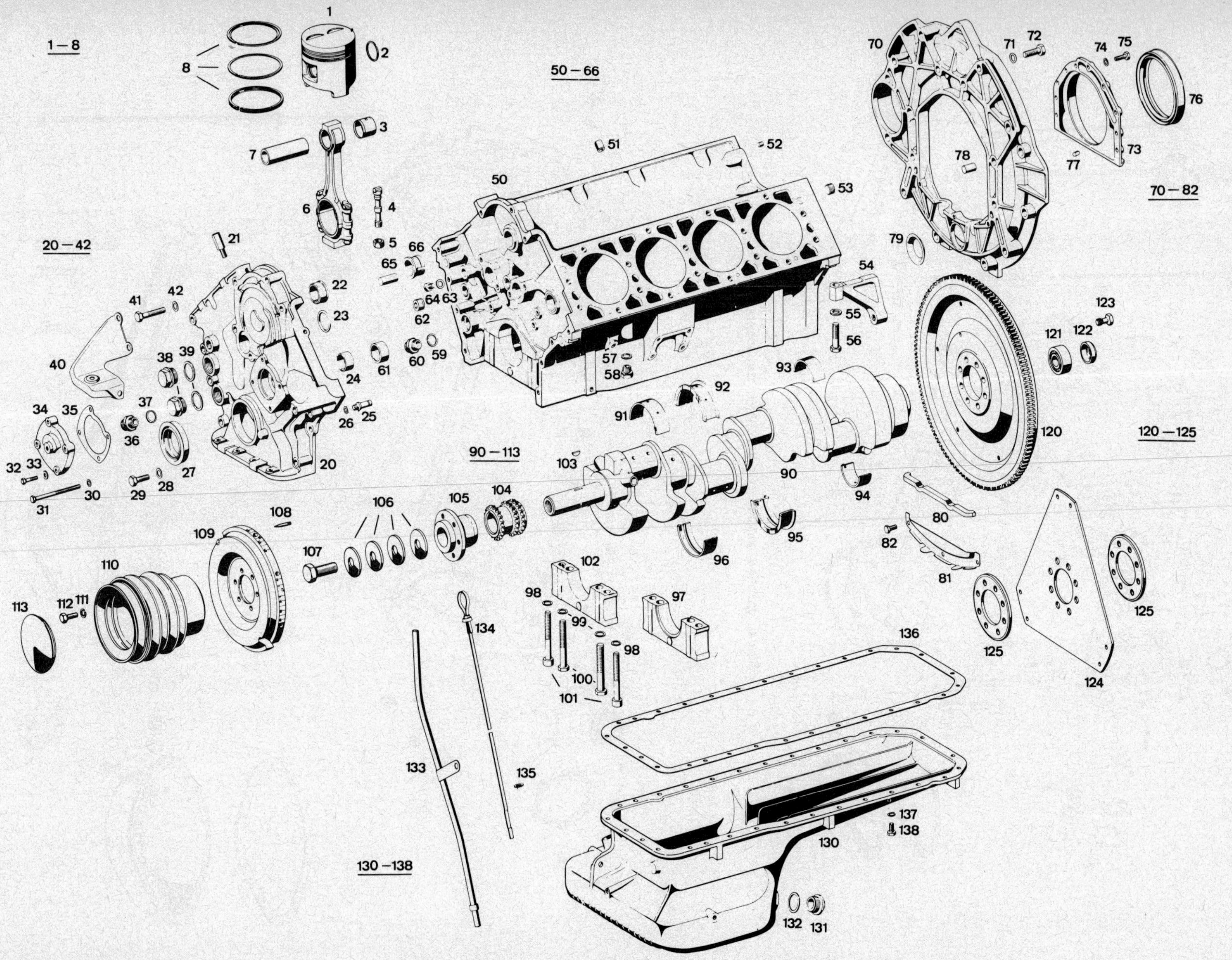

3.5 and 4.5 V-8 engine block and crankshaft components (6.3 V-8 is similar)

Piston and connecting rod 1-8

1. Piston
2. Circlip
3. Connecting rod bearing
4. Connecting rod bolt
5. Nut
6. Connecting rod
7. Wrist pin
8. Piston rings

Timing housing cover 20-42

20. Timing housing cover
21. Threaded bolts for adjusting lever of ignition distributor
22. Bearing bushing (guidewheel bearing)
23. 2 O-rings
24. Bearing bushing (intermediate gear shaft)
25. Bolt
26. Spring plate
27. Crankshaft sealing ring (front)
28. Washer
29. Screw
30. Washer
31. Screw
32. 4 Screws
33. 4 Washers
34. End cover
35. Gasket
36. Screw connection
37. Sealing ring
38. Plug
39. Sealing ring
40. Holder-engine damper
41. 6 Screws
42. 6 Washers

Cylinder crankcase 50-66

50. Cylinder block
51. 4 Hollow dowel pins
52. 3 Plugs (oil duct)
53. Plug (rear main oil duct)
54. 2 Supporting angle pieces
55. 2 Washers
56. 2 Screws
57. 2 Sealing rings
58. 2 Plugs
59. Sealing ring
60. Screw connection
61. Bearing bushing intermediate gear shaft rear
62. Plug (front main oil duct)
63. Sealing ring
64. Plug
65. 2 Cyl. pins
66. Idler gear bearing

Intermediate flange 70-82

70. Intermediate flange
71. 4 Spring washers
72. 4 Screws
73. Cover (crankcase sealing ring, rear)
74. 8 Washers
75. 3 Screws
76. Crankshaft sealing ring (rear)
77. 2 Cyl. pins
78. 2 Set pins
79. Cover
80. Sealing strip
81. Cover plate
82. 3 Screws

Crankshaft 90-113

90. Crankshaft
91. Main bearing shell (top)
92. Fitted bearing shell (top)
93. Connecting rod bearing shell (top)
94. Connecting rod bearing shell (bottom)
95. Fitted bearing shell (bottom)
96. Main bearing shell (bottom)
97. Crankshaft bearing cap (fitted bearing)
98. 10 Washers
99. 10 Washers
100. 10 Hex bolts
101. 10 Hex socket bolts
102. Crankshaft bearing cap (main bearing)
103. Key
104. Crankshaft gear
105. Vibration damper pulley
106. Plate springs
107. Bolt
108. Indicating needle
109. Vibration damper
110. Pulley
111. 6 Circlips
112. 6 Screws
113. Pulley cover

Flywheel and driven plate 120-125

120. Flywheel
121. Ball bearing 6202
122. Closing ring
123. 8 bolts
124. Driven plate
125. Spacers

Oil pan 130-138

130. Oil pan
131. Oil drain plug
132. Sealing ring
133. Guide tube (oil dipstick)
134. Oil dipstick
135. Stop-ring (oil dipstick)
136. Oil pan gasket
137. 30 washers
138. 30 Screws

3.5 and 4.5 V-8 engine block and crankshaft components (6.3 V-8 is similar)

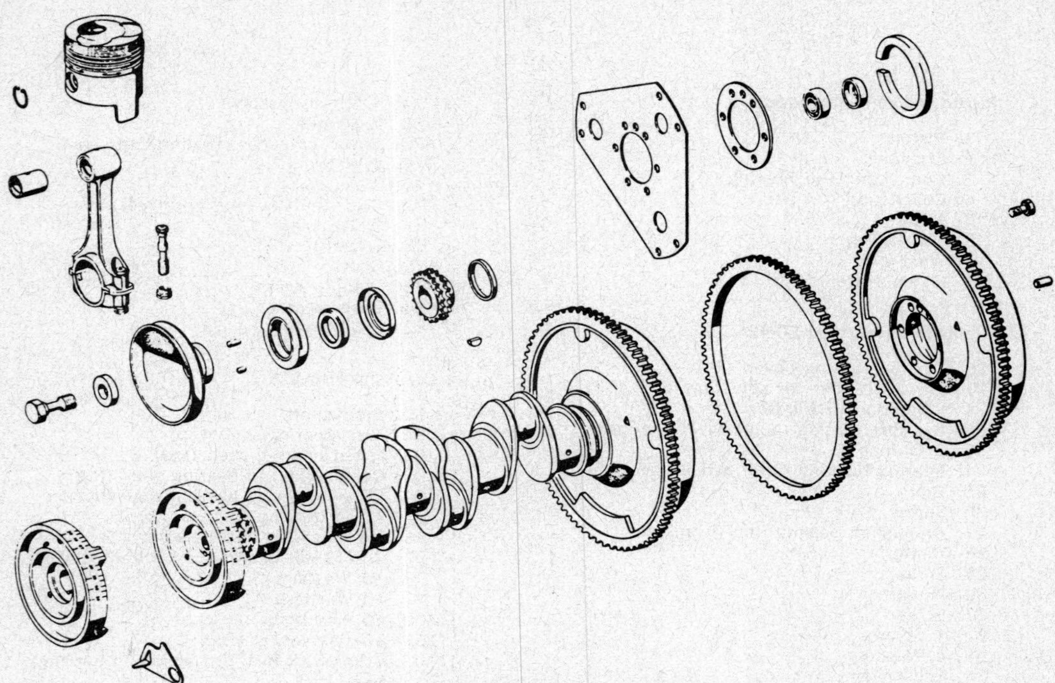

Diesel engine crankshaft and components

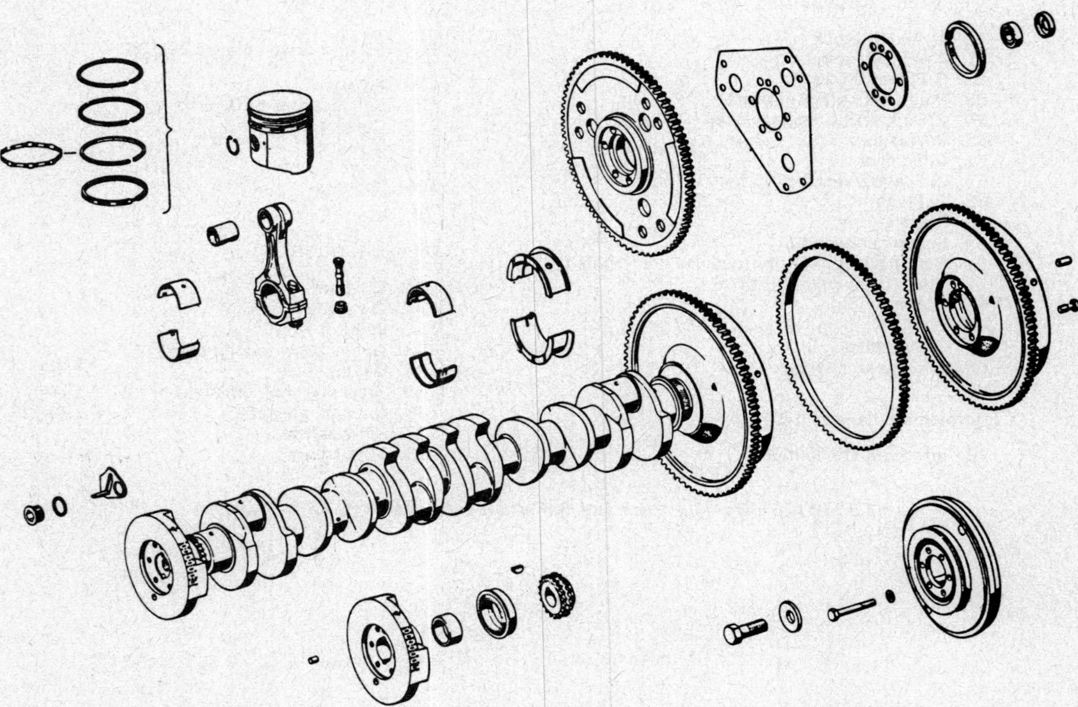

6-cylinder crankshaft and components (4- cylinder engine is similar).

around, then turn the engine right side up and install the cylinder head gasket and head. Make sure the gasket surfaces are clean before installation; a small dirt particle could cause gasket failure. Tighten the cylinder head bolts in sequence, in stages, to insure against distortion. Don't forget the small bolts at the front of the head.

7. Install the engine into the vehicle.

NOTE: *It is a good practice to retighten all bolts after about 500 miles of running, although this is not absolutely necessary. The cylinder head is the only exception to this and should be retightened to specifications after 500 miles. It is also a good practice to use a good break-in oil after an engine overhaul. Be sure that all fluids have been replaced and perform a general tune-up. Check the valve timing.*

8. Stretch bolts are used for the connecting rods of some phase II models, the 280 SL/8 AND 300 SEL/8 in particular. These bolts are tightened by angle of rotation rather than by use of a torque wrench. Make sure the stretch section diameter is greater than 0.35 in. (−0.003 in.). Remove the bolt from the rod and measure the diameter at the point normally covered by the rod; it should be at least 0.31 in. For reasons of standardization, the angle of rotation for all the screw connections tightened according to angle of rotation has been set to 90° + 10°. The initial torque for connecting rod bolts has been increased to 22–35 ft lbs.

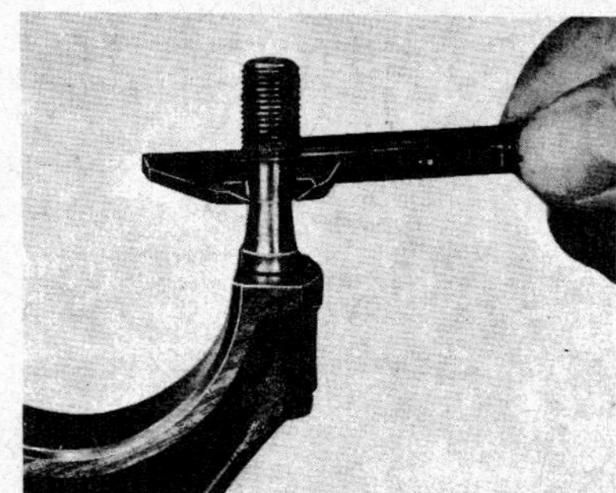

Checking stretchbolts (connecting rod stretchbolt illustrated).

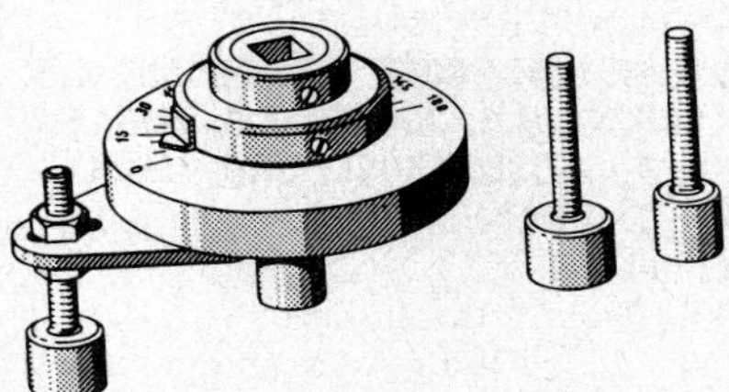

Prefered tools (in addition to a torque wrench) for torquing by angle rotation.

Valve Timing

Ideally, this operation should be performed by a dealer who is equipped with the necessary tools and knowledge to do the job properly.

All Engines

Checking valve timing is too inaccurate at the standard tappet clearance, therefore timing values are given for an assumed tappet clearance of 0.4 mm. The 280 and 280C engines is not measured at 0.4 mm. but rather at 2 mm.

1. To check the timing, remove the rocker arm cover and spark plugs. On 3.5, 4.5, and 280, 280C models, remove the tensioning springs. On the 280, 280C engine install the testing thrust pieces. Eliminate all valve clearance.

2. Cut the degree wheel from the back endpaper of this book and glue it to a piece of stiff cardboard, bakelite or aluminum.

3. A pointer must be made out of a bent section of 3/16 in. brazing rod or coathanger wire, and attached to the engine.

NOTE: *If the degree wheel is attached to the camshaft as shown, values read from it must be doubled.*

4. With a 22 mm wrench on the crankshaft pulley, turn the engine, in the direction of rotation, until the TDC mark on the vibration damper registers with the pointer and the distributor rotor points to the No. 1 cylinder mark on the housing.

5. Turn the loosened degree wheel until the pointer lines up with the 0° (OT) mark, then tighten it in this position.

6. Continue turning the crankshaft in the direction of rotation until the camshaft lobe of the associated valve is vertical (e.g., points away from the rocker arm surface). To take up tappet clearance, insert a feeler gauge (thick enough to raise the valve slightly from its seat) between the rocker arm cone and the pressure piece.

Dial indicator installed for checking valve timing.

1. Feeler gauge
2. Valve spring retainer
3. Dial indicator prod
4. Dial indicator holder
5. Dial indicator

7. Attach the indicator to the cylinder head so that the feeler rests against the valve spring retainer of No. 1 cylinder intake valve. Preload the indicator at least 0.008 in. then set to zero, making sure the feeler is exactly perpendicular on the valve spring retainer. It may be necessary to bleed down the chain tensioner at this time to facilitate readings.

8. Turn the crankshaft in the normal direction of rotation, again using a wrench on the crankshaft pulley, until

Engine set up for checking valve timing

1. Pointer for graduation on crankshaft
2. TDC mark or graudation on degree wheel of crankshaft
3. Degree wheel from end-paper
4. Pointer on camshaft
5. Dial micrometer with feeler and holder
6. Bracket for camshaft cover
7. Distributor rotor arm
8. Mark on distributor housing for cylinder No. 1

the indicator reads 0.016 in. less than zero reading.

9. Note the reading of the degree wheel at this time, remembering to double the reading if the wheel is mounted to the camshaft sprocket.

10. Again turn the crankshaft until the valve is closing and the indicator again reads 0.016 in. less than zero reading. Make sure, at this time, that preload has remained constant, then note the reading of the degree wheel. The difference between the two degree wheel readings is the timing angle (number of degrees the valve is open) for that valve.

11. The other valves may be checked in the same manner. comparing them against each other and the opening values given in "Tune-up Specifications." It must be remembered that turning the crankshaft contrary to the normal direction of rotation results in inaccurate readings.

12. If valve timing is not to specification, the easiest way of bringing it in line is to install an offset woodruff key in the camshaft sprocket. This is far simpler than replacing the entire timing chain and it is the factory-recommended way of changing valve timing provided the timing chain is not stretched too far or worn out. Offset keys are available in the following sizes:

Offset	Part No.	For a correction at crank-shaft of
2° (0.7)	621 991 04 67	4°
3°20′ (0.9)	621 991 02 67	6½°
4° (1.1)	621 991 01 67	8°
5° (1.3)	621 991 00 67	10°

13. The woodruff key must be installed with the offset toward the "right", in the normal direction of rotation, to effect advanced valve opening; toward the "left" to retard.

14. Advancing the intake valve opening too much can result in piston and/or valve damage (the valve will hit the piston). To check the clearance between the valve head and the piston, the crankshaft must be positioned at 5° ATDC (on intake stroke). The procedure is essentially the same as for measuring valve timing.

15. As before, the dial indicator is set to zero after being preloaded, then the valve is depressed until it touches the top of the piston. As the normal valve head-to-piston clearance is approximately 0.-035 in., you can see that the dial indicator must be preloaded at least 0.042 in. so there will be enough movement for the feeler.

If the clearance is much less than 0.035 in., the cylinder head must be removed and checked for carbon deposits. If none exist, the valve seat must be cut deeper into the head. Always set the ignition timing after installing an offset key.

Diesel Engines Only

1. After valve timing is checked, measure the distance between the exhaust valve and the piston at 5° BTDC as well as the intake valve to piston clearance at 5° ATDC. (All measurements taken at the top of the exhaust stroke.) The clearance must be at least 0.050 in., intake and exhaust.

ENGINE COOLING

Mercedes-Benz passenger car engines are all equipped with closed, pressurized, water cooling systems. Care should be exercised when dealing with the cooling system. Always turn the radiator cap to the first notch and allow the pressure to decrease before completely removing the cap. An audible hiss indicates that pressure is being released from the system.

Radiator

Removal and Installation

All Models

1. Remove the radiator cap.
2. Unscrew the radiator drain plug and drain the coolant from the radiator. If all of the coolant in the system is to be drained, move the heater controls to WARM and open the drain cocks on the engine block.
3. If the car is equipped with an oil cooler, drain the oil from the cooler.
4. If equipped, loosen the raiator shell.
5. Loosen the hose clips on the top and bottom radiator hoses and remove the hoses from the connections on th radiator.
6. Unscrew and plug the bottom line on the oil cooler.
7. If the car is equipped with an automatic transmission, unscrew and plug the lines on the transmission oil cooler.
8. Disconnect the right-hand and left-hand rubber loops and pull the radiator up and out of the body. On 350 and 450 SL and SLC models, push the retaining springs toward the fenders to remove the radiator from the shell.

Radiator retaining springs on 350SL, 450-SL, and 450SLC.

9. Inspect the replace any hoses which have become hardened or spongy.
10. Install the radiator shell and radiator (if the shell was removed) from the top and connect the top and bottom hoses to the radiator.
11. Bolt the shell to the radiator.
12. Attach the rubber loops or position the retaining springs, as applicable.
13. Position the hose clips on the top and bottom hoses.
14. Attach the lines to the oil cooler.
15. On cars with automatic transmissions, connect the lines to the transmission oil cooler.
16. Move the heater levers to the WARM position and slowly add coolant, allowing air to escape.
17. Check the oil level and fill if necessary. Run the engine for about one minute at idle with the filler neck open.
18. Add coolant to the specified level. Install the radiator cap and turn it until it seats in the second notch. Run the engine and check for leaks.

Water Pump

Removal and Installation

220/8, 220D/8, 230/8, 250/8, 250C, 280SE/8, 280SEL/8, 280SL/8, 280, 280C, and 300SEL/3

1. Drain the water from the radiator.
2. Loosen the radiator shell and remove the radiator.
3. Remove the fan with the coupling and set it aside in an upright position.
4. Loosen the belt around the water pump pulley and remove the belt.
5. Remove the bolts from the harmonic balancer and remove the balancer and pulley.
6. Unbolt and remove the water pump.
7. Installation is the reverse of removal. Tighten the belt and fill the cooling system.

280SE 3.5, 280SE 4.5, 280SEL 4.5, 300SEL 3.5, 300SEL 4.5, 300SEL 6.3, 350SL, 450SL, and 450SLC

1. Drain the water from the radiator and block.
2. Remove the air cleaner.
3. Loosen and remove the drive belt.
4. Disconnect the upper water hose from the radiator and thermostat housing.
5. Remove the fan and coupling.
6. On 3.5 engines, remove the bottom water hose from the water pump housing.
7. Remove the hose from the intake (top) connection of the water pump.

8. Set the engine at TDC. Matchmark the distributor and engine and remove the distributor. Crank the engine with a socket wrench on the crankshaft pulley bolt or with a screwdriver inserted in the balancer. Crank in the normal direction of rotation only.

9. Turn the balancer so that the recesses provide access to the mounting bolts. Remove the mounting bolts. Rotate the engine in the normal direction of rotation only.

10. Remove the water pump.

11. Clean the mounting surfaces of the water pump and block.

12. Installation is the reverse of removal. Always use a new gasket. Set the engine at TDC and install the distributor so that the distributor rotor points to the notch on the distributor housing. Fill the cooling system and check and adjust the ignition timing.

Thermostat

Removal and Installation

220/8, 220D/8, 230/8, 250/8, 250C, 280S/8, 280SE/8, 280SEL/8, 280SL/8, and 300SEL/8

The thermostat housing is a light metal casting attached directly to the cylinder head.

1. Open the radiator cap and de-pressurize the system.

2. Open the radiator drain cock and partially drain the coolant. Drain enough coolant to bring the coolant level below the level of the thermostat housing.

3. Remove the four bolts on the thermostat housing cover and remove the cover.

4. Note the installation position of the thermostat and remove it.

5. Installation is the reverse of removal. Be sure that the thermostat is positioned with the ball valve at the highest point and that the 4 bolts are tightened evenly against the seal.

6. Refill the cooling system and check for leaks.

280SE 3.5, 280SE 4.5, 280SEL 4.5, 300SEL 3.5, 300SEL 4.5, and 300SEL 6.3

1. Drain the coolant from the radiator and block.

2. Remove the air cleaner.

3. Disconnect the battery and remove the alternator.

4. Unscrew the housing cover on the side of the water pump and remove the thermostat. Note that the thermostat used on 3.5 and 4.5 liter V-8 models differs from the one used on other models due to a different positioning of the ball valve.

5. If a new thermostat is to be installed, always install a new sealing ring.

6. Installation is the reverse of removal. Be sure to tighten the screws on the housing cover evenly to prevent leaks. Refill the cooling system and check for leaks.

350SL, 450SL, and 450SLC

1. The procedure is the same as for all other vehicles equipped with 3.5 or 4.5 liter V-8 engines. On the 450SL and 450SLC, the battery and alternator need not be removed.

280 and 280C

1. Drain the coolant from the radiator.

2. Remove the vaccum pump and put the pump aside.

3. Remove the three bolts on the thermostat housing.

4. Remove the cover and the thermostat.

5. Installation is the reverse of removal. Install the thermostat so that the ball valve is at the highest point. Refill the cooling system.

EMISSION CONTROLS

Beginning in 1968, various modifications were incorporated on Mercedes-Benz engines to meet federal emission control regulations. Since 1968, these modifications have been continuallly updated and improved.

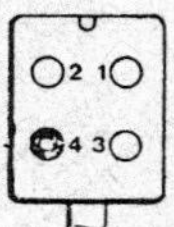

Terminals on 4 pole relay box (all models)

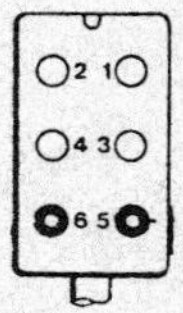

Terminals on 6 pole relay box (all models)

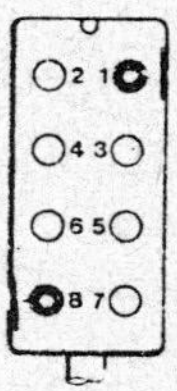

Terminals on 8 pole relay box (all models)

1968

General

The following emisssion controls were used on 1968 carbureted engines:

1. Modifications to the Manifold Air-Oxydation System.

2. Changes to the ignition timing and distributor advance curves to provide better combustion in the middle rpm ranges.

3. A Port Burning System, which uses a belt driven pump to force air directly behind the exhaust valves, creating an afterburning effect.

4. Modified carburetor jets to provide a leaner carburetor mixture.

Fuel injected engines required no modifications in 1968.

Testing the System

Due to the nature of the system, no testing of the system is required.

1969–71

General

The design of the combustion chambers was changed and the spark plugs are set deeper on 6-cylinder engines. Better cooling is accomplished by adding more cooling jackets. All 4 and 6 cylinder engines are equipped with a Fuel Evaporation Control System.

220/8

Description

In 1969, an ignition retard device was installed in conjunction with a temperature switch in the thermostat housing. At idle speed, manifold vacuum is ported to the distributor via a two-way valve and this retards the timing. When coolant temperatures reach 212° F., the temperature switch breaks the connection of manifold vacuum and prevents the retard device from functioning.

While decelerating, a throttle positioner is operated by the two-way valve and an rpm switch, which functions above 2000 rpm. At speeds below 1800 rpm, the throttle positioner is deactivated and manifold vacuum takes over.

Checking the System

Throttle Positioner

1. Connect a tachometer to the engine.

2. Start the engine and increase the speed to approximately 2500 rpm.

3. Release the accelerator linkage and observe the tachometer. At speeds above 1800 rpm, the adjusting screw should rest against the actuating lever. At speeds below 1800 rpm, the adjusting screw should be off the actuating lever.

RPM Switch

1. Connect a tachometer.

2. Remove the connector on the two-way valve and connect a voltmeter (do not use a test light).

3. Start the engine and increase engine speed. At approximately 2000 rpm, the voltmeter should indicate approximately 13 volts. As the speed falls off, the voltmeter should return to 0 at approximately 1800 rpm.

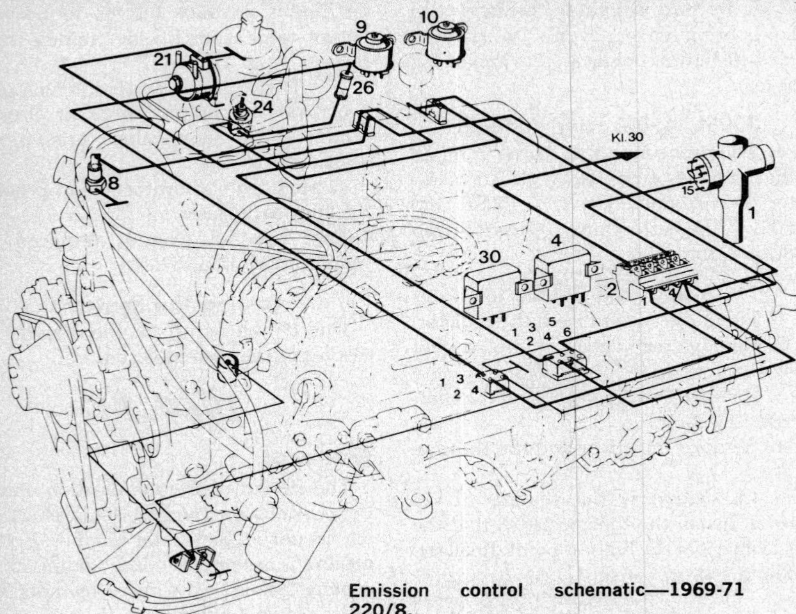

Emission control schematic—1969-71 220/8.

1. Ignition starter switch
2. Fuse box
3. Ignition coil
4. RPM switch
8. Temperature switch (212° F)
9. Two-way valve (ignition changeover)
10. Two-way valve (Throttle positioner lift)
21. Heating element for automatic choke
24. Idling speed shutoff valve
26. Connector
30. Delay switch

Ignition Retard

The following check applies only when the coolant temperature is below 212°F.

1. Connect a timing light.
2. Start the engine and run it at idle speed. Ground the temperature switch.
3. As a result, the engine speed should increase to approximately 1200–1500 rpm.

250/8 and 280S/8

Description

The ignition timing is either advanced or retarded depending on engine speed and coolant temperature. A three-way valve is operated by a 63°F. temperature switch in the cylinder head, a 212°F. temperature switch in the thermostat housing, and an rpm switch. The temperature switches are open between 63°F. and 212°F. When rpm drops below 2200, the distributor is retarded. When the coolant temperatures are in the same range and the rpm goes above 2400, the ignition timing is advanced. In addition, a throttle positioner is used similar to that on the 220/8.

Testing the System

Throttle Positioner

1. See the procedure under 220/8.

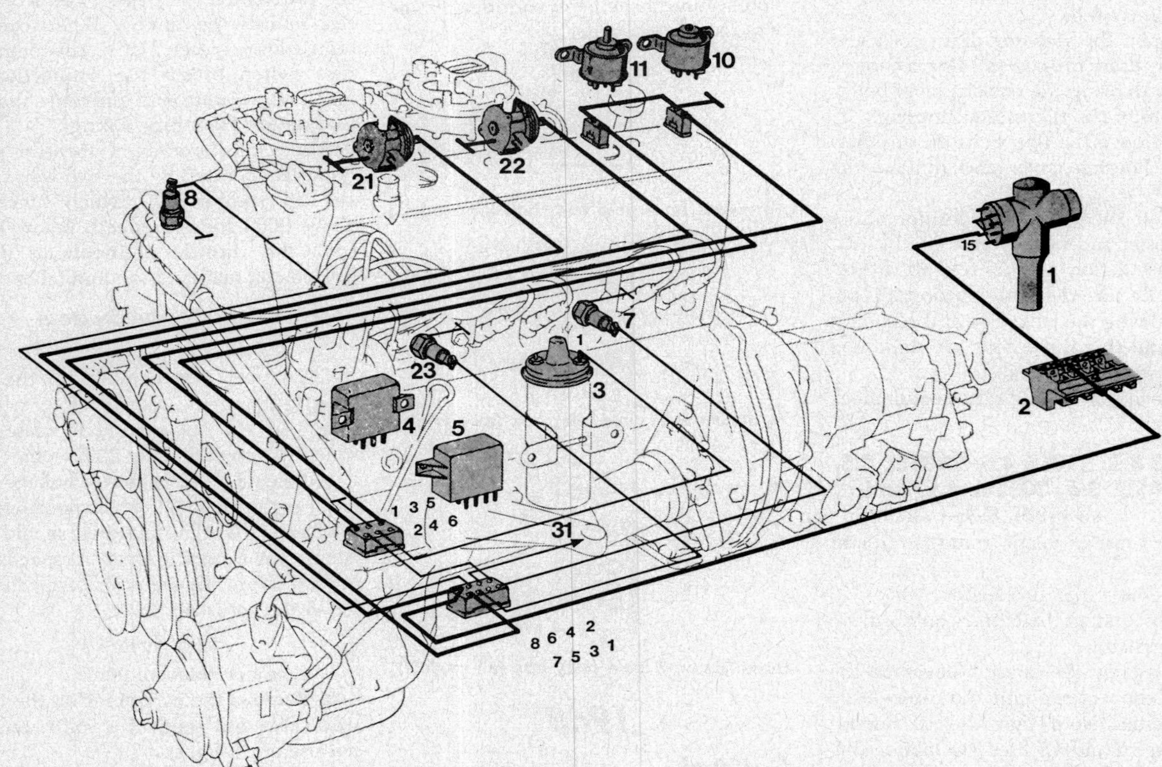

Emission control schematic—1969-71 250/8, 250C, and 280/8. NOTE: Location of components may vary.

1. Ignition starter switch
2. Fuse box
3. Ignition coil
4. RPM switch
5. Relay box
7. Temperature switch 63° F
8. Temperature switch 212° F
10. Two-way valve
11. Three-way valve
21. Front choke cover
22. Rear choke cover
23. Temperature switch 65° C(149° F)
31. To relay for supplementary fan

Ignition Changeover

1. The following check applies only when the coolant is between 63° and 212°F.
2. Connect a timing light.
3. Start the engine and increase speed.
4. Above approximately 2400 rpm, the ignition should be advanced; below 2200 the ignition should be retarded.

63° F. Temperature Switch

1. Remove the connector from the relay box and conect a test light to terminals 1 and 8.
2. Switch on the ignition. The test light should light up when the coolant temperature is below 63°F.

212°F. Temperature Switch

1. Remove the connector from the relay box and connect a test light to terminals 6 and 8.
2. Switch on the ignition. The test light should light up only if the coolant temperatute is above 212°F.

RPM Switch

1. The rpm switch is actually 2 switches.
2. Test the 1800/2200 switch point in the same manner as that for the 220/8.
3. Check the 2200/2400 rpm switch point by removing the connector from the three-way valve.
4. Connect a voltmeter.
5. Start the engine and increase speed.
6. Above 2400 rpm, the voltmeter should read approximately 0 volts. Below approximately 2200 rpm, the voltmeter should read approximately 13 volts.

280SE/8, 280SEL/8, 300SEL/8 with Automatic Transmission

Description

An ignition changeover device is installed to retard the ignition timing dependent on engine speed and coolant temperature. A two-way valve is installed in the vacuum line and is controlled by an rpm switch and by a 63°F. and 212°F. temperature switch. When coolant temperatures are between the range of the switches and engine speed is below 2200 rpm, the ignition is retarded. When the engine speed is above 2400 rpm, the ignition functions normally. In addition, a fuel shut-off solenoid on the injection pump shuts off fuel delivery under the following conditions:

1. Coolant temperature above 63°F.
2. Driving speed above 18–22 mph.
3. Accelerator pedal in the idling position, as determined by the idle speed switch on the venturi control unit.

Testing the System

Fuel Shut-Off Solenoid

1. Connect a test lamp to the fuel shutoff solenoid and to ground.
2. The test must be performed with the coolant temperature above 63°F.
3. Drive the vehicle on the road in driving position Four at approximately 30 mph.
4. At this speed the test lamp should not light.
5. Release the accelerator pedal and let the vehicle decelerate. The test light should light at about 18–21 mph.

Ignition Changeover Between 63°F. and 212°F.

1. Connect a timing light and tachometer.
2. Start the engine and increase speed.
3. At approximately 2400 rpm, the distributor should switch from retard to advance.

63°F. Temperature Switch

1. Remove the connector from the relay box and connect a test light to terminals 6 and 8.
2. Switch on the ignition.
3. The test light should light only below 63°F. oil temperature.

Idle Speed Switch on Venturi Control Unit

1. Ground the terminal of the oil pressure switch on the automatic transmission.
2. Remove the connector from the relay box and connect a test light to terminals 1 and 6.

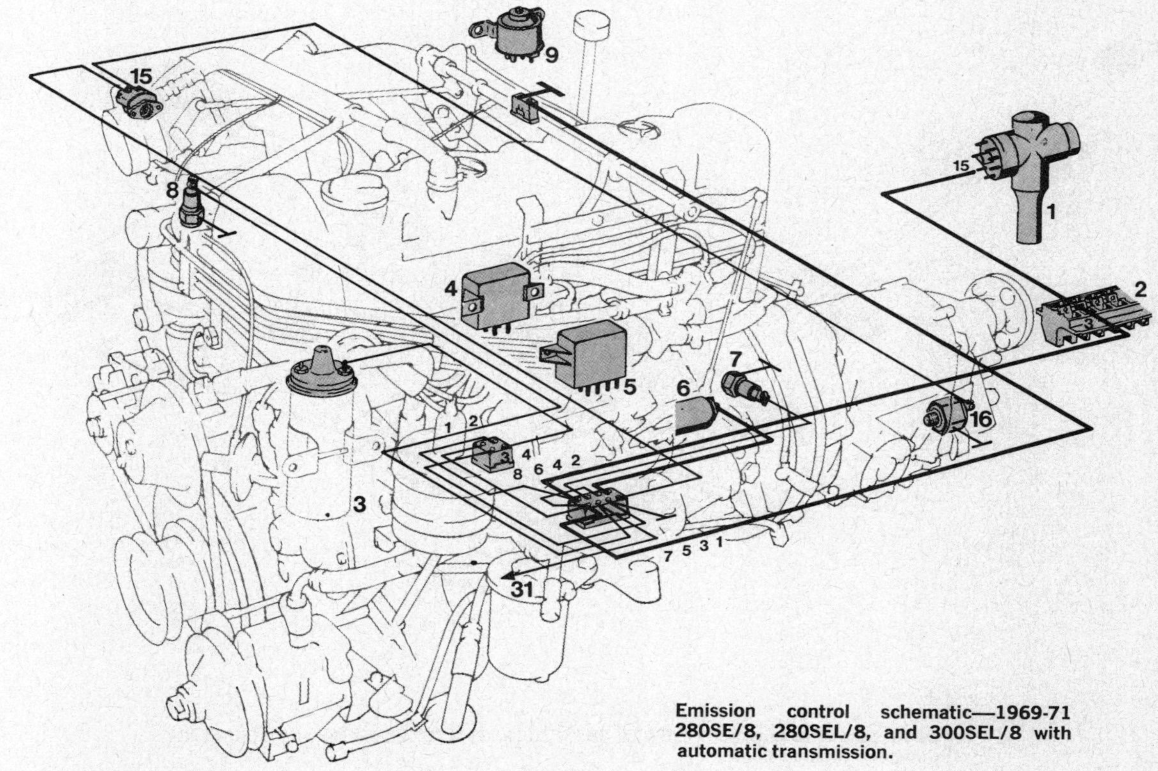

Emission control schematic—1969-71 280SE/8, 280SEL/8, and 300SEL/8 with automatic transmission.

1. Ignition starter switch
2. Fuse box
3. Ignition coil
4. RPM switch
5. Relay box
6. Shut-off solenoid
7. Temperature switch 17° (63° F)
8. Temperature switch 100°C (212° F)
9. Two-way valve
15. Idling speed switch
16. Oil pressure switch
31. To relay for supplementary fan

3. Switch on the ignition.

4. When activating the control linkage, the test light should imediately go out.

5. Be sure to reconnect the oil pressure switch.

Oil Pressure Switch on Automatic Transmission

1. Bridge the connecting terminals of the idle speed switch.

2. Remove the connector from the relay box. Connect a test light to terminals 1 and 8.

3. Drive the vehicle in position Four at approximately 30 mph. The test lamp should light up.

4. Decelerate. The test light should go out at approximately 18–21 mph.

RPM Switch

1. Use a voltmeter to test the rpm switch. Use of a test light may damage the switch.

2. Remove the connector from the two-way valve. Connect a voltmeter.

3. Start the engine and increase speed.

4. Above approximately 2400 rpm, the voltmeter should indicate approximately 13 volts, Below approximately 2200 rpm, the voltmeter should indicate approximately 0 volts.

212°F. Temperature Switch

1. Remove the connector from the relay box and connect a test light to terminals 5 and 8.

2. Switch on the ignition.

3. The test lamp should light when coolant temperature is above 212° F.

280SE/8, 280SEL/8, 280SL/8, and 300SEL/8 with Manual Transmission

Description

The emission system functions in the same manner as models with an automatic transmission except for the fuel shut-off solenoid. On vehicles with a manual transmission, the fuel shut-off solenoid is activated when the following conditions exist:

1. Coolant temperature is above 63°F.
2. Accelerator pedal is in the idling position as determined by the idle speed switch on the venturi control unit.
3. Clutch pedal is not depressed as determined by the switch on the pedal.
4. Third or Fourth gear is not engaged.

Testing the System

Fuel Shut-Off Solenoid

1. Connect a test lamp to the fuel shut-off solenoid and to ground.

2. Switch on the ignition.

3. The test lamp should light when Third or Fourth gear is engaged.

4. With Third or Fourth gear engaged, depress the gas and clutch pedal one at a time. The test lamp should go out each time.

Ignition Changeover Device

Refer to the test for the same models with automatic transmission.

63°F. Temperature Switch

Refer to the procedure for the same models with automatic transmission.

212°F, Temperature Switch

Refer to the procedure for the same models with automatic transmission.

RPM Switch

Refer to the test for the same models with automatic transmission.

Idle Speed Switch, Clutch Pedal Switch, and Gear Switches for Third and Fourth Gear

NOTE: *The gear switch is connected in series with the clutch pedal switch, except for the 280SL/8, on which the two switches are connected in parallel.*

1. Remove the connector from the relay box. Connect a test lamp to terminals 1 and 8.

2. Switch on the ignition.

3. The test lamp should light when Third or Fourth gear is engaged. Do not depress the clutch or accelerator pedal.

4. Actuate the accelerator and clutch pedal one after the other and engage Sec-

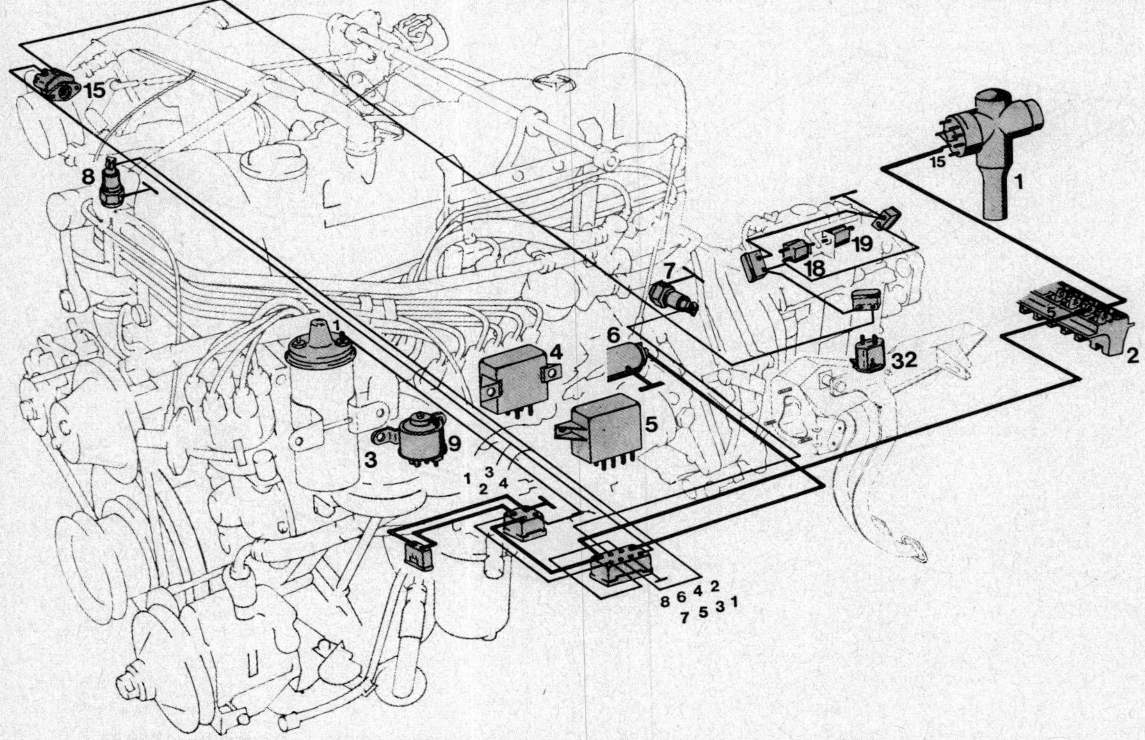

Emission control schematic—1969-71 280SE/8, 280SEL/8, 280SL/8, and 300SEL/8 with manual transmission.

1. Ignition starter switch
2. Fuse box
3. Ignition coil
4. RPM switch
5. Relay box
6. Shut-off solenoid
7. Temperature switch 17° C (63° F)
8. Temperature switch 100° C (212° F)
9. Two-way valve
15. Idling speed switch
18. 3rd gear switch
19. 4th gear switch
32. Clutch pedal switch

ond and Third gear. The test lamp should go out in each case.

5. If the test lamp does not go out, the defective switch can be located by bridging the terminals in turn.

6. The gear switches should also be adjusted so that they will be closed in Third and Fourth gear.

280SL/8 with Automatic Transmission

Description

The function of the system is the same as the 280SE/8, 280SEL/8, and 300SEL/8 with automatic transmission, except for the operation of the fuel shut-off solenoid. The fuel shut-off solenoid reduces the fuel delivery to zero when the following conditions are simultaneously attained:

1. Coolant temperatures above 63°F.
2. Transmission in Third or Fourth gear.
3. Engine speed above 1250 rpm.
4. Accelerator pedal position in the idle position as determined by the idle speed switch on the venturi control unit.

Testing the System

Fuel Shut-off Solenoid

1. Connect a test lamp to the solenoid and to ground. Connect a tachometer.
2. The test should be made with the coolant temperature at least 63°F.
3. Drive the car on the road at about 30 mph, with the transmission in position Four.
4. The test lamp should not light.
5. Release the pedal and let the car decelerate. The test light should light down to about 1250 rpm.

Ignition Changeover

Refer to the test for 280SE/8 and 300SEL/8 with automatic transmission.

63°F. Temperature Switch

Refer to the procedure for 280SE/8 and 300SEL/8 with Automatic Transmission.

Idle Speed Switch on Venturi Control Unit

The procedure is the same as that for 280SE/8 and 300SEL/8 with automatic transmission. Connect the light to the brown/white wire and ground.

Starter Lockout Switch

1. Remove the connector from the rpm switch and connect a test lamp to terminal 6 and to ground.
2. With the ignition switched on, the test lamp should light with the transmission selector lever in 2,3,4 and R.

RPM Switch

NOTE: *The rpm switch is actually two switches.*

1. Use only a voltmeter to test the rpm switch. Do not use a test lamp.
2. To check the 1250/1450 (shut-off) shift point, bridge the connecting terminals of the idle speed switch and switch on the ignition. Remove the connector from the starter lockout switch and connect terminal 5 to terminal 6. Remove the connector from the current relay and connect a voltmeter to terminal 4 and to ground. Increase the engine speed. At about 1200 rpm, the voltmeter should read approximately 13 volts. Below approximately 1000 rpm the voltmeter should read about 0 volts.
3. To check the 2200/2400 (ignition changeover) shift point, remove the connector from the two-way valve and connect a voltmeter. Start the engine and increase speed to approximately 2400 rpm, where the voltmeter should read about 13 volts. Below approximately 2200 rpm, the voltmeter should read 0 volts.

212°F. Temperature Switch

1. Refer to this test under 280SE/8 and 300SEL/8 with automatic transmission.

300SEL 6.3

Description

There is no ignition changeover device on this model. The fuel shut-off solenoid operates when the following conditions exist:

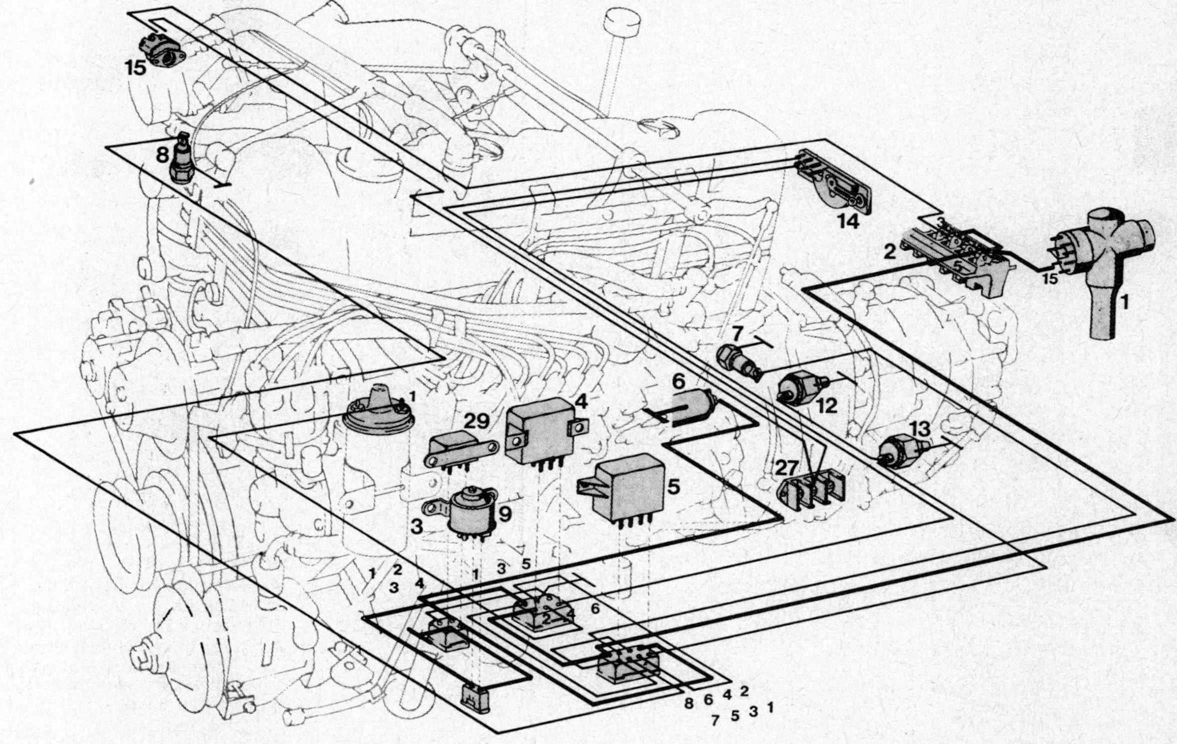

Emission control schematic—1969-71 280SL/8 with automatic transmission

1. Ignition starter switch
2. Fuse box
3. Ignition coil
4. RPM switch
5. Relay box
6. Shut-off solenoid
7. Temperature switch 17° C (63° F)
8. Temperature switch 100° C (212° F)
9. Two-way valve
12. Oil pressure switch
13. Oil pressure switch
14. Starter lockout and backup light switch
15. Idling speed switch
27. Cable connector
29. Current relay

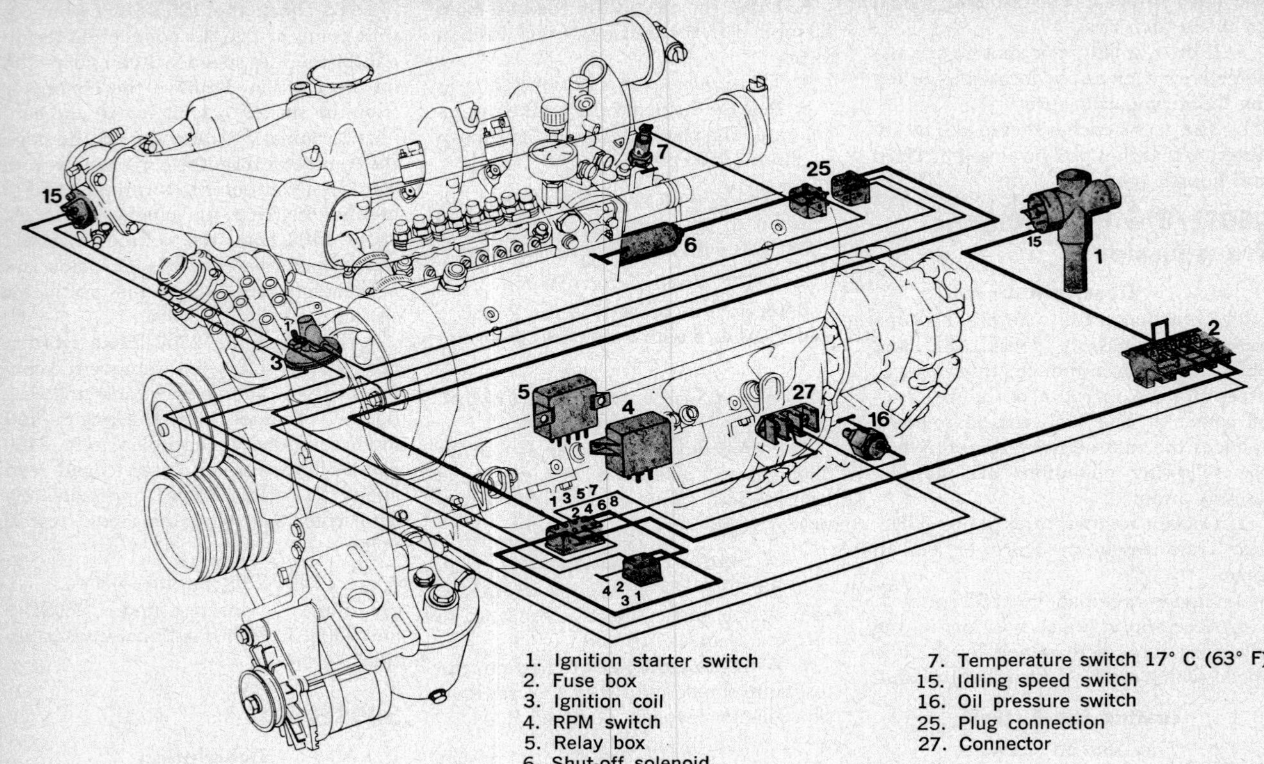

1. Ignition starter switch
2. Fuse box
3. Ignition coil
4. RPM switch
5. Relay box
6. Shut-off solenoid
7. Temperature switch 17° C (63° F)
15. Idling speed switch
16. Oil pressure switch
25. Plug connection
27. Connector

Emission control schematic—1970-71 300SEL 6.3

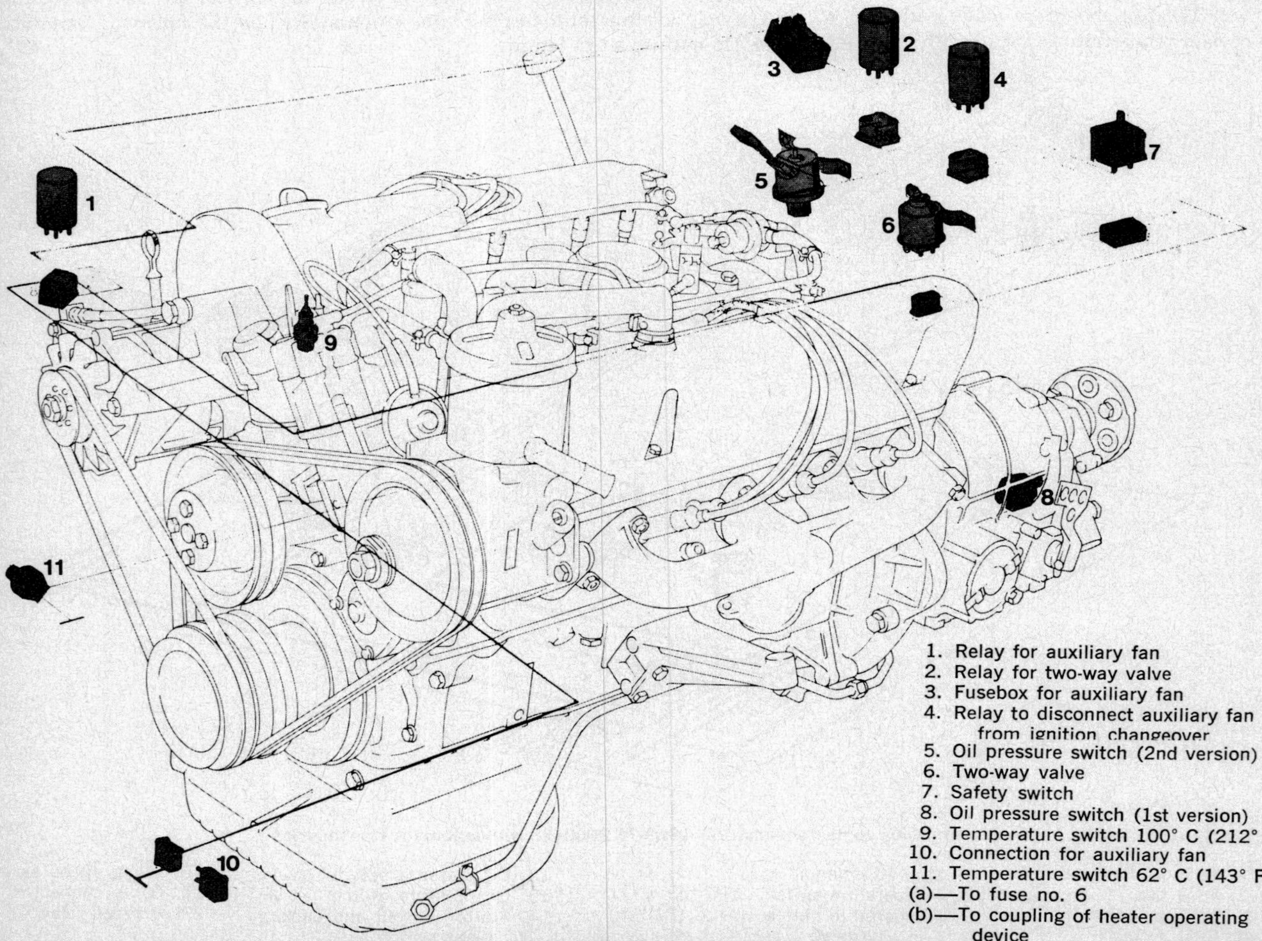

1. Relay for auxiliary fan
2. Relay for two-way valve
3. Fusebox for auxiliary fan
4. Relay to disconnect auxiliary fan from ignition changeover
5. Oil pressure switch (2nd version)
6. Two-way valve
7. Safety switch
8. Oil pressure switch (1st version)
9. Temperature switch 100° C (212° F)
10. Connection for auxiliary fan
11. Temperature switch 62° C (143° F)

(a)—To fuse no. 6
(b)—To coupling of heater operating device

Emission control schematic—1971 280SE 3.5 and 300SEL 3.5

1. Accelerator pedal in the idle position as determined by the idle speed switch on the venturi control unit.

2. Engine speed under deceleration above 750 rpm.

3. Transmission in Third or Fourth gear.

NOTE: *There is no fuel shut-off when coolant temperature is under 63°F.*

Testing the System

Fuel Shut-Off Solenoid

The fuel shut-off solenoid can only be checked when driving, either on the road or on a dynamometer.

1. Connect a test lamp to the solenoid and to ground.
2. Connect a tachometer.
3. Drive the vehicle on the road, in position Four at approximately 30 mph.
4. The test lamp should not light.
5. Decelerate and the test lamp should light, down to approximately 15 mph (750 rpm).

63°F. Temperature Switch

1. Remove the connector from the relay box and connect a test lamp to terminals 6 and 2.
2. Switch on the ignition.
3. The test lamp should light at a coolant temperature of below 63°F.

Idle Speed Switch

1. Remove the connector from the relay box and connect a test lamp to terminal 8 and to ground.
2. Switch on the ignition.
3. The test lamp should go out when the throttle is opened.

RPM Switch

1. Remove the connector from the relay box and connect a test lamp to terminal 7 and to ground.
2. Connect a tachometer.
3. Start the engine and increase speed to about 850 rpm, when the test lamp should light.
4. Reduce the rpm. The test lamp should go out at about 750 rpm.

1971 280SE 3.5 and 300SEL 3.5

Description

A two-way valve is installed in the vacuum line between the venturi control unit and the distributor. Ignition timing is retarded when the two-way valve is not energized, and advanced when the valve is energized (circuit completed to ground). The valve is controlled by an oil pressure switch on the automatic transmission, above a speed of 30–40 mph, and by a 212°F. temperature switch in the thermostat housing, which activates the valve above coolant temperatures of 212°F.

A fuel shut-off solenoid cuts off the delivery of fuel under the following conditions:

1. Acclerator pedal is in the idling position.

2. Engine speed is above 1500 rpm, determined by an electronic control unit. There is no fuel shut-off when coolant temperature is below −4°F.

Testing the System

Ignition Changeover Device

1. Connect a timing light and check the timing at idle. It should be as specified.
2. Ground the connection of the 212°F. temperature switch. The ignition timing should advance by 15° and engine speed should increase by about 300 rpm.
3. Check the oil pressure switch. This can only be done on the road or on a dynamometer. Connect a test lamp to the B+ terminal and terminal 87 of the relay. Disconnect the relay. Above a speed of 40 mph, the test lamp should light. Below approximately 30 mph, the light should go out.
4. Check the 212°F. switch by connecting a test lamp to the B+ terminal and to the switch. At a coolant temperature above 212°F., the light should come on.
5. If there is no ignition changeover and the oil pressure switch is working, check the following:

   a. Fuse no. 6 in the main fuse box.

   b. All vacuum and electrical connections on the two-way valve.

   c. The two-way valve. Switch on the ignition and ground the oil pressure switch. This should energize the two-way valve.

   d. The relay. Connect a test lamp to the plug of the two-way valve. Switch on the ignition and ground the 212°F. temperature switch. The relay is working if the lamp lights.

1972

General

Various modifications were made to the basic emission control system described previously. The engine compression ratio was reduced to 8.0:1 on all engines except the diesel. The shift points of the automatic transmission on the 250, 250C, and 280SE were modified. The fuel evaporation control system remains unchanged, but the evaporation valve unit was improved and relocated under the vehicle in the rear seat area.

220/8

Description

The function of the ignition changeover device and the throttle lifting device under deceleration remain basically unchanged for 1972. The distributor curve was changed and a new main jet, designated YA, is used in the carburetor.

Testing the System

Testing the 1972 system is the same as that for the 1969–71 system.

250/8 and 250C

Description

The 1972 250C and 280S/8 both use the 2.8 liter, 6-cylinder engine. A new type of air cleaner is used in conjunction with the 32/40 INAT carburetor. The distributor also has a modified advance curve and the 63°F. temperature switch has been relocated to the oil filter housing. Ignition changeover is accomplished by a three-way valve in the distributor vacuum line. The valve is controlled by a relay from the 63° F. switch, the 212°F. switch in the thermostat housing, and by the rpm relay. The ignition will be retarded at speeds below 2200 rpm, when the oil temperature is above 63°F. and the coolant temperature is above 212°F. The ignition is advanced when the engine speed is above 2500 rpm and when the temperatures are below the rated values of the switches.

A throttle positioner is also installed to slightly open the throttle valves depending on coolant and oil temperatures and engine speed.

Testing the System

Throttle Positioner

1. Make this test with the oil temperature above 63°F. and the coolant temperature above 212°F.
2. Connect a tachometer.
3. Start the engine and increase engine speed to approximately 2500 rpm.
4. Release the throttle linkage and observe the throttle control on the carburetor. At speeds in excess of 1800 rpm, the adjustment screw of the throttle control should rest against the accelerator linkage. Below 1800 rpm, the screw should be off the linkage.

Ignition Changeover

See this test under "250/8 and 280S/8, 1969–71".

63°F. Temperature Switch

See this test under "250/8 and 280S/8, 1969–71".

212°F. Temperature Switch

See this test under "250/8 and 280S/8, 1969–71".

1972 250/8 and 250C 3-way valve (11), 2-way valve (10), and relay (5).

RPM Switch

The rpm switch is actually two switches. Use only a voltmeter to test the rpm switch.

1. Remove the connector from the three-way valve and connect a voltmeter.
2. Start the engine and increase rpm.
3. At speeds between approximately 1800–2000 rpm, the voltmeter should indicate about 13 volts.
4. At speeds above approximately 2500 rpm, the voltmeter should read approximately 0 volts.

280SE/8

Description

The following modifications have been made to the system for 1972:

1. The injection pump has a modified cam.
2. The advance curve of the distributor is changed.
3. The 63°F. temperature switch is relocated to the oil filter housing.
4. When the ignition is shut off, the fuel shut-off solenoid is activated for a short time to prevent dieseling.

Basically, the function of the system has not changed except for the idle solenoid. The idle solenoid is activated under the following conditions:

1. The engine speed drops below 600 rpm due to increased load from the air conditioner or other power equipment.
2. The selector lever of the transmission indicates Slope or Drive.

Testing the System

Ignition Changeover

See this test under "1969–71 280SE/8 with Automatic Transmission".

Gulp Valve

1. Because the gulp valve must be checked either on the road or on a dynamometer, testing the mechanical function of the gulp valve should be sufficient.
2. Disconnect the air hose between the air cleaner and the gulp valve.
3. At engine speeds above 2900 rpm under deceleration, suction should be felt at the gulp valve.

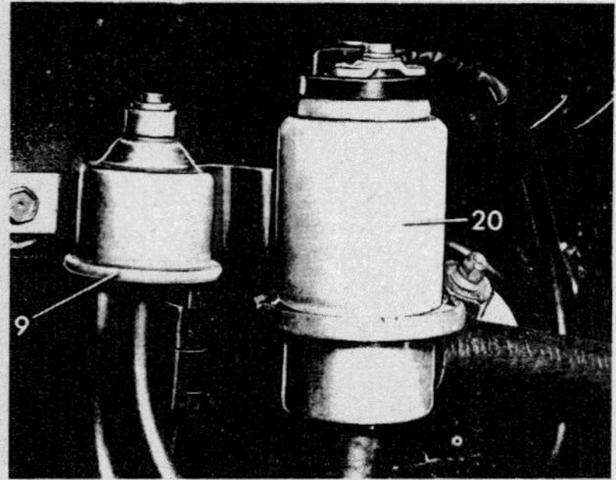

1972 280SE and 280SEL gulp valve (20) and valve for ignition retard (9).

Idle Solenoid

CAUTION: *To perform this test, the parking and service brakes must be firmly set.*

1. Connect a test lamp to the idle solenoid and run the engine at idle.
2. Switch on the air conditioner, turn the power steering to full lock, and engage reverse gear.

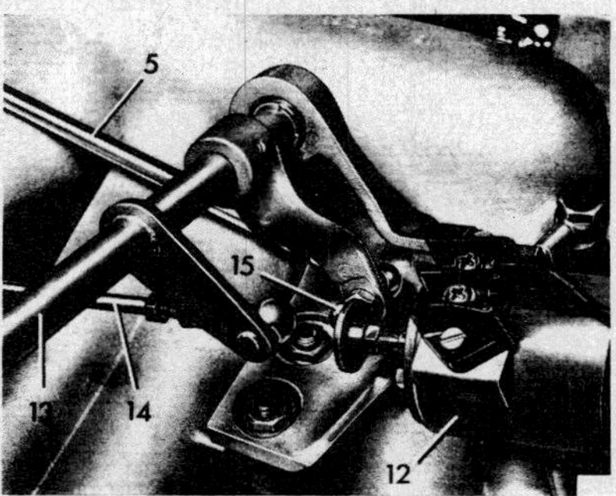

1972 280SE and 280SEL idle solenoid (12)

3. Should the idle drop below 600 rpm, the test lamp should light and the solenoid energize.
4. At speeds above approximately 1000 rpm, the test light should go out.
5. Place the transmission selector lever in Slope and Drive. At speeds up to approximately 2600 rpm, the test lamp should light. At speeds above approximately 2900 rpm, the test lamp should go out.

63°F. Temperature Switch

See this test under "1969–71 280SE/8 with Automatic Transmission".

212°F. Temperature Switch

See this test under "1969–71 280SE/8 with Automatic Transmission".

Idle Switch on Throttle Valve Housing

1. Remove the connector from the relay box and connect a test lamp to terminals 1 and 8. Ground terminal 6.
2. Turn on the ignition.
3. The test light should go out immediately when the throttle is depressed,

RPM Switch

See this test under "1969–71 280SE/8 with Automatic Transmission". In addition, perform the following test.

1. Remove the cable connector from the relay box.
2. Connect a voltmeter to terminal 4 and to ground.
3. Below approximately 2600 rpm, the voltmeter should indicate about 13 volts.
4. Above approximately 2900 rpm, the voltmeter should indicate about 0 volts.
5. Remove the connector from the relay box and connect a voltmeter to terminal 2 and ground.
6. At engine speeds below approximately 600 rpm, the voltmeter should indicate about 13 volts.
7. At engine speeds above approximately 1000 rpm, the voltmeter should read approximately O volts.

280SE 4.5, 280SEL 4.5, 300SEL 4.5 and 350SL

Description

The design and function of the exhaust emission control system used on vehicles with 4.5 liter engines is the same as the one on 1971 vehicles with 3.5 liter engines, except that the oil pressure switch on the automatic transmission is eliminated.

Testing the System

Testing each component of the system is the same as for 1971 3.5 liter vehicles.

1973

General

The fuel evaporation control system remains unchanged for 1973.

Beginning in 1973, the two-way valves used previously are replaced with switch-over valves that are externally identical. When new valves are installed, it is important that the vacuum line always be connected to the center connection, whether it is on the top or the bottom. To be able to distinguish the function of the individual valves, the covers are color

1973 220/8

9. Switch-over valve (ignition)
10. Swtch-over valve (throttle positioner)
12. Switch-over valve (exhaust recycling)

1973 220/8 EGR rpm switch (4)

4. RPM relay with two rpm switches
5. Relay box
30. Delay relay for idle cut-off valve

coded according to valve function, as follows:

WHITE—advanced ignition valve
RED—retarded ignition vlave
GREY—throttle opening valve
BROWN—exhaust gas recycling (EGR) valve.

Exhaust gas recirculation is not effective under the following conditions:
1. Oil temperature below 77°F.
2. Speed above 3600 rpm.

Testing the System

Ignition Timing

1. Check the ignition timing. It should be as specified earlier.
2. If not, check all vacuum connections and the 77°F. temperature switch before adjusting the timing.

77°F. Temperature Switch

1. Remove the plug from the relay.
2. Connect a test lamp to terminals 5 and 8.
3. The test lamp should light when the oil temperature exceeds 77°F.

RPM Switch

Use only a voltmeter to check the rpm switch.

1. Disconnect the plug on the switchover valve and connect a voltmeter.
2. Start the engine and increase speed.
3. Up to approximately 2000 rpm, the voltmeter should read about 13 volts. The voltage should be approximately 0 volts above 2000 rpm.

Ignition Switchover Valve

1. Connect the plug to the valve and increase rpm. At about 2000 rpm, the piston in the valve will be audibly heard to switch over.

Part No.		Dead	Live	Operation
001 540 04 97 001 540 07 97 001 540 08 97 001 540 09 97	white grey brown red	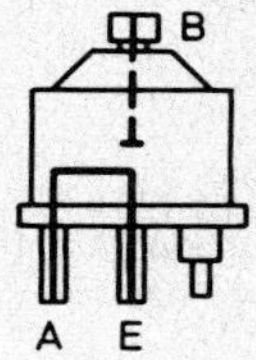 B A E	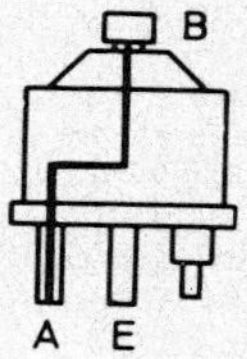 B A E	When de-energized, the air connection B is closed and the vacuum connections A and E are interconnected. When energized, the connection E is closed and only connection A is supplied with air. The connections E and A must under no circumstances be confused.
001 540 00 97	no color coding	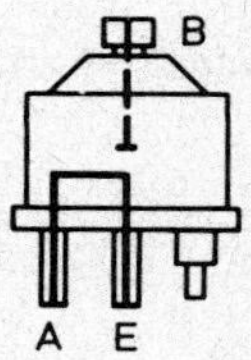 B A E	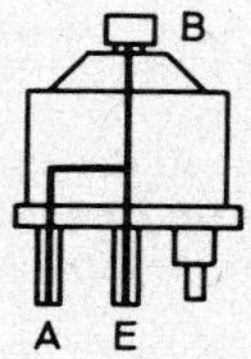 B A E	When de-energized, the air connection B is closed and the vacuum connections A and E are interconnected. When energized, the connections A and E are supplied with air. Air is taken in via the air cap B. The connections may be interchanged.
001 540 05 97 001 540 11 97	white brown	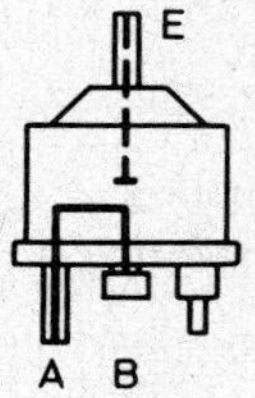 E A B	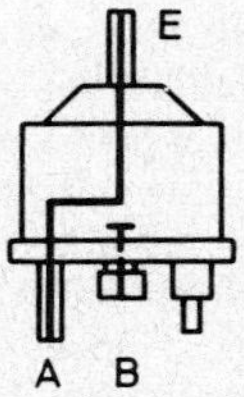 E A B	When de-energized, connection A is supplied with air and connection E is closed. When energized, connection A is connected to E and air connection B is closed. The connections E and A must under no circumstances be confused.

1973 switch valves

220/8

Description

Ignition changeover is accomplished through vacuum and oil temperature. Vacuum retard is only activated during acceleration, while vacuum advance is activated under the following conditions:

1. Oil temperature below 77°F.
2. Oil temperature above 77°F. and engine speed above 2000 rpm.

The throttle valve is also opened slightly during coasting, through a vacuum governor on the carburetor.

Exhaust gas is being recycled by the EGR valve under the following conditions:

1. Oil temperature above 77°F. up to 3600 rpm.

Throttle Valve Lift

See the test for the throttle positioner under 1969–71 220/8.

EGR Switch Valve

1. Connect a tachometer, start the engine, and increase speed. The switchover valve should be heard to switch over at approximately 3600 rpm.

EGR RPM switch

1. Disconnect the plug on the switch valve and connect a voltmeter (do not use a test lamp).
2. Start the engine and increase speed.
3. The voltmeter should indicate about 13 volts up to 3600 rpm and should drop to 0 volts above 3600 rpm.

EGR Valve

1. Start the engine and run it at idle.

2. Remove the lower, brown vacuum line from the EGR switchover valve and connect it to the carburetor in place of the blue vacuum line.

3. If the EGR valve is working, the engine will idle roughly or stop running. If the engine does not do one or the other, replace the EGR valve.

4. Do not forget to replace the vacuum lines.

1973 220/8 EGR valve (31)

280 and 280C

Description

An ignition changeover is installed to retard or advance the ignition. Ignition is retarded under the following conditions:

1. When the oil temperature is above 62°F. and coolant temperature is below 212°F.

2. Engine speed is below 3200 rpm. Ignition retard is negated under the following conditions:

1. Oil temperature below 62°F.
2. Coolant temperature above 212°F.
3. Engine speed above 3200 rpm and oil temperature above 62°F, and coolant temperature below 212°F.
4. When shifting into fourth gear.
5. When switching on the air conditioner.
6. With vacuum between 0 and 2.8 psi.

A throttle positioner is installed which will open the throttle slightly when the oil temperature is above 62°F., when the coolant temperature is below 212°F., and when engine speed exceeds 200 rpm.

Exhaust gases are recycled when engine oil temperature is above 62°F., when coolant temperature is below 212°F., and when manifold vacuum is between 0 and 2.8 psi, up to 3200 rpm.

Testing the System

Ignition Timing

1. Check the ignition timing. It should be as specified.

2. If not, check all vacuum connections and the temperature switches before adjusting the timing.

62°F. Temperature Switch

1. Disconnect the plug of the relay box.

2. Connect a voltmeter to terminals 5 and 8.

3. The voltmeter should indicate 0 volts when the oil temperature is above 62°F.

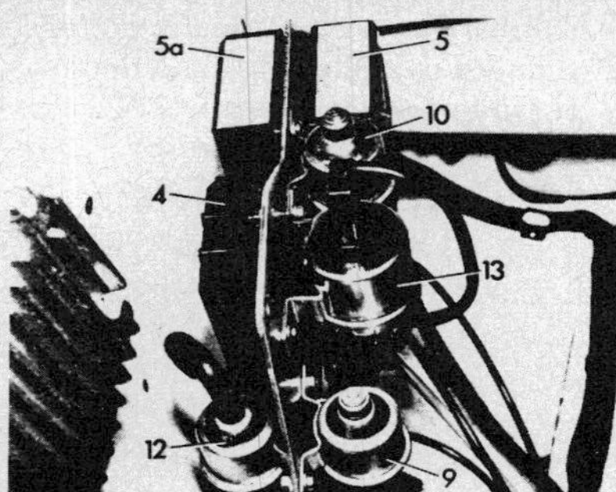

280 and 280C switch valves (1973)

5. Relay box 8-prong plug
5a. Relay box 12-prong plug
4. RPM relay with two rpm switches
9. Switch-over valve (ignition switch-over)
10. Switch-over valve (throttle positioner)
12. Switch-over valve (exhaust recycling)

212° F. Temperature Switch

1. Disconnect the plug from the relay box.

2. Connect a test lamp to terminals 4 and 8.

3. Switch on the ignition.

4. The test lamp should light when coolant temperature is above 212°F.

Throttle Positioner

See the test for the throttle positioner under "1969–71 220/8".

RPM Switch

Use only a voltmeter to test the rpm switch.

1. Disconnect the plug of the switch valve and connect a voltmeter.

2. Start the engine and increase speed.

3. The voltmeter should indicate about 13 volts, above 2000 rpm.

4. Decrease speed below about 1800 rpm and the voltmeter should read approximately 0 volts.

EGR Switch Valve

1. Disconnect the plug from the switch valve and connect a tachometer.

2. Connect a voltmeter and increase rpm.

3. The voltmeter should read about 13 volts up to 3200 rpm.

1973 280 and 280C 149° F. temperature switch (32).

149°F. Temperature Switch

1. Disconnect the plug from the relay box and connect a voltmeter to terminals 6 and 8.

2. The voltmeter should indicate approximately 13 volts above 149°F.

Vacuum Switch

1. Disconnect the plug from the relay box and connect a voltmeter to terminals 7 and 8.

2. Idle the engine.

3. The voltmeter should indicate 0 volts.

4. Disconnect the vacuum line from the switch. The voltmeter should now indicate about 13 volts.

EGR rpm Switch

1. Disconnect the plug from the relay box.

2. Connect a voltmeter to terminals 1 and 3.

3. Start the engine and increase speed.

4. The voltmeter should indicate 0 volts up to approximately 3200 rpm. Beyond that, voltage should be about 13 volts.

5. When rpm decreases, the voltmeter should return to 0 volts at about 2800 rpm.

EGR Valve

See this test under "1973 220/8".

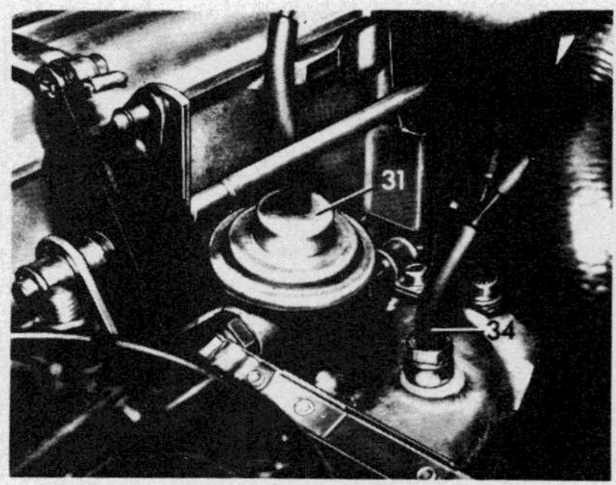

1973 280 and 280C EGR valve (31)

280SE 4.5, 280SEL 4.5, 300SEL 4.5, 450SL, and 450SLC

Description

The emission system used on these vehicles functions in the same manner as that used on 1972 3.5 and 4.5 engines. All tests are performed in a similar manner to those given under 1972 for these models.

❶ **Relay**
Auxiliary fan

Connection of test instruments shown with dotted lines.

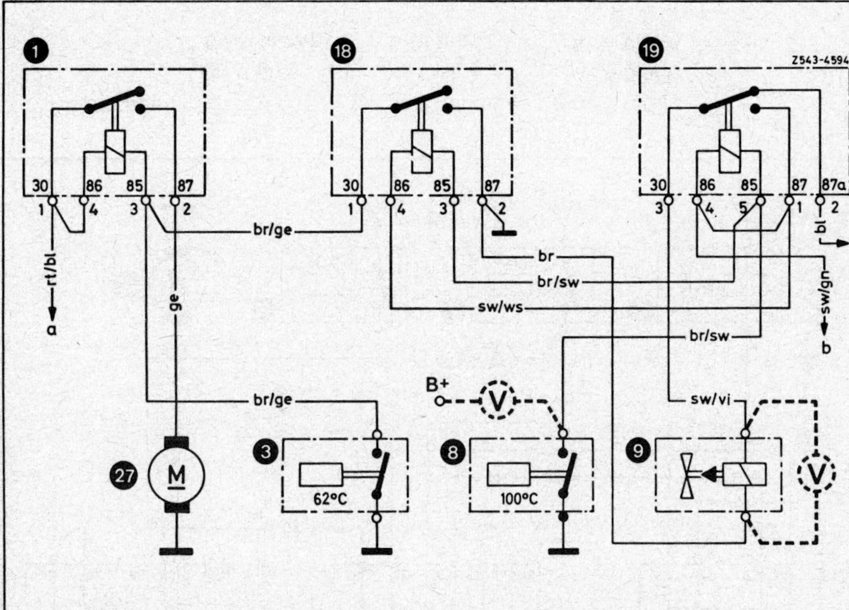

Emission schematic—1973 280SE 4.5 280SEL 4.5, 300SEL 4.5, 350SL

❽ **100°C (212°F) temperature switch**

❸ **62°C (144°F) temperature switch**

❾ **2-way valve**

Color code			
	ws = white	ge = yellow	rt = red
	gn = green	rs = pink	sw = black
	br = brown	bl = blue	li = violet

⓳ **Relay** 2-way valve.

㉗ **Auxiliary fan**

3 **62°C (144°F) temperature switch**

8 **100°C (212°F) temperature switch**

Connection of test instruments shown with dotted lines.

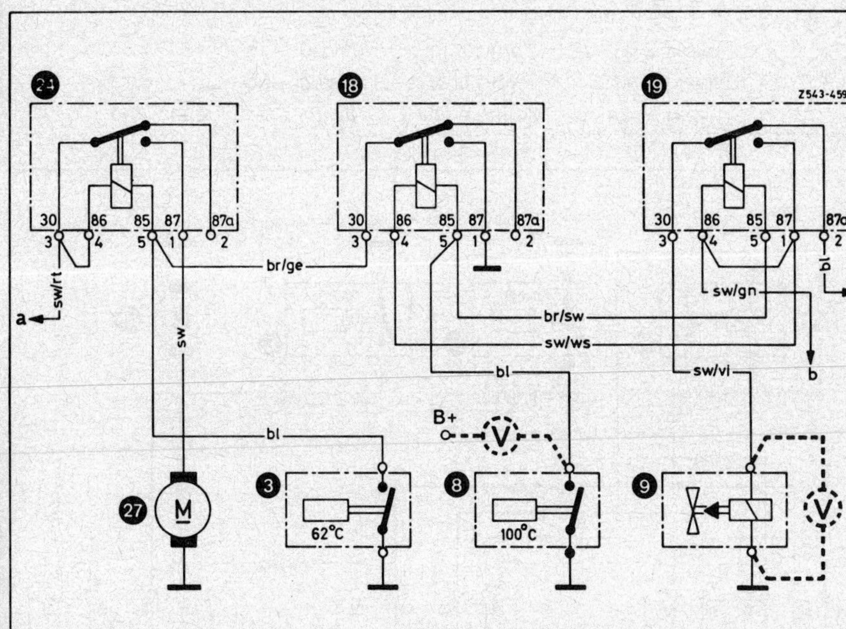

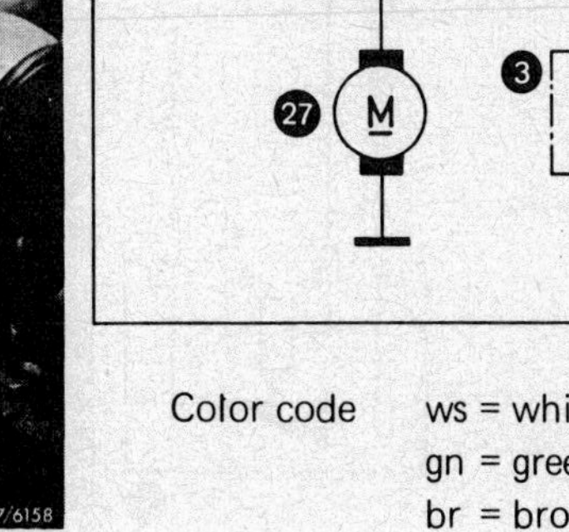

Color code

ws = white	ge = yellow	rt = red
gn = green	rs = pink	sw = black
br = brown	bl = blue	li = violet

Emission schematic—1973 450SL and 450SLC

9 **2-way valve**

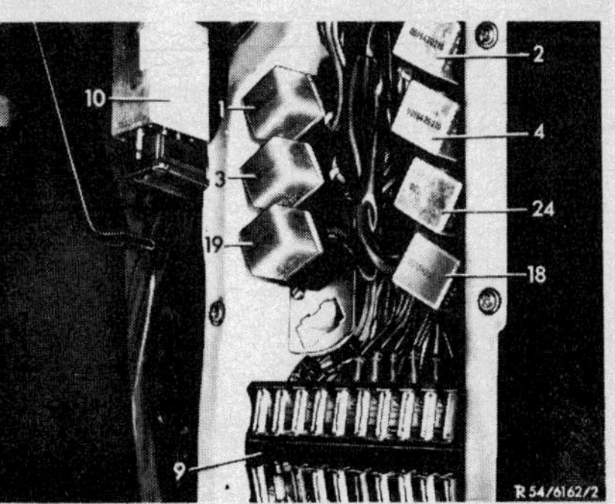

18 **Relay**

19 **Relay** 2-way valve.

24 **Relay** Auxiliary fan

27 **Auxiliary fan**

FUEL SYSTEM

Mechanical Fuel Pump

All Mercedes-Benz carbureted engines use a diaphragm type fuel pump, which is mounted on the side of the block. It is operated by a gear driven eccentric shaft through a rocker arm on the fuel pump.

Removal and Installation

1. Clean the joint around the fuel pump base and cylinder block.
2. One at a time, remove and plug the intake and outlet lines from the fuel pump.
3. Unbolt the retaining bolts and remove the fuel pump and gasket from the cylinder block.
4. Clean the mating surfaces of the engine and cylinder block.
5. Install a new gasket.
6. Insert the fuel pump into the block and install the retaining bolts. Be sure that the bolts are tightened evenly.
7. Reconnect the intake and outlet lines to the fuel pump.
8. Run the engine and check for leaks.

Testing Delivery Pressure

1. Remove the wire from the coil to prevent starting.
2. Connect a pressure gauge into the output line of the fuel pump.
3. Crank the engine and read the delivery pressure on the pressure gauge. The pressure should be a constant 1.5–2.5 psi.
4. If the pressure is not within specifications or is erratic, remove the pump for service or for replacement with a new or rebuilt unit. No adjustment is provided.

Electric Fuel Pump

NOTE: *Do not confuse the electric fuel pump with the injection pump.*

All Mercedes-Benz fuel injected engines are equipped with electric fuel pumps. The electric fuel pump is located under the left rear wheel housing, inboard of the shock absorber. In 1972, on 4.5 engined vehicles, the fuel pump was moved underneath the rear floor panel. The fuel return line was also eliminated and a check ball installed in its place.

Two types of fuel pumps have been used. One, the large pump, has been replaced with a new small design which has a bypass system to prevent vapor lock.

Removal and Installation

1. Jack the left rear of the car and support it on jackstands. This will provide sufficient working clearance.
2. Remove and plug the intake, outlet, and bypass lines from the pump.
3. Disconnect the electrical leads.
4. Unbolt and remove the fuel pump and vibration pads.
5. Install the fuel pump in the reverse order of removal. Be sure that the electrical leads are connected to the proper terminals. The negative wire (brown) is connected to the negative terminal (brown plastic plate) and the positive wire (black/red) is connected to the positive terminal (red plastic plate). If the terminals are reversed, the pump will operate in the reverse direction of normal rotation and will deliver no fuel.

Installation of Small Design Fuel Pump

In order to bring your 300SEL 6.3 or 280SL/8 to current Mercedes-Benz standards, the following procedure can be used to install the small design fuel pump.

1. An attaching plate for installing the fuel pump on various models is available.

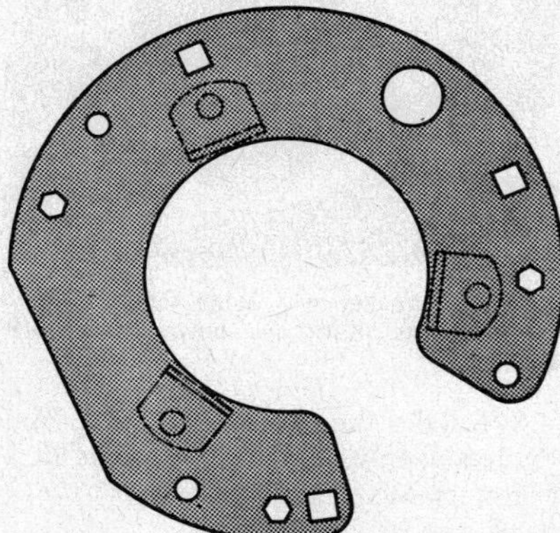

Mounting bracket for small design fuel pump.

2. Remove the present fuel pump with the vibration pads.
3. Leave the present mounting bracket attached to the floor.
4. Install the new vibration pads on the fuel pump.
5. Attach the adaptor to the fuel pump.
6. Attach the adaptor plate and fuel pump to the mounting bracket. Use the holes as shown in the illustration.
7. Install the fuel lines and T-fitting. Be sure that the intake line does not sag. If necessary, it should be cut to the proper length.
8. Connect the electrical leads, making sure that the proper polarity is obtained. The electrical leads are routed through the rubber sleeve.

Testing Fuel Pump Delivery Pressure

1. Reduce the pressure in the ring line by pulling the plug on the starting valve. Connect the terminals of the starting

Small design fuel pump installed

1. Fuel pressure line
2. Fuel bypass line
3. Fuel suction line
7. Vibration damper
6. Bracket
8. Attaching plate

valve to the positive and negative terminals of the battery for about 20 seconds. Reconnect the plug to the starting valve.

2. Remove the air filter and connect a pressure gauge at the branch connection of the ring line.
3. Run the engine at idle speed and measure the pressure in the ring line. The pressure should be 28.0–29.5 psi.
4. Stop the engine. The pressure may drop to 25 psi. Wait another five minutes and the pressure may drop to 22 psi. This is normal.
5. The pressure may drop uniformly to 0 psi. This indicates that there is a leak somewhere in the system.

Carburetors

Removal and Installation

Solex 36–40 PDSI (220/8)

1. Remove the air cleaner.
2. Remove the fuel lines and plug them.

CAUTION: *Do not pull the fuel lines from the carburetor. They should be pried off along with the securing discs.*

3. Disconnect the control linkage.
4. Remove the vacuum lines.
5. Loosen the carburetor attaching nuts and remove the carburetors from the manifold.

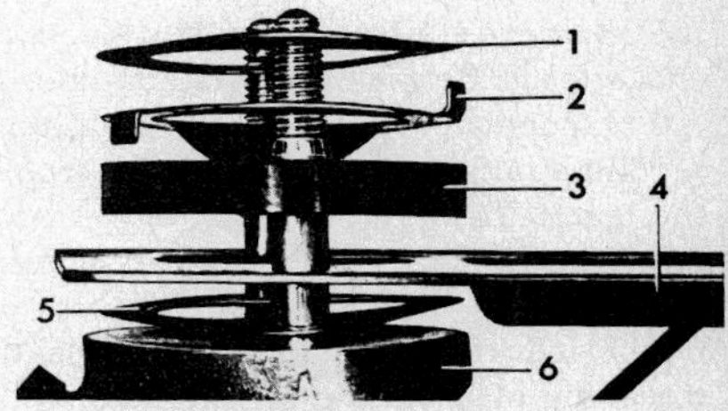

Gasket installation on Solex 36/40 PDSI

1. Gasket
2. Baffle plate
3. Insulating flange
4. Screening plate
5. Gasket
6. Intake manifold

6. Installation is the reverse of removal. The gaskets and metal plates should be installed as shown. Install the baffle plate so that the curvature points down. Adjust the carburetor. See "Tune-Up".

Stromberg 175CDT (220/8)

1. Remove the air cleaner.
2. Remove and plug the fuel lines.

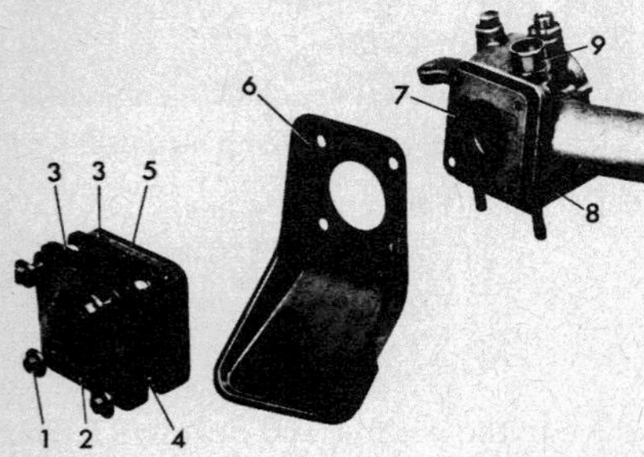

Gasket installation on Stromberg 175CDT

1. Carburetor retaining screw
2. Paper gasket
3. Rubber flange
4. Rubber flange fastening screw
5. Insulating flange
6. Deflector plate
7. Paper gasket
8. Intake manifold
9. Water separator

CAUTION: *Do not pull off the fuel lines. They should be pried off along with the securing discs.*

3. Disconnect the control linkage.
4. Remove the vacuum lines.
5. Disconnect the water hoses for the automatic choke.
6. Disconnect the leads for the automatic choke and fuel shut-off valve.
7. Remove the carburetor retaining nuts and remove the carburetor.
8. Installation is the reverse of removal. Adjust the carburetor. See "Tune-Up".

Zenith 35/40 INAT (230/8, 250/8, 250C, 280S/8)

1. Remove the air cleaner.
2. Pull the cable from the starter cover.
3. Unscrew and plug the fuel lines.
4. Detach the carburetor linkage from the carburetor body.
5. Remove any water lines and electric choke leads. Remove the vacuum line.
6. Loosen and remove the carburetor retaining nuts. Lift the carburetors from the manifolds.
7. Installation is the reverse of removal.
8. Place the insulating flanges and screening plate on the intake manifold.
9. Install the rubber rings on the carburetors. Slide the rubber ring on the water separator located at the bottom of the air cleaner.
10. Install the air cleaner so that the water separator empties into the funnel.
11. Tighten the retaining nuts and install the hot air line and engine vent line.

Solex 4 A 1 (280 and 280C)

1. Remove the air filter.
2. Remove the electric cable from the starter cover and cut-off valves.
3. Remove the vacuum lines.
4. To prevent corrosion from leaked coolant, cover the starter housing with a rag. Release the pressure in the cooling system by cracking the radiator cap until pressure has escaped. Install and tighten the radiator cap. Remove and plug the coolant water hoses from the carburetor.
5. Remove and plug the fuel lines.
6. Remove the retaining nuts and remove the carburetor from the manifold.
7. Installation is the reverse of removal. Install the insulating flange on the intake manifold as shown. The paper side of the insulating flange must face UP.

Install the gasket on a Solex 4 A 1 carburetor with the mark as shown (lower left corner).

8. Install the retaining nuts and tighten evenly, torquing the nuts in a crossing pattern. Torque the nuts to 7–11 ft lbs.
9. Be sure to adjust the idle speed. See "Tune-Up".

Overhaul

All Types

Efficient carburetion depends greatly on careful cleaning and inspection during overhaul. Since dirt, gum, water, or varnish in or on the carburetor parts are often responsible for poor performance.

Overhaul your carburetor in a clean, dust-free area. Carefully disassemble the carburetor, referring often to the exploded views. Keep all similar and look-alike parts segregated during disassembly and cleaning to avoid accidental interchange during assembly. Make a note of all jet sizes.

When the carburetor is disassembled, wash all parts (except diaphragms, electric choke units, pump plunger, and any other plastic, leather, fiber, or rubber parts) in clean carburetor solvent. Do not leave parts in the solvent any longer than is necessary to sufficiently loosen the deposits. Excessive cleaning may remove the special finish from the float bowl and choke valve bodies, leaving these parts unfit for service. Rinse all parts in clean solvent and blow them dry with compressed air or allow them to air dry. Wipe clean all cork, plastic, leather, and fiber parts with a clean, lint-free cloth.

Blow out all passages and jets with compressed air and be sure that there are no restrictions or blockages. Never use wire or similar tools to clean jets, fuel passages, or air bleeds. Clean all jets and valves separately to avoid accidental interchange.

Check all parts for wear or damage. If wear or damage is found, replace the defective parts. Especially check the following:

1. Check the float needle and seat for wear. If wear is found, replace the complete assembly.
2. Check the float hinge pin for wear and the float(s) for dents or distortion. Replace the float if fuel has leaked into it.
3. Check the throttle and choke shaft bores for wear or an out-of-round condition. Damage or wear to the throttle arm, shaft, or shaft bore will often require replacement of the throttle body. These parts require a close tolerance of fit; wear may allow air leakage, which could affect starting and idling.

NOTE: *Throttle shafts and bushings are not included in overhaul kits. They can be purchased separately.*

4. Inspect the idle mixture adjusting needles for burrs or grooves. Any such condition requires replacement of the needle, since you will not be able to obtain a satisfactory idle.
5. Test the accelerator pump check valves. They should pass air one way but not the other. Test for proper seating by blowing and sucking on the valve. Replace the valve if necessary. If the valve is satisfactory, wash the valve again to remove breath moisture.
6. Check the bowl cover for warped surfaces with a straightedge.
7. Closely inspect the valves and seats for wear and damage, replacing as necessary.
8. After the carburetor is assembled, check the choke valve for freedom of operation.

Carburetor overhaul kits are recommended for each overhaul. These kits contain all gaskets and new parts to replace those that deteriorate most rapidly. Failure to replace all parts supplied with the kit (especially gaskets) can result in poor performance later.

Some carburetor manufacturers supply overhaul kits of three basic types: minor repair; major repair; and gasket kits. Basically, they contain the following:

Minor Repair Kits:

- All gaskets
- Float needle valve
- Volume control screw

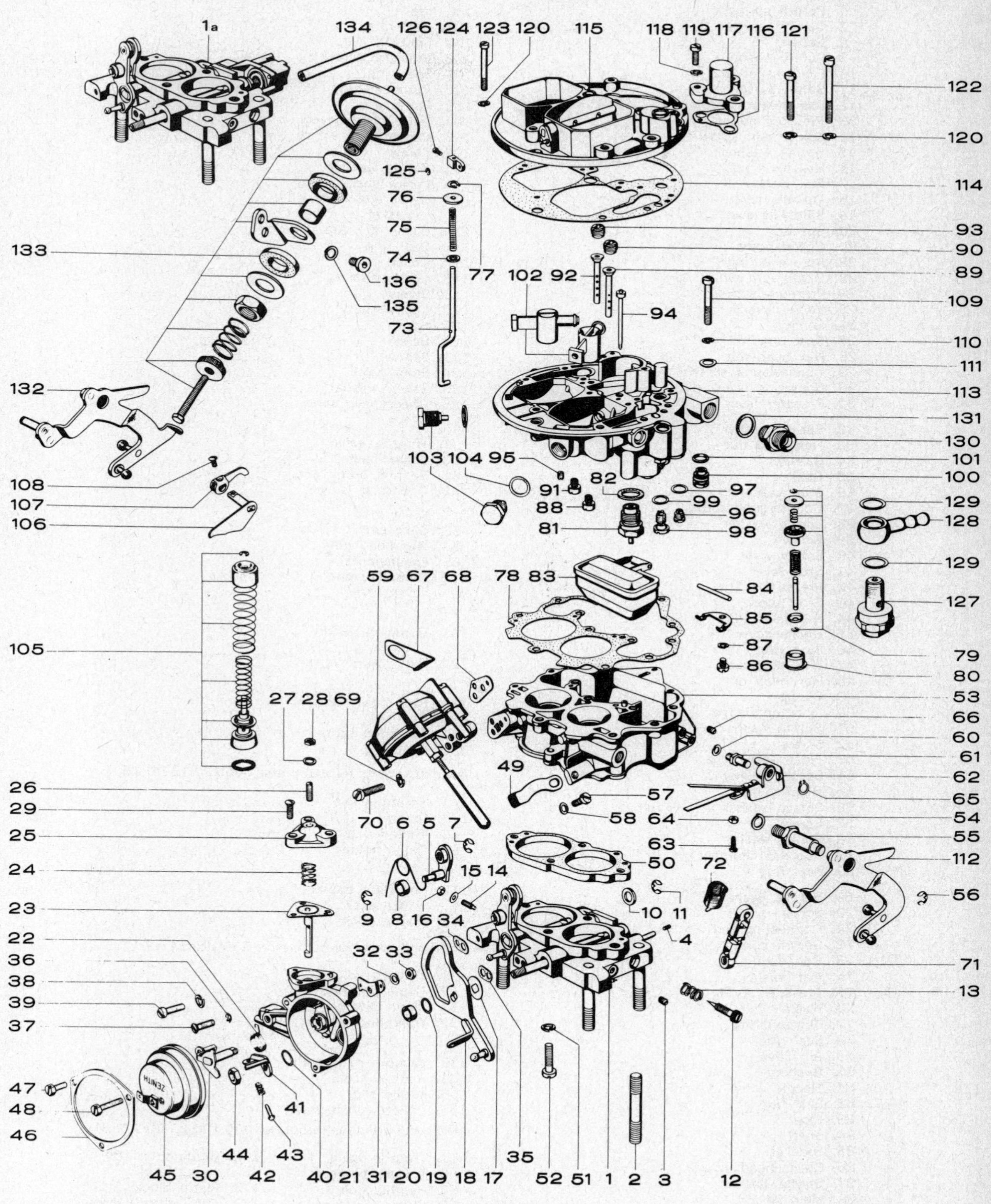

Zenith 35/40 INAT carburetor

2. Pin screw
3. Screw
5. Joint lever
6. Return spring
7. Safety washer
8. Roller
9. Safety washer
10. Flat washer
11. Safety washer
12. Idle mixture screw
13. Pressure spring
14. Adjustment screw
15. Spring washer
16. Hex head nut
17. Flat washer
18. Throttle lever
19. Safety washer
20. Spacer
21. Choke body
22. Return spring
23. Diaphragm spring
24. Pressure spring
25. Valve cover
26. Screw
27. Seal ring
28. Hex head nut
29. Countersunk screw
30. Operating lever
31. Transfer lever

32. Spring washer
33. Hex head nut
34. Gasket
35. Gasket
36. Star washer
37. Countersunk screw
38. Spring washer
39. Screw
40. Safety washer
41. Stop lever
42. Pressure spring
43. Stop screw
44. Hex head nut
45. Choke cover
46. Stop ring
47. Hex head nut
48. Hex head nut
49. Clamp
50. Isolation flange
51. Spring washer
52. Screw
53. Float bowl
54. Spring washer
55. Bearing bolt
56. Safety washer
57. Screw
58. Spring washer
59. Vacuum chamber
60. Seal ring

69. Spring washer
70. Screw
71. Connecting rod
72. Return spring
73. Connecting rod
74. Flat washer
75. Pressure spring
76. Washer
77. Tension ring
78. Seal ring
79. Air valve
80. Bushing
81. Needle valve
82. Seal ring
83. Float
84. Shaft
85. Bracket
86. Cheesehead screw
87. Spring washer
88. Main jet
89. Mixture tube
90. Air correction jet
94. Idle jet
95. Jet
96. Pump suction valve
97. Seal ring

98. Pump pressure valve
99. Seal ring
100. Jet
101. Seal ring
102. Sprayer
103. Pressure screw
104. Seal ring
105. Pump piston
106. Pump lever
107. Inner pump lever
108. Countersunk screw
109. Screw
111. Spring washer
110. Lockwasher
114. Carburetor body gasket
115. Carburetor top
116. Seal ring
117. Cover
118. Lockwasher
119. Screw
120. Lockwasher
122. Screw
121. Screw
123. Screw
124. Joint piece
125. Safety washer
126. Cheesehead screw

1. Throttle valve
60. Lockwasher
61. Bearing bolt
62. Operating lever

63. Cheesehead screw
64. Hex head nut
65. Expansion ring
112. Complete operating lever

113. Complete platin block
127. Fuel return valve

128. Ring hose piece
129. Seal ring
130. Threaded fitting
131. Seal ring

Additional parts for carburetor 000.120-13 DB 16

1. Throttle valve
4. Screw
66. Threaded pin
67. Cable holder

112. Complete operating lever
113. Platin block

Additional parts for carburetor 000.120-14 DB 17

1. Throttle valve
67. Cable holder
113. Platin block
132. Operating lever

133. Vacuum regulator
134. Rubber hose
135. Lockwasher
136. Cheesehead screw

Additional parts for carburetor 000.120-23 DB 27

1a. Throttle valve
60. Lockwasher
61. Bearing bolt
62. Operating lever

63. Cheesehead screw
64. Hex head nut
65. Expansion ring
67. Cable holder

112. Complete operating lever
113. Platin block
127. Fuel return valve

128. Ring hose piece
129. Seal ring
130. Threaded fitting
131. Seal ring

Zenith 35/40 INAT carburetor

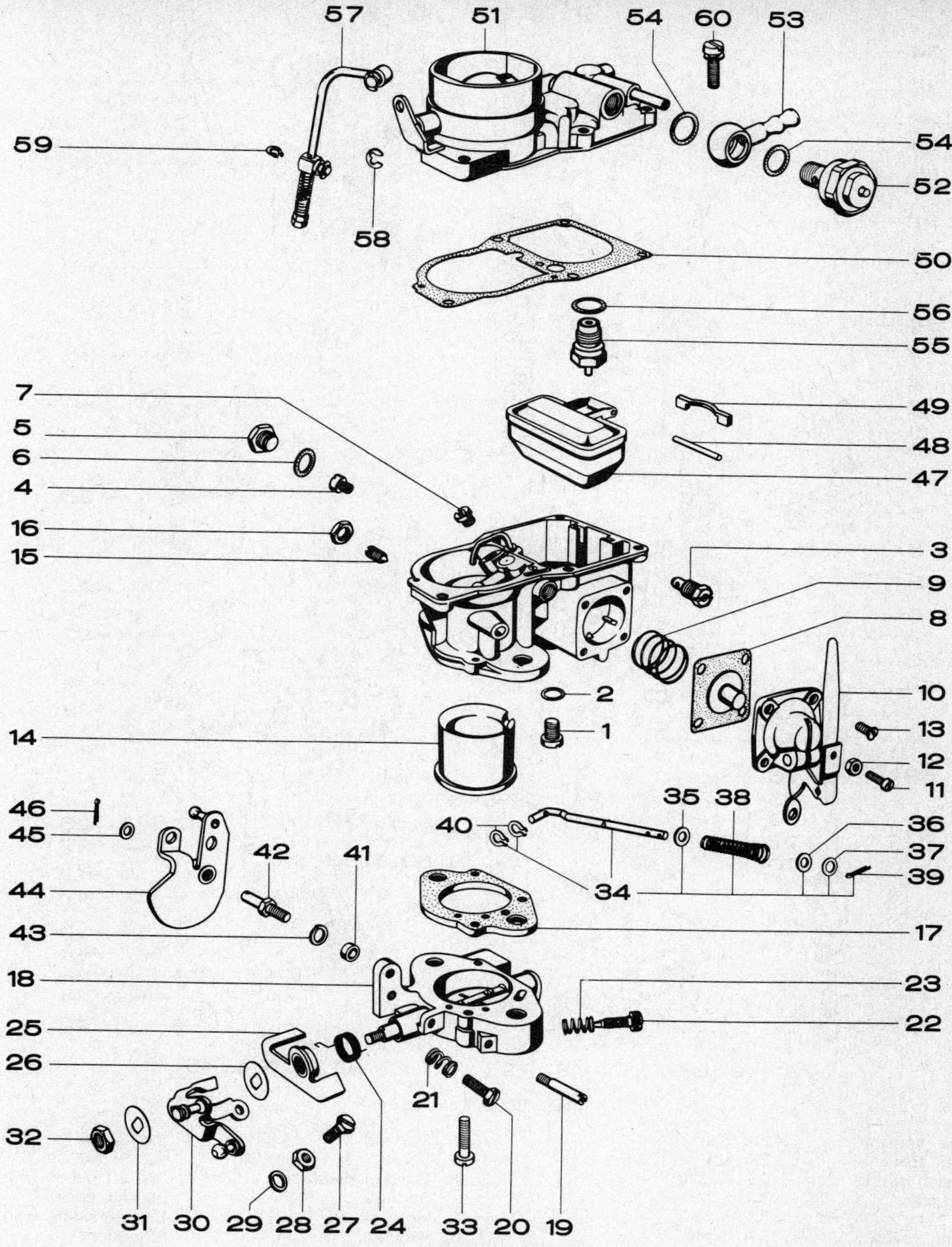

Solex 36/40 PDSI carburetor

1. Screw
2. Seal ring
3. Idle jet
4. Main jet
5. Plug screw
6. Seal ring
7. Air correction jet
8. Diaphrgm
9. Diaphragm spring
10. Pump cover
11. Screw
12. Hex head nut
13. Countersunk screw
14. Venturi
15. Venturi lockscrew
16. Hex head nut
17. Isolation gasket
18. Complete throttle valve
19. Connection tube
20. Idle adjustment screw
21. Pressure spring
22. Idle volume control screw
23. Pressure screw
24. Return spring
25. Operating lever
26. Spacer washer
27. Choke adjustment screw
28. Hex head nut
29. Lockwasher
30. Throttle lever
31. Safety washer
32. Hex head nut
33. Screw
34. Pump connecting rod
35. Flat washer
36. Flat washer
37. Flat washer
38. Pressure spring
39. Cotter pin
40. Expansion ring
41. Washer
42. Bearing bolt
43. Lockwasher
44. Choke lever
45. Washer
46. Cotter pin
47. Complete float
48. Float pin
49. Hold-down
50. Seal ring
51. Carburetor top
52. Fuel return valve
53. Ring hose piece
54. Seal ring
55. Needle valve
56. Seal ring
57. Choke connecting rod
58. Safety washer
59. Expansion ring
60. Screw

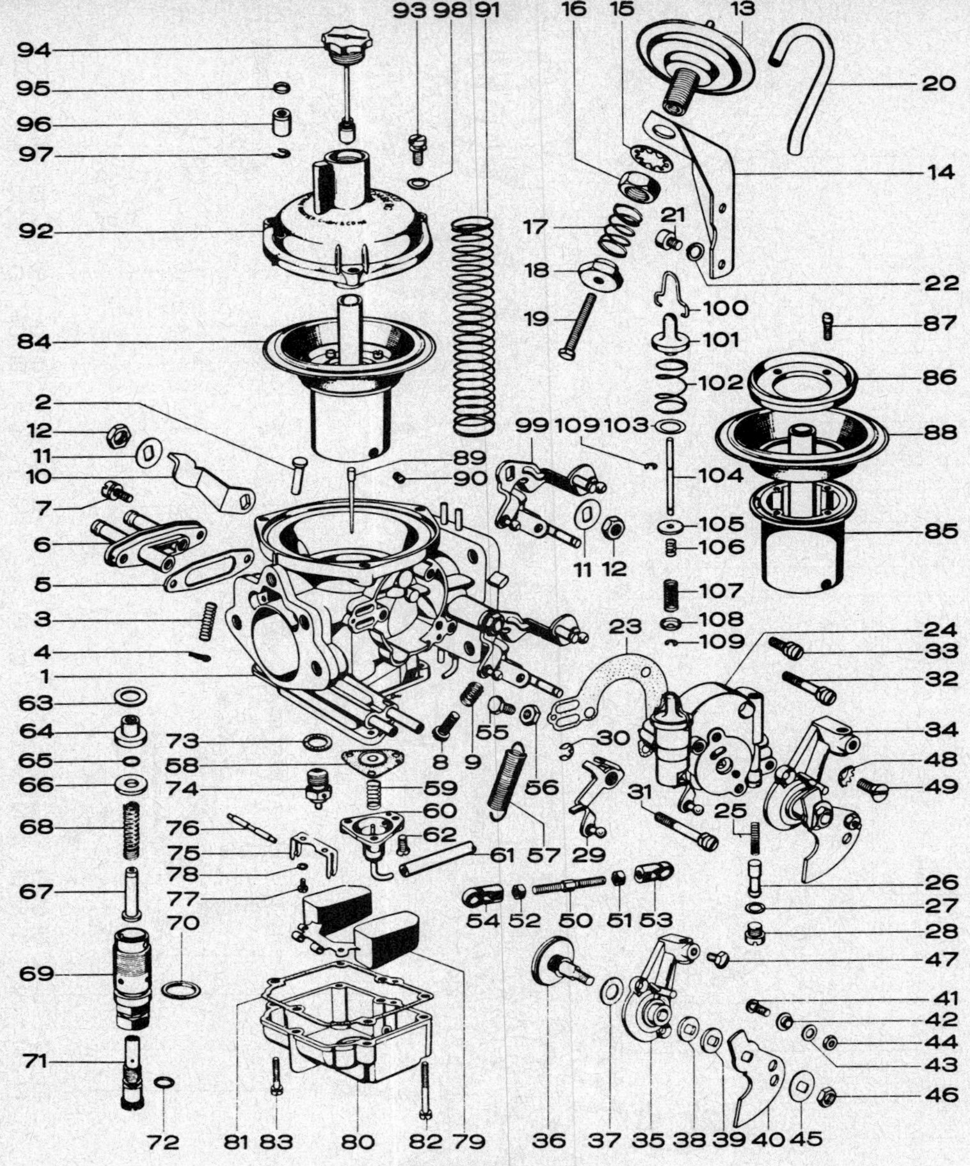

Stromberg 175CDT carburetor

1. Carburetor housing
2. Carburetor tickler
3. Compression spring
4. Locking spring
5. Gasket
6. Connecting cover
7. Screw
8. Idle adjustment screw
9. Spring
10. Control rod
11. Locking plate
12. Nut
13. Vacuum control
14. Bracket
15. Lockwasher
16. Hex nut
17. Spring
18. Adjustment nut
19. Screw
20. Vacuum hose
21. Screw
22. Lockwasher
23. Gasket
24. Starter housing
25. Spring (not installed)
26. Vacuum piston
27. Sealing ring
28. Plug
29. Starter lever
30. Circlip
31. Screw
32. Screw
33. Screw
34. Starter cover, compl.
35. Starter cover
36. Rotary slide valve
37. Gasket
38. Stop
39. Spacer
40. Starter lever
41. Clamp bolt
42. Bushing
43. Washer
44. Hex nut
45. Lock plate
46. Hex nut
47. Clamping bolt
48. Lockwasher
49. Countersunk screw
50. Connecting rod
51. Hex nut
52. Hex nut
53. Ball socket
54. Ball socket
55. Hex screw
56. Hex nut
57. Spring
58. Vacuum diaphragm
59. Spring
60. Valve cover
61. Vacuum hose
62. Countersunk screw
63. Sealing ring
64. Guide tube
65. Rubber ring
66. Washer
67. Needle valve
68. Spring
69. Lockscrew
70. Rubber ring
71. Idle mixture adjustment screw
72. Rubber ring
73. Sealing ring
74. Float needle valve
75. Bracket
76. Float spindle
77. Screw
78. Lockwasher
79. Dual float
80. Float chamber cover
81. Gasket
82. Screw
83. Screw
84. Air piston with diaphragm
85. Air piston
86. Retaining disc
87. Screw
88. Diaphragm
89. Nozzle needle
90. Clamping bolt
91. Compression spring
92. Carburetor cover
93. Screws
94. Damping element
95. Sleeve
96. Piston
97. Circlip
98. Washer
99. Throttle lever
100. Clamping spring
101. Cap
102. Spring
103. Washer
104. Rod
105. Valve disc
106. Spring
107. Spring
108. Spring retainer
109. Circlip

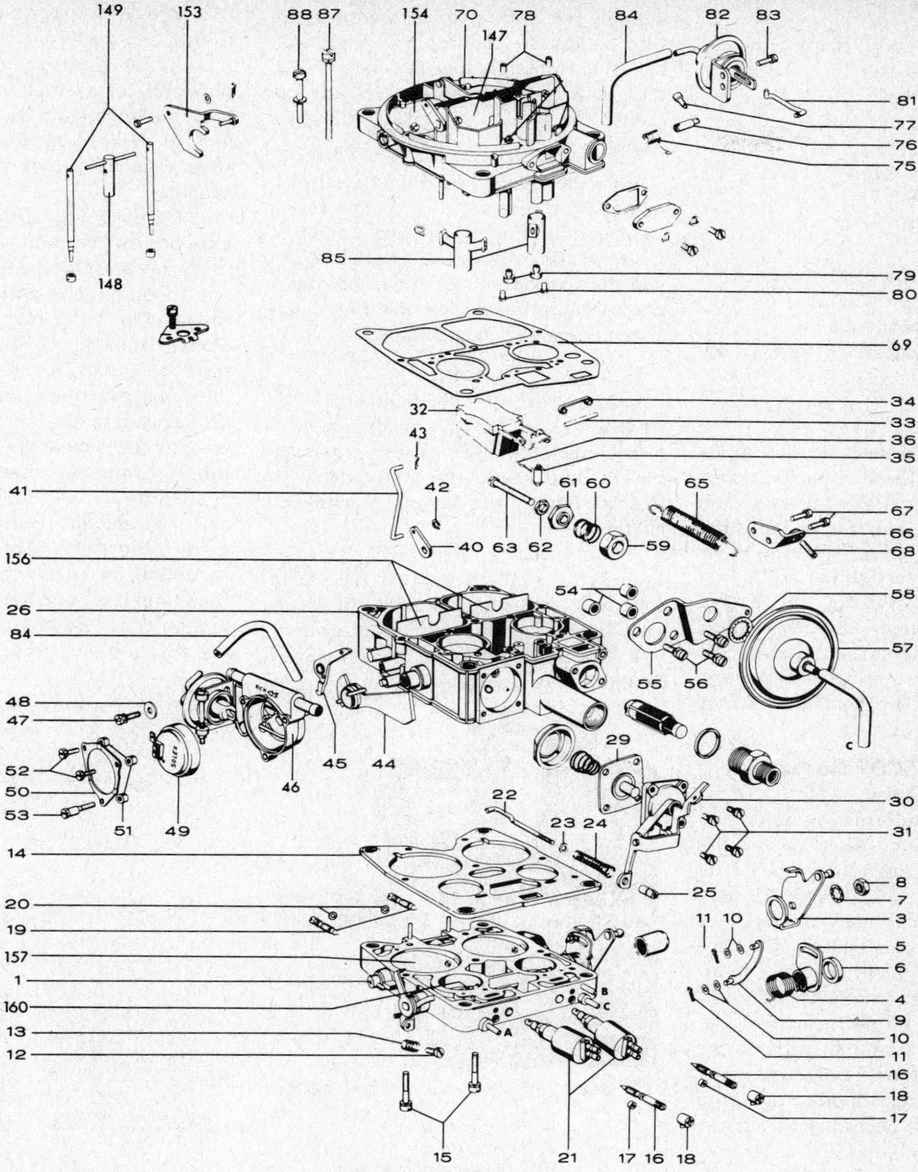

Solex 4 A 1 carburetor

1. Throttle valve housing
3. Bracket
4. Spring
5. Cam lever
6. Bushing
7. Washer
8. Nut
9. Secondary connecting rod
10. Washer
11. Cotter pin
12. Screw
13. Spring
14. Plate
15. Screw
16. Idle mixture adjusting screws
17. Idle mixture adjusting screws
18. Idle mixture adjusting screws
19. Secondary jets
20. Secondary jets
21. Idle speed solenoid
22. Actuating levers for accelerator pump
23. Actuating levers for accelerator pump
24. Actuating levers for accelerator pump
25. Actuating levers for accelerator pump
26. Float housing
29. Diaphragm
30. Accelerator pump cover
31. Screws
32. Float
33. Float shaft
34. Hold-down clamp
35. Float needle
36. Float needle
40. Choke connecting rod
41. Choke connecting rod
42. Circlip
43. Cotter pin
44. Cam lever
45. Step lever
46. Thermostat housing
47. Screw
48. Washer
49. Thermostat cover
50. Attaching plate
51. Bushing
52. Screws (short)
53. Screw (long)
54. Vacuum regulator with bracket
55. Vacuum regulator with bracket
56. Vacuum regulator with bracket
57. Vacuum regulator with bracket
58. Vacuum regulator with bracket
59. Nut
60. Spring
61,62. Nut
63. Screw
65. Throttle return spring
66. Idle stop screw with bracket
67. Idle stop screw with bracket
68. Idle stop screw with bracket
69. Gasket
70. Carburetor cover
75. Spring
76. Eccentric pin
77. Clamp screw
78. Primary idle air jets
79. Main jets
80. Screws
81. Vacuum diaphragm connecting rod
82. Vacuum diaphragm.
83. Screw
84. Vacuum line
85. Emulsion Tube
87. Screw
88. Screw
147. Choke plate
148. Guide pin
149. Secondary needle valve
153. Lever
154. Secondary choke plate
156. Secondary baffle plates
157. Throttle valve (primary)
160. Throttle valve (secondary)

All diaphragms
Spring for the pump diaphragm
Major Repair Kits:
All jets and gaskets
All diaphragms
Float needle valve
Volume control screw
Pump ball valve
Main jet carrier
Float
Complete intermediate rod
Intermediate pump lever
Complete injector tube
Some cover hold-down screws and washers
Gasket Kits:
All gaskets

After cleaning and checking all components, reassemble the carburetor, using new parts and referring to the exploded view. When reassembling, make sure that all screws and jets are tight in their seats, but do not overtighten, as the tips will be distorted. Tighten all screws gradually, in rotation. Do not tighten needle valves into their seats; uneven jetting will result. Always use new gaskets. Be sure to adjust the float level when reassembling.

Stromberg 175CDT Carburetor Only

The preceding information applies to Stromberg carburetors also, but the following, additional suggestions should be followed.

1. Soak the small cork gaskets (jet gland washers) in penetrating oil or hot water for at least a half-hour prior to assembly, or they will invariably split.
2. When the jet is fully assembled, the jet tube should be a close fit without any lateral play, but it should be free to move smoothly. A few drops of oil or polishing of the tube may be necessary to achieve this.
3. If the jet sealing ring washer is made of cork, soak it in hot water for a minute or two prior to installation.
4. Adjust the float height.
5. Center the jet so that the piston will fall freely (when raised) and seat with a distinct click. If the jet is not centered properly, it will hang up in the tube. Refer to the procedure for centering the jet in the adjustments section of the text.

Solex 36–40 PDSI Adjustments

Vacuum Control Valve

Automatic Transmission Models

1. Loosen bolt to give 0.040 in. clearance between it and the bellcrank.

NOTE: *The Transmission should be in Drive.*

Automatic Transmission Models with No Accessories or Air Conditioned Models, Any Transmission

1. Place the selector lever in Drive or, if equipped with manual transmission, turn on the air conditioner. Adjust the hex bolt to obtain specified idle speed, then adjust the polystop nut to rest against the stop.

Models with Two or More Accessories

Place the car in D or, if equipped with manual transmission, turn on one accessory (air conditioning, full lock on power steering, etc.). Adjust the hex bolt to obtain the specified idle speed, then adjust the polystop nut to give 0.080 in. clearance between it and the stop.

Choke

1. Adjust the idle speed and check the throttle linkage for ease of movement.
2. Detach the pushrod at the rear carburetor and clamp the choke cable so that its end is in alignment with the clamp.
3. Push the choke lever forward against the stop, then press the choke control in until there is 0.040 in. clearance between it and the dashboard.
4. Tighten the choke cable at the lever by tightening the screw.

Choke adjustment—Solex 36/40 PDSI

6. Starter link rod
7. Starter lever
8. Clamping screw
10. Stop
11. Bowden cable clamp
16. Follower link lever
18. Starter cable coil
19. Connecting rod

5. Turn the shoulder nut on the choke link so that the distance equals 1.12 in. at the rear carburetor.
6. Set lever as illustrated (arrow) by adjusting the connecting link.

Float Level

Remove the carburetor.

2. Remove the carburetor cover.
3. The float level is correctly adjusted if the specified seal ring (1.0 mm.) has been installed beneath the float needle valve.
4. Replace the carburetor cover and install the carburetor on the engine.

Accelerator Pump

1. Make sure that the connecting rod and pump lever move easily.
2. Remove the air cleaner and check the start of injection.
3. As the throttle valve is opened, a powerful jet of fuel must be pumped from the injection tube. It may be necessary to make sure that the pump diaphragm and injection tube are working properly.
4. On the front carburetor used in automatic transmission applications, the fuel spray must hit the side of the venturi, not shoot directly into the carburetor throat. On both carburetors used in manual transmission applications, and on the rear carburetor in automatic transmission applications, the fuel spray must be parallel to the venturi axis and go through the gap between the venturi and throttle butterfly when the butterfly is opened 20°.
5. The amount (volume) of fuel delivered by the accelerator pump is adjusted by adding or removing shims between the pump lever and the cotter pin on the pump rod. Adding shims increases volume, and vice-versa.

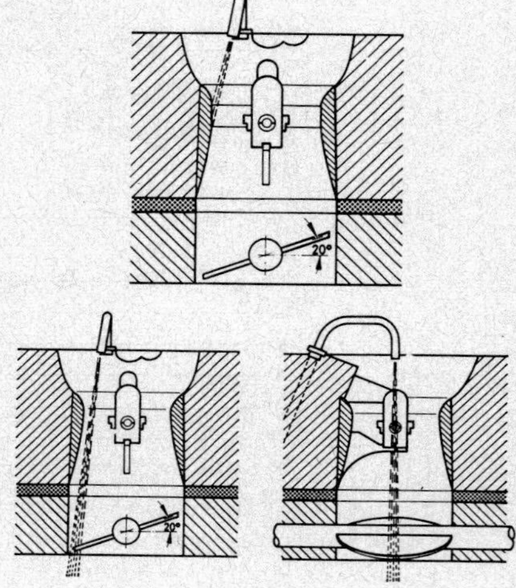

Fuel spray pattern—220/8

Accelerator pump adjustment—Solex 36/40 PDSI.

1. Fuel return valve
2. Flat spring
3. Adjusting screw
4. Shim
5. Pump lever
6. Connecting rod

Stromberg 175CDT Adjustments

Damper Fluid Level

1. Unscrew the top of the damper and check the fluid level.

2. If necessary, top up the reservoir with engine oil, or in cold weather, automatic transmission fluid (ATF).

3. The fluid level should be to the top edge of the piston ring.

4. Replace the top on the reservoir.

Float Adjustment

1. Remove the carburetor.

2. Remove the float chamber cover.

3. Do not loosen the lock screw from the needle, or the needle will have to be recentered.

4. Measure the distance between the edge of the carburetor housing and the upper edge of the float; it should be 15–17 mm.

Float level adjustment—Stromberg 175-CDT.

1. Float
2. Float arm
3. Needle valve
4. Sealing ring

5. To correct the float level, bend the float arm at the tang over the needle valve. The float arm must always remain perpendicular to the needle valve.

6. Replace the float chamber cover and install the carburetor.

7. Adjust the idle.

Automatic Choke

1. The idle should be set and the engine should be at normal operating temperature.

2. On vehicles with air conditioning, remove the air cleaner and air intake.

Stromberg 175CDT automatic choke adjustment.

1. Connecting rod
2. Hex nut
3. Threaded bolt
4. Hex nut
5. Actuating lever
6. Venting valve

3. Check the adjustment of the choke cover. The index marks should be aligned.

4. Raise the throttle linkage slightly and insert a screwdriver through the slot of the starter housing on the carburetor. Push the screwdriver against the engaging lever in the direction of the engine. Release the throttle linkage and engaging lever. This will set the engine at fast idle.

5. The fast idle speed should be 3300–3600 rpm. If the speed requires adjustment, loosen both locknuts on the connecting rod and turn the threaded bolt. A ½ turn of the bolt will change the engine rpm by about 200-300 rpm. Decreasing the length of the bolt will decrease rpm and increasing the length will increase rpm.

Zenith 35/40 INAT Adjustments

Float Level

1. Remove the carburetor.

2. Remove the float chamber cover with the float attached.

3. Measure the distance from the edge of the float housing to the top edge of the float.

4. The distance in Step 3 should be 21–23 mm if the float level is correct. If the float level requires adjustment, install a sealing ring, of the appropriate thickness, under the needle valve.

5. Install the carburetor cover using new gaskets; tighten the cover screws evenly.

6. Install the carburetor and adjust the idle and balance the carburetors.

Acclerator Pump

1. Be sure that the pump and lever are working smoothly.

2. Check the start of injection. As the throttle valve is opened, a powerful jet of fuel must emerge from the injection tube. It may be necessary to check the injection tube and the accelerator diaphragm for blockage.

3. The fuel jet must be sprayed against the wall of the air horn, 10–15 mm below the upper edge of the float chamber cover.

Dashpot

NOTE: *Apply the parking brake and chock the wheels.*

1. If the car is equipped with automatic transmission, place the selector lever in a drive range and, with the engine not running, back out the hex bolt until the vent valve is raised 0.020–0.040 in.

2. Then start the engine and adjust the compression spring by turning the nut to obtain the specified idle speed.

3. Place the selector lever in Neutral and make sure that the lever is against the idle stop.

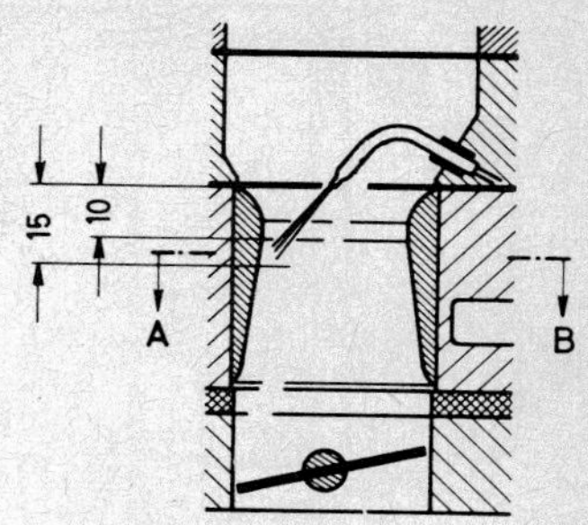

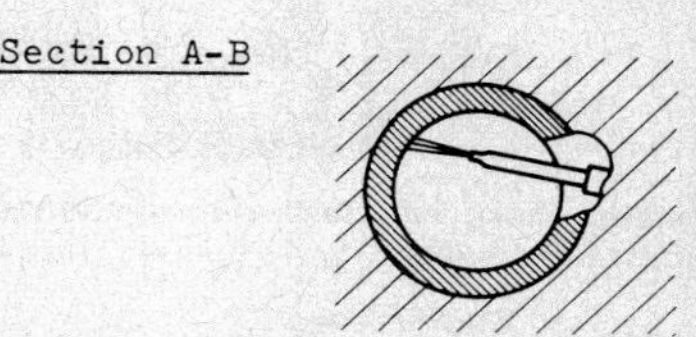

Fuel spray pattern—Zenith 35/40 INAT

4. If the lever touches the hex bolt, back out the bolt and readjust the spring with the car in Drive.

5. If the car is equipped with manual transmission, start the engine, make sure all accessories are turned off, and adjust the nut to give 0.004 in. clearance between the hex bolt and the actuating lever.

Dashpot adjustment—Zenith 35/40 INAT

1. Idle stop screw
2. Vent valve
3. Vacuum hose to valve
4. Vacuum hose connecting valve and control unit
5. Spring
6. Knurled nut
7. Adjustment screw
8. Actuating lever

Automatic Choke

1. Make sure that the choke butterflies operate without binding, then check the choke housing cover; the marks must align.

NOTE: *The spring is preloaded 0.20 in.*

2. Turn on the ignition switch and make sure the throttle butterflies open after a few minutes (engine cold).

3. To adjust the pilot throttle gap with the engine running, lift the accelerator linkage and insert a screwdriver between the choke housing and the throttle lever. Press the relay lever upward until it touches the stop on the diaphragm rod, then release the linkage.

4. Measure the clearance between the choke butterfly and the carburetor bore;

Automatic choke and fast idle adjustment —Zenith 35/40 INAT.

1. Starter cover
2. Starter housing
3. Adjustment screw

it should be 0.096 in. If necessary, adjust by turning the screw on the starter valve.

5. Start the engine and allow it to warm up.

6. Shut off the engine, raise the accelerator linkage and insert a screwdriver between the starter housing and the throttle lever of one carburetor. Press the relay lever upward and release the linkage. This should cause the adjustment screw inside the choke housing to come to rest on the top notch of the cam. The adjustment screw should only be turned with the engine off.

7. Hook up a tachometer and start the engine; adjust the screw to obtain the proper fast idle. Adjust the other carburetor in the same manner.

Solex 4 A 1 Adjustments

Fuel Level

1. There is no provision for measuring the fuel level, other than with the special Mercedes-Benz tool. It is a measuring rod which is inserted through the bore of the carburetor cover, and can be purchased from a dealer.

2. Run the engine briefly at fast idle and shut off the ignition.

3. Insert the measuring gauge through the bore of the carburetor cover as far as it will go.

4. Remove the gauge and read the fuel level. The reading should be within the

Measuring fuel level on Solex 4 A 1 with gauge (1).

tolerance range marked on the stick.

5. To adjust the level, remove the carburetor cover and adjust the float by bending it on the hinge.

6. Reinstall the cover and test the level again.

Vacuum Governor

1. Set the idle speed and make sure that the engine is at normal operating temperature.

2. Run the engine at idle and pull the vacuum hose from the governor.

Vacuum governor adjustment—Solex 4 A 1

3. Throttle valve lever
60. Spring
61. Adjusting nut
62. Counternut
63. Adjuting screw

3. Set the engine speed to approximately 1200–1400 rpm. Loosen the locknut and adjust the rpm with the adjusting screw. Hold the diaphragm rod and turn the adjusting nut.

4. Adjust the compression spring with the transmission in gear.

5. The speed should be 600–700 rpm. If necessary, adjust the compression spring with the adjusting nut.

6. Turn on the air conditioning, and turn the wheels to full lock. The engine should keep running. If it does not, adjust the speed with the adjusting nut again. See Step 3.

Automatic Choke

1. Check the choke for ease of operation.

2. Switch on the ignition and check to be sure that the choke opens after a minute or so.

3. Check the adjustment on the choke cover. The markings on the housing and cover should be aligned.

Choke Gap

1. Run the engine at idle until the diaphragm in the vacuum unit has been pulled completely against the stop.

2. Then clamp the hose to block all vacuum.

3. Be sure that the diaphragm is still against the stop and slightly raise the throttle valve lever. Position the stepped disc upward against the top stop. Release the throttle valve lever.

4. Push the lever of the bi-metallic spring until the stop is felt. The connecting rod will now be against the stop in the slot of the lever.

5. Measure the choke gap with a # 53 drill (0.060 in.) between the choke plate and the wall of the air horn.

6. To adjust the gap, remove the coolant hose from the choke housing. Cover the choke housing with a rag and release the pressure in the radiator. Tighten the radiator cap again. Remove the coolant hose and clamp it shut.

Automatic choke adjustment—Solex 4 A 1. If the choke gap is too large, push the bend apart; if the choke gap is too small, push the bend together.

7. Hold the connecting rod with a screwdriver. Bend the connecting rod with a second screwdriver.

8. While making the adjustment, be sure that the diaphragm in the vacuum unit is still against its stop.

Fast Idle

1. Adjust the idle speed and be sure that the engine is at normal operating temperature.

2. Run the engine at idle speed.

3. Raise the throttle valve lever slightly and position the stepped disc completely upward against the top stop.

4. Release the throttle valve lever.

5. Connect a tachometer and measure the engine speed. It should be 2400–2600. If required, adjust the fast idle with the fast idle speed adjusting screw.

Solex 4 A 1 fast idle adjustment screw (12)

Accelerator Pump

1. Move the throttle valve lever several times. A strong jet of fuel should be forced out of the fuel outlets.

2. If not, remove the accelerator pump cover and check the diaphragm. Blow out the ducts with compressed air.

3. Install the accelerator pump cover.

4. If there still is no fuel from the injection tube, remove the carburetor cover.

5. Actuate the accelerator pump. If fuel emerges from the ball valves, blow out the injection holes in the carburetor cover with compressed air.

6. Install the carburetor cover. Tighten the screws evenly to 11 ft lbs.

Fuel Return Valve

1. Pull the fuel return hose from the connection to the return line below the fuel pump.

2. Hold the return hose in a container and check whether a strong fuel jet comes from the line with the automatic transmission in Drive and the air conditioning on.

Fuel Injection (Mechanical and Electrical)

Two types of fuel injection are used on Mercedes-Benz gasoline engines. All 6-cylinder engines and the 6.3 V-8 use mechanical fuel injection, while all V-8's (except the 6.3) are equipped with electronic fuel injection. Due to the sensitive nature of these systems, and the numerous special tools required, it is best to refer any service or adjustment, other than idle speed adjustment, to a qualified Mercedes-Benz service facility.

CAUTION: *Even a seemingly minor adjustment, such as idle speed, can necessitate adjustments to other portions of the fuel injection system. Be extremely careful when adjusting the idle. If any difficulty at all is experienced, immediately refer the vehicle to a Mercedes-Benz dealer. Further attempts at adjustment will only upset the balance of an already delicate system.*

MANUAL TRANSMISSION

Removal and Installation

The transmission can be removed with the engine as a unit or it can be removed separately, whichever appears easiest. See the procedures under "Engine Removal and Installation" or those following for separate Removal and Installation. Once the engine/transmission unit has been removed from the vehicle, the transmission and bell housing must be separated from the engine, as follows:

Removal and Installation–with Engine

1. After removing the engine/transmission unit, unbolt the bellhousing from the engine. The bolts which hold the transmission to the bellhousing cannot be reached except from inside the bell housing.

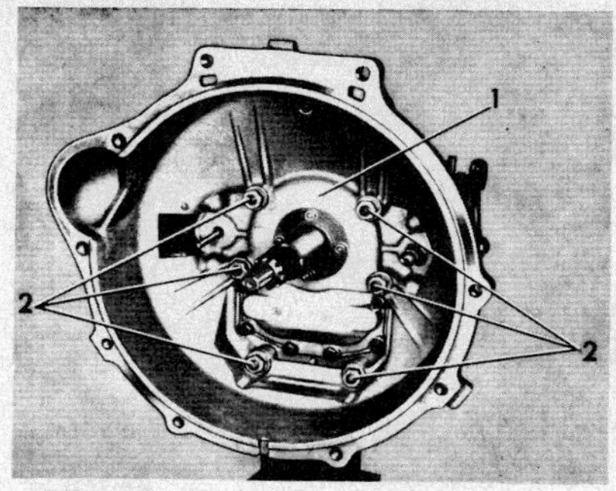

Clutch housing (1) and clutch housing attaching bolts (2) which can only be reached from inside the clutch housing.

2. Remove the starter from its mounting position and pull the transmission and bellhousing from the engine.

3. The bolts which secure the bellhousing to the transmission are now visible and can be removed to separate the bellhousing and transmission.

4. To install, connect the engine, bellhousing, and transmission, after coating the splines of the mainshaft with grease.

5. Install the starter.

6. Further installation is the reverse of removal.

Removal and Installation—Without Engine

1. First jack up the car at all four corners and place it on axle stands. Remove the negative battery cable and disconnect all shift rods.

2. With a column-mounted gearshift lever, remove the rods at the relay arm from under the hood.

Transmission viewed from below

5. Driveshaft for speedometer
6. Clamping screw
7. Pressure hose for clutch actuation
8. Pressure line for clutch actuation
10. Attaching screw for cross-member on frame floor
11. Attaching screw for cross member with rubber mount on transmission
12. Fastening nuts (covered) for exhaust support on transmission
13. Screws for clip of exhaust bracket

(a)—Connecting point pressure hose on pressure line

14. Clip

3. On floorshift models, unhook the rods at the transmission side cover by prying upward on the clips from the open end using a screwdriver.

4. On models having a top cover shift mechanism, the floor tunnel must be removed to reach the shift rods.

5. On older models having the clutch slave cylinder held to the clutch housing with two bolts, remove the cylinder completely and swing it out of the way. On newer models it is sufficient to remove the hose and plug it to prevent fluid loss.

6. Remove the speedometer cable and the exhaust pipe bracket and wire them out of the way.

7. If equipped, disconnect the back-up light switch

8. Disconnect the driveshaft by holding one nut with a wrench; loosen the other, then unbolt the shaft from the transmission tailshaft. Remove the center bearing support.

NOTE: *It is a good idea to scribe marks on the center bearing support bracket for ease in assembly.*

9. Mark the position of the rear crossmember and slightly jack up the engine with a block of wood between the jack and the oil pan. This serves to take the weight off the crossmember bolts during removal and prevents stripped threads.

10. Unscrew all crossmember bolts that hold it to the body and transmission and remove the crossmember.

11. Unbolt the bellhousing and starter bolts and pull the transmission straight backward, while rotating clockwise 90° to clear obstructions. *Make absolutely sure the mainshaft is out of the clutch before lowering the transmission, otherwise the clutch hub will be damaged.*

12. The reason for removing both the transmision and bellhousing together is immediately obvious when the unit is out: the transmission hold-down bolts can be reached only from the inside. Bolt configurations vary slightly with the different models, but, in general, removal procedure is identical.

13. To remove the housing, pull off the throwout bearing, then the throwout fork. The non-anchored end of the fork must be pulled outward, then to the left to disengage the ball socket pivot.

14. Unscrew the bolts that hold the transmission to the housing, then tap the housing lightly with a fiber hammer to separate it from the transmission nose piece. The housing is easily distorted, so never use a steel hammer.

15. Installation is the reverse of removal except that the rear U-joint must be split on some models and the driveshaft pushed further back for clearance.

16. Always coat the mainshaft splines and pilot bushing surfaces with Vaseline

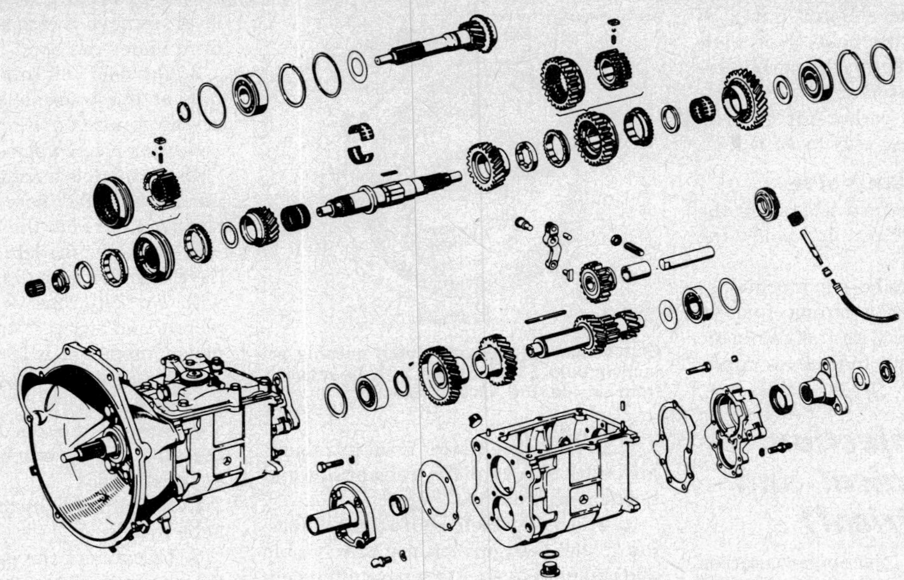

Topcover transmission and case—280- SE/8, 280S/8, and 280SL/8.

or Molykote grease before installing. Don't forget the ground cables under the nuts, and make sure that all bolts are tightened evenly. The center bearing support must not be cocked or it will soon disintegrate under torque loads, so tighten its mounting bolts finger tight until everything else is torqued, then tighten them.

17. The driveshaft double clamp nuts get torqued to about 140 ft lbs.

18. Bracing the hold-down wrench on the body pan is not recommended without some insulation to distribute the load.

Use a 24 in. section of pipe on the wrench handle, but don't put full weight on it or the nut might be distorted.

CAUTION: *On all Allen-head bolts, use the proper size key with a short extension. Use of too small American keys may round the bolt heads to such a degree that removal without drilling is impossible. Unfortunately, Allen bolts are extremely hard, and almost impossible to drill out with any success if they are in an awkward position. Grinding an oversize American key to fit is alright if the grinding is done slowly so as not to destroy the temper of the steel from frictional heating.*

Overhaul

Side Cover and Top Cover

NOTE: *Internal parts of both side cover and top cover transmissions are basically similar.*

1. Locked-up transmissions or shifting problems may be caused by defective parts in the shifting mechanism of the transmission itself.

2. After making sure that the shift rods are all in proper adjustment, check the first and second gear shift yoke needle bearings and the shift detent mechanism.

3. Drain the transmission oil and remove the clamp bolt and reverse shift lever at the transmission.

4. Remove the lock tab from the reverse shift shaft and unscrew the cover hold-down bolts.

5. Tap the cover with a fiber hammer

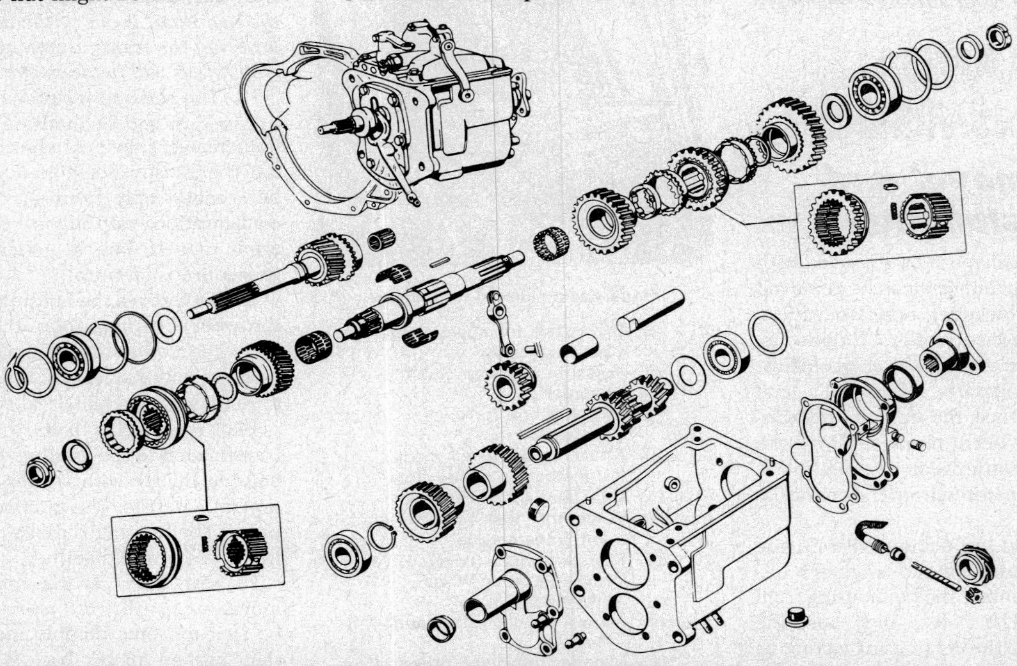

Internal transmission parts—top cover models.

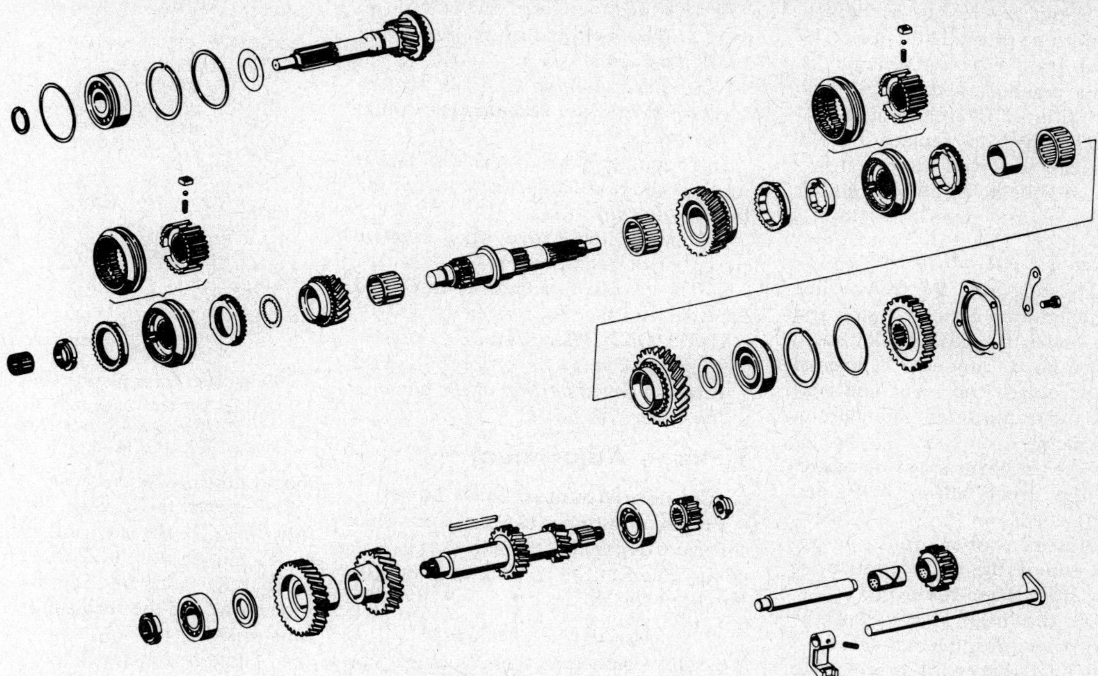

Internal transmission parts—side cover models.

to loosen it, while driving the reverse shift shaft upward with another fiber hammer.

6. When the cover is off about ¾ in. reach in and slide the shift forks out of the shift yokes, then pull the cover downward and upward.

7. The transmission gears are now visible for inspection, as is the shift mechanism. When inspecting gear teeth, rotate all the gears to make sure no part has been missed. A chipped tooth is as bad as a broken tooth, for it weakens the entire gear and can lead to transmission failure.

8. Work the gears by hand and check the synchronizers.

9. Badly burred or worn synchronizing rings usually cause grinding during shifting.

10. To disassemble the shift mechanism, loosen the clamp bolts and remove the shift levers from the outside of the cover.

11. Going to the inside, remove the circlips from the shafts and pull out shift yokes and the reverse detent lever.

12. Using a screwdriver, bend back the locktab on the bolt and unbolt the detent cage and locating pin.

13. The detent balls should not be scarred and should move in and out easily, although under spring tension. If they are immovable even under pressure, or if they flop in and out with ease, the detent cage should be replaced.

14. The shift yokes then must be checked for wear, as a burred shift yoke will more than likely ruin a new detent cage in a short time.

15. Check the bearings where the shift rods pass through the cover. If the caged

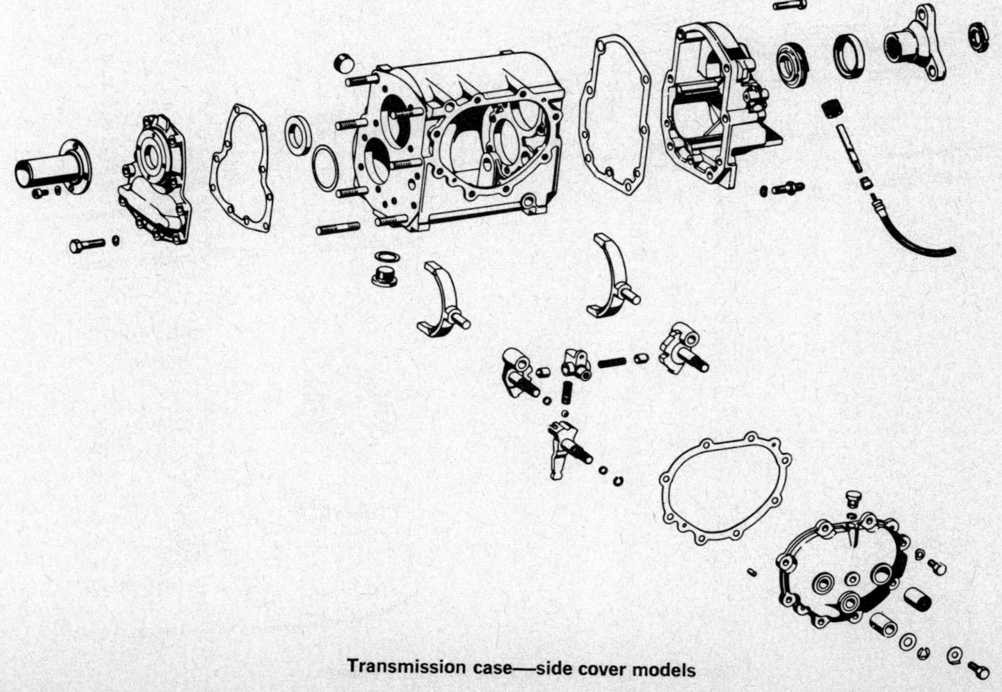

Transmission case—side cover models

needle bearings are scored or broken, new ones must be pressed into place. Use of an arbor press is recommended, although some ingenuity and a large bench vise can be utilized in an emergency.

16. Don't forget to replace the O-rings, because they will almost always leak after once being disturbed. Adjustment of the levers is described later.

Replacing Front and Rear Seals

1. Fluid leaking from the front seal is usually visible in the clutch housing and can cause clutch slippage if allowed to progress too far. In any case, it is good practice to replace the front and rear seals while the transmission is out, just on general principles.

2. After the clutch housing is removed, unscrew the front cover bolts and remove the cover.

3. The thrust washers must be replaced in exactly the same position, so note their order when removing.

4. Unbolt the nose piece from the front cover, then press the old seal out. It is recommended that an arbor press with a 1 ¾ in. adapter be used, but a slide hammer with a screw attachment can be used for this job.

5. It is important, however, that the new seal is *pressed* into the cover, not hammered.

6. The thrust washers can be held in place with wheel bearing grease during installation of the cover.

NOTE: *Use nonhardening Permatex® on the cover and bolt threads to prevent leaks.*

7. To remove the rear seal, insert a bar through the rear flange and remove the locktab and nut.

8. Remove the flange, then remove the cover bolts and cover.

9. The gear train can now be inspected for wear and the seal replaced.

CAUTION: *When installing, the reverse shaft must be properly aligned with the keyed portion of the cover or the cover will break.*

Linkage Adjustment

Column Mounted Shift Lever

Proper adjustment of the column shift linkage is dependent on both the position of the levers at the transmission and the length of the shift rods.

Top Cover Transmission

1. Make sure that the levers are not binding anywhere in their travel, then place the shift lever in Neutral and loosen the clamp bolt at the selector lever.

2. Then pull the selector lever forward in the direction of travel and pull the relay lever forward by the lower leg. This

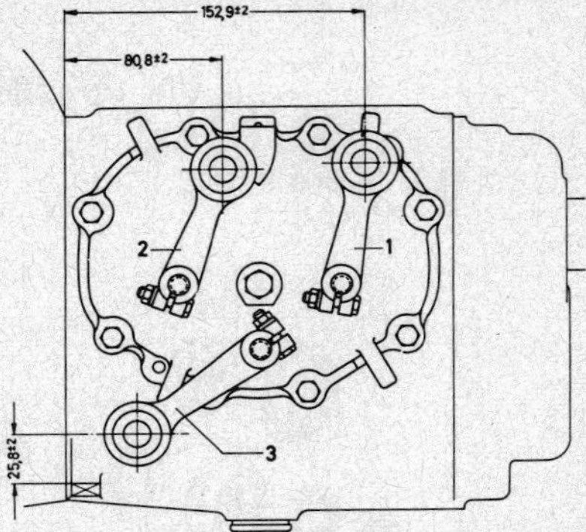

Side cover transmission shift levers

1. 1st and 2nd gear lever
2. 3rd and 4th gear lever
3. Reverse lever

should engage Fourth gear.

3. Remove the rubber cover on the shift lever at the steering column and have a helper pull the shift lever upward until about 0.080 in. separates the shift tube collar and the recess in the steering tube jacket.

4. Tighten the clamp bolts on the selector lever, preloading the spring washer while doing so.

5. Now, try shifting through all the gears, using the clutch of course. When engaging reverse, a resistance should be felt. If not, the reverse gear interlock on

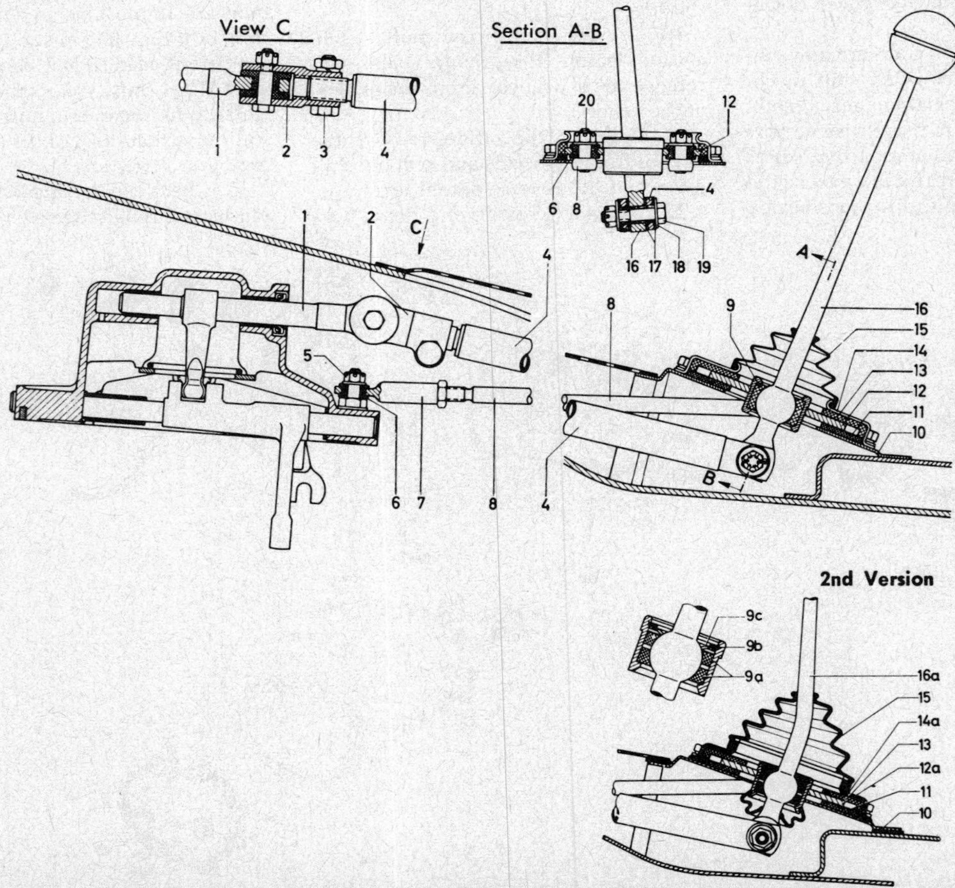

Top cover transmission with floorshift linkage.

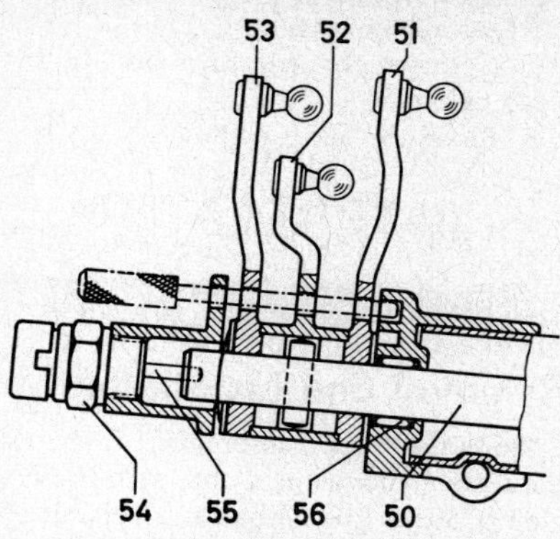

Locking the levers on column shift linkage

51. Reverse lever
52. 1st and 2nd gear lever
53. 3rd and 4th gear lever

the top cover probably is weak and a new spring should be installed. When the shift lever is in Second or Fourth gear, it should vary only about ⅝ in. from the horizontal. Small corrections to this can be made by shortening or lengthening the shift rod.

6. If shifting is hard, the shift tube may be touching the steering column passage or, in first version units, the lever may be binding in its bearing. To correct the latter condition, loosen the steering column strap and the firewall cover plate and correct any misalignment.

7. If the selector lever binds in the shift tube, it must be removed and checked for straightness. The selector lever dogs may be bent apart or ground down to fit. Grease all the ball sockets and make sure that the lower bearing assembly at the bottom of the steering column hasn't pulled off its studs.

8. The spring-loaded ball connector in the bearing assembly often wears and causes hard shifting. Replace it with the newer type connecting rod and adjust length to 67 mm (2⅝ in.).

Side Cover Transmission

1. Check the positioning of the shift levers at the transmission (see illustration) and correct by loosening the clamp bolts. The diagram shows the levers in neutral.

2. Next, go to the lower steering column and lock the three levers by inserting a 0.2156 in. rod (a No. 3 drill will do or other tool of approximately the same diameter) through the levers and the hole in the bearing block.

3. With the shift levers at the lower steering column locked and the levers at the transmission adjusted, try hooking the shift rods into their respective levers. If they are too long or short, adjust their length by loosening the locknuts and turning the ball socket ends. Remove the locking rod and try shifting through the gears. Very slight further adjustments may clear up any binding.

Floor Mounted Shift Lever

Top Cover Transmission

1. To adjust, move the shift shaft against the reverse gear stop and engage second gear by actuating the shaft.

2. Then move the shift lever into the first or second gear shifting plane and insert the shift tube into the yoke serrations at least ⅝ in. and tighten the clamp bolt.

3. Try shifting through all the gears. If the shift lever hits the bearing, adjust both pushrods an *equal* amount.

Side Cover Transmission

1. The adjustment procedure is the

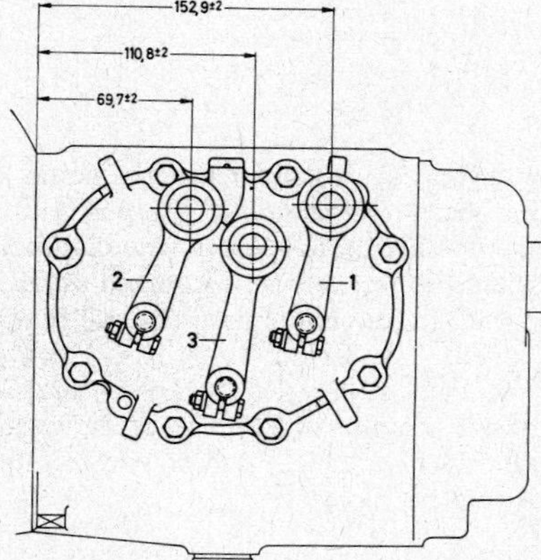

Side cover transmission with floorshift linkage.

1. 1st and 2nd gear lever
2. 3rd and 4th gear lever
3. Reverse lever

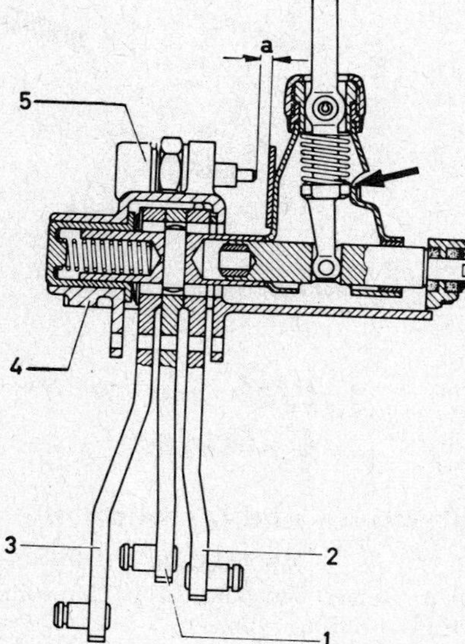

Floorshift levers with side cover transmission.

1. Shift lever for 1st and 2nd gear
2. Shift lever for 3rd and 4th gear
3. Shift lever for reverse gear
4. Bearing block
5. Backup light switch
6. Adjusting dimension for reversing light switch, 4±1 mm.—gearshift lever in shifting plane 1st or 2nd gear

same as that for side cover column shift transmissions, with the exception of the lever positioning at the transmission. The three shift levers and bearing block (where the locking rod is inserted) are found underneath the floor tunnel, which must be removed.

CAUTION: *On all types of transmissions, never hammer or force a new shift knob on with the shift lever installed, as the plastic bushing connected to the lever will be destroyed and cause hard shifting.*

CLUTCH

Removal and Installation

All Models

1. To remove the clutch, first remove the transmission and bellhousing.

2. Loosen the clutch pressure plate hold-down bolts evenly, 1–1½ turns at a time, until tension is relieved. Never remove one bolt at a time, as damage to the pressure plate is possible.

3. Examine the flywheel surface for blue heat marks, scoring, or cracks. If the flywheel is to be machined, always machine both sides.

4. To reinstall, coat the splines with high temperature grease and place the clutch disc against the flywheel, centering it with a clutch pilot shaft. A wooden shaft, available at automotive jobbers, is satisfactory, but an old transmission mainshaft works best.

5. Tighten the pressure plate hold-down bolts evenly 1–1½ turns at a time until tight, then remove the pilot shaft.

CAUTION: *Most clutch plates have the flywheel side marked as such (Kupplungsseite). Do not assume that the pressure springs always face the transmission.*

Checking Clutch Plate Wear

Apart from the usual slippage which accompanies severe wear of the clutch plate or disc, Mercedes-Benz has a simple tool, which can be purchased from a dealer that measures the amount of wear on the clutch plate. Actually, it is a simple "go-no go" gauge. This method can only be used on vehicles produced after May, 1969. On all other vehicles it is necessary to take an indirect measurement at the clutch slave cylinder.

Vehicles Produced Prior to May 1969

1. Push the end of the throwout fork (projecting from the bellhousing) in the direction of the slave cylinder.

2. If the resistance is firm and spongy the clutch still has miles left on it.

3. If the fork can be moved only very slightly (approx. 2 mm) in the direction of

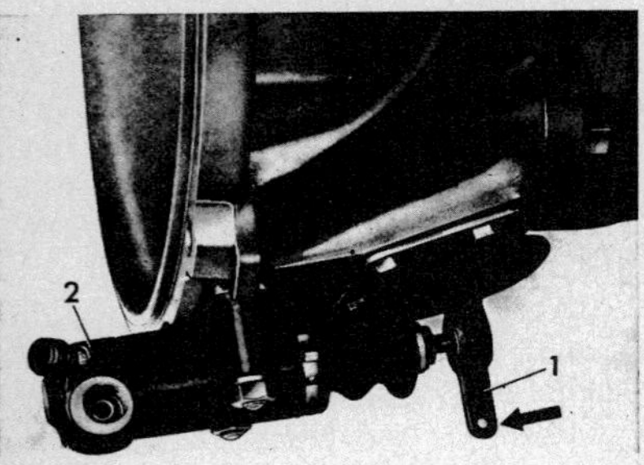

Checking clutch wear on vehicles produced prior to May, 1969.

1. Throwout fork 2. Slave cylinder

the slave cylinder, or not at all, the clutch plate should be replaced.

Vehicles Produced After May 1969

On these models the extent of wear on the clutch plate can be determined with the aid of a special measuring device, availalbe through a Mercedes-Benz dealer.

1. A plastic shim is installed between the slave cylinder and the bellhousing.

2. The shim is provided with two flat grooves running diagonally from bottom to center. When the shim is installed,

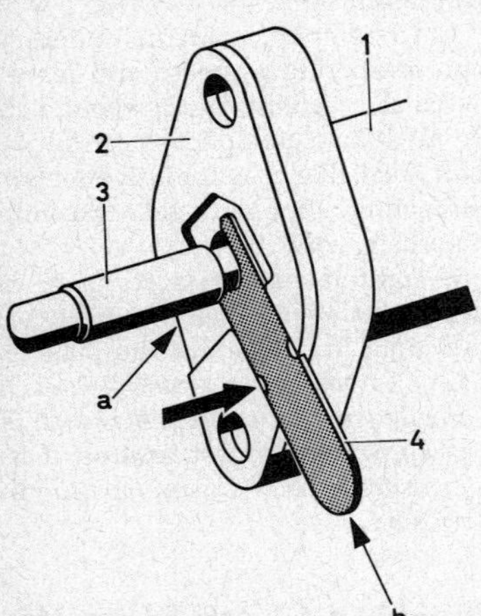

Wear limit has not been reached

1. Clutch slave cylinder
2. Plastic shim
3. Thrust rod
4. Measuring gauge (Part No. 115 589 07 23 00)

(a)—Direction of measuring on lefthand drive vehicle with steering wheel and center shift, as well as on righthand drive vehicles with center shift
(b)—Direction of measuring on righthand drive vehicles with steering wheel shift

these grooves appear as slots. Use groove (a) for left-hand drive vehicles and groove (b) for right-hand drive vehicles.

3. The clutch slave cylinder pushrod has two different diameters. The jaw

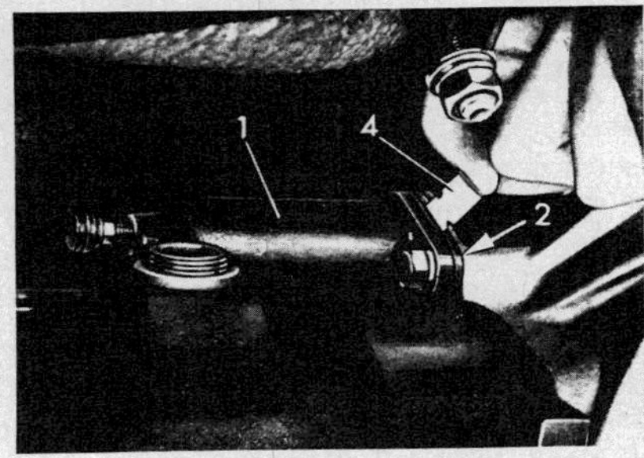

Measuring clutch wear on vehicles produced after May, 1969.

1. Slave cylinder
2. Plastic shim
3. Measuring gauge (Part No. 115 580 07 23 00)

width of the test device corresponds to the smaller diameter of the pushrod. If the notches on the test device disappear when the test device is inserted as far as it will go, the clutch plate is still operational.

4. If, however, the notches on the test device remain visible, this is an indication that the clutch plate is worn severely and should be replaced.

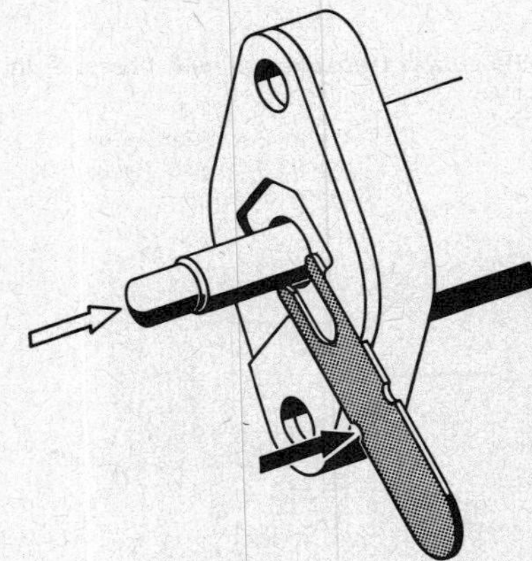

Wear limit has been reached

Clutch Slave Cylinder

Removal and Installation

All Models

1. Detach and plug the pressure line from the slave cylinder.

2. Remove the attaching screws from the slave cylinder.

3. Remove the slave cylinder, pushrod, and spacer.

4. To install, place the grooved side of the spacer in contact with the housing and hold it in position.

5. Install the slave cylinder and pushrod into the housing. Be sure that the dust cap is properly seated.

6. Install the attaching screws.

7. Connect the pressure line to the slave cylinder.

8. Bleed the slave cylinder.

AUTOMATIC TRANSMISSION

Removal and Installation

Mercedes-Benz automatic transmissions are removed as a unit with the engine. Consult the "Engine Mechanical" section for removal and installation procedures concerning a given engine.

In-Car Service

Because automatic transmission work is mainly done by specialty shops, only in-car service procedures are given here.

Before doing any work on the automatic transmission, consult the transmission identification chart to determine which transmission you are dealing with.

Filter Replacement

All Models

1. Drain the transmission of all fluid.

2. Remove the transmission oil pan.

3. Remove the bolt or bolts which retain the oil filter to the transmission.

4. Remove the filter and replace it with a new one.

5. Install the transmission oil pan, using a new gasket.

Transmission oil filter—K4C 025, K4A 040, and W3A 040.

4. Filter
5. Attaching bolts

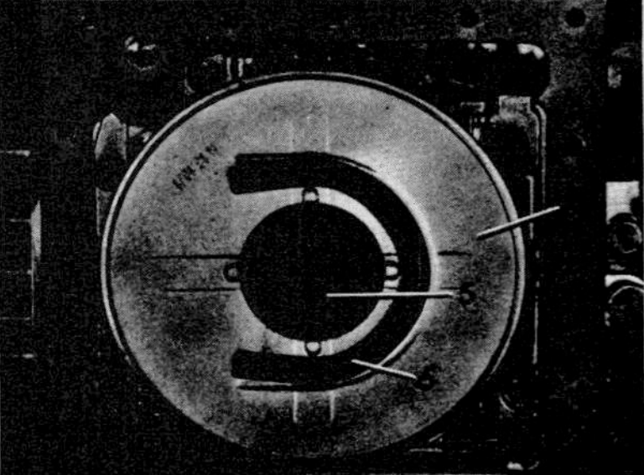

Transmission oil filter—K4A 025 and K4B 050.

4. Filter
5. Attaching screw
6. Rubber gasket

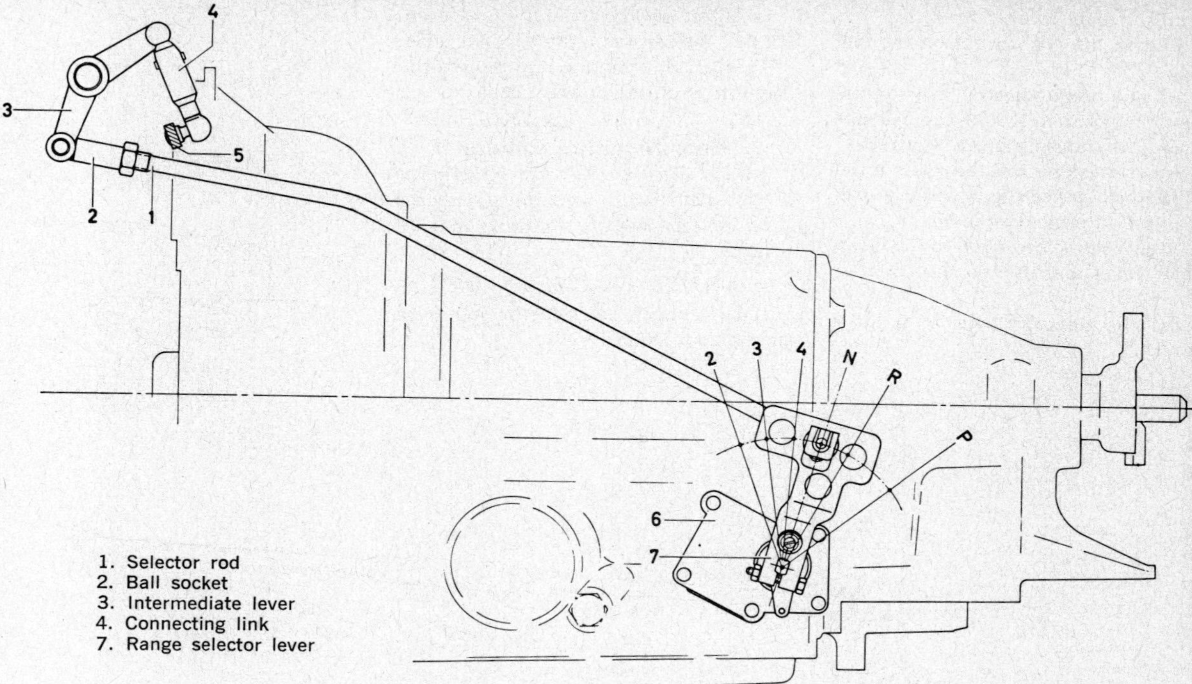

Selector rod linkage—column mounted (K4C 025, K4A 040, and W3A 404).

6. Refill the transmission to the proper level with the specified brand of fluid.

Selector Rod Linkage Adjustment

NOTE: *Before performing this adjustment on any Mercedes-Benz vehicle, be sure that the vehicle is resting on its wheels. No part of the vehicle may be jacked for this adjustment.*

Column Mounted Linkage

K4C 025, K4A 040, W3A 040

1. Loosen the counternut on the ball socket.
2. Disconnect the selector rod from the shift lever bracket.
3. Set the transmission selector lever and the selector rod in Neutral
4. Adjust the length of the selector rod until the ball socket aligns with the end of the ball on the intermediate lever.
5. Attach the ball socket to the intermediate lever, making sure that the play in the selector lever in position Three and Four is about equal.
6. Tighten the counternut on the ball socket.

K4B 050 and K4A 025

1. Disconnect the selector rod from

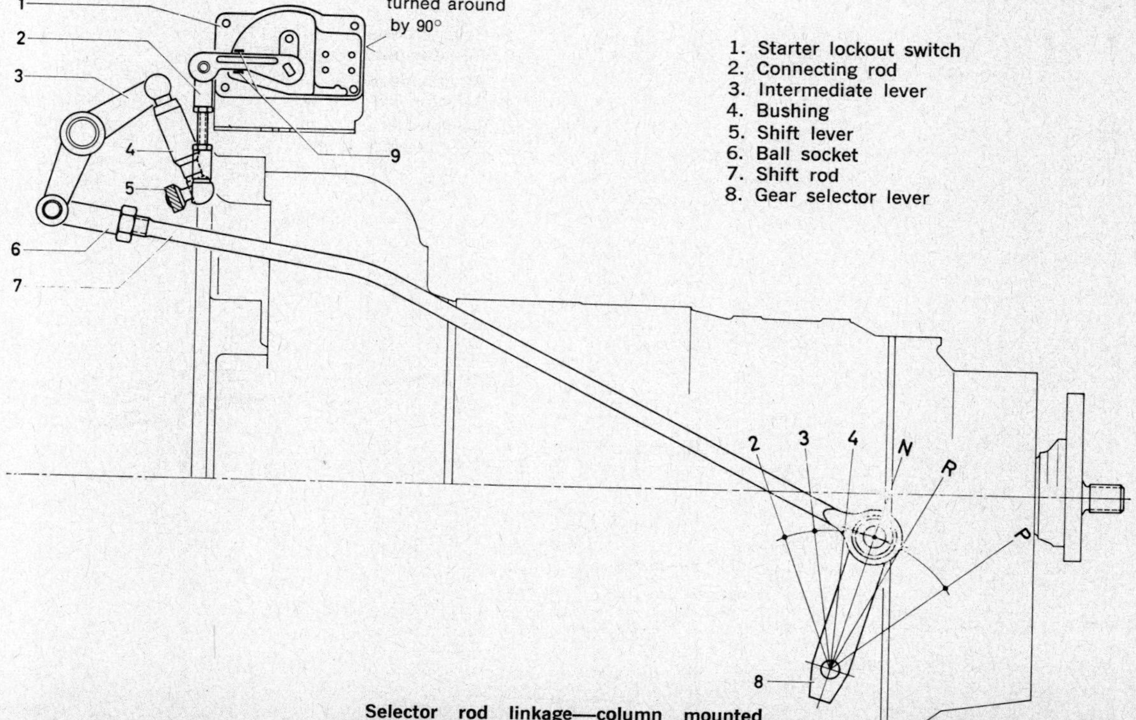

Selector rod linkage—column mounted (K4B 050 and K4A 025).

the intermediate lever.

2. Loosen the counternut on the ball socket.

3. Set the range selector lever on the column in position N and the selector lever on the transmission in Neutral.

4. Adjust the length of the selector rod until the ball socket aligns with the ball end on the intermeidate lever.

5. Attach the selector rod to the intermediate lever and tighten the counternut.

6. Set the selector lever in position Neutral.

7. Adjust the knurled nut after loosening the counternut on the bowden cable.

8. After adjusting the nut, tighten the counternut on the bowden cable.

Floor Mounted Linkage

NOTE: *The vehicle must be standing with the weight normally distributed on all four wheels. No jacks may be used.*

K4C 025, K4A 040, W3A 040

1. Disconnect the selector rod from the range selector lever.

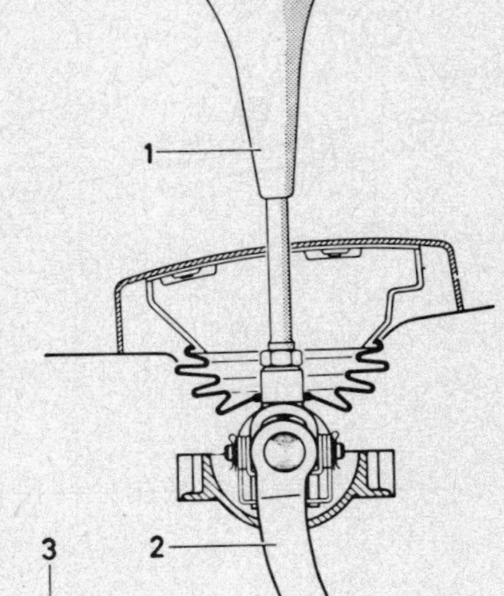

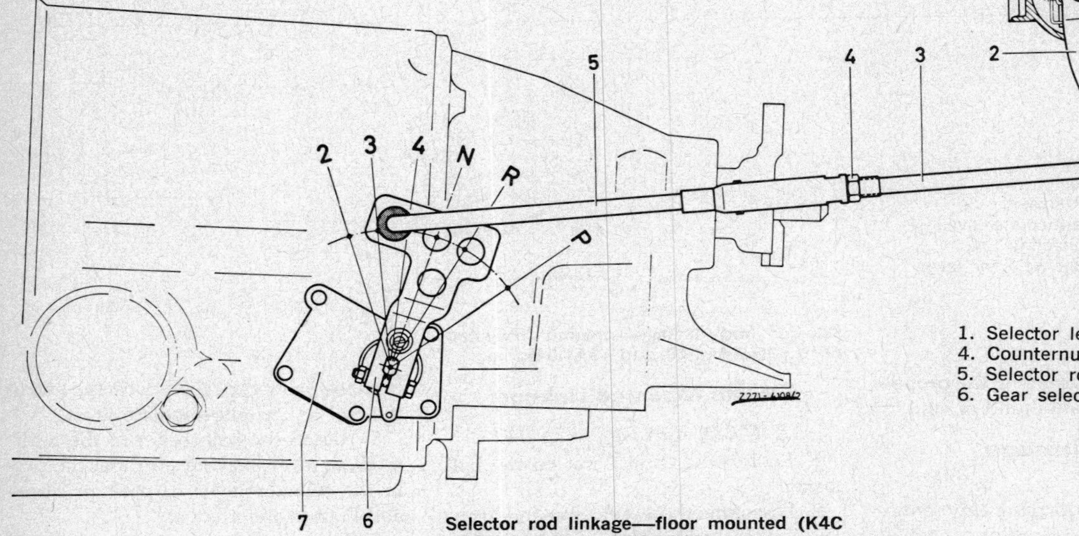

1. Selector lever
4. Counternut
5. Selector rod
6. Gear selector lever

Selector rod linkage—floor mounted (K4C 025, K4A 040, and W3A 040).

1. Selector lever
2. Selector lever, lower part
3. Adjustable lug
4. Selector rod
5. Auxiliary lever
6. Gear selector lever

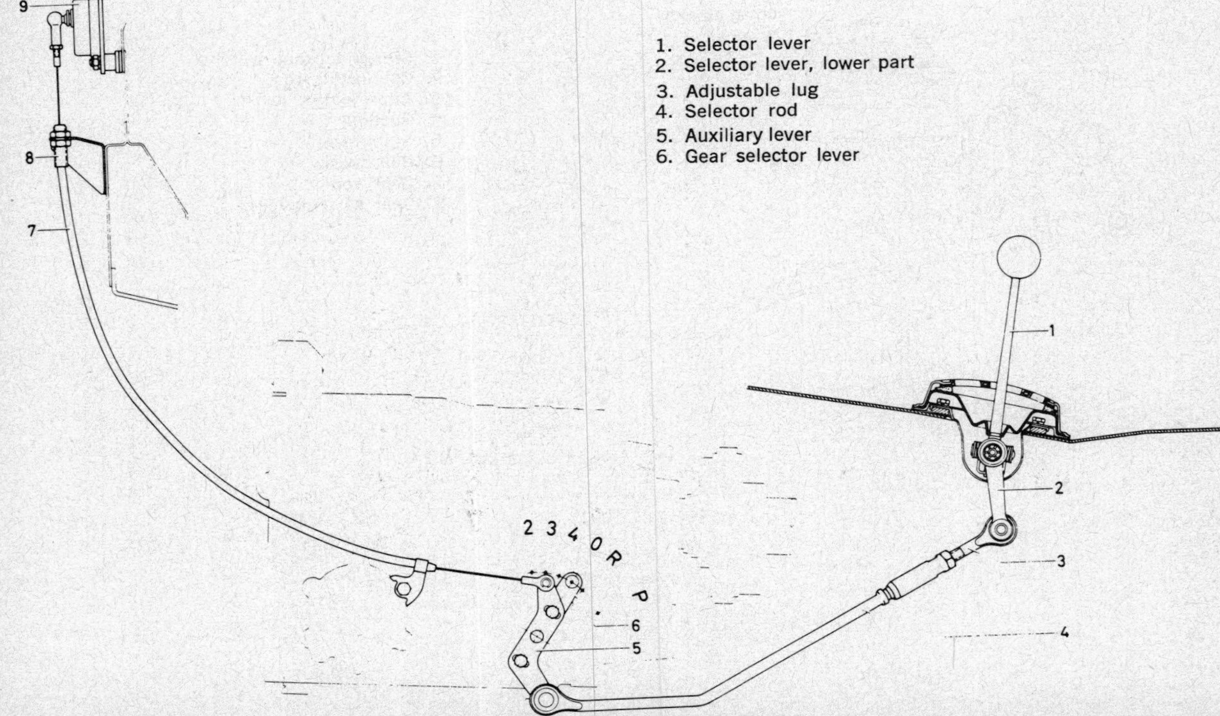

Selector rod linkage—floor mounted (K4B 050 and K4A 025).

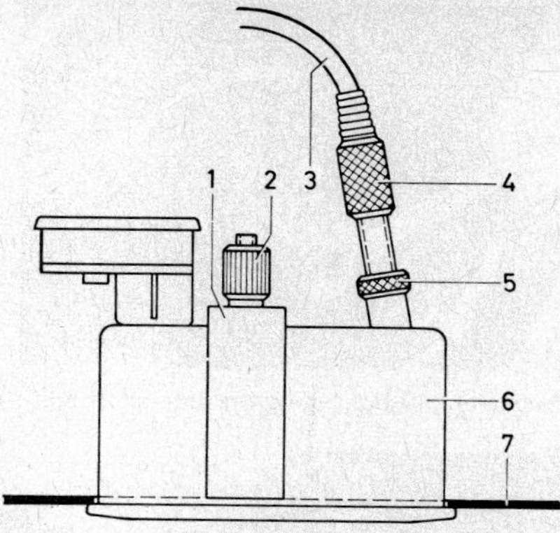

Adjust the knurled nut on the Bowden cable

1. Clamp
2. Clamp nut
3. Bowden cable
4. Knurled nut
5. Counternut
6. Housing
7. Instrument panel

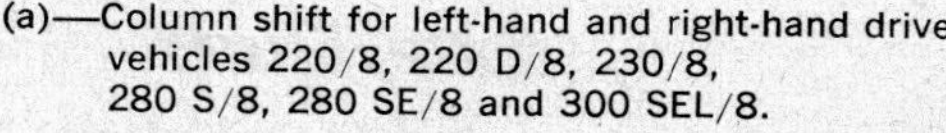

(a)—Column shift for left-hand and right-hand drive vehicles 220/8, 220 D/8, 230/8, 280 S/8, 280 SE/8 and 300 SEL/8.

(b)—Steering wheel shift for left-hand drive vehicles (220/8, 220 D/8, 230/8, 250/8)

(c)—Steering wheel shift for right-hand drive vehicles (220/8, 220 D/8, 230/8, 250/8)

(d)—Steering wheel shift for left-hand drive vehicles (280S/8, 280 SE/8, 300 SEL/8, 280 SE/3.5 and 300 SEL/3.5)

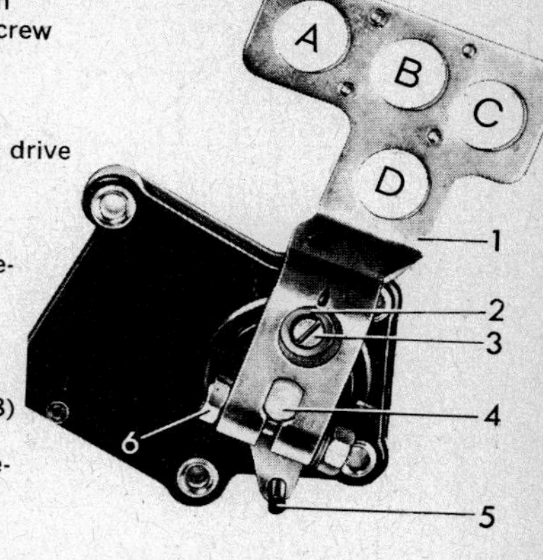

Starter lockout and back-up light switch adjustment (K4C 025, K4A 040, and W3A 040).

2. Set the range selector lever in Neutral and make sure that there is approximately 1 mm clearance between the selector lever and the N stop of the selector gate.

3. Adjust the length of the selector rod so that it can be attached free of tension.

4. Retighten the counternut.

K4B 050 and K4A 025

1. Disconnect the selector rod from the lower part of the selector lever.

2. Set the selector lever on the linkage, and the selector lever on the transmission, at Neutral.

3. Adjust the lug or the selector rod so that it aligns with the pivot pin on the lower part of the selector lever.

4. A finer adjustment can be made at the 2 slots in the auxilliary lever.

5. Press the selector rod onto the lower part of the selector lever and tighten the counternut.

Starter Lockout and Back-Up Light Switch Adjustment

K4C 025, K4A 040 and W3A 040

1. Disconnect the selector rod and move the range selector lever on the transmission to position Neutral.

2. Tighten the clamping screw prior to making adjustments.

3. Loosen the adjusting screw and insert the locating pin through the driver into the locating hole in the shift housing.

4. Tighten the adjusting screw and remove the locating pin.

5. Move the selector lever to position N and connect the selector rod so that there is no tension.

6. Check to be sure that the engine cannot be started in Neutral or Park.

K4A 025 and K4B 050

1. The bowden cable, which actuates the neutral starter lockout and the back-up light switch, should be adjusted so that the engine can be started only in Neutral or Park.

2. In all other positions, the starter lockout should be activated.

3. In addition, the back-up lights should light up in Reverse.

4. Any adjustment should be made at the adjusting stop on the other end from the transmisssion linkage.

DRIVE AXLES

Mercedes-Benz automobiles use either two or three piece driveshafts to connect the transmission to a hypoid independent rear axle. All models covered in this book use independent rear suspension with open or enclosed driveshafts to the rear wheels.

Driveshaft and U-Joints

Removal and Installation

220D/8, 220/8, 230/8, 250/8 250C, 280, and 280C

1. Remove the equalizer and disconnect the parking brake cables.

2. Remove the bolts which secure the two brackets to the chassis at the front and rear and remove the brackets. It may be necessary to lower the exhaust system slightly to allow access to the left-hand bolts on the rear bracket.

3. On three piece driveshafts, back off the nut on the front clamp only. On both two and three piece driveshafts, push back the rubber sleeve on the clamp nut.

4. Remove the nuts which secure the attaching plate to the transmission flange and rear axle.

5. Remove the bolts which secure the intermediate bearing(s) to the chassis. Push the driveshaft together and slightly down, and remove the driveshaft from the vehicle.

NOTE: *If possible, do not separate the parts of the driveshaft since each driveshaft is balanced at the factory. If separation is necessary, all parts must be marked and reassembled in the same relative positions to assure that the driveshafts will remain reasonably well balanced.*

6. Installation is the reverse of removal.

7. Pack the cavities of the two centering sleeves with special Mercedes-Benz grease.

8. Install the driveshaft and attach the intermediate bearing(s) to the chassis.

9. Rock the car backward and forward several times to be sure that the driveshaft is properly centered without forcing.

10. Prior to tightening the clamp nuts on a three piece driveshaft, be sure that the intermediate shaft does not contact either the front or rear intermediate bearing. The clearance between the intermediate shaft and the bearing should be the same at both ends.

All Other Models

NOTE: *Steps 1–3 apply to 280SE, 280SEL, and 300SEL models with V-8's only.*

1. Fold the torsion bar down after disconnecting the level control linkage (if equipped).

2. Remove the exhaust system.

3. Remove the heat shield from the frame.

4. Support the transmission with a jack and completely remove the rear engine mount crossmember.

5. Without sliding the rubber sleeve back, loosen the clamp nut approximately two turns (the rubber sleeve will slide along).

NOTE: *On 3 piece driveshafts, only the front clamp nut need be loosened.*

6. Unscrew the U-joint mounting flange from the U-joint plate.

7. Bend back the locktabs and remove

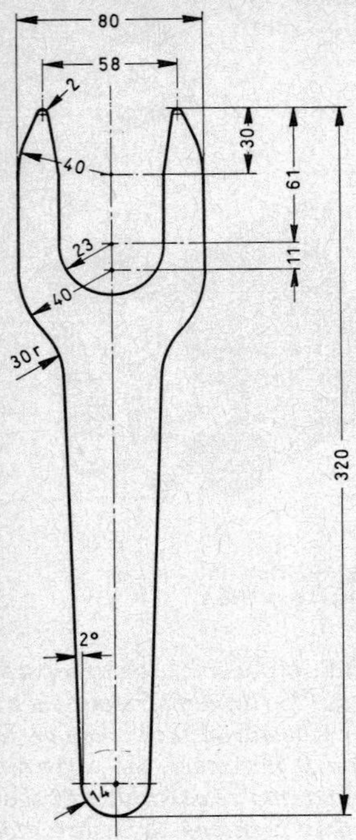

Fabricated tool for holding or turning the driveshaft.

the bolts that attach the driveshaft to the rear axle pinion yoke.

NOTE: *To hold and turn the driveshaft, a tool can be fabricated according to the accompanying diagram.*

8. Remove the bolts which attach the intermediate bearing(s) to the frame. Push the driveshaft together slightly and remove it from the vehicle.

9. Try not to separate the driveshafts. If it is absolutely necessary, matchmark all components so that they can be reassembled in the same order.

10. Installation is the reverse of removal. Always use new self-locking nuts and be sure that the arrow on the driveshaft mounting plate (300SEL 6.3 models) points forward (driving direction). After the driveshaft is installed, rock the car back and forth several times to settle the driveshaft. Make sure that neither intermediate shaft is binding against either intermediate bearing, and that the clearance between the intermediate bearing and the driveshaft is the same at both ends.

Rear driveshaft mounting flange

16. Rear axle carrier
17. Cheesehead bolts

Axle Shaft

Removal and Installation

220D/8, 220/8, 230/8, 250/8, 250/C, 280, and 280C

NOTE: *On the 280 and 280C, only axle shafts identified with a yellow paint dot or part no. 107 350 07 10 (left) or part no. 107 350 0810 (right) can be installed.*

1. Jack up the rear of the car and remove the wheel and center axle hold-down bolt (in hub).
2. Drain the differential oil and place a jack under the differential housing.
3. Unbolt the rubber mount from the chassis and the differential housing, then remove the differential housing cover to expose the ring and pinion gears.
4. Press the shaft from the axle flange.
5. Using a screwdriver, remove the axle lock ring inside the differential case.
6. Pull the axle from the housing by pulling the splined end from the side gears.

NOTE: *Axle shafts are stamped R and L for right and left units. Always use new lock-rings.*

7. Installation is the reverse of removal.

CAUTION: *Check end-play of the lock-ring in the groove. If necessary, install a thicker lock ring to eliminate all end-play, while still allowing the lock-ring to rotate. Do not allow the joints in the axleshaft to hang free or the joint bearing may be damaged and leak.*

280S/8, 280SE/8, 280SEL/8, 300SEL/8, 280SE 3.5, 280SE and SEL 4.5, 300SEL 3.5 and 4.5, 280SL/8

1. Jack up the rear of the car and remove the wheel, brake caliper, and disc.
2. Remove the parking brake shoes.
3. Unbolt the backing plate and dust cover and pull the axle from the housing using a puller or slide hammer.

NOTE: *Axle bearings must be removed with a special puller or slide hammer only. Never hammer on the bearings.*

NOTE: *The grooved nut is threaded to the shaft; bearings must be removed and replaced using an arbor press. Use a punch, as previously described, to anchor the sliding joint during axle installation.*

4. Installation is the reverse of removal.

Loosening or tightening the axle shaft bolt

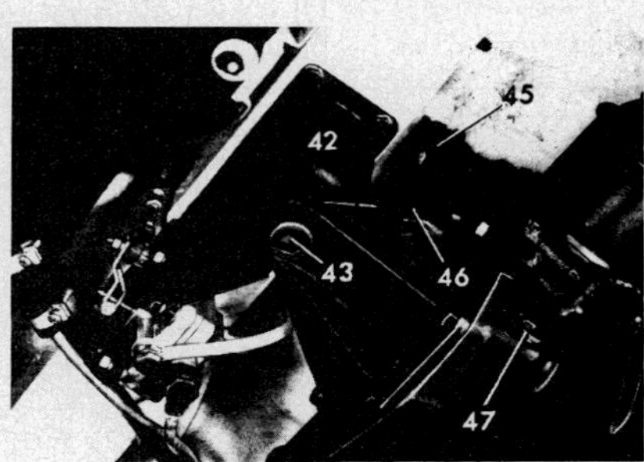

Differential attaching points

42. Rear rubber mounting
43. Hexagon socket bolt
45. Breather
46. Filler plug
47. Drain plug

Removing the lock-ring from the axle shaft

42. Rear rubber mounting
43. Hexagon socket bolt
45. Breather
46. Filler plig
47.cgdrain plug

350SL, 450SL and 450SLC

1. Drain the oil from the rear axle.
2. Disconnect and plug the brake lines.
3. Remove the bolt which attaches the rear axle shaft to the rear axle shaft flange.
4. Force the rear axle shaft out of the flange with a suitable tool.
5. Support the rear axle with a jack.
6. Remove the rear rubber mount.
7. Clean the axle housing and remove the cover from the housing.

NOTE: *The axle shafts are the floating type and can be compressed in the constant velocity joints approximately 15–20 mm.*

Removing the lock-ring (26) from the axle shaft with pliers (1) or a screwdriver.

8. Remove the locking ring from the end of the axle shafts which engage the side gears in the differential.

9. Disengage the axle shaft from the side gear and remove the axle shaft together with the spacer.

10. Installation is the reverse of removal.

11. If either axle shaft is replaced, be sure that the proper replacement shaft is installed. Axle shafts are marked L and R for left and right.

Axle shaft markings (R)

CAUTION: *Do not hang the outer constant velocity joint in a free position (without any support) as the shaft may be damaged and the constant velocity joint housing may leak.*

12. Check the end-play between the lock-ring on the axle shaft and the side gear. There should be no noticeable end-play, but the lock-ring should be able to turn in the groove.

13. Be sure to bleed the brakes and fill the rear axle with the proper quantity and type of lubricant.

Differential

Removal and Installation

Models With Enclosed Axle Shafts

1. Jack up the rear of the car and remove the rear wheels.

2. If equipped with air suspension, remove the sway bar.

3. Remove the rear exhaust pipe and the two mufflers, then loosen the parking brake adjuster wingnut and disconnect the brake cables.

4. Disconnect the rear universal joint and push the driveshaft forward, then remove the compensating spring.

5. Remove the rear coil springs.

6. On cars with air suspension, disconnect the spring piston from the torque arm.

NOTE: *Do not remove from the bellows.*

7. Disconnect the hoses from the lines at the calipers.

8. Remove the front link from the cross strut by loosening the bolts. Push the strut out of the way.

9. Remove the trailing arm brackets from the chassis.

Lowering the differential

NOTE: *Tape any shims found beneath the plate to the appropriate trailing arm.*

10. If equipped with air suspension, disconnect the brake support chassis mount by removing the rear seat and unscrewing the castle nut thus exposed.

11. Pull the bolt out from beneath the car.

12. Jack up the axle tubes slightly to unload the shock absorbers, then disconnect the lower shock mounts.

13. Raise the axle tubes to a horizontal position.

14. Place a 24 in. section of 2 x 4 (wood) over the top of the differential housing, the long axis lined up with the axle tubes, then, using short sections of chain or rope, fasten the axle tubes to the ends of the 2 x 4 so that the axle tubes remain in a horizontal position and do not sag at their ends. This is to prevent damage to the inner constant velocity joint of the axle shafts

15. From inside the trunk, unbolt the differential housing from the chassis, then gradually lower the entire rear differential housing and axle tube assembly to the floor.

16. Installation is the reverse of removal. Bleed the brakes.

Models With Exposed Axle Shafts

1. Jack up the rear of the car as high as possible.

2. Support the rear axle subframe on jackstands (both sides).

3. Drain the oil from the differential housing.

4. Remove the hubcaps and the two bolts (one per side) that hold the axle to the axle flange.

5. The rear axle splined shaft then must be pressed from the axle flange.

6. Place a jack under the differential housing and jack up the housing slightly. Then unscrew the Allen bolt.

NOTE: *This bolt is tightened to 87–115 ft lbs.*

7. From inside the trunk, remove the four plugs and unbolt the differential housing from the subframe (17 mm socket).

8. Loosen the driveshaft center bearing support bracket, push back the rubber dust cover, and loosen the locknut.

9. Disconnect the rear universal joint from the flange and push the driveshaft forward out of the way.

10. Lower the entire rear differential housing assembly and axle shafts to the floor.

11. Installation is the reverse of removal.

Overhaul

All Models

1. With the rear differential housing removed, first remove the right-hand axle and tube, then loosen the hold-down bolt and pull out the slip joint.

2. Remove the right- and left-hand axle shafts and unbolt the bearing flange and axle tubes from the housing.

3. The differential now can be removed.

4. Press the outer bearing race from the left axle tube, then remove the lock-tabs and unscrew the threaded ring from the housing.

5. Drive the outer bearing race from the right-hand side of the housing, then remove the grooved pinion nut while holding the flange steady in a vice. The pinion shaft can now be pressed into the empty differential case and removed.

6. Remove the pinion flange and cover and the inner pinion bearing; the outer bearing race must be pressed from the housing.

7. The inner bearing can now be pressed from the pinion shaft. Check the pinion for runout and the bearing seats for scoring. Don't forget to remove the collapsible spacer sleeve from the pinion shaft.

8. The ring and pinion gears have several markings etched on their surfaces: the serial number, the pinion depth tolerance deviation (in mm), the gear ratio

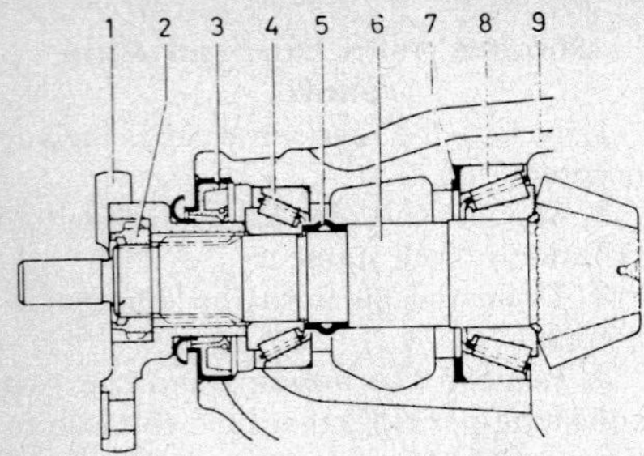

Detail of pinion and pinion seal

1. Joint flange
2. Self-locking grooved nut
3. Sealing ring
4. Front taper roller
5. Spacer sleeve
6. Drive pinion
7. Shim
8. Rear taper roller bearing
9. Rear axle housing

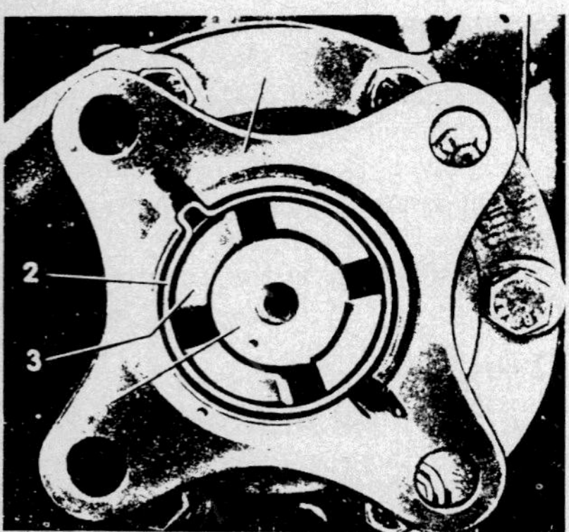

Grooved pinion nut

1. Joint flange
2. Locking plate
3. Grooved nut
4. Drive pinion

— 0.04 Deviation "a" from basic adjustment
0.16 "D nom." in the direction minus 0.04 mm.
Backlash
No. 355 Gear set (ring gear and pinion) No. 355
1:4.10 Gear ratio drive pinion to ring gear

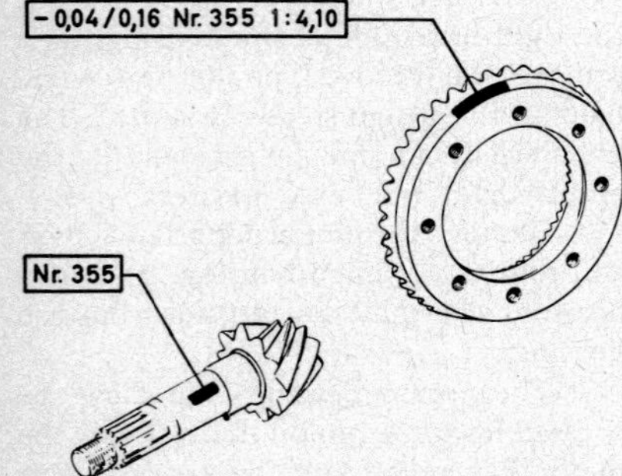

Ring gear and pinion markings

and the backlash clearance (in mm). Backlash is constant, being 0.0062 ± 0.-0008 in., while the individual gear markings indicate tolerance deviation from the norm for those *particular* gears. For instance, if the ring gear is marked with a minus (−) sign (and a dimension), it indicates the pinion deviation is away from the ring gear; a plus (+) sign indicates the reverse. The proper pinion depth can be computed for any combination of ring and pinion gears, and the thickness of the compensating washer determined from these markings. Since special tools are required for computation of the proper washer thickness, a "red lead" test will be described later.

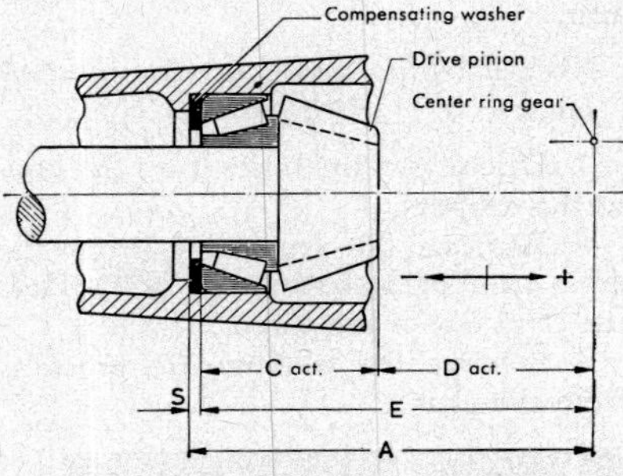

(c) act.—Actual height of drive pinion plus height of taper roller bearing
(d) act.—Actual distance between front face of drive pinion and center ring gear (adjusting dimension)
(e)—Distance between compensating washer and center ring gear
(a)—Distance between front face of bearing mount for the rear taper roller bearing and center ring gear
(s)—Thickness of compensating washer

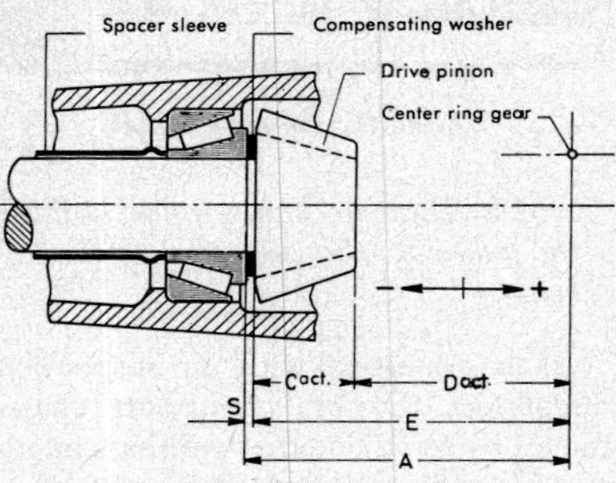

(c) act.—Actual height of drive pinion
(d) act.—Actual distance between front face of drive pinion and center ring gear (adjusting dimension)
(e)—Distance between compensating washer and center ring gear
(a)—Distance between inner race of rear taper roller bearing and center ring gear
(s)—Thickness of compensating washer

The factory procedure involves measuring distance B, the distance between the front end of a "perfect" dummy pinion shaft of known thickness (C nom.) and the center of the ring gear to determine distance A. Then the actual distance (D act.) is computed by adding to (or subtracting from, as the case may be) the "perfect" distance between the front of the pinion gear as installed, the dimension (a) etched on the gear to be used. (Dimension (a) is the amount of deviation from the "perfect" pinion thickness.) From the illustration, it can be seen that S, the thickness of the compensating washer needed to bring the pinion and ring gears into perfect mesh, is determined by subtracting distance E from the previously determined distance A. Distance E is found by adding the actual thickness of the pinion gear to be used (measured with a micrometer) to the distance D-act., also previously computed. This enables the washer thickness to be accurately determined before the components are assembled thus saving much time and trouble over the trial and error "red lead" method.

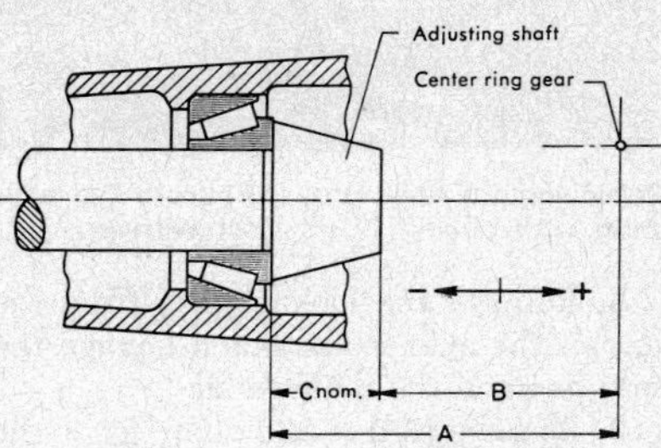

(c) nom.—Nominal height of adjusting shaft
(b)—Distance between front end of adjusting shaft and center ring gear
(a)—Distance between inner race of rear taper roller bearing and center ring gear

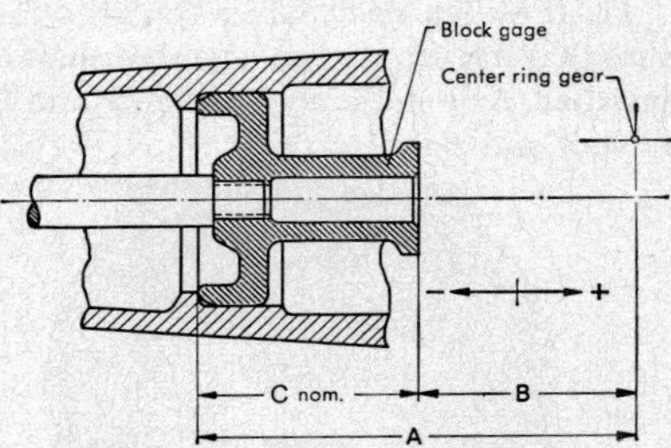

(c) nom.—Height of block gage
(b)—Distance between front fact block gage and center ring gear
(a)—Distance between front face of bearing mounting for the rear taper roller bearing and center ring gear

S = (B + 67.00) − [(66.00 ± a) + C act.]

S = thickness of compensating washer

B = distance between front of dummy "perfect" pinion and center of ring gear

± a = manufacturing tolerance deviation etched on gear

C act. = actual thickness of pinion to be used

NOTE: *C nom. = 67.00 (mm)*
D nom. = 66.00 (mm)

9. To assemble, first install the outer bearing races (front and rear) of the pinion shaft into the housing.

10. Push the compensating washer S onto the pinion shaft and press on the inner bearing race.

NOTE: *If "red lead" method of determining washer thickness is to be used, pick a washer on the basis of markings on old gears and old washer thickness. If ring and pinion gears are to be reused, a new washer of the same thickness as the one used before should be installed.*

11. Install the pinion into the differential housing, slide on a new collapsible spacer sleeve and press on the inner bearing race, after coating it with hypoid

Install outer bearing races

8. Front bearing outer race
11. Rear bearing outer race
20. Fixture (111 589 12 61 00) or homemade
20i. Hexagon screw
20k. Installing washer
20l. Installing washer

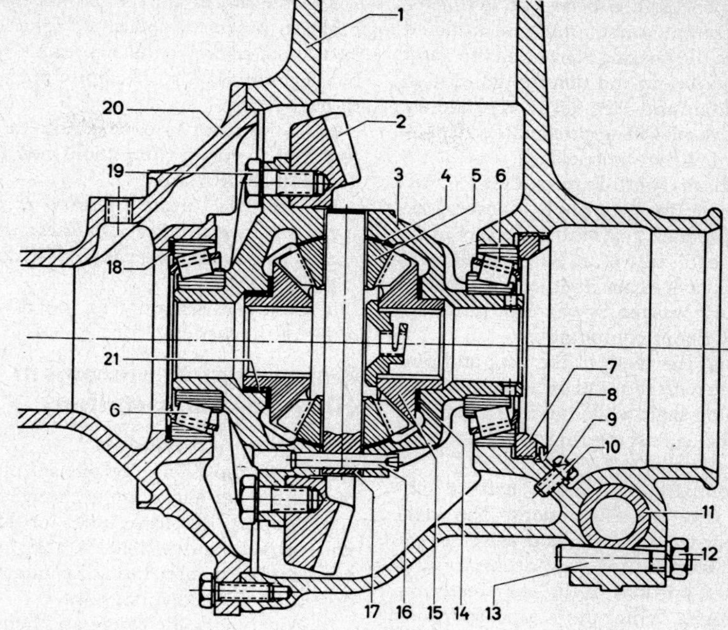

Standard differential

1. Rear axle housing
2. Ring gear
3. Differential gear housing
4. Dished washer
5. Differential pinion
6. Taper roller bearing
7. Threaded ring
8. Lock
9. Hexagon screw
10. Locking plate
11. Connecting pin
12. Hexagon nut with lock-washer
13. Conical screw wedge
14. Thrust washer
15. Differential side gear
16. Locking pin
17. Differential pinion shaft
18. Compensating washer
19. Hexagon screw
20. Bearing flange with left axle tube
21. Bearing ring

lubricant.

12. Press a new pinion seal into place in the housing cover and install the cover. Press the driveshaft universal joint flange onto the drive pinion splines, after coating splines with Molykote®.

NOTE: *Observe the matchmarks made during disassembly.*

13. Install the grooved nut and lockplate and tighten the nut until a torque of 16–18 cm kg. (14–15 in. lbs) for new bearings, or 5–10 cm kg (4–9 in. lbs) for old bearings, is needed to turn the drive pinion in its bearings.

14. Tap the housing gently with a fiber hammer to seat the bearings.

CAUTION: *Remember, as the grooved nut is tightened, the collapsible sleeve is deformed to provide proper bearing preload. As a consequence, the sleeve must be REPLACED if torque on the grooved nut is exceeded. Never loosen the pinion nut to obtain desired pinion rotating torque.*

15. Insert the compensating washer into the left axle tube flange and press in the outer race of the roller bearing. Screw in the threaded ring about three turns and press the outer bearing race into the differential housing until it rests against the ring.

16. Install the differential into the housing and attach the bearing flange and left axle tube to the housing.

17. Tighten the threaded ring to approximately 25 ft lbs and tap the housing gently with a fiber hammer to seat the bearing. There must be some play between the ring and pinion gears, otherwise the ring must be removed and a new washer (thinner) inserted.

18. Set up a dial indicator to measure ring gear backlash at the outer edge of the teeth. Check backlash at four or five points around the gear circumference–it should be 0.0062 ± 0.0008 in.

NOTE: *Clamp the drive pinion so that only ring gear backlash is measured.*

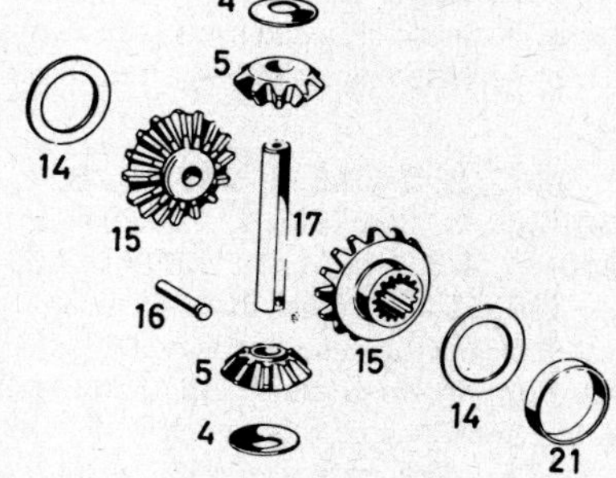

Pinion gears and side gears

4. Dished washer
5. Differential pinion
14. Thrust washer
15. Differential side gear
16. Locking pin
17. Differential pinion shaft
21. Bearing ring

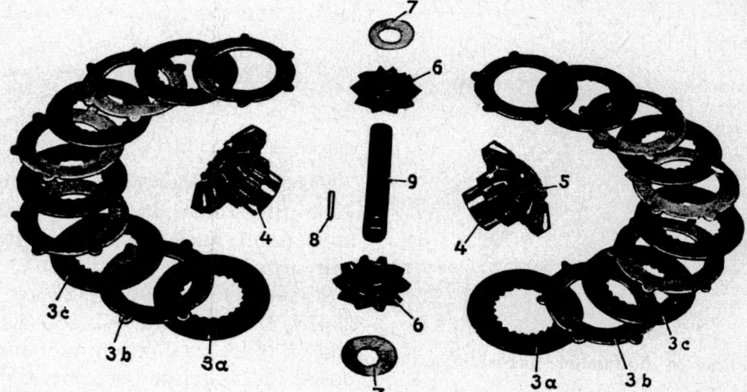

Positive traction differential parts

3a. Friction clutch with one-side sinter coating
3b. Friction clutch without coating
3c. Friction clutch with both-side sinter coating
4. Differential side gear
5. Nut for right differential side gear
6. Differential pinion
7. Dished washer
8. Locking pin
9. Differential pinion shaft

19. If backlash is excessive, a thicker compensating washer must be installed between the bearing flange and the outer bearing race (in the differential, *not* on the pinion) and vice-versa. A 0.040 in. washer results in approximately 0.003–0.004 in. change in backlash.

Red Lead Tooth Pattern Test

In order to determine whether the ring and pinion gears are in perfect mesh a "red lead" test must be made. This is especially necessary if pinion depth compensating washer S was arbitrarily selected without computation.

1. Coat the teeth of the ring and pinion gears with red lead or lipstick. Rotate the pinion shaft while holding a piece of soft wood against the ring gear (the wood acts as a brake).

2. Compare the tooth pattern obtained with the illustrations. The ideal ring gear wear pattern is usually not exactly as shown; it is only necessary that the outer portions of the gear teeth are not touched. If the outer (upper) portions of the teeth are covered, a thicker compensating washer S is indicated for the drive pinion. At the same time, a thinner washer is needed in the left axle tube flange to correct backlash. If the inner gear teeth surfaces are covered, a thinner compensating washer S and a thicker left axle tube washer are necessary. This will, of course, require complete disassembly of the unit and a new collapsible spacer on the drive pinion. For this reason it is best to have the proper equipment available for computation of compensating washer S thickness before assembly, as this trial and error method is most time consuming.

Correct Meshing

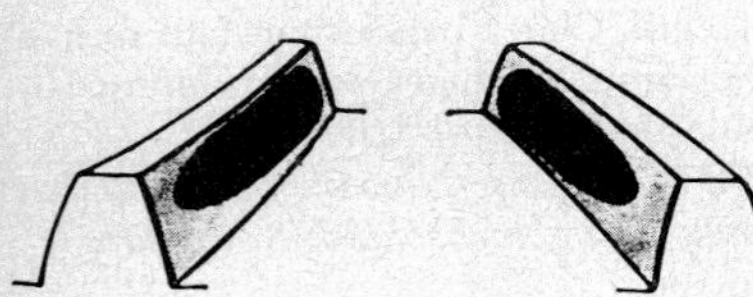

Contact at Dedendum (incorrect)

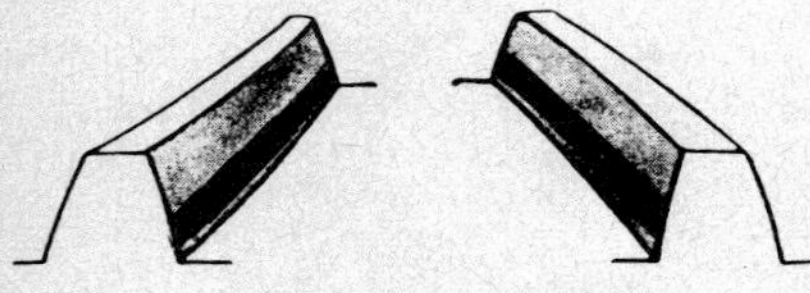

Contact at Addendum (incorrect)

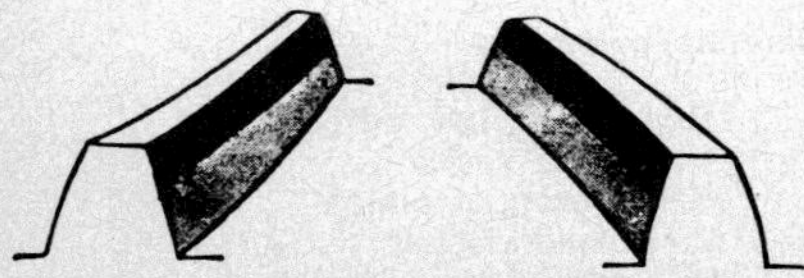

Ring gear tooth contact pattern

3. After the proper pinion depth and backlash has been achieved, adjust the initial tension on the differential bearings by tightening or backing out the threaded ring.

4. At the same time, check the torque required to rotate the pinion shaft (and complete gear train).

NOTE: *The torque required to turn the pinion shaft after installation of the ring gear should increase by 7–8 cm kg (6–7 in. lbs).*

5. Continue assembly in the reverse order of disassembly.

Pinion Seal Replacement (Differential Installed)

All Models

1. Drain the differential oil, jack up the rear of the car and remove the wheels.

2. Support the axle tubes or lower arms on jackstands so that the axles are in a horizontal position, then disconnect the driveshaft rear universal joint.

3. Punchmark the flange and housing, then remove the grooved nut.

4. Using a puller, remove the flange.

NOTE: *If the flange is scored, it must be replaced.*

5. Pull or pry the seal from the housing and install the new seal (press it into place).

6. Reinstall the components and carefully tighten the grooved nut until the torque required to turn the differential assembly at the pinion shaft is 26–30 cm kg (22–26 in. lbs) for models having enclosed axle shafts and 15–20 cm kg (13–17 in. lbs) for models having exposed axle shafts.

7. This corresponds to about 108–144 ft lbs on the pinion nut.

8. If the turning torque is excessive, a new collapsible spacer sleeve must be installed.

9. Never back off on the grooved nut to achieve desirable pinion turning torque, as the bearings will be improperly preloaded and eventually destroyed.

SUSPENSION

Basically, all Mercedes-Benz cars since 1968 use similar similar suspension systems. All cars use independent front and rear suspensions.

Smaller cars (220D/8, 220/8, 230/8, 250/8, 250C, 280, 280C, 350SL, 450SL, and 450SLC) utilize independent exposed halfshafts at the rear and upper and lower control arms at the front, with eccentric cam adjusters. These vehicles use steering knuckles with ball joints.

Larger vehicles (all 280 and 300 series cars, except 280 and 280C) use independent rear suspensions with enclosed halfshafts and upper and lower control arms at the front, supported on pivot pins. Steering knuckles on these cars contain kingpins.

REAR SUSPENSION

Springs

Removal and Installation

220D/8, 220/8, 230/8, 250/8, 250C, 280 280C, 350SL, 450SL, and 450 SLC

1. Jack up the rear of the car.

2. Remove the rear shock absorber.

3. With a floor jack, raise the control arm to approximately a horizontal position. Install a spring compressor to aid in this operation.

4. Carefully lower the jack until the control arm contacts the stop on the rear axle support.

5. Remove the spring and spring compressor with great care.

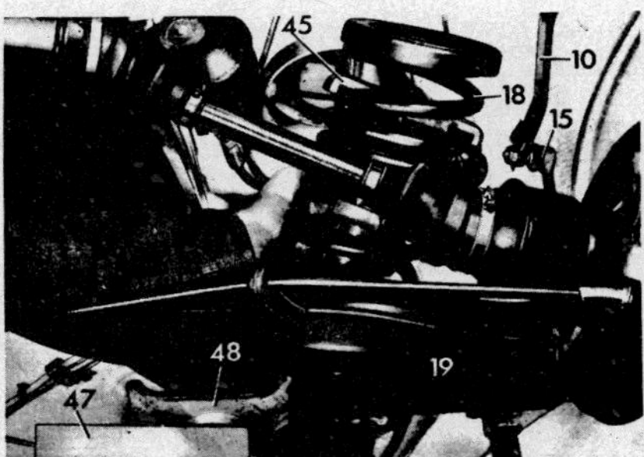

Removing rear coil spring—models with exposed axle shafts.

10. Torsion bar
15. Connecting rod
17. Rubber mounting
18. Rear spring
19. Control arm
45. Spring tensioner
47. Angeled intermediate brace
48. Jack cradle

6. Installation is the reverse of removal. For ease of installation, attach the rubber seats to the springs with masking tape.

280S/8, 280SE/8, 280SEL/8, 300SEL/8, 280SE 3.5, 280SE 4.5, 280SEL 4.5, 280SL/8, 300SEL 3.5, 300SEL 4.5, and 300SEL 6.3

1. Jack up the rear of the vehicle.

2. Support the trailing arm (thrust rod) with a floor jack or other jack.

NOTE: *For safety's sake, install a spring compressor on the rear spring and take up some of the tension.*

3. Loosen the fastening plate on the chassis and swing it aside.

4. Carefully lower the trailing arm (thrust rod) and remove the spring.

5. Installation is the reverse of removal. Be sure to have the camber of the rear wheels checked.

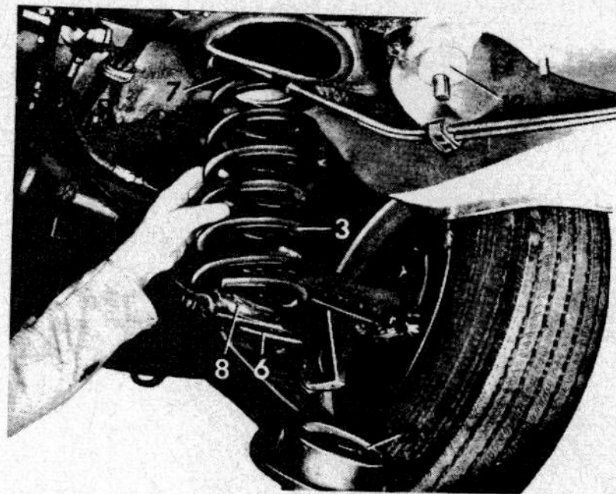

Coil spring removal—280 and 300 series (except 280 and 280C).

2. Thrust rod
3. Rear spring
6. Spring disc
7. Rubber mount (top)
8. Rubber mount (bottom)
13. Cup

Shock Absorbers

Removal and Installation

220D/8, 220/8, 230/8, 250/8, 250C, 280, 280C, 250SL, 450SL, and 450SLC.

1. Jack up the rear of the car and support the control arm.
2. From inside the trunk (sedans), remove the rubber cap, locknut, and hex nut from the upper mount of the shock absorber. On 350SL, 450SL, and 450SLC, the upper mount of the rear shock absorber is accessible after removing the top, top flap, rear seat, backrest, and lining.
3. Unbolt the mounting for the rear shock absorber at the bottom and remove the shock absorber.
4. Installation is the reverse of removal.

280S/8, 280SE/8, 280SEL/8, 300SEL/8, 280SE 3.5, 280SE 4.5, 280SEL 4.5, 280SL/8, 300SEL 3.5, 300SEL 4.5, and 300SEL 6.3

1. Jack up the rear of the vehicle.
2. Support the trailing arm (thrust rod) or axle tube with a floor jack or other jack.
3. On vehicles with air suspension, leave the pull knob for the valve in the driving position.
4. On sedans, open the trunk and remove the nut, washer, and rubber disc from the upper mount of the rear shock absorber. On the 280SL/8, these pieces are accessible from the top box when the roadster top is closed or when the coupe top is removed.
5. Loosen the lower shock absorber mounting bolt and remove the shock absorber.
6. Installation is the reverse of removal. With load on the wheels, jack the axle up to the level of the shock absorber lower mount and install the bolt.

Independent Rear Suspension Adjustments

Suspension adjustments should only be checked when the vehicle is resting on a level surface and is carrying the required fluids (full tank of gas, engine oil, etc.).

Camber

220D/8, 220/8, 230/8, 250/8, 250C, 280 and 280C 350SL, 450SL, and 450SLC

Rear wheel camber is determined by the position of the control arm. The difference in height (a) between the axis of the control arm mounting point on the rear axle sub frame and the lower edge of the cup on the constant velocity joint is directly translated in degrees of camber.

Rear Wheel Camber
350SL, 450SL, and 450SLC

Control Arm Position (mm)	Corresponds to Rear Wheel Camber of: (deg)
+ 50	+ 0°50′ ± 30′
+ 45	+ 0°35′ ± 30′
+ 40	+ 0°20′ ± 30′
+ 35	+ 0° 5′ ± 30′
+ 30	− 0°10′ ± 30′
+ 25	− 0°25′ ± 30′
+ 20	− 0°40′ ± 30′
+ 15	− 0°55′ ± 30′
+ 10	− 1°10′ ± 30′
+ 5	− 1°25′ ± 30′
0	− 1°40′ ± 30′
− 5	− 1°55′ ± 30′
− 10	− 2°10′ ± 30′
− 15	− 2°25′ ± 30′

280S/8, 280SE/8, 280SEL/8, 300SEL/8, 280SE 3.5, 280SE 4.5, 280SEL 4.5, 280SL/8, 300SEL 3.5, 300SEL 4.5, and 300SEL 6.3

The rear wheel camber, measured with the vehicle ready for the road, is the result of the installation height of the rear springs and of the compensating spring. On vehicles with a hydroneumatic compensating spring, only the basic pressure of the compensating spring is effective.

Toe-In

All Models

Toe-in, on the rear wheels, is dependent on the camber of the rear wheels.

Air Suspension System

NOTE: *Service of this system should be left to a qualified Mercedes-Benz dealer.*

The air suspension consists of three basic systems; the air suspension units (chambers, bellows, and air pistons) which take the place of traditional steel springs, the compressed air system, which encompasses the compressor, supply tank and anti-freeze device, and the level control equipment (valve unit and level control valves front and rear).

Ground clearance and vehicle level are kept constant by distributing the vehicle load on four bellows. Three level control valves, two at the front and one at the rear, permit balancing of unsymmetric loads.

FRONT SUSPENSION

Springs

Removal and Installation

All Models

NOTE: *Be extremely careful when at-*

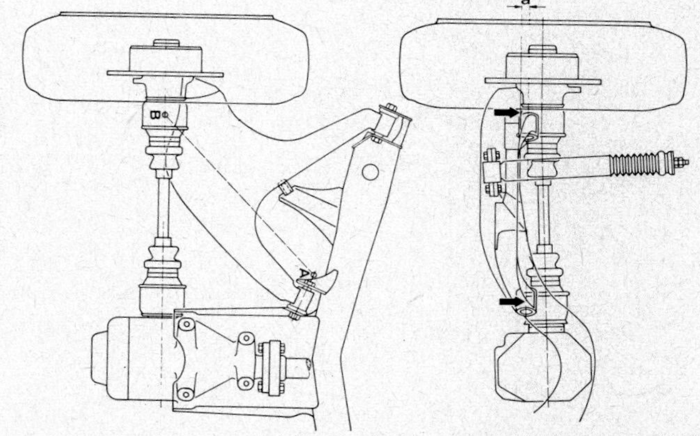

Rear wheel camber measurement on 220D/8, 220/8, 230/8, 250/8, 250C, 280, 280C, 350SL, 450SL, and 450SLC a = control arm position (difference in height between the axis of the rear control arm mount (A) and the lower edge of the cup on the outer constant velocity joint (B).

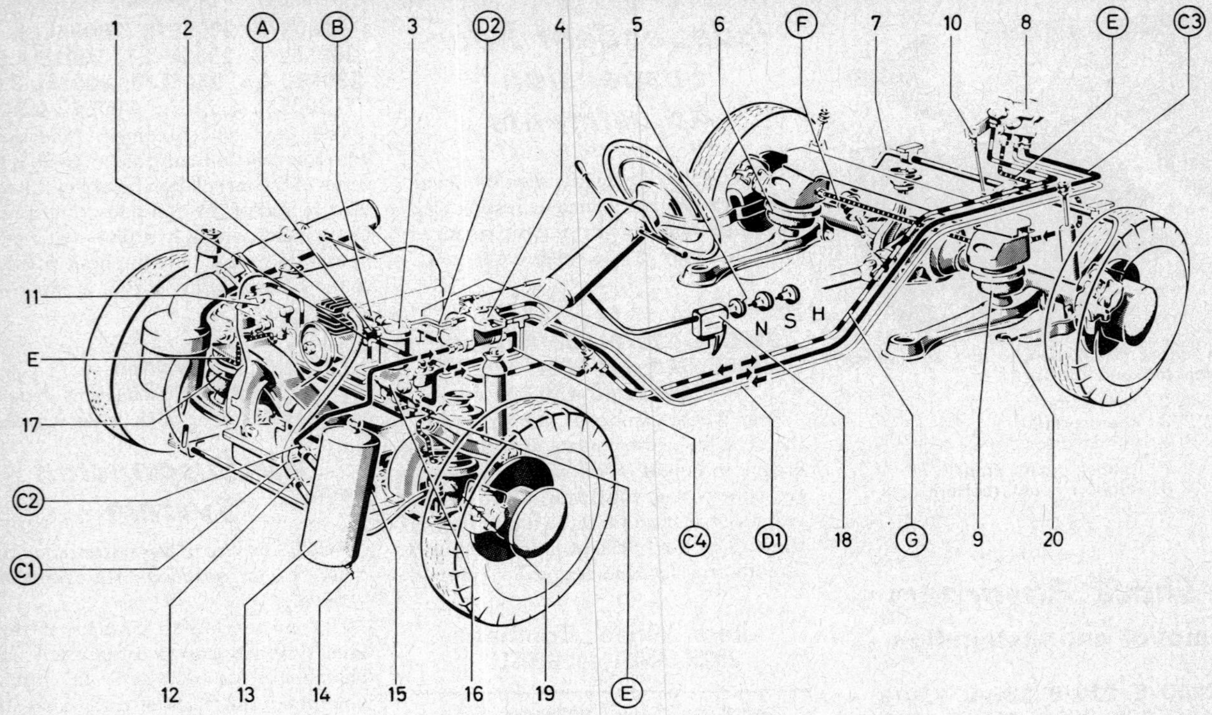

Air suspension system schematic

(a)—Intake air inlet and exhaust air outlet
(b)—Intake line anti-freeze device—air compressor
(c 1)—Pressure line (full operating pressure) air compressor—air supply tank
(c 2)—Pressure line (full operating pressure) air supply tank—valve unit
(c 3)—Pressure line (full operating pressure) valve unit—level control valve on rear axle
(c 4)—Pressure line (reduced) pressure) valve unit—level control valve on front axle
(d 1)—Return line to level control valve—valve unit
(d 2)—Return line valve unit—anti-freeze device
(e)—connecting line to level control valves—air suspension units
(f)—Compensating line between air suspension units on rear axle
(g)—pressure control line for higher level valve unit—level control valves

1. Air cleaner
2. Air compressor
3. Anti-freeze device
4. Valve unit
5. Warning light
6. Air chamber on rear axle
7. Torsion bar on rear axle
8. Level control valve on rear axle
9. Bellows on rear axle
10. Connecting rod for level control valve
11. Level control valve—right front
12. Check valve
13. Air supply tank
14. Drain valve
15. Filling valve
16. Level control valve—left front
17. Air chamber on front axle
18. Cable control for valve unit
19. Bellows on front axle
20. Lever for brake support

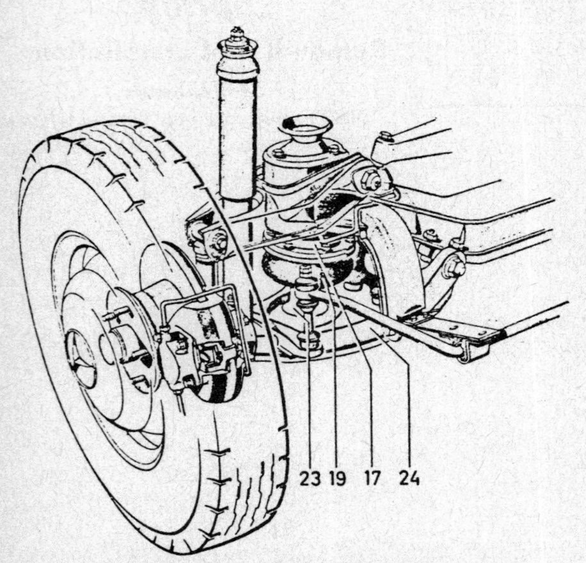

Schematic of air suspension system on the front wheel.

17. Air chamber
19. Bellows
23. Air piston
24. Lower control arm

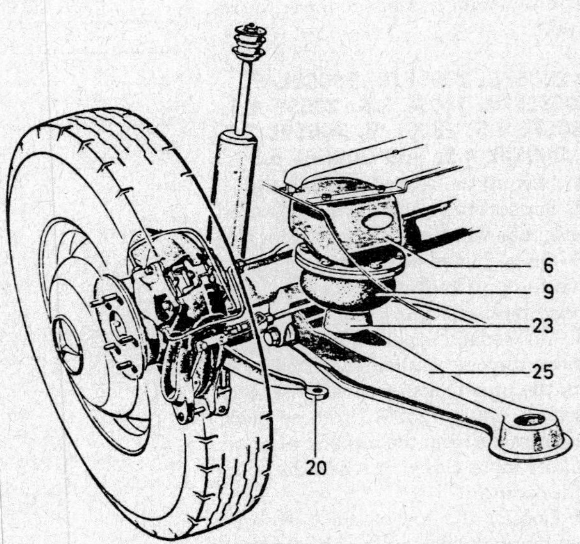

Schematic of air suspension system on the rear wheel.

6. Air chamber
9. Bellows
20. Lever for brake support
23. Air piston
25. Strut rod

tempting to remove front springs as they are compressed and under considerable load.

1. Jack up the front of the car, put on jackstands and remove the front wheels.

2. Remove the front shock absorber and disconnect the sway bar.

3. On cars having pivot pins and threaded bushings (all 280 and 300 series sedan except 280 and 280C), unscrew the two outer bolts that attach the pivot pin to the frame.

3a. Place a jack under the inner control arm, then remove the two inner bolts and gradually lower the jack and arm.

Front coil spring removal—cars with pivot pins.

1. Front axle carrier
3. Lower control arm
4. Upper control arm
5. Steering knuckle
6. Kingpin
7. Steering knuckle carrier
10. Front spring
11. Front shock absorber
12. Torsion bar
18. Brake caliper
27. Torsion bar connecting linkage
30. Cam bolt
31. Leaf spring
33. Bearing bolt
44. Center brake cable control
45. Brake lever

Front coil spring removal—cars with eccentric adjusters.

3. Lower control arm
4. Upper control arm
6. Guide joint
7. Suspension joint
10. Front spring
11. Front shock-absorber
12. Torsion bar
29. Rubber mounting
44. Jack cradle
47. Angled intermediate brace

3b. When the spring tension is relieved, remove the spring and its rubber bumpers.

4. On cars having eccentric adjusters (all others), first punchmark the position of the adjusters, then loosen the hex bolts.

4a. Support the lower control arm with a jack.

4b. Then knock out the eccentric pins and gradually lower the arm until spring tension is relieved.

4c. The spring can now be removed. **NOTE:** *Check caster and camber after installing a new spring.*

5. Installation is the reverse of removal.

6. For ease of installation, tape the rubber mounts to the springs.

7. If the eccentric adjusters were not matchmarked, install the eccentric bolts as illustrated under "Front End Alignment".

Shock Absorbers

Removal and Installation

All Models

Shock absorbers are normally replaced only if leaking excessively (oil visible on outside cover) or if worn internally to a point where the car no longer rides smoothly and rebounds after hitting a bump. A good general test of shock absorber condition is made by bouncing the front of the car. If the car rebounds more than two or three times it can be assumed that the shock absorbers need replacement.

1. For removal and installation of shock absorbers, it is best to jack up the front of the car until the weight is off of the wheels and support the car securely on jackstands.

2. When removing the shock absorbers, it is also wise to draw a simple diagram of the location of parts such as lock-rings, rubber stops, locknuts and steel plates, since many shock absorbers require their own peculiar installation of these parts.

3. Raise the hood and locate the upper shock absorber mount.

4. Support the lower control arm with a jack.

5. Unbolt the mount for the shock absorber at the top. On 350SL, 450SL, and 450SLC, remove the coolant expansion tank to allow access to the right front shock absorber.

6. Remove the nuts which secure the shock absorber to the lower control arm.

7. Push the shock absorber piston rod in, install the stirrup, and remove the shock absorber.

8. Remove the stirrup, since this must be installed on replacement shock absorbers.

NOTE: *220D/8 through 250C sedans, use both Bilstein and F&S shock absorbers. On Bilstein shock absorbers, never re-use the upper or lower cups.*

9. Installation is the reverse of removal. Always use new bushings when installing replacement shock absorbers.

Steering Knuckle and Ball Joints/Kingpins

Mercedes-Benz cars 220D/8, 220/8, 230/8, 250/8, 250C, 280, 280C, 350SL, 450SL, and 450SLC use steering knuckles with ball joints. All other models covered here use steering knuckles with kingpins.

Checking Ball Joints/Kingpins

1. To check the steering knuckles or ball joints, jack up the car, placing a jack directly under the front spring plate. This unloads the front suspension to allow the maximum play to be observed.

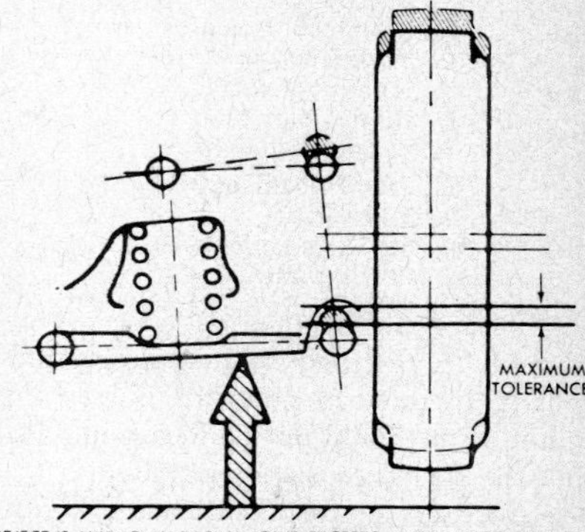

REJECT IF AXIAL PLAY IN BALL JOINT EXCEEDS MAXIMUM TOLERANCE.

2. On older models having kingpins, the maximum allowable play between the kingpin and bearing bushing is 0.016 in. The kingpin end-play is the same.

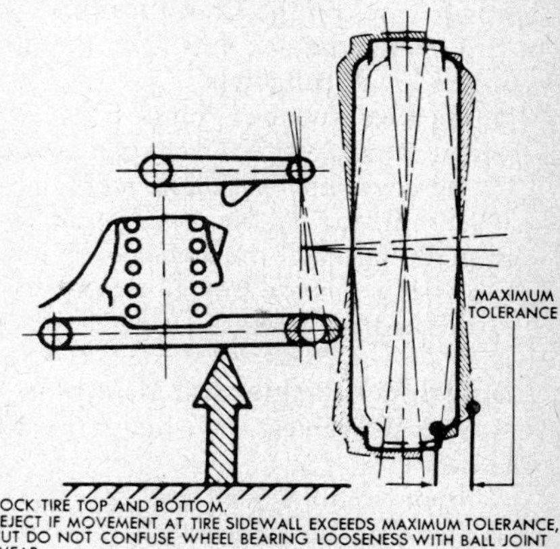

ROCK TIRE TOP AND BOTTOM.
REJECT IF MOVEMENT AT TIRE SIDEWALL EXCEEDS MAXIMUM TOLERANCE, BUT DO NOT CONFUSE WHEEL BEARING LOOSENESS WITH BALL JOINT WEAR.

3. Late model ball joints need be replaced only if dried out with plainly visible wear and/or play.

Removal and Installation

Steering Knuckle and Ball Joints

1. This should only be done with the front shock absorber installed. If, however, the front shock absorber has been removed, the lower control arm should be supported with a jack and the spring

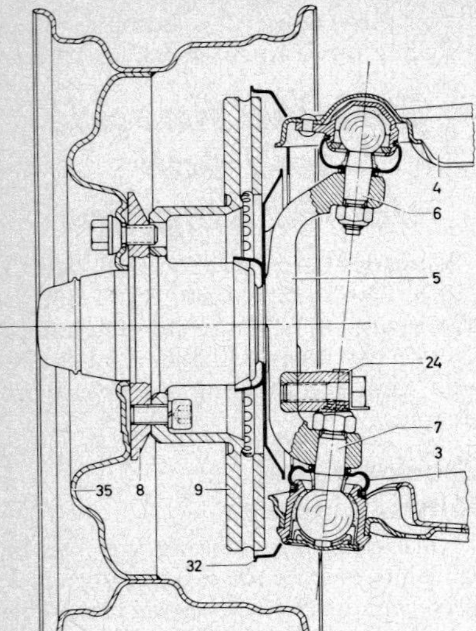

Steering knuckle and ball joints

3. Lower control arm
4. Upper control arm
5. Steering knuckle
6. Guide joint
7. Supporting joint
8. Front wheel hub
9. Brake disc
24. Steering knuckle arm
32. Cover plate
35. Wheel

should be clamped with a spring tensioner. In this case, the hex nut on the guide joint should not be loosened without the spring tensioner installed.

2. Jack up the front of the car and support it on jackstands.
3. Remove the wheel.
4. Remove the brake caliper.
5. Unbolt the steering relay lever from the steering knuckle. For safety, install spring clamps on the front springs.
6. Remove the hex nuts from the upper and lower ball joints.
7. Remove the ball joints from the steering knuckle with the aid of a puller.
8. Remove the steering knuckle.
9. Installation is the reverse of removal. Be sure that the seats for the pins of the ball joints are free of grease.
10. Bleed the brakes.

Steering Knuckle and Kingpins

1. Jack the vehicle and support it with jackstands.
2. Remove the wheel.
3. Remove the brake caliper.
4. On vehicles with air suspension, perform the following:
    a. Leave the pull knob for the valve in the driving position.
    b. Completely evacuate the compressed air from the compressor.
    c. Open the plug on the valve unit and plug it again after evacuating the air.
5. Remove the front shock absorber.
6. On vehicles with air suspension, disconnect the connecting rod for the front level control valve on the bottom of the control arm. Unscrew the ball pin.
7. Lift the lower control arm and attach the special holding tool to the upper and lower shock absorber mounts.
8. Remove the brake caliper. Remove the brake line from the steering knuckle and plug the line.
9. Loosen and remove the track rod from the steering knuckle arm.
10. Loosen and remove the cam bolt from the upper bearing of the steering knuckle.
11. Remove the steering knuckle by unscrewing the threaded bolt and castle nut from the bottom bearing of the steering knuckle.

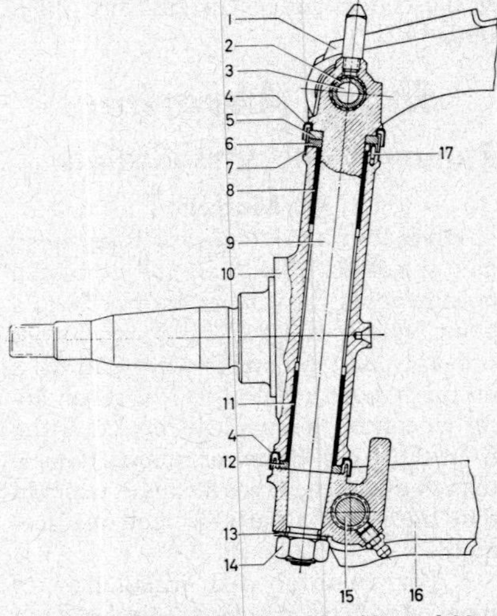

Cross-section of steering knuckle and kingpin.

1. Upper control arm
2. Threaded bolt
3. Cam bolt
4. Dust cap
5. Thrust washer (top)
6. Thrust washer (bottom)
7. Dust sleeve
8. Upper bearing bushing
9. Kingpin
10. Steering knuckle
11. Bottom bearing bushing
12. Compensating washer
13. Lockwasher
14. Hex nut
15. Steering knuckle carrier with threaded bolt
16. Lower control arm
17. Pin

12. Installation is the reverse of removal. Use new rubber rings throughout. The threaded bolt must be screwed in from the rear of the control arm so that the steering knuckle will not contact the castle nut at full lock. Be sure that the adjusting lug of the adjusting disc correctly enters the groove on the threaded bolt in the steering knuckle carrier.

Upper Control Arm

Removal and Installation

220D/8, 220/8, 230/8, 250/8, 250C, 280, 280C, 350SL, 450SL, and 450SLC

1. The front shock absorbers should remain installed. Never loosen the hex nuts of the ball joints with the shock absorber removed, unless a spring clamp is installed.
2. Jack the front of the car and remove the wheel.
3. Support the front end on jackstands.
4. Remove the steering arm from the steering knuckle.
5. Separate the brake line and brake hose from each other and plug the openings.
6. Support the lower control arm and unscrew the nuts from the ball joints.
7. Remove the ball joints from the steering knuckle.
8. Loosen the bolts on the upper control arm and remove the upper control arm.
9. Installation is the reverse of removal.

CAUTION: *Mount the front hex bolt from the rear in a forward direction, and the rear hex bolt from the front in a rearward direction.*

10. Bleed the brakes.

All 280 and 300 Series Cars (except 280 and 280C)

1. On models having threaded control arm supports, first remove the steering knuckle, then unscrew the threaded bushings and the pivot pin.
2. Remove the rubber seals and the control arm.
3. On models having hex bolt supports, support the control arm with a jack, then disconnect the sway bar and shock absorber.
4. Remove the front coil spring, then disconnect the brake hose from the steel line, plug the line to prevent fluid loss and unscrew the hex bolts.

NOTE: *The bolts are installed from the inside–the nut always goes on the outside of the control arm.*

5. To install, reverse the removal procedure. On models having threaded bushings, make sure the bushing rotates freely on the pivot pin.

Lower Control Arm

Removal and Installation

220D/8, 220/8, 230/8, 250/8, 250C, 280, 280C, 350SL, 450SL, and 450SLC

1. Since the front shock absorber acts acts a deflection stop for the front wheels, the lower shock absorber attaching point should not be loosened unless the vehicle is resting on the wheels or unless the lower control arm is supported.
2. Jack up the front of the vehicle and support it on jackstands.
3. Support the lower control arm.
4. Loosen the lower shock absorber attachment.

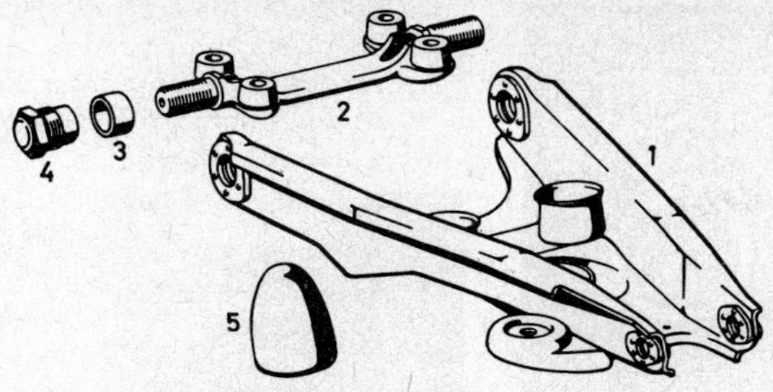

Lower control arm and pivot shaft

1. Lower control arm
2. Pivot pin
3. Rubber sealing ring
4. Threaded bushing
5. Additional rubber buffer

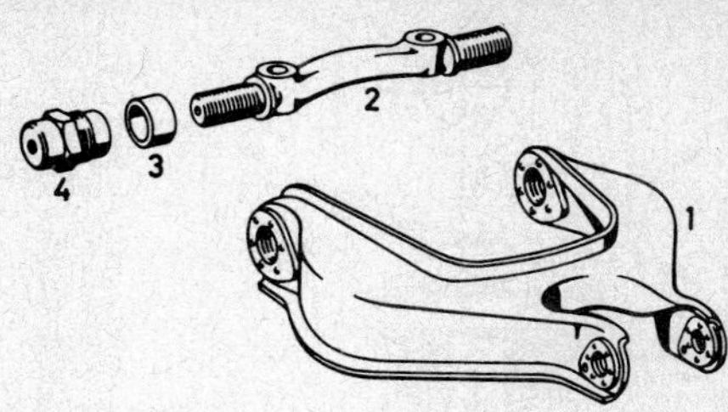

Upper control arm and pivot shaft

1. Upper control arm
2. Pivot pin
3. Rubber sealing ring
4. Threaded bushing

5. Unscrew the steering arm from the steering knuckle.

6. Separate the brake line and brake hose and plug the openings.

7. Remove the front spring.

8. Unscrew the hex nuts on the ball joints.

9. Remove the lower ball joint and remove the lower control arm.

10. Installation is the reverse of removal. Bleed the brakes and check the front end alignment.

Front End Alignment

Caster and Camber Adjustment

220D/8, 220/8, 230/8, 250/8, 250C, 280, 280C, 350SL, 450SL, 450SLC

Caster and camber are dependent upon each other and cannot be adjusted independently. They can only be adjusted simultaneously.

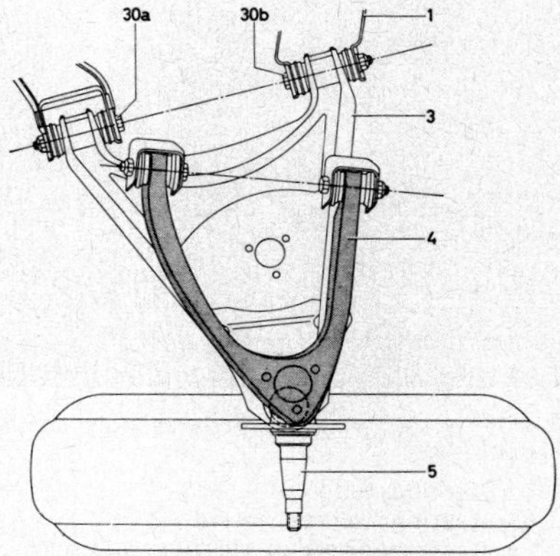

Caster and camber adjustment points on 220D/8, 220/8, 230/8, 250/8, 250C, 280, 280C, 350SL, 450SL, and 450SLC.

1. Front axle carrier
3. Lower control arm
4. Upper control arm
5. Steering knuckle

30a. Cam bolt front (caster)
30b. Cam bolt rear (camber)

Caster is adjusted by turning the lower control arm around the front mounting, using the eccentric bolt.

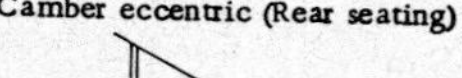

Camber eccentric (Rear seating)

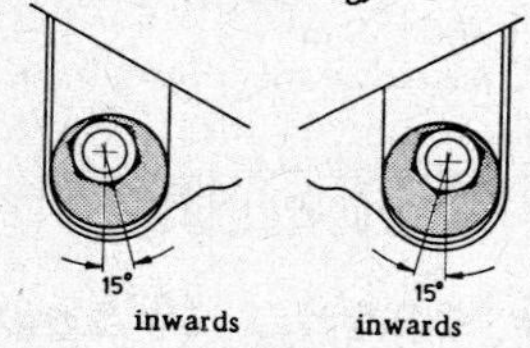

Caster eccentric (front seating)
Mechanical steering

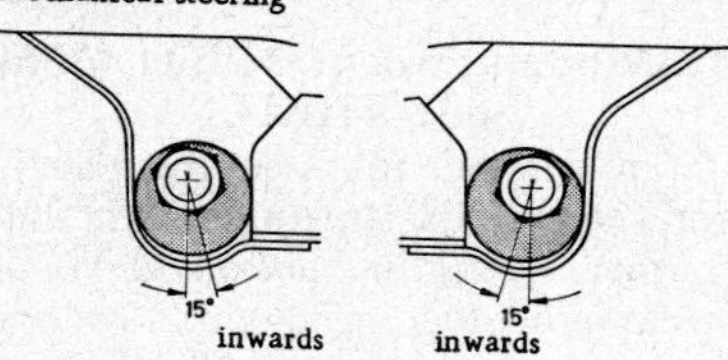

Caster eccentric (front seating)
Power steering

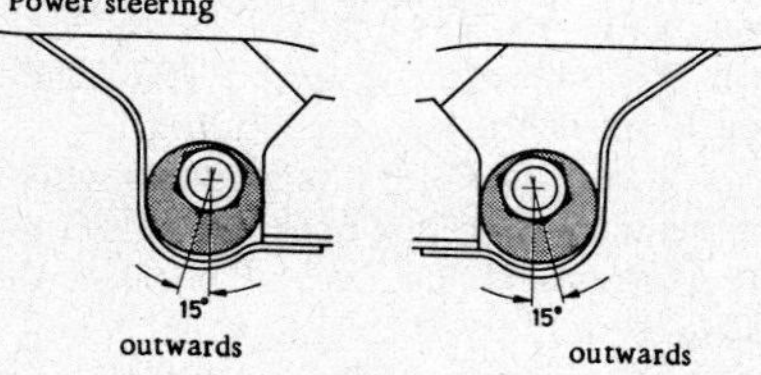

Basic caster and camber settings—220D/8, 220/8, 238/8, 250/8, 250C, 280, and 280C.

Camber is adjusted by turning the lower control arm about the rear mounting, using the eccentric bolt. Bear in mind that caster will be changed accordingly.

When camber is adjusted in a positive direction, caster is changed in a negative direction, and vice versa. Adjustment of camber by 0° 15' results in a caster change of approximately 0° 20'. Adjustment of caster by 1° results in a camber change of approximately 0° 7'.

Caster Adjustment

All 280 and 300 Series Vehicles (Except 280 and 280C)

Caster is adjusted by swivelling the front axle carrier by means of the eccentric bolts. Caster should be adjusted equally on the left and right, so as not to distort the rubber front axle mounts. Before adjusting the caster, the four hex bolts which attach the rear engine mount carrier to the front axle carrier should be

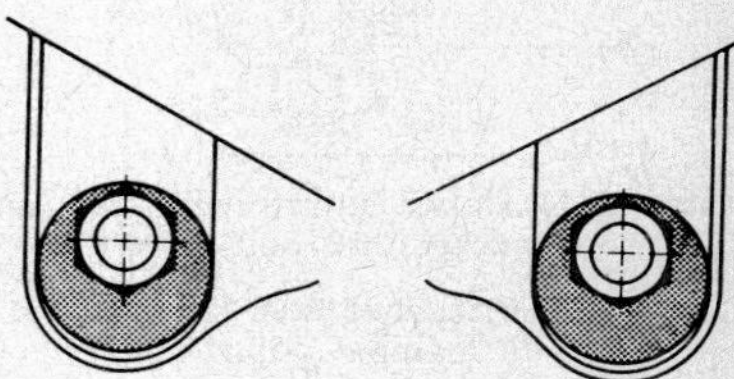

Basic adjustment of rear cams (camber) on 350SL, 450SL, and 450SLC.

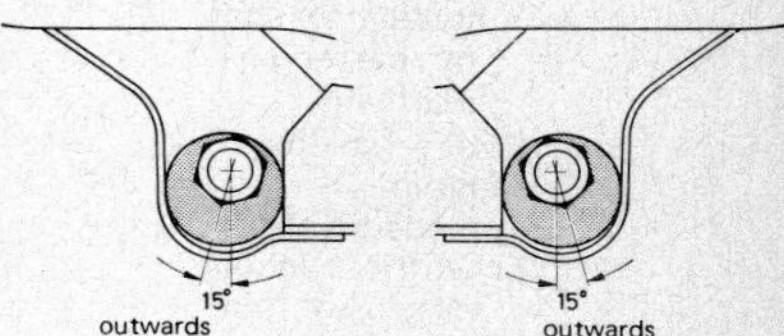

Basic adjustment of front cams (caster) on 350SL, 450SL, and 450SLC.

loosened to prevent any distortion. Tighten the nuts after adjustment.

Small differences in caster between the left and right can be adjusted (within minor limits) on the upper steering knuckle bearing at the bolt.

Camber Adjustment

All 280 and 300 Series vehicles (Except 280 and 280C)

Camber is adjusted at the upper steering knuckle bearing by turning the cam bolt. In special cases, if adjustment cannot be obtained at the bolt, camber can be adjusted by adding or removing some of the washers between the upper control arm bearing bolt and the front axle carrier. Washers should be added between the hex bolt and the lockwasher. One washer should always be used with each bolt.

Toe-In Adjustment

All Models

Toe-in is the difference of the distance between the front edges of the wheel rims and the rear edges of the wheel rims.

To measure toe-in, the steering should be in the straight ahead position and the marks on the pitman arm and pitman shaft should be aligned.

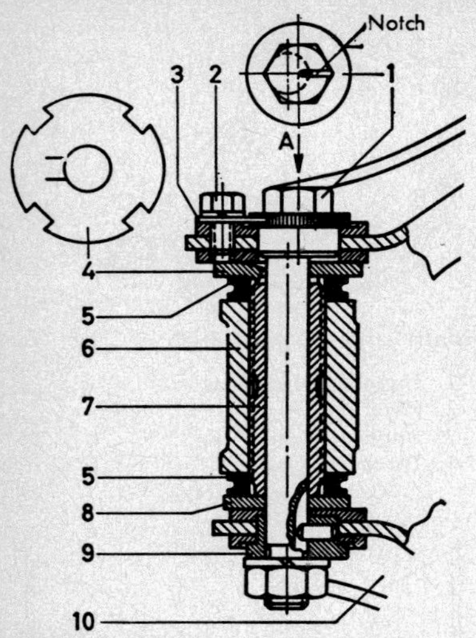

Caster and camber adjustment—280 and 300 series (except 280 and 280C).

1. Eccentric bolt for camber adjustment
2. Hex screw with lockwasher
3. Locking plate
4. Adjusting washer for caster adjustment
5. Rubber sealing ring
6. Kingpin
7. Threaded bolt
8. Eccentric bushing with drive pin
10. Upper control arm

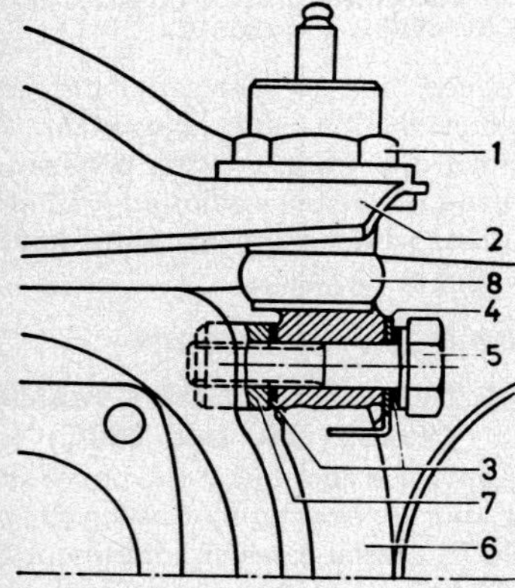

Upper control arm bushings on 280 and 300 series (except 280 and 280C).

1. Threaded bushing
2. Upper control arm
3. Shim
4. Lockplate
5. Bolt
6. Pivot pin
7. Front axle support
8. Rubber seal

Toe-in is adjusted by changing the length of the two tie-rods with the wheels in the straight ahead position. Some older models have a hex nut locking arrangement rather than the newer clamp, but adjustment is the same.

NOTE: *Install new tie-rods so that the left-hand thread points toward the left-hand side of the car.*

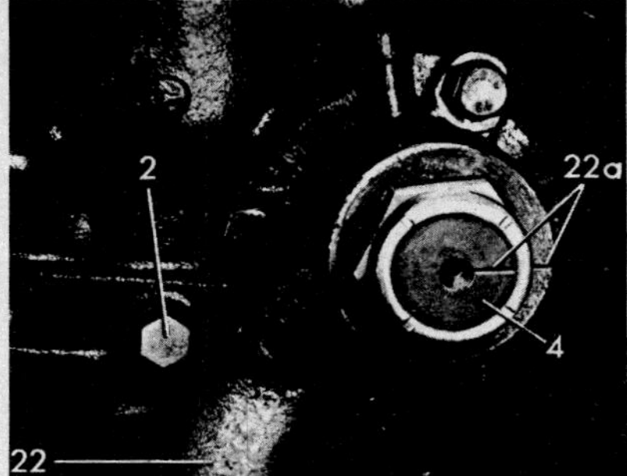

The steering is centered when the marks are aligned.

2. Closing plug in steering gear housing
4. Steering shaft
22. Pitman arm
22a. Assembly mark for pitman arm

STEERING

Steering Wheel

Removal and Installation

All Models Except 350SL, 450SL, and 450SLC

1. In general, the steering wheel is removed from the steering column shock absorber, while the shock absorber remains on the steering column. If work on the steering column jacket is required, the shock absorber and wheel must be removed.

2. Pry the three-pointed star trademark out of the center padding.

3. To remove only the steering wheel, unscrew the five hex nuts and lift off the steering wheel. Be careful because the cable is connected to the wheel.

Steering wheel only removal (except 350-SL, 450SL, and 450SLC).

2. Steering wheel 4. Hex nut

4. To remove the wheel and shock absorber, leave the five nuts intact and remove the center hex nut.

5. Remove the steering wheel and shock absorber carefully because the cable is still connected.

6. Installation is the reverse of removal, no matter which part was removed.

350SL, 450SL, and 450SLC

1. Pry the three-pointed star trademark from the center padding.

2. Unscrew the hex nut from the steering shaft and remove the spring washer and the steering wheel.

Align the marks on the wheel and shaft—350SL, 450SL, and 450SLC.

1. Steering wheel
2. Steering spindle
3. Hex nut with spring washer

3. Installation is the reverse of removal. Be sure that the alignment mark on the steering shaft is pointing upward and be sure that the slightly curved spoke of the steering wheel is down.

Manual Steering Gear

Removal and Installation

CAUTION: *The telescopic steering tube must be fixed in position with an assembly pin inserted through the hole as illustrated, otherwise the tube will be shifted out of position when the steering box is installed.*

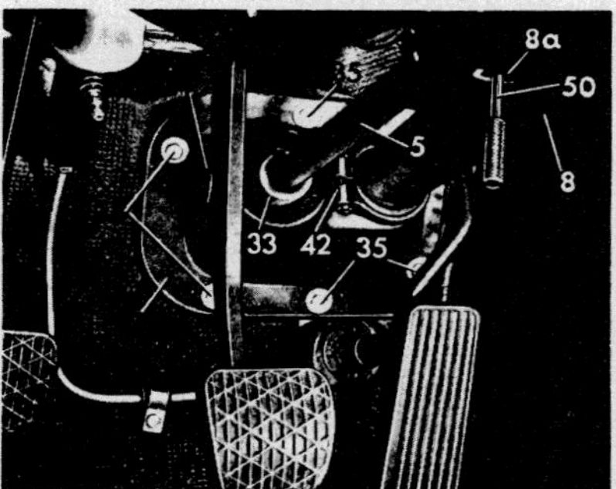

Assembly tool inserted in telescopic steering column.

5. Steering tube
8. Steering column jacket
8a. Assembly hole in steering column jacket
33. Rubber boot
34. Cover plate
35. Hexagon screw with washer
41. Rubber grommet
42. Fixing screw
50. Assembly pin

1. Remove the socket screw from the upper flange of the steering coupling.

2. Detach the tie-rod and center tie-rod from the pitman arm.

3. Remove the pitman arm from the gear box using a puller. The pitman arm can be removed from the gear box with

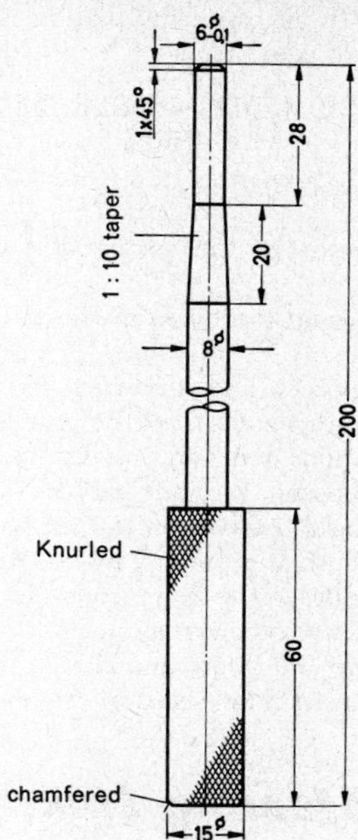

Dimensions for fabricating assembly tool

the two tie-rods still attached if desired. In any case, the pitman arm must be removed from the gear box before the box will come out of the car.

4. Detach the steering shock absorber from the bracket on the chassis, then remove the three hex-head bolts that secure the gear box to the frame side member.

5. Press the steering worm shaft off the coupling and remove the gear box from underneath the car.

6. To install, attach the pitman arm (observing matchmarks) to the gear box, then remove the oil fill plug and fill the box with the required lubricant.

7. Place the steering box in its centered position (this can be found by observing the steering worm shaft while looking down through the bore in the housing cover). Center the steering wheel and install the gear box from beneath the car.

8. Insert the steering shaft of the box into the lower coupling.

9. Install the three chassis-to-gear box bolts and tighten.

10. Tighten the lower clamp bolt, after making sure the steering wheel and gear box are both in centered positions.

11. Reattach the center tie-rod to the pitman arm.

Adjustment

All Models

Steering Worm

1. Remove the steering gear from the vehicle and clamp it in a vise between two pieces of wood.

2. Remove the hex nut from the adjusting screw.

3. Remove the steering housing cover and at the same time unscrew the adjusting screw.

4. Remove the steering shaft from the housing.

5. Measure the torque necessary to rotate the steering shaft.

6. The torque should be 4–5 in. lbs. To adjust the torque, unscrew the ring and remove the snap-ring. Tighten or loosen the adjusting ring until the specified torque is obtained.

7. Install the threaded ring and snap-ring and check the torque again.

8. Assembly is the reverse of disassembly. Adjust the pressure block.

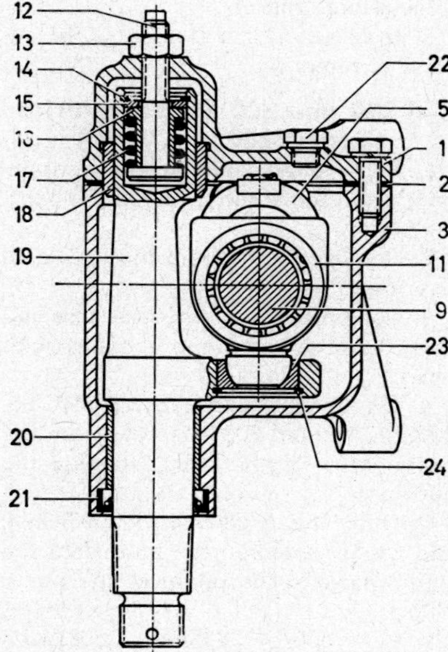

Schematic of typical steering box

1. Steering housing cover
2. Gasket
3. Steering housing
5. Ball guide tube
9. Steering worm
11. Steering nut
12. Adjusting bolt
13. Hex nut
14. Locking ring
15. Thrust washer
16. Thrust sleeve
17. Compression spring
18. Upper bearing bushing
19. Steering shaft
20. Lower bearing bushing
21. Sealing ring
22. Closing plug
23. Ball socket
24. Locking ring

Pressure Block

1. Center the steering gear.

2. Unscrew the plug from the steering housing and turn the steering worm until the center of the steering nut is exactly below the threaded bore for the plug.

3. Measure the torque needed to turn the steering worm beyond the center position. If necessary, adjust the torque using the directions below:

4. On 220D/8, 220/8, 230/8, 250/8, and 250C models, screw in the adjusting screw to increase the torque and screw out the screw to decrease the torque. Lock the adjusting screw.

CAUTION: *When the steering worm is turned over center, it should not bind although a definite resistance should be felt.*

5. On all other models, unscrew the adjusting bolt and tighten it to 7 ft lbs. Back off the bolt ¼ turn and tighten it to 3–4 ft lbs. Install a dial indicator on the adjusting bolt and zero the indicator. Screw the adjusting bolt down approximately ⅛ turn (0.1–0.15 mm) and tighten the hex nut to 18–22 ft lbs. The dial indicator should return to 0–0.03 mm.

6. After the adjustment, check the adjustment once again and install the steering gear.

7. Check the steering in the vehicle.

Power Steering Gear

Removal and Installation

1. Suck the oil from the power steering reservoir using a syringe.

2. Detach the high-pressure hose and oil return hose from the steering assembly.

3. Cap both lines to prevent entry of dirt, then remove the clamp screw from the lower part of the coupling flange.

4. Remove the rubber plug from the cover plate and remove the U-joint socket screw.

5. Detach the tie-rod and center tie-rod from the pitman arm, using pullers or a tie-rod splitter.

6. Remove the hex-head bolts that hold the gear box to the chassis, then press the worm shaft stub from the steering coupling and remove the gear box from underneath the car.

7. To install, first install the pitman arm (if it has been removed) aligning the matchmarks. Tighten the pitman arm nut to 110 ft lbs and install the cotter pin.

8. Remove the screw plug from the steering box. Turn the worm shaft until the center of the power piston is directly below the bore in the housing. Check dimension (a) which can be altered by changing the position of the pitman arm on its shaft.

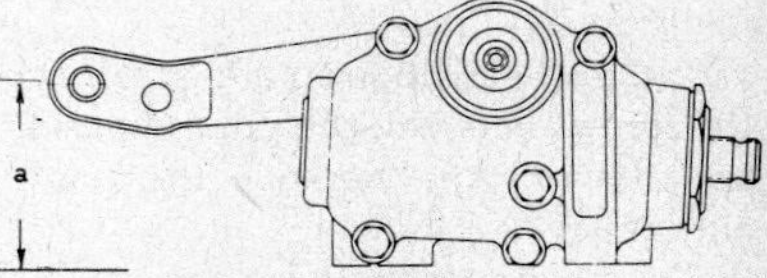

Dimension (a) can be altered by changing the position of the pitman arm on the shaft.

9. Center the steering wheel.

10. Press the worm shaft stub into the steering shaft coupling, making sure not to damage the serrations.

NOTE: *Install assembly pin as for manual steering.*

11. Install and tighten the hex-head screws that hold the gear box to the chas-

sis, then install and tighten the coupling clamp screw.

12. Install the plug in the gear box, using a new gasket; attach the tie-rods to the pitman arm and make sure that the steering knuckle arms rest against their stops at full left and right lock.

13. Check toe-in and correct if necessary. Remove the dust covers from the fluid lines, then reconnect the high- and low-pressure lines.

14. Fill the reservoir and connect a hose between the bleed screw on the steering and the reservoir.

15. Open the bleed screw and, with engine running, bleed the system and top up.

Power Steering Pump

Removal and Installation

Many types of power steering pumps are used on Mercedes-Benz vehicles. Use only the instructions that apply to your vehicle.

220D/8, 220/8, 230/8, 250/8, 250C

1. On all models:

a. Remove the wing nut on the oil reservoir and remove the cover, spring, and damping plate.

b. Suck the oil from the reservoir with a syringe.

c. Loosen the hose on the pump and plug both pump and hose.

d. On pumps with the oil reservoir attached, loosen the return hose and plug it.

e. On other types, loosen the connecting hose from the reservoir to the pump.

2. On 4 cylinder models:

a. On 220/8, loosen the four bolts on the mounting bracket, push the pump toward the engine, and remove the belt.

b. On 220D/8, loosen the three screws on the mounting bracket and push the pump toward the engine. Remove the belt.

c. On 220D/8, remove the supporting strut.

d. On all 4 cylinder models, remove the screws between the pump housing and the bracket. Remove the pump and pulley.

3. On 6 cylinder models:

a. Loosen the screws that are hidden by the pulley (mounting bracket) and the nuts on the clamp screw.

b. Loosen the rear screw and remove it together with the spacer. Push the pump toward the engine and remove the belt.

c. Remove the screws which attach the mounting bracket to the engine and remove the pump together with the pulley and mounting bracket.

4. On vehicles with Exhaust Emission Control:

a. Remove the radiator.

b. Remove the nut from the pulley shaft. On pumps with cylindrical shafts, remove the pulley.

c. On pumps with tapered shafts, pull the pulley from the shaft with a jaw type puller.

d. Unscrew both front mounting bolts.

e. Remove the rear mounting bolt with spacer.

f. Remove the pump from the mounting bracket.

5. Installation, in all cases, is the reverse of removal.

All 280 and 300 Series Vehicles (Except 280 and 280C)

1. Remove the wing nut on the supply tank and remove the spring and mounting plate.

2. Remove the oil from the tank with a syringe.

3. Loosen the high-pressure hose and close the hose and pump openings with plugs.

4. On models 280S/8, 280SE 3.5, 300SEL 3.5, and 300SEL 6.3, loosen the return hose on the tank and plug the openings.

5. On 280SE/8, 280SEL/8, 300SEL/8, and 280SL/8, loosen the hose from the supply tank to the pump at the pump elbow.

6. On 280S/8, 280SE/8, 280SEL/8, and 280SL/8:

a. Remove the radiator.

b. Remove the pulley from the pulley shaft.

c. Loosen the nuts on the clamp. Unscrew the bolt and note the arrangement of bolt and spacer on the rear mounting bolt.

d. Unscrew the bolts on the face end of the carrier and remove the pump.

7. On the 300SEL/8:

a. Remove the compressor and lay it aside. Do not detach the lines.

b. Remove the mounting bolts from the pump and remove the pump.

8. On the 300SEL 6.3:

a. Unscrew the mounting bolts behind the pump and remove it together with the spacers.

b. Remove the bolt which attaches the bracket to the cylinder head.

c. Remove the bolts which hold the pump to the air compressor and remove the pump.

9. On the 280SE 3.5 and 300SEL 3.5:

a. Remove the nuts from the attaching plate and from the support.

b. Push the pump toward the engine and remove the belt from the pulley.

c. Unbolt and remove the pump and mounting bracket. Separate the pump and mounting bracket.

10. In all cases, installation is the reverse of removal.

350SL, 450SL, 450SLC, 280, and 280C

1. Remove the nut from the supply tank.

2. Remove the spring and damping plate.

3. Drain the oil from the tank with a syringe.

4. Loosen and remove the expanding and return hoses from the pump. Plug all conections and pump openings.

5. Loosen the nut on the attaching plate and the bolt on the support.

6. Push the pump toward the engine and remove the belts from the pulley.

7. Unscrew the mounting bolts and remove the pump and carrier.

8. Installation is the reverse of removal.

Steering Linkage

220D/8, 220/8, 230/8, 250/8, 250C, 350SL, 450SL and 450SLC

Tie-Rod

Removal and Installation

1. Remove the cotter pins from the castellated nuts.

NOTE: *350SL, 450SL and 450SLC do not use cotter pins and castellated nuts, but do use self-locking nylon insert nuts.*

2. Remove the castellated nuts.

3. Remove the center tie-rod.

4. Press the tie-rod off the steering arm and the steering relay arm.

5. Installation is the reverse of removal. Be sure to install the tie-rods so that the rod with the left-hand thread is on the left (driving direction). Always use new cotter pins. Check and adjust the toe-in, if necessary.

Center Tie-Rod

Removal and Installation

1. Disconnect the steering damper from the center tie-rod.

2. After removing the cotter pins, remove the castellated nuts from the center tie-rod joints.

3. Press the center tie-rod off the steering gear and steering relay arm.

4. Installation is the reverse of removal. Use new cotter pins and adjust the toe-in if necessary. Install new plastic rings and plastic caps on the ball pins.

All 280 and 300 Series Vehicles (Except 280 and 280C)

Tie-Rod

Removal and Installation

1. Remove the cotter pins and remove the castellated nuts.

2. Press the tie-rod from the steering knuckle arm.

3. Press the tie-rod from the steering lever.

4. Installation is the reverse of removal. Always use new cotter pins. Be sure that the tie-rod with the left-hand threads is installed on the left (driving direction). Adjust the toe-in if necessary.

Center Tie-Rod

Removal and Installation

See this procedure under "Center Tie-Rod Removal and Installation for 220D/8 through 250C."

BRAKE SYSTEMS

All Mercedes-Benz cars imported into the United States since 1968 are equipped with four wheel disc brakes. The disc brake systems are basically similar on all models, although removal and installation procedures may vary slightly. In addition, caliper bore sizes differ, depending upon application. The bore size (in millimeters) is represented by the number stamped on the outside of the caliper.

Adjustment

Since disc brakes are used at all four wheels, no adjustments are necessary. Disc brakes are inherently self-adjusting. The only adjustment possible is to the handbrake, which is covered at the end of this section.

Master Cylinder

Removal and Installation

The dual master cylinder has a safety feature which the single unit lacks–if a leak develops in one brake circuit (rear wheels, for example), the other circuit will still operate.

Failure of one system is immediately obvious–the pedal travel increases appreciably and a warning light is activated. This warning light is operated by a simple switch attached to a float in the reservoir/s. When the fluid falls below a certain level, the switch activates the circuit.

CAUTION: *This design was not intended to allow driving the car for any distance with, in effect, a two-wheel brake system. If one brake circuit fails, braking action is correspondingly lower. Front circuit failure is the more serious, however, since the front brakes contribute up to 75% of the braking force required to stop the car. Repair any leaks immediately!*

All Models

1. To remove the master cylinder, first open a bleed screw at one front, and one rear, wheel.

2. Pump the pedal to empty the reservoir completely. Make sure both reservoirs are completely drained.

3. Disconnect the switch connectors using a small screwdriver. Disconnect the two brake lines to the front brakes and the brake line to the rear brakes. Plug the ends with bleed screw caps or the equivalent.

4. Unbolt the master cylinder from the power brake unit and remove. Be careful you do not lose the O-ring in the flange groove of the master cylinder.

5. Installation is the reverse of removal. Be sure to replace the O-ring between the master cylinder and the power brake unit, since this must be absolutely tight. Torque the nuts to 12–15 ft lbs. Be

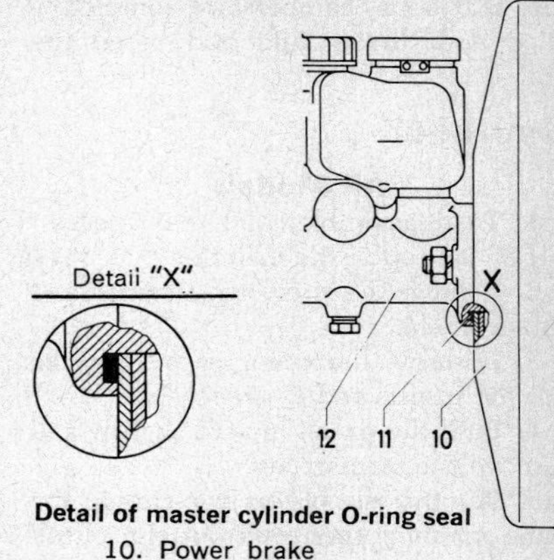

Detail of master cylinder O-ring seal

10. Power brake
11. O-ring
12. Tandem master cylinder

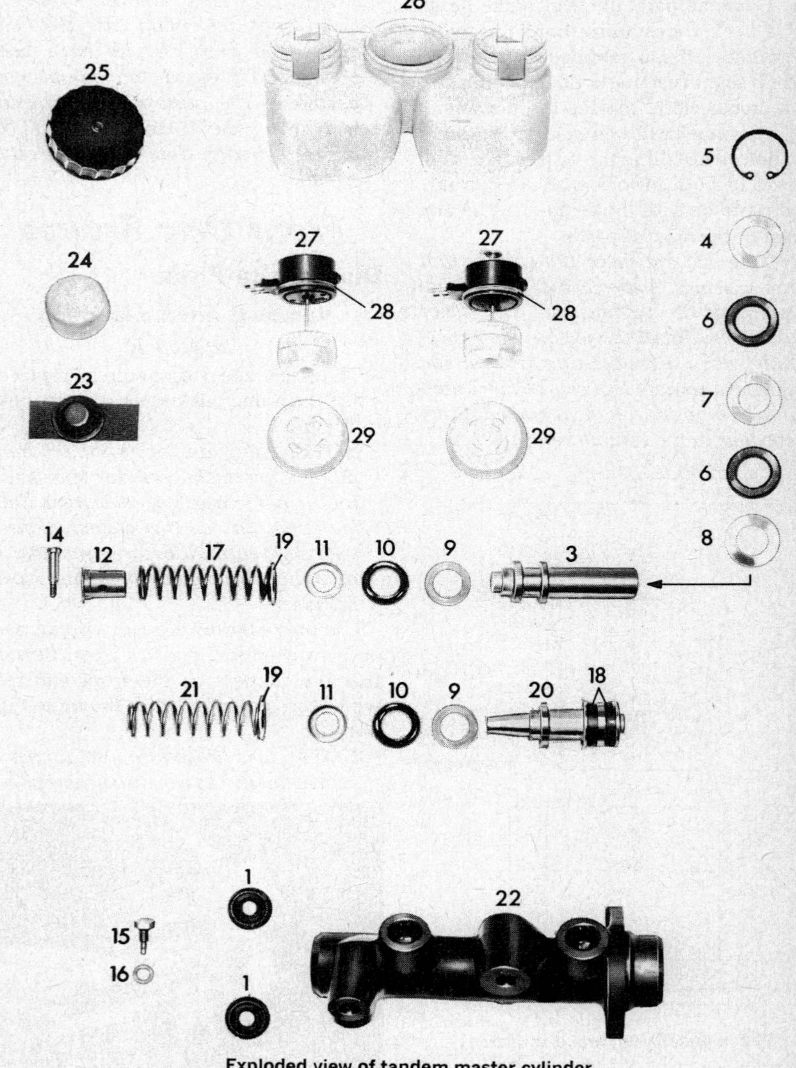

Exploded view of tandem master cylinder

1. Container plug
3. Piston (push rod circuit)
4. Stop washer
5. Lock ring
6. Vacuum seal
7. Intermediate ring
8. Bearing ring
9. Filler
10. Primary sleeve
11. Supporting ring
12. Spring retainer
14. Connecting screw
15. Stop-screw
16. Sealing ring (copper)
17. Compresion spring
18. Ring sleeve
19. Spring plate
20. Intermediate piston
21. Compression spring
22. Housing
23. Splash guard
24. Strainer
25. Closing cover
26. Compensating tank
27. Contact insert
28. O-ring
29. End cover

sure that both chambers are completely filled with brake fluid and bleed the brakes.

Overhaul

All Models

1. To disassemble, pull the reservoir out of the top of the cylinder.
2. Remove the screw cap, strainer, and splash shield.
3. Unscrew the cover caps and take out the inserts and O-rings.
4. Push the piston inward slightly and remove the stop screws.
5. Remove the piston stop-ring in the same manner, then pull out the piston and other components.
6. The spring must be unscrewed from the piston.
7. Clean all parts in clean brake fluid.
8. Check the housing bore for score marks and rust. Do not hone the cylinder bore. If slight rust marks do not come out with crocus cloth, replace the housing.
9. Assembly is the reverse of disassembly. Before installing the pistons, coat the sleeves of both pistons with ATE brake fluid paste or with brake fluid in the absence of the special paste.

NOTE: *Do not force the pistons into the housings. A special tool is available to install the pistons, but if it is not available, install the pistons very carefully with a slight twisting motion. The special assembly tool can be fabricated in the shop from light metal alloy, according to the dimensions given.*

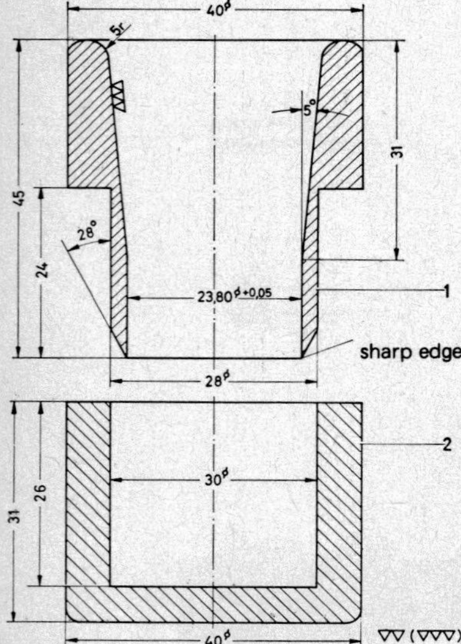

Piston installation tool (fabricated)

Brake Bleeding

All Models

Always bleed the brakes after performing any service, or if the pedal seems spongy (soft). The location of the bleed screws can be seen by consulting the illustrations throughout this section. Prior to bleeding each wheel, connect a hose to the bleed screw and insert the hose into a jar of clean brake fluid.

1. First have an assistant pump the brakes and hold the pedal.
2. Then, starting at the point farthest from the master cylinder, slightly open the bleed screw.
3. When the pedal hits the floor, close the bleed screw before allowing the pedal to return (to prevent air from being sucked into the system).
4. Continue this procedure until no more air bubbles exit from the bleed screw hole, then go to the next wheel. Fluid, which has been bled from the system, is filled with microscopic air bubbles after the bleeding process is completed, therefore it should be discarded.

NOTE: *On dual master cylinders, bleed only the circuit that has been opened. If both circuits have been opened, first bleed the circuit connected to the pushrod bore starting with the wheel farthest from the master cylinder, then bleed the other circuit.*

Front Disc Brakes

Disc Brake Pads

Removal and Installation

All Models

The disc brake pads should be replaced when the lining thickness has worn down to 2 mm.

NOTE: *The 2 mm (approx. 0.08) minimum lining thickness figure specified is the manufacturer's specification. State laws may vary on this subject. Consult your state authorities for any conflict in minimum acceptable lining (pad) thickness.*

Use only approved quality brake pads and always install pads as a set. Be sure that the calipers on the front and rear wheels are equipped with the same type of pads.

NOTE: *This procedure also applies to replacement of rear disc brake pads.*

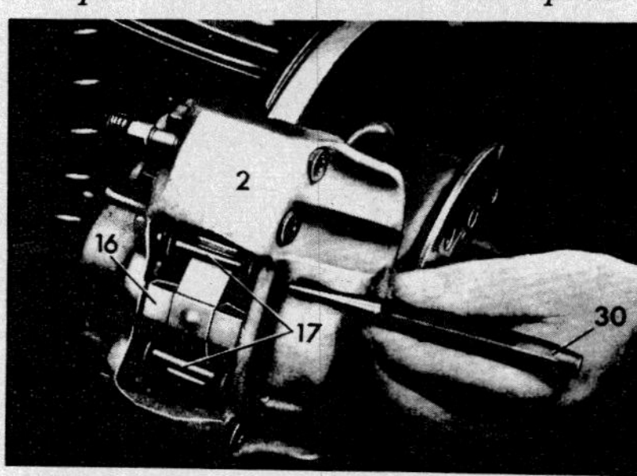

Drive out the retaining pins

2. Brake caliper
16. Anti-rattle spring
17. Retaining pin
30. Drift

1. Remove the cover plate (front calipers only) and drive the retaining pins out of the caliper, using a drift.

Removing one brake pad

2. Brake caliper
18. Brake pad
30. Removal tool

2. Remove the anti-rattle spring.
3. Then remove one pad only by pulling out on both tabs with bent pieces of welding rod. Always leave one brake pad in the caliper.
4. Blow off the brake assembly with compressed air and clean the pad guide in the caliper.
5. Check the dust covers for cracks. If cracks exist, the caliper must be disassembled (not separated) and the cover replaced.

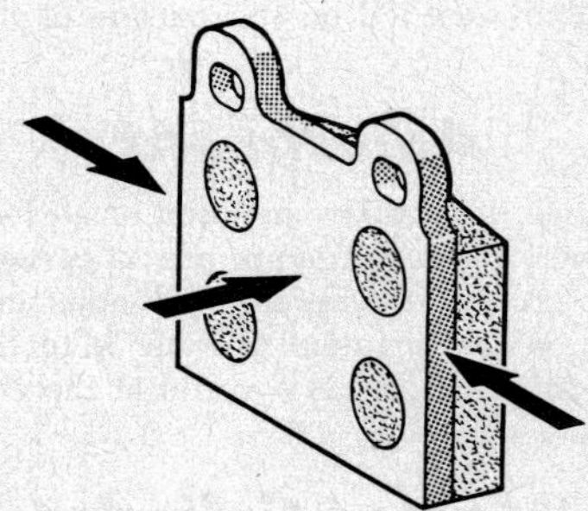

Lubricate the new pad at the areas indicated.

6. Press one piston back into its bore, using special pliers or a flat piece of steel bent to fit. Do not scratch the surface of the piston.

NOTE: *Fluid may be displaced from the master cylinder reservoir. It is wise to siphon off a small amount of fluid to avoid damaging the paint.*

7. Install one friction pad. Before installing the pad, grease the areas illustrated with special grease Molykote-Paste "U"®.

NOTE: *One pad must always remain in the caliper, because pushing one piston back would bring the other forward too far.*

8. Replace the other pad using the same procedure
9. Install the cross spring and retaining pins, then seat the pads by pumping the brake pedal a few times.
10. Hard stopping for the first few hundred miles could ruin the new pads by causing heat glazing.
11. Refill the master cylinder and bleed the brakes.

Disc Brake Calipers

Removal and Installation

All Models

1. Drain brake fluid from the front brake circuit through an open bleeder screw.
2. Disconnect the brake hose from the brake line (or, on some models, disconnect the brake line from the caliper).
3. Immediately plug the lines and openings to prevent loss of fluid.
4. On models where the brake line does not connect directly to the caliper, remove the hose from the caliper.
5. Remove the brake hose from the bracket.
6. Plug the connection at the brake caliper.
7. Unlock the lockwasher and remove the hex mounting bolts.

CAUTION: *The caliper mounting bolts should not be removed unless the calipers are at approximately room temperature.*

8. Remove the calipers from the steering knuckle. As the caliper is removed, take note of any shim that may be installed and tape these (if any) in their original position.

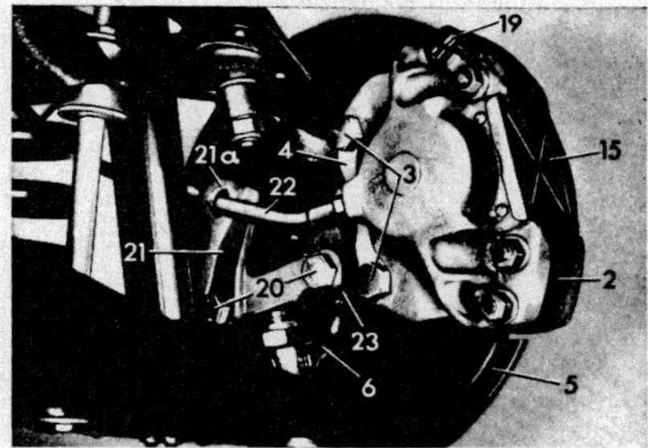

Front wheel disc brake caliper—220D/8 through 280C and 350SL, 450SL, 450SLC.

2. Brake caliper
3. Hex screw
4. Lock plate
5. Cover plate
6. Steering knuckle
15. Shaft cover plate
19. Bleed screw with rubber cap
20. Hexagon screw
21. Bracket
21a. Grommet
22. Brake hose
23. Steering relay lever

9. To install, use a new lockplate and attach the brake caliper to the steering knuckle. The proper torque for the mounting bolts is 82 ft lbs.

It is extremely important that the brake disc be parallel to the caliper. Using a feeler gauge, measure the clearance at the top and bottom of the caliper (between disc and caliper) and on both sides of the disc. The clearance should not vary more than 0.15 mm. If the clearance varies, position the brake caliper by adding or subtracting shims as required. This procedure only applies to models equipped with shims, usually on the rear brake calipers.

Front wheel disc brake caliper—all 280 and 300 series cars (except 280 and 280C).

9. Brake calipers
9a. Code No.
11. Brake line
13. Hex bolt
14. Lockwasher
17. Cover plate
18. Bleeder screw with rubber cap
25. Shaft cover plate

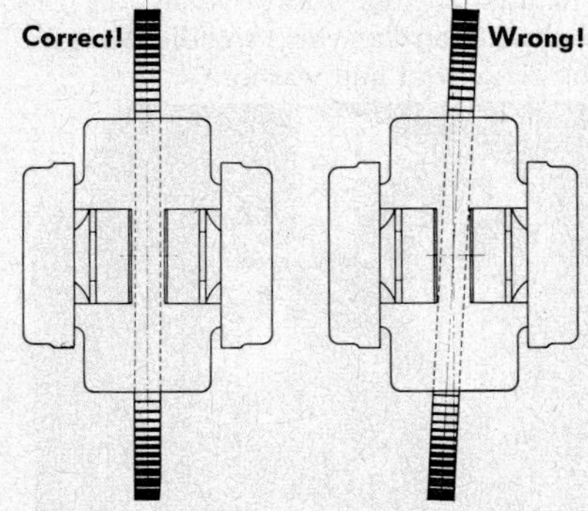

Uneven brake pad wear will result from misaligned calipers and discs.

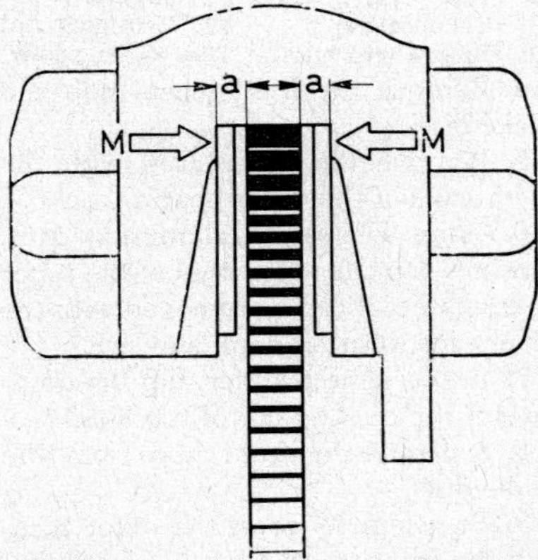

Measure the clearance (a) on each side of the disc at point (M).

10. On all 280 and 300 series cars (except 280 and 280C), the following mounting bolts are used:

a. On vehicles with solid brake discs, use a 34 mm bolt, part no. 111 421 00 71.

b. On vehicles with vented discs, use a 31.5 mm bolt, part no. 109 421 00 71. This bolt is identified with notches on the hex head.

11. Insert the brake hose into the bracket, making sure that the grommet is not damaged, or connect the brake line to the calipers. If applicable, connect the brake hose to the brake line. Make sure that the hose is not twisted.
12. On some models (220D/8, 220/8, 230/8, 250/8, 250C, 280, 280C, 350SL, 450SL, and 450SLC) a locking disc is attached to the brake line bracket. Install the brake hose into the disc so that the disc or hose does not bind.
13. Turn the steering lock-to-lock to make sure that the brake hose or lines do not bind.
14. Fill the master cylinder and bleed the brake system.
15. Before driving the car, depress the brake pedal hard, several times, to seat the pads.

Piston Seal Replacement (Front Brake Caliper)

All Models

CAUTION: *Do not unbolt the two caliper halves for any reason. Remove the brake caliper for easier service.*

1. Remove the friction pads, brake line, and dust cap, then pry the clamp ring from the housing.
2. Using a rubber-backed piece of flat steel, hold one piston in place while blowing the other one out with compressed air (7–8 psi).

NOTE: *If a piston is stuck, clamp the other piston in place and pump the brake pedal. The hydraulic pressure will force the piston out. This is a messy operation, so protect exterior paint from splashing brake fluid.*

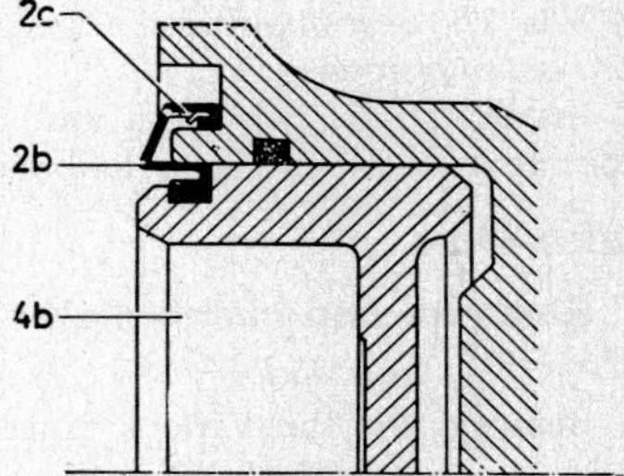

Piston seal and dust cover.

2b. Dust cap
2c. Closed clamp ring
4b. Piston

3. Remove the piston seals from the cylinder bores and examine the bores. Scored bores necessitate replacement of the entire caliper, since the inner surface is chrome plated and cannot be honed.
4. Clean the bores with crocus cloth only, never emery paper.
5. Install the new seals, coating them with brake fluid beforehand, then install the (front) piston so that the projection points downward. The rear caliper pistons must be installed with the projection facing downward.

NOTE: *If the projection is in any other position, the brakes may squeal badly.*

6. Install the dust cap, clamp ring and heat shield.

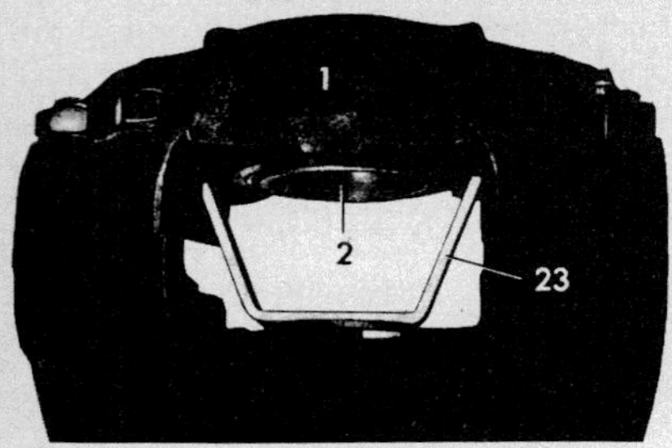

Piston holding fixture installed

1. Brake caliper
2. Piston
23. Holding fixture

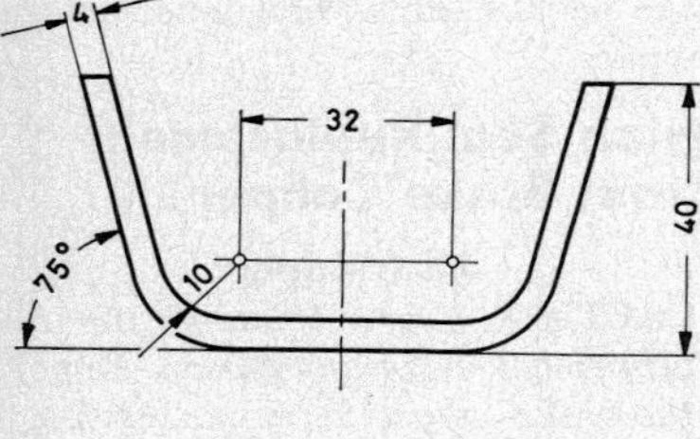

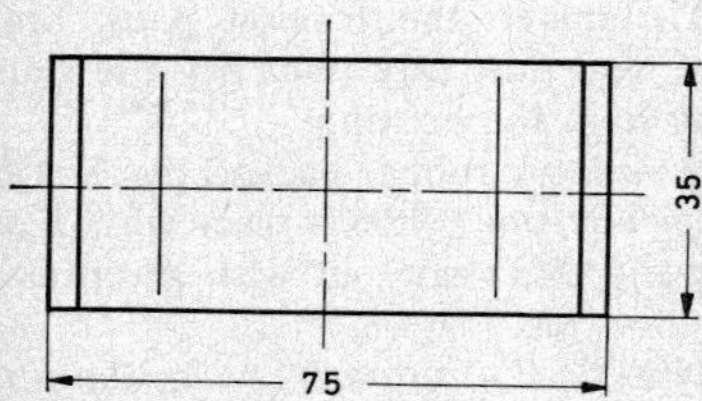

Dimensions for fabricating the piston holding fixture.

7. The recess in the heat shield must fit the piston projection, but be above the shield level by about 0.004 in.

NOTE: *The heat shields differ for inner and outer pistons.*

8. Install the friction pads and the caliper assembly, then bleed the brakes.

Brake Disc

Removal and Installation

All Models

1. Removal for the various types is similar.

2. First, remove the brake caliper, then the front hub. The hub and disc can be removed by prying off the dust cap, removing the socket screw and clamp nut, and pulling off the wheel hub.

3. Fasten the hub in a vise or holding fixture (be careful not to distort the housing), matchmark the disc and hub, then unbolt the brake disc.

4. Inspect the disc for burning (blue color), cracks and scoring. The disc becomes scored slightly in normal service; therefore, replace it only if the depth of individual scores exceeds 0.020 in.

5. To ensure proper alignment, clean the hub and disc with emery paper to remove all rust and/or burrs, then bolt the disc to the hub.

6. It is a wise precaution to use new lockwashers under the bolts.

7. Install the hub and disc, then check the disc for runout (wobble), using a dial indicator as illustrated.

8. If runout is excessive, it sometimes helps to remove the disc and reseat it on the hub. Install the caliper assembly and bleed the brakes.

NOTE: *If new brake discs are being installed, remove the anti-corrosion paint before installing it.*

Wheel Bearings

Removal and Installation

All Models

If the wheel bearing play is being checked for correct setting only, it is not necessary to remove the caliper. It is only necessary to remove the brake pads.

1. Remove the brake caliper.

2. Pull the cap from the hub with a pair of channel-lock pliers.

3. Loosen the socket screw of the clamp nut on the wheel spindle. Remove the clamp nut and washer.

Loosening the Allen screw in the clamp nut

1. Brake disc
2. Brake caliper
10. Front wheel hub
12. Washer
13. Clamping nut
13a. Allen screw

4. Remove the front wheel hub and brake disc.

5. Remove the inner race with the roller cage of the outer bearing.

6. Using a brass or aluminum drift, carefully tap the outer race of the inner bearing until it can be removed with the inner race, bearing cage, and seal.

7. In the same manner, tap the outer race of the bearing out of the hub.

8. Separate the front hub from the brake disc.

9. To assemble, press the outer races into the front wheel hub.

10. Pack the bearing cage with bearing grease and insert the inner race with the bearing into the wheel hub.

11. Coat the sealing ring with sealant and press it into the hub.

12. Pack the front wheel hub with 45–55 grams of wheel bearing grease. The races of the tapered bearing should be well packed and also apply grease to the front faces of the rollers. Pack the front bearings with the specified amount of grease. Too much grease will cause overheating of the lubricant and it may lose its lubricity. Too little grease will not lubricate properly.

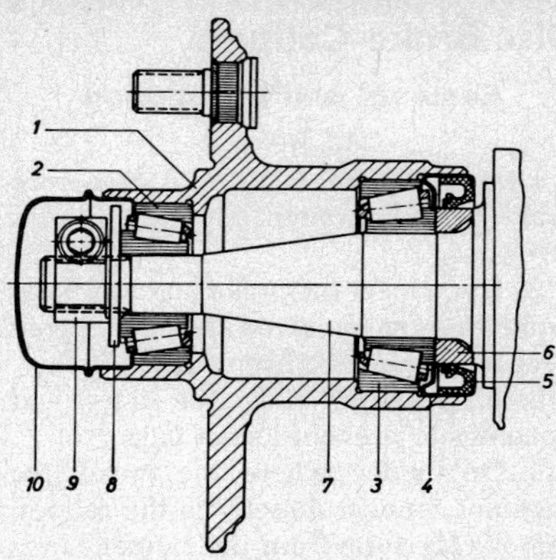

First version wheel bearings

1. Front wheel hub
2. Outer bearing
3. Inner bearing
4. Puller ring
5. Seal
6. Spacer
7. Wheel spindle
8. Washer
9. Clamp nut
10. Dust cap

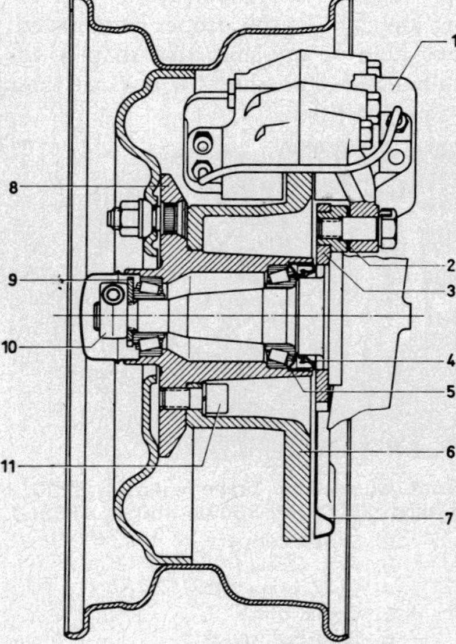

Second version wheel bearings

1. Brake caliper
2. Shim
3. Caliper bracket
4. Seal
5. Puller ring
6. Brake disc
7. Cover plate
8. Wheel hub
9. Washer
10. Clamp nut
11. Screw and lockwasher

13. Coat the contact surface of the sealing ring on the wheel spindle with Molykote® paste.

14. Press the wheel hub onto the wheel spindle.

15. Install the inner race and cage of the outer bearing.

16. Install the steel washer and the clamp nut.

Adjustment

1. Tighten the clamp nut until the hub

can just be turned.

2. Slacken the clamp nut and seat the bearings on the spindle by rapping the spindle sharply with a hammer.

3. Attach a dial indicator, with the pointer indexed, onto the wheel hub. Preload the dial indicator approximately 2 mm.

4. Check the end-play of the hub by pushing and pulling on the flange. The end-play should be approximately 0.0008 in.

5. Make an additional check by rotating the washer between the inner race of the outer bearing and the clamp nut. It should be able to be turned by hand.

6. Check the position of the suppressor pin in the wheel spindle and the contact spring in the dust cap.

7. Pack the dust cap with 20–25 grams of wheel bearing grease and install the cap.

8. Install the brake caliper and bleed the brakes.

Rear Disc Brakes

Disc Brake Pads

Removal and Installation

All Models

The procedure for removing the rear disc brake pads is the same as for front disc brake pads. Use the instructions given under "Front Disc Brake Pad Removal and Installation", with the accompanying illustrations.

Disc Brake Calipers

Removal and Installation

All Models

Use the procedure given under "Front Brake Caliper Removal and Installation". Some rear brake calipers have no disc run-out compensating feature. These calipers can only be installed on vehicles where the rear axle shaft is supported on grooved ball bearings. Calipers with a compensating feature may be installed on axles with grooved ball bearings or self-aligning bearings.

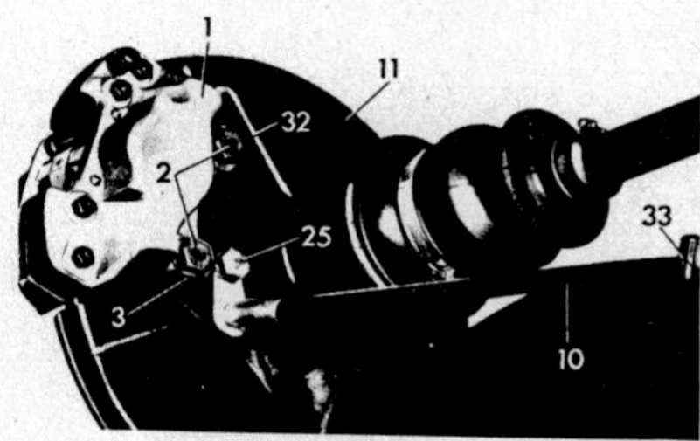

Rear wheel disc brake caliper (models with exposed axle shafts).

1. Brake caliper
2. Hexagon screw
3. Locking plate
10. Brake cable
11. Cover plate
25. Hexagon scrw
32. Brake line
33. Bracket for brake cable with rubber grommet

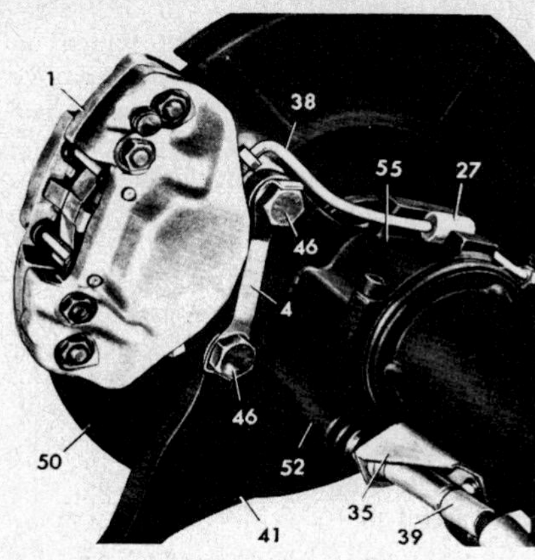

Rear wheel disc brake caliper (models with enclosed axle shafts and brake hold-down).

1. Brake caliper
4. Lockwasher
27. Rubber ring
35. Holder for brake cable control
38. Brake line
39. Brake cable control
41. Lever for brake holddown
46. Bolt
50. Cover plate
52. Rubber sleeve
52. Bearing body

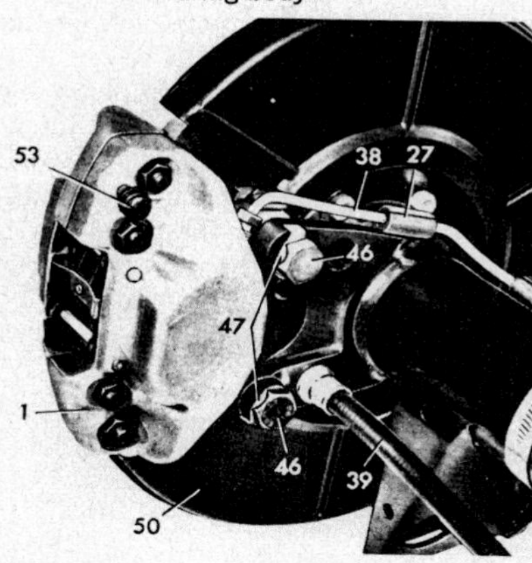

Rear wheel disc brake caliper (models with enclosed axle shafts and no brake hold-down).

1. Brake caliper
27. Rubber ring
38. Brake line
39. Brake cable control
46. Hex bolt
47. Lockwasher
50. Cover plate
53. Bleed screw with rubber cap

Overhaul

Rear disc brake caliper overhaul procedures are the same as those given for front disc brake caliper overhaul.

Brake Discs

Removal and Installation

All Models

1. Remove the brake caliper.

2. Remove the brake disc from the rear axle shaft flange. Jammed brake discs can be loosened from the axle shaft flanges by light taps with a plastic hammer. Be sure that the parking brake is fully released.

3. The air ducts on the vented discs used on the 300SEL 6.3 are provided with spring clips which serve as balancing weights. These should never be removed.

4. Installation is the reverse of removal.

5. Inspection procedures are the same as those for front brake discs.

Handbrake

Front Cable

Removal and Installation

220D/8, 230/8, 220/8, 250/8, 280, 280C

1. Remove the spring from the equalizer.

2. Back off the adjusting screw completely.

3. Detach the relay lever from the bracket on the frame and from the adjusting shackle.

4. Detach the cable from the relay lever by pulling the cotter pin out of the bolt.

5. Remove the clip from the cable guide. Remove the clips from the chassis.

6. Detach the brake cable from the parking brake link. Remove the clip from the cable guide and detach the brake cable from the parking brake.

7. Pull the cable downward from the chassis.

8. Installation is the reverse of removal.

280SL/8

1. Disconnect the return spring from the bracket and compensating lever.

2. Pull the cotter pin from the flange bolt and remove the flange bolt from the compensating lever.

3. Remove the handbrake lever.

4. Remove the brake cable control.

5. Remove the rubber sleeve from the brake cable control.

6. Installation is the reverse of removal.

All 280 and 300 Series Cars (Except 280, 280C, and 280SL/8)

1. Loosen the nut on the intermediate lever.

2. Remove the flange bolt from the intermediate lever.

3. Pull the cotter pin from the brake cable guide of the brake lever. Remove the brake cable control.

4. Installation is the reverse of removal.

350SL, 450SL, 450SLC

1. Remove the exhaust system.

2. Disconnect the spring.

3. Remove the bolts which attach the guide to the intermediate lever.

4. Remove the adjusting screw from

the adjusting bracket.

5. Loosen the brake control cables on the intermediate lever and pull the cotter pin from the flange bolt. Remove the flange bolt.

6. Remove the spring clamp from the cable guide and remove the cable control from the bracket.

7. Remove the tunnel cover.

8. Disconnect the brake control from the parking brake and remove the spring clamp from the cable guide. Remove the cable control from the parking brake.

9. Remove the brake control cable out of the frame toward the rear.

10. Installation is the reverse of removal.

Rear Brake Cable

Removal and Installation

220D/8, 220/8, 230/8, 250/8, 250C, 280, 280C

1. Remove the parking brake shoes after removing the wheel.

2. Remove the screw from the wheel support and detach the brake cable.

3. Back off the adjusting screw from the adjusting shackle.

4. Remove the spring clips, detach the cable, and remove the equalizer.

5. Installation is the reverse of removal.

All 280 and 300 Series Cars (Except 280 and 280C)

1. On all models except 280SL/8, loosen the nut on the intermediate lever and disconnect the return spring.

2. On 280SL/8's, loosen the capstan nut on the brake lever.

3. Loosen the flange nut which attaches the cable to the bracket. Remove the cable control from the bracket and compensating lever.

4. Remove the parking brake shoes.

5. Disconnect the brake control from the expanding lock.

6. On models with a brake hold-down, loosen the holder on the support tube and remove the brake cable together with the rubber sleeve.

7. On models without a brake hold-down, remove the safety from the brake cable and remove the brake cable from the carrier plate.

350SL, 450SL, 450SLC

1. Remove the parking brake shoes.

2. Remove the bolt from the wheel carrier and remove the cable.

3. Remove the exhaust system.

4. Disconnect the spring from the holder.

5. Detach the guide from the intermediate lever.

6. Remove the adjusting screw from the bracket.

7. Disconnect the intermediate lever on the bearing and remove it from the adjusting bracket.

8. Remove the holder, compensating lever, cable control plates, and intermediate lever from the tunnel.

9. Remove the spring clamps and disconnect the cable from the plate.

10. Installation is the reverse of removal.

Adjustment

All Models (Except 280SL/8)

1. If the floor pedal can be depressed more than two notches before actuating the brakes, adjust by jacking up the rear of the car, then removing one lug bolt and adjusting the star wheel with a screwdriver.

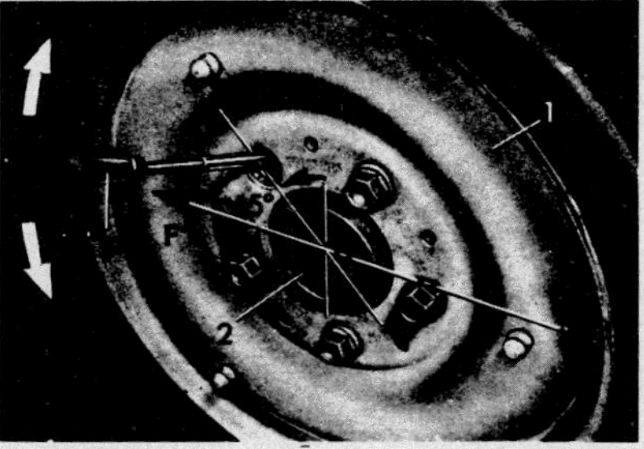

Parking brake adjustment with wheel installed—all models.

1. Disc wheel
2. Rear axle shaft
3. Screwdriver
(f)—Direction of travel

2. Move the screwdriver upward on the left (driver's) side, downward on the right (passenger's) side to tighten the shoes.

3. When the wheel is locked, back off about 2–4 clicks.

4. With this type system, the adjusting bolt on the cable relay lever only serves to equalize cable length; therefore, do not attempt to adjust the brakes by turning this bolt.

280SL/8

1. Adjust the drilled adjustment wheel by inserting a drill rod into the holes.

2. The lever should have to come up only three notches in order to hold the car on a slight grade.

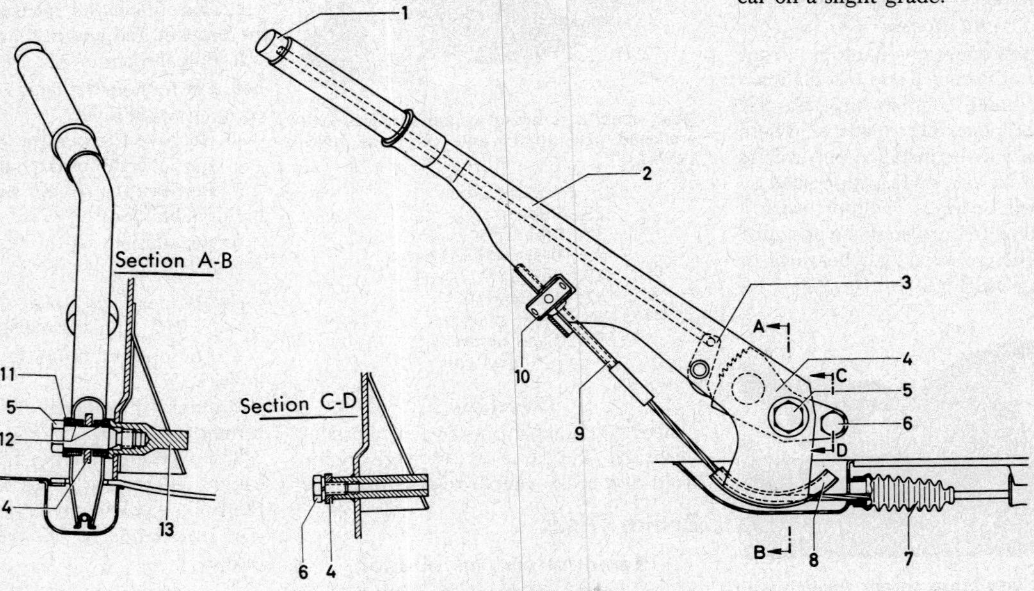

Parking brake adjustment—280SL/8

1. Push button
2. Handbrake lever
3. Pawl
4. Toothed segment
5. Pivot pin
6. Hexagon screw with lockwasher
7. Rubber sleeve
8. Brake cable guide
9. Front brake cable
10. Circular four-hole nut
11. Washer
12. Bearing bushing
13. Threaded member for fastening brake lever to chassis base panel

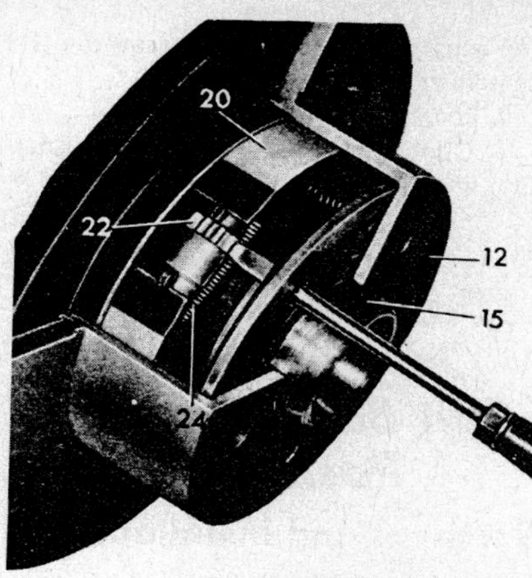

Parking brake adjustment with wheel removed—all models expect 280SL/8.

12. Brake disc
15. Rear axle shaft flange
20. Brake shoes
22. Adjustment device
24. Upper return spring

Parking Brake Shoes

Removal and Installation

All Models

1. Remove the brake caliper.
2. Remove the brake disc.
3. Disconnect the lower spring with brake pliers.
4. Turn the rear axle shaft flange so that one hole faces the spring. With brake spring removal pliers, disconnect and remove the spring from the cover plate.

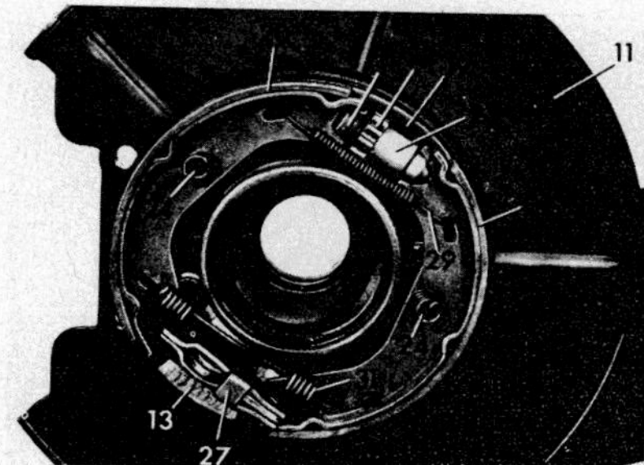

Parking brake shoes installed

11. Cover plate
13. Supporting web
20. Brake shoe
21. Thrust piece
22. Adjusting wheel
23. Thrust sleeve
24. Pressure spring
27. Expanding lock
29. Upper return spring
31. Lower return spring

5. Remove the spring on the other brake shoe in a similar manner.
6. Pull both brake shoes apart so that they can be removed past the rear axle shaft flange.
7. Disconnect the upper return spring from the brake shoes and remove the adjuster.
8. Force the pin out of the expanding lock and remove the expanding lock from the brake cable.
9. Remove the brake shoes.
10. Installation is the reverse of removal. Coat all bearing and sliding surfaces with Molykote® prior to installation. Attach the lower spring with the small eye to the brake shoes.
11. Adjust the parking brakes.

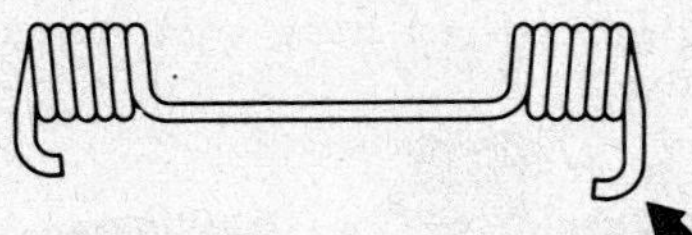

Install the lower parking brake shoe spring with the small eye to the brake shoes.

CHASSIS ELECTRICAL

Heater Box with Heat Exhanger

Removal and Installation

220D/8, 220/8, 230/8 and 250/8

1. Drain the coolant.
2. Detach the hose connections in the engine compartment.
3. Remove the heating duct from the rear seat heating by removing the center support at the top and bottom. Back out the screws on the heating duct and remove the duct.
4. Remove the right defroster vent by detaching the right cover from beneath the instrunment panel. Remove the glove compartment. Detach the connecting hose to the right vent and remove the two nuts from the defroster vent.
5. Remove the left cover from beneath the instrument panel.
6. Remove the two nuts on the supporting brackets.
7. Remove the screw from the transmission tunnel which holds the bottom of the securing bracket.
8. Reach through the glove compartment and remove the rubber sleeve from the center air duct on the heater casing.
9. Detach the ball joint on the linkage to the flap in the center air duct.
10. Remove the left-hand securing nut from the instrument panel.
11. Detach the cable connections from the right-hand side of the heater box.
12. Raise the instrument panel slightly.
13. Remove the heater box from the rubber grommets and remove it toward the right.
14. Removal is the reverse of installation. Lightly grease or wet the rubber grommets before installation. Refill the cooling system.

Heater Blower

Removal and Installation

220D/8, 220/8, 230/8, and 250/8

1. Remove the heater box.
2. Back out the three retaining screws.
3. Slightly pull out the blower and remove the electrical plug and the blower.

Heater blower (220/8 shown)

11,12. Rubber grommets
13. Blower screws
14. Heater box attaching screw

4. Installation is the reverse of removal. To prevent leaks, install the three screws with three new special washers exactly like those removed.

350SL, 450SL and 450SLC

1. Remove the panel which covers the heater blower.
2. Loosen the blower retaining nuts.
3. Pull the plug from the series resistance that is located on the firewall.
4. Remove the series resistance.
5. Lift the cable and remove the blower.
6. Installation is the reverse of removal. Be sure that the sealing frame is not damaged.

Windshield Wipers

Motor

Removal and Installation

220D/8, 220/8, 230/8 and 250/8

If the windshield wiper motor alone is to be removed, do not loosen the setscrew in the linkage, or the linkage will have to be adjusted.

1. Remove the copper plate at the left under the instrument panel.
2. Detach the ball joint from the link rod.
3. Remove the three nuts from the threaded pin.
4. Working from the engine compartment, remove the cable plugs from the motor and remove the motor.
5. Installation is the reverse of removal. Use new washers on the threaded studs.

Left Face Plate/Wiper Shaft Assembly

Removal and Installation

220D/8, 220/8, 230/8, and 250/8

1. Remove the windshield wiper arm.
2. Remove the bushing and nut.
3. Remove the washer and seal.
4. Disengage the ball joints.
5. Remove the retaining screws from the face plate.
6. Remove the face plate and wiper shaft assembly.
7. Installation is the reverse of removal. Be sure that the seal and rubber washer are securely installed.

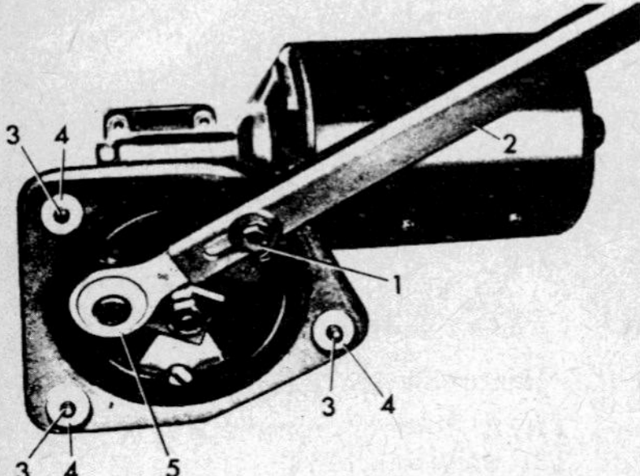

Windshield wiper motor (220/8 through 250/8).

1. Setscrew
2. Link rod
3. Threaded pin
4. Sealing washers
5. Ball joint on motor

Right Face Plate/Wiper Shaft Assembly

Removal and Installation

220D/8, 220/8, 230/8, and 250/8

1. Remove the right windshield wiper arm, bushing, nut, washer, and seal.
2. Remove the left and right cover plates under the dashboard.
3. Remove the glove compartment.
4. Detach the ball joint from the wiper linkage.
5. Remove the two retaining screws from the face plate.
6. Remove the face plate together with the wiper linkage toward the right.
7. Installation is the reverse of removal. Be sure that the seal and rubber washer are securely installed.

Instrument Cluster

Removal and Installation

350SL, 450SL, and 450SLC

1. Remove the padding from the steering wheel.
2. Remove the steering wheel.
3. The instrument cluster is held in place by a rubber ring which fits into a groove. Remove the ring and pull the instrument cluster slightly forward.
4. Loosen and disconnect the speedometer shaft, the electrical plug connections, and the oil pressure line.
5. Completely remove the instrument cluster.

CAUTION: *Do not bend the oil pressure line.*

6. Installation is the reverse of removal. Be sure that the speedometer is not bent excessively or it will vibrate when running.

All Other Models (Except 350SL, 450SL, and 450SLC

1. Remove the cover plate from the left side underneath the dashboard.
2. On vehicles with automatic transmission, disconnect the Bowden cable for the gear selector lever, after engaging Park.

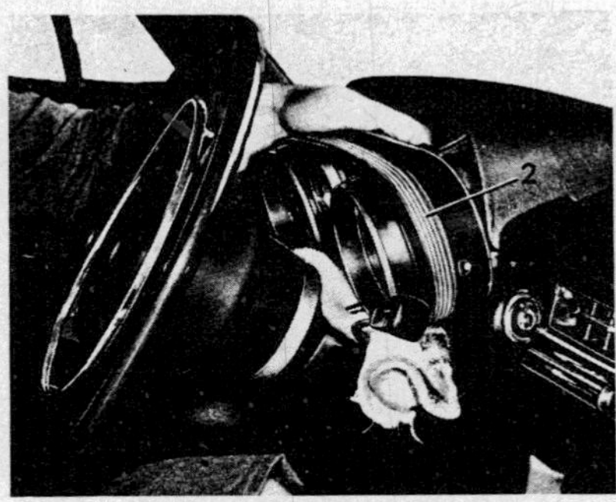

Instrument panel removal showing rubber retaining strip (2).

3. Remove the bracket holding the handbrake.
4. Unscrew the knurled nut and pull the instrument cluster slightly forward.
5. Disconnect the tachometer drive.
6. Cover the steering column to prevent scratches.
7. If only bulb replacement is desired, this is sufficient. To remove the entire cluster, continue with the remaining steps.
8. Disconnect the oil pressure line.
9. Remove the electrical plug connections.
10. Release the excess pressure in the cooling system and install the cap afterward.
11. Remove the temperature sensor from the cylinder head and plug the hole.
12. Carefully remove the instrument cluster with the capillary tube and temperature sensor.

CAUTION: *Do not bend the capillary tube.*

13. Installation is the reverse of removal.

Ignition Switch

Removal and Installation

All Models with Ignition Switch in Dashboard

1. Remove the instrument cluster.
2. Remove the right-hand cover plate under the dashboard.
3. Remove the plug connection from the ignition switch.
4. Remove the screws which hold the ignition switch to the rear of the lock cylinder and remove the ignition switch.
5. To install the ignition switch, attach the plug connection, after fastening the switch to the steering lock.
6. Install the instrument cluster.
7. Check the switch for proper function and install the lower cover.

Lock Cylinder (Dashboard Models Only Where Key Can Be Removed in Position 1)

Removal and Installation

All Models Equipped as Above

1. Turn the key to position 1 and remove the key.
2. Pry the cover sleeve from the lock cylinder with a small screwdriver.
3. Using a bent paper clip, hook onto the cover sleeve and remove the sleeve. Be sure that you do not remove the rosette in the dashboard also.
4. Insert the paper clip between the rosette and the steering lock and push in the lock pin. Remove the lock cylinder slightly with the key.
5. Insert the paper clip into the locking hole and pull the lock cylinder completely out.
6. Installation is the reverse of removal. Turn the lock cylinder to position 1 and insert it into the steering lock, making sure that the lock pin engages. Push the cover sleeve into position 1.
7. Make sure that the cylinder operates properly.

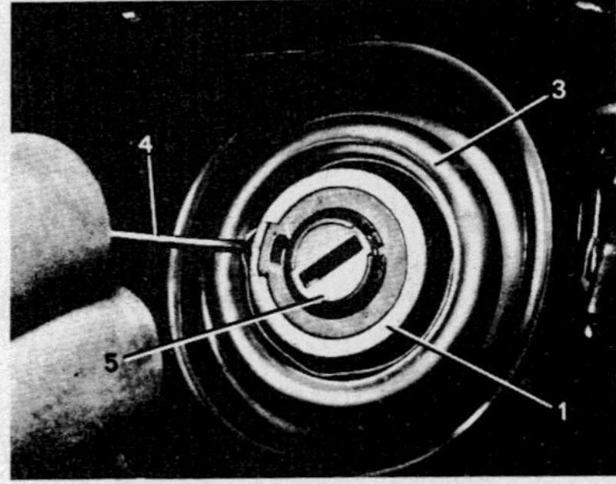

Ignition lock cylinder removal from the instrument panel (both types).

1. Steering lock
3. Rosette
4. Steel wire (paper clip)
5. Locking cylinder

Lock Cylinder (Dashboard Models Only Where Key cannot Be Removed in Position 1)

Removal and Installation

All Models Equipped As Above

Because of legal requirements, the lock was changed from the previous version, so that the key can only be removed in position 0.

1. Turn the key to position 1.
2. Lift the cover sleeve to the edge of the key and turn the key to position 0.
3. Remove the key and cover sleeve.
4. Insert the key into the lock cylinder and turn to position 1 (90° to the right), push in the lock pin and remove the lock cylinder.
5. To install the lock cylinder, turn the lock cylinder to position 1 and insert the lock cylinder, making sure that the locking pin engages.
6. Turn the key to position 0 and remove the key.
7. Place the cover sleeve on the steering lock, insert and turn the key, and push in the cover sleeve at position 1.
8. Check the locking cylinder for proper function.

Steering Lock

Removal and Installation

All Models With Ignition Switch in Dashboard

1. Disconnect the ground cable from the battery.
2. Remove the instrument cluster.
3. Remove the plug connection from the ignition switch behind the dashboard.
4. Pull the ignition key to position 1.
5. Loosen the attaching screw for the steering lock.
6. Remove the cover sleeve from the steering lock.
7. On vehicles with the latest version of the steering lock, pull the connection for the warning buzzer.
8. Push in the lock pin with a small punch.
9. Turn the steering lock and remove it from the holder in the column jacket. Be sure that the rosette is not damaged.

CAUTION: *The lock pin can only be pushed in when the cylinder is in position 1.*

10. To install the steering lock, connect the warning buzzer if so equipped.
11. Place the steering lock in position 1 and insert the lock into the steering column while pushing the lockpin in. Be sure that the lockpin engages.
12. Tighten the attaching clamp screw.
13. Attach the plug connection to the ignition switch.
14. Push the cover sleeve onto the lock in position 1.
15. Install the instrument cluster.
16. Check to be sure that the steering lock works properly.

Headlights

Removal and Installation

220D/8, 220/8, 230/8, 250/8, 250C, 280S/8, 280SL/8, 280 and 280C

1. Loosen the screw on the lower portion of the unit.
2. Remove the trim ring together with the lower part of the unit.
3. Push the retaining ring in and, at the same time, turn the ring left to the stop.
4. Remove the ring, sealed beam lamp, and disconnect the plug.
5. Installation is the reverse of removal. If installing a Mercedes-Benz replacement sealed beam, be sure that the number 2 is at the top in the center. Be sure to have the headlights adjusted.

280SE/8, 280SEL/8, 300SEL/8, 280SE 3.5, 300SEL 3.5, 280SE 4.5, 280SEL 4.5, 300SEL 4.5 and 300 SEL 6.3

1. Loosen and remove the attaching screw for the trim ring.
2. Raise the trim ring slightly and remove it.
3. Remove the attaching screws which hold the sealed beam unit.
4. Remove the attaching rings and sealed beam lights and remove the plug from the rear of the lights.
5. Installation is the reverse of removal. When installing a Mercedes-Benz replacement light, be sure that the number stamped in the glass is facing up and that the plug is tight. Be sure to have the headlights adjusted.

350SL, 450SL and 450SLC

1. Loosen the attaching screws and remove the cover.
2. Remove the headlight attaching screws and remove the retaining ring and light as a unit.
3. Pull the retaining ring and light slightly forward and disconnect the plug.
4. Remove the headlight and retaining ring.
5. Installation is the reverse of removal. Be sure that the plug and socket on the rear of the light are tight.

Fuses

Fuse Box Location

220D/8, 220/8, 230/8, 250/8 and 250C

The main fuse box is located in the engine compartment, on the fender, next to the master cylinder. The amperage of the fuses and protected circuits is stamped on the cover of the fuse box. In addition, various other electrical equipment is fused separately. The additional fuse boxes are also located in the engine compartment. Replacement fuses are located in the fuse box.

280S/8, 280SE/8, 280SEL/8, 300SEL/8, 280SE 3.5, 300SEL 3.5, 280SEL 4.5, 300SEL 4.5, 300SEL 6.3, 280, and 280C

The fuse box is located in the kick panel on the driver's side. Protected circuits and amperage of fuses is contained on the cover of the fuse box. Separate fuse boxes for additional equipment are located in the engine compartment.

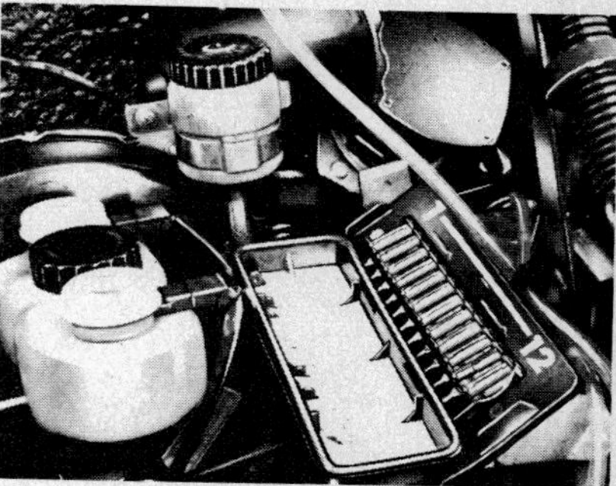

Fuse box—220D/8, 220/8, 230/8, 250/8, and 250C.

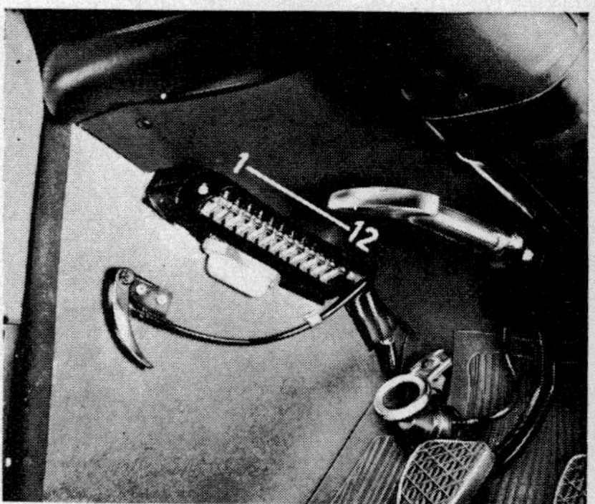

Fuse box—280S/8, 280SE/8, 280SEL/8, 300SEL/8, 280SE 3.5, 300SEL 3.5, 280-SEL 4.5, 300SEL 4.5, 300SEL 6.3, 280, and 280C.

280SL

The fuse box is located inside the engine compartment on the right-hand side of the firewall. The fuses are numbered 1–12 from inboard to outboard. In addi-

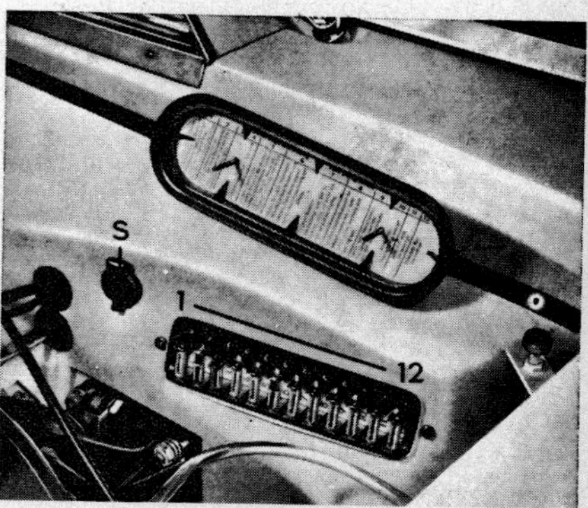

Fuse box 280SL/8 (S is a socket)

tion, there are several other small fuse boxes located in the engine compartment which protect other separate components.

350SL, 450SL and 450SLC

The fuse box is located in the kick panel on the right-hand (passenger) side. The protected circuits and fuse amperage are printed on the cover of the fuse box. Spare fuses and a fuse removal and installation tool are stowed with the tool kit.

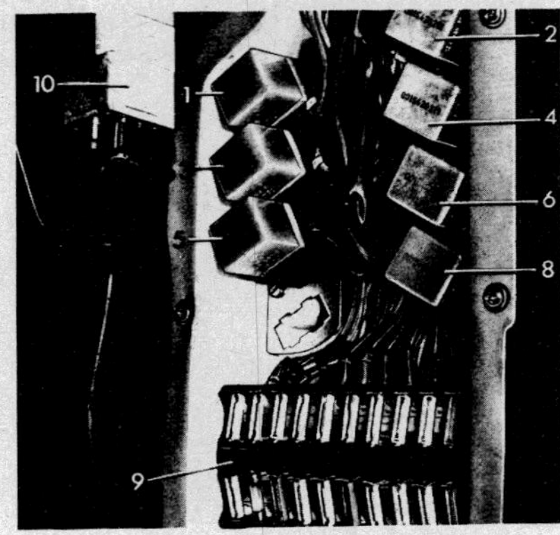

Fuse box and relays—350CSL, 450SL, and 450SLC.

1. Relay for fuel pump
2. Relay for starting valve automatic choke
3. Relay for electronic control unit
4. Relay for starter (terminal 50)
5. Relay for 2-way valve (exhaust emission control)
6. Relay for air conditioning (fan)
8. Relay for disconnecting electric fan when ignition is retarded

when ignition is retarded

9. Fuse box
10. Time switch for heated rear window

M G

Index

MODEL IDENTIFICATION

MGB 1961-70; MGC 1968-69

MGB-GT 1971-72

MGB 1971-72

MG Midget, 1961-70

MGB-GT 1966-70; MGC-GT 1968-69

MG Midget, 1971-72

SERIAL NUMBER IDENTIFICATION

Vehicle

The Vehicle Serial Number can be found stamped on a plate located on the inner fender panel of the engine compartment. Late model cars have this plate located on the top of the dashboard, visible through the windshield.

Vehicle Identification—Midget

Year	Model	Serial Numbers
1961-62	Mk. I	G-AN1/*101-16,183
1963-64	Mk. I	G-AN2/*16,184-25,787
1965-66	Mk. II	G-AN3/*25,788-52,389
1967-69	Mk. III	G-AN4/*52,390-74,885
1970-72	Mk. III	G-AN5/*74,886-**

Vehicle Identification—MGB

Year	Model	Serial Numbers
1961-67	Conv.	G-HN3/*101-138,400
1968-69	Conv.	G-HN4/*138,401-187,210
1970-72	Conv.	G-HN5/*187,211-**
1966-67	GT	G-HD3/*71,933-139,471
1968-69	GT	G-HD4/*139,472-187,840
1970-72	GT	G-HD5/*187,841-**

Vehicle Identification—MGC

Year	Model	Serial Numbers
1968-69	Conv.	G-CN1/*101-***
1968-69	GT	G-CD1/*101-***

Engine

The engine serial number is located on a plate riveted to the engine block on the distributor side.

Engine Identification—Midget

No. of Cylinders (All inline)	Displacement (cc.)	Type	Serial Number
4	948	OHV	9CG/Da/H 101-36,711
4	1,098	OHV	10CG/Da/H 101-21,048
4	1,098	OHV	10CC/Da/H 101-16,300
4	1,275	OHV	12CC/Da/H 101-16,300
4	1,275	OHV	12CE/Da/H 101-
4	1,275	OHV	12CD/Da/H 101-
4	1,275	OHV	12CJ/Da/H 101-
4	1,275	OHV	12V/587Z/L 101-

Engine Identification—MGB**

No. of Cylinders (All inline)	Displacement (cc.)	Type	Number Serial
4	1,798	OHV	18G/U/H 101-31,121
4	1,798	OHV	18GA/U/H 101-17,500
4	1,798	OHV	18GB/*/H 101-91,200
4	1,798	OHV	18GF/*/H 101-13,650
4	1,798	OHV	18GH/*/H 101-
4	1,798	OHV	18GJ/*/H 101-
4	1,798	OHV	18GK/*/H 101-
4	1,798	OHV	18/584Z/L 101-

**—In late 1967 and early 1968 a few cars with 18GD or 18GG engines may have been imported. Specifications for these engines are the same as for the 18GF engine except for carburetors, which are the same as those on the 18GB engine.

Engine Identification—MGC

No. of Cylinders	Displacement (cc.)	Type	Serial Number
6-inline	2,912	OHV	29GA/—/H 101-

FIRING ORDERS

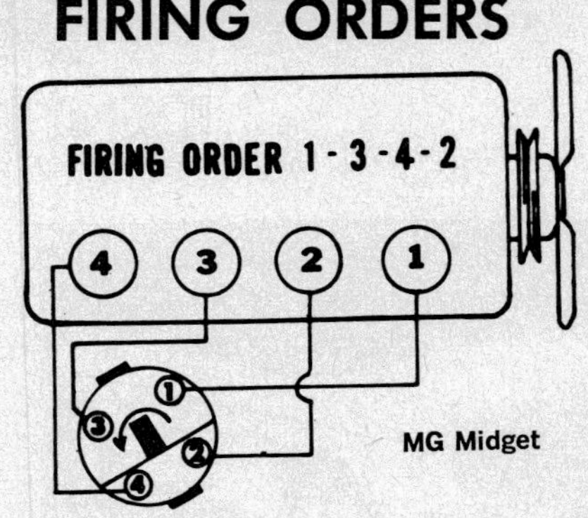

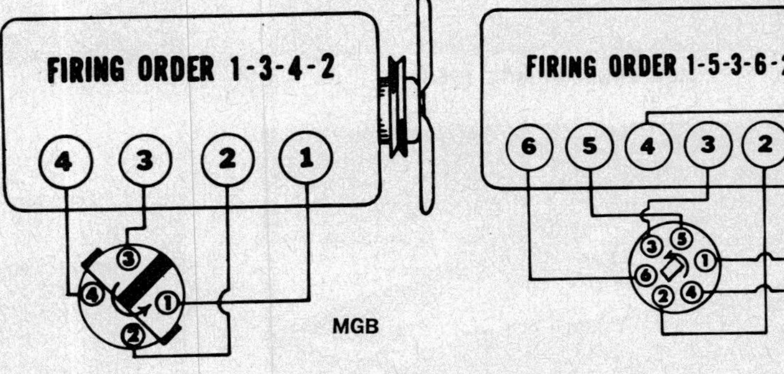

TUNE-UP SPECIFICATIONS

Model/Year	Engine Code	Spark Plugs Champion	Spark Plugs Gap (in.)	Distributor Dwell (deg.)	Distributor Gap (in.)	Timing Static (deg. BTDC)	Compression pressure (psi)	Valves Clearance (in.) Intake	Valves Clearance (in.) Exhaust	Valves Intake Opens (deg.)	Idle Speed (rpm)
Midget Mk. I											
1961-62	9CG	N5	0.025	60	0.015	4	165	0.012C	0.012C	5B	1,000
1963-64	10CG	N5	0.025	60	0.015	5	165	0.012C	0.012C	5B	1,000
Midget Mk. II											
1965-66	10CC	N5	0.025	60	0.015	5	165	0.012C	0.012C	5B	1,000
Midget Mk. III											
1967	12CC/12CE	N9Y	0.025	60	0.015	7	120	0.012C	0.012C	5B	700
1968-70	12CD	N9Y	0.025	60	0.015	4	120	0.012C	0.012C	5B	1,000
1971	12CJ	N9Y	0.025	60	0.015	4	120	0.012H	0.012H	5B	1,000
1972	12V	N9Y	0.025	60	0.015	10	120	0.012C	0.012C	5B	1,000
MGB											
1961-64	18G/18GA	N9Y	0.025	60	0.015	10	160	0.015C	0.015C	16B	500
1965-67	18GB	N9Y	0.025	60	0.015	10	160	0.015C	0.015C	16B	500
1968-69	18GF	N9Y	0.025	60	0.015	10	160	0.015C	0.015C	16B	900
1970	18GH	N9Y	0.025	60	0.015	10	160	0.015C	0.015C	16B	900
	18GJ	N9Y	0.025	60	0.015	10	160	0.015C	0.015C	16B	900
1971	18GK	N9Y	0.025	60	0.015	10	160	0.015C	0.015C	16B	900
1972	18V	N9Y	0.025	60	0.015H	10	160	0.015H	0.015H	16B	850
MGC											
1968-69	29GA	N9Y	0.025	35	0.015	TDC	155	0.015C	0.015C	16B	850
MGB											
1973	18V	N9Y	0.025	60	0.015	11	160	0.015H	0.015H	16B	1,500
MGB-GT											
1973	18V	N9Y	0.025	60	0.015	11	160	0.015H	0.015H	16B	1,500

B Before Top Dead Center.
C Engine cold.
H Engine hot.
* See text for dynamic timing specifications.

NOTE: If any discrepancies exist between the above information and the data on the Tune-up Specifications in the engine compartment, use the data on the sticker.

GENERAL ENGINE SPECIFICATIONS

Model/Year	Engine Code	Displacement	Carburetor Type (S.U.)	Advertised Horsepower @ RPM	Advertised Torque @ RPM	Bore and Stroke (in.)	Comp. Ratio	Oil Pressure
Midget Mk. I								
1961-62	9CG	948 cc.	HS2 (2)	46 @ 5,500	53 @ 3,000	2.478 x 3.000	8.9:1	30-60
1963-64	10CG	1,098 cc.	HS2 (2)	55 @ 5,500	62 @ 3,250	2.543 x 3.296	8.9:1	30-60
Midget Mk. II								
1965-66	10CC	1,098 cc.	HS2 (2)	59 @ 5,750	65 @ 3,500	2.543 x 3.296	8.9:1	30-60
Midget Mk. III								
1967	12CC/12CE	1,275 cc.	HS2 (2)	65 @ 6,000	72 @ 3,000	2.780 x 3.200	8.8:1	40-70
1968-70	12CD①	1,275 cc.	HS2 (2)	62 @ 6,000	72 @ 3,000	2.780 x 3.200	8.8:1	40-70
1971	12CJ②	1,275 cc.	HS2 (2)	62 @ 6,000	72 @ 3,000	2.780 x 3.200	8.8:1	40-70
MGB								
1961-64	18G/18GA	1,798 cc.	HS4 (2)	98 @ 5,400	110 @ 3,000	3.160 x 3.500	8.8:1	50-80
1965-67	18GB	1,798 cc.	HS4 (2)	98 @ 5,400	110 @ 3,000	3.160 x 3.500	8.8:1	50-80
1968-69	18GF①	1,798 cc.	HS4 (2)	92 @ 5,200	110 @ 3,000	3.160 x 3.500	8.8:1	50-80
1970	18GH①	1,798 cc.	HS4 (2)	92 @ 5,200	110 @ 3,000	3.160 x 3.500	8.8:1	50-80
	18GJ②	1,798 cc.	HS4 (2)	92 @ 5,200	110 @ 3,000	3.160 x 3.500	8.8:1	50-80
1971	18GK③	1,798 cc.	HS4 (2)	92 @ 5,200	110 @ 3,000	3.160 x 3.500	8.8:1	50-80
MGC								
1968-69	29GA①	2,912 cc.	HS6 (2)	145 @ 5,250	170 @ 3,500	3.280 x 3.500	9.0:1	50-70
MGB								
1972-73	18GK	1,798 cc.	HIF4 (2)	92 @ 5,200	110 @ 3,000	3.160 x 3.500	8.0:1	50-80
MGB-GT								
1972-73	18GK	1,798 cc.	HIF4 (2)	92 @ 5,200	110 @ 3,000	3.160 x 3.500	8.0:1	50-80

① Exhaust Emission Control System fitted.
② Exhaust Emission Control and Evaporative Loss Control Systems fitted.
③ Exhaust Emission Control, Evaporative Loss Control, and NOx Systems fitted.

PISTON AND RING SPECIFICATIONS

Model & Engine	PISTON SPECIFICATIONS (in.)				RING SPECIFICATIONS (in.)			
			SKIRT CLEARANCE		COMPRESSION		OIL CONTROL	
	Oversize Maximum	Wrist Pin Diameter	Top	Bottom	End-Gap	Side Clearance	End-Gap	Side Clearance
Midget								
9CG	+.040	0.6244-0.6246	0.0036-0.0032	0.0016-0.0022	0.007-0.012	0.0015-0.0035	0.007-0.012	0.0015-0.0035
10CG/10CC	+.020	0.6244-0.6246	0.0021-0.0037	0.0005-0.0011	0.007-0.012	0.002-0.004	0.012-0.028	0.0015-0.0035
12CC/12CE/12CD/12CJ	+.020	0.8123-0.8125	0.0029-0.0037	0.0015-0.0021	0.008-0.013①	0.0015-0.0035	0.012-0.028	0.0015-0.0035
MGB								
18G/18GA	+.040	0.7499-0.7501	0.0036-0.0045	0.0018-0.0024	0.012-0.017	0.0015-0.0035	0.012-0.017	0.0016-0.0036
18GB	+.040	0.8124-0.8127	0.0021-0.0033	0.0006-0.0012	0.012-0.017	0.0015-0.0035	0.012-0.017	0.0016-0.0036
18GF/18GH/18GJ/18GK	+.040	0.8125-0.8127	0.0021-0.0033	0.0006-0.0012	0.012-0.022	0.0015-0.0035	0.015-0.045	0.0016-0.0036
MGC								
29GA	+.040	0.8748-0.8750	0.0028-0.0040	0.0017-0.0023-	0.012-0.016	0.0025-0.0035	0.015-0.045	0.0016-0.0036

① Top compression ring—0.011-0.011 in.

VALVE SPECIFICATIONS

Model & Engine	Seat Angle (deg.)	Valve Lift (in.) In-take	Valve Lift (in.) Ex-haust	Valve Head Diameter (in.) Intake	Valve Head Diameter (in.) Exhaust	Valve Spring Free Length (in.) Inner	Valve Spring Free Length (in.) Outer	Spring Pressure (lbs.)② In-take	Spring Pressure (lbs.)② Ex-haust	Stem Diameter (in.) Intake	Stem Diameter (in.) Exhaust	Stem to Guide Clearance (in.) Intake	Stem to Guide Clearance (in.) Exhaust	Guide Height Above Head (in.)
Midget 9CG	45	0.312	0.312	1.151-1.156	1.000-1.005	1.672	1.750	118	118	0.2793-0.2798	0.2788-0.2793	0.0015-0.0025	0.002-0.003	19/32
10CG/10CC	45	0.312	0.312	1.213-1.218	1.000-1.005	1.672	1.750	118	118	0.2793-0.2798	0.2788-0.2793	0.0015-0.0025	0.002-0.003	19/32
12CC/12CE/12CD/12CJ	45	0.318	0.318	1.307-1.312	1.152-1.156	1.703	1.828	131	131	0.2793-0.2798	0.2788-0.2793	0.0015-0.0025	0.0015-0.0025	19/32③
MGB All Eng. Series	45.5	0.3645	0.3645	1.562-1.567	1.343-1.348	1.969	2.141	167	167	0.3422-0.3427	0.3417-0.3422	0.0015-0.0025	0.002-0.003	3/4
MGC 29GA	45	0.250 ①	0.250 ①	1.745-1.750	1.558-1.563	1.969	2.141	167	167	0.3422-0.3427	0.3422-0.3427	0.0016-0.0026	0.002-0.003	5/8

① From engine number 29GA/1401—0.3417-0.3422 in.
② Combined pressure of inner and outer valve springs with valve fully open.
③ 12CD and 12CJ engines should only use valve guides having an identification groove machined 0.187 in. from the guide top.

TORQUE SPECIFICATIONS (ft. lbs.)

Model & Engine	Cylinder Head Bolts	Main Bearing Bolts	Rod Bearing Bolts	Crankshaft Damper Bolt(s)①	Flywheel to Crankshaft Bolt(s)	Manifold Nuts Intake	Manifold Nuts Exhaust
Midget 9CG/10CG/10CC	40	60	35	70	40	15	15
12CC/12CE/12CD/12CJ	42②	60	45③	70	40	15	15
MGB All Engine Series	45-50	70	35-40	70	40	15	15
MGC 29GA	75	75	50	N.A.	50	42	42

① Torque figure given applies to crankshaft pulley on cars not equipped with damper.
② Studs stamped 22 or with small drill point—50.
③ Nylon-type locknut—32-34.

TIGHTENING SEQUENCES

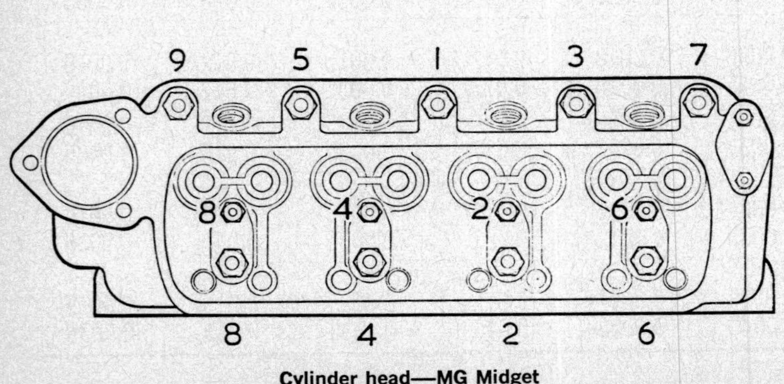

Cylinder head—MG Midget

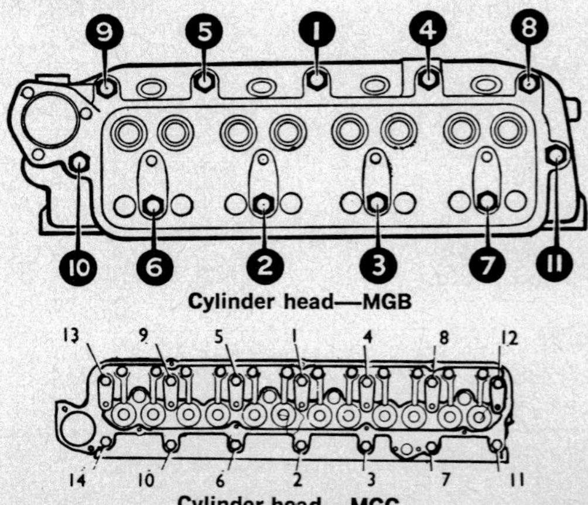

Cylinder head—MGB

Cylinder head—MGC

CAPACITIES AND PRESSURES

Model & Engine	CRANKCASE (qts.) With Filter	Without Filter	TRANSMISSION (pts.) 4-Speed	4-Speed with O.D.	Auto.	Drive Axle (pts.)	Fuel Tank (gals.)	Coolant with Heater (qts.)	Fuel Pressure (psi)	Coolant Pressure (max. psi)
Midget										
9CG/10CG	4.0	3.5	2.7	—	—	2.1	7.2	6.3	1.5-2.5	7
10CC/12CC/12CE	4.0	3.5	2.7	—	—	2.1	7.2	6.3	2.5-3.0	7
12CD/12CJ	4.0	3.5	2.7	—	—	2.1	7.2①	6.3	2.5-3.0	15
MGB										
18G	4.5	4.0	5.6	6.0	—	2.8	10.0	6.0	1.5-2.0	7
18GA	4.5	4.0	5.6	6.0	—	2.8	12.0	6.0	2.5-3.0	7
18GB	4.5	4.0	5.6	6.0	—	2.8	12.0	6.0	2.5-3.0	7
18GF/18GH/18GJ/18GK	4.5	4.5	6.0	7.0	12.7	2.0	12.0②	6.0	2.5-3.0	10
MGC										
29GA	8.5	8.5	6.3	7.2	17.3	2.0	14.0	11.0	3.5-4.0	14

① 12CJ—6.0 gallons.

② 18GJ and 18GK—10.0 gallons.

Brake Specifications (in.)

Model & Engine	TYPE (Lockheed) & DIAM. Front	Rear	BRAKE CYLINDER BORE Master Cylinder	WHEEL CYLINDER Front	Rear
Midget 9CG	drum 7.0	drum 7.0	7/8	15/16	3/4
10CG/ 10CC	disc 8 1/4	drum 7.0	3/4	2 1/4	3/4
12CC/ 12CE/ 12CD/ 12CJ	disc 8 1/4	drum 7.0	1 1/16	2 1/4	3/4
MCB All Eng. Series	disc 10 3/4	drum 10.0	3/4	2 3/8	3/4
MCG 29GA	disc 11.0	drum 9.0	1.0	N.A.	N.A.

WHEEL ALIGNMENT SPECIFICATIONS

Model & Engine	Wheelbase (in.)	TRACK (in.) Front	Rear	CASTER (deg.) Range	Ideal	CAMBER (deg.) Range	Ideal	Toe-In (in.)	Kingpin Inclination (deg.)	WHEEL PIVOT RATIO (deg.) Inner	Outer
Midget											
9CG/10CG/10CC	80	45 3/4	44 3/4	—	3P	—	3/4N	1/8	6 3/4	20	18 1/2
12CC/12CE/ 12CD/12CJ	80	46 5/16	45 1/4	—	3P	—	3/4N	1/8	6 3/4	20	19 3/4
MGB											
All Engine Series	91	49 1/4	49 1/4	5P-7 1/4P	7P	1/4N-1 1/4P	1P	1/16	8	20	19
MGC											
29GA	91	50	49 1/4	4P-5 1/4P	5P	1N-1/6P	0	1/16	9	18 3/4	20

CRANKSHAFT SPECIFICATIONS

Model & Engine	MAIN BEARING JOURNALS (in.) Journal Diameter New	Journal Diameter Minimum	Oil Clearance	Shaft End-Play	Thrust On No.	CONNECTING ROD BEARING JOURNALS (in.) Journal Diameter New	Journal Diameter Minimum	Oil Clearance	End-Play
Midget 9CG/10CG	1.7505-1.7510	−0.040	0.001-0.0025	0.002-0.003	2	1.6254-1.6259	−0.040	0.001-0.0025	0.008-0.012
10CC	2.0005-2.0010	−0.040	0.001-0.0025	0.002-0.003	2	1.6254-1.6259	−0.040	0.001-0.0025	0.008-0.012
12CC/12CE/12CD/12CJ	2.0005-2.0010	−0.010①	0.001-0.0027	0.002-0.003	2	1.6254-1.6259	−0.010①	0.001-0.0025	0.006-0.010
MGB 18G/18GA②	2.1262-2.1270	−0.040	0.001-0.0027	0.004-0.005	2	1.8759-1.8764	−0.040	0.001-0.0027	0.008-0.012
18GB/18GF/18GH/18GJ/18GK	2.1262-2.1270	−0.040	0.001-0.0027	0.004-0.005	3	1.8759-1.8764	−0.040	0.001-0.0027	0.008-0.012
MGC 29GA	2.3742-2.3747	−0.020	0.0009-0.0027	0.002-0.0036	3	2.0000-2.0005	−0.020	0.001-0.0027	0.008-0.012

① Maximum permissible without heat treatment.
② 18G and 18GA engines have 3 main bearings. All later engines have 5 main bearings.

CARBURETOR SPECIFICATIONS

Model/Engine	S.U. Type	Throat Diameter (in.)	Main Jet Size (in.)	JET NEEDLE④ IDENTIFICATION NO. Standard	Rich	Lean	Piston Spring Strength (Color identification)
Midget							
9CG	HS2	1.25	.090	V3	V2	GX	light blue
10CG	HS2	1.25	.090	GY	M	GG	blue
10CC	HS2	1.25	.090	AN	H6	GG	blue
12CC/12CE	HS2	1.25	.090	AN	H6	GG	light blue
12CD/12CJ	HS2	1.25	.090	AAC①	—	—	blue
MGB							
18G/18GA	HS4	1.50	.090	MB	6	21	red
18GB	HS4	1.50	.090	FX	6	21	red
18GF/18GH	HS4	1.50	.090	AAL②	—	—	red
178GJ	HS4	1.50	.090	AAE②	—	—	red
18GK	HS4	1.50	.090	AAL	—	—	red
MGC							
29GA	HS6	1.75	.100	BAD③	—	—	yellow

① Fixed needle—AN.
② Fixed needle—FX.
③ Fixed needle—KM.
④ Most emission control engines are fitted with spring-loaded jet needles.

ELECTRICAL SPECIFICATIONS

Model & Engine	Battery ②: Capacity (amp. hrs.)	Battery ②: Volts	Battery ②: Grounded Terminal	Starter (Lucas): Type	Lock Test: Amps	Lock Test: Volts	Lock Test: Torque (ft. lb.)	No Load Test: Amps	No Load Test: Volts	No Load Test: Rpm	Brush Spring Tension (oz.)
Midget 9CG/10CG/10CC	43	12	Pos.	M35G	250-365	7	6.7	60	11.5	8,000-11,500	25
12CC/12CE/12CD/12CJ	50	12	Neg.①	M35J	250-375	7	7.0	65	11.5	8,000-10,000	28
MGB 18G/18GA/18GB	58	12	Pos.	M418G	450	7	14.5	70	11.5	5,500-8,000	32
18GF/18GH/18GJ/18GK	60	12	Neg.③	M418G	465	7	17.0	70	11.5	5,800-6,500	36
MGC 29GA	64	12	Neg.	M418G	465	7	17.0	70	11.5	5,800-6,500	36

① Positive ground up to car number G-AN4/60,460. Positive ground cars (12CC engine only) use the M35G starter.
② MGB and MGC equipped with two 6-volt batteries. Specifications apply to the two batteries wired together in series.
③ Positive ground up to car number G-HN4/138,801 (Conv.), and G-HD4/139,824 (GT).

Model & Engine	Generator (Lucas): Type	Output (amps)	Brush Pressure (oz.)	Resistance (ohms)	Regulator (Lucas): Type	Cut-Out Relay: Points Close (volts)	Cut-Out Relay: Reverse Current (amps)	Cut-Out Relay: Points Air Gap (in.)	Maximum Current (amps)	Points Air Gap (in.)
Midget 9CG (1961)	C39	19	18-26	6.0-6.3	RB106	12.7-13.3	5.0	②	19	②
9CG (1962)	C39	19	18-26	6.0-6.3	RB106/2	12.7-13.3	5.0	②	19	②
10CG/10CC	C40/1	22	22-25	6.0	RB106/2	12.7-13.3	5.0	②	19	②
12CC/12CE/12CD/12CJ	C40/1	22	22-25	6.0	RB340①	12.7-13.3	5.0	②	22	②
MGB 18G/18GA/18GB	C40/1	22	22-25	6.0	RB340	12.7-13.3	5.0	②	22	②

① Early cars (12CC engine with positive ground) use the RB106/2 regulator.
② The settings of the points should never need adjustment. See text for further explanation.

Model & Engine	Alternator (Lucas): Type	Output @ Engine RPM (amps): 850	Output @ Engine RPM (amps): 3,300	Field Current Draw (amps @ 12V)	Brush Tension (oz.)	Regulator (Lucas): Type	Field Relay: Air Gap (in.)	Field Relay: Point Gap (in.)	Points Close (volts)	Air Gap (in.)	Volts @ 125 deg.
MGB 18GF	16AC	12-15	34	3	7-10	4TR	Transistor type—no adjustment				14.3-14.7
18GH/18GJ/18GK	16ACR	12-15	34	3	7-10	8TR 11TR	Integral with alternator, transistor type—no adjustment				14.0-14.4 14.0-14.4
MGC 29GA	16AC	12-15	34	3	7-10	4TR	Transistor type—no adjustment				14.3-14.7

WIRING DIAGRAMS

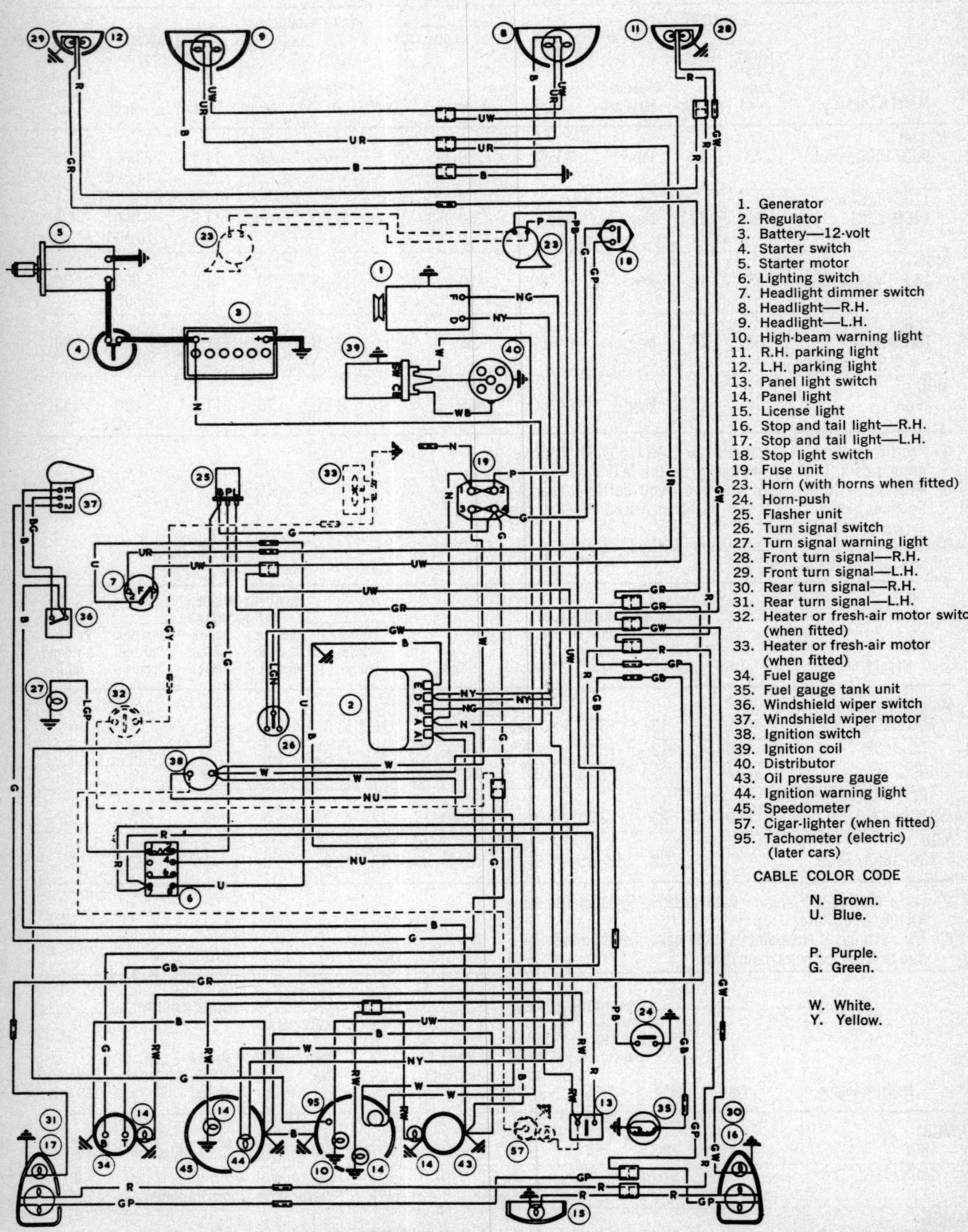

Midget Mk. I

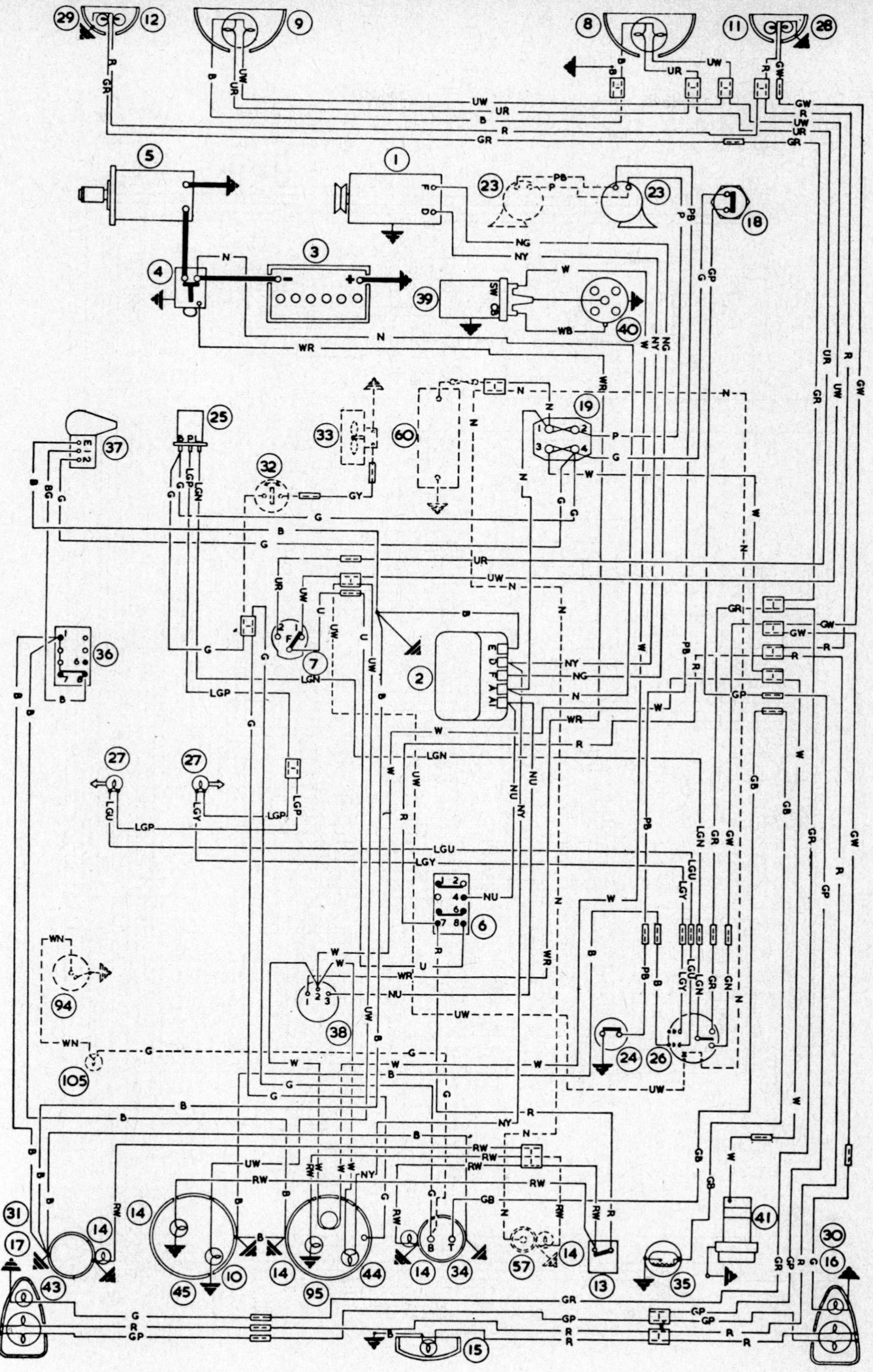

Midget Mk. I and II

See page 616 for key

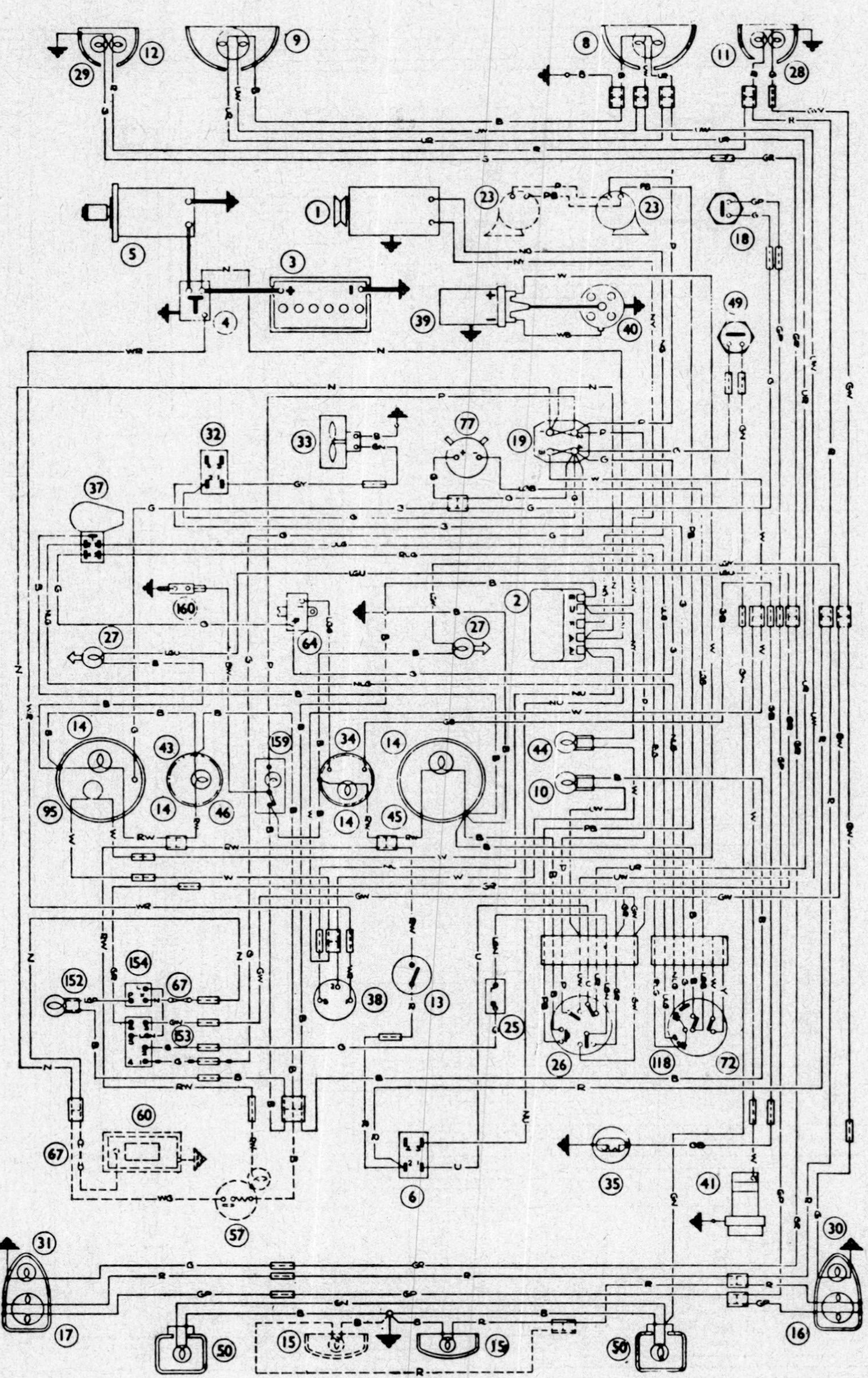

Midget Mk. III from Car Number G-AN4/60460, Neg. Ground

See page 616 for key

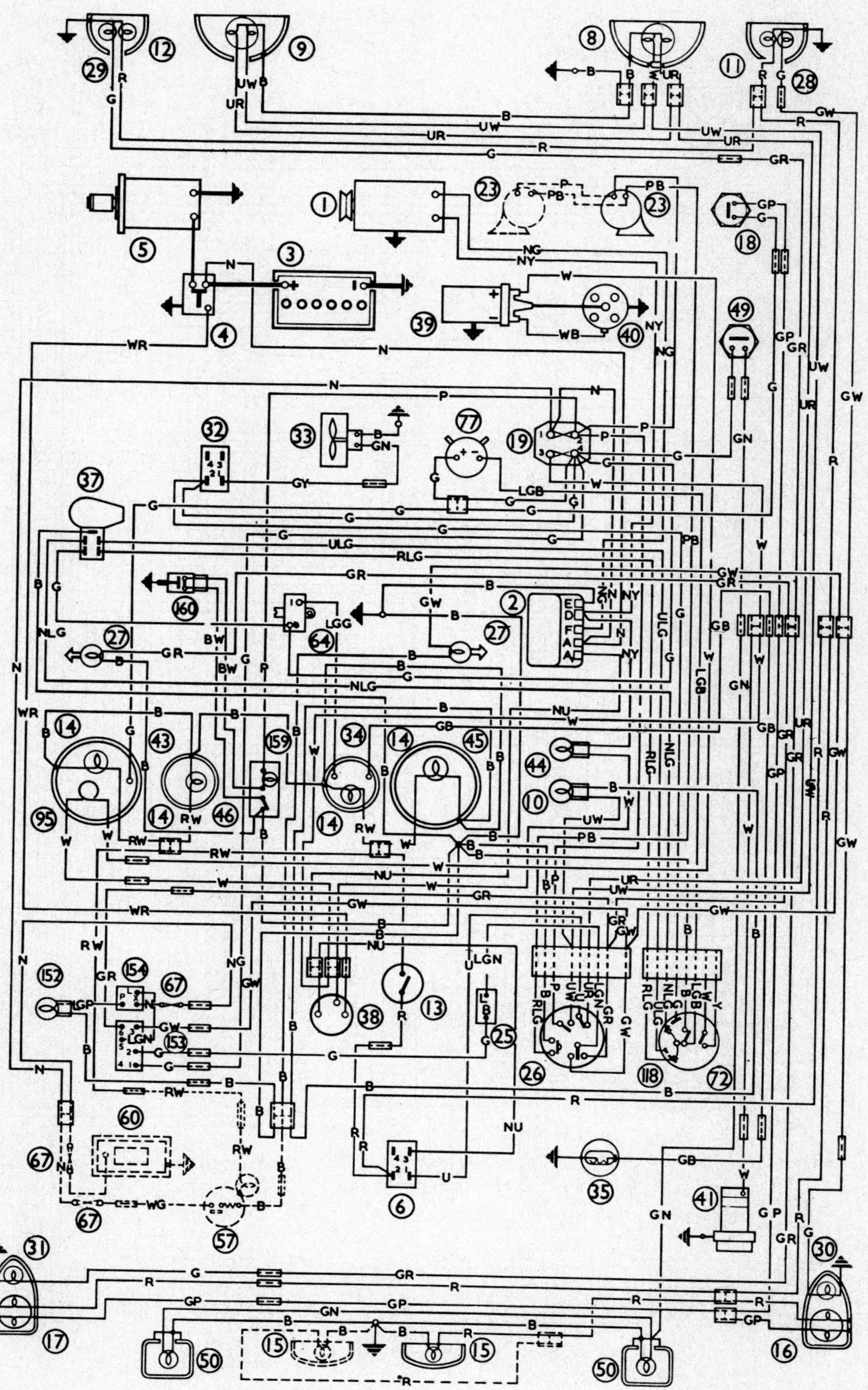

Midget Mk. III from Car Number G-AN4/66226 Neg. Ground

See page 616 for key

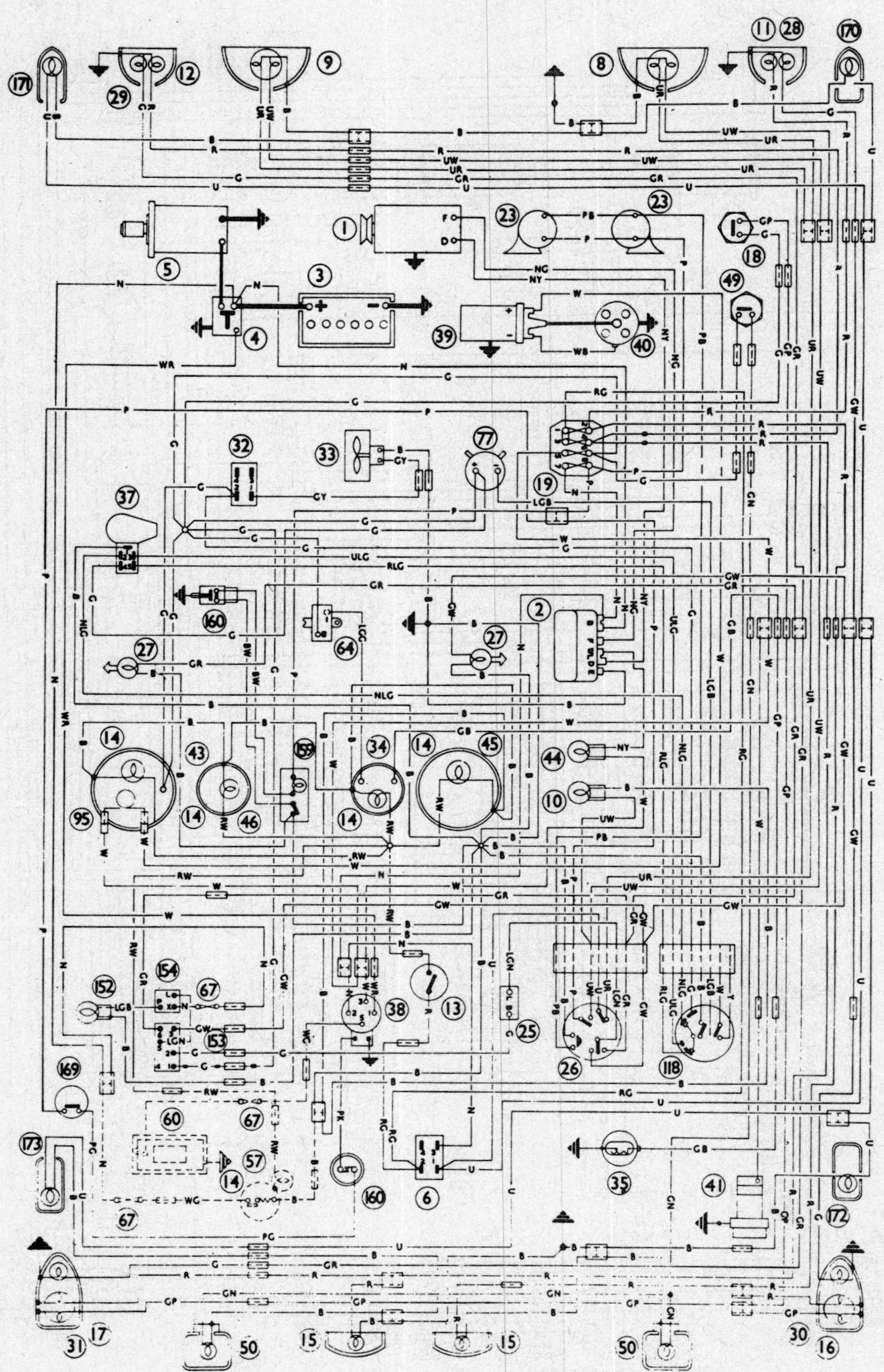

Midget Mk. III from Car Number G-AN5/74886 Neg. Ground

See page 616 for key

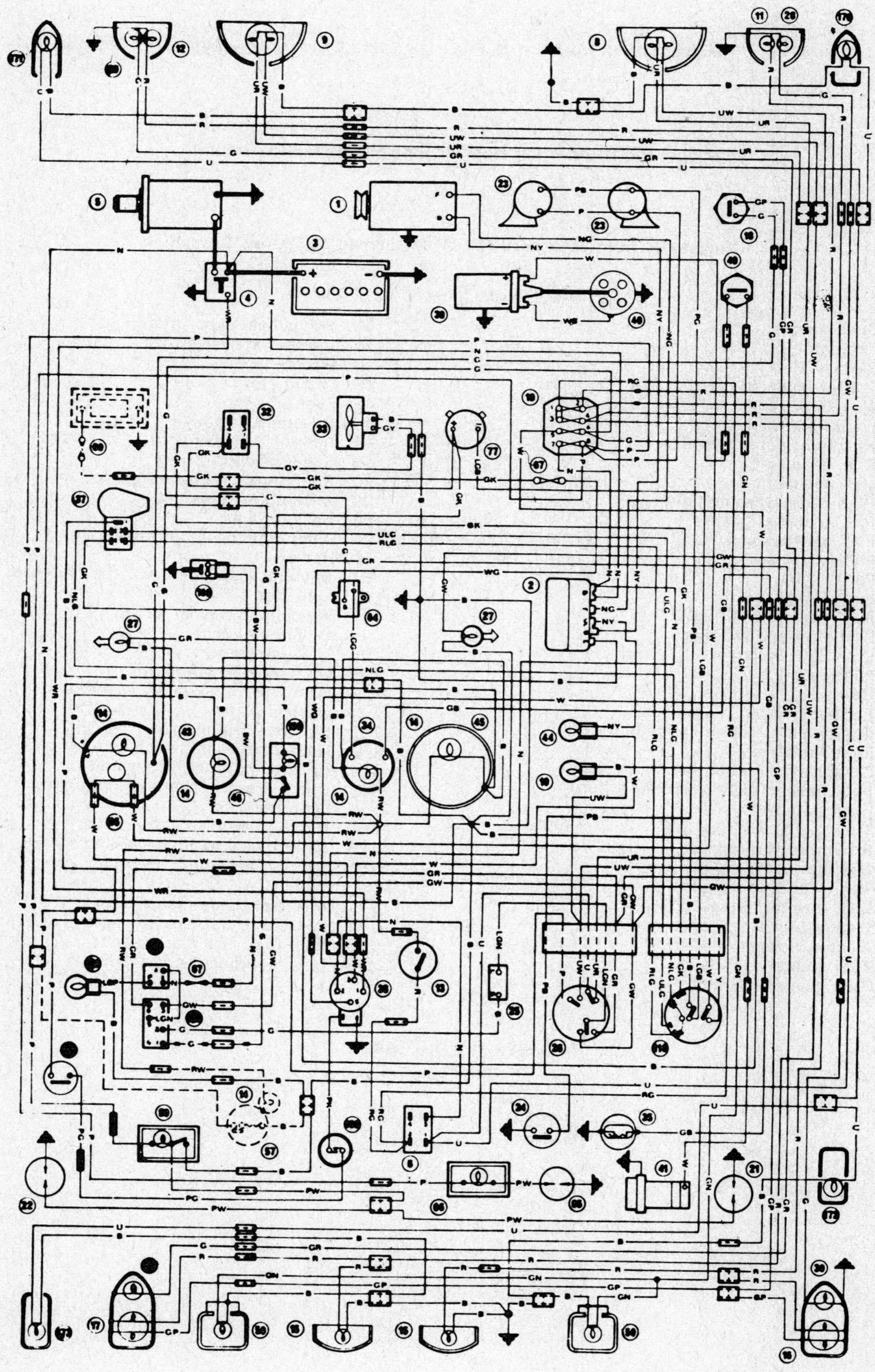

Midget Mk. from Late 1970 (12 CJ Engine) to 1972 Neg. Ground

See page 616 for key

Midget Mk. I and II

Midget Mk. III from Car Number G-AN4/60460, Neg. Ground

Midget Mk. III from Car Number G-AN4/66226 Neg. Ground

Midget Mk. III from Car Number G-AN5/74886 Neg. Ground

Midget Mk. from Late 1970 (12 CJ Engine) to 1972 Neg. Ground

1. Generator
2. Regulator
3. Battery
4. Starter solenoid
5. Starter motor
6. Lighting switch
7. Headlight dimmer switch
8. R.H. headlight
9. L.H. headlight
10. High-beam warning light
11. R.H. parking light
12. L.H. parking light
13. Panel light switch
14. Panel light
15. License light
16. R.H. stop and tail light
17. L.H. stop and tail light
18. Stop light switch
19. Fuse unit
23. Horns
25. Flasher unit
26. Combined direction indicator/headlight flasher or
26. Combined direction indicator/headlight flasher/high-beam lamp/horn-push switch
27. Turn signal warning light
28. R.H. front turn signal
29. L.H. front turn signal
30. R.H. rear turn signal
31. L.H. rear turn signal
32. Heater blower switch
33. Heater blower
34. Fuel gauge
35. Fuel gauge tank unit
37. Windshield wiper motor
38. Ignition/starter switch
39. Ignition coil
40. Distributor
41. Fuel pump
43. Oil pressure gauge
44. Ignition warning light
45. Speedometer
46. Radiator temperature gauge
49. Back-up light switch
50. Back-up light
57. Cigar-lighter—illuminated
60. Radio
64. Bi-metal instrument voltage stabilizer
67. Line fuse
77. Windshield washer pump
94. Oil filter switch
95. Tachometer
105. Oil filter warning light
118. Combined windshield washer and wiper switch
152. Hazard warning light
153. Hazard warning switch
154. Hazard warning flasher unit
159. Brake pressure warning light and light test push
160. Brake pressure failure switch
168. Ignition key audible warning buzzer
169. Ignition key audible warning door switch
170. R.H. front side marker light
171. L.H. front side marker light
172. R.H. rear side marker light
173. L.H. rear side marker light

CABLE COLOR CODE

N. Brown.
U. Blue.
R. Red.

P. Purple.
G. Green.
LG. Light Green

W. White.
Y. Yellow.
B. Black.

CABLE COLOR CODE

When a cable has two color code letters the first denotes the main color and the second denotes the tracer color.

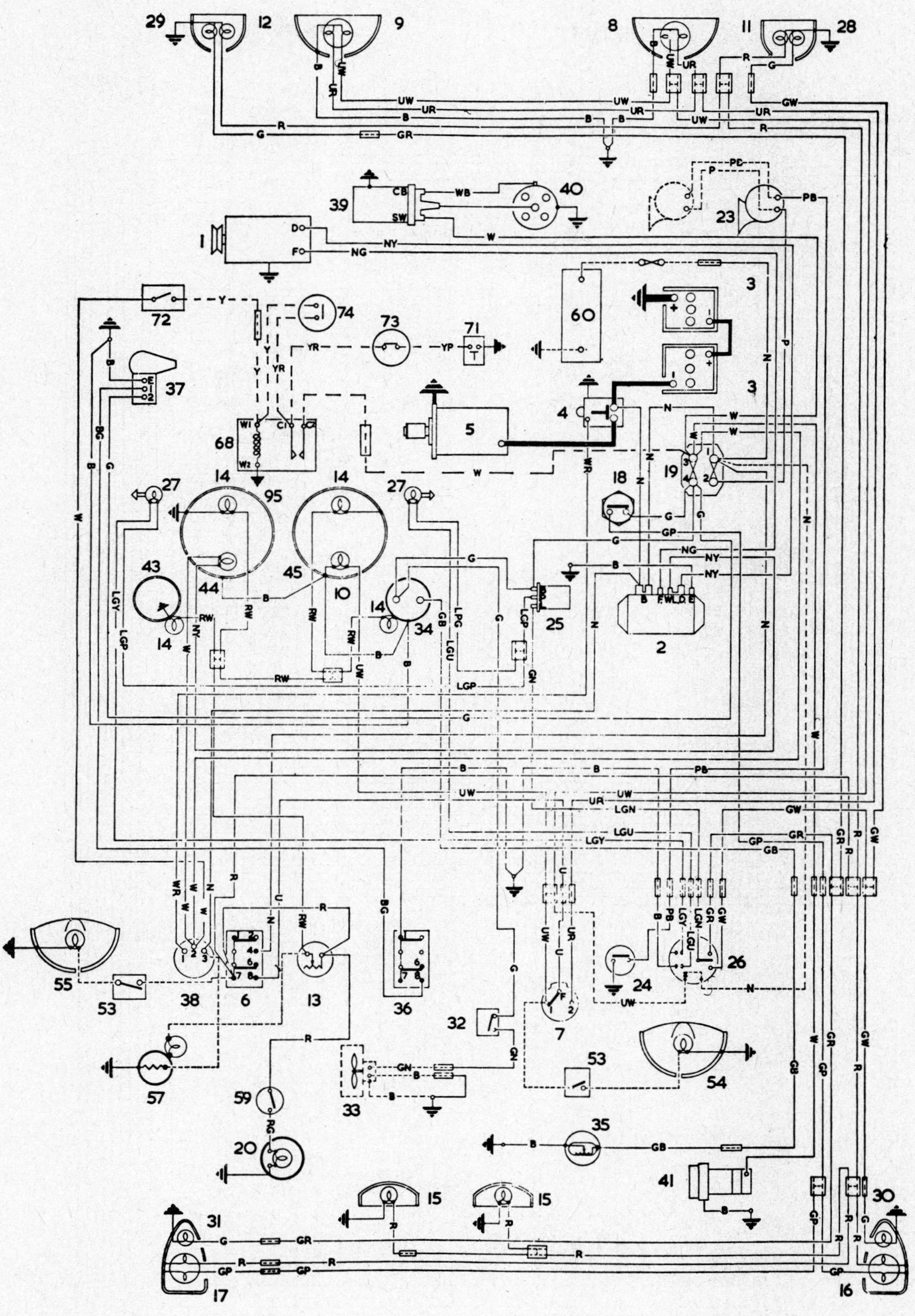

MGB Car Numbers G-HN3/101-48765 (conv) Positive Ground

See page 623 for key

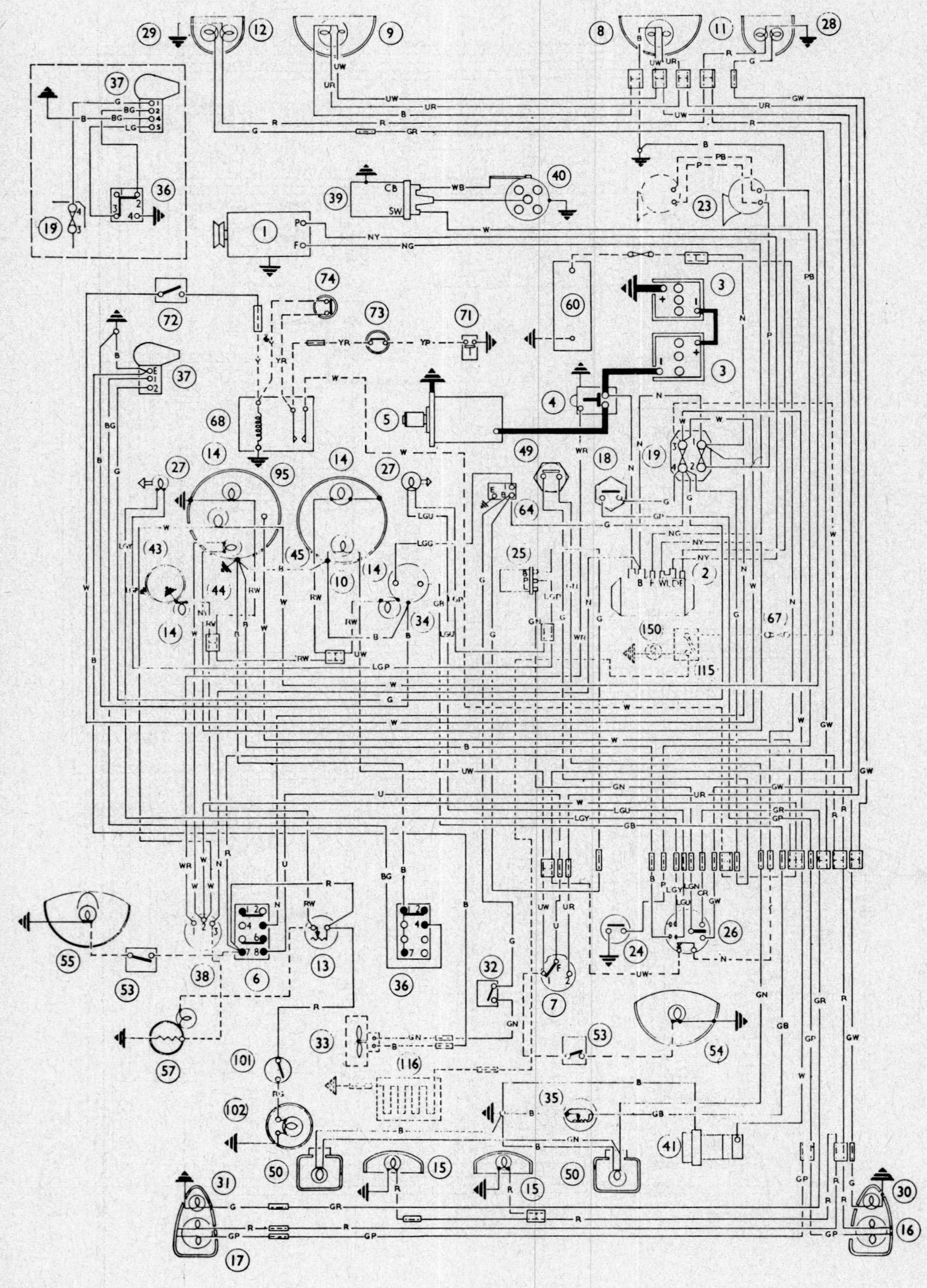

MGB Car Numbers G-HN3/48766 (conv) and G-HD3/71933 (GT) Positive Ground

See page 623 for key

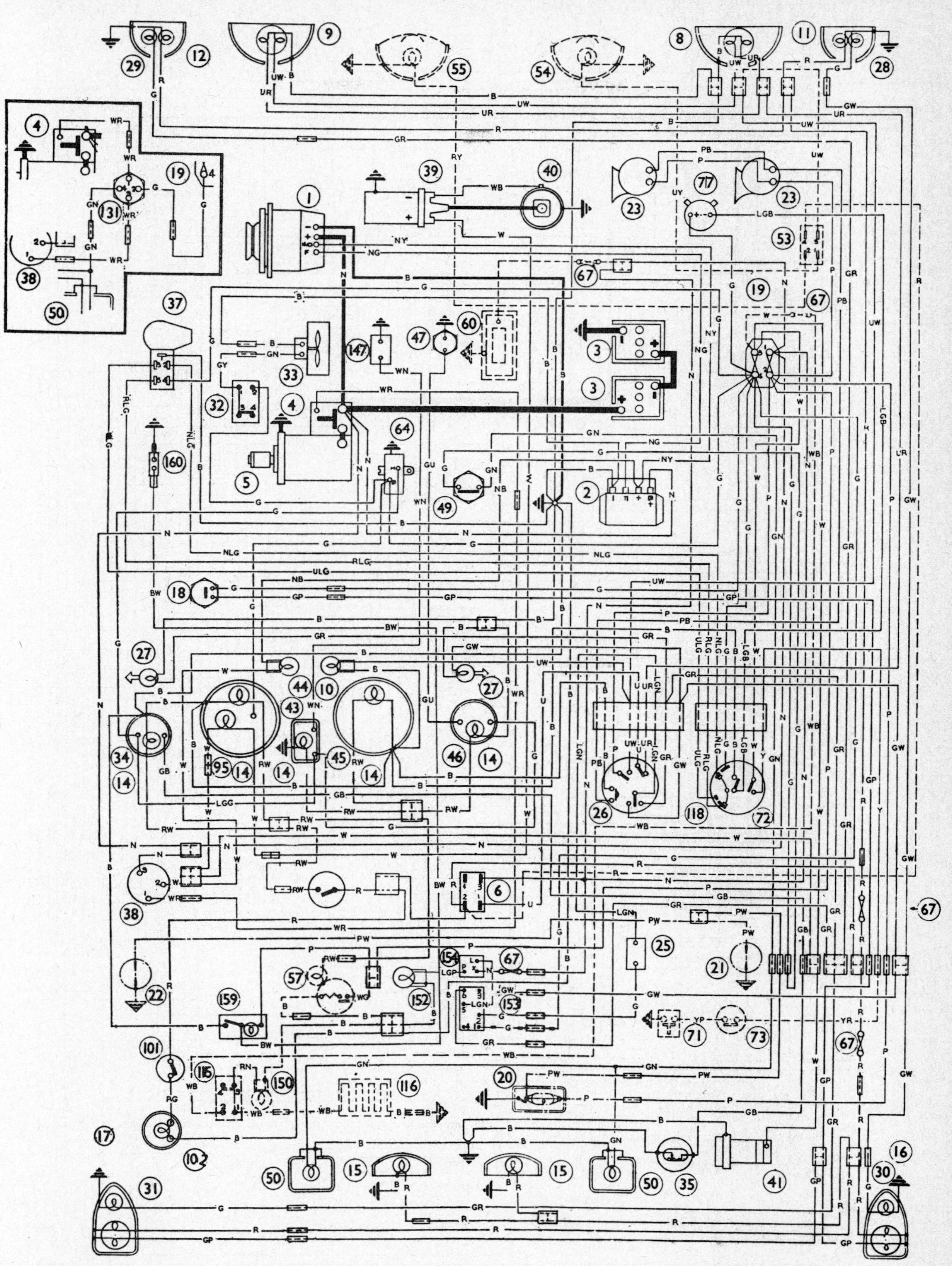

MGB from Car Numbers G-HN4/138401 (conv) and G-HD4/139472 (GT) Pos. Grd.

See page 623 for key

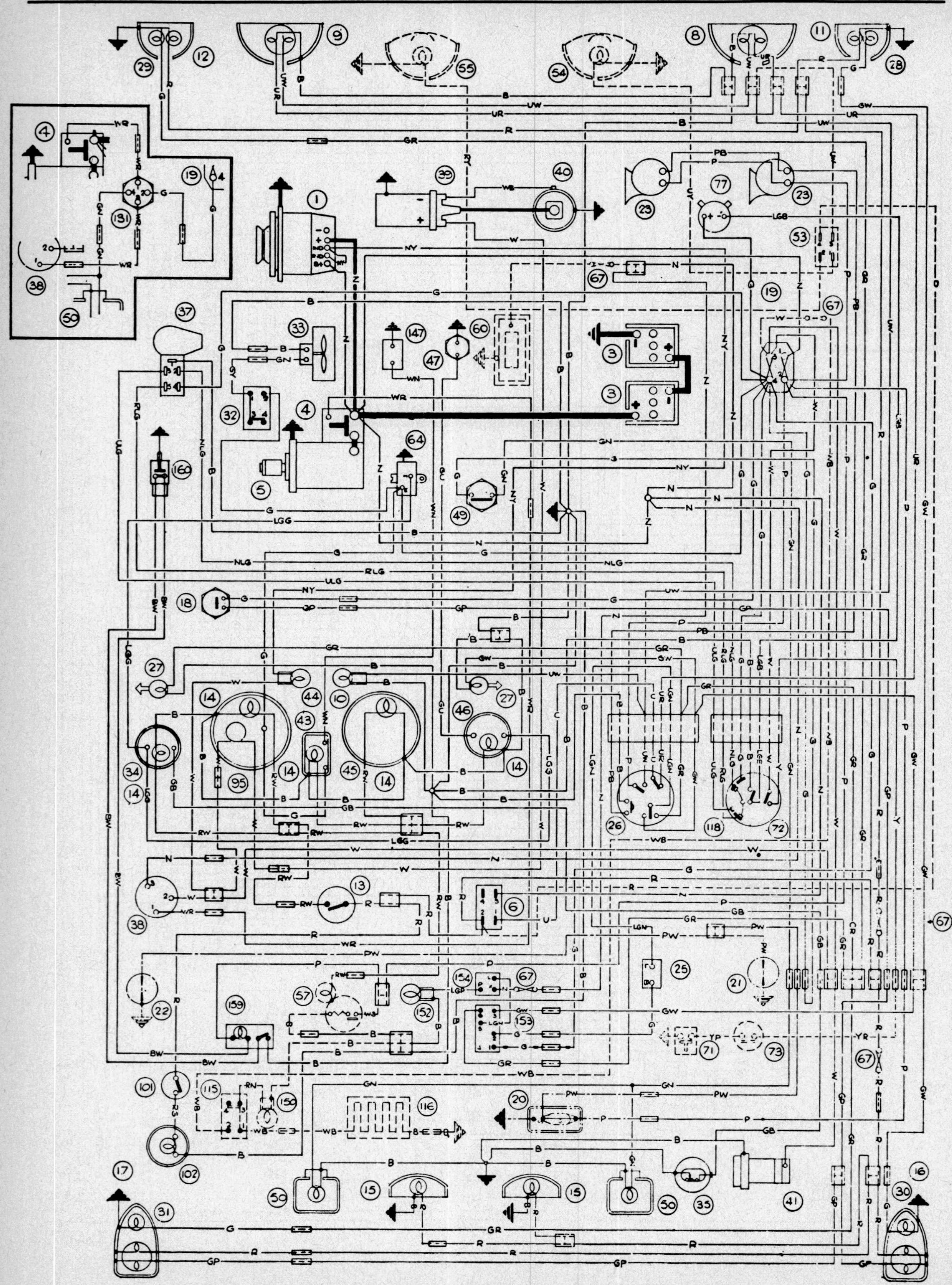

MGB from Car Numbers G-HN4/158233 (conv) and G-HD5/187841 (GT) Neg. Grd.

See page 623 for key

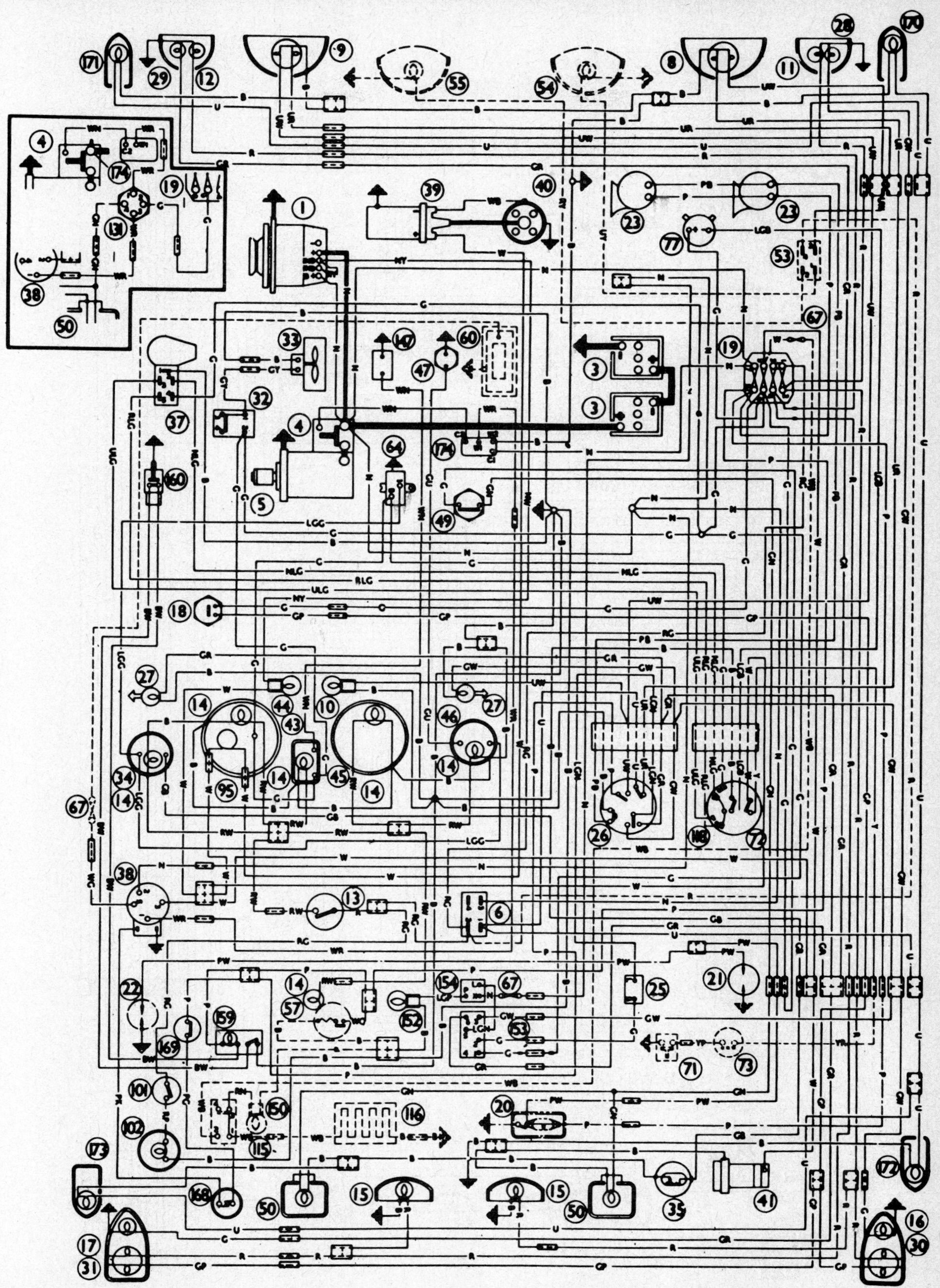

MGB Car Number from G-HNJ/187170 (conv) and G-HD5/187841 (GT) Neg. Ground

See page 623 for key

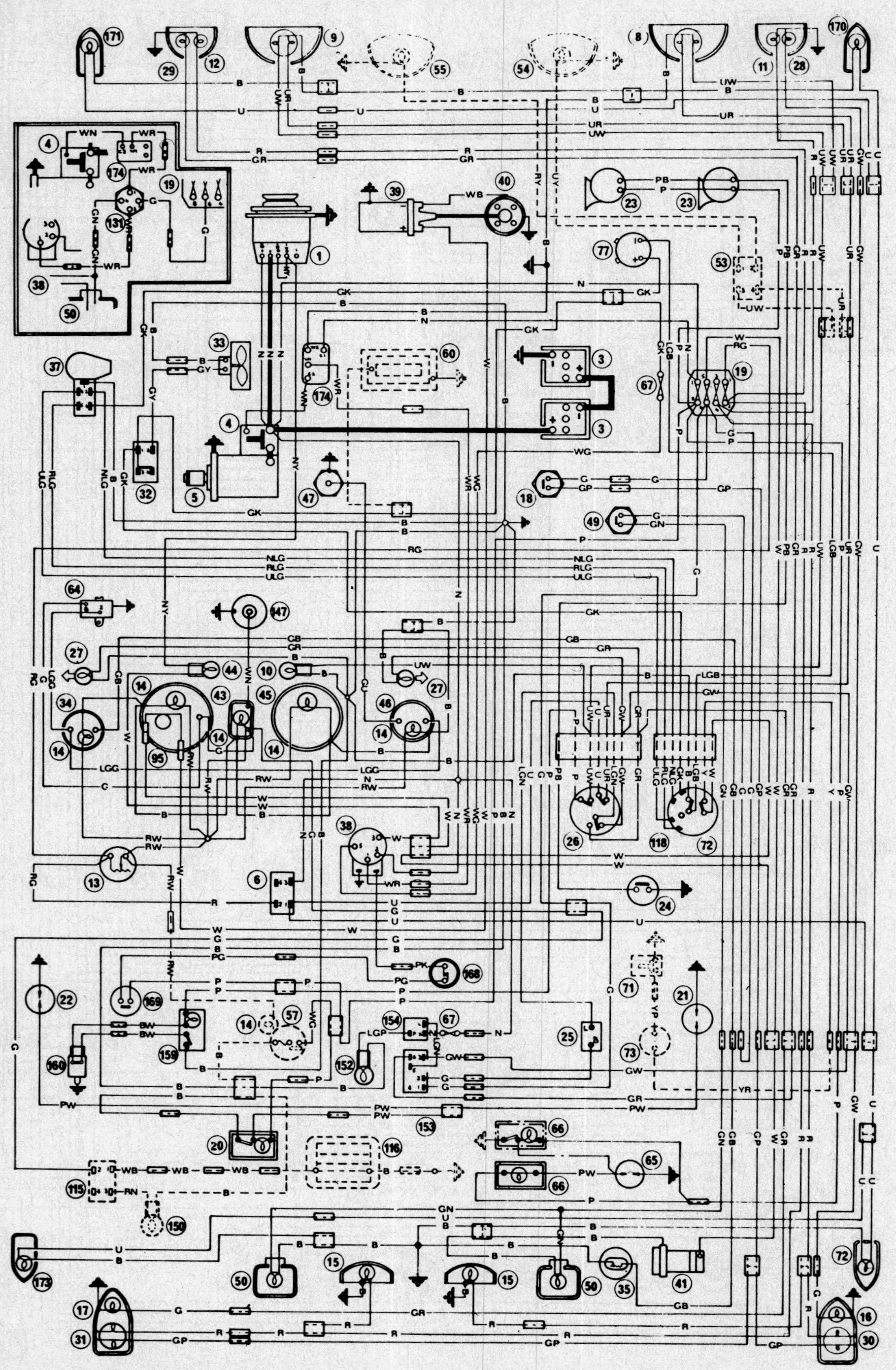

MGB from Late 1970 (18GJ and 18GK Engines) to 1972 Neg Ground

See page 623 for key

MGB Car Numbers G-HN3/101-48765 (conv) Positive Ground

MGB Car Numbers G-HN3/48766 (conv) and G-HD3/71933 (GT) Positive Ground

MGB from Car Numbers G-HN4/138401 (conv) and G-HD4/139472 (GT) Pos. Grd.

MGB from Car Numbers G-HN4/158233 (conv) and G-HD5/187841 (GT) Neg. Grd.

MGB Car Number from G-HNJ/187170 (conv) and G-HD5/187841 (GT) Neg. Ground

MGB from Late 1970 (18GJ and 18GK Engines) to 1972 Neg Ground

1. Alternator or generator
2. Regulator
3. Batteries—6-volt
4. Starter solenoid
5. Starter motor
6. Lighting switch
7. Headlight dimmer switch
8. R.H. headlight
9. L.H. headlight
10. High-beam warning light
11. R.H. parking light
12. L.H. parking light
13. Panel light switch or rheostat switch
14. Panel light
15. License light
16. R.H. stop and tail light
17. L.H. stop and tail light
18. Stop light switch
19. Fuse unit
20. Interior courtesy light or may light (early cars)
21. R.H. door switch
22. L.H. door switch
23. Horns
24. Horn-push
25. Flasher unit
26. Turn signal switch
    or
26. Turn signal/headlight flasher
    or
26. Combined turn signal/headlight flasher/headlight high-low beam/ horn-push switch
27. Turn signal warning light
28. R.H. front turn signal
29. L.H. front turn signal
30. R.H. rear turn signal
31. L.H. rear turn signal
32. Heater blower motor switch
33. Heater blower motor
34. Fuel gauge
35. Fuel gauge tank unit
36. Windshield wiper switch
38. Ignition/starter switch
39. Ignition coil
40. Distributor
41. Fuel pump
43. Oil pressure gauge
44. Ignition warning light
45. Speedometer
46. Radiator temperature gauge
47. Radiator temperature transmitter
49. Back-up light switch
50. Back-up light
53. Fog and driving light switch
54. Driving light
55. Fog light
57. Cigar-lighter illuminated
59. Map light switch (early cars)
60. Radio
64. Bi-metal instrument voltage stabilizer
65. Trunk light
65. Trunk light switch
67. Line fuse
68. Overdrive relay unit
71. Overdrive solenoid
72. Overdrive manual control switch
73. Overdrive gear switch
74. Overdrive throttle switch
76. Automatic gearbox gear selector illumination light
77. Windshield washer pump
82. Switch illumination light
95. Tachometer
101. Courtesy or map light switch
102. Courtesy or map light
115. Heated back-light switch
116. Heated back-light

GT only

118. Combined windshield washer and wiper switch
131. Combined back-up light switch and automatic transmission safety switch
147. Oil pressure transmitter
150. Heated back-light warning light (GT only)
152. Hazard warning light
153. Hazard warning switch
154. Hazard warning flasher unit
159. Brake pressure warning light and light test push
160. Brake pressure failure switch
168. Ignition key audible warning buzzer
169. Ignition key audible warning door switch
170. R.H. front side marker light
171. L.H. front side marker light
172. R.H. rear sider marker light
173. L.H. rear side marker light
174. Starter solenoid relay

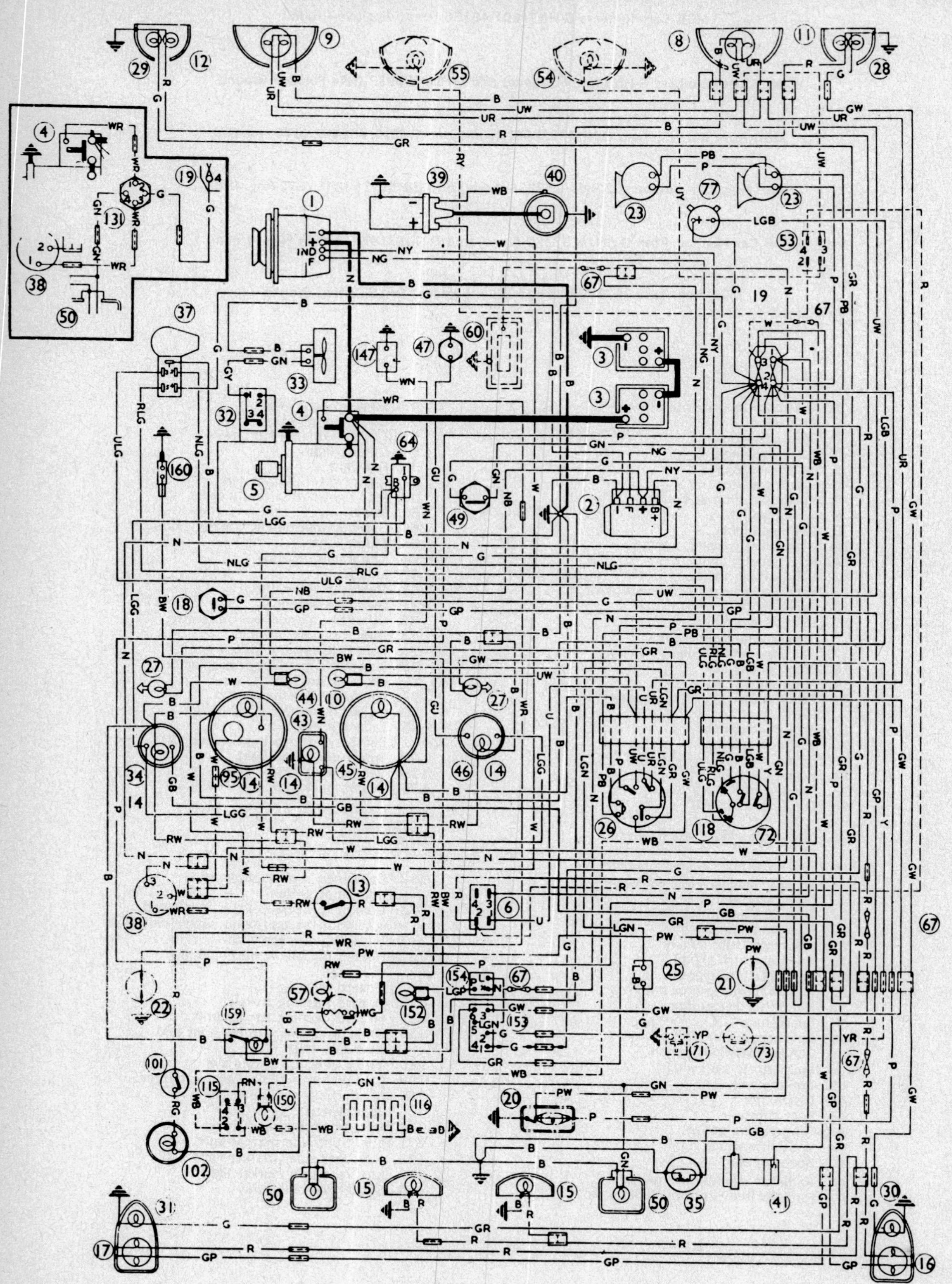

MGC Car Numbers G-CN1/101-4235 (conv) G-CD1/1014265 (GT)

See page 626 for key

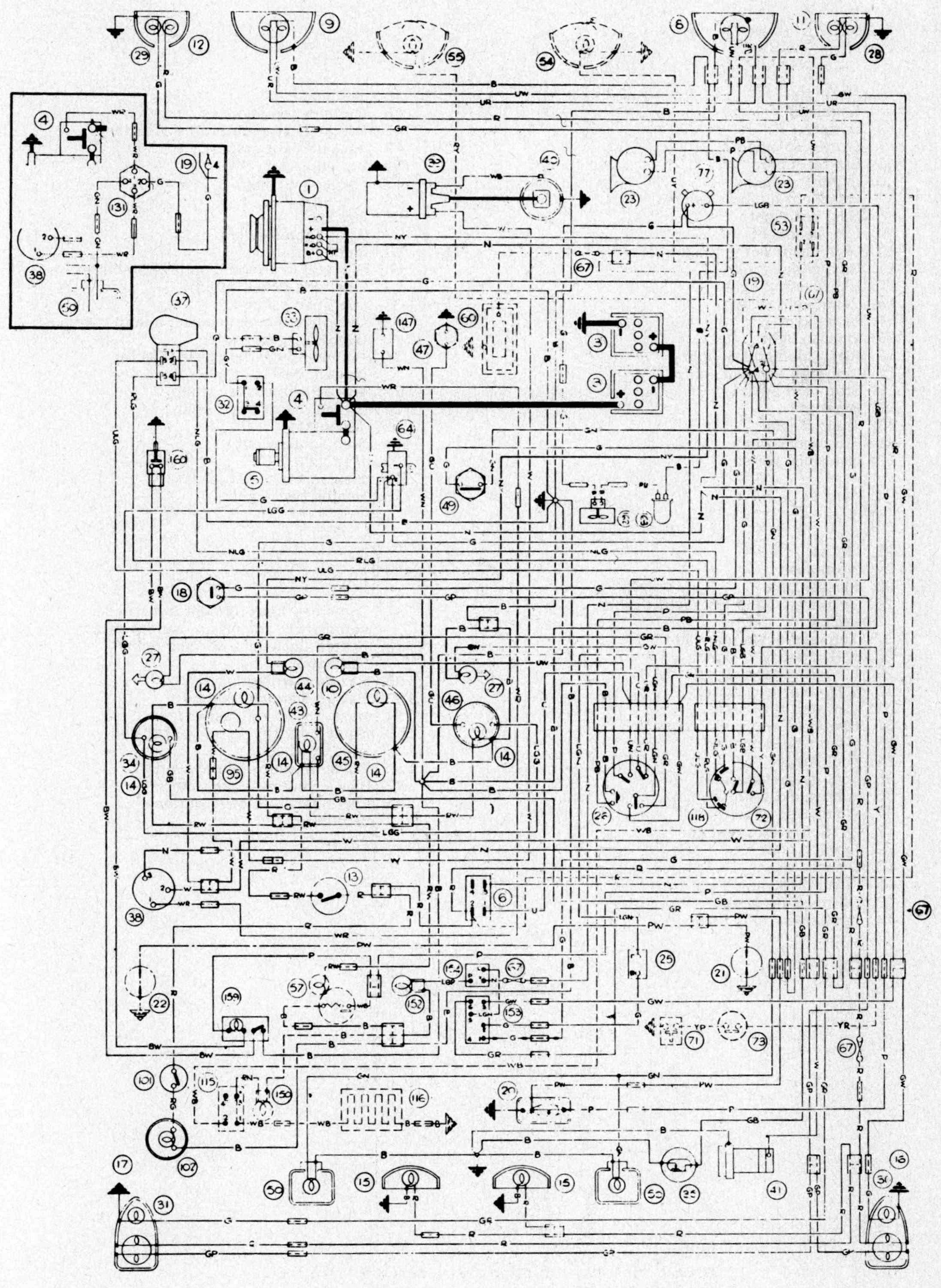

MGC Car Numbers G-CN1/4236 (conv) G-CD1/4266 (GT)

See page 626 for key

MGC Car Numbers G-CN1/101-4235 (conv) G-CD1/1014265 (GT)

MGC Car Numbers G-CN1/4236 (conv) G-CD1/4266 (GT)

1. Alternator
2. Regulator
3. Battery
4. Starter solenoid
5. Starter motor
6. Lighting switch
7. Headlight dimmer switch
8. R.H. headlight
9. L.H. headlight
10. High-beam warning light
11. R.H. parking light
12. L.H. parking light
13. Panel light switch
14. Panel light
15. License light
16. R.H. stop and tail light
17. L.H. stop and tail light
18. Stop light switch
19. Fuse unit
20. Interior light
21. R.H. door switch
22. L.H. door switch

GT only

23. Horns
24. Horn-push
25. Flasher unit
26. Turn signal and headlight flasher switch
27. Turn signal warning light
28. R.H. front turn signal
29. L.H. front turn signal
30. R.H. rear turn signal
31. L.H. rear turn signal
32. Heater blower motor switch
33. Heater blower motor
34. Fuel gauge
35. Fuel gauge tank unit
36. Windshield wiper switch
37. Windshield wiper motor
38. Ignition/starter switch
39. Ignition coil
40. Distributor
41. Fuel pump
43. Oil pressure gauge
44. Ignition warning light
45. Speedometer
46. Radiator temperature gauge
47. Radiator temperature transmitter
49. Back-up light switch
50. Back-up light
53. Fog and driving light switch
54. Driving light
55. Fog light
57. Cigar-lighter—illuminated
60. Radio
64. Bi-metal instrument voltage stabilizer
67. Line fuse (when fitted)
71. Overdrive solenoid
72. Overdrive manual control switch
73. Overdrive gear switch
76. Automatic gearbox gear selector illumination light
77. Windshield washer pump
82. Switch illumination light
95. Tachometer
101. Map light switch
102. Map light
115. Heated back-light switch
116. Heated back-light

GT only

131. Combined back-up light switch and automatic transmission safety switch
150. Heated back-light warning light (GT only)
152. Hazard warning light
153. Hazard warning switch
154. Hazard warning flasher unit
159. Brake pressure warning light and light test push
160. Brake pressure failure switch
162. Blower motor—carburetor
163. Thermostat—blower motor—carburetor

CABLE COLOR CODE

B. Black.
U. Blue.
N. Brown.

G. Green.
P. Purple.
R. Red.

W. White.
Y. Yellow.
LG. Light Green

When a cable has two color code letters the first denotes the main color and the second denotes the tracer color.

TUNE-UP PROCEDURES

Spark Plugs

Number each spark plug wire by placing a piece of tape on the wire indicating the cylinder number. Grasp each spark plug wire by the rubber boot on the end of the wire and remove the wire from the plug.

Using a socket and a ratchet remove the spark plugs. Before installing new plugs, gap each plug according to specification in the "Tune-up Specification Chart." Install the new plugs by hand then tighten them snugly with the wrench.

Breaker Points and Condenser

Removal and Installation

1. Remove the distributor. See the "Engine Electrical" section for distributor removal.
2. Lift the rotor from the distributor shaft. Make a careful note of the positions of the components so that they may be reassembled correctly.
3. Unscrew the nut from the moving contact return-spring locating pin and remove the plastic insulating sleeve and the condenser and low tension lead wires.
4. Remove the screw and washers holding the contact breaker plate and lift out the plate.
5. Remove the condenser screw and lift out the condenser.

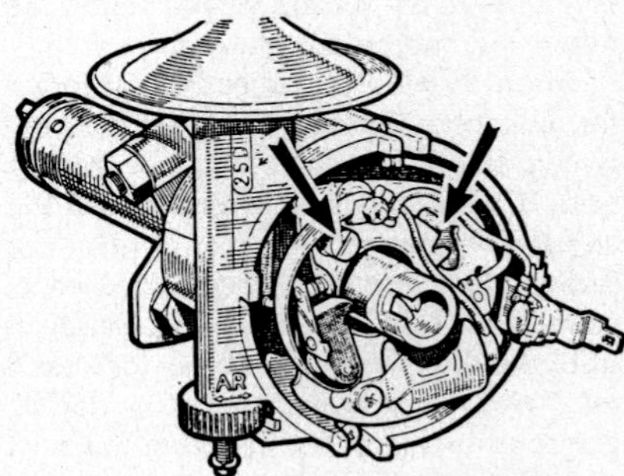

Location of the Breaker Points Adjusting Notch and Screw.

6. Thoroughly clean the distributor body and base plate, making sure that the base plate is left without an oily film that could insulate the contact breaker plate from the distributor base plate and prevent the ground circuit from being completed. The vacuum advance diaphragm may be checked by applying a suction where the line connects and watching for movement of the base plate.
7. Install the contact breaker points and condenser in reverse order of removal. Clean the surfaces of the contact points with a non-oily solvent such as alcohol to remove any preservative coating or dirt, and set the points gap to specification (see "Tune-Up Specifications").

CAUTION: *The order of installation of components on the moving contact return-spring locating pin must be followed exactly or the ignition spark will be short-circuited to ground. The fiber insulating washer must be installed first, followed by the return-spring end loop, the low-tension and condenser lead wires, the insulating sleeve (which slides down between the pin and the return-spring and wire end loops), and the nut.*

8. Apply one or two drops of engine oil to the felt in the top of the distributor shaft (if applicable). Lightly smear the distributor cam with engine oil or distributor cam lubricant.

Adjustment

Rotate the distributor camshaft until the points are fully open. Loosen the attaching nut on the securing plate and insert a screwdriver between the notches in the fixed plate. Turn the screwdriver until the gap between the two contacts is 0.15 in., using a feeler gauge. Tighten the attaching nut.

Dwell Angle

Dwell angle is the angle that the distributor cam rotates when the breaker points are closed.

This is a more accurate way of adjusting point gap than using a feeler gauge.

1. Remove the distributor cap and connect a dwell meter between the primary lead and the ground.
2. Crank the engine and observe the degree of dwell on the meter. Refer to the "Tune-Up Specifications Chart" for the proper dwell angle. If it is necessary to adjust this angle, adjust the points as previously described.

Ignition Timing

Static Timing Procedure

Satisfactory results on any MG engine without emission controls can be obtained through static (engine not running) timing if it is done carefully. The only equipment necessary is a test light, which is nothing more than a light bulb (12 volt) with two wires attached so that it will light when connected in parallel with a power source.

1. Turn the crankshaft in its normal direction of rotation until the notch in the crankshaft pulley aligns with the appropriate pointer on the front engine cover. See "Tune-Up Specifications" for correct settings.
2. Switch the ignition on.
3. Attach a test light wire to the low tension lead running from the coil to the distributor. Ground the other side of the test light.

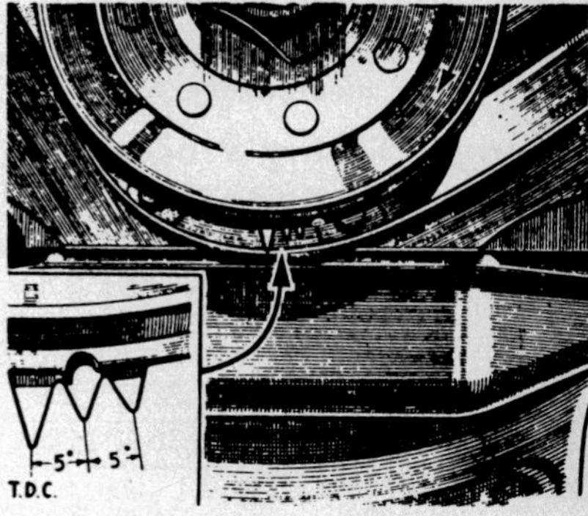

Timing Marks, Midget

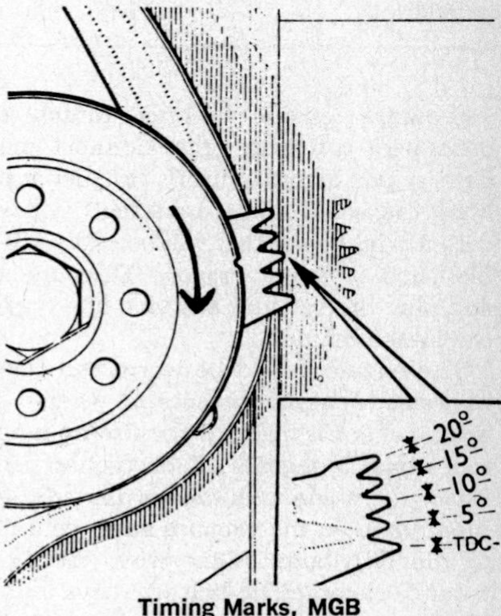

Timing Marks, MGB

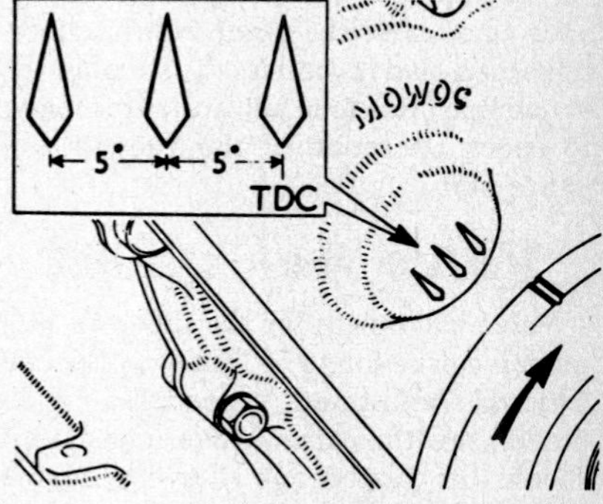

Timing Marks, MGC

4. Turn the distributor clockwise very slowly until the test light lights. This indicates that the points are just beginning to open. If the test light came on as soon as it was connected, turn the distributor counterclockwise until the light goes off and proceed as above.
5. Tighten the clamp pinch-bolt and recheck the timing by turning the crankshaft in the opposite direction of rotation until the light goes off and then *slowly* in the direction of normal rotation until the light goes on.
6. Check the alignment of the timing marks. Final small adjustments can be

made with the vernier adjustment knob on the vacuum advance unit of the distributor. (The space between each mark on the moving barrel equals approximately 5 deg. timing change.)

Dynamic Timing Procedure

Timing Specifications

Model & Engine	Deg. BTDC @ rpm
Midget	
12CC @ 12CE	22 @ 1,000
12CD/12CJ	10 @ 1,000
MGB	
18G/18GA/18GB	14 @ 600
18GF/18GH/18GJ	20 @ 1,000
18GK	15 @ 1,500

Valves No. 4 and 7 Open, Valves No. 5 and 2 Positioned for Adjustment.

Dynamic (engine running) timing is done with a timing light. Connect the light as per manufacturer's instructions. Mark the notch in the crankshaft pulley with a bright color that will be easily visible (such as yellow crayon). Disconnect and plug the vacuum advance line from the intake manifold.

The engine should be warm and running steadily at the correct rpm when the timing check is made. If the timing is no more than 5 degrees off, correction can usually be made with the vernier adjustment knob on the vacuum advance unit of the distributor. Otherwise, the distributor clamp pinch-bolt will have to be loosened and the distributor rotated to the correct position. Check the timing once again after the pinch-bolt has been tightened, and reconnect the vacuum advance line after final adjustment is made to check operation of the vacuum advance unit.

Valve Adjustment

Valve clearances for the different MG models can be found in "Tune-Up Specifications." Adjustment procedures for all models are the same. Valve adjustment should be carried out at every engine tune-up or whenever excessive valve train noise is noticed. Loose valve clearance will generally only cause a metallic thrashing sound, while over-tight adjustment can cause rough running and burnt valves.

To adjust the valves, remove the rocker cover and provide a means of turning the engine over slowly. Although the engine may be turned over by hand or with the ignition switch, the best methods are by manually operating the starter solenoid (early models only) or connecting an auxiliary starter wire to the solenoid. To operate the solenoid by hand on early models, simply push in the small shaft or rubber cover at the rear of switch or pull the actuation cable (Midget Mk. I only). An auxiliary starter wire can be either a two-position switch with one lead connected to the battery cable terminal at the solenoid and the other lead connected to the small gauge wire at the separate solenoid terminal, or simply a short length of wire connected momentarily in the above manner to turn the engine over.

Valve Adjustment Chart

Valve Open	Adjust this Valve Six Cylinder	Four Cylinder
1	12	8
2	11	7
3	10	6
4	9	5
5	8	4
6	7	3
7	6	2
8	5	1
9	4	1
10	3	
11	2	
12	1	

Valve rocker clearance adjusting sequence for four and six cylinder engines.

Measuring Valve Lash

CAUTION: *Make sure that the transmission is in Neutral before turning the engine over while outside the vehicle.*

In order to adjust an individual valve, it must be in a certain relationship to the camshaft; i.e., it must be on the low side of the camshaft lobe. Because the relationship of one valve to the action of another is known (through camshaft configuration), it is possible to position one of the valves in its fully opened position (valve spring compressed) and thus know that another valve is correctly positioned for adjustment. If a line is drawn at the midpoint of the head separating the valves into two equal groups, then this relationship is symmetrical. In other words, if one of the end valves is open, then the valve at the opposite end can be adjusted; if the second valve in from one end is open, the second valve in from the other end can be adjusted, etc.

When a valve is correctly positioned for adjustment, check the clearance between the valve stem and the rocker arm. If clearance is incorrect, loosen the adjusting screw locknut and turn the screw (clockwise to decrease clearance, counterclockwise to increase clearance) until the feeler gauge blade slides in and out with some resistance. To double check adjustment, try inserting the next size thinner and next size thicker feeler blade. If, for example, desired clearance is 0.010 in., the 0.009 in. blade should fit quite easily, while the 0.011 or 0.012 in. blade should be too thick to fit. When correct clearance has been obtained, hold the adjusting screw from turning and tighten the locknut. Recheck clearance in case the adjustment screw turned slightly when the locknut was tightened.

When all valves have been adjusted, reinstall the rocker cover. Make sure that the cover gasket is in good condition or an oil leak will develop. Breather hose connections at the rocker cover (if any) should be tight.

Carburetors

Idle Speed and Fuel Mixture, Balancing Dual Carburetors

Since 1930, when Morris Garages purchased the firm, MGs have been equipped with S.U. (Skinners Union) carburetors. All MG models covered in this book have twin HS type S.U. carburetors, while most earlier models have two H type carburetors. The maintenance and tuning procedures for HS carburetors are applicable to the H type as well.

Before the carburetors are adjusted, there are several preliminary checks that should be made.

1. Start the engine and spray a solvent such as an aerosol-type carburetor cleaner on the carburetor bodies where the throttle spindles pivot. If the engine speed varies, there is an indication of an air leak at those points and adjustment of the carburetors will prove to be futile. The carburetors should be rebuilt and the throttle spindles and bushings replaced if the carburetors are expected to respond to adjustment.

2. Check the carburetor pistons for sticking by lifting them all the way and letting them fall. Their descent should be steady, and a metallic click should be heard when they hit bottom. If there is evidence of sticking, remove and clean the pistons in solvent. Do not lubricate any part of the piston except the rod.

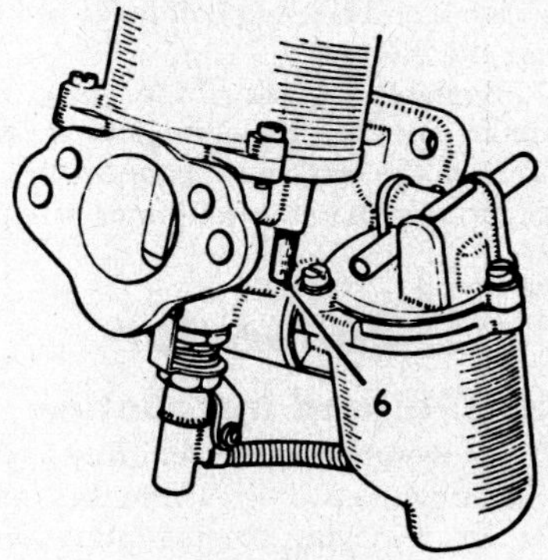

Piston Lifting Pin (6)

3. Check that the piston damper chambers have the proper amount of oil. On carburetors with vented damper caps the level should be ½ in. above the piston rod, and with non-vented caps the level should be ½ in. below the rod.

A dirty air filter will affect the carburetors quite noticeably. If carburetor adjustment is carried out with air filters off, the engine will run badly when they are replaced unless they are clean. MG uses replaceable paper filter elements.

The carburetor bodies and throttle linkage should be cleaned before adjustments are made. Check the manifold and carburetor nuts for looseness which could cause an air leak.

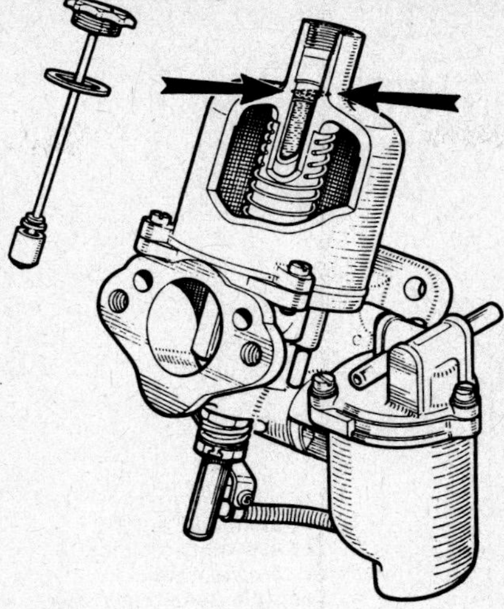

Oil Level 1/2 In Below the Tube

4. Start the engine and warm it to normal operating temperature.

5. Loosen the throttle linkage interconnection clamps so that the carburetor throttles may be synchronized.

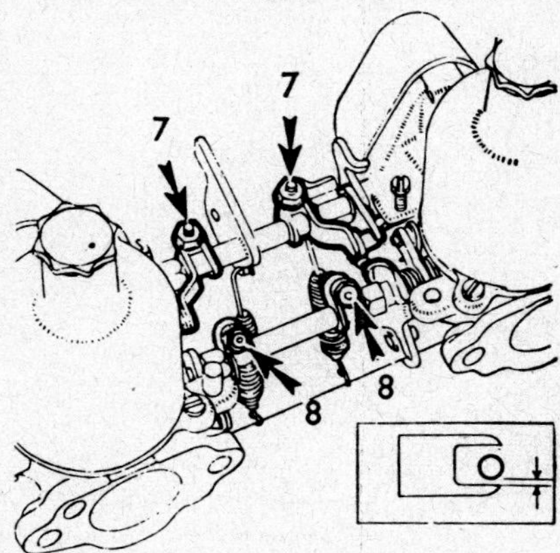

Throttle Interconnection Clamping Lever (7).

6. Loosen the choke (jet control) linkage interconnection clamps.

7. Run the engine at about 3,000 rpm for a few seconds to clear it out, and let it drop back to idle.

8. Using a Unisyn® or other carburetor balance meter, adjust the idle (see "Tune-Up Specifications") via the throttle adjusting screws so that when correct speed is obtained both carburetors register the same draw on the Unisyn.

The carburetors are now synchronized at idle, and must be set also for off-idle operation. Set the throttle interconnection clamps so that the link pin is 0.012 in. away from the lower edge of the fork (see illustration), and tighten the clamps. Open the throttles by pulling on the accelerator cable until the engine is just above idle speed, and check carburetor balance at this point with the Unisyn. If there is a balance difference of more than ½ in. on the meter, loosen one of the interconnection clamps and position it so that the carburetor drawing less in the meter will open slightly sooner than the other one. Tighten the clamp and recheck balance. Repeat the operation, if necessary, until balance is satisfactory.

Carburetor mixture strength is adjusted by turning the jet adjusting nut up to lean the mixture and down to richen it. Mixture strength is checked for the individual carburetors by lifting the piston very slightly (about 1/32 in.) and listening for a change in engine speed. If the engine slows down and remains at the lowered speed, the mixture is too lean. If the engine speeds up slightly and then returns to its original idle, the mixture is correct. If the engine speeds up and remains at the higher speed, the mixture is too rich. If jet adjustment is necessary, turn the adjusting nut one flat at a time and pause to check for any change in engine response.

On Emission Control System carburetors with jet adjusting nut restrictors, it will not be possible to adjust the mixture in the preceding manner because of the limited range of adjustment.

1. Turn the jet adjusting nut on both carburetors over the full range of adjustment, selecting the setting where maximum idle speed is consistent with smoothness. Do not remove or reposition

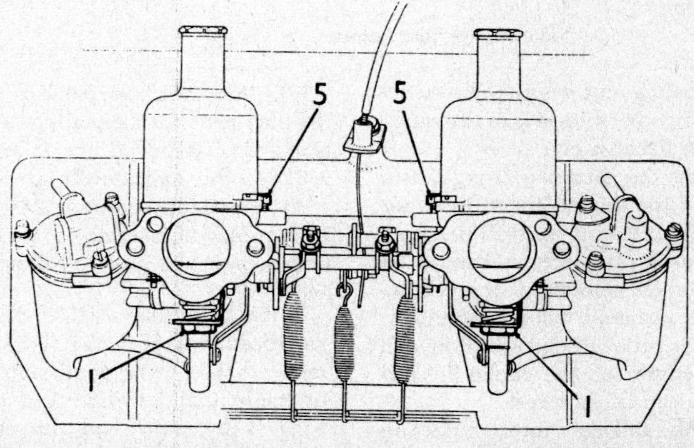

Idle Adjusting Screw (5), Jet Adjusting Nuts (1)

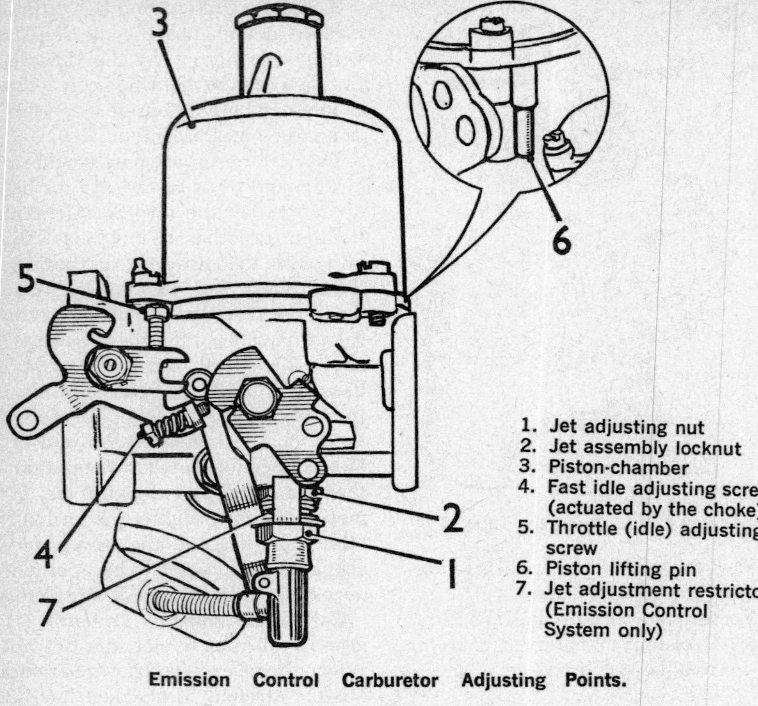

1. Jet adjusting nut
2. Jet assembly locknut
3. Piston-chamber
4. Fast idle adjusting screw (actuated by the choke)
5. Throttle (idle) adjusting screw
6. Piston lifting pin
7. Jet adjustment restrictor (Emission Control System only)

Emission Control Carburetor Adjusting Points.

4. Idle adjustment screws
8. Choke cable
9. Choke linkage and fast idle screw

Inset—The fast idle screws should be adjusted to raise the engine speed to 1,200 rpm with the choke knob ¼ in. from the dashboard, at which point the jet tubes have just begun to be lifted by the choke arms.

Idle Adjustment Points

the jet adjusting nut restrictors, as the adjusting range permitted is in the range of minimum exhaust emissions.

2. Altering the mixture strength will have altered the engine speed in either case, and the idle will have to be reset. Both of the throttle screws should be turned an equal amount so that carburetor synchronization will not be upset.

3. With throttle synchronization and mixture strength set, the choke (jet lifting) linkage can be adjusted.

4. Set the linkage interconnection clamps so that both jets are lifted simultaneously.

5. Adjust the choke cable so that when the jets are just beginning to lift, the choke knob is pulled out about ¼ in.

6. Set the engine idle at 1,200 rpm with the fast idle screws at this point. The Unisyn may be used to set up the choke linkage as it was used to balance throttle openings.

If the carburetors will not respond to jet adjustments and the engine cannot be made to idle or respond smoothly, it is probable that jet tube and jet needle wear is excessive and the carburetors should be overhauled.

ENGINE ELECTRICAL

Distributor

Removal and Installation

The distributor can be removed and replaced without disturbing the ignition timing, provided the pinch-bolt on the clamp that positions the distributor is not loosened.

1. Remove the distributor cap and disconnect the low tension lead from the terminal on the distributor.

2. Disconnect the vacuum advance line (if applicable) from the diaphragm unit at the distributor.

NOTE: *On Midgets equipped with mechanically driven tachometers it will be necessary to unscrew the tachometer drive from its connection at the rear of the generator.*

3. Remove the bolts securing the distributor clamp to the cylinder block and lift the distributor out.

4. To replace the distributor, insert the shaft into the housing until the driving dog rests on the distributor drive shaft.

5. Turn the rotor until the dog is felt to engage in the slot in the drive shaft. Both the driving dog and the slot are offset so that the distributor will not fall into place until it is properly positioned.

6. Turn the distributor body to align the clamp and housing bolt holes and replace the bolts.

7. Replace the distributor cap, the vacuum advance line, the low tension lead from the coil, and reconnect the tachometer drive to the generator (if applicable).

Generator

Removal and Installation

The generator may be removed by disconnecting the two wires from the terminals and removing the mounting bolts. When removing the regulator the battery cable leading to the starter should be disconnected at the battery to protect the wiring harness.

1. Disconnect the wires and unscrew the two bolts at the base to remove the regulator.

2. Mark the wires if unsure of their positions on the terminal block.

Both the generator and regulator may be polarized at the same time after they have been installed on the car. Reconnect the battery.

3. Disconnect the wire from regulator terminal F (field) and touch it momentarily to regulator terminal B or AI (battery). Do not hold the wire to the terminal for more than one second. Reconnect the wire to terminal F. The

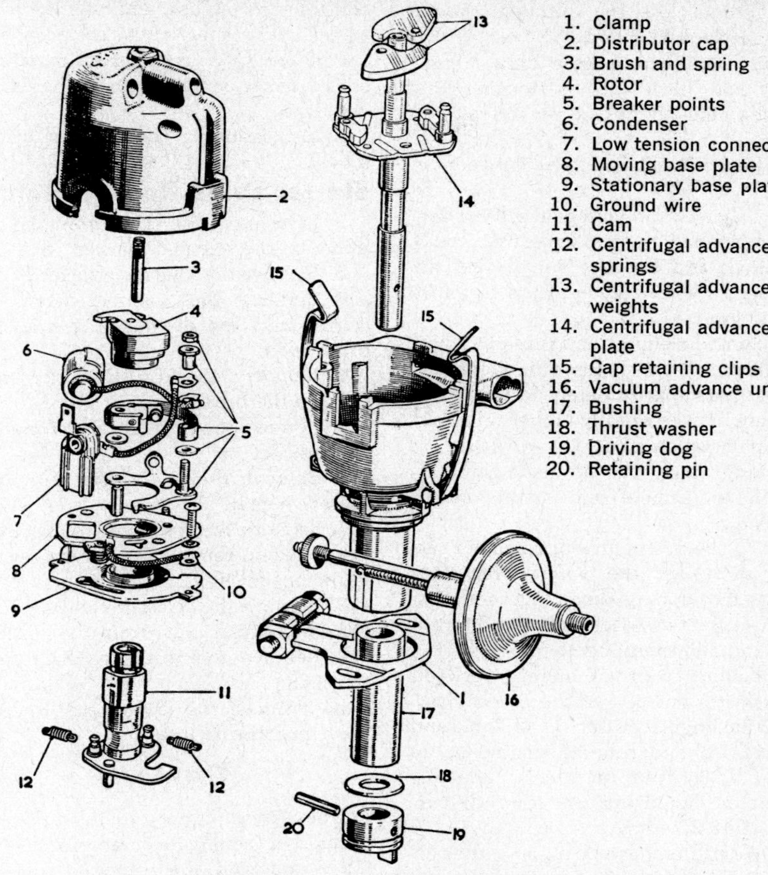

1. Clamp
2. Distributor cap
3. Brush and spring
4. Rotor
5. Breaker points
6. Condenser
7. Low tension connector
8. Moving base plate
9. Stationary base plate
10. Ground wire
11. Cam
12. Centrifugal advance springs
13. Centrifugal advance weights
14. Centrifugal advance plate
15. Cap retaining clips
16. Vacuum advance unit
17. Bushing
18. Thrust washer
19. Driving dog
20. Retaining pin

Lucas Distributor, Disassembled View

polarity of the generator and regulator will then be in line with the polarity of the vehicle electrical system.

Alternator

Alternator Precautions

4. Do not run the engine with the batteries out of the circuit or any of the charging circuits wires disconnected (except as given in test procedures). All charging circuit electrical connections must be clean and tight, and the drive belt properly adjusted.

5. Correct battery and alternator polarity (negative ground) must be maintained or the alternator will be destroyed. If arc welding equipment is used on the car the alternator and regulator leads must be disconnected.

Alternator and Regulator

Removal and Installation

16AC and 16ACR Alternators

To remove the alternator disconnect the hoses from the air pump outlets.

1. Loosen the air pump mounting bolt.
2. Remove the bolt from the air pump adjusting strut.
3. Slip the belt off the air pump pulley and raise the pump.
4. Disconnect the wires from the alternator (do not let the wire that connects to the B+ terminal on the alternator touch ground).
5. Remove the alternator mounting bolts, slip the belt from the pulley, and remove the alternator.
6. Installation is in reverse order of removal.

4TR, 8TR, and 11TR Regulators

The 4TR regulator is used only with the 16AC alternator and is conventionally mounted in the engine compartment. To remove this unit, simply pull the plug-in connector block from the base and remove the mounting screws.

The 8TR and 11TR regulators are used interchangeably with the 16ACR alternator. The regulator unit is located *inside the alternator.*

1. To replace it the alternator must be removed from the car. When the plastic alternator end-cover is removed the regulator is accessible. Note the positions of the regulator leads and remove them. Remove the lower mounting screw and the regulator will be free.

NOTE: *Never attempt to polarize an alternator or alternator regulator.*

Regulator Adjustments

RB106 Series Regulator

This regulator unit contains a cut-out relay and voltage regulator. The cut-out relay is a switch that makes and breaks connection between the battery and generator to prevent the battery from discharging through the generator when the engine is stopped or running slowly. The voltage regulator controls generator output in accordance with battery draw and its state of charge.

The settings of the contact breaker points of the voltage regulator and cut-out relay should not be disturbed. These were accurately set at the factory and should never need adjustment. They should never be disassembled because the regulator is only available as a unit; parts are not available. If necessary, the points may be cleaned using a strip of fine sandpaper and then wiped clean using a non-oily solvent.

The electrical settings of the cut-out relay and the regulator can be checked and adjusted.

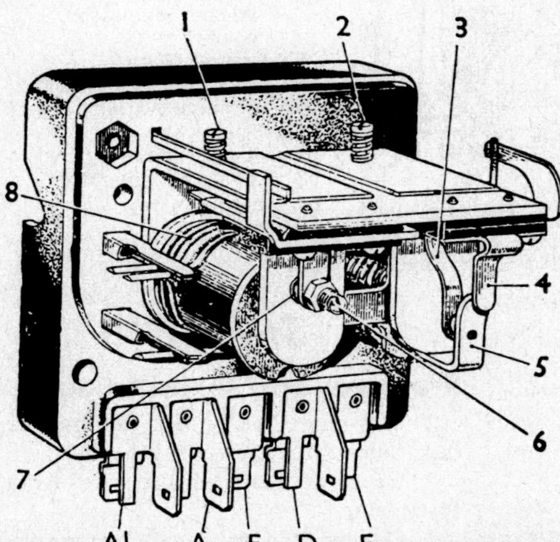

1. Regulator adjusting screw
2. Cut-out relay adjusting screw
3. Fixed contact blade
4. Stop arm
5. Moving contact
6. Fixed contact screw
7. Moving contact
8. Regulator series windings

AI—Battery input
A—Regulated generator output
F—Field
D—Armature (Generator)
E—Ground (Earth)

R 106 Series Regulator Unit

To check the voltage at which the cut-out operates connect a voltmeter to the terminals D and E.

1. Start the engine and slowly increase its speed until the cut-out points close. At the point just before the needle drops back, the voltmeter should read between 12.7 and 13.3 volts. If the reading is not within these limits adjustment can be made at the cut-out adjusting screw.

2. Recheck voltage after adjustment is made.

To check the regulator setting, disconnect wires AI and A and clip them together. Connect the negative lead of a voltmeter to the D terminal on the generator and ground the positive lead on the engine or chassis.

1. Start the engine and slowly increase the speed until the voltmeter "flicks" and then steadies. The voltmeter should indicate about 16 volts at this point.

2. Adjustment can be made with the regulator adjusting screw.

Both the cut-out and regulator adjustments should be made as rapidly as possible to avoid inaccuracy caused by temperature rise in the engine compartment.

RB340 Regulator

The regulator unit contains a cut-out relay, voltage regulator, and current regulator. Its functions are the same as the RB106 regulator except that the RB340 has the addition of the current (amperage) regulator to further monitor generator output.

As with the RB106 regulator, the settings of the contact breaker points in the RB340 unit should not be altered (see "Adjusting the RB106 Series Regulator").

1. Adjusting cams
2. Lucas adjusting tool (not essential)
3. Cut-out relay
4. Current regulator
5. Current regulator points
6. Voltage regulator
7. Voltage regulator points

E—Ground (Earth)
D—Armature (Generator)
WL—Charge Warning Light
F—Field
B—Battery input and regulated generator output

RB 340 Series Regulator Unit

The electrical settings of the cut-out relay and the two regulators can be checked and adjusted.

To check the voltage at which the cut-out operates, connect a voltmeter between the regulator terminal D and ground.

1. Start the engine, switch on the headlights, and slowly increase engine speed until the cut-out points close. At the point just before the needle drops back (points close) the voltmeter should read between 12.7 and 13.3 volts. If the reading is not within these limits, adjustment can be made by turning the toothed adjustment cam on the cut-out relay.

2. Recheck voltage after adjustment is made.

3. To check the voltage regulator setting disconnect the two wires from the B terminals and clip the wires together. Connect a voltmeter between terminal D and ground.

4. Start the engine and run it to about 2,000 rpm, at which point the voltmeter should read approximately 15 volts. The reading may be slightly higher on a cold day or lower on a hot day ±1 volt).

5. Adjustment can be made by rotating the adjustment cam on the voltage regulator.

6. To check the current regulator setting short out the *voltage* regulator points by clipping them together. Disconnect the two wires from the B terminals and clip them together.

7. Connect an ammeter between those wires and one of the B terminals. Start the engine, switch on all lights and accessories, and run the engine up to about 2,000 rpm, at which point the ammeter should indicate a steady current of 19-22 amps.

8. Adjustment can be made at the current regulator adjustment cam.

All adjustments should be made as quickly as possible to avoid inaccuracy caused by temperature rise in the engine compartment.

Unsteady readings obtained on any of the checks may be due to dirt or oil on the contact points.

Starter

Removal and Installation

1. Disconnect the battery. Remove the distributor (MGB and Midget only).

2. Disconnect and tag the wires from the starter.

3. On the MGC it is necessary to disconnect the steering column from the universal joint near the steering box, unbolt the steering box, and turn the front wheels out so that the box can be lowered out of the way. The starter mounting bolts can now be removed and the starter withdrawn.

4. Installation is the reverse of removal.

Starter Drive Replacement

1. Disconnect the cable from the terminal on the solenoid marked "STA".

2. Remove the solenoid attaching nuts.

3. Remove the solenoid from the starter case and disengage it from the drive lever.

4. Remove the brush cover and remove the brushes.

5. Remove the through-bolts from the end bracket.

6. Remove the lever pivot pin from the drive gear.

7. Separate the drive end bracket from the yoke and remove the drive gear engagement lever.

8. Remove the armature and separate the commutator plate from the yoke.

9. Remove the thrust washers from the shaft.

10. Remove the drive gear. Reverse the procedure to install.

Battery

The 12-volt battery in the Midget is located in the engine compartment. The MGB and MGC are equipped with two 6-volt batteries that are wired together in series to produce 12 volts. They are located just ahead of the rear axle and can be reached by lifting the carpet on the shelf behind the front seats (rear seat cushion on the GT), and turning the fasteners that secure the access panel counter-clockwise.

Batteries and connections may be cleaned with a baking soda and water solution. Care should be taken not to allow any of the solution to enter the cells. After cleaning, the battery cable ends and terminals should be coated with grease or paint to retard corrosion.

ENGINE MECHANICAL

Engine Removal and Installation

MG Midget

The engine of the Midget can be removed with or without the transmission. Either way, the preliminary steps are:

1. Drain the crankcase.
2. Disconnect the battery.
3. Remove the hood.
4. Disconnect the radiator and heater hoses and oil cooler lines (late models

only), and remove the radiator.

5. Disconnect the choke and throttle cables and tachometer cable (Mk. I only).

6. Disconnect the oil pressure gauge pipe from the engine.

7. Disconnect and tag all electrical connections to the engine.

8. Disconnect the high tension wires from the coil and spark plugs, and remove the distributor cap.

9. Unbolt the exhaust header pipe from the manifold and tie the pipe out of the way.

10. Remove the air cleaners and disconnect the fuel line.

At this point, the engine can be removed either with or without the transmission. If it is desired to remove only the engine:

1. Remove the starter motor.
2. Remove the fuel filter bowl (Mk. I only).
3. Support the transmission with a jack, and remove the bell housing bolts.
4. Connect a hoist to the engine and unbolt the right-side engine mount from the chassis bracket.
5. Disconnect the left-side engine mount from the front engine plate and lift the engine from the vehicle, taking care not to damage the transmission mainshaft.

If it is desired to remove the engine and the transmission as a unit:

1. Drain the transmission oil and disconnect the back-up light switch lead (later models only).
2. Remove the gearshift lever cover, and remove the spring cap, spring, and plunger.
3. Unbolt the shift lever retaining plate and lift out the lever.
4. With the carpet turned back, remove the rear transmission mount bolts.
5. From underneath the car, unscrew the speedometer cable from the transmission housing and release the cable support bracket from the bell housing.
6. Unbolt the clutch slave cylinder from the bell housing.
7. Unbolt the driveshaft from the differential flange and slide it out. Be sure to mark the flanges so that the driveshaft can be reinstalled correctly.
8. Connect a hoist to the engine and remove the remaining transmission mounting bolts.
9. Unbolt the right-side engine mount from the chassis bracket and disconnect the left-side mount from the front engine plate.
10. Lift the engine/transmission unit from the vehicle.

Installation of the engine or engine/-transmission unit is in reverse order of removal. Be sure to refill the engine, transmission, and radiator.

MGB

The engine of the MGB can be removed with or without the transmission. Either way, the preliminary steps are:

1. Drain the crankcase.
2. Disconnect the batteries.
3. Remove the hood.
4. Disconnect the oil cooler and pressure gauge lines from the engine.
5. Disconnect the heater and radiator hoses, and unbolt and remove the radiator, radiator shroud, and oil cooler as a unit.
6. Disconnect and tag all electrical connections to the engine.
7. Disconnect the high tension leads from the coil and spark plugs, and remove the distributor cap.
8. Disconnect the choke and throttle cables and the tachometer cable (early models only).
9. Unbolt the exhaust header pipe from the manifold, and disconnect the bell housing bracket.
10. Remove the air cleaners and disconnect the fuel line.

At this point, the engine can be removed either with or without the transmission. If it is desired to remove only the engine:

1. Support the transmission with a jack, and remove the bell housing bolts.
2. Remove the bolts holding the front engine mounts to the frame.
3. Connect a hoist to the engine and lift it from the chassis, taking care not to damage the transmission mainshaft or the oil pan.

If it is desired to remove the engine and transmission as a unit:

1. Drain the transmission oil and disconnect the back-up light switch lead (later models only).
2. Disconnect the overdrive solenoid wire or the automatic transmission starter lockout switch wire, where applicable.
3. Unbolt the clutch slave cylinder from the bell housing.
4. Disconnect the speedometer cable from the transmission.
5. Unbolt the driveshaft from the differential flange and slide it out. Be sure to mark the flanges so that the driveshaft can be reinstalled in its original position.
6. Lift the gearshift boot, unbolt the lever retaining screws, and remove the shift lever (manual transmission).
7. Disconnect the gearshift lever from the transmission shaft, and disconnect the downshift cable from the carburetors (automatic transmission).
8. Connect a hoist to the engine and remove the rear crossmember and the transmission mounts, along with the transmission stabilizer rod or bracket.
9. Remove the bolts securing the front engine mounts to the frame.
10. Lift the engine/transmission unit from the vehicle.

Installation of the engine or engine/-transmission unit is in reverse order of removal. Be sure to refill the engine, transmission, and radiator.

MGC

The engine and transmission of the MGC are removed as a unit. Removal is accomplished in the following manner:

1. Disconnect the batteries and remove the hood.
2. Drain the crankcase and the transmission.
3. Drain the radiator, disconnect the radiator and heater hoses and remove the radiator (see "Radiator Removal and Installation").
4. Disconnect and tag all electrical connections to the engine.
5. Disconnect the wires from the coil to the distributor.
6. Remove the air cleaners and disconnect the fuel line.
7. Disconnect the choke and throttle cables, and the throttle relay linkage (overdrive and automatic transmissions).
8. Disconnect the brake booster vacuum line from the intake manifold.
9. Disconnect the engine oil cooler and automatic transmission oil cooler lines (if applicable).
10. Disconnect the water temperature and oil pressure gauge lines from the engine.
11. Lift the gearshift boot, remove the lever retaining bolts, and remove the shift lever (manual transmission).
12. Disconnect the manual control rod from the shift lever, underneath the car (automatic transmission).
13. Disconnect the speedometer cable from the gearbox.
14. Unbolt the clutch slave cylinder from the bell housing.
15. Mark the flanges for replacement and disconnect the driveshaft.
16. Support the rear of the engine and disconnect the rear crossmember from the body.
17. Unbolt the exhaust header pipes from the manifold and tie them out of the way.
18. Attach a hoist to the engine and unbolt the engine mounts from the frame.
19. Raise the engine just enough to gain access to the transmission wires, and mark and disconnect the wires. Be sure to disconnect the harness clips from the transmission case.
20. Lift the engine/transmission unit from the vehicle.

Installation is in reverse order of removal. Be sure to refill the engine, transmission, and radiator when they have been reinstalled.

Cylinder Head

Removal and Installation

All MGs, with the exception of the MGA Twin-Cam which is not covered in this book, have water-cooled, inline, pushrod operated overhead valve engines with four or six cylinders. As such, cylinder head operations on the different models are closely related and some generalities can be assumed.

The cylinder head nuts should be loosened, gradually, in the same order as they are tightened, to prevent the head from warping (see "Tightening Sequences"). For the same reason, the head should be removed only when the engine is cold. When the cylinder head nuts and all accessories have been unbolted from the head, it may be necessary to tap each side of the head with a rubber mallet to break the head gasket seal. When the head is free, lift it evenly over the studs. If any water has found its way into the cylinders it should be immediately removed and the cylinder walls coated with oil. If the head is not to be reinstalled for a day or more, it is a good idea to stuff towels into the cylinders to protect them.

The cylinder head removal procedure for all models is as follows:

1. Drain the radiator.
2. Disconnect the radiator and heater hoses from the cylinder head.
3. Remove the heater control valve and unbolt the top radiator bracket.
4. Remove the carburetors and air cleaners, and unbolt the manifolds and pull them back out of the way.
5. Remove the rocker cover and remove the cylinder head nuts in the proper order (see "Tightening Sequences").
6. Lift the rocker shaft assembly off and remove the pushrods, keeping them in order.
7. Remove the spark plugs and disconnect the water temperature sending unit from the head.
8. Disconnect the air supply hose from the check valve (Emission Control models only).
9. Unbolt the air pump from its mounting point on the head (four-cylinder Emission Control models only).
10. Lift the head from the cylinder block.

Installation is in reverse order of removal. Thoroughly clean the mating surfaces of the cylinder block and head, and always use a new gasket. The gasket is marked Top and Front to facilitate correct installation. Gasket sealing compound is not necessary, but may be used. Cylinder head nuts should be tightened gradually, in the correct sequence (see "Tightening Sequences"), and to the proper torque value (see "Torque Specifications"). When the head has been tightened the valves must be adjusted (see "Valve Adjustment"). After running the engine for between 200 and 500 miles, the head should be retorqued and the valves readjusted. When retorquing the head, simply back off each nut slightly and retighten to specification, one at a time and in the proper sequence.

Overhaul

See "Engine Rebuilding Section".

Intake/Exhaust Manifold

Removal

Midget

1. Remove the carburetors and air cleaners (see "Carburetor Removal and Installation").
2. Unbolt the exhaust pipe from the exhaust manifold.
3. Unbolt the heater pipe clamps from the intake manifold.
4. Unscrew the PCV valve hose from the manifold connection (if applicable).
5. Disconnect the vacuum advance and gulp valve lines from the intake manifold (if applicable).
6. Unbolt and remove the manifolds.

MGB

1. Remove the carburetors and air cleaners (see "Carburetor Removal and Installation").
2. Disconnect the distributor vacuum advance line and the gulp valve line (if applicable).
3. Unscrew the PCV valve hose from the intake manifold connection (if applicable).
4. Unbolt the heater pipe clamps from the intake manifold (early models only).
5. Unbolt the exhaust header pipes from the exhaust manifold.
6. Unbolt and remove the manifolds.

MGC

1. Remove the carburetors and air cleaners (see "Carburetor Removal and Installation").
2. Disconnect the brake booster vacuum line from the intake manifold.
3. Disconnect the PCV valve hose, gulp valve line, and distributor vacuum advance line from the intake manifold.
4. Disconnect and temporarily relocate the throttle relay bracket assembly.
5. Disconnect the two fuel overflow pipes from the intake manifold.
6. Unbolt the exhaust header pipes from the exhaust manifold.
7. If the manifolds are to be separated, unbolt the intake manifold support brackets from the exhaust manifold.
8. Unbolt and remove the manifolds.

Installation—All Models

Manifold installation in all cases is in reverse order of removal.

1. Thoroughly clean the mating surfaces and use new gaskets. The perforated metal face of the gasket should face the manifold.
2. New exhaust header ring gaskets should be used on the MGB, MGC, and late Midget models. It may be necessary to use a new exhaust pipe clamp on the early Midget. Be sure to tighten the manifold studs evenly (see "Torque Specifications").

EXHAUST SYSTEM

The exhaust systems used on MGs are generally of a straightforward design, using, in most cases, straight-through mufflers and rubber-insulated hangers. However, new cars are equipped with exhaust systems that are welded into a solid unit, and when a muffler or other component requires replacement the defective part must be cut off. Except in the case of some Midget models, the exhaust system can be purchased in individual component pieces and does not have to be replaced as a complete unit. Welding may be necessary when only part of the original exhaust system, such as an intermediate pipe, is replaced on the MGB or MGC. Welding can be avoided by replacing the original exhaust system completely with component parts on those models. Normal U-clamps can then be used to fasten the parts together.

The Midget up to 1968 does not use any gasket between the front pipe and the exhaust manifold. A pinch-type clamp is used to join the pipe and manifold flanges together directly. It is important that a quantity of muffler sealer and a new clamp are used at this connection whenever the pipe has been removed. If the pipe flange is damaged or bent in any way, the pipe should be replaced, because the connection will inevitably leak or come apart.

In all cases, muffler sealer should be used at any joint in the exhaust system where a gasket is not used. U-clamps used at the joints should not be fully tightened until all components are in place, so that the entire system can be lined up with the hangers and prevented from making contact with the frame or underpan. When muffler sealer has been used, allow it to set for about two hours before driving the car.

An exhaust leak is dangerous because the effects of carbon monoxide poisoning are virtually undetectable until damage has been done. Check the exhaust system at least twice a year, and correct any leaks as soon as possible.

Timing Gear Cover and Oil Seal

Removal and Installation

MG Midget

To remove the timing gear cover:

1. Remove the radiator.
2. Loosen the generator adjustment bolts and remove the fan belt.

NOTE: *On 1968 and later Midgets it is necessary to unbolt the engine mounts and exhaust pipe in order to raise the front of the engine to provide clearance for removal of the pulley.*

3. Bend the locktab back and unscrew the crankshaft pulley nut.
4. Carefully pry the pulley from the crankshaft.
5. Unbolt and remove the timing gear cover.

To replace the timing gear cover oil seal:

1. Pry the old seal out of the cover.
2. Lubricate the new seal and install it evenly into the cover in the same position as the old one, taking care not to damage it.
3. If the seal is made of rubber, fill the groove between the seal lips with grease. Felt seals do not need to be lubricated in this manner.
4. Make sure that the oil thrower behind the crankshaft pulley is installed with the concave side (early engines) or the face marked F (later engines) away from the engine.

The cover and pulley are installed together to ensure that the oil seal is centered correctly. To reinstall:

1. Lubricate the hub of the pulley and insert it into the oil seal, turning the pulley in a clockwise direction to avoid damaging the seal.
2. Align the pulley keyway with the crankshaft key and push the pulley (with the cover and cover gasket) onto the crankshaft.
3. Replace the cover bolts and tighten them evenly.
4. Tighten and lock the crankshaft pulley nut.
5. Reinstall the fan belt, and replace and fill the radiator.

MGB

Timing gear cover removal and installation and oil seal replacement procedures for the MGB are the same as for the Midget, with one exception: on 18GB and later engines, the steering rack must be unbolted from the body and moved forward to provide clearance for removal of the crankshaft pulley. It is not necessary to raise the front of the engine to remove the pulley on the MGB.

MGC

To remove the timing gear cover:

1. Remove the radiator.
2. Drain the crankcase.
3. Remove the transmission stone guard.
4. Unbolt and lower the oil pan, allowing it to rest in the front crossmember.
5. Unbolt the alternator adjustment strut and loosen the adjustment (pivot) bolt.
6. Remove the fan belt and unbolt and remove the fan.
7. Remove the spacer and the water pump pulley.
8. Bend the locktab back and unscrew the crankshaft nut.
9. Remove the crankshaft pulley/-damper unit.
10. Unbolt and remove the timing gear cover.

To replace the timing gear cover oil seal:

1. Pry the old seal out of the cover.
2. Lubricate the new seal and install it evenly into the cover in the same position as the old one.

Installation of the cover is in reverse order of removal. Always use a new gasket between the cover and cylinder block. Torque the oil pan bolts to 6 ft lbs, and the cover bolts to 25 ft lbs. Do not forget to refill the crankcase with fresh oil.

Timing Gear and Chain

Removal and Installation

The camshafts in all MG engines are driven by a chain from the crankshaft. The Midget models have an endless, single-row timing chain without a tensioner, while the MGB and MGC have an endless, duplex chain and a chain tensiôner. Chain tensioner removal and service procedures can be found under "Timing Chain Tensioner Service—MGB and MGC."

The crankshaft and camshaft timing gears and the timing chain usually do not require service or replacement unless, due to high mileage or improper lubrication, gear tooth wear is noticeable. If wear is evident, replace all three components. Worn gears or chain stretch as isolated problems almost never occur.

1. To remove the chain and gears, first remove the timing gear cover (see preceding section). On the MGB and MGC, remove the chain tensioner or retract and lock the rubbing block by removing the plug from the tensioner body and turning the adjusting bolt clockwise (see following section).
2. Bend the locktab back and remove the camshaft timing gear nut. The camshaft and crankshaft timing gears may now be removed together with the chain by easing the gears off the shafts simultaneously, using a puller or suitable levers.

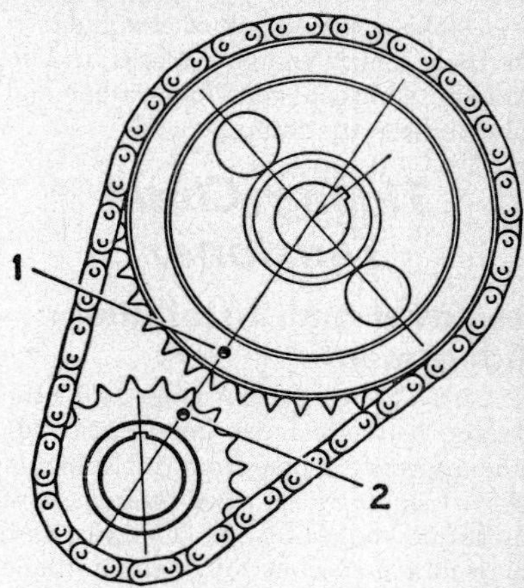

Timing Gear Marks—Midget, MGB

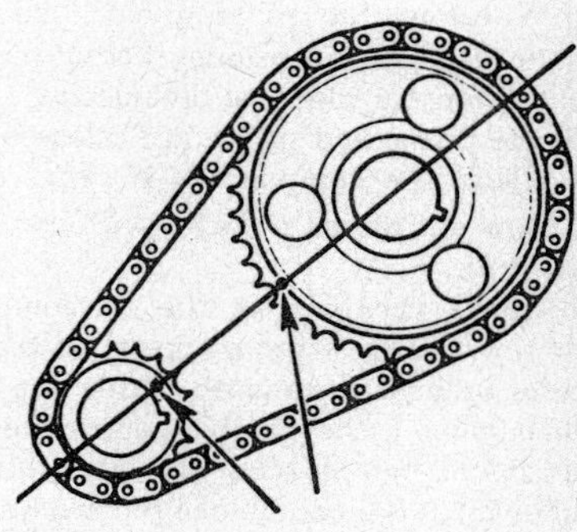
Timing Gear Marks—MGC

3. When replacing the timing chain and gears, set the crankshaft with its keyway at twelve o'clock and the camshaft with its keyway at one o'clock as seen from the front. The washers behind the crankshaft gear are spacers to align the two gears properly.
4. When reassembling, the same number of washers should be installed as were removed *unless* any of the following components have been replaced: crankshaft, crankshaft main bearings and thrust washers, crankshaft timing gear, camshaft, camshaft timing gear, or camshaft locating plate. If any of the above components have been replaced, timing gear alignment can be checked and adjusted by placing a straightedge across the gear sides and adding or subtracting washers to eliminate any gaps between the gear side surfaces and the straightedge (after the gears have been installed).
5. To install the timing gears and chain, assemble the chain onto the gears with the gear marks facing each other so that a line drawn through them would pass through the camshaft and crankshaft axes. Keeping the gears in this position, start the crankshaft gear onto the crankshaft (with the gear keyway and crankshaft key aligned).
6. Install the camshaft gear onto the camshaft, turning the camshaft to align the key with the keyway if necessary.

7. Make a final check of alignment of the timing gears and gear marks, and install the camshaft gear lockwasher and nut. Replace the timing cover.

Timing Chain Tensioner

Removal and Installation, Adjustment

1. To remove the tensioner (after the timing gear cover has been removed), first unscrew the plug from the tensioner body. Using a ⅛ in. Allen wrench, turn the tension adjusting bolt clockwise until the rubbing block is fully retracted and locked behind the limit peg.
2. Unbolt and remove the tensioner and its backing plate.
3. Withdraw the rubbing block and plunger from the tensioner body, and turn the tension adjusting bolt clockwise until the piston and spring are released.
4. Clean the components in solvent and blow out the oil passages with compressed air.
5. Check the bore of the tensioner body for ovality. If the diameter of the bore at or near the mouth varies more than 0.003 in., the complete tensioner unit should be replaced. If within the limit given, it is acceptable to replace just the rubbing block.
6. To reassemble the tensioner, insert the spring and piston into the bore and compress the spring.
7. Turn the piston clockwise until the inner end is below the peg. Install the rubbing block plunger into the bore.

CAUTION: *Do not attempt to turn the tension adjusting bolt counterclockwise.*

8. Bolt the backing plate and tensioner onto the cylinder block and lock the mounting bolts with the locktab.
9. Release the rubbing block for operation by turning the adjusting bolt clockwise until the block contacts the chain under spring pressure.
10. Check the rubbing block for freedom of movement and make sure that it does not bind against the backing plate.
11. Replace and lock the plug in the tensioner body.

Camshaft

Removal

Midget Mk. I and II

Removal of the camshaft from Mk. I and II Midgets can be accomplished without removing the engine from the chassis. The following procedure can, however, be utilized whether the engine is in or out of the car.

1. Drain the crankcase and remove the oil pan from the engine.
2. Remove the rocker cover from the head and unbolt and remove the rocker shaft assembly and pushrods (keeping the pushrods in order).
3. Remove the intake and exhaust manifolds.
4. Remove the lifter covers from the side of the cylinder block.
5. Remove the lifters, and, as with the pushrods, keep them in order.
6. Remove the timing cover and gears.
7. Remove the oil pump.
8. Remove the distributor.
9. Remove the camshaft locating plate.
10. Pull the camshaft from the front of the engine, rotating it slowly to assist removal.

NOTE: *Removal procedures for individual units such as the oil pump, timing gear cover, etc., can be found under appropriate subheads in the "Engine" section.*

Midget Mk. III

The 1,275 cc. engine does not have lifter covers on the side of the cylinder block; therefore, some method of holding the lifters all the way up in their bores must be employed so that the camshaft can be withdrawn without the cam lobes hanging up on them. There are two ways to accomplish this. The factory recommended method is to:

1. Drain the crankcase and remove the engine.
2. Remove the rocker cover and unbolt and remove the rocker shaft assembly and pushrods (keeping the pushrods in order).
3. Remove the timing cover and gears.
4. Remove the oil pan.
5. Remove the distributor.
6. Remove the camshaft locating plate.
7. Invert the engine to allow the lifters to fall into their bores.
8. Withdraw the camshaft, rotating it slowly to assist removal. If the oil pump drive flange comes away with the camshaft, replace it on the pump driveshaft with the drive lug towards the pump.

The alternative method of removing the camshaft does not require removal of the engine, but does necessitate a technique of retaining the lifters that is not factory approved. However, as with any repair procedure, if care and common sense are exercised, satisfactory results can be obtained. The procedure is as follows:

1. Drain the crankcase and remove the oil pan.
2. Remove the rocker cover, rocker shaft assembly, and pushrods. (Keep the pushrods in order.)
3. Remove the timing cover and camshaft gear.
4. Remove the distributor.
5. Remove the camshaft locating plate.
6. From underneath the car, coat the lifters with a thick lubricant such as a petroleum base grease and push them up into their bores. They should remain in this position long enough to remove and replace the camshaft.
7. Withdraw the camshaft while rotating it slowly. If the oil pump drive flange comes out with the cam, replace it on the pump driveshaft with the drive lug toward the pump.

NOTE: *Removal procedures for individual units such as the timing gear cover can be found under appropriate subheads in the "Engine" section.*

MGB

Camshaft removal procedures for the MGB are the same as for the Midget Mk. I and II, with one exception: if the car is equipped with a mechanically driven tachometer, disconnect the cable and unbolt and remove the drive gear.

MGC

Removal of the camshaft from the MGC can be accomplished without removing the engine from the chassis. The procedure is as follows:

1. Remove the radiator grille.
2. Remove the timing cover and gears.
3. Remove the rocker cover and unbolt and remove the rocker shaft assembly and pushrods (keeping the pushrods in order).
4. Remove the alternator and unbolt and remove the three lifter covers from the side of the cylinder block. Withdraw the lifters, keeping them in order.
5. Remove the distributor and lift out the distributor drive gear. The gear may be removed by screwing a 7/16 in. SAE bolt into the drive to provide a lifting point.
6. Remove the lines from the oil cooler and unbolt and remove the cooler.
7. Unbolt the camshaft locating plate.
8. Withdraw the camshaft gently from the engine.

NOTE: *Removal procedures for individual units such as the timing gear cover can be found under appropriate subheads in the "Engine" section.*

Installation

All Models

Camshaft installation in all cases is in reverse order of removal. Camshaft bearings, except in cases of insufficient lubrication, almost never need replacement. Clearance can be checked with a feeler gauge. Replacement of bearings requires special pullers and machine tools (for align-boring) and should be left to a machine shop.

Camshaft end-play can be checked before installation by assembling the locating plate and timing gear onto the camshaft and measuring fore and aft play. If it exceeds specification, the locating plate should be replaced.

Camshaft Specifications (in.)

Model	End Float	Oil Clearance
Midget	0.003-0.007	0.001-0.002
MGB	0.003-0.007	0.001-0.002
MGC	0.003-0.006	0.001-0.002
MG 1100	0.003-0.007	0.001-0.002

NOTE: Valve lift for the different engine models can be found under VALVE SPECIFICATIONS. Intake valve opening timing (deg. BTDC) can be found under TUNE-UP SPECIFICATIONS.

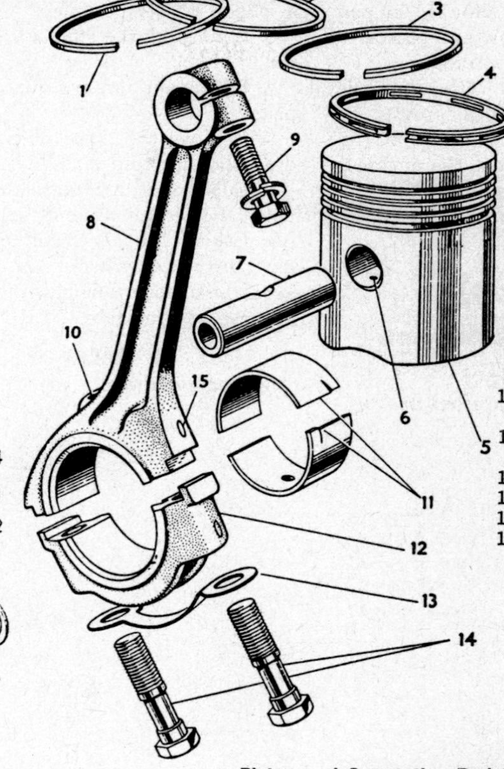

1. Piston ring—parallel
2. Piston ring—taper
3. Piston ring—taper
4. Piston ring—scraper
5. Piston
6. Piston pin lubricating hole
7. Piston pin
8. Connecting rod
9. Clamping screw and washer
10. Cylinder wall lubricating jet
11. Connecting rod bearings
12. Connecting rod cap
13. Lock washer
14. Bolts
15. Connecting rod and cap marking

Piston and Connecting Rod Components—Midget.

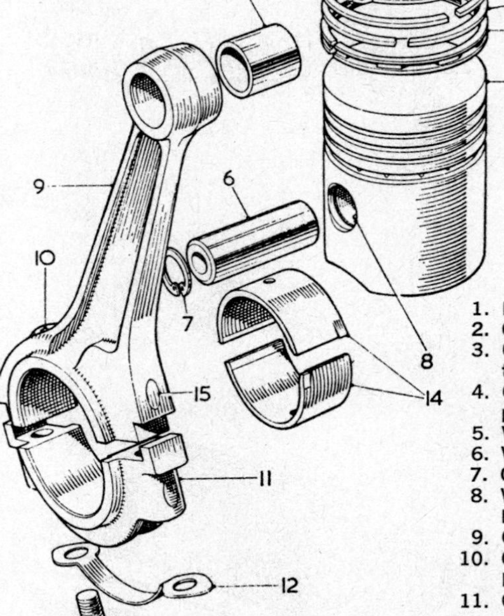

1. Piston
2. Oil ring
3. Compression rings—taper
4. Compression ring—parallel
5. Wrist pin bushing
6. Wrist pin
7. Circlip
8. Wrist pin lubrication hole
9. Connecting rod
10. Cylinder wall lubrication jet
11. Connecting rod bearing cap
12. Locktab
13. Rod bolts
14. Rod bearings
15. Connecting rod and cap assembly marks

Piston and Connecting Rod Components

Pistons and Connecting Rods

NOTE: *On engines with floating or press-fit type wrist pins, the pistons are select-fitted to the bores, and the piston crowns and cylinders are marked with identification numbers.*

Piston and connecting rod installation position for all models is indicated in the accompanying illustrations. Unmarked pistons must be identified with regard to cylinder and installation position prior to removal so that they may be reinstalled in the same position. Select-fitted pistons are identified by a number enclosed in a diamond stamped on the piston crown and block. Oversize dimensions are stamped on the piston crown, enclosed in some cases in an ellipse.

Oversize Piston Markings

ENGINE LUBRICATION

Oil Pan

Removal and Installation

Midget

1. Drain the oil and unbolt and lower the oil pan.
2. Always replace the two pan gaskets and the two main bearing cork seals when the pan has been removed. It may be necessary to soak the cork seals in hot water to keep them from breaking when installing them.

MGB

1. Drain the oil. Drain the radiator and disconnect the hoses.
2. Unbolt the engine mounts and lift the front of the engine enough to gain access to the front oil pan bolts.
3. Unbolt and lower the pan.
4. Clean the cylinder block and oil pan mating surfaces and replace the pan gasket to preclude the possibility of an oil leak.

MGC

Manual transmission models:

1. Remove the timing gear cover.
2. Unbolt the oil pan and let it rest on the crossmember.

3. Unbolt the engine mounts, lift the front of the engine, and slide the oil pan out. Be sure to use a new pan gasket.

Automatic transmission models:

On MGC's equipped with automatic transmission, the engine must be removed to provide clearance for removal of the oil pan. Once the engine is out of the car, the pan can simply be unbolted and removed. Be *sure* to use a new gasket.

Oil Pump

Removal and Installation

MG Midget

1. Remove the engine from the car.
2. Unbolt the clutch assembly from the flywheel.
3. Bend back the locktabs and unbolt the flywheel.
4. Unbolt and remove the rear engine plate.
5. Remove the three bolts and withdraw the oil pump assembly.

Installation is in reverse order of removal. Be careful, when installing the paper gasket, that the intake and delivery ports are not obstructed. Use a new gasket if the old one is damaged in any way, and use new locktabs.

MGB

1. Remove the oil pan.
2. Remove the three nuts that secure the pump to the crankcase and withdraw the pump assembly.

Installation is in reverse order of removal. Use a new gasket when the pump is reinstalled.

MGC

1. Remove the oil pan.
2. Unbolt and withdraw the oil pump assembly from the crankcase.
3. Installation is in reverse order of removal.

Oil Pump Clearances

MG Midget

Concentric Engineering pump:

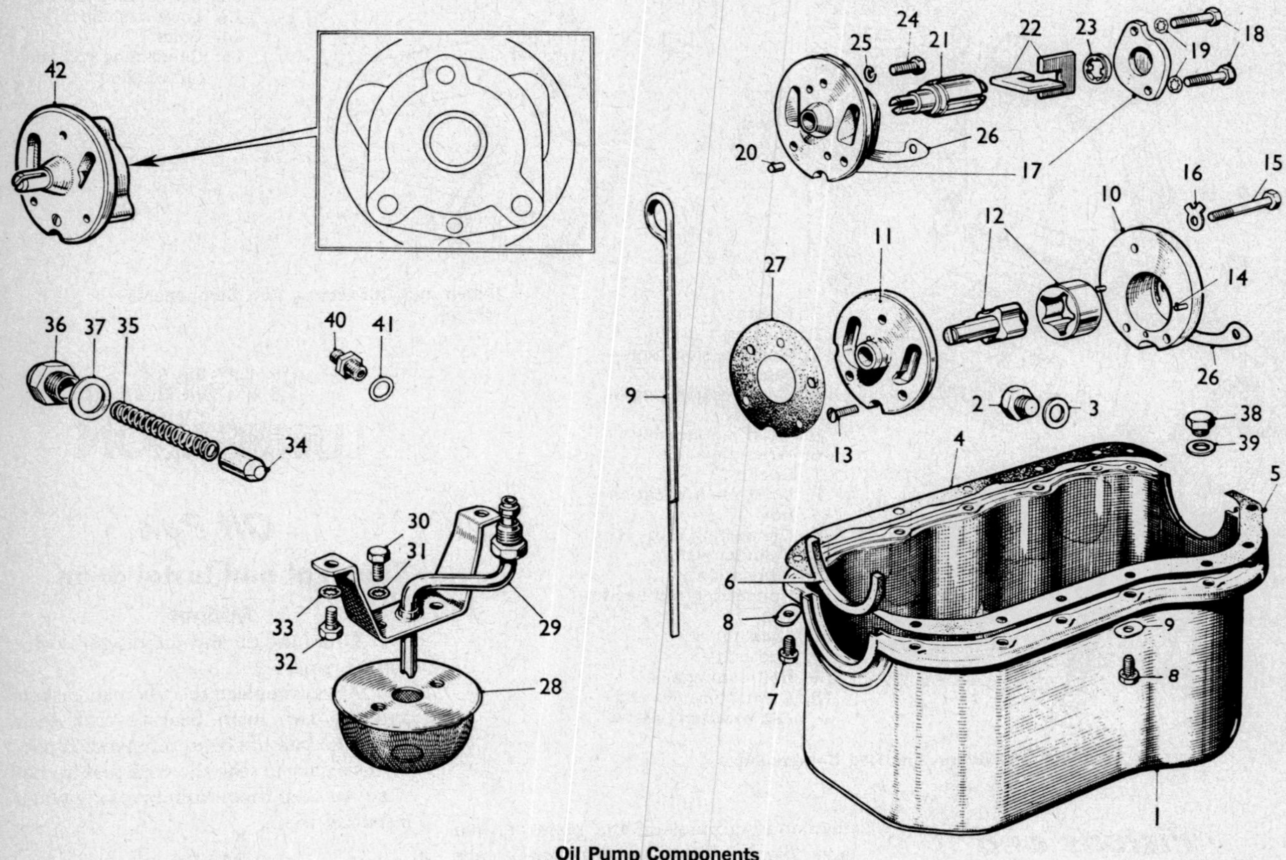

Oil Pump Components

1. Oil pan
2. Drain plug
3. Washer
4. Oil pan gasket
5. Oil pan gasket
6. Main bearing cork seal
7. Oil pan bolt
8. Washer
9. Dip stick
10. Oil pump body
11. Cover
12. Inner and outer rotors
13. Cover screws
14. Dowel
15. Pump mounting bolt
16. Lockwasher

(10–16: Hobourn-Eaton pump)

17. Body and cover assembly
18. Screw
19. Lockwasher
20. Dowel
21. Rotor
22. Vane
23. Sleeve
24. Pump mounting bolt
25. Lockwasher

(17–25: Burman pump)

26. Lockplate (all pumps)
27. Gasket
28. Wire mesh filter
29. Oil pickup pipe
30. Screw
31. Lockwasher
32. Screw
33. Lockwasher
34. Oil relief valve
35. Spring
36. Cap-nut
37. Washer
38. Oil priming plug
39. Copper washer
40. Oil pressure feed connection
41. Fiber washer
42. Pump assembly—Concentric Engineering type

The concentric pump is replaceable as a unit only; parts are not available.

Burman pump:

1. Remove the pump cover and withdraw the rotor and vane assembly. Remove the sleeve from the end of the rotor and remove the vanes.
2. Replace any worn or galled parts.
3. Coat all parts with motor oil before assembly.

Hobourn-Eaton pump:

4. Remove the pump cover and lift out the inner and outer rotors.
5. Check clearance between the outer rotor and the pump body. If the clearance exceeds 0.010 in., the complete pump assembly should be renewed.
6. Check clearance between the rotor lobes.
7. Replace the rotors if clearance exceeds 0.006 in.
8. Check the rotor end float. If the clearance exceeds 0.005 in., remove the dowels from the pump body mating surface and mill or lap the surface until clearance is within specification.
9. Coat all parts with fresh motor oil before assembling. Install the outer rotor in the pump body with the beveled end at the drive end of the pump body.
10. Check the pump for freedom of movement after assembly.

MGB

MGB oil pump service procedures are identical to those of the Hobourn-Eaton pump on the Midget.

MGC

The oil pump on the MGC is replaceable as a unit only; parts are not available.

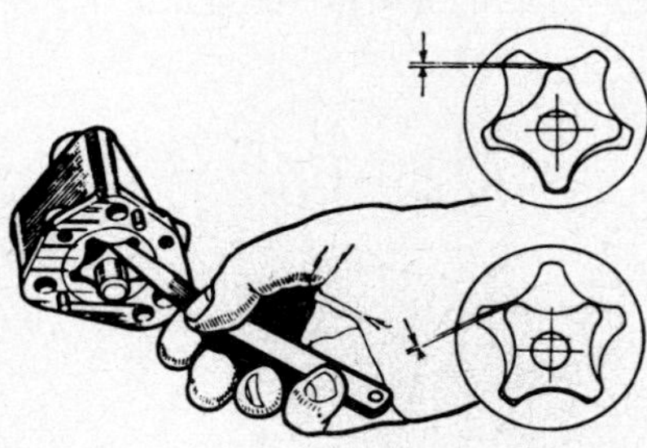

Oil Pump Rotor Position

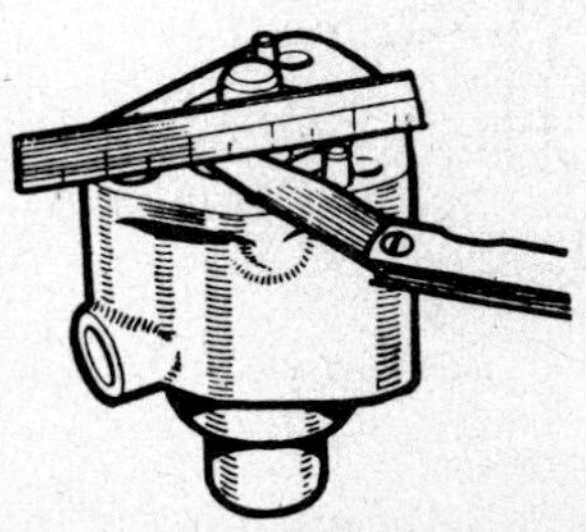

Checking Rotor End Play

Oil Cooler

Removal and Installation

On all models equipped with oil coolers, disconnect the lines from the cooler and unbolt and remove the cooler unit. When replacing, start the line fittings onto the connections by hand to avoid crossing the threads. Tighten the fittings, check the engine oil, and start the engine. Let the engine idle until oil pressure is developed, and check the oil lines for leaks. Shut the engine off and recheck the oil level.

ENGINE COOLING

Radiator

Removal and Installation

MG Midget

1. Drain the cooling system by opening the radiator tap.
2. Disconnect the upper and lower hoses from the radiator.
3. Disconnect the fresh air induction pipe from the front shroud.
4. Remove the temperature sending unit from the right side of the radiator (early models only).
5. Disconnect the oil cooler lines on cars so equipped.
6. Remove the radiator retaining bolts and lift the radiator out (complete with shroud, Mk. III).
7. Installation is in reverse order of removal.

MGB

1. Open the radiator tap and drain the coolant.
2. Disconnect the upper and lower radiator hoses.
3. If the car is not equipped with an oil cooler, remove the shroud bolts and remove the radiator and shroud as an assembly.
4. If the car has an oil cooler, loosen the shroud mounting bolts, remove the overflow hose clamp, and remove the radiator-to-shroud bolts. Withdraw the radiator from the shroud.
5. Installation is in reverse order of removal.

MGC

1. Open the radiator tap and drain the coolant.
2. Remove the washer bottle from the radiator shroud.
3. Disconnect the upper and lower hoses from the radiator.
4. Remove the expansion tank hose clamp from the radiator shroud.
5. Remove the bolt and remove the top radiator-to-shroud bridge piece.
6. Remove the radiator mounting screws, push the shroud over the fan, and lift the radiator out.
7. Installation is in reverse order of removal.

Water Pump

MG Midget—Removal

1. Remove the radiator.
2. Remove the fan retaining bolts and remove the fan.
3. Loosen the air pump mounting bolts, remove the adjusting strut bolt, remove the belt and swivel and pump up out of the way (Emission Control models only).
4. Loosen the generator mounting bolts, remove the belt, remove the top mounting bolts and lower the generator out of the way.
5. Disconnect the by-pass hose and lower radiator hose from the water pump.
6. Remove the water pump mounting bolts and remove the pump.

MGB—Removal

1. Remove the radiator.
2. Remove the generator or alternator.
3. Remove the fan and pulley retaining bolts and remove the fan.
4. Remove the water pump mounting bolts and remove the pump.

MGC—Removal

1. Remove the radiator.
2. Loosen the alternator mounting bolts and remove the fan belt.
3. Unbolt the fan and allow it to rest on the bottom radiator shroud.
4. Remove the fan-to-pulley spacer and remove the pulley.
5. Disconnect the hoses from the pump, unscrew the mounting bolts, and remove the water pump.

All Models—Installation

Installation in all cases is a reversal of removal procedures. Make sure that the mating surface of the cylinder block is cleaned of pieces of the old gasket that may remain. Always use a new gasket, and torque the mounting bolts evenly.

Thermostat

Removal and Installation

The thermostat on all MGs is located in the aluminum housing, bolted to the cylinder head, that connects to the upper radiator hose.

1. Replacement involves simply unbolting the housing and lifting out the thermostat.
2. Before unbolting the housing, drain (and save) about half of the coolant from the radiator to prevent loss when the housing is removed. Thermostats of three

different opening temperatures are available: 160° F., 180° F., and 190° F. The 180° thermostat is suitable for all around use in most climates, while the 160° and 190° thermostats can be used in very hot or cold weather, respectively.

3. The thermostat should always be installed with the bellows or spring facing downward toward the block.

4. Use a new gasket between the thermostat housing and the cylinder head. If the gasket is made of cork, as some replacements are, be careful not to overtighten the housing nuts or the cork will be completely crushed out and will not seal.

NOTE: *Never remove the thermostat in an attempt to cure overheating, as this may cause a blown head gasket, burnt valves, etc. due to localized overheating. Instead, install a restricting washer or a gutted thermostat body.*

EMISSION CONTROLS

Emission Control Applications

Model/ Year	Engine Code	Emission Control System Type
Midget		
1963-67	10CG/10CC/ 12CC/12CE	PCV
1968-70	12CD	PCV/EAI
1971	12CJ①	EAI/ELC
MGB		
1963-67	18GA/18GB	PCV
1968-69	18GF	PCV/EAI
1970	18GH② 18GJ	PCV/EAI EAI/ELC
1971	18GK	EAI/ELC/NOx
MGC		
1968-69	29GA	PCV/EAI

PCV Positive Crankcase Ventilation.
EAI Exhaust Air Injection.
ELC Evaporative Loss Control.
NOx Nitrogen Oxide control.
① Some 12CJ engines also incorporate the NOx modifications.
② 18GH engines have no PCV valve. Crankcase fumes are drawn through the oil separator to the intake manifold by carburetor vacuum. Service by simply replacing the oil filler cap at 12,000 mile intervals.

NOTE: Models equipped with the Evaporative Loss Control system are provided with a crankcase ventilation system integral with the ELC. The only service required is to replace the oil filler cap at 12,000 mile intervals.

Positive Crankcase Ventilation

The PCV system prevents crankcase fumes from venting to the atmosphere by routing them back to the intake manifold and reburning them in the combustion chambers. A non-operational PCV system can cause sludge formations and overheating. The only components in the system are the PCV valve and one-way breather type oil filler cap. To test the efficiency of the valve, remove the oil filler cap while the engine is idling. If the engine speed does not rise slightly (about 200 rpm), the valve is not operating properly and should be replaced. Valve components should be cleaned and inspected at 6,000 mile intervals, and the oil filler cap replaced every 12,000 miles.

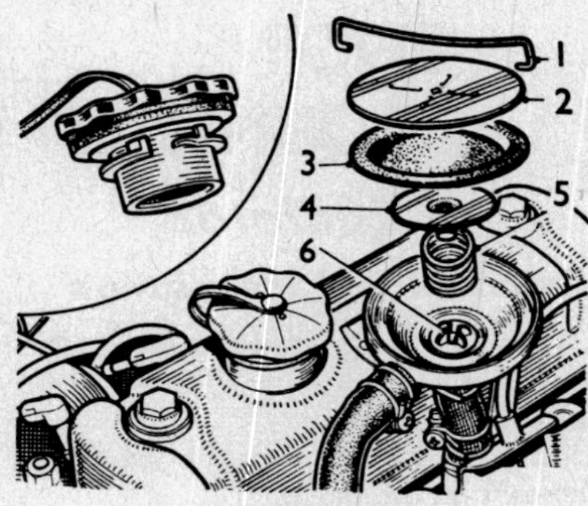

PCV Valve and Components

1. Retaining clip
2. Cover
3. Diaphragm
4. Metering valve
5. Spring
6. Guides (later type valves)

Exhaust Air Injection

Operation

The EAI system consists of a belt driven air pump that forces air into the exhaust port of each cylinder, causing a reburning of exhaust gases in order to reduce the number of harmful emissions.

Air is drawn into the pump through a replaceable paper filter.

A relief valve in the pump vents excessive air pressure, created by high rpm operation, to the atmosphere.

A check valve, located in the pump output line to the injection manifold, protects the pump from exhaust gas backflow.

A gulp valve, located in the pump output line to the intake manifold, leans out the rich fuel/air mixture that develops when the engine is decelerating (engine overrun). A line between the intake manifold and the gulp valve allows the valve to be activated by changes in manifold vacuum. On some engines a restrictor is located in the output line between the pump and valve to prevent engine surge when the valve is operating.

In addition to the air pump and its attendant equipment, all vehicles with emission control systems are equipped with the distributor and carburetors modified to meet emission standards. These units are covered separately in the "Engine Electrical" and "Fuel System" sections, as well as in the "Specifications" section.

The efficient and trouble-free operation of the emission control system depends to a large extent upon the engine being correctly tuned. Proper tuning specifications given for a particular engine should be strictly adhered to (see "Tune-Up Specifications").

Maintenance

At the time of an engine tune-up (6,000 miles recommended), the entire exhaust

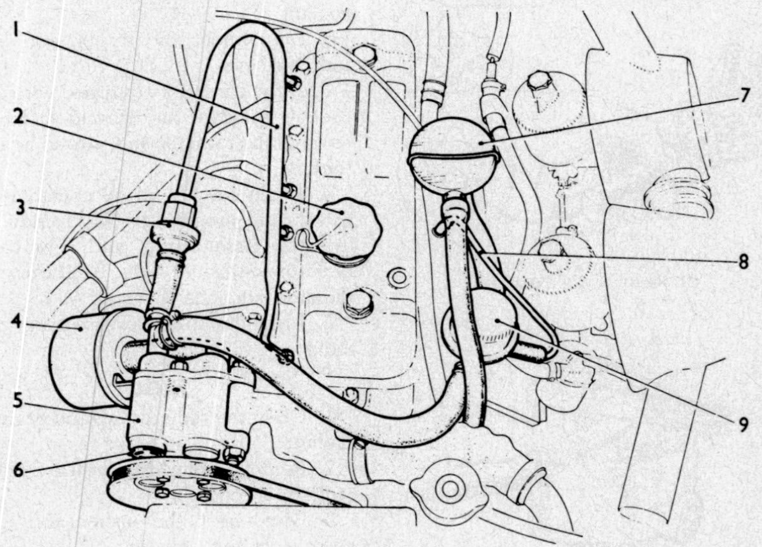

Exhaust Air Injection System

1. Air manifold
2. Oil filler cap
3. Check valve
4. Air pump air filter
5. Air pump
6. Relief valve
7. PCV valve
8. Vacuum sensing line
9. Gulp valve

air injection system should be inspected. Clean or replace the air pump air filter element. Check the air hoses and connections for any evidence of leaking. (This is very important, because an air leak can cause overheating, resulting in burnt valves, a blown head gasket, etc.) Check the air pump drive belt tension and adjust it if necessary. Properly adjusted, the belt should have a total defection of ½ inch midway between the pulleys. Adjustment is made by loosening the mounting bolt and adjusting strut bolts, in the same manner as generator adjustment.

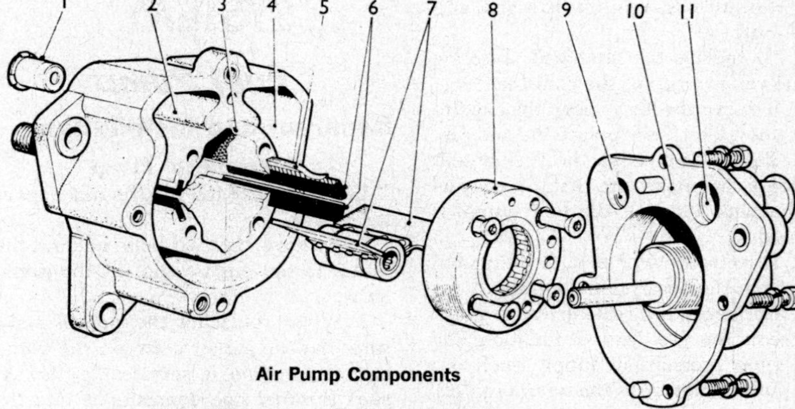

Air Pump Components

1. Relief valve
2. Intake chamber
3. Rotor
4. Output chamber
5. Spring
6. Carbons
7. Vane assemblies
8. Rotor bearing support plate
9. Output port
10. End-cover
11. Intake port

Component Testing

1. To check the air pump and relief valve, first make sure that the pump drive belt is properly adjusted and that the air filter is clean.

2. Disconnect and plug the air supply hose to the gulp valve. Disconnect the injection manifold air hose at the check valve, and connect a pressure gauge to the hose.

3. At an engine speed of 1,000 rpm (Midget—1,200 rpm), the pressure gauge should not read less than 2.75 lb./sq. in. If a lower reading is obtained, tape the relief valve shut and repeat the test. If the reading is now satisfactory, replace the relief valve (it can be removed by prying with a screwdriver or with a gear puller).

4. If the reading is still low, replace or overhaul the air pump unit.

NOTE: *If the pump is removed for service, do not hold it in a vise. Even a small amount of pressure will distort the pump body.*

5. To test the check valve, disconnect the air supply hose from the valve and unscrew it from the injection manifold. Blow through the valve at each connection (do not use compressed air). Air should pass through the valve only from

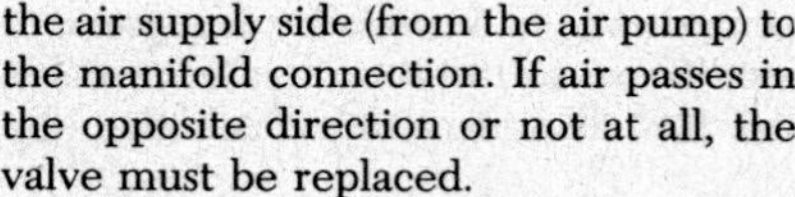

the air supply side (from the air pump) to the manifold connection. If air passes in the opposite direction or not at all, the valve must be replaced.

6. To test the gulp valve, disconnect the valve air supply hose from the air pump connection.

7. Start the engine and let it idle for a few seconds.

8. With the engine still idling, connect a vacuum gauge to the end of the gulp valve air hose that is disconnected from the air pump. The gauge should read zero for approximately fifteen seconds. If a vacuum is registered, the gulp valve should be replaced.

9. If the valve passes the test, snap the throttle open once and let it spring shut.

10. Repeat this test several times, breaking the connection between the vacuum gauge and the gulp valve hose before each operation of the throttle to return the gauge to zero. In every case the gauge should register a vacuum. If it does not, replace the gulp valve.

11. To check the intake manifold vacuum limit valve (integral with the carburetor throttle butterfly), disconnect the gulp valve sensing line from the intake manifold.

12. Connect a vacuum gauge to the sensing line connection at the manifold.

13. With the engine at normal operating temperature, increase the engine speed to 3,000 rpm and let the throttle snap shut. The vacuum gauge reading should immediately rise to between 20.5 and 22.0 in. vacuum. If the reading is outside these limits, the carburetors must be removed and the throttle butterflies replaced. Make sure, in each carburetor, that the butterfly is centered in the bore before the securing screws are tightened. Carburetor removal and tuning procedures can be found in the "Fuel System" section.

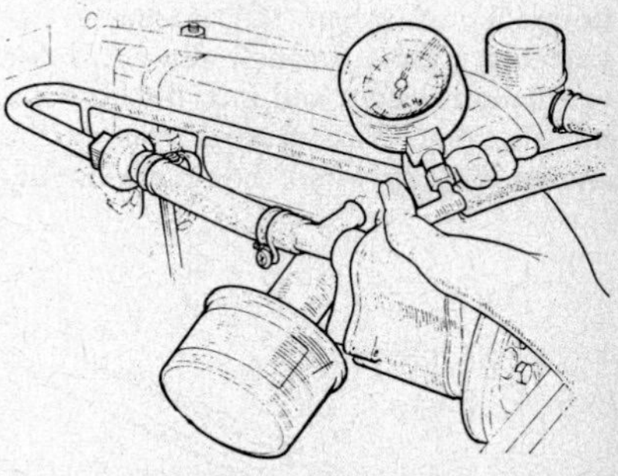

Vacuum Guage Connected to Gulp Valve

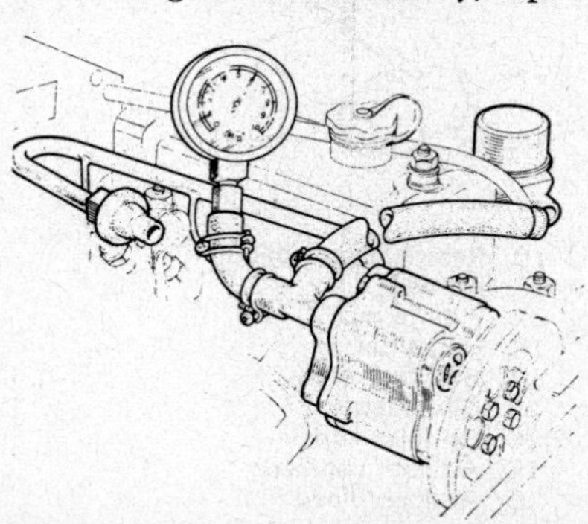

Air Pressure Check

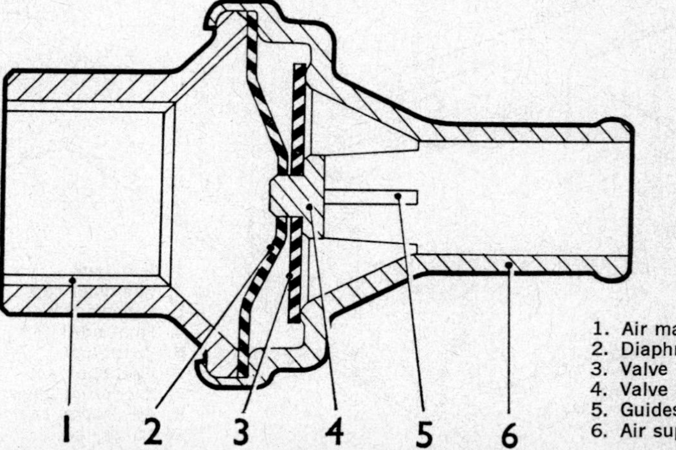

1. Air manifold connection
2. Diaphragm
3. Valve
4. Valve pilot
5. Guides
6. Air supply connection

Cross-section of Check Valve

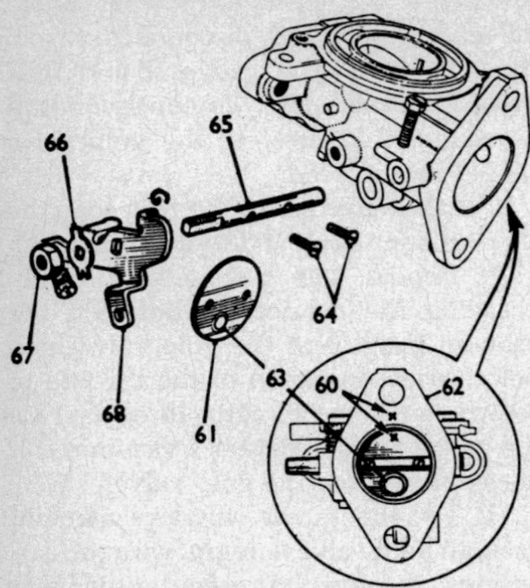

Throttle Butterfly and the Vacuum Limit Valve.

60. Alignment marks (scribed in)
61. Throttle butterfly
62. Carburetor body
63. Intake manifold vacuum limit valve
64. Butterfly retaining screws
65. Throttle shaft
66. Locktab
67. Spindle nut
68. Throttle lever

Evaporative Loss Control System

The system is designed to collect fuel vapor from the fuel tank and carburetor float chambers. The vapor is stored in the absorption canister while the engine is stopped, and when the engine is restarted it passes through the crankcase ventilation system and into the combustion chambers. Vapors are drawn into the engine directly when the engine is running. An air bleed chamber is located in the fuel tank to prevent overfilling, and a small separation tank, between the fuel tank and absorption canister, prevents liquid fuel from being drawn into the canister.

The only component of the system that needs servicing is the absorption canister. The filter pad should be replaced at 12,000 mile intervals, and the canister unit should be replaced at 50,000 miles. If the canister becomes saturated with fuel, it must be replaced sooner. Do not attempt to clear the canister with compressed air.

1. To remove the canister, disconnect the lines and loosen the clamp screw, and lift it out.
2. To replace the filter pad, unscrew the lower end cap of the canister.
3. Remove the filter, clean the cap, install a new filter, and replace the end cap.
4. To pressure check the fuel system for leaks, first make sure that there is fuel in the tank and that the fuel system is primed.
5. Disconnect the fuel tank ventilation line from the absorption canister.
6. Connect a low scale pressure gauge between the fuel tank ventilation line and a low pressure air supply (such as a tire pump). Pressurize the system to 1 psi. *Do not exceed this pressure at any time.* The pressure should not fall below ½ psi over a period of ten seconds. If there is evidence of a leak, check all fuel system components and connections beginning with the fuel filler cap. The cap is not vented and should not allow any pressure loss. When the test is completed, remove the fuel filler cap and check that the gauge returns to zero. Reconnect the fuel tank ventilation line to the canister.

NO_x Control System

The regulation of nitrogen oxide (NO_x) emissions is accomplished through slight modifications to engine components, and no special service is necessary. To ensure that the engine is within emission standards, particular attention should be paid to tune-up specifications and procedures.

FUEL SYSTEM

Fuel Pump

Removal and Installation

Mechanical Pump

1. Disconnect and cap the fuel lines at the pump.
2. Remove the two bolts holding the pump to the engine and lift the pump away.
3. When replacing the pump, make sure that the gasket between the pump and the engine is serviceable. Always start the fuel line connections into the pump by hand to avoid cross-threading the fittings.

S.U. Electric Pump

1. Disconnect the electrical supply and ground wires from the pump, and insulate the supply wire against grounding.
2. Disconnect the fuel lines and the

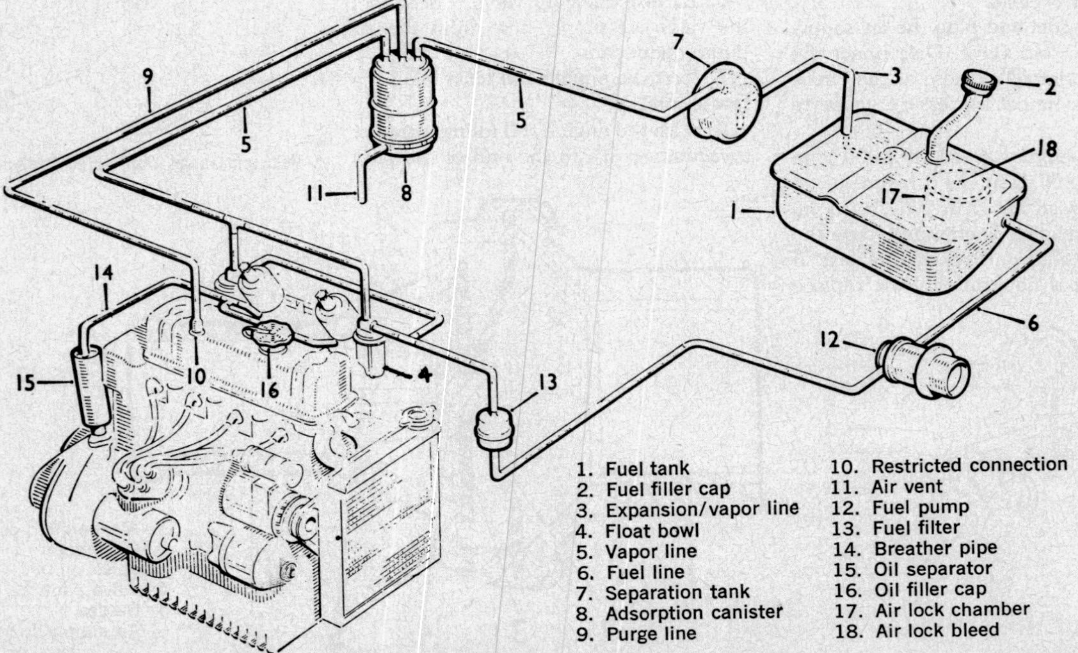

1. Fuel tank
2. Fuel filler cap
3. Expansion/vapor line
4. Float bowl
5. Vapor line
6. Fuel line
7. Separation tank
8. Adsorption canister
9. Purge line
10. Restricted connection
11. Air vent
12. Fuel pump
13. Fuel filter
14. Breather pipe
15. Oil separator
16. Oil filler cap
17. Air lock chamber
18. Air lock bleed

Evaporative Loss Control System

breather pipe (later cars) from the pump and cap the fuel lines.

3. Remove the pump bracket bolts and remove the pump.

4. When installing the pump, make sure that the ground wire makes a good connection and that the breather pipe is correctly routed.

Testing the Fuel Pump on the Vehicle

Mechanical Pump

The fuel pump pressure can be checked by disconnecting the pump output line at the carburetors and attaching a pressure gauge to it. Cranking the engine for a few seconds will show whether or not the pressure is within specification (see "Capacities and Pressures"). If pressure is low, disconnect the fuel pump intake line and check for fuel flow from the tank. If the line is not blocked, see "Servicing the Fuel Pump."

S.U. Electric Pump

S.U. electric fuel pumps maintain a low, constant pressure, thus making fuel delivery more even and easing the load on the tempermental carburetor needle and seat units. When fuel pressure drops below a predetermined level the pump will operate (audible as a series of clicks), and when pressure is built up again it will shut itself off.

1. To check pump operation, disconnect the fuel line at the carburetors and switch the ignition on.

2. The pump should be heard to operate and fuel should flow readily from the line.

If it does not, disconnect the output line at the pump and switch the ignition on again. If the pump now operates, the fuel line to the carburetors is blocked and should be cleared with compressed air. If the pump does not operate, disconnect the fuel intake line from the pump and check for a free flow of gasoline from the tank.

3. The line may be cleared, if necessary, with compressed air by pressurizing the gas tank through the tank filler tube.

CAUTION: *Never blow compressed air through the fuel pump, and on vehicles equipped with Evaporative Loss Control systems the fuel lines must never be pressurized unless the absorption canister is disconnected.*

If the fuel lines are clear and the pump will not operate, the electrical connections at the pump should be checked.

4. Switch on the ignition and connect a test light between the supply (battery) wire and ground. If it does not light, the pump is not being supplied with electricity. If it does light, check the ground wire continuity by connecting a jumper wire between the ground terminal on the pump and a good chassis ground.

5. If the pump still does not operate, the fault lies in the pump unit itself. Refer to the following section.

Servicing the Fuel Pump

Mechanical Pump

If the pump is not operating correctly, unscrew the top cover securing bolt and remove the cover and the thin disc-type filter. If the filter has obviously been restricting fuel flow, cleaning it may restore the efficiency of the pump. If the filter is not clogged or if pump pressure is still not acceptable after a dirty filter has been cleared, remove the upper casting screws, remove the casting, and inspect the diaphragm for cracks, holes, and rotting. The diaphragm may be removed by rotating it one-quarter turn in either direction.

The fuel pump unit should be replaced if the diaphragm appears to be in good condition or if pump pressure is still low when a new diaphragm has been installed.

S.U. Electric Pump

If the pump unit is not operating correctly, remove it from the vehicle.

1. Remove the intake and outlet line fittings from the pump body and remove the small fuel filter (if fitted).

2. Examine the ports for any foreign matter that may be lodged inside.

3. Clean the ports, if necessary, and clean and replace the filter and line fittings.

4. Remove the plastic end-cover by removing the electrical terminal retaining nut and the rubber or tape joint seal.

5. Examine the contact points for burning, and check the contact rotor assembly movement. If the end-cover was not sealed properly, the contact and rocker assemblies will have been exposed to water and dirt and should be thoroughly cleaned or replaced.

If the contacts are not badly burnt, they may be smoothed with fine sandpaper and cleaned with a non-oily solvent such as an aerosol-type carburetor cleaner.

6. When adjusting the points, make sure that when the outer rocker is pressed onto the pump housing, the contact blade rests on the narrow rib of the pedestal. The contact blade may be bent slightly if necessary.

7. Proper sealing of the plastic end-cover is very important.

8. Check that there are no cracks in it, and, after the cover is installed on the

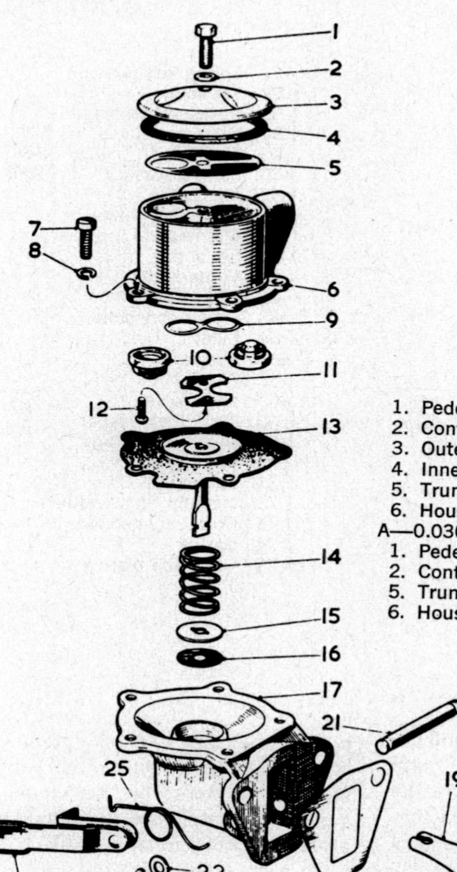

1. Pedestal
2. Contact blade
3. Outer rocker
4. Inner rocker
5. Trunnion
6. Housing

A—0.030 in.

1. Pedestal
2. Contact blade
5. Trunnion
6. Housing

1. Cover screw
2. Gasket
3. Filter cover
4. Filter cover gasket
5. Filter
6. Upper casting
7. Screw
8. Lockwasher
9. Valve gasket
10. Valve assembly
11. Valve retainer
12. Screw
13. Diaphragm
14. Spring
15. Metal washer
16. Fiber washer
17. Pump body
18. Rocker arm
19. Rocker arm link
20. Rocker arm spring
21. Rocker arm pin
22. Washer
23. Clip
24. Priming lever
25. Spring
26. Gasket

Mechanical Fuel Pump—Exploded View

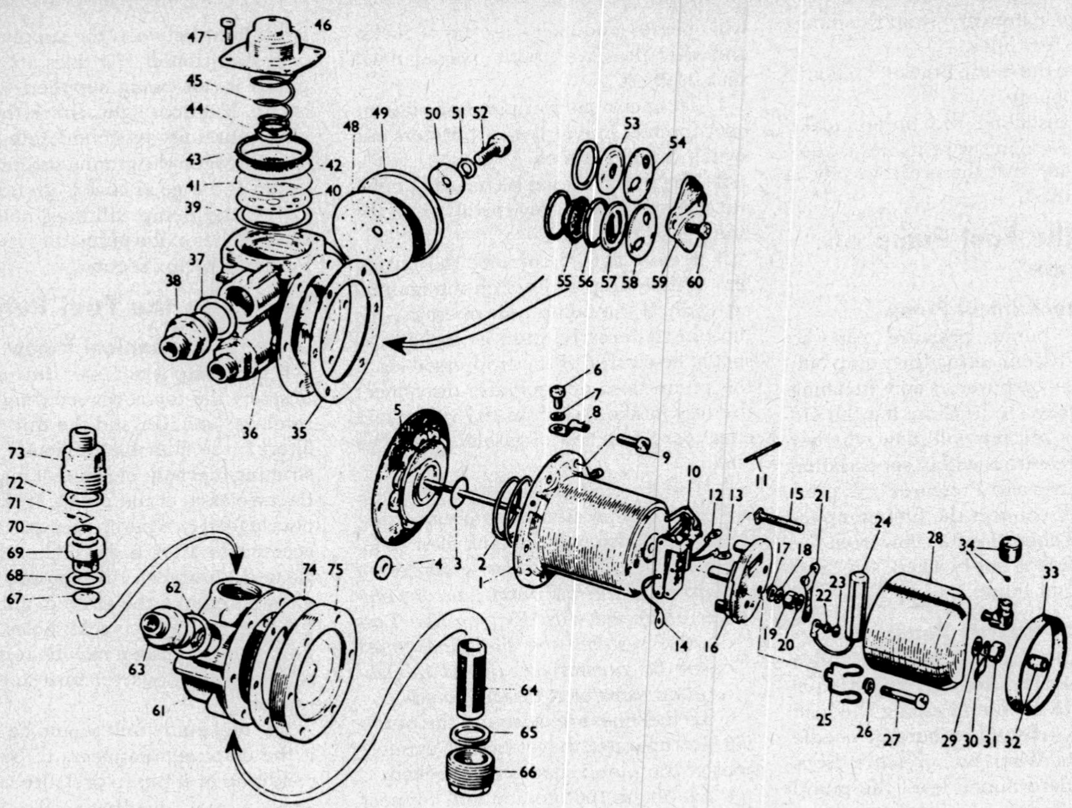

Electric Fuel Pump—Exploded View

1. Coil housing
2. Armature spring
3. Impact washer
4. Armature centralizing roller
5. Diaphragm and spindle assembly
6. Set screw
7. Spring washer
8. Ground connector
9. Set screw
10. Rocker mechanism
11. Rocker pivot pin
12. Terminal tag
13. Terminal tag
14. Ground tag
15. Terminal stud
16. Pedestal
17. Spring washer
18. Lead washer
19. Terminal nut
20. End cover seal washer
21. Contact blade
22. Washer
23. Contact blade screw
24. Condenser
25. Condenser clip
26. Spring washer
27. Pedestal screw
28. End cover
29. Shakeproof washer
30. Lucar connector
31. Nut
32. Insulating sleeve
33. Sealing band
34. Vent valve

AUF 300 type:

35. Gasket
36. Pump body
37. Fiber washer
38. Outlet connection
39. Sealing washer
*40. Diaphragm plate
41. Plastic diaphragm barrier
*42. Rubber diaphragm
43. Rubber "O" ring
*44. Spring end cap
*45. Diaphragm spring
†46. Delivery flow smoothing device cover
47. Set screw
48. Gasket
49. Inlet air bottle cover
50. Dished washer

AUF 300 type:

51. Spring washer
52. Set screw
53. Outlet valve
54. Valve cap
55. Filter
56. Sealing washer
57. Inlet valve
58. Valve cap
59. Clamp plate
60. Set screw

61. Pump body
62. Fiber washer
63. Outlet connection
64. Filter
65. Washer
66. Plug

HP type:

67. Inlet valve
68. Thin fiber washer
69. Outlet valve cage
70. Outlet valve
71. Spring clip
72. Medium fiber washer
73. Outlet connection
74. Gasket
75. Sandwich plate

* Early pumps
† Delivery air bottle (later pumps)

pump, wrap electrical tape around the mating surface of the pump housing and cover.

9. Pump operation should be checked by temporarily connecting the electrical wires and fuel lines to it and switching on the ignition.

10. Allow a few seconds for the pump to prime itself, and check fuel flow at the carburetors.

11. At this point, if the pump is still not operating correctly, the pump unit will have to be replaced. Do not discard the pump, as most MG dealers carry factory rebuilt S.U. fuel pumps instead of new ones (at a considerable savings), and will allow some trade-in on the old unit.

Fuel Filter

On vehicles equipped with the Evaporative Loss Control system an in-line filter is located on the fuel feed line to the carburetors. The filter element requires no maintenance, but should be replaced at 12,000 mile intervals.

On early MGBs with the 18G engine there is a filter located in the fuel pump. It can be removed for cleaning by unscrewing the plug, opposite the fuel output line, in the fuel pump body.

CARBURETORS

Removal and Installation

1. Remove the air filters.
2. Disconnect the fuel lines and remove the overflow tubes from the float chamber.
3. Disconnect the accelerator and choke cables.
4. Disconnect the vacuum advance line and remove the throttle return springs.
5. Unbolt the carburetor retaining nuts and remove the carburetors, being careful not to bend the throttle linkage.
6. Installation is in reverse order of removal. Make sure that the carburetor and manifold spacer gaskets are in good condition or an air leak will result. The carburetors and linkages will have to be adjusted after reinstallation.

OVERHAUL

All Types

1. Remove the carburetors from the vehicle.
2. If the throttle spindles are to be replaced remove the throttle levers and butterfly, and slide the spindle out.
3. Remove the retaining screws and lift the piston-chamber straight off.
4. Remove the spring and carefully lift the piston out. Unscrew the piston damper from the top of the piston-chamber.
5. Unscrew the fuel transfer line from the bottom of the float chamber.
6. Unbolt and remove the float chamber from the carburetor body.
7. Remove the float cover and remove the float by pressing out the hinge pin with an ice pick or small drift.
8. Unscrew the needle and seat from the cover.
9. Remove the pivot pin from the jet lifting (choke) arm at the bottom of the jet assembly.
10. Unscrew the jet assembly locknut and withdraw the jet assembly.
11. Pull the jet tube out and lift the top jet bearing off. The small spring, washers, and gaskets can now be removed. Unscrew the jet adjusting nut from the bottom jet bearing and remove the gaskets, the spring, and the washer.
12. All carburetor components except the float and seals should be soaked in acid-type carburetor cleaner for about an hour, then washed thoroughly with solvent and air dried. Components included in good carburetor rebuilding kits should include jet tubes, jet needles, needle and seat assemblies, and all gaskets and seals. If throttle spindles or bushings or any

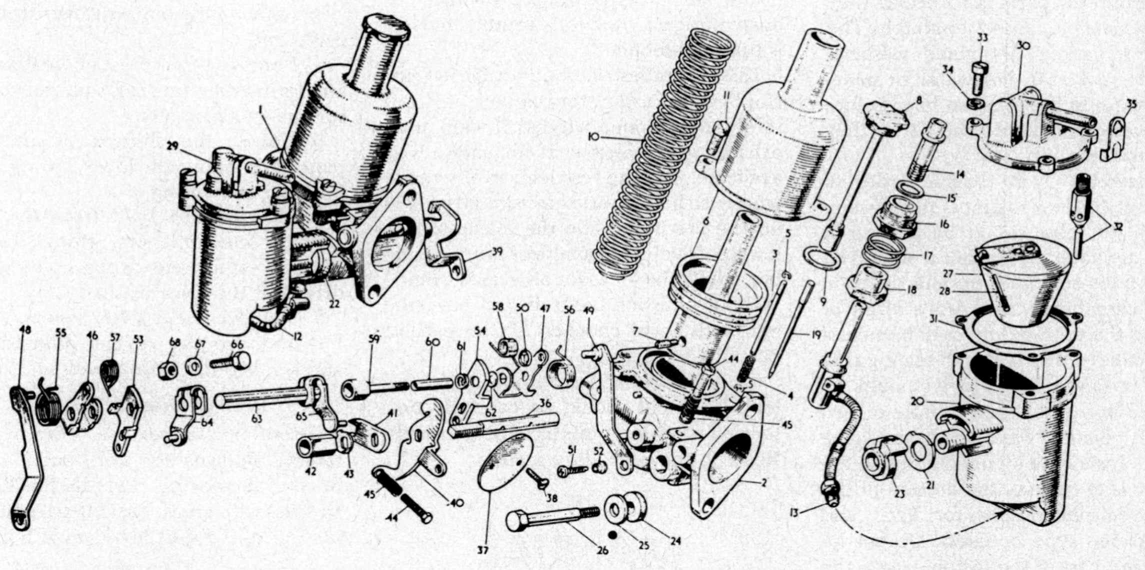

Dual Carburetor Set-up

1. Carburetor body (left)
2. Carburetor body (right)
3. Piston lifting pin
4. Spring
5. Circlip
6. Piston chamber assembly
7. Screw
8. Cap and damper assembly
9. Fibre washer
10. Piston spring
11. Screw
12. Jet assembly (left carburetor)
13. Jet assembly (right carburetor)
14. Bearing
15. Washer
16. Screw
17. Spring
18. Screw
19. Needle
20. Float-chamber
21. Support washer
22. Rubber grommet (left carburetor)
23. Rubber grommet (right carburetor)
24. Washer (rubber)
25. Washer (steel)
26. Bolt
27. Float assembly
28. Lever pin
29. Float-chamber lid (left carburetor)
30. Float-chamber lid (right carburetor)
31. Washer
32. Needle and seat assembly
33. Screw
34. Spring washer
35. Baffie plate
36. Throttle spindle
37. Throttle disc
38. Screw
39. Throttle return lever (left carburetor)
40. Throttle return lever (right carburetor)
41. Lost motion lever
42. Nut
43. Tab washer
44. Throttle screw stop
45. Spring
46. Pick-up lever (left carburetor)
47. Pick-up lever (right carburetor)
48. Link (left carburetor)
49. Link (right carburetor)
50. Washer
51. Screw
52. Bush
53. Cam lever (left carburetor)
54. Cam lever (right carburetor)
55. Pick-up lever spring (left carburetor)
56. Pick-up lever spring (right carburetor)
57. Cam lever spring (left carburetor)
58. Cam lever spring (right carburetor)
59. Bolt
60. Tube
61. Spring washer
62. Distance piece
63. Jet rod
64. Lever and pin assembly (left carburetor)
65. Lever pin assembly (right carburetor)
66. Bolt
67. Washer
68. Nut

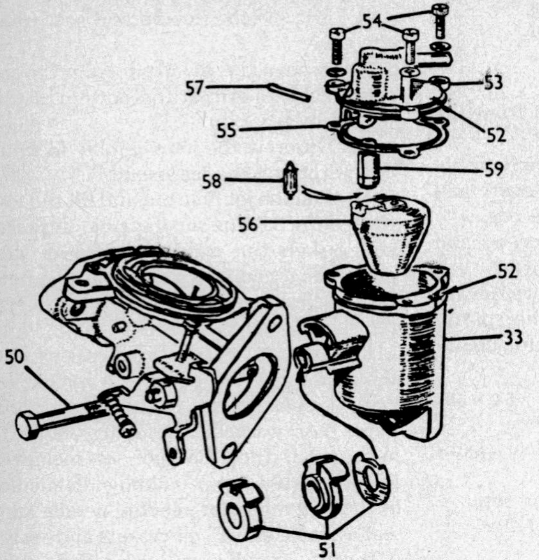

Float Bowl Components

other carburetor parts are needed they will have to be purchased separately. The small cork gaskets (jet gland washers) should be soaked in hot water or penetrating oil for at least half an hour before they are assembled onto the jet, or they will invariably split.

13. Assembly is in reverse order of disassembly. When the jet is fully assembled the jet tube should be a close fit without any lateral play, but it should be free to move smoothly up and down in the jet assembly. A few drops of oil or polishing the tube lightly may be necessary to achieve this. If the jet sealing ring washer is made of cork, it should be soaked in hot water for a minute or two before installation. Float height should be adjusted. Install the jet needle so that the shoulder is even with the bottom of the piston (see illustrations for fixed and spring-loaded type needles). Do not lubricate any part of the piston except the surface of the damper tube.

14. After the jet assembly is fitted into the carburetor body and before it is fully tightened, the jet will have to be centered so that the needle will fit into it evenly and without binding.

15. With the piston removed, look down into the bore and center the top of the jet in the hole by moving the bottom of the jet assembly. Partially tighten the jet assembly locknut.

16. Insert the piston, with the needle installed, into the bore. Push the jet tube all the way up in the jet assembly.

17. Temporarily install the piston-chamber over the piston. Lift the piston all the way and let it fall. It should fall smoothly and seat with a distinct click. If the jet is not centered properly the needle will hang up in the jet tube and the piston will not fall all the way. Several tries will probably be needed before the piston falls freely. Be sure to check it once more after the jet assembly locknut is fully tightened.

18. The jet restrictor on Emission Control System carburetors cannot be accurately repositioned without the aid of an exhaust gas analyzer. If an analyzer is available, lock the restrictor in the range where carbon dioxide emissions from the engine are just inside the maximum allowable level. If an analyzer is not available, adjust the jet as for an earlier engine without emission controls and have the emissions level checked at the earliest possible date.

19. Carburetor synchronization and jet adjustment should be carefully performed when the units have been rebuilt. Refer to the preceding section.

MANUAL TRANSMISSION

Removal and Installation

On all models the engine and transmission are removed as a unit (see "Engine Removal and Installation"). On the Midget, MGB, and MGC the transmission can be unbolted from the engine by simply removing the bell housing bolts.

Installation in all cases is in reverse order of removal. On the Midget, MGB, and MGC the clutch disc will have to be centered if the clutch assembly has been removed (see "Clutch Removal and Installation").

Overhaul

Midget 4-Speed Manual, 1961-71, Rebuilding Procedures

After the transmission is removed from the vehicle and separated from the engine, disassembly begins with:

Rear Extension Removal and Installation

1. Unbolt and remove the speedometer drive from the extension.
2. Unbolt and remove the shift linkage housing.
3. Unbolt the extension and remove it by pulling back slightly and turning it counterclockwise so that the selector lever will clear the selector forks.

At this point, if it is desired to rebuild the shift linkage, the extension components can be disassembled.

Installation of the extension is a reversal of removal procedures. To determine shim thickness, see "Transmission Assembly."

Rear Extension Disassembly

1. Unscrew the guide shaft locating bolt and remove the shaft.
2. Remove the selector lever nylon bushing.
3. Remove the bottom cover from the extension.
4. Remove the shift lever locating bolt and spring retaining cap, and remove the springs and plungers.
5. Unbolt the shift lever retaining plate and remove the lever, O-ring, pivot bushing, and spring.
6. Unscrew the bolts from the front and rear selector levers, remove the core plugs at either end of the housing, and drive out the selector shaft.
7. Remove the selector levers.
8. Remove the reverse plunger cap and remove the spring, ball, and pin.

Rear Extension Assembly

Assembly is in reverse order of disassembly. Replace any worn parts, and lubricate all moving parts in the linkage housing with grease (paying particular attention to the shift lever pivot bushing).

Transmission Disassembly

1. Remove the clutch release bearing.
2. Unscrew the locknut and pivot bolt, and remove the clutch release lever.
3. Unbolt and remove the front cover, and remove the gasket and shim.
4. Remove the side cover and gasket.
5. Remove the two springs from the front edge of the cover mating surface, and tilt the transmission to remove the two plungers.
6. Remove the two plugs from the side cover of the transmission case and remove the reverse plunger and springs and the selector interlock ball and spring.
7. Put the transmission into Neutral, and, working through the drain plug hole, remove the three selector fork lockbolts.
8. Tap the selector rods out through the back of the transmission. As the rods are being drawn out take care to remove the two interlock balls from the front of

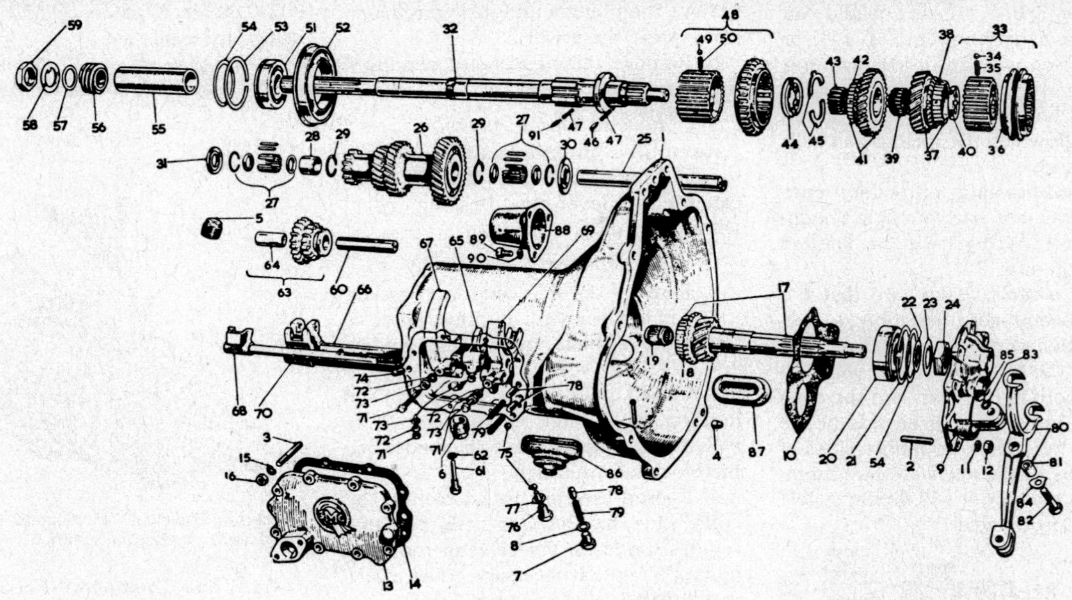

MG Midget Transmission

1. Case assembly
2. Stud
3. Stud
4. Dowel
5. Filler plug
6. Drain plug
7. Plug for reverse plunger spring
8. Washer
9. Front cover
10. Front cover gasket
11. Lockwasher
12. Nut
13. Side cover
14. Side cover gasket
15. Lockwasher
16. Nut
17. Input shaft with cone
18. Synchronizer
19. Needle-roller bearing
20. Ball bearing
21. Snapring
22. Washer
23. Lockwasher
24. Nut
25. Countershaft
26. Clustergear
27. Needle-roller bearing with snapring
28. Spacer
29. Snapring
30. Thrust washer (front)
31. Thrust washer (rear)
32. Mainshaft
33. Third and fourth gear synchronizer
34. Ball
35. Spring
36. Sleeve
37. Third gear with cone
38. Synchronizer
39. Needle roller
40. Third gear collar
41. Second gear with cone
42. Synchronizer
43. Needle roller
44. Second gear collar
45. Washer
46. Peg
47. Peg spring
48. First gear assembly
49. Ball
50. Ball spring
51. Ball bearing
52. Bearing housing
53. Snapring
54. Bearing shim
55. Spacer
56. Speedometer gear
57. Washer
58. Lockwasher
59. Nut
60. Reverse shaft
61. Screw
62. Lockwasher
63. Reverse gear and bushing
64. Bushing
65. Reverse fork
66. Reverse fork rod
67. First and second fork
68. First and second fork rod
69. Third and fourth fork
70. Third and fourth fork rod
71. Fork lockbolt
72. Lockwasher
73. Nut
74. Interlock plunger
75. Interlock ball
76. Plug
77. Washer
78. Fork rod plunger
79. Spring
80. Clutch release lever with bushing
81. Bushing
82. Bolt
83. Lockwasher
84. Locktab
85. Nut
86. Dust cover
87. Dust cover
88. Starter pinion cover
89. Screw
90. Washer
91. Peg

the transmission case.

9. Tap the countershaft out of the front of the case with a soft-metal drift.

10. Withdraw the mainshaft from the rear of the case.

11. Drive the input shaft out of the front of the case with a soft-metal drift.

12. Lift out the clustergear and thrust washers.

13. Remove the reverse shaft locating bolt. Place a screwdriver on the slotted end of the shaft and push it into the transmission with a twisting motion.

14. Remove the reverse gear and shaft.

Transmission Assembly

Assembly is the reverse of disassembly. The following points should be noted:

1. Clustergear end-play should be 0.001–0.003 in. (Mk. I and II) or 0.003–0.005 in. (Mk. III). If end-play exceeds these limits, the thrust washers should be replaced. Several thicknesses are available.

2. Determine shim thickness for the front and rear covers, when any mainshaft or input shaft components have been replaced, as follows: Measure the depth of the cover recess and the amount by which the bearing outer race protrudes from the case. Install and tighten the cover with the gasket in place to allow it to be compressed. Take off the cover and measure the gasket thickness. Add this measurement to the depth of the cover recess and subtract the amount by which the bearing protrudes. The result gives the thickness of shims to be used.

Gear Train Component Replacement

1. When rebuilding a transmission, all bearings should be replaced as a matter of course. Gear and synchronizer assemblies, if worn or broken, should be replaced as assembly units.

2. When disassembling the mainshaft components, do not disassemble the third and fourth gear synchronizer assembly or first gear assembly. A special tool is needed to install the spring-loaded balls that are released from the hub when the

unit is taken apart. British Leyland can supply the tool (part number 18G 144), or a piece of pipe with an inside diameter slightly larger than the hub diameter can be used. A hole must be drilled in the pipe through which the springs and balls can be loaded.

3. When assembling components onto the countershaft on early models, the uncaged needle bearings can be held in place with grease.

On later models, make sure that the first and second gear assembly is correctly positioned on the mainshaft. The plunger in the hub must align with the cut-away tooth in the gear, and the cone end of the hub and tapered side of the gear teeth must be on opposite sides of the assembly. If the gears are not assembled in this manner, it will be impossible to engage second gear.

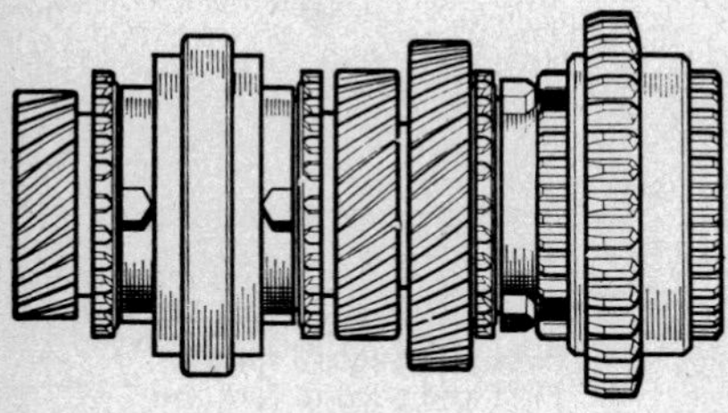

Cluster Gear

MGB and MGC 4-Speed Manual, 1961–67 (non-synchro first gear), Rebuilding Procedures

After the transmission is removed from the vehicle and separated from the engine, disassembly begins with:

Rear Extension Removal and Installation

1. Remove the dipstick, drain plug, and speedometer drive.
2. Remove the driveshaft flange.
3. Unbolt and remove the shift lever tower.
4. Remove the extension side cover.
5. Remove the interlock plate and bracket.
6. Loosen the clamp bolt on the front gear selector lever, and unbolt and remove the rear extension.

At this point, if it is desired to rebuild the shift linkage, the extension components can be disassembled. Installation of the extension is in reverse order of removal.

Rear Extension Disassembly

1. Withdraw the rear selector lever and the selector shaft from the extension.
2. Remove the circlip from the spring cover at the base of the shift lever and remove the two lever locating bolts. Remove the lever.
3. Unscrew the reverse plunger detent bolt from the rear of the shift lever tower and remove the spring and ball.
4. From the side of the tower remove the reverse plunger locating pin and remove the plunger and spring (released from inside the tower).
5. Remove the oil seal and bearing if they are to be replaced.

Rear Extension Assembly

Assembly is in reverse order of disassembly. Replace worn parts, and lubricate the shift lever pivot bushing (nylon) with motor oil.

Transmission Disassembly

1. Remove the side cover and gasket.
2. Cut the lockwire, unscrew the three selector lever bolts, and remove the levers.
3. Unbolt and remove the selector rod locating block, and remove the three balls and springs that are released when the block is withdrawn.
4. Loosen the shift fork locknuts and bolts, slide the selector rods out, and remove the forks. The selector rods may be tapped out, if necessary, using a soft-metal drift.
5. Unbolt and remove the front cover, the gasket, and the input shaft bearing shims.
6. Remove the cover oil seal if it is to be replaced.
7. Unscrew the reverse shaft locating bolt and remove the shaft and gear.
8. Using a soft-metal drift, drive the countershaft out toward the front of the transmission and leave the clustergear in the bottom of the case.
9. Pull the gear bearing housing from the case and withdraw the mainshaft assembly.
10. Withdraw the input shaft assembly from the front of the case, using a drift if necessary. Remove the clustergear and thrust washers.

Transmission Assembly

Transmission assembly is the reverse of disassembly. The following points should be noted:

1. Before the input shaft and mainshaft are installed assemble the clustergear and thrust washers onto the countershaft, install the assembly in the transmission case, and check clustergear end-play. End-play should not exceed 0.002–0.003 in. Washers of different thicknesses are available.

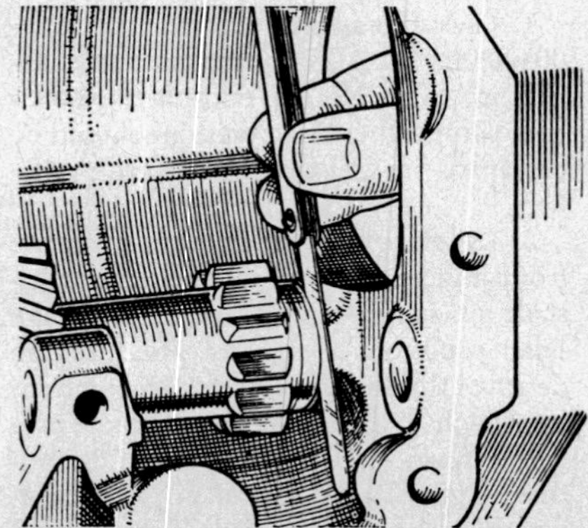

Checking Cluster Gear End Play

2. End-play of second and third gear on the mainshaft should be 0.004–0.006 in.

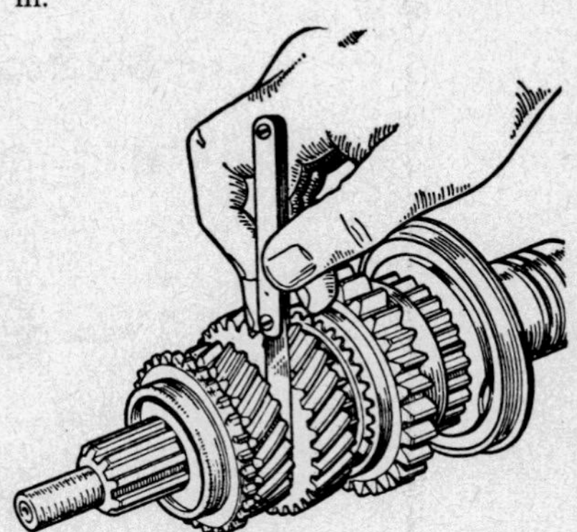

Checking End-float of Second Gear and Third Gear on the Mainshaft.

Gear Train Component Replacement

1. When rebuilding a transmission, all bearings should be replaced as a matter of course. Gear and synchronizer assemblies, if worn or broken, should be replaced as assembly units.
2. When disassembling the mainshaft components, do not disassemble the third and fourth gear synchronizer assembly or first gear assembly. A special tool is needed to install the spring-loaded balls that are released from the hub when the unit is taken apart. British Leyland can supply the tool (part number 18G 222), or a piece of pipe with an inside diameter slightly larger than the hub diameter can be used.
3. A hole must be drilled in the pipe through which the springs and balls can be loaded.

The uncaged roller bearings used in early transmissions can be held in position during assembly using grease.

4. To disassemble the input shaft assembly the large locknut must be removed. *This locknut has a left-hand thread.*

MGB/MGC 4-Speed Manual (fully synchronized), 1968–73

After the transmission is removed from the vehicle and separated from the engine, disassembly begins with:

Rear Extension Removal and Installation

1. Remove the driveshaft flange.
2. Unbolt and remove the shift linkage housing.
3. Withdraw the selector interlock arm and plate assembly.
4. Unbolt and remove the extension and mainshaft shims.

At this point, if it is desired to rebuild the shift linkage, the extension components can be disassembled.

Installation of the extension is in reverse order of removal. To determine

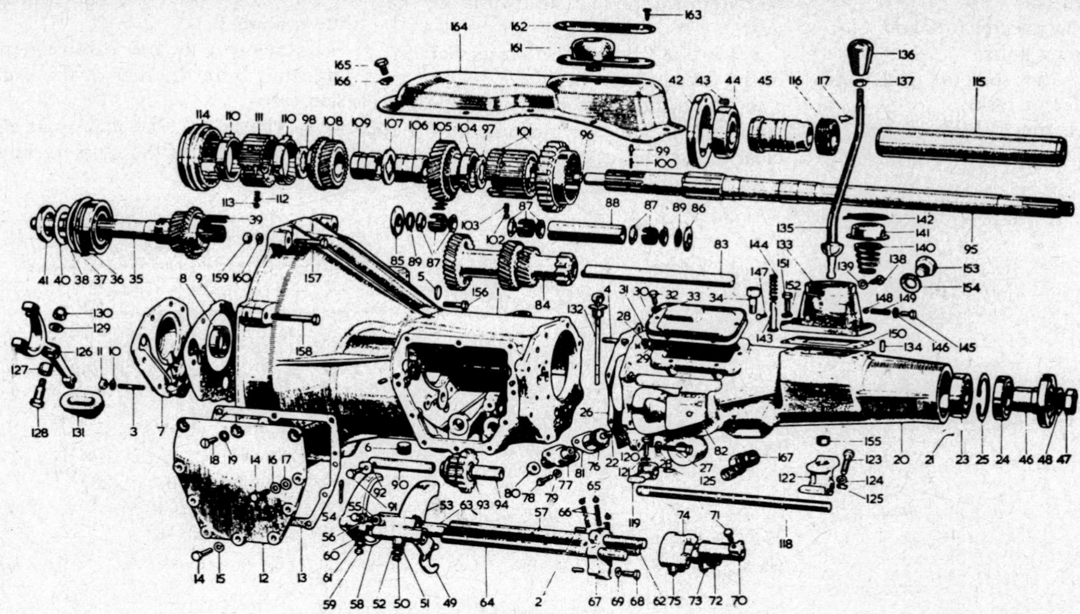

MGB Transmission, 1961-67

1. Transmission case
2. Dowel
3. Front cover stud
4. Rear extension
5. Core plug
6. Drain plug
7. Front cover
8. Oil seal
9. Gasket
10. Lockwasher
11. Nut
12. Side cover
13. Gasket
14. Bolt
15. Lockwasher
16. Washer
17. Fiber washer
18. Bolt
19. Lockwasher
20. Rear extension
21. Taper plug
22. Thrust button
23. Bearing
24. Oil seal
25. Circlip
26. Gasket
27. Bolt
28. Lockwasher
29. Nut
30. Extension side cover
31. Gasket
32. Bolt
33. Lock washer
34. Breather assembly
35. Input shaft
36. Bearing
37. Retainer ring
38. Shim (0.002 in.)
39. Uncaged roller bearing
40. Lockwasher
41. Nut
42. Rear bearing housing
43. Locating peg
44. Rear bearing
45. Spacer
46. Flange
47. Nut
48. Lockwasher
49. Reverse fork
50. Bolt
51. Lockwasher
52. Nut
53. First and second gear fork
54. Bolt
55. Lockwasher
56. Nut
57. Selector rod
58. Third and fourth gear fork
59. Bolt
60. Lockwasher
61. Nut
62. Selector rod
63. Spacer
64. Selector rod
65. Ball
66. Spring
67. Block
68. Bolt
69. Lockwasher
70. Selector lever
71. Bolt
72. Selector lever
73. Bolt
74. Selector lever
75. Bolt
76. Pinion (speedo)
77. Bushing
78. Bolt
79. Lockwasher
80. Oil seal
81. Gasket
82. Interlock arm
83. Countershaft
84. Clustergear
85. Thrust washer
86. Thrust washer
87. Uncaged roller bearing
88. Spacer
89. Retainer
90. Reverse shaft
91. Bolt
92. Washer
93. Reverse gear
94. Bushing
95. Mainshaft
96. Oil restrictor
97. Thrust washer
98. Thrust washer
99. Peg
100. Spring
101. First gear and synchronizer assembly
102. Ball
103. Spring
104. Synchronizer ring
105. Second gear
106. Bushing
107. Interlock ring
108. Third gear
109. Bushing
110. Synchronizer ring
111. Synchronizer assembly
112. Spring
113. Ball
114. Coupling
115. Spacer
116. Speedometer gear
117. Key
118. Shift linkage rod
119. Front selector lever
120. Bolt
121. Lockwasher
122. Rear selector lever
123. Bolt
124. Lockwasher
125. Key
126. Clutch release lever
127. Bushing
128. Bolt
129. Washer
130. Nut
131. Dust cover
132. Dipstick
133. Shift lever tower
134. Dowel
135. Shift lever
136. Knob
137. Locknut
138. Pin
139. Lockwasher
140. Spring
141. Cover
142. Circlip
143. Reverse selector plunger
144. Reverse plunger spring
145. Bolt
146. Lockwasher
147. Reverse plunger locating pin
148. Reverse plunger ball
149. Reverse plunger detent spring
150. Gasket
151. Bolt
152. Lockwasher
153. Back-up light switch
154. Fiber washer
155. Bushing
156. Bolt
157. Bolt
158. Bolt
159. Nut
160. Lockwasher
161. Grommet
162. Retainer
163. Bolt
164. Cover
165. Bolt
166. Lockwasher
167. Speedometer drive adaptor

shim thickness, see "Transmission Assembly."

Rear Extension Disassembly

1. Remove the snap-ring and oil seal from the rear of the extension and press the bearing out if it is to be replaced.
2. Remove the shift lever locating bolt from the shift linkage housing.
3. Remove the retaining cap and remove the damper and spring at the base of the shift lever.
4. Unbolt the shift lever retaining plate and remove the lever.
5. Loosen the clamp bolt at the selector lever and withdraw the linkage shaft.

Rear Extension Assembly

Assembly is in reverse order of disassembly. The nylon shift lever pivot bushing should be replaced and lubricated with motor oil.

Transmission Disassembly

1. Remove the clutch release bearing and release lever.
2. Unbolt and remove the front cover and bearing shims.
3. Unbolt and remove the side cover.
4. Remove the selector detent plunger

plugs and springs.

5. Remove the selector fork and selector lever retaining bolts.

6. Withdraw the selector rods and remove the selector forks.

7. Bend back the locktab on the reverse shaft retaining bolt and remove the bolt. Remove the shaft and withdraw the gear.

8. Carefully drive the countershaft out of the transmission case.

9. Drive the input shaft assembly forward out of the case, making sure it is clear of the clustergear.

10. Remove the spacer and shims from the mainshaft.

11. Remove the rear extension mounting studs from the rear of the transmission case.

12. Check that the mainshaft components are clear of the clustergear teeth,

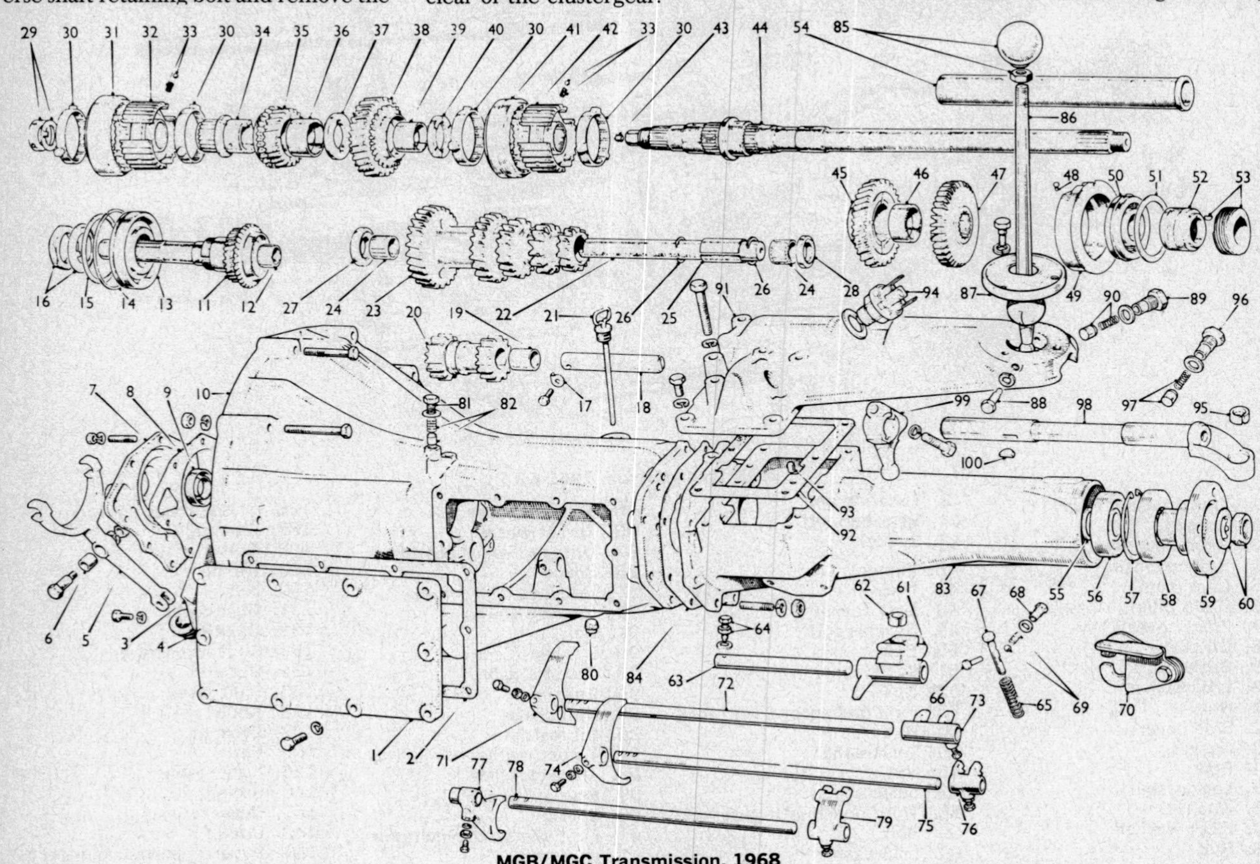

MGB/MGC Transmission, 1968

1. Side cover
2. Gasket for side cover
3. Stone guard
4. Dust cover
5. Clutch release lever
6. Bushing
7. Front cover
8. Gasket for front cover
9. Oil seal
10. Gearbox main casing
11. Input shaft
12. Needle roller bearing
13. Bearing
14. Snapring
15. Shim
16. Lockwasher and nut
17. Screw and lockwasher
18. Reverse idler shaft
19. Bushing
20. Reverse idler gear
21. Oil level indicator
22. Countershaft
23. Clustergear
24. Needle roller bearing
25. Spacer
26. Snapring
27. Front thrust washer
28. Rear thrust washer
29. Nut and lockwasher
30. Synchronizer ring
31. Sliding coupling for first and second gear
32. Synchronizer
33. Ball and spring
34. Sleeve
35. Third gear
36. Bushing
37. Interlocking thrust washer
38. Second gear
39. Bushing
40. Thrust washer
41. Sliding coupling for third and fourth gear
42. Synchronizer
43. Oil restrictor
44. Mainshaft
45. First gear
46. Bushing
47. Reverse gear
48. Locating peg
49. Bearing housing
50. Bearing
51. Shim
52. Spacer
53. Speedometer gear and driving gear
54. Spacer
55. Shim
56. Bearing
57. Circlip
58. Oil seal
59. Driving flange
60. Nut and lockwasher
61. Selector
62. Bushing
63. Selector levershaft
64. Locating bolt and locknut for selector shaft
65. Spring for reverse plunger
66. Locating pin for reverse plunger
67. Reverse plunger
68. Plug
69. Detent plunger and spring
70. Interlock arm
71. First and second selector fork
72. First and second selector rod
73. First and second selector
74. Third and fourth selector fork
75. Third and fourth selector rod
76. Third and fourth selector
77. Reverse selector fork
78. Reverse selector rod
79. Reverse selector
80. Drain plug
81. Plug
82. Detent spring and plunger
83. Rear extension
84. Gasket for rear extension
85. Knob
86. Shift lever
87. Retainer plate
88. Locating pin
89. Plunger retaining cap
90. Plunger and spring
91. Shift linkage housing
92. Gasket for remote control housing
93. Dowel
94. Back-up light switch
95. Bushing
96. Damper retaining cap
97. Damper and spring
98. Linkage shaft
99. Selector lever
100. Key for selector lever

and press the mainshaft assembly out the back of the transmission. Remove the clustergear.

Transmission Assembly

Transmission assembly is in reverse order of disassembly. The following points should be noted:

1. When the rear extension housing or any mainshaft components have been replaced, the shim thickness for the rear extension must be checked. Temporarily install the extension with the gasket, to allow the gasket to be compressed. Remove the extension and measure the amount that the bearing is recessed from the transmission case mating surface, and add to this the thickness from the extension bearing surface to the extension mating surface. Use the number of shims required to make the second distance equal to or 0.001 in. less than the first distance.

2. If the front cover or any of the input shaft components have been replaced, the shim thickness for the front cover must be checked. Temporarily install the cover with the gasket, to allow the gasket to be compressed. Measure the amount that the bearing protrudes from the transmission case. Measure the distance from the cover mating surface to the face of the cover bearing surface and add to this the thickness of the gasket. Use the number of shims required to make the second distance equal to or 0.001 in. less than the first distance.

Gear Train Component Replacement

Gear train replacement notes for the earlier non-synchromesh first gear transmission are applicable to the later type. See the preceding section.

CLUTCH

Removal and Installation

All Models

1. Remove the engine from the car, and, if the engine and transmission are removed as a unit, separate them.

2. Loosen the clutch pressure plate bolts gradually until the spring pressure is released, and remove the pressure plate and disc from the flywheel.

3. Examine the flywheel surface for scoring and signs of overheating. If scored at all, the flywheel should be turned down on a lathe or replaced. If it appears to have been overheated (blue discoloration), the surface should be checked for warpage and turned down if necessary. If disc wear is evident, the pressure plate and release bearing, as well as the disc, should be replaced. The pilot bushing in the end of the crankshaft should be checked for wear and replaced if galled or elongated. Lubricate the bushing with a graphite base grease or white grease such as *Molykote.*

4. Upon reinstallation of the disc and pressure plate, the disc must be centered so that the transmission mainshaft will engage the pilot bushing as well as the disc splines. To accomplish this, install the disc and pressure plate on the flywheel with the bolts only finger tight so that the disc can be moved.

5. At this point a dummy transmission mainshaft or clutch aligning tool (available from most tool manufacturers and from MG dealers) should be inserted through the disc hub and into the pilot bushing to hold the disc in position while the pressure plate bolts are tightened.

6. Tighten the bolts gradually and evenly, and remove the centering tool. If a new coil spring type pressure plate is used, be sure to remove the small U-shaped tabs that keep the springs slightly compressed. The tabs are used to prevent distortion of the plate, due to its unloaded condition, during storage and shipping.

7. Bolt the transmission back onto the engine if they were removed as a unit, and reinstall the engine in the chassis.

NOTE: *If a clutch centering tool is not available it is possible to center the disc by eye, if it is done very carefully. If trouble is experienced in mating the engine and transmission, the indication is that the disc is not centered properly and it should be rechecked.*

Adjustments

When the clutch has been replaced, it will be necessary to adjust the release lever stop and the release bearing stop. The lever stop should be adjusted first, and the procedure is as follows:

1. Pull the release lever outward until all free movement is taken up.

2. Using a feeler gauge, check the gap between the lever and the head of the adjustment bolt. The gap should be 0.020 in.

3. If adjustment is necessary, loosen the locknut and turn the adjustment bolt in the required direction until the proper clearance is obtained. Tighten the locknut.

Periodic adjustment of the release lever may be necessary as wear occurs; however, the release bearing stop should need adjustment only when the clutch is replaced. To adjust the bearing stop:

1. Screw the stop and locknut away

1. Pressure plate assembly
2. Spring
3. Release fork retainer
4. Eyebolt
5. Eyebolt nut
6. Release fork pin
7. Strut
8. Release fork
9. Thrust plate
10. Pressure plate
11. Anti-rattle spring
12. Release bearing
13. Retainer
14. Disc
15. Pressure plate mounting bolt
16. Lockwasher

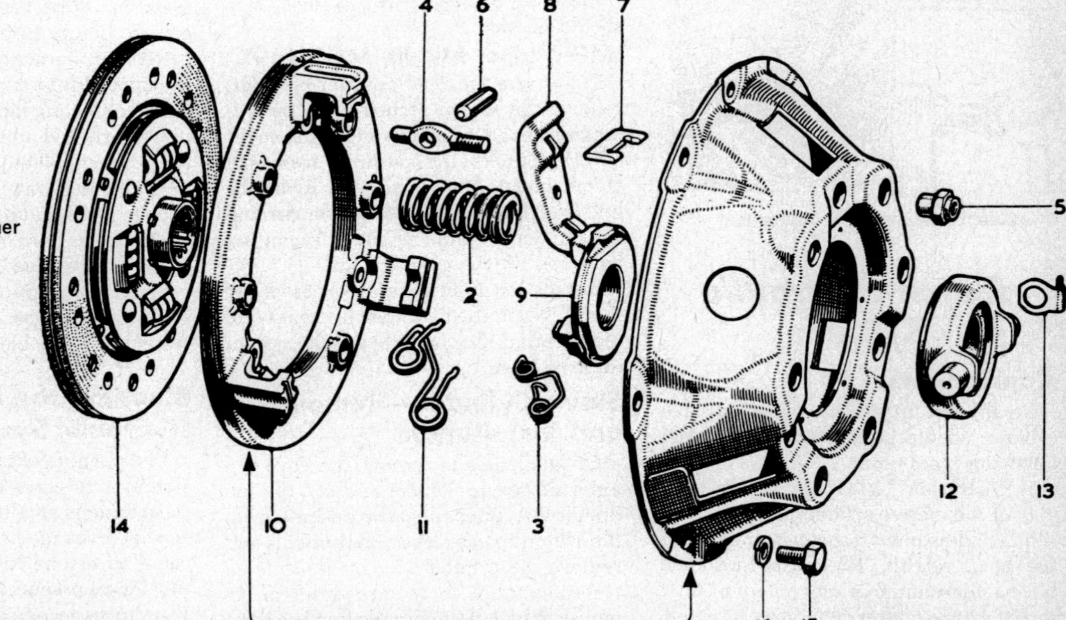

MG Midget Clutch Components

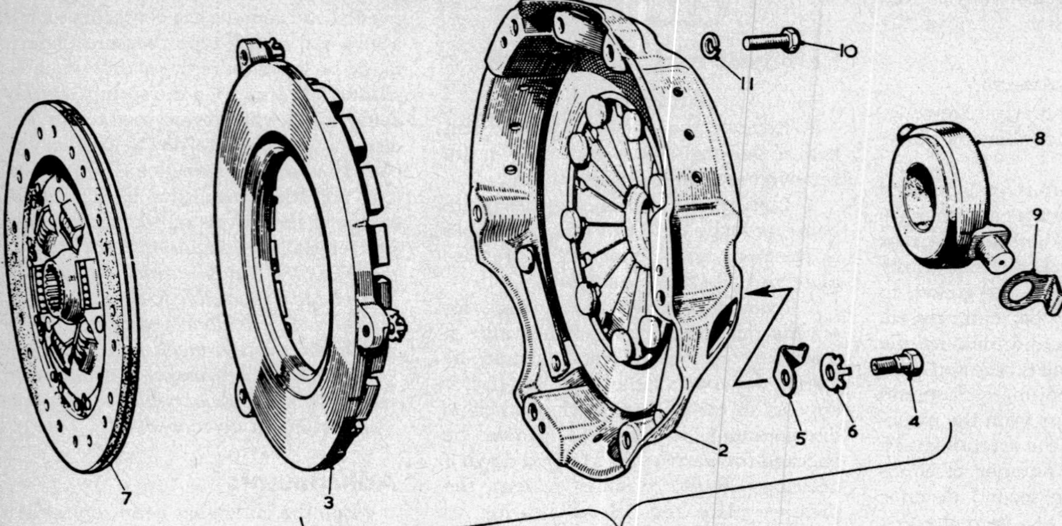

MGB/MGC Clutch Components

from the clutch cover housing to the limit of travel.

2. Have a helper fully depress and hold the clutch pedal. Screw the stop in until it contacts the housing.

3. Release the clutch pedal, and turn the stop in a further 0.002–0.005 in. (approximately 30° rotation).

4. Tighten the locknut, and recheck the release lever stop clearance.

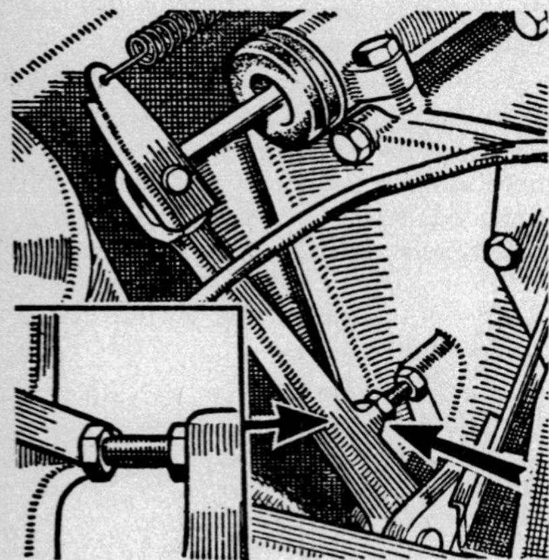
Clutch Release Lever Adjustment

Clutch Hydraulic System

Adjustments

No adjustments to the master or slave cylinder should be attempted, with the following exceptions:

1. On the Mk. I and II Midget, the free-play of the master cylinder pushrod may require adjustment if the master cylinder has been rebuilt. The pushrod should have a minimum free movement of 1/32 in. before the master cylinder is actuated. The movement can be checked at the pedal, which should travel a minimum of 3/16 in. before the cylinder is felt to operate. The clearance can be felt if the pedal is pushed by hand.

Master Cylinder—Removal and Installation

MG Midget Mk. I and II

On the Midget Mk. I and II the clutch and brake master cylinders are in the same body, and are removed at the same time. To remove the master cylinder, first disconnect the pushrods from the pedals. Disconnect the hydraulic lines from the cylinder body and cap them. Remove the two cylinder mounting bolts and lift the cylinder body out.

Installation is in reverse order of removal. When the lines have been reconnected, the brakes, as well as the clutch, should be bled.

MG Midget Mk. III, MGB, MGC

To remove the clutch master cylinder, remove the screws securing the mounting bracket cover plate and lift the cover off. Disconnect the pushrod from the clutch pedal. Disconnect the hydraulic line from the clutch master cylinder and cap it. Remove the cylinder mounting bolts and lift the cylinder out.

Installation is in reverse order of removal. When the hydraulic line has been reconnected the clutch hydraulic system must be bled.

Slave Cylinder—Removal and Installation

On all models, to remove the slave cylinder simply disconnect and cap the hydraulic line, disconnect the pushrod from the clutch release lever, and unbolt and remove the cylinder.

Installation is in reverse order of removal. When the hydraulic line has been reconnected, the clutch hydraulic system must be bled.

Master and Slave Cylinder Rebuilding

Rebuilding kits are available, and usually contain the rubber seals and metal washers. Pistons and springs are available as individual pieces.

When the piston assembly has been removed from the cylinder, examine the bore. If it is pitted or scored the entire cylinder assembly should be replaced. If bore damage is light it may be honed, but in most cases the repair will not be lasting and the cylinder may begin to leak again after a short time. When honing a cylinder, occasionally dip the hone in clean brake fluid for lubrication.

Whenever a cylinder is disassembled for inspection or rebuilding, the rubber seals should be replaced as a matter of course. Before installing the seals lubricate them thoroughly with brake fluid or the special lubricant that is included in some rebuilding kits. All internal components of the cylinder, especially the bore, must be completely free of dirt and grit or the cylinder may leak or fail to operate properly. When installing the piston and seals into the bore make sure that the seal lips are not turned back as they enter the cylinder. Once the cylinder has been installed on the car the clutch hydraulic system must be bled.

Bleeding the Clutch Hydraulic System

The purpose of bleeding the hydraulic system is to expel air that is trapped in the cylinders and lines. Air in the system is what gives the pedal a spongy feel, because air can be compressed while a liquid, for all practical purposes, cannot be. Bleeding is accomplished in the following manner:

1. Fill the master cylinder with brake

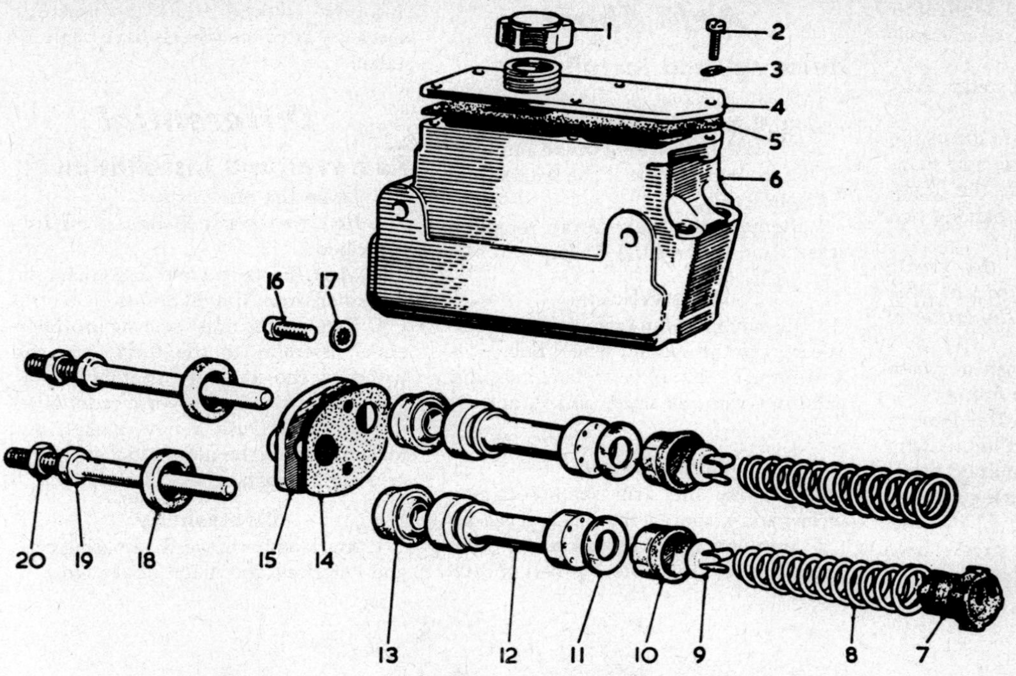

1. Filler cap
2. Screw
3. Washer
4. Tank cover
5. Gasket
6. Cylinder body
7. Check valve (brake only)
8. Return spring
9. Spring retainer
10. Main cup
11. Piston washer
12. Piston
13. Secondary cup
14. Gasket
15. Retaining plate
16. Screw
17. Lockwasher
18. Rubber boot
19. Pushrod
20. Pushrod adjuster

Midget Clutch and Brake Master Cylinder Components

fluid. (Recheck the fluid level often during bleeding.)

2. Attach a rubber tube to the slave cylinder bleed valve and immerse the other end of the tube in a jar or can containing a small amount of clean brake fluid.

3. With a helper in the car pump the clutch pedal several times until some resistance can be felt, hold the pedal down, and open the bleed valve about ½ turn.

4. With the bleed valve still open, pump the pedal slowly through its full travel several times. Close the bleed valve and check the pedal for firmness and proper free-play (about 0.5–1.0 in. free-play before the release bearing contacts the pressure plate).

5. If sponginess or excessive free-play indicates that some air is still in the system, it may be necessary to repeat Step 3 until the fluid running from the bleed valve is clear and free of air bubbles.

AUTOMATIC TRANSMISSION

Adjustments

MGB/MGC Automatic, 1968–71

Gear Selector Adjustment

1. Set the lever to the N position on the selector quadrant.

2. Disconnect the linkage rod from the linkage lever on the transmission. It may be necessary to temporarily remove the lever retaining nut to provide clearance for pulling the rod away from the lever.

3. Move the lever to the neutral position by moving it back (counterclockwise) as far as it will go and then forward two clicks.

4. Loosen the locknuts on the rod adjuster and turn the adjuster in the required direction until the linkage rod fits easily into the linkage lever.

5. Reconnect the rod and lever and tighten the adjuster locknuts.

Throttle Down-Shift Cable Adjustment

A high-pressure test gauge is required to test and adjust the down-shift mechanism. If a gauge is available, proceed as follows:

1. With the engine at normal running temperature and at the proper idle speed, check that the crimped stop on the down-shift valve inner cable just contacts the outer cable.

2. Remove the pressure take-off plug at the rear of the transmission just above the oil pan, and connect the gauge.

3. With the transmission in neutral and the engine at the correct idle speed, pressure should be 55–65 psi.

4. With the transmission in drive and the engine at 1,000 rpm (vehicle stationary), pressure should be 90–100 psi.

5. Pressures can be changed, if necessary, by resetting the cable adjuster.

DRIVE AXLES

Driveshaft

Removal and Installation

To remove the driveshaft on the Midget, MGB, and MGC mark the U-joint flanges and the transmission and differential flanges (for assembly purposes). Remove the nuts and bolts from the flanges and lower the driveshaft assembly. When reinstalling the driveshaft make sure that the alignment marks on the flanges are positioned correctly.

Universal Joint

Removal and Installation

MG Midget, MGB and MGC

NOTE: *If only the rear U-joint is to be replaced, unbolt the differential flange from the driveshaft flange and pull the driveshaft out toward the rear of the car to separate the driveshaft at the spline. On the MGC the spline cover (rubber boot) must be loosened before separation.*

After the driveshaft has been removed and the outside surfaces of the U-joints have been cleaned:

1. Remove all four snap-rings retaining the bearing cups. If the ring does not come out, tap the bearing cup lightly to relieve pressure on the ring.

2. Tap the flange and driveshaft yokes with a hammer until one of the bearings begins to come out. If difficulty is experienced, use a small screwdriver to tap the bearings out from the inside. Repeat this operation until all four bearing cups and their rollers have been removed.

3. Thoroughly clean the flange and driveshaft yokes.

4. Fill the reservoir holes in the spider journals with grease (sealed joints without grease fittings).

5. Fill the bearing cups to a depth of ⅛ in. with grease and install the needle rollers in the cups.

6. Install the seals on the spider journals (sealed joints).

7. Position the spider inside the flange yoke and install the bearings and snap-rings. Place the spider inside the drive-shaft yoke and install the remaining two bearings and snap-rings.

NOTE: *Make sure that the grease fittings on joints so equipped face away from the flanges, toward the center of the driveshaft.*

8. Lubricate the joint with a grease gun (early type with grease fitting).

9. Check the joint for freedom of movement. If it binds, tap it lightly with a soft-metal or wooden hammer to relieve pressure from the bearing cups on the ends of the journals.

10. Remove any surplus grease from the joint and replace the driveshaft.

Axle Shaft

Removal and Installation

1. Raise the rear of the vehicle and support it under the springs.

2. Release the parking brake and back off the brake adjusters if the wheel does not spin freely.

3. Remove the brake drum retaining screws and remove the drum.

Wire Wheels:

4. Remove the nuts which secure the axle hub to the splined wheel hub.

5. Remove the splined wheel hub, and withdraw the axle shaft, gasket, and O-ring.

Disc Wheels:

4. Remove the axle shaft retaining screws and withdraw the axle and gasket.

5. Installation is in reverse order of removal. Always use a new gasket and O-ring (wire wheels). Adjust the brakes if necessary after the wheels have been installed.

Differential

Removal and Installation

1. Drain the drive axle.

2. Remove the axle shafts as previously described.

3. Mark the flanges and disconnect the driveshaft from the differential.

4. Remove the nuts securing the differential assembly to the drive axle and withdraw the complete assembly.

5. Installation is in reverse order of removal. Always use a new gasket, and make sure that the differential and drive axle mating surfaces are clean.

Disassembly

1. Mark and remove the housing caps, and withdraw the differential cage.

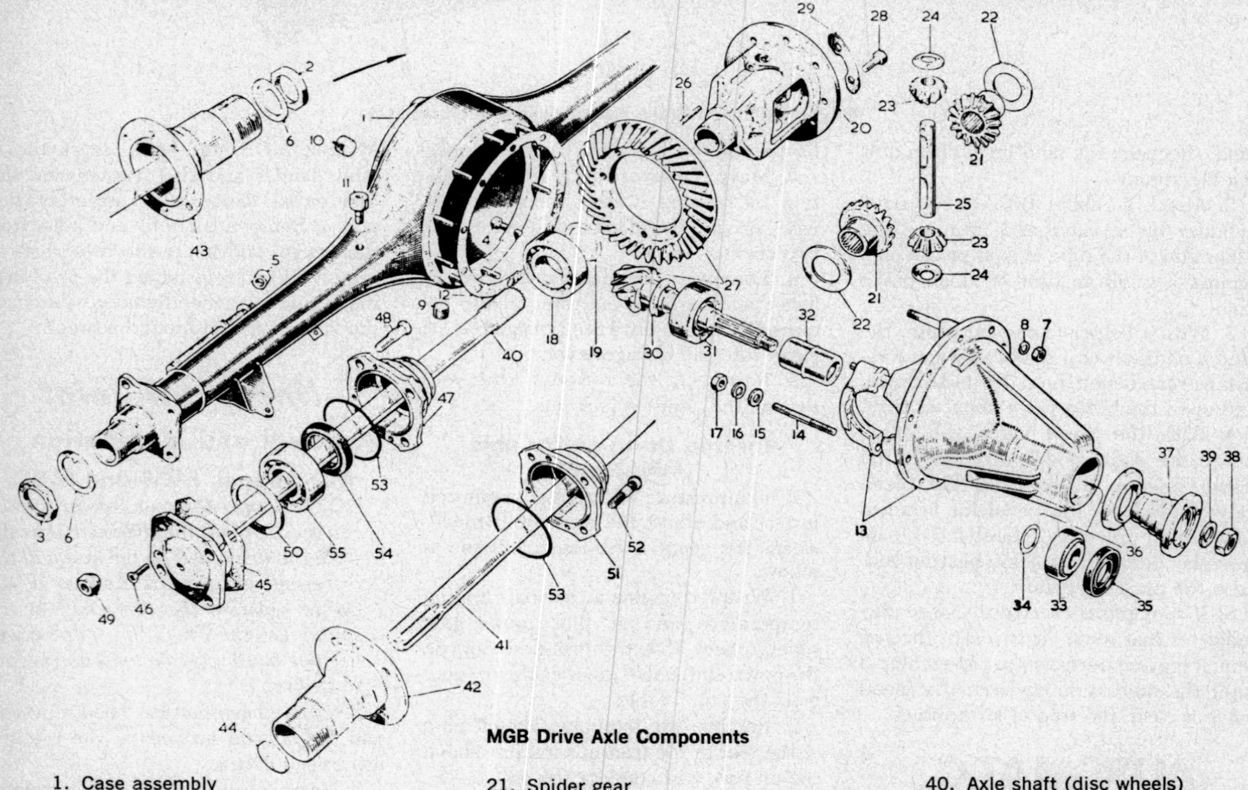

MGB Drive Axle Components

1. Case assembly
2. Nut
3. Nut
4. Gear carrier stud
5. Nut
6. Washer
7. Nut
8. Lockwasher
9. Drain plug
10. Filler plug
11. Breather
12. Gasket
13. Carrier assembly
14. Bearing cap stud
15. Washer
16. Lockwasher
17. Nut
18. Differential bearing
19. Shim
20. Differential cage
21. Spider gear
22. Thrust washer
23. Pinion
24. Thrust washer
25. Pinion shaft
26. Pinion shaft locating pin
27. Ring and pinion gearset
28. Bolt
29. Locktab
30. Thrust washer
31. Inner pinion bearing
32. Spacer
33. Outer pinion bearing
34. Shim
35. Oil seal
36. Dust cover
37. Differential drive flange
38. Nut
39. Lockwasher
40. Axle shaft (disc wheels)
41. Axle shaft
42. Wheel hub—RH
43. Wheel hub—LH
44. Core plug
45. Gasket
46. Screw
47. Axle hub
48. Wheel stud
49. Stud nut
50. Spacer
51. Axle hub
52. Wheel stud
53. O-ring
54. Oil seal
55. Hub bearing

wire wheels
disc wheels
wire wheels

2. Remove the bearings and shims from the cage.

3. Bend back the locktabs, remove the ring gear bolts, and remove the ring gear.

4. Drive out the dowel pin which locates the pinion shaft. The pin is ⅛ in. in diameter, and it must be driven out from the ring gear side of the differential cage.

5. Remove the pinions and thrust washers. Remove the pinion nut, drive flange, and end-cover.

6. Drive the pinion shaft toward the rear through the carrier. It will carry with it the inner race and rollers of the rear bearing.

7. Remove the inner race of the front bearing and the oil seal.

8. Remove the bearing outer races using a puller.

9. Slide off the pinion sleeve and shims.

10. Remove the rear bearing inner race, the spacer, and the bearing outer race.

Assembly

If no components other than the oil seal have been replaced, assembly is in reverse order of disassembly. Note that the thrust face of the differential bearings are marked with the word THRUST.

If any gears or bearings have been replaced, see "Differential Gear Adjustment."

MGB, BANJO-TYPE AXLE

The banjo axle was installed in MGB convertibles with engines 18G, 18GA, and 18GB. However, some cars with the 18GB engine were fitted with the tubed-type axle, as were all of the GTs. The only sure way to tell which axle is installed in a convertible with the 18GB engine is to look. The axle housing shapes are quite different.

The banjo axle is of the three-quarter floating type incorporating a hypoid ring and pinion gearset. The axle shafts, pinion oil seal, and differential assembly can be removed with the drive axle in place.

The rear suspension consists of leaf springs, serving also to locate the drive axle, and lever-type shock absorbers.

Overhaul

Midget, MGB and MGC

1. Mark and remove the housing caps, and withdraw the differential cage.

2. Remove the bearings and shims from the cage.

3. Bend back the locktabs, remove the ring gear bolts, and remove the ring gear.

4. Drive out the dowel pin which locates the pinion shaft. The pin is ⅛ in. in diameter, and it must be driven out from the ring gear side of the differential cage.

5. Remove the pinions and thrust washers. Remove the pinion nut, drive flange, and end-cover.

6. Drive the pinion shaft toward the rear through the carrier. It will carry with it the inner race and rollers of the rear bearing.

7. Remove the inner race of the front bearing and the oil seal.

8. Remove the bearing outer races using a puller.

9. Slide off the pinion sleeve and shims.

10. Remove the rear bearing inner race, the spacer, and the bearing outer race.

If no components other than the oil seal have been replaced, assembly is in reverse order of disassembly.

Adjustments

Pinion Depth Adjustment

Pinion depth adjustment is an adjustment of the pinion mounting distance D. In the absence of special factory tools for measuring this distance the pinion can be accurately positioned by taking note of the markings on the original and replacement pinions and using suitable shims behind the pinion head. A number with a plus or minus sign is etched into the pinion head C, which is the deviation (in thousandths of an inch) of pinion head thickness from nominal. If there is not an etched number on the pinion head the pinion is of nominal thickness. If, for example, the old pinion is marked −2 and the new pinion is marked −2, the same shims may be used behind the pinion head. If, however, the new pinion is marked −5 a shim or combination of shims 0.003 in. thick must be added as compensation. Therefore, if the new pinion is undersize as compared to the old one, shims must be added, and if the new pinion is oversize shim thickness must be decreased proportionately.

Pinion Bearing Preload

Preload adjustment is automatically made by the collapsible spacer when the differential drive flange nut is tightened. *It is of extreme importance that the nut is not overtightened.* See "Pinion Oil Seal Replacement" under the applicable model section for tightening procedures and torque values. The collapsible spacer should be replaced whenever the differential is disassembled.

Differential Bearing Preload and Ring Gear Mesh Adjustment

Bearing preload and mesh adjustment can be made simultaneously by first measuring total differential end-play, using a dial indicator to determine shim thickness needed. Either the ring or pinion must be removed to accurately measure end-play. To this measurement must be added 0.004 in., which is the amount of pinch needed to properly preload the bearings (all models).

1. With both gears in position, shift the differential assembly to one side so that the gap at Y is reduced to zero, and measure ring gear backlash with a dial indicator.

2. From the measurement obtained, subtract the correct backlash figure, which is etched into the rear face of the ring gear. This will give the shim thickness required at Y. Subtract this figure from A + 0.004 in., and the remainder will be shim thickness required.

Example:

End-float A	0.060
Plus 0.004 in. preload	0.004
Total shim thickness required	0.064
Shim thickness at Y:	
Backlash with zero gap at Y	0.020
Subtract specified backlash (Marked on ring gear.)	0.005
Shim thickness needed	0.015
Shim thickness at X:	
Total shim thickness	0.064
Subtract shims needed at Y	0.015
Shim thickness needed	0.049

If the above calculations have been done correctly, backlash should be within specification and the ring gear should be meshing properly with the pinion gear.

3. Gear mesh can be checked by painting the ring gear teeth with red lead or machinist's blue dye and rotating the gear to obtain a mesh pattern. If correction is necessary do not alter the total number of shims (total thickness), but increase or decrease thickness as needed.

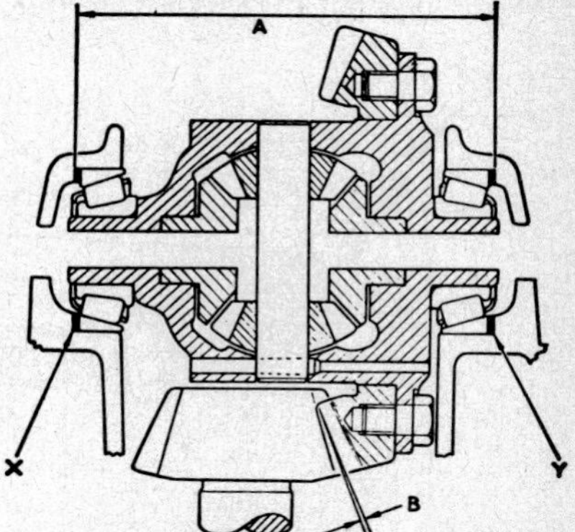

Preload and Ring Gear Mesh Adjustment

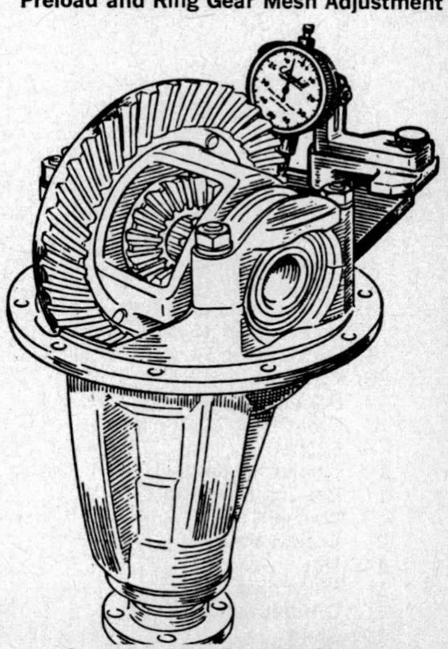
Checking Ring Gear Backlash

REAR SUSPENSION

Springs

Removal and Installation

Mk. I and II

1. Raise and support the rear of the car on the chassis, and place the jack under the axle to support it. The springs must be in the unloaded position.
2. Remove the forward spring mounting bolts.
3. Remove the U-bolt which secures the spring to the axle and pull the spring out of its mounting.
4. Installation is in reverse order of removal.

Mk. III

1. Raise and support the car as above.
2. Remove the wheels.
3. From inside the car remove the bolts which secure the spring anchor bracket to the body.
4. From beneath the car remove the two front bracket bolts.
5. Remove the four U-bolt nuts and the shock absorber anchor plate.
6. Remove the rear shackle nuts, pins, and plates, and remove the spring.
7. Installation is in reverse order of removal. The axle limit strap may be removed to facilitate U-bolt installation. Tighten the spring bolt fully after the car is lowered and the spring is loaded.

Shock Absorber

Removal and Installation

1. To remove a rear shock absorber simply disconnect the connecting link arm from the shock lever and unbolt the unit. Shock absorbers should be replaced in axle sets (pairs).
2. If a new shock absorber appears to operate erratically, allow the hydraulic fluid a few minutes to become deaerated.

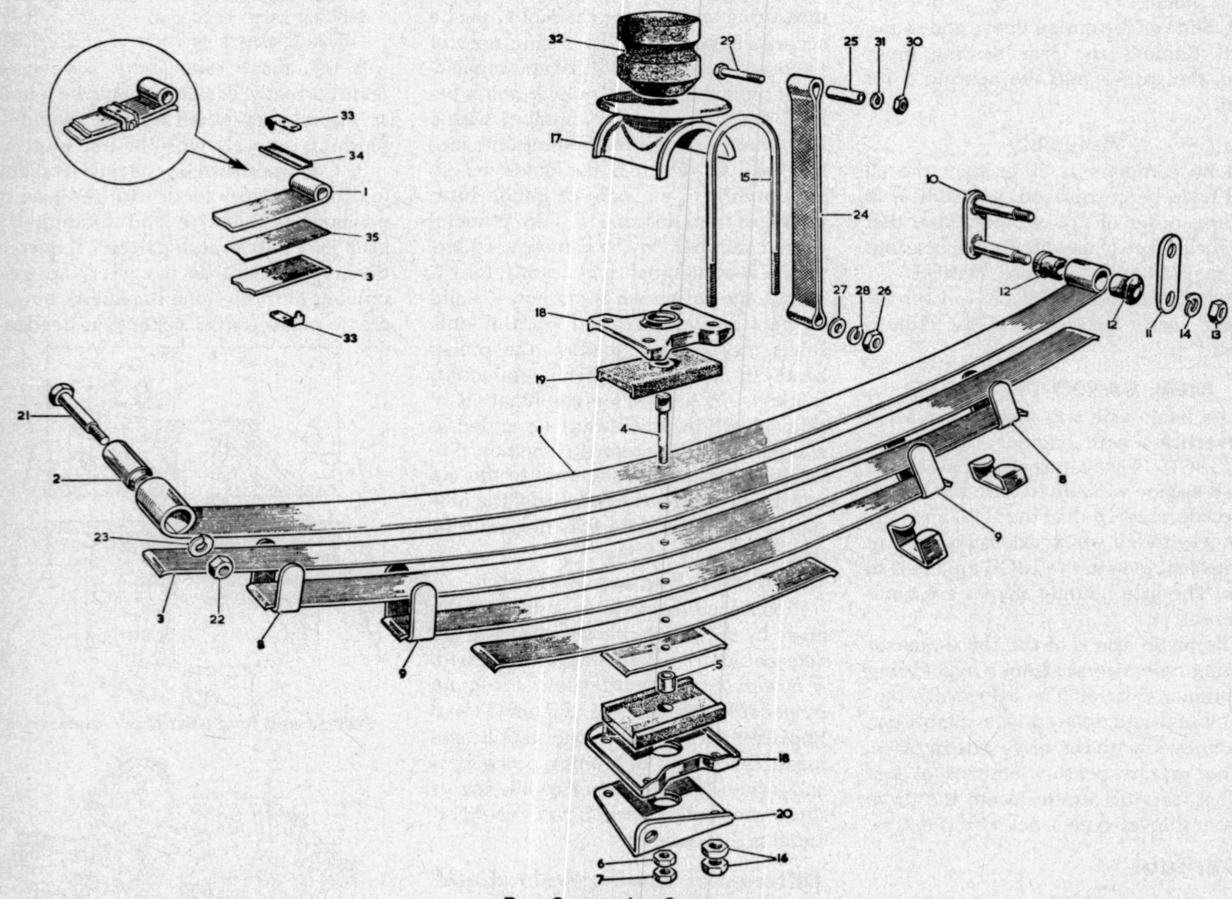

Rear Suspension Components

1. Case assembly
2. Gear carrier stud
3. Bearing retaining nut
4. Gear carrier to axle case nut
5. Lockwasher
6. Washer
7. Breather assembly
8. Drain plug
9. Gasket
10. Carrier assembly
11. Bearing cup stud
12. Washer
13. Lockwasher
14. Nut
15. Filler plug
16. Differential bearing
17. Shim
18. Differential cage
19. Spidergear
20. Thrust washer
21. Differential pinion
22. Thrust washer
23. Pinion pin
24. Pinion peg
25. Ring and pinion gearset
26. Bolt
27. Locktab
28. Pinion thrust washer
29. Inner pinion bearing
30. Bearing spacer
31. Pinion outer bearing
32. Oil seal
33. Dust cover
34. Differential drive flange
35. Pinion nut
36. Lockwasher
37. Hub assembly
38. Wheel stud
39. Nut
40. Oil seal
41. Hub bearing
42. Oil seal ring
43. Gasket
44. Axle shaft
45. Screw
46. Rubber block
47. Axle shaft
48. Hub assembly
49. Wheel stud
50. Hub extension
51. Core plug

FRONT SUSPENSION

Springs

Removal and Installation

MG Midget and MGB

1. Removal of a front spring requires a spring compressor. Once the spring is slightly compressed the spring seat can be unbolted and the spring withdrawn. If a spring compressor is not available, remove two of the spring seat mounting bolts as shown and substitute two long slave bolts that will allow the spring to expand slowly when unbolted evenly (Midget only).

2. Installation is in reverse order of removal.

Torsion Bar Adjustment

MGC

Torsion bar adjustment is made by turning the vernier lever adjustment bolt at the rear of the torsion bar. Turn the adjustment bolt in the required direction until ride height is 13 ⅞ ± ¼ in. Be sure to tighten the locknut when the adjustment is correct. For torsion bar removal procedures, see "Lower Wishbone Removal and Installation."

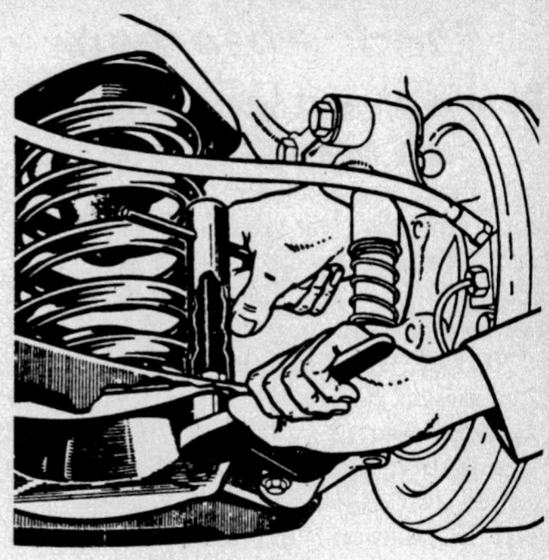

Spring Removal

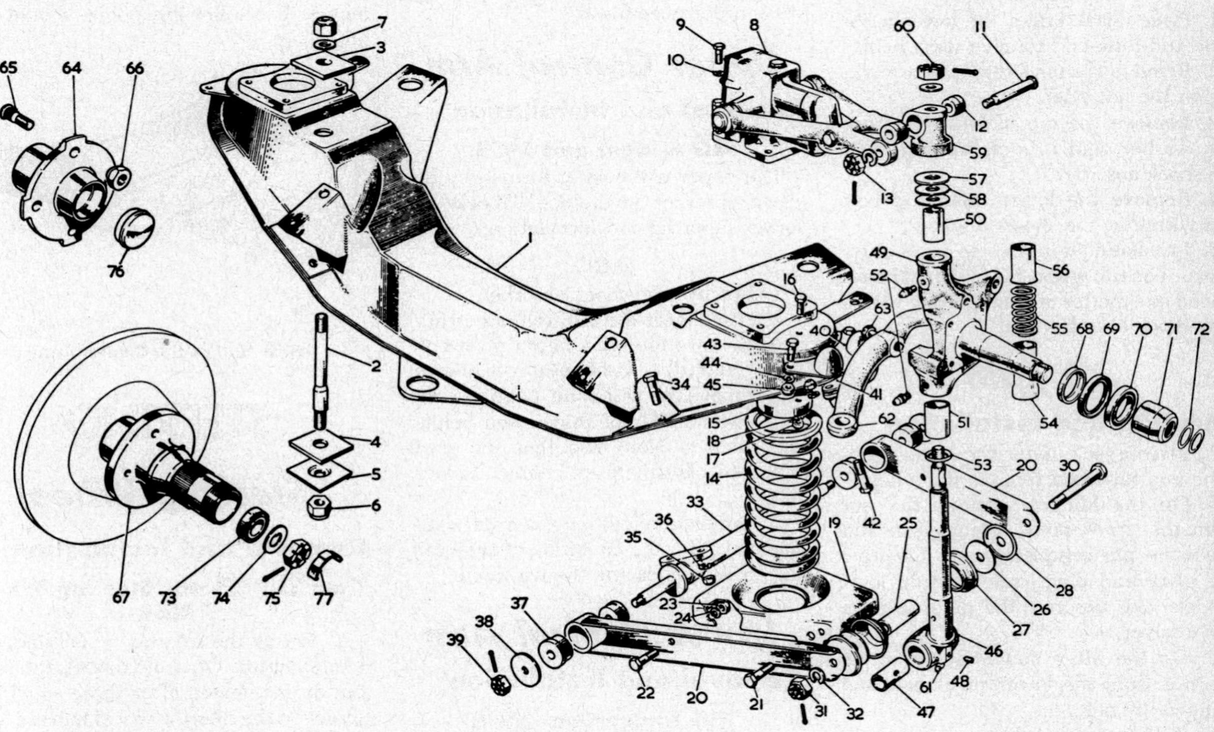

MGB Front Suspension

1. Crossmember
2. Bolt
3. Pad
4. Pad
5. Plate
6. Nut
7. Washer
8. Shock absorber
9. Bolt
10. Lockwasher
11. Pivot bolt
12. Bushing
13. Nut
14. Spring
15. Plate
16. Bolt
17. Nut
18. Lockwasher
19. Spring pan assembly
20. Wishbone assembly
21. Bolt
22. Bolt
23. Nut
24. Lockwasher
25. Spacer
26. Thrust washer
27. Seal
28. Support
29. Nut
30. Bolt
31. Nut
32. Lockwasher
33. Pivot bracket
34. Bolt
35. Nut
36. Lockwasher
37. Bushing
38. Washer
39. Nut
40. Buffer
41. Spacer
42. Bolt
43. Bolt
44. Lockwasher
45. Nut
46. Kingpin
47. Bushing
48. Setscrew
49. Stub axle assembly
50. Bushing
51. Bushing
52. Grease fitting
53. Seal
54. Spacer
55. Spring
56. Spacer
57. Thrust washer
58. Floating thrust washer—.052 to .057 in.
59. Trunnion—suspension link.
60. Nut
61. Grease fitting
62. Steering arm
63. Bolt
64. Hub assembly
65. Stud
66. Nut
67. Hub assembly
68. Collar
69. Oil seal
70. Bearing
71. Spacer
72. Shim—.003 in.
73. Bearing
74. Washer
75. Nut
76. Grease cap
77. Collar

Shock Absorbers

Removal and Installation

MG Midget and MGB

1. Place a jack under the lower wishbone and raise the wheel.

2. Remove the top kingpin pivot bolt and swing the wheel down, taking care not to strain the brake line.

NOTE: *The clamp bolt must be removed before the pivot bolt can be withdrawn.*

3. Unbolt and remove the shock absorber unit.

4. Installation is in reverse order of removal.

MGC

1. Place a jack under the lower wishbone and raise and remove the wheel.

2. Remove the air filters (when working on the left side).

3. Remove the top locknut, securing nut, washer, and rubber bushing from the shock absorber.

4. Remove the lower mounting bolt and withdraw the shock absorber.

5. Installation is in reverse order of removal. The rubber bushings should be replaced as a matter of course along with a new shock absorber unit.

Kingpin

Removal and Installation

1. Place a jack under the lower wishbone and raise and remove the wheel.

6. On the Midget, remove the nut from the lower pivot locating pin and drive the pin completely out. Unscrew the pivot end plug (core plug on later models) and unscrew the pivot using a screwdriver.

7. On the MGB and MGC, unscrew the nut from the lower pivot bolt and remove the bolt.

8. Withdraw the stub axle and kingpin assembly from the lower control arm.

9. Unscrew the nut from the top of the stub axle and kingpin assembly and remove the kingpin, washers, and seals.

10. Press the bushings out from the bottom of the axle.

11. Install the new bushings, taking care that the open end of the oil groove enters first and that the hole in the bushing is in line with the lubrication channel in the axle.

12. On the MGB and MGC the bushings must be line-bored after installation. (Most machine shops can perform this operation.)

The bushings should be machined to these dimensions:

MGB—top bushing: 0.7815–0.7820 in.; bottom bushing: 0.9075–0.9080 in.

MGC—top bushing: 0.8125–0.8130 in.; bottom bushing: 0.9375–0.9380 in.

13. On the Midget the kingpin bushings do not require reaming. However, the kingpin should be lubricated and installed to check the fit. If it takes excessive effort to rotate the kingpin, the bushing surfaces may be refinished using a brake cylinder hone.

14. Install the kingpin in the axle body along with the washers and seals, as removed, and tighten the nut.

15. Lubricate the bushings via the grease fittings using a high pressure grease gun, and check the resistance of the kingpin to rotation. If it is excessively stiff, remove the nut and substitute a thinner floating thrust washer (MGB and MGC) or a thicker adjustment washer (Midget).

From this point on, installation is in reverse order of removal.

Upper Control Arm

Removal and Installation

MG Midget and MGB

The upper wishbone is formed by the shock absorber lever. See "Shock Absorber Removal and Installation."

MGC

1. Remove the shock absorber.
2. Disconnect the anti-roll bar strut.
3. Remove the top kingpin pivot bolt.
4. Unbolt the wishbone pivot bracket and remove the wishbone, taking care to note the number of shims used behind the bracket. Note also that the pivot bracket lockwashers are behind the locktabs.
5. Installation is in reverse order of removal. Check the condition of the bushings before replacing the wishbone.

Lower Control Arm

Removal and Installation

MG Midget and MGB

1. Raise the front of the car and remove the wheel.
2. Remove the spring.
3. Disconnect the tie rod from the steering arm.
4. Remove the lower kingpin pivot. On the Midget it is necessary to remove the locating pin and pivot bolt end cap before the pivot can be unscrewed.
5. Swivel the stub axle and hub assembly up slightly and support it.
6. Unbolt the wishbone pivot bracket and remove the wishbone.

MGC

Removal of a lower wishbone requires unloading and removal of the torsion bar. The procedure is as follows:

1. Place a jack under the wishbone and raise and remove the wheel.
2. Disconnect the tie-rod from the steering arm.
3. Remove the shock absorber.
4. Remove the lower kingpin pivot bolt.
5. Place a jackstand under the chassis and lower the jack.
6. Remove the wishbone inner pivot nut and unbolt and remove the front half of the wishbone.
7. At the rear of the torsion bar remove the nut and small retaining plate from the vernier lever. Remove the lever and pull the bar out about two inches.

CAUTION: *Do not scratch or centerpunch the torsion bar or exchange the bars from right to left (when both are removed at the same time).*

8. Remove the rear half of the wishbone.
9. Installation is in reverse order of removal. The following points should be noted:

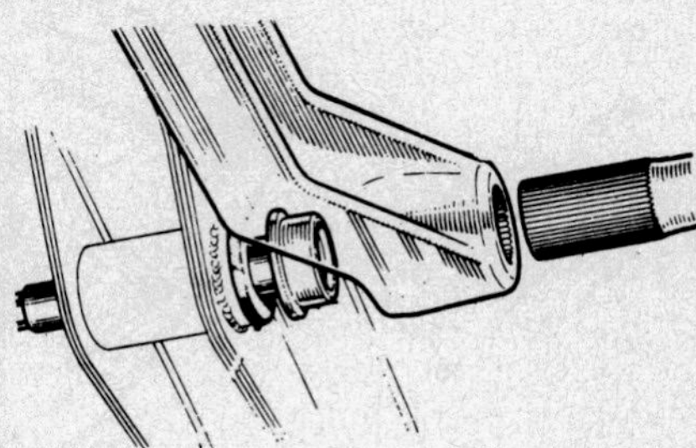

Rear Half of the Control Arm

STEERING

Steering Wheel

Removal and Installation

Cars With Plastic Steering Wheel Rims

1. Pry off the steering wheel hub emblem housing. On some models the horn button is released after three small setscrews in the steering wheel hub are loosened.
2. Remove the wheel retaining nut.
3. Mark the steering shaft and hub to facilitate correct installation and remove the wheel. It may be necessary to use a puller if the wheel does not come off easily.
4. Installation is in reverse order of removal. Make sure that the steering wheel is centered when the front wheels are straight ahead. The steering wheel nut in all cases should be tightened to 40 ft lbs.

Cars With Leather Covered or Wood Steering Wheel Rims

1. Pry off the steering wheel hub emblem housing.
2. Bend back the locktabs, remove the wheel retaining bolts, and remove the wheel.
3. Installation is in reverse order of removal. The retaining bolts should be tightened to 12–17 ft lbs.

Steering Gear

Removal and Installation

1967 and Earlier Cars

MG Midget

1. Remove the clamp bolt at the splined lower end of the steering column and disengage the column from the splines.
2. Disconnect the tie-rods from the steering arms.
3. Unbolt the steering rack brackets from the crossmember and remove the rack complete with tie-rods and brackets.

Installation is in reverse order of removal. The following point should be noted. To ensure correct pinion alighment, do not tighten the bolts securing the rack to the brackets until the rack has been attached to the steering column and the brackets attached to the crossmember.

MGB

1. Disconnect the tie-rods from the steering arms.
2. Turn the steering wheel to full right lock and remove the clamp bolt at the lower end of the steering column.
3. Unbolt the rack from the crossmember, noting the number of shims (if any)

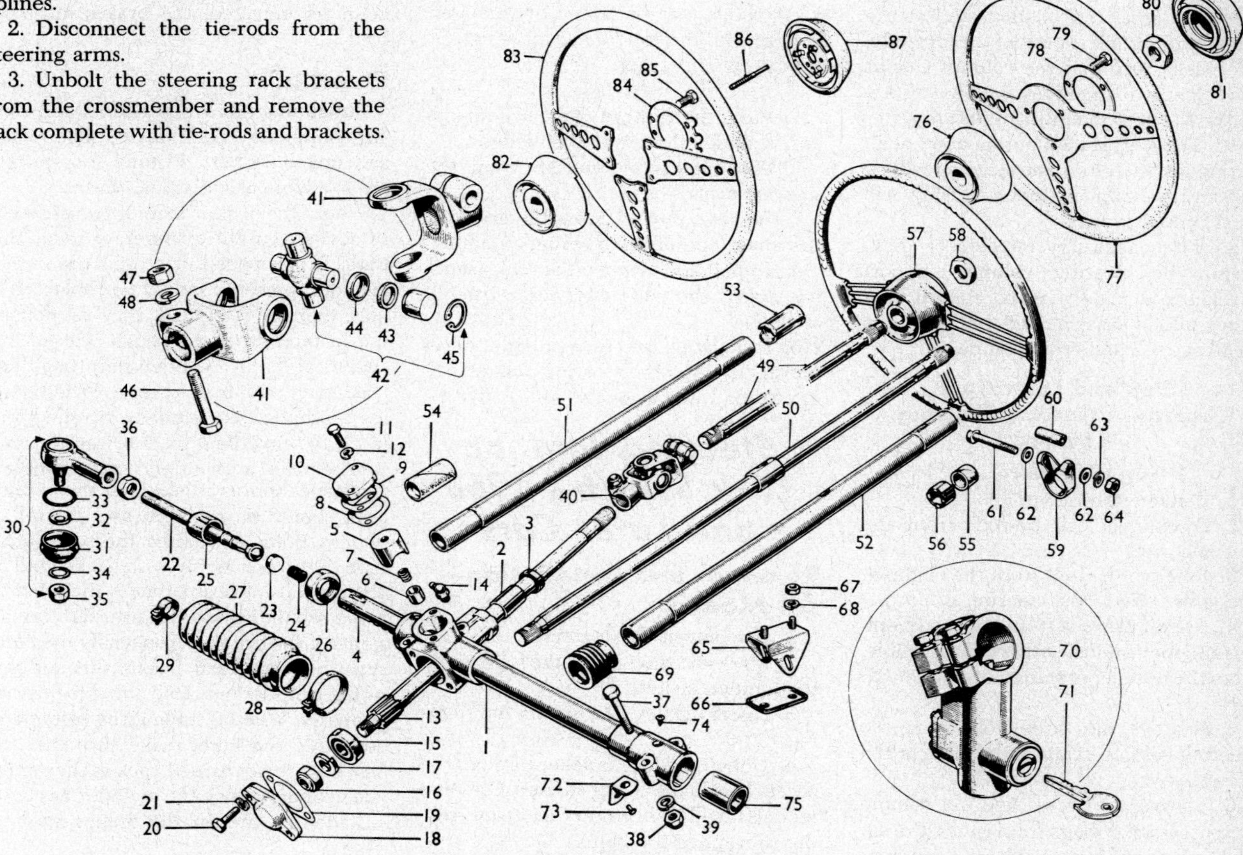

MGB/MGC Steering Components

1. Housing assembly
2. Bushing
3. Seal
4. Rack
5. Yoke
6. Damper
7. Spring
8. Shim
9. Gasket
10. Cover plate
11. Bolt
12. Lockwasher
13. Pinion
14. Grease fitting
15. Pinion bearing
16. Nut
17. Lockwasher
18. End cover
19. Gasket
20. Bolt
21. Lockwasher
22. Tie-rod
23. Ball seat
24. Thrust spring
25. Housing
26. Locknut
27. Seal
28. Clip
29. Clip
30. Socket assembly
31. Boot
32. Retainer
33. Spring
34. Washer
35. Nut
36. Locknut
37. Bolt
38. Nut
39. Lockwasher
40. Steering column U-joint
41. Yoke
42. Journal assembly
43. Seal
44. Retainer
45. Circlip
46. Bolt
47. Nut
48. Lockwasher
49. Column assembly—inner
50. Column assembly—inner—R.H.D.
51. Coumn tube
52. Column tube—R.H.D.
53. Bearing
54. Bearing
55. Bushing (felt)
56. Clip
57. Steering wheel
58. Nut
59. Clamp
60. Spacer
61. Bolt
62. Washer
63. Lockwasher
64. Nut
65. Bracket
66. Plate
67. Nut
68. Lockwasher
69. Boot
70. Lock assembly—steering and ignition
71. Key
72. Shim
73. Rivet
74. Bushing locating screw
75. Bushing
76. Wheel hub
77. Steering wheel
78. Ring
79. Bolt
80. Nut
81. Emblem housing
82. Wheel hub
83. Steering wheel
84. Ring
85. Bolt
86. Horn push contact
87. Horn push

When steering lock is fitted.
1970 and later cars.

between the rack and the bracket.

4. Remove the rack complete with tie-rods.

5. Installation is in reverse order of removal. To ensure correct steering column alighment the following procedure should be noted:

6. Set the steering in the straight-ahead position and make sure that that the turn signal cancellation stud at the top of the column is positioned correctly.

7. Make sure that the column U-joint has complete freedom of movement before the rack mounting bolts are tightened. The joint should not be offset at all during installation or the steering will be stiff and the pinion upper bearing will wear prematurely.

8. If it is necessary for correct alignment, the steering column support bracket and plate may be shifted, and shims added or removed between the steering rack and crossmember.

1968 and Later Cars (Energy-Absorbing Steering Column)

MG Midget

1. Remove the radiator.

2. Disconnect the tie-rods from the steering arms.

3. Remove the bolt from the clamp at the lower end of the steering column.

4. Unbolt the rack from the crossmember and move it forward as far as possible. Note the number of shims used under the rack.

5. Remove the three bolts from the steering column retaining plate near the firewall.

6. Loosen the three steering column support bracket bolts from inside the car and pull the column back far enough to disengage it from the rack.

7. Remove the right front wheel and withdraw the rack assembly.

8. Installation is in reverse order of removal. If the original rack is to be reused, the same shims that were removed may be used also and steering column alignment should be correct. If a new rack is to be used, alignment should be carried out as follows:

1. Push the steering column forward as far as it will go (after the rack is in position).

2. Tighten the three steering column support bracket bolts.

3. Check, by pushing and pulling, that the column slides reasonably freely over the steering rack pinion shaft. If the column is stiff, shims may be added or removed from behind the rack or the column support bracket.

MGB

Steering rack removal for the MGB with energy-absorbing steering column is the same as for the earlier type. Installation is in reverse order of removal. To align the steering column:

1. Remove the three bolts from the steering column retaining plate near the firewall.

2. Install the rack assembly with the shims that were originally removed and check, by pushing and pulling, that the column slides reasonably freely over the steering rack pinion shaft. If the column is stiff shims may be added or removed from behind the rack or the steering column support bracket.

MGC

1. Raise the front of the car and support it under the lower wishbones.

2. Disconnect the tie-rods from the steering arms.

3. Remove the bolt from the clamp at the lower end of the steering column.

4. Unbolt and remove the rack assembly, noting the number of shims used (if any).

5. Installation is in reverse order of removal. To align the steering column follow Steps 1 and 2 for the MGB, above.

Steering/Ignition Lock Switch—1968 and Later Cars

Removal and Installation—All Models

1. Disconnect the battery(s).

2. Mark and disconnect the wires from the ignition switch.

3. Insert the key and unlock the steering.

4. Unbolt the lock bracket through the access hole in the upper surface. On some models it will be necessary to use an *easy-out* to remove the bolts.

5. Loosen the steering column support bracket to aid in removal, and withdraw the lock switch assembly.

6. Installation is in reverse order of removal.

BRAKE SYSTEMS

Master Cylinder

Removal and Installation

MG Midget Mk. I and II

On the Midget Mk. I and II the clutch and brake master cylinders are in the same body, and are removed at the same time. To remove the master cylinder, first disconnect the pushrods from both the brake and clutch pedals. Disconnect the hydraulic lines from the cylinder body and cap them. Remove the two cylinder mounting bolts and remove the cylinder.

Installation is in reverse order of removal. When the lines have been reconnected, the clutch, as well as the brakes, should be bled.

MG Midget Mk. III, MGB, MGC

To remove the brake master cylinder, remove the screws which secure the mounting bracket cover plate and lift the cover off. Disconnect and cap the hydraulic line(s) from the cylinder. Remove the mounting bolts and lift the cylinder out.

Installation is in reverse order of removal. When the hydraulic lines have been reconnected, the brakes must be bled.

Overhaul

Rebuilding kits are available, and usually contain the check valve, rubber seals, and metal washers. Pistons and springs are available as individual pieces.

When the piston assembly has been removed from the cylinder, examine the bore. If it is pitted or scored the entire cylinder assembly should be replaced. If bore damage is light, it may be honed; but in most cases the repair will not be lasting and the cylinder may begin to leak again after a short time. When honing a cylinder, occasionally dip the hone in clean brake fluid for lubrication.

Whenever a cylinder is disassembled for inspection or rebuilding, the rubber seals should be replaced as a matter of course. Before installing the seals lubricate them thoroughly with brake fluid or the special lubricant that is included in some rebuilding kits. All internal components of the cylinder, especially the bore, must be completely free of dirt and grit or the cylinder may leak or fail to operate properly. When installing the piston and seals into the bore, make sure that the seal lips are not turned back as they enter the cylinder. Once the cylinder has been installed on the car the brakes must be bled.

Brake Bleeding

There are two methods of accomplishing this. The quickest and easiest of the two is pressure bleeding, but special pressure equipment is needed to externally pressurize the hydraulic system. The other, more commonly used method is gravity bleeding.

NOTE: *Only brake fluid conforming to SAE specification J1703 should be used.*

Gravity Bleeding Procedure

1. Clean the bleed valve at each wheel.

2. Attach a small rubber hose to the bleed valve on one of the rear wheel cylinders and place the other end in a container of brake fluid.

3. Top up the master cylinder with brake fluid (check often during bleeding).

4. Open the bleed valve about one-quarter turn, have assistant press the brake pedal to the floor and slowly release it. Continue until no more air bubbles are forced from the cylinder on application of the brake pedal.

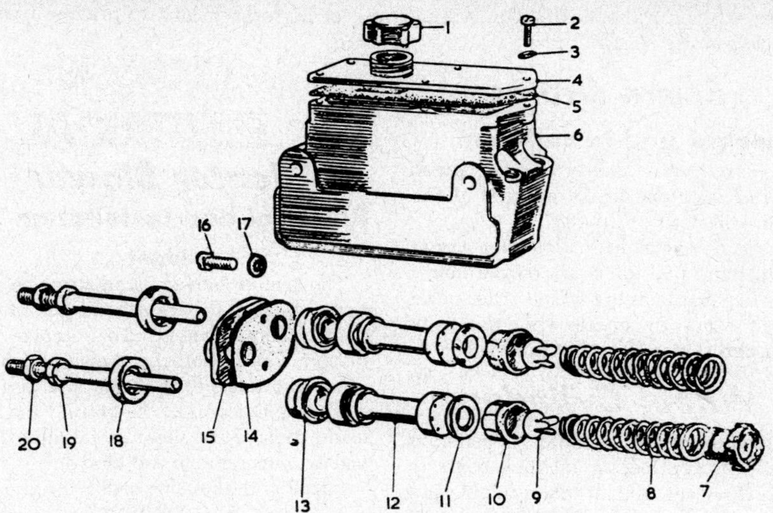

Clutch and Master Cylinder Components

1. Filler cap
2. Screw
3. Washer
4. Tank cover
5. Gasket
6. Cylinder body
7. Check valve (brake only)
8. Return spring
9. Spring retainer
10. Main cup
11. Piston washer
12. Piston
13. Secondary cup
14. Gasket
15. Retaining plate
16. Screw
17. Lockwasher
18. Rubber boot
19. Pushrod
20. Pushrod adjuster

5. Repeat for each of the remaining wheel cylinders, beginning with the other rear wheel.

FRONT DISC BRAKES

Disc Brake Pads

Removal and Installation

1. Raise the front of the car and remove the wheel.
2. Remove the two cotter pins that locate the pad retaining spring(s).
3. Remove the retaining spring and pull the pads and anti-squeal shims from the caliper.
4. Installation is in reverse order of removal. It may be necessary to push the pistons back into the caliper so that the new pads will fit. Be careful not to mar the disc in doing so. Install the anti-squeal shims in their original positions or they will not function properly. Pads should never be allowed to wear to a thickness of less than 1/16 in. Replace pads in axle sets (two pair).

Disc Brake Calipers

Removal and Installation

1. Remove the friction pads.
2. Disconnect the hydraulic line retaining plate and disconnect the line from the caliper.
3. Bend back the locktabs and unbolt and remove the caliper.
4. Installation is in reverse order of removal. Tighten the bolts to 40–45 ft lbs. It will be necessary to bleed the brakes after the hydraulic line is reconnected.

Overhaul

1. Remove the caliper and clean the exterior.
2. Temporarily reconnect the hydraulic line to the caliper and press the brake pedal until the pistons protrude far enough to be removed by hand.
3. Remove the dust seals and retainers, taking care not to damage the piston bores.
4. Remove the seals from the pistons using a non-metallic instrument.

NOTE: *It is not normally necessary to separate the caliper halves. If the separation is necessary the fluid transfer hole seal, bridge bolts, and bolt locktabs* must *be replaced with new parts. Only use bolts obtained from an MG dealer that are supplied for this special application. Torque the bolts to 34–37 ft lbs.*

5. Clean all components in solvent and dry thoroughly with compressed air.
6. Examine the pistons and bores for wear or damage. Damaged pistons should be replaced. Slight bore roughness can be removed with crocus cloth or a brake cylinder hone. Remove all traces of grit from the bore after refinishing. Badly pitted or damaged bores cannot be refinished; the caliper must be replaced.
7. Coat the pistons and piston seals with brake fluid and install the seals on the pistons.
8. Loosen the bleed valve one turn and install the pistons in the bores with the piston cut-away facing inward. Press the piston in until approximately 3/8 in. of the piston is protruding from the bore.
9. Install the dust seals on the pistons.
10. Install the caliper(s) and bleed the brakes.

Disc Brake

Removal and Installation

1. Remove the caliper.
2. Remove the grease cap and cotter pin, and remove the hub retaining nut. Withdraw the hub assembly.

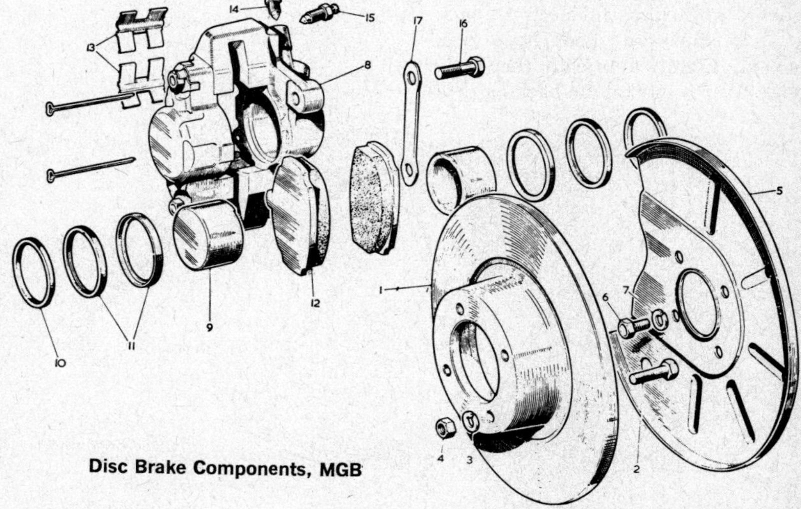

Disc Brake Components, MGB

1. Disc
2. Bolt
3. Lockwasher
4. Nut
5. Dust cover
6. Bolt
7. Lockwasher
8. Caliper
9. Piston
10. Piston seal
11. Dust seal and retainer
12. Pad
13. Retaining springs
14. Plug
15. Bleed valve
16. Bolt
17. Locktab

3. Unbolt and remove the disc from the hub.

4. Installation is in reverse order of removal.

Disc Resurfacing

Model	Orig. Thickness	Permiss. Regrind	Max. Runout	Parallel Variation	Surface Fin. (max. micro in.)
Midget	N.A.	none	0.006	N.A.	—
MGB	0.340-0.350	0.040	0.003	0.001	63
MGC	N.A.	none	0.003	N.A.	—

Any disc that is badly scored should be replaced. Light scoring is not detrimental to the operation of the brakes, but friction pad life will be reduced. Runout is measured at the outer edge of the disc friction surface with a dial indicator or runout gauge. Parallelism refers to variations in the thickness of the disc. The disc should be measured for parallelism at four equally spaced points around the friction surface.

Drum Brake Shoes

Removal and Installation

Brake shoes should always be replaced in axle sets. Replace riveted shoe assemblies or linings when they have less than 40% of original thickness left at the thinnest point, and bonded shoe assemblies or linings when they have less than 25% of original thickness left at the thinnest point. Examine the linings for signs of cracking and oil or brake fluid contamination.

With the drum off, examine the wheel cylinders for leakage. Check the brake springs for stretching and clean the backing plate after the shoes have been removed. Lightly lubricate the brake shoe contact points on the backing plate before installing the new shoes. Adjust the brakes after installation.

Brake Drums

Removal and Installation

1. Raise the car and remove the wheel.
2. Back off the brake adjuster if the drum will not spin freely.
3. Remove the drum retaining screws or nuts and pull the drum off the hub.
4. Installation is in reverse order of removal. Adjust the brakes when the drum has been replaced on the hub.

Wheel Cylinders

Ideally, wheel cylinder assemblies should be replaced when they begin to leak. However, seal kits are available and a rebuilt cylinder should function well if it has been rebuilt carefully. Use the illustrations at the beginning of the brake section for disassembly and assembly, and refer to "Master Cylinder Rebuilding" for inspection and rebuilding notes. It is possible to rebuild a wheel cylinder without removing it from the backing plate. In any case, cleanliness is of extreme importance. Adjust and bleed the brakes after the drum has been reinstalled.

Parking Brake

Adjustment

Adjustment can be made at the brake balance lever where the main parking brake cable splits into separate cables for each rear wheel, underneath the car near the axle. Adjust the cable so that the brake is fully applied when the lever is pulled up four or five notches. Some cars have grease fittings on the cables and balance lever pivot, and these points must be lubricated regularly to prevent brake drag.

CHASSIS ELECTRICAL

Heater Blower

Removal and Installation

Midget

The heater blower is adjacent to the heater box, on the right-hand side of the engine compartment. To remove the blower, loosen both hose clamps which retain the ducts to the unit, and pull off the ducts. Disconnect the ground and hot leads, remove the sheet metal mounting screws, and remove the blower.

Install in the reverse order of removal.

MGB/MGC

The heater blower is part of the heater assembly, mounted in the rear of the engine compartment, adjacent to the firewall. To remove the blower, separate the leads at the snap connectors, and remove the three blower mounting bolts.

Install in the reverse order of removal.

Heater Core

Removal and Installation

Midget

The heater core is located in the heater box, mounted directly in front of the battery in the engine compartment. To remove the core, it is necessary to drain the cooling system and proceed as follows:

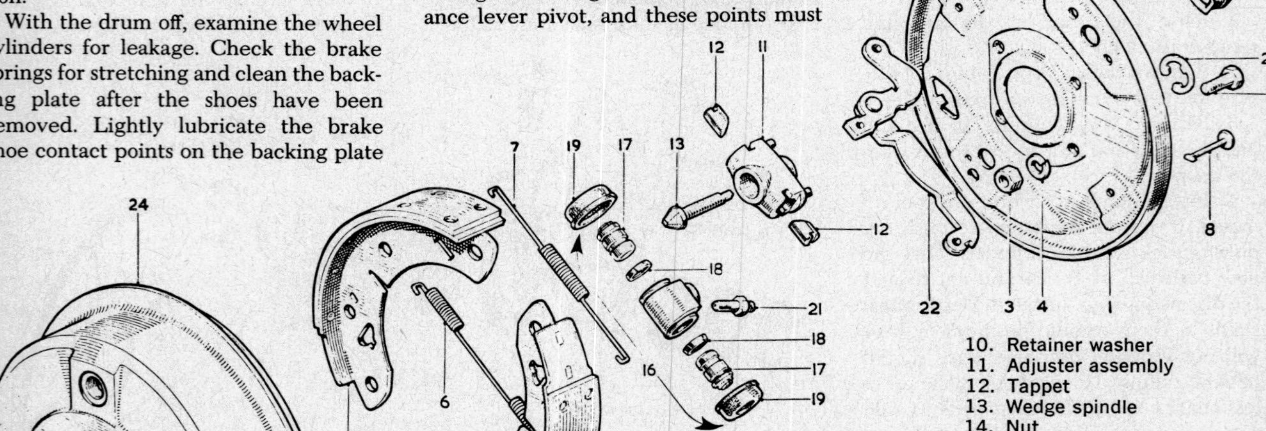

1. Backing plate
2. Bolt
3. Nut
4. Lockwasher
5. Shoe assembly
6. Spring
7. Spring
8. Shoe retaining pin
9. Brake-shoe retaining spring
10. Retainer washer
11. Adjuster assembly
12. Tappet
13. Wedge spindle
14. Nut
15. Washer
16. Wheel cylinder assembly
17. Piston
18. Piston seal
19. Piston boot
20. Wheel cylinder retaining clip
21. Bleed valve
22. Parking brake lever
23. Parking brake lever boot
24. Brake drum
25. Drum retaining screw
26. Drum retaining nut (wire wheels)

Rear Brake Components

1. Disconnect the battery cables, and the heater valve control cable. Remove the screws which retain the heater box to the tray.

2. Separate the water hoses and the blower duct from the heater box.

3. Lift the heater box out of the car as a unit.

4. The heater core may be removed from the heater box by removing the retaining sheet and metal screws.

5. Install in the reverse order of removal.

6. Bleed the system, if necessary, by removing the return hose from its connector, and extending it with an additional piece of hose, so that water may be returned to the radiator filler.

7. Plug the open connection, and run the engine until water flow into the radiator is free of bubbles.

8. Reconnect the hose as quickly as possible.

MGB/MGC

The heater core is located in the heater box, in the rear of the engine compartment, adjacent to the firewall.

1. To remove the heater core, it is necessary to remove the heater assembly as follows:

2. Disconnect the heater valve control cable (if the valve is mounted on the heater box).

3. Separate the blower motor leads at the snap connectors.

4. Drain the cooling system, and remove the water hoses from the heater unit.

5. Remove the screws which retain the heater box in the engine compartment.

6. Remove the center console (speaker panel).

7. Remove the defroster hose plate and pull the defroster tubes out of the heater box.

8. Remove the heater trim panel and loosen the clip which retains the air control cable.

9. Remove the heater air control from the dash panel, disconnect the control cable from it, and lift out the heater assembly.

10. To remove the core from the heater box, pry off the spring clips which retain the front panel to the assembly.

11. Assemble and install in the reverse order of disassembly and removal. Following installation, bleed the heater in the same manner as described for the Midget.

Radio

The radios used in MGs are dealer installed or aftermarket units. It is therefore impossible to give specific procedures for these radios. The following information applies generally to all radios installed in MGs.

Early MG models, equipped with positive ground electrical systems, must never be fitted with a negative ground radio which has been isolated from the chassis. This type of installation will result in a serious shock hazard, and possible severe damage to the electrical system.

Care should be exercised during installation to prevent reversing the ground and power leads. Reversal of the leads will result in serious damage to the radio. The power lead may be identified by an in-line fuse holder. The ground lead is not fused.

Should the speaker require replacement, it must be replaced with one of the same impedance. A speaker of the proper impedance must also be used during initial radio installation (consult the radio manual). Failure to observe proper impedance can result in rapid transistor failure. When installing a second speaker, it is also necessary to maintain impedance at the proper level by using a fader control or altering the entire system to maintain the specified load.

CAUTION: *Never operate a radio without load (no speaker), or with the speaker leads shorted together. This will result in transistor failure.*

Windshield Wiper Motor

Removal and Installation

1. Disconnect the electrical wires from the wiper motor.

2. Remove the wiper arms and wiper arm pivot nuts.

3. Unbolt the motor and withdraw the motor complete with drive cables and wiper arm pivots and gearboxes.

4. Loosen the cover screws in each wiper arm gearbox and remove the rack housings.

5. Remove the wiper motor gearbox cover and disconnect the cross-head and rack from the motor.

Installation is in reverse order of removal. Do not kink or bind the drive cable in any way, and make sure that the wiper arm gearboxes are aligned correctly.

OPEL

Index

INTRODUCTION

Opel A.G., owned by General Motors since 1929, began importing and selling the Opel Rekord through the Buick Motor Division dealer network in 1958. In 1964, the Opel line was expanded to include the Kadett Models, a sedan, a coupe and a station wagon. Since then the Opel has become more Americanized, adding such options as a fully automatic 3-speed transmission in 1969. A sport version of the Kadett, the Rallye, with improved performance and special trim, was introduced in 1967, followed by the Opel GT, a two seat sports coupe based on the Kadett Rallye running gear, in 1969.

In 1971, Opel introduced the 1900 series. It incorporates an all new sheet metal and interior design.

SERIAL NUMBER IDENTIFICATION

Vehicle Identification Number

Kadett

Opel Kadett vehicle-identification numbers run consecutively from the first Kadett produced in 1964. The first two digits of the serial number (reading from the left) indicate the model. The other numbers indicate production sequence. The identification plate is located in the engine compartment either on the right fender wall or on the left side of the fire wall.

GT

The GT is numbered in an identical manner to the Kadett. Identification plates are located on the right side of the cowl and on the left side of the instrument panel at the base of the windshield.

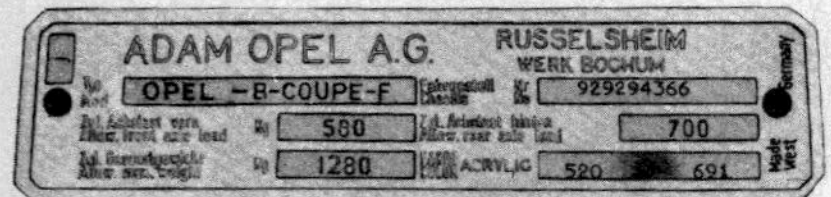

Model identification plate

Engine Serial Number

Kadett and GT

The engine number, stamped on the engine housing just above the crankcase dipstick, is prefixed with numbers and letters to indicate engine displacement and power. Reading from the left, the first two digits represent engine identification. Engines with an "S" designation are designed to run on premium gas.

MODEL IDENTIFICATION

1967-71 Opel Coupe

1967-71 Opel Rallye Coupe

1967-73 Opel Wagon

1971-73 Opel 1900 Coupe

1969-73 Opel GT

GENERAL ENGINE SPECIFICATIONS

Year	ENGINE Model	ENGINE Cu. In. Displacement	Carburetor Type	Horsepower @ rpm	Torque @ rpm (ft lbs)	Bore x Stroke (in.)	Compression Ratio
1966-1967	1.1	65.8	1-Solex 1 Bbl w/manual choke	54 @ 5600	59 @ 3000	2.95 x 2.40	7.8:1
	1.1S	65.8	1-Solex 1 Bbl w/manual choke	60 @ 5600	63 @ 3200	2.95 x 2.40	8.8:1
	1.1SR	65.8	1-Solex 1 Bbl w/manual choke	67 @ 6000	62 @ 5000	2.95 x 2.40	9.2:1
1968	1.1	65.8	1-Solex 1 Bbl w/manual choke	55 @ 5600	59 @ 2850	2.95 x 2.40	8.2:1
	1.5L	91.0	1-Solex 2 Bbl w/manual choke	80 @ 5100	87 @ 3400	2.95 x 2.40	9.0:1
	1.9L	115.8	1-Solex 2 Bbl w/automatic choke	102 @ 5200	115 @ 3100	3.66 x 2.75	9.0:1
1969	1.1US (AIR)	65.8	1-Solex 1 Bbl w/manual choke	55 @ 5600	59 @ 2850	2.95 x 2.40	8.2:1
	1.1SR (OECS)	65.8	2-Solex 1 Bbl w/manual choke	67 @ 6000	62 @ 5000	2.95 x 2.40	9.2:1
	1.9S	115.8	1-Solex 2 Bbl w/automatic choke	102 @ 5200	115 @ 3100	3.66 x 2.75	9.0:1
1970	1.1R (OECS)	65.8	2-Solex 1 Bbl w/manual choke	63 @ 6000	58 @ 4000	2.95 x 2.40	8.2:1
	1.1SR (OECS)	65.8	2-Solex 1 Bbl w/manual choke	67 @ 6000	62 @ 5000	2.95 x 2.40	9.2:1
	1.9S (OECS)	115.8	1-Solex 2 Bbl w/automatic choke	102 @ 5400	115 @ 3000	3.66 x 2.75	9.0:1
1971	1.1	65.8	2-Solex 1 Bbl w/manual choke	56 @ 5800	55 @ 4400	2.95 x 2.40	7.6:1
	1.9	115.8	1-Solex 2 Bbl w/automatic choke	90 @ 5200	111 @ 3400	3.66 x 2.75	7.6:1
1972-1973	1.9	115.8	1-Solex 2 Bbl w/automatic choke	90 @ 5200	111 @ 3400	3.66 x 2.75	7.6:1

AIR—Air Injection Reactor OECS—Opel Emission Control System

FIRING ORDER

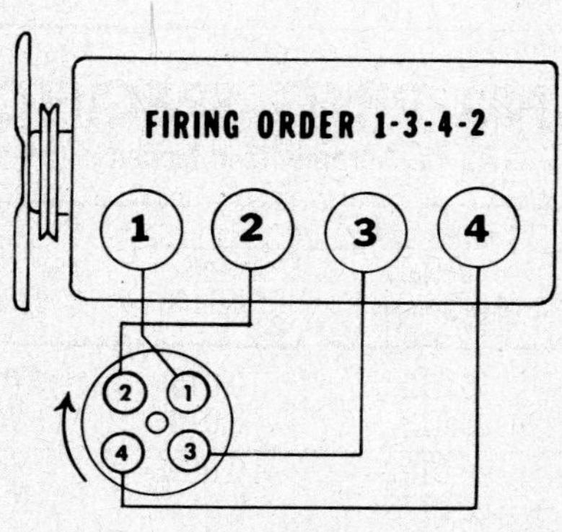

Firing order (All Models)

TUNE-UP SPECIFICATIONS

Year	Engine Model	Spark Plugs Type	Spark Plugs Gap (in.)	Distributor Point Dwell (deg)	Distributor Point Gap (in.)	Ignition Timing (deg)	Intake Valve Opens (deg)	Fuel Pump Pressure (psi)	Idle Speed (rpm) MT	Idle Speed (rpm) AT (Neutral)	Valve Clearance (in.) In	Valve Clearance (in.) Ex
1966	1.1	AC44F	0.030	48-52	0.018	(2)	36	3.1-3.7	750	N.A.	0.006	0.010
1967	1.1S	AC44F	0.030	48-52	0.018	(2)	36	3.1-3.7	750	N.A.	0.006	0.010
	1.1SR	AC44F	0.030	48-52	0.018	(2)	36	3.1-3.7	750	N.A.	0.006	0.010
1968	1.1	AC43FS	0.030	48-52	0.018	(2)	44	3.1-3.7	900	N.A.	0.006	0.010
	1.5S	AC44XLS	0.030	48-52	0.018	(2)	34	3.1-3.7	850	N.A.	0.012	0.012
	1.9S	AC42FS	0.030	48-52	0.018	(2)	44	3.1-3.7	750	800	0.012	0.012
1969	1.1R	AC43FS	0.030	47-53	0.016	(2)	44	3.1-3.7	950	N.A.	0.006	0.010
	1.1SR	AC43FS	0.030	47-53	0.016	(2)	46	3.1-3.7	950	950	0.006	0.010
	1.9S	AC42FS	0.030	47-53	0.016	(2)	44	3.1-3.7	750	800	0.012	0.012
1970	1.1R	AC43FS	0.030	48-52	0.018	(2)	46	3.1-3.7	950	N.A.	0.006	0.010
	1.1SR	AC43FS	0.030	48-52	0.018	(2)	46	3.1-3.7	950	900	0.006	0.010
	1.9S	AC42FS	0.030	48-52	0.018	(2)	44	3.1-3.7	900	850	0.012	0.012
1971	1.1	AC42FS(1)	0.030	48-52	0.018	(2)	—	3.1-3.7	900	N.A.	0.006	0.010
	1.9	AC42FS(1)	0.030	48-52	0.018	(2)	—	3.1-3.7	850	850	HYD.	HYD.
1972-73	1.9	AC42FS(1)	0.030	48-52	0.018	(2)	—	3.1-3.8	850	850	HYD.	HYD.

(1) If carbon fouling occurs, use AC43FS
(2) Align the timing marks. No timing scale is used.
— Not Available
NOTE: If the above specifications vary from those on the tune-up sticker, use the specifications on the sticker (under the hood).

CRANKSHAFT AND CONNECTING ROD SPECIFICATIONS

Year	Engine Displacement (liters)	Crankshaft Main Brg. Journal Dia.	Crankshaft Main Brg. Oil Clearance	Crankshaft Shaft End-Play	Crankshaft Thrust on No.	Connecting Rod Journal Diameter	Connecting Rod Oil Clearance	Connecting Rod Side Clearance
1966-1971	1.1	2.1260	0.0004-0.0022	0.004-0.008	1.1438	1.7711	0.0006-0.0025	0.004-0.010
1968-1973	1.5 1.9	2.2829-2.2835	0.0009-0.0025	0.0017-0.0061	1.0807-1.0831	2.0461-2.0467	0.0004-0.0025	0.0043-0.0095

PISTON AND RING SPECIFICATIONS

All measurements in inches

Year	Engine Displace. (liters)	Piston Clearance	Ring Gap Top Compression	Ring Gap Bottom Compression	Ring Gap Oil Control	Ring Side Clearance Top Compression	Ring Side Clearance Bottom Compression	Ring Side Clearance Oil Control
1966-1971	1.1	0.0004-0.0008	0.012-0.018	0.012-0.018	0.010-0.016	0.0024-0.0034	0.0013-0.0025	0.0013-0.0025
1968	1.5	0.0012	0.0118-0.0177	0.0118-0.0177	0.0098-0.0157	0.0024-0.0034	0.0013-0.0024	0.0013-0.0024
1968-1973	1.9	0.0012	0.0118-0.0216	0.0118-0.0216	0.0098-0.0157	0.0024-0.0034	0.0013-0.0024	0.0013-0.0024

VALVE SPECIFICATIONS

Year	Engine Displace. (liters)	Seat Angle (deg)	Face Angle (deg)	Spring Test Pressure (lb @ in.) Closed Intake	Closed Exhaust	Open Intake	Open Exhaust	Stem to Guide Clearance (in.) Intake	Exhaust	Stem Diameter (in.) Intake	Exhaust
1966-1967	1.1	45	44	34 @ 1.34	34 @ 1.34	91 @ 1.04	91 @ 1.04	0.0006-0.0018	0.0014-0.0026	0.2756-0.2760	0.2748-0.2752
1968-1969	1.1	45	44	34 @ 1.34	—	91 @ 1.04	—	0.0006-0.0018	0.0014-0.0026	0.2756-0.2760	0.2748-0.2752
	1.5 & 1.9	45	44	73 @ 1.63	68.3 @ 1.39	126 @ 1.32	132 @ 1.06	0.001-0.0025	0.002-0.0039	0.3538-0.3543	0.3524-0.3528
1970	1.1	45	44	33 @ 1.28	—	99 @ 0.91	—	0.0006-0.0018	0.0014-0.0026	0.2756-0.2760	0.2748-0.2752
	1.9	45	44	73 @ 1.63	68.3 @ 1.39	126 @ 1.32	132 @ 1.06	0.001-0.0025	0.002-0.0039	0.3528-0.3543	0.3524-0.3528
1971	1.1	45	44	33 @ 1.28	—	99 @ 0.91	—	0.0006-0.0018	0.0014-0.0026	0.2756-0.2760	0.2748-0.2752
	1.9	45	44	1.57 @ 81.6	1.36 @ 71.7	1.18 @ 153.2	0.96 @ 157	0.0014-0.0025	0.002-0.0039	0.3538-0.3543	0.3524-0.3528
1972-1973	1.9	45	44	1.57 @ 81.6	1.36 @ 71.7	1.18 @ 153.2	0.96 @ 157	0.0014-0.0025	0.002-0.0039	0.3538-0.3543	0.3524-0.3528

— Not Applicable
N.A. Information not available

TORQUE SPECIFICATIONS

Year	Model	Cylinder Head Bolts (ft. lbs.)	Main Bearing Bolts (ft. lbs.)	Rod Bearing Bolts (ft. lbs.)	Crankshaft Balancer Bolts (or nut) (ft. lbs.)	Flywheel to Crankshaft Bolts (ft. lbs.)	Manifold Bolts (ft. lbs.) Intake	Exhaust
1966-1967	1.0	35	45	20	30	25	33	33
1968	1.1	35	45	20	30	25	33	33
	1.5 } 1.9 }	{ 72 cold { 58 warm	72	36	54	43	33	33
1969	1.1	35	45	20	30	25	33	33
	1.9	72 cold 58 warm	72	36	72	43	33	33
1970	1.1	35	45	20	30	25	33	33
	1.9	72 cold 58 warm	72	36	72	43	33	33
1972-1973	1.9	72 cold 58 warm	72	36	72	43	33	33

TIGHTENING SEQUENCES

Cylinder head (CIH Engines)

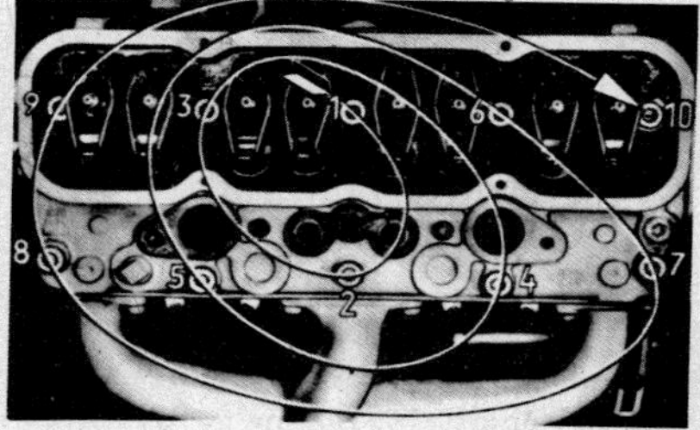

Cylinder head (OHV Engines)

Combination manifolds (CIH Engine)

CAPACITIES

Year	Model	Engine Displacement (liters)	Engine Crankcase (qts) With Filter	Engine Crankcase (qts) Without Filter	Transmission (pts) Manual 4-spd	Transmission (pts) Automatic	Drive Axle (pts)	Gasoline Tank (gals)	Cooling System (qts) Wo/AC
1966-71	All	1.1	3	2½	1¼	N.A.	1½	10½ 13¼ (GT only)	5½ w/heater
1968-71	All (except GT & 1900)	1.5 & 1.9	3¼	3	2½	10½	2½	10½	6
1969-73	GT & 1900	1.9	3¼	3	2½	10½	2½	13¼ ①②	6

① All 1900s use a gasoline tank of 11¾ gallons capacity.
② 71-73 GTs use a gasoline tank of 14½ gallons capacity.
— Not Applicable
N.A. Information not available

BRAKE SPECIFICATIONS

All measurements are given in in.

Year	Model Displacement (liters)	Master Cylinder Bore	Wheel Cylinder or Caliper Piston Bore: Front Disc	Front Drum	Rear Disc	Rear Drum	Brake Disc or Drum Diameter: Front Disc	Front Drum	Rear Disc	Rear Drum	New Pad or Lining Thickness
1966-1971	1.1	¾	N.A.	15/16	N.A. —	⅝	N.A.	7.88-7.91	N.A. —	7.88-7.91	0.197
1968-1972	1.5 & 1.9	13/16	1.77 1.89 (GT only)	N.A. —	N.A. —	⅝	9.37	N.A. —	N.A. —	9.06	0.394 front 0.20 rear
1973	1.9	13/16	1.89	N.A. —	N.A. —	⅝	9.37	N.A. —	N.A. —	9.06	0.394 front 0.20 rear

— Not Applicable
N.A. Information not available

WHEEL ALIGNMENT

Year	Model	Caster① Range (deg)	Caster① Pref. Setting (deg)	Camber Range (deg)	Camber Pref. Setting (deg)	Toe-in (in.)	Wheel Pivot Ratio (deg) Inner Wheel	Wheel Pivot Ratio (deg) Outer Wheel
1966-1969	All (except GT)	1-2	1½	½-1	¾	1/32-⅛	20	18½
	GT	1-2	1½	½-1	½	1/32-⅛	20	18½
1970	All (except GT)	1-3	2	½-1½	1	1/32-⅛	20	18½
	GT	2-4	3	½-1½	1	1/32-⅛	20	18½
1971-1973	Opel	1-3	2	½-1½	1	1/32-⅛	20	18½
	GT	2-4	3	½-1½	1	1/32-⅛	20	18½
	1900	3½-6½	5	1½N-½N	1N	⅛-3/16	20	19¼

① Permissible deviation from left to right wheel is 1 degree maximum
NOTE: All figures are given positive unless specified negative (N).

BATTERY AND STARTER SPECIFICATIONS

Year	Model	Battery: Cap. (Amp. Hours)	Battery: Volts	Battery: Grounded Terminal	Starter: Lock Test Amps	Starter: Lock Test Volts	Starter: No Load Test Amps	Starter: No Load Test Volts	Starter: No Load Test RPM	Starter: Brush Spring Tension (oz.)
1966-1967	1.1	44	12	Neg	270-310	7.5-8.5	25-45	11.5	8,000-9,500	28-32
	1.9	44	12	Neg	270-310	7.5-8.5	25-45	11.5	8,000-9,500	28-32
1968	1.1	44	12	Neg	270-310	7.5-8.5	25-45	11.5	8,000-9,500	28-32
	1.5 & 1.9	44	12	Neg	280-320	6 min	35-45	12	6,400-7,900	40-46
1969	1.1	44	12	Neg	270-310	7.5-8.5	25-45	11.5	8,000-9,500	28-32
	1.9	44	12	Neg	280-320	6 min	35-45	12	6,400-7,900	40-46
1970-1973	1.1	44	12	Neg	270-310	7.5-8.5	25-45	11.5	8,000-9,500	28-32
	1.9	44	12	Neg	280-320	6 min	35-45	12	6,400-7,900	40-46

ALTERNATOR AND REGULATOR SPECIFICATIONS

Year	Alternator: Part No. or Manufacturer	Alternator: Field Current Resistance (ohms)	Alternator: Test Output (amps.) @ 2500 RPM	Regulator: Part No. or Manufacturer	Regulator: Volts @ 2500 RPM
1966-1971	G114V28A22 (standard)	4-4.4	30 min.	ADN 1/14 V	13.5-14.5
1968-1971	K114V35A20 (option)	4-4.4	30 min.	AD 1/14 V	13.5-14.5
1972-1973	K114V35A20 (all)	4-4.4	30 min.	AD 1/14 V	13.5-14.5

WIRING DIAGRAMS

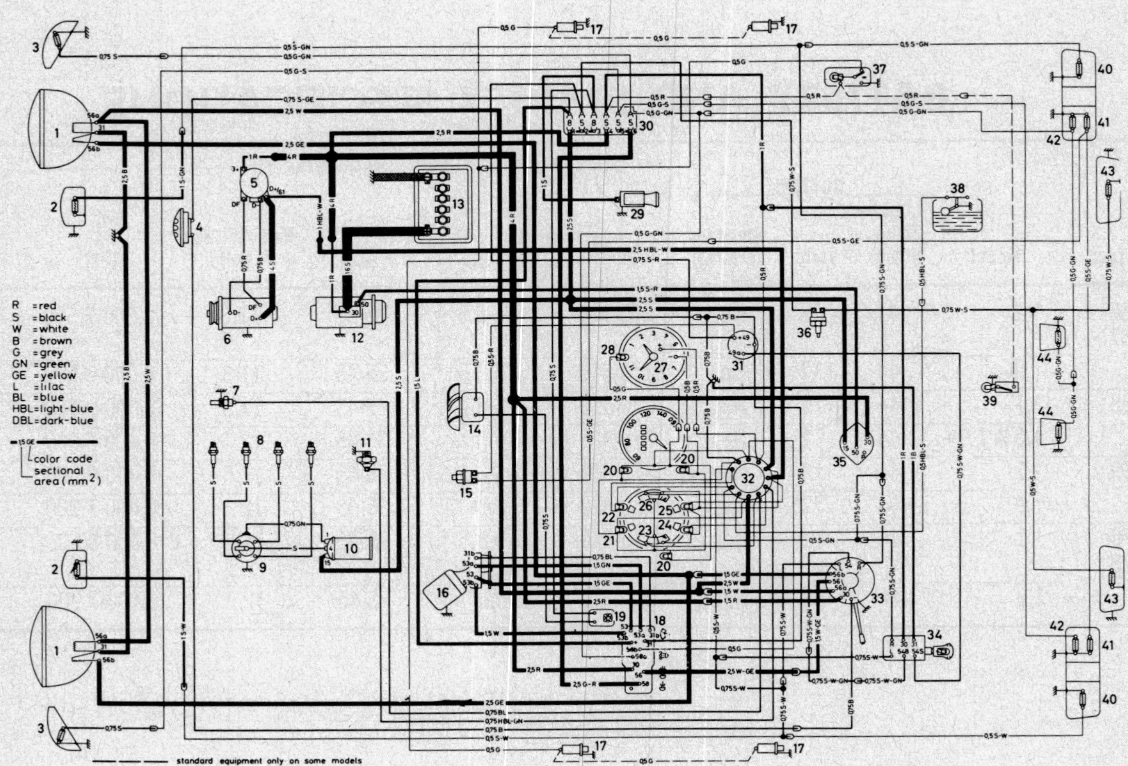

1966-67 Kadett (except Rallye)

1. Headlight
2. Front direction signal lamp
3. Parking lamp
4. Horn
5. Regulator
6. Generator
7. Temperature sending unit
8. Spark plugs
9. Distributor
10. Coil
11. Oil pressure switch
12. Starter
13. Battery
14. Heater blower motor
15. Stop light switch
16. Wiper motor
17. Interior lamp switch
18. Lights and windshield wiper switch
19. Heater blower motor switch
20. Instrument light
21. High beam lamp
22. Direction signal indicator light
23. Temperature gauge
24. Oil pressure light
25. Generator light
26. Fuel gauge
27. Clock
28. Clock light
29. Cigar lighter
30. Fuse box
31. Direction signal flasher
32. Printed circuit
33. Combination switch for turn signal, dimmer switch, horn and passing signal
34. Hazard warning switch
35. Steering—ignition lock
36. Back-up lamp switch
37. Dome light
38. Fuel gauge—tank unit
39. Luggage compartment light
40. Rear turn signal light
41. Stop light
42. Tail light
43. Back-up light
44. License plate light

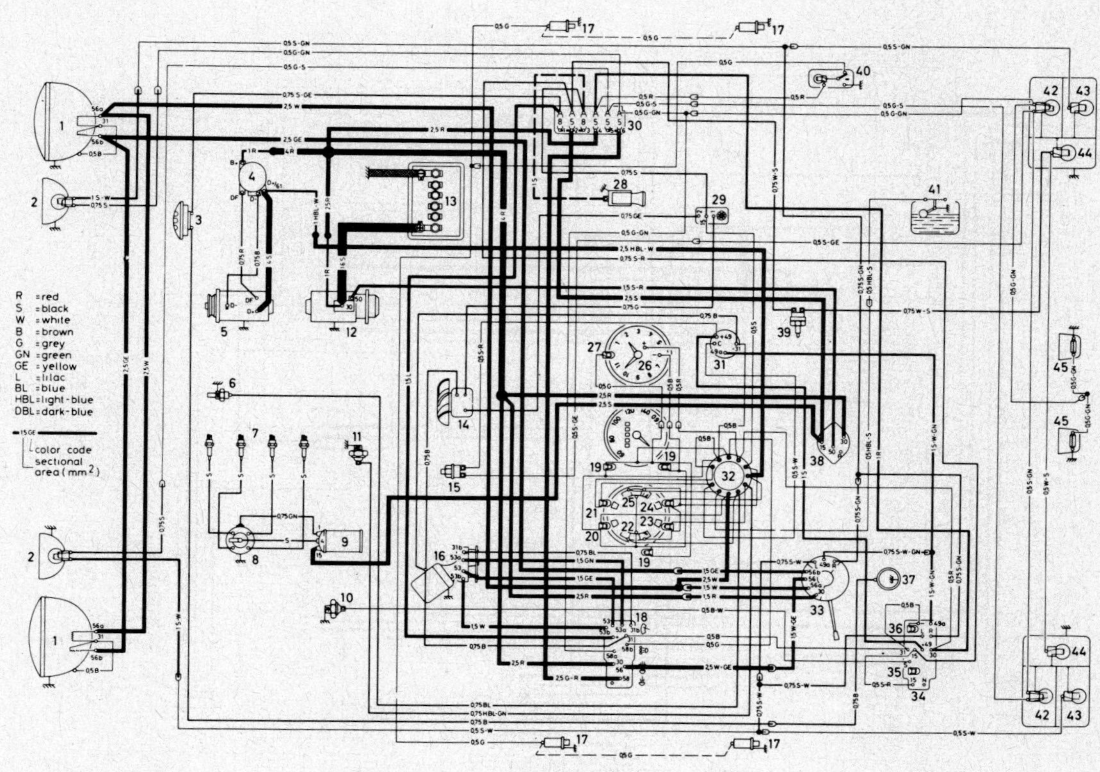

1968 Kadett

1. Headlight
2. Front direction signal lamp and parking lamp
3. Horn
4. Regulator
5. Generator
6. Temperature sending unit
7. Spark plugs
8. Distributor
9. Ignition coil
10. Switch, brake warning light control
11. Oil pressure switch
12. Starter
13. Battery
14. Heater blower motor
15. Stop light switch
16. Windshield wiper motor
17. Interior lamp switch
18. Combined lights and windshield wiper switch
19. Instrument lamp
20. High beam indicator lamp
21. Direction signal indicator lamp
22. Temperature gauge
23. Oil pressure indicator lamp
24. Generator light
25. Fuel gauge dash light
26. Electric clock
27. Electric clock light
28. Cigar lighter
29. Heater blower switch
30. Fuse box
31. Direction signal flasher unit
32. Printed circuit
33. Combination switch for turn signal and dimmer switch
34. Combined fog light, brake warning light and hazard warning light switch
35. Brake warning switch light
36. Hazard warning switch light
37. Horn button
38. Ignition and starter switch
39. Back-up lamp switch
40. Dome light
41. Fuel gauge-tank unit
42. Tail and stop lamp
43. Direction signal lamp
44. Back-up lamp
45. License plate lamp

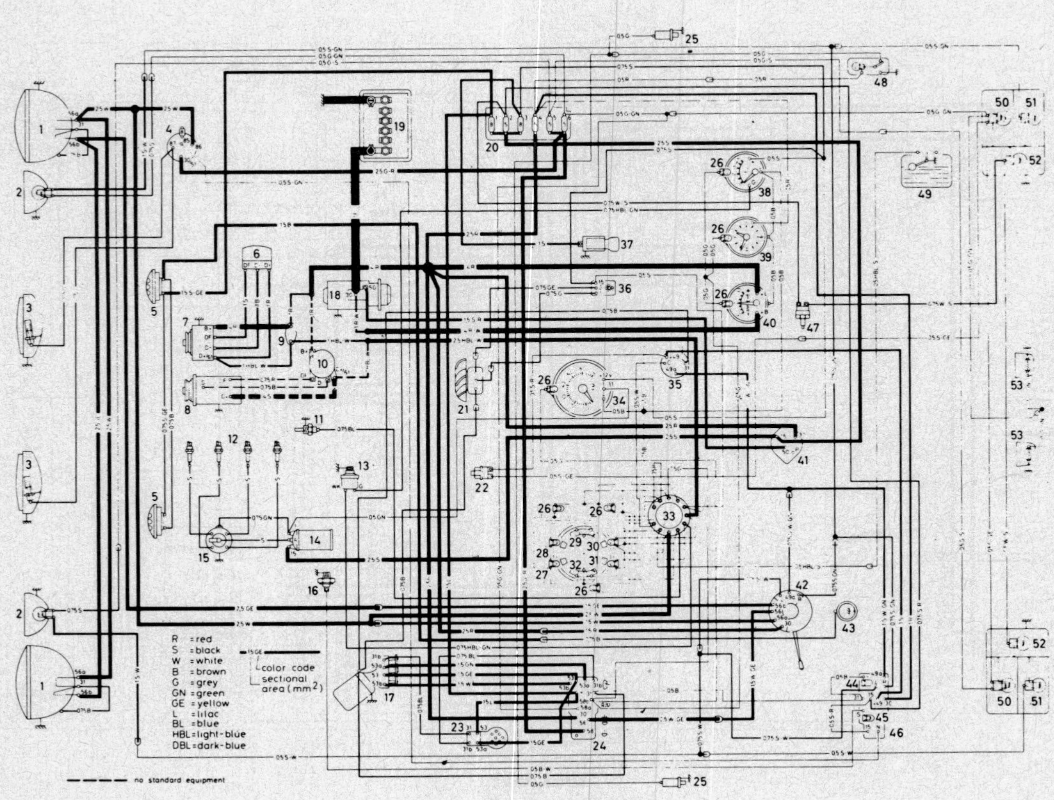

1968 Rallye

1. Headlight
2. Front direction signal lamp and parking lamp
3. Fog light
4. Fog light relay
5. Horn
6. AC regulator
7. AC generator
8. DC generator
9. Connector
10. DC regulator
11. Temperature sending unit
12. Spark plugs
13. Oil pressure switch
14. Ignition coil
15. Distributor
16. Switch, brake warning light control
17. Windshield wiper motor
18. Starter
19. Battery
20. Fuse box
21. Heater blower motor
22. Stop light switch
23. Electric windshield wiper switch (foot pump)
24. Combined lights and windshield wiper switch
25. Interior lamp switch
26. Instrument light
27. High beam idicator lamp
28. Direction signal indicator lamp
29. Fuel gauge dash unit
30. Generator light
31. Oil pressure indicator lamp
32. Temperature gauge
33. Printed circuit
34. Tachometer
35. Direction signal flasher unit
36. Heater blower switch
37. Cigar lighter
38. Oil pressure gauge
39. Electric clock
40. Ammeter
41. Ignition and starter switch
42. Combination switch for turn signal and dimmer switch
43. Horn button
44. Hazard warning switch light
45. Brake warning switch light
46. Combined fog light, brake warning light and hazard warning light switch
47. Back-up switch
48. Dome light
49. Fuel gauge-tank unit
50. Tail and stop lamp
51. Direction signal lamp
52. Back-up lamp
53. License plate lamp

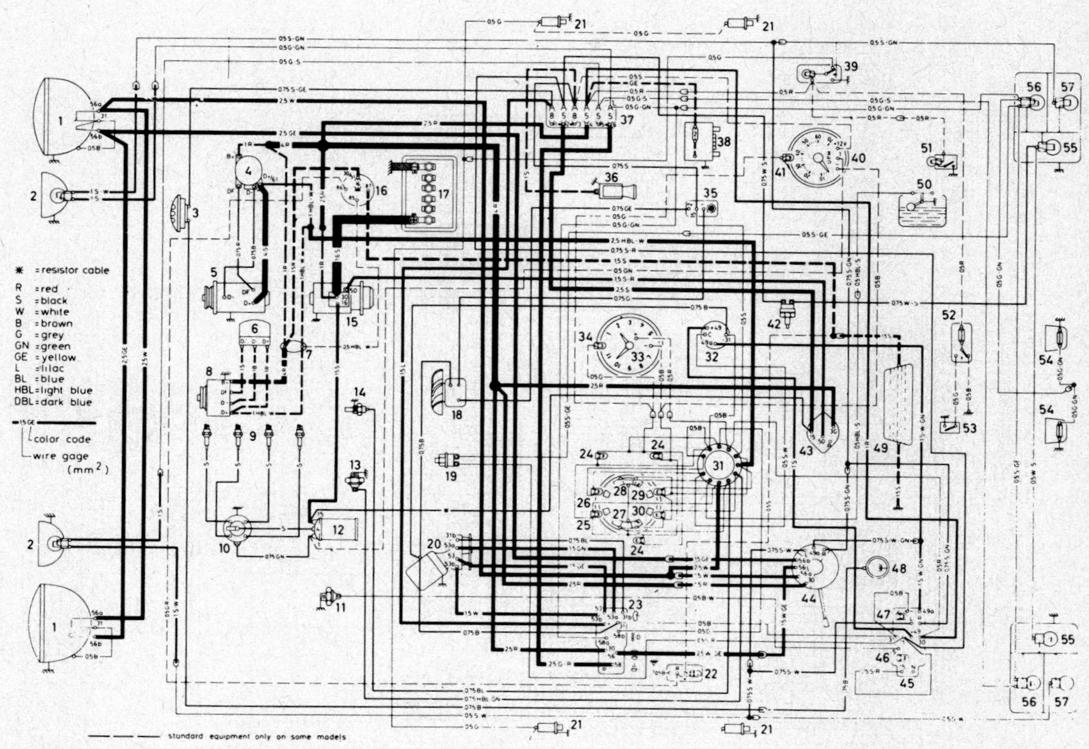

1969 Kadett

1. Headlight
2. Front direction signal lamp and parking lamp
3. Horn
4. Regulator
5. Generator
6. Alternator
7. Connector
8. Alternator—regulator
9. Spark plugs
10. Distributor
11. Low brake indicator switch
12. Coil
13. Oil pressure switch
14. Temperature sending unit
15. Starter
16. Relay, electrically heated back window
17. Battery
18. Heater blower motor
19. Stop light switch
20. Windshield wiper motor
21. Door jamb switch
22. Switch, electrically heated back window
23. Combined lights and windshield wiper switch
24. Instrument lamp
25. High beam indicator lamp
26. Direction signal indicator lamp
27. Temperature gauge
28. Fuel gauge dash unit
29. Generator light
30. Oil pressure indicator lamp
31. Printed circuit
32. Direction signal flasher unit
33. Clock
34. Electric clock light
35. Heater blower switch
36. Cigarette lighter
37. Fuse box
38. Radio
39. Dome light
40. Tachometer
41. Tachometer light
42. Back-up lamp switch
43. Ignition and starter switch
44. Combination switch for turn signal and dimmer switch
45. Fog light switch and hazard warning light switch
46. Low brake indicator light
47. Hazard warning flasher
48. Horn button
49. Electrically heated back window
50. Fuel gauge—tank unit
51. Trunk light
52. Luggage compartment light
53. Luggage compartment light switch
54. License plate lamp
55. Back-up lamp
56. Tail and stop lamp
57. Direction signal lamp

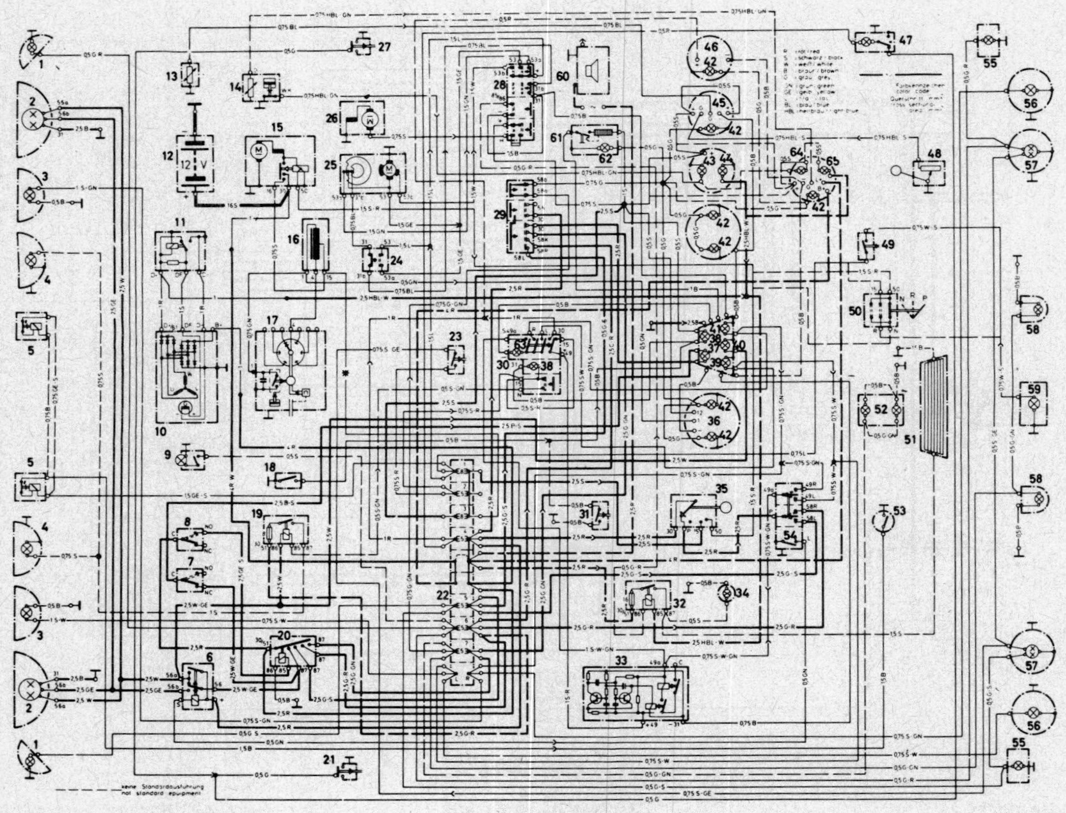

1969 Rallye

1. Headlight
2. Front direction signal lamp and parking lamp
3. Fog light
4. Fog light relay
5. Horn
6. AC regulator
7. AC generator
8. DC generator
9. Connector
10. DC regulator
11. Temperature sending unit
12. Spark plugs
13. Oil pressure switch
14. Ignition coil
15. Distributor
16. Switch, brake warning light control
17. Windshield wiper motor
18. Starter
19. Battery
20. Fuse box
21. Heater blower motor
22. Stop light switch
23. Electric windshield wiper switch (foot pump)
24. Combined lights and windshield wiper switch
25. Interior lamp switch
26. Instrument light
27. High beam indicator lamp
28. Direction signal indicator lamp
29. Fuel gauge dash unit
30. Generator light
31. Oil pressure indicator lamp
32. Temperature gauge
33. Printed circuit
34. Tachometer
35. Direction signal flasher unit
36. Heater blower switch
37. Cigar lighter
38. Oil pressure gauge
39. Electric clock
40. Ammeter
41. Ignition and starter switch
42. Combination switch for turn signal and dimmer switch
43. Horn button
44. Hazard warning switch light
45. Brake warning switch light
46. Combined fog light, brake warning light and hazard warning light switch
47. Back-up lamp switch
48. Dome light
49. Fuel gauge-tank unit
50. Tail and stop lamp
51. Direction signal lamp
52. Back-up lamp
53. License plate lamp

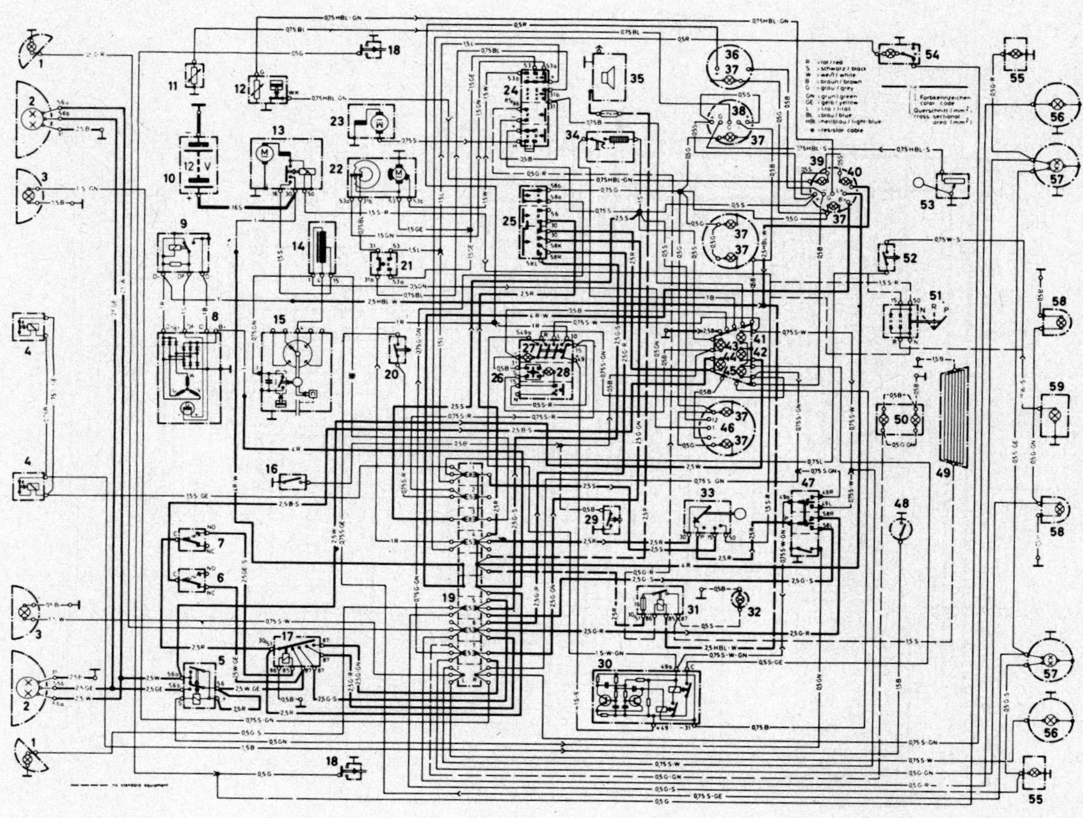

1969 Opel GT

1. Side marker and parking light
2. Headlamp high and low beams
3. Direction signal lamp
4. Horn
5. Dimmer relay
6. Headlamp indicator lamp switch
7. Headlamp relay switch
8. A.C. generator
9. Regulator
10. Battery
11. Temperature sender
12. Oil pressure sender
13. Starter
14. Ignition coil
15. Distributor
16. Brake warning light control switch
17. Headlamp relay
18. Interior lamp switch
19. Fuse box
20. Stop light switch
21. Wiper switch and pump assy
22. Windshield wiper motor
23. Blower
24. Windshield wiper, heatable back window and blower switch
25. Parking light and instrument light switch
26. Hazard warning flasher, brake system warning light switch
27. Hazard warning flasher indicator lamp
28. Brake system warning light
29. Parking brake indicator lamp switch
30. Flasher unit
31. Heatable back window relay
32. Heatable back window indicator light
33. Ignition and starter switch
34. Cigar lighter
35. Radio
36. Electric clock
37. Instrument light
38. Temperature indicator and fuel gauge dash unit
39. Oil pressure gauge with oil pressure indicator lamp
40. Ammeter with charging indicator light
41. Direction signal indicator lamp, right
42. Headlamp high beam indicator lamp
43. Parking brake indicator lamp
44. Headlamp high beam indicator lamp
45. Direction signal indicator lamp, left
46. Tachometer
47. Signal switch
48. Horn contact
49. Heatable back window
50. Selector lever indicator lamp
51. Selector lever switch
52. Back-up lamp switch
53. Fuel gauge tank unit
54. Interior lamp
55. Side marking light
56. Direction signal lamp
57. Stop and tail lamp
58. License plate lamp
59. Back-up lamp

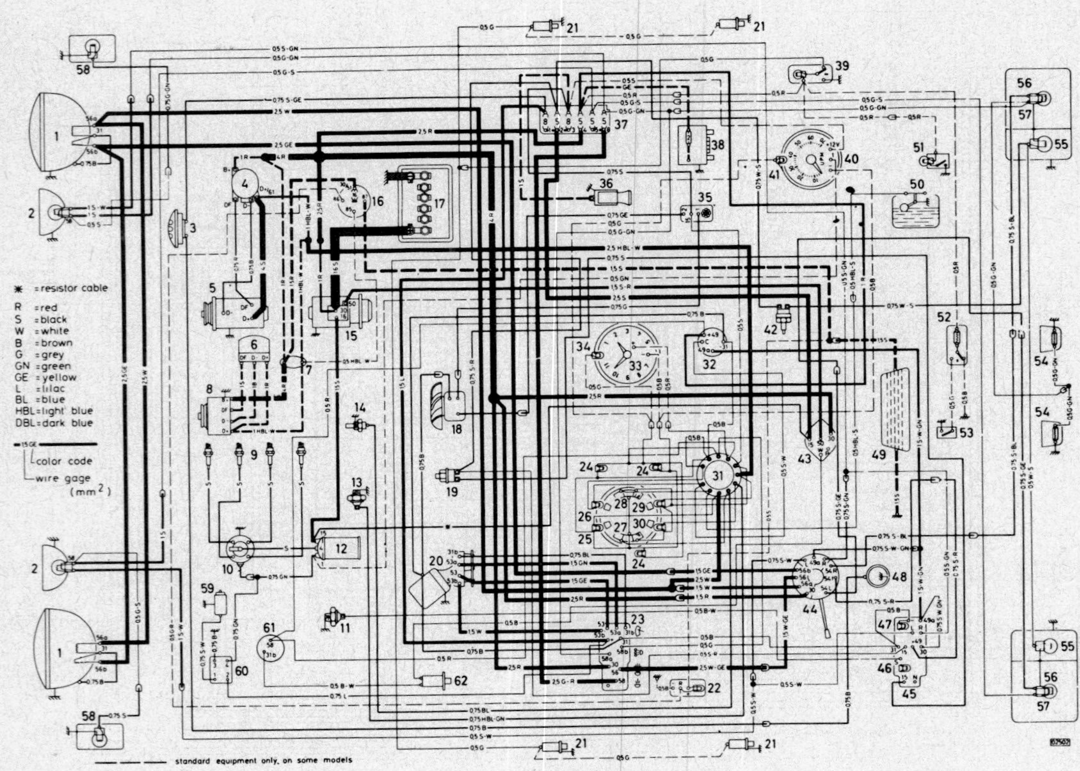

1970 Kadett

1. Headlamp, high and low beams
2. Direction signal and parking lamp
3. Horn
4. Regulator
5. Generator
6. A.C. regulator
7. Connector
8. A.C. generator
9. Spark plug
10. Distributor
11. Brake control switch
12. Ignition coil
13. Oil pressure switch
14. Temperature sending unit
15. Starter
16. Relay
17. Battery
18. Blower motor
19. Stop lamp switch
20. Windshield wiper motor
21. Door jamb switch
22. Electrically heated back window switch
23. Light and windshield wiper switch
24. Instrument lamps
25. Headlamp high beam indicator lamp
26. Direction signal indicator lamp
27. Temperature indicator
28. Fuel gauge dash unit
29. Charging indicator lamp
30. Oil pressure indicator lamp
31. Multiple plug
32. Direction signal flasher unit
33. Electric clock
34. Electric clock lamp
35. Blower switch
36. Cigar lighter
37. Fuse box
38. Radio
39. Interior lamp
40. Tachometer
41. Tachometer lamp
42. Back-up lamp switch
43. Ignition and starter switch
44. Signal switch
45. Fog lamp and hazard warning flasher switch
46. Brake control lamp
47. Hazard warning flasher indicator lamp
48. Horn button
49. Electrically heated back window
50. Fuel gauge tank unit
51. Luggage compartment lamp
52. Load compartment lamp
53. Load compartment lamp switch
54. License plate lamp
55. Back-up lamp
56. Direction signal lamp
57. Tail lamp
58. Side market light
59. Solenoid valve
60. Tachometer relay
61. Warning buzzer
62. Warning buzzer switch

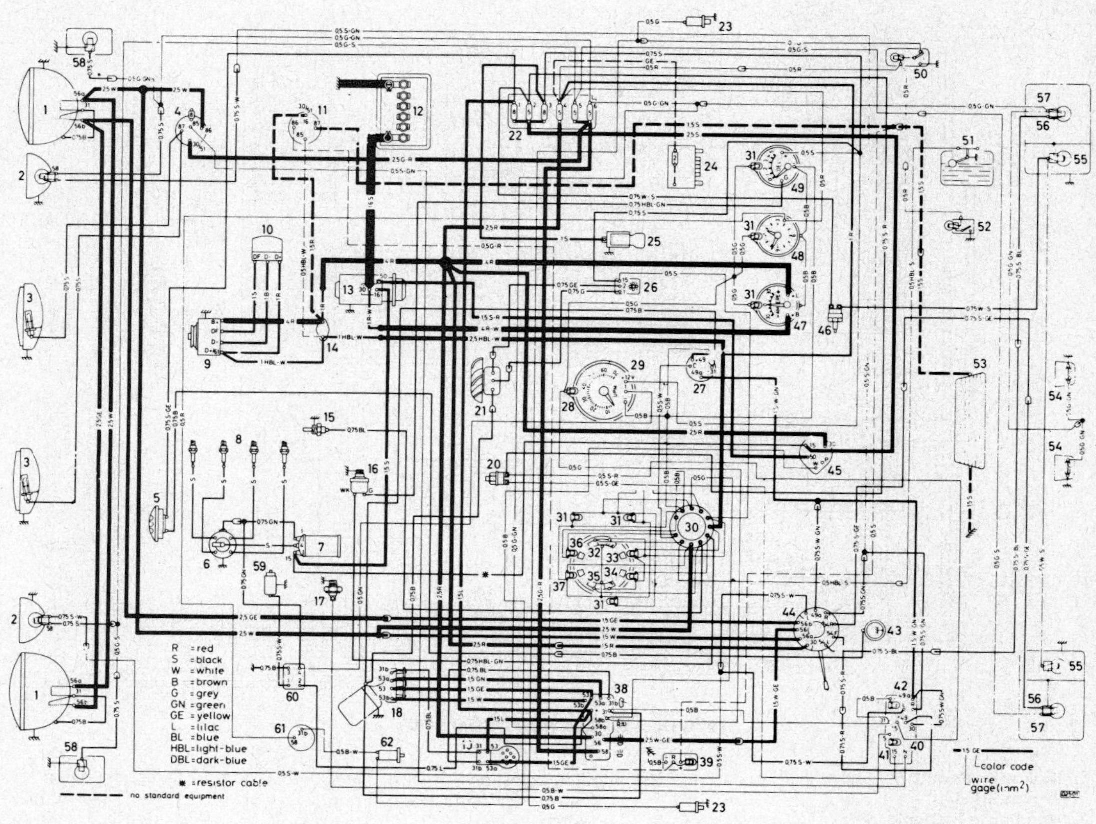

1970 Rallye

1. Headlamp
2. Direction signal lamp and parking lamp
3. Fog lamp
4. Fog lamp relay
5. Horn
6. Distributor
7. Ignition coil
8. Spark plugs
9. A.C. generator
10. Regulator
11. Electrically heated back window relay
12. Battery
13. Starter
14. Terminal
15. Temperature sending unit
16. Oil pressure switch
17. Brake warning light switch
18. Windshield wiper motor
19. Wiper switch and pump assembly
20. Stop lamp switch
21. Blower motor
22. Fuse box
23. Interior lamp switch
24. Radio
25. Cigar lighter
26. Blower motor switch
27. Direction signal flasher unit
28. Tachometer lamp
29. Tachometer
30. Multiple plug
31. Instrument lamps
32. Fuel gauge dash unit
33. Charging indicator lamp
34. Oil pressure indicator lamp
35. Temperature indicator
36. Direction signal indicator lamp
37. Headlamp high beam indicator lamp
38. Windshield wiper instrument light and light switch
39. Electrically heated back window with warning light
40. Fog lamp switch
41. Brake warning light
42. Hazard warning light switch
43. Horn button
44. Signal switch
45. Ignition and starter switch
46. Back-up switch
47. Ammeter
48. Electric clock
49. Oil pressure gauge
50. Interior lamp
51. Fuel gauge tank unit
52. Luggage compartment lamp
53. Electrically heated back window
54. License plate lamp
55. Back-up lamp
56. Direction signal lamp
57. Tail lamp
58. Side marker light
59. Solenoid valve
60. Solenoid valve relay
61. Warning buzzer
62. Warning buzzer switch

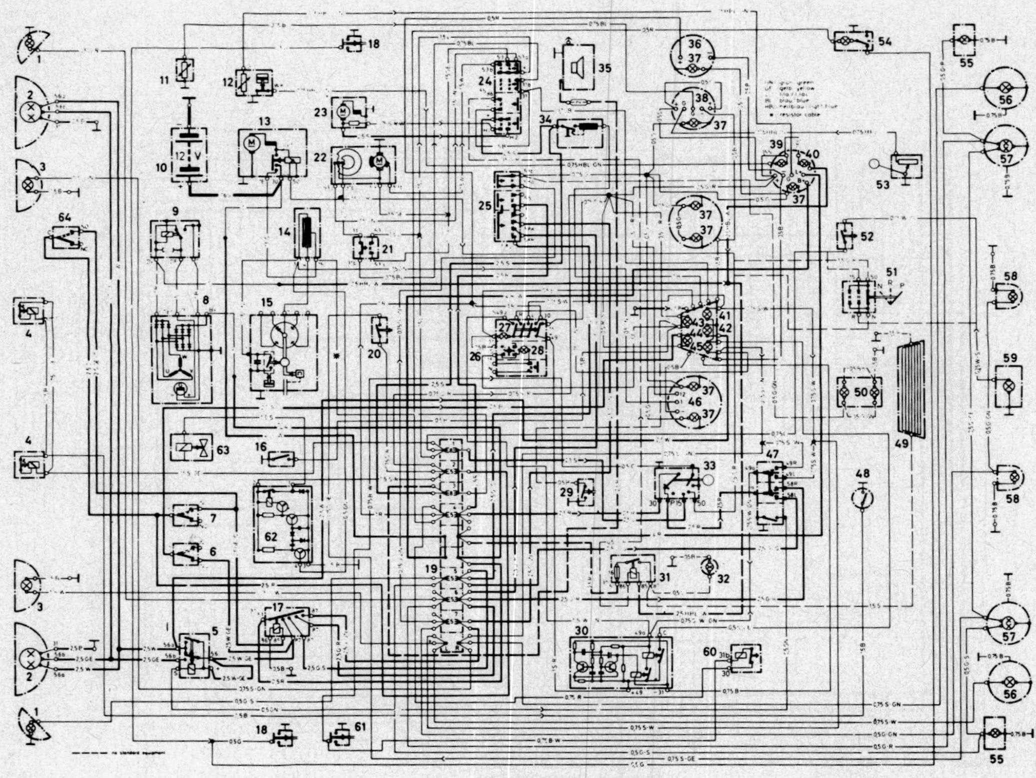

1970 Opel GT with manual transmission

1. Side marker and parking light
2. Headlamp high and low beams
3. Direction signal lamp
4. Horn
5. Dimmer relay
6. Headlamp indicator lamp switch
7. Headlamp relay switch
8. A.C. generator
9. Regulator
10. Battery
11. Temperature
12. Oil pressure sender
13. Starter
14. Ignition coil
15. Distributor
16. Brake warning light control switch
17. Headlamp relay
18. Interior lamp switch
19. Fuse box
20. Stop light switch
21. Wiper switch and pump assembly
22. Windshield wiper motor
23. Blower
24. Windshield wiper, heatable back window and blower switch
25. Parking light and instrument light switch
26. Hazard warning flasher, brake system warning light switch
27. Hazard warning flasher indicator lamp
28. Brake system warning light
29. Clutch warning switch
30. Flasher unit
31. Heatable back window relay
32. Heatable back window indicator light
33. Ignition and starter switch
34. Cigar lighter
35. Radio
36. Electric clock
37. Instrument lights
38. Temperature indicator and fuel gauge dash unit
39. Oil pressure gauge with oil pressure indicator lamp
40. Ammeter with charging indicator light
41. Direction signal indicator lamp, right
42. Headlamp high beam indicator lamp
43. Parking brake and clutch indicator lamp
44. Headlamp high beam indicator lamp
45. Direction signal indicator lamp, left
46. Tachometer
47. Signal switch
48. Horn contact
49. Heatable back window
50. Selector lever indicator
51. Selector lever switch
52. Back-up lamp switch
53. Fuel gauge tank unit
54. Interior lamp
55. Side marking light
56. Direction signal lamp
57. Stop and tail lamp
58. License plate lamp
59. Back-up lamp
60. Warning buzzer
61. Warning buzzer switch
62. Revolution relay
63. Solenoid valve
64. Headlamp relay switch

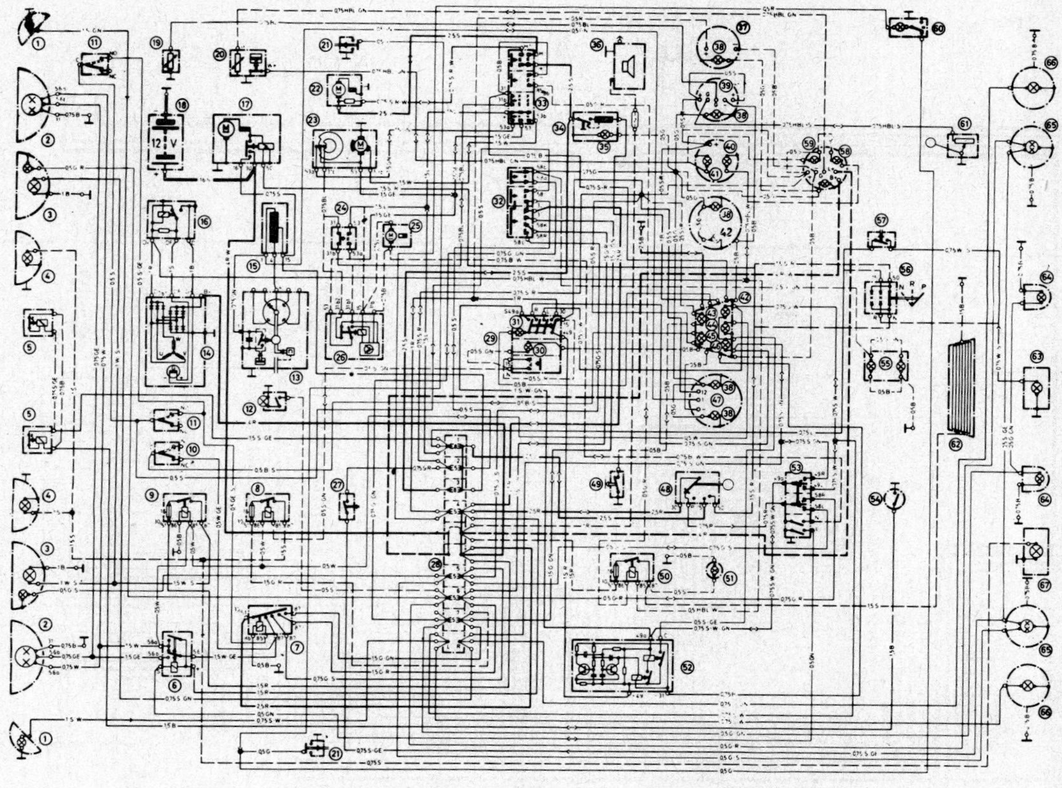

1970 Opel GT with automatic transmission

1. Direction signal lamp
2. Headlamp high and low beams
3. Long range headlamp with parking light
4. Fog lamp +)
5. Horn
6. Dimmer relay
7. Headlamp relay
8. Fog lamp and fog tail lamp relay +)
9. Long range headlamp relay
10. Headlamp indicator lamp switch
11. Headlamp and long range headlamp switch
12. Engine compartment lamp +)
13. Distributor
14. A.C. Generator
15. Ignition coil
16. Regulator
17. Starter
18. Battery
19. Temperature sender
20. Oil pressure sender
21. Interior lamp switch
22. Blower
23. Windshield wiper motor
24. Wiper switch and pump assy.
25. Windshield washer pump +)
26. Retarding relay +)
27. Stop light switch
28. Fuse box
29. Hazard warning flasher, fog lamp and fog tail lamp switch +)
30. Fog tail lamp indicator lamp +)
31. Hazard warning flasher indicator lamp
32. Parking light and instrument light switch
33. Windshield wiper, heatable back window +) and blower switch
34. Cigar lighter

+) Special Equipment

35. Cigar lighter lamp +)
36. Radio +)
37. Electric clock +)
38. Instrument lamp
39. Temperature indicator and fuel gauge dash unit
40. Charging indicator lamp
41. Oil pressure indicator lamp
42. Direction signal indicator lamp, right
43. Parking brake indicator lamp +)
44. Headlamp high beam indicator lamp
45. Headlamp indicator lamp
46. Direction signal indicator lamp, left
47. Tachometer
48. Ignition and starter switch
49. Parking brake inindicator lamp switch +)
50. Heatable back window relay +)
51. Heatable back window indicator lamp +)
52. Flasher unit
53. Signal and windshield washer switch
54. Horn contact
55. Selector lever lamp +)
56. Selector lever switch +)
57. Back-up lamp switch
58. Ammeter with charging indicator lamp +)
59. Oil pressure indicator lamp +)
60. Interior lamp
61. Fuel gauge tank unit
62. Heatable back window +)
63. Back-up lamp
64. License plate lamp
65. Tail and stop lamp
66. Direction signal lamp
67. Fog tail lamp +)

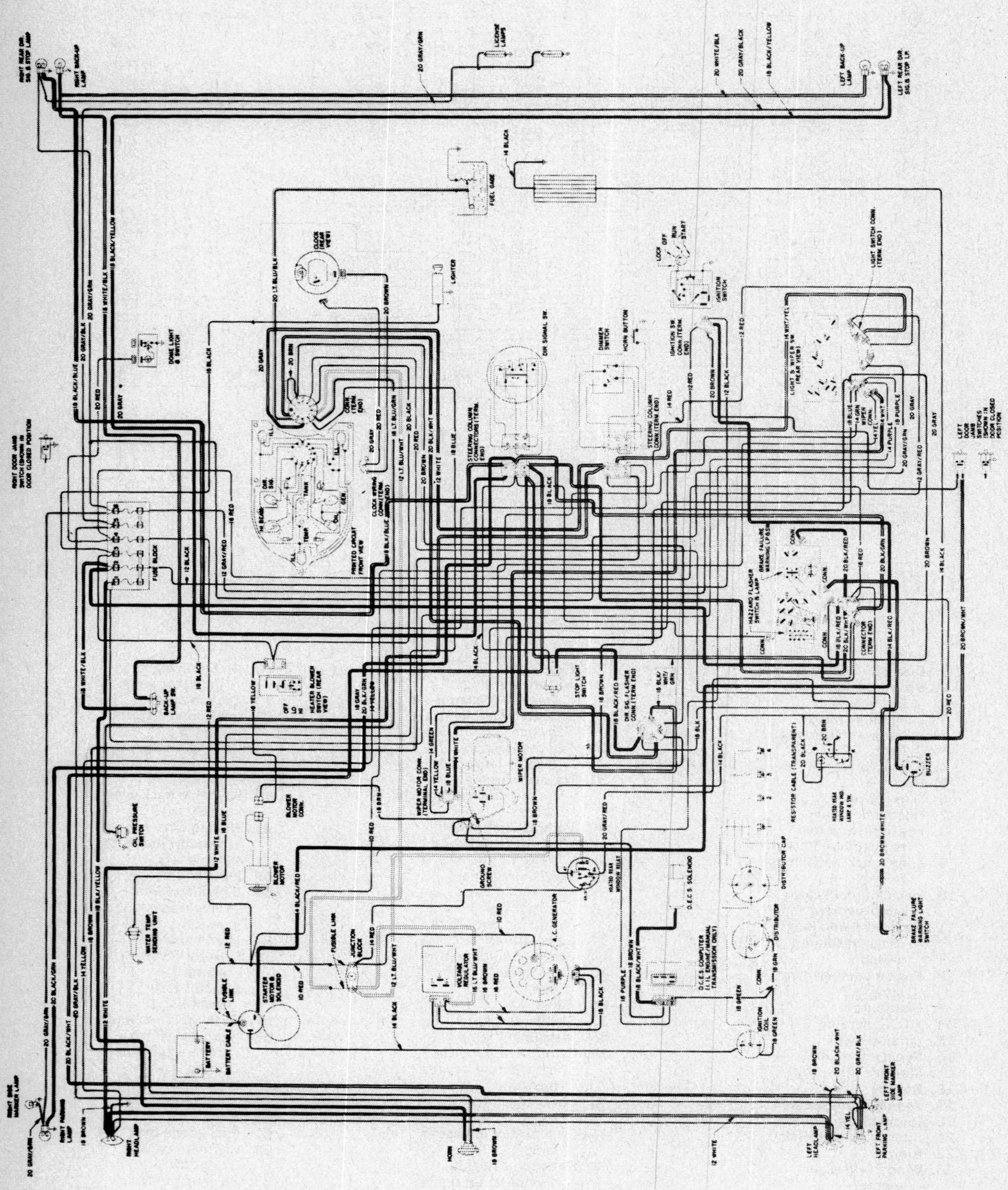

1971 Opel, 1900, and GT

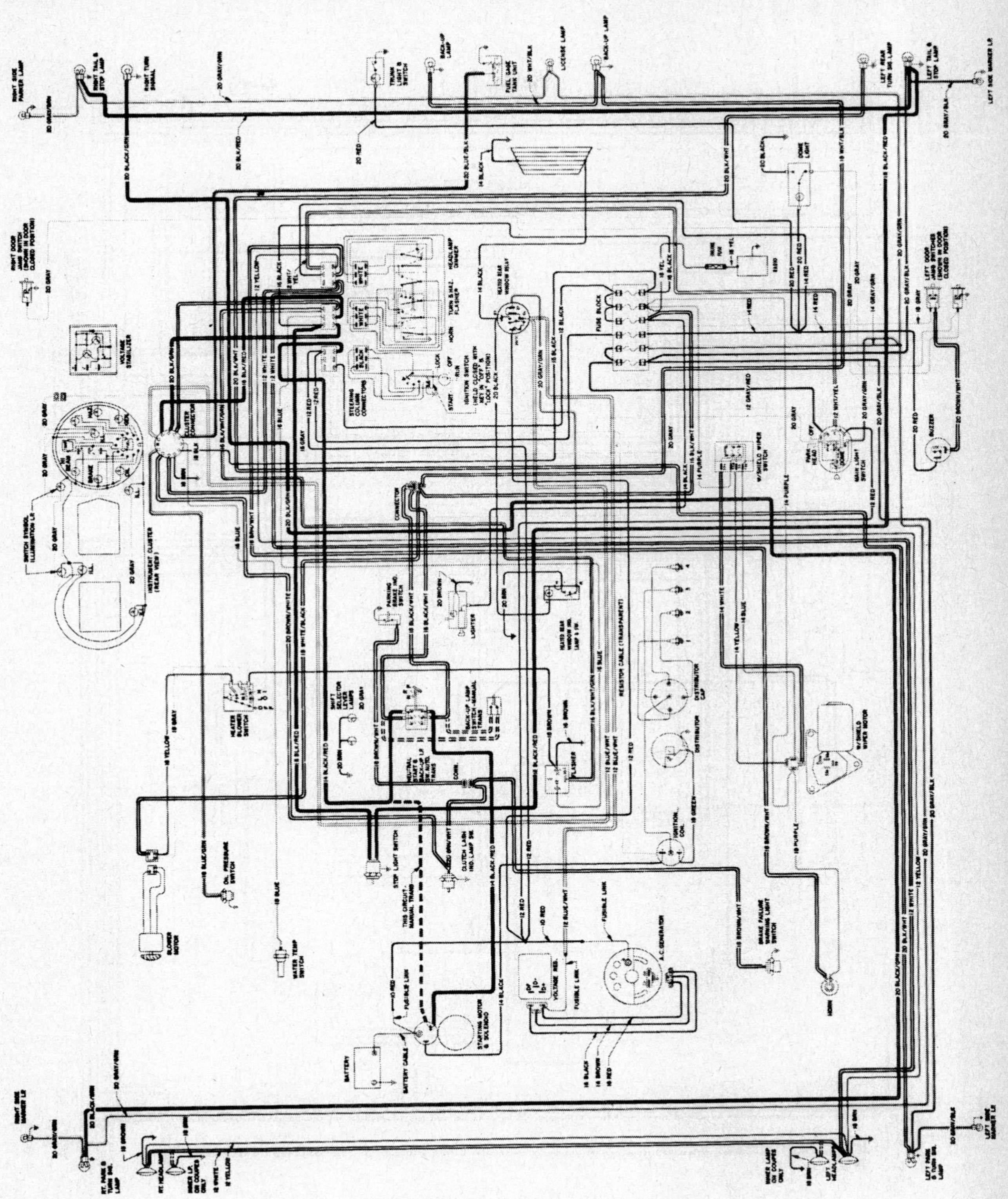

1972 Opel, 1900, and GT

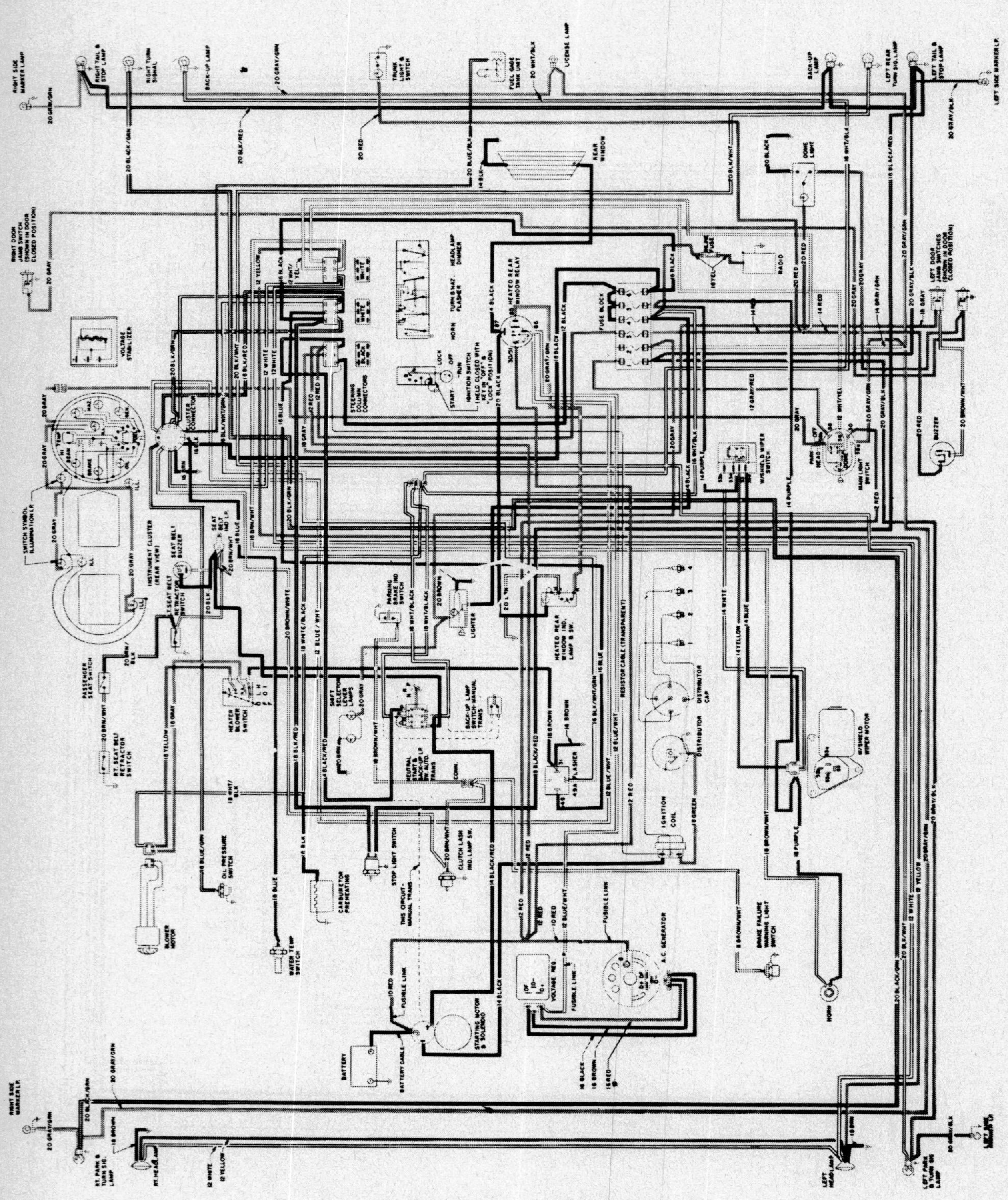

Wiring diagram—1973 Opel, 1900, & Manta

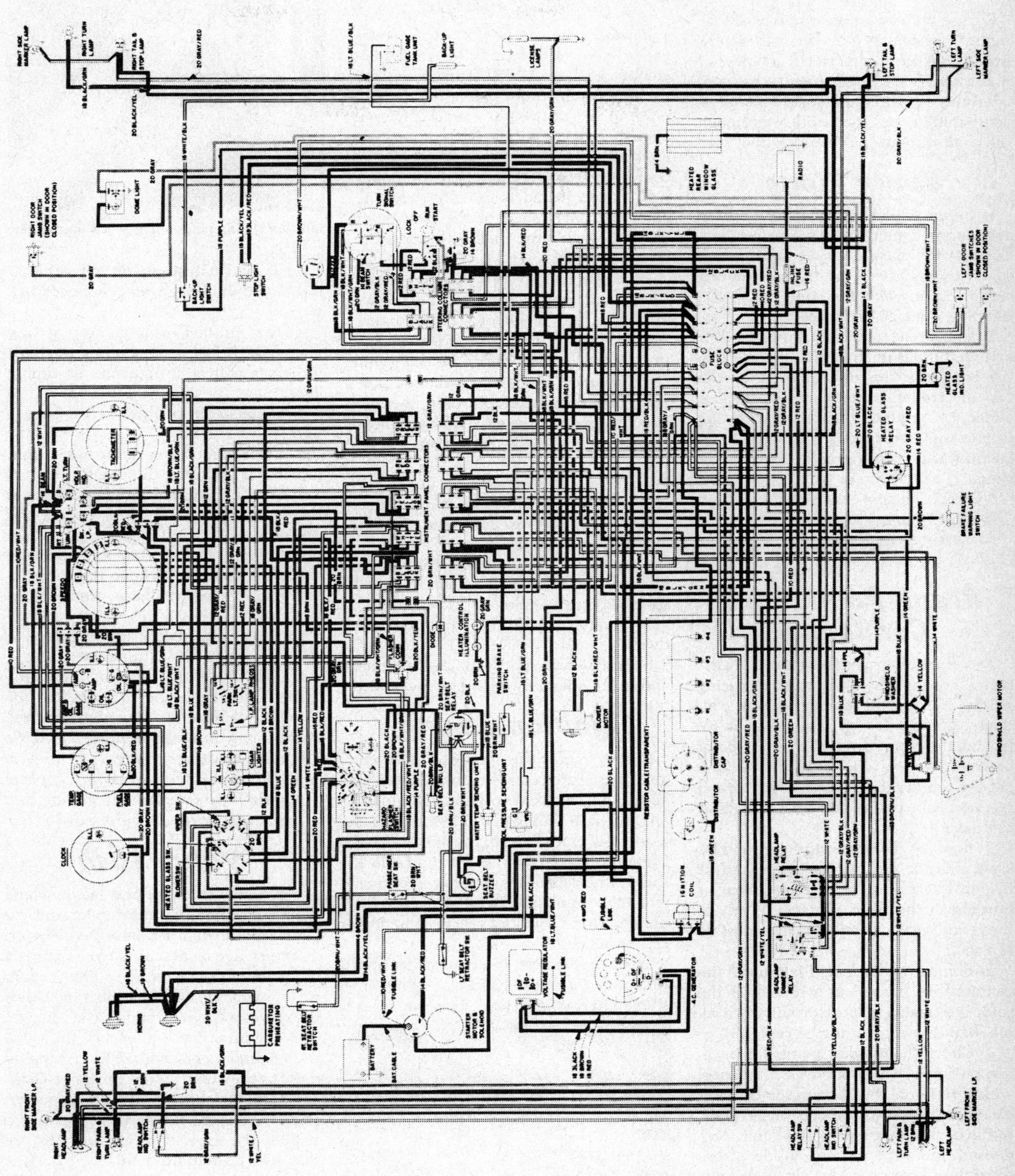

Wiring diagram—1973 GT

TUNE-UP PROCEDURES

Engine tune-up is performed to restore engine performance which has deteriorated due to normal wear and loss of adjustment. The three major areas considered in a routine tune-up are compression, ignition, and carburetion, although valve adjustment may be included.

Spark Plugs

1. Remove all spark plugs, noting the cylinder in which they were installed. Evaluate the spark plugs according to the spark plug chart in the troubleshooting section. If any of these conditions exist, the plug must be replaced.

2. Check the plug gap on both new and used plugs before installing them in the engine. If the air gap between the two electrodes is not correct, open or close the ground electrode, with the proper tool, to bring it to specifications. Such a tool is usually provided with a gap gauge.

NOTE: *Be sure to clean the seats before installing the plugs. After the correct gap is obtained, reinstall the plug.*

Break Points and Condenser

There are two rules that should always be followed when adjusting or replacing points. Neither the points nor the condenser should be replaced without replacing the other. If you change the point gap or dwell of the engine, you also change the ignition timing. Therefore, if you adjust the points, you must also adjust the timing.

1. Remove the distributor cap, and inspect it inside and out for cracks and/or carbon tracks, and for excessive wear or burning of the rotor contacts. If any of these faults are evident, the cap must be replaced.

2. Remove and inspect the rotor. If the contacts are burned or worn, or if the rotor is excessively loose on the distributor shaft, the rotor must be replaced.

3. Check the breaker points for burning, pitting or wear, and the contact heel which rests on the distributor cam for excessive wear. If defects are noted, remove the original points and condenser, and wipe out the inside of the distributor housing with a clean, dry rag.

NOTE: *A magnetic or locking screwdriver should be used to remove the points and attaching screws from the distributor.*

Lightly lubricate the contact heel and pivot point and install the new points and condenser. The points should then be set with a feeler gauge, (0.018) and rechecked with a dwell meter after the rotor and cap have been replaced.

Dwell Angle

If you adjust the points with a feeler gauge, you are setting the maximum amount the points will open when the rubbing block on the points is on a high point of the distributor cam. When you adjust the points with a dwell meter, you are measuring the number of degrees (of distributor cam rotation) that the points will remain closed before they start to open as a high point of the distributor cam approaches the rubbing block of the points.

Point gap can be set by using a feeler gauge or a dwell meter. Accurate measurements with a feeler gauge require careful, precise usage of the feelers.

1. A dwell meter should be calibrated first, switched to the four-cylinder position, and connected between the distributor primary terminal and ground.

2. Remove the distributor cap and rotor.

3. Loosen the breaker set screw approximately ⅛ turn. With a feeler gauge, check the gap between the contact point and correct it if necessary.

4. With a dwell meter, turn the reset screw of the stationary contact to obtain specified dwell angle.

5. Tighten set screw and recheck dwell.

6. Install rotor and cap, start engine, and make a final dwell angle check.

Ignition Timing

Timing marks for overhead-valve engines are located on the crankshaft pulley and timing chain cover. The 1.5S and 1.9S engines have timing marks in the form of a steel ball embedded in the flywheel and a pointer in a window on the right side of the flywheel housing. Timing is correct when the timing marks are aligned at the moment No. 1 cylinder reaches top dead center (TDC).

Basic timing is set by rotating distributor housing counterclockwise slightly until contact points just start to open.

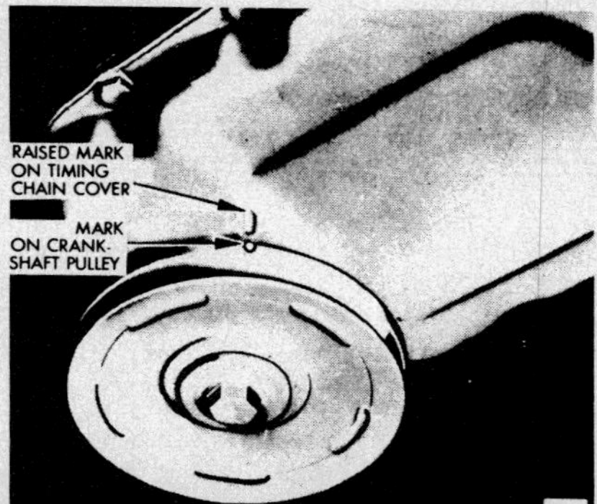

Ignition timing mark—1.1 liter engine

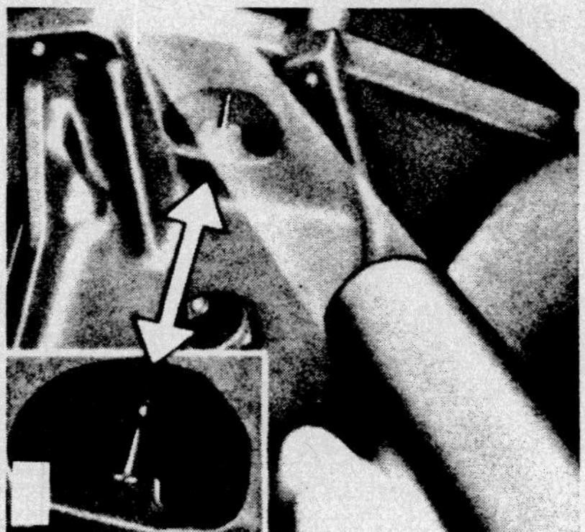
Ignition timing mark—1.5 & 1.9 liter engine

Timing marks must line up at this point. Install distributor cap, and connect spark plugs.

Adjust ignition timing after setting point gap. A fast and easy way to adjust timing is with a stroboscope or timing light.

1. Connect strobe light to No. 1 spark plug.

2. Disconnect all vacuum hoses from distributor and plug the hoses.

3. Start engine and reduce idle speed below 500 rpm for 1.1 liter engine and 700 rpm for 1.5 and 1.9 liter engines. Idle performance must be smooth. Slowing the idle is essential to keep the centrifugal advance, in distributor, from engaging.

4. Rotate distributor as necessary to align timing marks with strobe pulses.

CAUTION: *When working on a vehicle with the engine running, the following precautions must be observed: Work only in a well-ventilated area. Be certain the transmission is in neutral and the parking brake firmly applied. Always keep your hands, clothing, and tools clear of the moving radiator fan.*

Valve Lash

Valve adjustment is one factor which determines how far the intake and exhaust valves will open into the cylinder.

If the valve clearance is too large, part of the lift of the camshaft will be used up in removing the excessive clearance, thus the valves will not be opened far enough. This condition has two effects, the valve train components will emit a tapping noise as they take up the excessive clearance, and the engine will perform poorly, since the less the intake valves open, the smaller the amount of air/fuel mixture that will be admitted to the cylinders. The less the exhaust valves open, the greater the back-pressure in the cylinder which prevents the proper air/fuel mixture from entering the cylinder.

If the valve clearance is too small, the intake and exhaust valves will not fully seat on the cylinder head when they close. When a valve seats on the cylinder head it does two things; it seals the combustion chamber so none of the gases in the cylinder can escape and it cools itself by transferring some of the heat it absorbed from the combustion process through the cylinder head and into the engine cooling system. Therefore, if the valve clearance is too small, the engine will run poorly (due to gases escaping from the combustion chamber), and the valves will overheat and warp (since they cannot transfer heat unless they are touching the seat in the cylinder head).

While all valve adjustments must be as accurate as possible, it is better to have the valve adjustment slightly loose than slightly tight, as burned valves may result from overly tight adjustments.

1. *Adjust valves cold.*
2. Set each piston to TDC on the compression stroke and adjust intake valve to 0.008 in. lash and exhaust valve to 0.012 in. lash on pushrod engines.
3. Adjust valve clearance with engine *at operating temperature* (hot) and at slow idle to:

Push rod intake valve: 0.006 in.
Pushrod exhaust valve: 0.010 in.
CIH intake and exhaust valves: 0.012 in.

4. It is best to adjust valve clearances immediately after a road test.

Carburetor (See "Fuel Systems" for further adjustments)

When the engine in your Opel is running, air/fuel mixture from the carburetor is being drawn into the engine by a partial vacuum that is created by the downward movement of the pistons on the intake stroke of the four-stroke cycle of the engine. The amount of air/fuel mixture that enters the engine is controlled by throttle plate(s) in the bottom of the carburetor. When the engine is not running, the throttle plate(s) is (are) closed, completely blocking off the bottom of the carburetor from the inside of the engine. The throttle plates are connected, through the throttle linkage, to the gas pedal in the passenger compartment of the car. After you start the engine and put the transmission in gear, you depress the gas pedal to start the car moving. What you actually are doing when you depress the gas pedal, is opening the throttle plate in the carburetor to admit more of the air/fuel mixture to the engine. The further you open the throttle plates in the carburetor, the higher the engine speed becomes.

Idle Speed Adjustment

OHV Engines through 1967

Perform the following steps to adjust the idle speed of the Solex carburetors used on 1.1 liter engines.

1. If carburetor was disassembled, set the basic mixture adjustment by screwing the idle-mixture jet(s) closed until the screw gently touches its seat. Reopen the screw on Solex's 1 ½ turns.
2. Set the idle speed to highest rpm within specifications by adjusting the throttle stop screw.

Carburetor	*Standard engine*	*"S" engine*
Carter, 1.0-liter	600-800 rpm	750-800 rpm
Solex, 1.1-liter	600-800 rpm	800-900 rpm

3. Adjust idle-mixture screw(s) until the highest possible rpm is achieved.
4. Turn the throttle stop screw again, lowering rpm to normal engine idle.
5. Readjust the idle-mixture screw(s) until the engine runs perfectly. The engine should not die by quick-shutting of the throttle or quick release of the clutch pedal in Neutral.
6. Adjust throttle control linkage (if possible) so that it slips on without changing carburetor adjustment.

1968 Engines

The carburetors used on 1967 engines have an adjustable idle air-bypass system, with an air passage entrance above the throttle valve, a passage exit below the throttle valve, and an air (speed) adjusting screw in between. Idle speed adjustment is made only with the by-pass air adjusting screw, not by changing the throttle stop-screw position. However, if the stop screw setting has been disturbed accidentally, adjust it first with air cleaner installed and choke valve open. Follow the throttle stop-screw adjustment procedures below.

1. With engine idling, fully close idle air-adjustment screw (uppermost screw).
2. Adjust idle-mixture screw to achieve the highest possible idle speed. Idle speed should now be 650–700 rpm.
3. If idle is not 650–700 rpm, adjust *throttle stop screw* as required to obtain this speed. The throttle valve is now properly reset.
4. Continue with the air and mixture adjustments (taking care not to disturb the throttle stop screw) until engine idles perfectly.
5. With air cleaner installed and choke valve open, adjust idle speed with air adjusting screw (uppermost screw) to 850–900 rpm (750–800 rpm, CIH engines).
6. Adjust idle mixture needle (located in lower throttle body) until the highest possible rpm is achieved.
7. If idle speed is now over 900 rpm (800, CIH engines), readjust idle air screw to 850–900 rpm (750–800, CIH).
8. Whenever idle speed is changed, always make a careful mixture needle adjustment last.

OHV Engines—1969–71

The twin carburetor system has factory-balanced carburetors. Therefore, individual throttle stop screws and idle mixture needles should never be disturbed. If the adjustments are disturbed accidentally, a basic adjustment, as follows, must be performed to balance the carburetors.

1. Connect a tachometer, start the engine, and run it until operating temperature is reached.
2. Adjust idle speed, using idle speed screw in center unit between carburetors, to 975 rpm.
3. Adjust idle mixture screw, located at left of front carburetor, to obtain highest rpm. If idle speed exceeds 1,000 rpm, reduce speed using center unit idle speed screw, then readjust idle mixture screw for highest rpm.
4. For best performance, reduce engine speed by 50 rpm by slightly "leaning" the idle mixture screw.

On manual transmission cars, it may be necessary to adjust the deceleration mixture to obtain correct dashpot action. Connect a jumper wire between the battery positive post, and the solenoid valve terminal. This will hold the solenoid valve open so that the intake vacuum can open the diaphragm valve. Move carburetor linkage to give an engine speed of at least 3,000 rpm, then release. The engine should idle at 1,000–1,900 rpm. If it does not, turn deceleration speed screw in to decrease speed and check again.

To check operation of the computer, connect a test light between the solenoid valve and ground, then increase engine speed. Test light should come on between 2,100 and 2,500 rpm. If light does not come on, the computer must be replaced.

1969–73 1.9 Engines

The throttle valve has been properly positioned by the manufacturer and should not require adjustment. But should it be necessary to adjust it, use the following procedure.

1. Fully close the idle air adjusting screw until it is seated.
2. Adjust idle mixture needle and throttle stop screw at 650–700 rpm to obtain the best possible mixture.

NOTE: *Now that the throttle stop screw has been set, do not move it. All further adjustments are made with the idle air and mixture screws.*

3. If it was not necessary to adjust the throttle stop, proceed by raising the idle speed to 850 rpm with the idle air (speed) adjusting screw and the idle mixture needle.
4. Adjust idle mixture needle to midpoint of highest rpm range. If idle speed is too high, reset idle air speed adjusting screw to obtain 850 rpm.

Carburetor adjusting screws (twin carburetors)

1. Throttle stop screw
2. Idle mixture needle
3. Center unit air speed screw
4. Center unit mixture needle
5. Deceleration mixture screw

A. Carburetor linkage coupling screw
B. Choke stop screw

NOTE: *Always adjust idle speed after changing idle mixture.*

5. The fast idle speed is adjusted by turning the nuts on the throttle connecting rod. Shortening the rod decreases, and lengthening increases, engine speed.

6. The fast idle should be 2,700 $\pm$ 200 rpm, with the throttle lever resting on the highest step of the fast idle cam.

Synchronization of Twin Carburetors

1. Prior to adjusting the carburetors, the engine must be at operating temperature.

2. Loosen the screw on the coupling between the carburetors, leaving clearance between the screw and the shaft pick-up.

NOTE: *On cars equipped with Opel Emission Control System, shut off the center unit by pulling the hose from the front carburetor to the center unit and plugging the carburetor nipple and the intake manifold vacuum port.*

3. Back out the throttle idle adjust screw and close the idle mixture screw on the front carburetor, so that the engine runs on the rear carburetor only.

4. Start the engine and adjust the rear carburetor so that the engine runs as smoothly as possible at 700 rpm.

5. Reverse the procedure and adjust the front carburetor in a similar manner.

NOTE: *Record the number of turns as the idle mixture screw is closed on the rear carburetor.*

6. Back out the idle mixture screw on the rear carburetor the number of turns recorded, and adjust the idle, using the rear throttle screw, to 1,000 rpm.

ENGINE ELECTRICAL

Distributor

Removal and Installation

Kadett and GT

1. To overhaul distributor, remove distributor cap, place No. 1 cylinder in the firing position (timing marks aligned).

2. Disconnect vacuum line and primary ignition wire, and remove bolt, clamp and distributor.

3. Replace paper gasket on distributor housing if necessary.

4. Install distributor with vacuum advance unit pointing rearward and parallel with engine.

5. Turn rotor to align mark on tip with breaker point hold-down screw so that shaft seats itself.

6. If distributor was set in wrong, rotor will be 180° out of place.

7. Set distributor into position and hand tighten bolt.

8. The mark on the rotor should be nearly aligned with mark on distributor housing.

9. Align marks on rotor tip and housing, set breaker point gap or dwell angle, and adjust ignition timing.

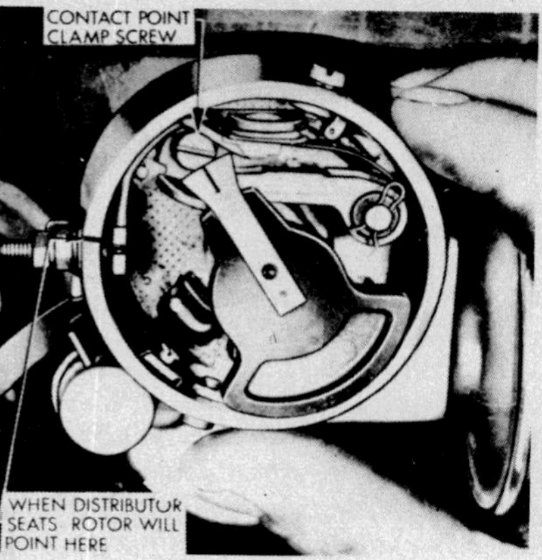

Distributor installation alignment marks

Alternator

The alternating current generator is a continuous-output, diode rectified generator. The rotor, which carries the field winding, is mounted in a ball bearing at both ends. Each bearing has a sealed-in grease supply which eliminates the need for periodic lubrication. Two brushes and two slip rings are used. One brush conducts the current provided by the voltage regulator to one end of the field coil; the other brush conducts the current from the other end of the rotating field coil to ground.

Alternator Precautions

If the generator will not meet output specifications when supplied with full field current, the assembly must be replaced. If the voltage regulator does not limit maximum voltage within specifications, adjust the voltage regulator. If steady voltage regulation, within specifications, cannot be achieved, the voltage regulator assembly must be replaced.

Removal and Installation

1. Disconnect battery ground strap.

2. Unplug wiring connector from generator.

3. Disconnect battery lead from generator.

4. Remove adjusting brace bolt, lockwasher, plain washer and nut.

5. Loosen pivot bolt. Push generator inward and remove belt from pulley.

6. Drop generator down and remove pivot bolt, nut, lockwasher and plain washer.

7. Remove generator.

8. Hold generator in position and install pivot bolt, plain washer, lockwasher and nut finger tight.

9. Install generator belt.

10. Install adjusting brace bolt, lockwasher, plain washer and nut finger tight.

11. Position a belt tension gauge on belt. Pull generator outward until gauge reads 45 lbs, then tighten adjusting brace bolt.

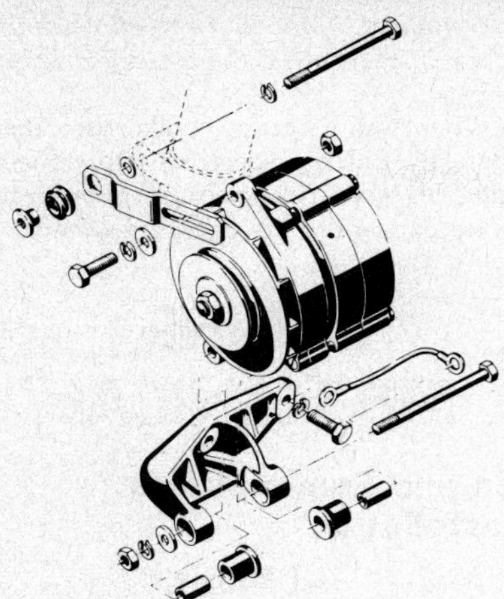

Alternator installation (CIH Engine)

12. Tighten generator pivot bolt.
13. Connect battery lead to generator.
14. Plug three-way wiring connector into generator and engage safety catch.
15. Connect battery ground strap.

Alternator and regulator tests

Test Current Output

1. Check alternator belt condition and tension. Adjust to 45 lbs.
2. Install a battery post adapter at the positive post of the battery.
3. Connect ammeter leads to adapter with red lead toward alternator and black lead toward battery positive post. Connect ground lead to battery negative post.

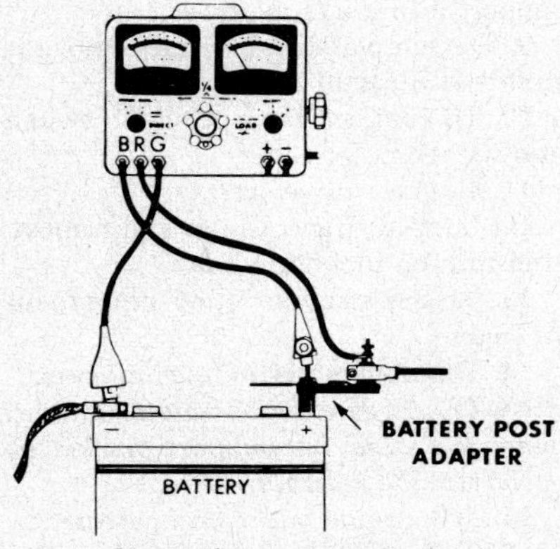

Connecting ammeter leads

4. Connect voltmeter across the battery: red lead at alternator side of battery post adapter and black lead to battery negative post.
5. Connect a tachometer to ignition system.
6. Make sure all electrical accessories are turned off. Start engine with battery post adapter switch closed; open switch as soon as engine is started.
7. Adjust engine speed to 2500 RPM.
8. Turn tester control knob to "LOAD" position and adjust knob to obtain highest possible ammeter reading. Output must be 30 amperes minimum. If output is okay, proceed to voltage regulator test below.
9. If output is low, defect may be in alternator or in regulator. To eliminate regulator, supply field current direct to cause full alternator output. On a D.C. generator system, *disconnect field lead (DF) from regulator* and connect a jumper from end to ground; on an A.C. generator system, unplug three-way connector from regulator, and plug in a jumper between the red and black leads.

Generator output check

NOTE: *Retest as described in Steps 7 and 8. In either charging system, if output is still low, generator is faulty and must be replaced.*

10. If output (using field jumper) is now okay, defect is in the regulator or wiring harness. Check all wiring connections. If all wiring is okay, try replacing regulator; if output now tests okay (without using field jumper), you have found the trouble.

NOTE: *Always follow-up with a voltage regulator test.*

Adjusting Voltage Regulator

1. Always test alternator output first. Leave all test instruments connected, but make sure field jumper is removed, if used.
2. With engine speed at 2500 RPM, turn tester control knob to "¼ OHM" position. Make sure all electrical accessories are turned off. After voltage reading stabilizes, any reading between 13.5 and 14.5 volts is okay.
3. If voltage reading is out of limits, remove regulator cover and adjust voltage regulator armature spring tension to obtain a middle reading of 14.0 volts. If reading fluctuates, voltage contacts are dirty.
4. Replace regulator cover and re-check voltage setting. A steady voltage reading between 13.5 and 14.5 volts means voltage regulator is okay.
5. Adjust engine speed to specified idle.

Cut-out Relay Adjustment Generator Equipped Cars Only

1. Connect voltmeter positive lead to regulator "61" (lower rear) terminal. Negative lead to ground.
2. Connect ammeter in series with "B+" (upper rear) terminal and disconnected red wire.
3. Increase engine speed while observing voltmeter. Voltage will increase until cutout relay points close, then drop slightly as circuit is completed to battery. The highest voltmeter reading, just before it drops off, is the closing voltage. *Closing Voltage: 12.3–13.4 Volts*
4. If closing voltage is not within limits, remove regulator cover (as in "voltage check") and adjust closing voltage, as required, by bending cutout relay spring support. Increase spring tension to increase closing voltage; -decrease spring tension to decrease closing voltage.
5. Reinstall cover and re-check cutout relay closing voltage with cover in place.

STARTER

Starter removal and Installation

1.1 Engine

1. Disconnect battery. Remove air cleaner for easier access.
2. Hoist front of car and support it securely.
3. Remove right side motor mount bolt from frame attachment.

Starter installed (OHV Engine)

4. Disconnect exhaust pipe at manifold.
5. Loosen bolts on the left side motor mount.
6. Jack engine up on starter side and remove the right side motor mount from attaching points on engine.
7. Disconnect all wiring and remove starter mounting bolts.
8. The starter is installed by reversing the removal steps.

CAUTION: *Care should be taken not to break seal on oil pan when removing the motor mount from engine.*

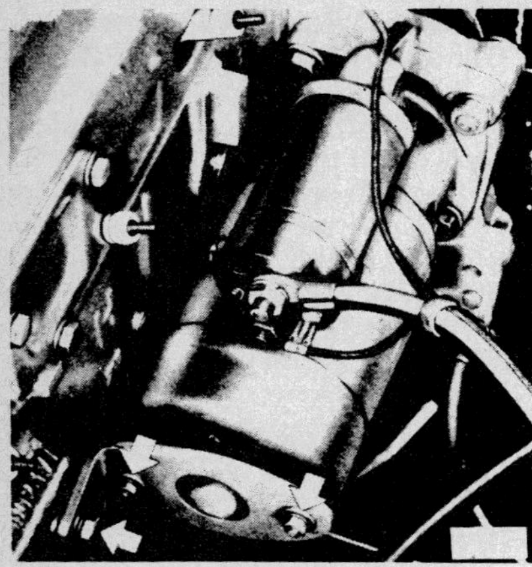

Starter installed (CIH Engine)

1.5 &1.9 Engines

1. Disconnect battery and starter wiring.
2. Unbolt and remove starter support bracket.
3. Remove starter bolts and nuts.
4. To remove starter, you must drive out stud.
5. To install the starter, reverse the removal steps.

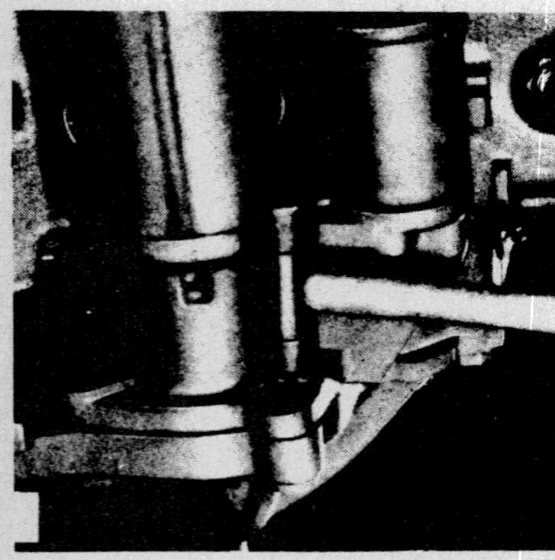

Removing starter stud (CIH Engine)

Starter Drive Replacement (all engines)

1. Remove the field connecting nut from terminal on the solenoid.
2. Remove screws which hold solenoid to the drive housing.
3. Remove two "thru" bolts and the solenoid shift lever pivot bolt.
4. Remove the armature and drive assembly, with the shift lever, from the drive housing.
5. To remove the drive assembly from the armature, tap the pinion stop retainer toward the armature to uncover the snap ring.
6. Remove snap ring from shaft, then slide pinion drive assembly from the shaft.
7. Clean all parts by wiping with a clean dry cloth.

NOTE: *Do not use any degreaser or high temperature solvents. This will damage the insulation and will cause shorts in windings.*

8. Carefully inspect all parts for wear or damage and replace all unserviceable parts.

NOTE: *When soldering use resin flux only.*

9. Reassemble the starter by reversing the previous steps. Make sure that the pinion stop retainers and assist spring are in proper position.

BATTERY

Opels use a 12 volt, 77 amp-hour Delco battery. The electrical system requires that the battery produce at least 9 volts while starter is cranking the engine.

Batteries should be checked periodically for proper output and good, clean connections. Inspect the case for cracks and weakness. Check the density (specific gravity) with a hydrometer.

NOTE: *All readings for each cell should produce a nearly equal charged condition. If one or two cell readings are sharply lower, the battery is defective.*

When jump starting, make sure that the cable polarity is correct. Disconnect cables as soon as engine starts in order to avoid damage to the charging system.

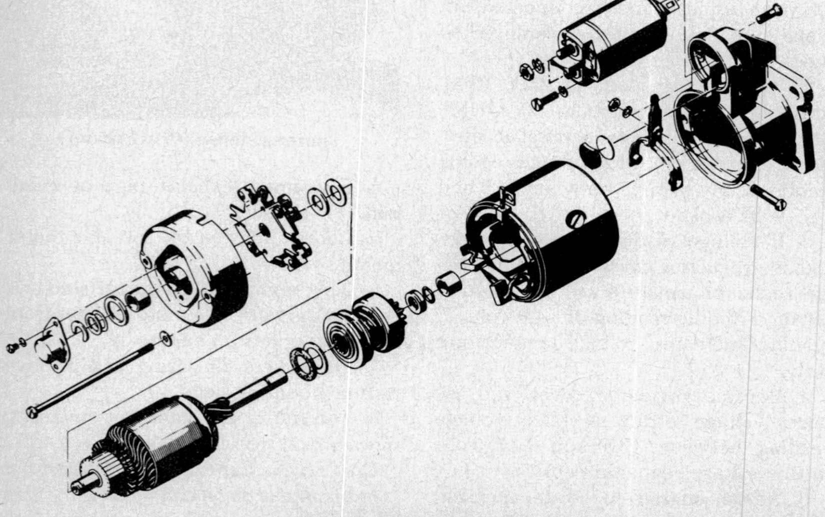

Starter motor exploded view

ENGINE MECHANICAL

Engine Removal and Installation

1.1 Engine

1. Mark hood hinge location and remove hood.
2. Disconnect battery cables.
3. Drain radiator. Disconnect and remove radiator, radiator hoses, and heater hoses.
4. Remove shift lever by placing shifter in Neutral, raising boot cover, and unscrewing locking capt. Push locking cap down and turn it counter clockwise. Some models use a snap ring to retain the shift lever. Remove snap ring and lift shifter out.
5. Detach throttle linkage from carburetor and remove the rear support, fuel lines, vacuum lines, heater control cables, and electrical connections to starter and generator.
6. Unbolt exhaust pipe from manifold.
7. Remove oil filter housing and filter.
8. Jack up front and rear of car and support it in a safe manner.
9. Detach clutch cable and remove it from transmission.
10. Disconnect back-up light switch and speedometer cable.
11. Remove drive shaft.
12. Support transmission and remove transmission mounting bolts.
13. Attach suitable lifting equipment to engine.
14. Disconnect both motor mounts.

NOTE: *Engine rubber motor mounts are the same, but support bracket on starter side is larger.*

15. Lift engine out of compartment.
16. To install the engine, lower engine into compartment.
17. With engine still supported, install the motor mounts, but do not tighten.
18. Install tramsmission mounting bolts. After all mounting bolts are in position, tighten all bolts.
19. Install oil filter housing using a new gasket to prevent leakage.
20. Reversing removal procedures, install all electrical connections, heater hose, linkage to carburetor, etc..

1.5 & 1.9 Engines

NOTE: *This engine assembly removal is only possible by lowering the engine out through the bottom of the car.*

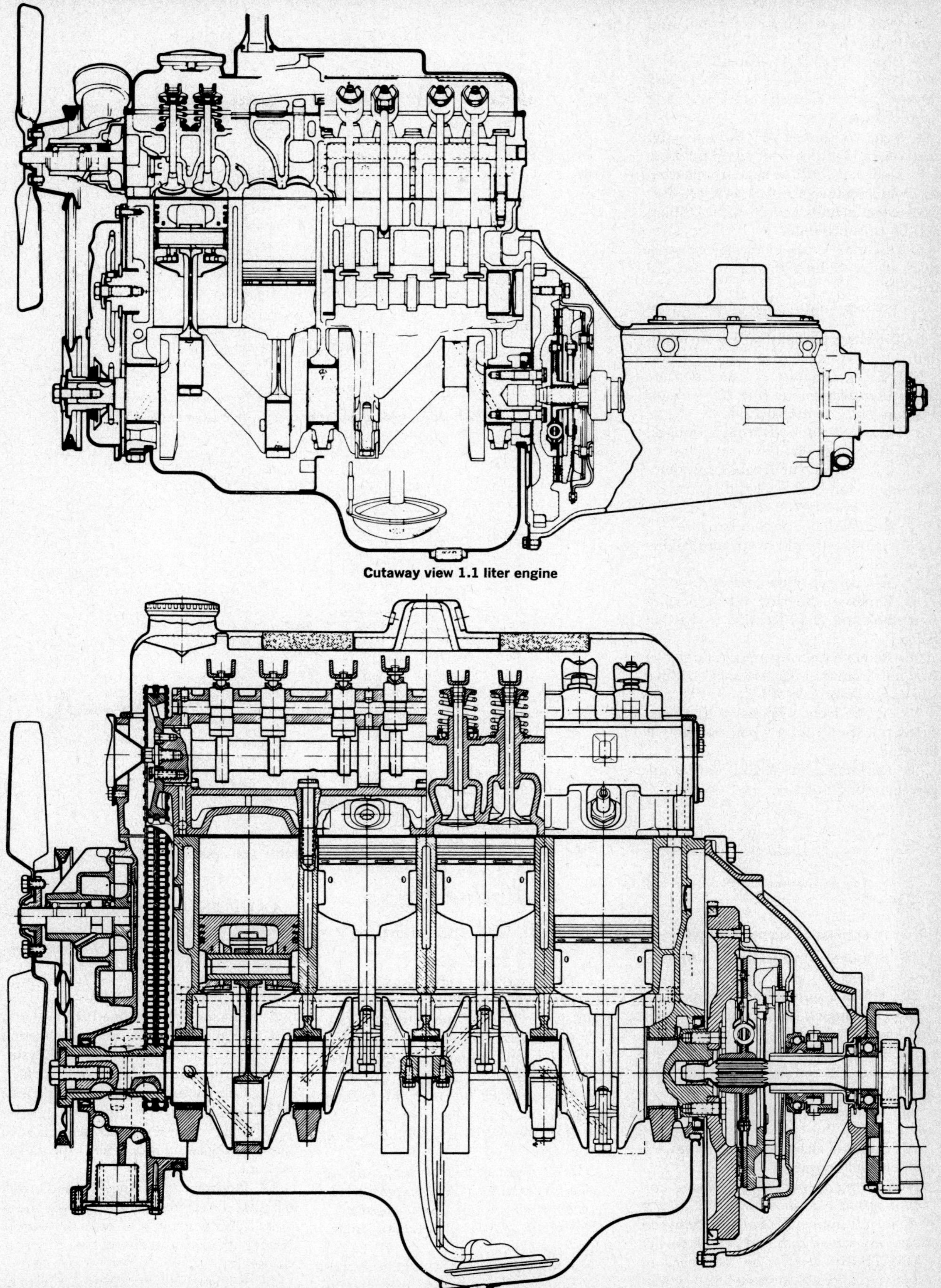

Cutaway view 1.1 liter engine

Cutaway view 1.9 liter engine

1. Mark hood hinge location and remove hood.
2. Disconnect battery cables.
3. Drain radiator. Disconnect and remove radiator, radiator hoses, and heater hoses.
4. Remove shift lever by removing snap ring and lifting lever out of position.
5. Detach throttle linkage from carburetor and remove the rear support, fuel lines, vacuum lines, heater control cables, and oil pressure lines.
6. Disconnect all electrical connections at the generator, starter, and distributor.
7. Remove T-fitting from intake manifold.
8. Disconnect exhaust pipe from manifold.

NOTE: *To facilitate reinstallation, do not completely unscrew the exhaust flange bolts on inboard side.*

9. Raise vehicle, both front and back, and support it safely.
10. Disconnect clutch cable, speedometer cable, and back-up lights.
11. Remove drive shaft.
12. Remove tailpipe and hangers.
13. Remove ground strap from engine to side rail.
14. Disconnect brake lines at hoses.
15. Remove steering shaft clamp pinch bolt and mark location of shaft on flange.
16. Remove steering mast guild sleeve stop bolt from mast jacket bracket. Move steering column out of way.
17. Attach front suspension to a hoist to keep it from tilting when assembly is lowered.
18. Disconnect shock absorbers at upper mounting bracket.

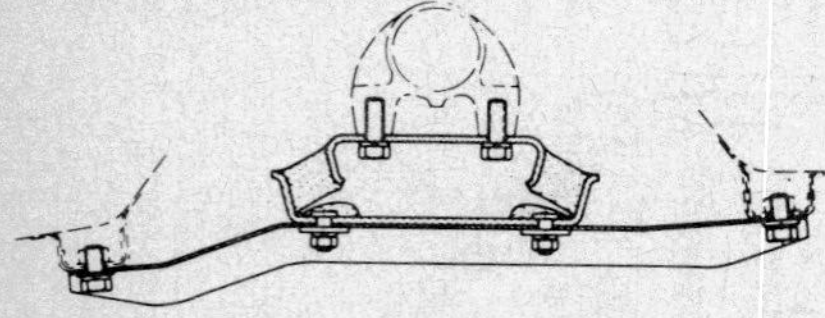

Transmission support bracket

19. Remove transmission support bracket bolts.
20. Attach a suitable hoist to engine.
21. Disconnect front cross member and lower complete assembly to floor.
22. To install, raise the complete engine and suspension into place and start all mounting bolts.
23. Tighten all bolts after engine has been aligned into position.
24. Reinstall all components by reversing removal operation.

NOTE: *When installing steering column, push column downward until a ⅛ in. clearance is obtained between steering wheel hub and switch cover.*

CAUTION: *'It will be necessary to bleed the brake system after system has been installed in car.*

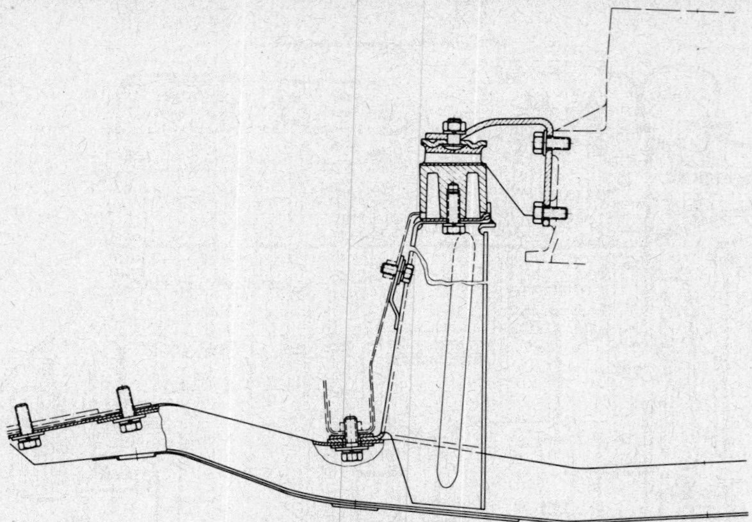

Left side engine support bracket with crossmember

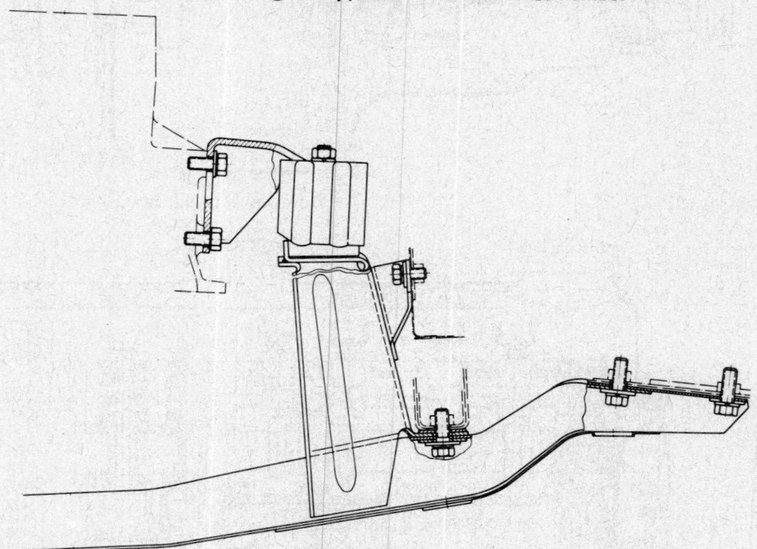

Right side engine support bracket with crossmember

Cylinder Head

Removal and Installation

1.1 Engine

1. Drain radiator and cylinder block. The drain plug for block is located on right side in front of motor mount.
2. Disconnect throttle linkage from carburetor and disconnect the choke control cable.
3. Detach fuel lines, vacuum lines, heater hoses, and radiator hoses.
4. Remove carburetors and rocker arm cover.

NOTE: *Remove O-ring seal from between carburetor and manifold. Replace it with a new one if possible.*

5. Unbolt intake and exhaust manifolds.
6. Remove rocker arms and push rods.
7. Remove the cylinder head bolts. A special star wrench must be used.

CAUTION: *Remove the cylinder head when it is cold, and in reverse of the tightening sequence, to prevent warpage.*

8. Remove cylinder head from block.
9. Clean piston tops and combustion chambers. Throughly clean all gasket surfaces on the cylinder head and block.
10. Lubricate cylinder walls and clean all foreign matter from the area.
11. Coat cylinder head gasket with grease on both sides or other type gasket cement.
12. Put head gasket in place and install cylinder head into place. Torque head bolts to 35 ft lbs in a circular sequence. (Check specification charts for proper sequence).
13. Reinstall all remaining equipment by reversing the removal sequence.

Removal and Installation

1.9 Engine

1. Drain radiator and cylinder block. The plug for block is located on right side in front of motor mount.

2. Disconnect radiator hoses, heater hoses, fuel lines, vacuum lines, and throttle linkage from manifolds.

3. Remove spark plug and cap along with any electrical connection.

4. Remove rocker arm cover and rocker arms.

5. Remove plate which is attached to front of cylinder head. Then remove the bolts from end of camshaft.

6. Unbolt cylinder head in proper sequence (reverse of tightening sequence).

7. Disconnect camshaft sprocket from cylinder head. Slide sprocket off of camshaft and remove cylinder head.

CAUTION: *Never place cylinder head, with installed camshaft and valves, on its machined surface on work bench.*

8. Clean piston tops and combustion chamber. Throughly clean all gasket surfaces on the cylinder head and block.

9. Lubricate cylinder walls with engine oil and clean all foreign matter from machined surfaces.

10. Coat cylinder head gasket with grease or gasket cement on both sides.

11. Install coolant passage rubber gasket ring in timing case.

Coolant passages rubber gasket ring in timing case.

1. Timing chain
2. Camshaft sprocket
3. Sprocket timing mark
4. Timing case
5. Support timing mark
6. Support
7. Cylinder block
8. Rubber gasket ring

12. Place gasket on cylinder block and install cylinder head into position.

NOTE: *Rotate camshaft to align recesses for installation of left row of bolts.*

13. Install head bolts and tighten to specified torque. (72 ft lbs)

14. Slide camshaft sprocket and chain onto camshaft and guide pin, then bolt them together. Install nylon adjusting screw. After sprocket is attached, recheck alignment to see that chain has not slipped.

15. Reinstall cover plate and procede to install in reverse of removal.

Overhaul (See "Engine Rebuilding Section")

Intake Manifold

Removal and Installation

1.1 Engine

1. Disconnect battery and remove air cleaner and silencer.

2. Detach fuel lines, choke cable, vacuum lines, and A.I.R. control valve from carburetor.

3. Disconnect throttle linkage.

4. Remove rocker arm cover-to-intake manifold hose.

5. Remove carbuertor and carburetor support bracket.

NOTE: *Remove O-ring seal from between carburetor and intake manifold.*

Intake manifold bolts location (OHV Engine).

6. Remove intake mamifold. The center bolt is accessible only after carburetor has been removed.

7. Installation is accomplished by reversing the removal process.

NOTE: *Use a new O-ring seal when replacing carburetor.*

1.9 Engine

To remove the intake manifold from the 1.5 or 1.9 engines, it is necessary to remove both the intake and exhaust manifolds together, then seperate them after removal. See the combination manifold section for the removal steps.

Exhaust Manifold

Removal and Installation

1.1 Engine

1. Disconnect exhaust pipe at manifold.

2. Remove carburetor support bracket from intake and exhaust manifolds.

3. Unbolt manifold from cylinder head and remove it from engine.

4. Clean surfaces of old gasket material.

5. Install a new gasket and replace manifold.

6. Torque bolts to 33 ft lbs in proper sequence.

7. Reinstall exhaust pipe and support bracket.

1.9 Engine

To remove the exhaust manifold from the 1.5 or 1.9 engines, it is necessary to remove both the intake and exhaust manifolds togther, then seperate them after removal. See the combination manifold section for removal procedures.

Combination Manifolds

Removal and Installation

1. Disconnect battery.

2. Remove air cleaner and disconnect throttle linkage, vacuum lines, and fuel lines from carburetor.

3. Drain radiator and remove water hoses to automatic choke.

4. Remove positive crankcase ventilation valve (PCV valve) at rocker arm cover.

5. Disconnect exhaust pipe.

6. Remove (6) bolts which attach the manifold assembly to cylinder head, and remove complete assembly.

NOTE: *To separate intake and exhaust manifolds, remove carburetor and the bolts which attach them together. Always replace gasket between the manifolds.*

7. Clean all surfaces where new gaskets are to be installed.

NOTE: *Never reuse old gaskets when replacing manifolds onto the engine.*

8. Place manifold assembly into position and install bolts.

9. Tighten bolts in proper sequence. Torque bolts to 33 ft lbs.

10. Reinstall vacuum lines, fuel lines, and throttle linkage.

11. Replace everything that was removed from engine.

Timing Gear Cover

Removal and Installation (All Models)

1. Remove fan belt, then remove crankcase pulley attaching bolt.

NOTE: *Usually, pulley will come off by hand. Tap pulley with a rubber hammer to free it.*

2. Unbolt timing gear cover.

3. Throughly clean surfaces of old gasket material and reinstall by reversing removal procedures.

Timing Chain and Tensioner

Removal and Installation

1. Follow removal procedure and remove timing chain cover.

2. Carefully remove tensioner making sure not to lose any parts.

3. Mark timing chain and sprockets for location, then unbolt sprocket from camshaft.

4. Slide off both the camshaft and crankshaft sprockets together with timing chain.

NOTE: *Check woodruff key on crankshaft for wear or cracking. Replace if necessary.*

5. Reinstall sprockets being careful to line up all marks exactly as before.

6. Reinstall cover, pulley, and fan belt.

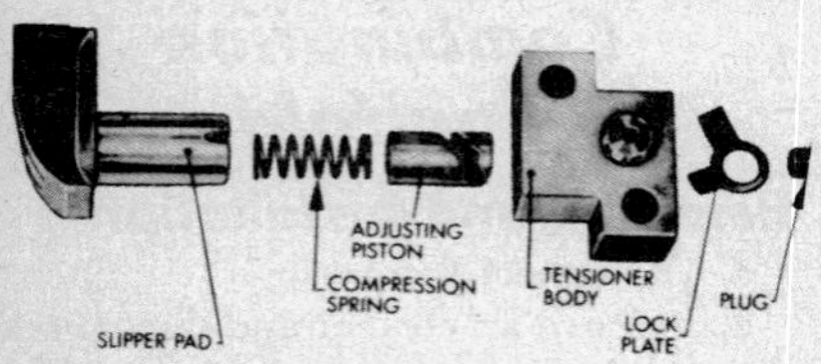

Chain tensioner assembly

Tensioner Adjustments

1. Check all parts for wear. If any are defective, replace complete unit.

2. Insert compression spring into adjusting piston and install plunger sleeve so that helical slot of adjusiting piston and guide pin (in tensioner body) fit into each other in plunger sleeve.

3. With a ⅛ in. allen wrench, turn clockwise until guide pin emerges on top of helical slot.

4. Remove end plug and install unit into place.

5. With an allen wrench, release adjusting piston. The timing chain now has the proper tension.

6. Install a new locking plate and end plug. Secure plug by bending tab up.

Timing Cover Crankshaft Seal Replacement

1. With timing chain cover supported, drive outer seal retainer and cork seal out of cover.

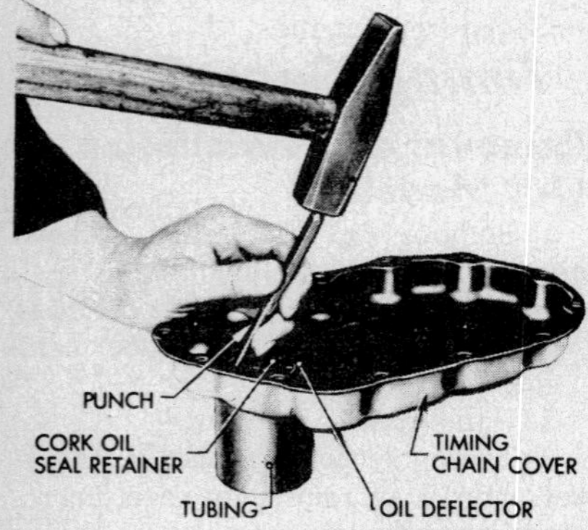

Removing outer-seal retainer and cork seal

CAUTION: *Do not try to remove inner seal retainer.*

2. Install timing cover seal through front of cover. Press or drive seal flush with cover.

Camshaft

Removal and Installation

(OHV)

NOTE: *To remove camshaft from engine, you must remove engine from car.*

1. To remove engine from car, follow removal procedures outlined in that section.

2. Remove timing chain cover and rocker arm cover, rocker arms, and push rods.

NOTE: *Align timing marks for easier installation of parts.*

3. Remove distributor.

4. Drain crankcase oil and invert engine.

NOTE: *If lifters are to be replaced, the oil pan must be removed.*

5. Unbolt camshaft thrust plate and carefully slide camshaft and front plate out.

6. Coat camshaft with engine oil before reinstalling it into crankcase.

7. Reverse removal procedure to install.

Removal and Installation

(CIH)

1. Remove cylinder head. Follow procedures outlined in that section.

2. Loosen rocker arms, swing arms off of the valve lifters and remove lifters.

NOTE: *The lifters must be installed in same position if not being replaced.*

3. Remove cover from access hole on left side of cylinder head.

4. Pull camshaft toward front, while supporting it with one hand through access hole. Be careful not to damage bearing surfaces or cam journals.

5. Before installing camshaft into head, lubricate journals liberally.

6. Reinstall valve lifters, push rods, and rocker arms.

7. Replace head gasket and reinstall head.

8. Reinstall other parts by reversing removal procedures.

Piston and Connecting Rods

Removal and Installation

(See "Engine Rebuilding" section)

1. Remove engine from car and support it safely.

2. Drain crankcase oil and remove oil pan.

3. Remove cylinder head assembly.

4. Check top of cylinder bore for a ridge above ring travel. If a ridge exsists, remove it with ridge reamer.

CAUTION: *Don't try to remove pistons before removing ridge. This is to avoid damage to the rings and their lands during removal.*

5. Remove cap and bearing shell and push the piston-rod assembly out through the top of the block. Replace cap onto rod to pervent loss.

NOTE: *Mark piston assemblies to show from which cylinder they were removed.*

6. Remove other pistons and rods in same manner

7. To install, reverse removal procedure.

NOTE: *After replacing worn or damaged pistons or rings, a ring compressor must be used to reinstall pistons into block.*

ENGINE LUBRICATION

Oil Pan

Removal and Installation

1. In order to remove the oil pan from an Opel, with the engine installed, the front suspension must be removed as an assembly (see "Suspension Section").

2. Support the engine slightly to remove weight from the engine mounts.

3. Disconnect the clutch cable at the pivot arm.

4. Remove the crossmember-to-frame and body bolts and remove the motor mount bolts.

5. Drain oil and unbolt oil pan.

6. Clean old gasket throughly to prevent fluid leakage.

7. Place new gasket end-tabs in slots in front and rear of the main bearing caps.

8. Install small gasket strips in grooves in front and rear main bearing caps

9. Torque oil pan bolts to 5 ft lbs

NOTE: *Flat washers are used on oil pan attaching bolts.*

Rear Main Oil Seal Replacement

1. Remove transmission and bell housing.

2. Unbolt the clutch and flywheel.

3. Punch a hole into oil seal, screw in a sheet metal screw, and then pull out old seal.

4. Lubricate new seal to asure proper sealing. Place seal on crankshaft flange and move lip of seal over rear of crankshaft.

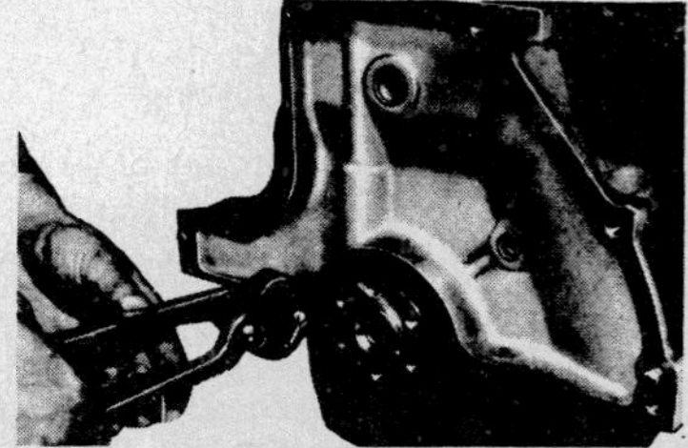

Removing rear main seal

5. Drive seal into position. Be careful not to tilt seal or it will not seal properly.

6. Reinstall flywheel, clutch, bell housing, and transmission.

NOTE: *When replacing flywheel, use new bolts and torque to 43 ft lbs.*

3. Reinstall, using new gasket, in the reverse of removal.

CIH

1. Unbolt oil pump cover from timing chain cover.

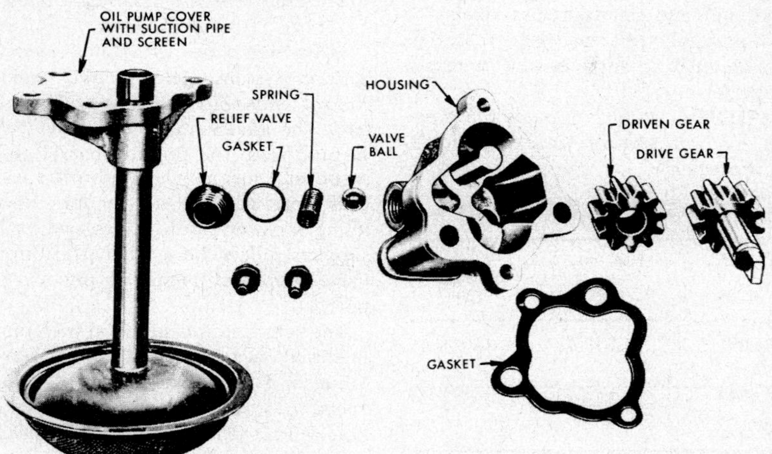

Exploded view of oil pump (OHV Engine)

Oil Pump

Removal and Installation

OHV

1. Remove oil pan. Follow procedures outlined in that section.

2. Remove two bolts which hold oil pump in place.

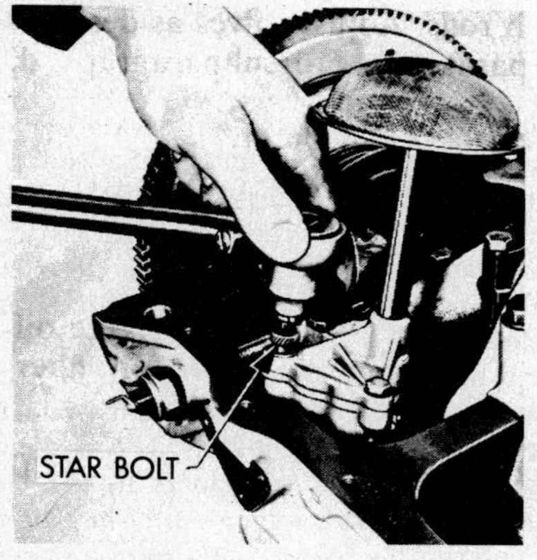

Installing oil pump assembly (OHV Engine).

2. Slide gears out of housing.

3. Clean and inspect gears and cover for scoring. Replace any part found unserviceable.

NOTE: *If pump housing or distributor shaft bushings are worn, the timing case and all pump parts must be replaced.*

Checking Clearances

1. With the pump removed from engine, remove oil pump cover and screen assembly.

2. Slide out pump gears and remove pressure relief valve plug, relief valve, spring, and check ball.

3. Throughly clean and inspect all parts for wear or scoring.

4. Install oil pump gears into housing. Check gear lash with a feeler gauge. Clearance must be 0.004–0.008 in.

5. Place a straight edge over gears and check clearance between top of the housing and the straight edge. Clearance should be 0.001–0.004.

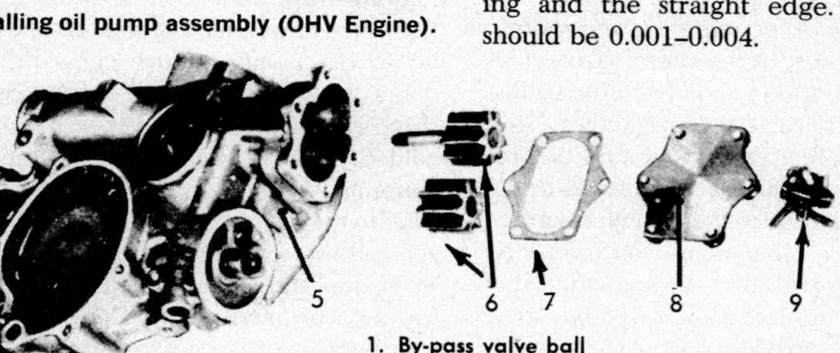
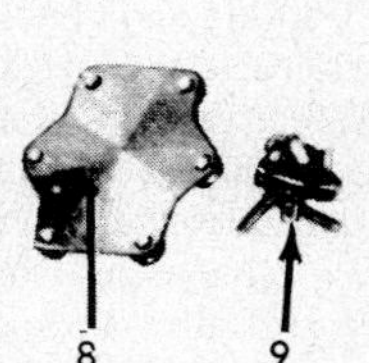

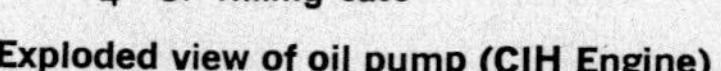

Exploded view of oil pump (CIH Engine)

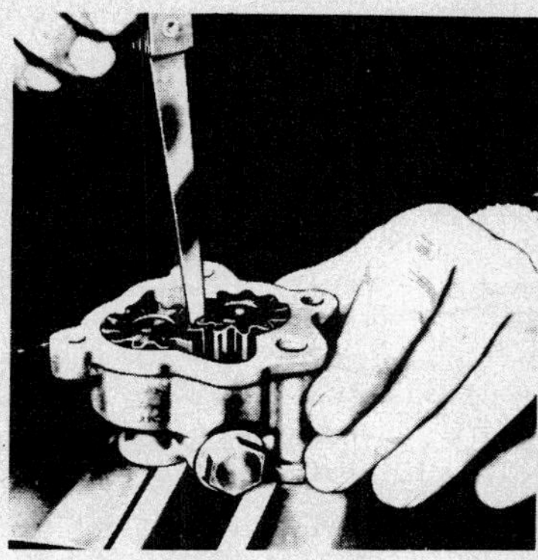

Checking gear backlash

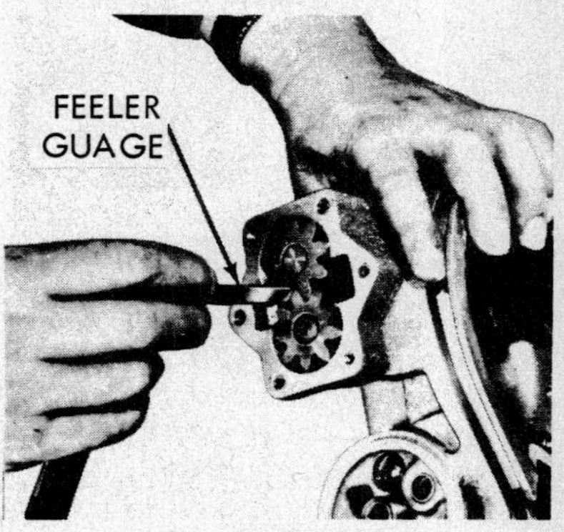

Checking gear backlash

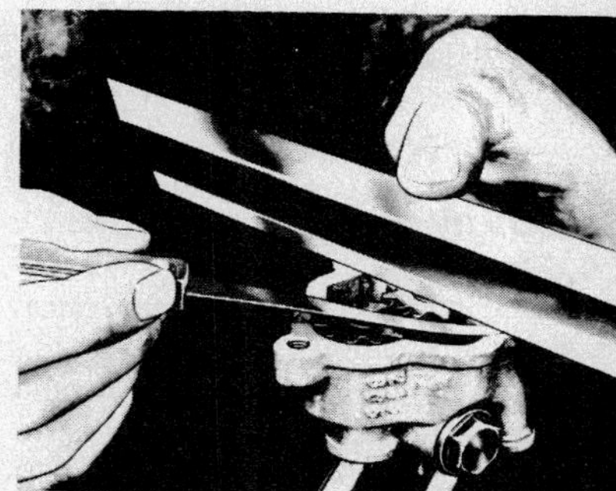

Checking gear end clearance

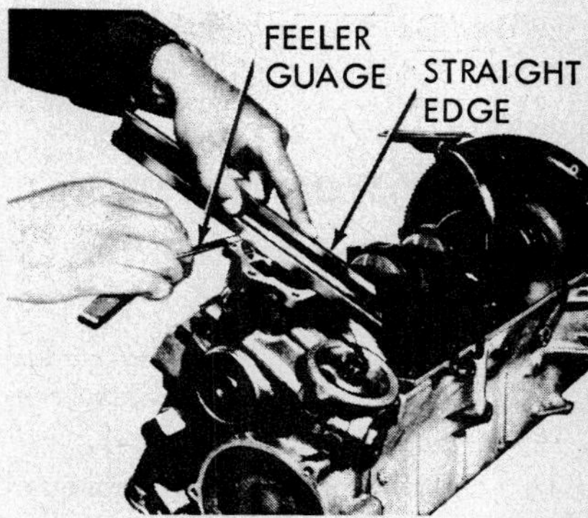

Checking oil pump gear end clearance

NOTE: *If gears are to be replaced, check timing case for "0.2" stamped on pump flange on left or right side. This indicates 0.008 in. oversize bores for pump gears and shaft. Order new parts accordingly.*

5. Lubricate spindles and gear teeth and replace them in housing.

6. Check oil pump relief valve, spring, and relief valve ball. Clean, inspect and replace any part found defective.

7. Install pump cover using a new gasket.

Oil pump pipe and screen assembly installed (CIH Engine).

NOTE: *To check oil pump pipe and screen assembly on CIH engines, the oil pan must be removed. Follow steps for removing the oil pan and unbolt pipe and screen assembly.*

ENGINE COOLING

Radiator

Removal and Installation

1. Drain system of all fluid.
2. Disconnect upper and lower radiator hoses at radiator.
3. Remove lower attaching nuts and slide radiator out of compartment.
4. Install by reversing removal process.

NOTE: *Be sure to add the proper amount of anti-freeze solution when filling the system with fluid.*

Water Pump

Removal and Installation

1. Drain radiator of fluid.

NOTE: *Remove radiator and shroud on cars equipped with overhead cam engines.*

2. Loosen alternator and remove fan belt.
3. Unbolt fan and pulley from water pump shaft
4. Remove water pump.
5. Before reinstalling pump, throughly clean old gasket material from the block and pump mating surfaces.
6. Install in reverse of removal.

Thermostat

Removal and Installation

1. Drain radiator.
2. Unbolt thermostat housing from block.
3. Remove thermostat from block.
2. Throughly clean old gasket material from the mating surfaces and reinstall thermostat.

CAUTION: *Be sure to place the thermostat right side up to allow fluid to flow properly.*

Thermostat Usage Chart

Year & Model	Maximum Pressure (psi)	Thermostat (°F)
1966-1971 1.1	10.4-12.4	180°
1968-1973 1.9	13.2-15.2	190°

EMISSION CONTROLS

Applications

1968–69

The exhaust emission control system on the 1968–69 Opel limits the amount of unburned hydrocarbons and carbon monoxide discharged into the atmosphere and is separated from the PCV system. The air pump injects clean filtered air into each exhaust port immediately after the exhaust cycle. This air allows the hot exhaust gases to burn any unburned fuel and carbon monoxide before it reaches the atmosphere. On sudden closing of the throttle, some of the air is fed into the intake manifold through the control valve to further reduce pollutants. The entire system is designed to be relatively maintenance free, and internal parts of the pump are not available separately—if the pump is defective it must be replaced.

To see if the pump is operating, remove the hose at the check valve while the engine is idling and check for air discharge. If there is no air delivery, the pump is defective and should be replaced, and the check valve must be inspected as a possible source of trouble.

The check valve should be examined occasionally and always checked, when the pump is replaced, for defective operation. If the valve leaks, hot exhaust gases may damage the pump. Check the hose from the pump to the check valve—if it is hot while the engine is running, or brittle, remove the air cleaner and the hose. If the black rubber on the valve is burned at all, replace the valve and check the pump for damage.

If backfiring occurs when the throttle is closed at high speeds, or while shifting, the control valve is malfunctioning and must be replaced.

NOTE: *When cleaning the engine compartment, mask off the centrifugal fan filter located behind the pulley assembly.*

The design of the 1969 1.9 liter engine ignition system includes two vacuum control units, one advance and one retard. The advance unit is supplied with vacuum from the primary barrel of the carburetor just above the throttle valve. This port supplies no vacuum during idling or closed throttle deceleration, but supplies full vacuum when the throttle valve is opened enough to uncover this port.

The retard unit is supplied with intake manifold vacuum at all times. During idling and deceleration, when there is vacuum to the advance unit, the retard unit will cause the timing to be retarded 4–9°. During partial throttle operation, there is vacuum to the advance unit and the retard unit has no effect on timing.

1970

The 1970 exhaust emission control system is designed to reduce unburned hydrocarbons and carbon monoxide through the use of: (1) leaned out carburetion, (2) heated air, (3) mixture control on engine deceleration, and, (4) tuned spark timing. This system does away with the air pump and related equipment as used on earlier cars.

The exhaust manifold provides heated air for a stable intake temperature and accurate mixture by means of a "stove" mounted on the exhaust manifold. This heated air is drawn through the heated air pipe into the snorkel of the air cleaner. The temperature control air cleaner has a sensor that is designed to mix the heated air with colder outside air so the carburetor inlet air temperature averages about 115±20°F. This is done with the sensor, two doors in the air cleaner, and a vacuum motor. The motor operates the doors so that as one opens the other closes, mixing heated and cold air to keep temperature constant. The doors are spring loaded, so that when there is no vacuum from the engine the cold air door is open. When the engine is running, the amount of vacuum delivered to the motor is regulated by the sensor and the amount of vacuum available from the engine. Thus when underhood temperature rises above 135°F., the sensor allows no vacuum to the motor and the door for the heated air closes completely, admitting only cold air. When accelerating hard, manifold vacuum drops and the motor gets no vacuum regardless of the temperature, so again the cold air door is open. When decelerating, the manifold vacuum is high and, if the underhood temperature is less than 135°F., the cold air door closes and only heated air is admitted. The hot air door opens fully at 9 in. of vacuum and the cold air door opens fully below 5 in. of vacuum.

1.1 engines now use two carburetors, and a leaner idle is achieved because of more accurate air metering and better distribution. An additional air-fuel mixture valve is attached to the balance tube on the intake manifold. This allows an additional fuel-air mixture to be drawn into the intake manifold when decelerating, keeping combustion efficiency high and reducing the harmful emissions. This valve draws in the additional fuel-air mixture from the front carburetor on deceleration at engine speeds above 1,800 rpm to prevent backfiring.

1971–73

All cars must be capable of passing certain tests which measure the quantity of unburned impurities in the exhaust system. Federal law places a limit on the hydrocarbon and carbon monoxide emissions from the exhaust system. These Federal standards are the same as the California standards which have been in effect for the past three years. The purpose of this law is to keep the atmosphere cleaner, particularly in populous areas where these impurities add to the smog problem. Basically, excessive exhaust emissions are caused by incomplete combustion of the air-fuel mixture in the cylinders.

The equipment used on 1971–73 cars is similar, except for modifications and improvements to meet each year's federal laws.

Testing (1968–69 Models)

Pump Assembly

1. Check belt tension.
2. If pump is noisy, remove belt to see whether pump is binding or seized.
3. Check all hose connections and hoses for tightness and to see if they are touching any other part in engine.
4. With engine running, check for leaks in the hoses and around clamps.
5. Check the mounting bracket for tightness.
6. Check the relief valve. If air escapes from the valve during engine idle, the pump must be replaced.

NOTE: *If the pump is found to be defective, check the relief valve for possible source of trouble.*

Check Valve

1. If hose is excessively hot or brittle, check inside hoses for burned rubber. If this is the case, replace the check valve.

NOTE: *If the check valve is defective, check pump for possible cause.*

Testing (1970–73)

Vacuum Motor

1. Check hoses for looseness, kinks, plugs, or damage.
2. With engine off, damper door should be open, if it isn't check for binding of the linkage.
3. Apply at least nine (9) in. HG of vacuum to diaphram assembly. Damper door should be closed. Check linkage for proper connection.
4. Apply vacuum and trap in system, damper door should remain closed. Check diaphram assembly for vacuum leakage.

Sensor Check

1. Observe, with engine cold, whether cold air door is open.
2. Start engine. The cold air door should close immediately.
3. As engine warms up, the cold air door should start to open, and the air cleaner should become warm.

Removal and Installation

Damper Door

The damper door is not serviceable. The air cleaner assembly must be replaced if damper door is found to be defective.

Vacuum Motor

1. Disconnect vacuum motor retainer spring clamp.

Vacuum motor assembly installed in air cleaner.

2. Remove vacuum lines, lift motor, and unhook vacuum motor control linkage at damper door.
3. Install in the reverse order of removal.

Sensor in Air Cleaner

1. Disconnect vacuum lines from sensor.
2. Remove retaining clips from sensor. and remove them from air cleaner.

NOTE: *Before removal of sensor, mark position of old sensor to assure installation of new sensor into same position.*

Sensor assembly installed in air cleaner

3. Reinstall retaining clip and vacuum lines.

Control Valve

1. Remove air cleaner and detach rubber hoses, air bleeder lines, and vacuum lines.
2. Remove attaching bolts and then remove control valve from bracket.
3. Reinstall by reversing removal procedures.

Air Pump

1. Remove fan belt from pump pulley.
2. Disconnect hoses from pump.
3. Remove bolts which hold pump to the mounting bracket.

CAUTION: *Do not prevent pulley from rotating by inserting something into filter fan.*

4. Reinstall in reverse order of removal.

NOTE: *Do not operate vehicle with pump removed or belt disconnected.*

FUEL SYSTEM

Mechanical Fuel Pump

The fuel pump for the 1.1 engine is the conventional rocker arm type. The 1.9 engine uses a push rod type pump.

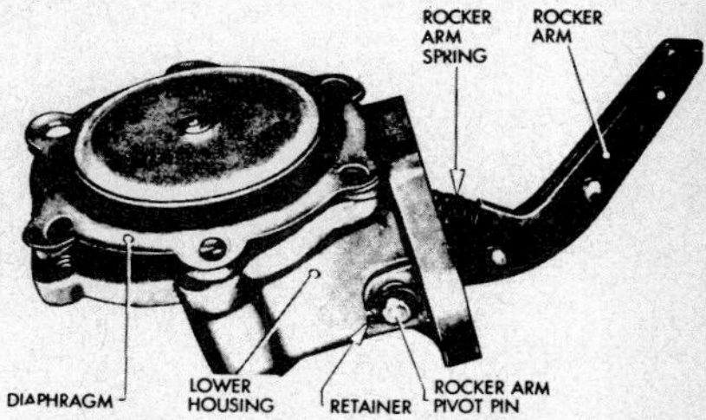

Fuel pump assembly (OHV Engine)

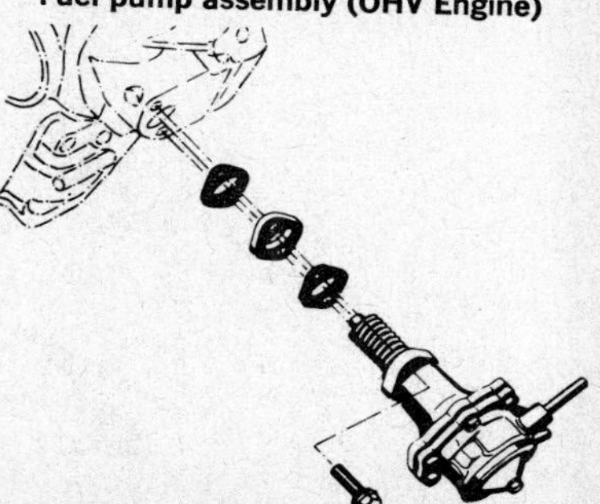
Fuel pump assembly (CIH Engine)

Removal and Installation

1. Remove fuel lines from pump and plug them.

CAUTION: *Because the fuel pump is higher than the pump, fuel will flow freely when the fuel line is disconnected.*

2. Unbolt the fuel pump from the engine block.

3. Reinstall fuel pump by reversing the removal procedures.

NOTE: *When replacing the fuel pump, be sure to use a new gasket to prevent leakage between pump and block assemblies.*

Testing and Adjustments

1. Disconnect fuel lines at carburetor.

2. Connect a pressure testing gauge to that end of the fuel line that comes directly from the pump.

3. Crank the engine. The pressure should read 3.1–3.7 PSI. Defective pumps should be replaced.

Carburetors

Removal and Installation

Solex 1 barrel carburetor

1. Remove the fuel lines and all vacuum hoses to the carburetor.

2. Disconnect the choke cable and the throttle control rods.

3. Unbolt two (2) mounting nuts, and remove carburetor.

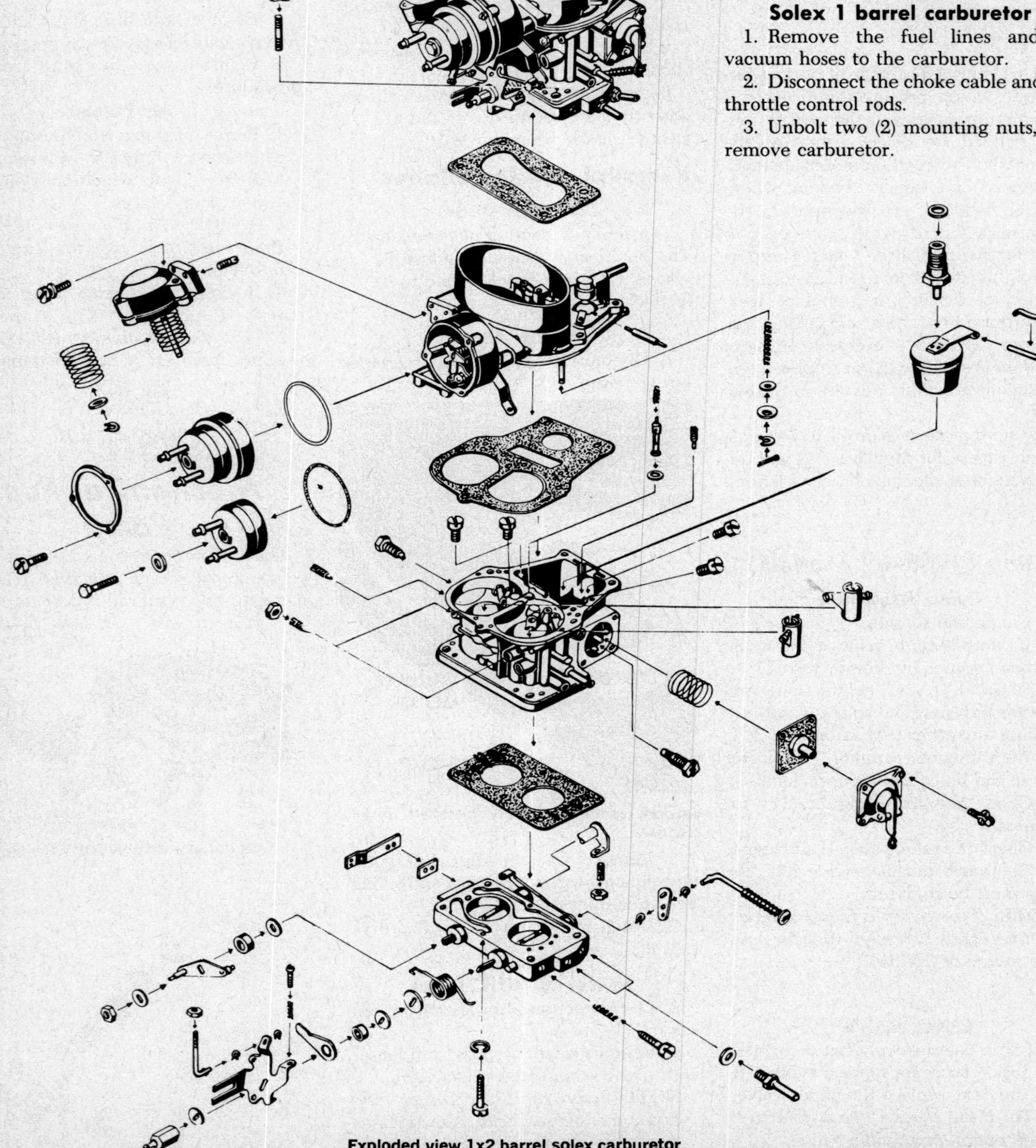

Exploded view 1x2 barrel solex carburetor

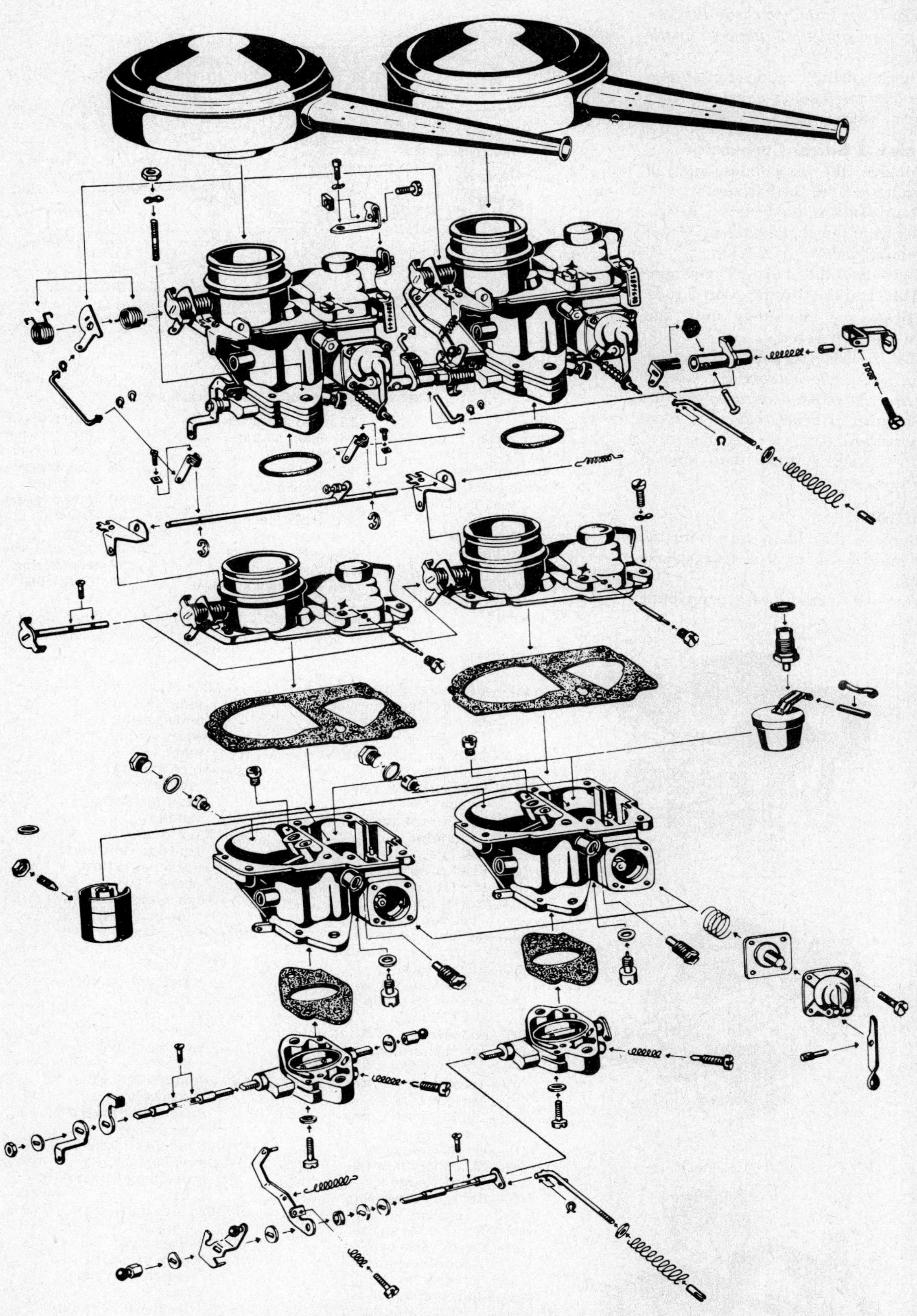

Exploded view 2x1 barrel solex carburetors

4. To install, reverse the removal procedures.

NOTE: *When installing carburetor, install a new rubber O-ring seal in the manifold.*

5. Check synchronization of multi-carburetor engines, if adjustments on either carburetor were made.

Solex 2 Barrel Carburetor

1. Remove the fuel lines and all vacuum hoses from the carburetor.
2. Drain radiator and remove the water hoses from the choke housing. (Automatic chokes only)
3. Disconnect the choke cable (where applicable) and the throttle control rods.
4. Unbolt the mounting nuts and remove the carburetor.

NOTE: *Before reinstalling the carburetor, adjust the automatic choke by rotating the choke housing so that the choke plate is nearly closed at room temperature.*

5. To install, reverse the removal procedures.

Overhaul

1. Remove the clamp ring from the lower end of the throttle lever choke linkage.
2. Remove vacuum case connecting lever.

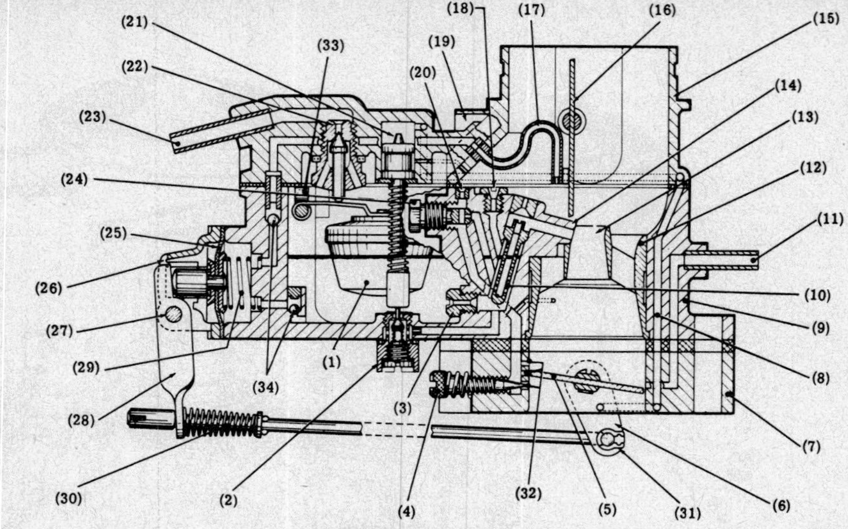

Cross-section of Solex 1 barrel carburetor

1. Float
2. Power valve
3. Main metering jet
4. Idle mixture screw
5. Throttle valve
6. Throttle lever
7. Throttle body
8. Vacuum passage to power valve
9. Float bowl
10. Main well tube
11. Vacuum fitting
12. Main venturi
13. Boost venturi
14. Main nozzle
15. Air horn
16. Choke
17. Accelerator pump nozzle
18. High speed bleeder
19. Bowl vent
20. Idle air bleed
21. Vacuum piston
22. Float needle valve
23. Fuel inlet
24. Idle jet
25. Pump diaphragm
26. Pump cover
27. Pump lever shaft
28. Diaphragm return spring
29. Pump lever
30. Duration spring
31. Clip
32. Idle and off-idle ports
33. Leaf spring
34. Check ball

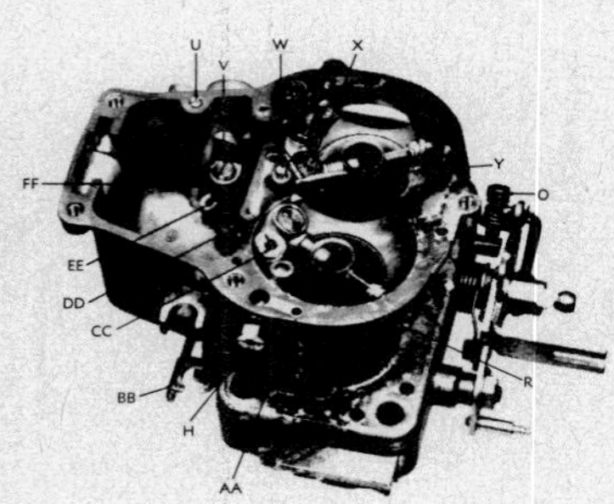

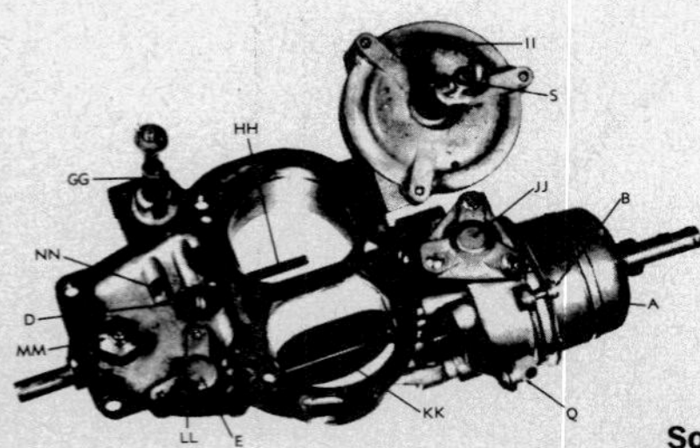

(a)—Automatic choke cover (water temp)
(b)—Choke adjustment screws
(c)—Cover of choke control mechanism
(d)—Float chamber vent tube
(e)—Enrichment diaphragm chamber
(f)—Fuel inlet
(g)—Float cover screws
(h)—Idle jet
(i)—Accelerator pump screws
(j)—Vacuum pipe for distributor advance
(k)—Idle air (speed) adjusting screw
(l)—Accelerator pump adjustment
(m)—Connection for A.I.R.
(n)—Idle mixture (volume) adjustment
(o)—Throttle stop screw
(p)—Throttle lever
(q)—Choke-throttle connecting rod
(r)—Venturi set screw
(s)—Secondary throttle control rod
(t)—Hot water hose connections
(u)—Enrichment air jet
(v)—Check valve carrier for accelerator pump
(w)—Injection nozzle for accelerator pump
(x)—Main nozzle bleed (emulsion tube underneath)
(y)—Primary venturi (choke tube)
(aa)—Air channel of progression circuit for secondary venturi
(bb)—Control arm for outside ventilation channel to float bowl
(cc)—High speed air bleed (main air jet)
(dd)—Primary main metering jet (secondary main metering jet not visible)
(ee)—Fuel inlet to check valve
(ff)—Enrichment fuel inlet
(gg)—Control rod for the inside-outside ventilator for the float bowl
(hh)—Enrichment tube
(ii)—Secondary-throttle diaphragm chamber
(jj)—Vacuum-choke diaphragm chamber
(kk)—Choke valve
(ll)—Vacuum passage to enrichment chamber
(mm)—Needle valve carrier
(nn)—Float bowl ventilation passage

Solex 2 barrel carburetor (automatic choke)

3. Disconnect vent valve rod and thrust spring.

4. Unscrew carburetor cover and remove float needle valve and sealing ring.

5. Remove vacuum diaphram cover from choke housing and remove enrichment system from carburetor cover

6. Unscrew retaining ring from automatic choke bódy and take off cover.

7. Unscrew vacuum diaphram cover and remove reduction jet.

8. Remove the injection tube with the ball valve and spring from the float chamber.

9. Remove the float with the spindle and leaf spring.

10. Unscrew the idle jets and the high speed jets.

11. Remove the metering jets and the accelerator pump inlet ball valve, then remove the enrichment jet.

12. Disconnect the retaining ring from the accelerator pump connecting rod and then remove the accelerator pump.

13. Remove the idle mixture adjusting screw and idle air adjusting screw from the throttle valve body.

CAUTION: *Never mix parts from the primary and secondary metering systems.*

14. Clean all parts and blow dry with compressed air. Replace all gaskets and sealing rings.

15. Check actuating parts in automatic choke body and check the diaphram pull rods for free operation.

16. Reinstall all main secondary metering jets.

17. With stop screws, adjust throttle valve of secondary barrel so that a gap of 0.002 in. exists; this prevents jamming in the throttle bore.

18. Install float needle valve together with a copper seal ring.

19. Install choke assembly in reverse of removal sequence and install it on carburetor.

20. Reinstall all adjusting screws and accelerator pump discharge nozzle assembly into carburetor housing.

21. Install float into float chamber and replace carburetor cover using a new gasket.

22. Arrange washers on vent valve, one on each side of the lever, and insert cotter pin.

23. The lower vent valve spring should be compressed ¼ in. with the throttle valve completely closed.

NOTE: *If the brass bushings in the vacuum diaphram case are worn, the vacuum case must be replaced.*

24. Check the hot idle compensator by heating it in water until it opens. Opening temperature should be 194 degrees F.

25. Install vacuum case diaphram assembly.

26. Replace gasket between automatic choke cover and choke body and install automatic choke cover so that the catch of the bi-metal spring is positioned on the bent end of the intermediate lever.

Alignment marks on choke housing

27. Align and tighten the automatic choke cover. The valve should be nearly closed at room temperature.

28. Reinstall all other parts by reversing their removal sequence.

Throttle Linkage Adjustments

Adjustments are made using the theaded end of the throttle rods. The throttle should be adjusted so that it operates freely and permits the throttle plates of the carburetor to open and close completely.

Choke Linkage Adjustments

The choke cable is adjusted so that the choke plate will be fully open when the control is pushed in completely.

Float and Fuel Level Adjustments

When overhauling the carburetor, the float should be checked to be sure that it is not bent or cracked. Never try to repair the float or arm, instead replace the float assembly.

Fast Idle Adjustments.

1. Warm engine up to operating temperature.

2. Turn engine off and manually operate the linkage while holding the choke plate closed.

NOTE: *The choke plate should open and close freely. There should be no binding of any parts if choke is to work properly.*

3. When the linkage is released, the choke plate should remain in the closed position.

4. Now restart the engine; do not touch the accelerator pedal or linkage.

NOTE: *The engine should be idling fast; if it doesn't, repeat steps 2,3, and 4 until properly set.*

5. Connect a tachometer (if available) to the engine and adjust the choke control arm. Fast idling rpm is 2700±.

Decreasing fast idle speed

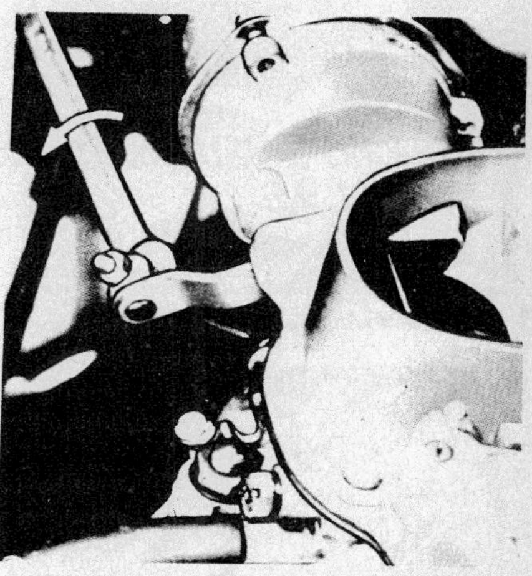

Increasing fast idle speed

Automatic Choke Adjustments

NOTE: *To adjust automatic choke, the engine must be cold.*

1. Remove the air cleaner. Check vacuum lines for cracks and loose connections.

2. Check choke plate for freedom of movement.

3. The choke plate should be nearly closed.

4. To adjust, loosen choke cover and rotate assembly until choke plate is nearly closed.

5. Tighten cover assembly and start engine. When operating temperature has been reached, the choke plate should be completely open.

MANUAL TRANSMISSION

Removal and Installation

All Models

1. Remove the air cleaner and throttle rod from the engine.

2. Remove the standard shift lever by pulling up the boot, pushing the lock cap down and turning it counterclockwise.

a. The sport shift lever is removed

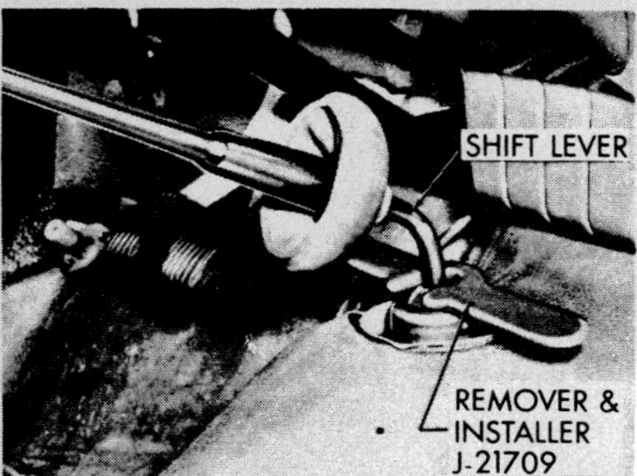

Removing standard shift lever

Removing sports shift lever

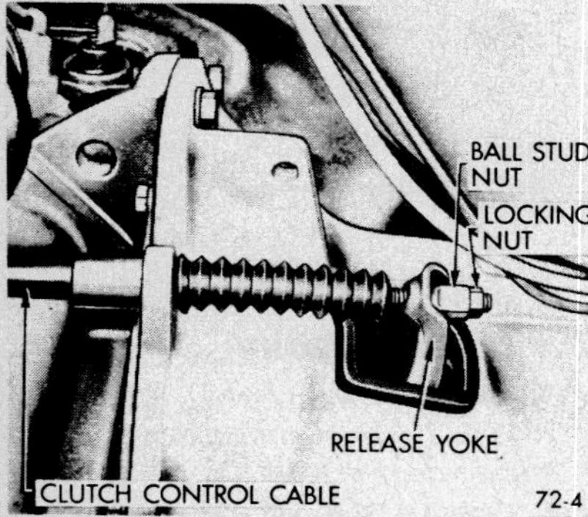

Clutch cable and attaching parts

by removing the boot, and removing the snapring that retains the lever.

3. Disconnect the clutch cable from the clutch fork, the speedometer cable from the speedometer drive housing, and the wires from the backup lamp switch.

4. Unhook the parking brake cable return spring, and remove the cable adjusting nut, equalizer, and spacer.

5. Mark the relative positions of the driveshaft U-joint flange and the drive pinion extension shaft flange at the central joint.

6. Support the vechicle at its rear jacket brackets, loosen the bolt locks and remove the flange bolts. Work the driveshaft slightly forward, swing the end of the shaft down, and remove the shaft and thrust spring.

NOTE: *Plug the end of the transmission to prevent fluid loss.*

7. Remove the lower bolt on each side of the crankcase, and install guide pins to prevent clutch disc warpage when removing the transmission.

8. Support the engine from below, and unbolt the right engine mount.

9. Remove one rear transmission mounting bolt, loosen the other, and raise the front of the engine to provide clearance for removal of the transmission.

10. Remove the remaining transmission to crankcase bolts, and the rear mounting bolt, and slide the transmission back and out of the vehicle.

11. Installation is the reverse of removal.

Overhaul

OHV Engines

1. Remove transmission case cover (6 bolts) that support shift housing and discard the gasket.

2. Invert transmission to drain oil.

3. Using suitable pliers, remove reverse gear stop spring from transmission case cover.

4. To remove speedometer driven gear, pry cover out of upper right side of rear bearing retainer (speedometer drive housing).

a. Using small punch, push speedometer driven gear out through upper opening and discard speedometer gear shaft seal.

5. Shift shafts, forks and detents are removed through top of case.

a. Take the six retaining snap rings from shift shafts (located at the front and rear of shift forks and shift head).

b. Pull the three detent (lock-ball) retaining plugs out, and remove the springs and balls.

NOTE: *For the following steps, be certain the shift shafts are in neutral position. This assures that the interlock pins at the rear of the shafts will not interfere with shaft removal.)*

6. Remove lower attaching bolt of rearbearing retainer and rotate bearing retainer until rear of 1st and 2nd speed (middle) shift shaft is exposed. Use a brass drift to drive shaft and end plug forward out of case.

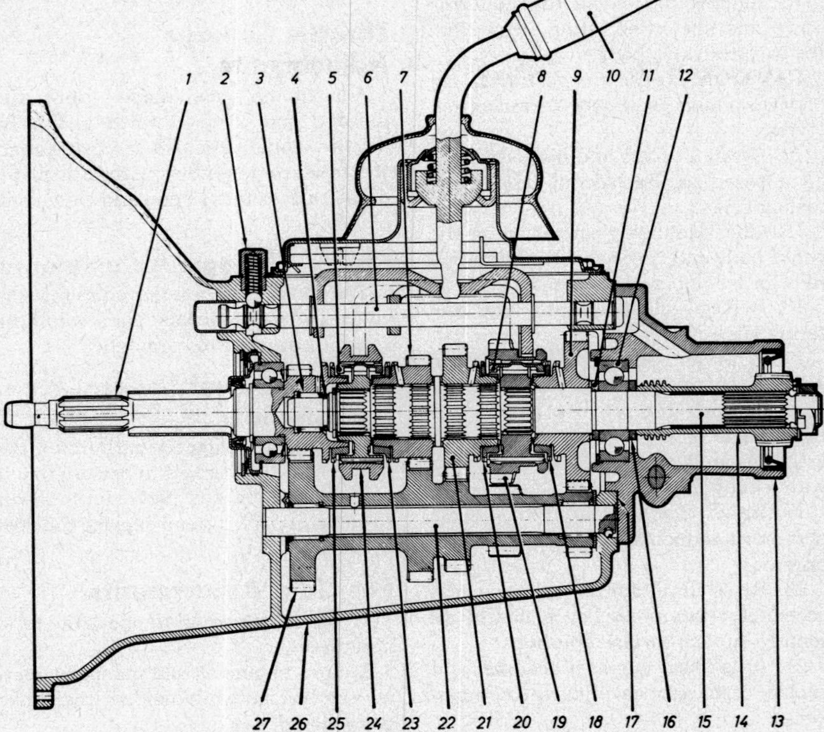

Cross section of standard transmission (OHV Engine).

1. Clutch gear
2. Lock ball and spring plug
3. Needle bearing assy.
4. Thrust ring
5. Key for 3rd-and-4th-speed clutch sleeve (3)
6. 1st-and-2nd-speed shifter shaft
7. 3rd-speed gear
8. Key for 1st-and-2nd-speed clutch sleeve (3)
9. 1st-speed gear
10. Gearshift lever
11. Spacer between 1st-speed gear and ball bearing
12. Ball bearing
13. Speedometer drive housing (bearing retainer)
14. Mainshaft sleeve
15. Mainshaft
16. Spacer between ball bearing and mainshaft sleeve
17. Gasket between speedometer drive housing and transmission case
18. 1st-speed synchronizer ring
19. 1st-and-2nd-speed sliding gear
20. 2nd-speed synchronizer ring
21. 2nd-speed gear
22. Countergear shaft
23. 3rd-speed synchronizer ring
24. 3rd-and-4th-speed clutch sleeve
25. 4th-speed synchronizer ring
26. Transmission case
27. Countergear

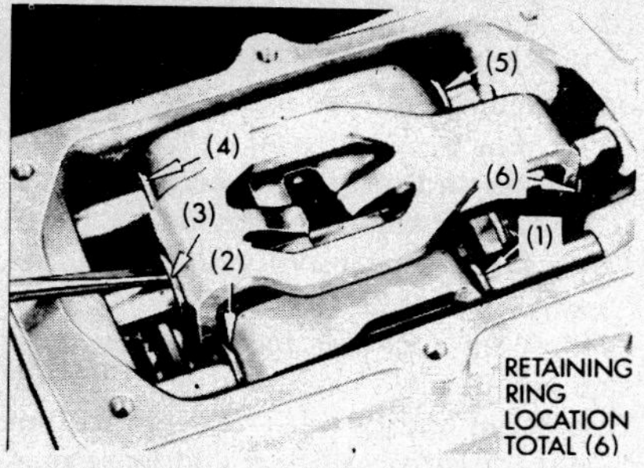

Removing snap-rings from shifting shafts

CAUTION: *During shaft removal or replacement, be certain that the spring washer on each shaft does not fall into retaining ring groove and block shaft movement, damaging shaft or washer.*

7. Rotate rear-bearing retainer until a hole lines up with 3rd and 4th speed shifter shaft and drive the shaft out toward the front. Remove spring washers and shaft end plugs.

8. Rotate rear bearing retainer until a hole lines up with the reverse-gear shifter shaft and drive the shaft out toward the front.

9. Lift out shift forks, shift head and reverse lever.

10. If removing and disassembling mainshaft assembly with rear-bearing retainer, mark with paint the relative position of 3rd-and 4th-speed clutch sleeve and 1st-and-2nd-speed sliding gear as well as corresponding synchronizer rings and clutch hubs. Marks are made to assure the same tooth or spline contact on reassembly.

11. Turn rear-bearing retainer so that hole for countergear shaft is accessible.

a. Dirve countergear shaft out of transmission case toward the rear.

CAUTION: *Use caution with lock ball on shaft.*

12. Pull mainshaft assembly and rear-bearing retainer out of transmission case together.

13. Slide 3rd-and-4th speed clutch sleeve from the clutch hub and remove keys and front clutch key spring.

14. Clamp mainshaft assembly into a vise having soft jaws and remove mainshaft nut and lockplate.

15. Press from mainshaft, the mainshaft ball bearing, the rear-bearing retainer, two spacers, the mainshaft sleeve, and 1st-speed gear.

16. Slide 1st-and-2nd-speed sliding gear from the clutch hub and remove keys and rear clutch key spring.

NOTE: *Keep synchronizer rings with their respective gears—perhaps by wiring them together. Always discard used synchronizer keys and key springs.*

17. Take snap-ring out of rear-bearing retainer and with a hammer handle carefully push put ball bearing.

a. Pull oil seal ring out of rear bearing retainer.

18. Remove snap-ring behind 1st and 2nd-speed clutch hub from mainshaft. Place next-to-largest slot in a press plate under 2nd-speed gear (between 2nd and 3rd gears) and press gear, 1st-2nd clutch hub and 2nd-speed synchronizer ring from the rear of shaft.

a. Remove front clutch-key spring.

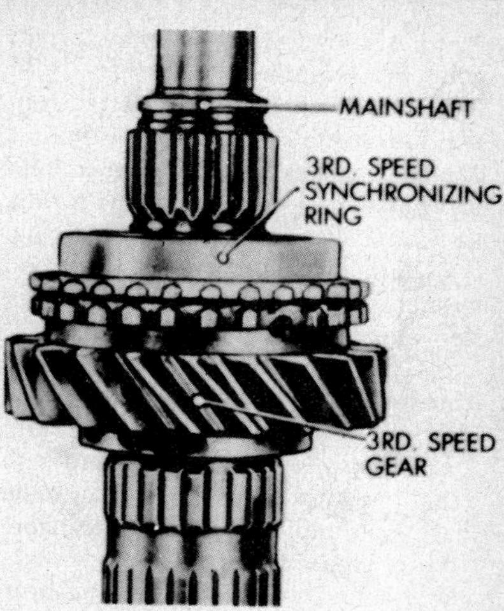

Assemblied gears on mainshaft

Clutch key spring position

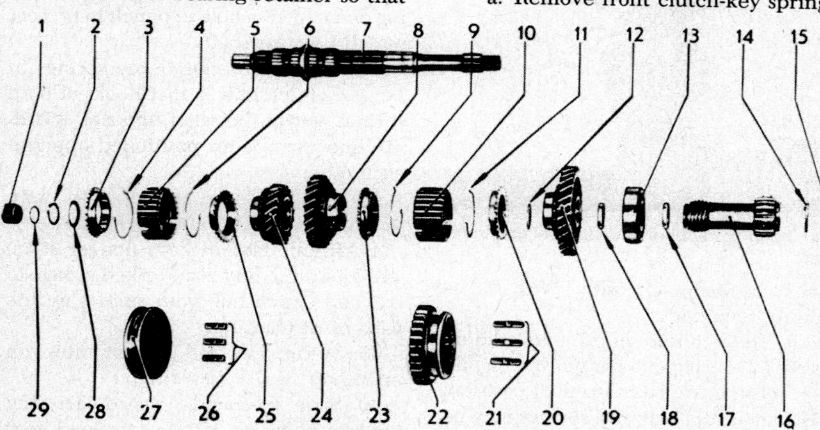

Mainshaft and component parts

1. Needle bearing assembly
2. Snap ring
3. 4th-speed synchronizer ring
4. Clutch key spring
5. 3rd-and-4th-speed clutch hub
6. Clutch key spring
7. Mainshaft
8. 2nd-speed gear
9. Clutch key spring
10. 1st-and-2nd-speed clutch hub
11. Clutch key spring
12. Snap ring
13. Ball bearing
14. Lock plate
15. Nut
16. Mainshaft sleeve
17. Spacer between ball bearing and sleeve
18. Spacer between bearing and 1st-speed gear
19. 1st-speed gear
20. 1st-speed synchronizer ring
21. Keys for 1st-and-2nd-speed sliding gear
22. 1st-and-2nd-speed sliding gear
23. 2nd-speed synchronizer ring
24. 3rd-speed gear
25. 3rd-speed synchronizer ring
26. Keys for 3rd-and-4th-speed clutch sleeve
27. 3rd-and-4th-speed clutch sleeve
28. Spring washer
29. Thrust ring

19. Remove snap-ring from front of mainshaft, insert mainshaft in press plate and press 3rd-speed gear, 3rd-4th clutch hub and 3rd-speed synchronizer ring from the front of mainshaft.

a. Remove rear clutch-key spring from clutch hub.

20. Inspection of mainshaft assembly.

a. Examine shaft, bearing, gears, hubs, and synchronizer rings for excessive wear, chipping, nicks or scoring.

b. Wash ball bearing in solvent, blow dry, and check for roughness or other wear.

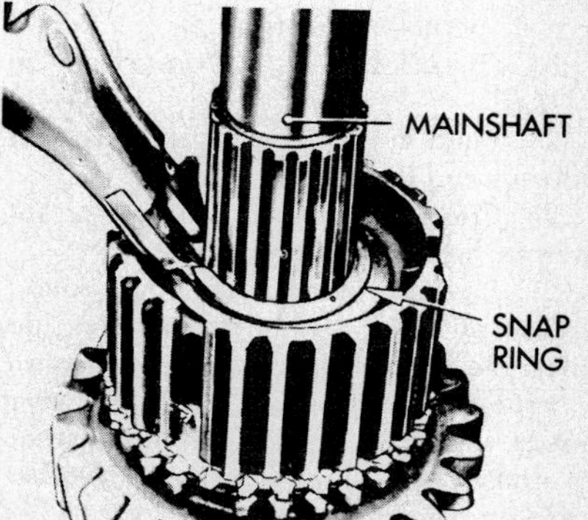

Removing snap-ring from 3rd-& 4th clutch hub.

c. Use new synchronizer key springs when reassembling.

d. Oil all parts with SAE 90 transmission lubricant.

21. To remove main drive gear and bearing assembly, disengage yoke spring, yoke (from ball stud) and release bearing.

a. Remove snap ring and dished washer that retains release-bearing sleeve and main drive gear.

b. The release-bearing sleeve (thrust-bearing guide) and seal assembly can be slid off front of pilot shaft.

c. Grasp pilot (spline) shaft and with a slight rocking motion, withdraw main drive gear and bearing assembly from front of transmission case.

d. Remove and discard O-ring from between clutch-gear bearing and case.

22. To disassemble main drive gear and bearing assembly:

a. Remove caged-needle bearing and thrust ring from gear end of shaft (this bearing may have come out with mainshaft assembly).

b. Remove ball-bearing retaining snap ring and dished washer over spline shaft.

23. Using a press plate and adapter, press bearing forward off main-drive-gear shaft.

NOTE: *When using press, do not allow shaft to tip or bend.*

a. Examine all parts and races for abnormal wear or damage.

b. Try spline for sliding fit into clutch disc hub.

c. Examine release bearing sleeve and inner seal for damage.

d. Remove seal by carefully driving it out with a punch from rear.

e. Using a seal driver for installation, drive seal in until it bottoms in sleeve.

24. Removal of countergear and reverse sliding gear.

a. Lift countergear assembly from bottom of transmission case and remove it through rear of case.

b. Remove thrust washers.

c. Use a long (12 in.) brass drift through pilot gear opening to drive reverse sliding gear shaft out toward rear of transmission case.

d. Remove gear from case.

NOTE: *Do not lose ball imbedded in shaft.*

25. Wash gears, bearings and shafts in solvent and blow dry.

26. Check all parts thoroughly for abnormal wear, nicks or scoring.

27. Reverse sliding gear should rotate freely on shaft without excessive side play (clearance). However, bushings are not serviced separately. If abnormal wear exists, replace gear and bushings. If wear is unusually severe, shaft may also require replacement.

NOTE: *If replacement of caged needle bearings is required, 26 individual needles are to be installed for service replacement instead of two caged bearing assemblies. Place new thrust washers on front and rear of countergear assembly (1966-up only).*

28. Clean transmission case thoroughly prior to reassembly and oil each part as it is reinstalled in housing.

29. Put reverse sliding gear in housing with the long bearing hub facing the rear.

30. Install shaft making sure ball is seated in its groove.

a. Using a plastic mallet, drive shaft until end is flush with the case.

b. Coat countergear thrust washers with petroleum jelly and position them in the case with dimples in slots provided.

31. Start countergear shaft through rear of transmission case.

a. Leave it flush with rear thrust washer.

b. Hold front thrust washer in place with a screwdriver.

c. Coat ends of the countergear assembly with petroleum jelly and insert new thrust washers. Using a countergear needle-bearing loader, install bearing needles into each end of assembly.

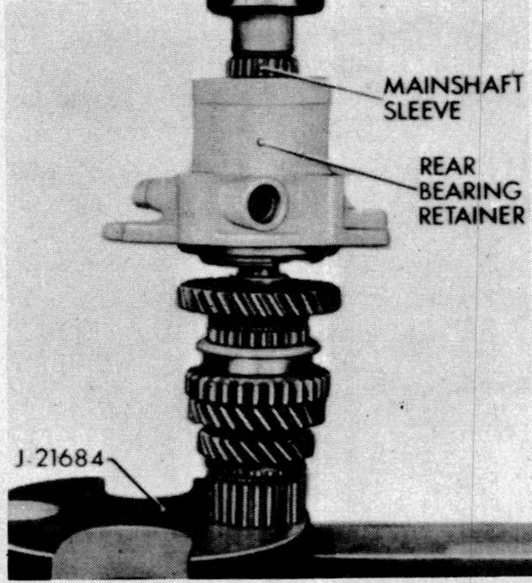

Rear bearing retainer and sleeve on mainshaft.

32. Mainshaft Assembly With Rear-Bearing Retainer.

a. The clutch hubs and sliding sleeves are factory mated and should be returned to their original position. However, the keys and springs may be replaced individually if worn or broken.

33. From front of the mainshaft install 3rd-speed gear on mainshaft. Assemble it so that the gear turns freely on mainshaft.

34. Place 3rd-speed synchronizer ring over 3rd-speed cone.

35. Install rear clutch-key spring in 3rd-4th clutch hub so that hooked spring end rests in a hub slot.

36. Using a press plate, press 3rd-4th clutch hub onto mainshaft so that the original tooth-alignment is restored. Secure clutch hub with a snap ring.

37. Slide 2nd-speed gear from the rear onto mainshaft. Gear must turn freely.

a. Place 2nd-speed synchronizer ring on 2nd-speed gear cone.

NOTE: *Install caged needle bearings in countergear assembly if bearing replacement is not required.*

38. With a loading tool in place, position countergear assembly in bottom of case, large end forward, taking care not to disturb thrust washers and loose needles.

NOTE: *Do not tap countergear shaft through its assembly until after installation of main drive gear and mainshaft.*

39. Place a spring washer over reverse shift lever pin and install lever.

40. To assemble main drive gear and bearing assembly, raise transmission case on end (bell housing up).

a. Lubricate and position new main-drive-gear bearing "O" ring in groove. Install main-drive-gear assembly.

b. Rap tool lightly with a plastic mallet until locating snap ring is against case.

c. Lubricate seal in release bearing sleeve and install sleeve over spline shaft until flange touches bearing.

d. Place dished washer on sleeve flange, dished-out side down, and install snap ring. It may be necessary to tap snap ring down with punch to start it into groove. To assure good snap ring engagement, grip ends of snap ring with expanding (external) snap-ring pliers and force ring back into the groove.

41. Place transmission case, bell housing down, over a hole in bench to protect maindrive-gear shaft.

42. Install both clutch key springs in 1st-2nd clutch hub so that hooks of both springs rest in the same hub slot as 3rd-4th hub springs are positioned opposite each other.

43. Press 1st-2nd clutch hub onto mainshaft so that original teeth mate.

44. Install 1st-2nd keys (longer style) and 1st-2nd sliding gear (forked groove to rear) on clutch hub with splines in line with paint markings.

45. Secure 1st-2nd clutch hub on mainshaft with a snap ring.

46. Slide 1st-speed synchrohizer ring (line up paint markings), 1st-speed gear and spacer onto mainshaft.

47. Oil sealring lips and drive seal ring into rear bearing retainer to its stop.

48. Press rear bearing into bearing retainer near outer race and install snap ring. If bearing has been replaced, a new snap ring must be selected according to width of bearing outer-race.

NOTE: *Replacement bearing boxes marked "A" use a silver snap ring. Boxes marked "B" use a blue snap ring. Boxes marked "C" use a black snap ring.*

49. Slide mainshaft assembly through rear bearing retainer, place spacer and mainshaft sleeve onto mainshaft and press all parts onto mainshaft.

50. Position front 3rd-4th clutch key spring.

51. Install the 3 keys (short design) and 3rd-4th sleeve over hub along with synchronizing ring—noting paint marks.

52. Install thrust ring and needle-bearing assembly onto the mainshaft.

53. Install 4th-speed synchronizer ring onto the clutch gear.

54. Place a new rear-bearing retainer gasket on retainer.

55. Place mainshaft assembly into transmission case.

56. Line up paint markings on 4th-speed synchronizer ring and 3rd-4th clutch sleeve.

57. Line up countergear assembly and its thrust washers with shaft holes in front and rear of case.

58. Coat inner surface of front shaft hole in case with sealer, rotate rearbearing retainer and gasket out of way and install countergear shaft. Make certain that the locating ball is in place and enters groove in case.

59. Tap shaft in until rear of shaft is flush with case.

60. Position rear-bearing retainer, coat lower attaching bolt with an appropriate sealer, and tighten bolt to a torque of 25 ft lbs.

61. Secure transmission firmly in a vise, loosely install nut and lockplate on mainshaft, place a drive-pinion-flange wrench on mainshaft sleeve.

62. Counterhold mainshaft sleeve and torque nut to 18 ft lbs. Secure nut with a lockplate.

NOTE: *On installed transmissions, with drive shaft removed, a drive-pin-*

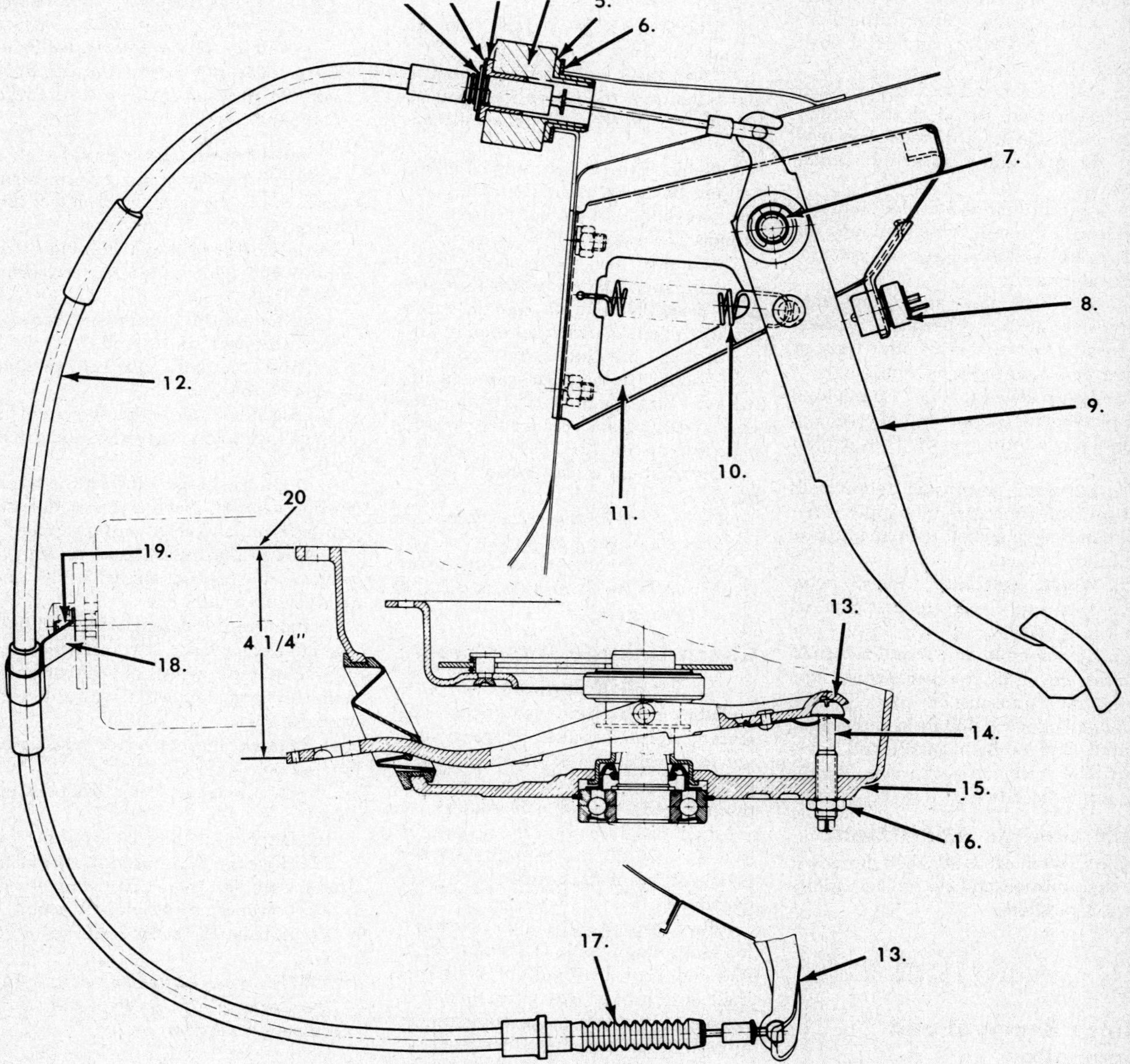

Clutch pedal and component parts

1. "E" ring
2. Washer
3. Rubber grommet
4. Clutch operating damper
5. Grommet
6. Washer
7. "E" ring
8. Adjustment switch
9. Clutch pedal
10. Return spring
11. Bracket
12. Cable
13. Release lever
14. Ball stud
15. Clutch housing
16. Ball stud lock nut
17. Rubber bellows
18. Cable support bracket
19. Nut, cable support bracket
20. Distance between release lever and clutch housing

ion-flange wrench can be used to counterhold mainshaft sleeve while checking torque of mainshaft nut.

63. Installing Shifter Shafts.

a. Lubricate and install interlock pins (passage in rear top of case).

b. Coat retaining plugs with sealer and drive them in until plugs bottom. Pins must be located between shift shafts.

64. Place mainshaft gear train in neutral and loosely position shift forks and shifter head in case.

65. From front of transmission, insert short shifter shaft into hole on right side.

66. Place shaft through reverse idler fork, install spring washer (dished-out side toward the front) and feed shaft through shifter head.

62. Next, insert 1st-2nd shifter shaft into center hole, install spring washer (dished-out side toward front) and feed shaft through shifter fork and shifter head.

68. Insert 3rd-4th shifter shaft into left hole, feed it through shifter fork and install spring washer (dished-out side toward the rear).

69. Install six new snap rings into shifter shaft grooves. The spring washers are located between the shifter forks or shifter head and the snap rings.

70. Apply sealer to shaft caps (plugs) and place them in front end of case. Tap in until plugs bottom on shoulder in shaft hole.

71. Lubricate and install detent balls and springs. Then carefully apply sealer to retainer plugs and drive them into case until they bottom.

72. When installing speedometer drive gear, apply sealer to gear cap and tap it into place.

73. To assemble and install transmission case cover, place reverse-speed stop spring into transmission cover, grease cover gasket, place shift forks and head in neutral, and position gasket and cover plate. Use sealer on all threads. Torque cap screws to 7 ft lbs.

Shift Linkage Adjustment

The shift linkage is attached directly to the transmission and no linkage adjustment is possible.

CLUTCH

Clutch Removal and Installation

OHV Engines

1. Remove the transmission from the vehicle (see procedure in manual transmission removal and installation section).

2. Check for assembly alignment marks on the clutch cover flange and flywheel. If no marks are present, punch or scribe marks for installation purposes.

3. Loosen the four clutch cover retaining bolts one turn at a time, and remove the pressure plate and driven disc.

4. Hold the clutch disc and pressure plate against the flywheel, and insert a clutch pilot tool.

5. Align the mating marks on the flywheel and clutch cover (if using the original pressure plate) and tighten the four retaining bolts evenly and gradually to 15 ft lbs. Install the transmission.

CIH Engines

1. Remove the transmission from the vehicle (see procedure in manual transmission, removal and installation section).

2. Unbolt the exhaust pipe from the exhaust manifold.

3. Disconnect the clutch return spring and cable from the clutch fork, and unbolt the starter from the flywheel housing.

4. Remove the clutch support-to-bellhousing bolts, back out the clutch support-to-cylinder block bolts, and swing support downward.

5. Remove the bellhousing lower cover and the bellhousing. If the pressure plate assembly is to be reused, ensure that alignment marks are present on the flywheel and the clutch cover flange.

6. Loosen the clutch cover retaining bolts one turn at a time until spring pressure is released, and remove the pressure plate and driven disc.

7. Installation is the reverse of removal.

NOTE: *When installing the clutch onto the flywheel, use a pilot tool, to ensure proper alignment of the driven disc, and torque the cover bolts gradually to avoid distortion.*

Clutch Linkage Adjustment

OHV Engines

Clutch pedal free play (pedal lash) must be adjusted occasionally to compensate for normal wear of the clutch facings. As the driven plate (clutch disc) wears thinner, pedal free play decreases.

Clutch pedal free play should measure ¾ to 1 in. (20–25 mm) from the released-pedal rest point to start of clutch disengagement.

Adjust free play at clutch housing by loosening clutch cable lock nut at release fork and screw ball-stud nut along cable shaft until proper play is reached. Hold hexagon end of cable to permit loosening of locknut and turning of ball stud.

CIH Engines

Clutch pedal free play should be adjusted to between ¾ and 1 ¾ in., by turning the ball stud located on the right side of the clutch housing. Cable length is not adjustable. Turning the ball stud clockwise decreases, and counterclockwise increases, pedal travel.

AUTOMATIC TRANSMISSION

The Opel three-speed automatic is a fully automatic unit utilizing a torque converter and a Ravigneaux planetary gear set, with three multiple disc clutches and a single band to provide three forward speeds and reverse. Automatic upshifts and downshifts are controlled by road speed, engine vacuum and an accelerator pedal connection to the transmission.

Removal and Installation

NOTE: *When removing or installing the automatic transmission, ensure that the front of the transmission is always above the rear of the transmission, to prevent the converter from falling out.*

All Models (Except GT)

1. From the top of the transmission, before the car is raised, disconnect the battery.

2a. Remove two upper housing bolts, remove the filler tube and converter housing bolt.

2b. On the 1.9 liter engine, remove the two upper starter bolts.

3. Raise the car and remove the flywheel cover pan.

4. Disconnect the exhaust system at exhaust manifold and remove the driveshaft.

5. Drain the oil pan, loosen the transmission support, place a jack under the transmission, and remove the support.

6. Lower the transmission enough to remove the speedometer cable and modulator vacuum line.

7. Remove the detent cable and linkage at selector lever or transmission.

8. Mark the flywheel and converter for assembly and remove flywheel-to-converter bolts.

9. Remove the converter housing-to-engine bolts.

11. Pry the transmission from the engine.

10. Disconnect the cooler lines.

12. Move the transmission back and install a clamping tool to hold converter.

13. Lower transmission to a bench.

14. Installation is the reverse of removal

NOTE: *When installing, ensure that the marks on the flywheel and on the converter align properly.*

GT

1. Disconnect the battery and pull the throttle control rod off of the ball pin.

2. Raise the car.

3. Remove the heat shield from the right side and the exhaust pipe.

4. Remove the driveshaft and detach rear engine support from the transmission crossmember.

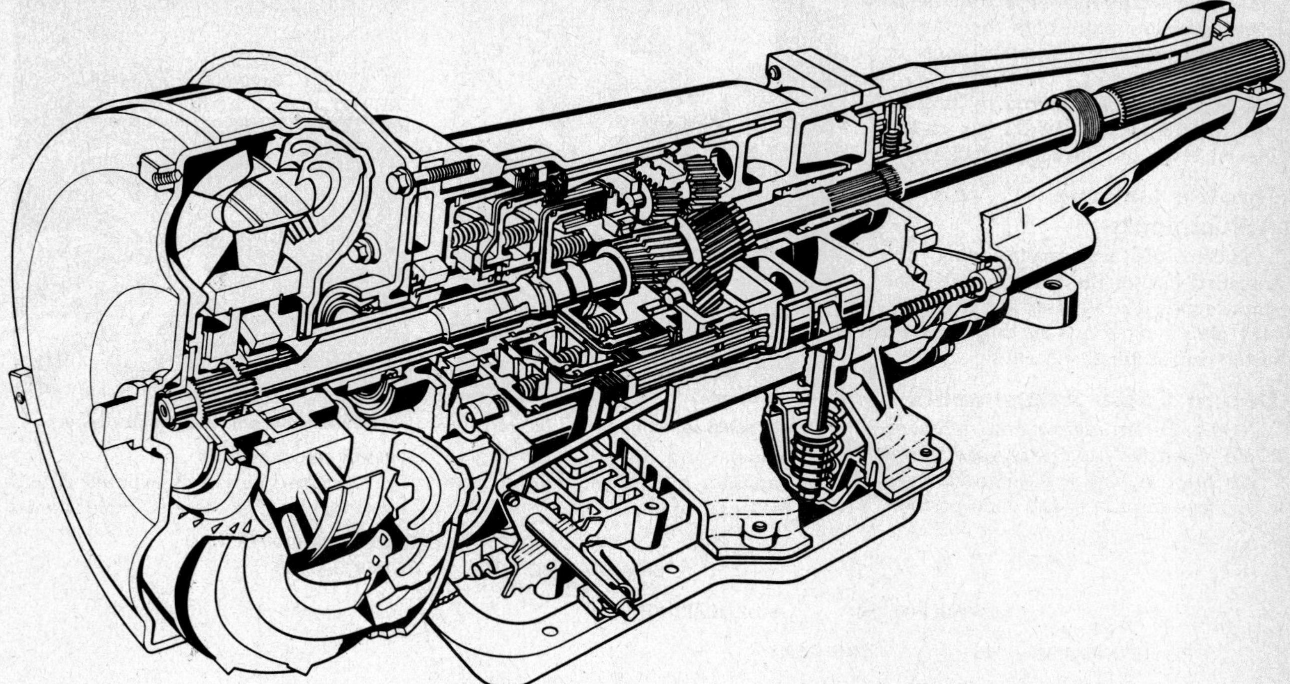

Cross-section of automatic transmission

5. Support the transmission with a jack.

6. Unscrew the transmission cross-member from side members.

7. Lower transmission as far as possible then drain the oil.

8. Detach selector rod from ball pin at the outer transmission selector lever.

9. Remove the cooler lines and pull vacuum line from modulator.

10. Detach detent cable from accelerator pedal and unscrew detent cable from transmission.

11. Remove speedometer cable, then unscrew engine support brackets from torque converter housing. Slacken only the front attaching bolt.

12. Remove the torque converter housing cover plate and mark flex plate and converter for assembly.

13. Unscrew the three torque converter-to-flex plate attaching bolts.

14. Pry the transmission loose from the engine.

15. Move transmission back and insert a clamping tool to hold converter, then lower transmission to a bench.

16. Installation is the reverse of removal.

NOTE: *When installing, rotate the converter to ensure that the marks on the flex plate and the converter align properly.*

Pan Removal and Installation

1. Raise the car and drain the oil.

2. Remove the twelve bolts which hold the oil pan to transmission.

3. Remove oil pan and gasket.

4. Installation is the reverse of removal.

NOTE: *Always replace old gasket and be careful not to over-tighten pan bolts.*

Filter or Strainer Service

1. Raise car and support it safely.

2. Drain fluid from oil pan.

3. Remove oil pan and gasket. Discard gasket.

4. Remove strainer assembly, strainer gasket and discard the gasket.

5. Install a new oil strainer gasket. Install new strainer assembly.

6. Install a new gasket on oil pan and install pan. Tighten attaching bolts to 7–10 ft. lb.

7. Lower car and add approximately three (3) pints of transmission fluid through filler tube.

8. With manual control lever in Park position, start engine. DO NOT RACE ENGINE. Move manual control lever through each range.

9. Immediately check fluid level with selector lever in Neutral, engine running, and vehicle on a LEVEL surface.

10. Add additional fluid to bring level to ¼ in. below the ADD mark on the dipstick. Do not overfill.

Servo Adjustment

1. Drain fluid from transmission and remove pan.

2. Use a 3/16 in. hex head wrench on servo adjusting bolt. Adjust servo apply rod by tightening adjusting bolt to 40 in. lbs. Back off bolt exactly five (5) turns.

3. Tighten lock nut while holding adjusting bolt and sleeve firmly with a hex-head wrench.

4. Reinstall pan, using a new gasket, and refill transmission.

Servo adjusting bolt

Locking servo into position

Shift Linkage Adjustment

1. Remove the lock clip which holds the control rod to the selector lever.

2. Remove the control rod from the selector lever and place both the selector lever and the transmission shift lever in the drive position.

3. Adjust the control rod by turning until it slides freely over the pin on the selector lever, and install the lock clip.

Throttle Linkage Adjustments

Adjustments are made using the threaded end of the throttle rods. The throttle should be adjusted so that it operates freely and permits the throttle plates of the carburetor to close fully.

Detent Cable Adjustments

NOTE: *Before adjusting the detent cable (downshift cable) it is essential that the throttle linkage be adjusted first.*

1. Place throttle in full open position.

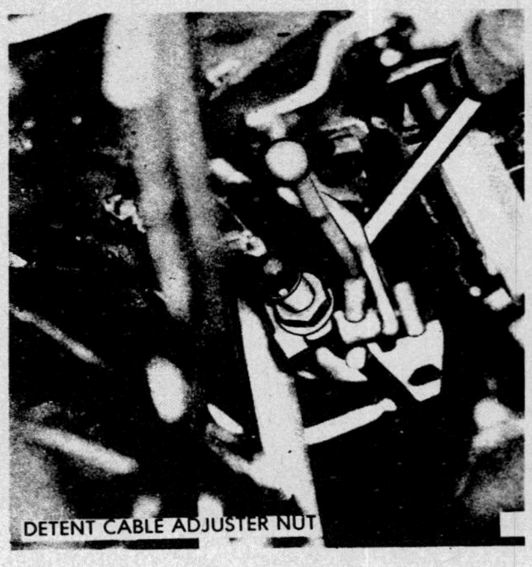

Detent cable adjusting points (Lower)

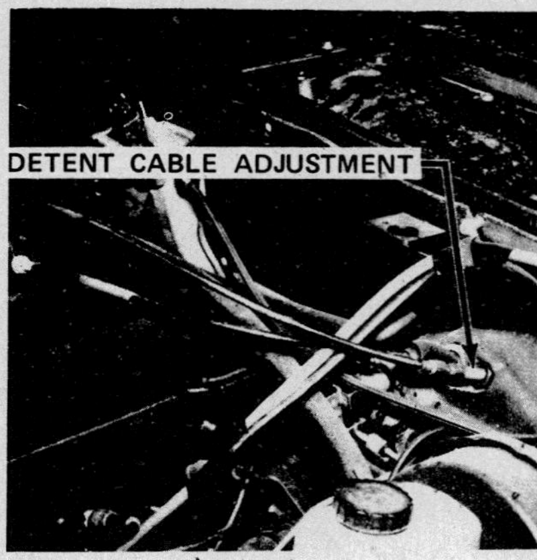

Detent cable adjusting point (Upper)

2. Loosen and tighten upper and lower adjustor nuts of the detent cable until ball end of the cable rests firmly against selector lever.

3. Measure length of exposed detent inner cable. The detent cable should

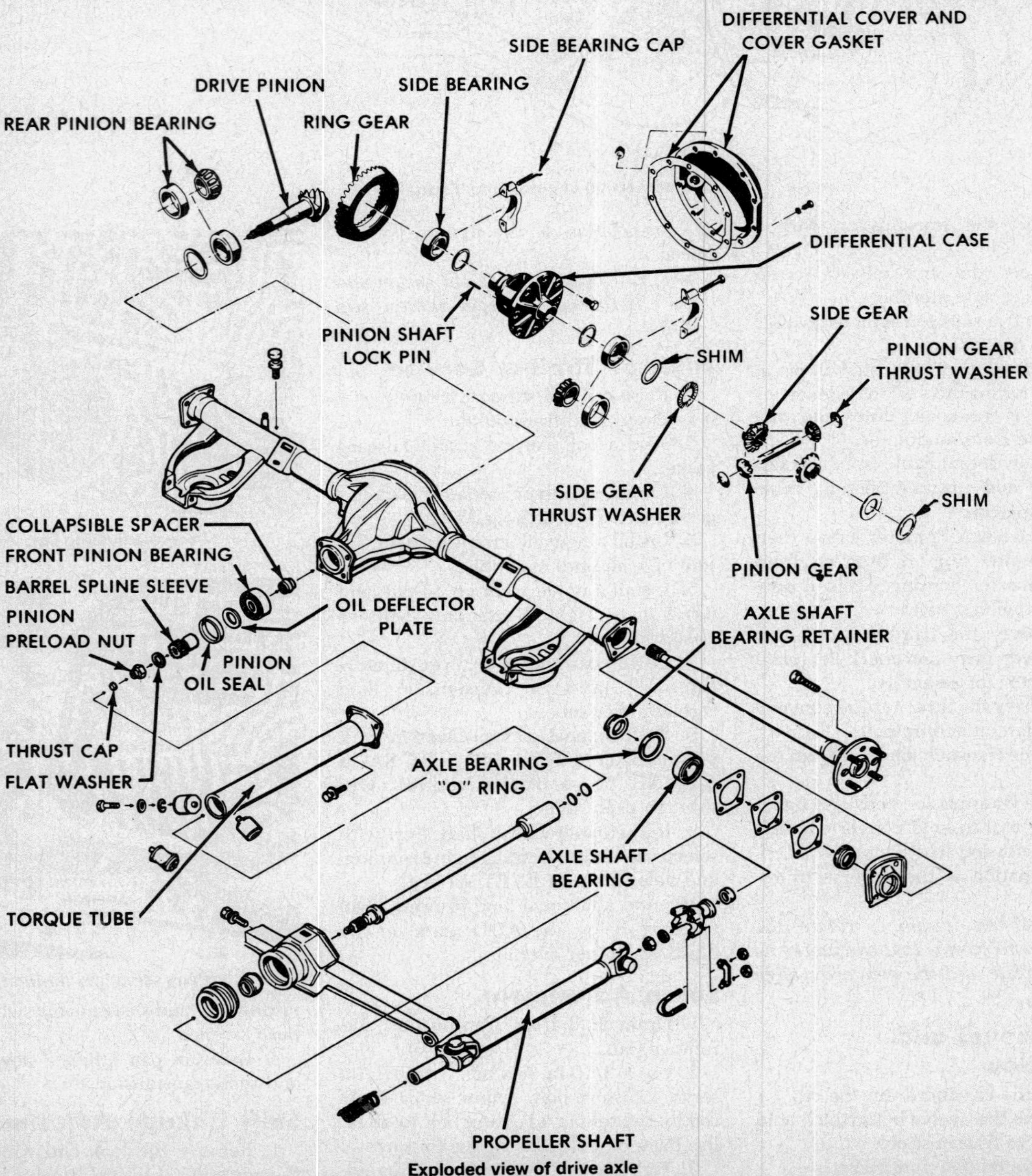

Exploded view of drive axle

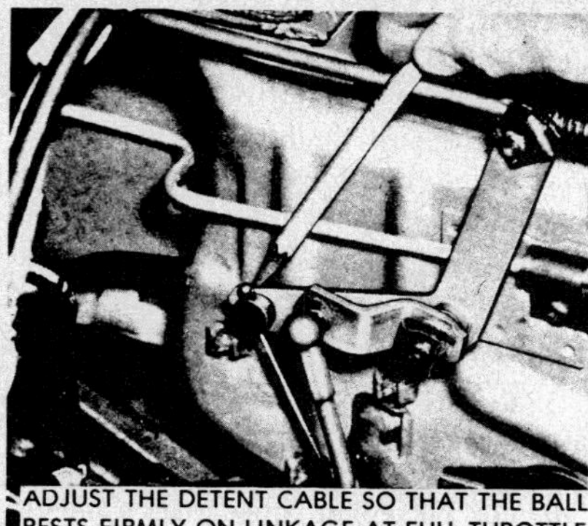

Detent cable ball position at full throttle

measure approximately ⅜ in.

Neutral Safety Switch Adjustment

The neutral safety switch has no adjustments on its mounting position. If switch needs an adjustment, adjust shift linkage to center neutral starting position in transmission.

DRIVE AXLES

General

Rear suspension on Kadetts from 1964 through 1967 is designed with leaf springs. The axle assembly is attached to the springs with support brackets. The attachment point of the axle to each rear spring is forward of center to reduce driving and coasting stresses on the springs. A plastic pad is placed between the leaves of each rear spring to prevent friction and squeaking. The rear springs have a progressive action, becoming stiffer with increased load.

Rear suspension for 1968–73 was completely redesigned with coil springs, a track bar, and a roll stabilizer.

Rear wheel rates were reduced, as a result of the design change, from 102 psi to 95 psi.

The coil springs are mounted on the axle. Two (lower) control arms connect the axle to the body. The differential torque-tube mount at the central joint is (in effect) an upper control arm. Using the torque tube as a control arm allows for a lower underbody and additional cushion depth in the rear passenger seat. Because this suspension design directs greater stress to the axle tube, metal thickness of the tube is increased.

Driveshaft and U-Joints

Removal and Installation

1966–71 OHV Engines

1. Raise the rear of the vehicle and disconnect the parking brake equalizer from the rod.
2. Remove one rear engine mount bolt and loosen the other.
3. Mark the mating parts of the driveshaft and pinion extension, and remove the mounting bolts.
4. Slide the shaft slightly forward, and remove the shaft and thrust spring.
5. Install a plug to avoid fluid loss from the transmission.
6. Install in the reverse order of removal.
7. Insert the small end of the thrust spring into the transmission, and torque the flange bolts to 18 ft lbs.

1968–73 CIH Engines

Removal and installation is similar to the OHV engine models, except that the rear engine mount need not be loosened. When installing, torque rear U-joint U-bolts to 11 ft lbs.

Center Joint Assembly

Removal and Installation

1. Remove driveshaft. Follow the procedure outlined in that section.
2. Support torque tube and remove center joint bracket.
3. Lower torque tube and disconnect it from differential carrier.
4. Install pinion flange holder and remove self-locking nut.
5. Pull pinion shaft from extension housing using a soft mallet.
6. Remove support bracket-to-support cushions.
7. Installation is the reverse of removal.

NOTE: *Check the support cushions and replace if necessary. The fasteners which hold the center joint should be replaced when overhauled. Also, use a new selflocking nut for pinion flange and torque to 87 ft lbs.*

Axle Shaft Assembly

Removal and Installation

1. Raise and support rear of the car.
2. Remove wheel and brake drum from the side to be removed.
3. Unscrew axle shaft retaining plate and pull axle from housing.
4. Installation is the reverse of removal.

Overhaul

1. Check radial runout (0.002 in.) and lateral runout (0.004 in.) of the axle shaft. If these tolerances are exceeded, the shaft must be replaced.
2. Press a new bearing onto shaft so that oil seal groove faces shaft splines.

NOTE: *When replacing bearing, always replace outer race which is located in housing.*

3. Check axle shaft end play.
   a. Measure depth of axle bearing seat in housing.

Measuring depth of axle shaft bearing

   b. Measure width of bearing outer race. The maximum end play is 0.002–0.006 in.

Differential

Removal and Installation

1. Raise the rear of the vehicle and support it with jack stands at the jack brackets.
2. Remove both rear wheels and one rear brake drum.
3. Disconnect the parking brake rod from the equalizer, and the cable from the actuating lever on the side with the drum removed.
4. Separate the cable from the lower control arm brackets and hang the free end over the exhaust pipe.
5. Unbolt the shock absorbers, the track rod, and (if so equipped) the stabilizer shackles, from the rear axle brackets.
6. Mark the mating parts of the driveshaft-to-pinion extension flange, separate the flange, and tie the driveshaft out of the way.
7. Disconnect and cap the brake hoses at the differential.
8. Lower the axle enough to remove load from the springs, and remove the springs.
9. Unbolt the central joint bracket from the under pan and the lower control arms from the axle brackets, and roll the axle out from under the vehicle.
10. Install in the reverse order of removal.

NOTE: *When installing the central joint to the underpan, place a load of approximately 350 lbs. in the trunk.*

11. Support the vehicle by the differential housing (raise off of the jack stands), and torque the bolts to 33 ft lbs.

NOTE: *Following installation of the axle, the brake system must be bled.*

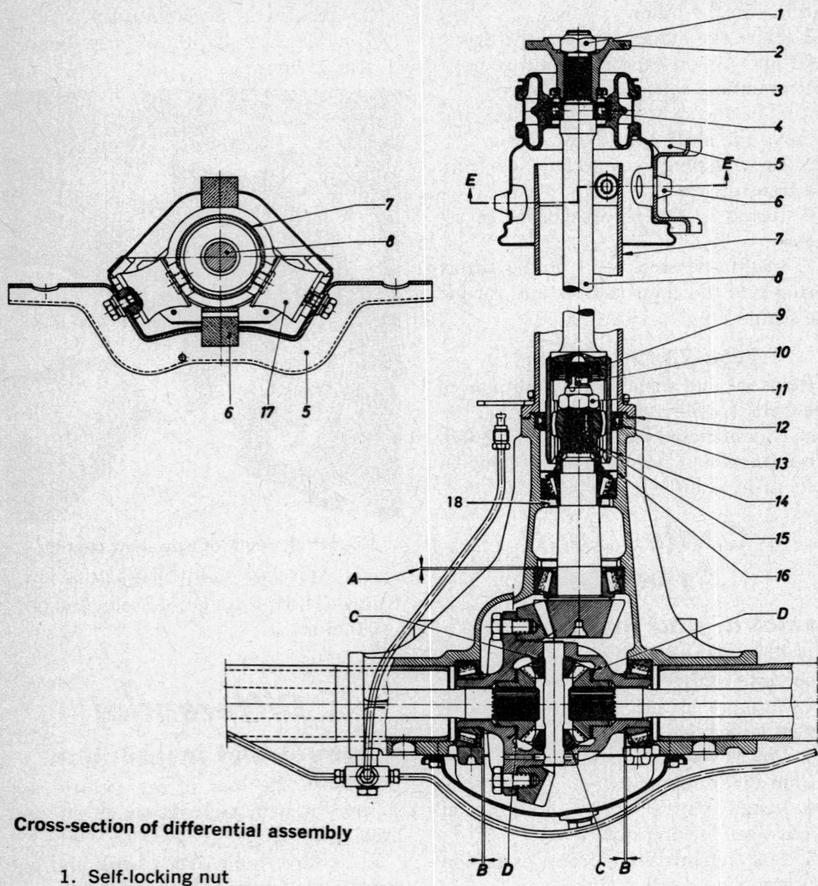

Cross-section of differential assembly

1. Self-locking nut
2. Drive-pinion-shaft extension flange
3. Rubber cushion
4. Ball bearing with sheet metal casing
5. Central joint support
6. Rubber cushion on central joint support
7. Torque tube
8. Drive pinion extension
9. Hard rubber disc
10. Thrust cap
11. Hex. nut
12. Paper gasket
13. Oil seal
14. Slip joint
15. Splined sleeve
16. Oil deflector
17. Rubber cushion
18. Collapsible spacer

(a)—Shims for drive-pinion height adjustment
(b)—Shims for ring gear and pinion backlash adjustment
(c)—Spherical washer
(d)—Shim for differential side gears

Overhaul

Disassembly of Differential and Pinion Assemblies

1. Raise rear of car and support it with jackstands.
2. Remove wheels and brake drums from both sides of the car.
3. Prior to draining differential, remove brake pipe assembly, including pipes which attach wheel cylinder, junction block at differential housing, and hose bracket on torque tube.

NOTE: *It is not necessary to remove brake hardware to remove differential and pinion assemblies.*

4. Loosen differential bolts and drain lubricant by breaking loose cover at bottom. Remove cover.
5. Next, check pinion depth, ring gear-to-pinion backlash, and side bearing preload. If adjustments meet specifications, it is not necessary to disassemble pinion and differential.

To remove the differential assembly procede as follows:

1. Mark side-bearing caps and housing with a punch for proper reinstallation.
2. Remove attaching bolts and caps. Using suitable wood levers (such as hammer handles), pry out differential assembly. Do not drop or interchange bearing races.
3. Remove both differential side bearings with a bearing puller.

NOTE: *Do not interchange bearings or shims.*

4. Remove bolts which attach the ring gear to differential case.
5. Evenly tap ring gear off of case with a brass drift and a hammer.

To remove the pinion shaft from the housing, procede as follows:

1. With driveshaft disconnected and central joint disassembled, remove bolts which attach the rear torque tube to axle housing and break the flange seal with a block of wood.
2. Withdraw pinion-shaft extension and torque tube from axle housing.
3. Remove pinion-shaft extension from torque tube using a soft mallet against shaft at central-joint end.
4. Remove ball bearing from its cushion.
5. Remove selflocking nut on pinion-shaft (immobilize flange with a wrench which can be clamped in a vise).
6. Pull off pinion flange with a puller, taking care to protect threads.
7. Using a suitable sharp-pointed tool, pry pinion oil seal from its seat.

NOTE: *To prevent damage to the flange, lay a screwdriver against the flange as a base for prying.*

8. Place a wrench on preload adjusting nut and continue disassembly by following steps below that apply.
   a. 1966-67 models have a pinion with a splined sleeve.
   b. 1968–73 models have pinions with barrel splines
9. Grip sleeve or barrel to hold pinion from turning while removing pinion nut. Remove thrust cap.
10. Tap pinion from housing with a soft-face hammer.
11. Tap out pinion bearing races, noting shims behind inner bearing outer race.
12. Press off pinion inner bearing.
13. Drive out pinion-shaft lock pin with a small punch.
14. Remove pinion gears, side gears, and shims.

Assembling Differential and Pinion Assemblies

1. Clean all mating surfaces of foreign matter or burrs.
2. Press on pinion bearings and races, lubricating bearings amply.
3. Check pinion depth in housing.

NOTE: *If an improper reading (see chart) is attained, place shims under pinion to reach proper pinion depth with no further end play.*

4. Tighten the pinion preload adjusting nut until preload specifications are nearly reached.
5. Check torque required to turn pinion (in inch-pounds) after turning it several times to seat bearings. Readjust pinion preload nut as requred, taking readings while pinion is turning.

CAUTION: *After preload has been checked final tightening must be done very carefully so as not to over-compress collapsible spacer.*

6. Stake adjusting nut to slots, drive thrust cap onto end of shaft (use a new cap if old fits loosely), and install a new seal after soaking in hypoid lube a few minutes.

7. Lubricate side gears, pinion gears and washers.

8. Install side gears and thrust washers into case.

9. Position one pinion (without washer) between side gears and rotate gears until pinion is directly opposite the loading opening in the case.

10. Place another pinion between side gears and align so that pinion-axle holes line up with holes in case.

11. When holes are aligned, rotate pinions back toward loading opening just enough to permit sliding pinion thrust washers in.

12. Reinstall with flange facing toward front of car.

13. Pack area in front of bearing with water-resistant grease.

14. Replace cushions if necessary. Torque new ones to 29 ft lbs.

15. Put central-joint support in place on one cushion and then pry the support over the other with a screwdriver.

16. Bolt together and torque to 15 ft lbs.

17. Inserting pinion-shaft extension into torque tube from the rear, tap it into place with a soft-face mallet.

18. Position pinion flange, tap it into place far enough to start pinion nut (use a soft-face mallet), install a new nut on flange, secure flange and torque nut to 73 ft lbs.

19. Install torque tube and central-joint assembly on rear axle housing using a new gasket.

20. Install pinion shaft so that the hole in shaft aligns with lock pin holes in case.

NOTE: *If clearance between side gears and differential case exceeds 0.006 in. install thicker shims.*

21. Slip lock pin in pinion shaft and secure by peening case.

22. Position ring gear on differential case (plate) so that holes in gear align with holes in case. Attach bolts and torque to 30 ft lbs.

Torqueing sequence on ring gear

23. *To adjust side-bearing preload* and to set proper ring gear-to-pinion backlash, the differential side bearings must be precisely shimmed.

a. Place differential side-bearing outer races on bearings and install differential case in carrier.

b. Insert two sets of feeler gauges between the differential case and each side-bearing outer race.

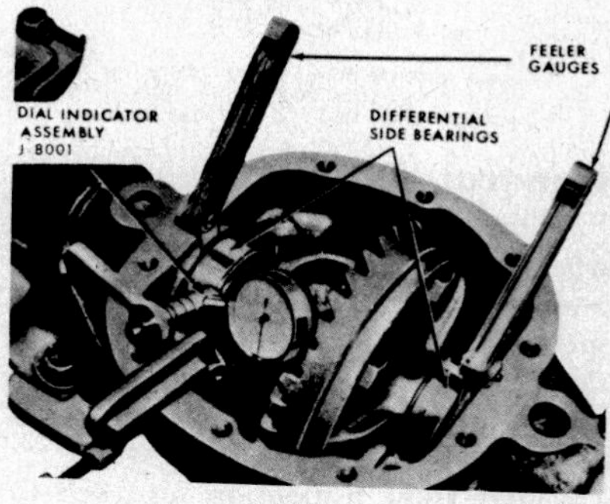

Adjusting differential tolerances

c. Work each gauge to the bottom of the pedestal bore.

d. Increase gauge thickness until all end play is removed.

e. Replace gauges with shims of same thickness.

24. *Ring gear backlash (clearance)* is set by readjusting differential case from side to side.

a. Set backlash by adding feelers at one side bearing and removing from other until gear tooth clearance is an average of 0.005 in. within a 0.004–.008 in. range.

b. A dial indicator that mounts at right angles with the ring gear teeth is available.

NOTE: *When end play is removed and backlash is correct, select shims to a thickness of feeler gauges. In addition add 0.002 in. to each side to obtain side bearing preload.*

25. Remove side bearings, fit shims behind respective bearings, and reseat the bearings.

26. Place outer races on side bearings and set differential case into its carrier.

27. Using a plastic hammer, tap case in until seated at bottom of bores.

28. Tighten bearing-cap bolts to 30 ft lbs.

29. Rotate case several times to seat bearings.

30. Check backlash and side bearing preload using an inch-pound torque wrench connected at right angles to the assembly. Preload should be 10–20 in. lbs.

DIFFERENTIAL SPECIFICATIONS—PINION BEARING PRELOAD

1.1 Liter Engine

	(Average)	(Range)
New bearings	8 in. lbs.	5-11 in. lbs.
Original bearings	4 in. lbs.	3-5 in. lbs.

1.5 and 1.9 Liter Engines

	(Average)	(Range)
New bearings	9 in. lbs.	7-12 in. lbs.
Original bearings	6 in. lbs.	5-7 in. lbs.

Pinion depth setting (from pinion marking) +0.002 to −0.001 in.

Shims for Setting Pinion Depth

Notches in shim	Shim thickness (in.)
One side flattened	0.0016-0.0024
0	0.0094-0.0102
1	0.0104-0.0112
2	0.0114-0.0122
3	0.0124-0.0132
4	0.0134-0.0142
5	0.0144-0.0152

Clearance from differential side gears to case max 0.006 in.

Shims for Setting Clearance

Notches in shim	Shim thickness (in.)
0	0.019-0.020
1	0.023-0.024
2	0.027-0.028
3	0.031-0.032

Maximum runout, axle shaft bearing-seat	0.002 in.
Maximum lateral runout, rear axle shaft-flange (at largest flange diameter)	0.004 in.
Maximum lateral runout, ring gear	0.003 in.
Lash, ring gear to drive pinion	0.004-0.008 in.
Differential side baring preload	
New bearings:	20-30 ft lbs.
Old bearings	10-20 ft lbs.

Shims for Setting Preload

Notches in shim	Shim thickness (in.)
0	0.0056-0.0062
1	0.0066-0.0072
2	0.0076-0.0082
3	0.0085-0.0092
4	0.0094-0.0102
5	0.0104-0.0112
6	0.0193-0.0201
7	0.0386-0.0398

REAR SUSPENSION

Spring

Removal and Installation

1. Raise the vehicle and support it at its rear jack brackets.
2. Disconnect the shock absorbers and (if equipped) the stabilizer and shackles from the rear axle brackets.
3. Lower the rear axle as far as possible and remove the springs.

NOTE: *When lowering rear axle, do not stress brake hose.*

4. Install the springs, checking to ensure that they are properly seated in the damper rings and seats.
5. Jack up the rear axle at the differential housing, compressing the springs in their seats.
6. Attach the shock absorbers to the rear axle, torquing the nuts to 15 ft lbs.
7. Attach stabilizer and torque bolts to 25 ft lbs.

Shock Absorber

Removal and Installation

1. Raise the vehicle and support it at its rear jacking brackets.
2. Disconnect the shock absorbers at lower mounting point.
3. Place a jack under rear and slightly raise rear.
4. Remove the shocks from their upper mounting position.
5. Installation is the reverse of removal.

FRONT SUSPENSION

General

All Opel models use independent front wheel suspension attached to a cross member and a transverse steel-band spring. Road shock is dampened by direct shock absorbers. The entire suspension can be removed as a unit. No maintenance lubrication is needed.

Kadett front suspension for 1966–67 models differs from earlier models, with a larger cross member, longer two-leaf spring, tapered seats for ball joints, and a rubber bumper to eliminate spring and cross member interference.

The 1968 suspension was modified from the 1967 design by a change to a softer spring. As a result, wheel rates dropped from 99 pounds per square inch to 80 psi and ride softness improved. Other changes were made to handle the additional weight of two optional engines but are adopted on all models for simplified part servicing. The modifications include the following:

. . . shaft for lower control arm is redesigned with a larger offset to accommodate three-leaf spring.

. . . lower ball-joint and stud are larger.

. . . Tapered roller bearings replace ball bearings.

. . . steering knuckle spindles and wheel hubs are changed to hold tapered bearings. (Drum-brake steering knuckles and front hubs for ball bearings on models prior to 1968 are not interchangeable to disc-brake knuckles and hubs).

. . . Rubber is vulcanized to inner sleeve of lower control arm for greater durability. Hardness of rubber is reduced for softer ride.

The front end for the 15S and 19S engines uses a three-leaf transverse spring to properly suspend the greater weight. A rubber bushing is vulcanized to the spring inner sleeve. The three-leaf assembly is not interchangeable with the standard suspension.

Removal and Installation as a Unit

1.1 Engine

1. Block and brake wheels, jack up front end (place block of wood between jack and cross member to prevent damage), and support car with stands at rear of front frame rails.
2. Support power plant at rear of

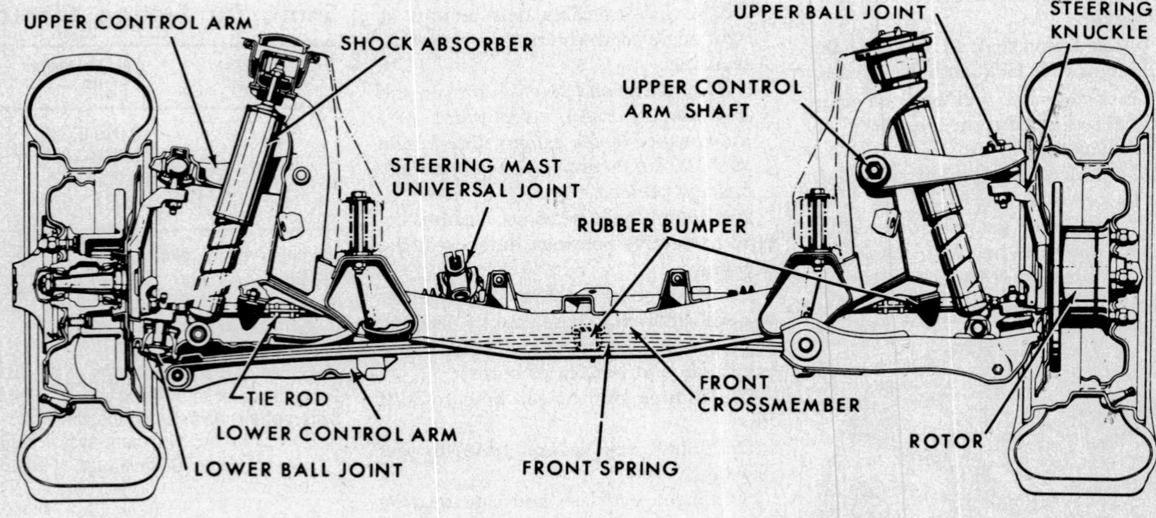

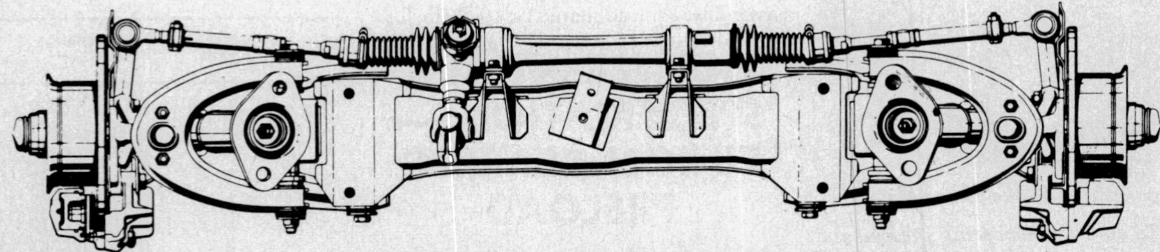

Front suspension (disc brakes)

transmission with a stand; remove clamping bolt and nut from steering mast flange, and take out stop bolt from mast guide below steering wheel.

3. Gently lift steering column from mast flange until it stops against direction signal mechanism.

4. Prop a wood spacer between housing and steering wheel hub.

5. Disconnect brake hoses, front engine support bolts, rubber mounts, clutch cable at engine mount, shock-absorber plastic cover, and upper shock-absorber attaching nuts.

6. Remove cross-member attaching nuts and lower the cross member. Make sure that the engine mounting bracket does not interfere with starter cables.

7. *Installation is easier if rubber dampening block is lubricated to reduce friction of mounting brackets.*

8. Slide engine mounting bracket over rubber block, attach cross member to front frame rail with new nuts, and torque to 30 ft lbs.

9. Bolt down engine and complete installation in reverse sequence of disassembly.

10. Make sure that the direction signal switch is in central (not engaged) position when lowering steering column into mast.

11. Tighten steering-mast clamp bolt to 25 ft lbs.

12. Adjust front end alignment.

1.9 Engine

1. For the GT, proceed as outlined above, but note the follwing steps: loosen the steering mast at the lower universal joint and take out the clamp bolt.

2. Loosen the clamp at the upper universal joint and lift the steering mast upward until it is free of the lower universal joint.

3. It is also necessary to remove the air cleaner.

4. Before removing the engine mount nuts, unscrew the radiator from the support on the crossmember.

5. Installation is the reverse of removal.

6. When installing the steering mast, center the steering wheel and front wheels.

7. Tighten the lower universal joint clamp bolt to 22 ft lbs. and then the upper bolt to 14 ft lbs.

Springs

Removal and Installation

NOTE: *Special hooks are needed on the upper control arms to remove the spring. The part number is J-23697.*

1. Install special hooks onto the upper control arms.

2. Raise car and support with a hoist to aid in spring removal.

Upper control arm hook installed

3. Remove front wheels and shock absorbers.

4. Disconnect lower control arm from steering knuckle (spindle), but do not remove nut from ball joint stud.

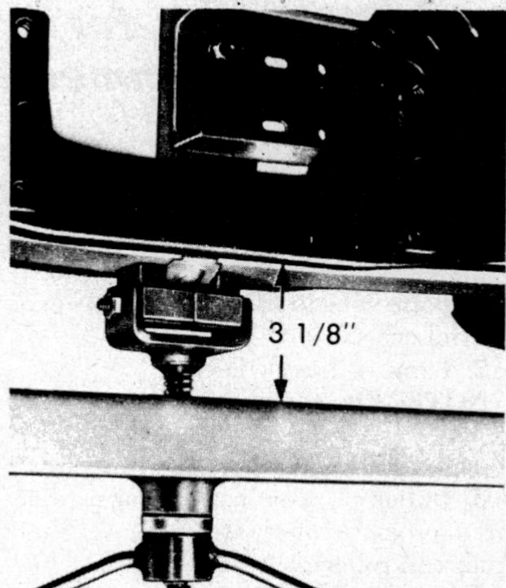

Leaf spring compression installed

5. Install a spring compressor and compress spring until a 3 ⅛ in. clearance is obtained.

6. Carefully lower car onto jack stands and remove lower control arm attaching bolts.

7. Remove lower control arm-to-spring nuts and remove the spring from car.

8. Installation is the reverse of removal.

Shock Absorber

Removal and Installation

1. Remove plastic cover from shock absorber upper attaching point.

2. Remove upper attaching nuts from shocks.

3. Raise car and support it on stands.

4. Remove lower attaching nuts and compress shocks.

5. Remove shock absorber from car.

6. Installation is the reverse of removal.

NOTE: *Always replace old bushings and lock washers.*

Ball Joint

Removal and Installation

Upper

1. Remove upper ball joint if there is excessive play in the ball stud.

2. With wheel off, unscrew castle nut from upper ball joint stud. Discard cotter pin.

3. Press ball stud from steering knuckle (spindle) and remove two bolts which attach the ball joint to upper control arm.

4. Replace ball joint if dust cap is damaged.

5. Install upper ball joint with the offcenter holes in flange showing toward the steering knuckle spindle.

6. Tighten control arm nuts to 18 ft lbs. and castle nut to 20 ft lbs.

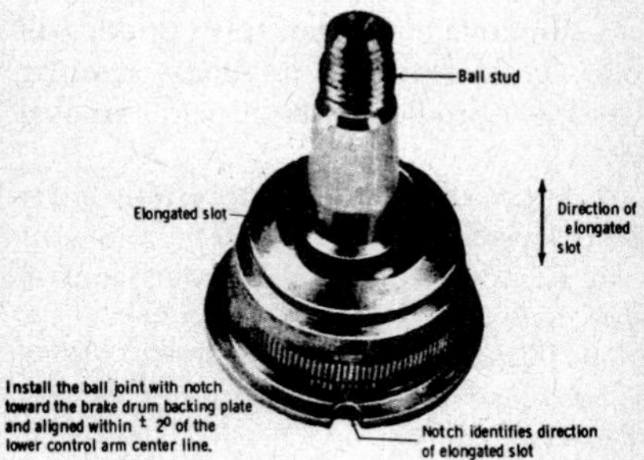

Lower ball joint assembly

Lower

NOTE: *Maximum axial play of Kadett lower ball joints is .080 inches. Greater play or worn parts require replacement of joint. New lower ball joints have axial play of .020 inches or less.*

1. *When removing lower ball joint,* back off castle nut only two turns.

2. Strike the ball stud to break it loose. Do not remove nut.

3. Compress transverse spring or coil spring 3 ⅛ in. from lower spring pad.

4. Disconnect shock absorber-to-lower control arm attachment, compress it and swing it aside.

5. Then remove castle nut from ball-joint stud.

NOTE: *Prior to the removal of the lower ball joint from the control arm, note the position of the locating notch, in the rim of the balljoint housing. Scribe or mark the control arm to facilitate realignment of the replacement ball joint.*

6. Pry off dust-cap retainer and dust cap carefully and press ball stud out of lower control arm.

7. *When reinstalling lower ball joint,* the notch in the ball joint bottom plate (identifying the direction of the elongated slot) must point toward the brake drum backing plate.

8. Alignment must be within 2° of lower control-arm centerline. Improper positioning of the ball joint will cause binding and fracture.

NOTE: *Do not press ball joint onto bottom plate, but only onto joint housing.*

9. Install dust cap on lower ball joint and fill with chassis lubricant. Attach dust cap retainer.

10. Press ball joint into steering knuckle.

11. Install castle nut and torque it to 45 ft lbs. Use new cotter pin.

Upper Control Arm

Removal and Installation

1. Raise front of car and support it securely.

2. Remove front wheel from the side to be worked on.

NOTE: *The front shock absorber must be disconnected and front spring must be compressed.*

3. Remove cotter pin from upper ball joint and separate it from steering knuckle (spindle) with tie rod removal tool.

4. Support brake drum assembly to relieve tension on brake hose.

5. Remove nut from upper control arm shaft and remove it from car.

NOTE: *If rubber bushings on control arms are worn, they should be replaced.*

6. Reinstall all parts in reverse order of removal.

NOTE: *After installation, the front end alignment should be checked and corrected if necessary.*

Lower Control Arm

Removal and Installation

1. Raise front of car and support it securely.

2. Remove front wheels.

3. Using a spring compressor, compress the spring to relieve tension.

4. Disconnect lower shock absorber attaching bolts to cross member. Shocks do not have to be removed from position.

5. Remove cotter pins from the lower ball joint stud. Use a tie rod removal tool to release the ball joint from the steering knuckle (spindle).

6. Support the brake drum assembly to relieve the tension on the brake hose.

7. Slightly lower the car to remove the bolt which holds the front spring to the control arm.

8. Remove lower control arm to cross-member attaching bolts.

9. Remove the control arm from the car.

10. Installation is the reverse of removal.

NOTE: *After installation, the front end alignment should be checked and corrected if necessary.*

Adjustments for Front End Alignment

Caster

NOTE: *To change caster either add or remove the toothed washers from the front and rear of the lower control arm shafts.*

1. Raise vehicle and support it at lower control arms.

2. Remove front wheels.

NOTE: *On some models it will be necessary to remove the shock absorber and compress the spring.*

3. Unbolt Upper control arm shaft from cross-member and remove shaft from control arm.

4. Adjust caster by adding or subtracting the tooth washers from the front and rear of the shaft, between the upper control arm and the shock absorber supports.

5. Replace shaft into the upper control arm and torque to 40 ft lbs. using new lock nuts.

6. Reinstall upper control arm to cross-member and reinstall the wheel.

7. Recheck caster setting after installation.

Camber

NOTE: *Camber is adjusted by turning the upper ball joint flange 180 degrees.*

1. Raise car and support it below lower control arms.

2. Remove front wheels.

NOTE: *On some models it will be necessary to remove the shock absorber and compress the spring.*

3. Unbolt upper ball joint from control arm and front steering knuckle.

4. Turn ball joint 180 degrees and reinstall it onto control arm.

5. Reinstall front wheels

6. Recheck camber settings.

Toe-In

NOTE: *To adjust toe-in, rotate the tie rod sleeves to lengthen or shorten the tie rod.*

1. Recheck caster and camber before adjusting toe-in.

2. Align wormshaft-to-steering gear high point.

3. Loosen wire clamps on tie rod ends and push back bellows.

4. Loosen clamp bolt on tie rod ends.

5. Unbolt tie rod from steering knuckle and disconnect tie rod.

6. Rotate tie-rod end to gain the correct settings. The toe-in should be 1/32–⅛ in. for all Opels and GT, and ⅛–3/16 in. for 1900's and Manta's.

7. Tighten clamp on tie-rod end and reinstall end onto steering knuckle.

8. Install wheels and recheck the complete front end alignment.

STEERING

Steering Wheel

Removal and Installation

Lower control arm attaching points

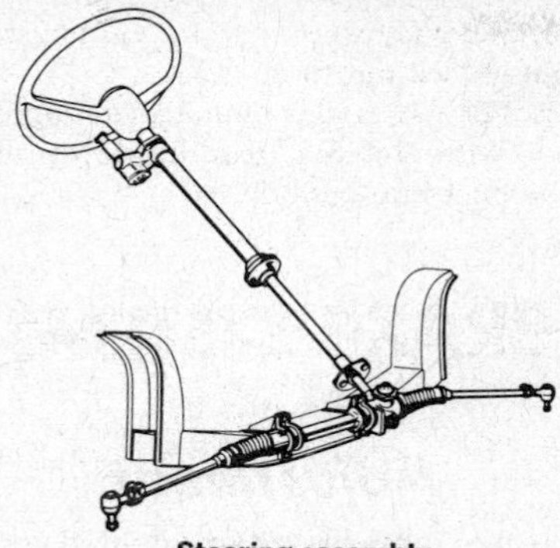

Steering assembly

1. Disconnect the ground strap from the battery, pry out the horn cap, and disconnect the horn wires.

2. Bend the lockplate tabs down, and remove the steering wheel nut and washer.

3. Mark the relative position of the steering wheel and shaft.

4. Install a conventional steering wheel puller, and remove the steering wheel.

5. Prior to installation, lightly lubricate the sliding parts of the turn signal mechanism with lubriplate.

6. Ensure that the match marks align, and install in the reverse order of removal

Turn Signal Switch Replacement

1. Remove steering wheel. Follow steps in that section.

2. Remove directional signal lever by pulling on lever to unlock ball seat.

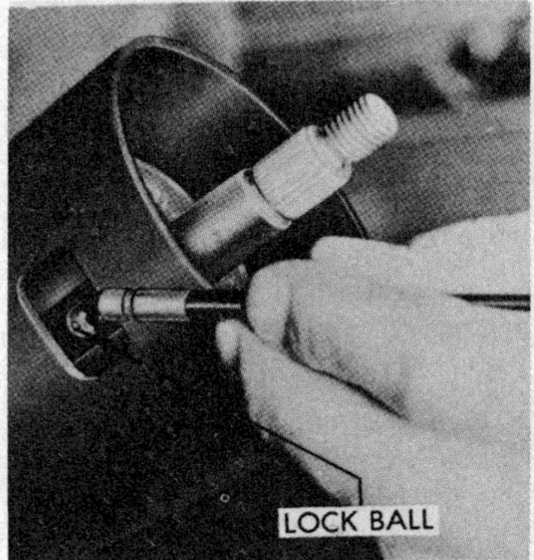

Removing directional signal lever

3. Unbolt all caps and attaching screws.

NOTE: *Some models have attaching screws that hold the switch housing cover halves together*

4. Remove switch housing cover and switch from the steering column.

NOTE: *Be careful not to lose guide ring on top of bearing housing.*

5. Disconnect wires from switch and remove switch from column.

7. Install turn signal switch in reverse order of removal.

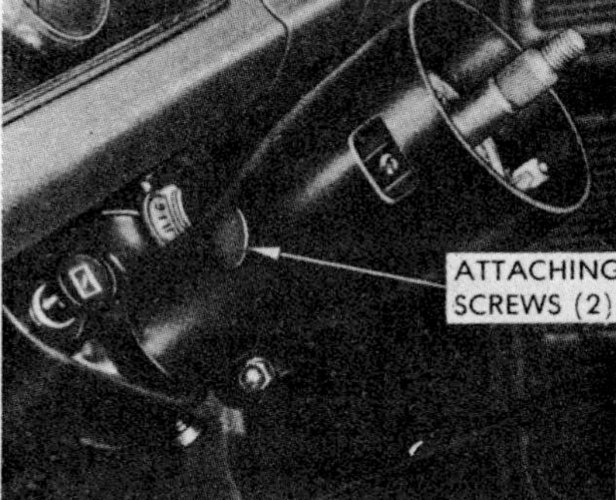

Steering column attaching points (upper)

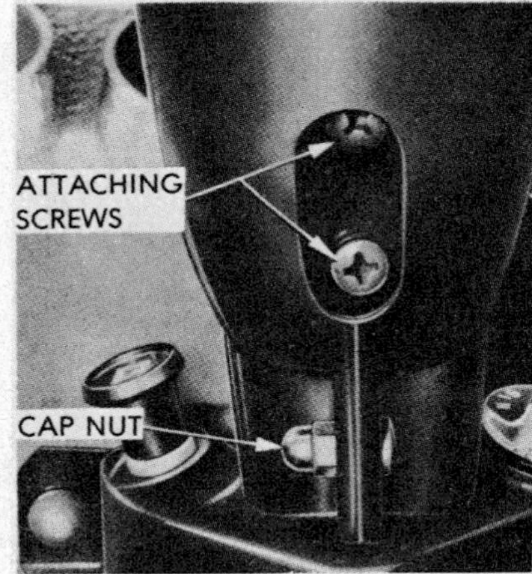

Steering column attaching points (lower)

Removing turn signal switch from steering column.

Steering Column

Removal and Installation

1. Disconnect battery and wires leading to the ignition switch and to the turn signal switch.

2. From underside of the car, remove clamps which secure the flexible steel ring coupling to the steering shaft.

3. Remove steering column, trim pan, and stop bolt from underside of column.

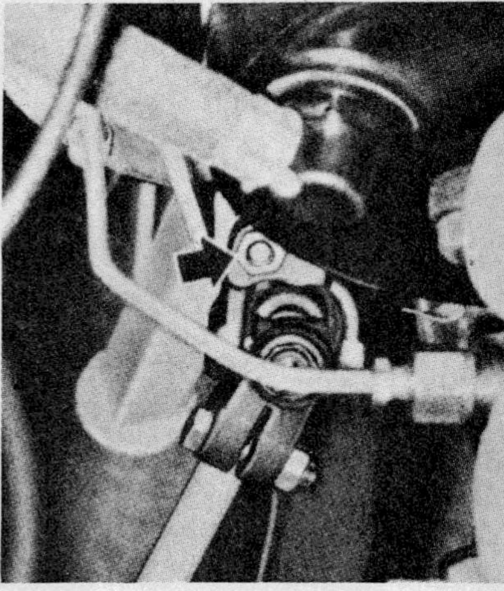

Steering column flexible steel ring coupling

4. Unbolt slide-off base attaching nuts and pull steering wheel rearward about 3 in.

5. Drill off head of rear attaching bolt and remove attaching bolt.

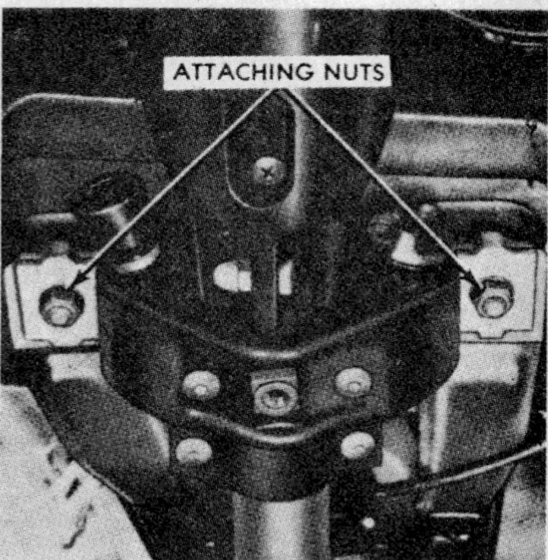

Slide-off base attaching bolts

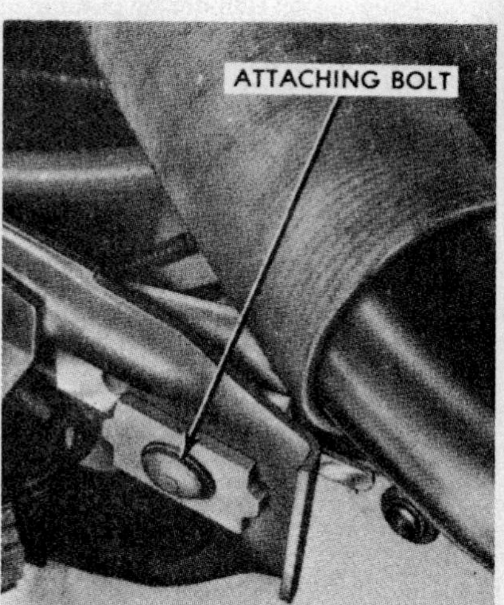

Rear attaching bolts

6. Remove steering column assembly from car. Carefully put down assembly to avoid breakage.

7. Installation is the reverse of removal.

Ignition Lock Switch (1969 and Later)

Removal and Installation

Opel and GT

1. Disconnect battery and turn ignition switch to the ON position.
2. Insert a rod into stop pin hole on the side of the ignition lock switch and remove cylinder assembly.

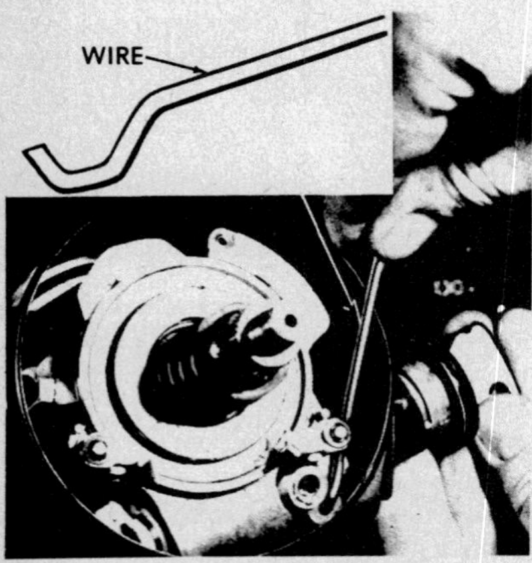

Removing ignition cylinder lock assembly (Opel & GT).

3. Remove screws which hold the electrical switch to ignition lock housing.
4. Remove switch from housing.
5. Install switch into steering and ignition lock housing and rotate switch. The assembly will lock itself into proper position.

1900 and Manta

1. Disconnect battery and turn ignition switch to the LOCK position.
2. Unscrew split signal switch housing covers and remove lower half.
3. Remove lock cylinder by pushing in lock spring of the cylinder.

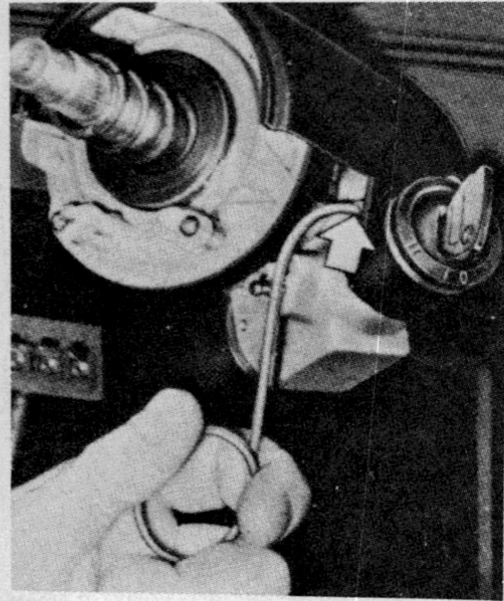

Removing ignition cylinder lock assembly (1990 & Manta).

4. To install, insert lock cylinder into housing and install lower half of the signal switch housing.

Steering Gear

Removal and Installation

1. Remove flexible-coupling bolt above gear box and the stop bolt located below steering wheel in steering mast jacket.
2. Lift out steering column from mast about three in. and position it with a block of wood.
3. Detach tie rod ends, pressing ball studs out of steering arms.
4. Unfasten steering gear assembly from suspension cross member and lift it off with tie rods.
4. Installing the steering gear, position steering gear on front suspension cross member and tighten bolts to 25 ft lbs.
5. Position tie-rod ball studs on steering arm; install castle nuts and torque to 30 ft lbs.
6. Lock it into position with new cotter pins.
7. Set steering wheel so that flat, lower portion of steering mast is parallel to ring-coupling bolt hole.
8. Position the mast in the flexible coupling and set clearance between steeringwheel hub and directional signal housing between 3/32 and ⅛ in.
9. Tighten flexible coupling to 23 ft lbs. Reinstall stop bolt in steering mast jacket.
10. Turn steering wheel ½ turn both right and left. If any resistance is noticeable, remove the steering mast and find the cause.

NOTE: *Do not over-tighten stop bolt in plastic bushing*

Steering Gear Adjustment

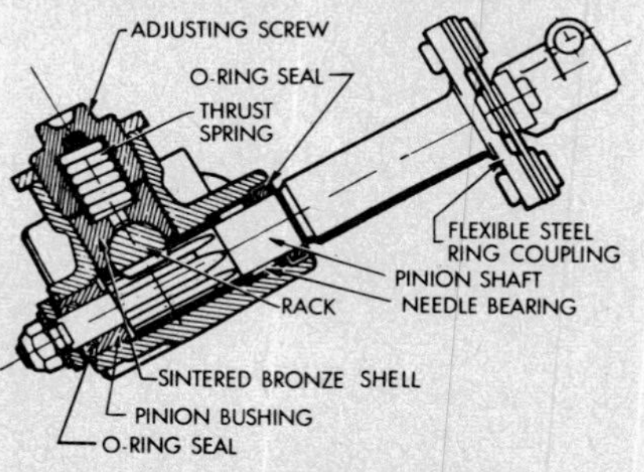

Steering gear assembly

1. Set steering gear to high point by positioning front wheels straight ahead with center steering wheel spoke pointing directly downward.
2. Flexible-coupling bolt hole will thereby be positioned parallel to the rack.
3. Thread adjusting screw into steering gear housing until resistance is felt. (The screw pushes the sintered bronze shell against the rack).
4. Back off adjusting screw 1/12 of a turn (a quarter turn = 3/12) and check for free movement of rack, left and right. If not free, delicately back off screw further until rack does move freely.
5. Hold adjuster screw in position and tighten lock nut to 65 ft lbs.
6. Fill area under pinion shaft rubber boot with steering gear lubricant and slide boot into position.

BRAKE SYSTEMS

Adjustment

1. The drum brakes are adjusted using two eccentrics mounted on the backing plate.
2. Turning the eccentrics in the direction of the arrows stamped on the backing plate increases shoe-to-drum contact.
3. When adjusting the front shoes, turn the eccentrics, while turning the wheel forward, until the wheel locks. Then back off the eccentric until the wheel is just free to turn.
4. Adjust the rear shoe in a similar manner, turning the wheel rearward rather than forward.

HYDRAULIC SYSTEM

Master Cylinder

The drum-type brake system requires a minimum static pressure of 4 ¼ psi on the brake fluid at all times to hold the wheel cylinder cups firmly against the cylinder walls, preventing loss of fluid or entrance of air. Disc brakes, on the other hand, require that all pressure be released to disengage brake pistons.

Removal and Installation (All Models)

1. Disconnect and plug brake lines where they enter the master brake cylinder.
2. Remove the two bolts that secure the master cylinder to cowl wall.
3. Depress brake pedal slightly and remove master cylinder from support bracket and brake booster.
4. Inside car, remove trim pad above pedal assembly. Then remove actuating pushrod nut from brake pedal and slide assembly out.
5. Pour out brake fluid and lift it out of position.
6. Installation is the reverse of removal.

Overhaul

Single Master Cylinder

1. Remove rubber dust cap.
2. Clean outside of master cylinder thoroughly before removing reservoir cover.

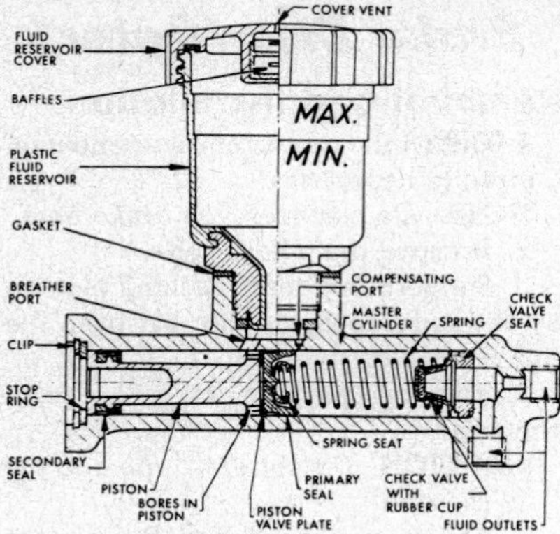

Single brake master cylinder assembly

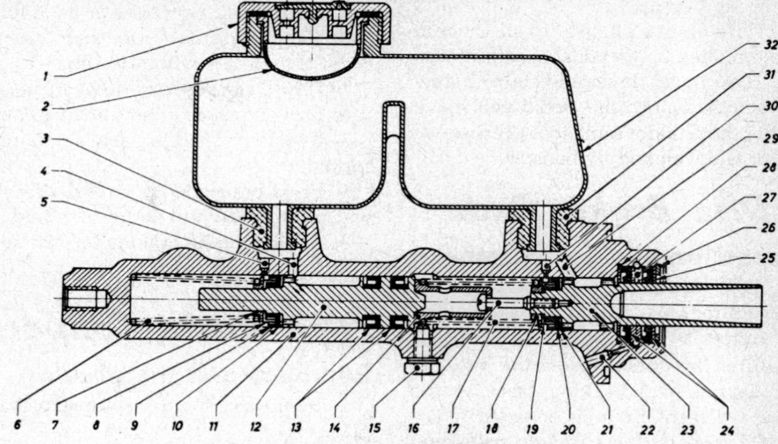

Dual brake master cylinder assembly

1. Cover with seal ring
2. Screen
3. Sealing plug
4. Feed port
5. Compensating port
6. Piston spring
7. Piston spring collar
8. Support ring
9. Primary seal
10. Plate
11. Dual brake master cylinder housing
12. Intermediate piston (for front brake circuit)
13. Secondary seal
14. Stop sleeve
15. Stop screw with seal ring
16. Stop screw
17. Piston spring
18. Piston spring collar
19. Support ring
20. Primary seal
21. Plate
22. Drain port
23. Piston (rear brake circuit)
24. Secondary seals
25. Stop plate
26. Circlip
27. Intermediate ring
28. Stop plate
29. Feed port
30. Compensating port
31. Sealing plug
32. Twin brake fluid container

3. Turn cylinder over and pump push-rod by hand to drain all brake fluid. Discard old fluid.

4. Remove snap ring and stop ring from end of master cylinder.

5. Remove piston with its components. Remove brake fluid reservoir, washer, and gasket.

NOTE: *Left hand threads on reservoir.*

6. Inspect master cylinder bore and clean with brake fluid and a brush. Check bypass and compensating ports for restrictions.

7. Reassemble single master cylinder by first installing reservoir, gasket and washer on cylinder.

NOTE: *Left hand threads.*

8. Dip all parts in brake fluid and install valve seat washer, check valve, spring and attached spring seat, primary cap, thin steel washer, and piston with secondary cup.

9. Push piston into bore; then install stop washer and lock ring.

10. Check for free operation.

11. Test proper seating of lock ring with a hard pull on rod.

Dual Master Cylinder

1. Screw static pressure valve out of housing.

2. Push piston into cylinder to a point where a rod 1/10 in. thick will slip into the feed port to hold piston in this position.

3. Remove stop screw at bottom and circlip at booster end of housing and take out both pistons together with springs.

4. Unscrew stop screw from rear-brake-circuit piston. Remove remaining parts.

5. Clean master cylinder parts with brake fluid and dry with compressed air. Clean the compensating and feed ports. Polish cylinder bore and pistons.

Maximum piston diameter: 0.82 in.
Minimum piston diameter: 0.81 in.

7. Replace rubber seals and static pressure valve.

8. Coat all parts with brake fluid for reassembly.

9. Assemble intermediate piston and insert it into cylinder bore with thrust spring and spring seat. The smaller diameter of the tapered thrust spring must face piston.

10. With a drift, push piston into housing and insert a rod into feed port.

11. Install stop screw with a new seal ring.

12. Insert preassembled piston for rear brake circuit into cylinder bore and install circlip into groove in housing.

13. Check piston for free movement.

NOTE: *If required, place washers under the head of the stop screw.*

14. Push piston partly into housing and remove rod from feed port.

15. Screw in new static pressure valves.

16. Coat new sealing plugs thinly with brake fluid and insert them into housing.

17. Push twin brake fluid container into sealing plugs.

Brake Booster

The brake booster available on 1967 and later Opels reduces required foot pressure for braking by approximately 25%. The booster is mechanically controlled by the foot pedal and conveys this pressure along with an engine vacuum assistance to the dual master cylinder. A vacuum control valve prevents air from flowing back into booster when engine is not running. The valve must be replaced when defective.

Checking Brake Booster Operation

The operation of the brake booster can

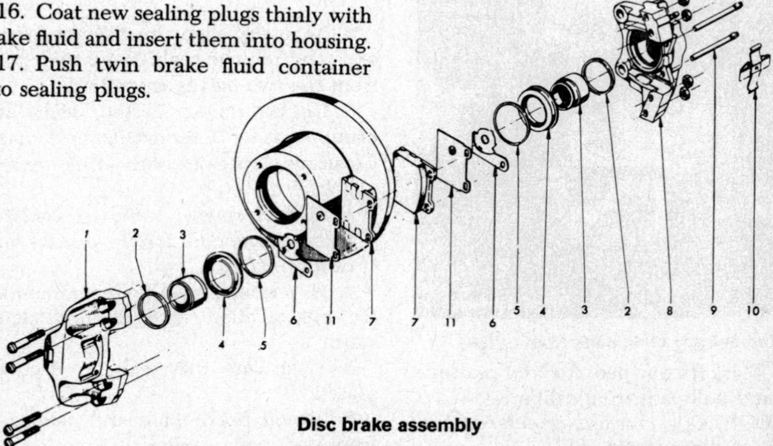

Disc brake assembly

1. Caliper rim half
2. Rubber fluid seals
3. Hollow pistons
4. Rubber seals
5. Clamp rings
6. Retainer plates
7. Friction pads
8. Caliper mounting half
9. Dowel pins for friction pads
10. Cross-shaped retaining spring
11. Pad backing plate

be checked easily.

1. With engine off, use up all vacuum by depressing brake pedal several times.

2. Hold pedal down and start engine. As vacuum builds, the pedal will move farther (held under same foot pressure) as power is developed by booster.

Disc Brake Pads

Inspection and Replacement

1. Disc brake friction pads can be checked for wear without disassembling the caliper if a gauge is available that measures the distance from the inside of one friction pad backing plate to the other when the brake is engaged.

NOTE: *Both brake friction pads must be replaced if either pad is worn down to a thickness of 0.08 in. or less.*

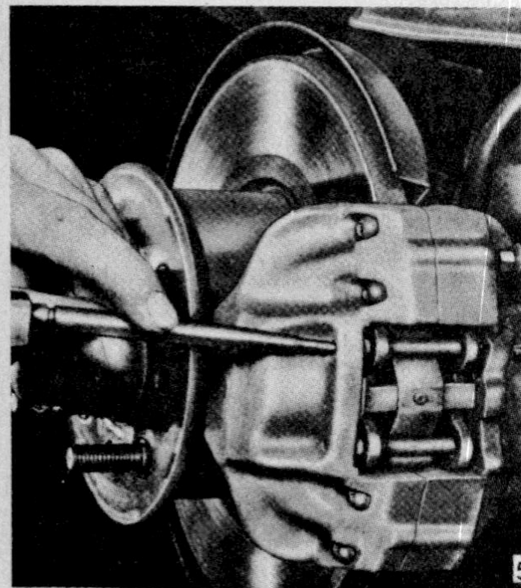

Removing dowel pins from calipers

2. If no gauge is available, tap dowel pins from brake caliper toward center of car after pin retainer has been removed.

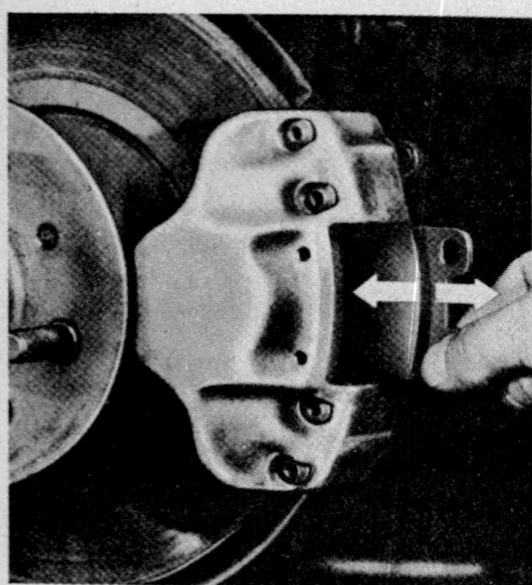

Removing friction pads from caliper

3. Mark friction pads for later reassembly and pull pads from caliper.

NOTE: *Oily, cracked, or defaced pads need replacement.*

4. Pads themselves must measure at all times greater than 0.08 in. thick.

5. Remove high spots on friction pads with a cut stone file before reinstalling.

6. *If installing new friction pads,* force both caliper pistons into their caliper bores completely with a clamp.

NOTE: *Open bleeder valve on caliper to prevent brake reservoir overflow.*

7. Replace friction pad retaining spring.

8. Press brake pedal several times to seat pads. Bleed and add brake fluid.

9. Avoid forceful braking for 125 miles to break in pads.

Disc Brake Calipers

Removal and Installation

1. Remove caliper from wheel backing plate.

2. Loosen brake line at union, unfasten caliper and brake hose bracket and remove brake pipe (plugging hose at union) on their collars and clamp rings are correctly positioned on the seals.

4. Push retainer plates into pistons with handle of a screwdriver.

Overhaul

NOTE: *Caliper halves are not disassembled for repair work.*

1. From opening for friction pads, lift retainer plates from each piston.

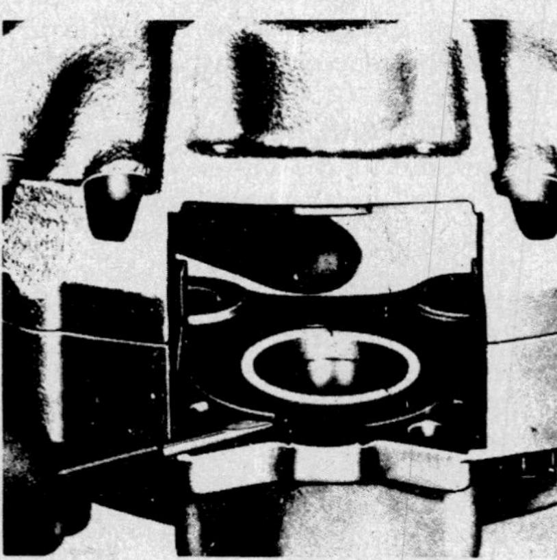

Removing rubber seal clamp ring

2. Next, pry clamp rings from rubber seals and remove seals. Keep twin parts from the two halves separated.

3. Check caliper piston seals and clamp rings for deterioration or damage. Clean ring recesses with *denatured* alcohol.

NOTE: *A special clamp (J-22429) is recommended for forcing pistons from caliper halves.*

4. New rubber seals are recommended for reinstallation with cleaned clamp rings.

5. Make sure that seals are securely seated

6. Attach brake pipe and caliper to front end, making sure that mating surfaces of caliper and steering knuckle are clean and smooth.

7. Tighten caliper attaching bolts to 50 ft lbs.

Brake Disc (Rotor)

Removal and Installation

1. Unbolt the caliper and suspend it on a piece of heavy wire.

NOTE: *Do not stress the brake hose.*

2. Remove the wheel hub.

3. Support the wheel backing plate in a vise, and unbolt the disc hat from the hub using a star wrench.

4. The disc may now be pulled from the hub.

CAUTION: *Do not drive the hub out of the disc.*

5. The disc is installed in the reverse order of removal.

6. When installing the disc on the hub, ensure that the mating surfaces are free of dirt, and torque the star bolts to 36 ft lbs.

7. Before installing the disc on the car, repack the wheel bearings.

Disc Inspection

Checking brake disc for lateral runout

The discs should be inspected visually for scratches, nicks, or scoring. The discs may be checked for lateral runout using a dial indicator, mounted perpendicular to the disc, ½ in. from its circumference. Disc parallelism is checked with a micrometer.

Minimum thickness of brake disc: 0.390 in.

Maximum unevenness: 0.002 in.

Maximum lateral runout: 0.001 in.

If runout or parallelism exceed the above specifications, the disc should be machined or replaced.

NOTE: *In no case should the disc be machined beyond the minimum thickness. If it is impossible to true disc without exceeding this figure, the disc*

Wheel Bearings

Removal and Installation

1. Remove front wheels.

2. Remove front wheel bearing hub cap and spindle nut.

3. Pull rotor hub assembly off of the

spindle. Be careful not to drop the outer bearing.

NOTE: *On cars equipped with disc brakes, it will be necessary to remove the caliper assembly before removing the rotor and hub assembly.*

4. Throughly clean bearings of old lubricant and press fresh grease into bearing.

NOTE: *Both inner and outer front bearings should be repacked with grease. For best results, both sides of the car should be repacked at the same time.*

5. Place hub assembly on spindle and install spindle nut in reverse order of removal.

Adjustments

When reinstalling the hub assembly onto the spindle, it is important to set the free play in bearing to prevent damage.

1. Install hub assembly onto spindle.
2. Place outer bearing into position and install spindle nut.
3. Tighten spindle nut until all free play is removed from the wheel bearing.

NOTE: *Do not overtighten nut. This will cause binding of the bearing on its race, and will cause excessive wear.*

4. Reinstall bearing hub cap and recheck free play.

Brake Drums

Removal and Installation

Front

1. Remove wheels, bearing hub cap, and spindle nut.
2. Pull drum and hub assembly from the spindle being careful not to drop the outer bearing.
3. Installation is the reverse of removal.

Rear

1. Support rear of car and remove rear wheels.
2. Remove rear drums by pulling them off of hub.
3. Install in the reverse order of removal.

Inspection

1. The drums should be checked for cracks, scoring and concentricity.
2. Slight scores may be polished out using emery cloth. Eccentricity or serious scores should be removed by turning the drum providing the maximum diameter is not exceeded.

Maximum eccentricity of drum: 0.004 in.

NOTE: *Eccentricity is measured by comparing the diameter of the inner and outer edge of the machined surface in two places, 90° apart.*

Standard drum inner diameter: 7.880 in.

Maximum diameter after turning: 7.910 in.

3. To regain center contact with brake shoes, grind linings to 0.02 in. under drum diameter.
4. Before reinstalling brake drum, inspect all brake pipe and hose connections for fluid leakage. Tighten these connections and apply heavy pressure to brake pedal to recheck seal.
5. Inspect rear wheel backing plate for leaks from wheel bearing oil seals. Replace seals if needed.
6. Check all backing plate bolts for tightness.
7. Clean away all dirt from assemblies and repack wheel bearings.
8. If rear wheel backing plate was removed, use new gaskets lightly coated with grease. Torque plate to 21 ft lbs.
9. Seal the outside of the backing plate near the brake shoe hold-down springs with body sealing compound.

Brake Shoes

Removal and Installation

Front or Rear

1. Raise front of car and support it safely.
2. Remove front wheels and drum assemblies.
3. Remove upper and lower brake shoe return springs.
4. Remove brake shoe hold down springs and retainers.
5. Remove shoes from backing plate.
6. Clean all dirt from drum and backing plate and inspect all fittings and parts.
7. Installation is reverse of removal.

Wheel Cylinders

Removal and Installation

1. Remove front wheels, drums, and brake shoes from backing plates.
2. Disconnect brake lines from back of wheel cylinder.
3. Unbolt wheel cylinder and remove it from backing plate.
4. Installation is the reverse of removal.

NOTE: *After installation be sure to bleed system of all air.*

Overhaul

1. Carefully pull lower edges of wheel cylinder boots away from cylinders and note if interior is wet—an indication of brake fluid seepage past the piston cup. If so, cylinder overhaul is required.
2. Clean dirt from all surrounding surfaces and then disconnect and seal off brake line (tape is often satisfactory for sealing).
3. Remove cylinder from backing plate.
4. Dismantle boots, pistons, cups and spring from cylinder.
5. Remove bleeder valve.
6. Discard boots and cups; clean other parts with fresh brake fluid.

NOTE: *Use no fluid containing even a trace of mineral oil.*

7. Light scratches and corrosion can be polished from pistons and bore with fine emery cloth or steel wool.
8. Dip all parts in brake fluid and reassemble.
9. After installation, adjust brakes and road test for performance.

Wheel Bearings

Removal and Installation

1. Remove front wheels and bearing hub cap. Unscrew spindle nut.
2. Pull drum and hub assembly from the spindle. Be careful not to drop outer bearing.
3. Throughly clean bearing of old lubricant and press fresh grease into bearing.

NOTE: *Both inner and outer front bearings should be repacked with grease. For best results, both sides should be repacked at the same time.*

4. Place drum and hub assembly onto spindle and install spindle nut.
5. Tighten until free play is removed and reinstall wheel onto car.

Adjustments

1. Install hub assembly onto spindle.
2. Place outer bearing onto the spindle and install spindle nut.
3. Tighten spindle nut until all free play is removed from the wheel bearing.

NOTE: *Do not tighten nut. It will cause binding of the bearing on its race and therefore, excessive wear.*

4. Reinstall bearing hub cap and recheck free play.

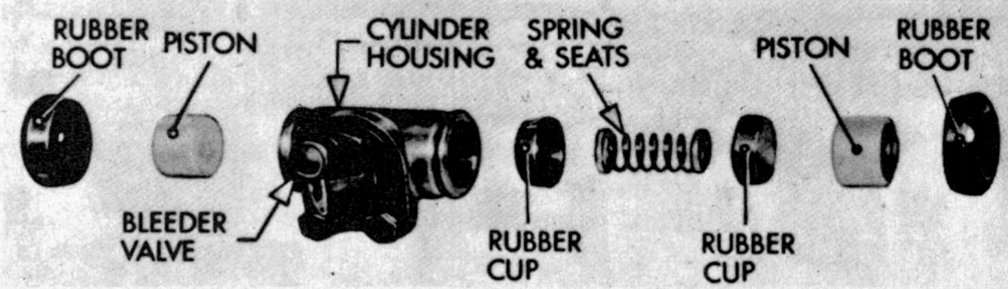

Wheel cylinder assembly

PARKING BRAKE

Cable

Removal and Installation

1. Raise car and support it securely.
2. Release parking brake and disconnect return spring.
3. Remove adjusting nut from parking brake equalizer.
4. Disconnect parking brake cable at rear connections.
5. Remove cable from car.
6. Install in reverse order of removal.

Adjustment

1. Lift the rear of the vehicle, and support it with jackstands.
2. Release the parking brake lever and loosen the nut in front of the equalizer.
3. Pull the brake lever up three notches (clicks), and tighten the nut behind the equalizer until the rear brakes begin to bind.
4. Tighten the nut in front of the equalizer.
5. Lubricate the cable in the area of the equalizer to ensure proper operation.

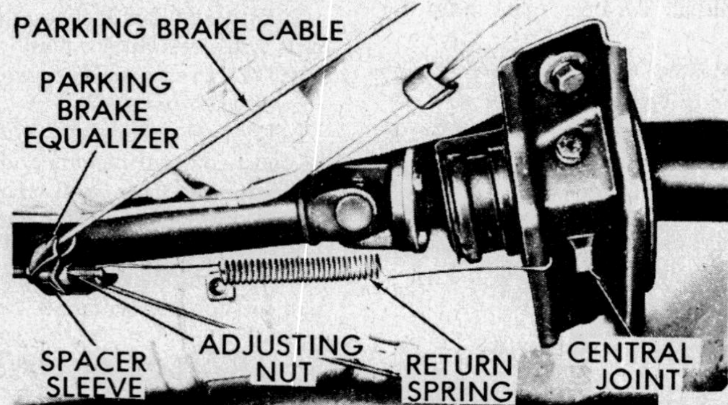

Parking brake assembly

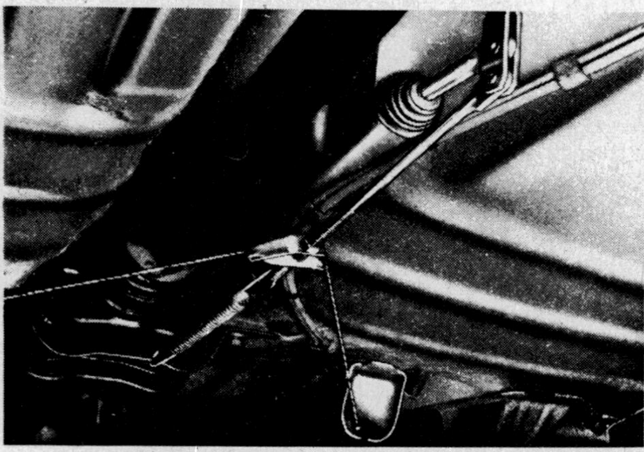

Parking brake equalizer assembly

Heater Blower

Removal and Installation

Kadett

1. Disconnect the wire leading to the blower and the air distributor door control cable.
2. Remove the hoses from the air distributor, and remove the air distributor.
3. Remove the screws which mount the blower to the housing, and remove the blower.
4. Install in the reverse order of removal.

GT and 1900's

1. Drain the coolant by removing the lower radiator hose, then remove the hoses from the heater in the engine compartment.
2. Disconnect the hood lock control cable from the lock bar.
3. Remove the console by removing two screws under the ash tray, two screws which retain the headlamp lever handle, and prying the console up to release four retaining snaps.
4. Lower the steering column, and separate the two plug connectors from it.
5. Remove the two plugs from the sides of the instrument panel, adjacent to the heater control, and remove the screws through the openings.
6. Detach the speedometer cable from the speedometer, and remove the flasher unit, located adjacent to the hood release.
7. Disconnect five plug connectors from the left underside of the instrument panel.
8. Remove two retaining screws from the radio bracket, and one nut from the left side of the instrument panel, and pull the panel out from the top.

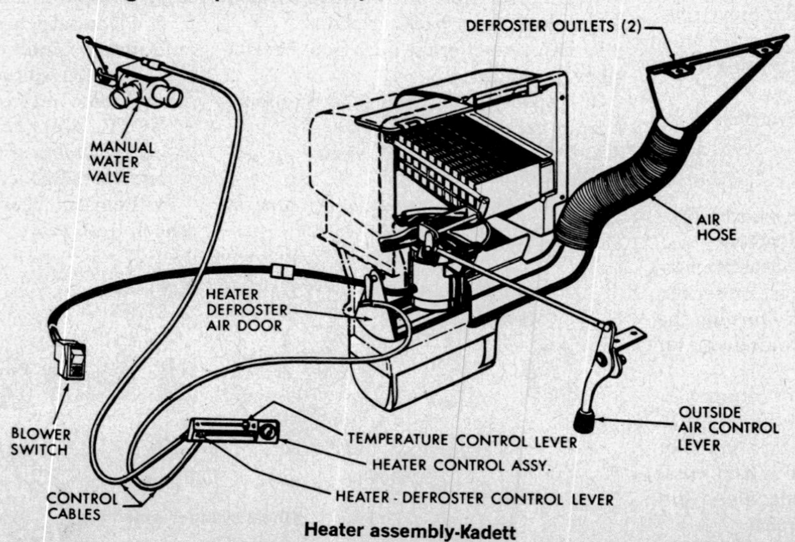

Heater assembly-Kadett

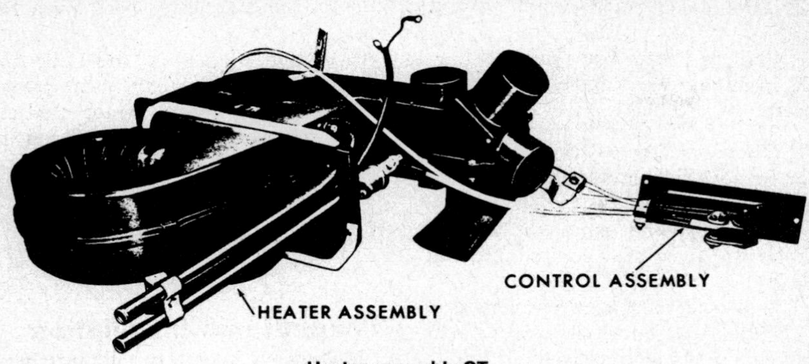

Heater assembly-GT

9. If so equipped, mark for identification and remove the wires from the ammeter.

10. Unbolt the heater control panel, and the heater support bracket, located at the upper right corner of the radio bracket.

11. Remove all screws from the dash panel padding, and remove it from the dash.

12. Disconnect all duct hoses, remove one bolt from the top and two nuts from the bottom of the case, and remove the heater assembly.

13. Install in the reverse order of removal, checking all connections such as hoses to ensure that they are airtight.

14. Correct any leaks with body sealer.

Heater Core

Removal and Installation

1. Drain the coolant by removing the lower radiator hose.

2. Disconnect the heater hoses at the heater.

3. Remove the housing retaining screws, and remove the core.

4. Install in the reverse order of removal.

Radio

Removal and Installation

Kadett and 1900

1. Disconnect the battery ground cable and the antenna and speaker connectors from the radio.

2. Remove the knobs from the radio and unbolt the mounting nuts.

3. Remove the receiver bracket lower screw from the receiver, loosen the upper bolt approximately three turns, and slide out the radio.

4. Install in the reverse order of removal.

NOTE: *When installing the radio, the antenna trimmer should be adjusted as follows: extend the antenna to a height of 31 in. tune the radio to a barely audible station around 1400 KC, and turn the trimmer screw (on the bottom of the receiver) until maximum volume is achieved.*

Rallye

The procedure is identical to the Kadett, except that the glove box and the right defroster duct must be removed, and the radio installed and removed through the glove box opening.

GT

1. In order to remove the radio from the GT, the dash and instrument panel must be removed (see "Heater Removal").

2. After this is complete, remove the radio knobs and the mounting nuts, disconnect the antenna and the speaker, and slide out the radio.

3. Install in the reverse order of removal, noting antenna trimmer adjustment above (Kadett).

Windshield Wipers

Motor Removal and Installation

Opel

1. Remove the crank arm nut and crank arm from the wiper motor drive shaft, located above the clutch and brake pedals.

2. Unbolt the three nuts which attach the motor and drive to the firewall and remove the wiper motor.

3. Install in the reverse order of removal.

GT

1. Unbolt the retaining nuts, and remove the wiper arms.

2. Remove the three bolts which retain the wiper posts to the deflector panels, and allow the posts to drop out of the panels.

3. Unscrew the left and center deflector panels, and remove the left panel, including the motor and linkage.

4. Remove the crank arm nut from the wiper drive, and separate the linkage from the motor.

5. Unbolt the three retaining nuts, and remove the motor from the deflector panel.

6. Install in the reverse order of removal.

NOTE: *When installing the wiper arms, ensure that they are in the proper position at rest.*

Instrument Cluster

Removal and Installation

Opels

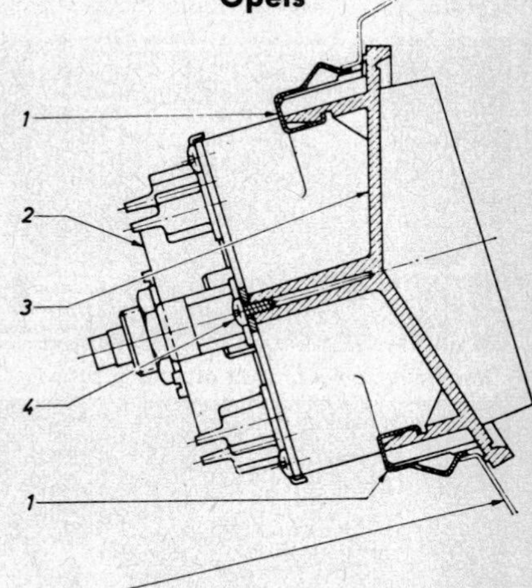

Cross-section of instrument panel

1. Retaining clamp
2. Speedometer
3. Instrument housing
4. Sheet metal screw
5. Instrument panel

1. Disconnect battery.

2. Disconnect speedometer cable at speedometer housing.

3. Reach under dash and push instrument cluster out of instrument panel.

NOTE: *The instrument cluster is held in position by four retaining clamps.*

4. To remove the cluster from the panel, disconnect all wires connected to the instrument cluster and remove it from dash.

5. Installation is the reverse of removal.

1900 Series

1. Disconnect battery cable.

2. Remove headlight switch knob by depressing retaining clip and pulling knob out.

3. Disconnect two plugs and screws behind plugs on front of cluster.

4. Remove heater control knob and pull cover from instrument panel.

5. Disconnect speedometer cable by turning coupling counterclockwise.

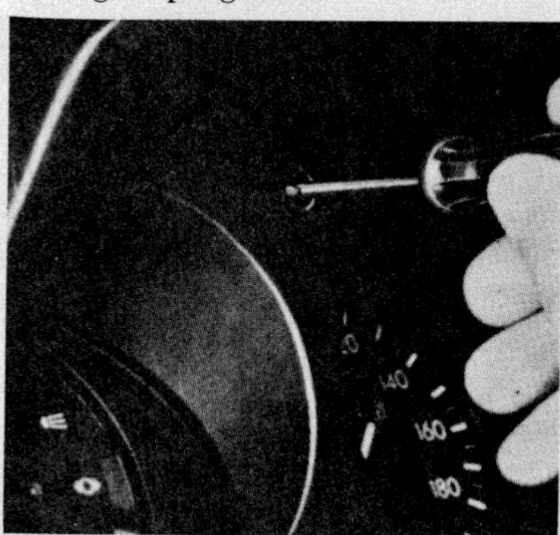
Removing upper cluster attaching screws

NOTE: *If equipped with a rear defogger or fog lamps, disconnect switch and remove it from panel.*

6. Remove two screws for lower attaching point and remove cluster partially. Disconnect wires from back of cluster.

Removing lower cluster attaching screws

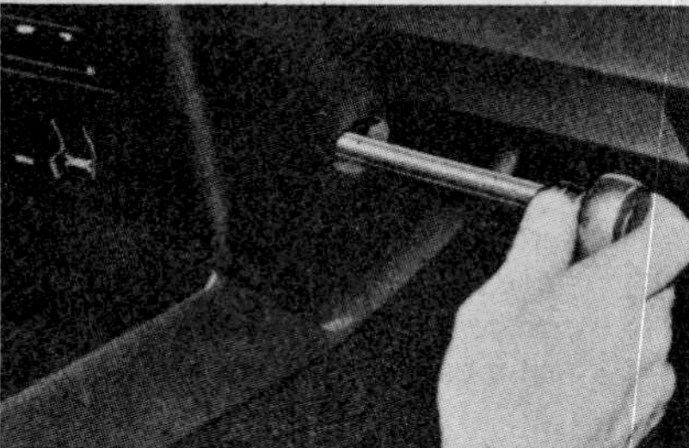

Removing right access cover and attaching bolts.

Removing left access cover and attaching bolt.

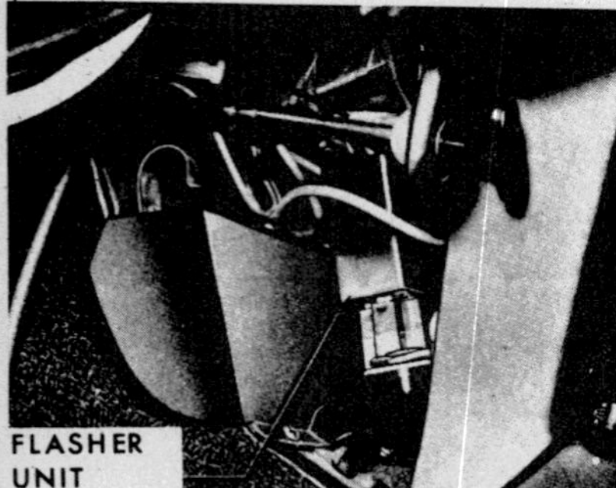

Flasher unit installed

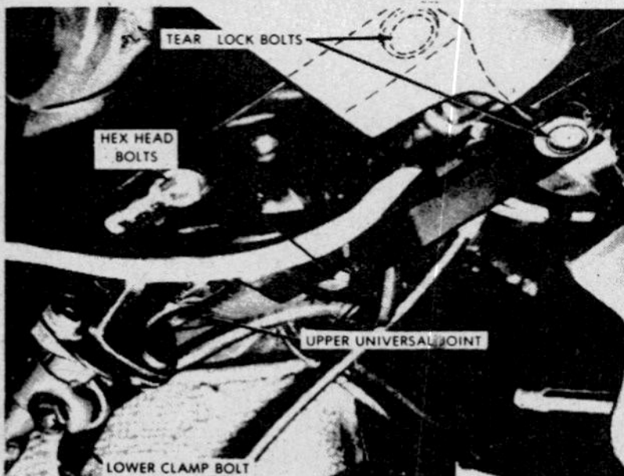

Steering column attaching bolts

7. Remove cluster from car.
8. Install by reversing removal procedures.

GT Models

1. Disconnect the battery cable.
2. Remove right and left access covers and remove screws.
3. Remove flasher unit and position wheels so they are pointed straight ahead.
4. Pull heads off of both rear bolts, drill a 3/16 in. hole, and then remove rear bolts by using a stud extractor.
5. Disconnect ignition and directional signal wire set plugs.
6. Remove steering column support bolts and drop column to floor.
7. Disconnect speedometer cable.
8. Remove six attaching screws and pull instrument cluster back from the top.
9. Unplug wires from the radio and other instruments, gauges, and switches.
10. Pull instrument cluster out and turn it sideways to remove any gauge or switch.
11. Install in reverse order of removal.

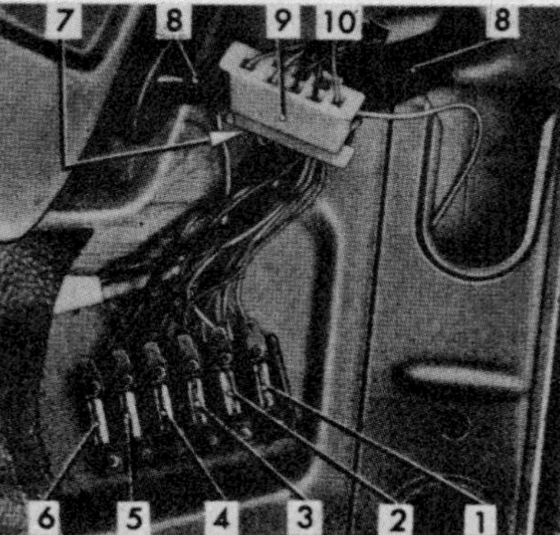

Fuse box location—1966 Kadett

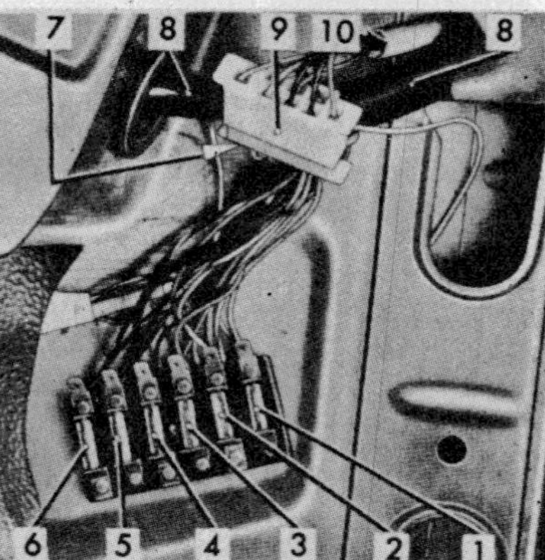

Fuse box location—1967 Opels & Rallye

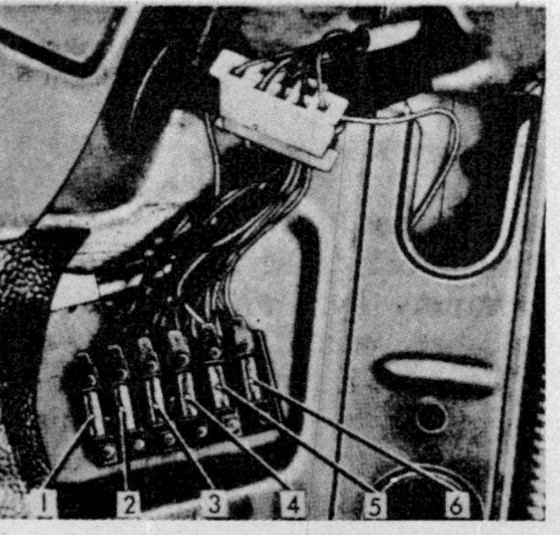

Fuse box location—1968-73 Opel, 1900, and GT.

Ignition Switch (Pre–1969)

Removal and Installation

1. Disconnect battery and turn ignition switch to the ON position.
2. Insert a rod into stop pin hole on the side of the ignition lock assembly and remove cylinder assembly.
3. Remove screws which hold the electrical switch to ignition lock housing.
4. Remove switch from housing.
5. Install switch into steering and ignition lock housing and rotate switch. The assembly will lock itself into proper position.

Fuse Box Location

Fuse	Circuit	Amps
1966	(Behind right kick pad through cutout covered by owner's protection plan book.)	
1	Right parking light, right tail light, license plate light and instrument light	5
2	Left parking light, left tail light	5
3	Interior light, glove box light, radio, electric clock and luggage compartment light	5
4	Heater motor	5
5	Direction signal lights, stop lights and back-up lights	5
6	Windshield wiper motor, signal horn and cigar lighter	8
1966-1967	(Behind right kick pad through cutout)	
1	Right parking light, right tail light, license plate light and instrument light	5
2	Left parking light and left tail light	5
3	Dome light, glove box light, radio, electric clock and hazard warning flasher	5
4	Heater motor and cigar lighter	8
5	Direction signal lights, stop lights and back-up lights	5
6	Windshield wiper motor and horn	8
1968-1973	(Behind right kick pad through cutout)	
1	Windshield wiper, horn	8
2	Direction signal, stop lights, back-up lights, brake system warning light	5
3	Heater, cigar lighter	
4	Dome light, glove box light, radio, electric clock and hazard warning flasher	5
5	Left parking light and left tail light	5
6	Right parking light, right tail light, license plate light and instrument lights	5
	Fog lights. (In relay switch in engine compartment)	8
	(In relay switch el. heated rear window. In engine compartment.)	16

PORSCHE

Index

INTRODUCTION

The name Porsche and the term sports car have always been synonymous. The current 911 and 914 series have continued the Porsche tradition of performance and reliability. Myriad competition victories in endurance racing, such as the 24 Hours of Le Mans and the Targa Florio, and in Sports Car Club of America production class racing have kept the marque in the vanguard of the high-performance car ranks. Remarkably, Porsche cars have been in production for only twenty-four years, which is difficult to comprehend in view of the legendary reputation and the legion of enthusiasts that the car has attracted. The first Porsches were built in Gmund, Austria, since, at that time, Professor Porsche was denied entrance to Germany. The factory was eventually moved to its present location near Stuttgart, Germany. Porsche has since grown into a multimillion dollar concern, but the painstaking attention to detail, inherited from the small group of men who produced the first cars, was not lost in the transition from workshop to large factory.

SERIAL NUMBER IDENTIFICATION

Chassis

In accordance with Federal standards, the chassis number on all 1969–73 912, 911, 914, and 914/6 models is located on the driver's side windshield post and is visible from the outside of the car. The chassis number on 912 and 911 models is also found in the luggage compartment under the rug and on the identification plate near the front hood lock catch. The 914 and 914/6 chassis number is stamped on the right front wheel well and on the identification plate on the right headlight housing inside the luggage compartment.

911 chassis serial number location

MODEL IDENTIFICATION

Front view of 911 through 1972 (1972 S is equipped with a spoiler)

Front view of 1973 911 E and S models (spoiler optional on T)

1970-1972 914 front and rear views

911 identication plate location

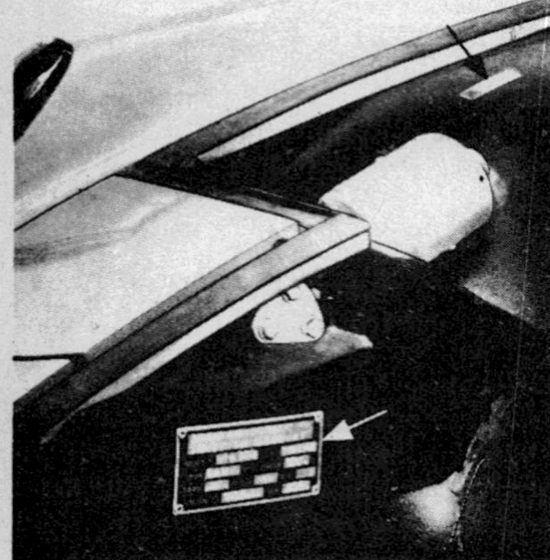

914 identification plate (bottom) and chassis serial number (top) location

The 911 series chassis identification number breaks down in the following manner:

	911 2 2 1 0001
Series type	11 (1969 only)
	911 (1970-73)
Model year	9 = 1969
	0 = 1970
	1 = 1971
	2 = 1972
	3 = 1973
Engine type	1 = T
	2 = E
	3 = S
Body type	0 = Porsche coupe
	1 = Targa
	2 = Karmann coupe
Four-digit sequential number	

The 914 series chassis identification number is broken down as follows:

	914 0 43 0001
Series type	914
Model year	0 = 1970
	1 = 1971
Engine and	4 = 6 cylinder
body number	3 = Roadster
Four-digit sequential number	

1973 914 front view

The 914/6 series chassis identification number breaks down in the following manner:

	47 12 000001
Series type	47 914 series
Model year	02 = 1970
	12 = 1971
	22 = 1972
	32 = 1973
Six-digit sequential number	

Chassis Identification Chart

Year	Model	Starting Number
1965	911	300236
	912	350001
1966	911	303391
	912	351971
1967	911	305101
	911S	305101S
	912	500001
1968	911	11835001
	911L	11805001
	912	12800001
1969	912 Coupe	129000001
	912 Targa	129010001
	911T (P)	119100001
	911T (K)	119120001
	911T Targa	119110001
	911E (P)	119200001
	911E (K)	119220001
	911E Targa	119210001
	911S	119300001
	911S Targa	119310001
1970	911T (P)	9110100001
	911T (K)	9110120001
	911T Targa	9110110001
	911E (P)	9110200001
	911E (K)	9110220001
	911E Targa	9110210001
	911S	9110300001
	911 Targa	9110310001
	914	4702900013
	914/6	9140430001

Chassis Identification Chart—(Continued)

Year	Model	Starting Number
1971	911T (P)	9111100001
	911T (K)	9111120001
	911T Targa	9111110001
	911E	9111300001
	911E Targa	9111210001
	911S	9111300001
1971	911S Targa	9111310001
	914	4712900001
	914/6	9141430011
1972	911T	9112100001
	911T Targa	9112110001
	911E	9112200001
	911E Targa	9112210001
	911S	9112300001
	911S Targa	9112310001
	914	4722900001
1973	911T	9113100001
	911T Targa	9113110001
	911E	9113200001
	911E Targa	9113210001
	911S	9113300001
	911S Targa	9113310001
	914	4732900001

(P) Porsche body
(K) Karmann body

Engine

The 912 engine number is stamped on the upper left side of the crankcase, below the breather column. The engine number for the 911 model is located on the right side of the crankcase adjacent to the blower. The 914/6 engine serial number is stamped on the upper left of the crankcase, below the breather column. The 1.7 liter, 914 engine number is stamped on the upper right of the crankcase, below the air intake runners. The 2.0 liter, 914 engine number is stamped on the upper part of the crankcase between the oil filler and the blower housing.

912 engine serial number location

911 identification plate location

914 1.7 liter engine serial number

914/6 engine serial number location

914 2.0 liter engine serial number

911 engine numbers are divided as follows:

	6 3 2 0001
Engine type	6 = cylinder
Engine model	1 = T
	2 = E
	3 = S
Model year	9 = 1969
	0 = 1970
	1 = 1971
	2 = 1972
	3 = 1973
Four-digit sequential number	

914 engine numbers are divided as follows:

	W 0 000 001
Engine type	W = 1.7 liter, 4 cylinder
	EA = 1.7 liter, 4 cylinder (except California)
	EB = 1.7 liter, 4 cylinder (California)
	GA = 2.0 liter, 4 cylinder
Seven-digit sequential number	

914/6 engine numbers are divided as follows:

	6 4 0 0001
Engine type	6 = 6 cylinder
Engine model	4 = 2 liter
Model year	0 = 1970
	1 = 1971
Four-digit sequential number	

Engine Identification Chart

Year	Model	Starting Number
1969	911T	6190001
	911E	6290001
	911S	6390001
1970	911T	6100001
	911E	6200001
	911S	6200001
	914	W0000001
	914/6	6400001
1971	911T	6110001
	911E	6210001
	911S	6310001
	914	W0000001
	914/6	6410001
1972	911T	6120001
	911E	6220001
	911S	6320001
	914	W0000001
1973	911T	6130001
	911E	6230001
	911S	6330001
	914 (1.7 except Calif.)	EA0057001
	914 (1.7 Calif.)	EB0000001
	914 (2.0)	GA0000001

GENERAL ENGINE SPECIFICATIONS

Year	Model	Engine Displacement cc (Cu in.)	Carburetor Type	Horsepower @ rpm ①	Torque @ rpm (ft lbs) ①	Bore x Stroke (in.)	Compress. Ratio (to 1)
1965-68	912	1582 (96.5)	(2) Solex 40 PII 4	102 @ 5800	91 @ 3500	3.25 x 2.91	9.3
	911	1991 (121.5)	(2) Weber 40 IDA	148 @ 6100	140 @ 4200	3.15 x 2.60	9.0
1966-67	911S	1991 (121.5)	(2) Weber 40 IDA	180 @ 6600	144 @ 5200	3.15 x 2.60	9.8
1967-68	911L	1991 (121.5)	(2) Weber 40 IDA	148 @ 6100	140 @ 4200	3.15 x 2.60	9.0
1969	912	1582 (96.5)	(2) Solex PII 4 2-bbl	102 @ 5800	98 @ 3500	3.25 x 2.91	9.3
	911T	1991 (121.5)	(2) Weber 40 IDT 3-bbl	125 @ 5800	131 @ 4200	3.15 x 2.60	8.6
	911E	1991 (121.5)	Fuel Injection	158 @ 6500	145 @ 4500	3.15 x 2.60	9.1
	911S	1991 (121.5)	Fuel Injection	190 @ 6800	152 @ 5500	3.15 x 2.60	9.8
1970	911T	2195 (134)	(2) Solex/Zenith 40 TIN 3-bbl	142 @ 5800	148 @ 4200	3.31 x 2.60	8.6
	911E	2195 (134)	Fuel Injection	175 @ 6200	160 @ 4500	3.31 x 2.60	9.1
	911S	2195 (134)	Fuel Injection	200 @ 6500	164 @ 5200	3.31 x 2.60	9.8
	914	1679 (102.5)	Fuel Injection	85 @ 5000	98 @ 2700	3.54 x 2.60	8.2
	914/6	1991 (121.5)	(2) Weber 40 IDT 3-bbl	125 @ 5800	116 @ 4200	3.15 x 2.60	8.6
1971	911T	2195 (134)	(2) Solex/Zenith 40 TIN 3-bbl	142 @ 5800	148 @ 4200	3.31 x 2.60	8.6
	911E	2195 (134)	Fuel Injection	175 @ 6200	160 @ 4500	3.31 x 2.60	9.1
	911S	2195 (134)	Fuel Injection	200 @ 6500	164 @ 5200	3.31 x 2.60	9.8
	914	1679 (102.5)	Fuel Injection	85 @ 5000	98 @ 2700	3.54 x 2.60	8.2
	914/6	1991 (121.5)	(2) Weber 40 IDT 3-bbl	125 @ 5800	116 @ 4200	3.15 x 2.60	8.6
1972	911T	2341 (142.8)	Fuel Injection	134 @ 5600	140 @ 4000	3.31 x 2.77	7.5
	911E	2341 (142.8)	Fuel Injection	157 @ 6200	147 @ 4500	3.31 x 2.77	8.0
	911S	2341 (142.8)	Fuel Injection	181 @ 6500	154 @ 5200	3.31 x 2.77	8.5
	914	1679 (102.5)	Fuel Injection	85 @ 5000	98 @ 2700	3.54 x 2.60	8.2
1973	911T	2341 (142.8)	Fuel Injection	134 @ 5600	140 @ 4000	3.31 x 2.77	7.5
	911E	2341 (142.8)	Fuel Injection	157 @ 6200	147 @ 4500	3.31 x 2.77	8.0
	911S	2341 (142.8)	Fuel Injection	181 @ 6500	154 @ 5200	3.31 x 2.77	8.5
	914	1679 (102.5)	Fuel Injection	76 @ 4900 ②	92 @ 2700 ③	3.54 x 2.60	8.2 ④
	914S	1971 (120.3)	Fuel Injection	91 @ 4900	105 @ 3500	3.70 x 2.80	7.6

① 1972 and 1973 horsepower and torque ratings are SAE net values.
② California: 69 @ 5000
③ California: 87 @ 2700
④ California: 7.3

TUNE-UP SPECIFICATIONS

Year	Model	Engine Displace. cc (Cu in.)	SPARK PLUGS Type *	SPARK PLUGS Gap (in.)	DISTRIBUTOR Point Dwell (deg)	DISTRIBUTOR Point Gap (in.)	IGNITION TIMING (deg) Basic	IGNITION TIMING (deg) Dynamic @ rpm	Intake Valve Opens (deg)	Com-press. Press. (psi)	IDLE SPEED (rpm) MT	IDLE SPEED (rpm) AT	VALVE CLEARANCE (in.) In	VALVE CLEARANCE (in.) Ex
1965-68	912	1582 (96.5)	W225-T1	0.020-0.024	47-53	0.016	3B	—	17B	①	800-900	—	0.004	0.006
1965-68	911, 911L	1991 (121.5)	W250-P21	0.014	35-41	0.016	5B	35 @ 6000	29B	128-156	850-950	—	0.004	0.004
1966-67	911S	1991 (121.5)	W265-P21	0.014	35-41	0.016	5B	31 @ 6000	29B	128-156	850-950	—	0.004	0.004

TUNE-UP SPECIFICATIONS (Continued)

1969	912	1582 (96.5)	W225-T7	0.024	50 ± 3	0.016	3B	—	17B	①	800-900	800-900	0.004	0.006
	911T	1991 (121.5)	W230-T30	0.024	38 ± 3 ②	0.016	0	35B @ 6000	17B	130-155	850-950	850-950	0.004	0.004
	911E	1991 (121.5)	W265-P21	0.014	38 ± 3	0.016	0	30B @ 6000	29B	130-155	—	—	0.004	0.004
	911S	1991 (121.5)	W265-P21	0.014	38 ± 3	0.016	5B	30B @ 6000	38B	130-155	—	—	0.004	0.004
1970	911T	2195 (134)	W250-P21	0.024	38 ± 3 ②	0.016	0	35B @ 6000	15B	①	850-950	850-950	0.004	0.004
	911E	2195 (134)	W265-P21	0.024	38 ± 3	0.016	5B	30B @ 6000	20B	①	—	—	0.004	0.004
	911S	2195 (134)	W265-P21	0.024	38 ± 3	0.016	5B	30B @ 6000	38B	①	—	—	0.004	0.004
	914	1679 (102.5)	W175-T2	0.028 ③	50 ± 3	0.016	5B	27B @ 3500	11°30′	①	850-950	—	0.006	0.006
	914/6	1991 (121.5)	W230-T30	0.024	40 ± 3	0.016	0	35B @ 6000	15B	130-155	850-950	—	0.004	0.004
1971	911T	2195 (134)	W250-P21	0.024	38 ± 3 ②	0.016	0	35B @ 6000	15B	①	850-950	850-950	0.004	0.004
	911E	2195 (134)	W265-P21	0.024	38 ± 3	0.016	5B	30B @ 6000	20B	①	—	—	0.004	0.004
	911S	2195 (134)	W265-P21	0.024	38 ± 3	0.016	5B	30B @ 6000	38B	①	—	—	0.004	0.004
	914	1679 (102.5)	W175-T2	0.028 ③	50 ± 3	0.016	5B	27B @ 6000	11°30′	①	850-950	—	0.006	0.006
	914/6	1991 (121.5)	W230-T30	0.024	40 ± 3	0.016	0	35B @ 6000	15B	130-155	850-950	—	0.004	0.004
1972	911T	2341 (142.8)	W265-P21	0.024	37 ± 3	0.016	5A	32-38B @ 6000	15B	①	—	—	0.004	0.004
	911E	2341 (142.8)	W265-P21	0.024	37 ± 3	0.016	5A	32-38B @ 6000	20B	①	—	—	0.004	0.004
	911S	2341 (142.8)	W265-P21	0.024	37 ± 3	0.016	5A	32-38B @ 6000	38B	①	—	—	0.004	0.004
	914	1679 (102.5)	W175-T2	0.028 ③	50 ± 3	0.016	5B	27B @ 3500	11°30′	①	850-950	—	0.006	0.006
1973	911T	2341 (142.8)	W235-P21	0.022	37 ± 3	0.014	5A	32-38B @ 6000	—	①	—	—	0.004	0.004
	911E	2341 (142.8)	W265-P21 5 ④	0.022	37 ± 3	0.014	5A	32-38B @ 6000	—	①	—	—	0.004	0.004
	911S	2341 (142.8)	W265-P21	0.022	37 ± 3	0.014	5A	32-38B @ 6000	—	①	—	—	0.004	0.004
	914 (1.7)	1679 (102.5)	W175-T2	0.028	47 ± 3	0.016	5B ⑤	27B @ 3500	—	①	850-950	—	0.006	0.006
	914S (2.0)	1971 (120.3)	W175-T2	0.028	47 ± 3	0.016	5B ⑤	27B @ 3500	—	①	850-950	—	0.006	0.008

* Bosch spark plugs
B Before top dead center
A After top dead center
MT Manual transmission
AT Automatic transmission

① All cylinders should be within 22 psi of the highest reading. Compression test to be performed with engine warmer than 140°F
② With Bosch distributor, 40° ± 3° with Marelli distributor
③ 0.016-0.020 in. for cold weather setting
④ W260T2 gapped at 0.028 in.
⑤ Static, 5°A at idle speed

Firing Orders

6 5 4

3 2 1

911

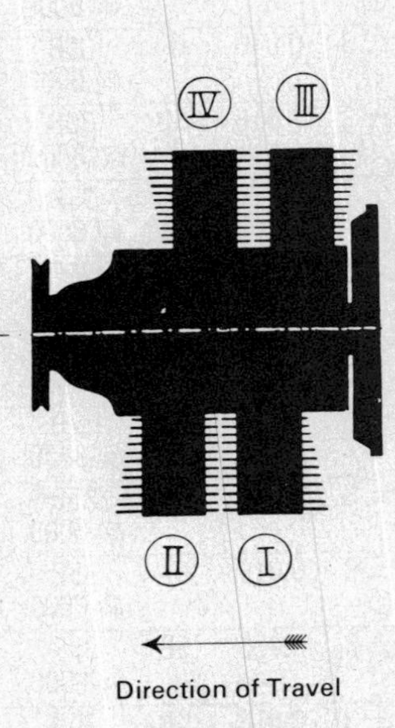

Four cylinder engines

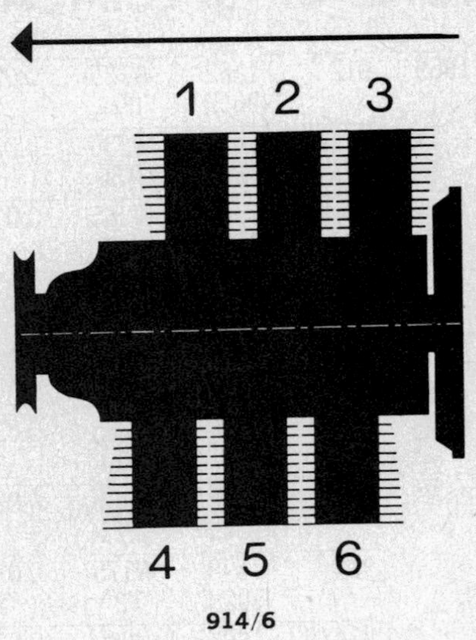

914/6

CRANKSHAFT AND CONNECTING ROD SPECIFICATIONS

All measurements are given in inches

Model	Engine Displace. cc (Cu in.)	CRANKSHAFT Main Brg. ▲ Journal Dia. ●	Main Brg. Oil Clearance	Shaft End-Play ①	Thrust on No.	CONNECTING ROD Journal Diameter ▲	Oil Clearance	Side Clearance
912	1582 (96.5)	2.1654 ②⑥	0.001-0.003⑤	0.005-0.007	1	2.0866	0.0016-0.0036	0.0039-0.0118
914/6	1991 (121.5)	2.2429-2.2437⑦	0.0004-0.0028	0.0043-0.0077	1	2.2429-2.2437	0.0011-0.0034	0.0078-0.0157
914	1679 (102.5)③	2.3610-2.3618⑧	N.A.	0.0028-0.0051	1	2.1646-2.1654	N.A.	0.004-0.016
911	1991 (121.5)④	2.2429-2.2437⑦	0.0004-0.0028	0.0043-0.0077	1	2.2429-2.2437	0.0011-0.0034	0.0078-0.0157
911	2341 (142.8)	2.2429-2.2437⑦	0.0004-0.0028	0.0043-0.0077	1	2.0476-2.0484	0.0011-0.0034	0.0078-0.0157

▲ Undersize bearings are available for all engines.

● Journal diameter for bearings 1-7 (six cylinder engines) and bearings 1-3 (four cylinder engines). Last bearing size is footnoted below.

① Measured at the thrust bearing

② Specification given is for no. 2 and 3 main bearings. No. 1 main bearing journal is 1.9865 in.

③ 1971 cc (120.3 cu in.) 914 engine also

④ 2195 cc (134 cu in.) engine also

⑤ No. 2 and 3 bearings: 0.0018-0.0039 in., no. 4 bearing: 0.0016-0.0041

⑥ No. 4: 1.5748 in.

⑦ No. 8: 1.2197-1.2202

⑧ No. 4: 1.5740-1.5748 in.

N.A. Not available

PISTON AND RING SPECIFICATIONS

All measurements in inches

Model	Engine	Ring Gap Top Compression	Ring Gap Bottom Compression	Ring Gap Oil Control	Ring Side Clearance Top Compression	Ring Side Clearance Bottom Compression	Ring Side Clearance Oil Control
912	1582 (96.5)	0.0030-0.0042	0.0018-0.0028	0.0012-0.0020	0.012-0.018	0.012-0.018	0.012-0.018
914/6	1991 (121.5)	0.0032-0.0043	0.0020-0.0032	0.0012-0.0024	0.0118-0.0177	0.0118-0.0177	0.0098-0.0157
914	1679 (102.5)①	0.0024-0.0035	0.0016-0.0028	0.0008-0.0020	0.0138-0.0217	0.0118-0.0217	0.0098-0.0157
911	1991 (121.5)②	0.0029-0.0042	0.0023-0.0028	0.0010-0.0020	0.0118-0.0177	0.0118-0.0177	0.0098-0.0157

① Also 914 2.0 liter engine
② Also 2195 cc and 2341 cc engines

VALVE SPECIFICATIONS

Model	Engine Displacement cc (Cu in.)	Seat Angle (deg)	Spring Test Pressure (lbs @ in.) Intake	Spring Test Pressure (lbs @ in.) Exhaust	Spring Installed Height (in.) Intake	Spring Installed Height (in.) Exhaust	Stem to Guide Clearance (in.) Intake	Stem to Guide Clearance (in.) Exhaust	Stem Diameter (in.) Intake	Stem Diameter (in.) Exhaust
912	1582 (96.5)	45	86.2 ± 3.32	86.2 ± 3.32	1.615	1.576	0.0014-0.0024	0.0022-0.0031	0.3929-0.3933	0.3921-0.3925
914/6	1991 (121.5)	45	176.4	165.3	1.417	1.417	0.0011-0.0022	0.0019-0.0030	0.3531-0.0005	0.3524-0.0005
914	1679 (102.5)	30②	N.A.	N.A.	1.18	1.18	0.0177	0.0177	0.3126-0.3130	0.3508-0.3512
911	All	45	176.4	165.3	1.40③	1.40③	0.0012	0.0020	0.3504-0.0005	0.3526-0.0005

① Valve guides on all models are replaceable
② Intake angle; Exhaust angle: 45°
③ E: Intake 1.398 in., exhaust 1.379 in.
S: Intake 1.398 in., exhaust 1.359 in.

TORQUE SEQUENCE

6 2 4 8

7 3 1 5

912 cylinder head

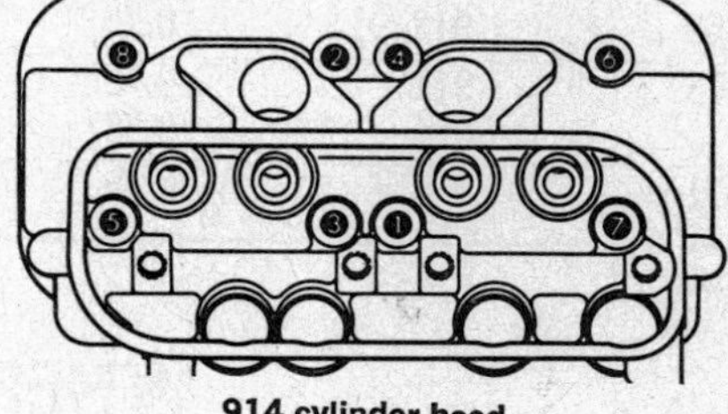

914 cylinder head

TORQUE SPECIFICATIONS

All readings in ft lbs

Model	Engine Displacement cc (Cu in.)	Cylinder Head Bolts	Rod Bearing Bolts	Main Bearing Bolts	Crankshaft Pulley Bolt	Flywheel To Crankshaft Bolts
914/6	1991 (121.5)	21.7-23.9	36.2	25.3	57.9	108.5
914	1679 (102.5)①	23.1	23.9	23.9	43.4	79.6
911	1991 (121.5)②	23.9	36.2	25.3	57.9	108.5
912	1582 (96.5)	21.7	32.5	28.9	N.A.	253-268

① 1971 cc (120.3 cu in.) 914 (2.0) engine also
② 2195 cc (134 cu in.) and 2341 cc (142.8 cu in.) engines also

CAPACITIES

Year	Model	Engine Displacement cc (Cu in.)	Engine Crankcase (qts)	Transaxle (qts)	Gasoline Tank ① (qts)
1965-69	912	1991 (121.5)	4.2	2.6	16.4
	911T	1991 (121.5)	9.5	2.6	16.4
	911E	1991 (121.5)	9.5	2.6	16.4
	911S	1991 (121.5)	9.5②	2.6	16.4
1970-71	911T	2195 (134)	9.5③	2.6	16.4
	911E	2195 (134)	9.5③	2.6	16.4
	911S	2195 (134)	9.5②③	2.6	16.4
	914	1679 (102.5)	3.7④	2.6	16.4
	914/6	1991 (102.5)	9.5	2.6	16.4
1972	911T	2341 (142.8)	9.5⑤	3.17	16.4
	911E	2341 (142.8)	9.5⑤	3.17	16.4
	911S	2341 (142.8)	10.5⑥	3.17	16.4
	914	1679 (102.5)	3.7④	2.6	16.4
1973	911T	2341 (142.8)	11.6⑦	3.17	16.4
	911E	2341 (142.8)	11.6⑦	3.17	16.4
	911S	2341 (142.8)	11.6⑦⑧	3.17	16.4
	914	1679 (102.5)	3.7④	3.7④	16.4
	914	1971 (120.27)	3.7④	3.7④	16.4

① Including 1.6 gal reserve
② Initial filling including oil cooler is 10.5 qts
③ Total capacity with Sportomatic is 11.6 qts; however, only 9.5 qts are added when refilling
④ With filter, 3.2 qts refill without filter
⑤ Total capacity with Sportomatic is 12.1 qts; however, only 9.5 qts are added when refilling
⑥ Total capacity with Sportomatic is 13.2 qts; however, only 9.5 qts are added when refilling
⑦ Total capacity with Sportomatic is 13.6 qts; however, only 10.4 qts are added when refilling
⑧ Total capacity of 14.2 qts with optional oil cooler. Capacity with oil cooler and Sportomatic is 16.9 qts. Normal refill for all models is 10.4 qts.

BRAKE SPECIFICATIONS

All measurements are given in inches

Year	Model	Master Cylinder Bore	Wheel Cylinder Bore Front	Wheel Cylinder Bore Rear	Brake Disc Diameter Front	Brake Disc Diameter Rear
1965-69	912, 911	0.75	1.891	1.480	9.25	9.61
1970-73	911	0.75	1.891	1.480	11.1	11.4
	914	0.687	1.7	1.3	11.0	11.4
1970-71	914/6	0.75	1.9	1.5	11.1	11.2

WHEEL ALIGNMENT

Year	Model	Caster Range (deg)	Caster Pref Setting (deg)	Camber Range (deg)	Camber Pref Setting (deg)	Toe-in (deg)
1969	912, 911	6°-7°30′	6°45′	−40′-(+)20′	0°①	0°②
1970-71	911	5°50′-6°20′	6°	−40′-(+)20′	0°①	0°②
1970-73	911	5°30′-6°30′	6°	−40′-(+)20′	0°③	+20′ ± 10′④
1972	911	6°20′-7°20′	6°50′	−50′-(+)10′	0°⑥	0°⑤
1973	911	5°50′-6°20′	6°5′	−50′-(+)10′	0°⑥	0°⑦

① Rear wheels: −50′ ± 20′
② Rear wheels: 0° ± 10′
③ Rear wheels: −30′ ± 20′
④ Rear wheels: 0° ± 15′
⑤ Front and rear wheels
⑥ Rear wheels: −1 ± 10′
⑦ Rear wheels: 0° ± 20′

BATTERY AND STARTER SPECIFICATIONS

	BATTERY			STARTERS						
				Lock Test			No-Load Test			
Model	Amp. Hour Capacity	Volts	Term. Ground.	Amps.	Volts	Torque (ft lbs) rpm	Amps.	Volts	RPM	Brush Spring Tension (oz)
912	(2) 36	12	Neg	160-200	9	1100-1400	33-50	11.5	6400-7900	42.3
911	(2) 36	12	Neg	160-200	9	1100-1400	33-50	11.5	6400-7900	42.3
914/6	45	12	Neg	160-200	9	1100-1400	35-50	12	6400-7900	N.A.
914	45	12	Neg	170-205	9	900-1300	35-45	12	7400-9100	N.A.

ALTERNATOR AND REGULATOR SPECIFICATIONS

	ALTERNATOR		REGULATOR						
					Field Relay			Regulator	
Model	Part No. or Manufacturer	Output (amps.)	Part No. or Manufacturer	Air Gap (in.)	Point Gap (in.)	Volts to Close	Air Gap (in.)	Point Gap (in.)	Volts @ 75°
911	Bosch	55	Bosch	Not Adjustable					
911	Motorola	55	Motorola	Not Adjustable					
914	Bosch	50	Bosch	Not Adjustable					
914/6	Bosch	55	Bosch	Not Adjustable					

GENERATOR AND REGULATOR SPECIFICATIONS

	GENERATOR				REGULATOR				
						Cut-out Relay			
Model	Part Number	Brush Spring Pressure (oz)	Field Resistance (ohms)	Output (amps)	Part Number	Volts to Close	Reverse Current (amps)	Maximum Current (amps)	Voltage Regulator Setting
912	Bosch EG (L) 14V 25A	15.8-21.1	3.5	N.A.	RS/VA 200/12 A5	12.4-13.1	2-7.5	N.A.	N.A.

N.A. Not available

Wiring Diagrams

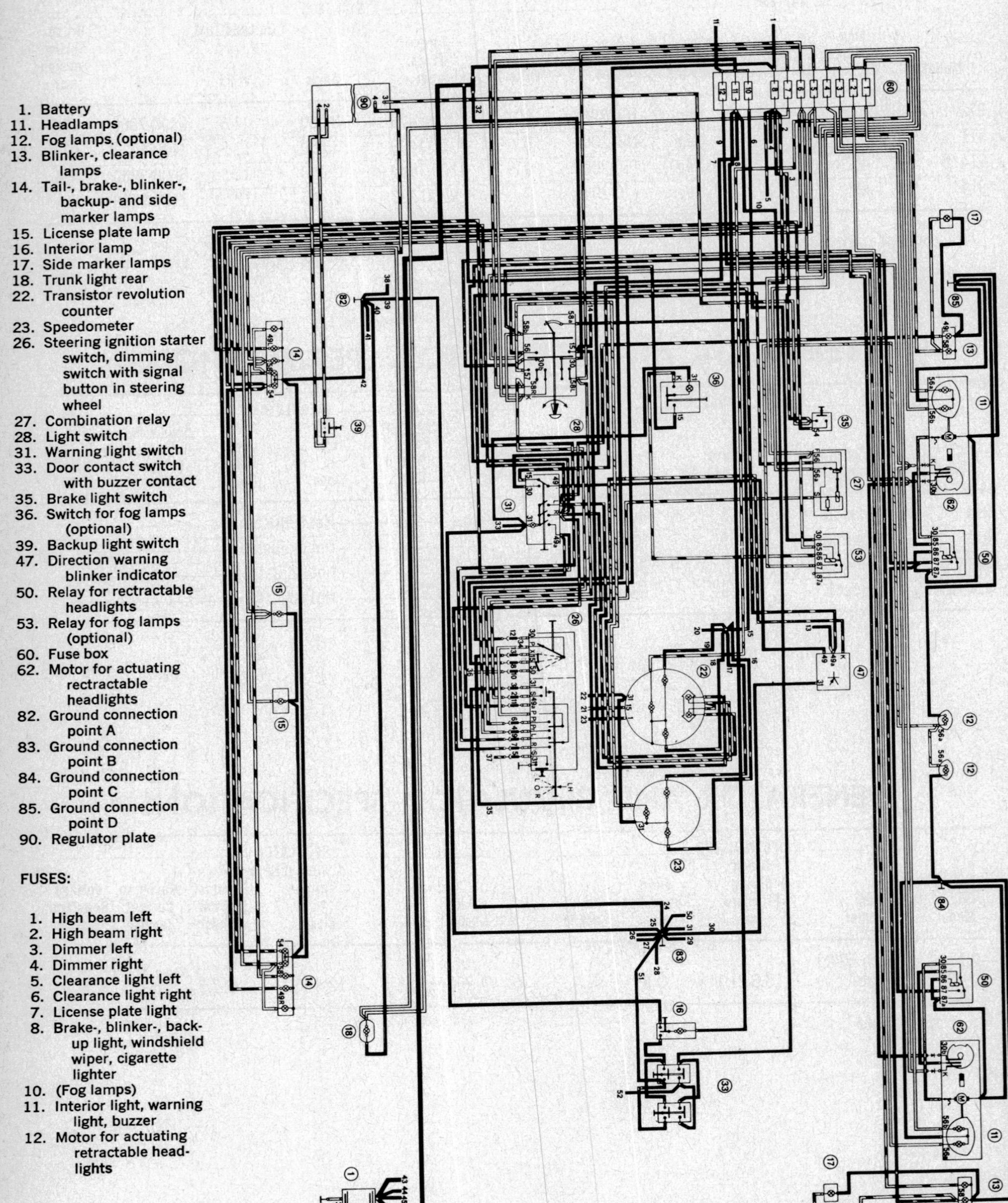

914 wiring diagram, part 1

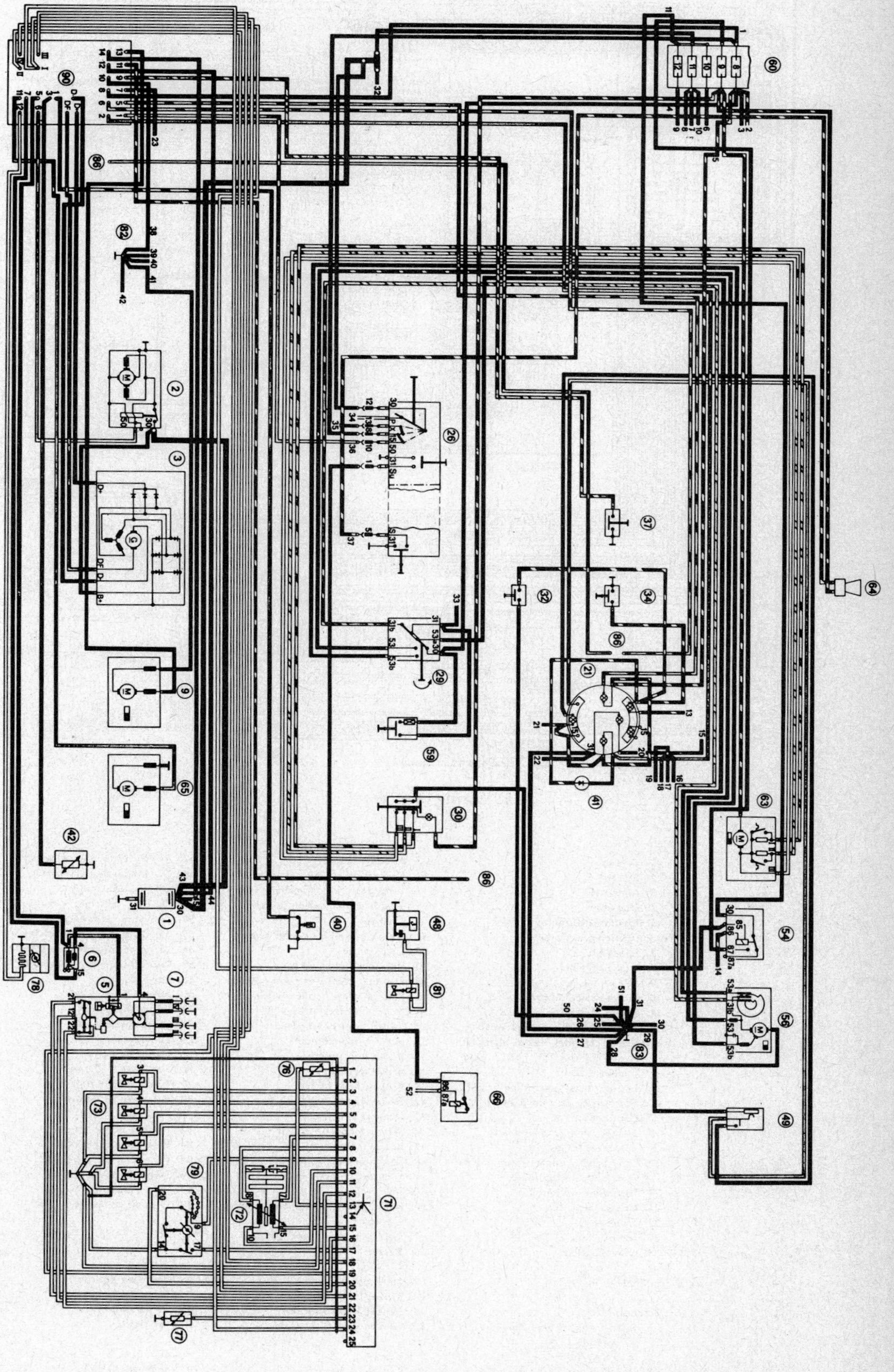

1. Battery
2. Starter
3. Alternator
5. Ignition distributor
6. Ignition coil
7. Spark plugs
9. Gasoline pump
21. Combination instrument
26. Steering ignition starter switch, dimming switch with signal button in steering wheel
29. Wiper-washer switch
30. Fan and separate heater switch
32. Brake warning switch
34. Hand brake contact
37. Switch for heater blower
40. Oil pressure switch
41. Diode
42. Oil temperature indicator (optional)
48. Thermoswitch
49. Indicator for fuel gauge
54. Relay for fresh air blower
56. Wiper motor
59. Cigarette lighter
60. Fuse box
63. Fresh air blower
64. Horn
65. Heater blower
66. Buzzer
71. Electronic control unit for fuel injection
72. Pressure sensor
73. Electric injection valve
76. Temperature sensor I
77. Temperature sensor II
78. Supplementary air
79. Throttle valve switch
81. Cold start valve
82. Ground connection point A
83. Ground connection point B
86. Sportomatic (optional)
90. Regulator plate

FUSES:

8. Brake-, blinker-, back-up light, windshield wiper, cigarette lighter
9. Fresh air blower, horn
10. (Fog lamps)
11. Interior light, warning light, buzzer
12. Motor for actuating retractable headlights

914 wiring diagram, part 2

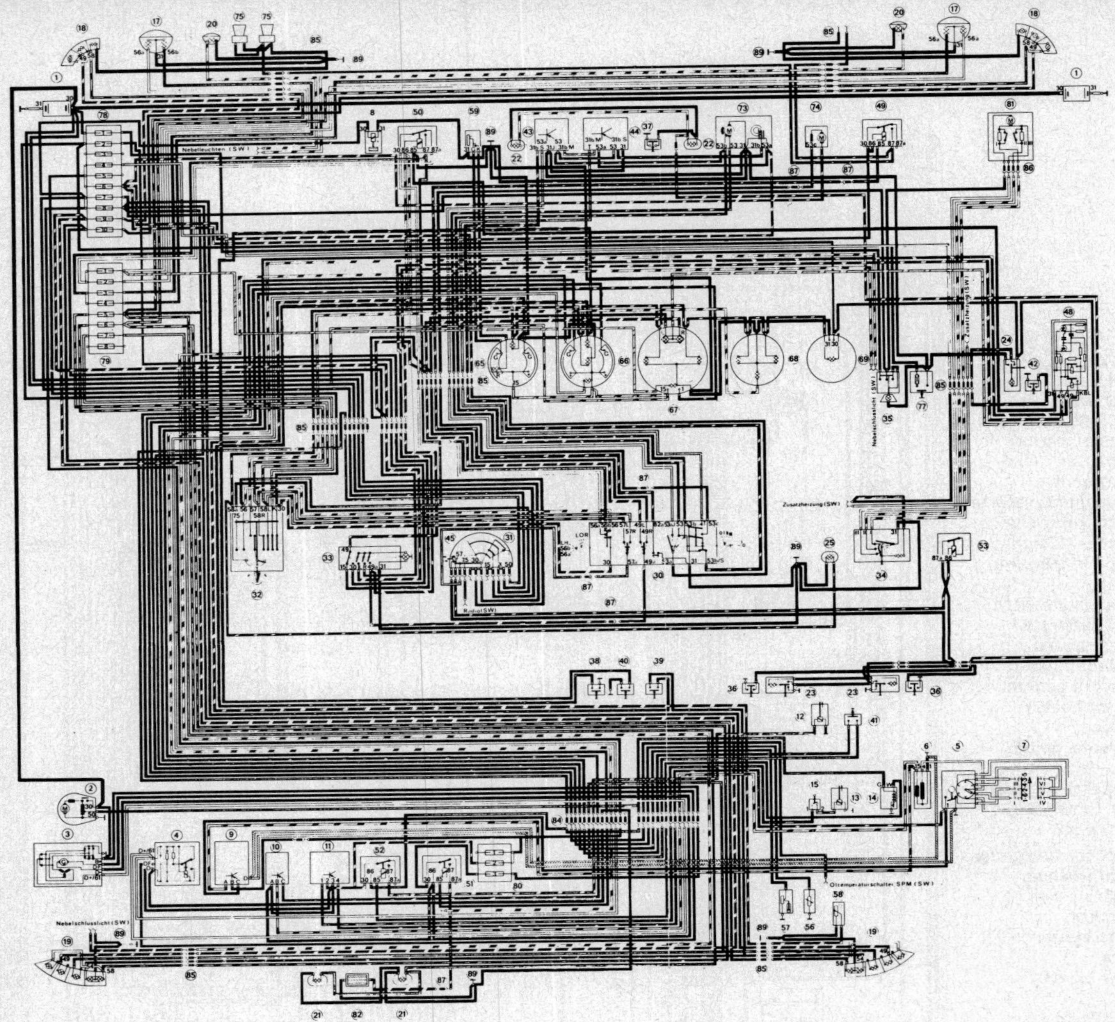

911 wiring diagram

1. Battery
2. Starter
3. Alternator
4. Governor
5. Ignition distributor
6. Ignition transformer
7. Spark plugs
8. Gasoline pump
9. BHKZ unit
10. Intermediate unit
11. Speed switch (only E and S)
12. Electromagnetic control valve
13. Lifting magnet (stop) (only E and S; on 911 T USA solenoid valve)
14. Temperature time switch
15. Microswitch (E and S only)
17. Headlamps
18. Blinker, clearance and side marker lamps
19. Tail, brake, blinker, side marker and backup lamps
20. Fog lamp (optional)
21. License plate lamp
22. Trunk lamp
23. Interior lamp
24. Glovebox lamp
25. Ashtray lamp
30. Blinker, dimming, headlamp flasher, wiper-washer switch with signal button in steering wheel
31. Steering ignition starter switch
32. Light switch
33. Warning light switch
34. Fan and separate heater switch
35. Rear window heater switch
36. Door contact switch
37. Switch for trunk light
38. Hand brake contact
39. Brake light switch
40. Brake warning switch
41. Backup light switch
42. Switch for glovebox light
43. Interval switch
44. Wiper follow-up switch
45. Buzzer contact
48. Direction warning blinker indicator
49. Horn relay
50. Headlight flasher changeover relay
51. Rear window heater relay
53. Buzzer
52. Auxiliary starting relay
56. Oil temperatuer indicator
57. Oil pressure indicator
58. Oil level indicator
59. Indicator for fuel gauge
65. Small combination instrument
66. Large combination instrument
67. Transistor revolution counter
68. Speedometer
69. Electric time clock
73. Wiper motor
74. Washer pump
75. Fanfare horn
77. Cigarette lighter
78. Fuse box I 10-pole
79. Fuse box II 8-pole
80. Fuse box III 3-pole
81. Fan motor
82. Heated pane
84. Plug-connection 14-pole
85. Plug-connection 6-pole
86. Plug-connection 4-pole
87. Plug-connection 1-pole
89. Ground connection—body

FUSES:

Fusebox I
1. Interior light, time clock, trunk light
2. Warning light
3. (Window lifter)
4. Cigarette lighter
5. (Slide roof)
6. Windshield wiper, washer pump
7. Fresh air fan
8. Brake, blinker, backup lights
9. Blinker light front left
10. Blinker light front right

Fusebox II
1. High beam left
2. High beam right
3. Dimmer left
4. Dimmer right
5. Clearance light left
6. Clearance light right
7. License plate light
8. (Fog lights)

Fusebox III
1. (Sportomatic)
2. Stop magnet, solenoid valve, starting valve
3. Rear window heater

TUNE-UP

Spark Plugs

In addition to performing their basic function of igniting the air-fuel mixture, spark plugs can also serve as very useful diagnostic tools. Once removed, compare your spark plugs with the samples in the "Troubleshooting" section. Typical plug conditions are illustrated along with their causes and remedies. Plugs which exhibit only normal wear and deposits can be cleaned, gapped, and reinstalled.

Before removing the spark plug leads, number the towers on the distributor cap with tape. Grasp each spark plug boot and pull it straight out. Check the condition of the rubber boot and/or shroud seals and replace them if necessary. Install the spark plug socket on the plug's hex and remove it. If removal is difficult, loosen the plug only slightly and drip some light oil onto the threads. Allow the oil to penetrate and then unscrew the spark plug. Proceeding this way will prevent damaging the threads in the cylinder head. Be sure to keep the socket straight to avoid breaking the ceramic insulator. Most spark plug sockets are lined with rubber for this reason. Inspect the plugs using the "Troubleshooting" section illustrations and then clean or discard them according to their condition. Recommended spark plug gap is given in the "Tune-Up Specifications Chart." Use a spark plug wire gauge for checking the gap. The wire should pass through the electrodes with just a slight drag. Using the electrode bending tool on the end of the gauge, bend the side electrode to adjust the gap. Never attempt to adjust the center electrode. Lightly oil the threads of the replacement plug and install it hand-tight. The spark plugs in all engines should be tightened to a torque of 18–21 ft lbs. Install the ignition wire boots firmly on the spark plugs. On the 912 and 914 models, be sure that the cooling shroud seals are snug or cooling efficiency will be lost.

Breaker Points and Condenser

Snap the two retaining clips off the distributor cap. Remove the cap and examine it for cracks, deterioration, or carbon tracks. Replace the cap, if necessary, by transferring one wire at a time from the old cap to the new one. Some 911 models have a dust cover which must be removed to service the points. Examine the rotor for corrosion or wear and replace it if necessary. **NOTE:** *Marelli rotors are retained by a screw.* Check the points for pitting and burning. Slight imperfections on the contact surface may be filed off with a point file (fine emery paper will also do), but it is usually wise to replace the breaker point set when tuning. Replace the condenser when you replace the point set. All Porsches are equipped with externally mounted condensers mounted on the body of the distributor. To replace the condenser, disconnect its lead from the distributor primary terminal and unscrew it from the mounting on the body. Reverse the removal procedure to install a replacement condenser.

Breaker Point Removal and Installation

912

1. Loosen the nut which retains the leaf spring of the moveable breaker contact.

912 distributor, arrow locates primary terminal

2. Pry the snap-ring off the breaker point pivot. Be careful not to allow the snap-ring to fall into the distributor, or you will have to remove the breaker plate to retrieve it.
3. Remove the breaker arm.
4. Unscrew the fixed contact retaining screw and remove the contact.
5. Install the replacement breaker point set using the reverse of the removal procedure.
6. Turn the crankshaft pulley until the breaker arm rubbing block is on the high point of one of the cam lobes.
7. A 0.016 in. feeler gauge should just slip through the contact points. If the gap is incorrect, loosen the retaining screw of the fixed contact and move it in or out as necessary. Tighten the retaining screw.
8. Lubricate the cam with silicone grease. (Special grease is available for this purpose.)
9. Install the rotor and distributor cap.
10. Check the dwell angle and the ignition timing as outlined in the following sections.

911, 914/6

NOTE: *Porsche recommends removing the distributor to replace the breaker points on these models. The problem is one of access and working space. Some mechanics find they are able to remove the points with the distributor in the car; however it is much easier to do it out of the car. Follow the directions in the "Engine Electrical" section to remove the distributor and then remove the points as outlined below.*

1. Undo the retaining screw(s), if so equipped, and remove the rotor.
2. Remove the breaker point retaining screw(s), disconnect the primary lead from the terminal, and lift out the breaker point set.

911 distributor showing breaker point retaining screws

NOTE: *When removing the points in the car, it is best to use a magnetic screwdriver to prevent dropping the screws.*

3. Install the replacement point set, but leave the adjustment screw hand-tight.
4. Turn the engine until the rubbing block of the breaker arm rests on the highest point of a cam lobe.
5. Insert a 0.016 in. feeler gauge between the two contact points. The gauge should pull through the points with just a slight drag.
6. When the gap is adjusted, tighten the retaining screw. Lightly lubricate the cam with silicone grease.
7. Install the rotor.
8. Install the distributor cap. Check the dwell angle and ignition timing as outlined in the following sections.

914

The 914, in addition to resistor spark plugs, is equipped with a resistor rotor. The rotor may be checked with an ohmmeter. If a resistance greater than 10k ohms is indicated, the rotor should be replaced.

1. Remove the breaker point retaining screw.
2. Unclip the wire lead and remove the point set.
3. Install the replacement point set, tightening the retaining screw only hand-tight.
4. Turn the engine (with a remote starter switch or by having an assistant "bump" the starter) until the rubbing

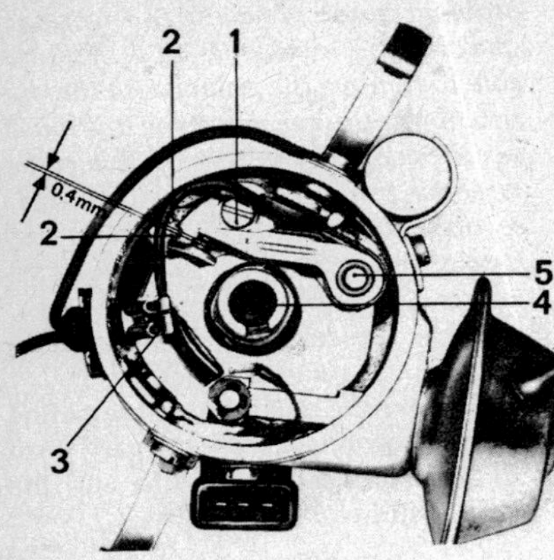

914 distributor

1. Retaining screw
2. Breaker plate
3. Primary connection
4. Distributor shaft felt
5. Breaker arm pivot (place a few drops of oil on 4 and 5)

block of the point set is on the high point of a cam lobe.

5. Using a 0.016 in. feeler gauge, adjust the point gap and then tighten the retaining screw.

6. Place a few drops of engine oil on the pivot bearing of the breaker arm and the felt in the center of the distributor shaft.

7. Install the rotor and distributor cap.

8. Check the dwell angle and ignition timing as outlined in the following sections.

Dwell Angle

The dwell angle or cam angle is the number of degrees that the distributor cam rotates while the points are closed. There is an inverse relationship between dwell angle and point gap. Increasing the point gap will decrease the dwell angle and vice versa. Checking the dwell angle with a meter is a far more accurate method of measuring point opening than the feeler gauge method.

After setting the point gap to specification with a feeler gauge, check the dwell angle with a meter. Hook-up the dwell meter according to the maker's instruction sheet. The negative lead is grounded and the positive lead connected to the primary wire (terminal no.1 on 911 models) that runs from the coil to the distributor. Start the engine, let it idle and reach operating temperature, and observe the dwell. The reading should fall within the allowable range. If it does not, the gap will have to be reset or the breaker points will have to be replaced.

911 dwell meter hook-up

1. Ground connection
2. Primary connection

Ignition Timing

CAUTION: *When performing this or any other adjustment with the engine running, be very careful of the fan belt and pulley.*

Ignition timing should always be checked as part of any tune-up. Timing is checked after the points have been adjusted or replaced. A stroboscopic timing light is a necessity for timing any Porsche and, in addition, a static 12 V timing light is necessary for the 911, 914/6, and the 914.

912

1. Measure 0.14 in. to the right of the TDC "OT" notch in the outer edge of the crankshaft pulley and scratch or paint a mark at that point. This is equivalent to 3° BTDC.

2. Attach a timing light to the no. 1 spark plug or its lead, according to the manufacturer's instructions.

3. Start the engine and allow it to idle until the normal operating temperature is reached.

4. Aim the light at the pulley. The timing light should flash (indicating that no. 1 cylinder has fired) when the mark aligns with the mating line of the two crankcase halves.

5. If the timing is not correct, loosen the distributor clamp and slowly rotate the distributor as necessary to align the mark and the crankcase centerline.

6. Tighten the clamp nut when the correct initial ignition advance is reached.

914/6

Basic timing is set first, and then the timing is dynamically checked at 6000 rpm.

1. Turn the engine until the "Z1" mark on the flywheel aligns with the crankcase centerline. The marks may be observed through the inspection hole in the transaxle housing.

2. Remove the distributor cap and check to make sure that the rotor is pointing to the no. 1 position. Remove the rotor.

3. Attach a 12 V static timing light to the coil-to-distributor primary terminal and ground.

4. Turn on the ignition switch. Loosen the distributor clamp and turn the distributor clockwise until the breaker points close. (The lamp will be out.)

914/6 timing mark

Slowly rotate the distributor in the opposite direction until the light just comes on, and then tighten the clamp.

5. Install the rotor and distributor cap. Remove the static timing light.

6. Install a stroboscopic timing light, according to the manufacturer's directions. Start the engine and allow it to reach normal operating temperature. Have an assistant accelerate the engine to 6000 rpm.

7. Looking through the transaxle inspection hole, you should see the "35" mark align with the crankcase centerline when the timing light flashes.

CAUTION: *Do not maintain this high an engine speed for any extended period. Revving an unloaded engine for more than a few seconds may prove hazardous to its health.*

8. Loosen the distributor clamp and slowly rotate the distributor as necessary to align the "35" and the crankcase centerline. Tighten the distributor clamp.

9. Disconnect the timing light.

1969–71 911

Basic timing is adjusted first with a static timing light, and then total advance is checked dynamically at 6000 rpm with a stroboscopic timing light.

1. Turn the crankshaft pulley until the correct basic timing mark on the pulley aligns with the reference notch on the blower housing. This is "Z1" (TDC) for 1969–71 T models and 1969 E models. For 1969–71 S models and 1970–71 E models, the basic timing is 5° BTDC. Scribe a mark 0.2 in. to the right of the TDC notch in the crankshaft pulley, and then align this mark with the blower housing notch.

2. Remove the distributor cap and the rotor.

3. Connect one lead of a 12 V static timing light to the primary terminal on the distributor and the other to ground.

4. With the ignition switch on, loosen the distributor clamp and rotate the distributor clockwise to make the timing light go out. The points will be closed.

911 timing light hook-up

1. Positive connection
2. Ground connection
3. No. 1 terminal
a. Idle speed screw
b. Idle mixture screw
c. Idle air screw

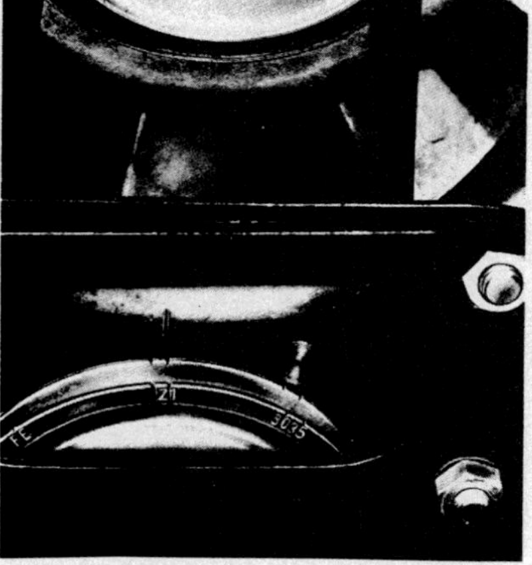

1972-1973 911 timing marks (pre-1972 is the same except for the 5° ATDC mark)

5. Slowly turn the distributor counterclockwise until the light comes on again. The points will be open at this point and the ignition will be timed to have just fired no. 1 cylinder.

6. Retighten the distributor clamp. Install the rotor and distributor cap.

7. Install a stroboscopic timing light according to the manufacturer's directions. Start the engine and allow it to reach normal operating temperature.

8. Have an assistant accelerate the engine to 6000 rpm while you aim the timing light at the crankshaft pulley. When the light flashes, the 30° or 35° (depending on the model) notch should be aligned with the reference notch in the blower housing.

CAUTION: *Do not maintain this high an engine speed for any extended period. Over revving an unloaded engine may prove hazardous to its health.*

9. If the marks do not align, loosen the distributor clamp and rotate the distributor as necessary to correct the total advance.

10. Tighten the distributor clamp and remove the timing light.

1972–73 911 T/E/S

These models are equipped with a vacuum retard unit which retards the ignition to 5° ATDC at idle. Ignition timing is checked both at idle and at 6000 rpm with a stroboscopic timing light. The crankshaft pulley has a TDC notch ("Z1"), a 5° ATDC notch directly to the left of the "Z1" notch, a 30° BTDC notch, and a 35° notch. The 1972–73 911 distributor has a slotted mounting flange on its base. The retaining nut is loosened and the distributor swivels on the mounting stud to make timing changes.

1. Start the engine and allow it to reach normal operating temperature.

2. Stop the engine and attach a timing light to no. 1 spark plug according to the manufacturer's instructions.

3. Restart the engine. Make sure that the idle speed is according to specifications and that the vacuum advance hose is connected.

4. When the timing light flashes, the 5° ATDC notch in the pulley should be aligned with the reference notch in the blower housing.

5. If the notches do not align, loosen the retaining nut and slowly rotate the distributor as necessary until they line up. Ignition timing is now correct at idle.

6. Dynamic timing is checked at this point. Total advance at 6000 rpm should be between 32° and 38°.

7. While you stand at the rear with the timing light aimed at the timing notches on the crankshaft pulley, have an assistant accelerate the engine to 6000 rpm for an instant.

CAUTION: *Do not hold the engine at this high speed for an extended period.*

8. The pulley has a 30° and 35° notch, so 32–38° would start the right of the 30° notch and end just to the right of the 35° notch. The blower housing reference notch should be aligned with the desired timing area on the crankshaft pulley when the light flashes.

9. If the timing is incorrect, loosen the nut and slowly rotate the distributor to adjust it.

10. Stop the engine and remove the timing light.

914

Basic timing is set at 5° BTDC and checked with a static timing light. Dynamic timing is set at 3500 rpm and checked with a stroboscopic timing light. 1973 models are equipped with vacuum retard ignition timing which should be checked dynamically at idle (5° A) in addition to 3500 rpm.

1. Loosen the clamp on the right hand heater hose, and pull the hose from the heater blower. Position the hose out of the way.

2. Unscrew the inspection hole cover from the cooling shroud.

3. Turn the engine until the black notch in the crankshaft pulley aligns with V-shaped notch in the blower housing. Remove the distributor cap and rotor.

914 timing marks

4. Attach one lead of a 12 V static timing to terminal no. 1 (primary) on the distributor and the other lead to ground. Switch on the ignition.

5. Loosen the distributor clamp and rotate the distributor clockwise until the light is out. The points will be closed.

6. Slowly turn the distributor counterclockwise until the breaker points open and the light just comes on. Tighten the distributor clamp.

7. Install the rotor and distributor cap.

8. Disconnect both vacuum hoses from the vacuum unit on the distributor. Install a stroboscopic timing light according to the manufacturer's instructions.

9. Start the engine and allow it to reach normal operating temperature.

10. On 1973 models, check the timing at idle speed first (5°A). While you aim the timing light through the inspection hole, have an assistant accelerate the engine to 3500 rpm for an instant.

11. The red notch (27°) on the crankshaft pulley should be aligned with the V-shaped notch in the blower housing.

12. If the notches are not in alignment, loosen the distributor clamp and slowly rotate the distributor until they do align.

13. Tighten the retaining clamp, stop the engine, and remove the timing light.

Valve Lash

Adjustment

1. The engine must be cold when adjusting the valves on any Porsche. Remove the rocker arm covers, two per head in the case of the 911 and 914/6.

2. The valves of each cylinder are adjusted with that piston at the top of its compression stroke. Both the intake and exhaust valves will be closed at this point. Turn the engine to align the TDC mark ("Z1" for the 911 and 914/6, "OT" for the 912, and the black notch on 914 models) with the reference mark.

3. Using a feeler gauge (thickness equal to the figure given in the "Valve Clearance" column of the "Tune-Up Spe-

912 valve clearance adjustment

914 valve clearance adjustment (special adjusting tool shown)

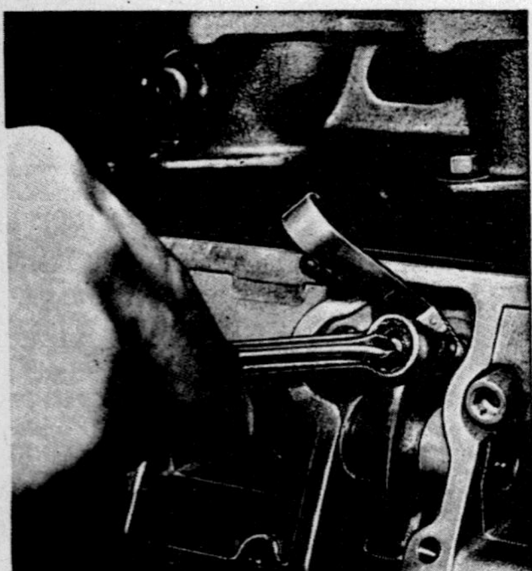

911 and 914/6 valve clearance adjustment

cifications Chart"), check the clearance between the valve stem and the rocker arm. The feeler gauge should just slip through; if it has to be forced the clearance will be incorrect.

4. If the clearance is not within specifications, loosen the locknut with a box wrench and, using a screwdriver, turn the rocker arm adjusting screw while holding the locknut. A tool to simplify this procedure is available from automotive suppliers. It has a screwdriver bit which can be turned while the locknut is held with a socket.

5. Tighten the locknut while holding the adjusting screw. Recheck the valve clearance to ensure that it wasn't changed when the locknut was tightened. Repeat this procedure on the other valve of no. 1 cylinder.

6. Proceed to adjust the valves of the remaining cylinders in an order of 1–2–3–4 for four-cylinder engines or 1–6–2–4–3–5 for six-cylinder engines. The piston of the cylinder on which the valves are being adjusted must be at TDC. Turn the engine until both valves of the cylinder being adjusted are closed. Six-cylinder engines have TDC marks for each cylinder on the crankshaft pulley. Adjust the valves in the same manner as no. 1 cylinder.

7. Install the rocker arm or camshaft housing covers with new gaskets. Start the engine and check for leaks.

Carburetor

Idle speed and Mixture

912

NOTE: *A Unisyn® or other carburetor synchronizer will make for a much more accurate adjustment.*

1. Start the engine and run it until it reaches normal operating temperature.

2. Detach the crankcase breather hose and remove the air cleaners from both carburetors.

3. Remove both idle mixture adjusting screws from each carburetor. Check the tips of the screws for damage or wear. Replace the screws with new units if there is any question about their condition. Install the screws.

4. Remove the throttle rods from the throttle arms.

5. Attach a dwell/tachometer to the engine, or have an assistant observe the instrument panel tachometer while you adjust the idle speed screws to obtain 1000 rpm.

6. Turn both idle mixture screws on each carburetor in to its seat (not tight, or you'll damage the needles) and then back them out 1 ½ turns.

7. Turn the idle mixture screws in or out as necessary to obtain the smoothest and fastest idle.

CAUTION: *Never leave the screws in a fully turned-in position.*

8. Adjust the idle speed screws for a normal idle of 800–900 rpm. This as far as you can go in adjusting without a Unisyn gauge.

912 idle mixture screw

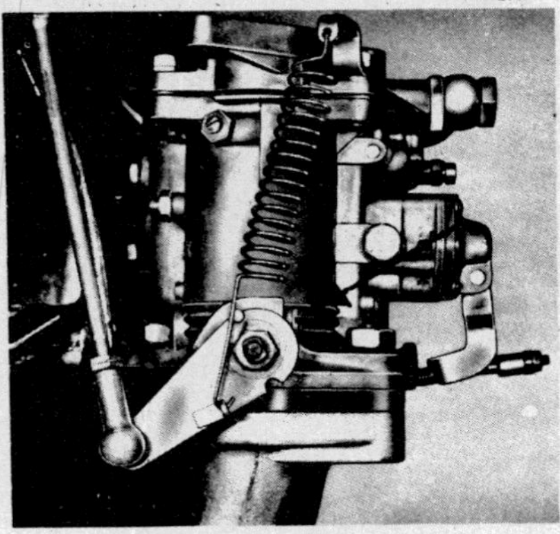

912 idle speed screw location

9. Position the Unisyn gauge on one carburetor throat. Adjust the synchronizer so that the plunger is halfway between the two calibration rings in the center of the tube. The synchronizer is now set for the engine and should not be changed.

10. Move the gauge to the other throat of the carburetor. If the reading changes, the throttle valves are not in alignment. Twist the throttle shaft to correct this condition. Double check the throttle valve synchronization by comparing readings from both carburetor throats.

11. Transfer the gauge to the other carburetor. Adjust the throttle valve with the idle speed screw so that the plunger moves to the same position as on the other carburetor. Check the throttle valve synchronization as performed in the previous step.

12. If the idle speed has changed during the adjusting, reset the idle speed screws and recheck carburetor synchronization with the gauge.

13.Connect the throttle rods to the throttle arms. There should be no preload on either part.

14.Run the engine up to 1200–1300 rpm. Recheck the carburetor synchronization. If the gauge indicates unequal values, shorten or lengthen the carburetor throttle rods.

15. Check to see that the idle speed is correct. Install the air cleaners and the breather hose.

1969–71 911T and 1970–71 914/6 (Weber and Solex/Zenith)

NOTE: *A Unisyn or other carburetor synchronizer is the only way to obtain an accurate adjustment.*

1. Run the engine until normal operating temperature is reached.

2. Shut the engine down and remove the air cleaner. Disconnect the throttle linkage ball joints from the cross-shaft connecting linkage.

3. Attach a dwell/tachometer to the engine or have an assistant observe the

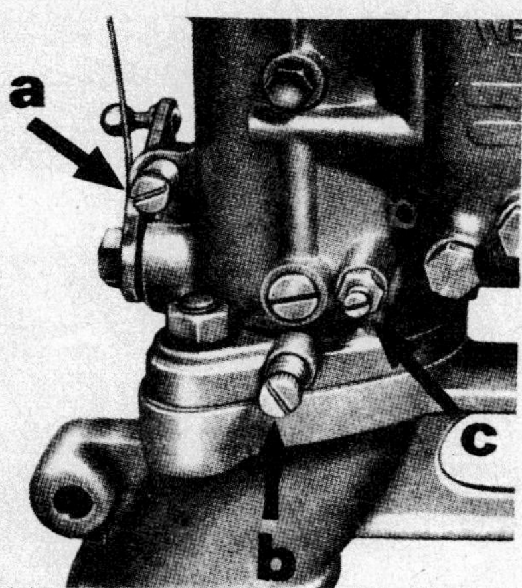

Weber 40 IDT adjustment screws

Solex/Zenith 40 TIN adjustment screws

a. Idle speed screw
b. Idle mixture screw
c. Idle air screw

instrument panel tachometer. Adjust the idle stop screws on each carburetor so that the engine idles between 1000 and 1200 rpm. Both screws must be equally adjusted.

4. Adjust the idle mixture screws on all carburetors.

CAUTION: *Never leave the screws in a fully turned-in position.*

5. Place the Unisyn gauge on the throat of one carburetor and adjust the gauge so that the piston is about halfway up the glass indicator tube. No other adjustment should be performed on the gauge itself.

6. Move the gauge to the next carburetor. The indicator piston should move to the same position as on the first carburetor. If it does not, adjust the idle air screw until the piston stays at the halfway level. Repeat this procedure for each carburetor.

NOTE: *Turn the idle air adjusting screws out as little as possible. If a satisfactory adjustment cannot be obtained, turn all the screws and restart the adjustment.*

7. Turn the idle stop screw on each set of carburetors until the engine idles at 850–950 rpm. Recheck the adjustment on each carburetor with the gauge.

8. Install the air cleaner. Readjust the idle mixture screws to smooth out the idle.

9. Adjust the cross-shaft carburetor connecting linkage and reconnect them.

10. Using an exhaust gas analyzer, check to see that the CO content is no more than 3.5% $\pm$ 0.5%.

Fuel Injection

Idle Speed

911

Procedures for adjusting the fuel injection system are not included for several reasons. It's an absolute necessity to have the specific factory tools and equipment when adjusting or repairing this system.

914

1. Remove the air filter and connect a tachometer to the engine.

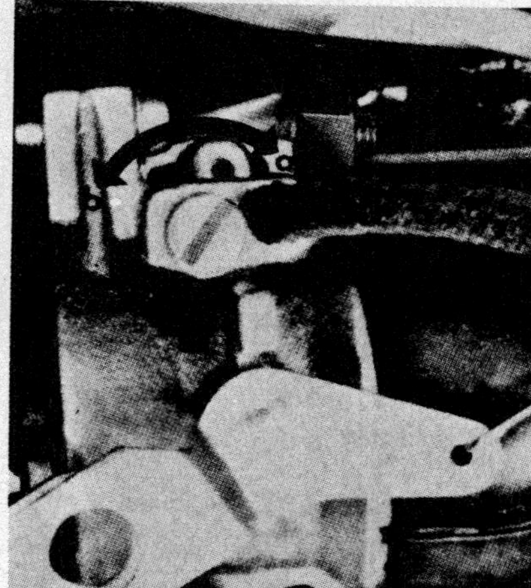

914 idle speed screw

2. Start the engine and set the idle speed to 850 $\pm$ 50 rpm. Turning the adjustment screw (see illustration) clockwise, in the direction of (a) increases the idle speed. Turning the screw in the direction of (b), or counterclockwise, decreases the idle speed.

ENGINE ELECTRICAL

Distributor

Removal and Installation

912

1. Locate the no. 1 spark plug wire location in the distributor cap. Scribe or mark this location with chalk on the body of the distributor.

2. Unsnap and remove the distributor cap.

3. Turn the engine over until the rotor points toward the no. 1 cylinder mark.

4. Detach the two distributor leads.

5. Loosen the clamp bolt at the base and remove the distributor from the engine.

If the engine has not been disturbed, install the distributor as follows:

6. Ensure that the spring is replaced in the center bore of the drive gear. A length of wire may be utilized to install the spring if it has been removed.

7. Insert the distributor, making sure that the dog on the distributor engages the slot in the drive gear. Turning the rotor a few times will ease the installation.

8. Push the distributor in firmly. Tighten the clamp bolt hand-tight.

9. Install the distributor leads and the cap. Check the ignition timing and then tighten the clamp bolt.

If the engine has been disturbed while the distributor was out, install it in the following manner:

10. Turn the engine over until the slot in the drive gear is parallel with the engine centerline. The smaller side of the gear should be facing the center of the engine. No.1 piston should now be at TDC.

11. Proceed with steps 6 through 9. Double check that the rotor faces the no.1 terminal in the distributor cap.

911, 914/6

1. Remove the heated air intake duct on 1972–3 911's.

2. Unsnap and remove the distributor cap. Position it out of the way.

3. Mark the direction in which the rotor is pointing on the body of the distributor.

NOTE: *Some models have a scribe mark indicating the correct rotor positioning for no. 1 cylinder. On these models it will be more convenient to turn the engine so that the rotor points to this mark before removing the distributor.*

4. Detach the distributor leads. Remove the vacuum line on 1972–3 911 models.

5. Loosen and remove the retaining nut from the base of the distributor. Pull the distributor straight out of the engine. Check and, if necessary, replace the sealing ring on the distributor housing.

6. Insert the distributor into the engine. Turn the rotor back and forth to engage the distributor and crankshaft gears. If the engine has been turned while the distributor was out, bring no. 1 cylinder to TDC as described below under "Ignition Timing".

7. Adjust the static and dynamic timing as described below.

914

1. Remove the air cleaner.

2. Loosen the clamp on the right-hand

heater hose and pull it from the heater. Position the hose out of the way.

3. Screw the inspection hole cover out of the cooling shroud.

4. Turn the engine until the black notch in the crankshaft pulley aligns with v-shaped notch in the blower housing.

5.Remove the distributor cap and check that the rotor is, indeed, pointing towards the no. 1 cylinder position.

6. Detach the two electrical leads and vacuum hoses from the distributor.

7. Loosen the retaining nut on the base of the distributor and pull it out of the engine.

To install the distributor with the engine undisturbed:

8. Ensure that the spring is in place in the center bore of the drive gear. A length of wire may be used to install the spring if it has been removed.

9. Insert the distributor, making sure that the dog on the distributor engages the slot in the drive gear. Turning the rotor a few times will ease installation.

10. Push the distributor in firmly. Tighten the clamp nut.

11. Install the distributor leads and vacuum hoses. Install the distributor cap.

12. Check the ignition timing as described below. Install the inspection cover, heater hose, and air cleaner.

Install the distributor in the following manner if the engine has been disturbed:

914 distributor drive gear positioning

13. Turn the engine to bring no. 1 cylinder up to TDC. At this point, the black notch in the crankshaft pulley should be aligned with the V-shaped notch in the blower housing and the slot in the distributor drive gear should be at approximately a 12° angle to the engine centerline. The slot should be pointing toward the rear retaining screw of the air filter support and the smaller side of the gear should be facing the center of the engine.

14. Install the distributor using steps 8 through 12.

Generator

Carbon Brush and Commutator Checking

1. Remove the generator cover plate. Lift the brush springs and extract the brushes.

2. Examine the carbon brushes for excessive wear and for free travel in their guides. Replace worn or oily brushes.

3. If necessary, clean the commutator with a solvent-wetted cloth. The cloth can be wrapped around a paint brush or a piece of wood. Be careful not to get any dirt on the bearing. Allow the solvent to evaporate before starting the engine.

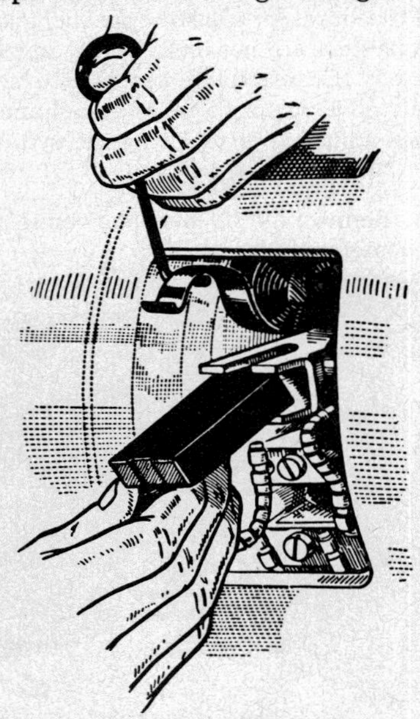

Carbon brush replacement

NOTE: *If there is excessive dirt or oil on the brush holders or if the brushes show evidence of arcing, the generator should be removed and checked. Take the generator to a dealer or shop which specializes in electrical repair.*

4. If you have access to a spring gauge, check the tension of the brush springs. Spring tension will be found under "Generator Specifications".

5. Reinstall the brushes and springs. Replace the cover strap.

Removal and Installation

912

1. Tag (for reinstallation) and disconnect the leads to the generator.

2. Remove the upper pulley nut by holding the pulley in place with a screwdriver (a square slot is provided in the pulley for this purpose).

3. Remove the outer pulley half and adjustment shims.

4. Remove the drive belt.

5. Remove the generator-to-bracket clamp.

6. Remove the four generator bracket bolts and then the bracket.

Generator removal

7. There are four bolts retaining the generator/cooling blower assembly to the cooling shroud. Remove the bolts and then pull the generator/blower assembly out of the shroud.

8. Install the generator/blower assembly in the cooling shroud and tighten the four bolts.

9. Install the engine-to-bracket gasket and install the bracket.

10. Install the generator-to-bracket clamp. Install the electrical leads to the generator.

11. Polarize the generator by connecting the battery lead to the 61D+ terminal of the regulator for an instant. The generator should turn in the direction of engine rotation.

12. Install the drive belt, outer pulley half, spacers, and the nut. Check the belt tension and, if necessary, adjust it as outlined below.

Belt Tension Adjustment

1. Check the drive belt tension by pushing it in with your thumb at a point about midway between the pulleys. Belt deflection should be between 5/8 in. and 3/4 in. If the belt deflection does not fall within these limits, it must be adjusted or replaced.

2. Insert a screwdriver into the slot in the inner edge of the pulley and brace it on the top generator bolt. While holding the pulley in this manner, loosen and remove the pulley nut.

3. Remove the outside of the pulley.

4. Remove adjustment spacers to increase the belt tension. Add spacers to decrease belt tension.

5. When the correct spacer grouping is achieved, install the belt, pulley half, spacers, and the nut.

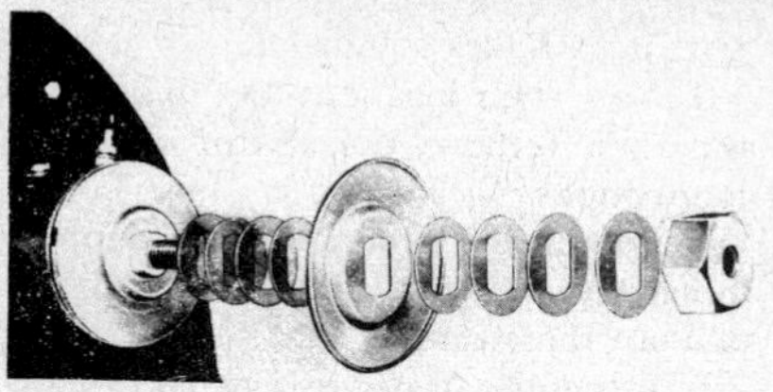
912 pulley adjustment spacers

NOTE: *If you have removed spacers, install the extra spacers on the outside of the pulley so they won't become lost or misplaced.*

6. Recheck the belt tension after about 60 miles of driving.

Alternator

Alternator Precautions

A few precautions should be observed when servicing an electrical system that uses an alternator. Failure to do so can result in serious damage to the charging system. The negative terminal(s) of the battery(ies) is (are) always grounded. Always connect the correct battery terminals when attaching a battery charger or replacing a battery. Never operate the alternator on an open, uncontrolled circuit. Never ground or short across any regulator or alternator terminals. Never attempt to polarize the alternator. Remove the battery cables from the terminals when charging the battery in the car.

Removal and Installation

911

The alternator is located in the blower housing.

1. Disconnect the battery ground straps.
2. Remove the air cleaner assembly.
3. Remove the upper shroud retaining bolts.
4. Hold the alternator pulley and remove the pulley nut.
5. Remove the drive belt.
6. Remove the blower housing strap retaining bolts.
7. Pull the blower housing/alternator towards the rear until there is enough clearance to disconnect the wiring.
8. Remove the alternator.
9. Install the alternator in a reverse order of the removal. Be sure that the blower housing is seated on the dowel in the crankcase.
10. Tighten the pulley nut to 29 ft lbs.

911 alternator pulley nut removal

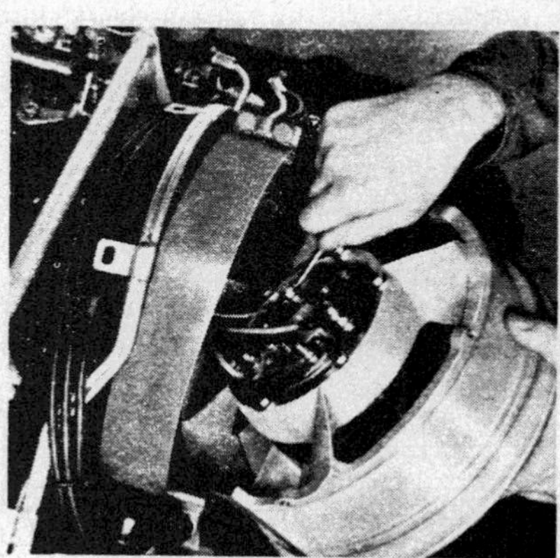
911 alternator removal

914/6

1. Disconnect the battery ground strap.
2. Remove the carburetors and intake stacks. This procedure is described in the "Fuel System" section.
3. Remove the coil.
4. Remove the retaining bolts and then detach the shroud.
5. Hold the alternator pulley and remove the pulley nut.
6. Remove the pulley and spacers.
7. Remove the air duct and ground strap from the rear of the fan housing.

914/6 shroud retaining bolts (arrows)

8. Detach the wires and plug from the alternator.
9. Remove the retaining strap and remove the alternator.
10. Install the alternator in a reverse

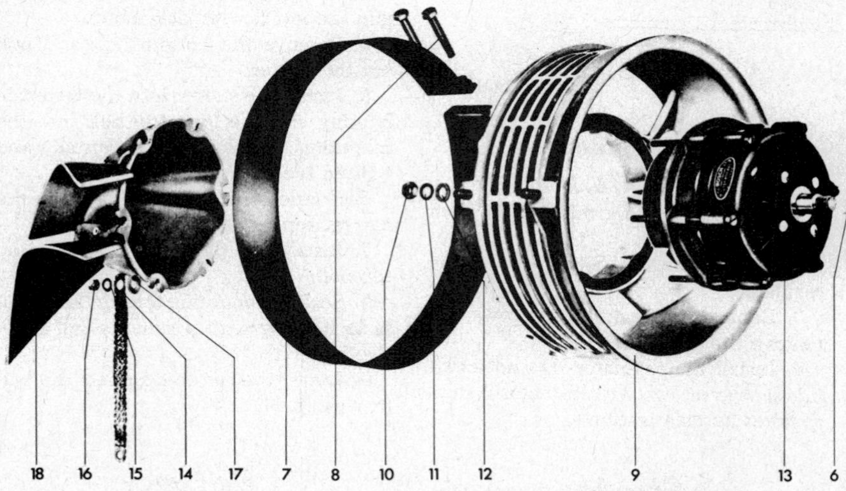

Exploded view of 914/6 alternator and blower

1. Nut
2. Dished washer
3. Outer pulley half
4. Washer
5. Blower fan
6. Woodruff key
7. Retaining strap
8. Bolt
9. Fan housing
10. Nut
11. Washer
12. Lockwasher
13. Alternator
14. Ground strap
15. Washer
16. Nut
17. Washer
18. Air duct

order of the removal. Be sure that the blower housing is seated on the dowel in the crankcase.

11. Tighten the pulley nut to 29 ft lbs.

Belt Tension Adjustment

911, 914/6

A correctly tensioned belt can be deflected ½—¾ in. by light hand pressure. If the tension is not within specifications, follow the steps below to adjust or replace the belt.

1. Remove the pulley nut as outlined

Loosening 914/6 alternator pulley nut

above in "Alternator Removal and Installation". The 914/6 will require infinitely more patience and an assistant because of the inaccessibility of the pulley, so take your time. While you hold the pulley, have an assistant remove the nut. Don't drop the nut or spacers, or you'll be a long time fishing them out of the engine compartment.

2. Remove the outside half of the pulley.
3. Remove adjustment spacers to increase belt tension. Add spacers to decrease belt tension.
4. When the correct spacer grouping is achieved, install the belt, pulley half, spacers, and nut.
5. Tighten the nut to 29 ft lbs.

914/6 and 911 adjustment spacer arrangement

NOTE: *If you have removed spacers, install the extra spacers on the outside of the pulley so they won't become lost or misplaced.*

6. Recheck the belt tension after about 60 miles of driving.

914

A correctly tensioned belt will be able to be deflected approximately ½ in. by light hand pressure. If the tension is not within specification, follow the steps below to adjust or replace the belt.

1. Remove the small cover plate from the alternator cover.
2. Loosen the socket screw and slide the alternator left or right as necessary.
3. Tighten the screw and replace the cover.

Regulator

Removal and Installation

912

1. Disconnect the battery ground cable.
2. Disconnect the wiring from the regulator.
3. Remove the retaining screws and remove the regulator.
4. Install the replacement regulator in a reverse manner of the removal procedure. New regulators generally have a wiring diagram on the case.
5. Polarize the generator as described under "Generator Removal and Installation."

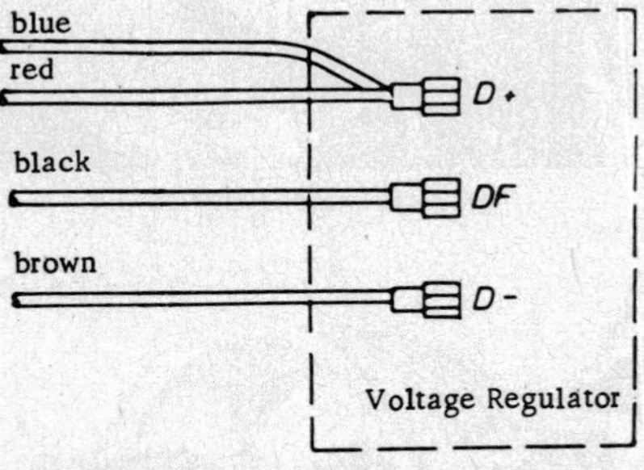

911 voltage regulator wiring schematic

911, 914/6, 914

1. Disconnect the ground cable from the battery.
2. Disconnect the wiring from the regulator.
3. Remove the mounting screws and remove the regulator.
4. Install the regulator. Do not overtighten the screws. An alternator system requires no polarization.

Starter

Removal and Installation

912, 911

1. Disconnect the battery(ies) ground strap(s).
2. Jack up the rear of the car and support it with jack stands.
3. Note their locations (tag to be sure) and then remove the starter electrical connections.
4. Loosen the retaining bolts, support the starter, remove the bolts, and then pull out the starter.
5. Install the starter using a reverse order of the removal procedure. Ensure that the terminal connections are correctly installed and tight.
6. Lower the car and connect the battery(ies) ground strap(s).

914/6

1. Disconnect the battery ground strap.
2. Raise and support the starter side of the car.
3. Disconnect the electrical leads from the starter. Remember their locations or tag the leads so that you won't reinstall them incorrectly.
4. Assemble an 8mm allen head socket, universal joint, extension, and ratchet handle. Using this set-up, remove the upper bolt.
5. Remove the lower hex bolt and pull out the starter.
6. Install the starter using a reverse order of the removal procedure. Be sure that the electrical leads are installed on the correct terminals. Install a hose clamp to retain the electrical cable to the solenoid.

914

1. Open the engine compartment lid. Disconnect the battery ground cable.
2. The top retaining bolt is accessible from within the engine compartment. Remove the nut.
3. Jack up the starter side of the car and support it with jack stands.
4. Remove the bottom bolt and pull out the starter.
5. Install the starter into the transaxle housing and the long top bolt into the mounting bracket hole. Install and tighten the bottom bolt.
6. Connect the electrical leads to the correct terminals.
7. Install and tighten the nut on the top bolt.
8. Seal the mounting bracket and transaxle housing with a suitable self-adhesive sealer.
9. Lower the car and connect the battery cable.

Battery

The 911 and 912 batteries are located in the front luggage compartment. One battery is located in each fender well behind the headlights. The 914 and 914/6 battery is located in the engine compartment.

ENGINE MECHANICAL

Engine Removal and Installation

All Porsche engines are removed and installed with the transaxle attached. The recommended method for removal is to raise the rear of the car high enough for working clearance and then support it on jack stands. A hydraulic transmission/-differential jack or service jack of at least 800 lbs. capacity is required for lowering the engine/transaxle and raising it back into the chassis. A flat steel plate should be used on the jack pad to evenly support the engine during the removal and installation procedures. Proceed slowly and carefully as the engine/transaxle combination is both heavy and delicate.

912 & 911

1. Disconnect the battery. Drain the engine and transaxle oil.
2. Open the engine compartment lid and detach the hot air ducts from the air gates and exhaust manifold heat exchangers.
3. Detach the two heater control cables.
4. Remove the hot air ducts from the T-union between the air cleaners and then remove the T-union from the blower housing.
5. Remove the tops of the air cleaners.
6. Tag for installation and then remove the electrical cables from the generator and blower housing.
7. Tag for installation and remove the wires from the coil.
8. Remove the connections from the oil temperature and pressure sending units.
9. Remove the fuel line from the fuel pump and detach its clip from the engine shield.
10. Remove the allen bolts retaining the axle shaft flange to the transaxle. Free the axle shaft from the transaxle and drop them out of the way.
11. Remove the starter electrical leads.
12. Disconnect the clutch cable from the control lever.
13. Remove the ground strap.
14. Detach the back-up light lead.
15. Disconnect the throttle linkage from the cross-shaft at the transaxle.
16. Remove the cover in the center of the rear floor.
17. Detach the rubber shift lever cover from the flange on the body and pull it forward on the control lever.
18. Remove the safety wire from the square-headed from the joint. Loosen the screw and slide the shift rod off its base.
19. Position the jack, including the flat support plate, under the engine/transaxle. The jack should be under the point of balance of the powertrain.

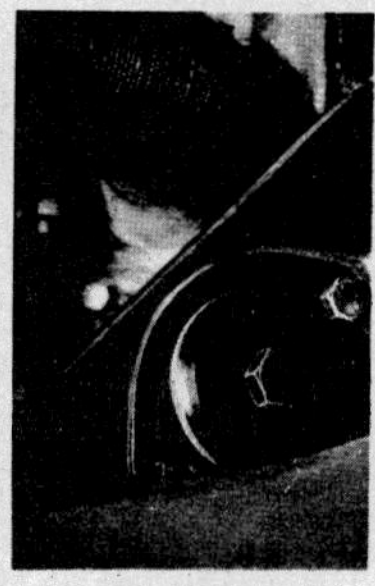

912 and 911 rear engine-to-body mounts

912 and 911 transaxle crossmember mounting

20. Raise the jack a slight amount.
21. Remove the body mounting bolts on either side of the engine compartment.
22. Remove the body mounting bolts from the short transaxle crossmember. The engine is removed with this crossmember attached.

912 and 911 engine/transaxle removal

23. Very carefully lower the engine, while your assistants help balance it.
24. Roll the engine/transaxle out from under the car.

Follow steps 26 through 31 for engine and transaxle separation. Step 25 is for 1970 and later 911 models only.

25. Remove the starter. Turn the engine until the three threaded rivets in the pressure plate (spaced 120° apart) are visible throughout the starter opening. A spacer sleeve (see figure) should be fastened to each rivet with an allen screw (M6 x 12). Tightening the screws will release the tension on the throwout bearing.

Releasing throwout bearing tension

NOTE: *On cars equipped with an adjustable throwout fork, some 1970–71 models, it is possible to release tension by unscrewing the adjusting screw on the fork.*

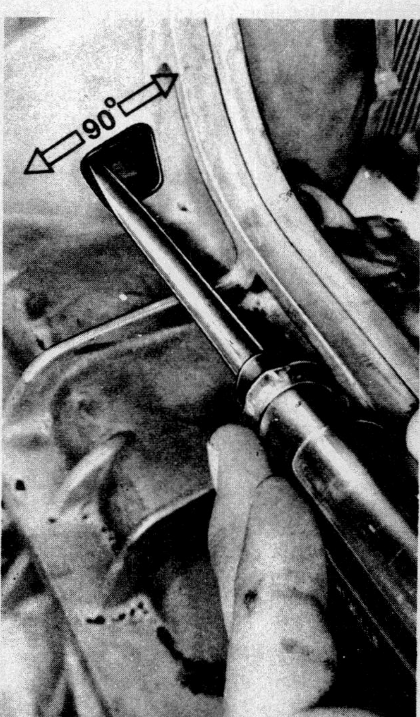

Sliding the fork past the throwout bearing

After releasing throwout bearing tension through one of the above methods it is necessary to slide the throwout fork past the bearing. To do this, insert a screwdriver in the opening in the transaxle and turn the bearing 90°. Slide the fork past the bearing. The transaxle may now be separated from the engine.

26. Remove the engine-to-transaxle bolts and nuts. Carefully pull the transaxle away from the engine. Be sure that the full weight of the transaxle is supported, so as not to damage the pilot bushing, throwout bearing, clutch disc, or pressure plate.
27. Whichever component you are repairing, rebuilding, or replacing may now be moved to a suitable workbench,

dolly, or engine stand.

28. Before reinstalling the transaxle, fill the pilot bushing in the gland nut with a small amount of graphite grease (no more than 3cc, or 1/10 oz).

29. Lightly grease the transmission input shaft splines, starter shaft bushing, and the starter and flywheel gear teeth.

30. Carefully attach the transaxle to the engine. Remember the transmission input shaft will be passing through the throwout bearing, pressure plate, clutch disc, and pilot bushing, so give it ample support during the attachment procedure.

NOTE: *If the clutch disc splines and the input shaft splines don't line up, as they so often won't, have an assistant turn the crankshaft pulley until they do.*

31. Push the transaxle home so that the mounting flanges are flush. Align the bottom holes and install the bolts. Install the top bolts, and then tighten all of the retaining bolts evenly.

32. The engine/transaxle is installed by following the removal steps in reverse order.

33. After the engine is installed, check the clutch adjustment as described in below.

34. Refill the engine and transaxle with the correct lubricant. Lower the car.

35. Start the engine and check for leaks.

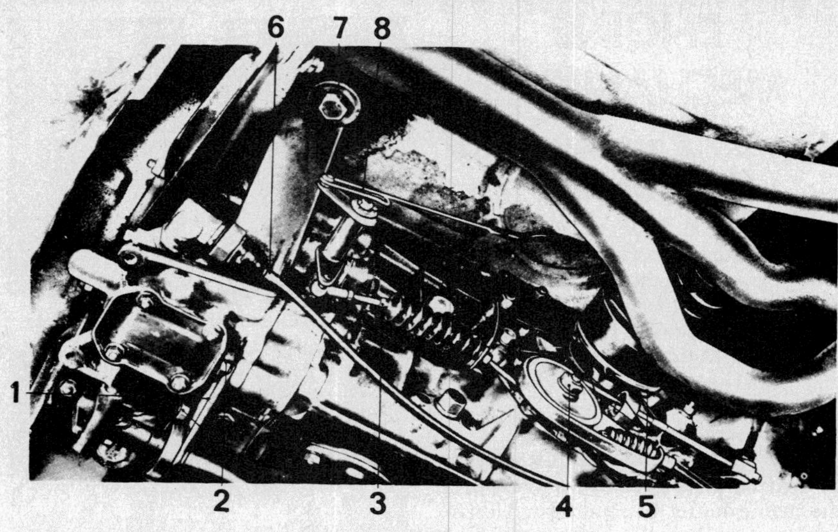

914/6 under chassis connections

1. Transaxle support
2. Nut
3. Throttle cable
4. Cable pulley nut
5. Allen bolt
6. Speedometer cable
7. Transaxle support nut
8. Throttle rod

914/6

1. Disconnect the battery cables.

2. Remove the air cleaner and oil tank ventilation hose.

3. Remove and plug the fuel line to the carburetors.

4. Detach the oil breather hose from the filler neck.

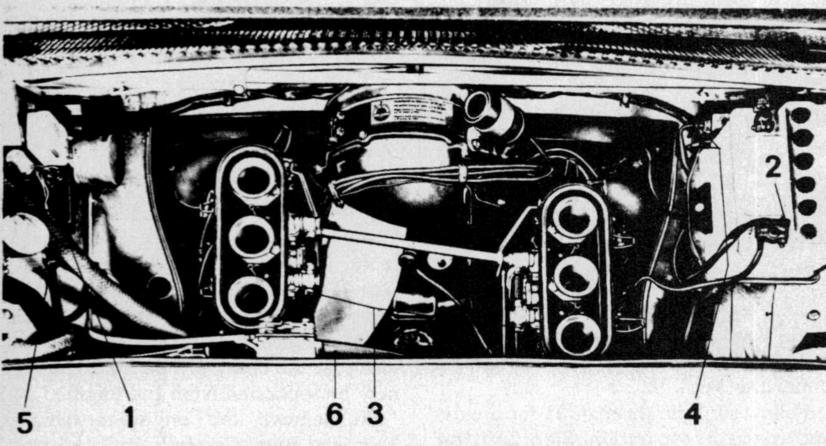

914/6 engine compartment connections

1. Multiple connector
2. Battery cable
3. Fuel line
4. Multiple connector
5. Wire retainer
6. Oil breather hose

5. Remove the electrical connector plugs located under the battery.

6. Jack up the car and support it on stands.

7. Remove the muffler shrouding.

8. Remove the cover and unscrew the transmission shift rod retainer.

9. Remove the protective cover. Unscrew the nuts and remove the shift rod bracket. Pull out the shift rod.

10. Remove all warm air ducts, flaps, and their control cables.

11. Disconnect the lines and drain the oil tank as described above. Drain the transaxle.

12. Unscrew the clutch cable adjusting nut and the cable pulley retaining nut.

13. Bend the plate and pull the clutch cable toward the front.

14. Disconnect the speedometer cable.

15. Detach the carburetor linkage from the cross-shaft.

16. Disconnect the throttle pull rod and remove it from its retainer.

17. Remove the axle driveshafts from the transmission as outlined in the "Drive Axle" section.

18. Remove the ground strap from the underbody.

19. Disconnect the back-up light switch wire.

20. Position the hydraulic jack, with a flat plate, under the engine/transaxle.

21. Raise the jack slightly so that the engine is supported.

22. Remove the transaxle mount retaining nuts. Detach the front support.

23. Position the axle driveshafts out of the way, and then carefully lower the engine/transaxle down and out of the car.

914/6 engine removal

24. Engine/transaxle separation is similar to that given above for the 912 and 911.

25. Reverse the removal steps to install the engine/transaxle.

26. Adjust the clutch as described later. Refill the engine and transaxle with lubricant. Lower the car.

27. Start the engine and check for leaks.

914

1. Scribe the hinge positioning, and then remove the engine compartment lid.

2. Disconnect the battery cables.

3. Remove the air cleaner and attendant hoses.

4. Tag each of the eleven cables for the fuel injection (for correct reinstallation) and then disconnect them. Tape the cables to the engine compartment sides so that they are out of harm's way.

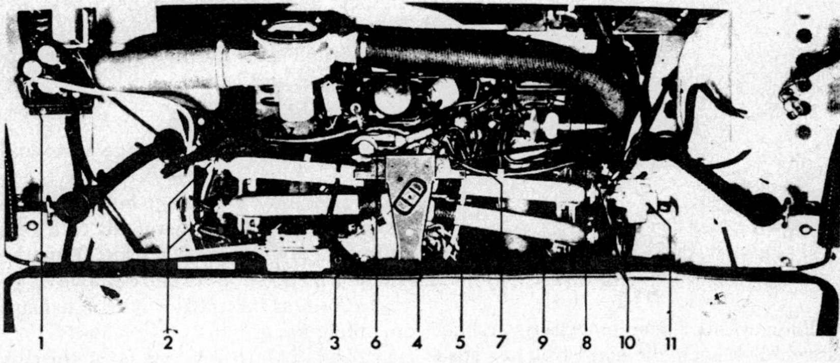

914 fuel injection connections

1. Voltage supply relay 4-pole
2. Two injection valves left 2-pole
3. One throttle valve switch 4-pole
4. Temperature feeler 1-pole
5. Mass connections 3-pole
6. Cold starting valve 2-pole
7. Thermal switch 1-pole
8. Ignition distributor release contact 3-pole
9. Temperature feeler 1-pole
10. Two injection valves right 2-pole
11. Pressure feeler 4-pole

5. Disconnect the throttle cable and push it through the front engine firewall.

6. Open the fuel line retaining clip: Disconnect and plug the fuel lines near the pressure regulator.

7. Remove the top retaining nut for the starter (accessible from the engine compartment).

8. Jack up the car and support it safely with stands.

9. Remove the muffler shrouding. Drain the engine and transaxle.

10. Remove the lower heater components.

11. Detach the dust cover and then unscrew the shift rod retainer.

12. Remove the protective cover, unscrew the retaining nuts, and remove the rear shift rod.

13. Remove the heater box, hoses, and control cables.

14. Loosen the cable pulley adjusting nut and retaining nut. Bend the retaining bracket and pull the clutch cable towards the front.

15. Loosen the speedometer cable and pull it forward.

16. Remove the starter. Detach the ground strap from the underbody.

17. Detach the axle driveshafts from the transaxle as described below. Wire the driveshafts out of the way.

18. Position the jack and plate under the engine/transaxle and raise it slightly.

19. Unscrew the four transaxle support retaining nuts. Remove the two allen bolts on the front engine mount.

20. Lower the engine/transmission down and out of the car.

21. Engine/transaxle separation is similar to that given for the 912 and 911, with exception of step 25.

22. Installation is essentially a reverse of the removal procedure, with the addition of the following steps.

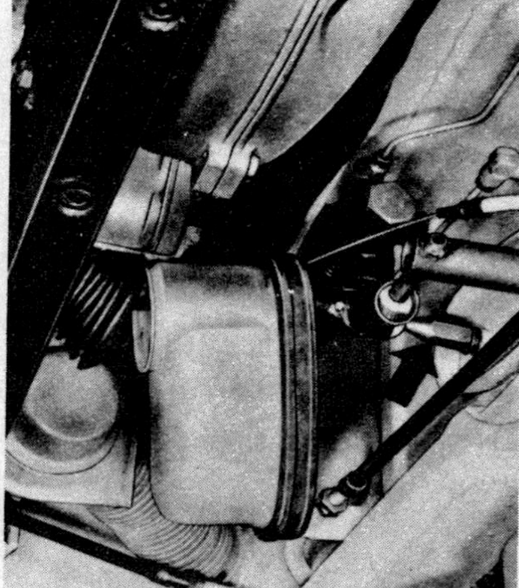

914 shift rod retainer

23. Be especially careful that the injector valve fuel lines aren't squashed when repositioning the engine. The parking brake cables go above the engine mount.

24. Torque the engine mount allen bolts to 22 ft lbs. The transmission mount nuts are tightened to 15 ft lbs. Tighten the axle driveshaft bolts to 33 ft lbs.

25. Adjust the clutch as described later.

26. Adjust the throttle cable.

27. Refill the engine and transaxle with lubricant.

28. Lower the car. Start the engine and check for leaks.

Rocker Shafts

Removal and Installation

912

This operation may be performed with the engine in the car. The center two rocker arms share a common shaft, while the end rockers each have an individual shaft.

1. Remove the rocker arm cover.

2. Remove the seven nuts which retain the rocker arm shafts.

3. Remove the rocker shafts and arms.

4. The rocker shaft assembly retainer may be removed from the head by unscrewing the three retaining bolts.

5. Before installation, coat all threads with an anti-seize compound or oil.

6. Bolt the rocker shaft retainer to the cylinder head. Tighten the bolts to 36 ft lbs.

7. Position the rocker shaft assemblies on the retainer and tighten the nuts to 18 ft lbs.

8. Adjust the valve clearance as described earlier.

9. Oil the shafts and rocker arms. Install the rocker arm cover.

911 and 914/6

Each rocker arm has an individual shaft on this single overhead camshaft engine. One or all of the shafts and rocker arms may be removed with the engine in the chassis.

1. Remove the camshaft housing cover nuts and spring washers. Remove the covers.

2. Scribe the rocker arms being removed so that they can be returned to the same position.

3. Unscrew the allen bolt in the rocker shaft. Push the shaft out of its bore and remove it along with the rocker arm.

NOTE: *If the rocker is under pressure, you won't be able to push the shaft out. Turn the camshaft until the rocker rests on the heel of the cam lobe.*

4. Check the rocker arm and shaft for excessive wear or damage. Replace any suspect pieces.

NOTE: *End rockers are installed with the allen screw heads facing towards cylinders no. 2 and 5 respectively.*

5. Place the rocker arm on its shaft.

6. The rocker arm shaft should be centered in its bore so that each groove is recessed 0.059 in (1.5mm).

a. Insert a 0.06 in. feeler gauge in the groove on one side of the shaft. Push the shaft in until the feeler gauge is held tight against the edge.

b. Carefully remove the gauge and

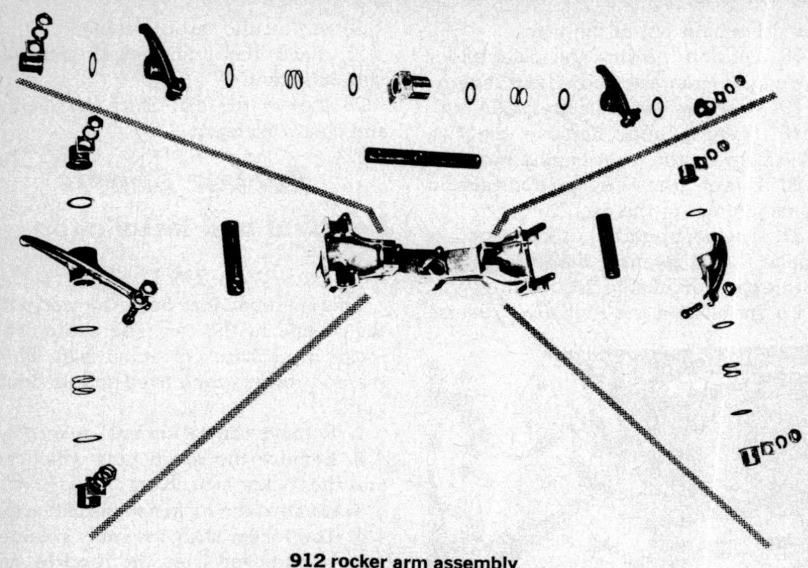
912 rocker arm assembly

push the shaft in approximately 0.06 in. more, using the feeler gauge to judge the distance.

7. Tighten the allen bolt to 156 in lbs.
8. Install the camshaft cover.

911 and 914/6 rocker arm removal

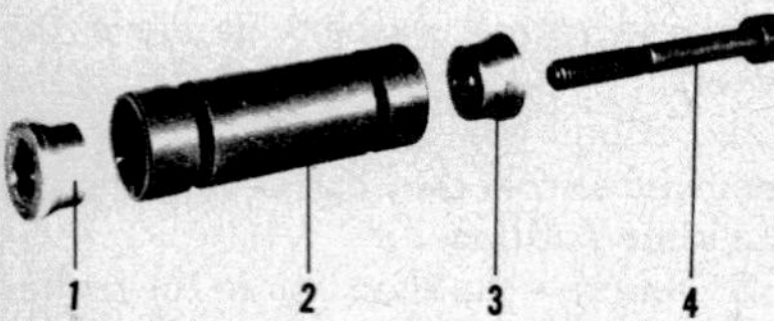

911 and 914/6 rocker arm shaft assembly

1. Allen nut cone
2. Shaft
3. Bushing cone
4. Allen bolt

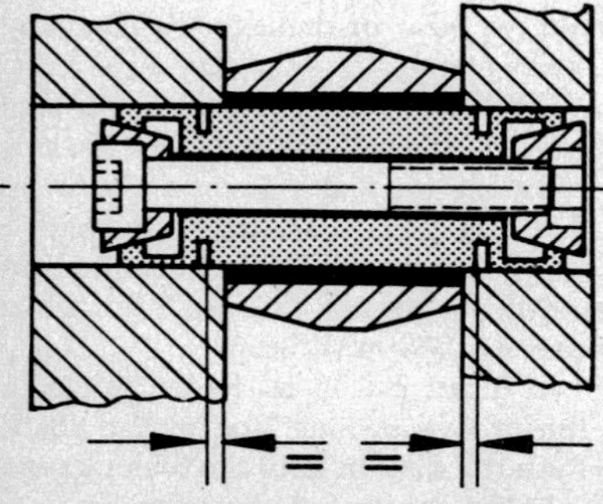
Correct rocker arm shaft positioning

914

Each cylinder head mounts two rocker assemblies, each one consisting of a shaft and two rocker arms. Each shaft is mounted in two bearings which are positioned on studs and retained by nuts. The rocker arm shaft assemblies can be removed with the engine in the car.

1. Remove the rocker arm cover.
2. Unscrew the retaining nuts and lift the rocker arm assemblies off the cylinder head.
3. When installing the rocker arm assemblies, the open slots of the bearings must face down.
4. With the rocker assemblies mounted on the head, tighten the retaining nuts to 120 in. lbs.

Exhaust Pipe and Muffler

Removal and Installation

911

1. Remove the flange nuts and bolts.
2. Loosen the retaining clamps and detach the muffler from its support.
3. Position the muffler on its support and then fit the clamps.
4. Install new gaskets between the muffler and exhaust manifold/heat exchanger.
5. Install and alternately tighten the flange nuts and bolts.

914/6

1. Remove the four flange nuts and bolts.
2. The inner two flange bolts hold the muffler and exhaust manifolds to a rear support. Pry the muffler free from the manifold and support and remove it.
3. Position the muffler on the exhaust manifold flanges.
4. Install the retaining bolts through flanges, making sure that the rear support is aligned. Use new gaskets.
5. Alternately tighten the four flange bolts.

914

To remove only the exhaust pipe:

1. Remove the two tailpipe-to-muffler retaining bolts.
2. Pull the tailpipe out of the muffler.
3. Install the tailpipe using two new gasket rings. Tighten the two retaining bolts.

To remove the tailpipe and muffler:

1. Remove the three flange nuts on each side.

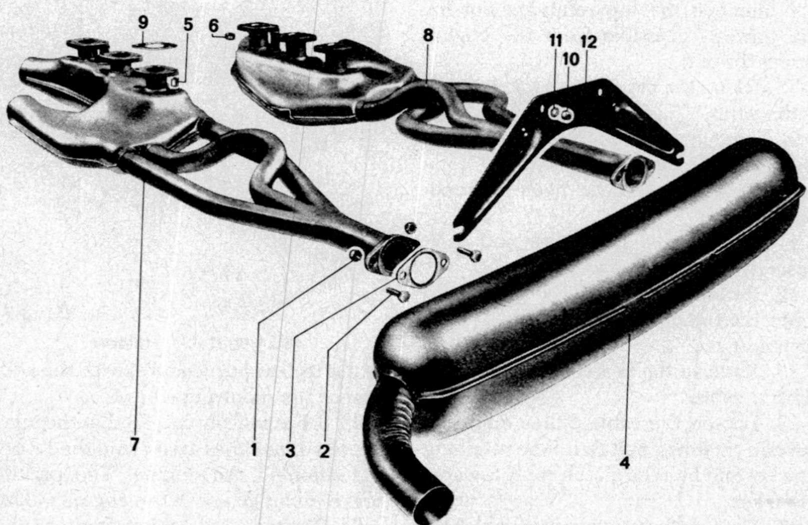

914/6 exhaust system

1. Nut
2. Bolt
3. Seal
4. Muffler
5. Spring washer
6. Nut
7. Heat exchanger
8. Heat exchanger
9. Seal
10. Nut
11. Washer
12. Support

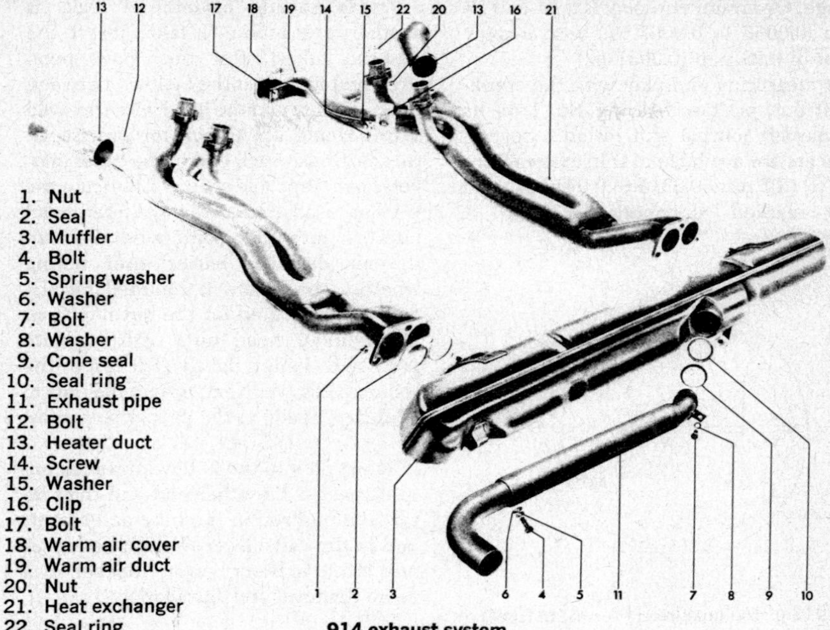

914 exhaust system

2. Pry the muffler loose and remove it.
3. Use new flange gaskets when installing the muffler. Tighten the six flange retaining nuts alternately.

Exhaust Manifold/Heat Exchanger

Removal and Installation

911, 914/6, and 914

1. Remove the muffler as previously outlined. Detach and remove the connecting hose from the heat exchanger to the heater valve chamber.
2. Detach the heater hose from the heat exchanger.
3. Remove the three sunken bolts from the bottom of the heat exchanger.
4. Remove the six cylinder head-to-heat exchanger nuts using a universal socket set-up.

NOTE: *For 914/6 models, skip step 3. For 914 models, skip steps 3 and 4 and loosen the four retaining clamps.*

5. Remove the heat exchanger.
6. Examine the heat exchanger for damaged flanges or cracks. Replace it, if necessary.
7. Install the heat exchanger in a reverse order of the removal procedure. Use new flange gaskets and tighten the retaining nuts and bolts alternately.

Engine Disassembly and Assembly

Further component removal and installation requires engine removal and disassembly. Follow the steps of engine disassembly and then assembly for the part being replaced. A general engine rebuilding section is included at the end of the book.

912

Place the engine on a stand and drain the oil. Remove the front, rear and side engine shrouds. Remove the muffler, exhaust pipes and heat exchangers. Both supports for the engine rear shield must be off. Loosen the exhaust pipe clamps behind the heat exchangers and the straps supporting the muffler. Break away stuck pipe connections by tapping the joints lightly with a rubber mallet.

Detach the coil wires at the distributor and remove the distributor cap. Disconnect the leads from the spark plugs. Remove the air cleaners, throttle linkage, fuel lines, carburetors (cover the intake openings) and the fuel pump with its insulating flange. Disconnect the oil lines to the filter. After the actuating plunger of the fuel pump is out and the hex nut which holds the distributor base plate is removed, lift out the distributor and withdraw the distributor pinion shaft by pushing up and turning to the left through the orifice of the fuel pump flange. Cautiously pick up the thrust washer from the base of the pinion shaft so it won't fall into the crankcase. Take the spring from the pinion shaft.

912 blower housing removal

Remove the V-belt and oil filter. Unscrew the retaining bolts on the blower housing. Unfasten the generator from the support and detach the wiring. Disconnect the hot air duct from the blower housing. Lift off the blower housing (the generator and blower can be removed without removing entire housing). Detach the oil cooler. Remove the cylinder shrouds (and lower air ducts if the export heater is standard equipment). Remove the generator carrier and then seal off the opening to eliminate foreign matter.

Remove the rocker covers, rocker arms, and rocker arm carriers. Pull out the pushrods and mark them for reassembly. Remove the intake manifolds, cylinder heads (allen-wrench nuts), pushrod tubes and air deflector baffles. Remove the cylinders and the pistons, marking each for reassembly. Remove the crankshaft pulley with the woodruff key. Detach the exhaust muffler brackets.

912 cylinder removal

Remove the oil pump cover and take out the gears. Remove the timing gear cover and the counter-pressure oil line with the rubber plugs. Remove the oil seal, deflector, bearing No. 4 and bypass valve located in the timing gear cover. *Note for removing bearing:* After deforming the oil seal at the recess slot in the seat (strike the seal through the recess slot with a punch and hammer), pry out the seal with a screwdriver, withdraw the oil deflector, remove the bearing set screw, and take out bearing No. 4. Remove any burrs from the oil-seal seat, heat the timing cover to 140°F and punch out the bearing.

Remove the clutch and flywheel. Evenly loosen the clutch retaining bolts, slackening each by one or two turns at a time in a cross sequence until spring pressure is relieved to avoid distortion of the spring housing. Slip off the clutch assembly and disc. Loosen the flywheel gland nut and remove the flywheel and the soft iron gasket. If the oil seal is removed, clean the seat for the oil seal and hone down sharp edges from the outer surface perimeter, making sure to clean away any metal filings.

Remove the oil drain plug, bypass and pressure relief valves, oil strainer and magnetic element.

Disassemble the crankcase by removing the crankcase retaining nuts and the two retaining nuts for the camshaft bearing at the flywheel end. Break the crankcase halves free with a rubber mallet. *Prying the halves apart will damage the mating surfaces.* Unbolt the crankshaft and the camshaft. Remove the camshaft end plug. Withdraw the valve lifters. Remove the bearing inserts and the crankshaft oil seal at bearing No. 1. Mark the bearing inserts.

Assembly is similar to that for the 914, noting the following.

The crankshaft drive pinion for the timing gear and the drive gear for the distributor are locked onto the crankshaft by a woodruff key. Using lock ring pliers (VW 161a), remove the gear lock ring from the crankshaft. Remove the distributor drive gear, spacer and camshaft drive gear from the crankshaft using a puller and block. Polish out minor scoring in the seating surface with fine grit polishing cloth saturated with engine oil. Inspect gears for wear and tooth contact.

912 timing gear positioning

To install the distributor and camshaft drive gears, insert a woodruff key for each gear, heat each gear to 175°F and press them onto the crankshaft using a special guide tube (VW 427). Fit the camshaft gear with the beveled edge facing the flywheel. Install the gear lock-ring on the crankshaft and check the gears for firm seating when they have cooled.

End-play of the crankshaft is measured at the crankshaft pulley when the engine is installed in the chassis, and at the flywheel when the engine is disassembled. In both cases use a dial gauge for precision. When measuring end play at the crankshaft pulley, attach a gauge holder to a stud in the timing gear cover; when measuring at the flywheel, attach the holder to the engine mounting flange. Optimum end play is 0.14 to 0.17 mm (0.0055 to 0.0067 in.) with a wear limit of 0.22 mm (0.0087 in.)

If measuring end-play with the crankshaft out, position bearing No. 1 on its crankshaft journal and install a spacer, Spacers are available in thicknesses from 0.8 to 1.05 mm (0.0315 to 0.0413 in.) and are marked alphabetically from A through F.

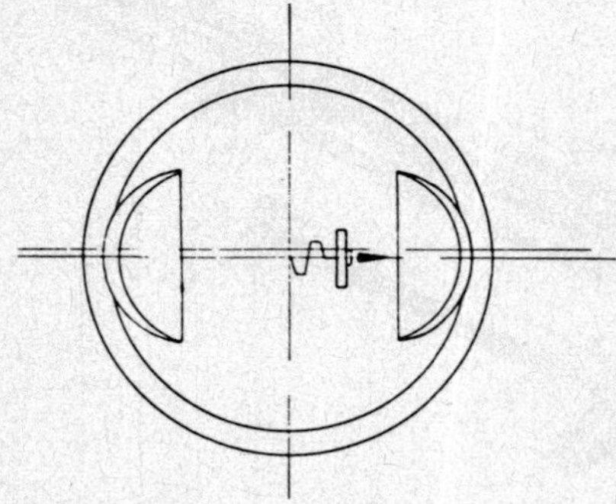

912 piston positioning (arrow to front)

Attach the flywheel to the crankshaft and torque the gland nut to 253–271 ft lbs. (35–37.5 mkg). Measure the end-play with a feeler gauge.

With the crankshaft mounted in the crankcase, end-play is calculated as follows:

1. Place the gauge base on the end of the crankshaft and measure the distance from the crankshaft end to the thrust flank of bearing no. 1 while the crankshaft is pushed to the flywheel.
2. Place the gauge base on the flywheel hub and measure the depth of seat (flywheel hub takes up the thrust, hub seat rests on crankshaft end).
3. From the difference in readings, and adding the thickness of the soft iron gasket, the thickness of the required spacer can be determined. Thickness of soft iron gaskets ranges between 0.10 to 0.14 mm (0.004–0.006 in.) but only one gasket can be used.

Example:	
Crankshaft-end to Bearing 1 thrust flank	4.015 mm
Crankshaft seat depth in flywheel hub	−3.025 mm
	0.990 mm
Soft iron gasket thickness	+0.100 mm
	1.090 mm
Required end-play	−0.140 mm
Spacer Thickness	= 0.950 mm

To install the pistons correctly on the connecting rods, attach the piston to the connecting rod with the arrow on the piston crown facing the flywheel.

Installation of the cylinder head must be made carefully to ensure proper seating. The head will warp when tightened if it is not properly seated on the cylinders.

Proper sealing against oil leaks is another precaution to take. Insert the pushrod tubes, after they have been stretched slightly at the bellows, between the crankcase and the head with the weld seams facing up. Check for precise O-ring seating at each end of the tubes (gaskets have trapezoid shape). Lubricate the O-rings used under the cylinder head nuts (use no sealing compound). Position the air deflector baffles after noting whether the cutout is rounded for the cap nut or squared for the hex nut. Coat the cylinder head nuts with graphite paste and tighten lightly (7 ft lbs) in the sequence shown. Next, torque the nuts to 22 ft lbs (3 mkg) in the proper sequence.

6-2-4-8-7-3-1-5

Squirt oil into the hollow pushrods until it reaches the other end and then insert the pushrod in the tube and seat its end in the valve lifter. Install the rocker arm shafts as described in "Rocker Arm Shaft Removal and Installation".

911 and 914/6

Follow the disassembly procedure for four cylinder Porsche engines up to the rocker carriers and the cylinder heads. Further disassembly of the 911 engine is as follows:

Removal of the cylinder heads on the 911 involves removing the overhead camshafts. All three cylinder heads on each bank can be removed as a unit complete with the camshaft and rockers or each cylinder head can be removed individually. For access to the cylinder heads and valves, the camshaft housing must be disassembled and removed.

Rockers. Scribe a mark on the rockers for later installation. Remove the 5 mm allen retaining screws in the rocker shafts, holding the cone-nut that is released on the other end of the shaft. Push out the shafts and lift away the rockers. *Position the camshaft so that the cam lobe does not press against the rocker being removed.*

Camshaft. Remove the timing chain cover at each camshaft. Unbolt the chain tensioner and the intermediate wheel, using tools P 202 and P 203. Withdraw the dowel pin from the camshaft wheel with tool P 212. Remove the sliding wedges and withdraw the wheel and flange. Take the key from the camshaft, unscrew the three sealing ring screws, and remove the sealing ring together with the O-ring and the gasket. Withdraw the camshaft toward the rear. Note that both camshafts turn in the same direction and therefore require that the cam lobes be positioned differently.

Cam housing. Unscrew the hex nuts and the three allen screws to lift off the camshaft housing. Each housing fits either cylinder bank.

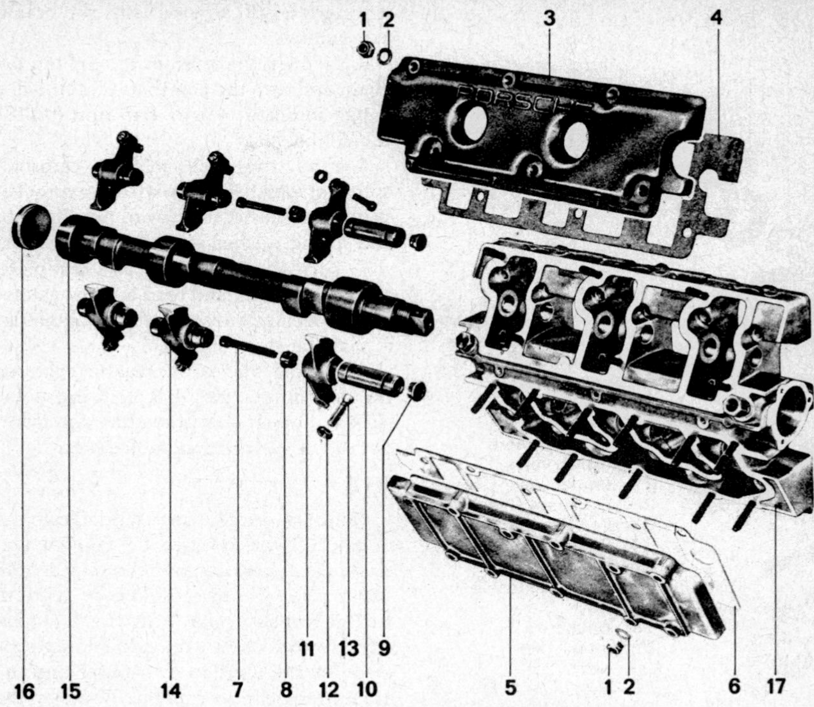

Six cylinder camshaft housing assembly

1. Nut
2. Aluminum washer
3. Cover
4. Gasket
5. Cover
6. Gasket
7. Bolt
8. Bushing
9. Nut
10. Rocker arm shaft
11. Rocker arm
12. Nut
13. Adjusting screw
14. Rocker arm assembly
15. Camshaft
16. Cover
17. Housing

Cylinder head. Loosen the cylinder head securing nuts (using tool P 119) and remove the cylinder head. Cylinders are numbered from the crankshaft pulley on the left bank as 1, 2 and 3 (left when facing the front of the car), and on the right bank as 4, 5 and 6.

The upper and lower sealing surfaces of the cylinder head (between the head and the camshaft and between the head and the cylinder) should not be machined. Permitted distortion at the cylinder seating surface must not exceed 0.15 mm (0.0059 in.). Examine the mating surfaces to ensure that they are in good condition.

Removing the camshaft housing and cylinder heads as a unit

When installing the cylinder heads, use new cylinder head gaskets with the perforations set toward the cylinder. Carefully position each head, insert the washers and tighten the hex nuts lightly.

The camshaft housing is sealed to the cylinder heads only with sealing compound. Assemble the camshaft housing and oil return pipes on the cylinder heads, but only handtighten.

The Porsche factory workshop manual suggests that at this point in reassembly, the cylinder head be torqued down first and then the camshaft housing. Some mechanics prefer to torque the camshaft housing first for more accurate tensioning. Either way, the camshaft must be checked frequently for free turning. If tightening one side binds the crankshaft, tightening the opposite side must free it again. If not, the housing must be loosened and tightening steps must be made in a different sequence.

Tighten the cylinder head to 21.6–23.8

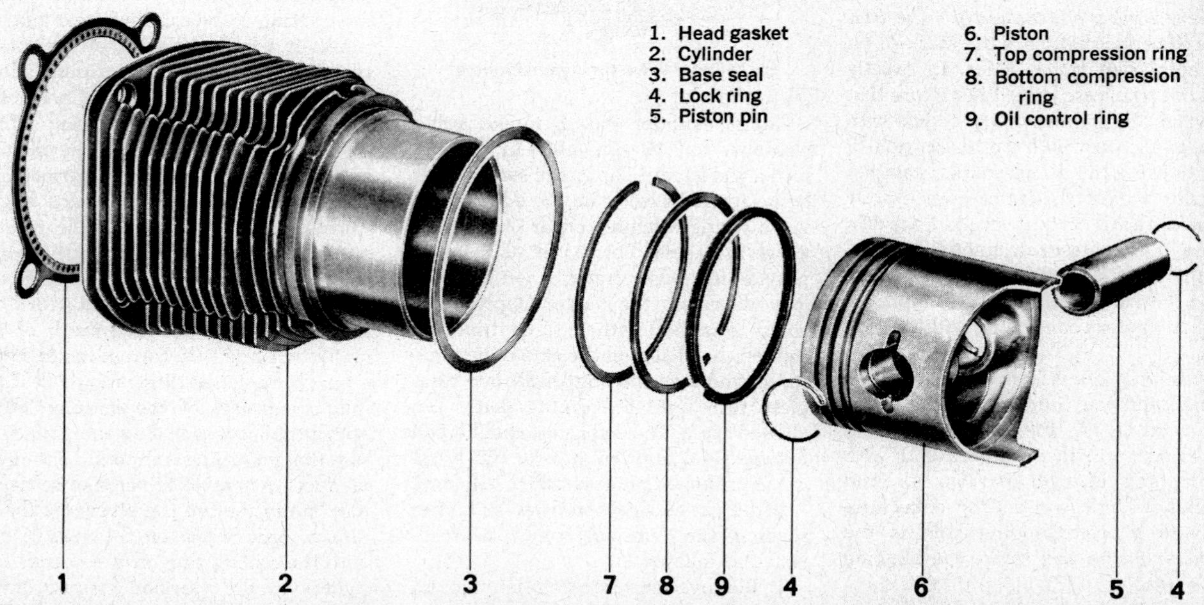

1. Head gasket
2. Cylinder
3. Base seal
4. Lock ring
5. Piston pin
6. Piston
7. Top compression ring
8. Bottom compression ring
9. Oil control ring

911 and 914/6 cylinder and piston assembly

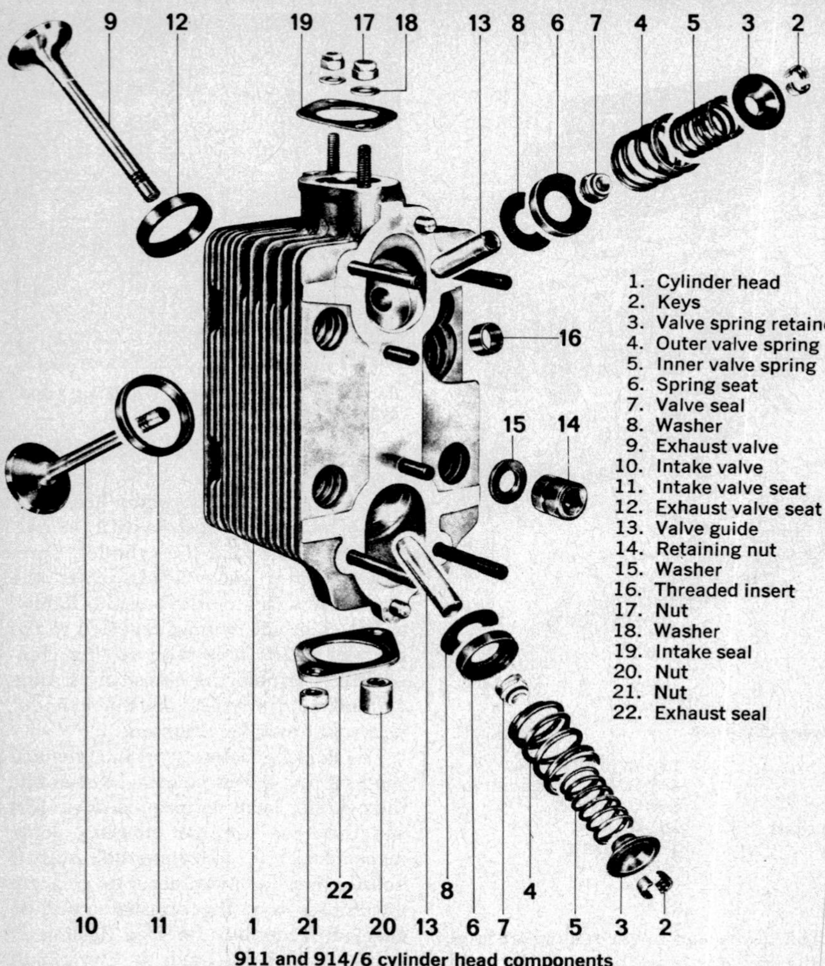

911 and 914/6 cylinder head components

ft lbs (3.0–3.3 mkg). Tighten the camshaft housing to 15.9–18.1 ft lbs (2.2–2.5 mkg).

From this point, further disassembly of the 911 engine is the same as the four-cylinder procedure. Valve timing is outlined below.

Valve timing adjustment for the 911. Turn the crankshaft until the mark Z1 on the crankshaft pulley lines up exactly with the crankcase joint. Taking care that the valves and pistons do not collide with each other, turn both camshafts (tool P 202) to bring the punch marks, stamped on the face of the camshafts, exactly above the shaft vertical center. Back off a little if the slightest resistance is felt during the turn. Then turn the free shaft to bring the valves and pistons into proper harmony before continuing with the first shaft.

With the crankshaft timing marks aligned and the camshaft punch marks exactly on the top, the engine is timed at the firing point in cylinder No. 1 with overlapping in cylinder No. 4. Find which hole in the camshaft sprocket lines up with a corresponding hole in the sprocket flange and insert the aligning dowel pin.

Slip on the washer and tighten the retaining nut to 72.3 ft lbs (10 mkg).

Six cylinder valve timing positioning

Adjust cylinder No. 1 intake valve clearance to 0.10 mm (0.004 in.) and attach a dial gauge. The gauge sensor must be positioned exactly on the edge of the valve spring retaining collar. Adjust the gauge to a preload of 10 mm (0.39 in.) to provide for sensor travel when the cam lobe depresses the valve. Depress the chain tensioner with a screwdriver to tighten the chain (on the side to be measured) and turn the crankshaft one complete turn until the timing marks are aligned again. The dial gauge should read between 4.2 and 4.6 mm (0.165–0.181 in.). A preferred range is 4.25 to 4.45 mm.

If the gauge shows a lower or higher reading, the camshaft has to be readjusted as follows:

1. Remove the sprocket retaining nut, spring washer and aligning dowel pin.

2. Make sure that the crankshaft pulley mark is still aligned with the crankcase joint.

3. Depress the tensioner to tighten the chain and turn the camshaft until the dial gauge indicates 4.4 to 4.45 mm (0.173–0.175 in.).

4. Find the hole in the camshaft sprocket which lines up with the sprocket flange and insert the dowel pin. Replace the spring washer and nut and tighten.

5. Turn the crankshaft two complete turns to the right and read the dial gauge. If the specified value is still not obtained, repeat the steps above.

When the valves overlap in cylinder No. 1, cylinder No. 4 is at firing point (TDC). Repeat the procedure for cylinder No. 4 valve timing adjustment.

914

Mount the engine on a stand. Drain the engine oil and remove the muffler and heat exchanger. Remove the rear engine cover plate. Remove the intake distributor and intake pipe with the injection valves (on fuel injection engines). Remove the ignition distributor and the front engine cover plate. Remove the cooling blower impeller. Remove the cooling blower housing with the alternator attached. Remove the engine mount. Remove the front and rear cylinder jackets with the warm air guides. Remove the oil cooler, oil filter and oil pump. Remove the rocker arm shafts with the protective tubes, pushrods and tappets. Remove the cylinder heads, cylinders and pistons. Remove the clutch and flywheel. Disassemble the crankcase, being careful not to score any of the mating surfaces by trying to pry the halves apart. Remove the camshaft and crankshaft with the connecting rods.

Assembly is the reverse of disassembly, noting the following procedures. Check the riveting of the camshaft gear and the camshaft. Check the camshaft for out-of-true using V-blocks. The maximum allowable wear is 0.0016 in. Check the end-play of the guide bearing which should be 0.0016–0.0051 in. The oil holes in the crankshaft bearing journals and bearings should have no sharp edges. Carefully remove any metallic foreign substances. Install the crankshaft and connecting rods. Install the camshaft and gear so that the tooth marked with a 0 is located between the two teeth of the crankshaft gear which are identified with a punch mark (see illustration). Coat the mating surfaces of the housing halves with a thin coat of sealing compound. Be sure that no sealing compound enters the oil ducts. Assemble the crankcase halves and lightly tighten the screw for the oil intake pipe. Screw on the sealing nuts with the sealing ring on the outside and tighten to the specified torque. Rotate the crankshaft to ensure free rotation. Grease the needle bearing in the

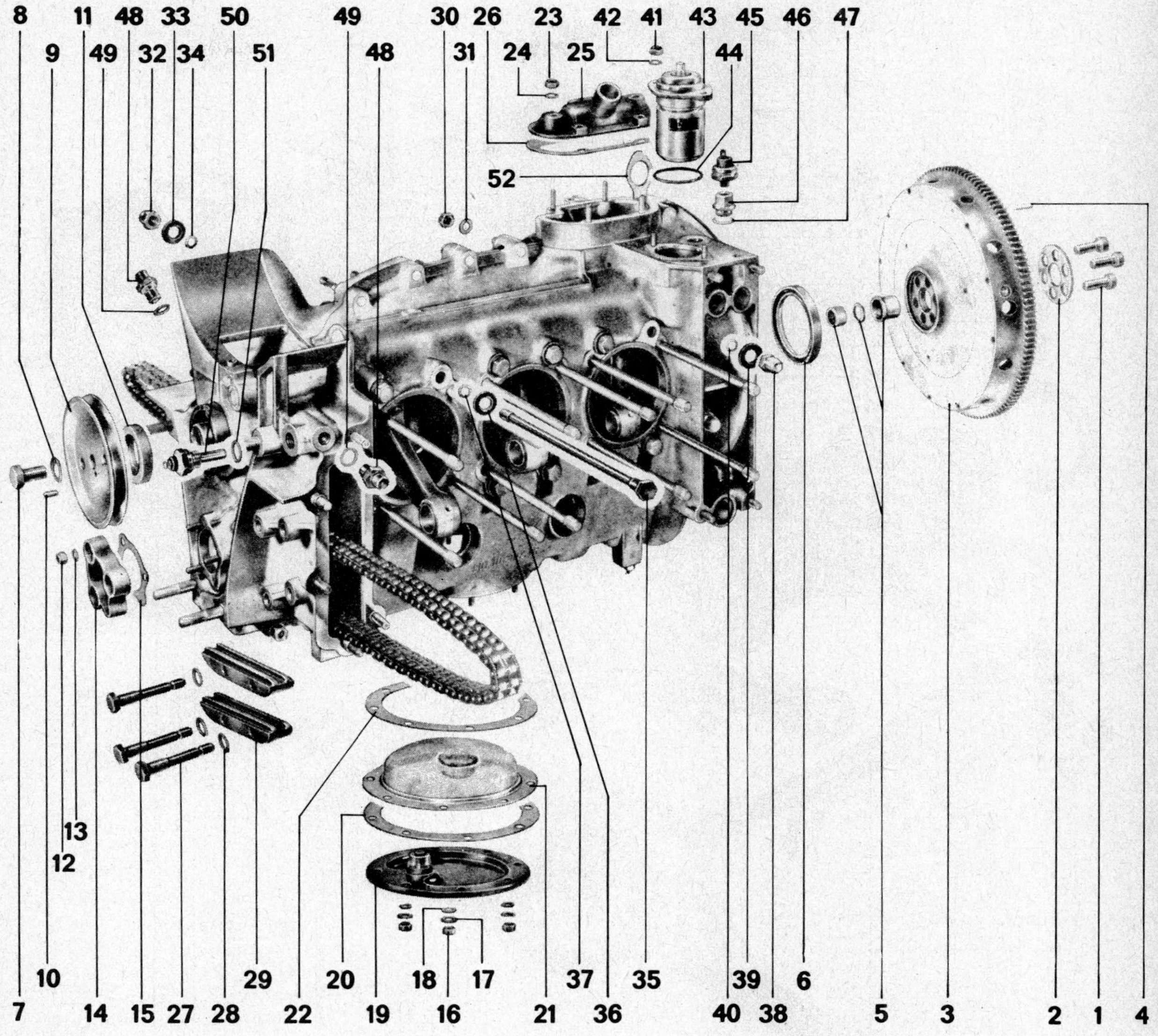

Six cylinder crankcase assembly

1. Bolt
2. Washer
3. Flywheel
4. Pin
5. Bushing
6. Seal
7. Bolt
8. Spring washer
9. Pulley
10. Pin
11. Seal
12. Nut
13. Washer
14. Cover
15. Seal
16. Nut
17. Spring washer
18. Washer
19. Cover
20. Seal
21. Oil strainer
22. seal
23. Nut
24. Washer
25. Breather cover
26. Seal
27. Slide rail bolt
28. Seal
29. Slide rail
30. Nut
31. Washer
32. Nut
33. Washer
34. Seal
35. Crankcase bolt
36. Washer
37. Seal
38. Nut
39. Washer
40. Seal
41. Nut
42. Spring washer
43. Thermostat
44. Seal
45. Oil pressure switch

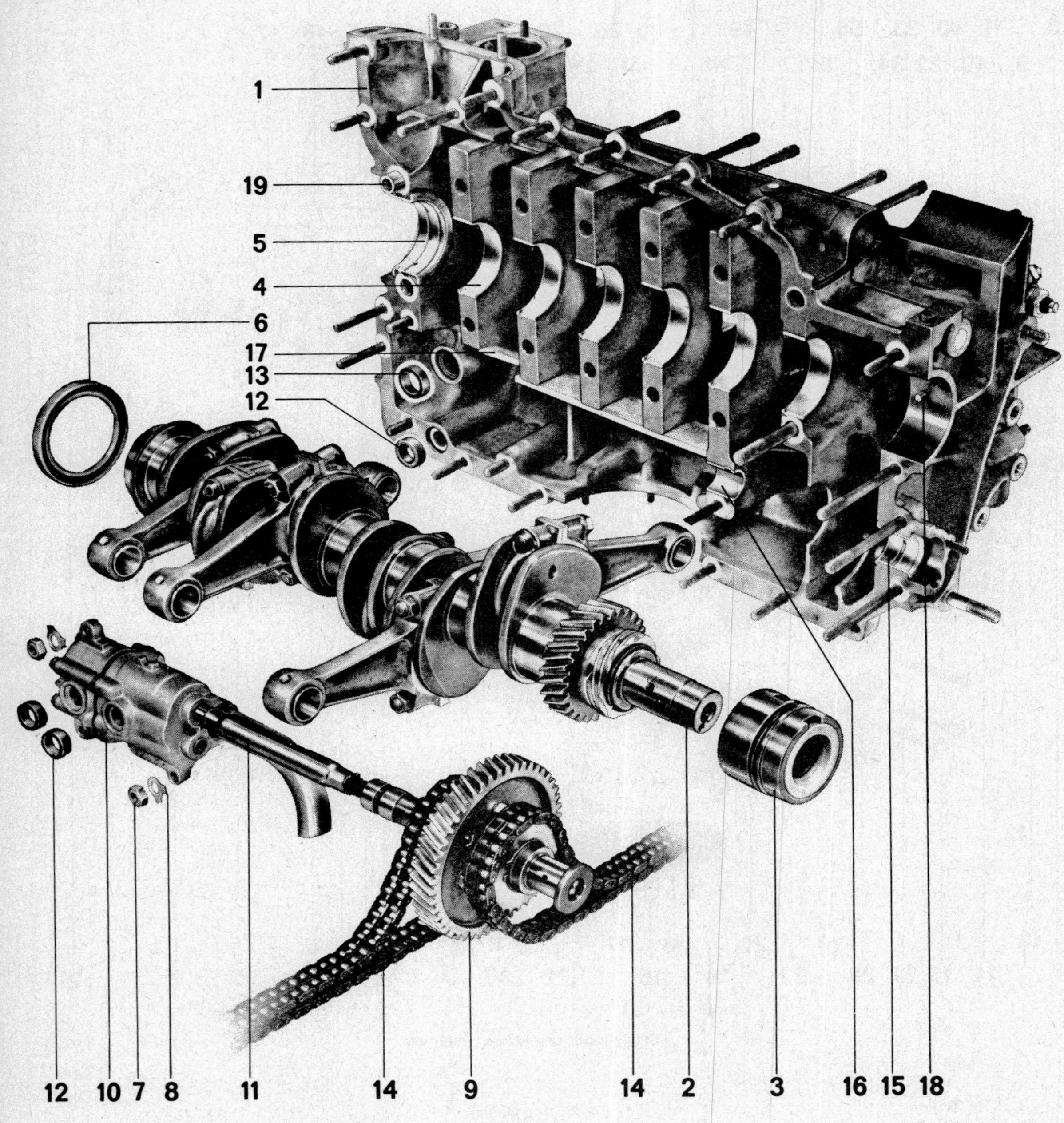

Six cylinder crankcase assembly

1. Crankcase half
2. Crankshaft assembly
3. No. 8 bearing
4. Bearing shell
5. Thrust bearing shell
6. Seal
7. Nut
8. Lockwasher
9. Intermediate shaft
10. Oil pump assembly
11. Connecting shaft
12. Seal
13. Seal
14. Camshaft chain
15. Intermediate shaft thrust bearing
16. Intermediate shaft bearing
17. Oil strainer
18. pin
19. bushing

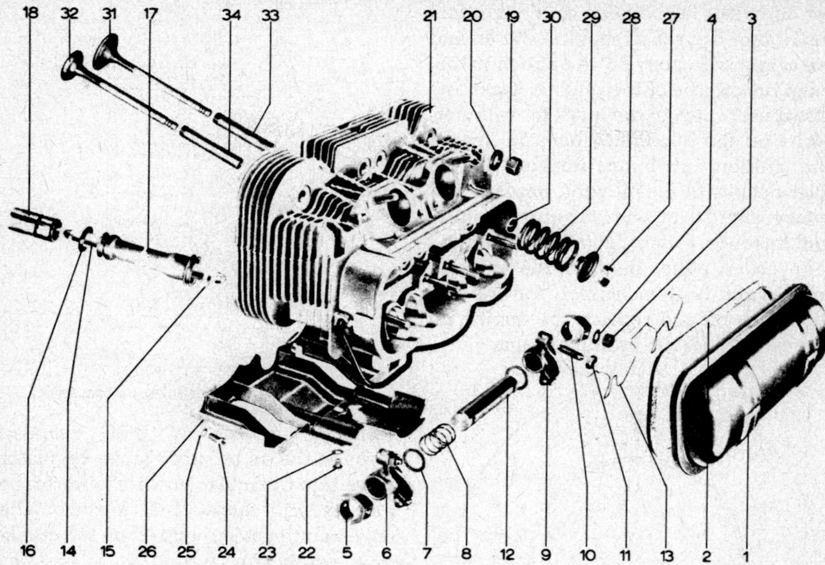

914 cylinder head components

1. Rocker arm cover
2. Gasket
3. Nut
4. Spring washer
5. Rocker arm bearing
6. Exhaust rocker arm
7. Thrust washer
8. Spring
9. Intake rocker arm
10. Valve adjusting screw
11. Nut
12. Rocker arm shaft
13. Rocker arm cover retainer
14. Pushrod
15. Pushrod tube seal (white)
16. Pushrod tube seal (black)
17. Pushrod tube
18. Valve lifter
19. Nut
20. Washer
21. Cylinder head
22. Bolt
23. Washer
24. Bolt
25. Washer
26. Baffle plate
27. Valve keys
28. Valve spring retainer
29. Valve spring
30. Valve stem seal
31. Intake valve
32. Exhaust valve
33. Intake valve guide
34. Exhaust valve guide

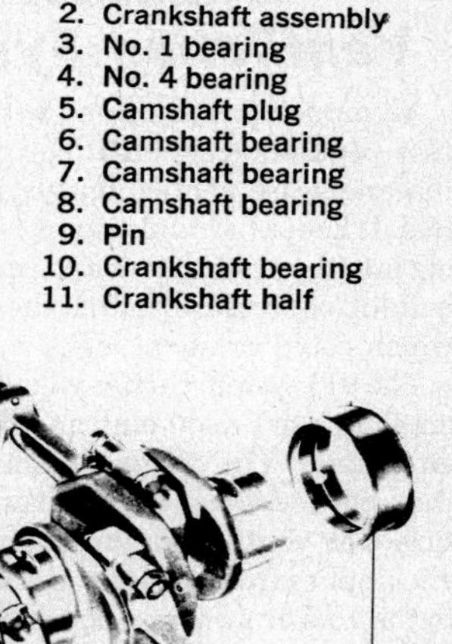

1. Camshaft
2. Crankshaft assembly
3. No. 1 bearing
4. No. 4 bearing
5. Camshaft plug
6. Camshaft bearing
7. Camshaft bearing
8. Camshaft bearing
9. Pin
10. Crankshaft bearing
11. Crankshaft half

914 crankcase and crankshaft assembly

flywheel with a small amount of multipurpose grease. Moisten the left ring with engine oil, wiping off any excess. Install the flywheel and adjust the axial play of the crankshaft. Measure the axial play by installing the flywheel with two spacing washers but without the sealing rings. Using a dial gauge, measure the play by rotating the flywheel. The thickness of the third spacer can be computed by subtracting 0.0039 in. from the measured result. Remove the flywheel and install the sealing ring, felt ring, and three spacers. Three spacers must always be installed for the required thickness. Spacers are available in the following sizes: 0.0094, 0.0118, 0.0126, 0.0134, 0.0142 and 0.0150 in. Each spacer is marked for proper identification. The axial play of the crankshaft, measured with the engine assembled and the flywheel screwed on, should be 0.0028–0.0051 in. Clean the contact surface of the clutch disc and flywheel. Check the splining of the input shaft and coat lightly with molybdenum disulphide powder, applied with a brush. The clutch disc should slide easily. Check the throwout bearing. Do not wash in any solvent but wipe it clean. Replace bearings which are contaminated or noisy. Grease the guide bushing lightly with molybdenum disulphide paste. Center the clutch disc and clutch on the flywheel using an input shaft. When a new clutch is installed, the balancing marks should be 180° apart. A white paint stripe on the outside edge of the flywheel indicates the heavy end, and a white paint stripe indicates the heavy end of the clutch. Tighten the bolts to 14.5 ft lbs. Clean all pistons and check for wear. Check the marking of the pistons according to the following designations:

A.—The letter next to the arrow is the index of the spare parts number.

B.—The punched in arrow indicates that the piston must be installed with the arrow facing the flywheel.

C.—The color dot (blue, pink or green) indicates the paired size of the piston.

D.—A statement of weight class (+ or −) is punched in or printed.

E.—The weight class is indicated by a color dot (brown equals (−) weight and grey equals (+) weight).

F.—Number indicates the piston size in mm.

Fit the compression and oil scraper rings. The designation TOP should face up. Insert the locking rings of pistons 1 and 2 on the side facing the flywheel. The locking rings of pistons 3 and 4 should be fitted on the impeller side. Fit the piston pin. The piston pin may slide in easily by hand, which is normal. Should the pin not fit easily, heat the piston to approximately 176°F. and slide in the piston pin without bottoming the pin on the locking ring.

914 timing marks

Seat the second locking ring. Lubricate the piston and piston pin. Compress the piston rings. Lubricate the cylinder bore and fit the cylinder bore. The sealing ring must also be fitted. The studs of the crankcase may not touch the cooling fins of the cylinder. Check the cylinder head for cracks and the spark plug threads for damage. Replace the sealing ring and the cylinder head. Pre-tighten the cylinder head nuts slightly and finally tighten according to sequence. Replace the baffle plate. Insert the tappets with engine oil. Slide the protective tubes with new sealing rings up to the stop, taking care not to damage the sealing rings. Slide the bearing pieces on the rocker arm shafts so that the slots face downward and the broken edges outward when settling on the studs. The clip which secures the protective tubes should enter the slots of the bearing pieces and rest against the bottom edges of the protective tubes. Lubricate the gear wheel and driveshaft and insert into the oil pump housing. Install the oil pump cover with the lubricated rubber sealing ring. Check the gear wheels for proper running. Install the oil pump, with a new seal, into the crankcase. The journal of the driveshaft should be in alignment with the slot in the camshaft gear. Center the oil pump by two crankshaft revolutions and tighten the nuts. Clean the sealing surface on the flange for the oil filter. Lubricate the rubber seal slightly and screw the filter in until the filter is seated. Tighten the oil filter. Replace the oil cooler after checking for leaks and tightening all welded seats. Replace the front and rear cylinder jackets and warm air guides. Replace the engine mount. Replace the cooling blower housing with the alternator and adjust the V-belt tension. Replace the cooling blower impeller and the front engine cover plate. Replace the ignition distributor. Bring cylinder No. 1 to the firing point. The black notch should be in alignment with the reference mark. The center offset slot in the head of the ignition distributor driveshaft should be at an angle of approximately 12° in relation to the longitudinal axis of the engine. Turn the distributor rotor to the mark for cylinder No. 1 on the distributor housing. Insert the ignition distributor. Replace the oil filler neck with the oil vent. Replace the intake distributor with the intake pipes and injection valves. Mount the rear engine cover plate. Replace the exhaust muffler and heat exchanger. Fill the engine with oil and replace the engine in the car. Adjust the ignition timing.

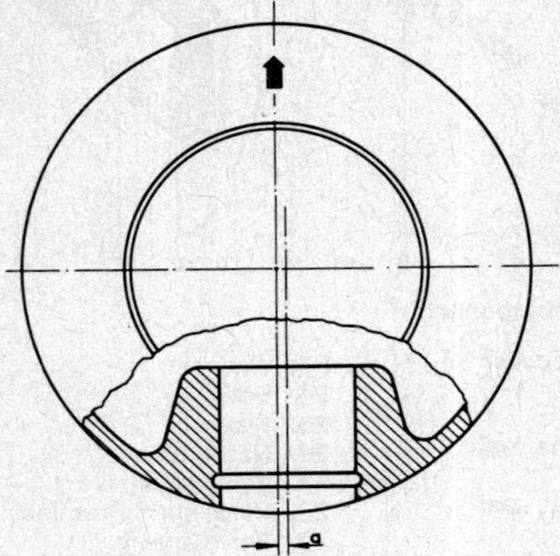

914 piston positioning

EMISSION CONTROLS

Crankcase Ventilation System

All models are equipped with a crankcase ventilation systems. The purpose of the crankcase ventilation system is twofold. It keeps harmful vapors from escaping into the atmosphere and prevents the buildup of pressures within the crankcase which could cause oil leaks.

The 911 system carries vapors from the crankcase to the oil tank and then to the air cleaner. The crankcase emissions are then burned along with the air/fuel mixture. The ventilation system on 914 models supplies fresh air from the air cleaner to the rocker arm covers, where it mixes with crankcase vapors and continues through the pushrod tubes and into the crankcase. The mixture of fresh air and crankcase vapors is then released through the oil breather and a regulator valve into the intake air distributor to be burned with the air/fuel mixture. The only maintenance required on the crankcase ventilation system is a periodic check. At every tune-up, examine the hoses for clogging or deterioration. Clean or replace the hoses as required.

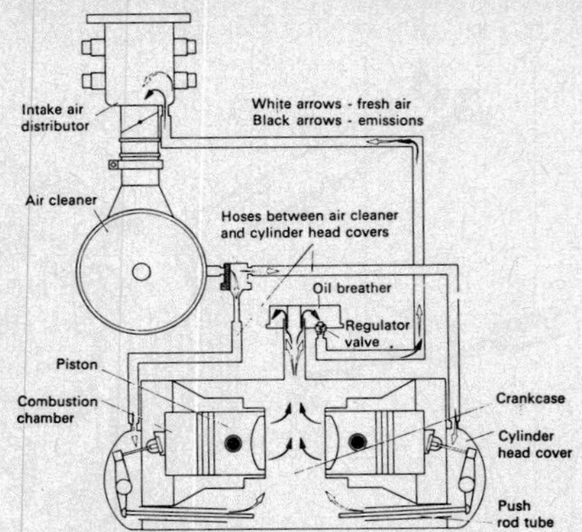

914 crankcase ventilation schematic

Evaporative Emission Control System

Required by California in 1970 and nationwide in 1971, this system has been standard equipment on Porsches imported to the United States since 1970. Fuel vapors are no longer vented into the atmosphere. The systems used on the 911 and 914 are basically similar and consist of an expansion chamber, evaporation chamber, and an activated charcoal filter. Fuel vapors which reach the filter deposit hydrocarbons on the surface of the charcoal element. The engine fan forces fresh air into the charcoal filter when the engine is running. The air purges the filter and the hydrocarbons are sent into the air cleaner where they become part of the air/fuel mixture and are burned.

Maintenance on this system consists of checking the condition of the various connecting lines and the charcoal filter at 10,000 mile intervals. The charcoal filter, which is located in the front luggage compartment on all models, should be replaced at 50,000 mile intervals.

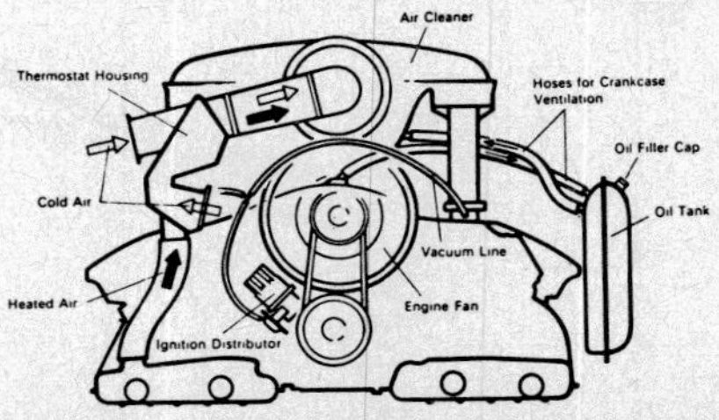

911 crankcase ventilation schematic

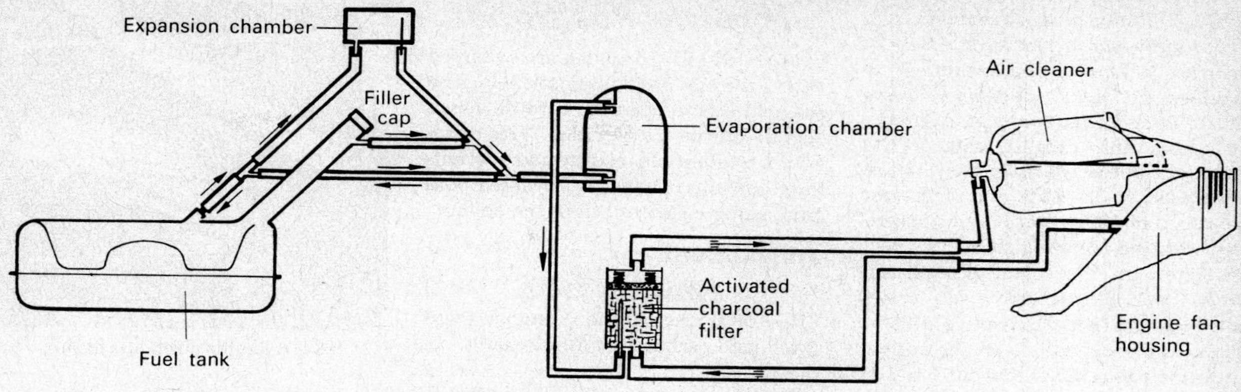

911 evaporative emission control system

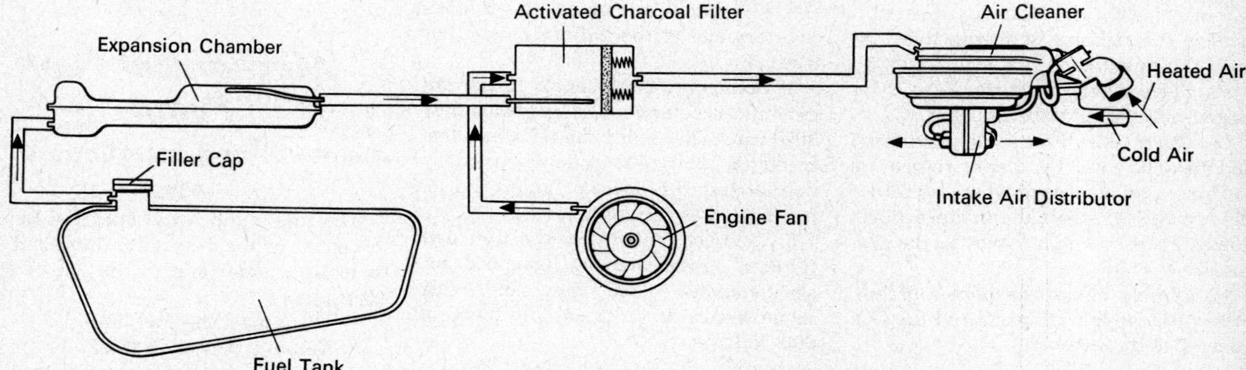

914 evaporative emission control system

Dual Diaphragm Distributors

The purpose of the dual diaphragm distributor is to improve exhaust emissions during idling. The distributor has a vacuum retard diaphragm, in addition to a vacuum advance diaphragm. The 911 series was equipped with the vacuum retarding distributor in 1972 and the 914 in 1973. Both models retard the ignition advance to 5° ATDC at idle speed.

Testing

All Models

1. Connect a timing light to the engine. Check the ignition timing.
2. Remove the retard hose from the distributor and plug it. Increase the engine speed. The ignition timing should advance. If it doesn't, then the vacuum unit is faulty and must be replaced.

Deceleration Valve

1970–71 911T models are equipped with an additional mixture valve on each carburetor. During deceleration, with the throttles closed and the engine speed high, there is little opportunity for complete combustion due to the excessively rich mixture. A deceleration valve mounted on each carburetor supplies a fresh mixture to aid combustion. In this manner, exhaust emissions during deceleration are considerably reduced. The system consists of the mixture valve, an electromagnetic valve, and an electronic engine speed switch. On deceleration, with the engine speed above 1350 rpm, the speed switch causes the electromagnetic valve to allow intake manifold vacuum to reach the mixture valve and open it. Additional mixture is then passed into the intake of each cylinder. When the engine speed drops below 1300 rpm, the idle system comes into operation. A micro switch disconnects the mixture valve when the throttles are opened.

Beginning with the 1972 models, the 914 is equipped with a vacuum deceleration valve. On deceleration, with the throttles closed and engine speeds high, the valve opens and allows additional air from the air cleaner to flow into the intake air distributor. The mixture is leaned out and the exhaust emissions lowered.

Adjustment

1970–71 911T

1. Turn in the adjusting screw on the micro switch until you can hear the switch just starting to operate.
2. Disconnect the wire from the engine speed switch to the left terminal of the micro switch (P).
3. Using a jumper wire, connect terminal 30 of the rear fuse box to the terminal on the micro switch and energize the mixture valve for adjustment.
4. Start the engine and run it until it reaches normal operating temperature. The idle speed will be higher than usual because the mixture valve is energized.
5. Turn out the mixture valve flow rate adjusting screw (no. 1) until the idle speed reaches approximately 1200 rpm.
6. Using a Unisyn or similar gauge, check the air flow rate on the center cylinders. Equalize the cylinders, if necessary, by readjusting the flow rate screws.

Deceleration valve adjusting screws

1. Flow rate adjusting screw
2. Mixture control screw

(a)—idle speed screw
(b)—idle mixture screw
(c)—idle air screw

NOTE: *If the idle speed changes, turn both screws in or out as necessary to correct it. Turning the screws out increases the engine speed and turning them in decreases the engine speed.*

7. Check the exhaust with a CO analyzer, if one is available. The CO content should be 3.5–4.5% at an increased idle speed of 1200 rpm. If it is not, proceed with the following steps.

8. Screw in the mixture regulating screws (no. 2, above the flow rate screws) on the left and right carburetors until the increased idle speed just begins to slow. Screw the regulating screw out 1 or 1 ½ turns.

9. Adjust both screws as necessary to bring the CO content of the exhaust within specifications. Screwing them out richens the mixture; screwing them in leans the mixture.

10. Recheck the mixture valve synchronization as described in step 6.

11. Open the throttle momentarily and make sure that the engine returns to the increased idle speed when the throttles are closed. Adjust the mixture valve flow rate screws evenly to correct the idle speed.

12. Double check the center carburetor throat synchronization and the CO content of the exhaust.

Testing

1972–1973 914

1. Disconnect the vacuum valve hose at the air cleaner.
2. Start the engine and increase the speed momentarily to 3000 rpm. Close the throttle.
3. A suction should be evident at the end of the hose removed from the air cleaner. If there is no suction, replace the valve.

Throttle Positioner

1970–1971 914/6 models are equipped with a throttle positioning solenoid. The solenoid acts to open the throttle valves slightly during deceleration. This maintains a combustible mixture and prevents large amounts of unburned hydrocarbons from being exhausted from the engine.

Adjustment

1970–1971 914/6

1. Adjust the ignition timing, point dwell, and carburetors as previously outlined.
2. Disconnect the wire from the insulated connector on the throttle positioner.
3. Connect this terminal to the positive terminal of the battery or any hot wire.
4. Connect a dwell meter to the engine and accelerate it to approximately 3000 rpm. The engine should return to a speed of 1250–1300 rpm when slowly decelerated. If it does not, adjust the actuating rod as necessary.
5. Connect the wire to the insulated terminal on the solenoid. Again accelerate the engine to 3000 rpm. The engine should return to a normal idle speed of 900–950 rpm.

Testing

1970–1971 914/6

1. Connect a 12V test light to both electrical terminals on the throttle positioner solenoid.
2. Accelerate the engine. The light should go on at 2000–3000 rpm.
3. Reduce the engine speed. The light should go out at about 1500 rpm.
4. If the light doesn't go out, replace the rpm transducer.

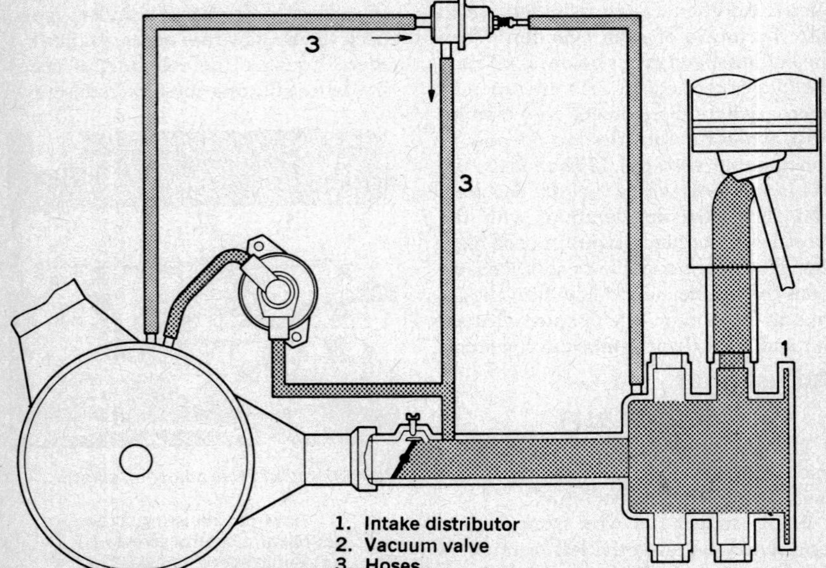

Vacuum deceleration valve system

914/6 throttle positioner testing

FUEL SYSTEM

Mechanical Fuel Pump

Removal and Installation

912

The fuel pump is rod operated by an eccentric off the distributor driveshaft. It is located under and to the left of the distributor.

1. Disconnect the fuel lines.
2. Remove the pump shield.
3. Remove the two retaining nuts at the base of the fuel pump.
4. Remove the fuel pump and insulating gasket.
5. Replace the O-ring on the fuel pump and install it in a reverse order of removal.

912 fuel pump location

Electric Fuel Pump

Removal and Installation

The electric fuel pumps used on 1969–1970 911 models are located at the front of the car adjacent to the fuel tank. Starting in 1971, the fuel pump was relocated to the left rear of the car near the trailing arm. The 914 and 914/6 electric fuel pumps are located in the engine compartment.

911

1. Remove the cap nuts.
2. Withdraw the pump with its mounting bracket.
3. Loosen the hose clamp and remove the pump from the bracket.

911 fuel pump removal

4. Loosen the hose clamps and remove the three fuel lines from the pump.
5. Install the pump using a reverse of the removal procedure. Coat both electrical terminals with grease and make sure that the rubber boot is firmly seated.

914/6

1. Remove the right-hand hot air hose.
2. Detach the electrical plug.
3. Loosen the retaining nuts on the anti-vibration mount.

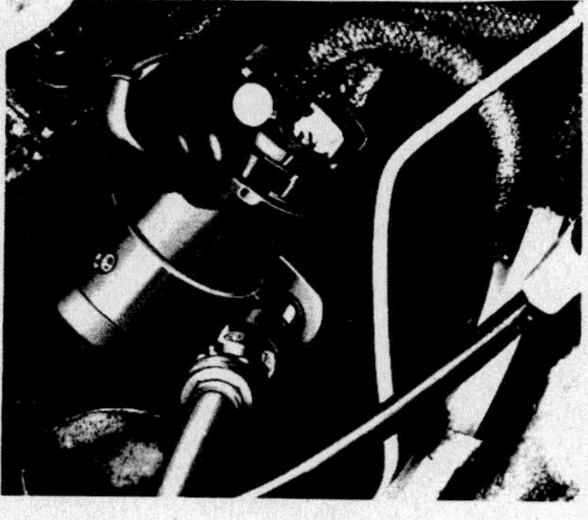

914/6 fuel pump removal

4. Remove the clip from the pressure line.
5. Disconnect the fuel lines by loosening the clamps. Catch any spilled fuel with a rag.
6. Remove the fuel pump.
7. Install the pump using a reverse of the removal procedure. Do not distort the anti-vibration mounting. Make sure that the protective cap is properly seated.

914

1. Pinch the fuel hoses to prevent spillage and remove the cable plug.
2. Cut the hose clamps and pull the hoses from the pump, catching any fuel with a rag.
3. Raise the fuel pressure hose to prevent draining any fuel.
4. Unscrew the retaining nuts and remove the pump.
5. Fit the hoses to the pump. Use new hose clamps.
6. Mount the pump on its supports and remove the clamps used to pinch the hoses.
7. Replace the cable plug, ensuring that the protective cap is correctly installed.

Carburetors

Removal and Installation

1. Remove the air cleaners and attendant hoses.
2. Disconnect and plug the fuel lines.
3. Disconnect the throttle linkage.
4. Remove the vacuum lines and deceleration mixture lines, if so equipped.
5. Remove the retaining nuts and carefully lift the carburetors from the engine.
6. Install the carburetors using a reverse of the removal procedure.

Overhaul

All Types

Efficient carburetion depends greatly on careful cleaning and inspection during overhaul since dirt, gum, water, or varnish in or on the carburetor parts are often responsible for poor performance.

Overhaul your carburetor in a clean, dust-free area. Carefully disassemble the carburetor, referring often to the exploded views. Keep all similar and look-alike parts segregated during disassembly and cleaning to avoid accidental interchange during assembly. Make a note of all jet sizes.

When the carburetor is disassembled, wash all parts (except diaphragms, electric choke units, pump plunger, and any other plastic, leather, fiber, or rubber parts) in clean carburetor solvent. Do not leave parts in the solvent any longer than is necessary to sufficiently loosen the deposits. Excessive cleaning may remove the special finish from the float bowl and choke valve bodies, leaving these parts unfit for service. Rinse all parts in clean solvent and blow them dry with compressed air or allow them to air dry. Wipe clean all cork, plastic, leather, and fiber parts with a clean, lint-free cloth.

Blow out all passages and jets with compressed air and be sure that there are no restrictions or blockages. Never use wire or similar tools to clean jets, fuel passages, or air bleeds. Clean all jets and valves separately to avoid accidental interchange.

Check all parts for wear or damage. If wear or damage is found, replace the defective parts. Especially check the following:

1. Check the float needle and seat for wear. If wear is found, replace the complete assembly.
2. Check the float hinge pin for wear and the float(s) for dents or distortion. Replace the float if fuel has leaked into it.
3. Check the throttle and choke shaft bores for wear or an out-of-round condition. Damage or wear to the throttle arm, shaft, or shaft bore will often require replacement of the throttle body. These parts require a close tolerance of fit; wear may allow air leakage, which could adversely affect starting and idling.

   NOTE: *Throttle shafts and bushings are not included in overhaul kits. They can be purchased separately.*
4. Inspect the idle mixture adjusting needles for burrs or grooves. Any such condition requires replacement of the needle, since you will not be able to obtain a satisfactory idle.
5. Test the accelerator pump check valves. They should pass air one way but not the other. Test for proper seating by blowing and sucking on the valve. Replace the valve if necessary. If the valve is satisfactory, wash the valve again to remove breath moisture.
6. Check the bowl cover for warped surfaces with a straightedge.
7. Closely inspect the valves and seats for wear and damage, replacing as necessary.
8. After the carburetor is assembled, check the choke valve for freedom of operation.

Carburetor overhaul kits are recommended for each overhaul. These kits contain all gaskets and new parts to replace those that deteriorate most rapidly. Failure to replace all parts supplied with the kit (especially gaskets) can result in poor performance later.

Some carburetor manufacturers supply overhaul kits of three basic types: minor repair; major repair; and gasket kits. Basically, they contain the following:

Minor Repair Kits:
- All gaskets
- Float needle valve
- Volume control screw
- All diaphragms
- Spring for the pump diaphragm

Major Repair Kits:
- All jets and gaskets
- All diaphragms
- Float needle valve
- Volume control screw
- Pump ball valve
- Main jet carrier
- Float
- Complete intermediate rod
- Intermediate pump lever
- Complete injector tube
- Some cover hold-down screws and washers

Gasket Kits:
- All gaskets

After cleaning and checking all components, reassemble the carburetor, using

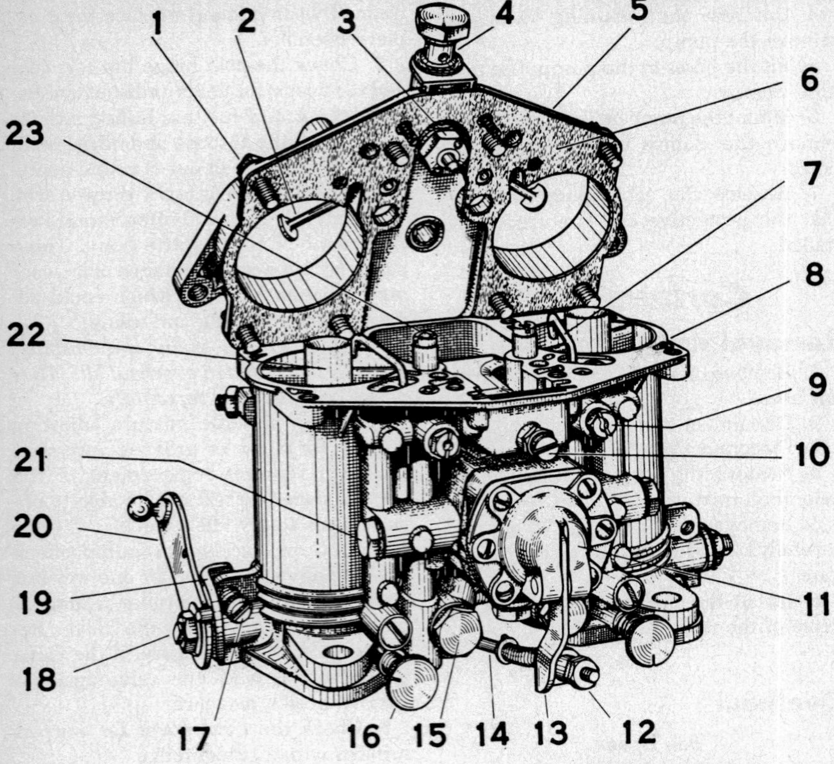

Solex PII 4 carburetor

1. Cover retaining screws
2. Power enrichment nozzle
3. Float needle valve
4. Fuel line connector
5. Carburetor cover
6. Cover gasket
7. Accelerating pump nozzle
8. Carburetor body
9. Idle jet
10. Float level adjustment
11. Accelerating pump
12. Accelerating pump adjustment
13. Accelerating pump lever
14. Accelerating pump rod
15. Main jet carrier with jet
16. Idle mixture adjustment
17. Idle speed adjustment
18. Throttle return stop
19. Throttle return stop
20. Throttle arm
21. Accelerating pump jet
22. Preatomizer
23. Air correction jet

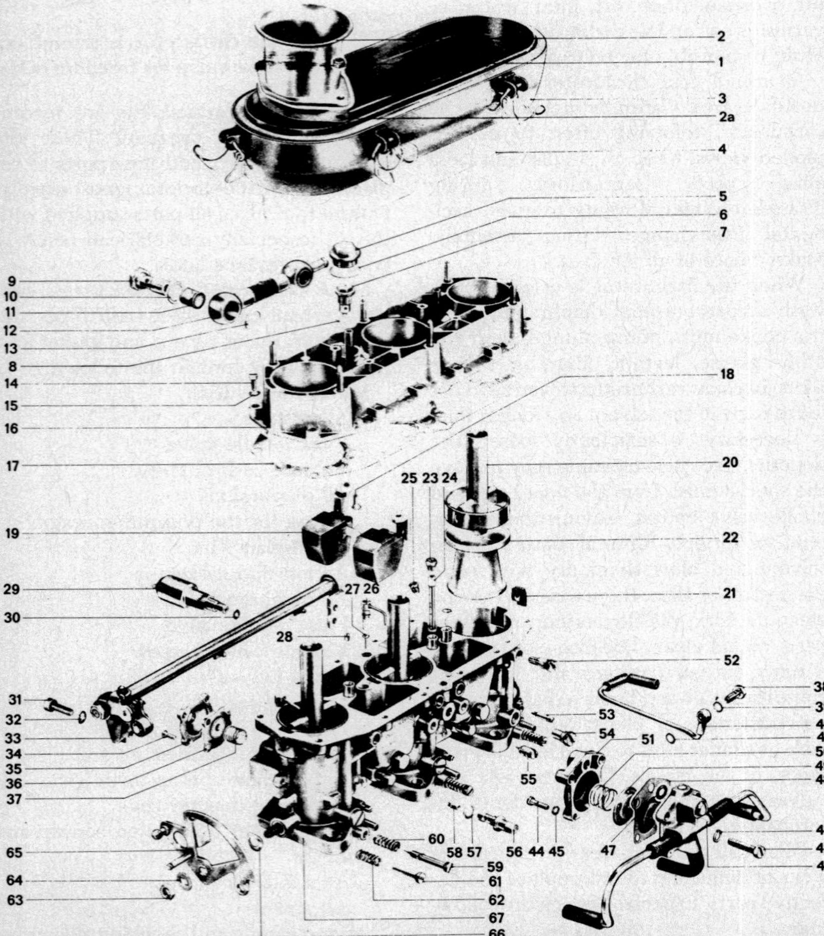

Solex/Zenith 40 TIN carburetor

1. Nut
2. Velocity Stack
3. Gasket
4. Clamp
5. Gasket
6. Threaded plug
7. Float needle valve
8. Gasket
9. Fitting
10. Gasket
11. Filter
12. Connector
13. Gasket
14. Screw
15. Lock washer
16. Top cover
17. Gasket
18. Screw
19. Float assembly
20. Upper venturi
21. Clip
22. Venturi
23. Air correction jet
24. Emulsion tube
25. Pump inlet valve
26. Injection tube
27. Plug
28. Enrichment valve fuel jet
29. Enrichment solenoid
30. Gasket
31. Screw
32. Lock washer
33. Pump shaft
34. Shrew
35. Pump cover
36. Diaphragm
37. Pump spring
38. Fitting
39. Gasket
40. Fuel line assembly
41. Gasket
42. Screw
43. Lock washer
44. Screw
45. Lock washer
46. Enrichment valve top
47. O-ring
48. Diaphragm

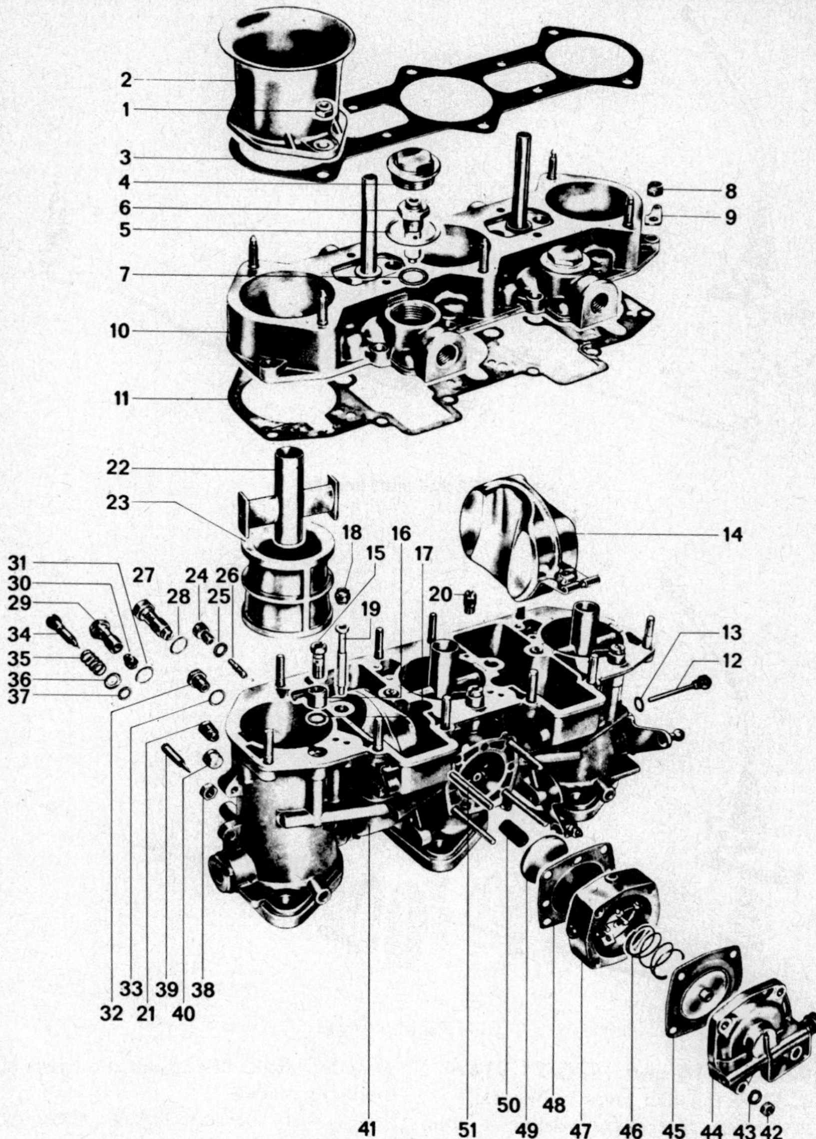

Weber 40 IDT carburetor

1. Nut
2. Velocity stack
3. Gasket
4. Plug
5. Gasket
6. Float needle valve
7. Gasket
8. Nut
9. Lock
10. Top cover
11. Gasket
12. Float shaft screw
13. Gasket
14. Float
15. Pressure valve
16. Pump nozzle
17. Gasket
18. Air correction nozzle
19. Mixing tube
20. Suction valve
21. Venturi screw
22. Venturi top
23. Venturi
24. Jet carrier
25. Gasket
26. Idle jet
27. Main jet
28. Gasket
29. Jet carrier
30. Main jet
31. Gasket
32. Drain screw
33. Sealing ring
34. Idle speed adjusting screw
35. Spring
36. Spacer
37. O-ring
38. Nut
39. Air adjusting screw
40. Inspection plug
41. Carburetor body
42. Nut
43. Lock washer
44. Pump cover
45. Diaphragm
46. Spring
47. Pump base
48. Diaphragm
49. Plunger
50. Spring
51. Stud

new parts and referring to the exploded view. When reassembling, make sure that all screws and jets are tight in their seats, but do not overtighten, as the tips will be distorted. Tighten all screws gradually, in rotation. Do not tighten needle valves into their seats; uneven jetting will result. Always use new gaskets. Be sure to adjust the float level when reassembling.

Float Level Adjustment

912 (Solex PII–4)

1. Position the car on a level surface.
2. Start the engine and allow it to run for a few moments.
3. Remove the float level inspection plug.
4. If the float level is correct, you will be able to see fuel in the machined groove within the threaded section of the port, or some fuel will spill out.

Solex PII 4 float level inspection plug

5. Adjust the fuel level by turning the adjusting screw. Turning the screw in lowers the level; turning the screw out raises the level.

NOTE: *When turning the screw in, some fuel may run out of the inspection port due to displacement of the float. Allow the engine to use up the excess before making your final adjustment.*

911 and 914/6 (Weber and Solex/Zenith)

Both the Weber and Solex/Zenith carburetors have two float chambers per unit. They differ in that the Weber has one accelerator pump for all of its three throats, while the Solex/Zenith has an accelerator pump for each throat. Porsche tool P226a or its equivalent is required to accurately set the float level on these carburetors. The two lower lines on the gauge apply to the Solex/Zenith; the top two lines apply to the Weber.

Float level gauge for Weber and Solex/Zenith carburetors

1. Place the car on a level surface.
2. Remove the plug from the float chamber on one carburetor and install the gauge.
3. Start the engine and observe the

fuel level. It should be between the lines for that carburetor.

4. Fuel level is adjusted by placing thicker or thinner gaskets under the needle valve for that float.

a. Remove the air cleaner

b. Remove the top of the carburetor

c. Remove the plug for the float needle valve.

d. Unscrew the float needle valve.

e. Install the desired gasket.

A thicker gasket raises the float level; a thinner gasket lowers the level.

5. Repeat the above operation for the other float chamber of that carburetor, and then the two chambers of the second carburetor.

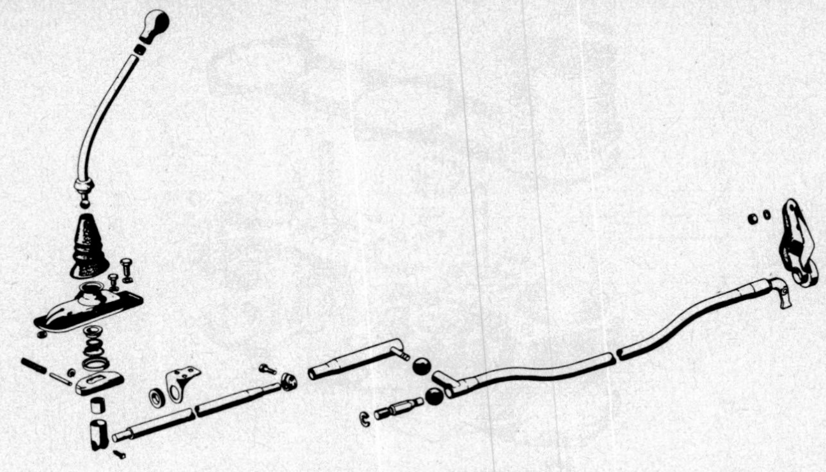

1970-1972 914 shift lingake

Fuel Injection

The 911 mechanical fuel injection and the 914 electronic fuel injection systems require special tools and training for any adjustment or repair. For this reason, only those having access to these tools and possessing this training should work on these systems.

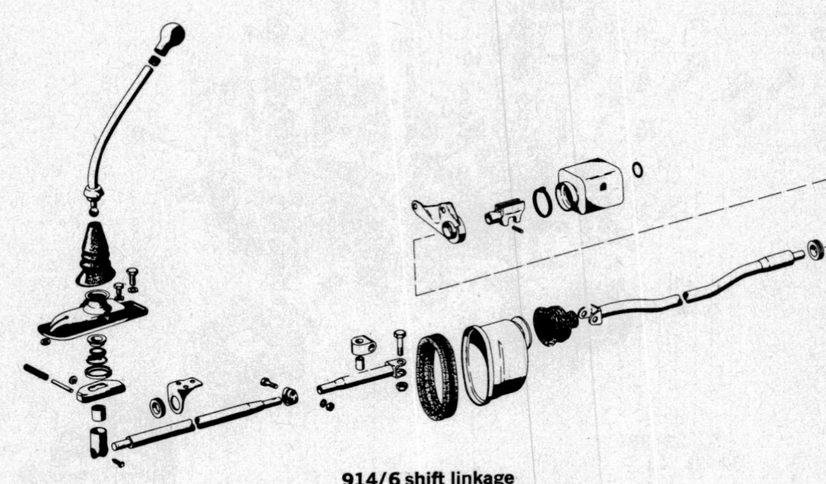

914/6 shift linkage

TRANSAXLE

Transaxle separation is covered in the "Engine Removal" procedure.

Shift Linkage Adjustment

912 and 911

1. Position the shift lever in Neutral. Remove the rear tunnel cover in front of the rear seat.

2. Pull the rubber dust cover forward on the shift rod.

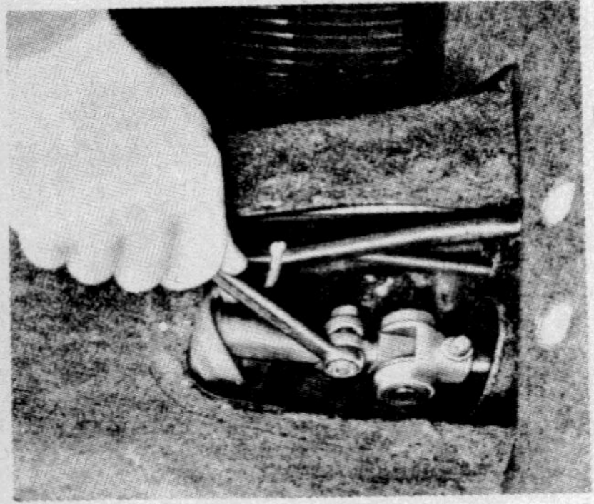

911 and 912 linkage adjustment

3. Loosen the clamp bolt on the shift rod.

4. Move the transmission selector shaft all the way to its left stop, keeping it in Neutral.

5. With the transmission still in Neutral, move the gearshift rod to the right to its stop.

6. Tighten the clamp bolt to 18 ft lbs.

7. Test the shift lever. Play should be the same in all gears in all directions.

1970–72 914 and 1970–71 914/6

1. Place the shift lever in Neutral.

2. Loosen the clamp between the front rod and the center rod.

3. The bottom of the shift lever should be straight up and down.

4. Set the shift lever against the left stop.

5. Loosen the dust cap clamp and remove the cap.

6. Place the transmission selector lever into Neutral and center the selector lever by moving the rear shift rod.

7. Tighten the front and center rod clamps.

8. Shift the lever into Third gear. Make sure that the transmission selector lever is correctly engaged.

9. Adjust the linkage again, if necessary.

10. Road test the car.

1973 914

For 1973, the transaxle was modified for a side shift configuration. This change eliminated the inner selector levers and selector shaft in the rear transmission cover. The linkage goes straight back to the side shift lever without the twists of the older models.

1. Loosen the shift linkage retaining bolt on the shift mount.

2. Place the shift lever in Neutral and to the right (toward the Fourth and Fifth gear side).

3. Remove the rear tunnel cover in the passenger compartment.

4. Rotate the shift rod clockwise (facing toward the front of the car).

5. Tighten the mounting screw hand tight.

6. Shift lever travel must be the same for Second, Third, Fourth, and Fifth gears. Make sure that First and Reverse are easily engaged.

7. Finally tighten the mounting bolt to 18 ft lbs.

CLUTCH

Removal and Installation

All Models

Each Porsche covered in this section is equipped with single dry disc clutch and diaphragm pressure plate. Clutch actuation is controlled by a cable.

1. Separate the engine/transaxle.

2. Gradually loosen the pressure plate bolts one or two turns at a time in a criss-cross pattern to prevent distortion.

3. Remove the pressure plate and clutch disc.

4. Check the clutch disc for uneven or excessive lining wear. Examine the pressure plate for cracking, scorching, or scoring. Replace any questionable components.

5. On 912 and 911 models, fill the pilot bearing with about 2 cc of grease.

6. Install the clutch disc and pressure plate. Use a pilot shaft or an old transaxle input shaft to keep the disc centered.

Clutch disc centering

7. Gradually tighten the pressure plate-to-flywheel bolts in a criss-cross pattern. Torque the bolts to 25 ft lbs on the 912, 914/6, and 1969 911 models. Tighten the bolts on the 914 to 15 ft lbs. On 1970 and later 911s, tighten the bolts to 18 ft lbs.

8. Install the throwout bearing.

9. Install the transaxle on the engine.

Free Play Adjustment

912 and 911

This adjustment is made at the throwout arm on the transaxle. Free play should be between ¾ in. and 1 in.

1. Jack up the rear of the car and support it on stands.

2. On older models, loosen the locknut on the clevis and turn the adjusting nut as necessary to obtain the correct free play.

Free-play adjustment

3. A threaded cable extension is provided on later models. While holding the flats on the cable end to prevent it from turning, screw the self-locking nut in or out for the correct free play.

914 and 914/6

1. Raise the rear of the car and support it on jack stands.

2. Hold the threaded cable end with pliers and turn the self-locking adjustment nut in or out until the free play is ½ in. to ¾ in.

Pedal Travel Adjustment

All Models

1. Pull the front carpeting back.

2. Loosen the two retaining bolts on the pedal stop.

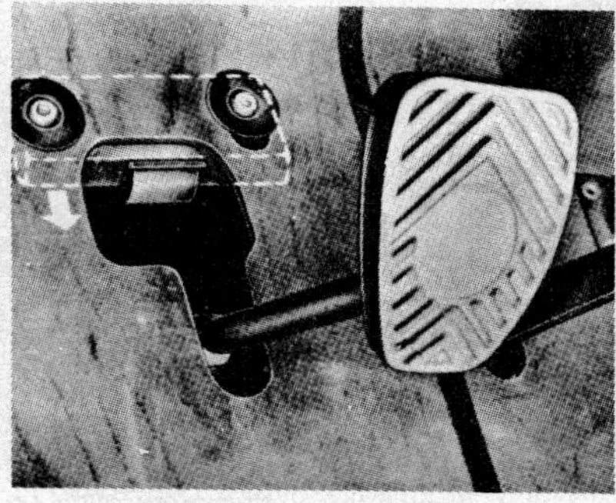

911 and 912 pedal travel adjustment

3. Move the pedal up or down until reverse can be engaged with only a slight amount of gear clash.

4. Tighten the pedal stop bolts.

5. Double check the adjustment by shifting into reverse several times. Reinstall the floor carpeting.

DRIVE AXLES

Axle Driveshaft

Removal and Installation

912 and 911

1. Jack up the rear of the car and support it on stands.

2. Remove the wheels. Remove the brake caliper and disc.

3. Raise the trailing arm with a hydraulic jack.

4. Remove the lower shock absorber mounting.

5. Install a fixture similar to Porsche tool P36b to hold the hub.

6. Remove the cotter pin and using a long ratchet handle extension, remove the hub nut.

7. Remove the allen bolts at the axle driveshaft/transaxle flange.

8. Use a flat chisel to pry the flanges apart.

CAUTION: *Don't damage the flanges when separating them.*

9. Check the axle driveshaft joints for excessive play and replace them if necessary.

Hub nut removal (Porsche tool P36b shown)

Disconnecting inner driveshaft joint at transaxle

10. Use a new gasket on the transaxle flange. Ensure that the flanges are clean and free from burrs.

11. Pack the joints with a moly grease.

12. Install the axle drive-shaft using a reverse of the removal procedure.

13. Tighten the flange bolts to 60 ft lbs. The hollow side of the lock washer should face the spacer slate.

14. Using a long extension handle wrench, tighten the castellated nut to 217–253 ft lbs and install a new cotter pin.

NOTE: *Be prepared to apply considerable force on this nut.*

15. Tighten the shock absorber bolt to 54 ft lbs.

16. Install the brake caliper and disc.

17. Install the wheels and lower the car.

914 and 194/6

1. Raise the rear of the car and support it on jack stands.

2. Remove the wheels.

3. Remove the brake caliper and disc as described in the brake section.

4. Using a ratchet handle with a long extension (a pipe will provide more leverage), remove the castellated hub nut.

5. Remove the heat exchangers.

6. Unscrew the allen bolts at the transaxle/driveshaft flange.

7. Using a chisel or flat-edged screw-

driver, pry the flanges apart and separate the driveshaft.

8. Pull the driveshaft from the hub and down out of the case. Be careful not to damage the flange surfaces.

9. Clean the flanges and install a new gasket.

10. Install the axle driveshaft and tighten the flange bolts to 31 ft lbs. Use new lock washers and install them so that their hollow ends are against the spacer plate.

12. Tighten the hub nut to 217–253 ft lbs, using a long extension on the wrench handle and plenty of muscle.

13. Install the brake disc and caliper.

14. Install the wheels and lower the car.

REAR SUSPENSION

All models covered in this section have independent rear suspension. The 912 and 911 rear suspension is a semi-trailing arm design. Springing is provided by transverse torsion bars located forward of each trailing arm. Telescopic shock absorbers at each wheel provide dampening. A rear stabilizer bar is standard equipment on the 911S and optional on the other two 911 models.

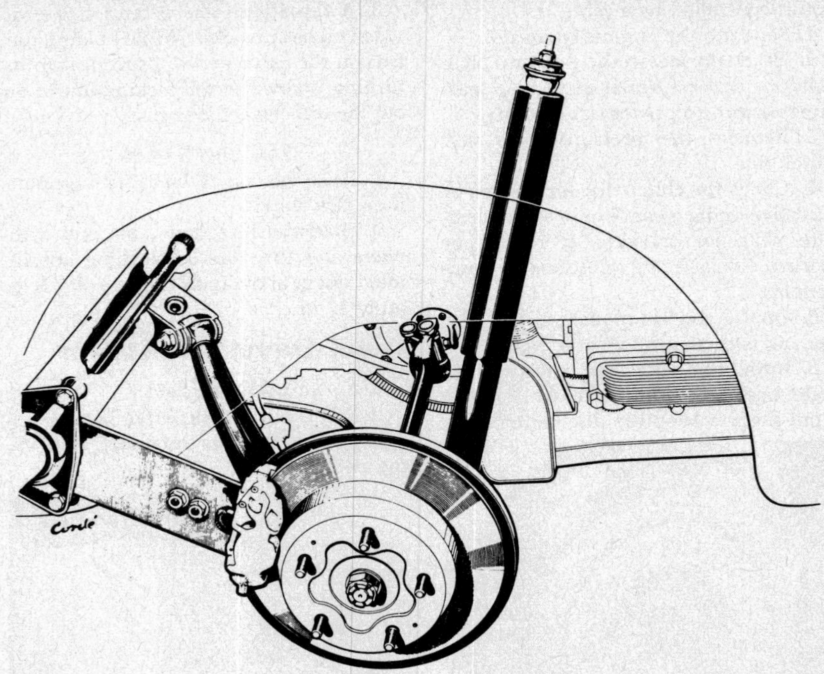

911 and 912 rear suspension

The 914 and 914/6 are also equipped with trailing arms, but they are one piece arms as opposed to the two piece arms on the 912 and 911. Telescopic strut/shocks with concentric coil springs support the weight of the car. A rear stabilizer bar is optionally available on later models.

1
2
3
4

914 and 914/6 rear suspension

Torsion Bars

Removal and Installation

912 and 911

1. Jack up the rear of the car and support it safely with stands.
2. Remove the wheel on the side where the torsion bar is being removed.
3. Fabricate a fixture similar to the one shown. The fixture is necessary to hold the trailing arm while it is raised and lowered. The special Porsche tool for this purpose is number P 289.

Raising the trailing arm

4. Using a hydraulic jack under the holding fixture, raise the trailing arm.
5. Remove the lower shock absorber bolt.
6. Remove the trailing arm retaining bolts. Remove the toe and camber adjusting bolts.
7. Remove the four retaining bolts from the trailing arm cover. Withdraw the spacer.
8. Using two screwdrivers, pry off the trailing arm cover.
9. Remove the holding fixture.
10. Knock out the round body plug and remove the trailing arm.
11. Paint a reference mark on the torsion bar support, matching the location of the "L" or "R" side identification letter, so that the torsion bar may be installed in the same position.

NOTE: *The torsion bars are splined to allow adjustment of the rear riding height.*

12. Remove the torsion bar. Do not scratch the protective paint on the torsion bar, or it will corrode and possibly develop fatigue cracks.

NOTE: *If you are removing a broken torsion bar, the inner end can be knocked from its seat by removing the opposite torsion bar and tapping through with a steel rod. Torsion bars are not interchangeable from side-to-side and are marked "L" and "R" for identification.*

13. Check the torsion bar splines for damage and replace it if necessary. If any corrosion is present on the bar, replace it.
14. Coat the torsion bar lightly with a multi-purpose grease. Carefully grease the splines.
15. Apply glycerine or another rubber preservative to the torsion bar support.
16. Install the torsion bar, matching the "L" or "R" with the paint mark you made before removal.
17. Install the trailing arm cover into position and start the three accessible bolts.

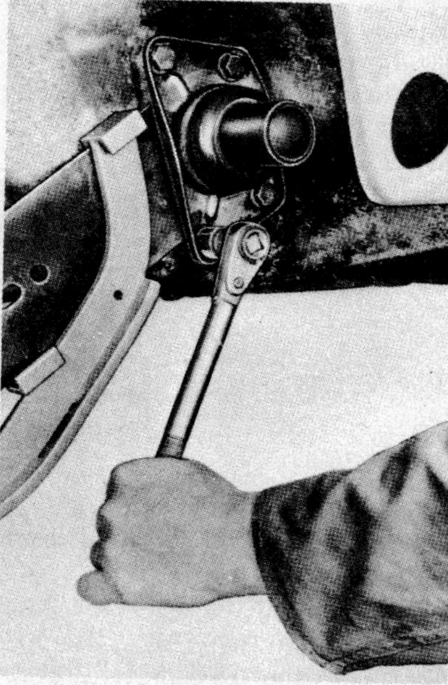

Installing the trailing arm cover

18. Raise the trailing arm into place with the holding fixture (or special tool P 289) until the spacer and the fourth bolt can be installed.
19. Assemble the remaining components in a reverse order of their removal.
20. Tighten the trailing arm cover bolts to 34 ft lbs. Tighten the trailing arm retaining bolts to 65 ft lbs.
21. Tighten the camber adjusting bolt to 43 ft lbs. and the toe-in adjusting bolt to 36 ft lbs. Tighten the shock absorber bolt to 54 ft lbs.
22. Adjust the rear wheel camber and toe-in.

Spring Strut

Removal and Installation

914 and 914/6

1. Jack up the rear of the car and support it safely with stands.
2. Support the wheel on the side where the spring strut is being removed.
3. Loosen and remove the bottom through-bolt and nut from the trailing arm.
4. Loosen and remove the nut at the top of the strut. Hold the strut shaft while loosening the nut.
5. Remove the strut by pulling it down and out of the car.
6. When reinstalling the strut, use a nut at the top. Install the bottom nut and bolt.
7. Tighten the top nut to 36–43 ft lbs. Torque the bottom bolt to 72–87 ft lbs.
8. Lower the car.

Disassembly

914 and 914/6

1. Remove the strut as outlined above.
2. Install the strut in a vise. Grip at the bottom spring retainer.
3. Install a compressor on the coil spring.
4. Alternately tighten the compressor bolts to hold the spring.

Compressing the coil spring

CAUTION: *Be sure that the lips of the compressor are gripping the coils firmly.*

5. Remove the two threaded bushings and remove the top spring retainer.
6. Gradually release the spring compressor. When the spring tension is fully released, remove the spring, bushing, and washer.
7. Using a drift, drive the cap off the shock absorber.
8. Remove the bottom spring retainer by pulling over the top of the shock absorber.
9. Check the shock absorber for correct action by pushing and pulling on the rod. If there is any sloppiness present, replace the shock absorber.
10. Slight oil leakage is within tolerance, but if the shock is leaking badly replace it.
11. Reassembly is basically a reverse of the disassembly steps. The threaded bushing on the top should be tightened to 11–14 ft lbs.

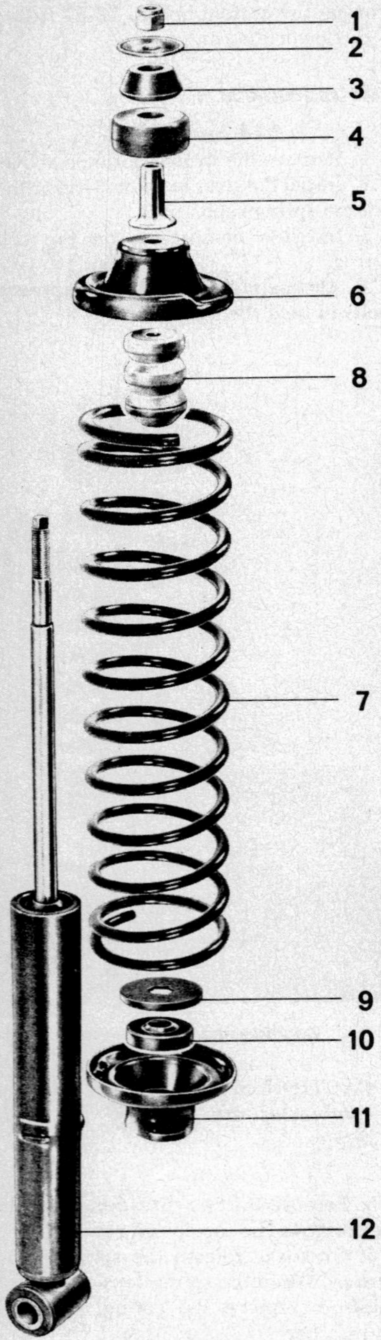

Strut components

1. Nut
2. Washer
3. Bushing
4. Bushing
5. Threaded bushing
6. Top spring retainer
7. Coil spring
8. Bumper
9. Stop washer
10. Cap
11. Bottom spring retainer
12. Shock absorber

Shock Absorbers

Removal and Installation

912 and 911

1. Leave the car standing on the ground, so that the shock absorber is not tensioned.
2. Open the engine compartment lid and remove the rubber cover from the top of the shock absorber.
3. Hold the shock absorber shaft and remove the nut.
4. On the bottom, remove the retaining nut and bolt.
5. Remove the shock absorber.
6. If the shock exhibits excessive free travel or is leaking, replace it.

Top shock absorber mounting

Bottom shock absorber mounting

7. Install the shock up through the body and screw the nut on hand-tight.
8. Align the shock absorber eye with the hole in the trailing arm and install the nut and bolt.
9. Tighten the top nut and install the rubber cover.
10. Tighten the bottom retaining bolt to 54 ft lbs.

Stabilizer

Removal and Installation

911

1. Jack the rear of the car and safely support it with stands.
2. Using a large screwdriver, pry the upper eyes of the stabilizer bar off the studs in the trailing arm.
3. Remove the body mounting brackets.
4. Remove the stabilizer.
5. Check the rubber bushings for wear or damage and, if necessary, replace them.
6. Install the stabilizer bar using a reverse of the removal steps.

Adjustments

Camber Adjustment

912 and 911

The rearmost of the two allen bolts on the trailing arm provides camber adjustment. Tighten the bolt to 43 ft lbs. after the camber is adjusted to specifications.

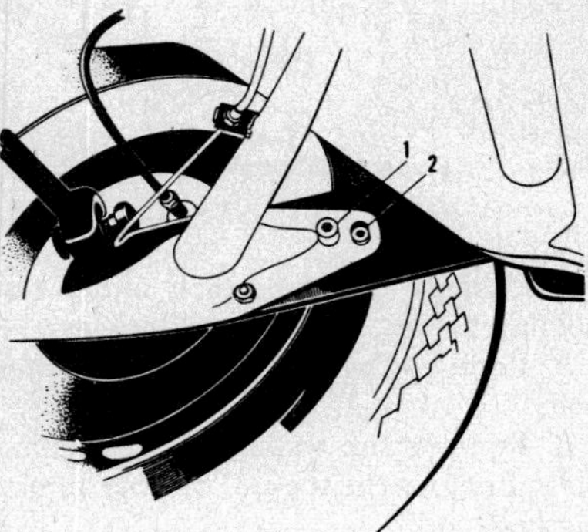

911 and 912 rear wheel alignment adjustment points

1. Camber
2. Toe-in

914 and 914/6

Camber is adjusted by removal or insertion of shims under the trailing arm bearing plate. Scribe the plate's position, so the toe-in setting isn't lost, and then remove the center bolt and loosen the two end bolts. Each 1 mm shim results in a 10′ change chamge in camber. Tighten the bolts to 18 ft lbs after the correct camber is reached.

914 and 914/6 rear wheel alignment adjustment point

Toe-in Adjustment

912 and 911

The front allen bolt on the trailing arm adjusts the toe-in. Tighten the bolt to 36 ft lbs after toe-in is adjusted to specification.

914 and 914/6

Loosen all three bolts on the trailing arm bearing plate and push the arm forward or backward as necessary to correct the toe-in. Tighten the bolts to 18 ft lbs when the adjustment is complete.

FRONT SUSPENSION

Front suspension is similar in design on all models; but parts are not interchangeable from one type to the other. Springing is provided by a longitudinal torsion bar at each wheel. A triangular lower arm links the torsion bar to the shock absorber strut and steering knuckle. A permanently lubricated ball joint is located at the bottom of the strut. A stabilizer bar is standard equipment on 912 and 911 models and available optionally on 914 and 914/6 models.

Up until 1972, 911E models were equipped with self-leveling hydropneumatic suspension struts. This suspension package was optionally available on the T and S, but few were so equipped. In this design, the strut acts as shock absorber, spring, and locating member and the torsion bars are replaced by a shaft in the lower arm.

Torsion Bars

Removal and Installation

912 and 911

1. Jack up the front of the car and support it safely with stands.
2. Remove the torsion bar adjusting screw.
3. Take the adjusting lever off the torsion bar and withdraw the seal.
4. Unscrew the retaining bolts from the front mount cover bracket and remove the bracket.
5. Using a drift, carefully drive the torsion bar out of the front of the arm.
6. Check the torsion bar for spline damage and rust. If necessary, replace the bar.
7. Give the torsion bar a light coating of grease before installing it.

NOTE: *Torsion bars are marked "L" or "R" to identify them and are not interchangeable.*

8. Insert the end cap of the torsion bar, protruding side out, into the control arm. Drive the torsion bar into position with a drift. Carefully.
9. Tighten the retaining bolts on the front mount to 34 ft lbs.
10. Slide the seal onto the torsion bar from the open side of the crossmember.
11. Using a tire iron, or other suitable lever, pry the control arm down as far as possible. While holding the control arm, slide the adjusting lever onto the splines of the torsion bar. There should only be a slight amount of clearance at the lever adjusting point.
12. Grease the adjusting screw threads with a moly grease and hand tighten the screw.
13. Check that the end cap is properly seated in the control arm.
14. Install the rubber mount cover

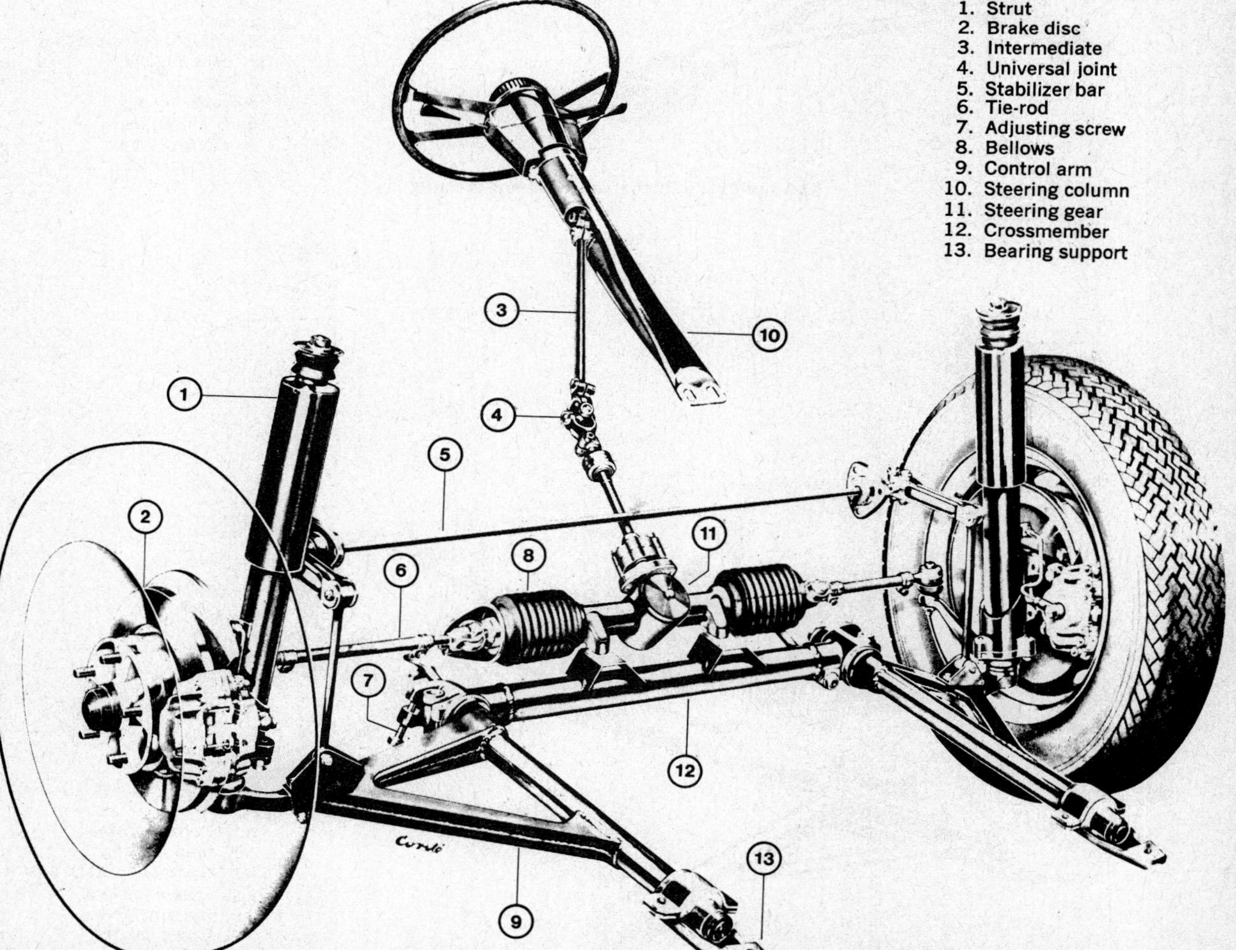

911 and 912 front suspension and steering

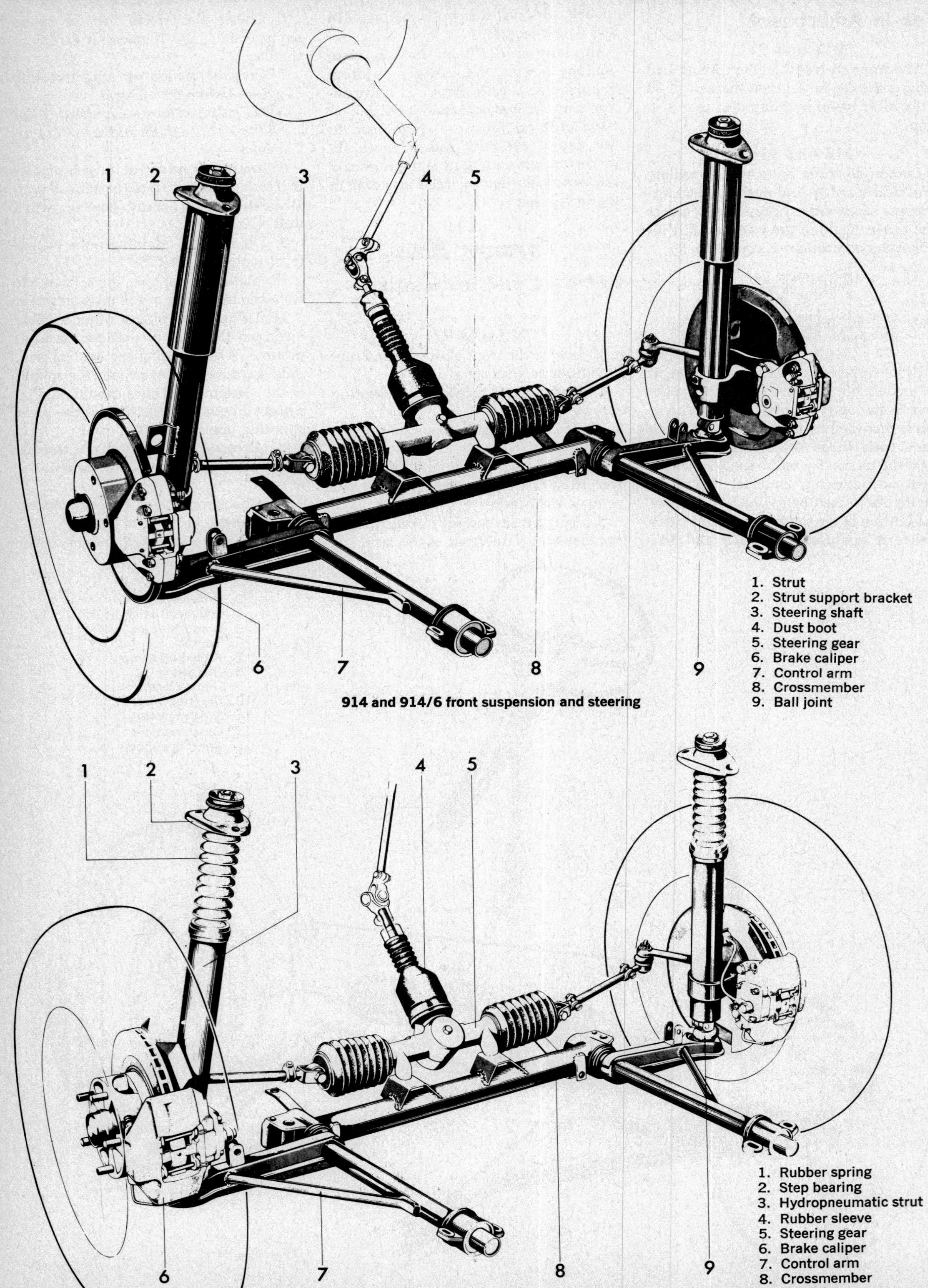

914 and 914/6 front suspension and steering

911 hydropneumatic suspension

bracket. Tighten the retaining bolts to 34 ft lbs.

15. Lower the car.
16. Check the front wheel alignment.

914 and 914/6

1. Jack up the front of the car and support it safely with stands.
2. Unscrew the torsion bar adjusting screw.

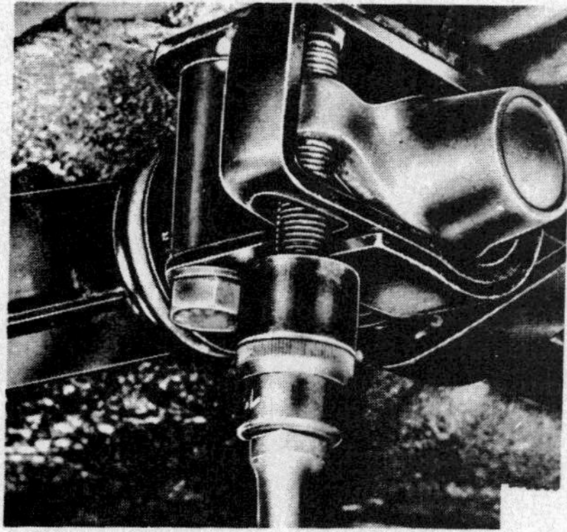

Loosening torsion bar adjusting screw

3. Pull the adjusting lever off the torsion bar and remove the seal.
4. Loosen the cheesehead screw for the front mount cover and remove the cover.
5. Carefully drive the torsion bar out of the rear of the control arm with a drift.
6. Check the torsion bar for spline damage and rust. If necessary, replace the bar.
7. Give the torsion bar a light coating of grease before installing it.

NOTE: *Torsion bars are marked "L" or "R" for identification and are not interchangeable from side-to-side.*

8. Slide the seal onto the torsion bar.
9. Using a tire iron, or other suitable lever, pry the control arm down as far as possible against the stop in the shock absorber strut. Push the adjusting lever onto the torsion bar as closely as possible against the stop.
10. Grease the adjusting screw threads and then install it hand-tight.
11. Make sure that the cover in the control arm is correctly seated. Improper assembly of the adjusting lever may force the torsion bar out of the control arm splines at the front.
12. Screw on the front mount cover.
13. Lower the car.
14. Check the front wheel alignment.

Shock Absorbers

Removal and Installation

912 and 911

NOTE: *This procedure also applies to cars equipped with hydropneumatic struts.*

1. Jack up the front of the car and support it safely on stands. Remove the wheels.
2. Remove the brake line from the clip on the suspension strut. A small amount of brake fluid will run out of the line, plug it so that dirt cannot enter the system.
3. Unscrew the retaining bolts and remove the caliper.
4. Using a soft mallet, tap the hub cap to loosen it.
5. Pry the hub cap off with a screwdriver.
6. Loosen the allen screw in the wheel bearing clamp. Unscrew the clamp nut and remove the nut and washer.
7. Remove the wheel hub along with the brake disc and wheel bearing.
8. Remove the backing plate retaining bolts and remove the plate.
9. Withdraw the cotter pin from the castellated nut on the steering tie-rod end and remove the nut. Using a suitable puller, remove the tie-rod joint from the strut.
10. Remove the control arm-to-strut ball joint retaining bolt and pull the ball joint out of the strut by pulling down on the lower control arm.

Loosening ball joint retaining bolt

NOTE: *If the car is not equipped with hydropneumatic struts, the torsion bar adjusting screw will have to be loosened and the adjusting arm removed.*

11. Remove the keeper for the nut on the top of the strut. Unscrew the nut and remove it, the keeper plate, and washer.

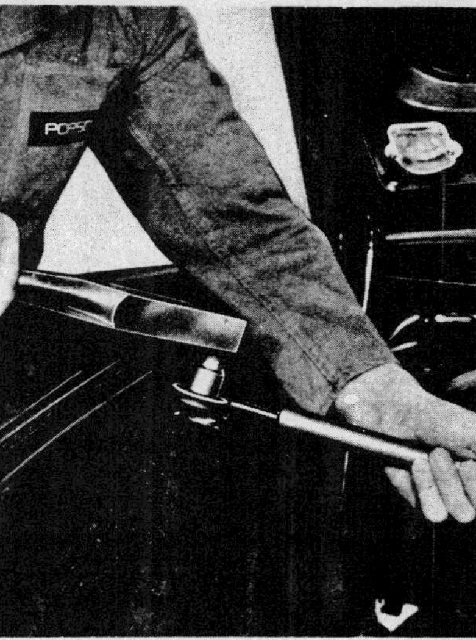

Top mounting nut removal

12. Remove the strut from the bottom. It will be necessary to loosen and pull the side of the luggage compartment out for clearance.
13. Check the shock absorber strut for excessive free travel and leaking. Replace the shock absorber if it is at all suspect.
14. Install the strut in a reverse order of the removal.
15. Tighten the top nut to 58 ft lbs. Use a new keeper plate and ensure that the peg on the plate is pointing up.
16. Tighten the ball joint bolt to 47 ft lbs.

NOTE: *Remember to install the washer between the ball joint seal and strut.*

17. On non-hydropneumatic strut equipped cars, install the torsion bar adjusting lever as described in "Torsion Bar Removal and Installation".
18. Tighten the tie-rod nut to 33 ft lbs and install a new cotter pin.
19. Torque the backing plate bolts to 18 ft lbs.
20. Install and adjust the wheel bearings as outlined in the "Brake" section.
21. Tighten the caliper retaining bolts to 50 ft lbs.
22. Bleed the hydraulic system as outlined in the "Brake" section.
23. Install the wheels and lower the car.
24. Check the wheel alignment.

914 and 914/6

1. Jack up the front of the car and support it safely with stands. Remove the wheels.
2. Remove the brake line from its retainer on the shock absorber strut.
3. Remove the retaining bolts and detach the caliper.
4. Carefully pry the hub cap off.
5. Loosen the screw in the wheel bearing clamp nut. Unscrew the clamp nut and remove the washer.
6. Remove the brake disc and the wheel bearings.
7. Remove the retaining bolt and remove the splash shield.
8. Remove the cotter pin and nut and remove the tie-rod joint from the strut with a suitable puller.
9. Loosen the torsion bar adjusting screw and remove the adjusting lever.
10. Loosen the ball joint retaining bolt on the strut. Pull the control arm down to free the strut from the ball joint.
11. Open the front luggage compartment lid. Remove the strut retaining nut, lock washer, and tab washer.
12. Pull the strut down and out of the car.

13. Check the shock absorber strut for excessive free travel and leaking and replace it, if necessary.

14. Installation of the strut is essentially a reverse order of the removal. Remember to install the washer on the ball joint before attaching the strut.

15. Tighten the top nut to 58 ft lbs. Use a new lock washer and ensure that its tab points up. Torque the ball joint bolt in the strut to 47 ft lbs.

16. Reinstall the torsion bar adjusting lever as outlined in "Torsion Bar Removal and Installation".

17. Tighten the tie-rod end nut to 33 ft lbs and install a new cotter pin. Torque the three splash shield bolts to 18 ft lbs.

18. Install and adjust the wheel bearings as described in the "Brake" section.

19. Install new lock washer, or spring washers in the case of the 914/6, on the caliper retaining bolts. Tighten both bolts to 51 ft lbs.

20. Bleed the brake system.

21. Install the wheels and lower the car.

22. Check the wheel alignment.

Stabilizer Bar

Removal and Installation

912 and 911

1. Jack up the front of the car and safely support it on stands.
2. Loosen the stabilizer clamp bolts and pry the lever ends off their mounts.
3. Remove the stabilizer bar along with the levers.
4. Check the rubber bushings for deterioration and, if necessary, replace them. Lubricate the bushings with glycerine or some other rubber preservative.
5. Install the stabilizer bar in a reverse order of the removal.
6. The square end of the stabilizer should protrude slightly above the clamp. Tighten the clamp nuts to 18 ft lbs.

Adjustments

Camber Adjustment

All Models

Camber is adjusted at the top of the strut. Pull back the luggage compartment rug to expose the three mounting bolts. Scrape the undercoating from the bolts and plates. Scribe the positions of the two plates under the bolts. Loosen the bolts and move the strut in or out as necessary to correct the camber angle.

Caster and camber adjustment location

Caster Adjustment

All Models

Caster is adjusted in the same manner as camber, except that the strut is moved forward or backward to change the caster angle.

Toe-in Adjustment

All Models

Toe-in is set with the front wheels straight ahead. Tie-rod length is adjusted by loosening the tie-rod clamps and moving them an equal amount in or out to obtain the correct toe-in.

STEERING

All models are equipped with rack and pinion type steering gear. No maintenance is required on the steering system. It is filled with a special lubricant at the time of manufacture and does not require checking or filling.

Steering Wheel

Removal and Installation

All Models

1. Disconnect the battery(ies). Place the wheels in a straight ahead position.
2. Twist the center cover to the left and remove it.
3. Remove the horn contact pin.
4. Remove the steering wheel nut.

Steering wheel center cover removal

5. Mark the steering wheel and the shaft so that it can be reinstalled in the same position.
6. Remove the steering wheel. Catch the bearing support ring and spring.
7. Install the spring and bearing support ring on the wheel hub.
8. Lightly grease the horn contact ring.
9. Install the wheel. Make sure that you align the match marks before removal.
10. Tighten the steering wheel nut to 58 ft lbs on 912 and 911 models, 54 ft lbs on the 914/6, and 36–43 ft lbs on 914s.
11. Twist the center cover back on to the right to snap it into place.

Turn Signal/Headlight Flasher Switch

Removal and Installation

912 and 911

The combination turn signal, headlight dimmer, and flasher switch is located in the steering column housing. The wiper/washer switch removal and installation procedure is identical.

1. Remove the steering wheel as outlined above.
2. Reach under the instrument panel and disconnect all wiring to the switch.
3. Remove the two horn contact ring screws, disconnect the wire, and remove the ring.
4. Remove the two upper housing retaining nuts. Pull the entire assembly off the column, leading the switch wires through the hole in the housing.
5. Remcve the three retaining screws and remove the switch.
6. Reverse the removal steps to reinstall the switch.

914 and 914/6

Both the turn signal/headlight dimmer and wiper/washer switches are located within the steering column cover halves.

1. Remove the steering wheel as previously outlined.
2. Unscrew and remove the horn contact ring.
3. Remove the screw retaining the horn ground wire and remove the wire.
4. Remove the retaining screw from the top and bottom covers. Detach the covers.
5. Remove the switch attaching screws and remove the switch.
6. Installation is a reverse of the removal procedure. Make sure that the turn signal switch is in neutral, or the cancelling cams will be damaged.

Ignition Switch/Steering Lock

Removal and Installation

912 and 911

1. Remove the ignition switch cover.
2. Drill out the two shear bolts which retain the switch.
3. Remove the steering lock and spacer.
4. Disconnect the electrical wiring

and remove the switch.

5. Place the steering lock into position.
6. Insert the protective plate.
7. Install and evenly tighten the shear bolts until their heads break off.

Steering Gear

Removal and Installation

912 and 911

1. Remove the front luggage compartment carpeting. Jack up the front of the car and support it safely with stands.
2. Remove the auxiliary heater duct from the steering post and position it to one side.
3. Open the access door and the intermediate steering shaft cover by prying the spring clips off with a screwdriver.
4. Remove the three heater fuel pump retaining bolts and position the pump to one side.
5. Remove the cotter pin from the lower universal joint bolt and loosen the castellated nut. Pull the universal joint off the steering shaft.
6. Remove the allen bolts from the steering shaft bushing bracket. Remove the bracket and pull the bushing and dust cover.
7. Loosen and remove the steering coupling bolts.

Disconnecting steering coupling

8. Remove the retaining bolts and remove the bottom shield.
9. Remove the cotter pins and nuts, and then pull the tie-rod ends out of the suspension struts with a suitable puller.

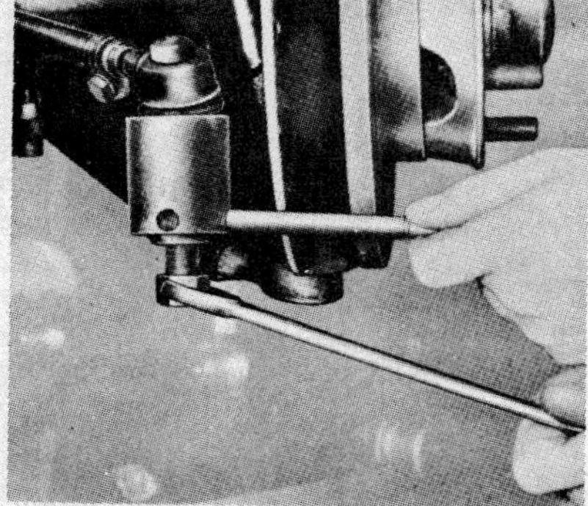
Removing tie-rod ends

10. Remove the two rack and pinion housing retaining bolts.

Rack and pinion retaining bolts

11. Remove the right side crossmember brace.
12. Pull the steering assembly out the right side of the car.
13. Remove the retaining bolts from the tie-rod yokes.
14. Installation is the reverse of the removal procedure.
15. Tighten the yoke bolts to 34 ft lbs.
16. Make sure that the crossmember brace mounts without binding. Tighten the nuts to 47 ft lbs and the bolts to 34 ft lbs.
17. Install the steering housing bolts with new lockwashers and tighten to 34 ft lbs.
18. Tighten the tie-rod end nuts to 33 ft lbs and install new cotter pins.
19. Tighten the steering bushing bracket allen bolts to 18 ft lbs.
20. Install new washers on the steering coupling bolts and tighten them to 18 ft lbs.
21. Lower the car

914 and 914/6

1. Raise the front of the car and support it safely on stands.
2. Remove the nut and bolt from the bottom universal joint.
3. Remove the cotter pins and castellated nuts from the tie-rod ends. Using a suitable puller, remove the tie-rod ends from the struts.
4. Remove the front shield.
5. Loosen the crossmember retaining bolts for the steering gear.
6. Loosen the torsion bar adjusting screws.
7. Remove the adjusting levers and seals from the torsion bars.
8. Remove the crossmember and control arm retaining bolts and remove the crossmember.
9. Remove the steering gear and tie-rods.
10. Detach the tie-rods from the steering gear by removing the yoke bolts.
11. Installation is essentially a reverse of the removal procedure. Reinstall the torsion bar adjusting levers as described in "Torsion Bar Removal and Installation".
12. The tie-rod yoke bolts are tightened to 34 ft lbs, the steering housing mounting bolts to 34 ft lbs, and the crossmember mounting bolts to 65 ft lbs.
13. Torque the tie-rod end nuts to 33 ft lbs. Tighten the steering coupling bolts and universal shaft nut to 18 ft lbs.

BRAKE SYSTEMS

All models are equipped with four wheel disc brakes. Fixed, two-piston calipers are utilized on each system. The discs on the 1969 911T with manual transmission, 912, and 914 are solid. 911's are equipped with internally vented discs at each wheel, while the 914/6 has internally vented front and solid rear brake discs. Disc brakes on all of these models are self-adjusting and require no periodic adjustment.

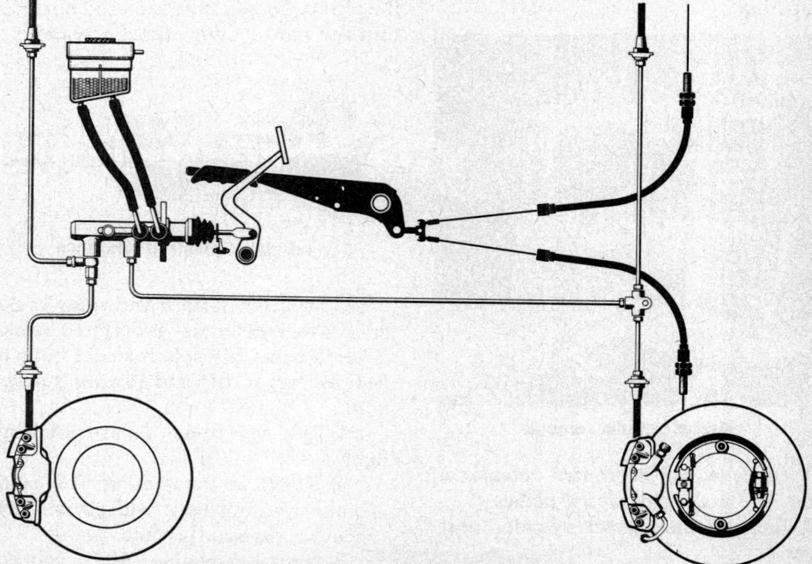
911 and 912 brake system

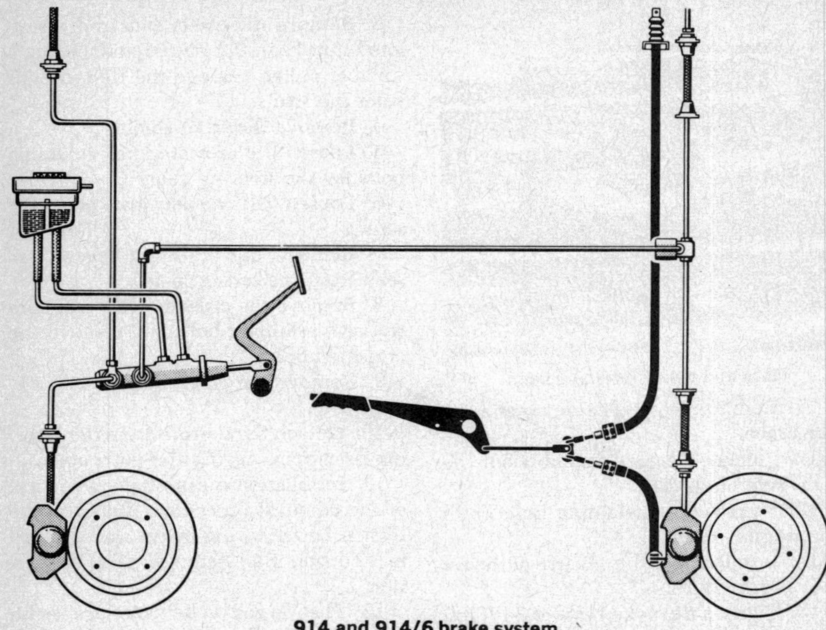

914 and 914/6 brake system

Hydraulic System

Each car has a tandem master cylinder, remote reservoir (mounted in the front luggage compartment for convenience), and separate hydraulic circuits for the front and rear brakes. The 914 and 914/6 rear circuit includes a pressure regulator which maintains maximum rear brake pressure at a predetermined level to prevent rear wheel lockup under hard braking.

Master Cylinder

Removal and Installation

All Models

1. Pull the accelerator back and out of its pushrod. Pull back the driver's side carpeting.

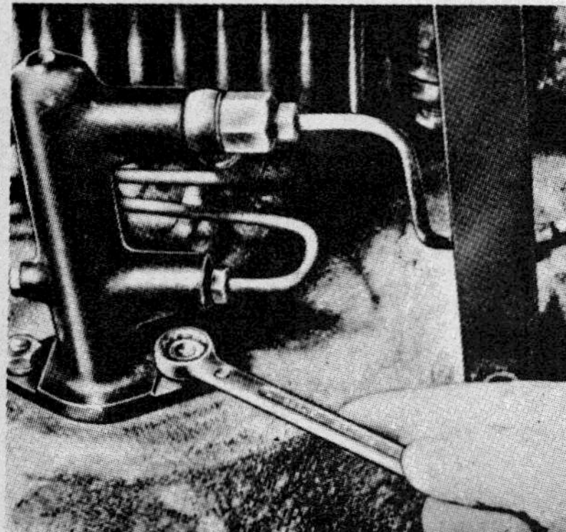

Master cylinder removal

2. Unscrew the floorboard retainer(s) under the brake and clutch pedals.
3. Remove the master cylinder dust cover.
4. Jack the front of the car up and support it with stands.
5. Siphon the brake fluid out of the reservoir. Discard the fluid, don't save it for reuse.
6. Unbolt the front splash shield.
7. Remove the brake lines from the master cylinder. Disconnect the brake failure warning light sending unit wire.
8. Remove the two master cylinder mounting nuts.
9. Disconnect the reservoir lines and remove the master cylinder.
10. Before installing the master cylinder, apply body sealer around the mounting flange.
11. Install the cylinder, making sure that the piston pushrod is correctly positioned. Torque the mounting nuts to 18 ft lbs.
12. The piston pushrod should have 0.04 in. (1 mm) clearance between it and the piston. Loosen the piston rod nut and turn the rod to adjust the clearance.

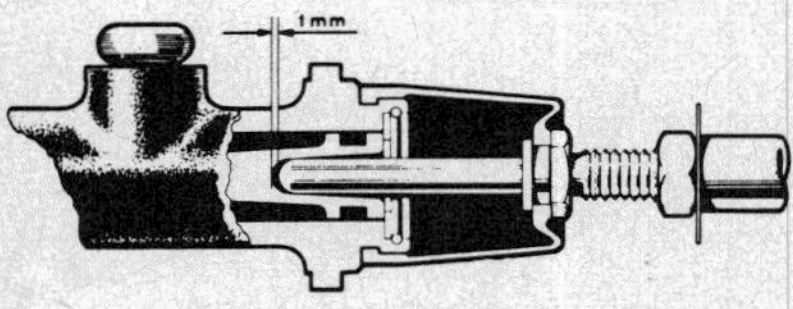

Correct piston pushrod clearance

13. Refill the system with new brake fluid. Bleed the brakes as outlined below.
14. Tighten the splash shield bolts to 34 ft lbs (larger bolt) and 18 ft lbs (smaller bolt).
15. Test the brake failure warning light.
    a. Switch on the ignition. The handbrake warning light will go on. If it doesn't, replace the bulb.
    b. Start the engine. While you depress the brake pedal, have an assistant open a bleeder valve on one of the wheels to simulate a brake failure. The light should go on.
    c. When your assistant closes the valve, the light should go out.
    d. Repeat the test on the other brake circuit.

If the light fails to light during one of the tests, check the circuit failure sender which screws into the master cylinder.

Overhaul

All Models

1. Mount the master cylinder in a vise. Use cloths to protect the cylinder from the vise jaws.
2. Using a small screwdriver, carefully pry out the lock ring in the end of the master cylinder.
3. Remove the stop plate and the complete primary piston assembly.
4. Unscrew the secondary piston stop bolt and blow the piston out with compressed air.
5. Remove the spring, spring seat, and the support washer.
6. Carefully clamp the primary piston in a vise. Slightly compress the spring and screw out the stroke limiting bolt.
7. Remove the primary piston stop sleeve, stop-bolt, spring, spring seat, and support washer.
8. Replace the used parts with those supplied in the overhaul kit.
9. Clean all metal parts in denatured alcohol and dry them with compressed air.
10. Check every part you are reusing. Pay close attention to the cylinder bores. If there is any scoring or rust, replace the master cylinder.
11. Lightly coat the bores and cups with brake fluid. Assemble the cylinder components in the sequence shown in the illustration.
12. Insert the secondary piston into the cylinder, along with the filler disc, primary cup, supporting washer, spring seat, and the spring.

    NOTE: *The large coil of the spring must face the bottom of the housing.*
13. Using a plastic rod or other nonmetallic tool, push the secondary piston into the housing until the stop-bolt and washer can be screwed in and tightened (7–9 ft lbs).

    NOTE: *Check the stop-bolt seating. It must be ahead of the secondary piston and the piston must move freely to the bottom of the housing.*
14. Assemble the filler disc, primary cup, and supporting washer onto the primary piston. Fasten the spring, spring seat, and stop sleeve to the piston with the stroke limiting bolt.
15. Assemble the remaining master cylinder components in a reverse order of disassembly. Ensure that the lock ring is fully seated and that the piston cups are

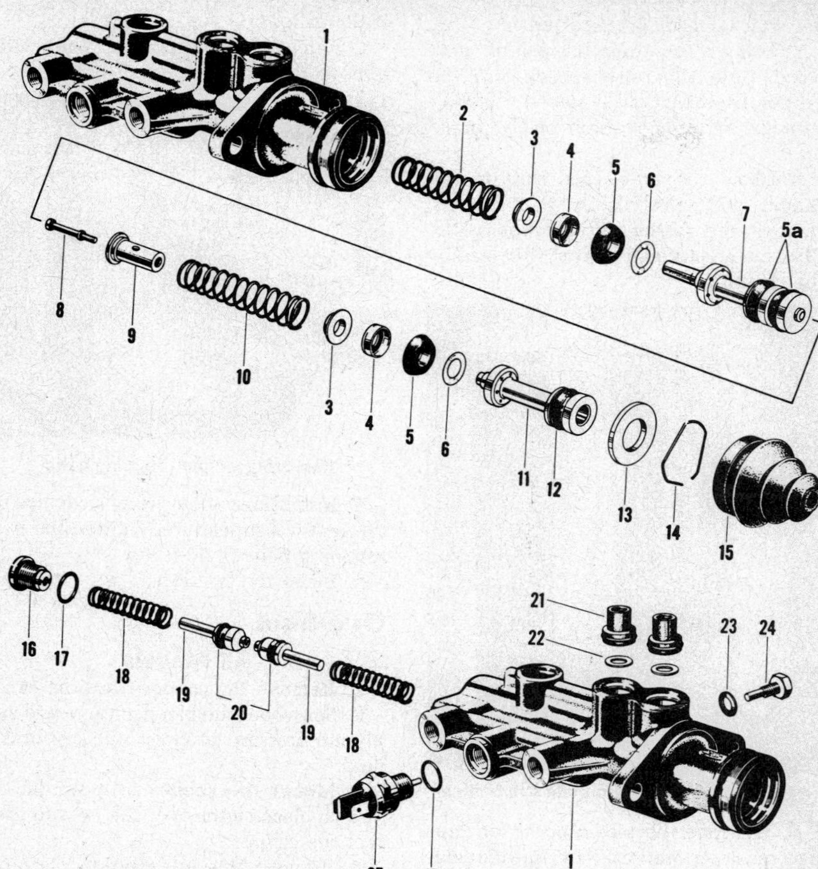

Exploded view of master cylinder

1. Housing
2. Secondary piston return spring
3. Spring seat
4. Supporting washer
5. Primary cup
5(a) Primary collar or separating collar
6. Filler disc
7. Secondary piston
8. Stroke limiting bolt
9. Travel stop
10. Primary piston return spring
11. Primary piston
12. Secondary cup
13. Stop plate
14. Lock ring
15. Dust boot
16. Bolt
17. O-ring
18. Spring
19. Piston
20. Piston cup
21. Grommet
22. Washer
23. Gasket
24. Stop bolt
25. Circuit failure sender

properly positioned.

16. Torque the cap bolt and brake failure warning sending unit to 11 ft lbs.

Pressure Regulator Valve

Removal and Installation

914 and 914/6

1. Have an assistant slightly depress the brake pedal to prevent the fluid in the reservoir from running out.
2. Disconnect the brake lines at the brake pressure regulator.
3. Remove the retaining bolts and remove the valve.
4. Install the regulator valve.
5. Bleed the brakes.

Checking and Adjustment

914 and 914/6

The brake pressure regulator is not repairable and must be replaced if defective. To check if the valve is operating, have an assistant depress the brake pedal while you hold your hand on the valve. When your assistant releases the brake pedal, you should feel a slight knock in the regulator. High pressure gauges are required to thoroughly check and adjust the valve. If you suspect the valve, replace it.

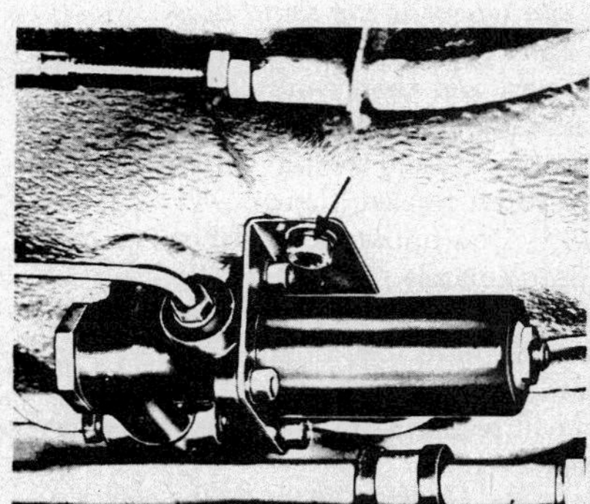

914 and 914/6 brake pressure regulator

Bleeding

Anytime a brake line has been disconnected, the hydraulic system should be bled. The brakes should also be bled when the pedal travel becomes unusually long ("soft pedal") or the car pulls to one side during braking. You will require one assistant to bleed the brakes. The proper bleeding sequence for 912 and 911 models is: left rear wheel (outer bleeder valve and then the inner), right rear wheel (outer bleeder valve and then the inner), right front wheel, and then left front wheel. 914 and 914/6 models use the following sequence: right rear, left rear, left front, and then right front.

NOTE: *If the system has been drained, first refill it with fresh brake fluid. Following the above sequence, open each bleeder valve ½ to ¾ of a turn and pump the brake pedal until fluid runs out of the valve. Proceed with the bleeding as outlined below.*

1. Remove the bleeder valve dust cover and install a rubber bleeder hose.

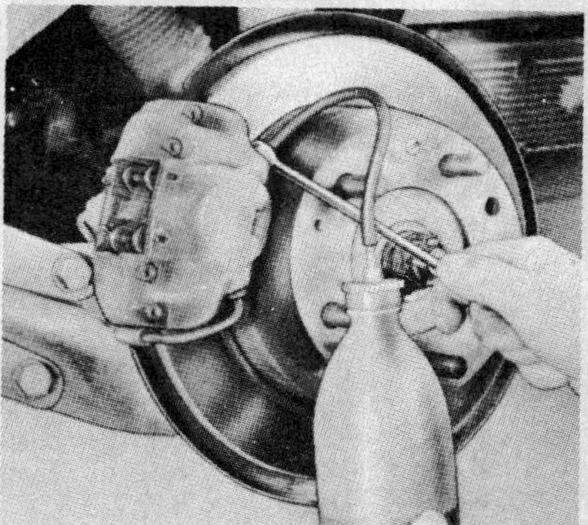

Brake bleeding

2. Insert the other end of the hose into a container about 1/3 full of brake fluid.
3. Have your assistant pump the brake pedal several times until the pedal pressure increases.
4. Hold the pedal under pressure and then start to open the bleeder valve about ½ to ¾ of a turn. At this point, have your assistant depress the pedal all the way and then quickly close the valve. The helper should allow the pedal to return slowly.

NOTE: *Keep a close check on the brake fluid in the reservoir and top it up as necessary throughout the bleeding process.*

5. Keep repeating this procedure until no more air bubbles can be seen coming from the hose in the brake fluid.
6. Remove the bleeder hose and install the dust cover.
7. Continue the bleeding at each wheel in sequence.

FRONT DISC BRAKES

Brake Disc Pads

Removal and Installation

Brake pads should be replaced when there is no visible clearance between the pads and the cross-spring or when they are worn to a thickness of 0.08 in. (2 mm) or less.

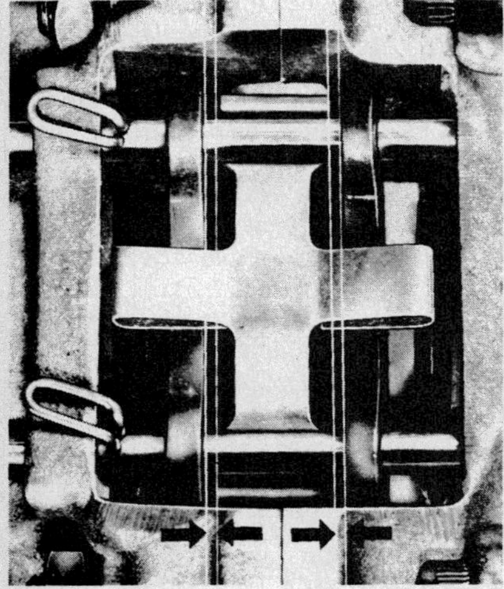

Brake pad wear indication

All Models

1. Jack up the front of the car and support it on stands. Remove the wheels.
2. Using pliers, pull out the pin retaining clips.

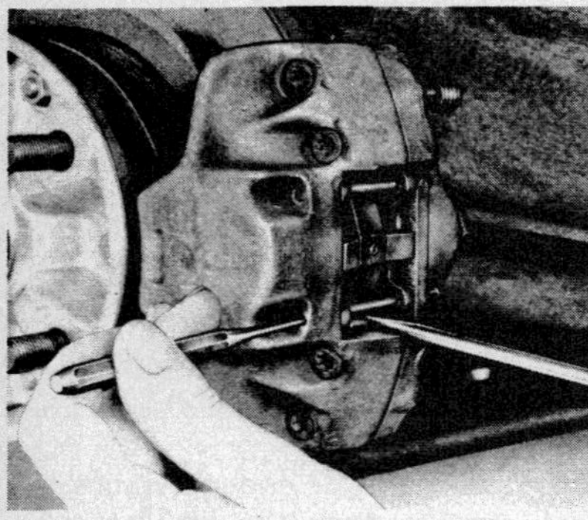

Retaining pin removal

3. While pressing down on the cross-spring, push the pad retaining pins out with a drift or small screwdriver.
4. Reference mark the positions of the brake pads if they are being reused.
5. Remove the brake pads from the caliper.

NOTE: *Porsche has a special tool for this purpose, P 86, but using a small drift or punch you can pry the pad out of the caliper until it can be gripped by a pair pliers and removed.*

6. Siphon out half of the brake fluid in the reservoir to prevent it from overflowing when the pistons are pushed in and new thicker pads are inserted.
7. Using a flat, smooth piece of hardwood, push the pistons back into the caliper. Do this carefully so that you don't damage either the piston or the brake disc.
8. Clean the brake pad slots in the caliper with alcohol. On 914 models, remove the piston anti-rotation plate. Blow out any foreign matter dislodged by the cleaning.

914 piston anti-rotation plate positioning

9. Examine the piston boots for damage or deterioration. Any questionable parts should be replaced.
10. Dress any ridges on the disc edge with crocus cloth.
11. On 914 models, install the anti-rotation plate onto the piston.
12. Install the brake pads into the caliper. Pads must be free in their slots, there should be no binding.

NOTE: *Replace used pads in the side of the caliper from which they were removed. When installing new pads, always replace the pads on the opposite wheel at the same time.*

13. Position a new cross-spring in the caliper, and then carefully tap the pad retaining pins into place with a small hammer. Install the pin clips. If the clips are rusty, replace them.
14. New brake pads must be run-in for approximately 100 miles. During this period, try not to apply the brakes extremely hard. Use them moderately and gradually during break-in. Failure to do so will result in the loss of full brake pad effectiveness.

Brake Calipers

Removal and Installation

All Models

1. Jack up the front of the car and support it on stands.
2. Remove the brake pads as outlined above.
3. Disconnect and plug the brake line at the caliper.
4. Remove the retaining bolts and remove the caliper.

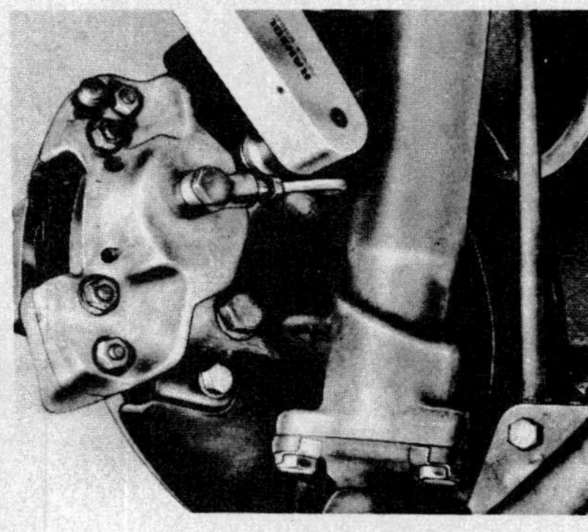

Removing caliper retaining bolts

5. Install the caliper using a reverse of the removal procedure. Tighten the two retaining bolts to 50 ft lbs.
6. Bleed the brakes.

Overhaul

All Models

1. Remove the caliper from the car.
2. Screw out the bleeder valve and apply air pressure to clean out any brake fluid.
3. Mount the caliper in a soft-jawed vise or place cloths over the jaws to protect the caliper.
4. Remove the anti-rotation plate on 914 models.
5. Using a screwdriver, pry out the retaining ring and remove the boot from one piston.

Removing piston retaining ring

6. Depress the other piston with a C-clamp and a flat piece of wood or metal. This setup will do the same job as Porsche tool P83.
7. Insert another flat piece of wood or metal in the caliper to protect the piston which is being removed. Apply an initial air pressure of 30 psi to the bleeder valve to force the piston from its bore in the caliper.

CAUTION: *Keep your hands away from the inside of the caliper. Air pressure of 147 psi produces an equivalent pressure of 550 lbs.*

8. When the piston pops out of the caliper, remove the rubber seal with a

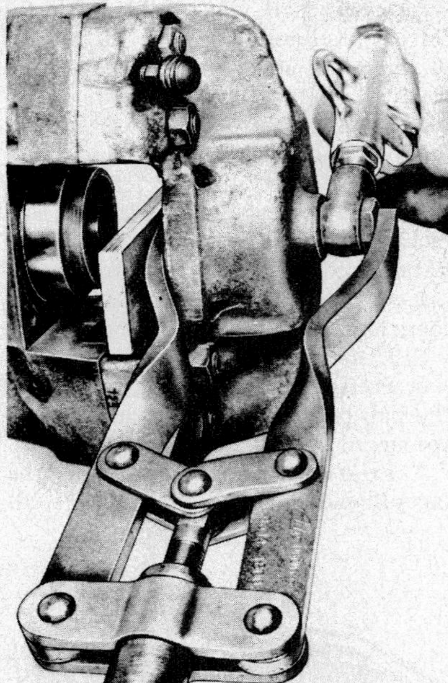

Forcing the piston out of the caliper

wood or plastic pin to avoid damaging the seal groove.

9. Clean all metal parts with denatured alcohol. Never use any mineral based solvents such as gasoline, kerosene, acetone, or the like. These solvents deteriorate rubber parts. Inspect the pistons and bores. They must be free of scoring and pitting. Replace the caliper if there is any damage.

10. Discard all rubber parts. Caliper rebuilding kits include new boots and seals which should be used as the caliper is reassembled.

11. Lightly coat the cylinder bore, piston, seals with a brake cylinder assembly paste.

12. Install the piston seal in the cylinder groove. Install the piston into its bore.

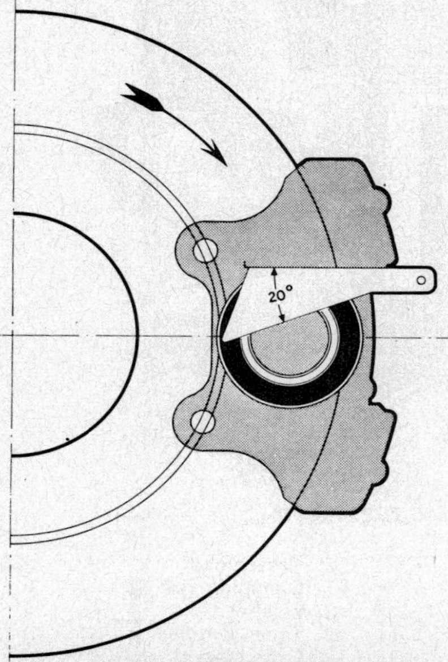

Piston alignment gauge

13. Fabricate a 20° piston alignment gauge, similar to the one in the illustration, from heavy cardboard. Using the gauge, position the step-down on the piston so that it faces the direction of brake disc rotation.

14. Wipe off any excess assembly paste on the piston and install the boot and retaining ring. Install the anti-rotation plate on 914 models.

15. Repeat the above operation on the second piston. Overhaul is complete at this point, unless the caliper half O-rings are leaking. In this case, the caliper must be split.

NOTE: *Light alloy calipers on some 911S models are one piece and cannot be disassembled. Do not remove the caliper side cover on these models.*

16. Remove the four caliper assembly bolts.

17. Remove the caliper cover housing. Remove the spacer plate on vented disc models.

18. Install two fresh O-rings in the fluid passages. Replace the assembly bolts and nuts. The outside bolts are shorter.

19. Align the halves and place the caliper in a soft-jawed vise. On 914 and 914/6 models, tighten the bolts to 7 ft lbs in the sequence shown. 912 and 911 models use the same tightening sequence, but are first torqued to 12.5 ft lbs and then final torqued to 25 ft lbs (6.5 and 13 ft lbs for rear calipers).

Brake Disc

Removal and Installation

912, 911, and 914/6

1. Jack up the front of the car and place it on stands. Remove the wheels.
2. Remove the brake caliper as outlined above.
3. Using two screwdrivers, pry off the hub cap.
4. Loosen the screw in the hub clamp nut. Unscrew the clamp nut and thrust washer.
5. Grip the disc with both hands and give it a sharp pull to remove it. A stubborn disc should be removed with a puller. Never strike the disc with a hammer.
6. Match mark the hub and disc, if the disc is being reused, and separate them.
7. The disc is installed in a reverse order of removal. Install the disc-to-hub bolts from the inside out and tighten the nuts to 17 ft lbs.
8. Install the disc/hub assembly on the spindle. Install the thrust washer and clamp nut.
9. Install the brake caliper.
10. Adjust the wheel bearings as outlined below.
11. Bleed the brakes.

914

1. Jack up the front of the car and sup-

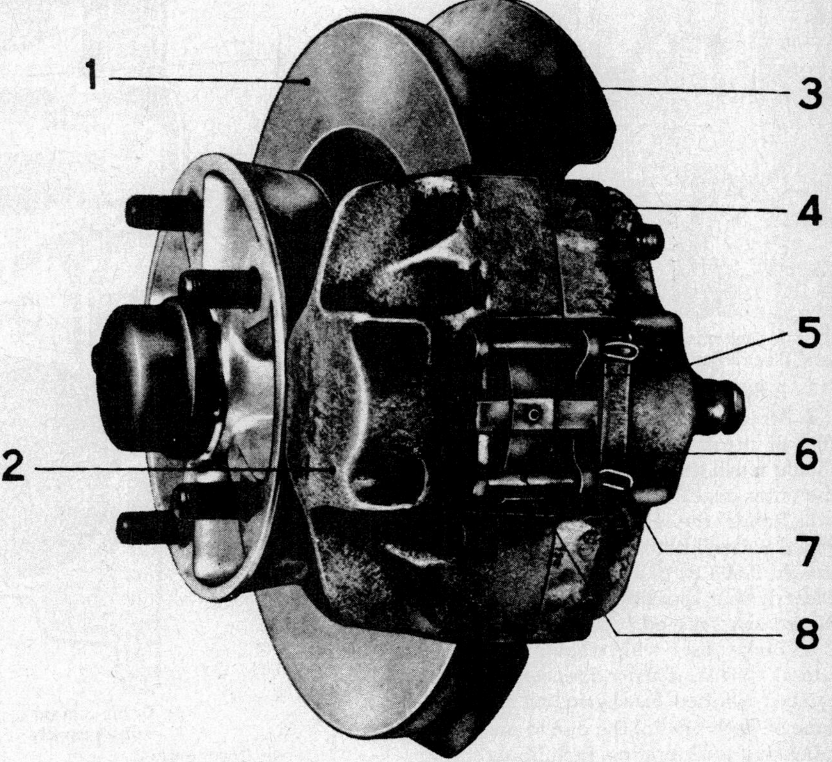

912 and 911 front disc brake components

1. Brake disc
2. Caliper cover
3. Disc shroud
4. Caliper base housing
5. Brake pad segment
6. Cross-spring
7. Pin retainer
8. Retaining pin

port it safely on stands. Remove the wheels.

2. Remove the brake caliper as described above.

3. Pry off the hub cap.

4. Loosen the screw in the hub clamp nut and unscrew the clamp nut.

5. Pull off the brake disc along with the inner and outer wheel bearings.

6. Installation is the reverse of removal.

7. Adjust the wheel bearings as outlined below.

8. Bleed the hydraulic system.

Inspection and Checking

Brake discs may be checked for lateral runout while installed on the car. This check will require a dial indicator gauge and stand to mount it on the caliper. Porsche has a special tool for this purpose which mounts the dial indicator in the brake pad slots of the caliper, but a dial indicator can also be mounted on the shaft of a C-clamp attached to the outside of the caliper.

Dial indicator set-up for determining lateral disc run-out

1. Adjust the front wheel bearings.

2. Mount the dial indicator using either of the above methods. The feeler should touch the disc about ½ in. below the outer edge.

3. Rotate the disc and observe the gauge. Lateral runout (wobble) must not exceed 0.008 in. (0.2 mm). A disc which exceeds this specification must be replaced or refinished.

4. Brake discs which have excessive lateral runout, sharp ridges, or scoring can be refinished. Final grinding must be done on both sides of the disc to prevent squeaking and vibrating. Refinishing specifications are provided below. Discs which have only light grooves and are otherwise acceptable can be used without refinishing.

NOTE: *Ventilated brake discs (911 and 914/6) are balanced by special clips inserted into the vent fins of the disc. Do not remove the clips or the original balance will be lost.*

Wheel Bearings

Removal and Installation

912, 911, and 914/6

NOTE: *The inner bearing, seal, and outer bearing may be removed and lubricated once the hub/disc assembly is off the car. If after cleaning, the bearings are noticeably worn or damaged they should be replaced along with their races. If the bearings are satisfactory, skip the race removal steps.*

1. Remove the brake disc/hub assembly.

2. Match mark the hub and disc for correct reassembly, remove the five assembly bolts, and separate the hub and disc.

3. Pry the inner seal out of the hub. Remove the inner bearing and outer bearing.

4. Wash the bearings in solvent and blow them dry. Examine the bearings for pitting, scoring, or other damage. Replace the bearing and race as a unit if there is any question as to their condition.

5. Heat the wheel hub to 250°–300° F.

6. Press the inner bearing race out of the hub on a press table, using suitable spacers to prevent damaging the hub.

7. Press out the outer bearing race, using suitable spacers and a support fab-

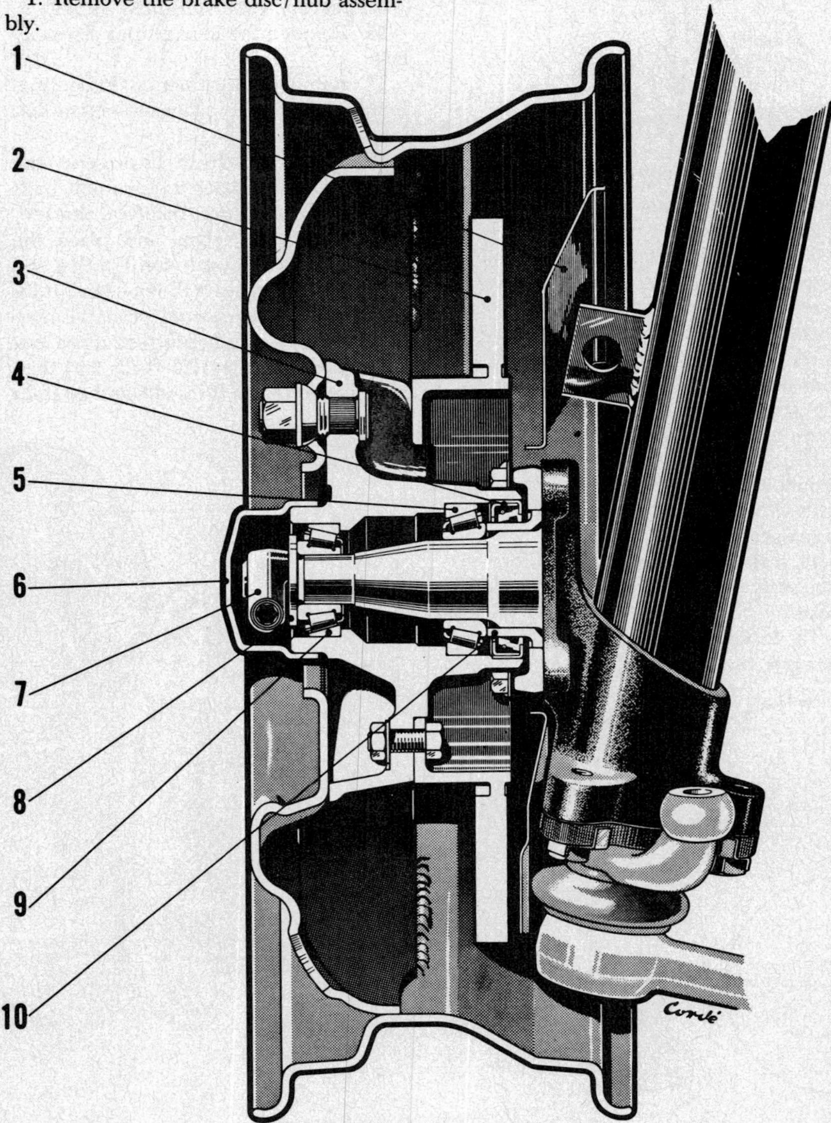

Cross-section of 911 and 912 brake disc/hub assembly

1. Cover shroud
2. Brake disc
3. Front wheel hub
4. Seal
5. Tapered roller bearing
6. Grease cap
7. Clamping nut
8. Washer
9. Tapered roller bearing
10. Distance ring

ricated from the accompanying drawing.

8. Press a new inner bearing race into the hub and then press in a new outer bearing race.

9. Pack the bearings with a lithium multipurpose grease.

10. Align the match marks and install the hub on the disc. Insert the assembly bolts from the inside out and tighten them to 17 ft lbs.

11. Lightly coat the spindle with grease. Fill the hub with about 2 oz of grease. Lubricate and install the bearings.

12. Grease the sealing edges of a new inner oil seal and carefully tap it into place. The oil seal must be flush with the hub.

13. Install the hub/disc assembly on the car.

14. Adjust the wheel bearings.

914

Wheel bearing procedures are similar to those for the above models, except that the hub and disc are one piece and the bearing races can be driven out with a brass or copper drift.

Adjustment

Check and adjust the front wheel bearings when the car has not been run for a few hours, the bearings will be cold then.

All Models

1. The front wheel bearings are correctly adjusted when the thrust washer can be moved slightly sideways under light pressure from a screwdriver, but no bearing play is evident when the wheel hub is shaken axially.

2. Jack up the front of the car, support it on stands, and remove the wheels. Turn the hub several times to seat the bearings.

3. Pry the hub cap off with a screwdriver and perform the check described in step 1.

NOTE: *Don't press the screwdriver against the hub. Hold it lightly in your hand so you get a better feel.*

4. If the bearings require an adjustment, loosen the allen screw and turn the clamp nut in or out as necessary.

5. Tighten the clamp nut allen screw to 11 ft lbs without altering the adjusted position of the clamp nut.

6. Double check the adjustment and readjust, if necessary.

7. Give the clamp nut and thrust washer a light coating of lithium grease. Tap the hub cap into place with a plastic or rubber mallet.

8. Install the wheels and lower the car.

Checking wheel bearing play

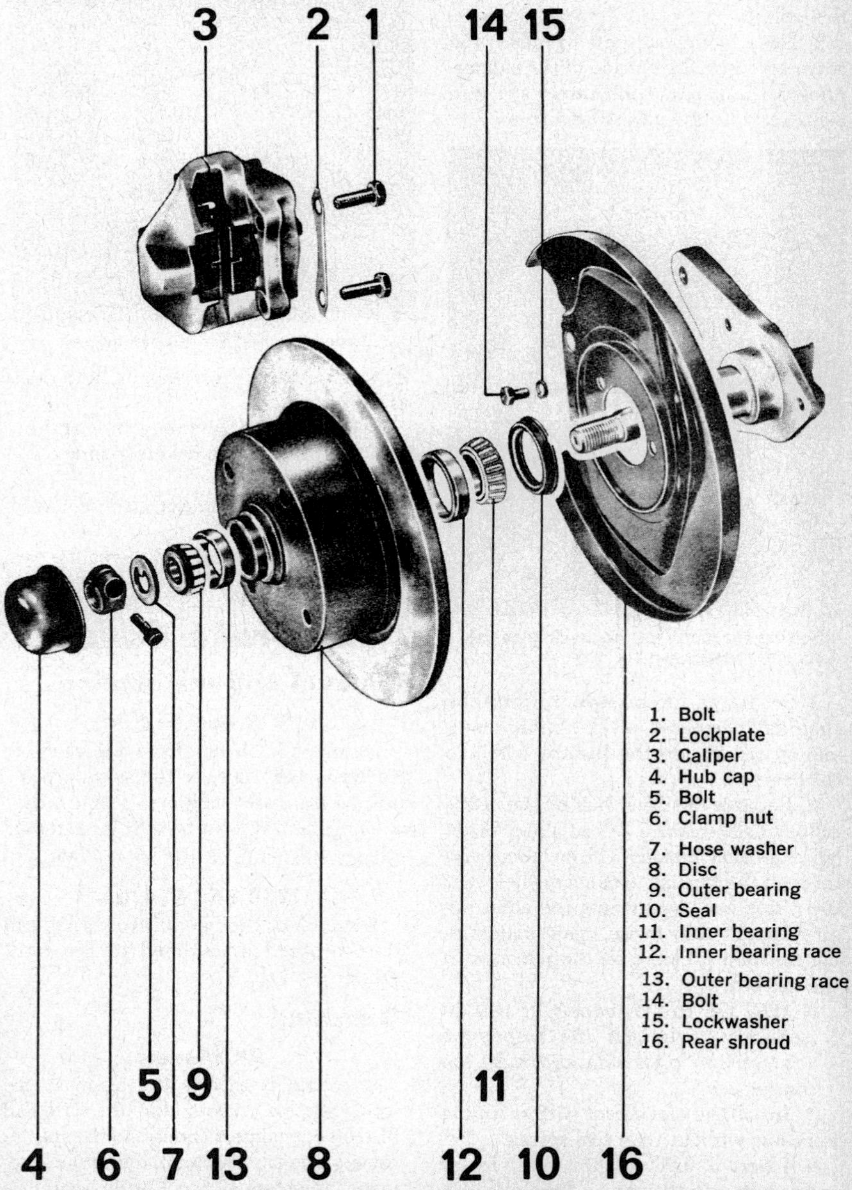

Final tightening of the wheel clamp nut —check play again before installing hub cap

1. Bolt
2. Lockplate
3. Caliper
4. Hub cap
5. Bolt
6. Clamp nut
7. Hose washer
8. Disc
9. Outer bearing
10. Seal
11. Inner bearing
12. Inner bearing race
13. Outer bearing race
14. Bolt
15. Lockwasher
16. Rear shroud

Exploded view of 914 brake disc/hub assembly

REAR DRUM BRAKES

Disc Brake Pads

Removal and Installation

912 and 911

Brake pad removal and installation is identical to that for front pads.

914 and 914/6

Removal of the rear brake pads is the same as that for the front pads. Installation, however, differs due to the automatic adjuster mechanism necessary for the handbrake.

1. Using two flat pieces of hardwood, or Porsche tool P 83, lightly pre-load the pistons. Unless you have four hands, an assistant becomes just about a necessity at this point.
2. Have your assistant remove the cover screw on the outside of the caliper. Loosen the locknut and insert a 4 mm allen key into the adjusting screw.

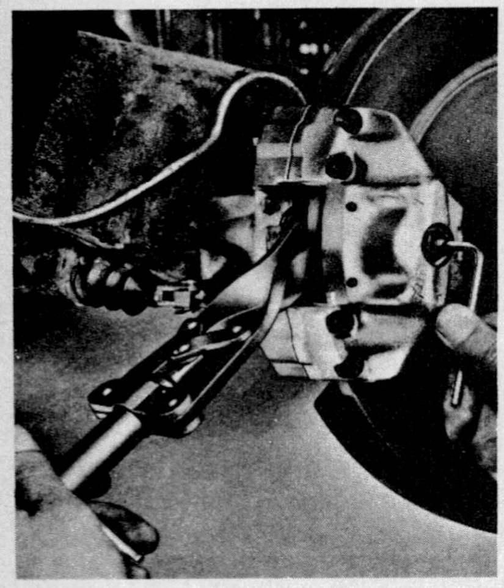

Setting the outer piston back (special Porsche tool shown)

3. Set the piston back by turning the allen key clockwise, all the while maintaining tension on the pistons with the flat boards.
4. Remove the cover bolt on the inside caliper half. Insert a 4 mm allen socket (an extension handle will be necessary) through the trailing arm access hole. Set the piston back by turning the adjusting screw counterclockwise, again maintaining constant pressure on the piston with the flat board.

NOTE: *On 914/6 models, it will be necessary to detach the suspension strut on the right side and raise the trailing arm.*

5. Install the brake pads with retaining pins, but without the cross-spring.
6. Insert a 0.08 in. (0.2 mm) feeler gauge between the pad and the disc. Adjust the pistons for that much clearance

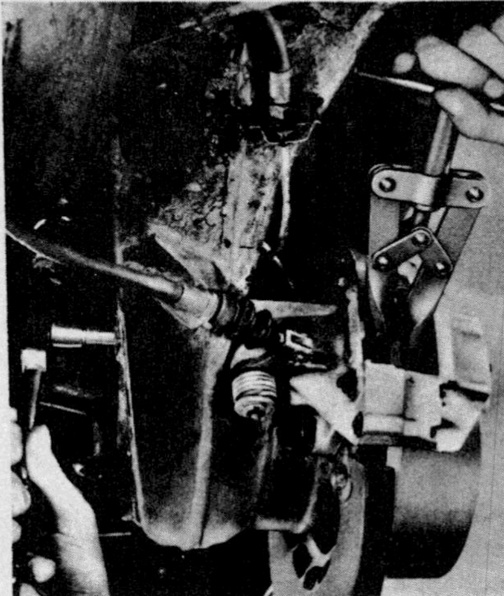

Setting the inner piston back

Adjusting pad and disc clearance

by turning the allen screws on both sides as necessary.

7. Remove the retaining pins and install them again with the cross-spring. Install the pin clips.
8. Install the suspension strut on 914/6 models.
9. Install the wheel and lower the car.

Disc Brake Caliper

Removal and Installation

912 and 911

Remove the shields from the rear of the brake and then use the same procedure as the front calipers. Tighten the caliper retaining bolts to 44 ft lbs and the shield bolts to 18 ft lbs.

914 and 914/6

Disconnect the handbrake cables and then proceed as outlined in the front caliper section.

Overhaul

All Models

Overhaul is exactly the same as the front calipers, except that the 914 and 914/6 rear calipers should not be split as their is a possibility of damaging the automatic adjuster. If the O-ring seals are leaking, replace the caliper.

Brake Discs

Removal and Installation

All Models

1. Remove the rear shroud on 912 and 911 models. Detach the handbrake cables on 914 and 914/6 models.
2. Remove the brake caliper.
3. Remove both countersunk screws from the disc and pull it off the car.
4. Installation is the reverse of the removal procedure.

Inspection and Checking

All Models

The rear brake disc procedure is similar to that for the front, except that the disc must be fastened to the hub. Install the wheel nuts on 912, 911, and 914/6 models and tighten them in a criss-cross pattern to 72 ft lbs. On 914 models, install the wheel bolts and tighten them to 80 ft lbs.

Handbrake

The 912 and 911 models are equipped with a separate handbrake system. The center, pull-up lever mechanically operates a pair of brake shoes inside each rear disc, which act as drums through a pot-shaped center section.

The 914 and 914/6 handbrake mechanically applies the rear service brakes. The rear calipers are equipped with automatic adjusting mechanisms.

Cable

Adjustment

912 and 911

1. Jack up the rear of the car and support it on stands. Remove the wheels.
2. Release the handbrake lever.
3. Push the brake pads away from the disc so that it can be turned by hand.
4. Loosen the cable adjusting nuts to release tension.
5. Insert a screwdriver into the disc access hole and rotate the handbrake star wheel until the disc can no longer be

Adjusting the handbrake

turned by hand.

6. Repeat this operation on the other side.

7. Readjust the cable nuts to take up the slack.

8. Pull up the center tunnel cover and handbrake lever boot at the rear. By looking through the two inspection holes, see if the cable equalizer is exactly perpendicular to the car's centerline.

9. If the equalizer positioning is off, correct it by loosening or tightening the cable adjusting nuts. Tighten the locknuts after the adjustment is correct.

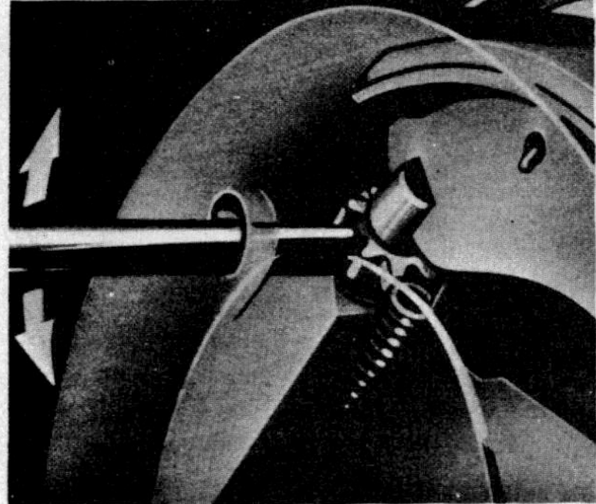

Handbrake star wheel adjustment

10. Back off each brake star wheel by four or five teeth until the disc can be turned by hand.

11. Check the handbrake lever clearance. There should be a slight clearance at the lever. The handbrake should be set when the lever is pulled up.

12. After completing the handbrake adjustment, depress the brake pedal several times to reposition the rear caliper pistons. Check the fluid level in the reservoir and top it up, if necessary.

Removal and Installation

1. Jack up the rear of the car and support it on stands. Remove the wheels.
2. Remove the center tunnel cover and handbrake lever boot.
3. Remove the heater control knob.
4. Undo the handbrake support housing bolts.
5. Unscrew the heater control lever nut. Remove the cup spring, discs, and the lever.
6. Slightly raise the handbrake support housing. Snap off the retaining clip and pull out the cable equalizing stud.
7. Disconnect the handbrake light switch wire.
8. Remove the handbrake support housing.
9. Detach the cables from the cable equalizer.
10. Remove the rear brake calipers.
11. Remove the rear brake discs and spacer rings.
12. Remove the cotter pin, castellated nut, and disc from each cable. Pull the cables toward the center of the car.
13. Pull the cables out from the center tunnel in the passenger compartment.
14. Lubricate the replacement cables with multipurpose grease and then feed them into the tube.
15. Place a washer between the spacer sleeve and the brake expander. Place another washer under the castellated nut.
16. Tighten the nut until a new cotter pin can be inserted. Make sure that the brake expander is correctly seated.
17. Install the brake discs and calipers.
18. Connect the handbrake light wire to the switch.
19. Insert the heater control lever into the handbrake support housing.
20. Install and clip the equalizer stud. Ensure that the handbrake cables are correctly seated.
21. Torque the handbrake support housing bolts to 18 ft lbs.
22. Install a friction disc, the heater control lever, another friction disc, pressure disc, cup spring, and the nut.
23. Tighten the nut so that the lever doesn't slip back when the heater is on full, and yet isn't too tight to operate.
24. Bleed the brakes.
25. Check the handbrake adjustment.
26. Install the wheels and lower the car.

Brake Shoes

Removal and Installation

912 and 911

1. Jack up the rear of the car and support it on stands. Remove the wheels.
2. Remove the brake calipers.
3. Detach the brake discs.
4. Remove the cotter pin, castellated nut, and washer from the brake cable.
5. Pull the cable out toward the center of the car.
6. Remove the expander and spring.
7. Depress the upper spring and twist the holddown cup to remove it and the spring.
8. Pull the brake shoe outward and remove the pin through the rear.
9. Using a screwdriver, raise the upper brake shoe and remove the star wheel assembly. Unhook the spring.

Star wheel assembly removal

10. Repeat steps 7 and 8 for the bottom shoe.
11. Unhook the front return spring and remove both shoes.

NOTE: *Complete the brake shoe removal and installation one side at a time, so the opposite side can be used as a reference.*

12. Clean all metal parts in alcohol. Contaminated or worn brake shoes should be replaced.
13. Insert the brake cable from the back and slide the inner part of the expander onto the cable. Don't forget to install a washer between the spacer tube and the expander.
14. Install the front return spring (two coils) so that the coils point towards the center of the axle.
15. Install the upper and lower brake shoes.
16. Install the pins, springs, and holddown cups.
17. Insert the inner expander into the seats in the brake shoes.
18. Raise the upper brake shoe with a screwdriver and install the star wheel assembly so that the adjusting sprocket is on both brakes shoes.
19. Install the other brake return spring.
20. Turn the cable adjusting nut in the tube all the way back.
21. Install the spring, second expander half, washer, and castellated nut. Tighten the nut until a new cotter pin can be installed.

Correct handbrake lining and spring installation

22. Install the brake discs and calipers.
23. Bleed the hydraulic system.
24. Adjust the handbrake.
25. Install the wheels and lower the car.

CHASSIS ELECTRICAL

Heater

The primary heating system in all models uses fresh air drawn in by the engine cooling fan, directs it to heat exchangers around the exhaust pipes, through a muffler, and distributes warm air into the passenger compartment via a system of ducts. A variable speed blower, located in the front luggage compartment on all models, speeds the circulation of heated and/or fresh air. 914 models are equipped with a blower motor in the engine compartment. An auxiliary, gas-fired heater is an option on 912 and 911 models.

Blower

Removal and Installation

912 and 911

1. Disconnect the battery cables.
2. Remove the front luggage compartment carpeting.
3. Open the blower compartment lid. Remove the steering shaft cover.
4. Disconnect the electrical wiring.
5. Loosen the hose clamps and disconnect the hoses from the blower.
6. Pull the blower off the air intake stack and remove it from the car.
7. Install the blower on the intake stack. Make sure that the sealing ring is correctly seated.
8. Fasten the hoses on the blower and tighten the hose clamps.
9. Connect the electrical wiring.
10. Install the steering shaft cover and close the blower compartment lid.
11. Cement the carpeting to the right front side panel.
12. Connect the battery cables.

914 and 914/6

1. Remove the front luggage compartment lid.
2. Remove the fuel tank.
3. Unscrew the mounting bolt on each end of the fresh air intake box.
4. Loosen the hose clamps on the two air hoses and pull them from the blower.
5. Squeeze the corbin clamps on the two water drain hoses and pull them from the fresh air box.
6. Loosen the cable clamp nut and detach the cable from the blower by pushing the retaining clip off. Be careful not to bend the cable.
7. Disconnect the electrical wiring.
8. Remove the fresh air box and blower as an assembly.
9. Unscrew the attaching bolts and separate the fresh air box and blower.
10. Install the blower in the fresh air box.
11. Install the cable on the blower. The cable casing should protrude from the retaining clip by about ¼ in.
12. Install the fresh air box/blower assembly in a reverse manner of removal. Adjust the cable, if necessary.

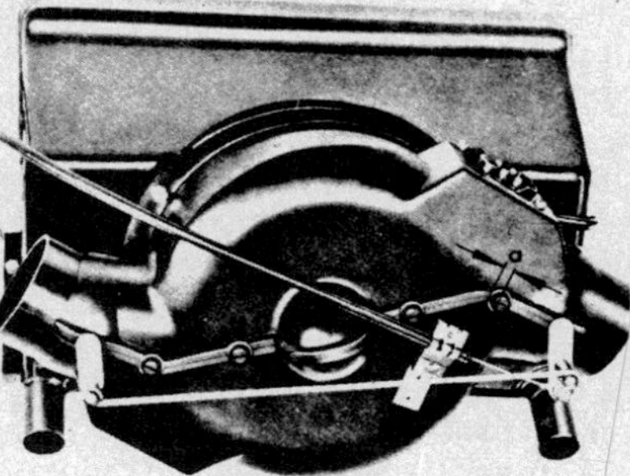

Correct blower cable installation

Auxiliary Heater

The 912 and 911 auxiliary heater assembly is mounted in the front luggage compartment in the place of the standard blower.

Removal and Installation

1. Jack up the front of the car and support it on stands.
2. Disconnect the battery cables.
3. Remove the luggage compartment lid.
4. Open the heater compartment lid.
5. Loosen the clamp on the hot air hose and pull the hose off the heater unit.
6. Remove the three mixture pump retaining bolts and remove them from the bracket.
7. Disconnect the fuel lines and wiring from the pump.
8. Working under the car, loosen the front muffler clamp. Disconnect the exhaust pipe and bend it down and out of the way.
9. Remove the muffler clamp and slide the white collar onto the heater unit.
10. Disconnect all wiring to the heater and carefully lift it out of the car.
11. Installation is the reverse of the removal procedure. Ensure that the wiring is correctly reinstalled.

Windshield Wipers

Motor and Linkage

Removal and Installation

912 and 911

The windshield wiper motor and linkage are located in front of the instrument panel.

1. Pull back the front luggage compartment carpeting. Disconnect the battery cables.
2. Remove the retaining clip and air duct. Remove the fresh air box.
3. Disconnect the blower motor wires.
4. Remove the wiper arms. Remove the rubber bushings under the arms and unscrew the shaft retaining nuts.
5. Pull the motor and linkage down as a unit. Separate the motor and linkage.
6. Installation is the reverse of the removal procedure.

914 and 914/6

The windshield wiper motor and linkage are mounted on a common frame.

1. Disconnect the battery.
2. Unscrew the retaining nut on each wiper arm.
3. Remove the rubber bearing cap.
4. Unscrew the retaining nut and remove the washers and seals.
5. Remove the fuel tank.
6. Remove the evaporative emission charcoal canister.
7. Remove the fresh air box and blower as previously described.
8. Remove the anti-vibration bearing retaining nut from under the instrument panel. Make sure that the bearing isn't twisted.
9. Pull the windshield wiper assembly down and out.
10. Disconnect the electrical wires.
11. To separate the motor and linkage:
    a. Remove the wiper motor shaft nut and washer.
    b. Using a puller, remove the linkage drive crank from the motor shaft.
    c. Remove the three retaining bolts and remove the motor.
12. To install the motor onto the linkage:
    a. The motor must be in the park position. Ground the motor and connect terminals 53 and 53a to a positive battery wire.
    b. Run the motor for a few seconds and then disconnect terminal 53. The motor will be parked.
    c. Position the drive crank parallel to the drive rod.
    d. Attach the motor with a washer and nut. Install the three retaining bolts.
13. Connect the electrical wiring.
14. Install the wiper arms in a reverse order of removal. Ensure that they are in the parked position.
15. Install the fresh air box/blower assembly.
16. Connect the battery.

911 Rear Window Wiper

1. Pull the wiper arm back off the rear window.
2. Open the engine compartment lid.
3. Disconnect the wiper motor electrical wiring.
4. Disconnect the wiper arm linkage at the bellcrank.
5. Remove the three wiper motor bracket bolts and remove the motor/-linkage assembly.
6. Install the wiper motor/linkage assembly in a reverse order of removal.
7. Adjust the linkage at the bellcrank for correct wiper operation.

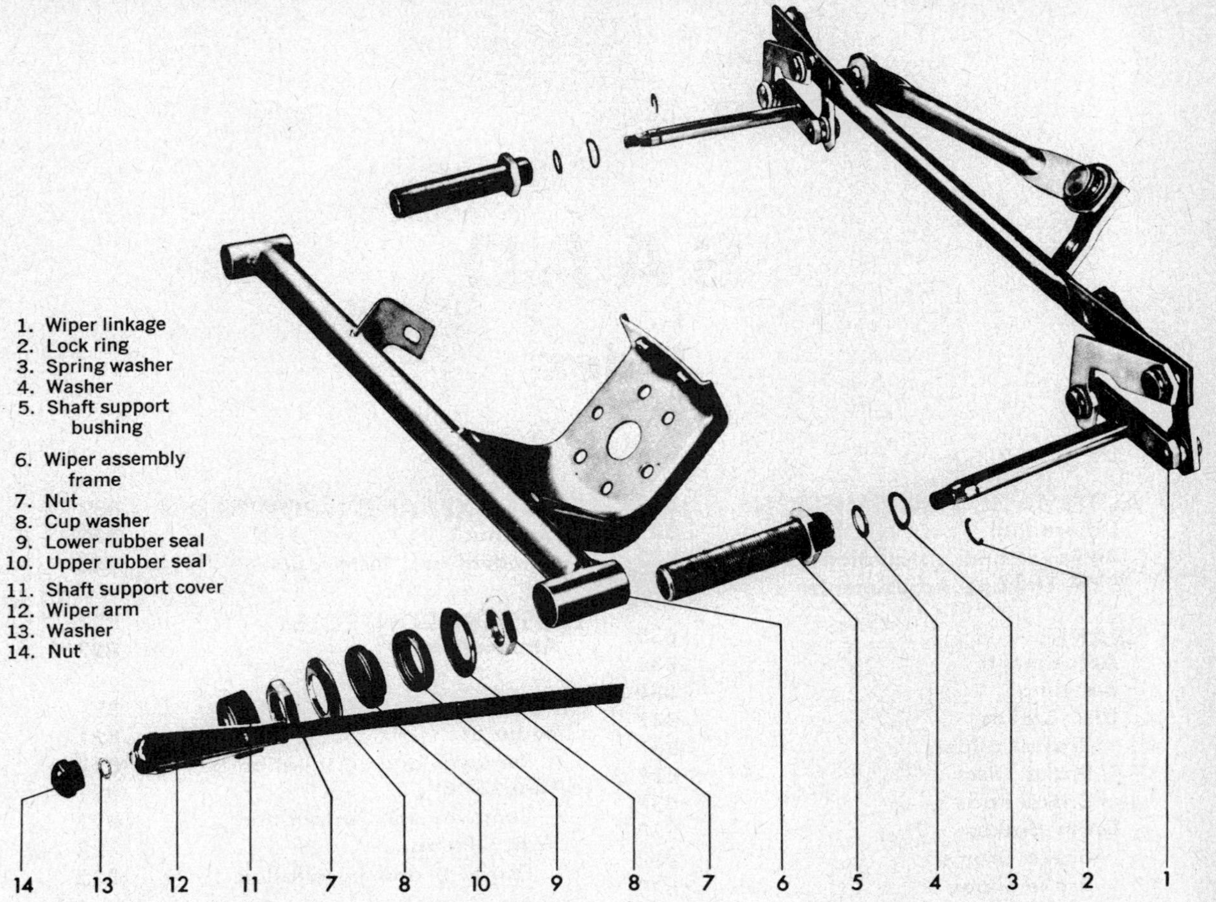

1. Wiper linkage
2. Lock ring
3. Spring washer
4. Washer
5. Shaft support bushing
6. Wiper assembly frame
7. Nut
8. Cup washer
9. Lower rubber seal
10. Upper rubber seal
11. Shaft support cover
12. Wiper arm
13. Washer
14. Nut

14 13 12 11 7 8 10 9 8 7 6 5 4 3 2 1

914 and 914/6 windshield wiper assembly

Instrument Panel

Removal and Installation

1969 912 and 911

1. Pull back the front luggage compartment carpet.

2. Detach the electrical wires from the gauge being removed. In the case of the speedometer, also disconnect the cable from the gauge.

3. Remove the small knurled nuts which retain the gauge, withdraw the retaining clamp, and carefully remove the gauge from the instrument panel.

4. Install the replacement gauge using the reverse of the removal procedure.

1970–73 911

Beginning with 1970, the gauges are mounted in individual rubber rings.

1. Pry the gauge out until you can grip it firmly, and then pull it out of the instrument panel.

2. Disconnect the wiring and/or cable and remove the gauge.

3. Connect the wiring or cable and position the gauge in its opening.

4. Align the gauge and then push it into place.

1970-1973 911 instrument removal

NOTE: *Use the later model rubber rings when reinstalling gauges in 1969 models.*

914 and 914/6

1. Disconnect the battery.

2. Remove the steering wheel as outlined in the "Steering" section.

3. Remove the four Phillips retaining screws.

4. Disconnect the speedometer cable and the trip odometer cable.

5. Pull the instrument panel out.

6. Individual gauges are retained by rubber rings. Push the gauge out towards the front to remove it.

7. Be sure that the wires are correctly reinstalled on the gauge.

8. Install the instrument panel in a reverse order of removal.

Fuse Box Location

The 911 and 912 fuse box is located in the left front of the luggage compartment. The 914 and 914/6 fuse box is located under the instrument panel to the left of the steering column.

914 and 914/6 instrument panel service

SAAB

Index

INTRODUCTION

The SAAB, a product of the Swedish aircraft firm SAAB Aktiebolag, was first introduced in 1949 to meet the demand for economical, dependable automobiles in the immediate post-war period. Designated the Model 92, the original design proved so sound that it has lasted to this day in the form of the Model 96, and its station wagon version, the Model 95. The Sonett, SAAB's sports car, shares many components with the Monte Carlo 850 and V4 models.

The SAAB 99, a new and entirely different design from earlier SAAB models, was made available to the public in 1969, after extensive development. A newly designed, aerodynamic sedan body, and an in-line, overhead cam four cylinder engine, designed by Ricardo Engineering in England are used. The Model 99 is the largest, most powerful SAAB yet produced.

In 1970, a fully automatic transmission coupled with electronic fuel injection was made available. In 1971 a four door version and electronic fuel injection with the standard manual transmission were made optional. The electronic fuel injection, manufactured by Bosch, improves engine performance and driveability, while reducing harmful pollutant emissions.

In 1973, SAAB started making their own overhead cam, four cylinder engine for the SAAB 99. Basic design is very similiar to past models, except for minor modifications made to the internal machining of the engine.

SAAB 96 sedan

SAAB 95 station wagon

SAAB 96—1973 model

SAAB 99 4 door

SAAB 99EMS 2 door

SAAB Sonnet

SERIAL NUMBER IDENTIFICATION

SAAB

The chassis number is stamped on a plate attached to the firewall under the hood, as well as on the left-hand side of the support member underneath the front edge of the back seat. On 1969–73 models, however, the number is embossed on a tab visible through the driver's side windshield.

SAAB 99

The vehicle serial number is stamped both on a plate located at the lower left-hand corner of the windshield, and on the left body sill.

Vehicle serial number and paint number location—SAAB 95, 96.

1. Serial number sign
2. Paint color code sign

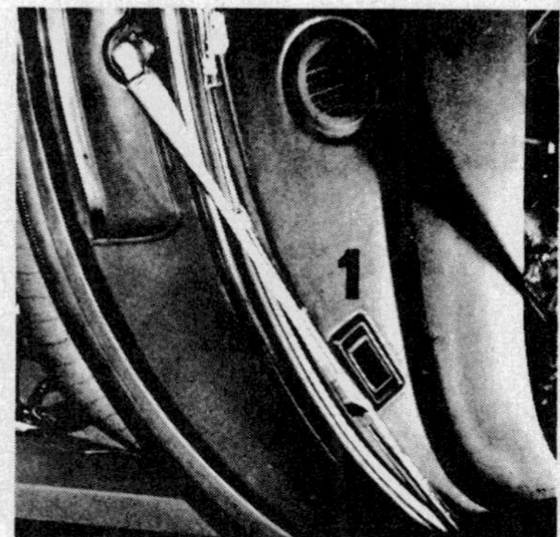

Vehicle serial number—SAAB 99

Engine Number Identification

On all V-4 engines, the number is on the block, directly forward of the left valve cover.

The Saab 99, with the OHC engine, has its engine number located on a boss at the left rear of the engine, just below the valve cover. On 1970–73 models, the engine number is located below the No. 1 and 2 spark plugs.

Engine serial number—V-4 engine

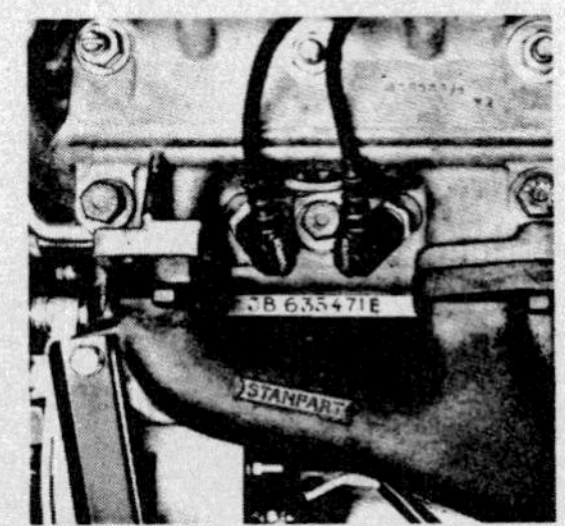

Engine serial number—OHC engine, 1970-73.

Engine serial number—OHC engine, 1969 location.

GENERAL ENGINE SPECIFICATIONS

Year	Model	Engine Displace. Cu. In. (cc)	Carburetor Type	Horsepower @ RPM	Torque @ RPM	Bore & Stroke (in.)	Com-press. Ratio	Oil Pressure (PSI)
1967-70	All (except V-4 Saab 99)	91.4 (1498)	Autolite 1 bbl. Down-draft	65 @ 4700	85 @ 2500	3.54 x 2.32	9.0:1	47-55.5
1971-73	All (except V-4 Saab 99)	103.6 (1698)	Autolite 1 bbl. Down-draft	65 @ 4700	85 @ 2500	3.54 x 2.63	8.0:1	47-55.5
1969-70	Saab 99 (only)	OHC 104.2 (1709)	Zenith-Stromberg	80 @ 5200	94 @ 3000	3.288 x 3.017	9.0:1	Single Rotary Type 54-60
			Bosch Fuel Injection	87 @ 5200	95 @ 3000			Dual Rotary Type 47-57
1971-72	Saab 99	OHC 113.1 (1854)	Zenith-Stromberg	88 @ 5000	108 @ 3000	3.425 x 3.017	9.0:1	Single Rotary Type 54-60
			Bosch Fuel Injection	95 @ 5200	105 @ 3200			Dual Rotary Type 47-57
1973	Saab 99	OHC 121.1 (1985)	Zenith-Stromberg	—	—	3.54 x 3.07	8.7:1	—

— Not applicable

TUNE-UP SPECIFICATIONS

NOTE If these specifications differ from those on the engine compartment stickers, use the sticker figure

Year	Model	Engine Displacement (cc)	SPARK PLUGS Type	SPARK PLUGS Gap	DISTRIBUTOR Point Dwell (deg)	DISTRIBUTOR Point Gap (in.)	Basic Ignition Timing (deg)	Intake Valve Opens (deg)	Fuel Pump Pressure PSI	Idle Speed rpm	VALVE CLEARANCE (warm) Intake	VALVE CLEARANCE (warm) Exhaust
1967	Sonnett II	3 cyl. 850	MGV 260 T31S	0.022-0.024	75-82	0.014-0.018	10 BTDC	—	2.1-3.5	600-750	—	—
	95 & 96	3 cyl. 850	M 240 T1	0.032	75-82	0.014-0.018	10 BTDC	—	2.1-3.5	600-750	—	—
	95, 96 Sonnett	V-4 1498	①	0.024-0.028	50 ± 2	0.016	6 BTDC	21 BTDC	3.4-4.3	600	0.014	0.016
1968	95, 96 Sonnett	V-4 1498	①	0.024-0.028	50 ± 2	0.016	10 BTDC	21 BTDC	3.4-4.3	900	0.014	0.016
1969-70	95, 96 Sonnett	V-4 1498	①	0.024-0.028	50 ± 2	0.016	6 BTDC	21 BTDC	3.4-4.3	900	0.014	0.016
1971-73	95, 96 Sonnett	V-4 1698	①	0.024-0.028	50 ± 2	0.016	3 BTDC	N.A.	3.4-4.3	900	0.014	0.016
1969-71	Saab 99	Carburetor 1709	②	0.024-0.028	40 ± 2	0.012-0.016	9 BTDC	12 BTDC	2.15-2.9	800	0.008-0.010	0.016-0.018
	Saab 99	Fuel Injected 1709	②	0.024-0.028	50 ± 2	0.014 (min.)	5 BTDC	12 BTDC	—	800	0.008-0.010	0.016-0.018
1971-72	Saab 99	Carburetor 1854	②	0.024-0.028	40 ± 2	0.012-0.016	9 BTDC	12 BTDC	2.15-2.9	800	0.008-0.010	0.016-0.018
	Saab 99	Fuel Injected 1854	②	0.024-0.028	50 ± 2	0.014 (min.)	5 BTDC	16 BTDC	—	800	0.008-0.010	0.016-0.018
1973	Saab 99	Carburetor 1985	②	0.025-0.030	40 ± 2	0.012-0.016	14 BTDC	N.A.	—	800 std 850 auto	0.006-0.012③	0.016-0.020③
	Saab 99	Carburetor 1985	②	0.025-0.030	40 ± 2	0.012-0.016	14 BTDC	N.A.	—	800 std 850 auto	0.006-0.012③	0.014-0.020③
	Saab 99	Fuel Injected 1985	②	0.025-0.030	50 ± 2	0.012-0.016	8 BTDC	N.A.	—	800 std 850 auto	0.006-0.012③	0.014-0.020③

NOTE: Manufacturer's recommend CO level at 1000 rpm: 2.5 percent

① Short reach plugs for silver and black painted engines; Long reach plugs for engines painted blue

Short reach plugs
Autolite—AE22
Champion—L82Y
Bosch—W225T35
NGK—B-7H

Long reach plugs
Autolite—AG22
Champion—N9Y
Bosch—W200T30
NGK—BP7E

② Autolite—AG22
Champion—N11Y
Bosch—W175T30
NGK-BP6E

③ Valves cold

FIRING ORDER

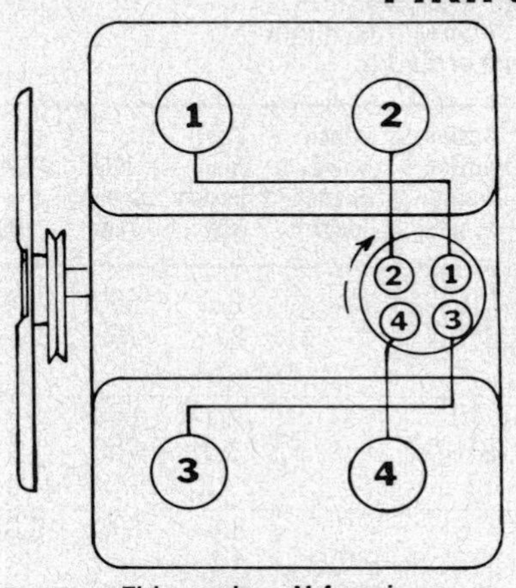

Firing order—V-4 engine

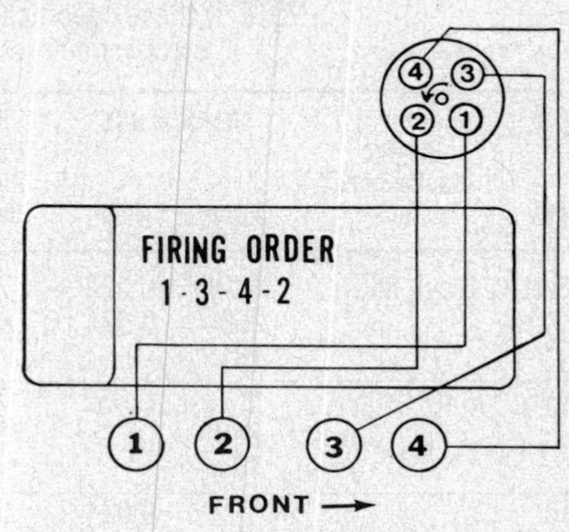

Firing order—OHC engine

CRANKSHAFT AND CONNECTING ROD SPECIFICATIONS

Year	Engine Type	CRANKSHAFT Main Brg. Journal Dia. (mm.)	Main Brg. Oil Clearance (in.)	Shaft End-Play (mm.)	Thrust on No.	CONNECTING ROD Journal Diameter (mm.)	Oil Clearance (in.)
1967-73	V-4	Red 57.000-56.990	0.0005-0.002	0.102-0.203	Center Main Bearing	Red 56.820-56.830	0.0006-0.002
1969-72	OHC	Blue 56.990-56.980			3	Blue 56.830-56.840	
		44.450-44.463	0.0009-0.002	0.08-0.25	3	48.146-48.158	0.0009-0.002

PISTON AND RING SPECIFICATIONS

Year	Engine Model	Piston Diameter (mm.)	RING GAP (mm.) Top Compression	Bottom Compression	Oil Control	RING SIDE CLEARANCE (in groove) (mm.) Top Compression	Bottom Compression	Oil Control
1967-73	V-4 (All models)	89.978-90.002	0.25-0.50	0.25-0.50	0.380-1.40	0.0394-0.077	0.040-0.078	0.026-0.196
1969-70	OHC	83.464-83.475	0.30-0.45	0.30-0.45	0.40-1.40	—	—	—
1971-72	OHC	86.962-86.976	0.30-0.45	0.30-0.45	0.40-1.40	—	—	—

VALVE SPECIFICATIONS

Year	Engine Type	Seat Angle (deg)	Face Angle (deg)	Spring Test Pressure (lbs @ in.)	Spring Installed Height (in.)	STEM TO GUIDE CLEARANCE (mm.) Intake	Exhaust	STEM DIAMETER (mm.) Intake	Exhaust
1967-72	V-4	45	—	1967 39-47 @ 1.13 1968-72 60-68 @ 1.13	1967 1.78 1968-72 1.91	0.020-0.063	0.046-0.089	8.043-8.025	8.017-7.999
1969-72	OHC	45	—	110 ± 10 lbs	36.322 mm	0.037	0.057	7.89-7.90	7.87-7.88

— Not Available

TORQUE SPECIFICATIONS

Year	Engine Type	Cylinder Head Bolts	Rod Bearing Bolts	Main Bearing Bolts	Crankshaft Pulley or Gear Bolt	Flywheel to Crankshaft Bolts	Camshaft Thrust Plate	Intake Manifold
1967-73	V-4	68	25	72	36	50	15	21
1969-72	OHC	54	40	58	62	44	17	—

— Not Available

TORQUE SEQUENCES

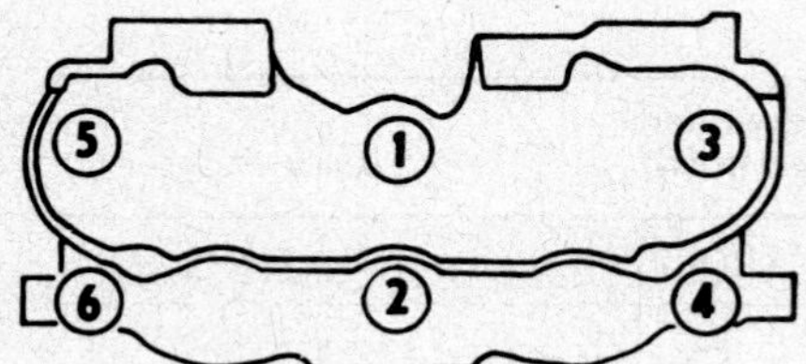

Torque sequences—cylinder head assemby, V-4 engine.

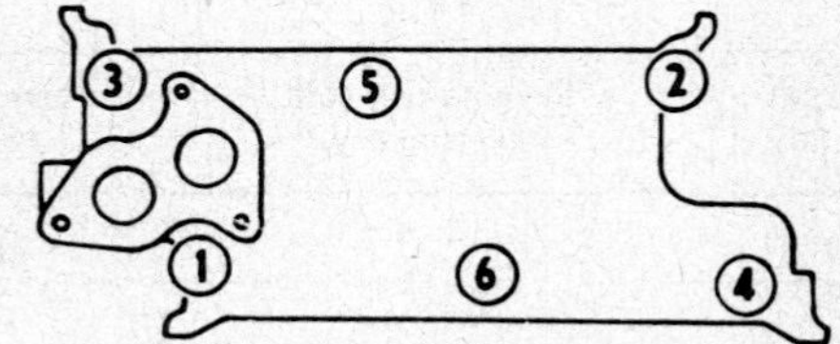

Torque sequences—intake manifold, V-4 engine.

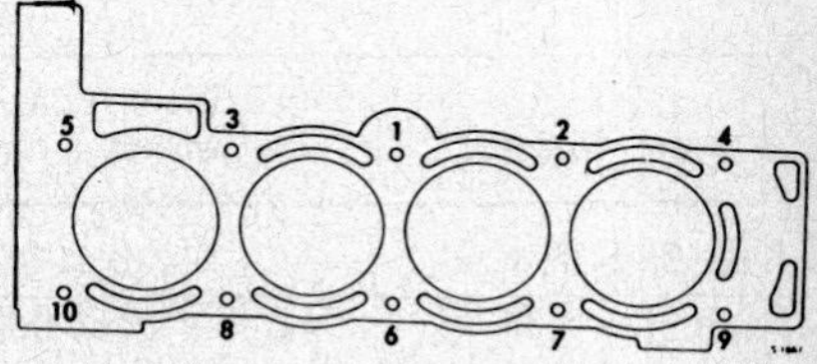

Torque sequences—cylinder head assembly, OHC engine.

CAPACITIES

Year	Model	Engine Displacement (cc)	Engine Crankcase (qts) With Filter	Engine Crankcase (qts) Without Filter	Transmission (pts) Manual 4-spd	Transmission (pts) Automatic	Drive Axle (pts)	Gasoline Tank (gals)	Cooling System (qts) W/O AC
1967	95	850 2 stroke	—	—	3	—	—	11.5	6.9
	96	850 2 stroke	—	—	3	—	—	10.5	6.9
1967-73	95	V-4 1498, 1698	3.5	3	3	—	—	11.5	7.5①
	96	V-4 1498, 1698	3.5	3	3	—	—	10.5	7.5①
1969-71	99	1709 OHC	4	3.5	6	18	2	12	8
1971-72	99	1854 OHC	4	3.5	6	18	2	12	8
1967-73	Sonett 97	V-4 1498, 1698	3.5	3	3	—	—	15.8	7.4
1973	99	1985 OHC	4	3.5	6	18	2	11.9	10

① 1967-1968 cooling system capacity 7.9 qts.
— Not Available

BRAKE SPECIFICATIONS

Year	Model	Master Cylinder Bore (in.)	Wheel Cylinder or Caliper Piston Bore: Front Disc	Wheel Cylinder or Caliper Piston Bore: Rear Disc	Wheel Cylinder or Caliper Piston Bore: Rear Drum	Brake Disc or Drum Diameter (in.): Front Disc	Brake Disc or Drum Diameter (in.): Rear Disc	Brake Disc or Drum Diameter (in.): Rear Drum
1967-72	All (except Saab 99)	1967-68 3/4 1969-72 13/16	2	—	5/8 Model 95 1967-69 3/4	10 1/2 (266.7 mm)	—	8 (203.2 mm)
1969-72	Saab 99	0.687 (17.46 mm)	1.890 (4.80 mm)	1.063 (48.0 mm)	—	10.614 (269.5 mm)	10.614 (269.5 mm)	—

WHEEL ALIGNMENT

Year	Model	Caster Range (deg)	Caster Pref. Setting (deg)	Camber Range (deg)	Camber Pref. Setting (deg)	Toe-in (in.)	Steering Axis Inclination	Wheel Pivot Ratio (deg) Inner Wheel	Wheel Pivot Ratio (deg) Outer Wheel
1967-73	All 95 & 96	1.5-2.5	2	1/2-1	3/4	0.08	6-8	21-24	20
	Sonett	1.5-2.5	2	N3/4-P1/4	0	0.04	6-8	21-24	20
1969-71	99	1-1 1/2	1 1/4	1/2-1	3/4	0.00	11.5	21.5 ± 1	20
1972-73	99	1/2-1	3/4	1/2-1	3/4	0.00	11.5	21.5 ± 1	20

REAR WHEEL ALIGNMENT

Model	Toe-in: sum of both wheels at rims (in.)	Toe-in: sum of both wheels in deg.	Max. toe-in for 1 wheel in deg.	Camber in deg.
Saab 95 & 96	0 ± 0.2	0 ± 0.7	0 ± 0.6	0 ± 1
Saab 99	0 ± 0.28	0 ± 1	0 ± 3/4	0 ± 1

BATTERY AND STARTER SPECIFICATIONS

Year	Engine Type	Battery: Ampere Hour Capacity	Battery: Volts	Battery: Term. Grd.	Starters Lock Test: Amps.	Lock Test: Volts	Lock Test: @ RPM	No-Load Test: Amps.	No-Load Test: Volts	No-Load Test: @ RPM	Brush Spring Tension (oz.)
1967-68	V-4	67-70 44	12	Neg	170-200	9	1150-1450	30-50	11.5	6500-7700	40.5-46
1969-72	V-4	60	12	Neg	205-235	9	1000-1300	35-55	11.5	6500-8500	41-46
	OHC	60	12	Neg	205-235	9	1000-1300	35-55	11.5	6500-8500	11.3-12.8(N)

ALTERNATOR AND REGULATOR SPECIFICATIONS

Year	Alternator: Part No. or Manufacturer	Alternator: Field Current @ RPM	Alternator: Output (amps.)	Regulator: Part No. or Manufacturer	Field Relay: Air Gap (in.)	Field Relay: Point Gap (in.)	Field Relay: Volts to Close	Regulator: Air Gap (in.)	Regulator: Point Gap (in.)	Regulator: Volts
1967-72	Bosch (Std) KI-14V 35A20 Bosch (Opt) KI-14V 55A20 (Std equipment) on all Saab 99)	14V @ 2000	35 (Std) 55 (Opt)	Bosch AD 114V	—	—	—	—	—	—

— Not Available

WIRING DIAGRAMS

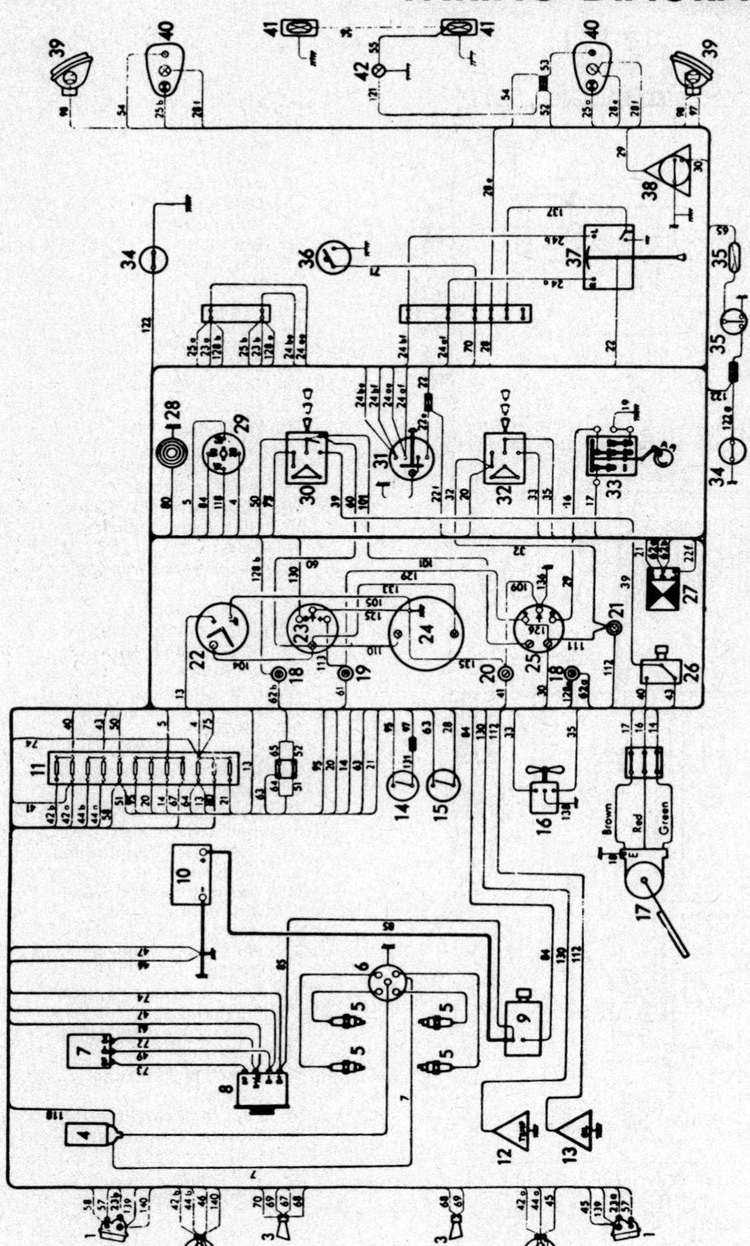

1. Turn signal indicators and side lights
2. Headlights
3. Horn
4. Distributor
5. Spark plugs
6. Voltage regulator
7. Alternator
8. Starter
9. Battery
10. Fuse box
11. Ignition coil
12. Back-up light switch
13. Stop light switch
14. Heater fan motor
15. Wiper motor
16. Direction indicator repeater light
17. Charge indicator light
18. High beam indicator light
19. Electric clock
20. Temperature gauge
21. Speedometer with odometer
22. Fuel gauge
23. Dimmer switch
24. Flasher
25. Ignition and starter switch
26. Headlight switch and instrument illumination
27. Warning flasher switch with control lamp
28. Heater fan switch
29. Windshield wiper switch
30. Courtesy light switch
31. Courtesy light with switch
32. Horn button
33. Direction indicator switch
34. Fuel tank gauge
35. Back-up lights
36. Stop lights, direction indicators and tail lights
37. License plate light
38. Trunk light

1967 SAAB 96, V-4 engine

Wiring diagram—SAAB 96 1967 USA version

Black: 7, 7b, 18, 19, 45, 46, 47, 49, 71, 105, 109, 135, 136, 138, 139, 140.

Red: 5, 21, 28, 28e, 28f, 32, 39, 61, 63, 65, 67, 68, 72, 126, 129.

Green: 16, 22, 22e, 22f, 50, 51, 52, 53, 54, 55, 56, 57, 58, 60, 101, 104, 110, 121, 133.

Grey: 4, 25b, 29, 35, 44a, 62a, 64, 69, 70, 74, 75, 85.

White: 20, 23b, 24b, 24be, 24bf, 40, 42b, 66, 95, 97, 98, 118, 122, 122e, 128a, 131.

Yellow: 17, 23a, 24a, 24ae, 24af, 33, 43, 44b, 73, 84, 128b.

Brown: 14, 15, 30, 137.

Blue: 13, 25a, 41, 42a.

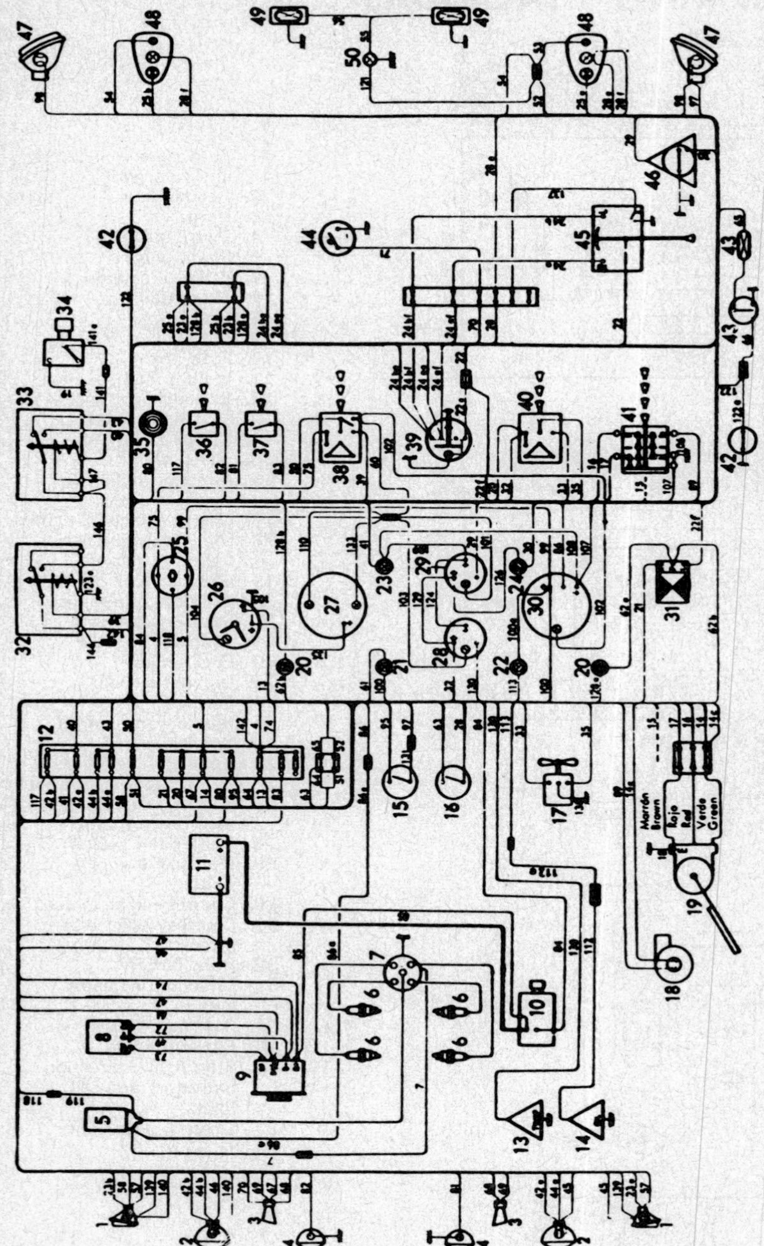

1. Parking and turn signal indicator lights
2. Headlights
3. Horns
4. Ignition coil
5. Spark plugs
6. Distributor
7. Voltage regulator
8. Alternator
9. Starter motor
10. Battery
11. Fuse box
12. Temperature gauge sending unit
13. Oil pressure switch
14. Stop light switch
15. Heater motor
16. Windshield wiper motor
17. Turn signal indicator warning lights
18. Charge indicator light
19. High beam indicator light
20. Oil pressure warning light
21. Electric clock
22. Temperature gauge
23. Speedometer with odometer
24. Fuel gauge
25. Foot dimmer switch
26. Flasher
27. Cigarette lighter
28. Ignition and starter switch
29. Headlight and parking light switch with instrument illumination rheostat
30. Warning flasher switch with control light
31. Heater switch
32. Windshield wiper switch
33. Automatic door switch for dome light
34. Dome light with switch
35. Horn ring
36. Direction indicator switch
37. Fuel tank sending unit
38. Stop light and direction indicator light
39. Tail lights
40. License lights

1967 SAAB Monte Carlo, V-4 engine

Black: 7, 18, 19, 45, 46, 47, 49, 71, 80, 105, 109, 125, 135, 136, 138, 139, 140.

Red: 5, 21, 28, 28e, 28f, 28g, 32, 39, 61, 63, 65, 67, 68, 72, 92, 111, 113, 126, 129.

Green: 16, 22, 22e, 22f, 50, 51, 53, 54, 55, 57, 58, 60, 86, 87, 88, 101, 104, 110, 133.

Grey: 4, 25b, 29, 35, 44a, 62a, 62b, 64, 69, 70, 74, 75, 85, 93.

White: 20, 23b, 24b, 24be, 24bf, 40, 42b, 66, 82, 83, 118, 122, 122e, 128a.

Yellow: 17, 23a, 24a, 24ae, 24af, 33, 43, 44b, 73, 84, 128b.

Brown: 14, 30, 130, 137.

Blue: 13, 25a, 41, 42a, 112.

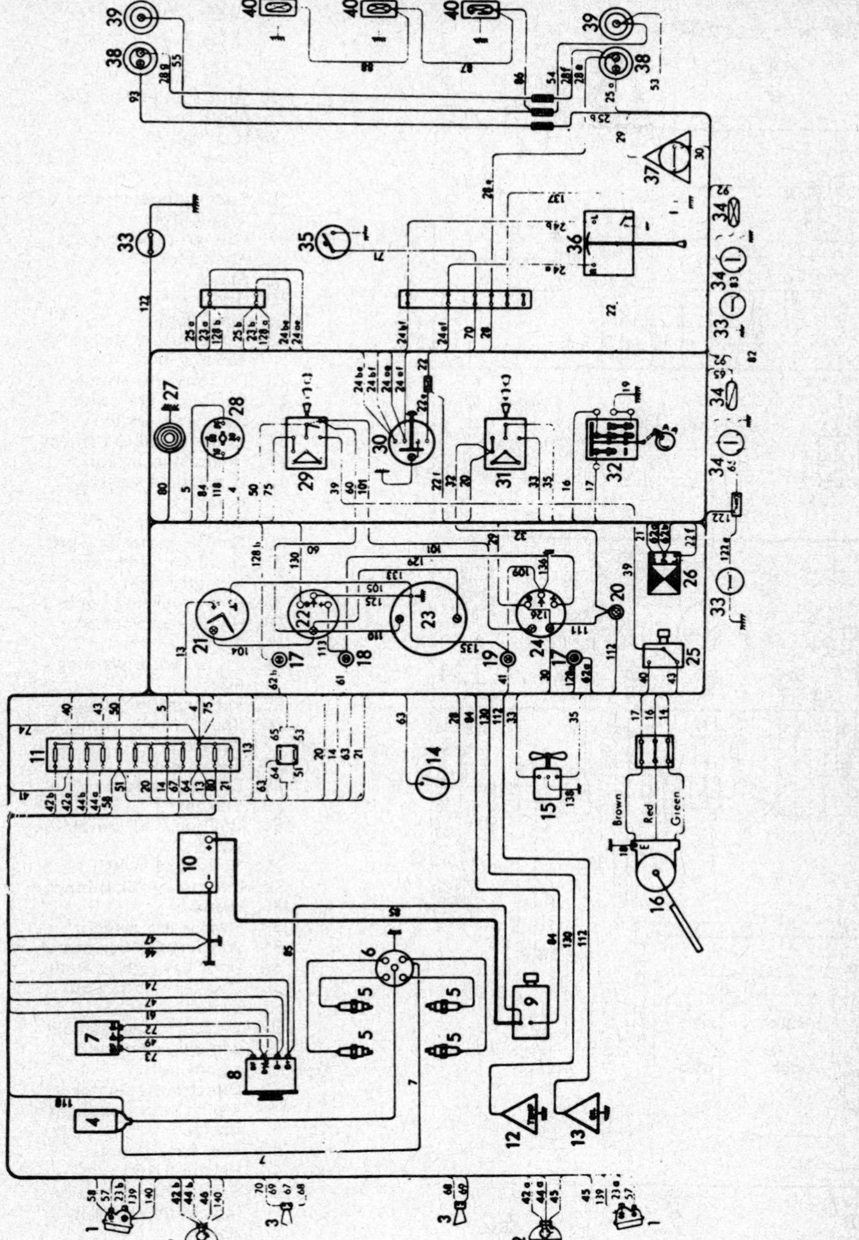

1967 SAAB 95, V-4 engine

1. Parking and turn signal indicator lights
2. Headlights
3. Horns
4. Ignition coil
5. Spark plugs
6. Distributor
7. Voltage regulator
8. Alternator
9. Starter motor
10. Battery
11. Fuse box
12. Temperature gauge sending unit
13. Oil pressure switch
14. Stop light switch
15. Heater motor
16. Windshield wiper motor
17. Turn signal indicator warning lights
18. Charge indicator light
19. High beam indicator light
20. Oil pressure warning light
21. Electric clock
22. Temperature gauge
23. Speedometer with odometer
24. Fuel gauge
25. Foot dimmer switch
26. Flasher
27. Cigarette lighter
28. Ignition and starter switch
29. Headlight and parking light switch with instrument illumination rheostat
30. Warning flasher switch with control light
31. Heater switch
32. Windshield wiper switch
33. Automatic door switch for dome light
34. Dome light with switch
35. Horn ring
36. Direction indicator switch
37. Fuel tank sending unit
38. Stop light and direction indicator light
39. Tail lights
40. License lights

Black: 7, 18, 19, 45, 46, 47, 49, 71, 80, 105, 109, 125, 135, 136, 138, 139, 140.

Red: 5, 21, 28, 28e, 28f, 28g, 32, 39, 61, 63, 65, 67, 68, 72, 92, 111, 113, 126, 129.

Green: 16, 22, 22e, 22f, 50, 51, 53, 54, 55, 57, 58, 60, 86, 87, 88, 101, 104, 110, 133.

Grey: 4, 25b, 29, 35, 44a, 62a, 62b, 64, 69, 70, 74, 75, 85, 93.

White: 20, 23b, 24b, 24be, 24bf, 40, 42b, 66, 82, 83, 118, 122, 122e, 128a.

Yellow: 17, 23a, 24a, 24ae, 24af, 33, 43, 44b, 73, 84, 128b.

Brown: 14, 30, 130, 137.

Blue: 13, 25a, 41, 42a, 112.

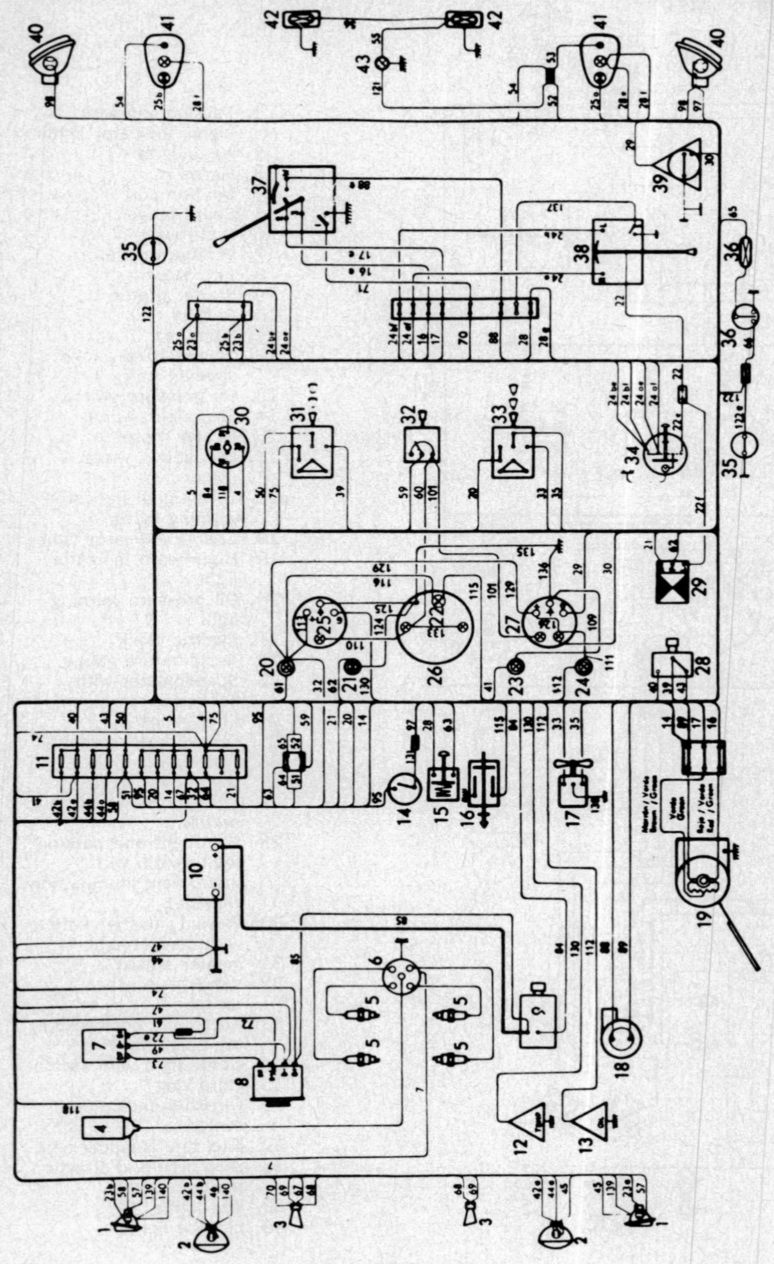

1968 SAAB 96, V-4 engine

1. Turn signals and side lights
2. Headlights
3. Horn
4. Ignition coil
5. Spark plugs
6. Distributor
7. Voltage regulator
8. Alternator
9. Starter
10. Battery
11. Fuse box
12. Temperature gauge, sending unit
13. Oil pressure switch
14. Back-up light switch
15. Stop light switch
16. Brake warning contact
17. Heater fan motor
18. Windshield washer pump
19. Wiper motor
20. Charge indicator light
21. Direction indicator repeater light
22. Brake warning light
23. High beam indicator light
24. Oil pressure warning light
25. Temperature gauge
26. Speedometer with odometer
27. Fuel gauge
28. Dimmer switch
29. Flasher
30. Ignition and starter switch
31. Headlight switch
32. Instrument illumination rheostat
33. Heater fan switch
34. Warning flasher switch
35. Courtesy light switch
36. Courtesy light with switch
37. Switch for windshield wiper, washer and signal horn
38. Direction indicator switch with headlight flasher
39. Fuel tank gauge
40. Back-up light
41. Stop lights, direction indicators and tail lights
42. License plate light
43. Trunk light

Black: 7, 45, 46, 47, 69, 70, 71, 88, 88e, 109, 124, 125, 135, 136, 138, 139, 140.

Red: 5, 21, 28, 28e, 28f, 32, 39, 61, 63, 65, 67, 68, 72, 72e, 111, 113, 116, 126, 129.

Green: 22, 22e, 22f, 50, 51, 52, 53, 54, 55, 56, 57, 58, 59, 60, 101, 110, 121, 133.

Grey: 4, 16, 16e, 25b, 29, 35, 44a, 62, 64, 74, 75, 85.

White: 20, 23b, 24b, 24be, 24bf, 40, 42b, 66, 95, 97, 98, 118, 122, 122e, 131.

Yellow: 23a, 24a, 24ae, 24af, 33, 43, 44b, 73, 84, 115.

Blue: 17, 17e, 25a, 41, 42a, 112.

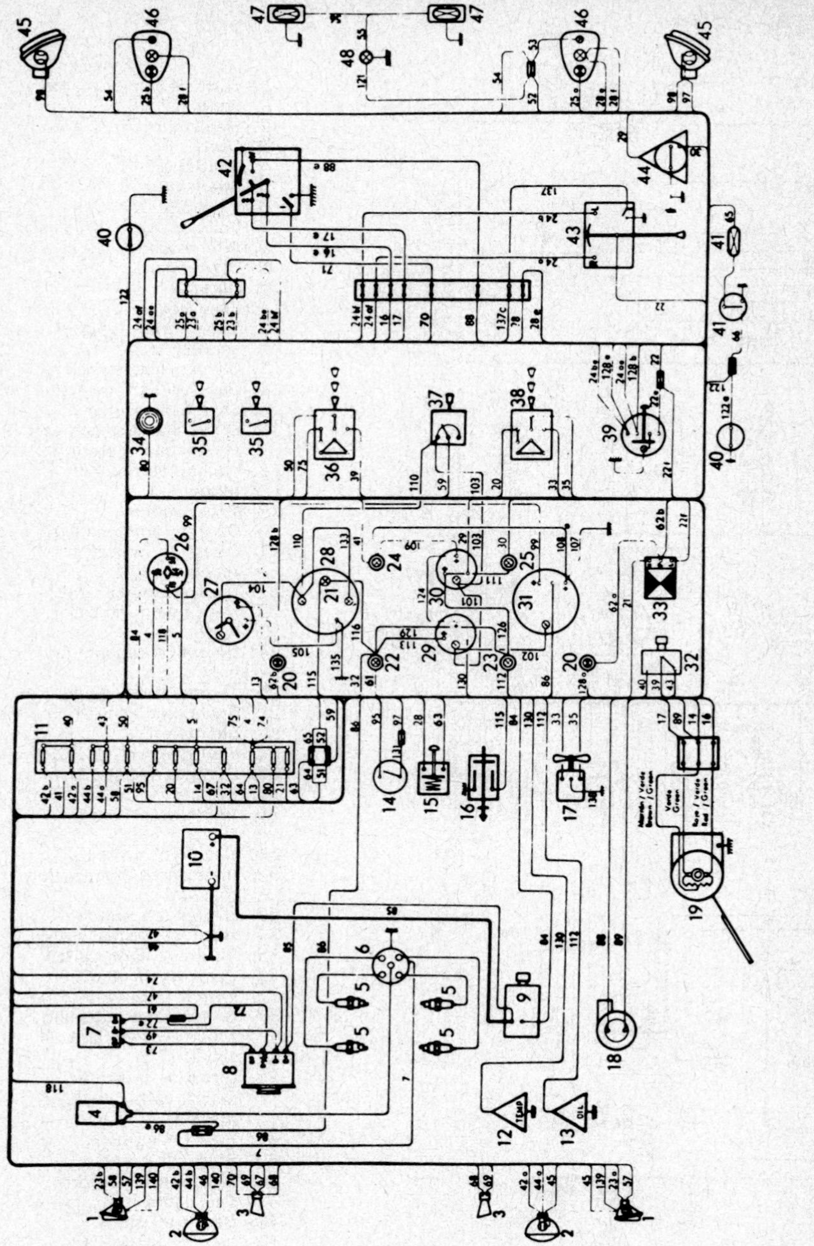

1968 SAAB Deluxe

1. Turn signals and side lights
2. Headlights
3. Horn
4. Ignition coil
5. Spark plugs
6. Distributor
7. Voltage regulator
8. Alternator
9. Starter
10. Battery
11. Fuse box
12. Temperature gauge, sending unit
13. Oil pressure switch
14. Back-up light switch
15. Stop light switch
16. Brake warning contact
17. Heater fan motor
18. Windshield-washer pump
19. Wiper motor
20. Direction indicator repeater light
21. Brake warning light
22. Charge indicator light
23. Indicator light, oil pressure
24. High beam indicator light
25. Indicator light, fuel
26. Ignition and starter switch
27. Electric clock
28. Speedometer, odometer and trip meter
29. Temperature gauge
30. Fuel gauge
31. Tachometer
32. Dimmer switch
33. Flasher
34. Cigarette lighter
35. Switches for extra equipment
36. Headlight switch
37. Instrument illumination rheostat
38. Heater fan switch
39. Warning flasher switch
40. Courtesy light switch
41. Courtesy light with switch
42. Switch for windshield wiper, washer and signal horn
43. Direction indicator switch with headlight flasher and dimmer switch
44. Fuel tank gauge
45. Back-up lights
46. Stop lights, direction indicators and tail lights
47. License plate light
48. Trunk light

Black: 7, 23a, 45, 46, 47, 49, 71, 80, 88, 88e, 105, 107, 108, 109, 124, 135, 138, 139, 140.

Red: 5, 21, 28, 28e, 28f, 32, 39, 61, 63, 65, 67, 68, 72, 72e, 86e, 111, 113, 116, 126, 129.

Green: 22, 22e, 22f, 50, 51, 52, 53, 54, 55, 56, 57, 58, 59, 101, 102, 103, 104, 110, 121, 133.

Grey: 4, 16, 16e, 25b, 29, 35, 44a, 62a, 62b 64 69, 70, 74, 75, 85.

White: 20, 23b, 24b, 24be, 24bf, 40, 42b, 66, 95, 97, 98, 99, 118, 122, 122e, 128a, 131.

Yellow: 24a, 24ae, 24af, 33, 43, 44b, 73, 84, 115, 128b.

Brown: 14, 30, 89, 130, 137, 137c.

Blue: 13, 17, 17e, 25a, 41, 42a, 112.

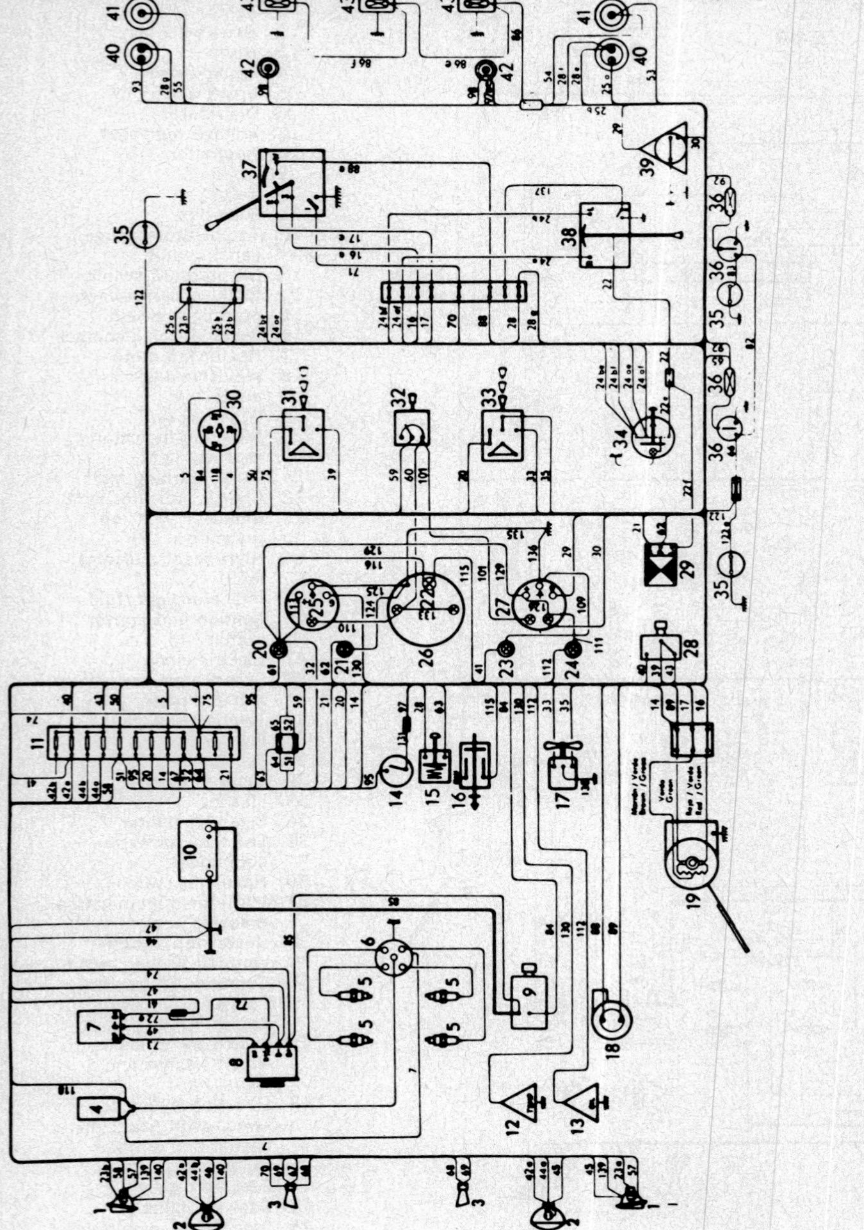

1968 SAAB 95, V-4 engine

1. Turn signals and side lights
2. Headlights
3. Horn
4. Ignition coil
5. Spark plugs
6. Distributor
7. Voltage regulator
8. Alternator
9. Starter
10. Battery
11. Fuse box
12. Temperature gauge sending unit
13. Oil pressure switch
14. Back-up light switch
15. Stop light switch
16. Brake warning contact
17. Heater fan motor
18. Windshield washer pump
19. Wiper motor
20. Charge indicator light
21. Direction indicator repeater light
22. Brake warning light
23. High beam indicator light
24. Oil pressure warning light
25. Temperature gauge
26. Speedometer with odometer
27. Fuel gauge
28. Dimmer switch
29. Flasher
30. Ignition and starter switch
31. Headlight switch
32. Instrument illumination rheostat
33. Heater fan switch
34. Warning flasher switch
35. Courtesy light switch
36. Courtesy light with switch
37. Switch for windshield wiper, washer and signal horn
38. Direction indicator switch with headlight flasher
39. Fuel tank gauge
40. Stop lights and direction indicators
41. Tail lights
42. Back-up lights
43. License plate light

Black: 7, 45, 46, 47, 49, 69, 70, 88, 88e, 109, 124, 125, 135, 136, 138, 139, 140.

Red: 5, 21, 28, 28e, 28f, 28g, 32, 39, 61, 63, 65, 67, 68, 72, 72e, 92, 111, 113, 116, 126, 129.

Green: 22, 22e, 22f, 50, 51, 53 54, 55, 57, 58, 59, 60, 86, 86e, 86f, 101, 110.

Grey: 4, 16, 16e, 25b, 29, 35, 44a, 62, 64, 74, 75, 85, 93.

White: 20, 23b, 24b, 24be, 24bf, 40, 40c, 42b, 66, 82, 83, 95, 97, 97ae, 98, 118, 122, 112e, 131.

Yellow: 23a, 24a, 24ae, 24af, 33, 43, 44b, 73, 84, 115.

Brown: 14, 15, 30, 89, 130, 137.

Blue: 17, 17e, 25a, 41, 42a, 112.

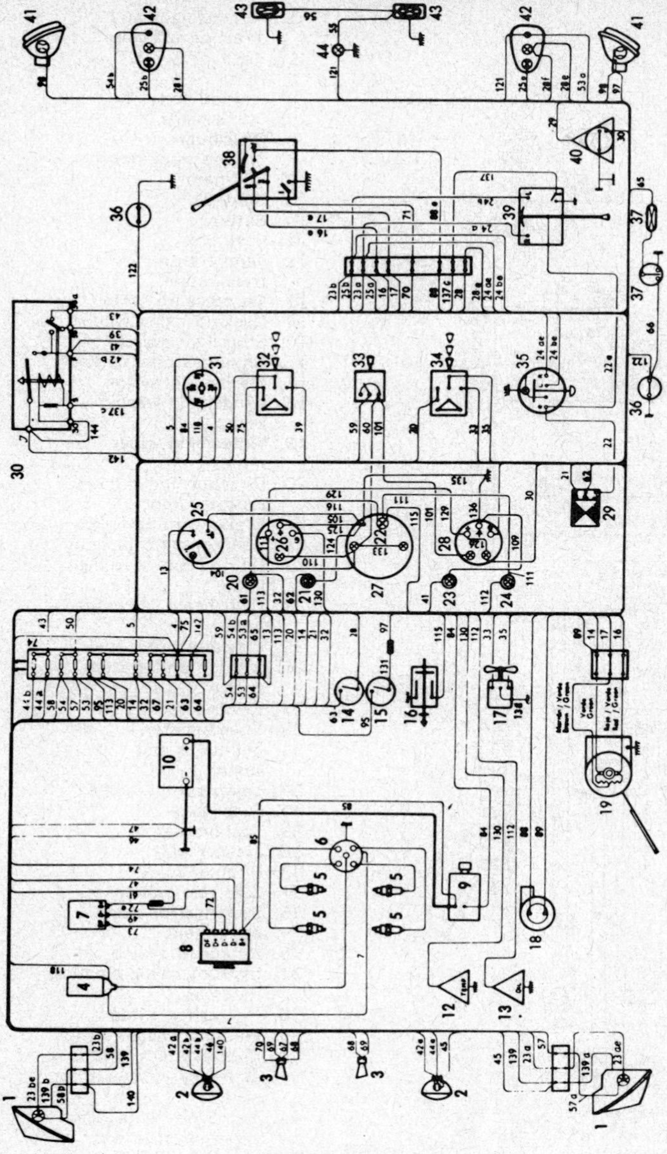

1969 SAAB 96

1. Parking light and direction indicators
2. Headlights
3. Horn
4. Ignition coil
5. Spark plugs
6. Distributor
7. Voltage regulator
8. Alternator
9. Starter
10. Battery
11. Fuse box
12. Temperature transmitter
13. Oil pressure switch
14. Stop light switch
15. Back-up light switch
16. Brake warning contact
17. Heater fan motor
18. Windshield washer pump
19. Windshield wiper motor
20. Charge indicator light
21. Direction indicator repeater light
22. Brake warning light
23. High beam indicator light
24. Oil pressure warning light
25. Electric clock (Extra equipment)
26. Temperature gauge
27. Sppedometer with odometer
28. Fuel gauge
29. Flasher unit
30. Dimmer relay
31. Ignition and starter switch
32. Headlight switch
33. Instrument illumination rheostat
34. Heater fan switch
35. Warning flasher switch
36. Courtesy light switch
37. Courtesy light with switch
38. Switch for windshield wiper washer and signal horn
39. Direction indicator switch with headlight flasher and dimmer switch
40. Fuel transmitter
41. Back-up lights
42. Stop lights, direction indicators and tail light
43. License plate light
44. Trunk light

4 grey
5 red
7 black
13 blue
14 brown
16 grey
16e grey
17 blue
17e blue
20 white
21 red
22 green
22e green
23a yellow
23ae yellow
23b white
23be white
24a yellow
24ae yellow
24b white
24be white
25a blue
25b grey

28 red
28e red
28f red
29 grey
30 brown
32 red
33 yellow
35 grey
39 red
41 blue
42a blue
42b white
43 yellow
44a grey
44b yellow
45 black
46 black
47 black
49 black
50 green
53 blue
53a blue
54 green

54b green
55 green
56 green
57 blue
57a blue
58 green
58b green
59 green
60 green
61 red
62 grey
63 red
64 grey
65 red
66 white
67 red
68 red
69 black
70 black
71 black
72 red
72e red
73 yellow

74 grey
75 grey
84 yellow

85 grey
88 black
88e black
89 brown
95 white
97 white
98 white
101 green
104 green
105 black
109 black
110 green
111 red
112 blue
113 white
115 yellow
116 red
118 white

121 green
122 white
124 black
125 black
126 white
129 white
130 brown
131 white
133 green
135 black
136 black
137 brown
137c brown
138 black
139 black
139a black
139b black
140 black

142 grey
144 grey

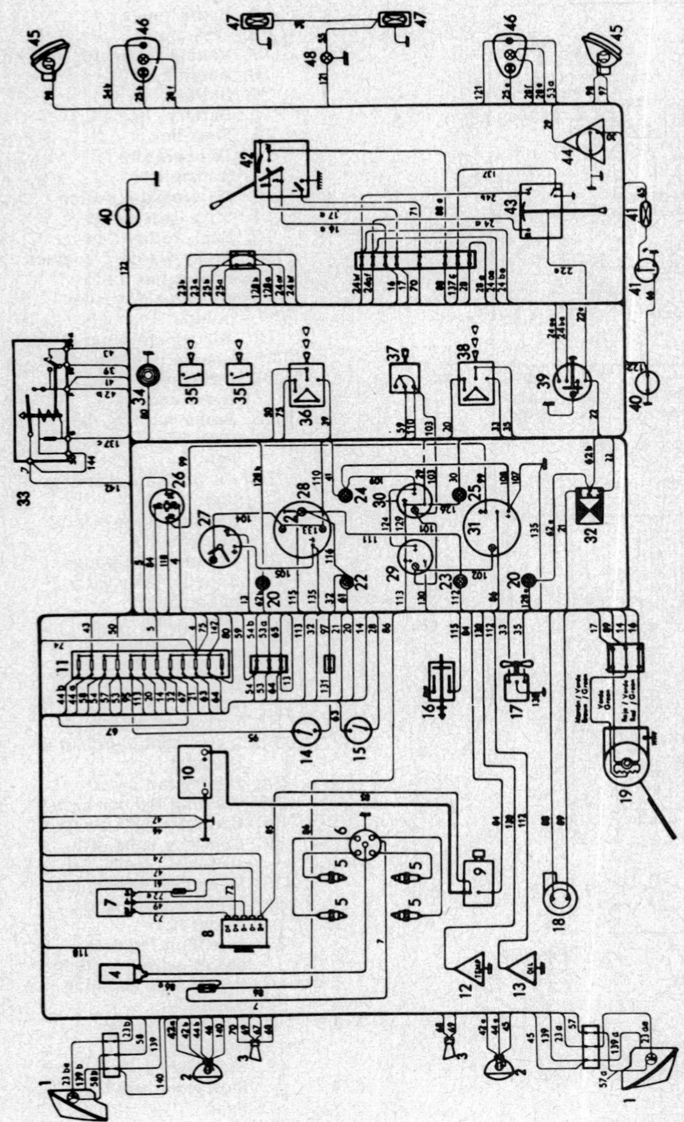

1969 SAAB Deluxe

1. Parking light and direction indicators
2. Headlights
3. Horn
4. Ignition coil
5. Spark plugs
6. Distributor
7. Voltage regulator
8. Alternator
9. Starter
10. Battery
11. Fuse box
12. Temperature transmitter
13. Oil pressure switch
14. Back-up light switch
15. Stop light switch
16. Brake warning contact
17. Heater fan motor
18. Windshield washer pump
19. Windshield wiper motor
20. Direction indicator repeater light
21. Brake warning light
22. Charge indicator light
23. Oil pressure warning light
24. High beam indicator light
25. Indicator light, fuel
26. Ignition and starter switch
27. Electric clock
28. Speedometer, odometer and trip meter
29. Temperature gauge
30. Fuel gauge
31. Tachometer
32. Flasher unit
33. Dimmer relay
34. Cigarette lighter
35. Switches for extra equipment
36. Headlight switch
37. Instrument illumination rheostat
38. Heater fan switch
39. Warning flasher switch
40. Courtesy light switch
41. Courtesy light with switch
42. Switch for windshield wiper, washer and signal horn
43. Direction indicator switch with headlight flasher and dimmer switch
44. Fuel transmitter
45. Back-up lights
46. Stop lights, direction indicators and tail lights
47. License plate light
48. Trunk light

4 grey
5 red
7 black
13 blue
14 brown
16 grey
16e grey
17 blue
17e blue
20 white
21 red
22 green
22e green
23a yellow
23ae yellow
23b white
23be white

24a yellow
24ae yellow
24af yellow
24b white
24be white
24bf white
25a blue
25b grey
28 red
28e red
28f red
29 grey
30 brown
32 red
33 yellow
35 grey
39 red

41 blue
42a blue
42b white
43 yellow
44a grey
44b yellow
45 black
46 black
47 black
49 black
50 green
53 blue
53a blue
54 green
54b green
55 green
56 green

57 blue
57a blue
58 green
58b green
59 green
61 red
62a grey
62b grey
63 red
64 grey
65 red
66 white
67 red
68 red
69 black
70 black
71 black

72 red
72e red
73 yellow
74 grey
75 grey
80 black
84 yellow
85 grey
86 red
86e red
88 black
88e black
89 brown
95 white
97 white
98 white
99 white

101 green
102 green
103 green
104 green
105 black
107 black
108 black
109 black
110 green
111 red
112 blue
113 white
115 yellow
116 red
118 white
121 green
122 white

124 black
126 white
128a white
128b yellow
129 white
130 brown
131 white
133 green
135 black
137 brown
137c brown
138 black
139 black
139a black
139b black
140 black
142 grey
144 grey

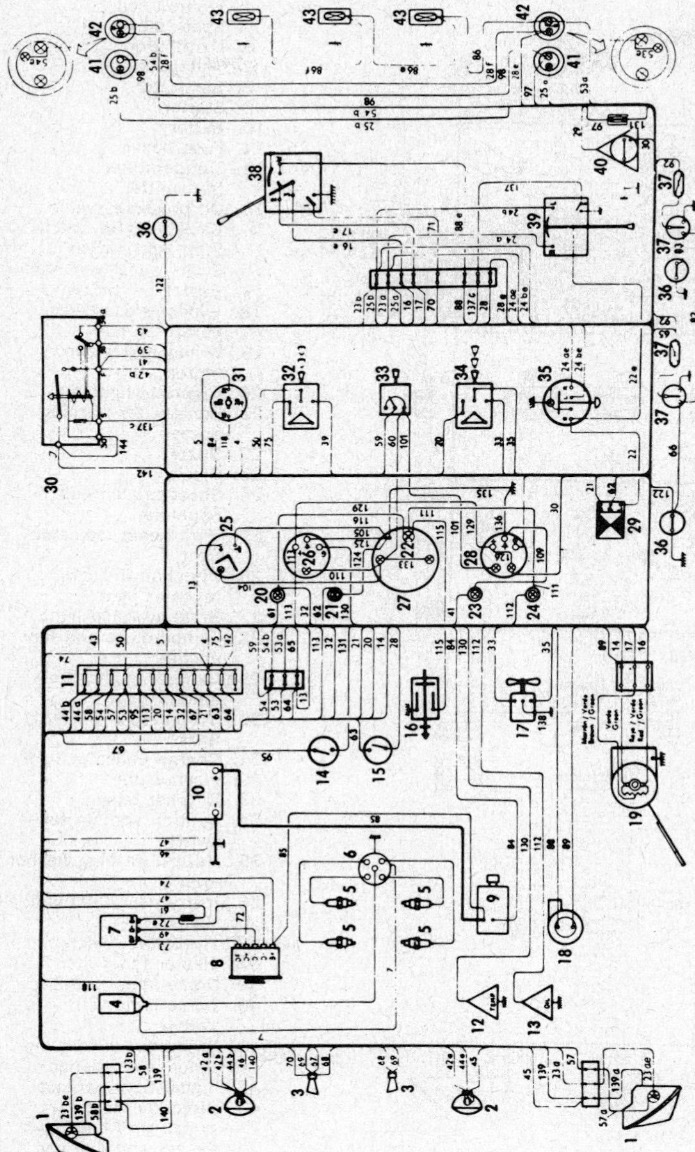

1969 SAAB 95

1. Parking light and turn signals
2. Headlights
3. Horn
4. Ignition coil
5. Spark plugs
6. Distributor
7. Voltage regulator
8. Alternator
9. Starter
10. Battery
11. Fuse box
12. Temperature transmitter
13. Oil pressure switch
14. Back-up light switch
15. Stop light switch
16. Brake warning contact
17. Heater fan motor
18. Windshield washer pump
19. Windshield wiper motor
20. Charge indicator light
21. Direction indicator repeater light
22. Brake warning light
23. High beam indicator light
24. Oil pressure warning light
25. Electric clock (Extra equipment)
26. Temperature gauge
27. Speedometer and odometer
28. Fuel gauge
29. Flasher unit
30. Dimmer relay
31. Ignition and starter switch
32. Headlight switch
33. Instrument illumination rheostat
34. Heater fan switch
35. Warning flasher switch
36. Courtesy light switch
37. Courtesy light with switch
38. Switch for windshield wiper, washer and signal horn
39. Direction indicator switch with headlight flasher and dimmer switch
40. Fuel transmitter
41. Back-up light and direction indicators
42. Tail light and stop light
43. License plate light

4 grey
5 red
7 black
13 blue
14 brown
16 grey
16e grey
17 blue
17e blue
20 white
21 red
22 green
22e green
23a yellow
24a yellow
24ae yellow
24b white
24be white
25a blue
25b grey
28 red
28e red
28f red
29 grey
30 brown
32 red
33 yellow
35 grey
42b white
43 yellow
44a grey
44b yellow
45 black
46 black
47 black
49 black
50 green
53 blue
53a blue
53e green
54 green
54b green
58 green
58b green
59 green
60 green
61 red
62 grey
63 red
64 grey
65 red
66 white
67 red
68 red
69 black
70 black
73 yellow
74 grey
75 grey
82 white
83 white
84 yellow
85 grey
86 green
86e green
86f green
88 black
88e black
89 brown
92 red
101 green
104 green
105 black
109 black
110 green
111 red
112 blue
113 white
115 yellow
116 red
118 white
122 white
124 black
125 black
131 white
133 green
135 black
136 black
137 brown
137c brown
138 black
139 black
139a black
139b black
140 black
142 grey
144 grey

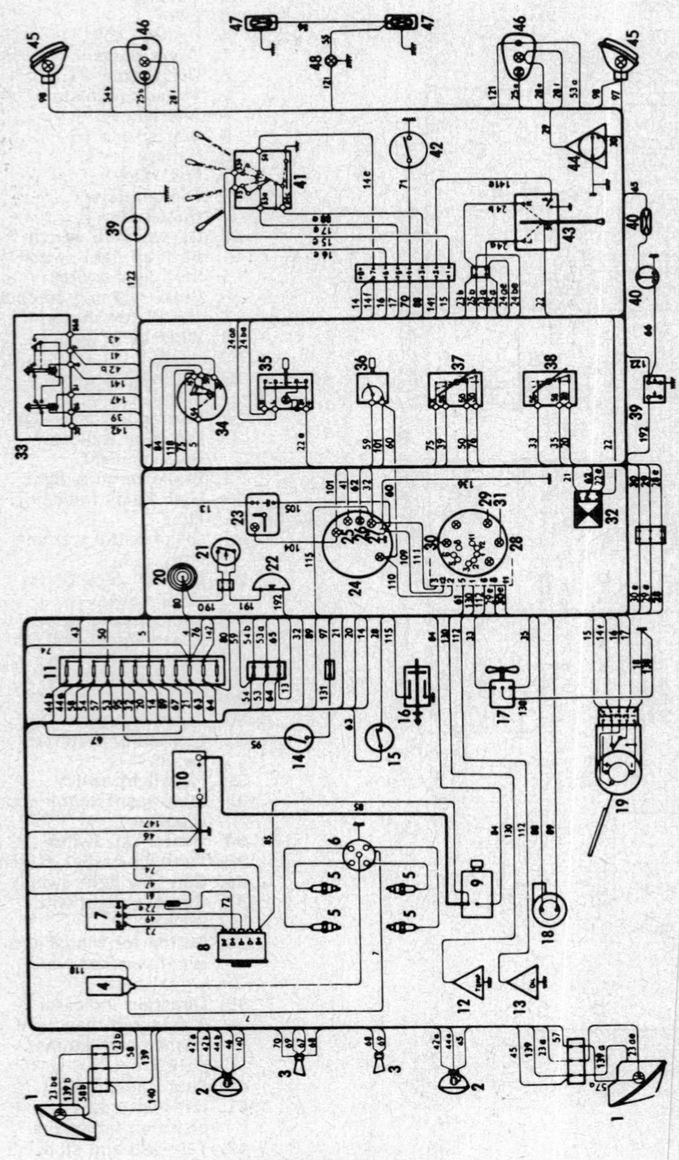

1970 SAAB 96

1. Parking light and direction indicator
2. Headlights
3. Horn
4. Ignition coil
5. Spark plugs
6. Distributor
7. Voltage regulator
8. Alternator
9. Starter
10. Battery
11. Fuse box
12. Temperature transmitter
13. Oil pressure switch
14. Back-up light switch
15. Stop light switch
16. Brake warning contact
17. Heater fan motor
18. Windshield washer pump
19. Windshield wiper motor
20. Cigarette lighter
21. Contact for warning buzzer
22. Buzzer
23. Clock
24. Speedometer with odometer
25. High beam indicator light
26. Direction indicator repeater light
27. Brake warning light
28. Temperature and fuel gauges
29. Indicator light, fuel amount
30. Oil pressure warning light
31. Charge indicator light
32. Flasher unit
33. Dimmer relay
34. Ignition and starter switch
35. Hazard warning flasher switch
36. Instrument illumination rheostat
37. Headlight switch
38. Heater fan switch
39. Dome lamp switch
40. Dome lamp with switch
41. Switch for windshield wiper, and washer
42. Signal horn contact
43. Direction indicator switch with headlight flasher and dimmer switch
44. Fuel transmitter
45. Back-up light
46. Stop lights, direction indicators and tail light
47. License plate light
48. Trunk light

4 grey
5 red
7 green
13 blue
14 brown
14e brown
14f brown
15 red
15e red
16 grey
16e grey
17 blue
17e blue
18 black
20 white
21 red
22 green

22e green
23a yellow
23ae yellow
23b white
23be white
24a yellow
24ae yellow
24b white
24be white
25a blue
25b grey
28 red
28e red
28f red
29 grey
29e green
30 brown

30e brown
32 red
33 yellow
35 grey
39 yellow
41 blue
42a blue
42b white
43 yellow
44a grey
44b yellow
45 black
46 black
47 black
49 black
50 green
53 blue

53a blue
54 green
54b green
55 green
56 black
57 blue
57a blue
58 green
58b green
59 green
60 green
61 red
62 grey
63 red
64 grey
65 red
66 white

67 red
68 red
69 black
70 black
71 black
72 red
72e red
73 yellow
74 grey
75 red
76 grey
80 black
84 yellow
85 grey
88 black
88e black
89 brown

95 white
97 white
98 white
101 green
104 green
105 black
109 black
110 green
111 red
112 blue
115 yellow
118 white
121 green
122 white
130 brown
131 white
136 black

138 black
139 black
139a black
139b black
140 black
141 brown
141e brown
142 grey
147 black
190 yellow
191 grey
192 black

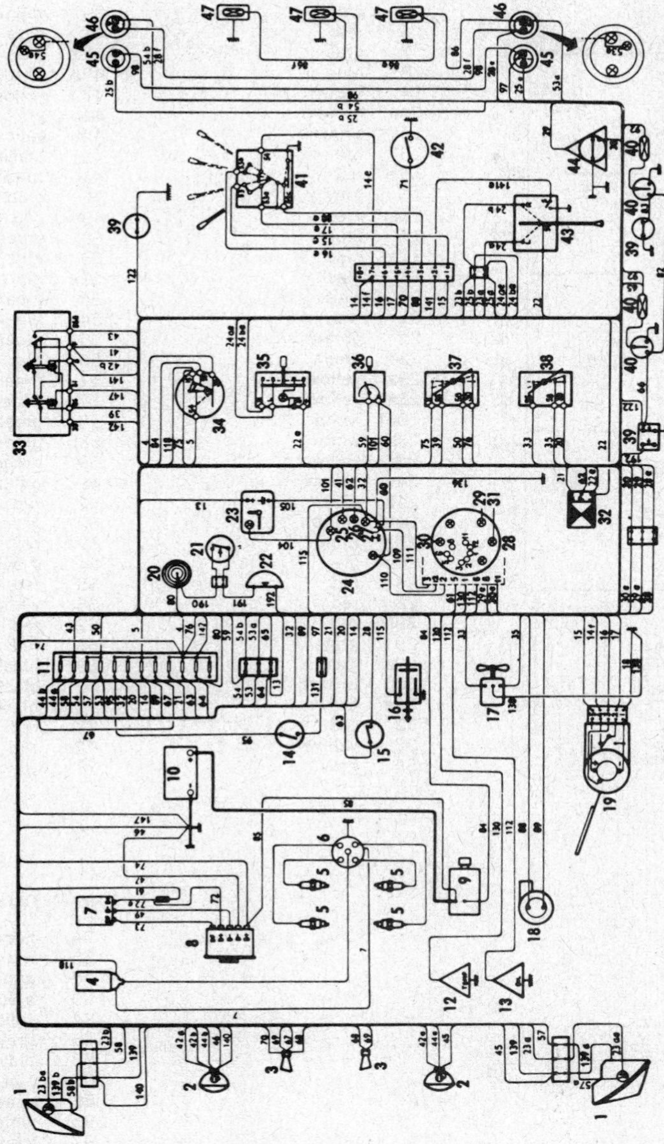

1970 SAAB 95

1. Parking light and direction indicators
2. Headlights
3. Horn
4. Ignition coil
5. Spark plugs
6. Distributor
7. Voltage regulator
8. Alternator
9. Starter
10. Battery
11. Fuse box
12. Temperature transmitter
13. Oil pressure switch
14. Back-up light switch
15. Stop light switch
16. Brake warning contact
17. Heater fan motor
18. Windshield washer pump
19. Windshield wiper motor
20. Cigarette lighter
21. Contact for warning buzzer
22. Buzzer
23. Clock
24. Speedometer and odometer
25. High beam indicator light
26. Direction indicator repeater light
27. Brake warning light
28. Temperature and fuel gauges
29. Indicator light, fuel amount
30. Oil pressure warning light
31. Charge indicator light
32. Flasher unit
33. Dimmer relay
34. Ignition and starter switch
35. Hazard warning flasher switch
36. Instrument illumination rheostat
37. Headlight switch
38. Heater fan switch
39. Dome lamp switch
40. Dome lamp with switch
41. Switch for windshield wiper, and washer
42. Signal horn contact
43. Direction indicator switch with headlight flasher and dimmer switch
44. Fuel transmitter
45. Back-up light and direction indicators
46. Tail light and stop light
47. License plate light

4 grey
5 red
7 green
13 blue
14 brown
14e brown
14f brown
15 red
15e red
16 grey
16e grey
17 blue
17e blue
18 black
20 white
21 red
22 green
22e green
23a yellow
23ae yellow
23b white
23be white
24a yellow
24ae yellow
24b white
24be white
25a blue
25b grey
28 red
28e red
28f red
29 grey
29e green
30 brown
67 red
68 red
69 black
70 black
71 black
72 red
72e red
73 yellow
74 grey
75 red
76 grey
80 black
82 white
83 white
84 yellow
85 grey
86 green
30e brown
32 red
33 yellow
35 grey
39 yellow
41 blue
42a blue
42b white
43 yellow
44a grey
44b yellow
45 black
46 black
47 black
49 black
50 green
53 blue
53a blue
53e green
54 green
54b green
54e green
57 blue
57a blue
58 green
58b green
59 green
60 green
61 red
62 grey
63 red
64 grey
65 red
66 white
86e green
86f green
88 black
88e black
89 brown
92 red
95 white
97 white
98 white
101 green
104 green
105 black
109 black
110 green
111 red
112 blue
115 yellow
118 white
122 white
130 brown
131 white
136 black
138 black
139 black
139a black
139b black
140 black
141 brown
141e brown
142 grey
147 black
190 yellow
191 grey
192 black

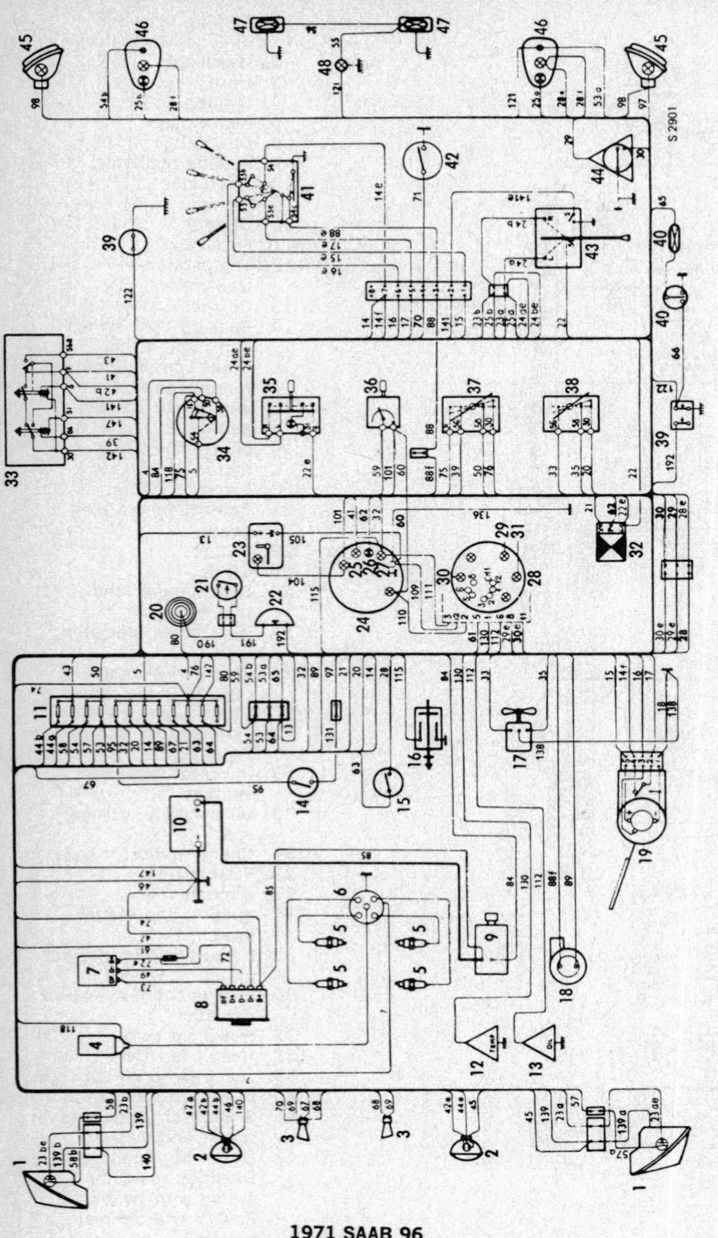

1971 SAAB 96

1. Parking light and direction indicators
2. Headlights
3. Horn
4. Ignition coil
5. Spark plugs
6. Distributor
7. Voltage regulator
8. Alternator
9. Starter
10. Battery
11. Fuse box
12. Temperature transmitter
13. Oil pressure switch
14. Back-up light switch
15. Stop light switch
16. Brake warning contact
17. Heater fan motor
18. Windshield washer pump
19. Windshield wiper motor
20. Cigarette lighter
21. Contact for warning buzzer
22. Buzzer
23. Clock
24. Speedometer with odometer
25. High beam indicator light
26. Direction indicator repeater light
27. Brake warning light
28. Temperature and fuel gauges
29. Indicator light, fuel amount
30. Oil pressure warning light
31. Charge indicator light
32. Flasher unit
33. Dimmer relay
34. Ignition and starter switch
35. Hazard warning flasher switch
36. Instrument illumination rheostat
37. Headlight switch
38. Heater fan switch
39. Dome lamp switch
40. Dome lamp with switch
41. Switch for windshield wiper, and washer
42. Signal horn contact
43. Direction indicator switch with headlight flasher and dimmer switch
44. Fuel transmitter
45. Back-up light
46. Stop lights, direction indicators and tail light
47. Number plate light
48. Trunk light

Cable numbers

No.	Color
4	grey
5	red
7	green
13	blue
14	brown
14e	brown
14f	brown
15	red
15e	red
16	grey
16e	grey
17	blue
17e	blue
18	black
20	white
21	red
22	green
22e	green
23a	yellow
23ae	yellow
23b	white
23be	white
24a	yellow
24ae	yellow
24b	white
24be	white
25a	blue
25b	grey
28	red
28e	red
28f	red
29	grey
29e	green
30	brown
30e	brown
32	red
33	yellow
35	grey

No.	Color
39	yellow
41	blue
42a	blue
42b	white
43	yellow
44a	grey
44b	yellow
45	black
46	black
47	black
49	black
50	green
53	blue
53a	blue
54	green
54b	green
55	green
56	black
57	blue
57a	blue
58	green
58b	green
59	green
60	green
61	red
62	grey
63	red
64	grey
65	red
66	white
67	red
68	red
69	black
70	black
71	black
72	red
72e	red
73	yellow

No.	Color
74	grey
75	red
76	grey
80	black
84	yellow
85	grey
88	black
88e	black
89	brown
95	white
97	white
98	white
101	green
104	green
105	black
109	black
110	green
111	red
112	blue
115	yellow
118	white
121	green
122	white
130	brown
131	white
136	black
138	black
139	black
139a	black
139b	black
140	black
141	brown
141e	brown
142	grey
147	black
190	yellow
191	grey
192	black

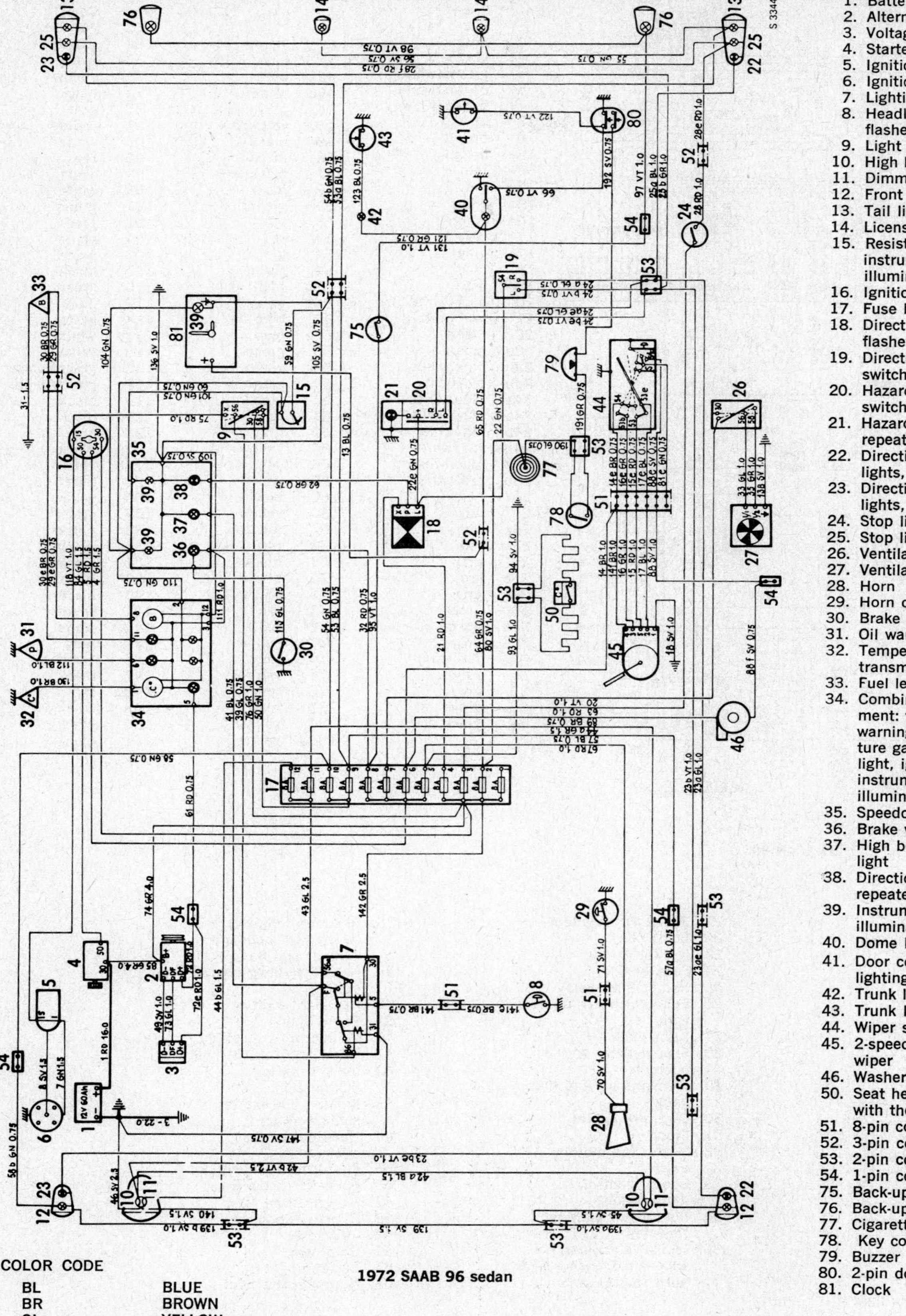

1972 SAAB 96 sedan

1. Battery
2. Alternator
3. Voltage regulator
4. Starter motor
5. Ignition coil
6. Ignition distributor
7. Lighting relay
8. Headlight dimmer/ flasher switch
9. Light switch
10. High beam
11. Dimmed beam
12. Front parking light
13. Tail light
14. License plate light
15. Resistance switch, instrument panel illumination
16. Ignition switch
17. Fuse box
18. Direction indicator flasher unit
19. Direction indicator switch
20. Hazard warning signal switch
21. Hazard warning signal repeater
22. Direction indicator lights, L
23. Direction indicator lights, R
24. Stop light contact
25. Stop lights
26. Ventilator fan switch
27. Ventilator fan motor
28. Horn
29. Horn contact
30. Brake warning contact
31. Oil warning contact
32. Temperature transmitter
33. Fuel level transmitter
34. Combination instrument: fuel gauge, fuel warning light, temperature gauge, oil warning light, ignition light, instrument panel illumination
35. Speedometer
36. Brake warning light
37. High beam indicator light
38. Direction indicator repeater light
39. Instrument panel illumination
40. Dome light
41. Door contact, interior lighting
42. Trunk light
43. Trunk light contact
44. Wiper system switch
45. 2-speed windshield wiper
46. Washer motor
50. Seat heating element with thermostat
51. 8-pin connector
52. 3-pin connector
53. 2-pin connector
54. 1-pin connector
75. Back-up light contact
76. Back-up lights
77. Cigarette lighter
78. Key contact (buzzer)
79. Buzzer
80. 2-pin door contact
81. Clock

COLOR CODE

BL	BLUE
BR	BROWN
GL	YELLOW
GN	GREEN
RD	RED
SV	BLACK
VT	WHITE

4 GR 1,5

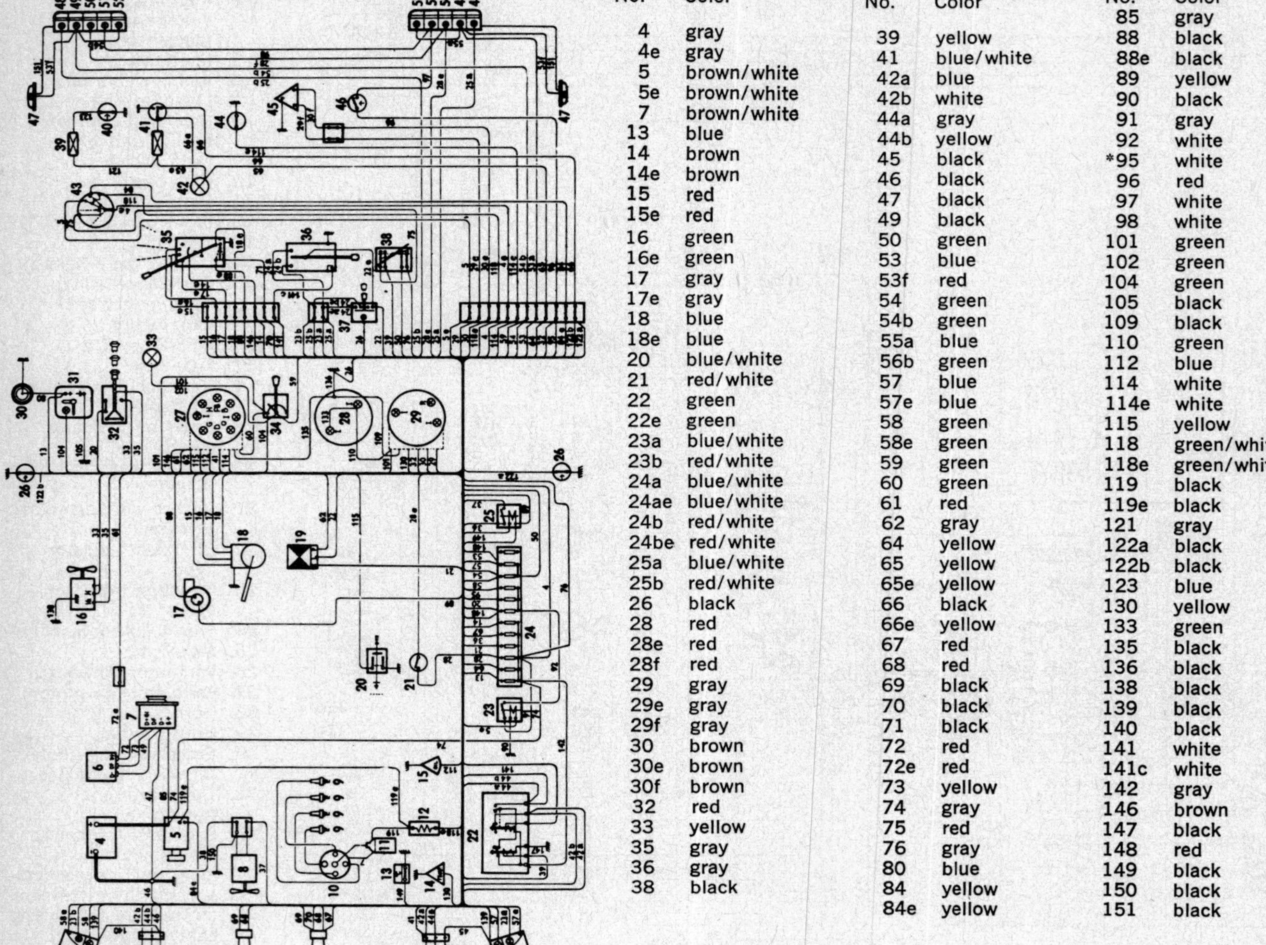

No.	Color	No.	Color	No.	Color
4	gray	39	yellow	85	gray
4e	gray	41	blue/white	88	black
5	brown/white	42a	blue	88e	black
5e	brown/white	42b	white	89	yellow
7	brown/white	44a	gray	90	black
13	blue	44b	yellow	91	gray
14	brown	45	black	92	white
14e	brown	46	black	*95	white
15	red	47	black	96	red
15e	red	49	black	97	white
16	green	50	green	98	white
16e	green	53	blue	101	green
17	gray	53f	red	102	green
17e	gray	54	green	104	green
18	blue	54b	green	105	black
18e	blue	55a	blue	109	black
20	blue/white	56b	green	110	green
21	red/white	57	blue	112	blue
22	green	57e	blue	114	white
22e	green	58	green	114e	white
23a	blue/white	58e	green	115	yellow
23b	red/white	59	green	118	green/white
24a	blue/white	60	green	118e	green/white
24ae	blue/white	61	red	119	black
24b	red/white	62	gray	119e	black
24be	red/white	64	yellow	121	gray
25a	blue/white	65	yellow	122a	black
25b	red/white	65e	yellow	122b	black
26	black	66	black	123	blue
28	red	66e	yellow	130	yellow
28e	red	67	red	133	green
28f	red	68	red	135	black
29	gray	69	black	136	black
29e	gray	70	black	138	black
29f	gray	71	black	139	black
30	brown	72	red	140	black
30e	brown	72e	red	141	white
30f	brown	73	yellow	141c	white
32	red	74	gray	142	gray
33	yellow	75	red	146	brown
35	gray	76	gray	147	black
36	gray	80	blue	148	red
38	black	84	yellow	149	black
		84e	yellow	150	black
				151	black

1969 SAAB 99

1. Parking light and direction indicator
2. Headlight
3. Horn
4. Battery
5. Starter
6. Voltage regulator
7. Alternator
8. Radiator fan motor
9. Spark plug
10. Distributor
11. Ignition coil
12. Series resistance
13. Radiator fan thermostat switch
14. Temp. transmitter
15. Oil pressure switch
16. Heater fan motor
17. Windshield washer pump
18. Windshield wiper motor
19. Flasher unit
20. Brake warning light contact
21. Brake light contact
22. Light relay
23. Ignition switch relay
24. Fuse box
25. Radiator fan relay
26. Door switch for dome light
27. Instrument light
28. Speedometer and odometer
29. Temperature and fuel gauge
30. Cigarette lighter
31. Clock
32. Heater fan motor switch
33. Heater control illumination
34. Instrument lighting rheostat
35. Windshield wiper, windshield washer and horn control switch
36. Direction indicator switch with highlight dimmer and flasher
37. Hazard warning signal switch
38. Headlight switch
39. Trunk light
40. Contact for trunk light
41. Dome light with switch
42. Ignition switch illumination
43. Ignition and starter contact switch
44. Handbrake light contact
45. Fuel level transmitter
46. Back-up light contact
47. Side position light
58. Direction indicator
49. Tail light
50. Stop light
51. Back-up light
52. Number-plate light

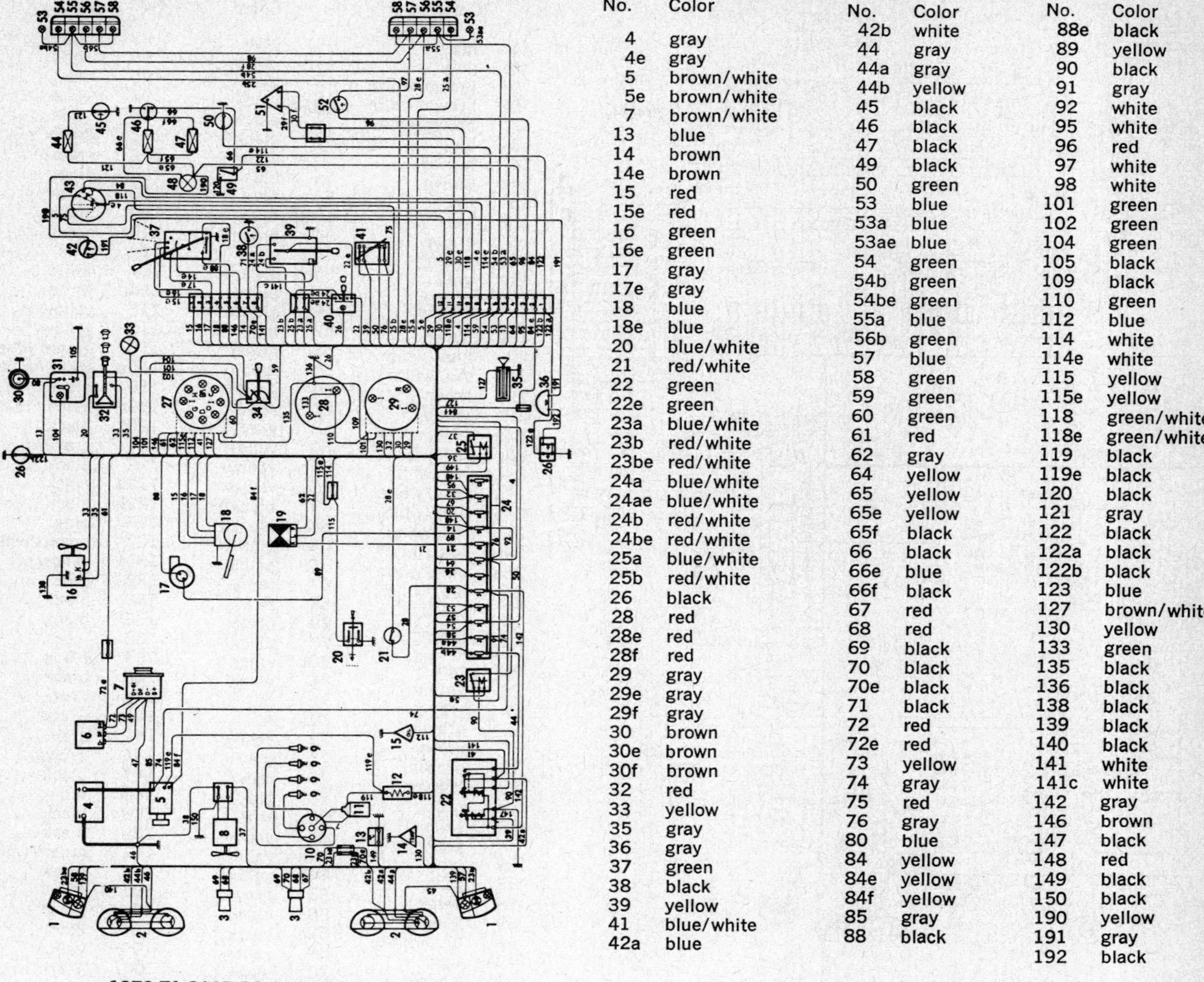

No.	Color
4	gray
4e	gray
5	brown/white
5e	brown/white
7	brown/white
13	blue
14	brown
14e	brown
15	red
15e	red
16	green
16e	green
17	gray
17e	gray
18	blue
18e	blue
20	blue/white
21	red/white
22	green
22e	green
23a	blue/white
23b	red/white
23be	red/white
24a	blue/white
24ae	blue/white
24b	red/white
24be	red/white
25a	blue/white
25b	red/white
26	black
28	red
28e	red
28f	red
29	gray
29e	gray
29f	gray
30	brown
30e	brown
30f	brown
32	red
33	yellow
35	gray
36	gray
37	green
38	black
39	yellow
41	blue/white
42a	blue

No.	Color
42b	white
44	gray
44a	gray
44b	yellow
45	black
46	black
47	black
49	black
50	green
53	blue
53a	blue
53ae	blue
54	green
54b	green
54be	green
55a	blue
56b	green
57	blue
58	green
59	green
60	green
61	red
62	gray
64	yellow
65	yellow
65e	yellow
65f	black
66	black
66e	blue
66f	black
67	red
68	red
69	black
70	black
70e	black
71	black
72	red
72e	red
73	yellow
74	gray
75	red
76	gray
80	blue
84	yellow
84e	yellow
84f	yellow
85	gray
88	black

No.	Color
88e	black
89	yellow
90	black
91	gray
92	white
95	white
96	red
97	white
98	white
101	green
102	green
104	green
105	black
109	black
110	green
112	blue
114	white
114e	white
115	yellow
115e	yellow
118	green/white
118e	green/white
119	black
119e	black
120	black
121	gray
122	black
122a	black
122b	black
123	blue
127	brown/white
130	yellow
133	green
135	black
136	black
138	black
139	black
140	black
141	white
141c	white
142	gray
146	brown
147	black
148	red
149	black
150	black
190	yellow
191	gray
192	black

1970-71 SAAB 99 (carbureted engine)

1. Parking light and direction indicator
2. Headlight
3. Horn
4. Battery
5. Starter
6. Voltage regulator
7. Alternator
8. Radiator fan motor
9. Spark plug
10. Distributor
11. Ignition coil
12. Series resistance
13. Radiator fan thermostat switch
14. Temp. transmitter
15. Oil pressure switch
16. Heater fan motor
17. Windshield washer pump
18. Windshield wiper motor
19. Flasher unit
20. Brake warning light contact
21. Brake light contact
22. Light relay
23. Ignition switch relay
24. Fuse box
25. Radiator fan relay
26. Door switch for dome light
27. Instrument indicator light
28. Speedometer and odometer
29. Temperature and fuel gauges
30. Cigarette lighter
31. Clock
32. Heater fan motor switch
33. Heater control illumination
34. Instrument lighting rheostat
35. Contact for choke indicator light
36. Buzzer
37. Windshield wiper and windshield washer control switch
38. Horn contact
39. Direction indicator switch with headlight dimmer and flasher
40. Hazard warning signal switch
41. Headlight switch
42. Contact for warning buzzer
43. Ignition and starter contact
44. Trunk light
45. Contact for trunk light
46. Dome light with switch
47. Rear-view mirror light
48. Ignition switch illumination
49. Switch for interior light
50. Handbrake light contact
51. Fuel level transmitter
52. Back-up light contact
53. Side position light
54. Direction indicator
55. Tail light
56. Stop light
57. Back-up light
58. Number-plate light

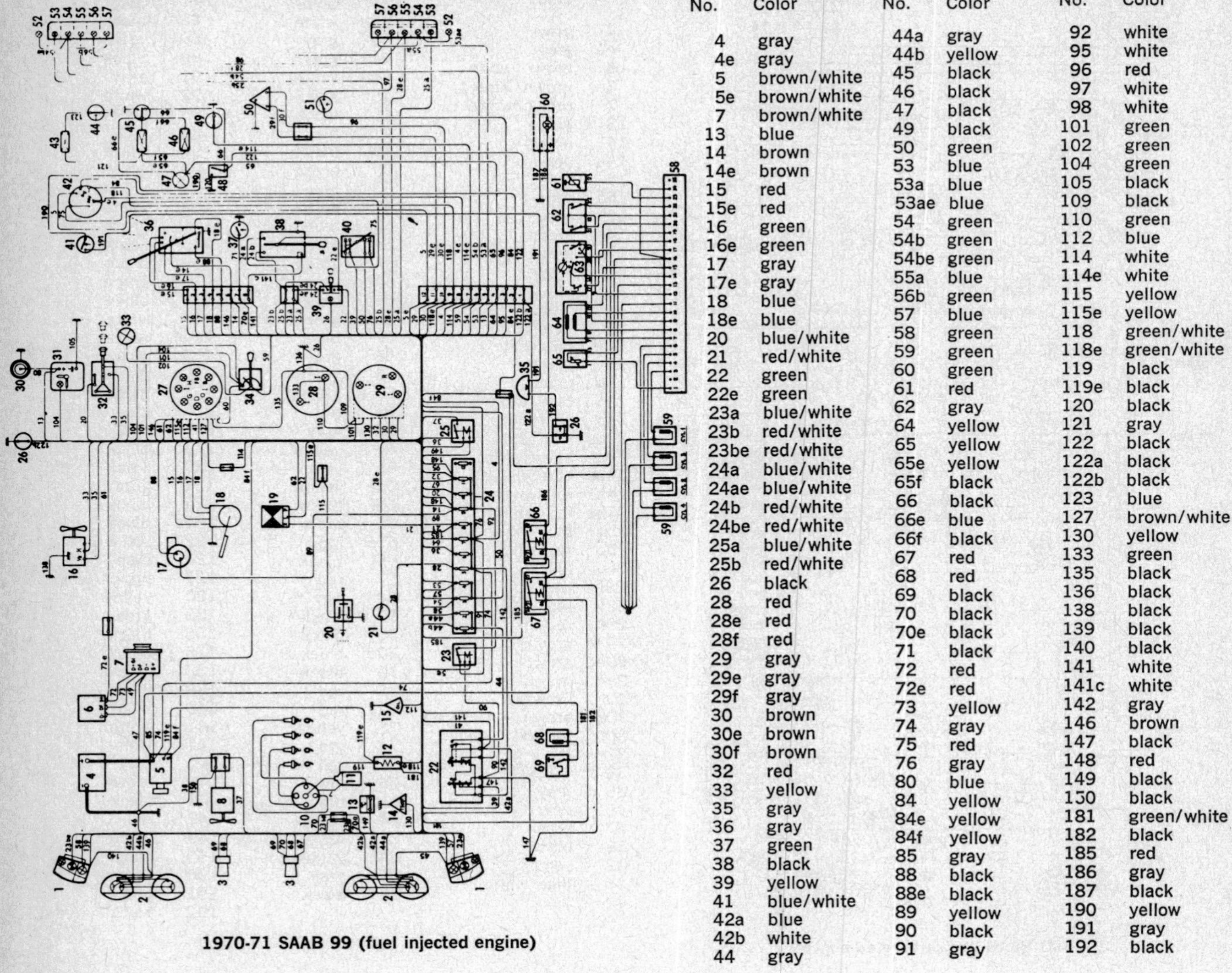

1970-71 SAAB 99 (fuel injected engine)

No.	Color	No.	Color	No.	Color
4	gray	44a	gray	92	white
4e	gray	44b	yellow	95	white
5	brown/white	45	black	96	red
5e	brown/white	46	black	97	white
7	brown/white	47	black	98	white
13	blue	49	black	101	green
14	brown	50	green	102	green
14e	brown	53	blue	104	green
15	red	53a	blue	105	black
15e	red	53ae	blue	109	black
16	green	54	green	110	green
16e	green	54b	green	112	blue
17	gray	54be	green	114	white
17e	gray	55a	blue	114e	white
18	blue	56b	green	115	yellow
18e	blue	57	blue	115e	yellow
20	blue/white	58	green	118	green/white
21	red/white	59	green	118e	green/white
22	green	60	green	119	black
22e	green	61	red	119e	black
23a	blue/white	62	gray	120	black
23b	red/white	64	yellow	121	gray
23be	red/white	65	yellow	122	black
24a	blue/white	65e	yellow	122a	black
24ae	blue/white	65f	black	122b	black
24b	red/white	66	black	123	blue
24be	red/white	66e	blue	127	brown/white
25a	blue/white	66f	black	130	yellow
25b	red/white	67	red	133	green
26	black	68	red	135	black
28	red	69	black	136	black
28e	red	70	black	138	black
28f	red	70e	black	139	black
29	gray	71	black	140	black
29e	gray	72	red	141	white
29f	gray	72e	red	141c	white
30	brown	73	yellow	142	gray
30e	brown	74	gray	146	brown
30f	brown	75	red	147	black
32	red	76	gray	148	red
33	yellow	80	blue	149	black
35	gray	84	yellow	150	black
36	gray	84e	yellow	181	green/white
37	green	84f	yellow	182	black
38	black	85	gray	185	red
39	yellow	88	black	186	gray
41	blue/white	88e	black	187	black
42a	blue	89	yellow	190	yellow
42b	white	90	black	191	gray
44	gray	91	gray	192	black

1. Parking light and direction indicator
2. Headlight
3. Horn
4. Battery
5. Starter
6. Voltage regulator
7. Alternator
8. Radiator fan motor
9. Spark plug
10. Distributor
11. Ignition coil
12. Series resistance
13. Radiator fan thermostat switch
14. Temp. transmitter
15. Oil pressure switch
16. Heater fan motor
17. Windshield washer pump
18. Windshield wiper motor
19. Flasher unit
20. Brake warning light contact
21. Brake light contact
22. Light relay
23. Ignition switch relay
24. Fuse box
25. Radiator fan relay
26. Door switch for dome light
27. Instrument indicator lights
28. Speedometer and odometer
29. Temperature and fuel gauge
30. Cigarette lighter
31. Clock
32. Heater fan motor switch
33. Heater control illumination
34. Instrument lighting rheostat
35. Buzzer
36. Windshield wiper and windshield washer control switch
37. Horn contact
38. Direction indicator switch with headlight dimmer and flasher
39. Hazard warning signal switch
40. Headlight switch
41. Contact for warning buzzer
42. Ignition and starter contact switch
43. Trunk light
44. Contact for trunk light
45. Dome light with switch
46. Rear-view mirror light
47. Ignition switch illumination
48. Switch for interior light
49. Handbrake light contact
50. Fuel level transmitter
51. Back-up light contact
52. Side position light
53. Direction indicator
54. Tail light
55. Stop light
56. Back-up light
57. Number-plate light

Electronic fuel injection units:

58. Control unit
59. Injection valves
60. Fuel pump
61. Temp. sensor II
62. Trigger contacts
63. Throttle valve switch
64. Pressure sensor
65. Temp. sensor I
66. Pump relay
67. Main relay
68. Start valve
69. Temp. switch

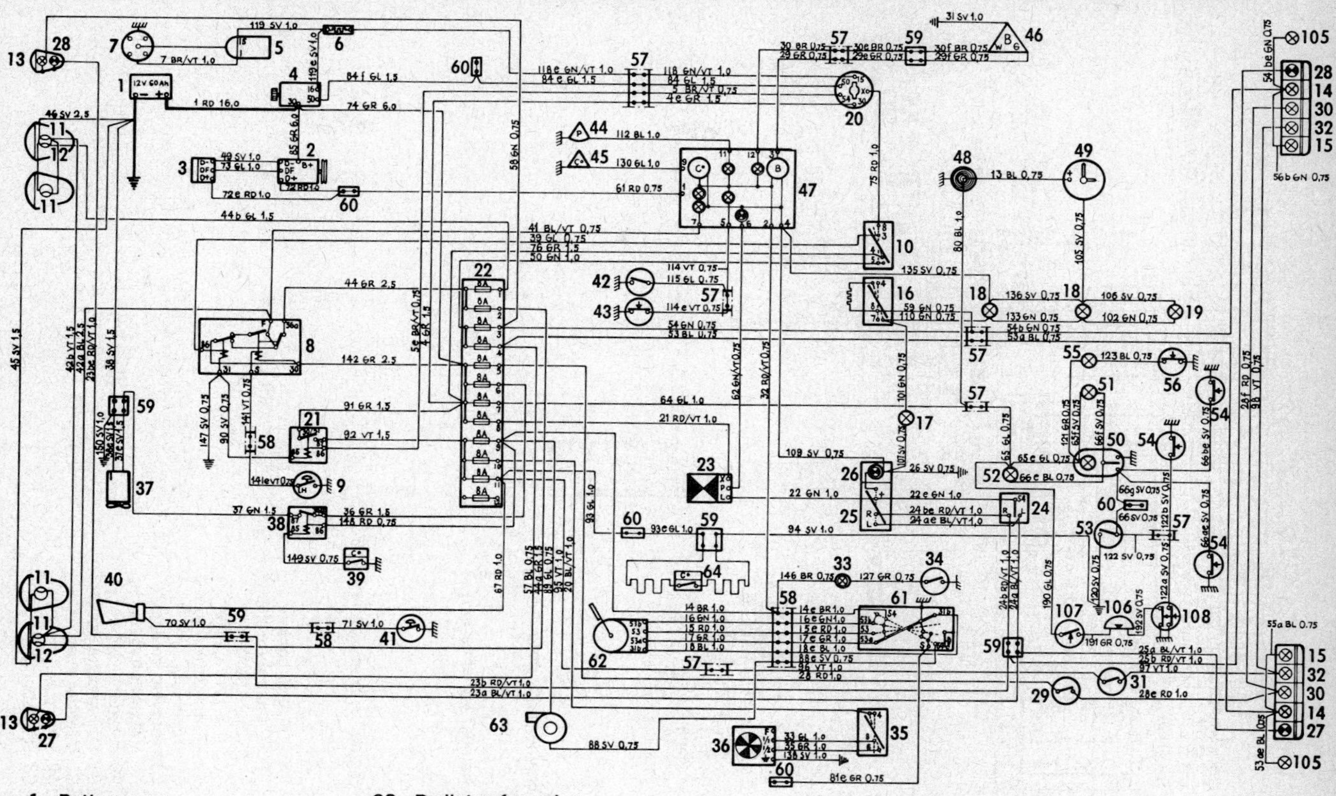

1972 SAAB (carbureted engine)

1. Battery
2. Alternator
3. Voltage regulator
4. Starter motor
5. Ignition coil
6. Serial resistance
7. Ignition distributor
8. Lighting relay
9. Headlight dimmer/ flasher switch
10. Light switch
11. High beam
12. Dimmed beam
13. Front parking light
14. Tail light
15. License plate light
16. Rheostat switch, instrument panel illuminator
17. Switch light
18. Instrument panel light
19. Glove compartment and heater control light
20. Ignition
21. Ignition relay
22. Fuse box
23. Direction indicator flasher unit
24. Direction indicator switch
25. Hazard warning signal switch
26. Hazard warning signal repeater
27. Direction indicator lights, L
28. Direction indicator lights, R
29. Stop light contact
30. Stop lights
31. Back-up light contact
32. Back-up lights
33. Choke warning light
34. Choke control contact
35. Ventilator fan switch
36. Ventilator fan motor
37. Radiator fan motor
38. Radiator fan relay
39. Radiator fan thermostat contact
40. Horn
41. Horn contact
42. Brake warning contact
43. Handbrake contact
44. Oil warning contact
45. Temperature transmitter
46. Fuel tank gauge
47. Combination instrument: fuel gauge, fuel warning light, temperature gauge, oil warning light, ignition light, brake warning light, high beam indicator light, direction indicator repeater
48. Cigarette lighter
49. Clock
50. Dome light, side
51. Dome light, forward
52. Ignition switch light
53. Interior lighting switch
54. Door contact, interior lighting
55. Trunk light
56. Trunk light contact
57. 12-pin connector
58. 8-pin connector
59. 2-pin connector
60. 1-pin connector
61. Wiper system switch
62. 2-speed windshield wiper
63. Washer motor
64. Seat heating element with thermostat
104. Side position light (front)
105. Side position light (rear)
106. Buzzer
107. Key contact (buzzer)
108. 2-pin door contact

COLOR CODE

BL	BLUE
BR	BROWN
GL	YELLOW
GN	GREEN
GR	GREY
RD	RED
SV	BLACK
VT	WHITE
BL/VT	BLUE/WHITE
BR/VT	BROWN/WHITE
GN/VT	GREEN/WHITE
RD/VT	RED/WHITE

4 GR 1.5

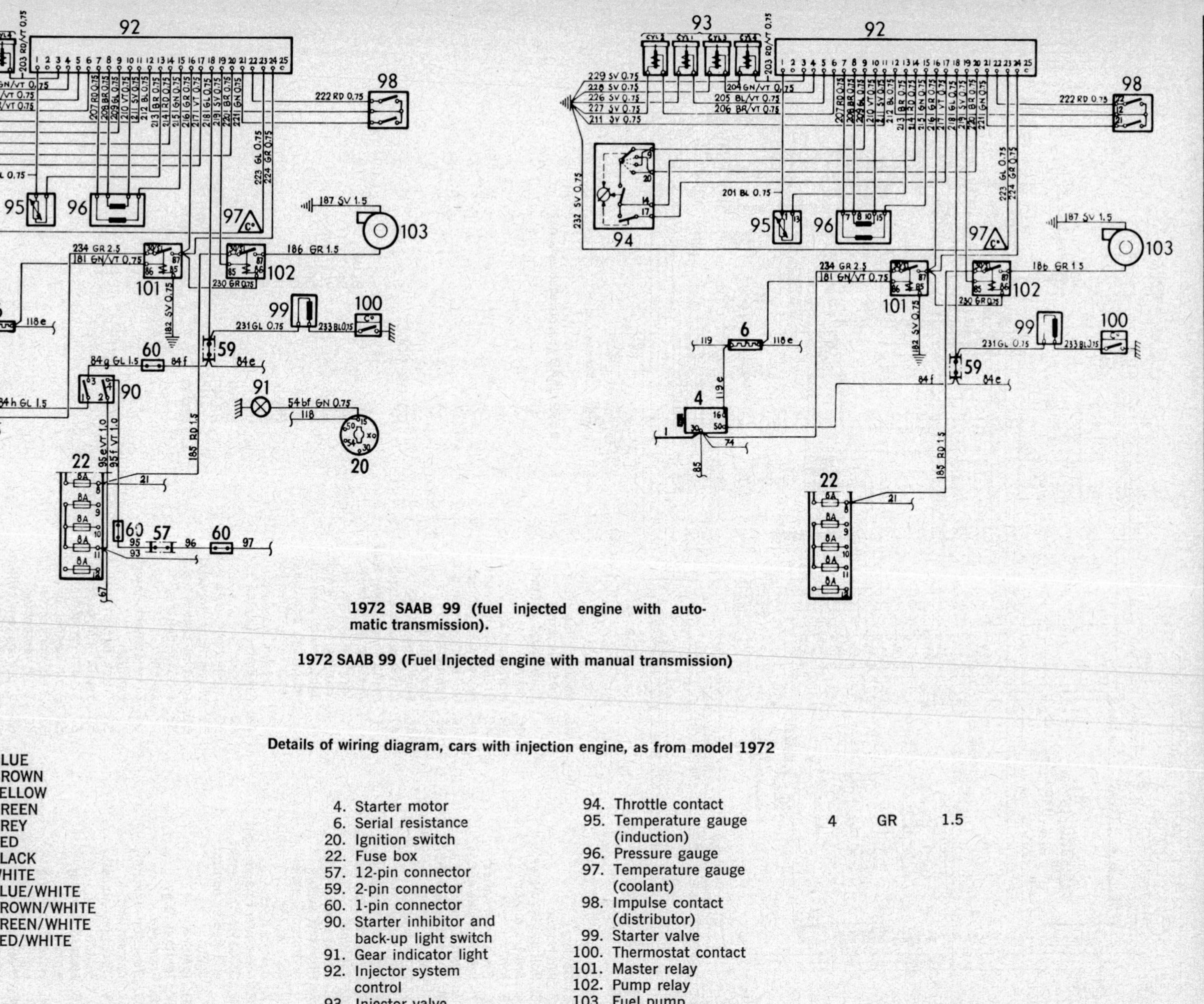

1972 SAAB 99 (fuel injected engine with automatic transmission).

1972 SAAB 99 (Fuel Injected engine with manual transmission)

COLOR CODE

BL	BLUE
BR	BROWN
GL	YELLOW
GN	GREEN
GR	GREY
RD	RED
SV	BLACK
VT	WHITE
BL/VT	BLUE/WHITE
BR/VT	BROWN/WHITE
GN/VT	GREEN/WHITE
RD/VT	RED/WHITE

Details of wiring diagram, cars with injection engine, as from model 1972

4. Starter motor
6. Serial resistance
20. Ignition switch
22. Fuse box
57. 12-pin connector
59. 2-pin connector
60. 1-pin connector
90. Starter inhibitor and back-up light switch
91. Gear indicator light
92. Injector system control
93. Injector valve
94. Throttle contact
95. Temperature gauge (induction)
96. Pressure gauge
97. Temperature gauge (coolant)
98. Impulse contact (distributor)
99. Starter valve
100. Thermostat contact
101. Master relay
102. Pump relay
103. Fuel pump

4 GR 1.5

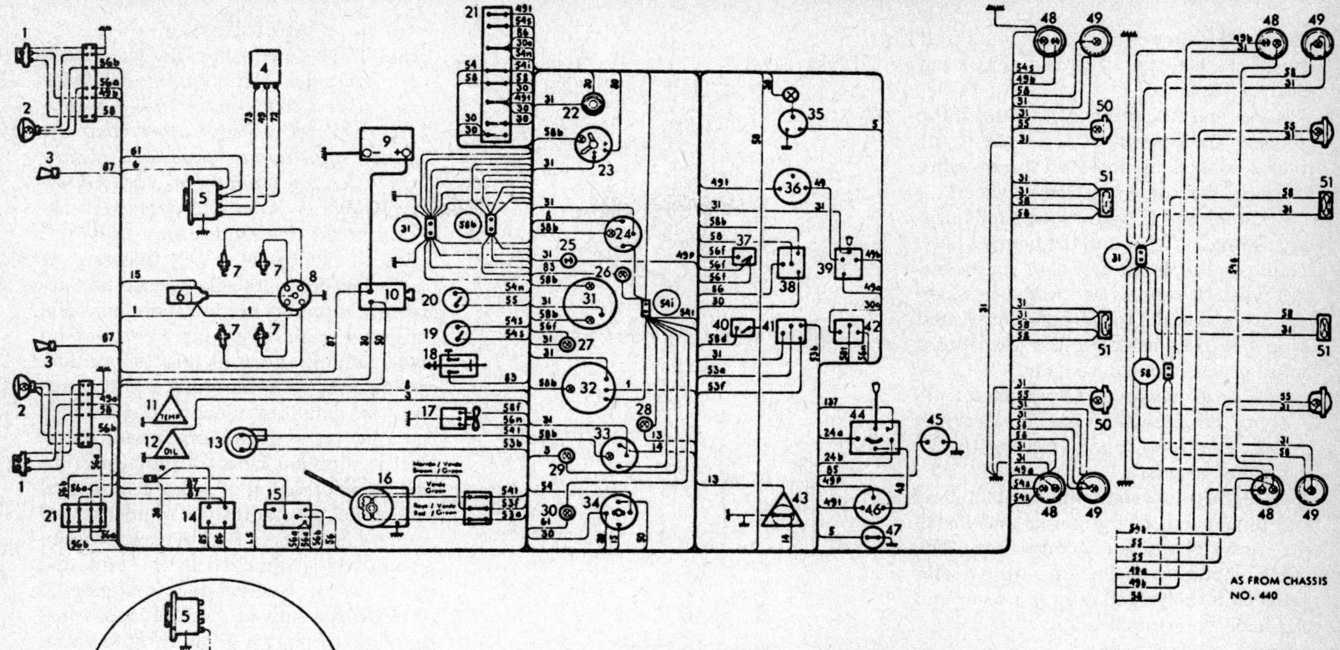

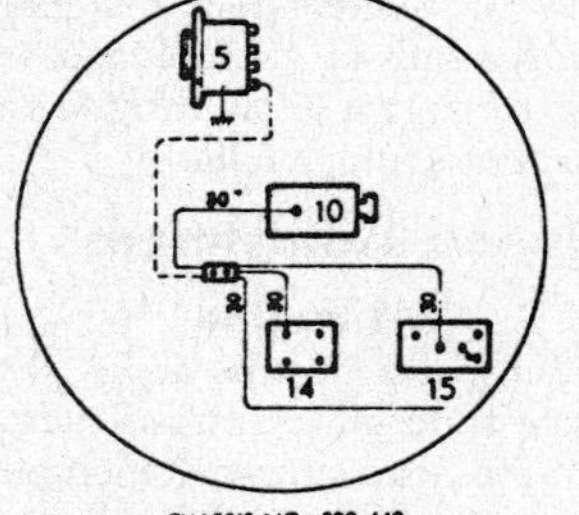

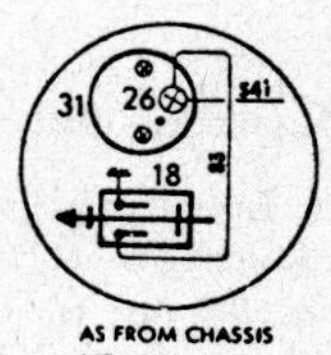

AS FROM CHASSIS NO. 416

Black: 31, 85, LS

Red: 1, 6, 15, 30, 30a, 49t, 50, 54, 54i, 54n, 54r, 54s, 54t, 61, 72, 86, 87

White: 24b, 49b, 55, 56a

Green: 49, 53a, 58, 58b, 58d

Yellow: 8, 24a, 49p, 53f, 54h, 56b, 73

Blue: 49b, 56a, 56f

Grey: 14, 49a, 53b, 56, 58t

Brown: 3, 5, 13, 83, 137

SAAB Sonnet, V-4 engine

TUNE-UP PROCEDURES

Engine tune-up is performed to restore engine performance which has deteriorated due to normal wear and loss of adjustment. The three major areas considered in a routine tune-up are compression, ignition, and carburetion, although valve adjustment may be included.

Spark Plugs

1. Remove all spark plugs, noting the cylinder in which they were installed. Evaluate the spark plug according to the spark plug chart in the "Troubleshooting" section and proceed as indicated in the chart.
2. Check the plug gap on both new and used plugs before installing them into the engine. If the air gap between the two electrodes is not correct, open or close the ground electrode with the proper tool to bring the gap to specifications. Such a tool is usually provided with a feeler or gap gauge. After the correct gap is obtained, reinstall it into the engine.

NOTE: *Be sure to clean the seats in the block before installing the plugs.*

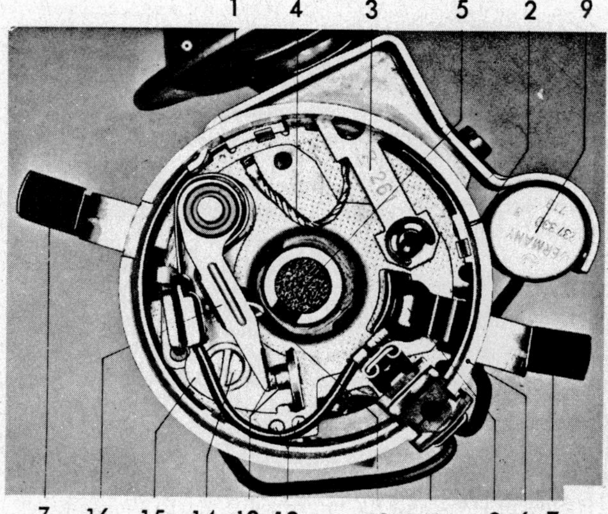

Distributor plate components

1. Vacuum chamber
2. Adjustment mark
3. Adjustment rod
4. Ground lead
5. Lubricating felt
6. Assembly mark
7. Retaining spring
8. Bearing
9. Capacitor
10. Primary cable
11. Fiber peg
12. Adjuster for fixed breaker point
13. Breaker points
14. Locking screw
15. Fixed breaker point
16. Movable breaker point

Breaker Points and Condenser

There are two rules that should always be followed when adjusting or replacing points. Neither points nor condenser should be replaced without replacing the other. If you change the point gap or dwell of the engine, you also change the ignition timing. Therefore, if you adjust the points, you must also adjust the timing.

1. Remove the distributor cap and inspect it inside and out for cracks and/or carbon tracks, and inside for excessive

wear or burning of the rotor contacts. If any of these faults are evident, the cap must be replaced.

2. Remove and inspect the rotor. If the contacts are burned or worn, or if the rotor is excessively loose on the distributor shaft, the rotor must be replaced.

3. Check the breaker points for burning, pitting, or wear and the contact heel, resting on the distributor cam, for excesssive wear. If defects are noted, remove the original points and condenser, and wipe out the inside of the distributor housing with a clean, dry rag.

NOTE: *To remove the points, a magnetic or locking type screwdriver should be used to avoid losing the attaching screws.*

4. Lightly lubricate the contact heel and pivot point of the points and install the new points and condenser. The points should then be set with a feeler gauge and rechecked after the rotor and cap have been replaced.

Dwell Angle

1. Point gap can be set by using a feeler gauge or a dwell meter. Accurate measurements with a feeler gauge require careful, precise use of the gauge.

2. A dwell meter should be calibrated first, switched to the four cylinder position, and connected between the distributor primary terminal and ground.

3. Remove the distributor cap and rotor.

4. Loosen the breaker set screw approximately ⅛ turn.

5. Observing the dwell meter, reset the stationary contact screw to obtain the specified dwell angle.

6. Tighten the set screw and recheck the dwell.

7. Install the rotor and cap, start the engine, and make a final dwell angle check.

Ignition Timing

Timing marks for V-4 engines are located on the crankshaft pulley and timing chain cover. On the SAAB 99, the timing marks are located on the rim of the flywheel and are visible through a port in the clutch housing which is adjacent to the distributor. The marks are graduated in five degree increments, those before dead center being numbered.

NOTE: *Adjust ignition timing after setting the point gap. A fast and easy way to adjust timing is with a timing light.*

1. Connect a timing light to the No. 1 spark plug.

2. Disconnect all vacuum hoses from the distributor and plug the hoses.

3. Start the engine and reduce idle speed to 500 rpm for the V-4 engine and

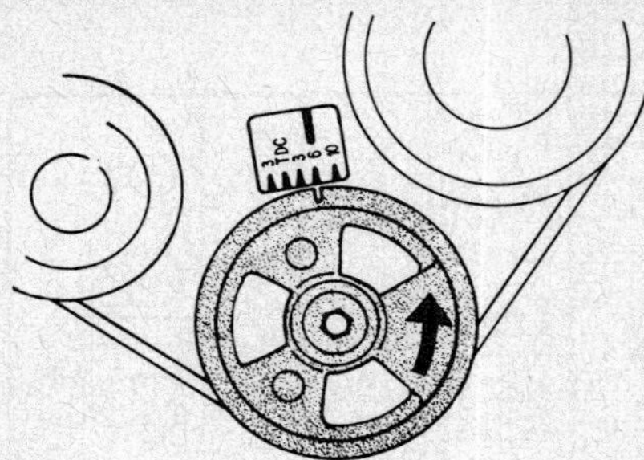

Ignition timing marks—V-4 engine

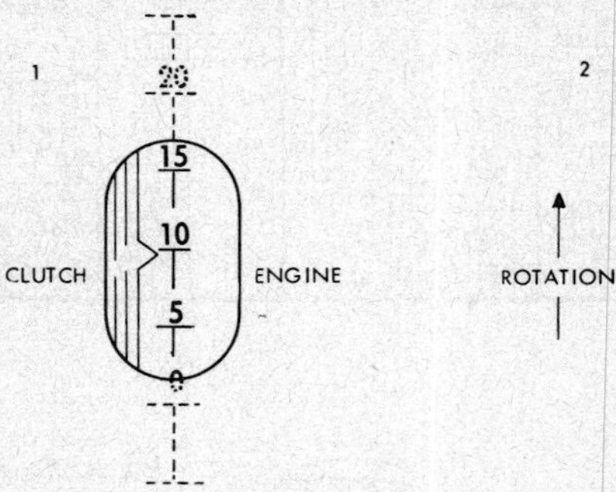

Ignition timing marks—OHC engine

below 850 rpm for all overhead cam (OHC) engines. The idle must be smooth.

NOTE: *Slowing the idle is essential to keep the centrifugal advance in the distributor from engaging.*

4. Rotate the distributor as necessary to align the timing marks with the strobe or timing light.

CAUTION: *When working on a vehicle with the engine running, the following precautions must be observed:*

1. Work only in a well ventilated area.

2. Be certain that the transmission is in Neutral and the parking brake is firmly applied.

3. Always keep your hands, clothing, and tools clear of the moving radiator fan.

Valve Lash

While all valve adjustments must be as accurate as possible, it is better to have the valve adjustment slightly loose than slightly tight, as burned valves may result from overly tight adjustments.

1. Adjust the valves cold.

2. Set each piston to top dead center (TDC) of the compression stroke and adjust the intake valve to 0.014 in. and the exhaust valve to 0.016 in. For overhead cam engines, turn to the "engine" section for OHC valve clearance adjustments.

NOTE: *For best results, recheck the valve clearance immediately after a road test.*

Carburetor and Fuel Injection

(See "Fuel Systems" for further information and adjustments)

Fuel Injection

CAUTION: *Electronic fuel injection is a highly complex system, requiring specialized tools and training to service. Do not attempt other than the basic adjustments described below without this equipment and knowledge, otherwise serious damage to the system and the engine may result.*

Bosch Electronic Fuel Injection is based on a computer-like device that accurately monitors engine functions. The computer monitors engine speed, engine load (manifold vacuum), throttle position, coolant and air temperature and translates this data into injection duration for the injectors and the enrichment valve. Fuel is supplied by a constant pressure fuel loop consisting of an electronic fuel pump, fuel line, a pressure regulator, and return line. Excess fuel bypasses the injectors and is returned to the tank and pump to be recirculated, maintaining constant pressure in the fuel loop. Air is supplied, through a single throttle valve, by a four branch manifold.

Idle Speed Adjustment

V-4 Engine

The idle speed must be adjusted with the engine at normal operating temperature and the headlights switched on.

1. Turn the slow speed adjustment screw slightly clockwise so that the engine speed is slightly increased.

2. Slowly turn in the volume control screw until the engine begins to run unevenly, then slowly back off approximately ¼ turn to achieve the best idle setting. The volume control screw must never be screwed in so hard that it bottoms.

3. Screw the volume control screw slowly in or out until the engine runs at the prescribed idling speed.

Fuel Injected Engines

To adjust the idle speed, turn to the "Fuel System" section and follow the procedures for checking and adjusting fuel injection.

ENGINE ELECTRICAL

Distributor

V-4 Engines

The distributor, Bosch JFUR 4, is installed at the rear of the engine; it rotates in a clockwise direction. It is equipped with both centrifugal and vacuum advance; centrifugal advance regulating ignition timing with relation to engine speed and vacuum advance regulating ignition timing with relation to load.

OHC Engines

The SAAB 99 uses two types of distributors, depending on engine equip-

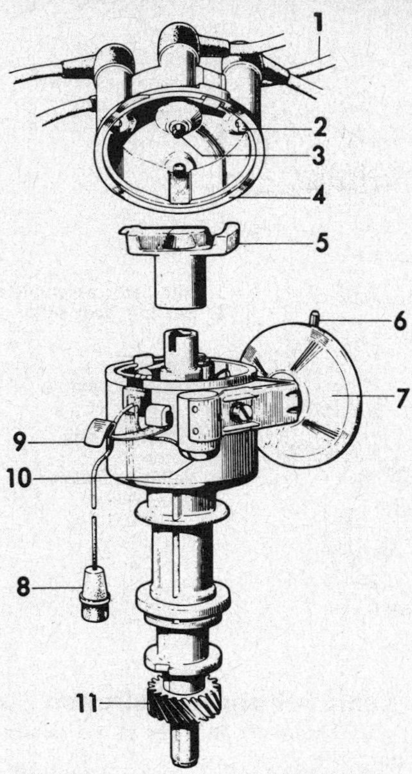

Distributor exploded view—V-4 engine

1. Spark plug wire
2. Contact
3. Center carbon button
4. Distributor cap
5. Rotor
6. Vacuum hose connection
7. Vacuum chamber
8. Ignition primary wire
9. Retaining spring
10. Condenser
11. Drive gear

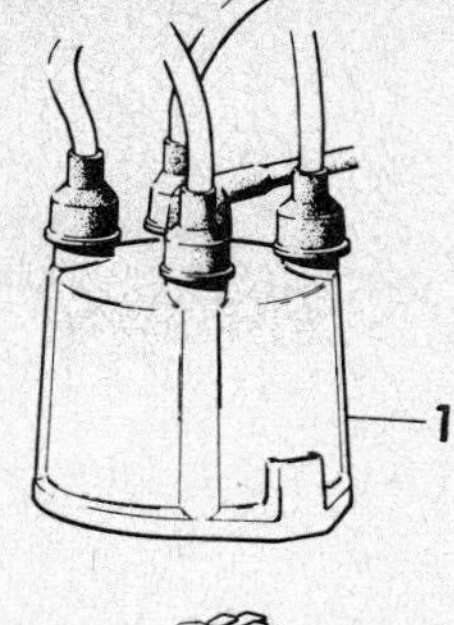

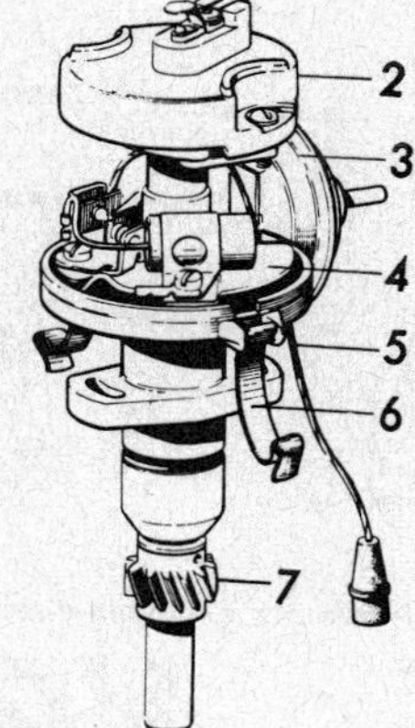

Distributor—Delco, OHC engine

1. Distributor cap
2. Rotor
3. Vacuum control unit
4. Breaker plate
5. Low-voltage wire
6. Spring clip
7. Drive gear

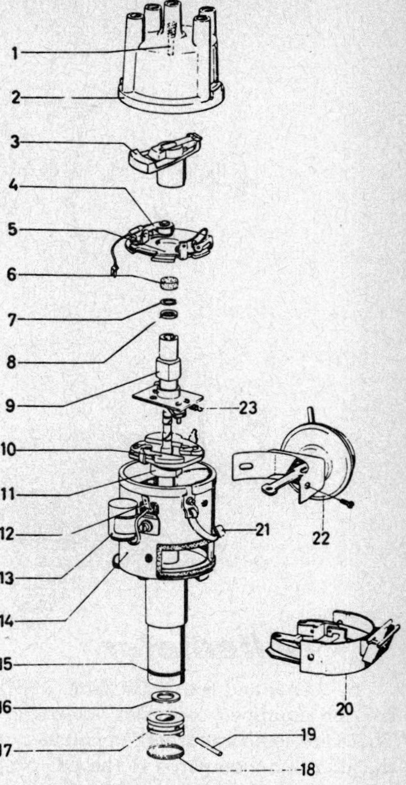

Distributor—Bosch, OHC engine

1. Rod brush (carbon)
2. Distributor cap
3. Distributor arm
4. Contact breaker
5. Breaker plate
6. Lubricating felt
7. Circlip
8. Washer
9. Breaker cam
10. Centrifugal weight
11. Cam for triggering contacts
12. Primary terminal
13. Capacitor
14. Distributor body
15. Rubber seal
16. Washers
17. Driving collar
18. Resilient ring
19. Lock pin
20. Contact device
21. Lock clasp for dist. cap
22. Vacuum regulator
23. Centrifugal governor spring

ment. Carbureted versions use a Delco distributor, while fuel injected engines use a Bosch distributor. The Bosch unit is equipped with a secondary set of contacts, mounted in the distributor lower housing, used to signal engine speed to the fuel injection computer.

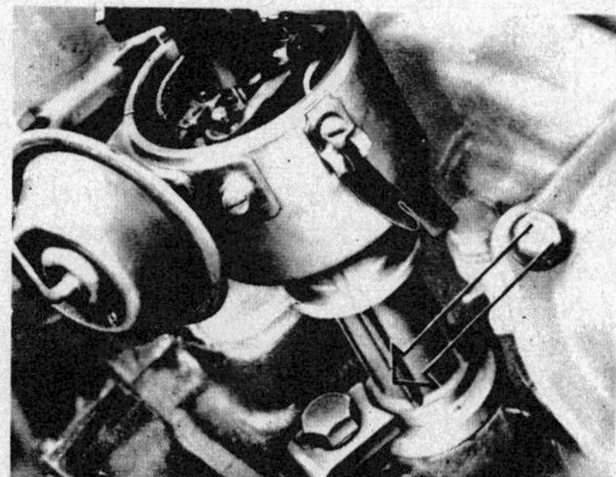

Distributor hold down clamp

Removal and Installation

All Models

1. Remove the wires from the spark plugs.
2. Release the retaining springs and remove the cap.
3. Remove the primary wire.
4. Remove the vacuum hose.
5. Crank the engine until the mark on the rotor and the mark on the distributor housing are directly opposite each other. This is the firing position for No. 1 cylinder (6° BTDC).
6. Unscrew the retaining clamp screw and remove the clamp.
7. Remove the distributor from the engine.
8. Turn the distributor until the rotor is directly opposite the assembly mark.
9. Insert the distributor into the engine.
10. See that the gears mesh properly. Rock the engine back and forth until the distributor shaft engages the oil pump driveshaft properly.
11. Make sure that the mark on the pulley coincides with the 6° mark on the transmission cover (firing position for No. 1 cylinder).
12. Turn the distributor housing so that the mark on the rotor is directly opposite the mark on the edge of the distributor housing.
13. Adjust the ignition timing.
14. Tighten the retaining clamp slightly with the screw so that the distributor can still be turned.
15. Connect the primary wire.
16. Connect a dwellmeter and adjust the dwell angle at starter rpm.
17. Install the cap (the correct position is indicated by the rear retaining spring). Secure it with retaining springs and connect the spark plug wires.
18. Connect a timing light and adjust ignition timing at starter rpm, or start the engine and let it run at 500 rpm. At higher engine speeds, the centrifugal governor begins to operate and invalidates the reading.
19. Tighten the distributor clamp.
20. Adjust the idle speed rpm.

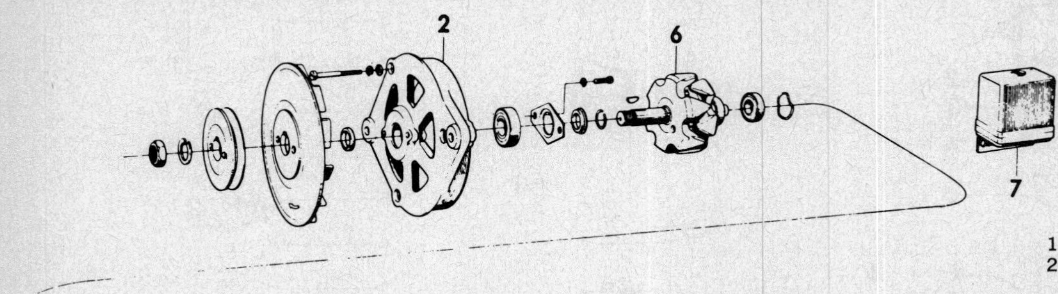

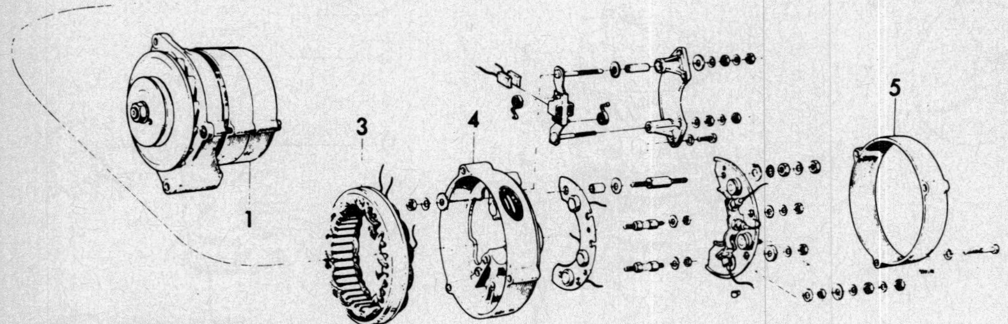

1. Alternator assembly
2. Bearing, gear side
3. Stator
4. Slip ring bearing
5. Protective ring
6. Rotor
7. Voltage regulator

Alternator exploded view

Alternator

The SAAB and SAAB 99 (from 1967) are all equipped with an alternator. There are some important advantages of the alternator compared to the DC generator. For example, the charging current begins earlier with an alternator and supplies the battery and electrical components at engine idle speed. Return current relays and current regulators are not used; only a voltage regulator is required. The alternator requires very little maintenance, because carbon brushes and commutators are not needed. Repair of the alternator should be done by a specialized shop.

Alternator Precautions

When servicing the charging system of vehicles equipped with an AC generator, the following precautions should be taken to avoid damaging the system:

1. Never operate the alternator on an open circuit (battery disconnected).
2. When installing a battery, connect the ground terminal (negative) before connecting the positive terminal.
3. When arc welding *anywhere* on the vehicle always disconnect the alternator.

Removal and Installation

Disconnect the battery ground cable and all wires from the alternator. Remove the two mounting bolts and the fanbelt, and remove the alternator. Install in the reverse order of removal.

Belt Tension Adjustments

1. Loosen the two (2) screws which attach the alternator so it will move freely.

Checking the belt tension

1. Adjusting screw
2. Retaining screw

2. Adjust the tension of the drive belt. The tension should be depressed about 0.4 in. (10mm) under thumb pressure, or a load of 3.5 lbs (1.5kp).
3. Tighten the two (2) attaching screws and recheck the belt tension.

Regulator

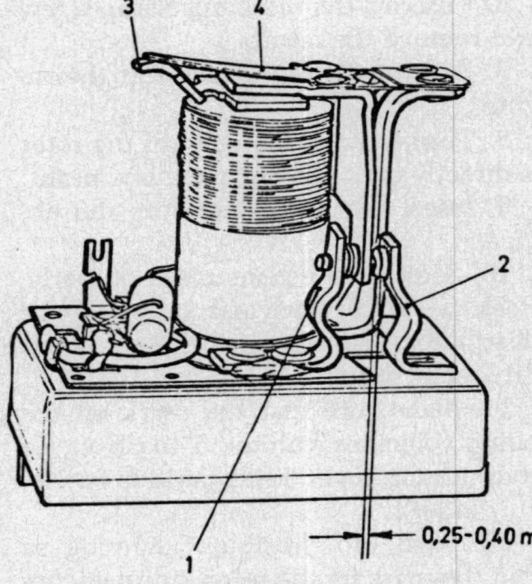

Voltage regulator

1. Lower contact
2. Upper contact
3. Adjusting arm
4. Spring

Removal and Installation

1. Disconnect all wires to the regulator.
2. Remove the attaching screws from the base of the regulator and remove the voltage regulator from the car.

Cut-in, Cut-out, Air Gap Adjustments

1. To test the regulator cut-out/cut-in voltage, connect an ammeter between the B+ terminal of the alternator and ground.
2. Start the engine, adjust the idle to 2000 rpm, and observe the ammeter reading. The alternator should produce 2/3 of its maximum output.
3. If the ammeter reading is outside specifications, remove the regulator cover and adjust by bending the spring tensioner rod.

NOTE: *Bending the tensioner downward will lower the cut-in voltage and bending it upward will increase cut-out voltage.*

4. Check the air gap with a feeler gauge and adjust by bending the upper contact arm.

NOTE: *After making each adjustment, lower the engine speed to idle and recheck the charging system.*

Starter

The starter is an electric motor which, at the moment of starting, turns the flywheel through a pinion and ring gear. The starter pinion can slide on the armature shaft and is designed to mesh with the ring gear through operation of a solenoid. As soon as the engine has started, the pinion, driven by the flywheel ring gear, is released from the armature shaft

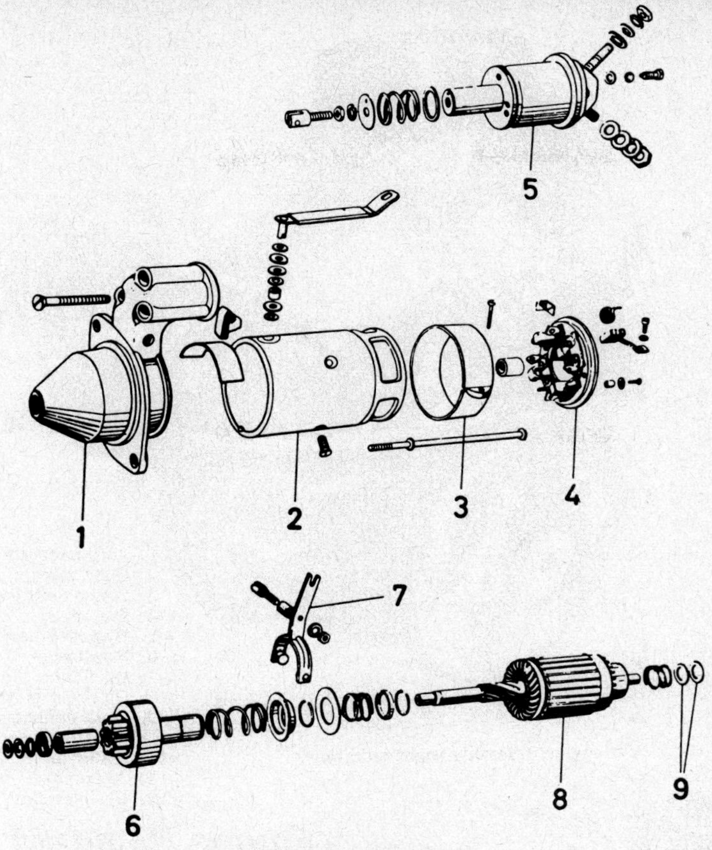

Starter motor assembly

1. Pinion housing
2. Starter housing
3. Cover band
4. Commutator end frame
5. Operating solenoid
6. Starter drive
7. Solenoid lever
8. Armature
9. Armature brake washers

by a freewheel mechanism, but remains in mesh with the ring gear as long as the solenoid is kept activated by the ignition key. The pinion is returned by a spring as soon as the current for the solenoid is cut off with the key.

Removal and Installation

1. Disconnect the negative battery cable.

NOTE: *If equipped with 55 Amp alternator, remove the cooler lines from the back of the alternator.*

2. Disconnect the wires from the starter motor.
3. Loosen the bolts which hold the starter to the crankcase lower half. (Use a short, ½ in. open end wrench with two ends.)
4. Pull back the starter until it is clear, then lift it out of the engine compartment.
5. Install in the reverse order of removal.

Starter Drive Replacement

1. Remove the starter from its mounting position on the engine.
2. Disconnect the wire which runs from the solenoid to the starter housing.
3. Remove the solenoid retaining screws.
4. Unhook the solenoid from the engaging lever arm and remove the solenoid.
5. Remove the two screws which hold the drive housing to the starter housing.
6. Pull the drive housing from the starter housing.

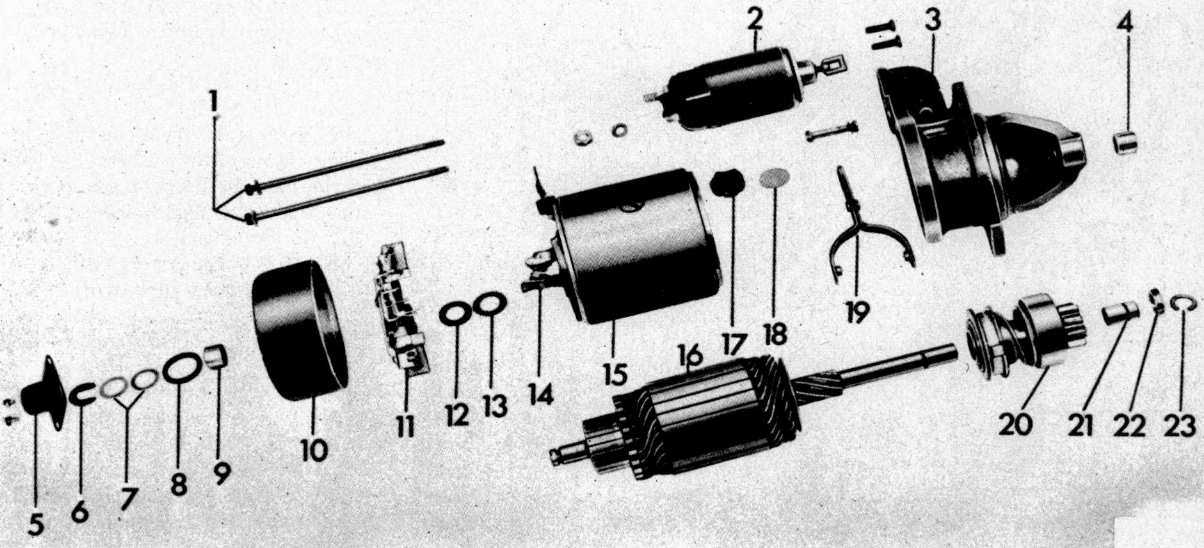

Starter motor exploded view

1. Screws, commutator end frame
2. Solenoid switch
3. Pinion housing
4. Bearing bushing, drive side
5. Protective cap
6. U-shaped washer
7. Shims
8. Rubber gasket
9. Bearing bushing, commutator side
10. Commutator end frame
11. Brush plate assembly
12. Fiber washer
13. Steel washer
14. Field winding
15. Starter housing
16. Armature
17. Rubber washer
18. Steel washer
19. Engaging lever
20. Starter pinion
21. Bearing, bushing, starter pinion
22. Stop ring
23. Retaining ring

7. Push down the stop-ring and remove the lock-ring with lock-ring pliers.

8. Remove the stop-ring and pull the starter drive from the armature shaft.

9. Remove any burrs on the armature shaft and check all other parts for cracks or excessive wear.

10. Install in the reverse order of removal.

Battery

The battery is a 12-volt, lead-acid type with six cells. The electrolyte is dilute sulfuric acid having a normal specific gravity of 1.28 at 68° F. with the battery fully charged. From 1967–1970, all cars are equipped with 44 Amp./hr. batteries. The output is 2.2 Amps. for 20 hours. 1971–73 models have a 60 Amp./hr. battery. The positive terminal of the battery is connected to the starter and other units, the negative terminal is grounded to the chassis.

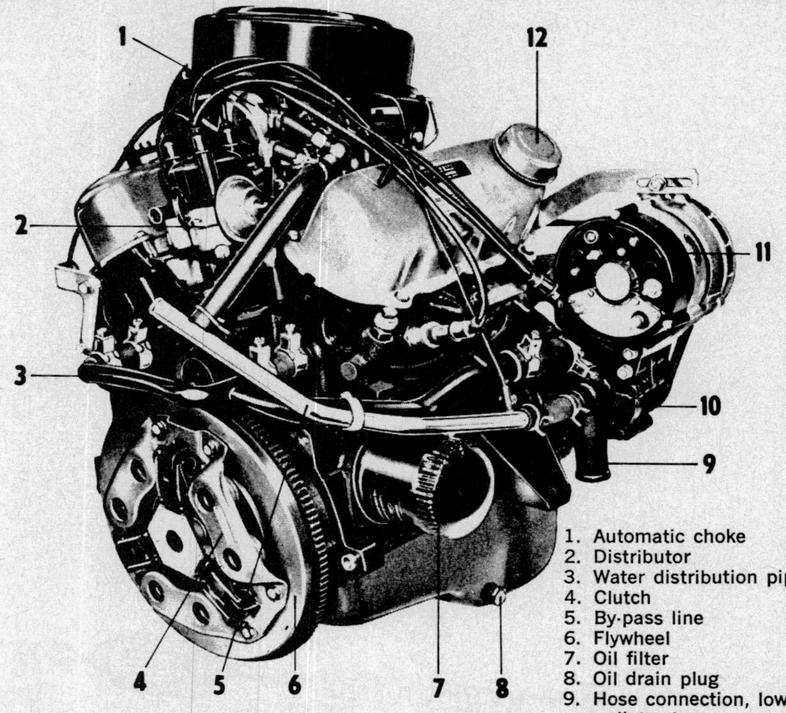

V-4 engine assembly (right side view)

1. Automatic choke
2. Distributor
3. Water distribution pipe
4. Clutch
5. By-pass line
6. Flywheel
7. Oil filter
8. Oil drain plug
9. Hose connection, lower radiator hose
10. Water pump
11. Alternator
12. Oil filler cap

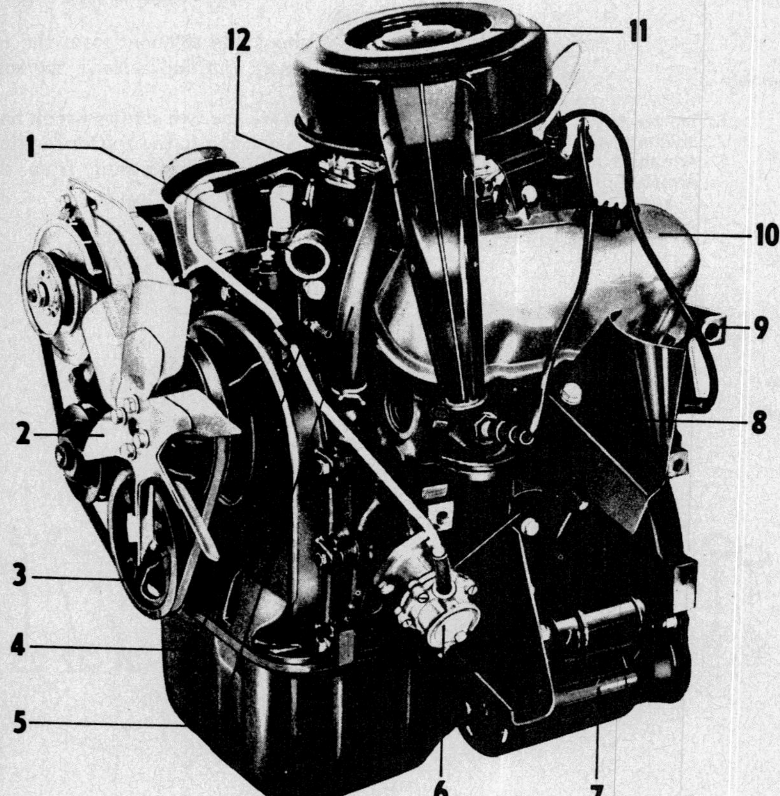

V-4 engine assembly (left side view)

1. Hose connection, upper radiator hose
2. Water pump
3. Balance shaft pulley
4. Temperature transmitter
5. Hose, crankcase ventilation
6. Fuel pump
7. Starter
8. Preheater plate
9. Bracket, engine side stay
10. Valve casing
11. Air filter
12. Carburetor

Engine Removal and Installation

V-4 Engine

NOTE: *If work is to be done on the engine only, the entire power unit should be removed and the engine separated from the transmission. Removal of the engine alone is not recommended.*

1. Disconnect the battery ground cable.

2. To remove the hood, first open it wide enough to remove the locking springs for the hood hinges. Now, bend the hood brace slightly inward to release the pin on one side.

NOTE: *On the Sonett V4, remove the two pivot bolts, then, with the help of an assistant, lift off the hood.*

3. Drain the engine oil and cooling water.

4. Disconnect the headlight and turn signal wires.

NOTE: *This must be done before removing the hood on Sonetts.*

5. Loosen the four screws that hold the grille panel and remove the two radiator supports. Detach the clamping straps from the radiator, then remove the hood lock and control wire.

6. Remove the grille panel, being careful not to damage the paint.

7. Disconnect the upper and lower radiator hoses.

8. Loosen the lower radiator retaining bolts and remove the radiator.

OHC engine assembly (right side, carbureted engine).

1. Carburetor
2. Crankcase ventilation valve
3. Camshaft cover
4. Alternator
5. Front axle universal joint
6. Engine bracket
7. Transmission
8. Starter
9. Primary gear housing
10. Clutch cover
11. Distributor

OHC engine assembly (left side, carbureted engine)

1. Air cleaner
2. Oil pressure switch
3. Oil pump
4. Oil filter
5. Oil dipstick
6. Gear control
7. Crankshaft pulley

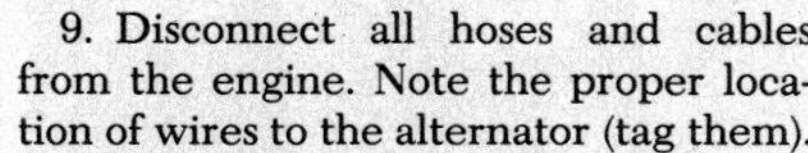

9. Disconnect all hoses and cables from the engine. Note the proper location of wires to the alternator (tag them).

10. Remove the air cleaner.

11. Disconnect the throttle control, engine side support, and air preheat casing.

12. Remove the flange nuts for the exhaust pipes at the cylinder heads. Remove the lower exhaust pipe clamps at the engine mounting pads.

13. Remove the rubber cushions for the middle exhaust pipe (under the floor).

14. Remove the spacers at the cylinder heads and lower the muffler as far as possible.

15. Remove the two front engine mounts (from above).

16. Disconnect the freewheel control.

17. Remove the rear retaining bolt for the clutch cylinder and wire the unit out of the way. Collect and save any shims used between the cylinder and transmission.

18. Remove the gearshift joint from the transmission, after removing the tapered pin.

19. Disconnect the speedometer cable.

20. Lift the floor mat and remove the rubber plug so the center bolt of the rear engine bracket becomes accessible. Remove the bolt, using a 9/16 in. socket and extension.

21. Jack up the car and place jackstands under the front edges of the sills so that the front wheels clear the floor.

22. Remove the large clamps from around the rubber boots on the universal joints.

23. Attach a suitable lifting device to the engine.

24. Connect the lifting device to a suitable lifting hook, carefully lift the engine about 2 in. and pull the transmission stub out of the rear engine bracket.

25. Disconnect the inner universal joints, first on the right side, then on the left. Do this with the T-shaped pieces of the driveshafts located vertically and with the engine pushed as far as possible in the opposite direction.

Lifting engine assembly with special tool

26. Lift the engine transmission unit out of the engine compartment. Make sure the distributor vacuum chamber does not hit the cross brace.

27. Before installing make sure that the inner universal joints are filled with the proper grease.

28. Lower the engine-transmission unit into the engine compartment, using the lifting device.

29. Lower it just far enough so that the engine brackets are about 0.2 in. from the engine mounts.

30. Place the T-pieces of the inner shafts into the inner universal joints. Do this with the T-pieces located vertically and with the power unit pushed over as far as possible in the opposite direction. First assemble the left side, then the right.

31. Attach the engine side support; tighten it after the engine is in place.

32. Install the engine in the reverse order of removal.

NOTE: *After installation has been completed, be sure to check all fluid levels in the engine and transmission.*

CAUTION: *When the engine is started after installation, be sure to check oil pressure immediately.*

OHC Engine

NOTE: *The power train is removed as a unit. Removing only the engine is not recommended.*

1. Mark the position of the hood brackets on the hood hinges, loosen the mounting bolts, and with an assistant, lift off the hood.

2. Detach both battery cables, unclamp and lift out the battery.

3. Disconnect the coil and ballast resistor, temperature and oil pressure senders, radiator fan and thermostat contact.

4. Drain the coolant from the radiator and engine block, and disconnect the upper and lower radiator hoses from the engine.

5. Disconnect the brake assist vacuum hose from the intake manifold, and (if

carbureted) the suction line from the fuel pump. If fuel injected, disconnect all injection wiring connectors, vacuum lines, and fuel input and return lines from the engine.

6. Remove the air cleaner and preheater casing, disconnect the throttle linkage from the throttle shaft, and the choke cable from the carburetor (if so equipped).

7. Unbolt the slave cylinder and hang it in an out-of-the-way position.

8. Move the freewheel lever into the locked position, and disconnect the cable from the transmission.

9. Disconnect the exhaust pipe from the exhaust manifold, and remove the ground cable from the transmission.

Gear shift rod joint assembly—SAAB 99

10. Raise the front end of the car, put the gear lever in Neutral, knock out the front taper pin from the shift rod joint, and separate the shift rod joint from the gear selector rod.

11. Remove the speedometer cable from the transmission.

12. Unbolt all engine mounts and support the power train at its lifting brackets with a hoist.

13. Remove the larger clips on the rubber bellows which cover the inner U-joints.

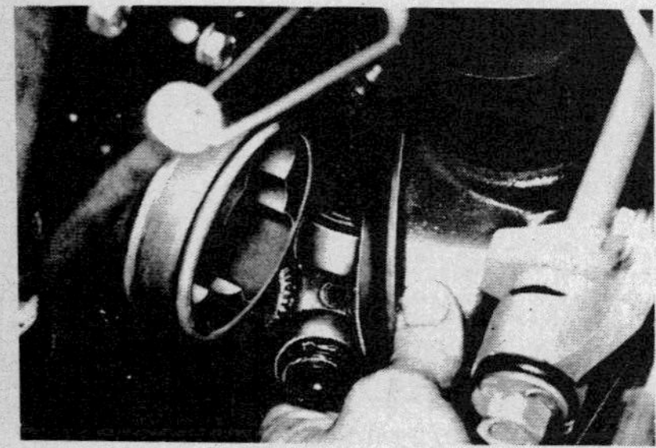

Removing the inner U-joint

14. On 1969 models, rotate the axle until the U-joint trunnions are horizontal, raise the power train approximately 2 in., move it as far right as possible, and separate the left U-joint. Move the power train as far left as possible and separate the right U-joint.

NOTE: *Ensure that the needle bearing caps remain on the U-joint.*

15. On 1970–73 models, unbolt the right-hand lower ball joint from the lower control arm. Turn the steering wheel to left lock, and separate the right U-joint. Raise the power train slightly, and separate the left U-joint.

16. On all models, raise the power train to gain access, and disconnect all wires from the starter and alternator.

17. Lift the power train out of the car.

18. Installation of the power train is the reverse of removal.

19. When installing, pack the inner U-joints with grease.

20. After lowering the power train onto its mounts, ensure that the throttle control shaft is inserted into its bearing.

NOTE: *When installing carbureted engines, ensure that adequate clearance (½ in.) exists between the alternator belt and the fuel line.*

Cylinder Head

Removal and Installation

V-4 Engine

NOTE: *To ease cylinder head removal, remove the hood.*

1. Remove the air cleaner, distributor cap, and wires.

2. Disconnect the vacuum lines to the distributor, carburetor, and intake manifold.

3. Unbolt the distributor and remove it from the engine.

4. Disconnect the fuel lines and any electrical wires to the carburetor.

5. Remove the carburetor and valve covers.

6. Unbolt the intake manifold and remove it from the engine.

Removing the rocker arm assembly—V-4 engine.

1. Rocker shaft and arms
2. Oil return plate

7. Remove the rocker arm assembly by alternate slackening of the two (2) bolts and remove the oil return plates.

8. Pull the pushrods out and be sure to keep them in the correct sequence.

9. Unbolt the cylinder head and remove it from the engine.

10. Remove all old head gasket material and thoroughly clean all contact surfaces.

11. Using a new gasket, replace the cylinder head onto the engine and tighten the bolts in three (3) stages to the prescribed torque.

12. Continue installation in reverse of the removal sequence.

OHC Engine

CAUTION: *Remove the cylinder head only with the engine cold, to prevent warpage.*

1. Drain the coolant from the radiator, engine block and heater bleeder, and disconnect all coolant hoses from the cylinder head.

2. Remove the air cleaner, the preheater hose and the preheater casing, and disconnect the brake assist vacuum line from the intake manifold.

3. On carbureted engines, remove the fuel output line from the fuel pump and disconnect the throttle and choke control from the carburetor.

4. On fuel injected engines, disconnect all hoses and electrical connectors from the intake manifold and disconnect the throttle control.

5. Unbolt the exhaust pipe from the exhaust manifold.

Camshaft index marks—OHC engine

6. Remove the camshaft cover and rotate the engine until the camshaft index marks align. Screw a nut onto the threaded stud in the camshaft sprocket and tighten securely against the mounting plate.

NOTE: *The nut must prevent movement of the camshaft sprocket, otherwise the chain tensioner will adjust and the engine will have to be removed to readjust the tensioner.*

7. Loosen and remove all cylinder head bolts and nuts in the reverse of the torque sequence.

8. Remove two cylinder head studs using a large screwdriver and screw them into two lower bolt holes to act as guides for removal.

9. Remove the remaining studs and lift off the cylinder heads.

10. Carefully scrape all old gasket material from the mating surfaces (do not use emery cloth) and check both the cylinder head and block for distortion using a straightedge.

11. Install a new gasket (uncoated) using the studs as locating pins.

12. Align the camshaft index marks and install the cylinder head over the locating studs.

13. Screw the center studs into their

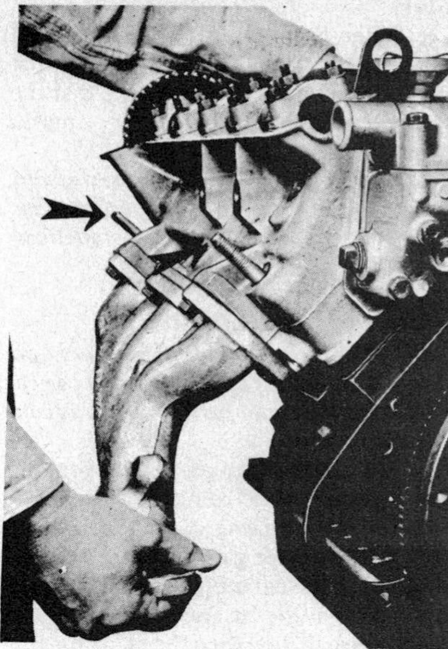
Cylinder head locating pin—OHC engine

original position, then relocate the studs used as locating pins to their original position.

14. Install the nuts and bolts, torque as specified, and mount the camshaft sprocket on the camshaft.

NOTE: *Do not remove the nut from the camshaft sprocket center stud until the sprocket is mounted on the camshaft.*

15. Lock the camshaft sprocket bolt and continue in the reverse of removal.

Overhaul

(See "Engine Rebuilding")

Rocker Shafts

Removal and Installation (V-4 Engine Only)

1. Remove the valve cover from the side to be worked on.
2. Release the rocker arm assembly by alternately loosening the two (2) bolts.
3. Remove the rocker arm assembly and the oil return plates.
4. Install in the reverse of the removal sequence.

Intake Manifold
Removal and Installation
V-4 Engines

1. Remove the air cleaner and drain the radiator.
2. Disconnect the battery.
3. Remove the distributor cap and ignition wires.
4. Unbolt the distributor and remove it from the engine.
5. Disconnect the fuel lines, vacuum lines, and the throttle linkage to the carburetor.
6. Remove the carburetor and the valve covers.
7. Unbolt the intake manifold and remove it from the engine.

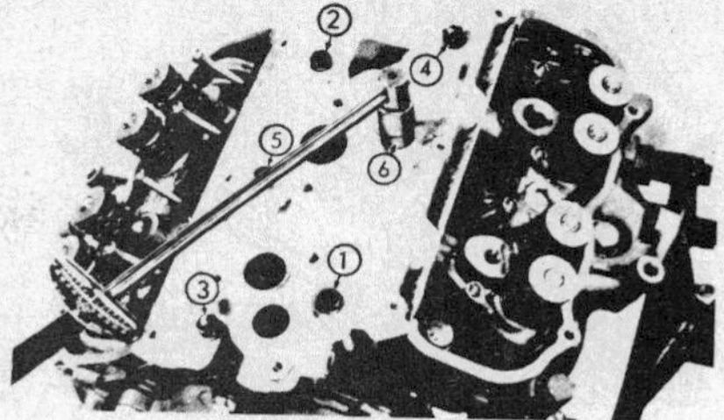

Installing the intake manifold—V-4 engine

8. Install in the reverse of the removal sequence.

NOTE: *Be sure to thoroughly clean all machined surfaces before reinstalling the cylinder head.*

OHC Engines

1. Detach all fuel and vacuum lines and electrical connectors from the intake manifold and carburetor (if so equipped).
2. On fuel injected engines, separate the fuel distributor tube from the injectors and the enrichment valve, and cap the injectors and the valve to prevent dirt from entering.
3. Remove the preheater hose and the air cleaner and disconnect the throttle and choke control (if so equipped).
4. Unbolt the mounting bolts, and remove the manifold.

NOTE: *Cover the inlets in the cylinder head.*

5. Install in the reverse order of removal.

Exhaust Manifold

Removal and Installation

V-4 Engine

The exhaust system on the V-4 engine consists of a front muffler, exhaust pipes, and a rear muffler. There is no exhaust manifold used on this engine because the front mufffler is bolted directly to the cylinder head.

In the event of leakage, either tighten the bolts or, if necessary, replace the gasket between the muffler and the cylinder head.

OHC Engine

1. Remove the air cleaner and the preheater hose and casing.
2. Unbolt the exhaust pipe from the exhaust manifold.
3. Remove the manifold mounting bolts and remove the manifold from the cylinder head.
4. Install in the reverse order of removal.

Front Muffler

Removal and Installation

V4 Engine

1. Disconnect the battery ground cable.

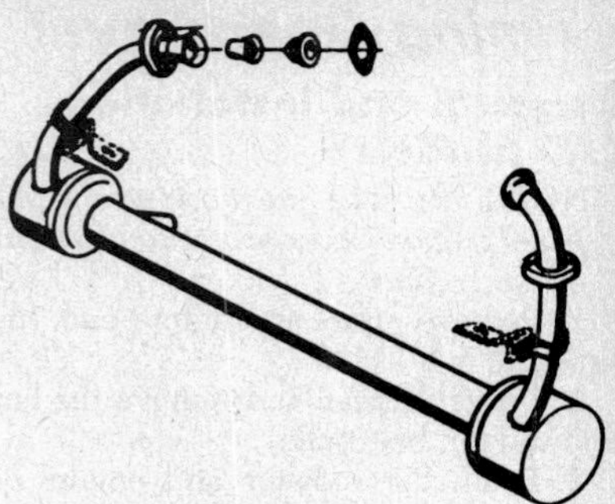
Front muffler—V-4 engine

2. Disconnect the cables and remove the starter.
3. Unbolt the flanges from the engine. Remove the spacers and flange gaskets. Unbolt the muffler support brackets from the engine.
4. Loosen the exhaust pipe clamp. Separate the exhaust pipe from the muffler. There are two exhaust pipes on the Sonett.
5. Lower the muffler. Pull the right muffler inlet pipe through the engine compartment floor and turn it forward between the front panel and the bumper. Pull out the left muffler inlet pipe.
6. Reverse the procedure to install, using new flange gaskets.

Rear Muffler

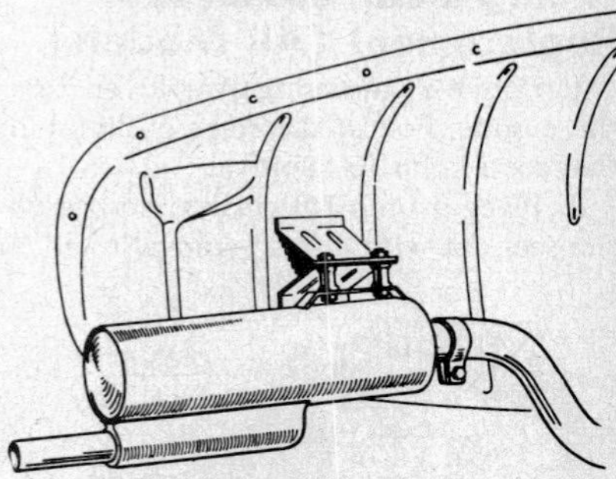
Rear muffler

Removal and Installation

All Models

1. Remove the right rear wheel.
2. Remove the two muffler support bolts. On the Sonett II, there are additional muffler support bolts.
3. Loosen the muffler clamp and remove the muffler.
4. Reverse the procedure to install.

Exhaust Pipe

Removal and Installation

All Models

1. Remove the rear muffler.
2. Loosen the exhaust pipe clamp(s) and hangers.
3. Remove the exhaust pipe.
4. Reverse the procedure to install.

Timing Gear Cover

Removal and Installation (All Models)

NOTE: *Remove the hood and front panel to gain easier access to the front of the engine.*

1. Remove the alternator and its bracket.
2. Unbolt the fan and remove the fan and the fan belt pulley.
3. Drain the radiator and engine of coolant and remove the water pump.
4. Unbolt the front of the oil pan (connected to the bottom of the timing gear cover).
5. Remove the balance shaft pulley.
6. Unbolt the timing gear cover from the front of the engine and remove it from the car.

CAUTION: *Extreme care must be taken to prevent damage to the oil pan gasket. If the oil pan gasket is damaged, it must be replaced to prevent leakage after installation of the timing cover is completed.*

7. Place a rag in the front of the oil pan to prevent foreign matter from dropping into the engine.
8. Thoroughly clean all old gasket material from the timing gear cover and the cylinder block.
9. Install in reverse of the removal procedure.

Timing Gear Cover Seal Replacement (All Models)

1. Remove the timing gear cover from the engine. Follow the steps outlined in that section for its removal.
2. Place it on a flat surface and drive the seal out with a seal removal tool.

Installing the timing gear cover oil seal—V-4 engine.

3. Drive the new seal into position and install in reverse of the removal procedure.

Timing Chain or Gear and Tensioner

Removal and Installation

V-4 Engine

1. Remove the timing gear cover by following the steps outlined in that section.

Removing the crankshaft timing gear—V-4 engine.

2. Unbolt the camshaft and crankshaft gears and, using a gear puller, remove them from the engine.
3. Remove the balance shaft gear.

Timing gear alignment marks—V-4 engine

NOTE: *Before removing any of the timing gears, align the timing marks on the gears. This will aid in installation.*

4. Install in the reverse order of removal.

CAUTION: *The timing marks must be aligned exactly as they were removed or the engine will not start.*

OHC Engine

1. With the front panel removed for easier access, unbolt and remove the crankshaft pulley using a slide hammer.
2. Remove the camshaft and timing chain covers.
3. Rotate the engine until the 0° mark on the flywheel and the mark on the side of the block align, and the camshaft index marks align.

NOTE: *The marks on the idler shaft sprocket will be horizontal.*

4. Install a nut on the camshaft sprocket stud, securely tightening the sprocket to the mounting plate.
5. Unbolt and remove the chain tensioner and the curved guide plate.
6. Unbolt the camshaft sprocket from the camshaft and the sprocket mounting plate from the block and remove the timing chain from the engine.
7. Installation is the reverse of removal.
8. When installing, apply light tension to the curved chain guide, rotate the crankshaft two turns, and ensure that the flywheel, camshaft, and idler index marks are properly aligned.

NOTE: *When installing a used chain, install so that the sides are positioned as they were in the original installation.*

Timing Gear Backlash Check (OHC Engine)

NOTE: *To check timing gear backlash, the engine must be mounted in the car with the front panel and radiator removed.*

1. Remove the timing gear cover. See that section for the removal procedure.
2. Align the timing gear marks.
3. With a feeler gauge or other means of measuring clearances, check the backlash between the balance shaft gear and the crankshaft gear. See the chart for correct tolerances.
4. Check the camshaft gear backlash to the crankshaft gear. See the chart for the correct tolerances.

	Camshaft gear in. (mm)	Balance shaft gear in. (mm)
New gears	0.0020-0.0079 (0.05-0.20)	0.0020-0.0055 (0.05-0.14)
Max backlash (wearing limit)	0.0157 (0.4)	0.0157 (0.4)

NOTE: *The camshaft gear can be replaced only with the engine in the car. If the crankshaft or balance shaft gears have to be replaced, the engine must be removed from its mounting position.*

Timing Chain Tensioner Adjustments

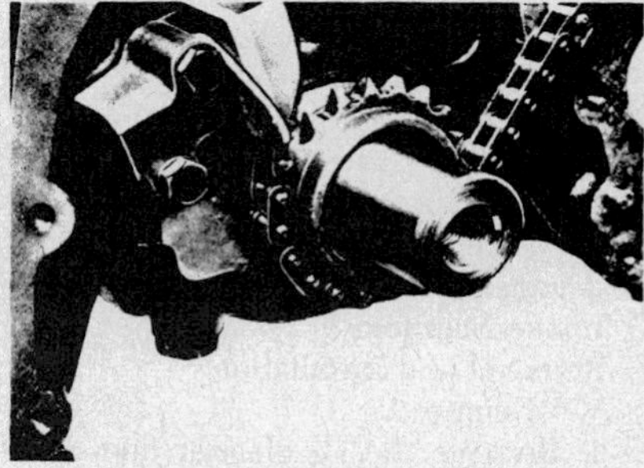

Chain tensioner assembly—OHC engine

1. With the hood removed for easier access, unbolt and remove the crankshaft pulley using a slide hammer.
2. Remove the timing chain cover and the bolt from the back of the tensioner.
3. Insert a hex key, and turn clockwise to slacken chain tension.
4. Unbolt the tensioner mounting bolts and remove the tensioner.
5. Install the tensioner as follows: Loosen the curved chain guide mounting

bolts and slacken the chain.

6. Relieve spring tension by rotating the tensioner sleeve clockwise, and insert a 0.12 in. shim on the tensioner neck (shim is supplied with the tensioner).

7. Mount the tensioner on the block with the shim installed.

8. Press firmly on the curved chain guide while removing the shim from the tensioner neck, causing the tensioner to bottom, and release slightly to actuate the tensioner.

9. Tighten the curved chain guide mounting bolts and continue installing in the reverse order of removal.

Camshaft

Removal and Installation

V-4 Engine

1. Remove the air cleaner and disconnect all the vacuum lines, fuel lines, and electrical connections to the carburetor.

2. Unbolt the fuel pump from the cylinder block

3. Remove the intake manifold and clean old gasket material from the mating surfaces.

4. Remove the valve covers and unbolt the rocker arm assemblies by slackening the bolts.

5. Take the push rods from the engine and keep them in correct sequence.

6. Remove the cylinder heads by following the steps outlined in "Cylinder Head Removal".

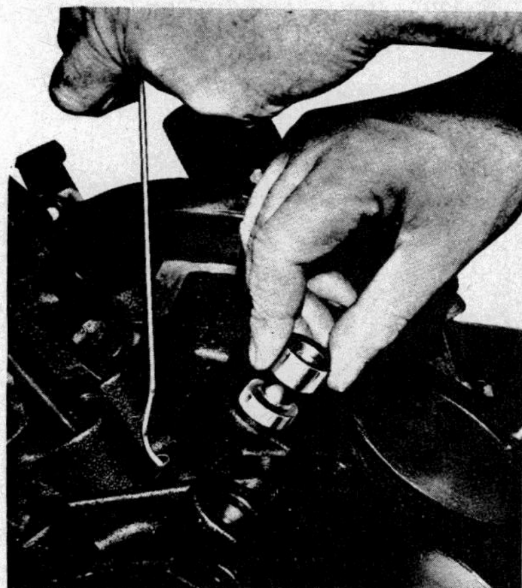

Removing tappets from the block

7. With the aid of a bent wire, remove the lifters from the cylinder block. Be sure to keep the lifters in the order of removal.

NOTE: *Extreme care must be used when removing the timing gear cover to prevent damage to the oil pan gasket.*

8. Remove the timing gear cover by following the steps outlined in that section.

9. Unbolt the camshaft gear and remove it from the engine.

10. Remove the camshaft thrust plate and pull the camshaft from the engine.

NOTE: *Care should be taken when removing the camshaft from the engine, as the bearings are of different diameters.*

11. Installation is the reverse of removal.

NOTE: *Lubricate the camshaft bearings and camshaft before reinstalling them into the engine.*

Installing camshaft thrust plate—V-4 engine.

12. When installing the thrust plate, the spacer should be checked to provide the proper end-play. A red spacer gives a smaller clearance, and a blue one gives a larger clearance. End-play is 0.00098–0.-0030 in. (0.025–0.076mm).

OHC Engine

1. Remove the camshaft cover and rotate the engine until the camshaft index marks align.

2. Install a nut on the camshaft sprocket stud and tighten, securely clamping the sprocket to the mounting plate.

NOTE: *The nut must prevent movement of the camshaft sprocket, otherwise the chain tensioner will adjust, making it impossible to install the sprocket on the camshaft.*

3. Remove the sprocket mounting bolts, gradually loosen the camshaft bearing cap nuts until valve spring pressure is released, and remove the bearing caps and camshaft.

4. Installation is the reverse of removal.

5. When installing, ensure that the camshaft index marks align.

Idler Shaft

Removal and Installation (All Models)

1. With the engine mounted in a work stand, rotate the flywheel until the camshaft index marks align.

2. Remove the intake manifold, the water pump, and the water pump shaft.

3. Mark the position of the distributor body on the block, and the rotor on the distributor body, and remove the distributor.

4. Detach the fuel lines from the fuel pump (if so equipped), and remove the pump.

5. Unbolt and remove the crankshaft pulley using a slide hammer.

6. Remove the timing chain or gear cover, and mark the position of the idler shaft sprocket on the block and the timing chain or gear.

7. Unbolt and remove the chain tensioner, loosen the curved guide rail mounting bolts, and move the rail away from the timing chain.

NOTE: *On V-4 engines, remove the timing gears with a gear puller.*

8. Lift the chain away from the idler shaft or balance shaft sprocket, remove the idler shaft or balance shaft retaining plate bolts, and slide the idler shaft out of the block.

9. Insert the idler shaft into the block and tighten the retaining plate bolts.

10. Align the index marks and engage the chain and sprocket.

11. Return the curved guide rail to its original position and tighten the mounting bolts.

12. Install the timing chain tensioner and adjust.

13. Check the condition of the timing cover seal and replace if necessary.

14. Continue installation in the reverse order of removal.

ENGINE LUBRICATION

Oil Pan

Removal and Installation

NOTE: *The oil pans on the V-4 and OHC engines are not removable with the engine installed in the car.*

V-4 Engine

1. With the engine mounted on an engine stand, drain the oil pan.

2. Unbolt all the oil pan bolts and remove the oil pan from the engine.

3. Thoroughly clean old oil pan gasket material from the mating surfaces of the oil pan.

4. Install a new oil pan gasket and continue installation in the reverse of removal.

OHC Engine

OHC engines are not equipped with an oil pan. The transmission is bolted directly to bottom of the cylinder block. To separate the engine from the transmission, follow these steps:

Manual Transmission

1. Drain the engine and transmission.

2. Remove the clutch cover and the starter.

3. Unbolt the alternator and remove the alternator drive belt.

4. Remove the clutch shaft and unbolt the clutch throw out bearing.

5. Disconnect the clutch lever.

6. Unbolt all the screws which hold the engine to the transmission and the two screws located under the transmission.

7. Lift the engine from the transmission. At the same time remove the release bearing guide sleeve.

8. Installation is the reverse of the removal procedure.

CAUTION: *The screws inserted from the block into the transmission have different threads from the ones inserted from the transmission into the engine block. Do not mix these screws or damage will occur.*

Automatic Transmission

1. Drain the engine and transmission.

NOTE: *On 1970 models, unbolt the screw located inside the crankcase using a ½ in. socket and an extension. This screw can be reached at an inward angle through the drain plug opening.*

2. Remove the flywheel ring gear cover.

3. Loosen the alternator and remove the drive belt.

4. Disconnect the throttle control cable from the throttle housing.

5. Remove the crankcase ventilation device from the engine.

6. Unbolt the engine from the transmission at the mating surfaces.

Location of the flywheel-to-torque converter attaching bolts.

7. Remove the four (4) screws which fasten the flywheel ring gear to the converter. These screws can be reached through a recess in the starter mount.

8. Carefully lift the engine from the transmission.

9. Thoroughly clean old gasket material from the mating surfaces of the engine and transmission.

10. Install in the reverse order of the removal sequence.

Rear Main Seal Replacement

V-4 Engine

1. Remove the clutch cover and unbolt the clutch, pressure plate, and fylwheel from the engine.

Separating the engine from the transmission.

2. Pull off the crankshaft seal with a seal removal tool. This tool is available through any SAAB dealer (part number 786216).

3. To install, lubricate the inner surface of the new crankshaft seal with engine oil.

4. If available, use special tool number 786217 to drive the new seal into the main bearing until it bottoms out.

5. Clean all foreign matter from the crankshaft and install the flywheel, clutch, and pressure plate.

OHC Engine

The flywheel end oil seal may be replaced with the drive train installed in the vehicle.

1. Remove the flywheel housing, the clutch and throwout bearing, and the flywheel.

2. Unbolt and remove the seal cap from the engine.

Removing the rear crankshaft seal

Removing the flywheel side crankshaft seal.

3. Pry the old seal out of the seal cap using a screwdriver and hammer.

4. Tap the new seal into the cap, lubricate the seal, and install the seal cap.

5. Ensure that the seal seats properly on the crankshaft.

NOTE: *When installing the flywheel, always use new bolts.*

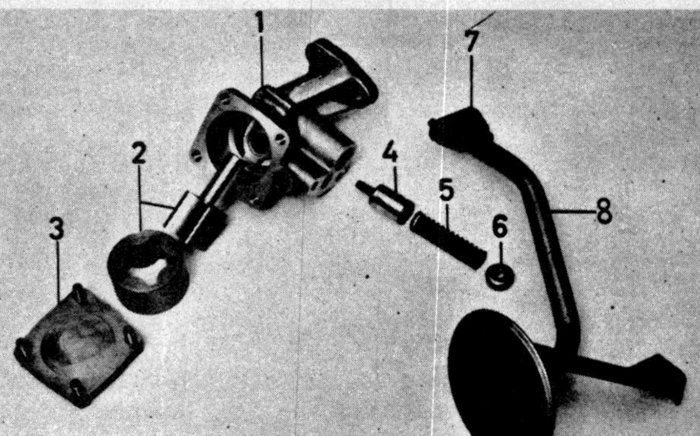

1. Housing
2. Inner and outer rotor (rotor with birotor)
3. Cover
4. Relief valve
5. Spring
6. Cover plate
7. Gasket
8. Pick-up tube

Oil Pump assembly—V-4 engine

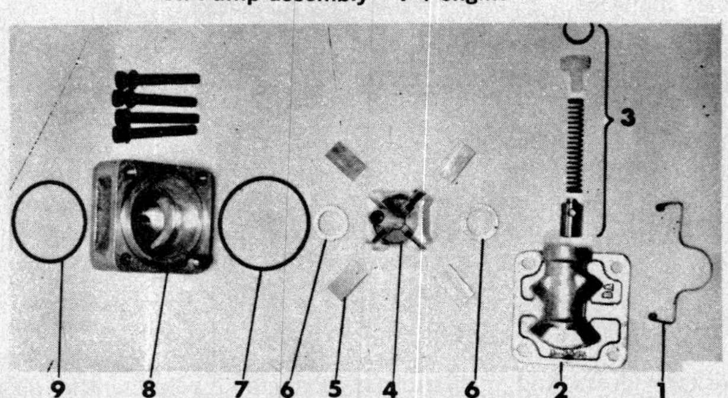

1. Spring
2. Cover
3. Pressure reducing valve
4. Rotor
5. Rotor vanes
6. Spacer rings
7. O-ring
8. Pump housing
9. O-ring

Oil Pump assembly—OHC engine

Oil Pump

Removal and Installation

V-4 Engine

1. Remove the engine from the car and support it on a suitable engine stand.
2. Drain the oil from the crankcase and unbolt the oil pan.
3. Unbolt the oil pump and pick-up tube from the engine block.
4. Remove the oil pump assembly and its drive shaft.
5. Installation is the reverse of the removal procedure.

NOTE: *When installing the oil pump drive rod, the pointed end must face the distributor.*

OHC Engine

NOTE: *To remove the oil pump from the engine, the engine must be removed from the car.*

1. Follow the steps in the "Oil Pan Removal" section for the separation of the engine from the transmission.
2. Unbolt the oil pump from the cylinder block.
3. Remove the pump with the drive rod attached.
4. When installing, always use a new sealing ring between the pump and the cylinder block.
5. Install in the reverse of the removal procedure.

Oil Pump Clearances (All Models)

1. Remove the oil pump as described under "Oil Pump Removal and Installation". Remove the oil pump cover.

Checking axial clearance in the oil pump

2. Check the clearance between the sealing surface of the pump housing and the front sides of the outer and inner rotor, using a straightedge and a feeler gauge. If necessary, grind the sealing surface of the pump housing or the rotor sides with fine emery cloth on a face plate. New inner and outer rotors are available as replacement parts.

NOTE: *All grinding dust must be removed before reassembly.*

3. Check the clearance between the outer rotor and the pump housing with a feeler gauge. If the clearance exceeds 0.012 in. with new rotors, the pump housing must be replaced.

Oil Pump Clearance Chart

Engine	Radial Clearance (in.)	Axial Clearance (in.)
V-4	0.012	0.004
OHC	0.012	0.00197-0.00354

Checking clearance of rotor-to-oil pump housing.

ENGINE COOLING

Radiator

Removal and Installation (All Models)

1. Drain the coolant from the radiator, loosen the upper and lower radiator hose clamps, and separate the hoses from the radiator.
2. Disconnect the wiring terminals from the cooling fan and thermoswitch.
3. Unbolt the four radiator retaining bolts, and lift out the radiator, the expansion tank, and the fan assembly.
4. Remove the sheet metal screws which retain the fan housing to the radiator and remove the fan housing.
5. Installation is the reverse of removal.

NOTE: *When filling with coolant, open the heater core bleeder, and set the heater control at its maximum heat position.*

6. Fill the system with coolant, start the engine, and allow it to run at moderate speed until coolant flows from the bleeder without air bubbles.
7. Close the bleeder, stop the engine, and fill the radiator to capacity.

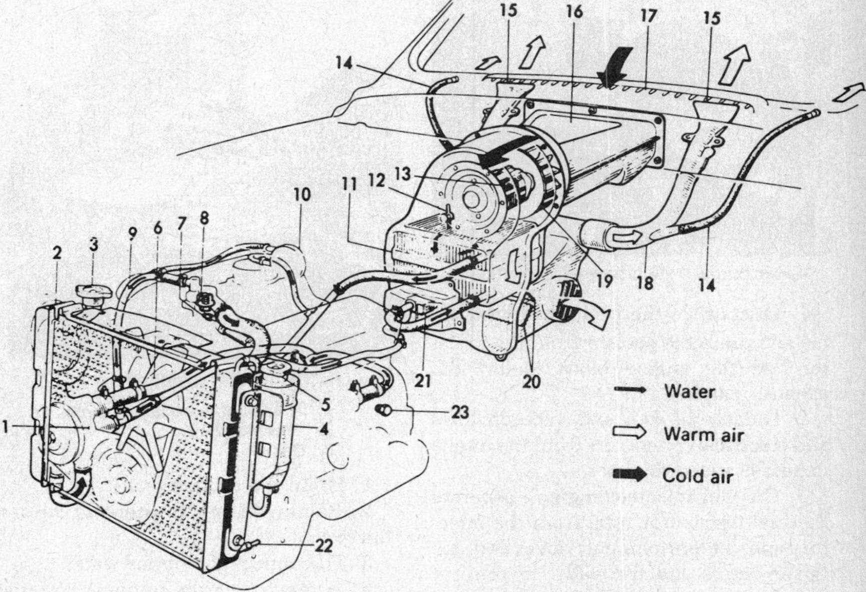

Cooling and heating systems

1. Water pump
2. Radiator
3. Radiator cap
4. Expansion tank
5. Pressure cap
6. Fan
7. Temperature transmitter
8. Thermostat
9. By-pass
10. Water jacket, automatic choke
11. Heat exchanger
12. Bleeding nipple
13. Fan motor
14. Side defroster hose
15. Defroster jet
16. Collector box
17. Cold-air intake
18. Defroster pipe
19. Fan wheel
20. Air distributor
21. Thermostat valve
22. Drain valve
23. Drain plugs (one on each side)

Water Pump

Removal and Installation

V4 Engine

Removing the water pump—V-4 engine

1. Drain the coolant.
2. Remove the alternator and bracket. Remove the belt.
3. Unbolt and remove the pump.

To replace:

Bolt the pump in place with a new gasket.

Install the alternator and bracket.

Adjust the belt. The correct belt play is 0.3 in. for all SAAB models.

OHC Engine

Water pump installation—OHC engine

1. Disconnect the battery ground cable and drain the coolant from the radiator and the engine block (below the exhaust manifold).
2. Detach all fuel and vacuum lines and electrical connectors from the intake manifold and carburetor.
3. On fuel injected engines, separate the fuel distributor tube from the injectors and the enrichment valve, and cap the injectors and the valve to prevent dirt from entering.
4. Remove the preheater hose and air cleaner and disconnect the throttle and choke control (if so equipped).
5. Unbolt the intake manifold mounting bolts, and remove the manifold.

NOTE: *Cover the inlets in the cylinder head.*

6. Remove the water pump cover (tap lightly with a plastic hammer to unseat) and turn the impeller bolt clockwise to screw the pump shaft assembly out of the block.
7. With the impeller removed, slide the pump shaft into the block, engaging the drive gears.
8. Seat the bearing housing, using a large piece of tubing and a hammer, so that the housing butts against the plane of the engine block.
9. Install the impeller and washer, tightening the bolt counterclockwise (left-hand thread).
10. Place a 0.02 in. spacer between the impeller bolt and the pump cover. Measure the clearance between the block and the cover and select the appropriate spacers. Gaskets are available in three thicknesses–0.01, 0.02, and 0.03 in.
11. Remove the shim and tighten the cover mounting bolts.
12. Install the remaining parts in the reverse of removal.

Thermostat

When servicing the thermostat, examine the check valve in the thermostat housing. If the valve is pitted or worn, it must be replaced.

NOTE: *Portions of the cooling system will not function if the check valve is not installed.*

Removal and Installation

All Models

Thermostat installation

1. Thermostat housing cover
2. Thermostat
3. Gasket

1. Drain the coolant.
2. Remove the air cleaner and the carburetor.
3. Disconnect the upper water hose.
4. Remove the bolts, upper thermostat housing, and thermostat.

To replace:

1. Insert the thermostat with the retaining bracket perpendicular to the front-rear centerline of the car. If this is not done, the thermostat will be bent, rendering it useless.
2. Install a new gasket and bolt down the upper thermostat housing.
3. Replace the water hose, carburetor, and air cleaner.
4. Refill the cooling system.

EMISSION CONTROLS

To comply with the emission control regulations in the USA, SAABs are fitted with a charcoal filter which absorbs vapor from the fuel tank. The charcoal canister is located in the engine compartment and is connected to the vent hose from the fuel tank, via a hose connected to the air cleaner. When the engine runs, fresh air is sucked through the charcoal filter and then to the carburetor.

Applications

The emission control system consists of:

1. A deceleration valve.
2. A carburetor with connections for the deceleration valve and modulating choke.
3. A modified distributor advance curve.
4. An air cleaner incorporating a thermostatically controlled valve assembly.

FUEL SYSTEM

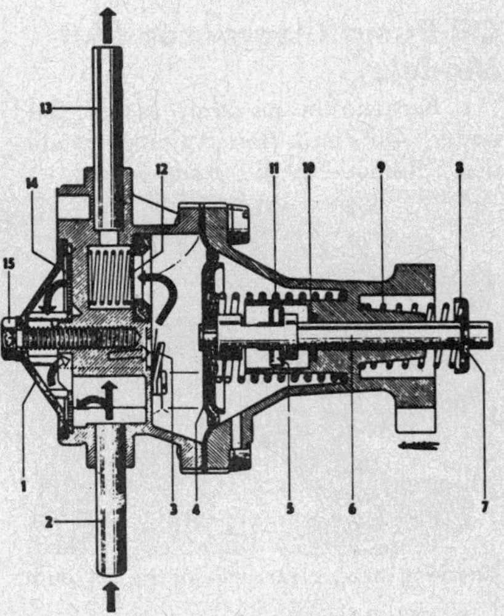

Mechanical fuel pump assembly

1. Cover
2. Fuel inlet
3. Inlet valve
4. Diaphragm
5. Retaining pin
6. Diaphragm rod
7. Lock washer
8. Retaining washer
9. Return spring
10. Seal
11. Compression spring
12. Outlet valve
13. Fuel outlet
14. Filter
15. Screw for cover

Mechanical Fuel Pump

The fuel pump is a diaphragm type and is located on the left-hand side of the engine.

Removal and Installation

1. Remove the fuel line from the pump.
2. Remove the nuts and lockwashers, then remove the pump, pushrod, and the old gasket.
3. Always use a new gasket and mark the end of the pushrod which rests against the camshaft for easy assembly.
4. Installation is the reverse of removal.

Testing and Adjustments

The fuel filter and the pump diaphragm are the only serviceable parts.

1. To replace the filter, remove the cover retaining bolt, the cover, and the filter (the filter may be serviced with the pump installed in the vehicle).
2. To replace the diaphragm, remove the pump and mark the relative position of the upper and lower pump halves.
3. Separate the pump halves, press the diaphragm down and rotate it ¼ turn clockwise and remove the diaphragm.
4. Install in the reverse order of removal, checking to ensure that the index marks on the pump halves align.

Electric Fuel Pump (Fuel Injected Engines)

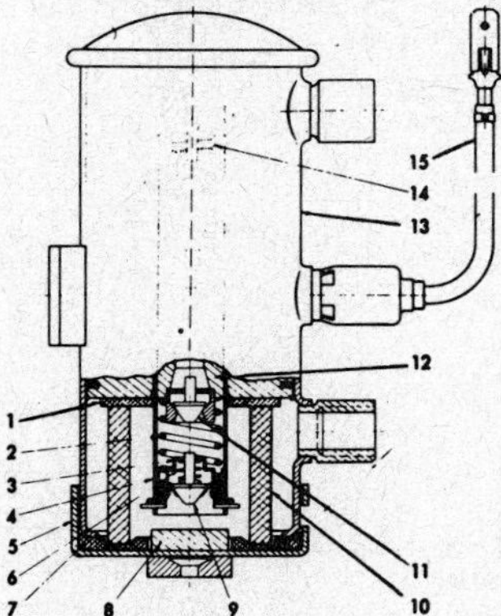

Electric fuel pump assembly

1. Gasket
2. Plunger spring
3. Spring retainer
4. Valve housing
5. Bayonet cap
6. Valve spring
7. Gasket
8. Magnetic body
9. Valve
10. Filter
11. Valve
12. Plunger
13. Pump housing
14. Damping spring
15. Electrical connection

Removal and Installation (All Models)

1. Remove the panelling to the left of the spare tire in the trunk.
2. Loosen the three retaining screws and pull the fuel pump panel forward.
3. Clamp off and code the fuel hoses for identification.
4. Unbolt the two attaching nuts, and remove the fuel pump together with the rubber pads and the fuel lines.
5. Remove the fuel lines from the pump.
6. Install in the reverse order of removal.

NOTE: *Install the fuel hoses in the following sequence: suction side, pressure side, and return side.*

Testing and Adjustments

The electric fuel pump is sealed and therefore is serviced as a unit. A fuel filter, which must be replaced every 6,000 miles, is also mounted on the fuel pump panel in the trunk. When replacing the filter, ensure that the arrow embossed on the filter housing points in the direction of fuel flow.

Carburetors

The carburetor used on the V-4 engine, up to and including all 1968 models, is a Solex down-draft. The model used most commonly is a 32 PDSIT-4.

For 1969–70, the Solex carburetor was replaced with a FoMoCo carburetor. The difference is that the main metering jet is removable and it is equipped with an automatic choke.

In 1971, to meet federal regulations, the FoMoCo carburetor was modified with narrower tolerances and each carburetor has been subjected to a flow test.

The overhead cam (OHC) engine in the SAAB 99 uses a Zenith-Stromberg cross-flow carburetor, model 175CD-2SE. This carburetor uses non-adjustable metering jets, an overflow valve, an air adjusting screw, and vacuum line connections for the emission control system.

Removal and Installation (All Models)

1. Drain some of the cooling water.
2. Remove the air filter.
3. Disconnect the lines from the automatic choke.
4. Disconnect the throttle control linkage and the vacuum line.
5. Disconnect the fuel line.

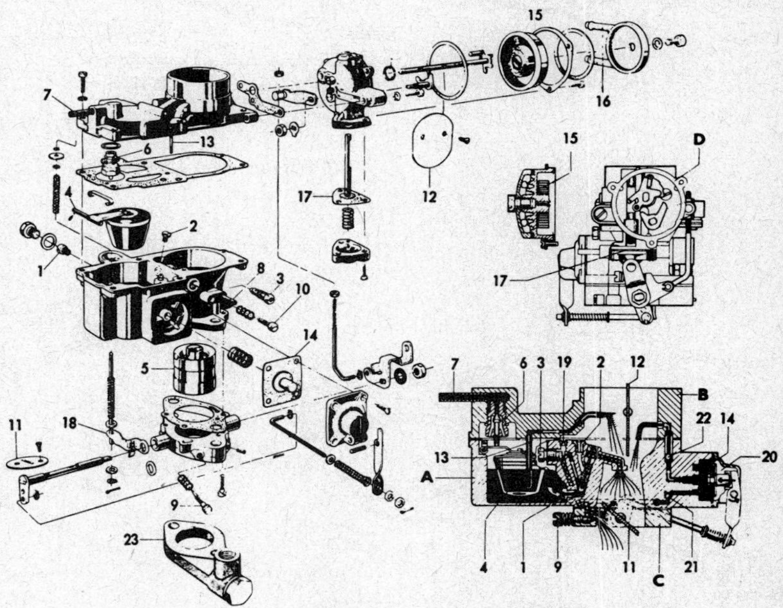

Carburetor—V-4 engine 1967-70

1. Main jet
2. Emulsion jet
3. Idling jet, fuel
4. Float
5. Choke tube
6. Float valve
7. Connection, fuel hose
8. Connection, vacuum hose distributor
9. Air-regulating screw, idling mixture
10. Adjusting screw, idling
11. Throttle flap
12. Choke flap
13. Ascending pipe, addition system (Econostat)
14. Diaphragm, acceleration pump
15. Bimetal spring, automatic choke
16. Water connections
17. Diaphragm for vacuum control of automatic choke
18. Retaining device, float chamber ventilation
19. Idling air jet (drilling)
20. Acceleration pump
21. Inlet valve, acceleration pump
22. Outlet valve, acceleration pump
23. Intermediate flange

A. Float chamber
B. Float chamber cover
C. Throttle body assembly
D. Housing automatic choke

1. Automatic choke housing
2. Choke plate
3. Connection for float chamber vent
4. Step cam
5. Idle adjusting screw
6. Vacuum nipple
7. Idle mixture control screw
8. Accelerating pump
9. Fuel supply tube
10. Thermostatic spring
11. Vacuum piston
12. Vacuum passage
13. Idle air jet
14. Idle air channel
15. Idle fuel channel
16. Air correction jet
17. Mixing tube
18. Full load enrichment
19. Control piston
20. Vacuum passage
21. Ball check valve (inlet)
22. Vent
23. Pump discharge passage
24. Ball check valve (discharge) and weight
25. Pump jet
26. Vent tube, float chamber
27. Main jet

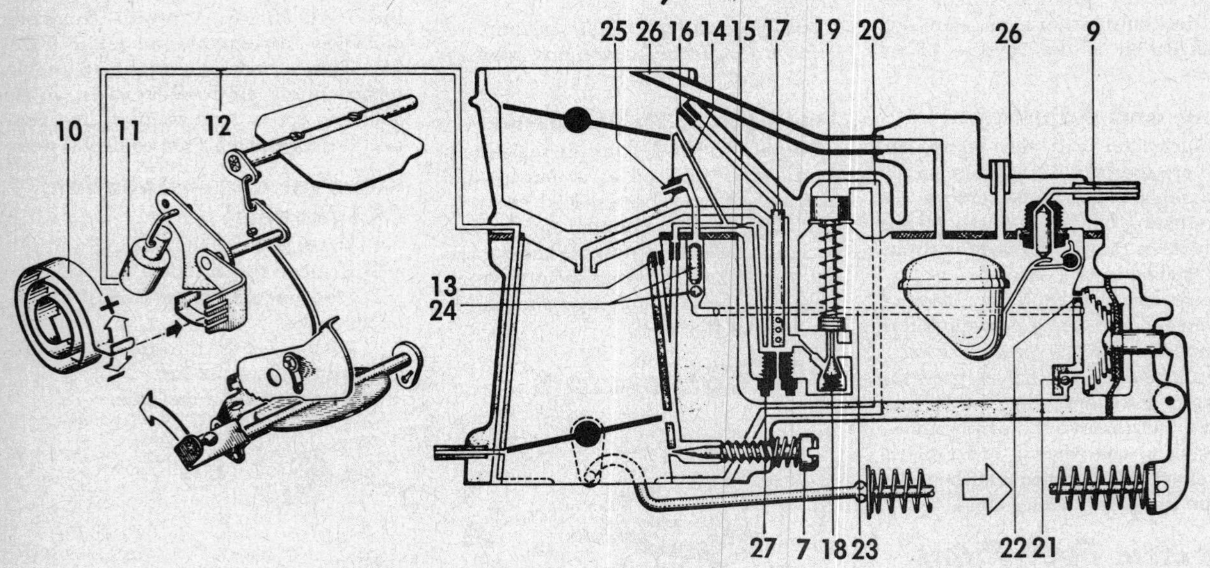

Carburetor—V-4 engine 1971-73

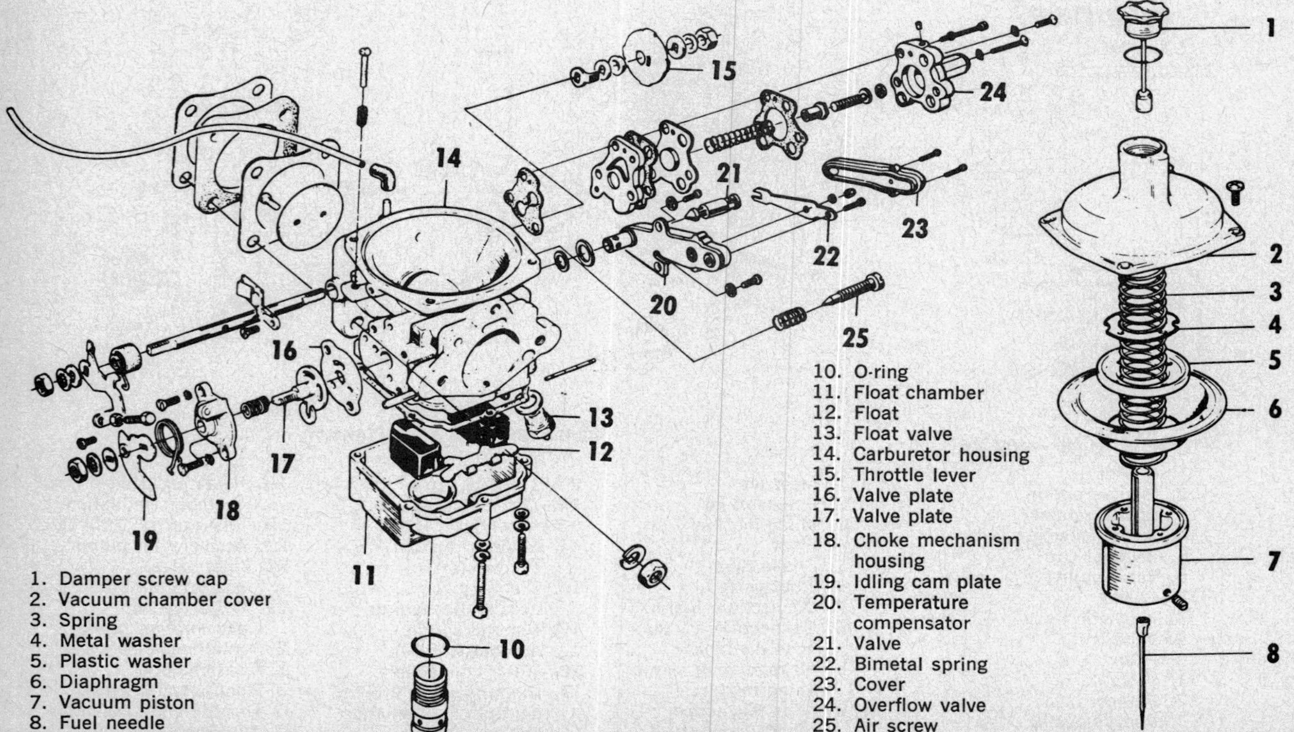

1. Damper screw cap
2. Vacuum chamber cover
3. Spring
4. Metal washer
5. Plastic washer
6. Diaphragm
7. Vacuum piston
8. Fuel needle
9. Float chamber plug
10. O-ring
11. Float chamber
12. Float
13. Float valve
14. Carburetor housing
15. Throttle lever
16. Valve plate
17. Valve plate
18. Choke mechanism housing
19. Idling cam plate
20. Temperature compensator
21. Valve
22. Bimetal spring
23. Cover
24. Overflow valve
25. Air screw

Carburetor—OHC engine 1969-73

6. Remove the carburetor.
7. Install in the reverse order of removal.

Overhaul

1. Remove the retainer from the control rod between the automatic choke and the throttle butterfly, then detach the link from the throttle butterfly arm.
2. Unscrew and lift off the float chamber cover; remove the gasket.
3. Unscrew the needle valve.
4. Take out the float and the float chamber.
5. Remove the plug from the float chamber and remove the main jet.
6. Pull off the accelerator pump jet (over the accelerator pump).
7. Unscrew the idle and emulsion tube jets.
8. Unscrew the accelerator pump cover and check the diaphragm.
9. Unscrew the idle mixture air regulating screw.
10. Remove the intermediate flange valve, if equipped.
11. Install the spring, diaphragm, and cover for the accelerator pump.
12. Insert the accelerator pump jet.
13. Screw in the idle and emulsion tube jets.
14. Advance the idling mixture air screw carefully until it bottoms, then back it off one complete turn.
15. Insert the float.
16. Screw the needle valve and gasket into the float chamber cover.
17. Install a new cover gasket.
18. Install the float chamber cover.
19. Install the rod between the automatic choke and the throttle butterfly arm; fasten with the retaining ring.
20. Set the butterfly arm in the semi-open position and, at the same time, fully close the choke butterfly with your fingers. Hold the butterfly arm firmly and make sure the throttle butterfly is ajar.

Throttle Linkage Adjustments

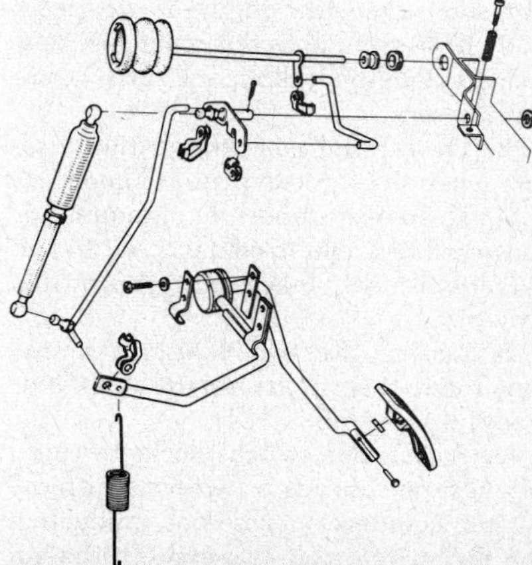

Throttle linkage

1. Make sure that the throttle plate in the carburetor opens completely when the pedal is depressed.
2. After adjusting the engine idling speed, check the movements of the accelerator pedal to the throttle shaft.
3. Turn the adjusting screw until there is no noticeable play.

NOTE: *there should be about 4.9 in. between the accelerator pedal and the bottom of the dash panel.*

4. Lubricate the throttle control joints and bearings with oil.

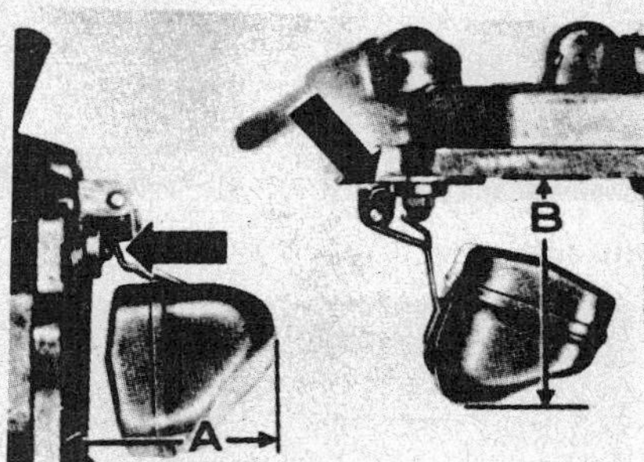

Checking the float level—V-4 engine

Float Level Adjustments

V-4 Engine

1. When checking the measurement (A), which must be 1.08 in., hold the float chamber cover vertically without pressing on the spring-loaded ball of the float valve. When adjusting, bend the stop gently at the arrow.
2. The lower end position of the float is checked by measuring at (B)—1.34 in. When adjusting, bend the stop gently at the arrow.

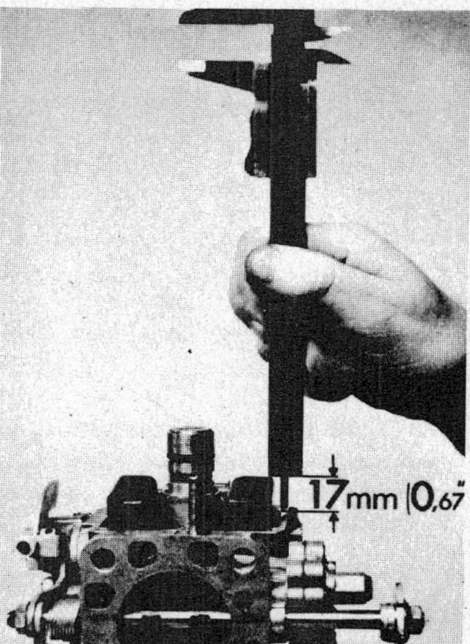

Checking the float level—OHC engine

OHC Engine

1. The float level is checked and adjusted with the carburetor removed from the vehicle and inverted, with the float cover removed.
2. At the highest point, the float should be 0.63–0.71 in, and at the rear end of the float 0.39–0.47 in. above the float cover mounting flange.
3. Adjust the float level by bending the tang that rests on the float needle.

Checking fast idle adjustment

Choke plate arm (B) and step cam stop (A)

Fast Idle Speed Adjustment

All Models

1. Bring the engine to operating temperature; remove the air cleaner.
2. Connect a tachometer between the distributor-to-coil primary wire and ground.
3. Hold the throttle shaft and step cam, so that the stop dog contacts the mark on the third catch of the step cam.
4. The engine speed now should be 1,800 rpm. To adjust, bend the stop of the throttle valve shaft.
5. Check the fast idle speed setting.
6. Reinstall the air cleaner.

Automatic Choke Adjustment

All Models

Normally the automatic choke setting should not need to be altered in any way. The setting mark on the thermostatic spring housing is normally in line with the center mark on the automatic choke housing, with the free end of the thermostatic spring fitted into the center slit of the thermostatic spring lever.

Fuel Injection

Removal and Installation

Pressure Sensor

The pressure sensor is mounted to the left inner fender panel.

1. Disconnect the pressure lines to the sensor unit.
2. Remove the electrical connections by disconnecting the four-pole plug.
3. Unbolt the sensor unit from its mounting bracket and remove the sensor from the car.
4. Install in the reverse order of removal.

Throttle Valve Switch

1. Remove the air cleaner.

Pressure sensor unit—fuel injected OHC engine

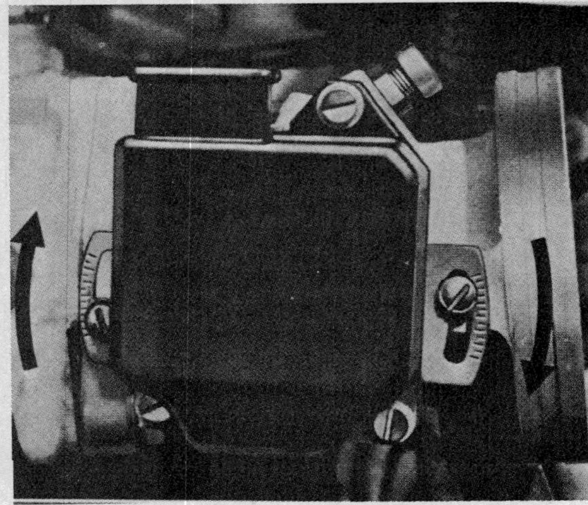

Throttle valve switch—fuel injected OHC engine

2. Disconnect the electrical connection at the switch.

3. Loosen both fastening screws and draw the switch off of the throttle valve shaft.

4. Install in the reverse order of removal.

Temperature Sensor (Inlet Air)

Unbolt the temperature sensor with a ½ in. (13mm) box wrench.

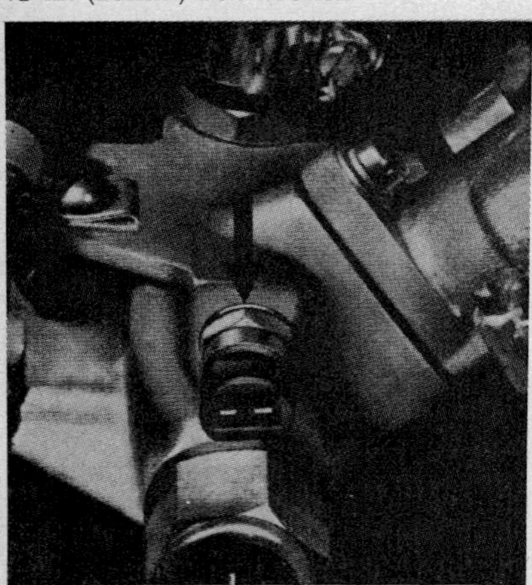

Temperature sensor (cooling system)—fuel injected OHC engine.

Temperature Sensor (Cooling Liquid)

1. Drain some coolant from the radiator.

2. Remove the air cleaner and preheat pipe.

3. Loosen the electrical plug connection and unscrew the sensor unit with a ½ in. open end wrench.

NOTE: *When reinstalling the temperature sensor, be sure to install a new sealing ring.*

4. Install in the reverse order of removal.

Auxiliary Air Regulator

1. Drain some coolant from the radiator.

2. Remove the air cleaner and the preheat pipe.

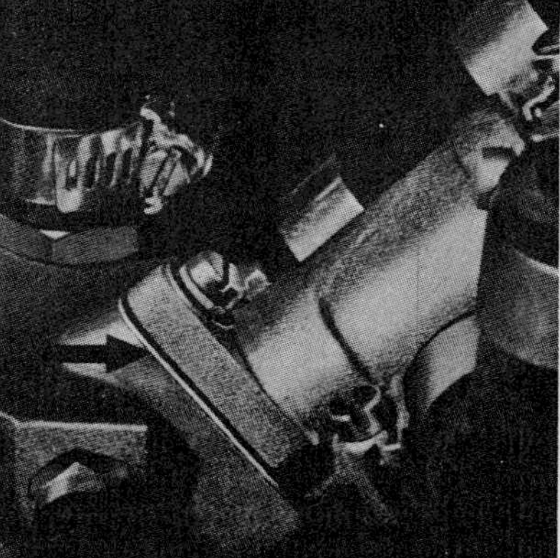

Auxiliary air regulator—fuel injected OHC engine.

3. Disconnect the air hoses from the auxiliary air regulating unit.

4. Unbolt the regulator from its mounting position and remove it from the engine.

5. Install in the reverse order of removal.

Starter Valve

1. Disconnect the fuel lines from the main fuel manifold.

2. Loosen the two (2) attaching screws which hold the starter valve to the intake manifold.

NOTE: *Do not forget to install the seal between the starter valve and the intake manifold.*

3. Install in the reverse order of removal.

Fuel Injectors

NOTE: *Before removing any of the injectors, all the fuel lines must be removed.*

1. Remove the electrical wiring from the injector.

2. Unscrew the fuel line fastening clip which is located next to the auxiliary air regulator.

3. Disconnect and remove the fuel lines from the injectors.

Fuel injectors—fuel injected OHC engine

4. Unbolt the injector from the engine.

CAUTION: *Cover the injector inlet immediately after the injector is removed from the engine.*

5. Install in the reverse order of removal.

Adjustments

1. The pressure regulator is checked by inserting a pressure gauge, on a T-fitting, into the line leading to the regulator, and running the engine at idle speed.

2. If pressure does not meet specifications, loosen the locknut and turn the adjusting screw.

3. The throttle valve switch must actuate when the throttle plate is opened 2°.

4. To adjust, connect an ohmmeter or powered test light to contacts No. 14 and 17 (right-hand, looking at the switch cover).

5. Loosen the two adjusting screws and rotate the switch until the ohmmeter reads 0 (light off).

6. Rotate the switch clockwise until the resistance reads 8 (light on), turn the switch counterclockwise one graduation on the switch scale and tighten the adjusting screws.

7. If no fuel reaches the regulator, make sure that the curved fuel pump suction line (in the trunk) has not collapsed.

8. If the line has collapsed, it must be replaced.

9. If the engine fails to start and the ignition and fuel systems appear to be functioning properly, remove the connector from the coolant temperature sensor.

10. Short across the cable plug terminals and try to start the engine.

11. If the engine starts, the temperature sensor must be replaced.

MANUAL TRANSMISSION

Removal and Installation.

NOTE: *SAAB recommends that the engine and transmission be removed together, and then separated.*

1. Remove the engine.
2. Disconnect the freewheel control.
3. Remove the rear clutch cylinder bracket and wire the cylinder out of the way.
4. Remove the gearshift shaft joint from the transmission. If both ends of the conical pin are threaded, transfer the nut and use it to remove the pin. A conical pin threaded on only one end is removed by means of tool 784083 or by backing off the nut until it is flush with the threads, then tapping gently with a hammer.
5. Disconnect the speedometer cable from the transmission.
6. Peel back or remove the front floor mat, then remove the rubber plugs to provide access to the rear engine mount center bolt. On older models, a section of the pedal housing must be removed. Remove the center bolt, using a 9/16 in. socket wrench.
7. If the tapered engine mount will not move, tap it off with a punch.
8. Remove the steering arm from the upper ball joint on the right steering knuckle housing, then pull the middle driveshaft from the inner joint. On the SAAB Sport, 1966 up, model 95 and 96, and the Monte Carlo 850, the steering knuckle need not be loosened.
9. As the transmission is lifted, move it slightly to the right so that the left driveshaft comes out of the joint.
10. Install in the reverse order of removal.

Overhaul

The methods described here are derived from factory-recommended procedures, which require special tools. Substitutes for these tools will become obvious as the job progresses. For example, it would be impractical to buy the special transmission jig that the dealer uses, but a large bench vise and suitable arbors and sleeves cut from pipe or other stock can serve the same purpose.

1. Clean the outside of the transmission and drain all the oil.
2. Remove the inner universal joint with the shafts. On the SAAB 96, the joints are connected to the side gears by means of a bolt which passes through the shaft centers.
3. Separate the transmission unit at the joint between the clutch housing and the transmission case. The clutch shaft will have to be turned to a certain position while removing the differential case.
4. Install the transmission case onto a stand.
5. Check the location of the pinion and measure the ring gear backlash for correct setting, as described later.
6. Remove the two bearing caps and lift out the differential. Keep the spacers and shims for each of the two bearings separate and note their positions.
7. Remove the freewheel hub, with the six rollers, from its sleeve, using tool No. 784068 and a strong rubber band to prevent the spring-loaded rollers from being thrown out. Next, remove the needle bearing. Make certain none of the rollers are missing.
8. If the pinion shaft or bearings are to be removed, measure the location of the pinion shaft before removing the end cover.

Gearshift Forks

9. Remove the end cover bolts and drive out the 1st, 2nd and 3rd, and 4th gearshift fork shaft (from the front).
10. Remove the cover rearward, keeping the gearshift forks in position. Note

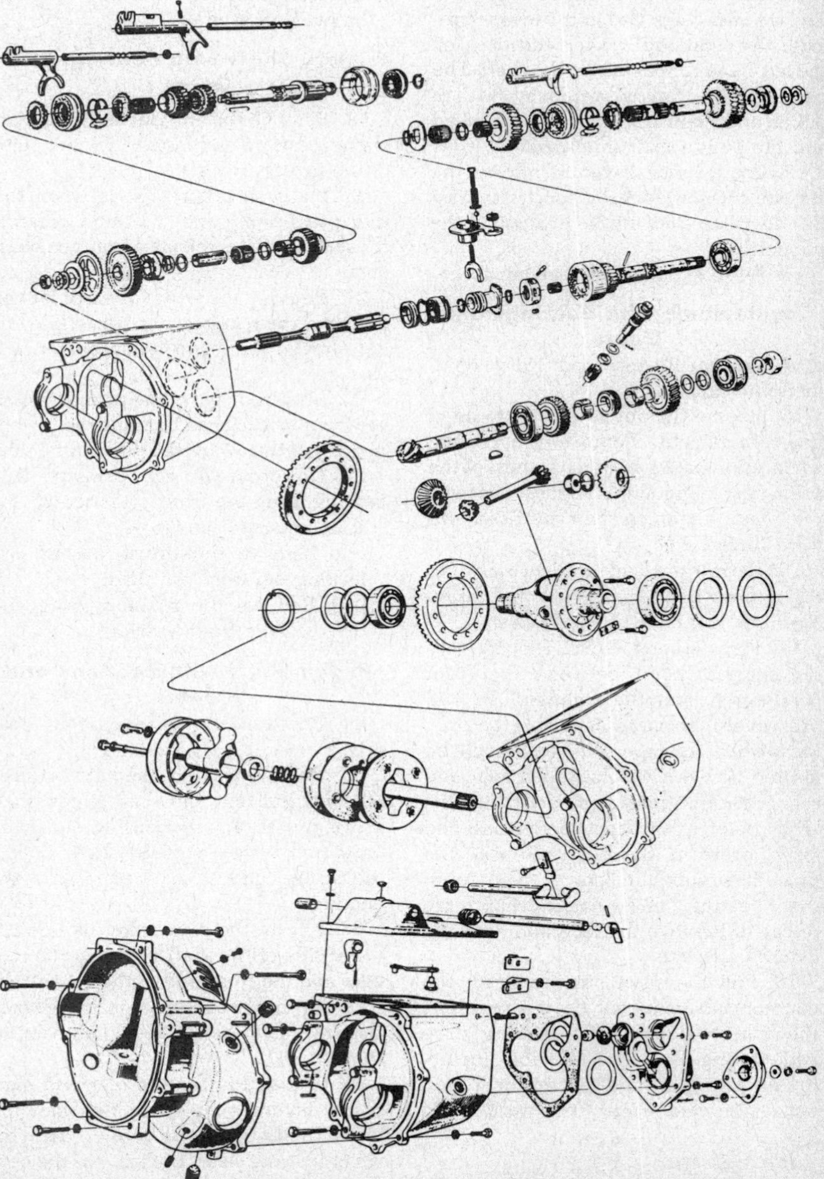

4-speed transmission—exploded view

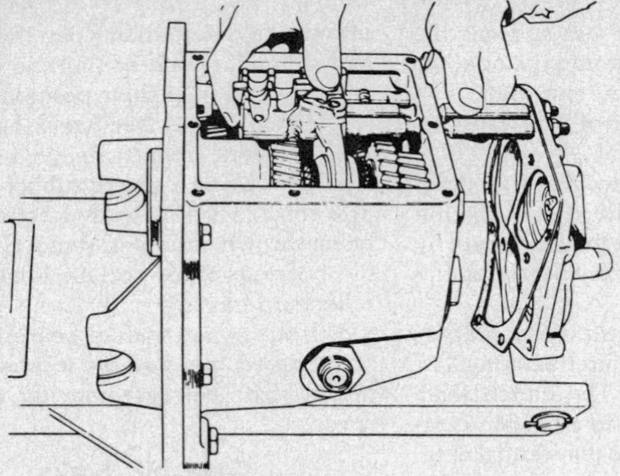

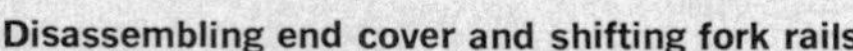
Disassembling end cover and shifting fork rails

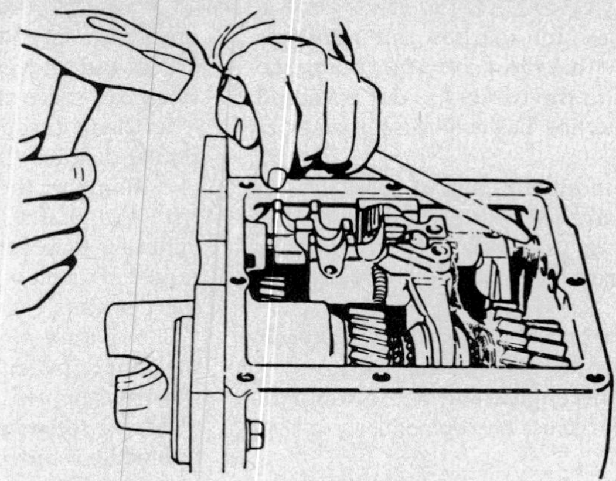
Driving out reverse shifting fork rail

the location of the shims and collect them. Prevent the ejection of the poppet balls in the gearshift forks.

11. If only the rear pinion shaft bearing is to be removed, it can be done now. Engage two gears (3rd and Reverse), release the retaining washer and back off the left-hand thread nut on the shaft. The bearing now can be removed with a puller, and a new bearing can be installed and the pinion shaft shimmed.

12. Use a brass driver to release the reverse gearshift fork shaft and withdraw it to the rear. Prevent the ejection of the poppet ball.

13. Lift out the three gearshift forks.

Countershaft with Bearings and Gears

14. Engage Reverse and 3rd gears at the same time.

15. Loosen the nut at the front end of the countershaft. Remove the friction wheel and washer. Loosen the nuts of the primary and pinion shaft if these are to be removed; the pinion shaft nut has a left-hand thread.

16. Return the synchronizer sleeve to the neutral position. Lift up and fasten the front end plate of the fixture.

17. Place arbor tool No. 786058, with the shortest point between the front press screw and the countershaft, and press in until the arbor is against the gear. Meanwhile, the supporting tool should be located between the 1st speed gear and rear of the transmission case. Change the arbor point to the next longer one and again press in the shaft. Repeat the procedure with the longest point until the bearing and countershaft are released. Remove the tools and drop the fixture end plate.

18. Pull the shaft out rearward; the countershaft gear will be released. Let the spacer at the front bearing drop while lifting the entire assembly, including the two gears and synchronizer unit, out of the case. Collect the washer and key.

If necessary:

a. Remove the retaining ring from the shaft and drive off the rear ball bearing and bearing seat in order to remove reverse gear.

b. The front countershaft bearing cannot be changed without removing the primary shaft.

Primary Shaft with Bearings and Gears

19. Remove the end nut and retaining washer. Lift up and fasten the rear plate of the fixture.

20. Place an arbor tool between the rear press screw and shaft and press in the shaft until it is released from the bearings.

21. Remove the shaft forward; let the spacer at the rear bearing drop while lifting out the gears and synchronizer as a unit.

22. After removal of the primary shaft, the front bearing can be removed by tapping it gently toward the differential side.

23. Drive out the rear primary shaft bearing using the front press screw.

If necessary:

a. Remove the thrust washer and locking pin from the shaft.

b. Remove the retaining ring and drive off the front bearing.

Pinion Shaft with Bearings and Gears

24. Remove the speedometer gear drive.

25. Remove the left-hand thread shaft nut and pull out the rear pinion shaft bearing with a puller, using the front press screw to support the shaft. Collect the spacer and shims from inside the bearing.

26. Locate the supporting tool on the lower side of the shaft between the rear gear and the front end of the case. Make sure the tool is centered on the gear so that the gear does not tip and bind on the shaft.

27. Lift and fasten the rear end plate of the fixture, then drive the shaft forward using the press screw, until the roller bearing clears the front of the case. Remove the tool and drop the end plate of the fixture. Lift out the 3rd gear while drawing the shaft from the case. Retrieve the woodruff key.

If necessary:

a. Press the front roller bearing and pinion shaft 4th gear from the shaft as follows: Remove the retaining ring from the roller bearing. Place the pinion shaft and supporting tool in a press and drive out the shaft.

CAUTION: *Make sure the outer bearing race is flush against the gear. The bearing should not be taken apart if it is to be reused; make sure that the rollers do not fall out and install the retaining ring immediately.*

b. Press the oil collector gently out of the case.

NOTE: *When installing new gears, remember that the 3rd speed gear and pinion shaft 3rd gear are supplied in matched sets, as are the 4th speed gear and the pinion shaft 4th gear. Quiet operation is assured only if the gears are replaced in sets. The pinion shaft and ring gear are also matched sets and must be replaced as sets. Install the gears so that the matching numbers face the same way.*

Installation

Pinion Shaft with Bearings and Gears

1. Locate the front roller bearing, pinion shaft 4th gear, spacers, and speedometer drive gear on the pinion shaft. Using a press and tool, drive in the bearing and pinion shaft 4th gear until the inner bearing race is flush with the drive pinion.

NOTE: *Make sure that the matching number faces the same way as on the 4th speed gear.*

2. Next, put the pinion shaft into the case from the differential side and place the pinion shaft 3rd gear on the shaft inside the case. Be certain the woodruff key for the 3rd gear is in the pinion shaft. In some older units, the pinion shaft 4th gear is also held by a key.

3. Turn the shaft to line up the woodruff key and the keyway in the 3rd gear.

4. Place a guiding arbor tool in the rear bearing seat so that the pinion shaft passes into it.

5. Secure the arbor with the rear press screw so that the flange is flush with the case.

6. Drive the pinion shaft into place using the front press screw. Be certain the key enters the groove in the 3rd gear.

7. Loosen the rear press screw and remove the arbor from the bearing seat.

8. Place a 0.14 in. spacer on the end shaft. If the rear pinion bearing has a split inner ring, the spacer must be placed next to the bearing.

9. Using the press screw and arbor, press the rear ball bearing, with retaining ring, into the case. Use the press screw at the front end of the pinion shaft for support. In the case of a split bearing, first fit the inner ring, then the remaining part, and press in as described above.

10. Loosen the rear press screw and drop both fixture end plates.

11. Install a new tabbed washer onto the pinion shaft, with the tab facing out. Install the left-hand thread nut, but don't tighten it with a torque wrench until the primary shaft and countershaft are installed.

Primary Shaft with Bearings and Gears

12. Up to and including transmission No. 276503: refit the front bearing, using tool No. 784107, and place the retaining ring, locking pin thrust washer and 4th speed gear needle bearing on the primary shaft. Be certain the locking pin prevents the thrust washer from rotating.

NOTE: *From Transmission No. 276504: fit the oil slinger and front bearing, using tool No. 784107, and place the retaining ring, washer, and 4th speed gear needle bearing on the primary shaft.*

13. Before pressing in the primary shaft, the countershaft front bearing must be in position. Press in the bearing from the front, using the arbor tool No. 786134, until it is hard against the retaining ring in the bearing seat.

14. Assemble the primary shaft components, the 3rd and 4th speed gears, and the synchronizer sleeve and rings, then place the entire assembly into the case while passing the aligning arbor (No. 784114) into the 3rd speed gear through the rear bearing seat. Secure the arbor with the press screw.

15. Slide in the shaft from the front until its splines enter the synchronizer hub.

16. Put arbor tool No. 784104 into the freewheel hub. The needle bearing must be removed from the freewheel sleeve while this is being done.

17. Lift and fasten the front end plate of the fixture and carefully drive in the primary shaft against the arbor in the freewheel sleeve, using the press screw if a fixture is available, until the 3rd speed gear is tight against the rear case. Make sure that the synchronizer hub does not tip and bind.

18. Remove the aligning arbor from the 3rd speed gear and place the needle bearing spacer sleeve and bushing for this gear onto the shaft inside the gear hub.

19. Place the spacer, with the beveled side facing outward and the rear bearing on the primary shaft, and drive in the bearing using tool No. 784109. The front press screw and the arbor in the freewheel sleeve will support the shaft.

20. Loosen the press screws and drop the rear fixture end.

21. Place a new tabbed washer, with tab facing outward, and a nut on the shaft. Do not tighten with a torque wrench until the countershaft is installed.

Countershaft with Bearings and Gears

22. Raise and fasten the front plate of the fixture and place the countershaft gear in position with the machined part facing the clutch bearing. Use the front press screw and tool No. 786134 to hold the countershaft gear and shaft gear.

23. Reassemble the 1st and 2nd speed gears, the 2nd speed complete with needle bearing, spacer, and bushing, and synchronizer unit with its rings.

24. Place this assembly into the case, passing the countershaft needle bearing, complete with 1st speed gear, through the rear of the case at the same time. If the rear bearing, bearing seat, and reverse gear have not been removed, they may remain on the shaft during reassembly. In this case, however, the bearing must first be pressed into the seat and the rear retaining ring removed from the shaft.

25. Put the spacer on the shaft between the 2nd speed gear and the front ball bearing, then slide the shaft through the front bearing and into the countershaft gear.

26. Drive in the countershaft with the press screw. Make certain that the shaft splines engage with the synchronizer hub and the shaft passes into the countershaft gear. Use a pin wrench, to turn the shaft. Drop both fixture end plates and fasten the rear bearing with the retaining ring (after pressing it in).

NOTE: *If the countershaft is reinstalled complete with reverse gear and bearing, use tool No. 784109. This tool also is used if the reverse gear and the seat with the bearing are mounted separately.*

27. Engage 2nd and 4th gears at the same time and turn the 3rd speed gear in order to align the keyway in the countershaft gear. Drive in the key using an arbor.

28. Refit the friction wheel, together with new friction and star washers. Tighten the countershaft end nut to 60 ft lbs. Tighten the pinion shaft nut initially to 90 ft lbs, back off and retighten to 45 ft lbs. The primary shaft nut must be tightened to 35 ft lbs. Make sure that the friction wheel is not located outside the opposing gear and that there is enough clearance between the primary shaft ball bearing and the countershaft gear. Lock the nuts on the main and pinion shafts by bending down the tabs on the washers.

Gearshift Forks

29. Put the synchronizer sleeve and reverse gear in neutral position and insert the gearshift forks. The poppet balls and springs must be fitted and secured before the forks are placed in the case.

30. Install the reverse gearshift shaft through the rear end and retrieve the tool used to hold the poppet ball in position.

31. Make sure the rubber washer and plastic plug are mounted in the end cover and the oil collector is in place in the case end.

32. Check the shims in the end cover.

33. Pass the 1st, 2nd, 3rd, and 4th gearshift fork shafts through the rear end, positioning them so that the forks engage their respective shafts.

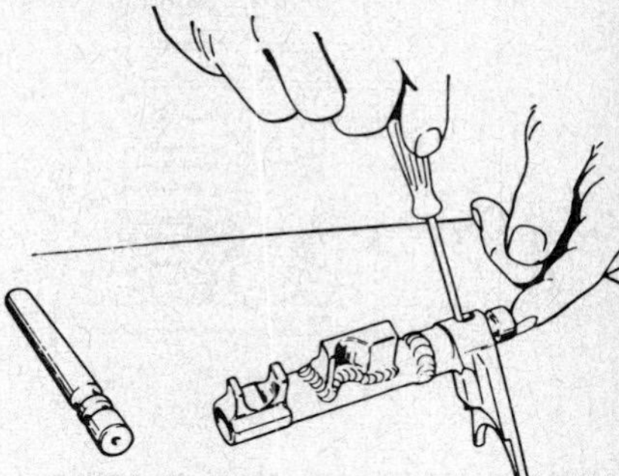

Installing poppet ball into reverse shifting fork with factory special tool.

34. Fit the poppet balls in the forks. This is simplified if the balls are held with two tools (No. 784069) while the cover is pressed in.

35. Retrieve the two tools as they are pressed out of the front ends of the forks, then tighten the end cover bolts to 18 ft lbs. Make sure that the bolt opposite the reverse gearshift fork is not too long (which would impede fork movement).

36. If necessary, adjust the gearshift fork shafts, so that the forks are not subjected to axial pressure when a gear is engaged. Roughly the same clearance should exist between each synchronizer sleeve and the gear concerned in all gear positions.

Differential

37. Reinstall the differential assembly and spacers and tighten the bearing cap bolts to 28 ft lbs. Be sure the short bolts

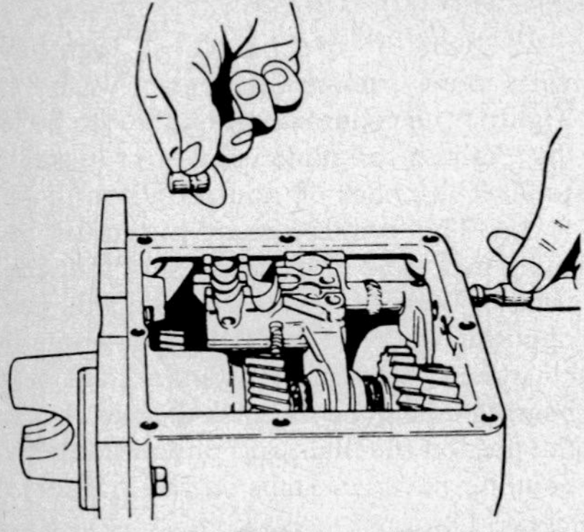

Removing the special tool with the shift fork rails installed.

are installed in the small bearing cap.

38. If the pinion shaft setting has been altered, or parts in the differential were replaced, always check the side clearance of the bevel gear.

39. Reinstall the speedometer drive gear.

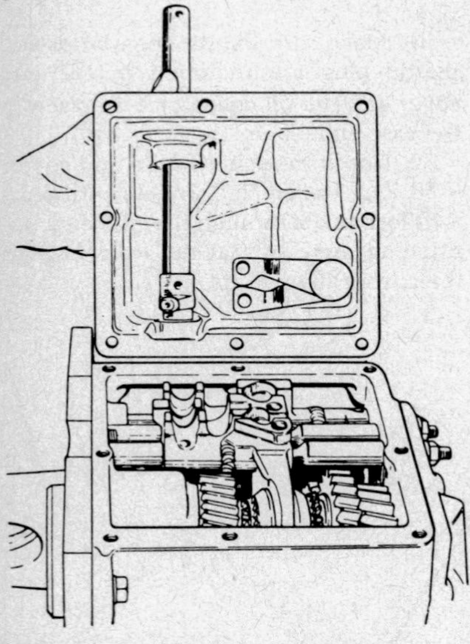

Shift mechanism and catch in transmission case cover.

40. Coat the top cover with sealing compound and make sure that the three gearshift forks, the dogs, and the catch in the cover are in neutral, then fit the cover. Check the function of the gearshift mechanism.

41. Insert the freewheel hub, using tool No. 784068 in the freewheel sleeve. Be sure an undamaged needle bearing is installed.

42. Check the clutch shaft seal and the driveshaft seals and replace if necessary. Install the seals so that the dust guard lips face outward; fill the space between the lips with chassis grease.

43. Coat the sealing surface of the clutch housing with Permatex® No. 3 and attach the clutch housing to the transmission case. Turn the clutch shaft so that it clears the differential. Be certain the clutch shaft is not subjected to lateral stress and that the freewheel hub engages the clutch shaft splines.

44. Coat the clutch shaft splines with graphite grease and fill the transmission with oil.

Transmission Rebuilding Chart

4-Speed Transmission

Location of Shims or Part	Spare-Part No.	Thickness (in.)	Thickness (mm)
On primary shaft	708093	0.004	0.10
	708101	0.006	0.15
	708102	0.012	0.30
On countershaft	708094	0.004	0.10
	708103	0.006	0.15
	708104	0.012	0.30
On pinion shaft	708095	0.004	0.10
	708105	0.006	0.15
	708106	0.012	0.30
End cover	708058		
Gasket	716754		(thin)

Linkage Adjustments

Saab 96

NOTE: *Make sure the steering column stand is adjusted in the vertical direction.*

1. Place the shaft lever into First gear and move the gear shift lever in all directions.

2. Movement should not exceed 0.3–0.5 in. (8–12mm).

NOTE: *Readjust the lock plunger after any adjustment to the shift mechanism.*

Saab 99

1. Place the gear shift lever into Reverse position and turn the ignition to LOCK position.

2. Move the gear lever back and forth. The gear rod should not move more than 0.06–0.1 in. (1.5–2.5mm).

3. Adjust by moving the gear lever housing backward or forward.

CLUTCH

Removal and Installation

V-4 Engine

1. Remove the engine from the car. Follow the procedures outlined in "Engine Removal".

2. Separate the engine from the transmission.

3. Slacken off the six (6) bolts which hold the pressure plate assembly to the flywheel.

4. Remove the pressure plate assembly and the clutch disc.

5. Installation is in the reverse order of removal.

NOTE: *When installing the clutch and pressure plate assembly onto the flywheel, use a pilot shaft or other suitable means to align the clutch assembly.*

OHC Engine

NOTE: *A clutch-throwout bearing compression tool (SAAB No. 839207) is necessary to remove and install the clutch from the SAAB 99 drive train. Do not attempt to remove the clutch unless this tool is available.*

1. Mark the position of the hood brackets on the hood hinges, loosen the mounting bolts, and with an assistant, lift off the hood.

2. Disconnect the battery ground cable, all wiring from the front sheet, the coil high tension lead from the coil, and the temperature and oil pressure switches.

3. Drain the radiator coolant and remove all hoses from the radiator.

4. Remove the headlight trim frames.

5. Disconnect the hood lock from its connections at the firewall and the fender.

6. Remove the eight retaining screws, and lift off the entire front sheet.

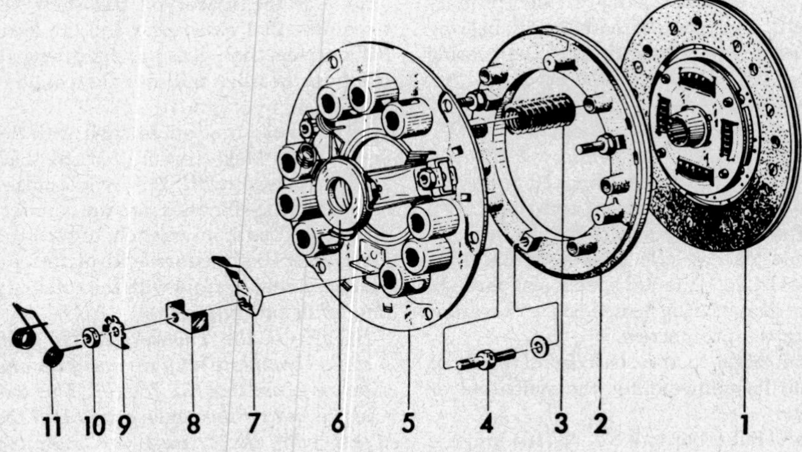

Clutch assembly—exploded view

1. Disc
2. Release plate
3. Spring
4. Lever screw
5. Clutch cover
6. Release bearing
7. Clutch lever
8. Bracket
9. Washer
10. Nut
11. Spring

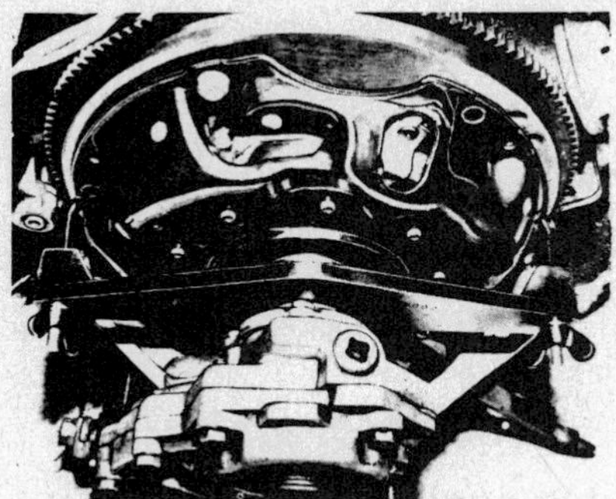

Clutch compression tool installed

7. Remove the clutch cover.
8. Unbolt the slave cylinder and support it in an out of the way position; remove the clutch lever.
9. Remove the lock ring, the clutch shaft end cap, and the clutch shaft center bolt, washer, and O-ring.
10. Pull the clutch shaft using a slide hammer threaded into the shaft.
11. Back off all clutch retaining bolts, one turn at a time, until clutch pressure is released, and remove all bolts except the top two.
12. Unbolt the throwout bearing guide sleeve.
13. Install and tighten the clutch-throwout bearing compression tool.
14. Remove the remaining clutch retaining bolts and lift out the clutch disc, pressure plate, throwout bearing, and guide sleeve.
15. To install, assemble the pressure plate, throwout bearing and guide sleeve using the compression tool.
16. Insert the clutch disc into the flywheel, and lower the pressure plate assembly into position.
17. Install the clutch shaft, align the pressure plate with the locating pins, and tighten the clutch bolts finger tight.
18. Tighten the guide sleeve retaining bolts, remove the compression tool, and tighten the clutch retaining bolts.
19. Continue installation in the reverse order of removal.

Clutch Pedal Free-Play Adjustment

The clearance between the release bearing and release plate is gradually decreased by wear of the clutch linings.

1. Adjust the clutch pedal free-play by turning the screw on the clutch housing.
2. The free movement is increased by loosening the screw (turning to the left).
3. The clearance is checked by moving the slave cylinder connection to the clutch arm. A movement of 0.16 in. here indicates the correct clutch clearance.

Clutch Linkage Adjustments

The clutch linkage consists of a vertical master cylinder, actuated directly by the clutch pedal, and a slave cylinder which operates the clutch lever.

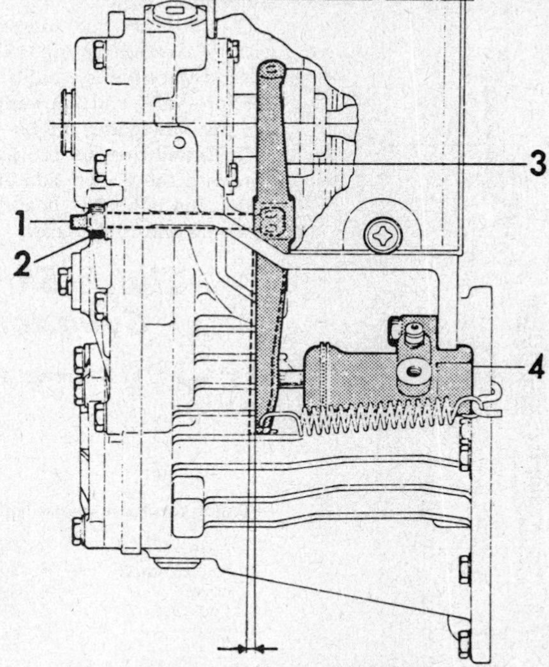

Clutch free-play adjustment

1. Adjusting screw
2. Lock nut
3. Clutch lever
4. Slave cylinder

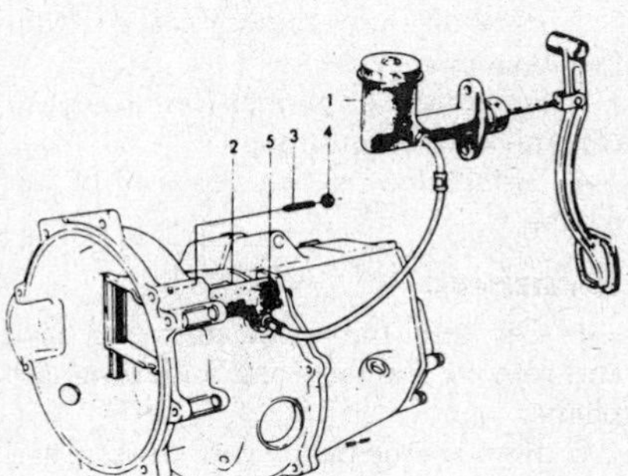

Clutch linkage

1. Master cylinder
2. Slave cylinder
3. Adjustment screw
4. Stop nut
5. Bleedscrew

Bleeding

NOTE: *The conventional method of bleeding the linkage, pumping the pedal to expel air, is not recommended on the SAAB 99, and can cause damage to the system.*

1. Connect a hose to the slave cylinder bleeder and immerse the free end in a container of brake fluid.
2. Fill the master cylinder reservoir with brake fluid, and open the slave cylinder bleeder ½ turn.
3. Place a cooling system pressure tester over the master cylinder reservoir and pump until no air bubbles leave the bleeder hose.
4. Close the bleeder and check the action of the clutch pedal.

Clutch Master Cylinder

Removal and Installation (All Models)

1. Disconnect the hose from the slave cylinder and remove all fluid from the master cylinder.
2. Unbolt the pushrod from the pedal assembly by removing the cotter pin.
3. Remove the master cylinder attaching bolts and remove it from the dash.
4. Install in the reverse order of removal.

Overhaul

1. To examine or renew parts, disconnect the pushrod from the pedal and remove it from the dash panel.
2. Carefully move back the dust cap.
3. Use longnose pliers to remove the lockring. After removing the pushrod, the entire piston assembly can be removed.
4. The piston assembly can be disassembled by lifting the retainer spring leaf over the tongued end of the piston.
5. Carefully remove the piston seal and the end seal.
6. Push down on the piston return spring, allowing the valve spindle to slide through the key-shaped hole in the retainer so that the spring lets go.
7. Remove the valve spacer carefully so as not to damage the elastic washer under the valve head.
8. Remove the seal from the valve head.

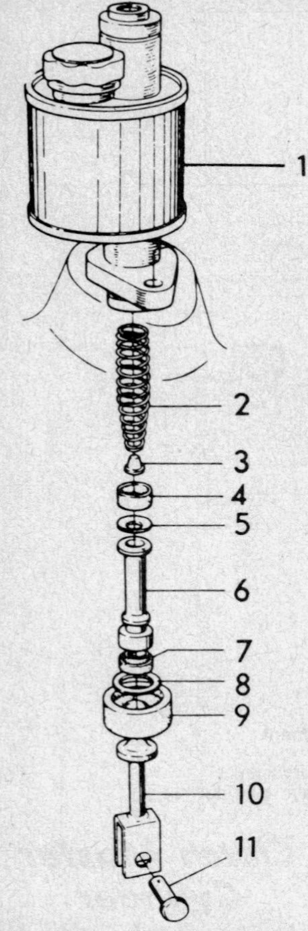

Clutch master cylinder—exploded view

1. Housing
2. Spring
3. Spring retainer
4. Seal
5. Washer
6. Piston
7. Seal
8. Lock ring
9. Sealing boot
10. Push rod
11. Shaft bolt

NOTE: *If the cylinder bore is smooth, not scored or distorted, new seals may be installed safely.*

9. Place the valve seal with its flat side properly located on the valve head.

10. Put on the elastic washer with the dished side facing the lower side of the valve head, holding it in position by means of the valve spacer with the legs turned toward the valve seal.

11. Replace the piston return spring, centering it on the washer, then insert the valve spring retainer into the spring and press down until the valve spindle bottoms through the keyshaped hole.

12. At the same time, make certain the spindle is correctly located in the middle of the retainer.

13. Make certain the spring is still centered on the spacer.

14. Put a new piston seal onto the piston, with the flat side turned toward the front of the piston.

15. Install a new end seal, with its lip facing the piston seal.

16. Insert the small end of the piston into the retainer until the retainer spring engages the piston tongue; press the retainer fully home.

17. Lubricate the piston thoroughly with Wakefield/Girling rubber grease #3 and place the assembly into the cylinder bore, valve end first, easing the piston seal lips slowly into the bore.

18. Install the pushrod into the cylinder, with the dished side of the washer under the spherical head, then install lock-ring and rubber cap.

Clutch Slave Cylinder

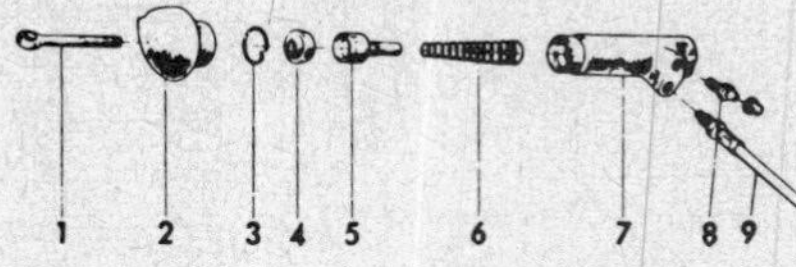

Clutch slave cylinder—exploded view

1. Pushrod
2. Rubber dust cover
3. Lockring
4. Seal
5. Piston
6. Spring
7. Cylinder body
8. Bleedscrew
9. Hose

Removal and Installation

All Models

1. Disconnect the hose from the master cylinder and remove the fluid from the system.

2. Back off the retaining screws from the slave cylinder.

3. Separate the cylinder from the push rod and clutch housing.

4. Installation is the reverse of removal.

Overhaul

1. Carefully move the dust cap back and remove the lock-ring with longnose pliers.

2. Remove the piston with the seal and spring.

NOTE: *If the bore is smooth, not scored or distorted, a new seal may be installed.*

3. Reverse the disassembly procedure, taking care to lubricate the seal and pack the rubber boot with Wakefield/Girling rubber grease #3.

NOTE: *Always lubricate the cylinder bore with brake fluid.*

AUTOMATIC TRANSMISSION

The automatic transmission consists of a three-element hydrokinetic torque convertor and a hydraulically operated gearbox which contains a planetary gear set providing three forward ratios and reverse.

Removal and Installation

See "Engine Removal".

Shift Linkage Adjustments

1. Remove the gear selector lever cover.

2. Loosen the gear selector lever housing to gain access to the adjusting cable nut.

3. Adjust by turning the nut on the outer cover so that the cable will move inward or outward.

4. Reassemble the gear selector housing and recheck.

Differential

Removal and Installation

The differential and transmission are enclosed into one housing and are removed from the car as a unit.

Overhaul

See "Manual Transmission Overhaul" for separation and repair of the differential assembly.

DRIVE AXLES

The SAAB drive axle consists of an inner U-joint, an axle shaft, an outer U-joint, a stub shaft, and a wheel hub. Due to the configuration of the U-joints, the axle shaft can slide axially as well as being jointed. 1969 models utilize an inner U-joint with two trunnions, while 1970 and later models use a joint with three trunnions.

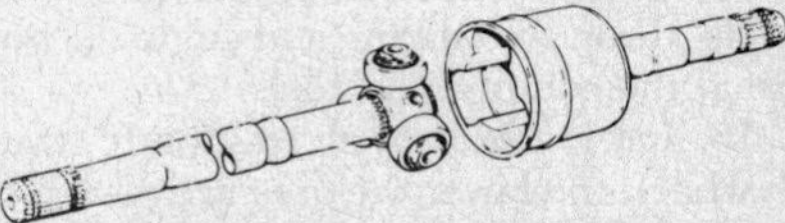

Inner U-joint—1970-73 model

Removal and Installation

1. Loosen the wheel nuts, remove the cotter pin, and loosen the castle nut.

2. Raise the front of the car, and remove the wheel.

3. Dismount the brake caliper and support it, so as not to stress the brake hose, in an out of the way position.

4. Remove the brake disc and disconnect the handbrake cable.

5. Remove the large clamp from the inner U-joint boot.

6. Free the tie-rod end from the steering arm using a puller and unbolt the upper and lower ball joints from the control arms.

7. Pull out the entire assembly and install a cap over the end of the inner U-joint boot to prevent damage to the joint.

8. Install in the reverse order of removal.

NOTE: *When installing, pack the inner U-joint with grease and tighten the castle nut to 145 ft lbs.*

Overhaul

1. Using a puller attached to the wheel

mounting studs, extract the stub shaft from the wheel hub.

2. Pull the wheel hub out of the suspension upright and pry out the seals with a screwdriver.

NOTE: *Seals are not reusable.*

3. Pull the bearing from the wheel hub, check the condition of all bearings, and replace if necessary.

4. Fill half the space between the bearing outer races and coat the inner bearing races with chassis lube.

5. Mount the bearings and spacer in the suspension upright, and press in the seals.

NOTE: *The seals are pressed flush with the flange. Pressing the seals further can cause bearing interference and result in excessive bearing wear.*

6. Mount the drive axle assembly, the suspension upright, and the wheel hub in a press and press into their installed position.

7. Install the castle nut, torque to 145 ft lbs and install the cotter pin.

8. Continue assembly in the reverse order of disassembly.

REAR SUSPENSION

All Models

Removal and Installation

1. Raise the rear of the car, and support it by the underbody.

2. Disconnect the brake hoses in front of the rear axle and plug them.

3. Support the axle with a jack and unbolt the shock absorbers from the trailing arms, the Panhard rod from the body, and the upper links from the axle.

4. Lower the jack and remove the coil springs.

5. Unbolt the axle from the trailing arms and remove it from the car.

6. Install in the reverse order of removal.

NOTE: *When installing, bleed the brake system.*

7. Torque all suspension bolts with the weight of the car supported by the wheels.

Hub Bearing Replacement

1. Remove the wheel, unbolt the caliper, and hang it in an out of the way position so as not to stress the brake hose.

2. Remove the brake disc, pry out the cap, and unbolt the castle nut.

3. Pull off the hub, using a slide hammer if necessary.

4. Pry out the seal and remove the bearing inner races.

NOTE: *The seal must be renewed when removed from the hub.*

5. Inspect the bearings, and if necessary, tap out the outer race, using a suitable drift, and replace.

6. Fill half the space between the bearing outer races and coat the bearing inner races with chassis grease.

NOTE: *If used bearings are installed, they must be in their original position.*

7. Install the inner bearing and the seal and mount the hub.

8. Install the outer bearing and tighten the castle nut to zero play.

9. Continue installation in the reverse order of removal.

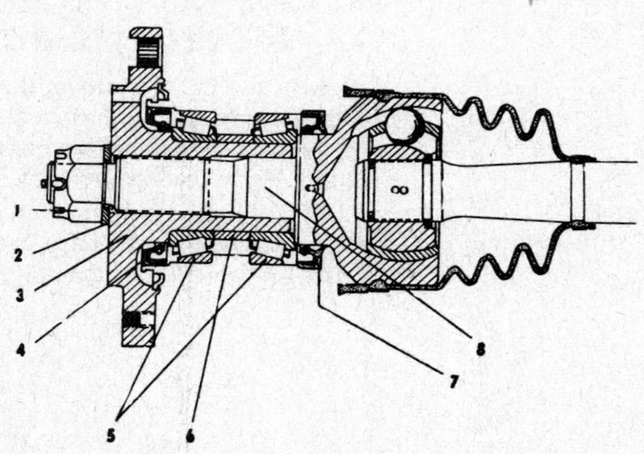

Outer U-joint

1. Castle nut
2. Washer
3. Hub
4. Outer shaft seal
5. Wheel bearings
6. Spacer sleeve
7. Inner shaft seal
8. Outer drive shaft

A rigid tubular rear axle is mounted by lower trailing arms and upper links. A Panhard rod is used to control lateral movement. Stub axles, pressed into the end pieces of the axle tube, support the wheel hubs on conical roller bearings. Coil springs and shock absorbers are mounted on the trailing arms. Upward suspension movement is limited by a rubber bump stop, while downward travel is limited by the shock absorbers.

CAUTION: *Never jack or support the car on its rear axle tube. To do so could distort the axle.*

Rear Suspension

1. Rear axle
2. End piece
3. Stub axle
4. Spring links
5. Rear links
6. Cross bar
7. Spring seat
8. Coil spring
9. Spring insulator
10. Bump stop
11. Stop
12. Shock absorber

FRONT SUSPENSION

The front suspension consists of unequal length upper and lower A-arms, mounted directly to the unit body on brackets. The suspension upright, with the steering arm, is mounted on ball joints bolted to the A-arms. The coil spring is mounted over the upper control arm, while the shock absorber is mounted on a stud on the lower arm. Upper and lower bump stops are utilized, the upper being progressive.

Ball Joint

Removal and Installation

Raise the car and remove the wheel. Unbolt the caliper and hang it in an out of the way position so as not to stress the brake hose. Servicing the upper ball joint is aided by compressing the coil spring. Unbolt the ball joint from the control arm and remove the stud retaining nut. Remove the ball joint from the suspension upright with a puller. Install in the reverse order of removal.

Adjustments

Toe-In

Toe-in is the difference between measurements taken at the forward extremes of the tires and the rearward extremes of the tires. In the illustration, this is shown as the difference between X and Y.

The correct setting is 0.08 ± 0.04 in. (i.e., measurement Y should be 0.04–0.12 in. less than measurement X). Toe-in is adjusted by changing the length of the tie-rod with the wheels in the straight-ahead position. Toe-in is 0.04 ± 0.04 in. for Sonett II models.

Caster

Caster is the amount that the king pin

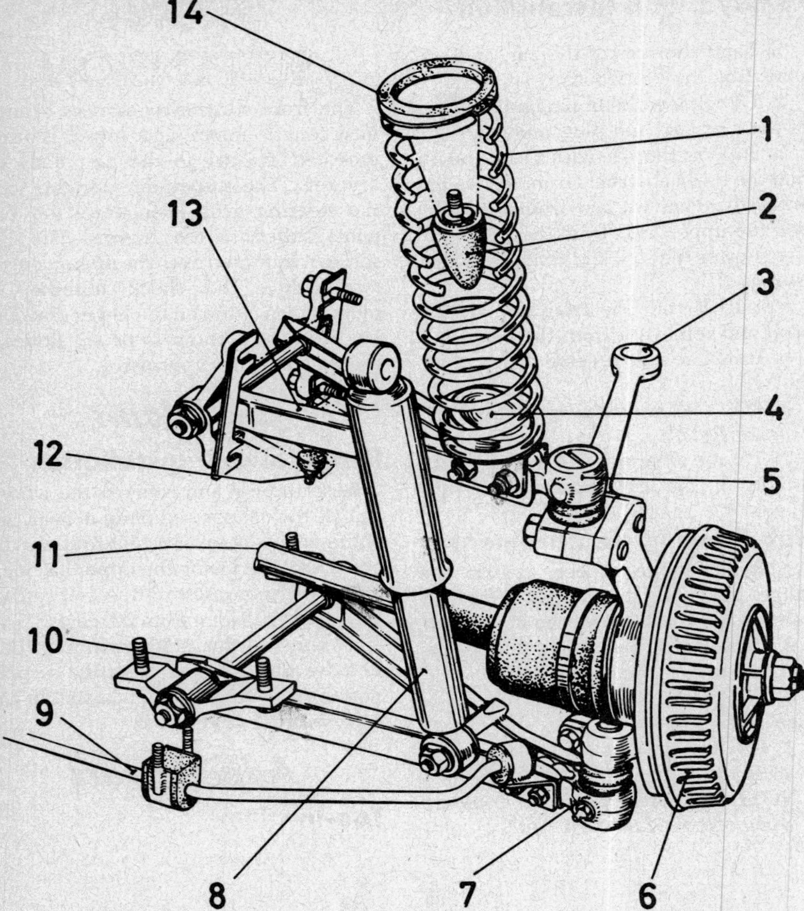

Left-front suspension (typical)

1. Coil spring
2. Rubber bumper
3. Steering arm
4. Spring seat
5. Upper ball joint
6. Brake drum
7. Lower ball joint
8. Shock absorber
9. Stabilizer bar
10. Lower control arm
11. Inner driveshaft
12. Rubber bumper
13. Upper control arm
14. Rubber spacer

is tilted toward the rear of the car, expressed in degrees. Positive caster means that the top of the king pin is tilted toward the rear; negative caster that the top is tilted toward the front. The correct caster setting for SAAB models, including the Sonett II, is +2° ± ½°.

Camber

Camber is the amount, expressed in degrees, that the front wheels are inclined outward at the top. The purpose of camber is to take some of the load from the outboard spindle bearing. If the wheel is tilted outward at the top, the camber is positive; if inward, the camber is negative. The correct camber for SAAB models is +¾° ± ¼°, with the exception of the Sonett II, which requires 0° ± ¼°.

STEERING

Steering Wheel

Removal and Installation (All Models)

1. Remove the steering wheel padding and the steering wheel bearing lower cover.

2. Remove the steering wheel nut and mark the position of the wheel and the shaft for installation.

3. Install a steering wheel puller and remove the steering wheel.

4. Install the steering wheel in the reverse order of removal.

CAUTION: *Extreme care must be exercised to avoid damaging the collapsible steering column. In no case should the steering wheel be forced or hammered onto the shaft.*

Steering Column

Removal and Installation (All Models)

1. Loosen the lock bolt at the intermediate shaft.

2. Unbolt the column at the pedal bracket and the instrument panel.

3. Separate the electrical connector and lift out the column.

4. Install in the reverse order of removal.

Steering Gear

A helical rack and pinion, directly actuating the steering arms by means of tie rods ball jointed at each end of the rack, is used. Early models (up to vehicle No. 99.022.278) can be lubricated and adjusted externally, later units are permanently lubricated and non-adjustable.

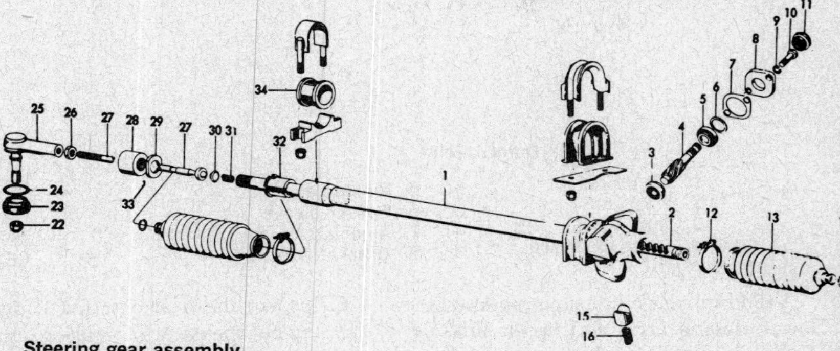

Steering gear assembly

1. Steering gear housing assembly
2. Rack
3. Ball bearing
4. Pinion
5. Ball bearing
6. Shim
7. Gasket
8. Cap
9. Washer
10. Screw
11. Seal ring
18. Gasket
19. Cap
20. Washer
21. Screw
22. Nut
23. Boot
24. Ring
25. Tie rod end
26. Lock nut
27. Tie rod
28. Outer ball joint cup
29. Lock nut
30. Inner ball joint cup
31. Spring
32. Bushing
33. Cotter pin
34. Rubber bushing

Removal and Installation

1. Raise the car and remove the front wheels.
2. Unbolt and remove the tie rod ends from the steering arms using a puller.
3. Roll back the carpet and loosen the lower intermediate shaft joint.
4. Unbolt the steering column and pull back and separate the intermediate shaft from the pinion shaft.
5. Loosen the retaining clamp nuts and slide the steering gear out through the left wheel well.
6. Install in the reverse order of removal.

NOTE: *When installing, place the brake discs in a straight ahead position, center the rack (equal distance from each lock), and place the steering wheel in its centered position.*

7. Adjust the tie rod ends so that they insert into the steering arms as positioned above and fasten the intermediate shaft to the pinion shaft.
8. Adjust the toe-in to specifications and center the steering wheel.

Adjustments

1. Rack backlash may be adjusted on early units using a bolt on the underside of the pinion housing.
2. Loosen the locknut and tighten the adjusting bolt to zero lash.
3. Back off the bolt ⅛–¼ turn, tighten the locknut, and check to ensure that the unit does not bind from lock to lock.

BRAKE SYSTEMS

SAAB has used three separate and distinct brake systems, although some minor similarities exist. The first type (Type I) is a four-wheel drum system having self-energizing front shoes, each shoe having a single wheel cylinder. The rear shoes are actuated by a single cylinder, but the cylinder is movable—the pushing action against one shoe resulting in an opposite reaction to move the other shoe against the drum.

The second type (Type II) is also a four-wheel drum system. It, however, has standard double-ended wheel cylinders at the rear, fixed to the backing plate.

The third type (Type III) is a four-wheel, dual-circuit system utilizing either a front drum/rear drum or a front disc/rear drum configuration. With this system, the master cylinder controls the left front and the right rear independently of, and simultaneously with, the right front and left rear wheels. If hydraulic fluid leakage occurs, braking effect will be lost only on one diagonal pair of wheels. Leakage manifests itself by long pedal travel and by a tendency of the car to swerve toward the side where brake pressure is the greatest. A warning light system is used after 1968, consisting of a light in the speedometer housing and a switch on the pedal mechanism.

Brake Adjustment

Brake wear is revealed by excessive travel of the brake pedal or handbrake lever before the brakes take effect. The distance between the fully depressed pedal and the floor board should be not less than 2.5 in. Since the front brakes are self-adjusting, only the rear brakes require adjustment.

1. Jack up the car so that the rear wheels clear the ground. It is possible to adjust the brakes without removing the wheels.
2. Release the handbrake and make sure that the brake levers return all the way. If the cable seems to bind, the levers must be returned by hand.
3. Press the brake pedal hard several times to center the brake shoes.
4. The adjusting screw for the rear brakes is the square peg located on the rear of the backing plate.

HYDRAULIC SYSTEM

CAUTION: *Do not permit brake fluid to contact painted surfaces.*

Master Cylinder

Removal and Installation

1. Disconnect the brake outlet lines from the master cylinder.
2. Remove the rubber boot from the pushrod or back off the locking nut and unscrew the pushrod from the clevis on the brake pedal.
3. Loosen and remove the two master cylinder retaining bolts. The lower one is a stud bolt and the nut is reached from the engine compartment. The upper one is a standard bolt, accessible from inside the car.
4. Remove the master cylinder.
5. Cover all openings to prevent the entry of dirt during installation.
6. Attach the brake cylinder to the cowl plate.
7. Install the rubber boot onto the pushrod. Reassemble the pushrod if it has been disassembled.
8. Connect the brake outlet lines and refill the system with brake fluid.
9. Adjust the brake pedal free-play.
10. Bleed the hydraulic system.

Overhaul

Disassembly

1. Remove the rubber boot from its retaining plate, together with the pushrod.

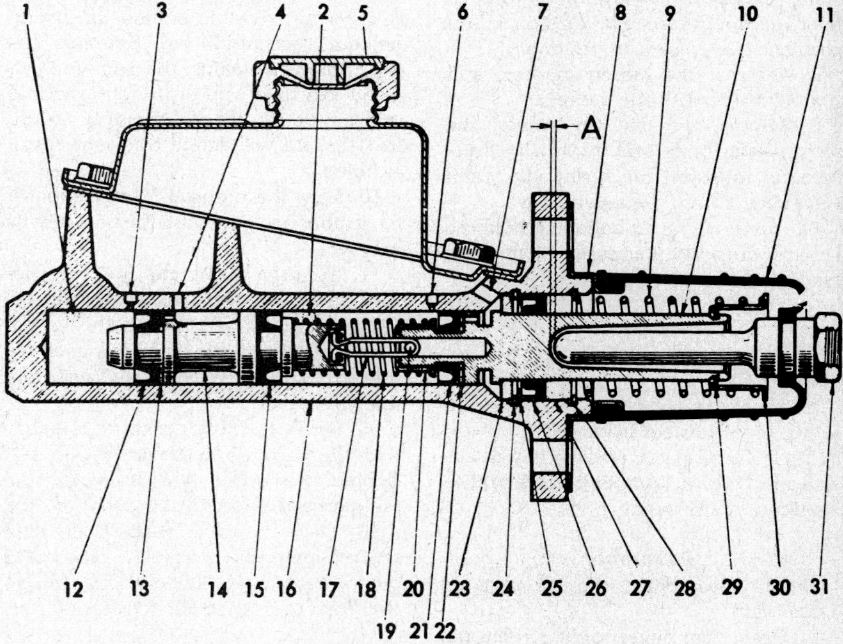

Brake system master cylinder

1. Outlet to one circuit
2. Outlet to other circuit
3. Bypass port
4. Feed hole
5. Brake fluid reservoir
6. Bypass port
7. Feed hole
8. Retaining plate
9. Spring
10. Primary piston
11. Rubber boot
12. Primary piston
13. Piston washer
14. Secondary piston
15. Secondary cup
16. Body
17. Clip
18. Spring
19. Retaining pin
20. Spring holder
21. Primary cup
22. Piston washer
23. Piston stop ring
24. Circlip
25. Washer
26. Secondary cup
27. Guide bearing
28. Circlip
29. "Spirol ox" circlip
30. Spring retainer
31. Pushrod

Bend the four ears of the boot retaining plate away from the mounting flange and remove it from the end of the cylinder.

2. Depress the spring retainer and, using a small screwdriver, unwind the "Spirolox" circlip from the groove on the primary piston, taking care not to distort the coils; remove the spring retainer together with the spring.

3. Remove the circlip, taking care not to damage the surface finish of the primary piston. Lightly tap the mounting flange of the cylinder body on the bench and remove the nylon guide bearing, the secondary cup, and the plain washer.

4. Using special snap-ring pliers with long narrow jaws, tool No. 784199, remove the inner snap-ring, taking care not to damage the surface finish of the primary piston.

5. Removal of the snap-ring will allow both pistons to be withdrawn together with the piston stop.

6. Compress the intermediate spring, together with spring holder, then drive out the retaining pin using a suitable pin punch. This will separate the two pistons, and allow the withdrawal of spring and spring holder.

7. Remove the primary cups, together with the piston washers, from the primary and secondary pistons. Remove the secondary cup from the back of the secondary piston. Do not attempt to remove the clip from the secondary piston, as it is permanently peened in position.

8. Unscrew the outlet adapters and remove them with the gaskets.

9. Remove the one-way valves, the spring, valve body, and spring clip. Take care not to distort the spring clip when removing it from the valve body.

10. Remove the six bolts that hold the cover of the brake fluid reservoir (5), then take off the cover and gasket.

Inspection

1. Make sure the cylinder bore is not scored.

2. Check the bypass holes; probe with a thin piece of steel piano wire.

3. Check all parts; replace any defective ones. Internal rubber parts should be replaced in any event.

Assembly

Before assembling, dip all parts in brake fluid.

1. Using your fingers only, stretch the secondary cup over the large end of the secondary piston with the lip pointing toward the peened clip. Gently work around the cup with your fingers to ensure correct seating.

2. Install the piston washer onto the secondary piston, as illustrated, so that the convex edge faces the rear of the cup. Using your fingers only, ease the primary cup over the nose and into the groove, with the lip of the cup pointing away from the head of the piston.

3. Use the same procedure with the primary cup and piston washer (22) of the primary piston. Ease the spring holder into the end of the spring (18) and fit the other end of the spring over the rear of the secondary piston (14).

4. Place the retaining pin in the hole in the primary piston; do not seat fully. Compress the spring until the secondary piston clip is visible. Place the clip in position in the primary piston and secure it by pushing the retaining pin fully home. Release the spring and make sure that the spring holder is correctly positioned.

5. Ease the pistons gently into the cylinder bore and slide the piston stop over the primary piston. Install the snap-ring into the inner groove, using snap-ring pliers. Do not damage the surface finish of the primary piston because this could cause leakage past the secondary cup.

6. Install the plain washer into the cylinder bore against the snap-ring, followed by the secondary cup.

7. Place the nylon guide bearing in position and secure the outer snap-ring.

8. Fit the boot retaining plate in position over the mounting flange and bend the four ears over to hold it in position.

9. Mount the spring retainer with the return spring on the primary piston. Compress the spring until the piston circlip groove is visible behind the spring retainer, then install the "Spirolox" circlip. Before installing the rubber boot, smear the small end of the pushrod and its groove with silicone grease to ensure that the rod will rotate freely when assembled.

10. Ease the pushrod into position in the rubber boot and push the boot into its groove.

11. Ease the spring clip into the one-way valve body and make sure that it is correctly positioned. Install the return spring over the valve body and assemble the parts within the outlet port, inserting the spring first.

12. Screw the outlet adapter, together with the gasket, into the outlet port and tighten to a torque of 28 ft lbs. Use the same procedure for the other outlet port.

13. Place the cover of the brake fluid reservoir in position, with the gasket, and secure it using the six bolts and tightening them to a torque of 6 ft lbs.

Brake Bleeding

Bleeding is not a routine procedure and is necessary only when part of the system has been disassembled or when the brake fluid has been drained. Indications that air has entered the system are excessive pedal travel, spongy pedal action or absence of braking effect until the pedal has been pumped several times.

A bleed screw is provided for each brake. Bleed screws for the disc brakes are located on the inner part of the caliper up to and including 1966. From 1967, the screws are located on the brake cylinder.

When bleeding the rear brakes on the SAAB Sport and 99, the pressure regulating valves will shut off the supply of brake fluid to the rear wheels if the brake pedal is depressed too hard before the bleed screw is opened.

To bleed the system, proceed as follows:

1. Make sure that the reservoir is full and the air vents are not blocked.

Location of bleeding screws—disc brakes

Location of bleeding screws—drum brakes

2. Since the master cylinder has tandem pistons, it is necessary to bleed both rear wheels and both front wheels at the same time in order to purge the system. Begin with the rear wheels and bleed the front wheels afterward.

3. Fit suitable hoses to the bleed screws.

4. Dip the hose ends into a glass jar full of clean brake fluid.

5. Back off both screws ½–1 turn.

6. Have another person quickly push the pedal down and allow it to come up slowly.

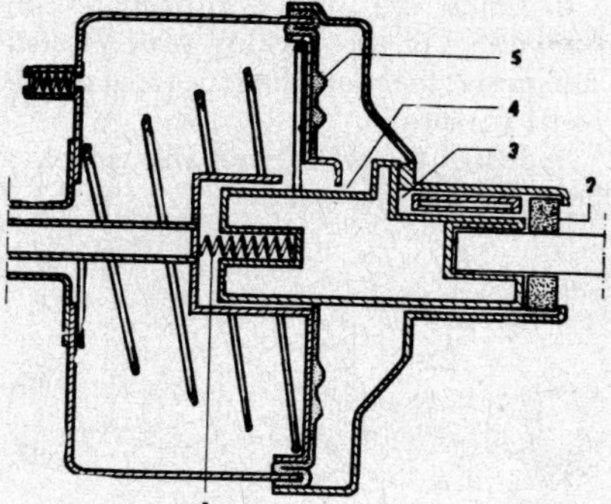

Power assist unit

1. Return spring
2. Air filter
3. Atmospheric channel
4. Vacuum channel
5. Diaphragm

Power Assist

The vacuum power assist unit cannot be disassembled and therefore is nonserviceable.

Removal and Installation

1. Remove the air cleaner.
2. Disconnect and plug the master cylinder brake lines and the power assist unit vacuum line.
3. Unscrew the clip that holds the speedometer cable to the power assist unit.
4. Disconnect the push rod from the brake pedal, unbolt the power assist unit from the firewall, and remove the unit.
5. Remove the retaining nuts and separate the master cylinder from the power assist unit.
6. Install in the reverse order of removal and bleed the brake system.

DISC BRAKES

Ate disc brakes with dual piston calipers and solid discs are used. A disc throw compensator, consisting of a spring assembly behind each piston, maintains proper pad-to-disc clearance. The pad retaining spring also acts as a warning device in case of excessive pad wear, causing high pedal effort when pads reach their minimum thickness.

Disc Brake Pads

Removal and Installation (All models)

1. Jack up the car and remove the wheel.
2. Remove the cotter pins and the springs that hold the friction pads. Remove the friction pads.
3. Clean the exposed part of the piston, making sure there is no rust or dirt on the friction pad surfaces which contact the bracket and yoke.

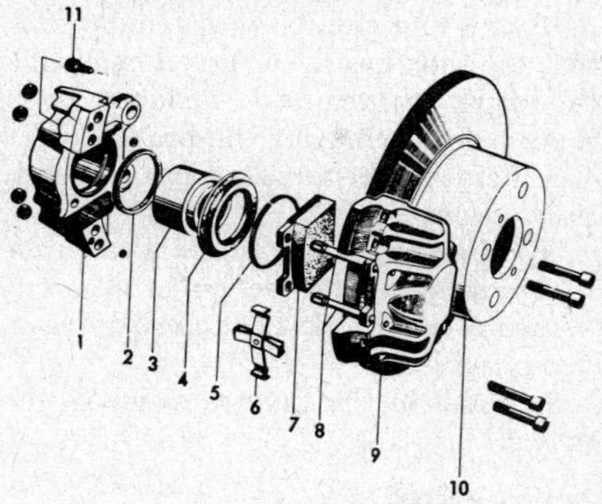

Disc brake assembly

1. Caliper half
2. Piston seal
3. Piston
4. Gasket
5. Gasket retainer
6. Retaining spring
7. Brake pad
8. Locking pins
9. Brake housing half
10. Brake drum and disc
11. Bleeder screw

NOTE: *When cleaning, use only brake fluid or methylated spirits.*

4. Drive the piston back into the brake housing, with a small C-clamp. When the piston is forced back, the fluid in the reservoir will be displaced and it may be necessary to drain off the excess.
5. Clean the brake disc with a solvent which leaves no residue, such as trichloroethylene.
6. Turn the movable brake component toward the wheel and install the outer friction pad. Make sure it moves easily in its yoke. Protruding pad parts can be trimmed with a file. If used friction pads are installed, they must be placed in their original positions.
7. Turn the movable brake component backward as far as possible.
8. Fit anti-squeak shims to the back of the friction pads, making sure they don't exceed the contours of the pressure plate.
9. Make sure the shims are installed with the two recesses directed downward in such a way that they are centered on the ends of the piston recess. Install the inner friction pad. Make sure that the recess in the piston is directed downward.
10. Install the spring. The recess in the spring should be as near as possible to the outer friction pad. Install new cotter pins, the upper cotter pin first.

NOTE: *To install the lower cotter pin, press the spring upward using a screwdriver.*

11. Pump the brake pedal a few times to seat the pads.
12. Top up the brake fluid reservoir.

Disc Brake Caliper

NOTE: *Never separate the caliper halves.*

Removal and Installation

1. Remove the brake pads.
2. Disconnect and plug the caliper brake line.
3. Unbolt the caliper from the suspension upright and remove it from the car.
4. Installation is the reverse of removal.

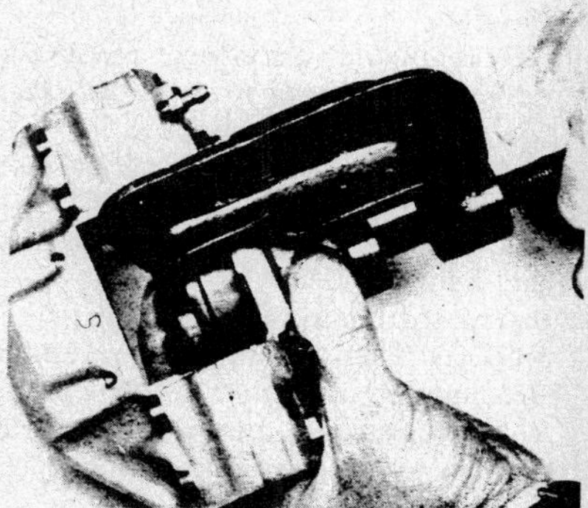

Pressing piston into disc brake caliper

Overhaul

1. With the caliper removed from the wheel, press one piston into the caliper and force the other out of the caliper using compressed air.
2. Pry the seal out of the caliper bore.
3. Coat the new seal with special disc brake lubricant and install it into the caliper.
4. Coat the piston with the same lubricant and insert it into the caliper, using a template to locate the recess in the piston face.
5. After installation, ensure that the recess is in the proper position. If necessary, rotate the piston into position.
6. Coat a new dust cover with the special lubricant and press the cover and retainer onto the piston and caliper.
7. Repeat the operation on the other piston.
8. Install the caliper in the reverse order of removal and bleed the brake system.

Checking caliper piston alignment with template.

Brake Disc (Rotor)

Removal and Installation (All Models)

1. Remove the hubcap and loosen the spindle nut.
2. Jack up the front of the car, take off the wheel, and remove the spindle nut.
3. Remove the two bolts that hold the brake to the steering knuckle housing. These bolts are accessible from inside the brake disc. Lift the caliper clear of the brake disc.

NOTE: *Do not disconnect the brake hose; wire the brake in such a way that the hose is not damaged.*

4. Pull off the wheel hub, with the disc attached, using a wheel puller.
5. Detach the brake disc from the wheel hub.
6. Reassemble in reverse order.

NOTE: *When installing the caliper bolts, always use a new tab lock plate.*

7. After assembly, pump the pedal a few times to seat the brake pistons.

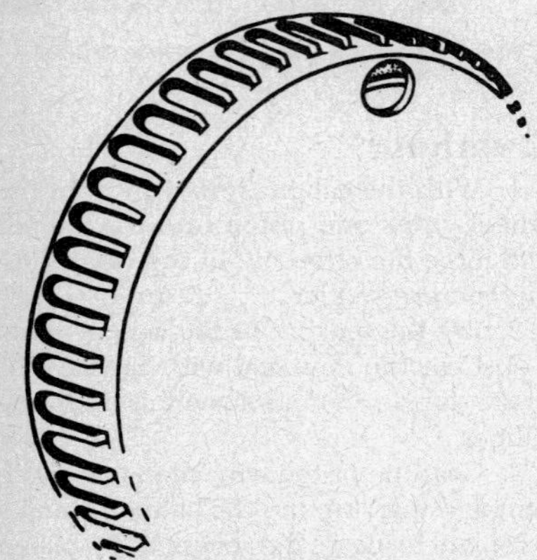

Inspection hole in brake drum

DRUM BRAKES

Because the front shoes are self-adjusting, it is not possible to detect worn linings by excessive pedal travel. It is, therefore, important to remove the wheels at regular intervals in order to check lining wear through the inspection holes in the drum. If the linings are less than 1.0 mm. (0.040 in.) thick, replacement is necessary.

Brake Drum

Removal and Installation

1. Remove the cotter pin and spindle nut.
2. Jack up the car.
3. Remove the wheel.

4a. *Rear wheels:* Release the handbrake and adjust the rear shoes with the adjusting screw.

4b. *Front wheels:* The front shoes must be adjusted in the following manner.

Insert a screwdriver into the extra hole in the brake drum, then into the hole (6) in the brake shoe. Then, with another screwdriver or bar bearing against the hub nut, press the brake drum and shoe against the normal direction of rotation until a grating sound is heard, indicating that the shoe has been forced back and the pawl has released. Readjust both shoes before removing the brake drum.

5. Remove the brake drum, using a brake drum puller.

NOTE: *If the proper puller is not available, a standard wheel puller will do if used carefully. Never remove by hammering.*

6. Install in the reverse order of removal.

Inspection

1. Examine the linings on all the shoes. If they are worn below inspection limits, cracked, burned, charred, worn unevenly, or covered with grease, new linings must be installed. Never install new lingings on only one side.
2. If linings are replaced, they must be ground in a special machine to a radius of about 0.010–0.012 in. less than that of the drum for perfect contact. The edges of the linings must *not* be chamfered, they should be left as sharp as possible.

Brake Shoes

Removal and Installation

1. Use a piece of wire or clamp to keep the brake pistons in the wheel cylinder.
2. Remove the springs which hold the shoes to the backing plate.

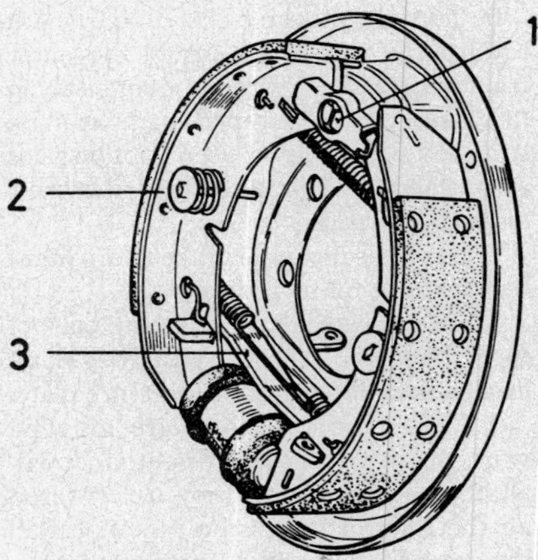

Rear brake assembly

1. Adjuster
2. Spring
3. Handbrake link

3. Remove the shoes from the cylinder and handbrake levers; first the top, then the bottom.
4. Hook the springs between the shoes.
5. Install the front shoe, with the handbrake lever in the oblong hole.
6. Lift the rear shoe with the handbrake lever into the large hole. Make sure the spring presses against the lever as illustrated.
7. Remove the wire or clamp used to keep the brake pistons in place.
8. Adjust the shoes approximately in the center of the backing plate. Install the springs that hold the shoes against the backing plate.
9. Install the wheel hub and wheel.
10. Adjust the brakes.

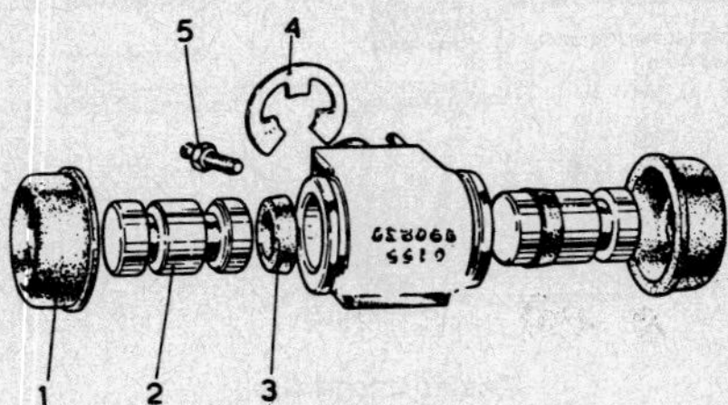

Wheel cylinder—drum brakes

1. Rubber boot
2. Piston
3. Piston seal
4. Locking washer
5. Bleed nipple

Wheel Cylinder

Removal and Installation

NOTE: *The locations of the anchor pins differ from model to model. These pins must not be removed.*

1. Remove the wheel, brake drum, and brake shoes.
2. Disconnect the handbrake cable from the levers.
3. Disconnect the brake line from the rear of the backing plate.
4. Remove the wheel cylinder retaining ring and the bleed screw from the rear of the backing plate.
5. Remove the wheel cylinder.
6. Bolt the wheel cylinder to the backing plate and locate the retaining ring and bleed screw. The cylinder has an anchor pin which fits in a hole in the backing plate.
7. Connect the brake line.
8. Install the brake shoes, brake drum, and wheel, taking care not to damage the axle seal.
9. Connect the handbrake cable. The handbrake lever must be installed with the bent part upward.

NOTE: *Bleed the system whenever a cylinder has been removed or a line disconnected.*

Overhaul

1. Remove the rubber boots from the cylinder.
2. Pull out the pistons.
3. Take the rubber seals off the pistons.
4. Clean and dry all parts. Do not allow gasoline or grease to come in contact with the rubber seals.
5. Make sure the cylinder bore is not scored.
6. Make sure that all the rubber seals and cups are in perfect condition.

NOTE: *Utmost cleanliness must be observed when assembling the wheel cylinder.*

7. Lubricate all parts with brake fluid when assembling.

8. Assemble, making certain the piston seal is facing the correct way; use no sharp tools.

PARKING BRAKE

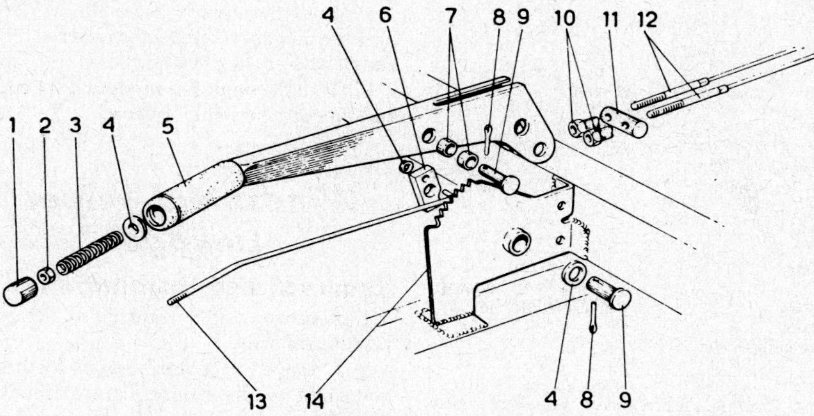

Handbrake components—parking brake

1. Release button
2. Nut
3. Return spring
4. Washer
5. Handbrake lever
6. Pawl
7. Spacer sleeve
8. Cotter pin or circlip
9. Pin
10. Adjustment nut
11. Cable pin
12. Threaded wire rods
13. Pawl rod
14. Ratchet

All SAABs are equipped with a parking brake which is actuated through cables to the rear drum brake shoes.

The SAAB 99, which utilizes four wheel disc brakes, also uses a drum type parking brake. Located inside the rotor hub of the front discs, it is very similar in construction and service procedures, to a conventional drum brake.

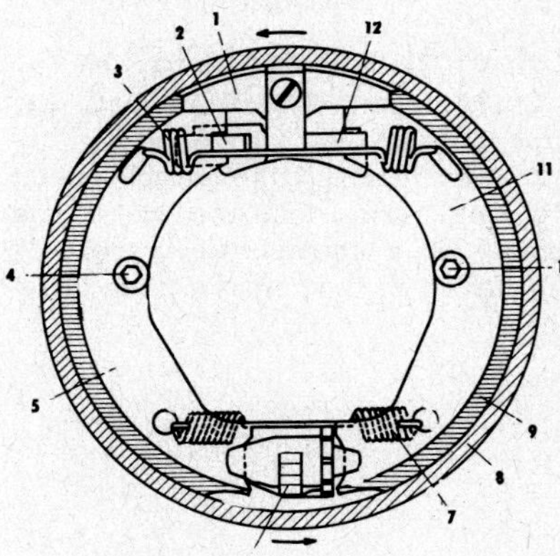

Parking brake—disc brakes

1. Support piece
2. Lever arm
3. Upper tension screw
4. Compression screw
5. Primary brake shoe
6. Adjustment
7. Lower tension spring
8. Brake drum
9. Brake lining
10. Retaining spring
11. Secondary brake shoe
12. Pressure rod

Parking Brake Shoes

Removal and Installation (SAAB 99 Only)

1. Raise the front end of the car and remove the wheels.

2. Unbolt the brake caliper and hang it in an out of the way position so as not to stress the brake line.

3. Release the parking brake and remove the disc.

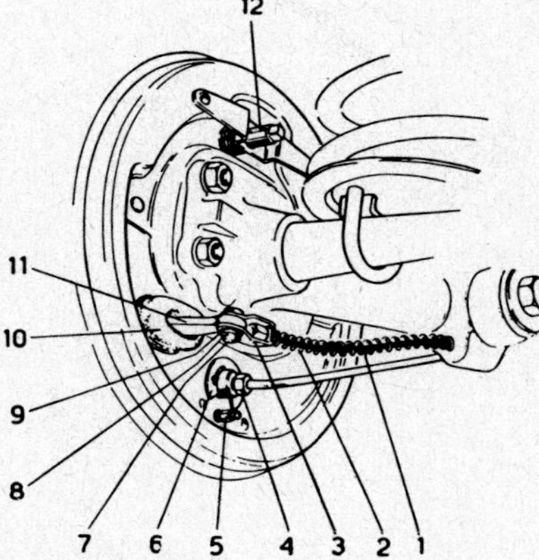

Reverse side of the backing plate—drum brakes.

1. Handbrake wire
2. Coil spring
3. Clevis
4. Brake pipe connection
5. Bleed nipple
6. Lockwasher
7. Pin
8. Cotter pin
9. Washer
10. Rubber boot
11. Parking brake lever
12. Adjustment device

4. Using a piece of welding rod with a hook formed on the end, release the upper return spring.

5. Rotate the hub until the hole is over the shoe hold down springs, and remove the hold down springs.

6. Remove the shoes by pulling them down.

7. Loosen the cable at the lever arm end, install the shoes in the reverse order of removal, and adjust the parking brake.

Adjustments

All Models (Except SAAB 99)

Adjustment of the handbrake lever travel or of the brake cables should always be preceded by adjustment of the rear brakes. If the handbrake still requires adjustment, proceed as follows:

1. Jack up the car so that both rear wheels clear the floor.

2. Remove the right front seat and move the lever to its lowest position.

3. Tighten the left-hand adjusting nut until the brake shoes contact the left brake drum.

4. Back off the nut just enough to permit the wheel to rotate, then back off one more full turn.

5. Repeat this procedure for the right-hand adjusting nut.

6. Test by pulling the handbrake all the way on, then releasing it. The wheels should still rotate freely with the lever pulled up two notches from off, but should be locked at the third-notch.

7. Make sure the braking effect is equal for both wheels.

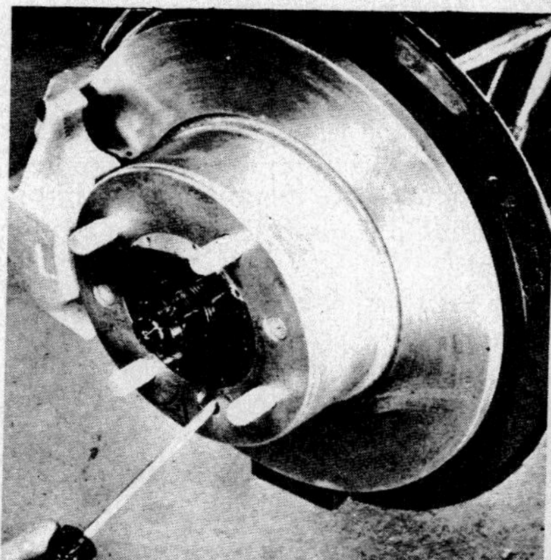

Adjusting parking brake—disc brakes

SAAB 99

NOTE: *When properly adjusted, the parking brake should begin to engage by the second ratchet notch and fully lock the wheels by the third notch.*

1. To adjust, raise the front of the car and support it under the suspension arms.

2. Release the parking brake and rotate the front wheels to ensure that no binding exists.

3. Rotate the disc until the hole aligns with the adjuster and, using a screwdriver, tighten the adjuster until the disc can just be turned.

4. Back off the adjuster until the shoes do not bind (1 or 2 teeth) and check the adjustment.

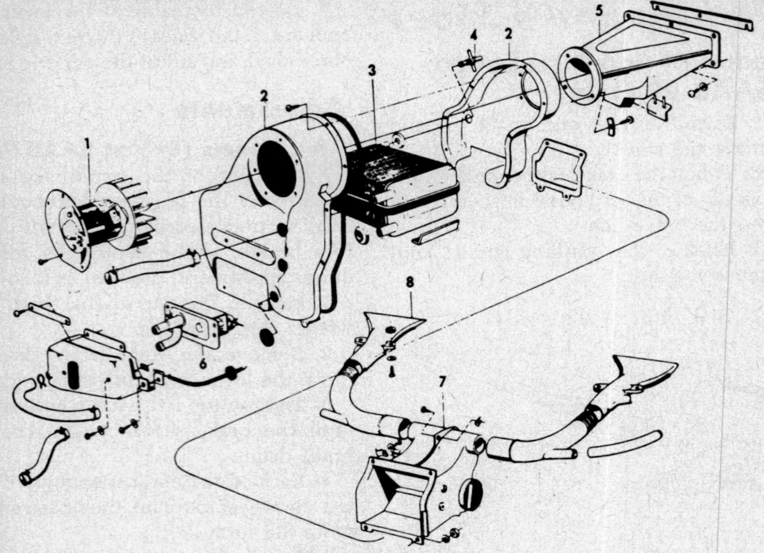

Heating system

1. Fan and motor
2. Casings
3. Heat exchanger
4. Bleeder screw
5. Fresh-air duct
6. Thermostat valve
7. Damper housing
8. Defroster jet

CHASSIS ELECTRICAL

Heater Blower

Removal and Installation

1. Code for identification and remove the three wires from the blower motor.
2. Remove the mounting screws from the front plate and lift out the blower motor.
3. Installation is the reverse order of removal.

Heater Core

Removal and Installation

1. Open the heater bleeder, drain the coolant from the heater core, and disconnect the hoses from the heater.
2. Disconnect and remove the throttle control shaft and disconnect the heater water valve.
3. Separate all air hoses from the heater casing.
4. Unbolt and remove the left hand cover plate and the fan casing and fan (as a unit).
5. Disconnect the engine brace from the firewall.
6. Remove the screws under the dash panel that retain the air control valve to the heater casing.
7. Unbolt the casing mounting bolts on the firewall and remove the heater casing.
8. Remove the clips that hold the halves of the casing together and lift out the core.
9. Installation is the reverse of removal.
10. Install the seal rings on the water pipes before assembling the casing.
11. Start the engine, close the heater bleeder, and open the heater water valve and fill the cooling system.
12. Run the engine at moderate speed, and bleed the cooling system.

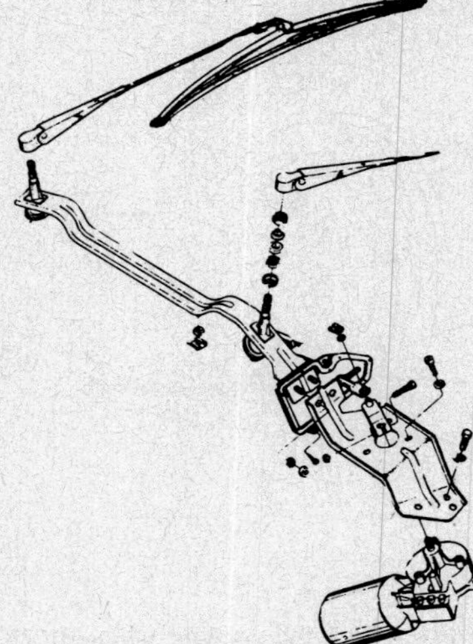

Windshield wiper assembly

Windshield Wiper Linkage

Removal and Installation

1. Remove the windshield wiper blades and arms.
2. Remove the heater hoses on the left and right of the engine compartment, unbolt and remove the heater fan housing.
3. Unscrew the nuts from the spindles, and unbolt the motor mounting bracket.
4. Push the spindles into the body, and slide out the linkage.
5. Install in the reverse order of removal.

NOTE: *Ensure that the wiper arms are installed in the parked position with the motor in the same position.*

Windshield Wiper Motor

Removal and Installation

1. The motor is removed with the wiper linkage.
2. After removing the linkage, unbolt the crank arm from the motor and remove the motor from the bracket.
3. Install in the reverse order of removal.

SUBARU

Index

INTRODUCTION

The Subaru model Star (FF-1) with an 1100 cc engine was introduced into America in 1970. In 1971, the model 1300 Star FF-1G was introduced and displacement was increased to 1267 cc. The Star is available in both a sedan and a station wagon version. In 1973 the Model DL sedan, the DL station wagon, and the model GL, which is the sporty version of the model G, were introduced. The DL station wagon and the GL have a 1361 cc engine (1400 Models) and the DL sedan and the G have the 1267 cc engine (1300 Models).

MODEL IDENTIFICATION

FF-1 Sedan

FF-1 Station Wagon

FF-1 Model G Sedan

FF-1 Model GL Sedan

FF-1 Model DL Sedan

FF-1 Model DL Station Wagon

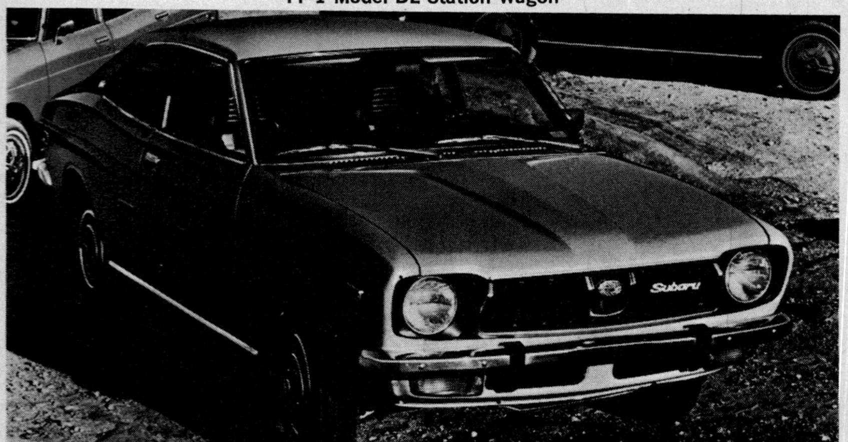

FF-1 Model GL Sports Coupe

Vehicle and Engine Serial Numbers

FF-1

The Vehicle Identification Number is stamped on a tab located on the top of the dashboard on the driver's side, visible through the windshield. The Vehicle Identification Plate is on the bulkhead in the engine compartment, behind the windshield washer reservoir. The engine number is stamped on the crankcase, behind the distributor. The 1100 cc. engine code is EA61. The 1300 cc. (Model G) engine code is EA62.

The engine code of the 1400 engine is EA63A.

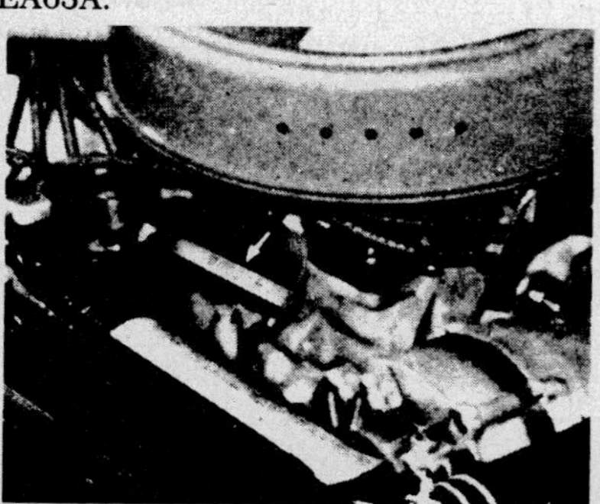

Engine number location

VEHICLE IDENTIFICATION

Year	Model	Body Style	Code
1970-71	FF-1 (1100)	Sedan Station Wagon	A14L A43L
1971-72	FF-1 G (1300)	Sedan Station Wagon	A15L A44L
1972-73	FF-1 (1300)	Sedan and Coupe Station Wagon	A23L A63L
	FF-1 (1400)	Sedan and Coupe (GL, GSR) Station Wagon	A22L A62L

TUNE-UP SPECIFICATIONS

Year	Engine Displace. Cu in.	SPARK PLUGS Type	SPARK PLUGS Gap (in.)	DISTRIBUTOR Point Dwell (deg)	DISTRIBUTOR Point Gap (in.)	Ignition Timing (deg)	Intake Valve Opens (deg)	Cranking Compression Pressure (psi)	IDLE SPEED (rpm)	VALVE (in) CLEARANCE In	VALVE (in) CLEARANCE Ex
1970-71	1100	NGK (B6E)	0.030	49-55	0.020	TDC @ 850	20B	178	850	0.008-0.009	0.010-0.011
1971-72	1300	NGK (BP-6ES)	0.032	49-55	0.020	TDC @ 750 ①	24B	178	750	0.011-0.013	0.011-0.013
1973	1400	NGK (B-6ES)	0.030	49-55	0.020	10 @ 700	24B	178	700	0.011-0.013	0.011-0.013

B Before Top Dead Center
TDC Top Dead Center
① 6B on 1972 model

TORQUE SEQUENCES

1100, 1300, and 1400 engines

FIRING ORDER

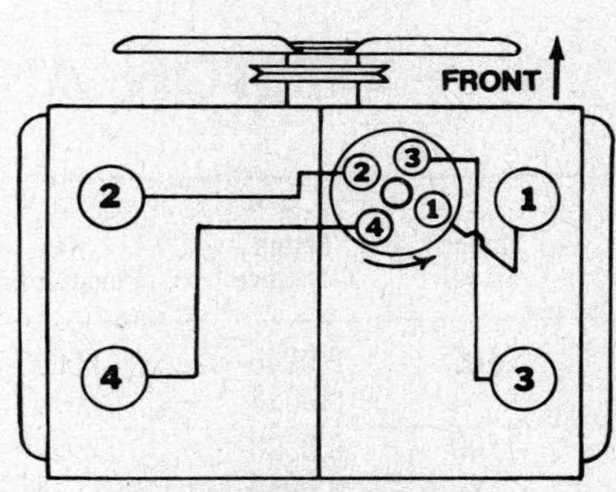

1100, 1300, and 1400 engines

GENERAL ENGINE SPECIFICATIONS

Year	Type	Displace. Cu. In. (cc.)	Carburetor	Advertized Horsepower @ rpm (SAE)	Advertized Torque @ rpm (SAE)	Bore and Stroke (in.)	Comp. Ratio	Normal Oil Pressure (psi)
1970-71	4 cylinder horizontally opposed	66.4 (1088)	2 bbl	62 @ 6000	62.9 @ 3200	2.99 x 2.36	9.0:1	42-57
1971-72	4 cylinder horizontally opposed	77.3 (1267)	2 bbl	61 @ 5600	65.1 @ 4000	3.23 x 2.36	9.0:1	42-57
1973	4 cylinder horizontally opposed	83.2 (1361)	2 bbl	80 @ 6400	76 @ 4000	3.35 x 2.36	9.0:1	42-57

CRANKSHAFT AND CONNECTING ROD SPECIFICATIONS

All measurements are given in inches

		CRANKSHAFT				CONNECTING ROD		
Year	Engine Model	Main Journal Dia.	Main Brg. Oil Clearance	Shaft End-Play	Thrust On No.	Journal Diameter	Oil Clearance	Side Clearance
1970-73	1100 1300 1400	1.9669- 1.9468	0.0012- 0.0026	0.0016- 0.0049	2	1.7719- 1.7515	0.0012- 0.0026	0.0039- 0.0073

VALVE SPECIFICATIONS

Year	Engine Model	Seat Angle (deg)	Face Angle (deg)	Spring Test Pressure (lbs @ in.)	Stem to Guide Clearance (in.) Intake	Stem to Guide Clearance (in.) Exhaust	Stem Diameter Intake	Stem Diameter Exhaust	Valve Guides Removable
1970-71	1100	45	45	Inner 48.7 @ 1.02 Outer 110.9 @ 1.10	0.0010- 0.0022	0.0016- 0.0030	0.3134- 0.3140	0.3125- 0.3134	Yes
1971-73	1300- 1400	45	45	Inner 43 @ 1.14 Outer 98 @ 1.22	0.0010- 0.0022	0.0020- 0.0032	0.3130- 0.3136	0.3124- 0.3130	Yes

PISTON AND RING SPECIFICATIONS

All measurements in inches

			RING GAP			RING SIDE CLEARANCE		
Year	Engine Model	Piston Clearance	Top Compression	Bottom Compression	Oil Control	Top Compression	Bottom Compression	Oil Control
1970-71	1100	0.0006- 0.0018	0.0079- 0.0157	0.0079- 0.0157	0.0118- 0.0354	0.0014- 0.0029	0.0010- 0.0025	None
1971-72	1300	0.0008- 0.0019	0.0079- 0.0196	0.0079- 0.0196	0.0118- 0.0354	0.0014- 0.0029	0.0010- 0.0025	None
1973	1400	0.0008- 0.0020	0.008- 0.020	0.008- 0.020	0.012- 0.035	0.0014- 0.0029	0.0010- 0.0025	None

TORQUE SPECIFICATIONS

All readings in ft lbs

Year	Engine Displacement (cc)	Cylinder Head Bolts	Rod Bearing Bolts	Crankcase Halves	Crankshaft Pulley Bolt	Flywheel To Crankshaft Bolts	Manifold Intake	Manifold Exhaust
1970-71	1100	30-35	35-38	10mm bolts 26-31 8mm bolts 17-20 6mm bolts 3-4	39-42	30-33	13-16	7-9
1971-72	1300	37-42	35-38	Same as for the 1100	39-42	30-33	13-16	7-9
1973	1400	37-43	29-32	Same as for the 1100	39-42	30-33	13-16	7-9

BATTERY AND STARTER SPECIFICATIONS

Year	Engine Model	BATTERY Amp. Hour Cap.	Volts	Term. Ground.	STARTERS Lock Test Amps.	Volts	Torque (ft lbs)	No-Load Test Amps.	Volts	RPM	Brush Spring Tension (oz)
1970-71	1100	32	12	Neg	430	8.5	8.0	55	11	3500	35-54
1971-72	1200	35	12	Neg	470	9.5	9.4	50	11	5000	35-54
1973	1400	50	12	Neg	470	7.7	9.4	50	11	5000	35-54

ALTERNATOR AND REGULATOR SPECIFICATIONS

Year	ALTERNATOR Part No. or Manufacturer	Output (amps.)	REGULATOR Part No. or Manufacturer	Field Relay Air Gap (in.)	Field Relay Point Gap (in.)	Volts to Close	Regulator Air Gap (in.)	Regulator Point Gap (in.)	Volts
1970-71	LT13059A	30 @ 5000	TL1Z27	0.035	0.020	15	0.024-0.039	0.014	10.5 @ 68°F
1971-72	LT17075	30 @ 5000	TL1Z54	0.035	0.020	15	0.024-0.039	0.014	10.5 @ 68°F
1973	LT13520	35 @ 5000	TL1Z64	0.035	0.020	10	0.024-0.039	0.014	10.5 @ 68°F

CAPACITIES

Year	Model	Engine Displacement cu in. (cc)	Engine Crankcase (qts) Without Filter	Transaxle (pts)	Gasoline Tank (gals)	Cooling System (qts)
1970-71	1100	1088 (1100)	2.8	5.2	11.9① 9.5②	6.2
1971-72	1300	1267 (1300)	3.4	5.2	13.2① 9.5②	6.2
1973	1400	1361 (1400)	3.4	5.2	13.2① 9.5②	6.2

① Sedan and Coupe ② Station Wagon

WHEEL ALIGNMENT

Year	Model	CASTER Range (deg)	CASTER Pref. Setting (deg)	CAMBER Range (deg)	CAMBER Pref. Setting (deg)	Toe-in (in.)	Steering Axis Inclination	WHEEL PIVOT RATIO (deg) Inner Wheel	Outer Wheel
1970-71	1100	1°30′-2°	2°	1°20′-1°50′	1°50′	0.20	2°20′	36°20′	34°20′
1972-73	1300 1400	0-1°30′	45′	50′-1°50′	80′	0.20	—	35°-37°	34°-36°

— Not Available

BRAKE SPECIFICATIONS

All measurements are given in inches

Year	Model	Master Cylinder Bore	Wheel Cylinder or Caliper Piston Bore: Front Disc	Front Drum	Rear Disc	Rear Drum	Brake Disc or Drum Diameter: Front Disc	Front Drum	Rear Disc	Rear Drum	New Pad or Lining Thickness
1970-73	1100 1300 1400	0.7489- 0.7501	2.125	0.937- 0.939	—	0.625- 0.627①	7.24	8.01②	—	7.09	Drum-0.20③ Disc-0.35④

① 0.687-0.689 in the Station Wagon
② 9.01 in the Station Wagon
③ 0.16 Front Primary Shoe
④ 0.20 Rear
— Not applicable

FUSES AND CIRCUIT BREAKERS

Year	Model	Circuit	Type	Amp.
1970-71	1100	Ignition, horn, key warning buzzer	Fuse	25
		Headlights, parking lights, instrument lights, windshield washers	Fuse	25
		Lighter, radio, interior light, wipers	Fuse	20
		Back-up light, turn signals, stop lights, charge indicator, oil pressure indicator, instruments, brake warning light, fuel pump, blower motor	Fuse	10
		Side marker lights, tail lights, license plate lights, instrument lights, map light	Fuse	10
1972-73		Lighting switch	Fuse	25
		Key warning buzzer, interior light, clock, stop light, hazard flasher, turn signal lamp, cigar lighter	Fuse	20
		Ignition starter switch	Fuse	30
		Horn, radio, heater fan, windshield wiper and washer	Fuse	10
		Illumination lamp for the tachometer, front combination lamp, tail lamp, side marker lamp, license lamp	Fuse	10
		Back-up lamp, turn signal flasher, ignition switch, fuel pump, wiper motor, heated rear window, fuel gauge, cooling fan motor, thermostat, voltage regulator, alternator, brake fail warning light, oil pressure warning light, charge warning light	Fuse	10
		Headlights—high and low beams	Fuse	10

LIGHT BULB SPECIFICATIONS

Year	Model	Usage	Type	Watt.
1970-71	1100	Headlight	Two staged Sealed Beam	50/40
		Front turn signal and parking light	Dual Filament (amber)	23/8
		Rear turn signal, stop and parking light	Dual Filament	23/8
		Back-up light	Single Filament	23
		License Plate light	Single Filament	8
		Front side marker light	Single Filament (amber)	6
		Rear side marker light	Single Filament (red)	6
		Instrument light, map light	Single Filament	3
		Charge, turn signal, high beam, and oil pressure indicator lights, brake warning light	Single Filament (red)	3
		Interior light	Single Filament	8
1972-73	1300	Front and rear turn signal light (and stop in rear)	Single Filament	23
	1400	Front and rear parking light	Single Filament	8
		Head light	Two staged Sealed Beam	50/40
		Front and rear side marker lights	Single Filament	8
		License Plate light	Single Filament	8
		Interior light	Single Filament	8
		Illumination light	Single Filament	3
		Back-up light	Single Filament	23

WIRING DIAGRAMS

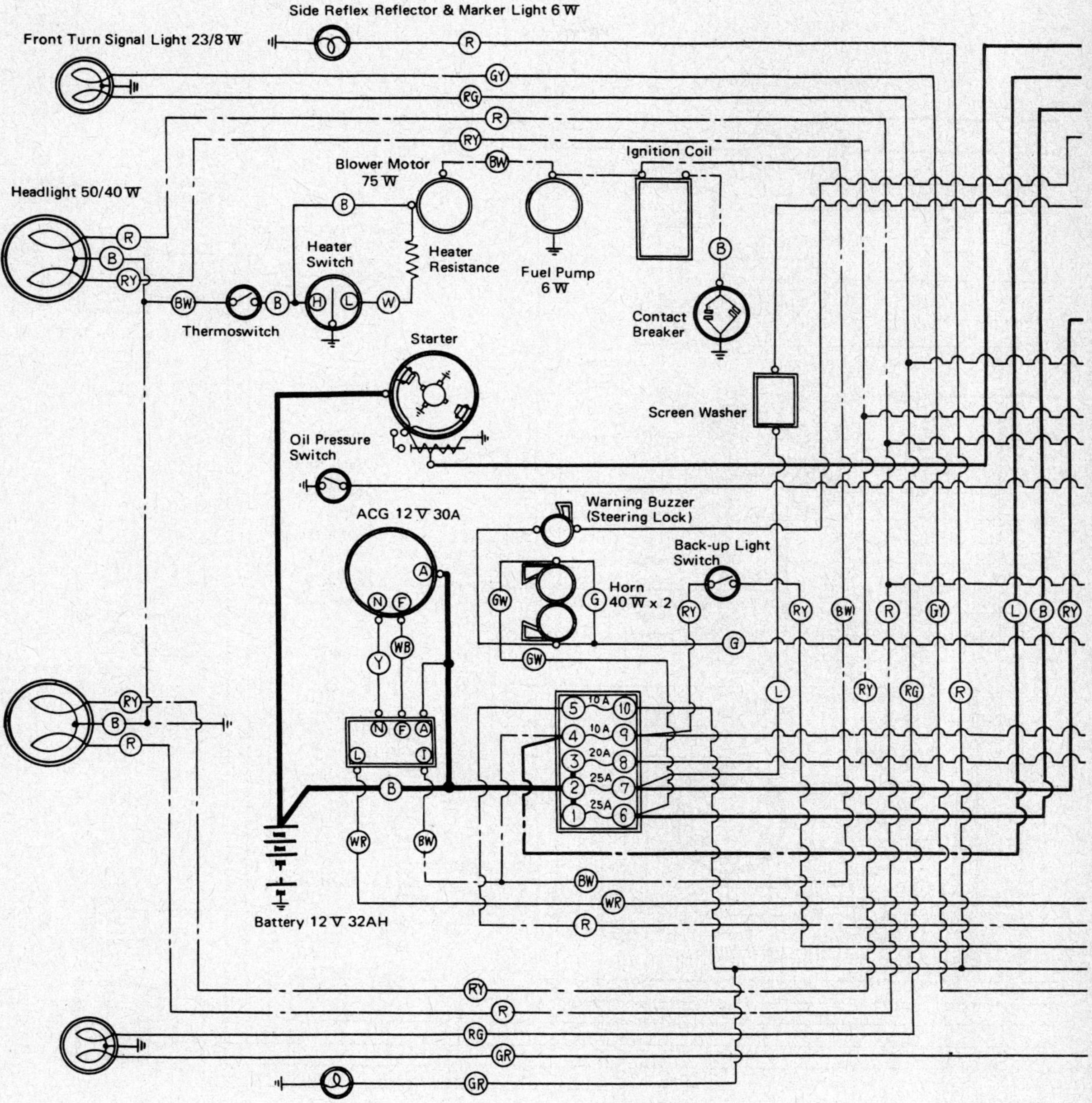

L	Blue	LW	Blue-white	LR	Blue-red				
R	Red	RW	Red-white	RG	Red-green	RY	Red-yellow	RB	Red-black
G	Green	GW	Green-white	GR	Green-red	GY	Green-yellow		
Y	Yellow	YR	Yellow-red	YG	Yellow-green				
W	White	WB	White-black	WR	White-red				
B	Black	BW	Black-white	BY	Black-yellow				
Color Code of Electric Wires									

1100 and 1300 Sedans

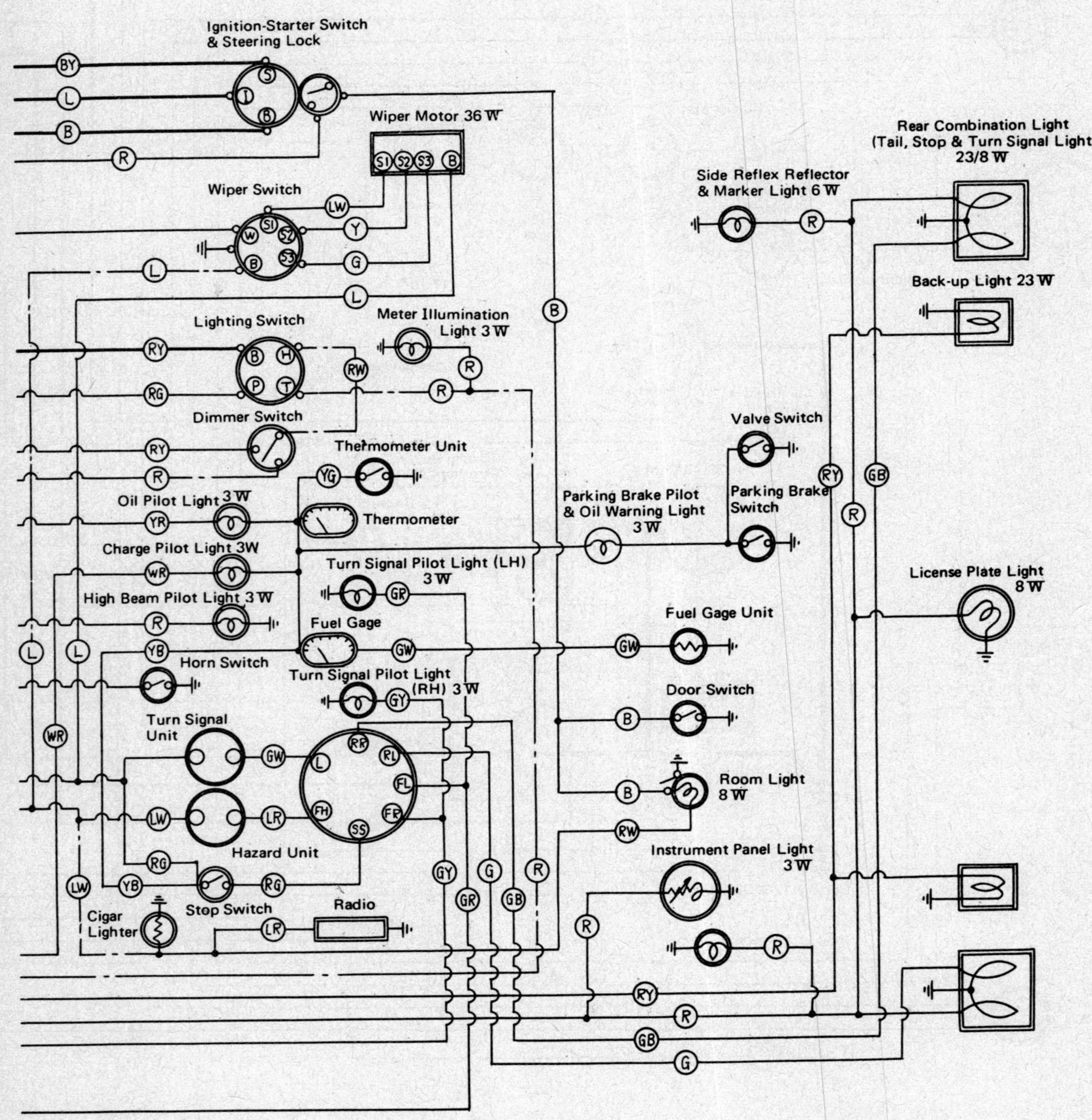

1100 and 1300 Sedans

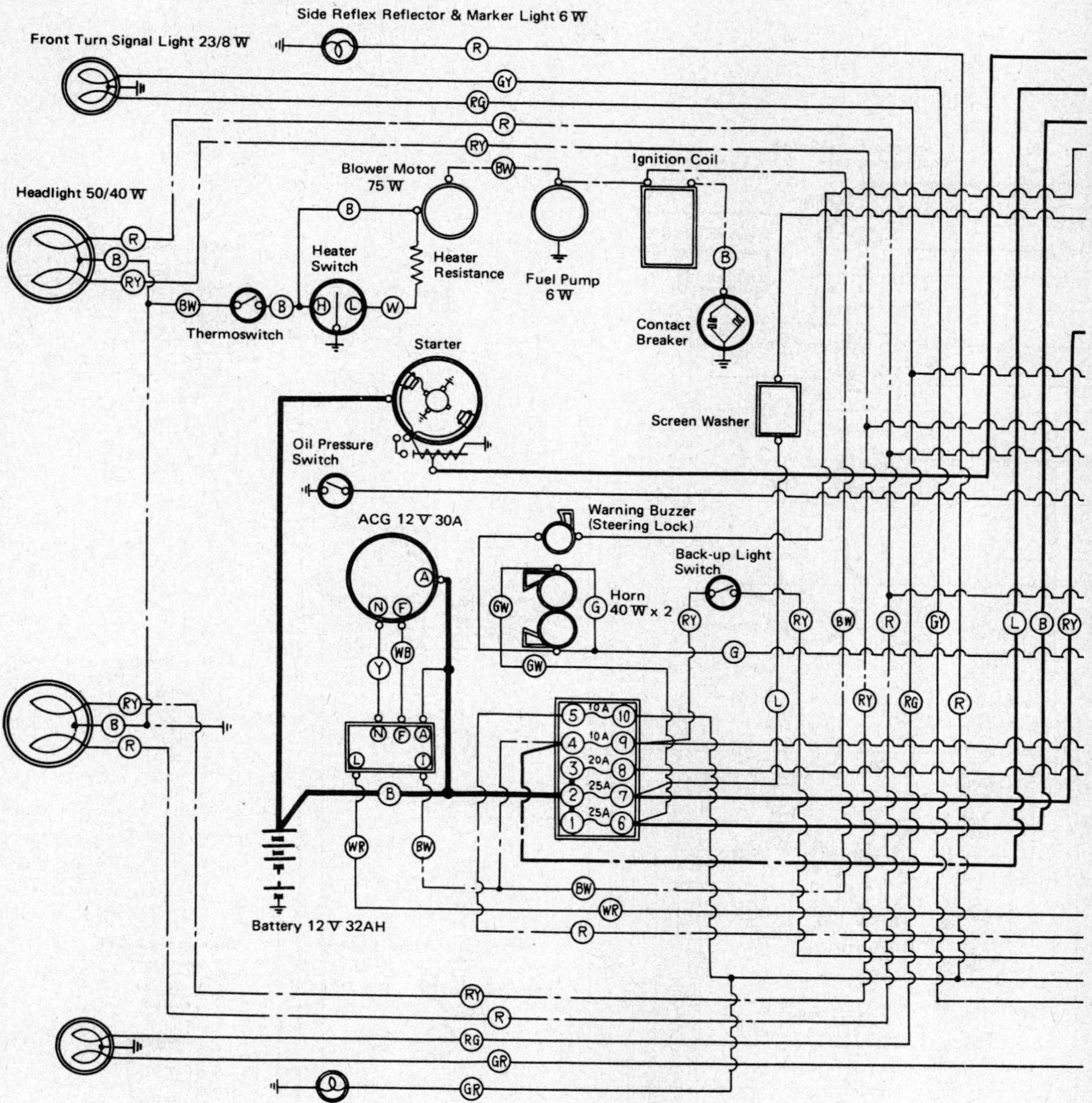

L	Blue	LW	Blue-white	LR	Blue-red				
R	Red	RW	Red-white	RG	Red-green	RY	Red-yellow	RB	Red-black
G	Green	GW	Green-white	GR	Green-red	GY	Green-yellow		
Y	Yellow	YR	Yellow-red	YG	Yellow-green				
W	White	WB	White-black	WR	White-red				
B	Black	BW	Black-white	BY	Black-yellow				

Color Code of Electric Wires

1100 and 1300 Station Wagons

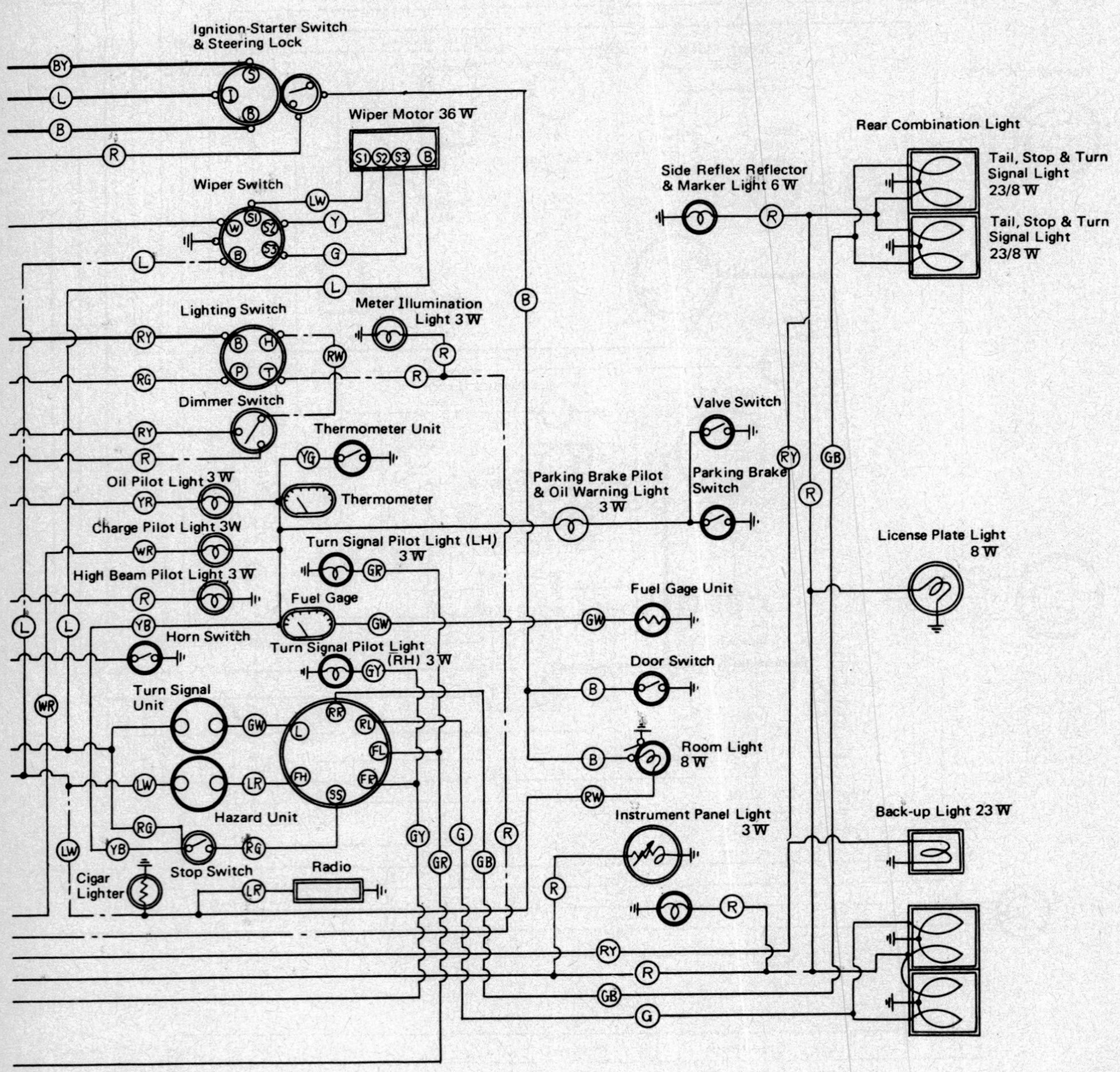

1100 and 1300 Station Wagons

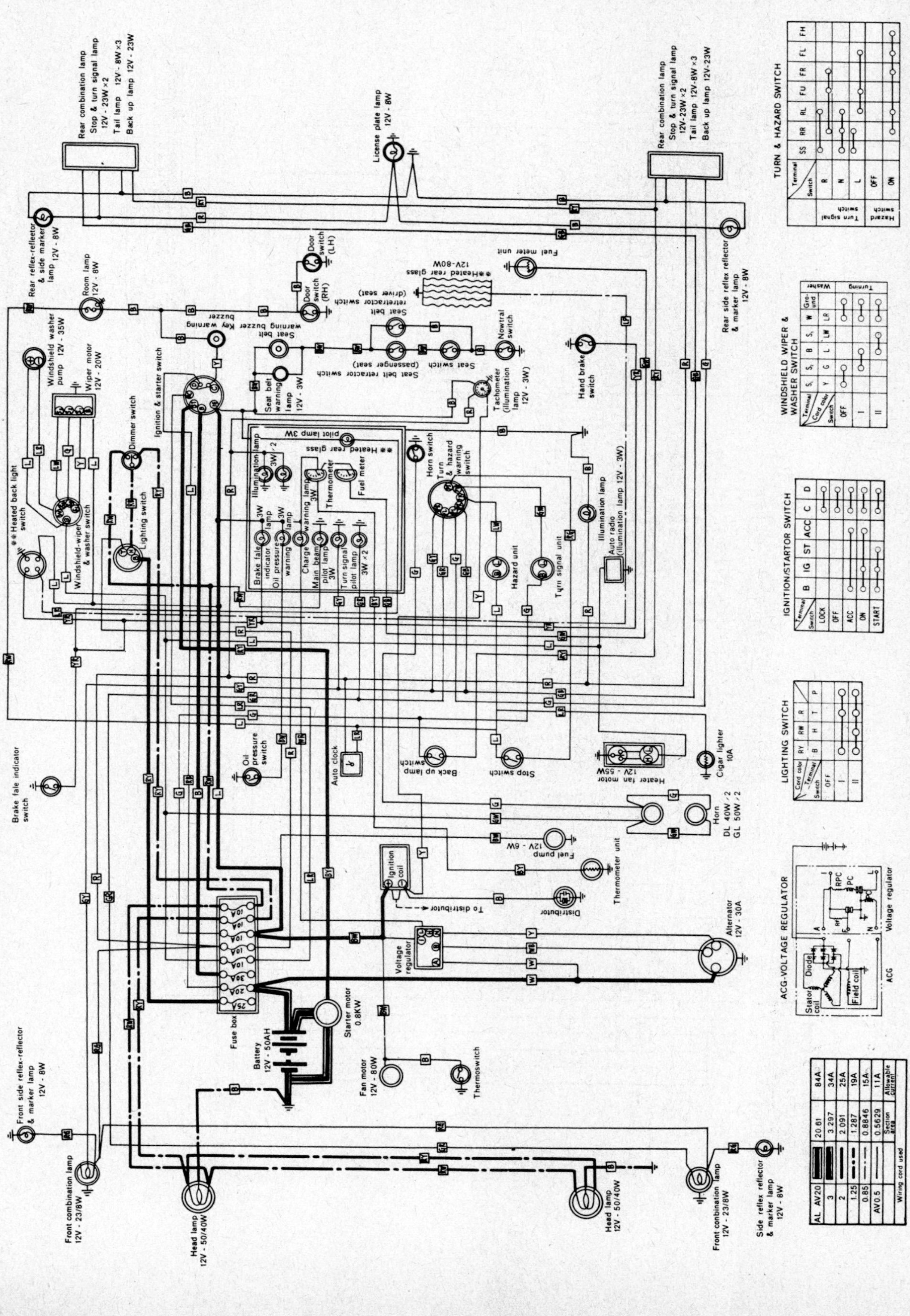

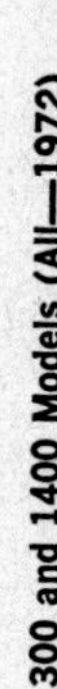

1300 and 1400 Models (All—1972)

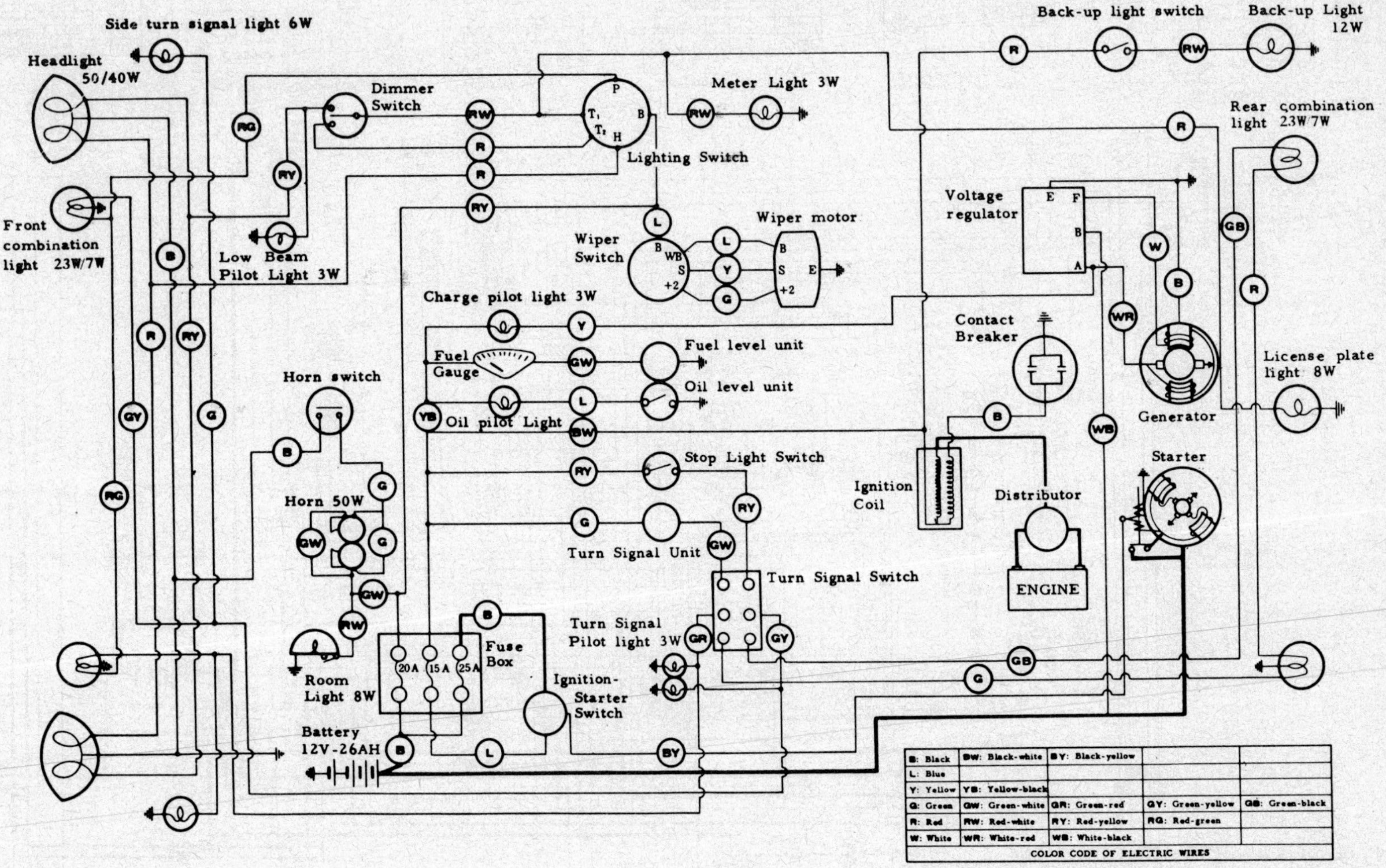

Wiring diagram for 360 Sedan

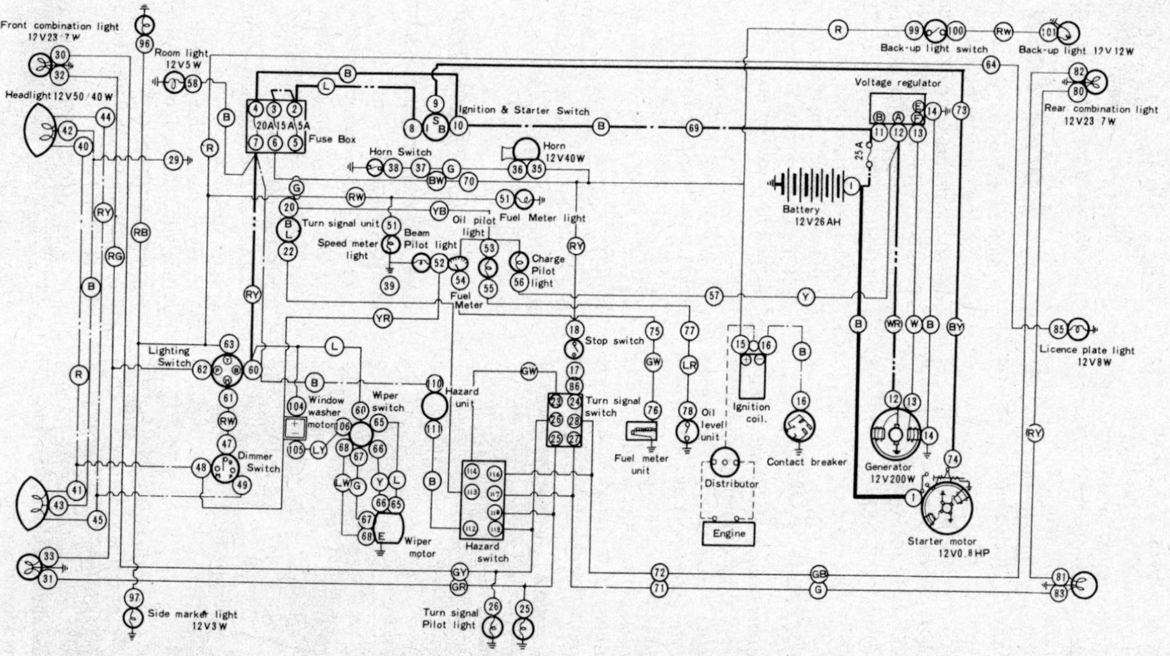

Circuit	Mark	Color	Mark	Color	Mark	Color	Mark	Color	Mark	Color
Ground	B	Black								
Others	L	Blue	LW	Blue/White	LR	Blue/Red				
Meters	Y	Yellow	YG	Yellow/Green	YR	Yellow/Red	YW	Yellow/White	YB	Yellow/Black
Signals	G	Green	GR	Green/Red	GY	Green/Yellow	GW	Green/White	GB	Green/Black
Illumination	R	Red	RG	Red/Green	RY	Red/Yellow	RW	Red/White		
Charging	W	White	WR	White/Red						
Starting	B	Black	BW	Black/Yellow	BY	Black/Yellow				

Wiring diagram for 360 Truck and Van

TUNE-UP PROCEDURES

Spark Plugs

1. Using a plug wrench, remove all of the spark plugs.

2. Check them for damage or wear and clean or replace them. Refer to the "Troubleshooting" section for more information pertaining to spark plugs.

3. Set the gap between the two electrodes, using a spark plug gap gauge.

4. Install the spark plugs in the engine, tightening to 13-17 ft lbs.

Breaker Points and Condenser

The breaker points are under the distributor cap. To inspect or adjust the points the cap must be removed. It is not necessary to remove the spark plug wires from the top of the distributor cap when removing the cap from the top of the distributor. After removing the cap, pry open the points with a screwdriver. Inspect the condition of the points. If they are excessively pitted or worn they must be replaced.

Checking the breaker point gap

1. To replace the points, remove the hold down screws, the ground lead and the condenser lead.

2. Lift out the point assembly and insert the new assembly.

NOTE: *Always replace the condenser when replacing the points.*

3. Install the hold down screws and the leads in their proper positions. Do not tighten the attaching screws, just leave them snug so the point gap can be adjusted.

4. Adjust the gap by placing the proper size feeler gauge between the contacts and turning the adjusting eccentric with a screwdriver.

5. The breaker point arm must be on the high point of the cam lobe. Turn the eccentric screw until there is a slight drag present when the gauge is drawn through the gap.

6. Lubricate the cam surface with cam lube.

7. Replace the distributor cap, making sure that the spark plug wires are installed tightly in the top of the cap.

Dwell Angle

1. Hook-up a dwell meter according to the manufacturer's instructions. Start the engine and read the dwell on the meter. If the dwell is correct, then shut off the engine and remove the dwell meter.

2. If the dwell must be adjusted, shut off the engine, remove the distributor cap and adjust the point gap.

3. Open the points to decrease the amount of dwell, close them to increase the dwell.

4. Replace the cap and start the engine. Check the dwell. If it is correct, shut off the engine and remove the dwell meter. If the dwell is not correct, repeat the above steps.

Ignition Timing

The ignition timing marks are located on the edge of the flywheel, graduated in 2° increments from 0° to 16°. The marks are visible through a port in the flywheel housing, just behind the dipstick.

1. After cleaning the timing marks, hook a timing light to the positive battery terminal and the number one spark plug.

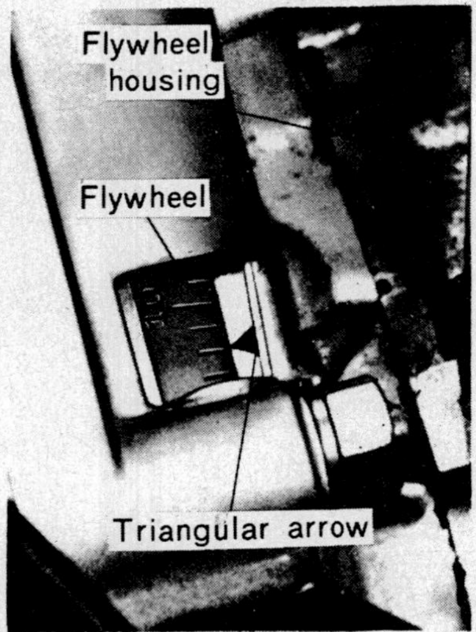

Ignition timing marks

2. Start the engine and aim the timing light at the timing marks on the flywheel.

3. Adjust the ignition timing by loosening the bolt opposite the octane selector on the retaining plate, and rotating the distributor clockwise to advance the timing or counterclockwise to retard the timing.

4. After adjusting the timing and removing the timing light, adjust the octane selector so that the engine knocks very slightly under sudden acceleration from low speeds in fourth gear.

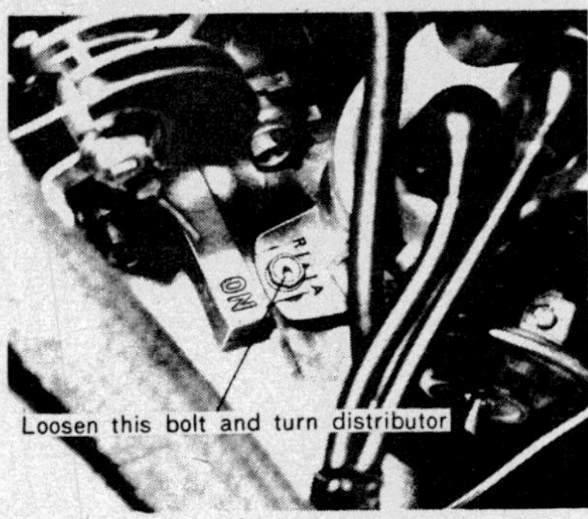

Adjusting the octane selector

Valve Lash

1. Before adjusting the valves, make sure that the cylinder head bolts are torqued to the proper specifications. The adjusting sequence for the valves is the same as the firing order which is 1-3-2-4.

2. Position No. 1 piston at TDC of the compression stroke, and adjust the valves for that cylinder. The valves are adjusted with the engine cold. Use a feeler gauge between the rocker arm and the valve stem.

3. Adjust the gap by loosening the locknut and turning the adjusting bolt.

4. When the proper gap is reached, tighten the adjusting locknut and the adjusting bolt.

5. Turn the engine 180° (indicated on the flywheel) for each cylinder's valves thereafter. This places the next cylinder to be adjusted at TDC.

Carburetor

Idle Speed and Mixture Adjustment

The idle adjustment is made when the engine is at operating temperature.

1. Disconnect the vacuum hose leading to the distributor.

2. Adjust the ignition timing to the proper specification.

3. By turning the throttle adjusting screw, adjust the engine idle speed to the proper specification.

4. Replace the vacuum hose onto the distributor.

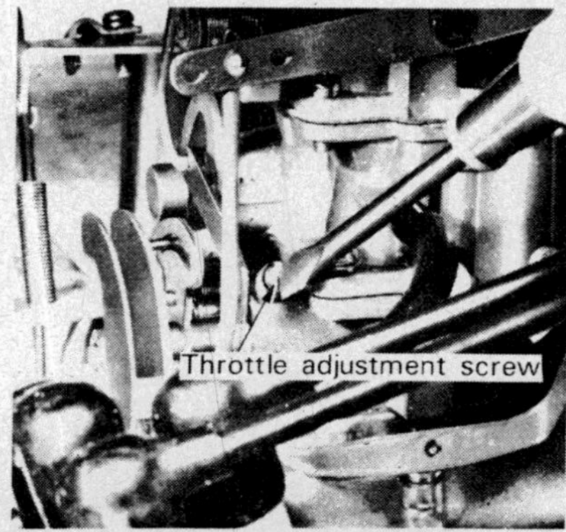

Throttle adjustment

5. Adjust the idle mixture screw so that the highest RPM reading is obtained after the throttle has been adjusted to 850 RPM. There is a limiter cap installed on the top of the idle mixture adjusting screw that should not be removed unless the proper carbon monoxide reading on a CO meter cannot be obtained.

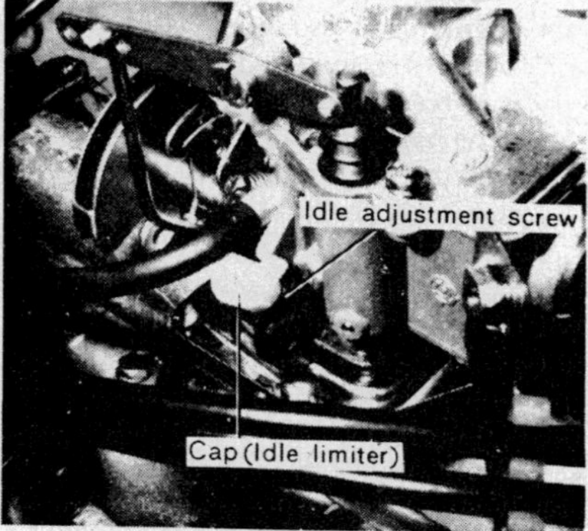

Idle mixture adjustment

6. After adjusting the idle mixture to the best idle speed or the proper CO reading on a CO meter, (replace the limiter cap) adjust the throttle adjustment screw to the proper idle speed. See "Fuel System" for further adjustments.

ENGINE ELECTRICAL

Distributor

Removal and Installation

1. Disconnect the distributor primary wire from the coil, and the vacuum hose from the distributor.
2. Remove the distributor cap, and mark the position of the rotor in relation to the distributor body. Note the position of the octane selector pointer on the octane selector scale.
3. Remove the bolt which retains the distributor at the octane selector and remove the distributor, retainer plate, and the octane selector pointer.
4. If the engine has not been disturbed since removal of the distributor, align the marks on the distributor rotor and body, and insert the distributor so that the octane selector is positioned as it was prior to removal.
5. Install the distributor cap, connect the primary wire at the coil, and check the ignition timing.
6. If the engine was disturbed while the distributor was removed, position the No. 1 cylinder on its compression stroke, and align the red mark on the flywheel housing with the TDC (0°) mark on the flywheel.
7. Insert the distributor so that the rotor points toward the number one tower in the distributor cap, and the points are just beginning to open.

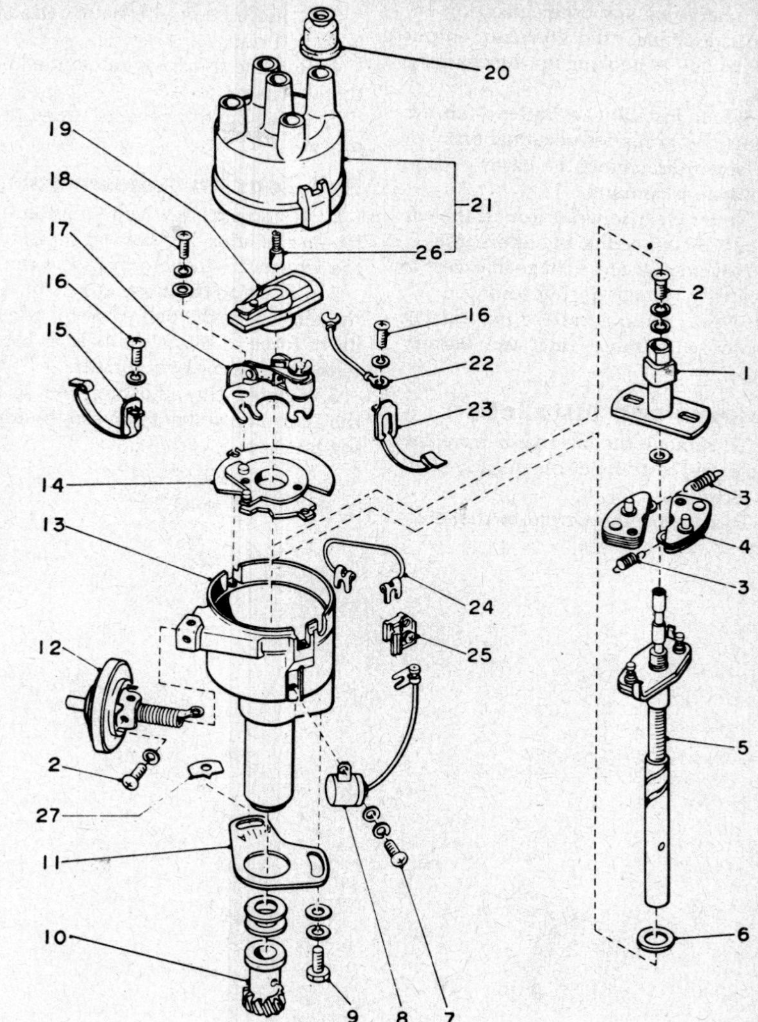

An exploded view of the distributor

1. Cam
2. Screw
3. Governor spring
4. Governor weight
5. Shaft
6. Washer
7. Screw
8. Condenser
9. Bolt
10. Gear
11. Plate
12. Vacuum unit
13. Housing
14. Breaker plate
15. Clamp
16. Screw
17. Breaker points
18. Breaker point set screw
19. Rotor
20. Boot
21. Cap
22. Ground wire
23. Clamp
24. Lead wire
25. Terminal
26. Carbon brush
27. Pointer

8. Center the octane selector between A and R, and tighten the retaining bolt.
9. Install the distributor cap, connect the primary wire, and check the ignition timing.

Alternator

Alternator Precautions

1. Pay particular attention to the polarity connections of the battery when connecting the battery cables. Make sure that you connect the correct cable to the corresponding terminal.
2. If a jumper battery is used to start the vehicle, make sure that the cables leading from the jumper battery are matched with the terminals on the battery being jumped, positive to positive and negative to negative.
3. When testing or adjusting the alternator, install a condensor between the alternator output terminal and the ground. This is to prevent the diode from becoming damaged by a spark which occurs due to testing equipment with a defective connection.
4. Do not operate the alternator with the output terminals disconnected. The diode would be damaged by the high voltage generated.
5. When recharging the battery by a

quick charge or any other charging apparatus, disconnect the alternator output terminal before hooking up the charging leads.

6. When installing a battery, always connect the grounded terminal first.

7. Never disconnect the battery while the engine is running.

8. Never electric weld around the car without disconnecting the alternator.

9. Never apply any voltage in excess of the battery voltage during testing.

10. Never jump a battery for starting purposes with more than the battery voltage.

Removal and Installation

1. To remove the alternator from the vehicle, first disconnect the negative battery terminal.

2. Disconnect the wiring to the alternator.

3. Remove the alternator attaching bolts and nuts.

4. Remove the drive belt and take out the alternator.

5. Install in the reverse order of removal.

Belt Tension Adjustment

1. To adjust the belt tension, first loosen the adjusting bolt on the right of the alternator (looking from the rear).

2. Lift up on the alternator to increase the tension on the belt. When it takes 22 lbs of force to move the belt ½ in., the tension adjustment is correct.

3. Tighten the adjusting bolt so that the alternator will not move in the adjusting bracket.

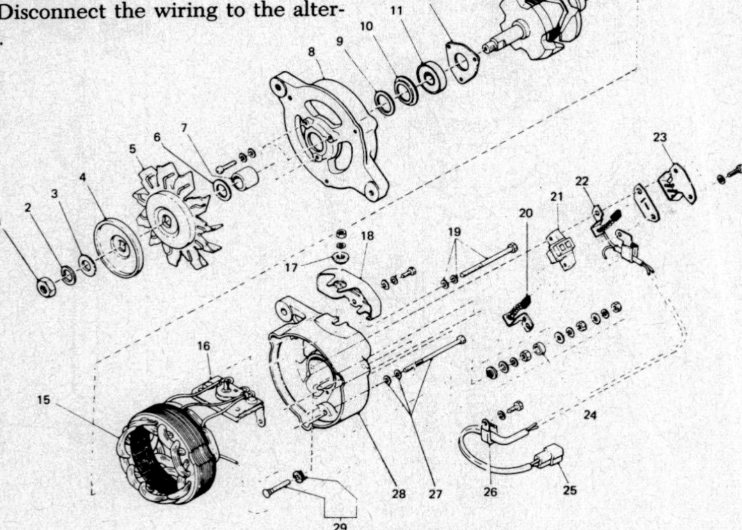

An exploded view of the alternator

1. Nut
2. Spring washer
3. Washer
4. Pulley
5. Fan
6. Washer
7. Spacer
8. Front cover
9. Packing
10. Retainer
11. Ball bearing
12. Bearing retainer
13. Rotor assembly
14. Ball bearing
15. Stator assembly
16. Diode
17. Insulator
18. Cover
19. Through bolt
20. Brush (E)
21. Brush holder
22. Brush (F)
23. Brush cover
24. Insulator tube
25. Lead wire
26. Clip
27. Thru-bolt
28. Rear cover
29. Terminal bolt set

Regulator

Removal and Installation

1. Disconnect the negative battery cable from the battery.

2. Disconnect the wires leading to the regulator.

3. Remove the screws which attach the regulator to the fender well.

NOTE: *Whenever the regulator is removed from a DC charging system, the circuit must be polarized upon installation. Momentarily connect a jumper wire between the battery (B or 51) and armature (A or D+) terminals of the regulator to ensure the proper polarity.*

4. Install the regulator in the reverse order of removal.

Air Gap Adjustment

After measuring the air gap of the voltage regulator and the charge relay, and finding them incorrect, proceed as follows to correct the gaps.

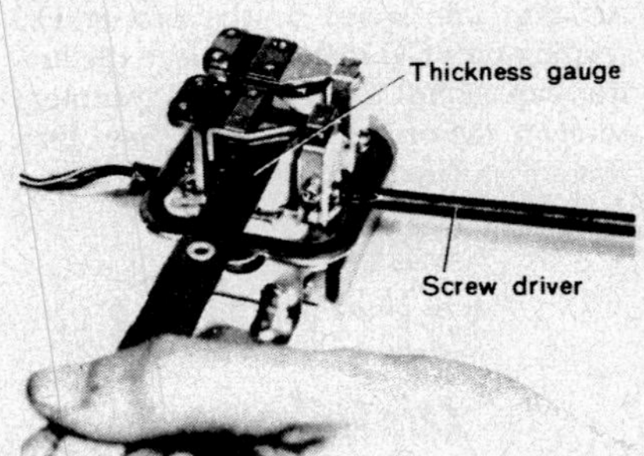

Adjusting the core gaps

Adjusting the point gaps

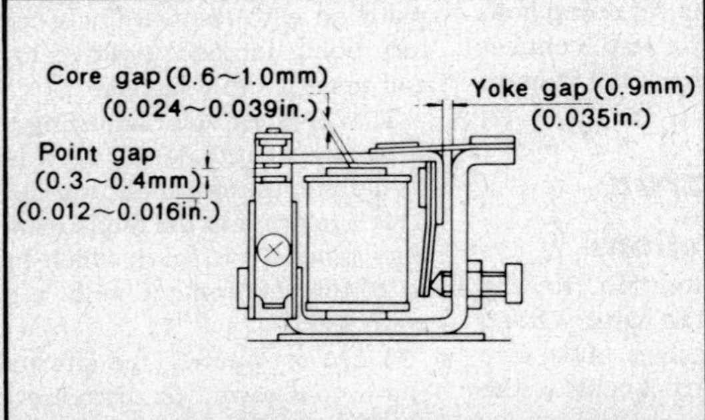

Adjusting specifications for the voltage regulator.

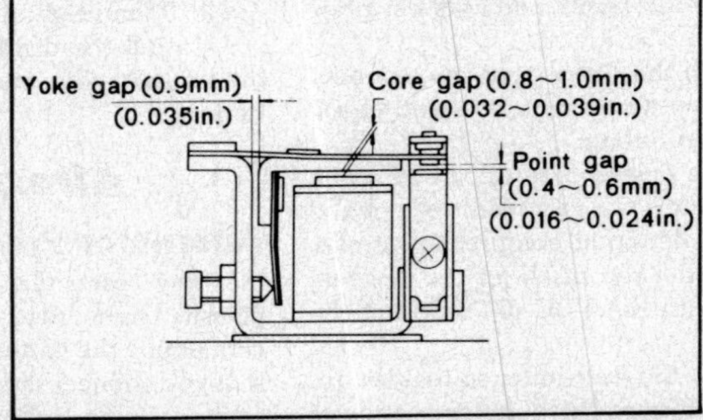

Adjusting specifications for the charge relay.

Adjust the point gap by shifting the upper contact set up and down after loosening the screw which holds the upper contact set.

Starter

Removal and Installation

1. Disconnect the battery terminal before touching the starter.
2. Disconnect the lead wires to the starter.
3. Remove the starter from the engine after removing the two bolts which attach the starter to the flywheel housing.
4. When reinstalling the starter, make sure that the mating surfaces of the flywheel housing and the starter fit flush against each other.
5. Install the starter in the reverse order of removal.

Starter Drive Replacement

1. Remove the starter from the engine. Remove the two thru-bolts that run through the length of the starter housing.
2. Remove the pinion housing from the end of the starter. Using a length of pipe the same diameter as the armature shaft, tap the pinion stop collar down toward the starter drive so that it is off the snap ring. Use a pair of snap ring pliers to remove the snap ring from the armature shaft.

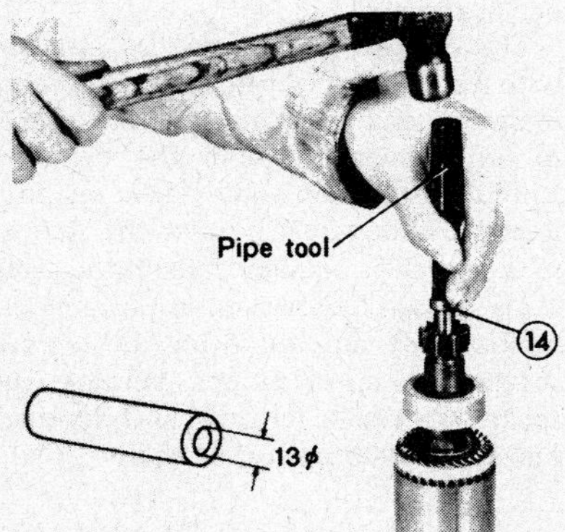

Removing the pinion stop collar with a length of pipe.

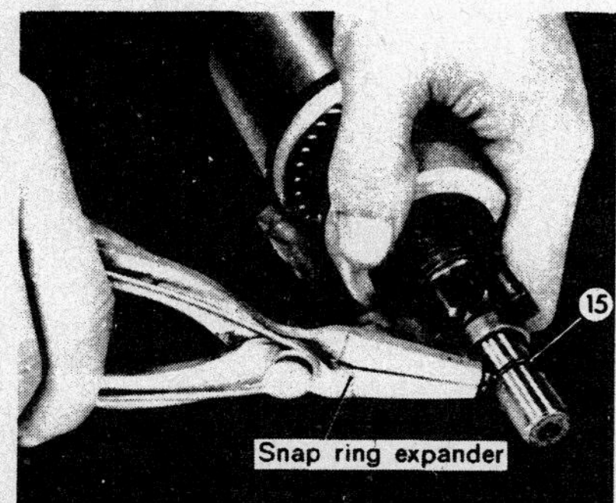

Removing the snap ring

3. Remove the starter drive from the threaded spline, taking care not to damage the threaded spline.

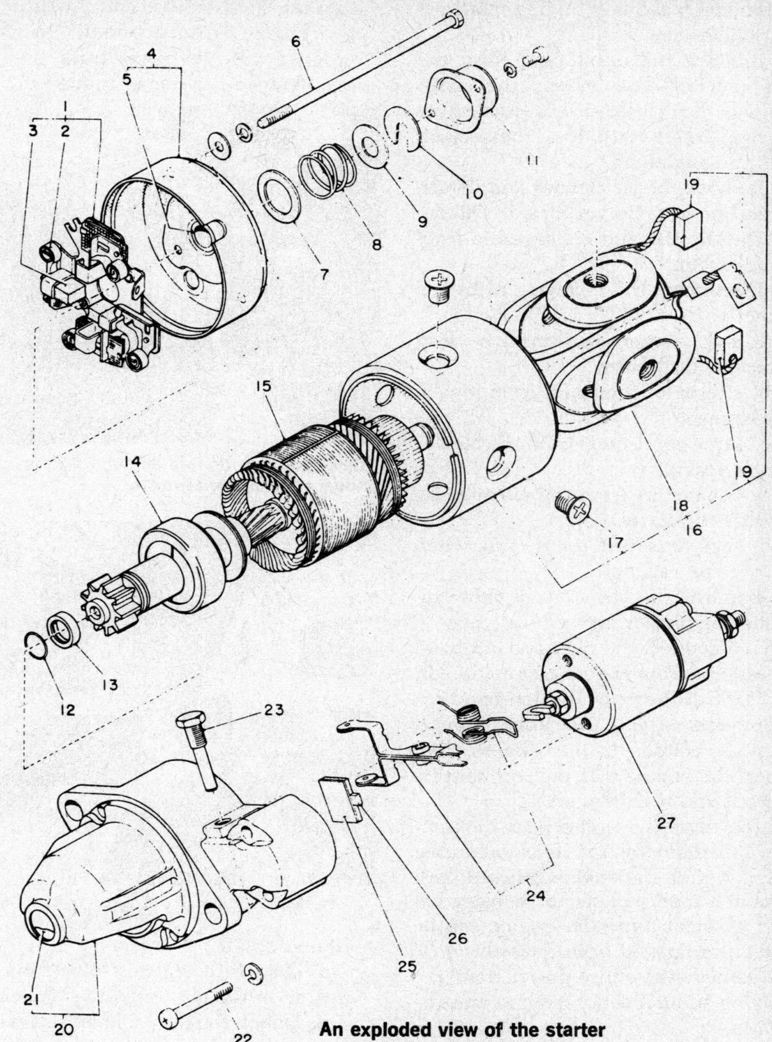

An exploded view of the starter

1. Brush holder plate assembly
2. Spring type brush holder
3. Brush
4. Commutator frame assembly
5. Bushing
6. Thru-bolt
7. Rubber parts
8. Spring
9. Washer
10. Lock plate
11. End frame cap
12. Snap ring
13. Pinion stop collar
14. Over running clutch assembly
15. Armature assembly
16. Yoke assembly
17. Pole core screw
18. Field coil assembly
19. Brush
20. Housing assembly
21. Housing bushing
22. Screw
23. Lever set bolt
24. Drive lever assembly
25. Plate
26. Rubber parts
27. Magnet switch assembly

4. To install the starter drive, slip the starter drive onto the armature shaft and install the snap ring into position. Drive the pinion stop collar down onto the snap ring with the length of pipe. Assemble and install the starter in the reverse order of disassembly and removal.

ENGINE MECHANICAL

Engine Removal and Installation

The FF-1 engine may be removed individually (late models only) or as a part of the power train assembly. To remove only the engine, proceed as follows:

1. Disconnect the battery positive terminal.
2. Separate the horn wire connectors and the hood stay lower retaining nut. Remove the hood hinge-to-body mounting bolts, leaving the hinges mounted on the hood, and lift off the hood.
3. Remove the grill, the front bumper, and the front skirt. On 1972 and '73 models this is not necessary.
4. Detach the hood lock mechanism from the radiator bracket.

NOTE: *Do not separate the cables from the lock mechanism.*

5. Disconnect the ground cables from

the cylinder head and engine compartment bulkhead.

6. Remove the drain plug from the main radiator and loosen the drain fittings on the cylinder heads (adjacent to the engine mounts) to drain the coolant. Drain the engine oil.

7. Remove the air cleaner and detach the fuel line from the carburetor. Disconnect the throttle and choke cable from the carburetor.

8. Disconnect the following electrical connections:

a. high tension and primary lead from the distributor,

b. alternator connector from regulator connector,

c. three connectors from the blower motor casing,

d. connectors from the oil pressure and thermostat switch,

e. two wires from the thermoswitch on the sub radiator.

9. Remove the radiator assembly including the blower casing.

10. Disconnect the right and left-hand exhaust pipe from the exhaust manifolds.

11. Unbolt the right and left-hand engine mounts, leaving the rubber mounting pads bolted to the engine, and support the engine with a chain hoist by the front and rear hangers.

12. Separate the engine from the transaxle by removing the four mounting bolts, and slide the engine forward until the clutch shaft and starter housing are clear, at which time the engine can be lifted and removed from the vehicle.

To remove the entire power train, the following additional procedures must be performed:

After step 9:

a. Disconnect the brake pipe from the brake hose (have a container available to prevent fluid spillage) and plug both fittings.

b. Remove the clutch return spring and pedal control rod, and dismount the clutch cross-shaft bracket on the body side. Remove the transmission side ball stud using an adjustable wrench.

c. Lock the handbrake, and separate the double-offset joints from the brake drums by removing the three retaining bolts, or driving out the spring pins (outboard brakes). Lower the joints away by turning the steering wheel to full lock.

d. Release the handbrake, and disconnect the cable so that it may be withdrawn with the power train.

e. Remove the carpeting and cover plate from the front floorboard center hump. Loosen the clamp, and slide the shift rod cover tube rearward. Separate the shifter shaft from the shift rod by tapping the roll pin out of the shaft.

f. Detach the speedometer cable from the speedometer and pull it into the engine compartment, to be removed with the power train.

g. Remove the starter motor.

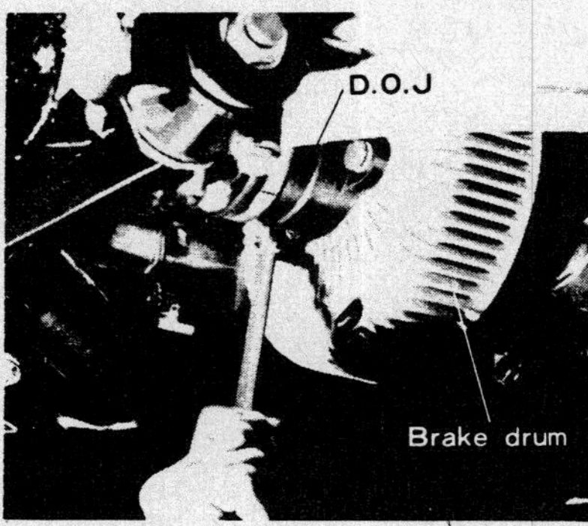

Unbolting the double offset joint on a model with inboard brakes.

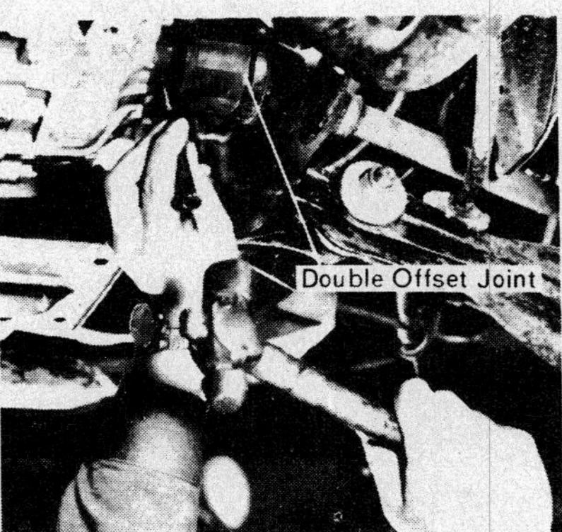

Driving out the spring pin

After step 10:

a. Detach the exhaust pipe from its mount on the bottom of the transaxle.

b. Unbolt the right and left-hand engine mounts, leaving the rubber mounting pads bolted to the engine. Unbolt the transaxle rear mount. Support the power train with a chain hoist attached to the front and rear hangers.

c. Slowly lift the engine, until clearance exists for the brake drums to clear the crossmember, and pull the power train forward and out of the vehicle.

Install in the reverse order of removal. When mounting the engine, ensure that the locator dimples on the front crossmember enter the holes on the mounting pads. Torque the front mounts 15-21 ft lbs, the large rear mount bolt 33-40 ft lbs, and the small rear mount bolts 18-25 ft lbs.

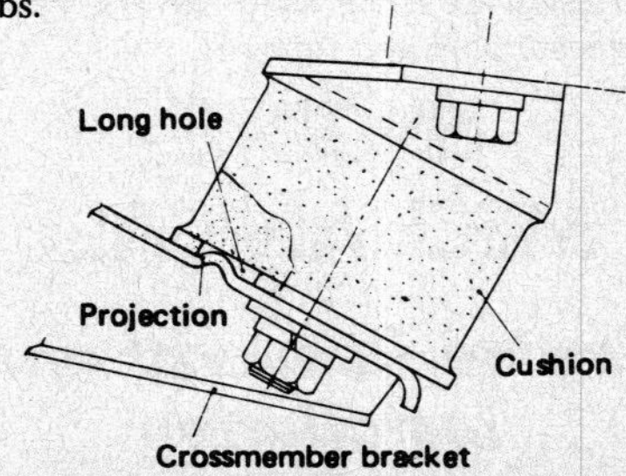

Engine mount alignment

Cylinder Head

Removal and Installation

FF-1

The engine must be removed from the vehicle to remove the cylinder heads. Although it is physically possible (on some models) to remove the cylinder heads with the engine installed, head gasket failure will result upon installation, due to misalignment of the cylinders. The cylinder heads should be removed with the engine cold to prevent warpage.

1. Remove the engine from the vehicle and mount it on a work stand.

2. Unbolt and remove the intake and exhaust manifolds.

3. Remove the spark plugs.

4. Disconnect the crankcase ventilation hose(s) and remove the valve covers.

5. Loosen the alternator adjusting bolts, and unbolt the alternator bracket from the cylinder head.

6. Remove the air injection distributor tubes from the cylinder heads by unscrewing the fittings.

NOTE: *Do not distort the injection tubes.*

7. Gradually loosen the head bolts in the reverse of the tightening sequence, and remove the cylinder heads and pushrods.

8. Install the heads in the reverse order of removal.

The cylinder heads must be installed with the cylinders vertical, to avoid misalignment, and to permit the head gasket to crush evenly around the cylinder. Prior to installation of the heads, cylinder liner projection must be checked. Torque in the specified sequence, in stages, using a spacer (see illustration) in place of the rocker shaft support. After the head is torqued to specifications, remove the rocker shaft bolts (or nuts) and the spacers, and install the rocker shafts.

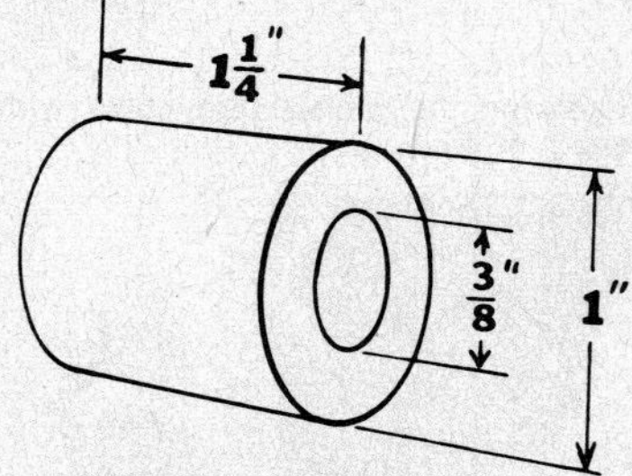

Cylinder head installation spacer

Service

Using a straight edge, check the cylinder heads for warpage. Should warpage exceed 0.002 in., the cylinder head must be resurfaced (grinding limit 0.0197 in.). Should the valve sinks exceed approximately 0.040 in., they must be replaced. The valve guides are pressed in, and should be replaced if clearance exceeds

0.0022 in. (intake) or 0.003 in. (exhaust). On the 1100, the intake valve guide should extend 0.59 in. and the exhaust 0.79 in. from the spring seat. On the 1300 and 1400, the intake valve guide should extend 0.71 and the exhaust 0.91 in. from the spring seat. See the "Engine Rebuilding" section for further details about cylinder head reconditioning.

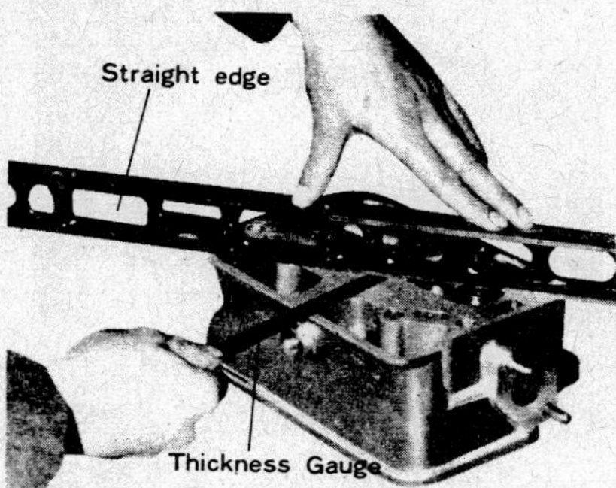

Checking the cylinder head for warpage

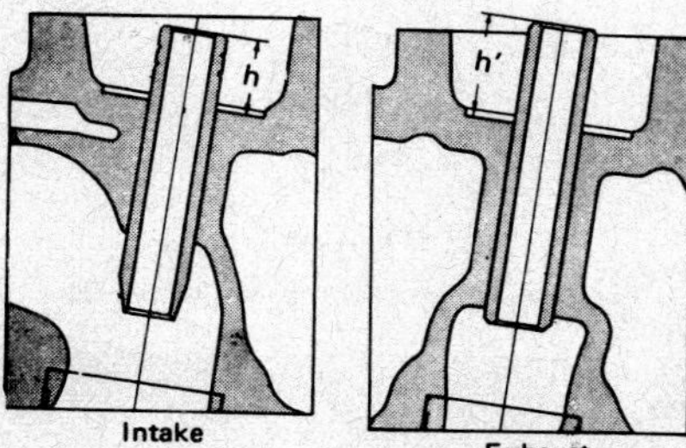

Valve guide installed height

Rocker Shafts

With the engine removed from the vehicle, remove the rocker arm covers and gaskets from the cylinder heads. Unscrew the nuts which hold the rocker arm assemblies to the cylinder heads and lift the rocker arm assemblies from the engine. Identify the push rods so they can be replaced in their original positions. Install in the reverse order of removal.

Removing the rocker arm

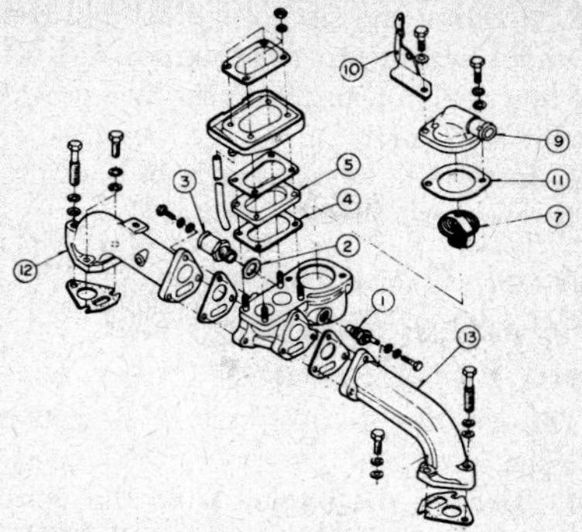

Exploded view of an 1100 intake manifold.

1. Thermoswitch
2. Washer
3. Fitting
4. Gasket
5. Insulator
7. Thermostat
9. Thermostat cover
10. Accelerator cable bracket
11. Gasket
12. Intake manifold
13. Intake manifold

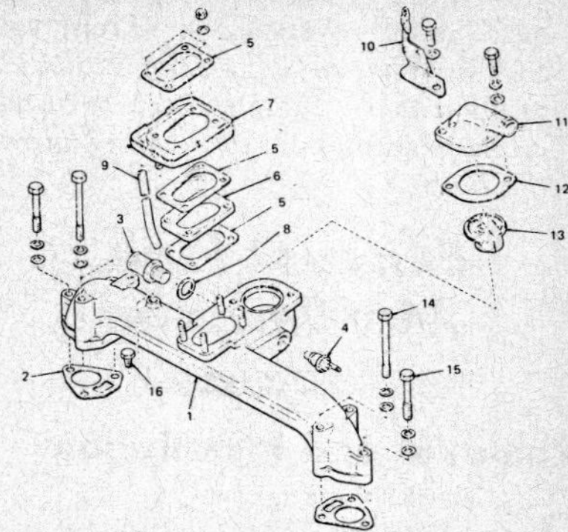

Exploded view of a 1300 intake manifold (Model G).

1. Intake manifold
2. Gasket
3. Fitting
4. Thermoswitch
5. Gasket
6. Insulator
7. Tray
8. Aluminum gasket
9. Overflow tube
10. Accelerator cable bracket
11. Thermostat cover
12. Gasket
13. Thermostat
14. Bolt
15. Bolt

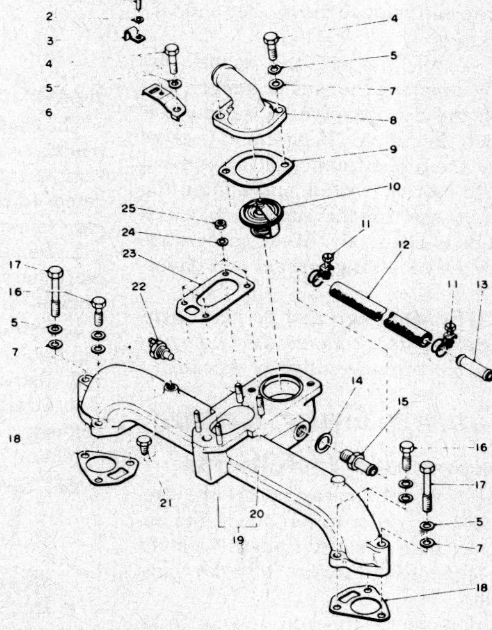

1. Screw
2. Spring washer
3. Accelerator cable clamp
4. Bolt
5. Spring washer
6. Accelerator cable bracket
7. Washer
8. Thermostat cover
9. Thermostat cover gasket
10. Thermostat
11. Hose clamp
12. Water bypass hose
13. Water bypass connector
14. Gasket
15. Water bypass connector
16. Bolt
17. Bolt
18. Intake manifold gasket
19. Intake manifold
20. Stud
21. Plug
22. Temperature sending unit
23. Carburetor gasket
24. Spring washer
25. Nut

Exploded view of a 1400 intake manifold

Intake Manifold

Removal and Installation

FF-1

The intake manifold may be removed with or without the carburetor. If the carburetor is to remain on the manifold, the throttle and choke cables and brackets must be disconnected, and the fuel line detached.

1. Detach all coolant hoses from the thermostat case and cover, and disconnect the wiring connector from the thermoswitch.
2. Remove all lines from the anti-afterburn valve (leave the valve mounted on the manifold).
3. Unbolt the air injection distributor mounting brackets from the manifold, and remove the air bypass valve (if so equipped).
4. Unbolt the intake manifold from the cylinder heads, and remove the manifold assembly. The intake manifold (not Model G) may be disassembled further by unbolting the manifold halves from the thermostat case.

NOTE: *Cover the intake ports in the cylinder heads while the manifold is removed.*

5. Install in the reverse order of removal.

Exhaust Manifold

Removal and Installation

Disconnect the left and right-hand exhaust pipes from the manifolds. Loosen (do not remove) the brass exhaust manifold retaining nuts, and swing the manifolds around until the slots in the flanges permit removal.

Install in the reverse order of removal.

NOTE: *When attaching the manifolds to the exhaust pipes, be sure to install insulator washers, to prevent seizure of the bolts.*

Exhaust Pipe, Muffler, and Tailpipe

Removal and Installation

FF-1

Disconnect the exhaust pipe from the right and left-hand exhaust manifolds, and from the muffler extension pipe (adjacent to the rear crossmember), and unbolt the hanger at the rear crossmember. Remove the front mounting bracket from the bottom of the transaxle, and lower the exhaust pipe away.

Install in the reverse order of removal.

Disconnect the muffler from the exhaust pipe, unbolt the tail pipe hanger bracket, and remove the muffler and tailpipe assembly.

To install, support the muffler by loosely attaching the muffler hanger, and attach the exhaust pipe to the muffler. Position the tailpipe hanger and bracket so that the rubber support is not stressed front to rear or twisted, and tighten the bolts. If the rubber support block is stretched excessively, insert spacers between the mounting bracket and underpan.

NOTE: *Make sure that no part of the exhaust system contacts the underpan, to avoid excessive noise or vibration.*

Timing Gear Cover

Removal and Installation

The flywheel housing covers the timing gears. In order to remove it, the engine has to be removed from the vehicle.

1. Separate the engine from the transmission.
2. Remove the flywheel and clutch assembly.

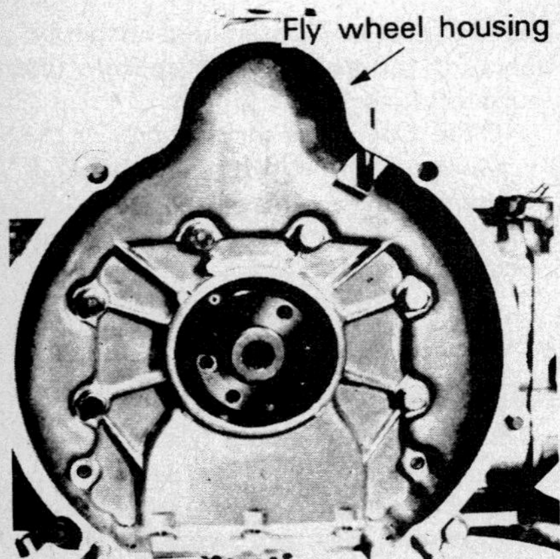

The flywheel housing covers the timing gears

3. Remove the six bolts that hold the flywheel housing to the engine, and lift the flywheel housing from the two dowel pins it rests on.
4. Install the cover (flywheel housing) in the reverse order of removal.

Timing Gear Cover (Flywheel Housing) Oil Seal Replacement

The flywheel housing cover oil seal is pressed in.

1. Remove the engine from the vehicle, separating the transmission from the engine.
2. Remove the flywheel and clutch assembly from the engine.
3. Remove the flywheel housing from the engine and remove the oil seal from the housing.
4. Install the new oil seal, pressing it into place.
5. Reassemble the engine and install it in the reverse order of disassembly and removal.

Camshaft

Removal and Installation

The camshaft turns on journals that are machined directly into the crankcase. To remove the camshaft, the engine must be removed from the vehicle and the crankcase separated.

1. Remove the engine from the vehicle, separating the transmission from the engine.
2. Remove the clutch and flywheel assembly.
3. Remove the flywheel housing.
4. Straighten the lockwashers and remove the bolts that hold the camshaft retaining plate to the crankcase. The lockwashers are straightened and the bolts removed through the access holes in the camshaft gear.

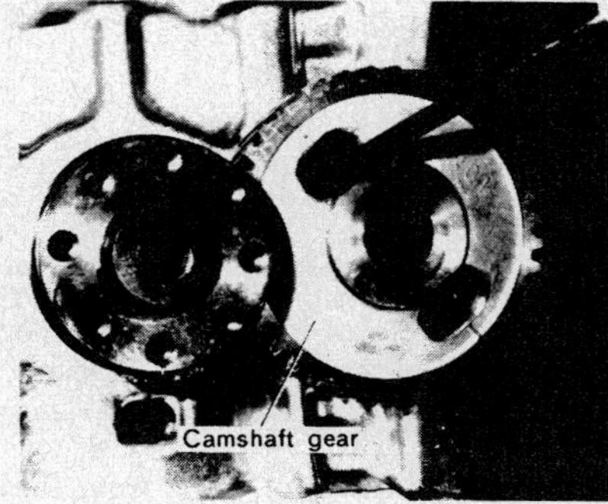

Straightening the lock washer of the camshaft retaining bolts.

5. Remove the intake manifold and separate the two halves of the crankcase and remove the camshaft.
6. Before installing the camshaft, measure the end play of the camshaft, using a feeler gauge. The end-play should be 0.012 in. or less. Install the camshaft in the reverse order of removal.
7. Assemble the engine and reinstall it in the vehicle in the reverse order of disassembly and removal.

Flywheel alignment marks

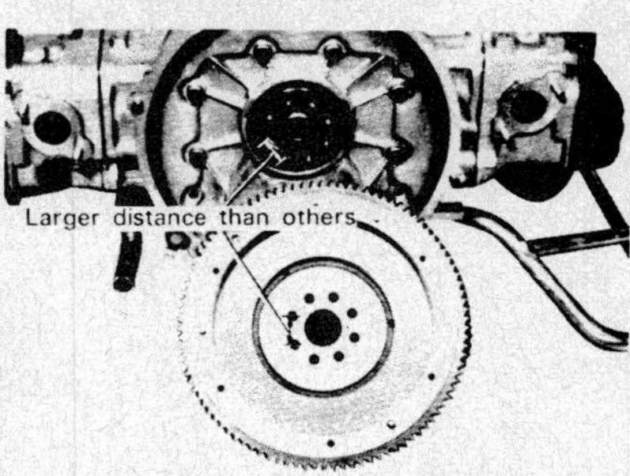

Flywheel alignment marks (Model G)

Camshaft timing marks

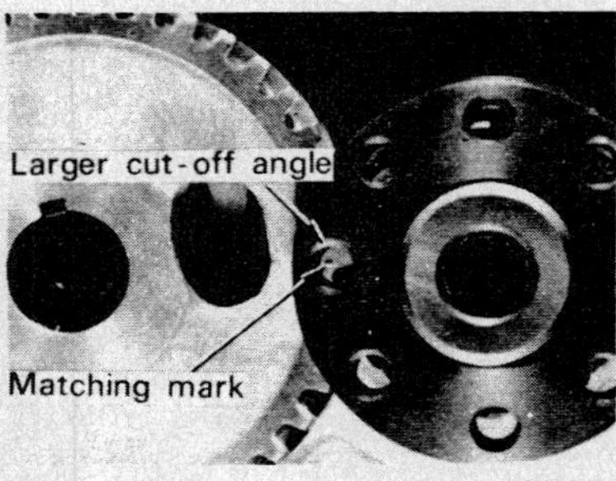

Camshaft timing marks (Model G)

Pistons and Connecting Rods

Removal and Installation

To remove the pistons and connecting rods, it is necessary that the engine be removed from the vehicle.

1. Separate the engine and the transmission.
2. Remove the intake manifold, oil pan, flywheel and clutch assembly,

flywheel housing, cylinder heads and gaskets.

3. Unscrew and remove the two bolts and lockwashers that hold the camshaft retaining plate in place. The bolts and lockwashers are removed through two access holes in the camshaft gear.

4. Remove the crankcase plug from the crankcase by using an Allen wrench.

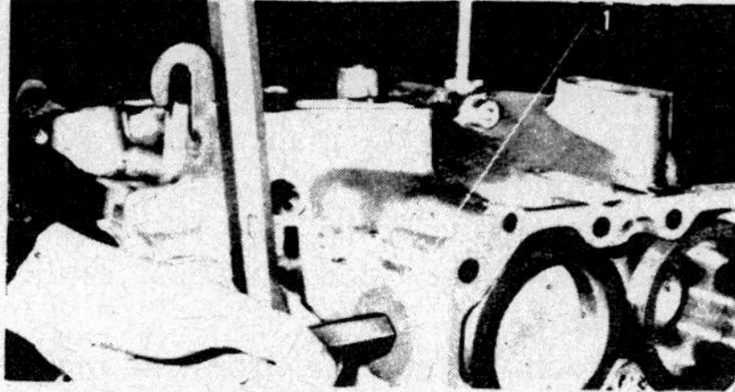

Removing the crankcase access plugs

5. Remove the cylinder liners by using a cylinder liner puller.

6. Remove the cylinder liner gaskets, keeping the cylinder liners and the gaskets of each cylinder together. The flanges of the liner should be marked so that they can be reinstalled in the correct positions.

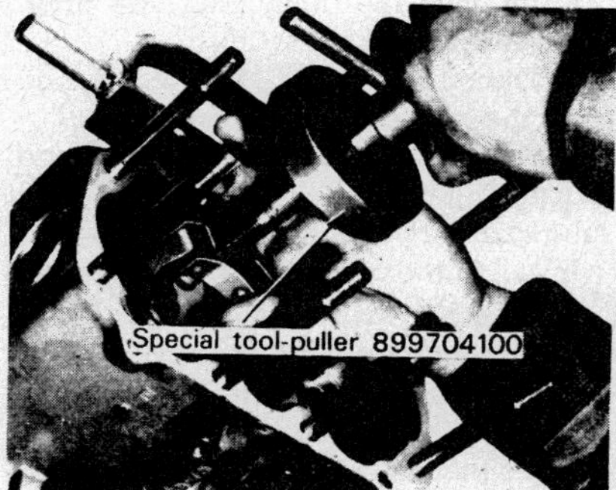

Removing the cylinder liners

7. Remove the circlips that hold the wrist pins in the pistons by inserting the piston circlip pliers through the crankcase plug holes.

Removing the circlips

8. Remove the wrist pins by inserting the wrist pin remover through the crankcase plug holes. Keep the pistons and the wrist pins together for each cylinder so that they do not become mixed. Make marks on the pistons and the liners so as not to change the direction in which they are installed.

Removing the piston pins

9. Separate the crankcase halves. Remove the oil seal. Be sure to replace it with a new one when reassembling the engine.

10. Remove the crankshaft together with the connecting rod and the distributor gear as an assembly.

11. Mark the connecting rods for identification purposes so they can be installed in the same position from which they were removed.

12. Install and reassemble the engine in the reverse order of removal.

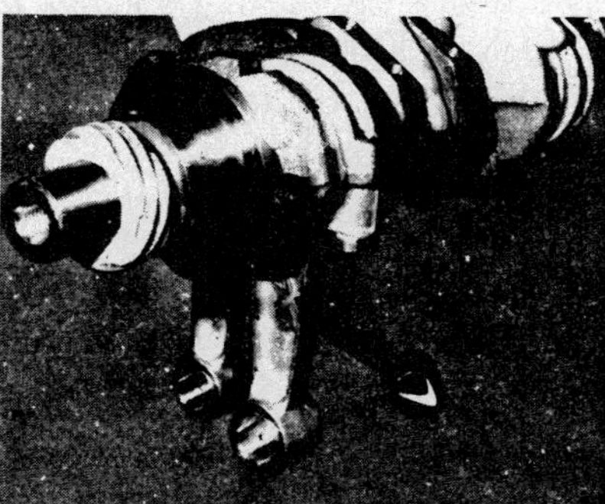

Position each connecting rod with the side marked ⊕ facing forward toward the distributor drive gear.

ENGINE LUBRICATION

Oil Pan

Removal and Installation

1. To remove the oil pan, it is not necessary that the engine be removed from the vehicle.

2. Remove the attaching bolts that hold the oil pan to the bottom of the crankcase, and remove the oil pan.

3. Remove the oil pan gasket and clean the mating surfaces of the oil pan and the crankcase.

4. Install in the reverse order of removal.

Rear Main Oil Seal Replacement

The rear main oil seal is located in the flywheel housing (timing gear cover). See "Timing Gear Removal and Installation" for the rear main oil seal replacement procedures.

Oil Pump

Removal and Installation

The oil pump can be removed with the engine in the vehicle. The oil pump and the oil filter can be removed as a unit. Remove the four attaching bolts, and remove the oil pump from the engine along with the gasket. The oil pump is driven directly by the camshaft. The oil pump shaft fits into a slot in the end of the camshaft. When the oil pump is reinstalled, make sure that the oil pump shaft fits into the slot in the end of the camshaft and that the mating surfaces are flush. Install in the reverse order of removal.

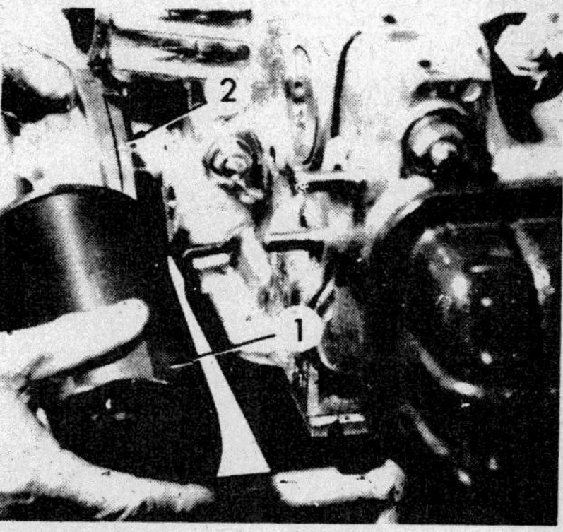

Removing the oil pump and the filter as an assembly.

Checking Clearances

1. Remove the oil pump from the engine.

2. Remove the oil filter from the oil pump.

3. Remove the screws that hold the oil pump body in place and remove body.

4. With a feeler gauge, measure the tip clearance between the inner and outer rotor, when one of the lobes of the inner rotor is on the very top of one of the lobes of the outer rotor. The tip clearance should be between 0.0008 in. and 0.0079 in. If the clearance is more than this, the oil pump should be replaced.

5. Measure the side clearance by placing a straightedge across the top of the pump body and the inner and outer rotors and measuring the gap between the straight edge and the rotors. The clearance should be between 0.0020 in. and 0.0079 in. If the clearance is more than allowed, either the rotors or the pump housing must be replaced.

6. Measure the radial clearance between the outer rotor and the pump housing with a feeler gauge The clearance should be between 0.0059 in. and 0.0098 in.

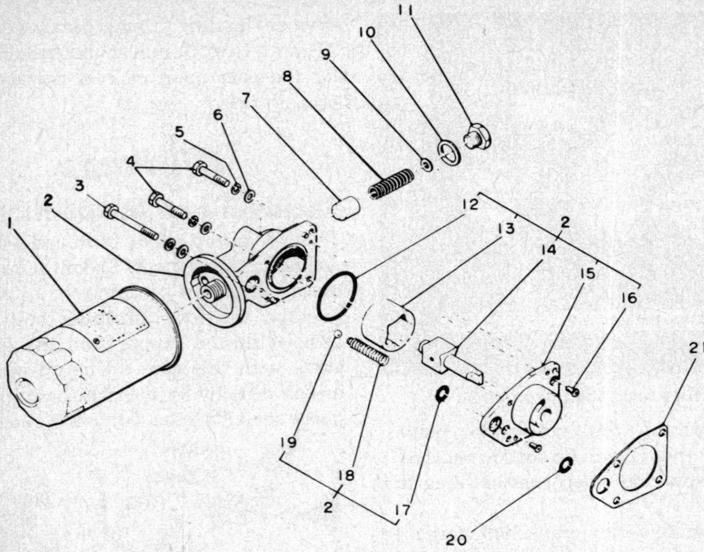

Exploded view of the oil pump

1. Oil filter
2. Oil pump body
3. Bolt (6X54 mm)
4. Bolt (6X32 mm)
5. Spring washer
6. Washer
7. Oil relief valve
8. Relief valve spring
9. Washer (6 mm)
10. Washer
11. Plug
12. O ring
13. Rotor
14. Gear
15. Oil pump holder
16. Screw
17. O ring
18. Bypass valve spring
19. Ball
20. O ring
21. Gasket

Measuring the tip clearance

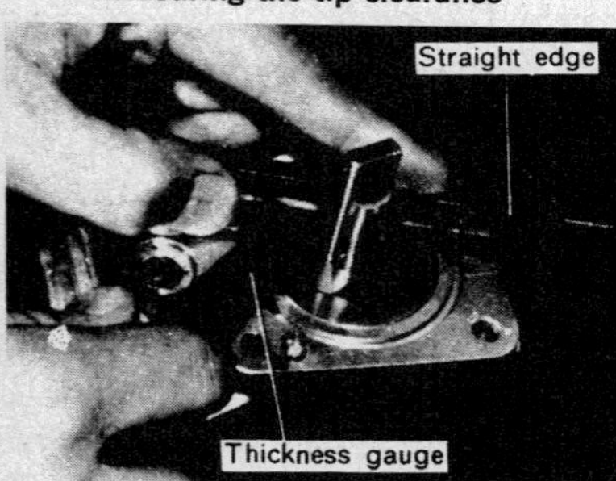

Measuring the side clearance

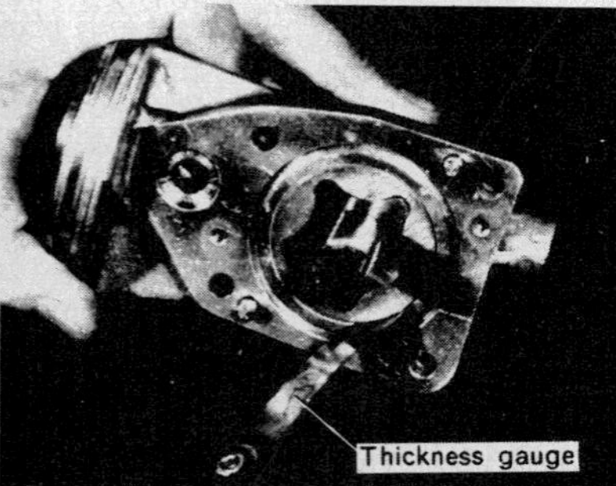

Measuring the clearance between the outside rotor and the pump body.

ENGINE COOLING

Radiators

Removal and Installation

Dual Radiator System

A main radiator, sub-radiator, and reservoir tank are utilized. They can be removed individually or as an assembly. To remove as an assembly proceed as follows:

1. Remove the grill.
2. Remove the drain plug, and drain the coolant.
3. Disconnect the radiator hoses from the top of the main and sub-radiators, and from the bottom of the main radiator (water pump side).

When removing the engine:

4. Disconnect the heater control cable, by removing the circlip which retains the inner cable, and the nut which retains the sheath to the bracket. Loosen the clamp that retains the heater duct to the blower casing, and remove the blower casing mounting bolts.

When not removing the engine:

4. Remove the bolts that retain the sub-radiator shroud to the blower casing.
5. Remove the four screws and two bolts that retain the radiator bracket, and remove the radiator assembly.

NOTE: *Do not remove the bolt between the radiators.*

To remove only the main radiator proceed as follows:

1. Remove the grill.
2. Remove the drain plug and drain the coolant.
3. Disconnect all hoses from the main radiator.
4. Remove the center and right-hand radiator mounting bolts, and the four screws which retain the radiator bracket.
5. Remove the main radiator and bracket, leaving the sub-radiator suspended on the left-hand mounting bolt and the blower motor casing.

To remove only the sub-radiator:

1. Remove the grill.
2. Remove the drain plug and drain the coolant.
3. Disconnect the radiator shroud from the blower casing.
4. Remove the center and left-hand radiator retaining bolts, and remove the sub-radiator.

Install in the reverse order of removal.

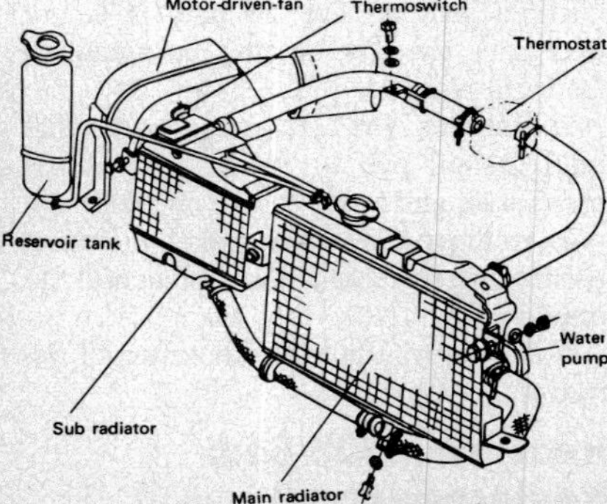

The dual radiator cooling system

Single Radiator System

1. Drain the cooling system by removing the drain plug in the bottom of the radiator. After loosening the drain plug, remove the radiator cap, which will allow the coolant to drain faster.
2. Loosen the hose clamps and remove the inlet (upper) and outlet (lower) hoses from the radiator.
3. Remove the two radiator mounting bolts.
4. Before removing the radiator from the vehicle, disconnect the wiring harness of the following items: thermostat and thermoswitch wiring, oil pressure switch wiring, fan motor wiring, and secondary terminal of the distributor.
5. Remove the fan and motor assembly from the radiator by removing the four bolts which hold the assembly to the radiator.
6. Install the radiator in the reverse order of removal.

Water Pump

Removal and Installation

A centrifugal water pump, mounted on the front of the engine, is utilized. To remove, drain the coolant, and remove the radiator hose from the pump. Remove the drive belt, unbolt and lift out the pump.

Install in the reverse order of removal.

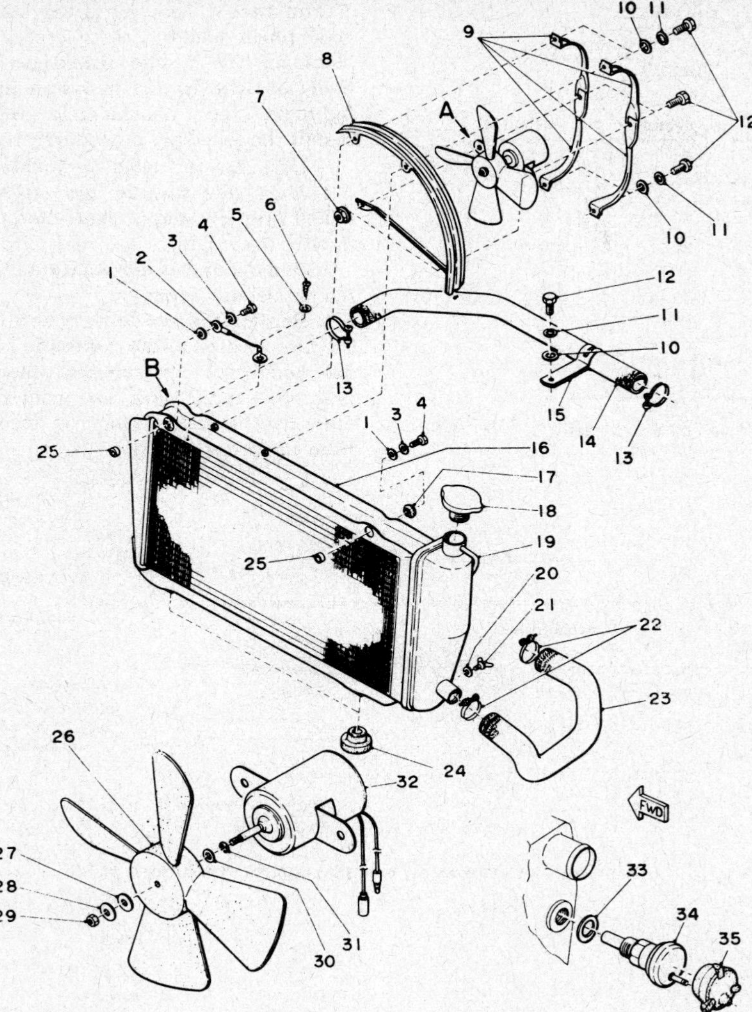

An exploded view of the single radiator cooling system

1. Washer
2. Radiator ground wire
3. Spring washer
4. Bolt
5. Lockwasher
6. Tapping screw
7. Flange nut
8. Fan protector
9. Fan motor stays
10. Washer
11. Spring washer
12. Bolt
13. Clip
14. Radiator inlet hose
15. Clamp
16. Radiator
17. Grommet
18. Radiator cap
19. Overflow tube
20. Gasket
21. Drain plug
22. Clip
23. Radiator outlet hose
24. Cushion for the radiator
25. Spacer
26. Fan
27. Washer
28. Washer
29. Nut
30. Washer
31. Circlip
32. Motor
33. Thermoswitch packing
34. Thermoswitch
35. Thermoswitch cap

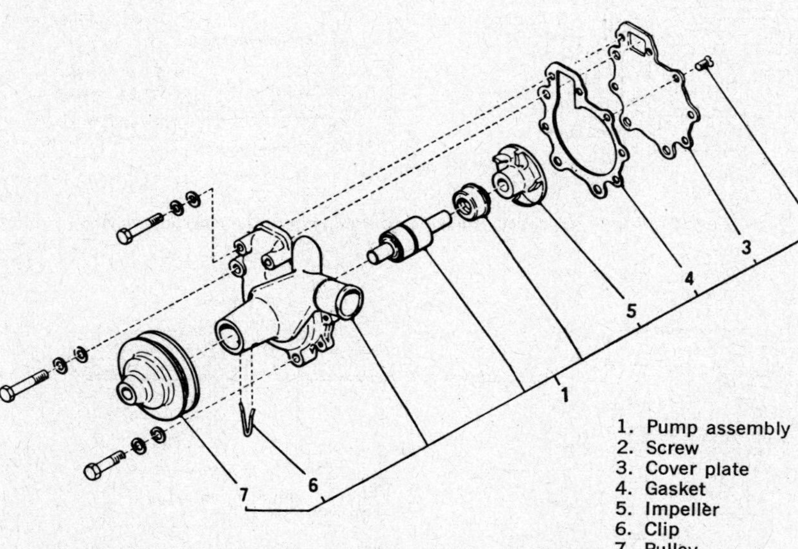

1. Pump assembly
2. Screw
3. Cover plate
4. Gasket
5. Impeller
6. Clip
7. Pulley

An exploded view of the water pump

Thermostat

Removal and Installation

A wax pellet type thermostat, which opens fully by 203° F. is used. It is removed by removing the air cleaner assembly and the thermostat cover, which is adjacent to the carburetor.

Install in the reverse order of removal.

NOTE: *It is essential to the proper operation of the cooling system that the thermostat be installed in the proper direction.*

EMISSION CONTROLS

Crankcase Emission Control System

Testing

The sealed crankcase emission control system takes blow-by gas emitted from the crankcase and routes the gas through the air cleaner and into the intake manifold for recombustion.

The system consists of a sealed oil filler cap, a rocker cover with an outlet pipe, an air cleaner with an inlet pipe to receive the connecting hoses and the connecting hoses and clamps.

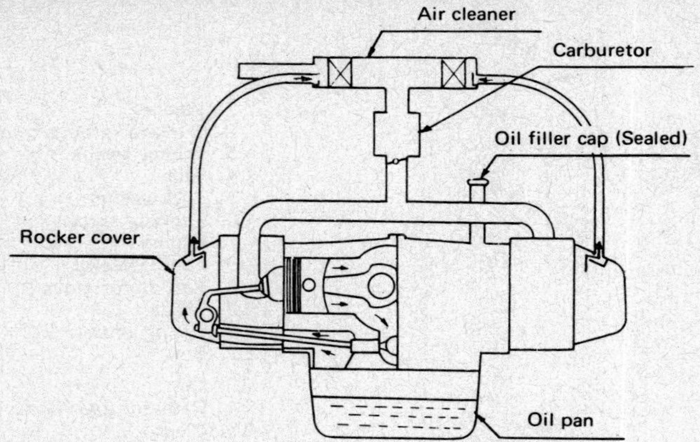

Diagram of the crankcase emission control system

There are no tests to insure operation of the system other than making sure that the system is kept clean.

Removal and Installation

To remove the crankcase ventilation system, remove all of the clamps and hoses.

Service

Replace the air cleaner element every 18,000 miles or 18 months, whichever comes first. Check the hoses and connections for leaks every 12,000 miles or 12 months. Clean the inside of the hoses. Remove the air cleaner case and wipe the inner face with rags to clean out accumulated dirt and oil.

Evaporative Emission Control System

Evaporative gas from the fuel tank is not discharged into the ambient atmosphere but conducted to the air cleaner unit and then burned in the combustion chamber. No absorbent is used.

The system consists of a sealed fuel tank and filler cap, two reservoir tanks on the station wagon, an air breather valve, breather hoses, breather pipe and the air cleaner with fixtures to receive the breather hoses.

While the engine is running, evaporative gas is absorbed into the intake manifold due to the suction pressure of the manifold, and never discharged directly into the atmosphere. While the engine is stopped, the gases collect on the inner wall of the element of the air cleaner.

There is an air breather valve located at the filler cap. When the flap (door) is opened, a spring exerts pressure on the rubber breather hose and pinches it shut.

The vacuum relief valve filler cap relieves any vacuum condition that might arise in the gas tank.

Service

To service the evaporative emission control system, keep all of the lines in good repair and free from cracks and blockage. The system should be relatively air tight. To test the system for air tightness, the manufacturer recommends the following procedure:

1. Drain the fuel from the fuel tank.
2. Make sure that the gas cap is installed properly and is tight, then close the flap door tight.
3. Remove the evaporation tube from the air cleaner housing.
4. Remove the fuel delivery hose from the pipe located in the underside of the floor and install a manometer (water column type) to the pipe. The manometer must have a scale which can measure from 17.55 in., or over.

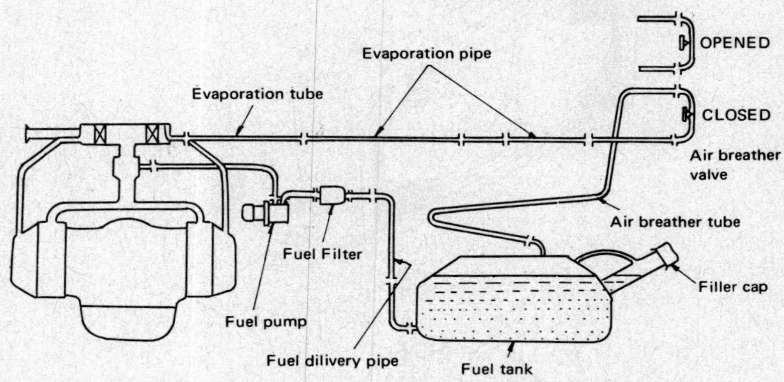

Diagram of an evaporative emission control system for a sedan

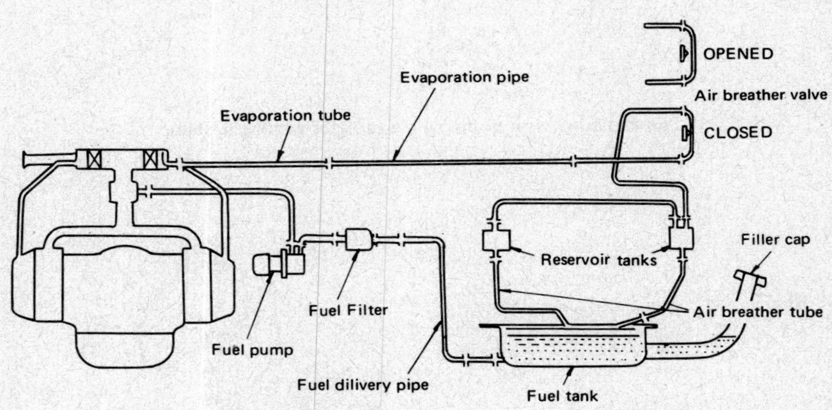

Diagram of an evaporative emission control system for a station wagon

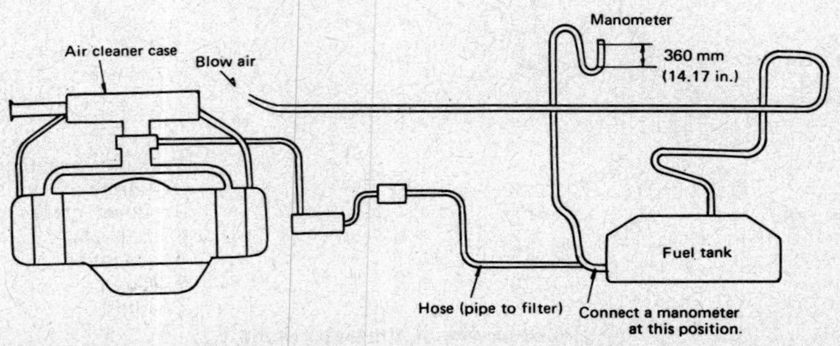

Air tight test of the fuel vapor lines

5. Send clean compressed air into the air cleaner side of the evaporation tube until the manometer indicates up to 14.17 in. The compressed air being blown into the system should not exceed 4.5 psi.

6. Measure the decrease of the water column in the manometer. The level should decrease from 14.17 in. by no more than 1.97 in. in no less than 5 minutes.

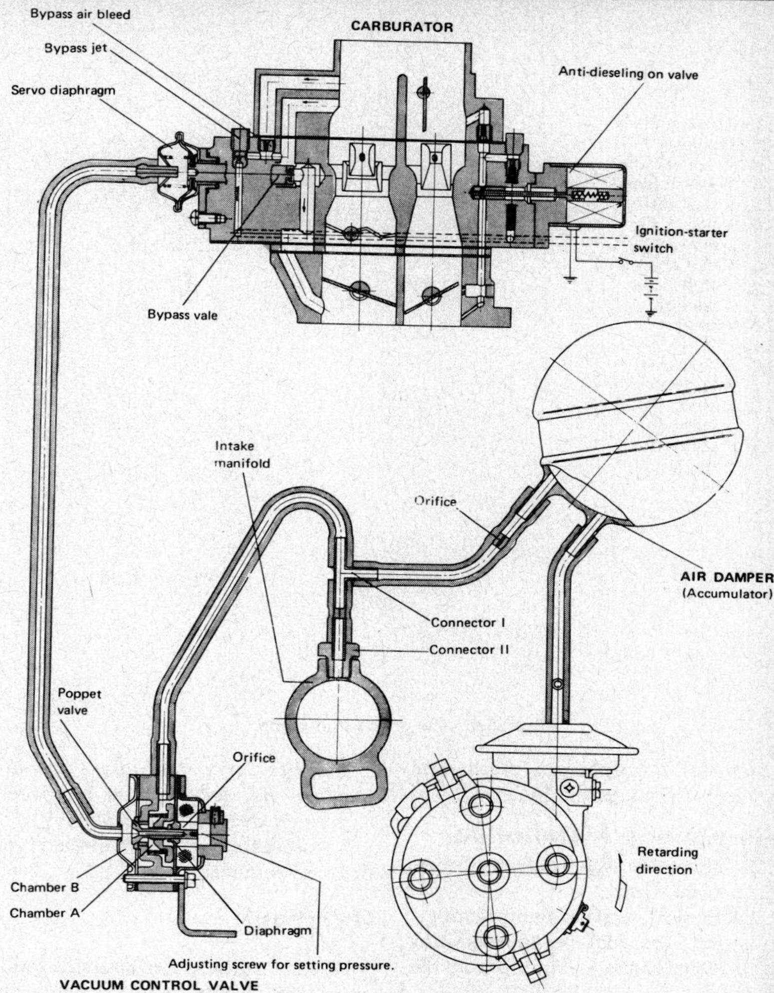

Exhaust emission control system

Exhaust Emission Control System

The operating principle of this system is not only to obtain correct air/fuel mixture while the vehicle is decelerating, but also to promote complete combustion by retarding the ignition timing, thus reducing the amount of harmful gases ejected into the ambient atmosphere.

While the vehicle is decelerating, the primary throttle valve is closed, causing a large vacuum condition to occur in the intake manifold. This vacuum pressure is conducted through a vacuum control and on to the carburetor where a by-pass jet is opened and extra air is allowed to enter the venturi below the throttle plates. This leans out the mixture and promotes cleaner combustion.

The vacuum is also routed to the distributor vacuum retarder. After passing through an air damper which regulates the vacuum to a smooth application, the vacuum actuated retarder retards the ignition spark in order to promote complete combustion in the cylinders.

While the primary throttle plate is opened during acceleration or while cruising or idling, the bypass air valve in the carburetor does not open because the vacuum pressure does not reach the specified operating pressure. However, the ignition retarder mechanism on the distributor operates at a much lower vacuum condition. Thus it is operating more often than the by-pass valve in the carburetor.

There is an anti-dieseling switch mounted on the side opposite the float bowl on the carburetor. The purpose of this switch is to prevent the engine from dieseling when the ignition switch is turned off. When the ignition switch is turned off, the electrical current which supplies an electromagnet in the switch is also cut off. A spring inside of the housing forces a plunger into position, blocking the fuel passages leading to the opening below the throttle plates. When the ignition switch is turned on, it energizes the electromagnet in the switch and pulls the plunger out of the fuel passage, thus allowing fuel to reach the opening below the throttle plates.

Service

Centrifugal Advance and Vacuum Retarder Check

The functions of the vacuum retarder and the centrifugal advance should be checked every 12,000 miles or 12 months.

Remove the vacuum retarder hose from the distributor and set the ignition timing to 6° BTDC at 700 rpm.

Connect the vacuum retarder hose to the distributor. At this time the engine idling speed will go down. Adjust the idle speed to 800 rpm. If the ignition timing is about 6° ATDC then the vacuum retard mechanism is working correctly.

Disconnect the vacuum retarder hose from the distributor. The engine rpm should jump up to about 1200 rpm. If the ignition timing is 9° BTDC then the centrifugal advance mechanism is working correctly. If any of these readings are wrong, the distributor must be replaced.

Vacuum Control Valve and Servo Diaphragm Check

The vacuum control valve and the servo diaphragm should be checked after the first 1,000 miles and every 12,000 miles or 12 months afterward.

Adjustment of the Operative Vacuum Pressure

Warm up the engine to operating temperature. Rev the engine up to 3,000 rpm without a load and then immediately release the throttle linkage lever. Using a stop watch or a wrist watch with a second hand, time how long it takes the engine to reach 1,000 rpm. Normally it takes from 3 to 5 seconds. If the time elapsed is less than 3 seconds, turn the adjustment screw of the vacuum control valve clockwise until the correct adjustment is reached. Turn the adjustment screw counter-clockwise if the time is over 5 seconds.

Check all of the connecting hoses to ensure against leaks and damage.

FUEL SYSTEM

Fuel Pump

Location and Type

The fuel pump is located in the engine compartment, mounted on the right side. It is an electromagnetic type. The mag-

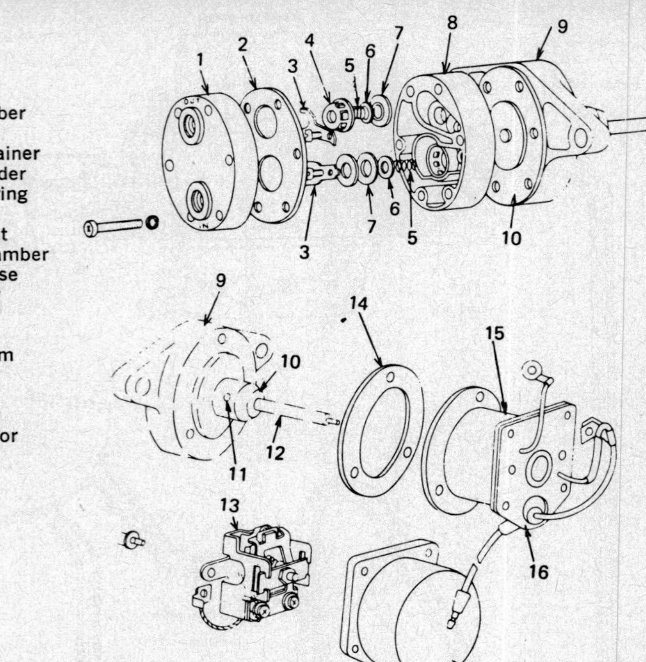

Exploded view of the fuel pump

net actuates a diaphragm mechanism which in turn pumps the fuel.

Removal and Installation

1. Remove the fuel delivery hoses from the fuel pump.
2. Disconnect the fuel pump wiring.
3. Loosen the fuel pump mounting nuts and remove the fuel pump from the vehicle.
4. Install in the reverse order of removal.

The fuel pump mounted under the hood

Carburetor

Removal and Installation

1. Unbolt and remove the air cleaner assembly.
2. Disconnect the fuel and distributor vacuum lines from the carburetor.
3. Disconnect the choke cable from the choke lever and the spring hanger, and the throttle cable from the throttle lever.
4. Remove the four carburetor mounting bolts and remove the carburetor.

NOTE: *Cover the intake manifold while the carburetor is removed to prevent dirt from entering.*

5. Install the carburetor in the reverse order of removal.

Overhaul

Efficient carburetion depends greatly on careful cleaning and inspection during overhaul since dirt, gum, water, or varnish in or on the carburetor parts are often responsible for poor performance.

Overhaul your carburetor in a clean, dust-free area. Carefully disassemble the carburetor, referring often to the exploded views. Keep all similar and look-alike parts segregated during disassembly and cleaning to avoid accidental interchange during assembly. Make a note of all jet sizes.

When the carburetor is disassembled, wash all parts (except diaphragms, electric choke units, pump plunger, and any other plastic, leather, fiber, or rubber parts) in clean carburetor solvent. Do not leave parts in the solvent any longer than is necessary to sufficiently loosen the deposits. Excessive cleaning may remove the special finish from the float bowl and choke valve bodies, leaving these parts unfit for service. Rinse all parts in clean solvent and blow them dry with compressed air or allow them to air dry. Wipe clean all cork, plastic, leather, and fiber parts with a clean, lint-free cloth.

Blow out all passages and jets with compressed air and be sure that there are no restrictions or blockages. Never use wire or similar tools to clean jets, fuel passages, or air bleeds. Clean all jets and valves separately to avoid accidental interchange.

Check all parts for wear or damage. If wear or damage is found, replace the defective parts. Especially check the following:

1. Check the float needle and seat for wear. If wear is found, replace the complete assembly.
2. Check the float hinge pin for wear and the float(s) for dents or distortion. Replace the float if fuel has leaked into it.
3. Check the throttle and choke shaft bores for wear or an out-of-round condition. Damage or wear to the throttle arm, shaft, or shaft bore will often require replacement of the throttle body. These parts require a close tolerance of fit; wear may allow air leakage, which could affect starting and idling.

NOTE: *Throttle shafts and bushings are usually not included in overhaul kits. They can be purchased separately.*

4. Inspect the idle mixture adjusting needles for burrs or grooves. Any such condition requires replacement of the needle, since you will not be able to obtain a satisfactory idle.
5. Test the accelerator pump check valves. They should pass air one way but not the other. Test for proper seating by blowing and sucking on the valve. Replace the valve if necessary. If the valve is satisfactory, wash the valve again to remove breath moisture.
6. Check the bowl cover for warped surfaces with a straightedge.
7. Closely inspect the valves and seats for wear and damage, replacing as necessary.
8. After the carburetor is assembled, check the choke valve for freedom of operation.

Carburetor overhaul kits are recommended for each overhaul. These kits contain all gaskets and new parts to replace those that deteriorate most rapidly. Failure to replace all parts supplied with the kit (especially gaskets) can result in poor performance later.

Some carburetor manufacturers supply overhaul kits of three basic types: minor repair; major repair; and gasket kits. Basically, they contain the following:

Minor Repair Kits:
- All gaskets
- Float needle valve
- Volume control screw
- All diaphragms
- Spring for the pump diaphragm

Major Repair Kits:
- All jets and gaskets
- All diaphragms
- Float needle valve
- Volume control screw
- Pump ball valve
- Main jet carrier
- Float
- Complete intermediate rod
- Intermediate pump lever

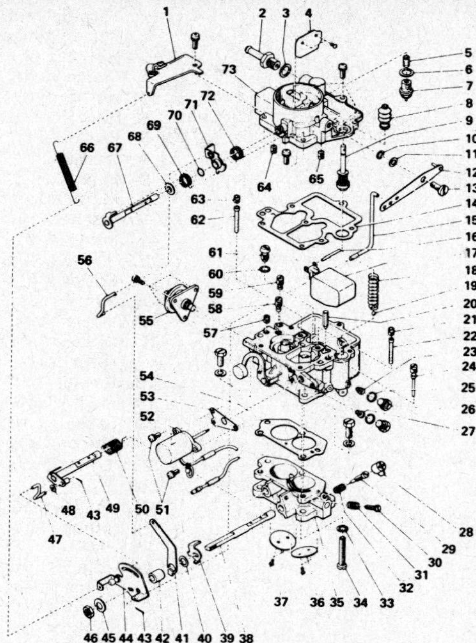

Exploded view of the carburetor (Early model)

1. Spring hanger
2. Nipple
3. Washer (12ϕ)
4. Choke valve
5. Filter
6. Washer (10ϕ)
7. Needle valve (1.5ϕ)
8. Cover (Pump)
9. Piston
10. Spring washer
11. Washer
12. Lever (Pump)
13. Shaft (Pump lever)
14. Gasket (Float chamber)
15. Connecting rod (Pump)
16. Shaft (Float)
17. Float
18. Piston return spring
19. Ball (5/32")
20. Weight A (Injector)
21. Primary main air bleed (#60)
22. Primary emulsion tube
23. Primary main jet (#95)
24. Primary slow jet (#43)
25. Washer (9ϕ)
26. Drain plug (Float chamber)
27. Secondary main jet (#155)
28. Cap (Idle limiter)
29. Idle adjustment screw
30. Throttle adjustment screw
31. Spring (Throttle adjustment screw)
32. Spring (Idle adjustment screw)
33. Washer
34. Screw
35. Throttle chamber
36. Primary throttle valve
37. Secondary throttle valve
38. Primary throttle shaft
39. Adjusting plate
40. Washer
41. Connecting lever
42. Sleeve
43. Cotter pin
44. Throttle lever
45. Spring washer
46. Nut
47. Connecting rod
48. Washer
49. Secondary throttle shaft
50. Spring (Secondary throttle)
51. Screw
52. Anti-dieseling switch
53. Anti-dieseling switch gasket
54. Gasket (Throttle chamber)
55. Servo diaphragm
56. Connecting rod (Choke)
57. Bypass air bleed (#320)
58. Secondary slow jet (#60)
59. Bypass slow jet (#55)
60. Washer
61. Power valve (#45)
62. Secondary emulsion tube
63. Secondary main air bleed (#90)
64. Secondary slow air bleed (#70)
65. Primary slow air bleed (#200)
66. Throttle return spring
67. Choke shaft
68. Sleeve (A)
69. Choke valve spring
70. Clip
71. Choke lever
72. Choke spring
73. Choke chamber

Complete injector tube
Some cover hold-down screws and washers

Gasket Kits:

All gaskets

After cleaning and checking all components, reassemble the carburetor, using new parts and referring to the exploded view. When reassembling, make sure that all screws and jets are tight in their seats, but do not overtighten, as the tips will be distorted. Tighten all screws gradually, in rotation. Do not tighten needle valves into their seats; uneven jetting will result. Always use new gaskets. Be sure to adjust the float level when reassembling.

Throttle Linkage and Fast Idle Adjustment

The throttle linkage is adjusted with the carburetor removed from the vehicle. It is adjusted so that when the connecting rod contacts the end of the groove in the secondary actuating lever, the primary throttle is open approximately ¼ in. (this may be measured with the shaft of a drill bit). Adjust by bending the secondary connecting rod. The fast idle is adjusted by bending the choke connecting rod so that the throttle plate is open approximately 0.035 in. in the fast idle position.

Float and Fuel Level Adjustment

The float level may be adjusted with the carburetor installed on the engine, by removing the air horn as follows:

1. Disconnect the accelerator pump actuating rod from the pump lever.
2. Remove the throttle return spring.

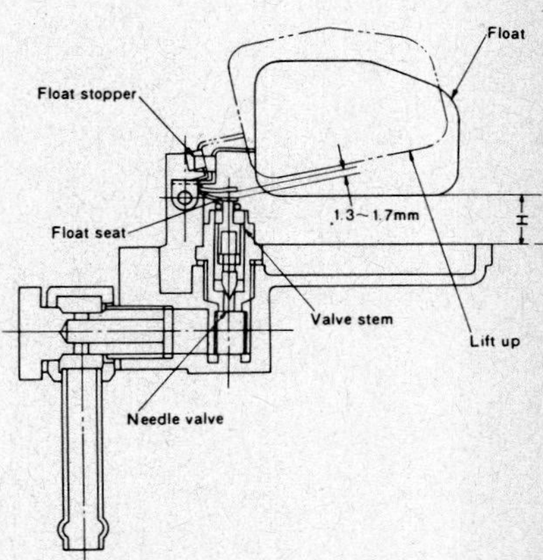

Float adjustment

3. Disconnect the choke cable from the choke lever, and remove it from the spring hanger.
4. Remove the spring hanger, the choke bellcrank, and the remaining air horn retaining screws.
5. Lift the air horn slightly, disconnect the choke connecting rod, and remove the air horn.
6. Invert the air horn (float up), and measure the distance between the surface of the air horn and the float.
7. Bend the float arm until the clearance is approximately 0.41 in.
8. Invert the air horn to its installed position, and measure the distance between the float arm and the needle valve stem. This dimension should be 0.050–0.065 in., and is adjusted by bending the float stops.

Choke Linkage Adjustment

The choke cable is adjusted by loosening the retaining nut, pulling the cable lightly to remove any slack, and tightening the retaining nut. When adjusting, ensure that both the choke plate and the choke control are in the full open position and that the accelerator and throttle plate are fully closed. To adjust the choke connecting rod and the connecting lever that actuates the opening of the throttle valve (when the choke is fully closed for starting), bend the connecting rod until the throttle valve is slightly open and the choke is not fully closed.

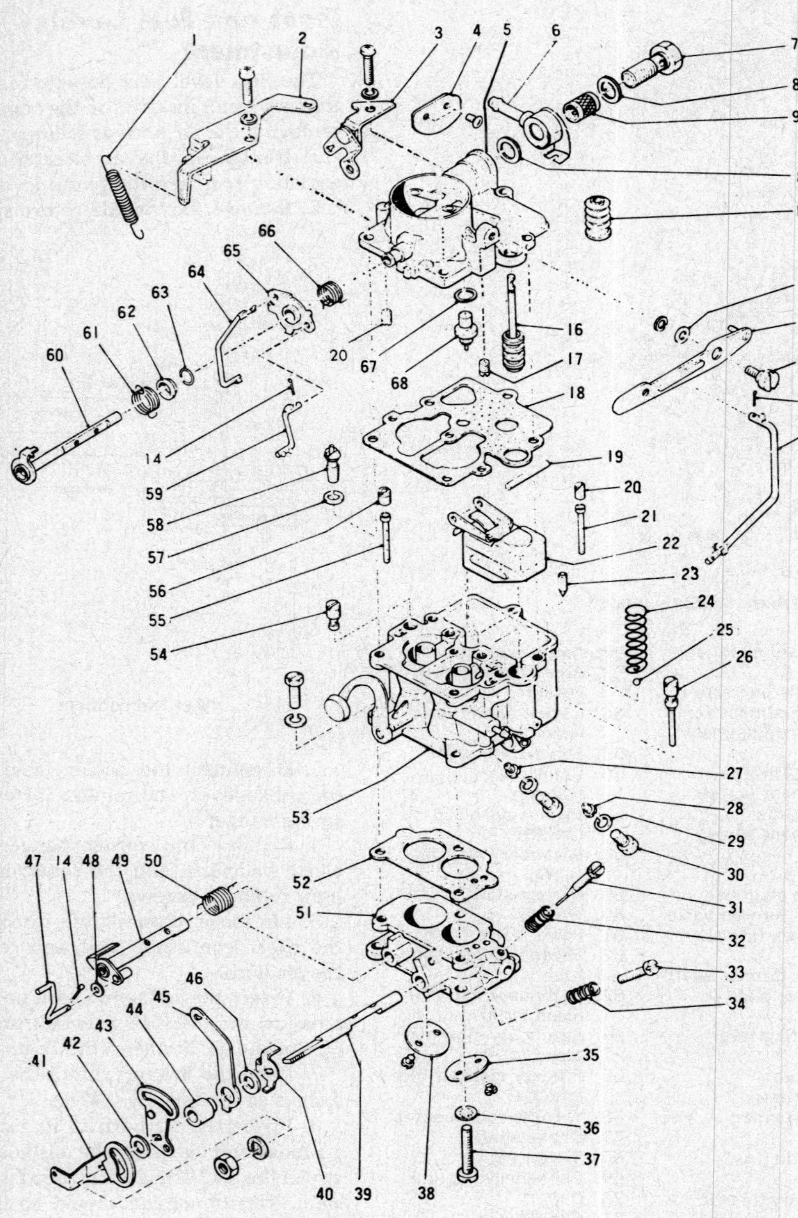

1. Throttle return spring
2. Spring hanger
3. Bell crank
4. Choke plate
5. Air horn
6. Banjo
7. Banjo bolt
8. Gasket
9. Filter
10. Pump cover
11. Washer
12. Pump arm
13. Pump arm pivot
14. Cotter pin
15. Pump rod
16. Pump shaft
17. Idle air bleed (primary)
18. Gasket
19. Float pivot
20. Idle air bleed (secondary)
21. Emulsion tube
22. Float
23. Pump needle
24. Pump return spring
25. Ball
26. Idle jet (primary)
27. Main jet (secondary)
28. Main jet (primary)
29. Washer
30. Drain plug
31. Idle mixture screw
32. Spring
33. Idle speed screw
34. Spring
35. Throttle plate (primary)
36. Washer
37. Screw
38. Throttle plate (secondary)
39. Throttle shaft (primary)
40. Throttle stop
41. Throttle lever
42. Washer
43. Secondary actuating arm
44. Sleeve
45. Choke unloader
46. Washer
47. Secondary link
48. Washer
49. Throttle shaft (secondary)
50. Spring
51. Throttle body
52. Gasket
53. Body
54. Idle jet (secondary)
55. Emulsion tube (secondary)
56. High speed air bleed (secondary)

Exploded view of the carburetor (Late model)

MANUAL TRANSMISSION

Removal and Installation

Refer to the "Engine Removal and Installation" section.

Overhaul

A split case transaxle is used. Because the components are pressed onto the transmission shafts, a considerable number of factory tools are required for reconditioning. For this reason, it is suggested that transaxle reconditioning be referred to a Subaru dealer.

Shifter and Linkage Adjustment

There are no adjustments that can be performed on the linkage and shifter. If there is too much play or looseness, a sign of worn parts, the worn parts must be replaced.

CLUTCH

Removal and Installation

1. To remove the clutch, the engine must be removed from the vehicle, and the engine and transmission separated.
2. Gradually unscrew the six bolts that hold the pressure plate assembly to the flywheel. Loosen them only a turn at a time and rotate around the pressure plate. Do not unscrew all of the bolts on one side at the same time.
3. When all of the screws have been removed, remove the clutch plate and disc.
4. When installing the clutch, use a pilot shaft to ensure the proper alignment of the disc.
5. Gradually tighten the pressure plate retaining screws one turn at a time, rotating around the pressure plate assembly.
6. Tighten the bolts to about 7-9 ft lbs.

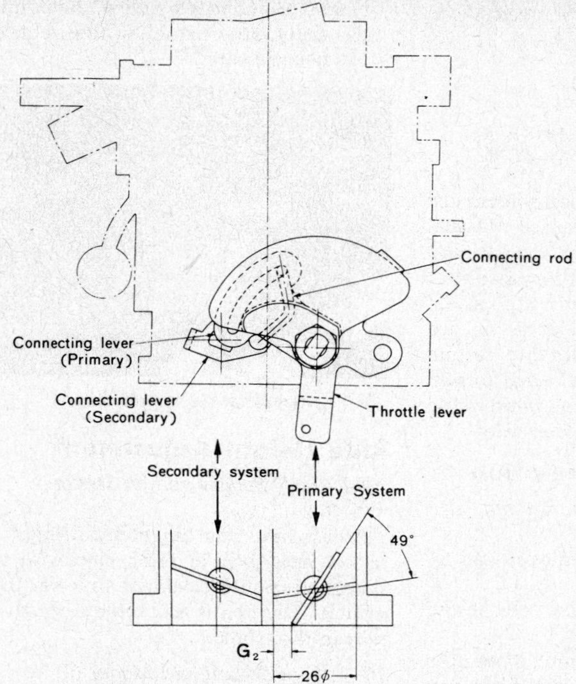

G_2=6.0mm when primary throttle valve opening is 49° from full close. (EA63A)

Throttle linkage adjustment

G_1=1.07mm when primary throttle valve opening is 16° from full close. (EA63A)

Choke linkage adjustment

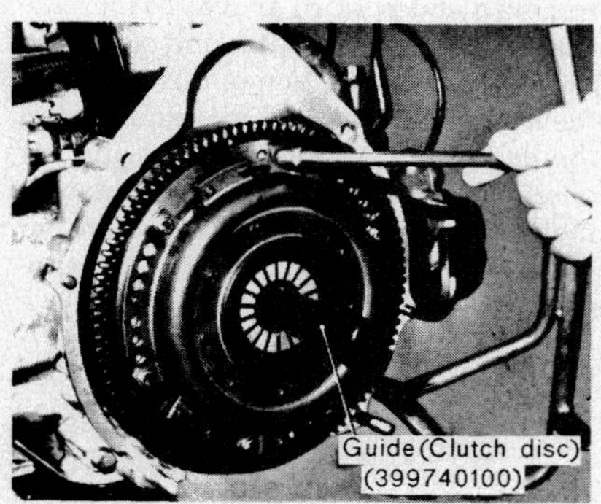

Removing the clutch from the flywheel

NOTE: *When installing the clutch pressure plate assembly, make sure that the O marks on the flywheel and the clutch pressure plate assembly are at least 120° apart. These marks indicate the direction of residual unbalance. Also, make sure that the clutch disc is installed properly, noting the FRONT and REAR markings.*

Clutch Pedal Adjustment

To adjust the free play at the clutch release fork, loosen the lock nut and adjust the free play to be 0.14 to 0.18 in. by turning the adjusting nut. When the adjustment is complete, tighten the lock nut.

Adjust the free play of the clutch pedal by adjusting the clutch pedal adjusting bolt. There should be about 0.94 to 1.18 in. of free play.

The clutch cable can be adjusted at the cable bracket where the cable is attached

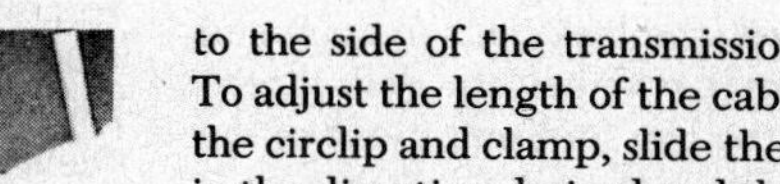

to the side of the transmission housing. To adjust the length of the cable, remove the circlip and clamp, slide the cable end in the direction desired and then replace the circlip and clamp into the nearest gutters on the cable end. The cable should not be stretched out straight nor should it have right angle kinks in it. Any curves should be gradual.

DRIVE AXLES

Driveshaft and U-Joints

Removal and Installation

The drive axle consists of a double-offset joint, an axle shaft, a constant velocity joint, and a stub axle. To remove the drive axle proceed as follows:

1. Engage the parking brake and remove the wheel and tire.
2. Flatten the lockplate, and remove the hub nut.
3. Remove the retaining bolts, and separate the double-offset joint from the brake drum.
4. Detach the inner panel from the wheel well.
5. Turn the steering knuckle to full lock, and pull the stub shaft out of the hub.
6. Slide the axle shaft out of the wheel well.
7. Install in the reverse order of removal.

Drive axle removal

8. Tighten the hub nut to 87–101 ft lbs, and bend the locktab.

NOTE: *Excessive torque will cause bearing damage.*

U-Joint Overhaul

1. Remove the bands from the boots at both the constant velocity and double-offset joints, and slide the boots away from the joints.

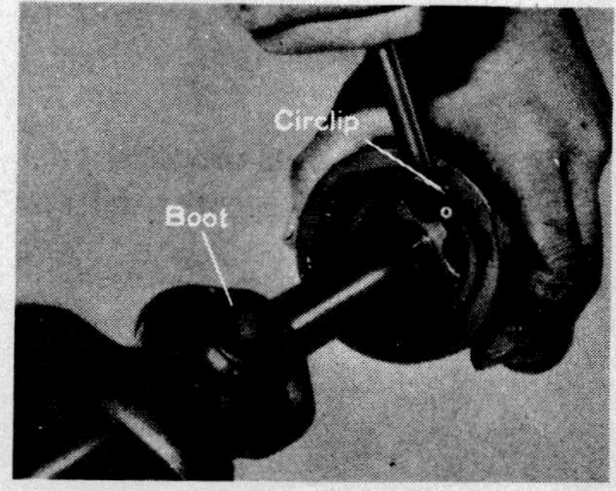

Removing the double-offset joint circlip

2. Pry the circlip out of the double-offset joint, and slide the outer race of the joint off the shaft.

3. Remove the balls from the cage, rotate the cage slightly, and slide the cage inward on the axle shaft.

4. Using snap-ring pliers, remove the outer snap-ring which retains the inner race to the shaft.

5. Slide the inner race, cage, and boot off the axle shaft.

NOTE: *Exercise care to avoid damaging the boot on the inner snap-ring.*

6. Pull back the constant velocity joint boot and pivot the stub axle around the joint far enough to expose a ball.

7. Remove the exposed ball, and continue this procedure until all balls are removed, at which time the outer race (stub axle) may be removed from the axle shaft.

8. Remove the retaining snap-ring, and slide the inner race off the shaft.

9. Inspect the parts of both joints for wear, damage, or corrosion, and replace if necessary. Examine the axle shaft for bending or distortion, and replace if evident. Should the boots be dried out, cracked, or distorted, they must be replaced.

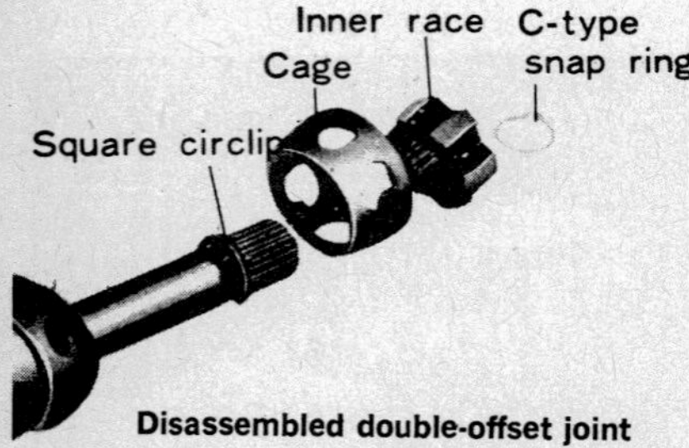

Disassembled double-offset joint

10. Install the constant velocity joint inner race on the axle shaft, and retain with a snap-ring.

11. Assemble the joint in the opposite order of disassembly.

12. Slide the double-offset joint cage onto the shaft, with the counterbore toward the end of the shaft.

13. Install the inner race on the shaft, and install the retaining snap-ring.

14. Position the cage over the inner race, and fill the cage pockets with grease.

15. Insert the balls into the cage.

16. Fill the well in the outer race with approximately 1 oz. grease, and slide the outer race onto the axle shaft.

17. Install the retaining circlip, and add 1 oz. more grease to the interior of the joint. Fill the boot with approximately 1 oz. grease, and slide it into position over the double-offset joint.

18. Fill the constant velocity joint boot with 3 oz. grease, and install the boot over the joint.

19. Band the boots on both joints tightly enough that they cannot be turned by hand.

NOTE: *Use only grease specified for use in constant velocity joints.*

REAR SUSPENSION

Early sedans and all station wagons utilize full trailing arms, mounted to transverse torsion bars, with an auxiliary center spring. Shock absorbers mount to the trailing arm, close to the stub axle.

Late sedans and Model G sedans use semi-trailing arms mounted to torque tubes, which act on an internal torsion bar. Shock absorbers are mounted to the trailing arm, close to the stub axle.

Removal and Installation

FF-1 (Early Sedans and all Station Wagons)

The torsion bars are removed and installed as follows:

1. Raise the rear of the vehicle and remove the wheel.

2. Using a hex key (8 mm), loosen the center arm and spring to relax the torsion bars.

3. Remove the nut and retaining plate from the crossmember mounting bracket.

4. Back out the lock bolts at each end of the torsion bar to be removed, thread a bolt into the bar, and pull it out of the crossmember.

Torsion bars are marked R or L, and must be installed on the correct side.

CAUTION: *Installation on the incorrect side will result in premature failure of the bars.* Install in the reverse order of removal, and adjust ride height (see below).

FF-1 (Late and Model G and DL Sedans)

The torsion bars are removed and installed as follows:

1. Remove the shock absorber lower retaining nut, and separate the shock absorber from the trailing arm.

2. Raise the vehicle and remove the rear wheel.

3. Index mark the splines on the outside and inside of the torsion bar, to indicate mounting position for installation.

4. Remove the lockbolt from the outer torsion bar bushing.

5. Position the trailing arm so as to remove all load from the torsion bar, and tap the torsion bar out.

6. Install the torsion bars in the reverse order of removal. Each torsion bar is marked R or L, on the outer end, to indicate on which side it is installed.

CAUTION: *Installation on the incorrect side will result in premature failure of the bars.* Index the splines according to the marks made during removal, install the wheel and check ride height. If necessary, adjust ride height as indicated below. Remount the shock absorber after the vehicle has been lowered.

Removing the torsion bars

Ride Height Adjustment

FF-1 (Early Sedans and all Station Wagons)

Adjust rear ride height by turning a socket head bolt (8 mm), clockwise to raise, and counterclockwise to lower the vehicle. The bolt is accessible through a port in the trunk.

FF-1 (Late Sedans and Model G Sedans)

No routine ride height adjustment is provided. Should it be necessary to adjust ride height, the torsion bar(s) must be removed as described above. To increase ride height, turn the outer end of the torsion bar in the direction of the arrow (on the end of the bar), and the inner end in the opposite direction an equal number of teeth. Decrease ride height by reversing the above. Shifting the torsion bar one tooth will alter ride height approximately 0.2 in.

FRONT SUSPENSION

McPherson Strut

Removal and Installation

It is desirable that removal and installation of the front suspension be performed with the car up on a lift or over a pit. If this is not possible, then you will need a jack and jackstands to raise and support the vehicle.

1. Remove the battery cable from the negative terminal of the battery.

2. Remove the hub caps, loosen the lug nuts, jack up the vehicle until the tire clears the ground and remove the lug nuts and the wheel/tire assembly. Place the jackstands under the vehicle and remove the jack. Perform this operation on the opposite side if the suspension is to be removed from both sides of the vehicle.

3. Remove the hand brake cable bracket and the hand brake cable hanger from the transverse link and the tie rod end. Remove the hand brake cable end.

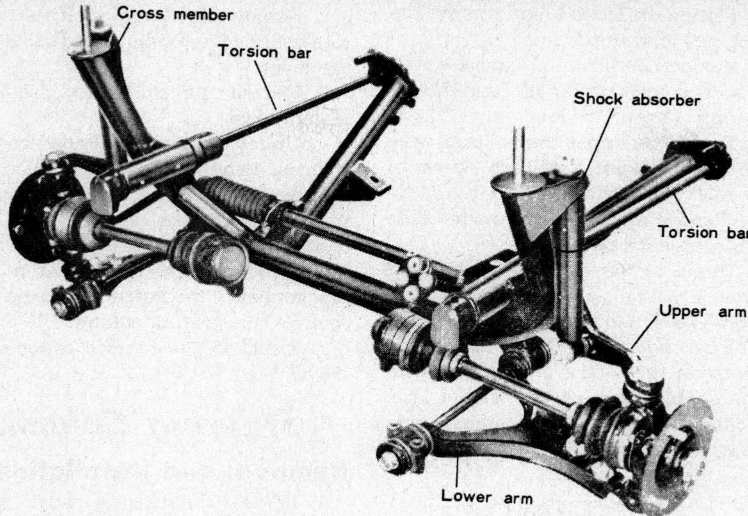

Assembled view of an early model front suspension (FF-1)

4. Remove the axle nut, lock plate, washer, and center piece and remove the front brake drums by using a puller.
5. Disconnect the brake hoses from the brake fluid pipes.
6. Remove the backing plates with the brake assemblies attached.
7. On cars equipped with front disc brakes, remove the hand brake cable end from the caliper lever. Remove the outer cable clip from the cable-end support bracket at the caliper. Remove the hand brake cable bracket from the housing mount by loosening the nuts.
8. Drive out the spring pins of the double offset joint side by using a drift pin and a hammer. The double offset side of the axle is the side closest to the transaxle.
9. Remove the transverse link by loosening the self locking nut which holds the transverse link to the inner pivot shaft of the cross member. Loosen and remove the nuts which clamp the transverse link to the stabilizer. Remove the transverse link rearward from the cross member by

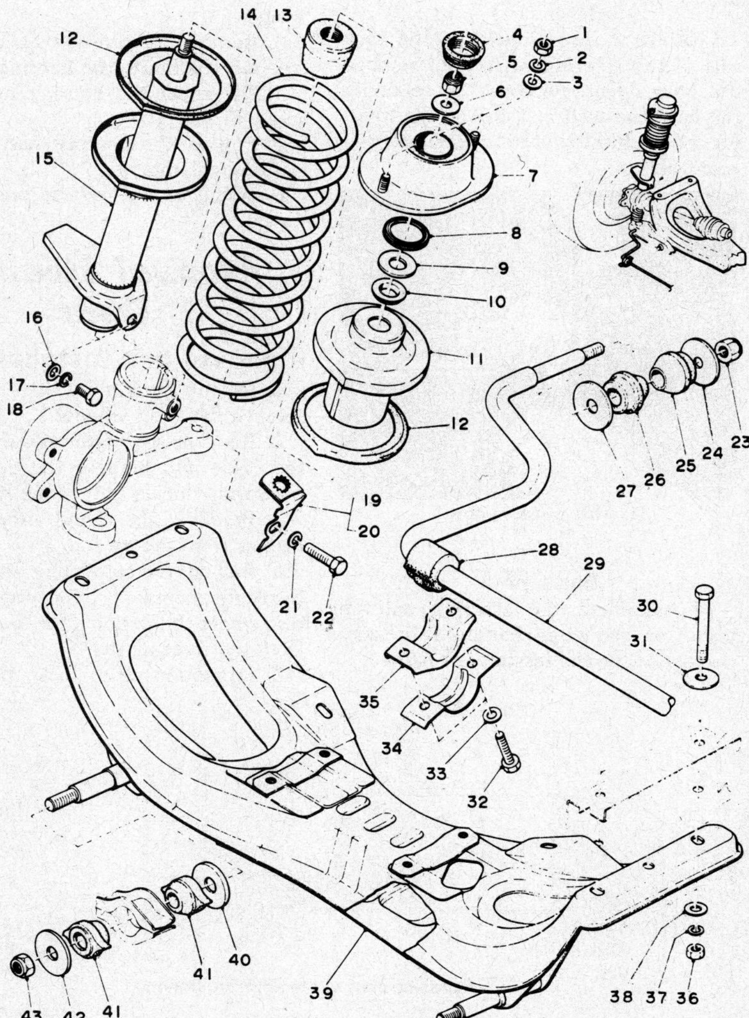

Exploded view of a later model front suspension (FF-1)

1. Nut
2. Spring washer
3. Washer
4. Cap (strut mount)
5. Self locking nut
6. Washer
7. Strut mount
8. Oil seal (strut mount)
9. Washer (thrust bearing)
10. Thrust washer
11. Spring retainer (upper)
12. Rubber seat (coil spring)
13. Helper
14. Coil spring
15. Shock absorber complete
16. Washer
17. Spring washer
18. Bolt
19. Bracket compl. (brake hose: RH)
20. Bracket compl. (brake hose: LH)
21. Spring washer
22. Bolt
23. Self locking nut
24. Washer (transverse link inner)
25. Bushing (link outer)
26. Bushing (link outer)
27. Washer (transverse link outer)
28. Bushing (stabilizer)
29. Stabilizer
30. Bolt
31. Washer
32. Bolt (10 x 40)
33. Washer
34. Lock plate
35. Bracket (stabilizer)
36. Nut
37. Spring washer
38. Washer
39. Crossmember compl. (F)
40. Washer (transverse link inner)
41. Bushing (inner pivot)
42. Washer (transverse link outer)
43. Self locking nut

using a lever and pulling the transverse link out from the end of the stabilizer.

10. Remove the cotter pin from the castle nut and remove the nuts and ball stud from the knuckle arm of the tie-rod end ball joint housing. Take care not to bend the housing.

11. Remove the nuts that hold the strut mount to the body (suspension assembly upper mounting nut-top of the shock absorber tower).

12. Pull the double offset joint out of the drive shaft and then remove the suspension assembly from the body.

13. Install the suspension assembly in the reverse order of removal.

Adjustments

Caster and camber are not adjustable on later models. If either of these specifications is not within the factory recommended range, this would indicate bent or damaged parts that must be replaced. Camber should be set at 1° ± 50'. Caster should be set at 45' ± 45'. The toe-in adjustment is made in the traditional manner, shortening or lengthening the tie rod. The toe-in adjustment should be 0.20 in. ± 0.12 in.

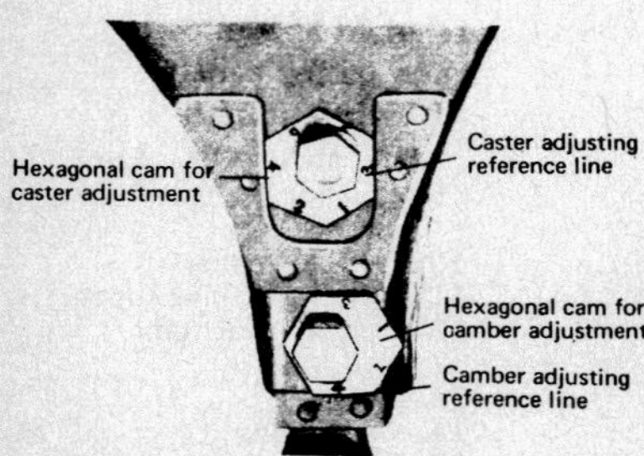

Caster and camber adjustment cams for early models.

Early FF-1

Unequal length upper and lower control arms are utilized. The lower arm is a wishbone type, and the upper a single link type. The torsion bar and shock absorber both mount to the upper arm, and the steering knuckle is mounted to both arms with ball joints. Unsprung weight is greatly reduced, and center-point steering (centerline of the ball joint pivots on the tire centerline) is facilitated by the use of inboard brakes. Caster and camber are controlled by hexagonal cams which control the position of the lower ball joint on the control arm. Rotating the inner (caster) or outer (camber) cam by two flats changes caster or camber by 1°. Toe-in is adjusted by loosening the lock nuts and turning the tie rods.

Torsion Bars

Removal and Installation

1. Raise the vehicle, and loosen the ride height adjusting cam retainer.

2. Remove the shock absorber upper retaining nuts.

3. Flatten the locktab, and remove the upper ball joint upper nut.

4. Remove both torsion bar lock bolts and nuts, at the adjuster arm and the upper control arm.

5. Rotate the upper control arm away from the ball joint, and then down, to fully relax the torsion bar.

6. Remove the adjuster arm, and slide the torsion bar out.

7. Install in the reverse order of removal.

CAUTION: *Do not interchange torsion bars side-to-side.* Index the missing tooth on the torsion bar splines with the double tooth on the anchor arm. Following installation, adjust ride height.

STEERING

Steering Wheel

Removal and Installation

Late FF-1

Loosen the three screws on the back side of the steering wheel and remove the horn cover. Remove the retaining nut from the shaft and pull off the steering wheel. Install in the reverse order of removal.

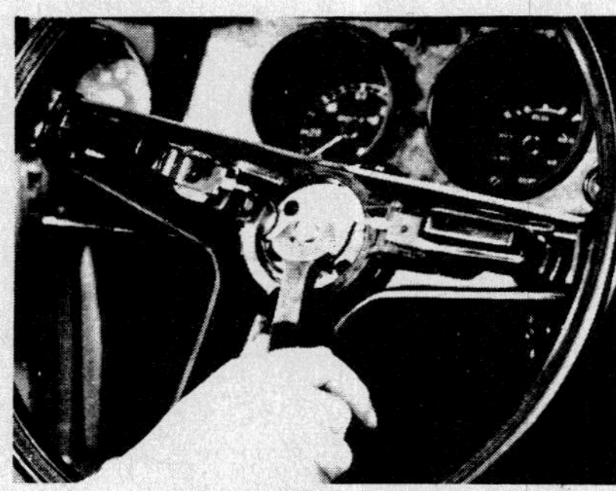

Steering wheel removal

Early FF-1

1. Disconnect the steering column leads from the wiring harness at the connectors below the instrument panel.

2. Remove the parcel shelf, and separate the accelerator pedal and cable from the lever.

3. Detach the clutch rod from the clutch pedal.

4. Unbolt the master cylinder from the steering column.

5. Separate the steering shaft from the steering gear at the rubber U-joint adjacent to the double-offset joint.

6. Unbolt the steering column support bracket below the instrument panel, and remove the steering column.

7. Install in the reverse order of removal.

Steering Column

Removal and Installation

1. Remove the steering wheel. Loosen the screw that fits the column cover to the steering column and the hazard knob. Pull the steering shaft out of the column cover.

2. Remove the snap ring and take out the spacer, washer, and the rubber washer.

3. Remove the screws which hold the steering column to the housing.

4. Drive out the housing by using a screw driver.

5. Pull out the steering shaft from the steering column.

6. Install in the reverse order of removal.

Manual Steering Gear

Removal and Installation

1. Jack up the front of the vehicle and remove the front wheels.

2. Remove the cotter pin and loosen the castle nut. Remove the tie rod end from the knuckle arm of the housing.

3. Remove the hand brake cable hanger from the tie rod.

4. Pull out the cotter pins and remove the rubber coupling connecting bolts and disconnect the pinion with the gear box from the steering shaft.

5. Straighten the lock plate and

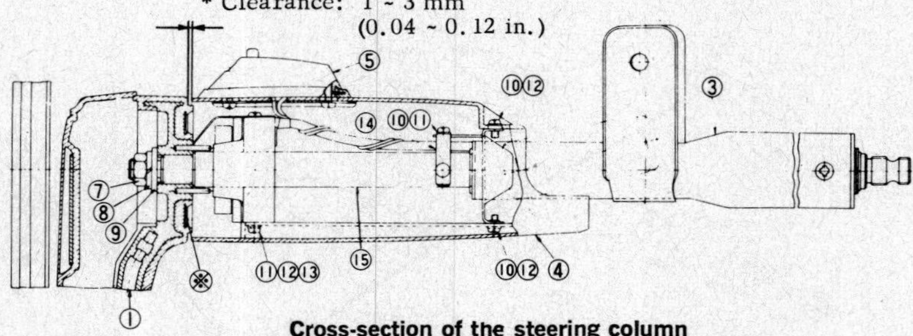

Cross-section of the steering column

1. Steering wheel
3. Steering column
4. Column cover
5. Illumination lamp
7. Nut
8. Spring washer
9. Washer
10. Screw
11. Spring washer
12. Washer
13. Washer
14. Brush
15. Steering shaft

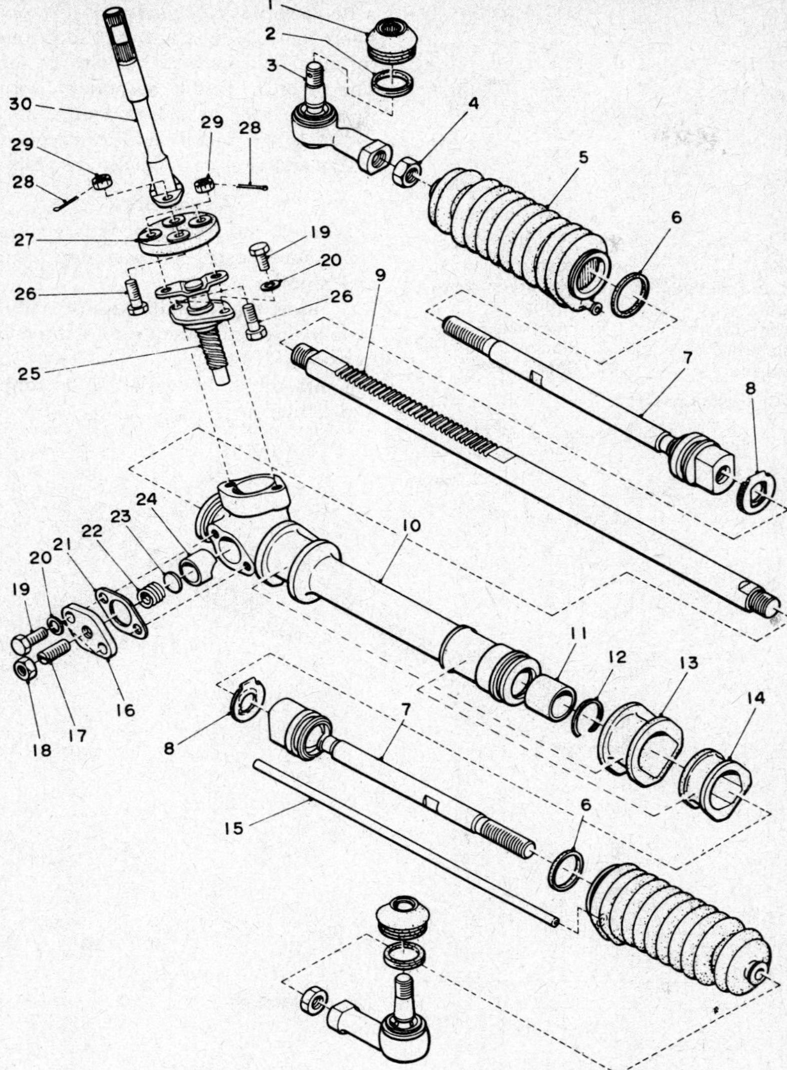

Exploded view of the manual steering gear

1. Dust seal
2. Snap ring
3. Tie rod end
4. Lock nut
5. Boot
6. Snap ring (boot)
7. Ball joint ass'y
8. Lockwasher
9. Rack
10. Gear box unit
11. Bushing-A
12. Clip
13. Adapter-A
14. Adapter-B
15. Air vent tube
16. Cap (steering gear box)
17. Adjusting screw
18. Lock nut
19. Bolt
20. Spring washer
21. Packing
22. Spring (sleeve)
23. Plate (sleeve)
24. Sleeve
25. Pinion
26. Bolt
27. Rubber coupling
28. Cotter pin
29. Castle nut
30. Torque rod

remove the bolts which hold the gear box bracket to the cross member.

6. Loosen the front engine mounting bolts and lift up the engine by about 0.2 in. to avoid touching the gear box with the engine. Remove the gear box from the vehicle.

7. Install in the reverse order of removal.

BRAKES

Brake System

Adjustment

The front brakes are self-adjusting and seldom, if ever, require manual adjustment. For this reason, prior to manual adjustment, ensure that the self-adjuster is functioning, and that brake linings are not excessively worn. To adjust the front brakes, remove the rubber inspection plug, insert a tool through the hole, and turn the star wheel to adjust the brakes. Pushing the handle of the tool will reduce shoe-to-drum clearance.

The rear brakes are adjusted by turning a wedge located at the bottom of the backing plate. Turn the wedge clockwise to lock the brake, and back off 180° to obtain the proper adjustment. Secure the wedge with its locknut.

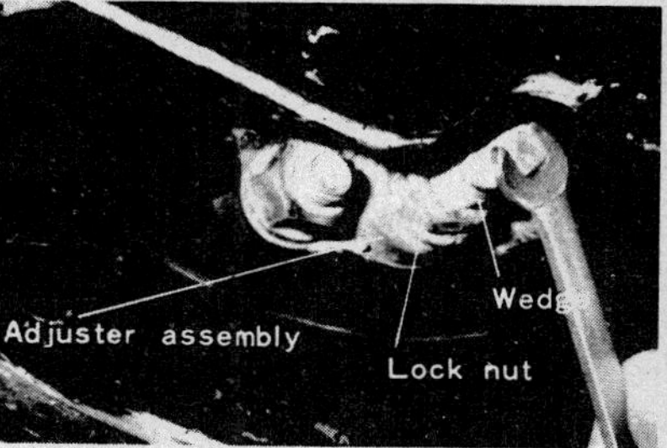

Adjusting the rear brakes

The parking brake is adjusted by removing the shift shaft cover (tunnel), loosening the locknut, and turning the turnbuckle. Adjust so that the parking brake is fully engaged when the lever is pulled 7 or 8 notches. Ensure that the brake releases fully when the lever is lowered.

HYDRAULIC SYSTEM

Master Cylinder

Removal and Installation

1. Remove the brake line from the master cylinder.
2. Remove the nuts which connect the master cylinder to the pedal bracket.
3. Pull the master cylinder assembly forward and out.
4. Install in the reverse order of removal.

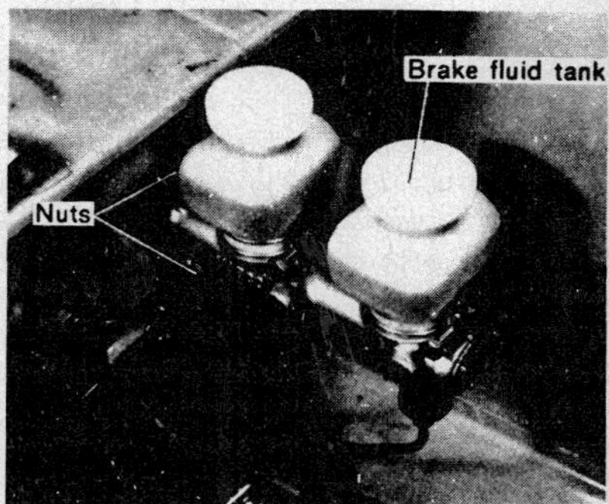

Removing the master cylinder

Power Brake Vacuum Booster

Removal and Installation

1. Disconnect the push rod from the brake pedal by pulling the cotter pin out and removing the head pin.
2. Loosen the master cylinder tightening nuts and disconnect the vacuum hose from the master vac (vacuum booster chamber).
3. Remove the master vac bracket tightening nuts from the passenger compartment side.

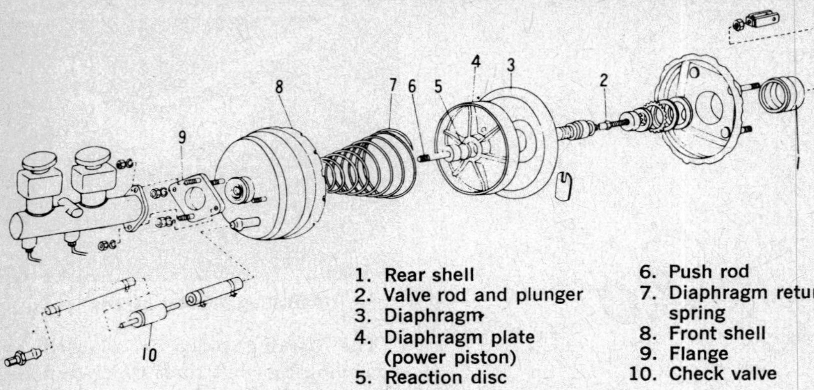

1. Rear shell
2. Valve rod and plunger
3. Diaphragm
4. Diaphragm plate (power piston)
5. Reaction disc
6. Push rod
7. Diaphragm return spring
8. Front shell
9. Flange
10. Check valve

Exploded view of the power brake booster

4. Remove the master cylinder tightening nut, and remove the master vac.

5. Install in the reverse order of removal, making sure that the arrow marking on the check valve of the master vac is facing toward the engine. Check for fluid leakage after the master cylinder has been installed and the brake pedal is fully depressed for 10 seconds, three or four times.

Overhaul

Disassembly

1. Remove the boot from the cylinder body.
2. Remove the stop ring and the stop plate.
3. Remove the stopper pin and the gasket.
4. Pull out the primary and the secondary piston assembly.
5. Pull out the return spring.
6. Loosen and remove the screw and remove the retainer, return spring and secondary cup.

NOTE: *When removing the stop ring, do not snap the ring away and be careful not to damage the cylinder, piston and cup with the screwdriver.*

Checking the Master Cylinder

Make sure that the bore of the master cylinder is smooth and perfectly round. If the bore is step-worn or scarred, replace the master cylinder. It is not advisable to correct the bore by honing with emery cloth. Use only genuine rubber parts. The sliding parts used in the cylinder should be washed in clean brake fluid before assembling. Do not allow dust or other foreign matter to enter the cylinder.

The inside diameter of the master cylinder should be 0.7489 in. to 0.7501 in.

The outside diameter of the piston should be 0.7476 in. to 0.7491 in.

The cylinder-to-piston clearance should be within the following limits: 0.-0008 in. to 0.0059 in.

Check the master cylinder rubber cup for scars, splits, wear, and other damage, and even if the damage is only slight in the case of the rubber cup, the cup must be replaced.

Replace the return spring if it is excessively worn. The length of the primary spring should be 2.32 in. with no load. The length of the secondary spring should be 1.99 in. with no load.

Check the brake fluid reservoir for cracks and replace if cracks are visible.

Assembly

1. Insert the return secondary spring.
2. Assemble the primary cup, spring and retainer.
3. Insert the secondary piston and the primary piston assembly into the cylinder body.
4. Assemble the gasket and stopper and tighten it.

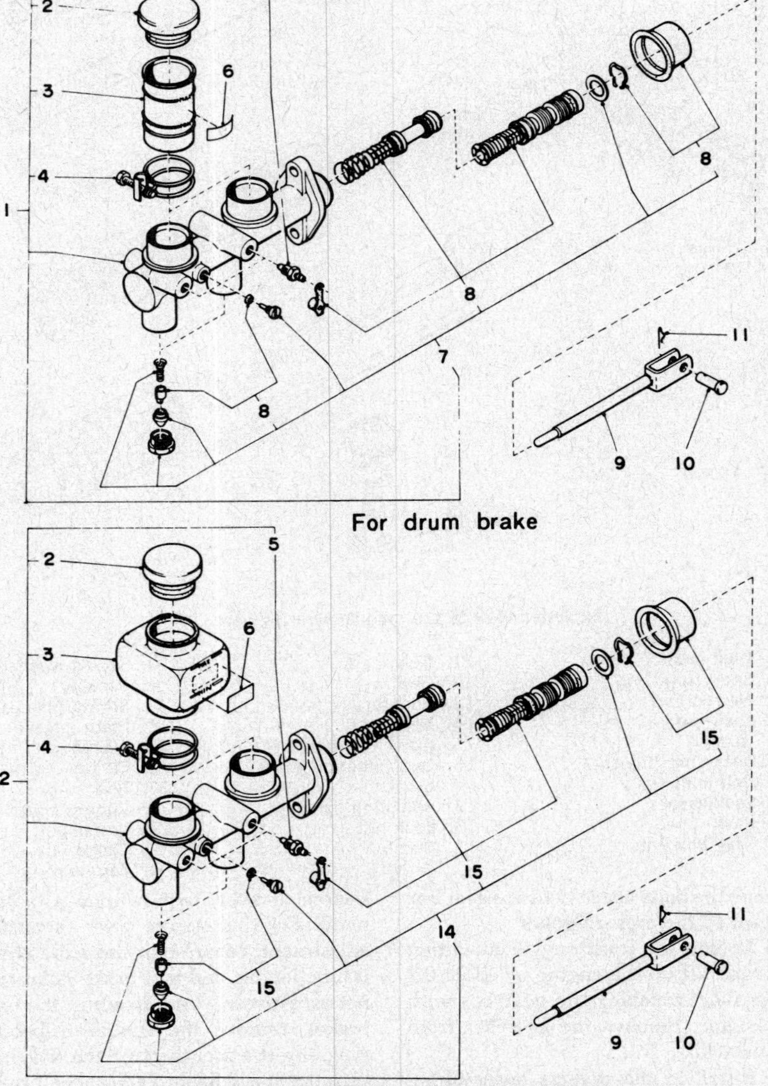

Exploded view of the two types of master cylinders

1. Master cylinder ass'y
2. Cap complete (reservoir)
3. Brake fluid reservoir (master cylinder)
4. Reservoir band (master cylinder)
5. Breeder screw
6. Lavel (brake oil tank)
7. Master cylinder repair kit (B)
8. Master cylinder repair kit (A)
9. Push rod
10. Head pin
11. Cotter pin (master cylinder)
12. Master cylinder ass'y
13. Brake fluid reservoir
14. Master cylinder repair kit (B)
15. Master cylinder repair kit (A)

5. Install the stop plate and stop-ring in the cylinder.

6. Install the boot on the cylinder body.

Bleeding the Brakes

1. Before beginning to bleed the air from the brake lines, check the pedal play and the level of the brake fluid in the master cylinder. Fill the master cylinder with brake fluid.

2. Begin bleeding the brake lines at the wheel farthest away from the master cylinder.

3. During the bleeding process, fill the reservoir with brake fluid and keep it full during the bleeding process.

4. Remove the bleeder screw cap and wipe away any adhering dust. Then insert the end of the vinyl pipe into the bleeder screw end.

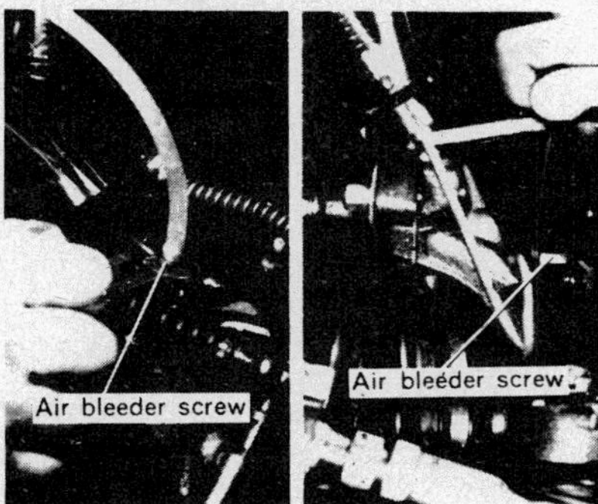

Bleeding the brakes

5. Insert the other end of the vinyl pipe in a glass or tin receptacle containing clean brake fluid.

6. Loosen the bleeder screw with a spanner, and have the person assisting you slowly depress the brake pedal.

7. Continue to depress the pedal until no air bubbles are observed in the vinyl pipe.

8.When bubbles are no longer present, tighten the bleeder screw (with the pedal depressed), and then release the pedal.

9. Remove the vinyl pipe from the bleeder screw, mount the cap, and apply the same procedure to the next wheel.

10. Upon completion of bleeding the air at all four wheels, check the level of the brake fluid in the master cylinder reservoir and add fluid to the level line. Do not reuse old brake fluid.

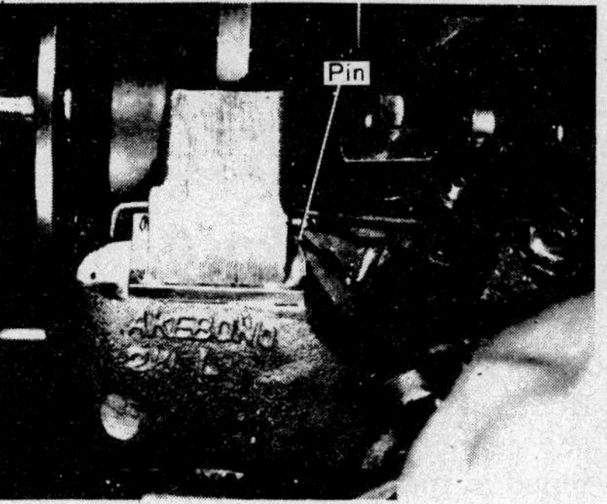

Removing the pins

Removing the stoppers

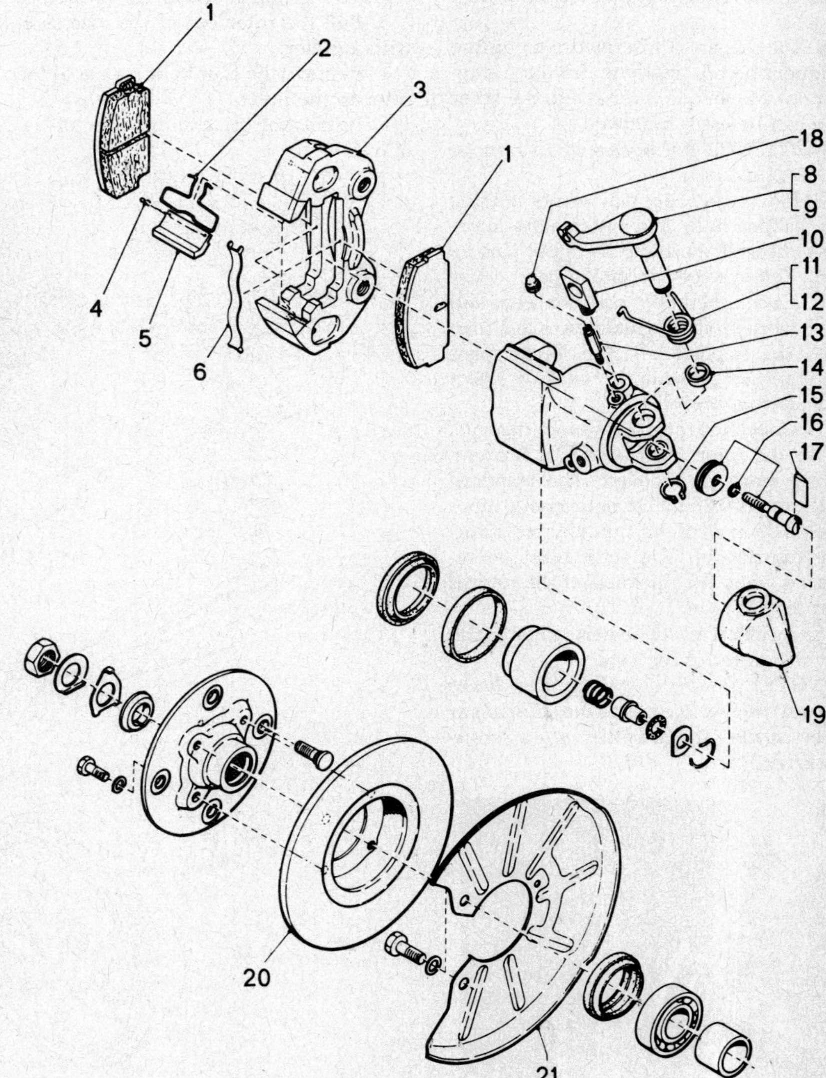

Exploded view of the disc brake assembly

1. Pad (disc brake F)
2. Spring (caliper)
3. Bracket (mounting)
4. Pin (caliper)
5. Stopper (plug)
6. Spring (pad)
7. Body caliper ass'y
8. Lever & spindle ass'y (LH)
9. Lever & spindle ass'y (RH)
10. Bracket (hand brake)
11. Spring (hand brake lever return LH)
12. Spring (hand brake lever return RH)
13. Bleeder screw (wheel cylinder)
14. Bushing (hand brake)
15. Retaining spring
16. Spindle ass'y
17. Connecting link
18. Cap (air bleeder)
19. Cap (lever)
20. Brake disc (F)
21. Cover (disc)

FRONT DISC BRAKES

Disc Brake Pads

Removal and Installation

1. Jack up the front of the vehicle and support it with jackstands. Remove the wheel and tire.

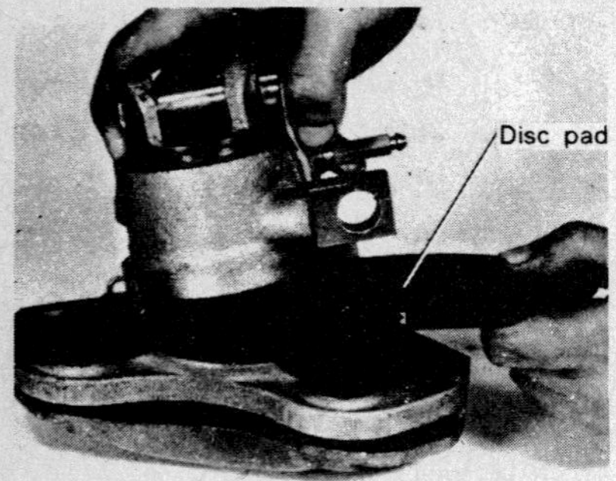

Removing the disc brake pads

2. Remove the hand brake cable by removing the outer cable clip.

3. Remove the four pins from the stoppers.

4. Fit the tip of a screwdriver on the stopper and tap lightly to drive the stopper out. When one is removed, the other one can be easily removed.

NOTE: *It is not necessary to remove the brake pipe.*

Remove the caliper by firmly holding the caliper body and pulling the lower part out while pushing the upper part in.

5. Remove the disc brake pad.

6. Check the brake pads for wear and replace them if the thickness is less than 0.06 in. Replace all four brake pads together to prevent the braking effect from being uneven.

7. Check the rotor for wear or damage. Have the rotor resurfaced if it is excessively worn or grooved. The standard thickness is 0.39 in. Do not remove more than 0.06 in. of metal from the rotor during resurfacing. The rotor must be replaced when the thickness of the rotor is less than 0.33 in.

8. Installation can be performed in the reverse order of removal.

NOTE: *Before installing the brake pads, replace the piston into the caliper by turning it clockwise with a screwdriver.*

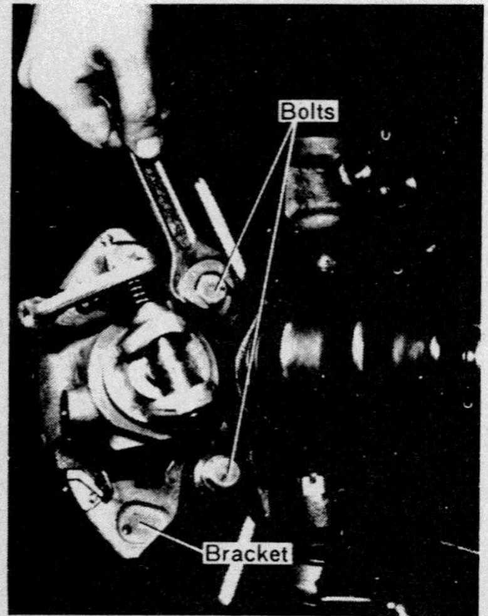

Removing the two bolts that hold on the caliper bracket.

Disc Brake Calipers

Removal and Installation

The calipers are removed as outlined in the disc brake pad removal procedure.

Disc Brake Rotor

Removal and Installation

1. Jack up the vehicle and remove the front wheel, hand brake cable, stoppers, and caliper in the same manner as outlined in the brake pad removal and installation procedure.

2. Remove the two bolts that hold the caliper bracket to the housing and remove the bracket from the rotor.

3. Pull the rotor out of the axle shaft with a puller.

4. Remove the four bolts that hold the rotor to the hub.

5. Installation is the reverse of removal.

Removing the hub/rotor assembly

Removing the disc from the hub

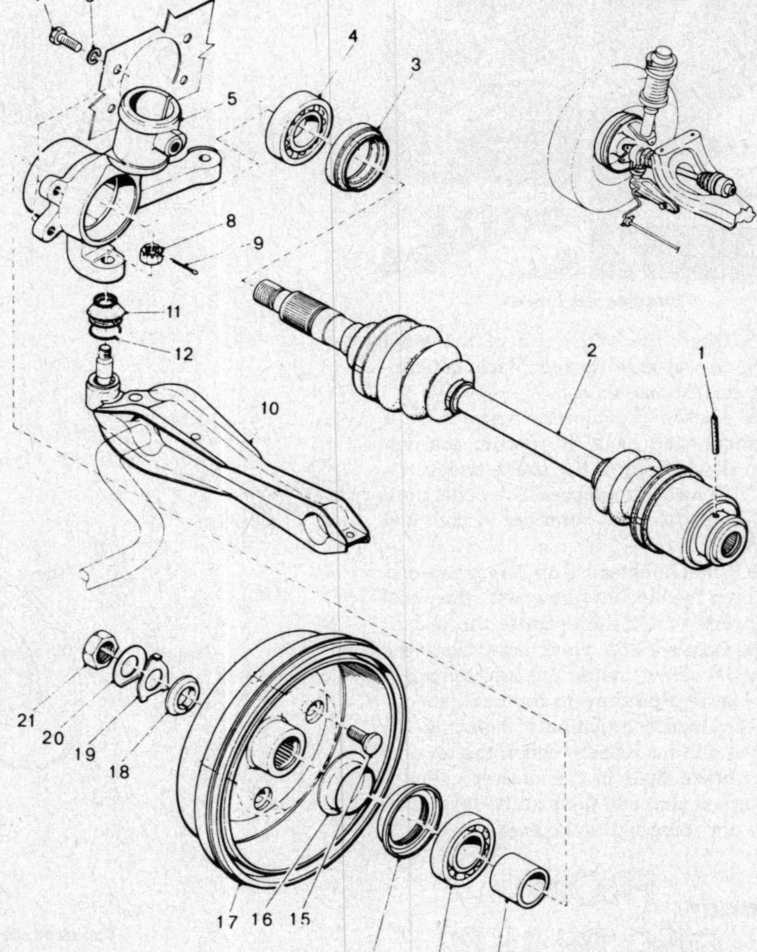

Exploded view of the front axle assembly (drum brakes)

1. Spring pin
2. Axle shaft
3. Oil seal
4. Bearing
5. Housing
6. Spring washer
7. Bolt
8. Castle nut
9. Cotter pin
10. Transverse link
11. Dust seal (Ball joint)
12. Circlip
13. Spacer
14. Oil seal (out)
15. Hub bolt
16. Sleeve
17. Brake drum
18. Center piece
19. Lock washer
20. Lock plate
21. Nut

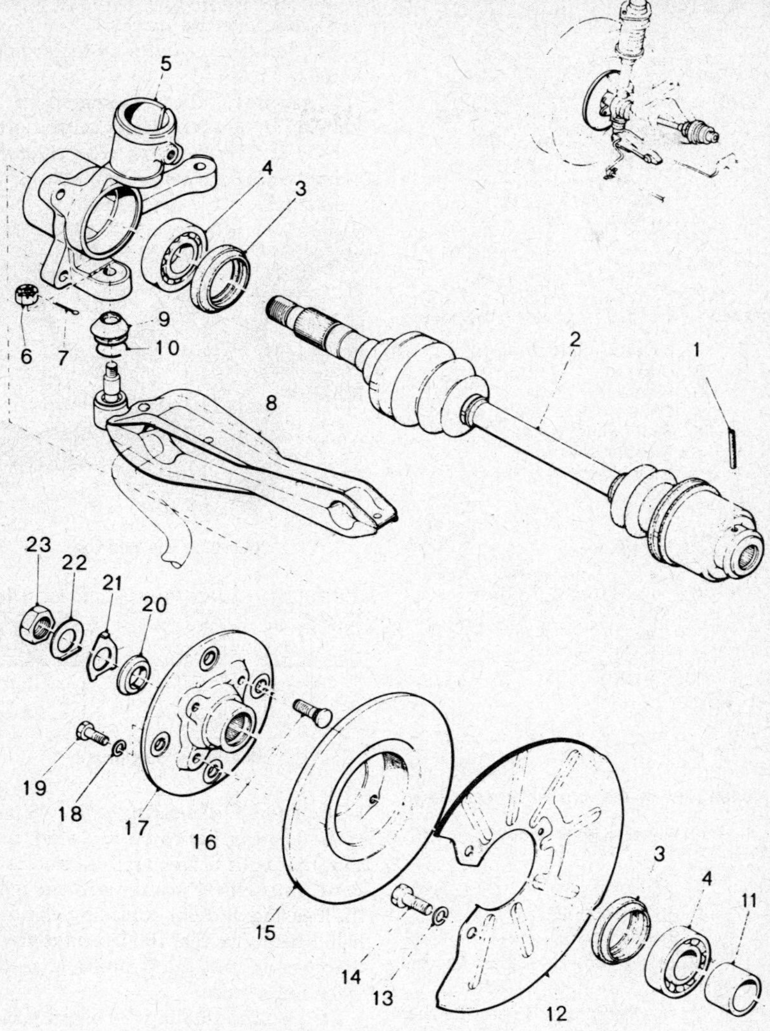

Exploded view of the front axle assembly (disc brakes)

1. Spring pin
2. Axle shaft
3. Oil seal
4. Bearing
5. Housing
6. Castle nut
7. Cotter pin
8. Transverse link
9. Dust seal (Ball joint)
10. Circlip
11. Spacer
12. Disc cover
13. Spring washer
14. Bolt
15. Disc
16. Hub bolt
17. Disc hub
18. Spring washer
19. Bolt
20. Center piece
21. Lock washer
22. Lock plate
23. Nut

Inspection

See "Disc Brake Pad Removal and Installation" for inspection of the rotor.

Wheel Bearings

Removal and Installation (Packing)

1. Jack up the vehicle and remove the front tire and wheel.
2. Remove the hand brake cable from the lever of the body caliper and disconnect the brake pipe from the body caliper.
3. Remove the stopper (plug) from the caliper bracket.
4. Remove the caliper bracket (mounting) from the disc hub by loosening the two bolts which hold it to the backing plate.
5. Remove the bolts which connect the damper strut to the housing.
6. Remove the hand brake hanger on the tie rod end. Remove the cable bracket from the housing.
7. Remove the tie rod ball joint from the housing knuckle by using a puller.
8. Carefully pull the housing downward and out to separate the damper strut from the housing.
9. Remove the transverse link ball joint from the housing. Loosen the castle nut and pry the castle nut by using a lever with the hub as the base.
10. Pull the rotor and rotor hub out of the axle shaft using a puller.
11. If the inner bearing and inner oil seal are left on the axle shaft, pull them off using a puller.
12. Move the spacer up or down with your finger.
13. Apply a brass or copper bar to the inside surface of the inner race of the bearing.
14. Lightly knock the bar with a fiber hammer to drive the bearing out of the housing together with the oil seal.

Removing the bearing

NOTE: *Don't hit the bearing with hard steel. When hitting the bearing, apply the bar all around the inner race.*

15. Pull out the spacer.
16. Apply a brass or copper bar to the inside surface of the outer race. Lightly tap the bar with a fiber hammer to drive the bearing out of the housing together with the oil seal. Apply the bar all around the outer race while tapping it out. Discard both of the oil seals and replace them.
17. The bearings are pressed into the housing in the reverse order of removal.

FRONT DRUM BRAKES

Brake Drums

Removal and Installation

1. Jack up the front of the vehicle and remove the front wheels.
2. Loosen the three bolts on the double offset joint (DOJ) side, and remove the DOJ from the drum.
3. Remove the drum cover attached to the brake assembly.
4. Remove the interior portion of the hand brake cable assembly into the engine compartment.
5. Straighten the brake drum locking cotter pin and remove it. Unscrew the nut and remove the drum in parallel with the splined shaft.
6. Inspect the inside surface of the brake drum. If it is excessively scored, it should be resurfaced or cut. The standard inside diameter for the sedan should be 8

in. and the maximum inside diameter is not to exceed 8.08 in. The standard inside diameter for the station wagon is 9 in. and the maximum inside diameter is not to exceed 9.08 in.

7. Replace the brake drums in the reverse order of removal.

Brake Shoes

Removal and Installation

1. Remove the brake drums.
2. Loosen and remove the brake line from the rear of the backing plate.
3. Unscrew the four brake backing plate bolts and remove the brake assembly from the vehicle.
4. Before disassembling, make sure that the automatic adjuster assembly movement is correct by pulling the cable.
5. Lift the automatic adjuster assembly cable by pulling it out from the shoe side and removing it from the shoe hole.
6. Remove the automatic adjuster assembly from the shoe.
7. Remove the shoe return spring and cable from the anchor pin by using a brake tool.
8. Remove the shoe set spring with a brake tool to set the shoe free. Then remove the hand brake cable from the shoe.
9. Remove the hand brake shoe strut.
10. Install in the reverse order of removal.

Wheel Cylinders

Removal and Installation

1. Remove the brake drum and the brake shoes from the backing plate.
2. Remove the wheel cylinder from the backing plate by unscrewing the attaching bolts.
3. Remove the rubber boots from both ends of the wheel cylinder and push out the inner pistons and spring together with the rubber cups.
4. Inspect the inside of the wheel cylinder bore. If it is worn or scratched in any way, it should be honed with a wheel cylinder hone or a piece of crocus cloth until the scratches are removed.
5. Replace the rubber cups with new ones. The internal replacement parts are usually supplied in a wheel cylinder rebuilding kit.
6. Reassemble the wheel cylinder and replace it on the backing plate in the reverse order of removal.
7. After reinstalling the brake line and the brake assembly, together with the brake drum, bleed the brake system.

Wheel Bearings

Removal, Packing and Installation

1. In order to remove the wheel bearing, the steering knuckle has to be removed.
2. Jack up the vehicle and remove the wheel and tire.
3. Straighten the lock plate at the wheel hub on the constant velocity joint side, loosen the wheel hub nut, and remove the nut with the lock plate.
4. Remove the tie rod end from the knuckle arm.
5. Remove the two cotter pins, castle nuts, spring washers, and the lower arm ball joint.

NOTE: *When the camber and caster adjusting cams are removed, remember the setting number for reassembly.*

6. After flattening the lock washer, remove the nut and lock plate which join the upper arm and the upper arm joint.
7. Remove the hub and knuckle assembly from the splined section of the axle shaft constant velocity joint side.
8. Separate the hub from the knuckle.
9. Remove the upper and lower ball joint and then remove the steering knuckle from the vehicle.
10. Straighten out the lock plate, loosen the bolt, and remove the bolt together with the spring washer and the lock plate.
11. Remove the inner oil seal from the bearing nut.

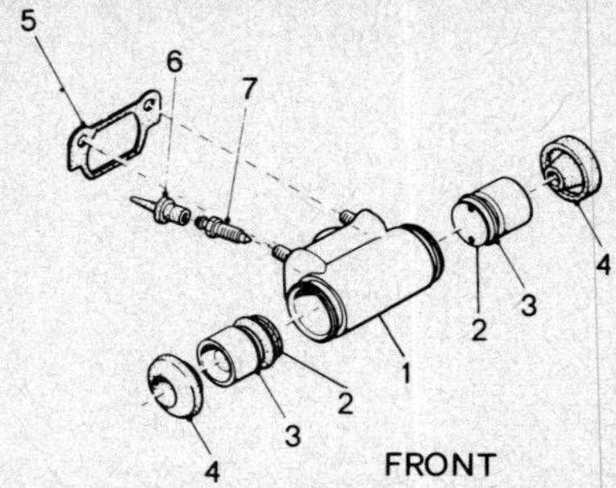

Exploded view of the front wheel cylinders

1. Wheel cylinder body
2. Cup
3. Piston
4. Boot
5. Seal (wheel cylinder)
6. Bleeder cap
7. Bleeder screw

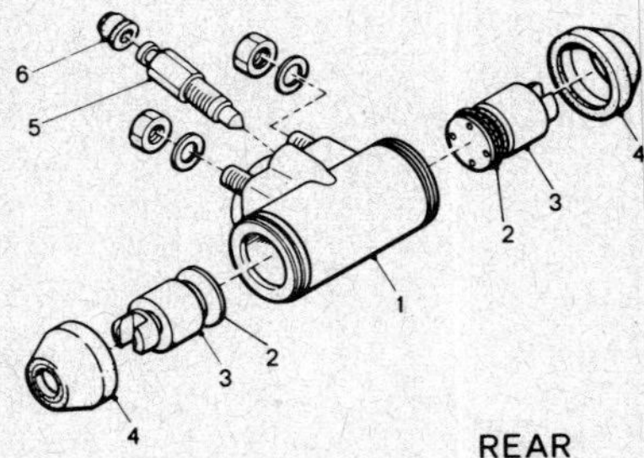

Exploded view of the rear wheel cylinders

1. Wheel cylinder body
2. Cup
3. Piston
4. Boot
5. Bleeder screw
6. Bleeder cap

12. Remove the nut from the knuckle.
13. Remove the spacer.
14. Remove the outer oil seal from the knuckle.
15. Remove the bearing from the knuckle by pressing it out with a press.

NOTE: *The bearing race cannot be removed because of its peculiar construction.*

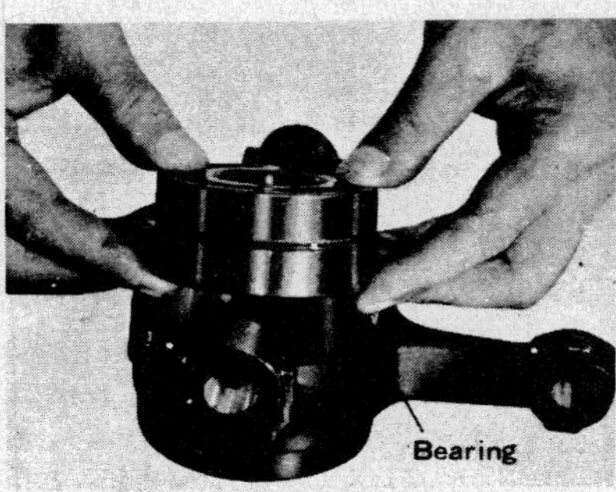

Installing the bearings

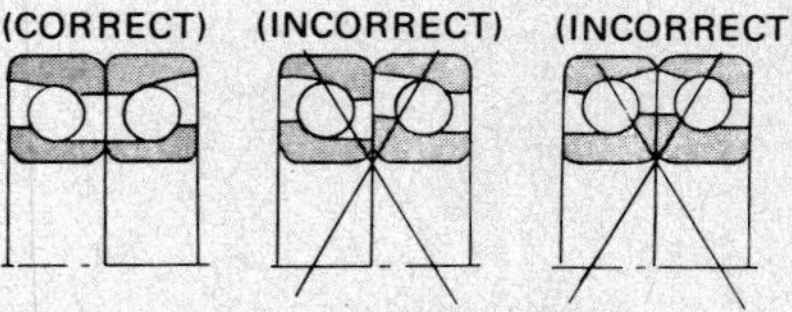

Bearing arrangement

16. The wheel bearing is in two parts. If the bearing has to be replaced, make sure that both halves are replaced at the same time. Never just replace one half of the bearing without replacing the other half. Make sure that the bearings are put together in the same position as they were removed.
17. Before installing the bearing, clean and inspect it for damage. Repack the bearing with wheel bearing grease.
18. Press the outer oil seal into the knuckle. Insert the outer oil seal so that it

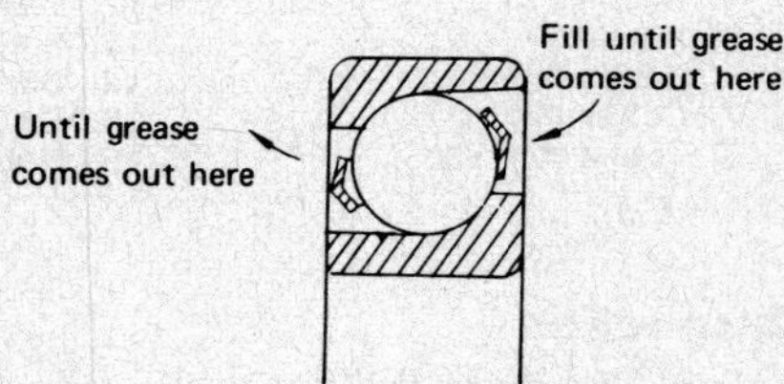

Packing the bearing with grease

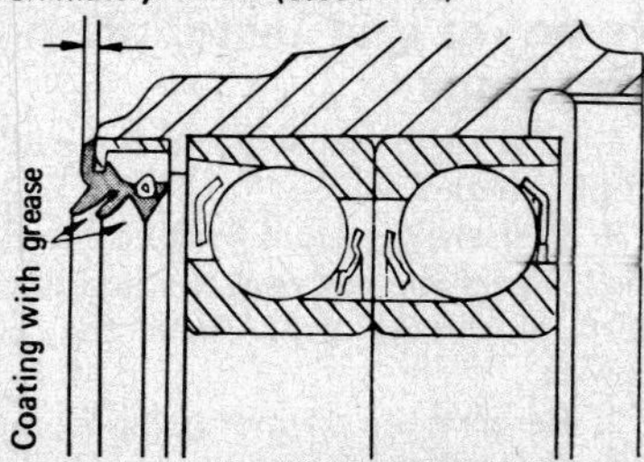

Installation of the outer oil seal

protrudes from the knuckle end surface about 0.04 in. Coat the outer seal lip with grease when installing.

19. Insert the spacer making sure that the lip of the oil seal is not tucked up.

20. Tighten the bearing nut to 115–133 ft lbs.

21. Align the lock plate groove with the nut groove and bend the lock plate and lock the nut.

22. Press the inner oil seal into the nut. Be careful not to damage the side lip of the oil seal. Coat the inner oil seal lip surface with grease when installing.

23. Assemble the steering knuckle to the vehicle in the reverse order of removal.

FRONT DRUM BRAKES

Brake Drums

Removal and Installation

1. Jack up the vehicle and remove the wheel and tire.

2. Remove the axle nut, release the hand brake if applied, and remove the brake drum using a puller.

3. Install in the reverse order of removal.

Inspection

After removing the brake drum, inspect the inner braking surface for excessive wear or damage. If it is unevenly worn, streaked or cracked, either have it resurfaced or replaced. The standard inside diameter of the brake drum is 9 in. The maximum inside diameter is to be no more than 9.08 in.

Brake Shoes

Removal and Installation

1. Jack up the vehicle then remove the wheel and tire and the brake drum.

2. Remove the automatic adjuster spring with a screwdriver and then remove the automatic adjuster lever.

3. Remove the lower shoe return spring and the automatic adjuster.

4. Remove the hand brake cable end from the hand brake lever. Remove the clamp nut with a box wrench. Remove the washer and pull the hand brake cable out.

5. Remove the upper shoe return springs from the anchor pin with a brake tool and remove the automatic adjuster.

6. Remove the shoe set springs with the brake tool and free the brake shoes.

7. Install in the reverse order of removal.

Wheel Cylinders

Removal and Installation

See the "Inboard Drum Brake" section for procedures on removing, installing, and rebuilding the wheel cylinders.

Wheel Bearings

Removal and Installation

1. In order to remove the wheel bearings, the steering knuckle has to be removed from the vehicle.

2. Jack up the vehicle and remove the front wheel and tire.

3. Remove the lock plates and nuts which connect the brake drum to the axle shaft assembly spindle. Removal of the lock plates will be easier if the hand brake is applied.

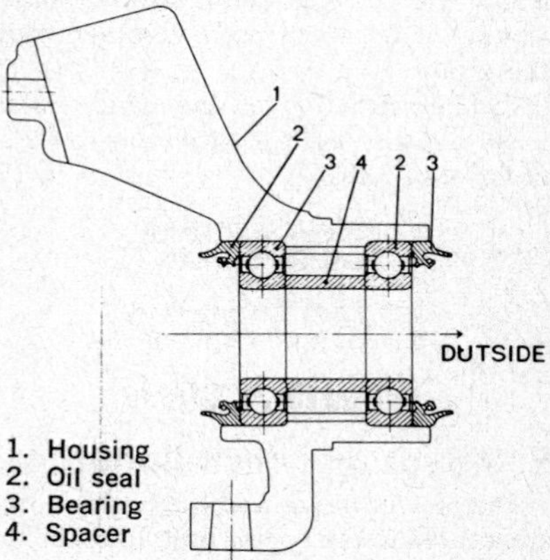

Bearing and oil seal arrangement

4. Pull the brake drum off the splines by using a gear puller.

5. Remove the backing plate with the brake assembly by removing the four attaching bolts.

6. Remove the bolts which connect the damper strut to the housing.

7. Remove the tie rod ball joint from the housing knuckle by using a puller.

8. Carefully pull the housing downward to separate the damper strut from the housing.

9. Remove the transverse link ball joint from the housing. Install a spacer between the housing and the castle nut and loosen the castle nut.

10. Use a puller to remove the housing from the axle shaft.

11. Move the spacer either up or down using your finger.

12. Insert a brass or copper drift in the inside surface of the inner race of the bearing and lightly tap on the drift with a hammer to drive the bearing out of the housing together with the oil seal.

13. Remove the spacer from the housing.

14. Use the drift to remove the outer race from the housing.

15. Install the bearing by pressing it into the housing. Assemble in the reverse order of disassembly.

REAR DRUM BRAKES

Brake Drums

Removal and Installation

1. Jack up the vehicle and remove the wheel and tire.

2. Remove the three cap installing bolts, spring washers, cap, and bearing stopper plate.

3. Remove the cotter pin and loosen the castle nut taking care not to damage the bearing seal.

4. Remove the brake drum with a puller.

5. Install in the reverse order of removal.

Inspection

After removing the brake drum, inspect the inner braking surface for excessive wear or damage. If it is unevenly worn, streaked, or cracked, have it resurfaced or replaced. The standard inside diameter of the brake drum is 7.09 in. The maximum allowed thickness is 7.17 in.

Brake Shoes

Removal and Installation

1. Jack up the vehicle and remove the wheels.

2. Remove the brake drums.

3. Remove the shoe setting spring with a pair of pliers.

4. Remove the anchor side of the shoe first by removing the return springs on the bottom.

5. Remove the cylinder side of the shoe by removing the upper return springs.

6. Remove the brake shoes from the backing plate.

7. Install in the reverse order of removal.

Wheel Cylinders

Removal and Installation

See the "Inboard Front Drum Brake" section for removal, installation, and rebuilding of the wheel cylinders.

PARKING BRAKE

Cable

Removal and Installation

1. Jack up the vehicle and remove the wheel and tire.

2. Remove the brake drum (drum brake type).

3. Remove the hand brake cover and console box.

4. Loosen the cable adjusting nut.

5. Remove the cable end from the equalizer.

6. Remove the cable end tightening clip.

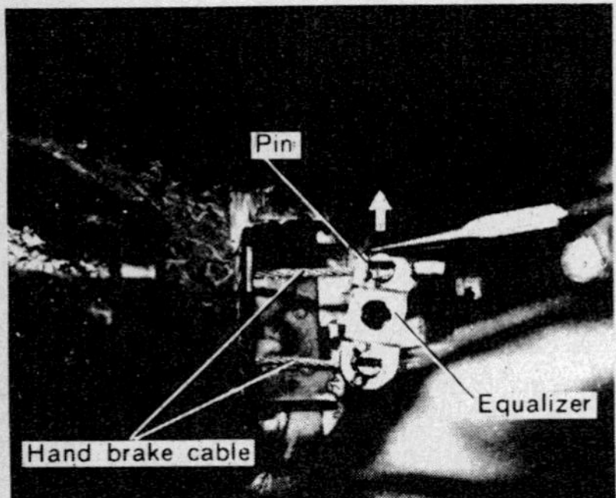

Removing the hand brake cable from the equalizer.

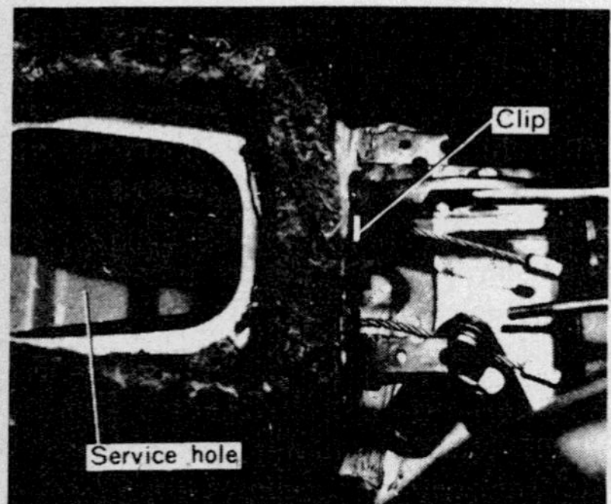

Removing the end clip

7. Remove the service hole attachment on the tunnel.

8. Remove the cable clamp from the cross-member.

9. Remove the cable installing bracket from the transverse link.

10. Remove the handbrake cable hanger from the tie-rod end.

11. Remove the handbrake cable end from the hand brake lever by removing the secondary shoe.

12. Remove the cable end nut, washer, and spring washer from the inside of the backing plate and pull the hand brake cable out from the backing plate (drum brakes).

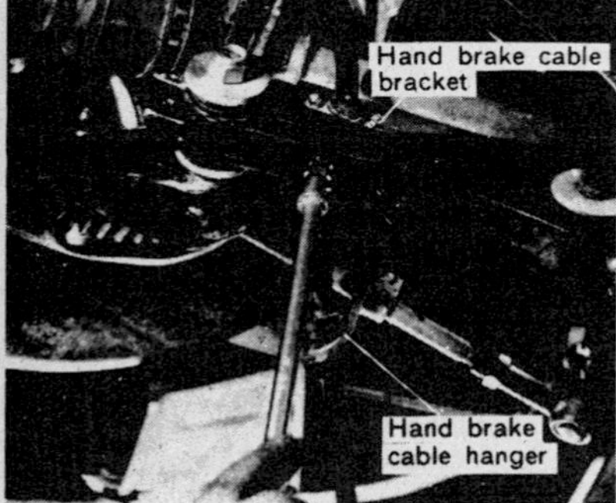

Removing the bracket from the transverse link.

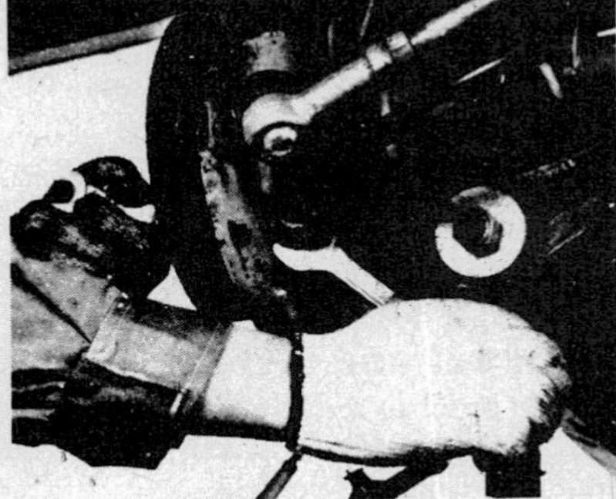

Removing the end nut

13. Pull the brake hose clamp out and remove the hand brake cable end from the lever and spindle assembly (disc brakes).

14. Pull the handbrake cable assembly from the engine compartment and remove it from the body together with the grommet.

15. Reinstallation of the hand brake cable can be performed in the reverse order of removal.

CHASSIS ELECTRICAL

Heater Unit

Removal and Installation

The blower motor and the heater core are located in the heater unit. In order to service either of these components, the heater unit must be removed from the vehicle. In order to remove the heater unit from the vehicle, the entire instrument panel has to be removed.

1. Disconnect the negative terminal of the battery.

2. Unscrew the nuts which retain the instrument panel to the body at both ends.

3. Remove the screws which hold the upper panel face of the instrument panel to the body bracket which is attached to the firewall.

4. After removing the bolts which retain the steering stay and the steering shaft, loosen the nuts which hold the lower side of the instrument panel to the steering stay.

5. Disconnect the defroster hoses.

6. Disconnect the heater control rod and wiring harness.

7. Disconnect the following wirings and cables and label them for identification when reinstalling them:

8. Remove the speedometer cable hanger spring.

9. Disconnect the speedometer cable from the speedometer.

10. Disconnect all of the electrical wirings connected to the instrument panel.

11. Disconnect the antenna feeder cord.

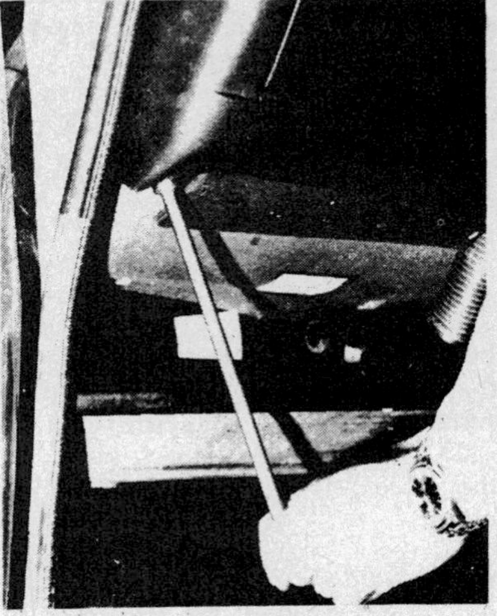

Removing the retaining screws from either end of the dash.

Removing the retaining screws from the top of the dash.

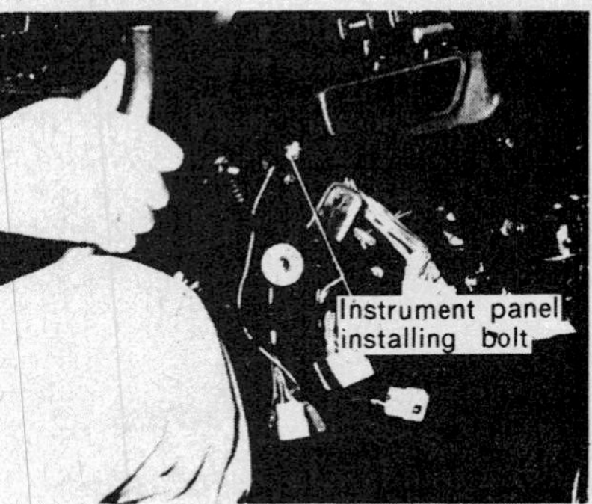

Removing the bolts from the steering stay.

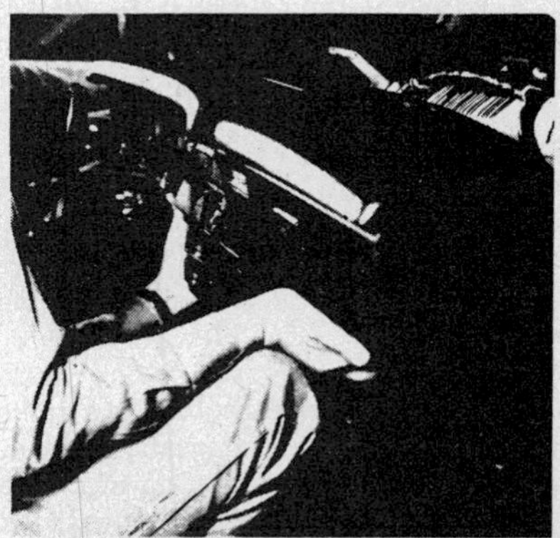

Removing the instrument panel (dash) from the vehicle as an assembly.

12. Remove the instrument panel from the vehicle being careful of interference between the side end of the instrument panel and the front pillars.

13. Drain the coolant from the radiator.

14. Disconnect the heater hoses on the engine side, both the inlet and the outlet hoses.

15. Remove the console box by removing the six attaching screws.

16. Disconnect the heater control assembly and the heater unit by disconnecting the room shutter cable and the two air inlet control rods.

Removing the shutter cable

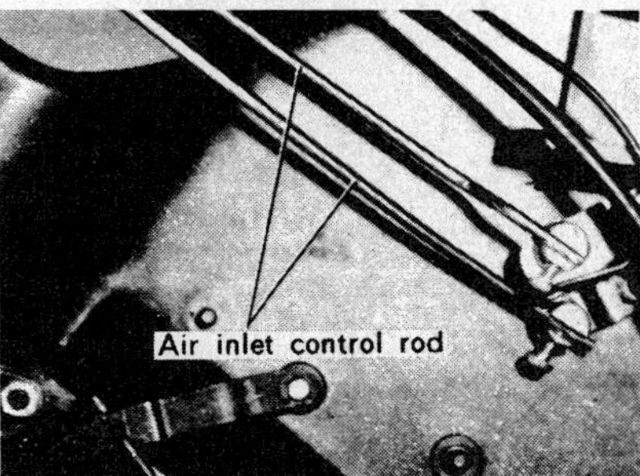

Remove the air inlet control rods

Remove the heater unit mounting bolts

Pulling out the heater core

17. Disconnect the wiring harnesses of the fan motor, the main harness, and the motor control switch wirings.

18. Remove the heater unit mounting bolts.

19. Lift the assembly to the side being careful of the stopper at the bottom of the unit. Remove the grommet on the firewall at this time.

20. Remove the unit assembly.

21. Remove the blower fan, motor,

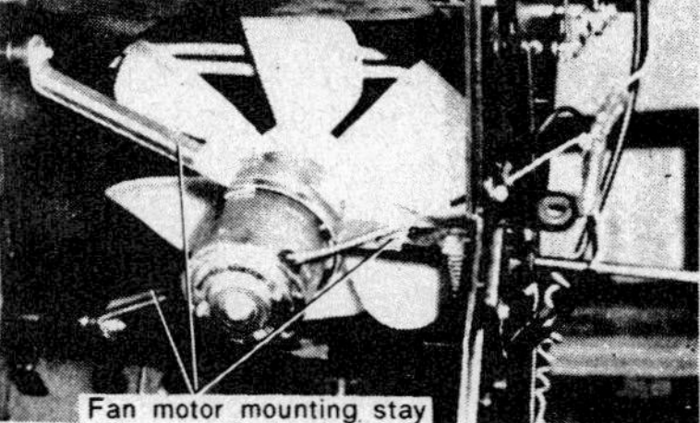

Removing the fan and motor assembly

and the heater core. There is no set procedure other than removing other components that are in the way of removal of the motor and the core.

22. Install in the reverse order of removal.

Radio

Removal and Installation

1. Remove the center panel of the instrument panel by first removing the radio installing nut. Remove the bolt which holds the center panel to the instrument panel. It can be reached by removing the ash tray. Remove the lighting switch and the wiper switch knobs by loosening the screw and removing the dress nut. Remove the heater shutter control knobs by loosening the screw. Remove the hanger spring of the speedometer cable. Disconnect the speedometer cable from the back side of the combination meter. Disconnect the junction block from the back side of the combination meter. Disconnect the wiring harness from the cigar lighter. Remove the center panel from the instrument panel.
2. Remove the speaker grille by loosening the two attaching screws.
3. Pull out the feeder cord from the radio plug.
4. Loosen the radio mounting bolt.
5. Loosen the radio mounting screws.
6. Disconnect the radio wiring and remove the radio.
7. Install in the reverse order of removal.

Removing the radio installing nut

Remove the bolt under the ash tray

Removing the dress nuts

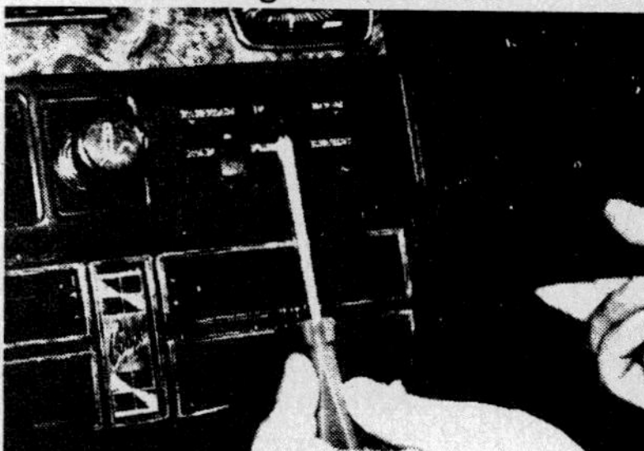
Removing the heater control knobs

Removing the center panel

Windshield Wiper Motor

Removal and Installation

The wiper motor is located on the firewall under the hood. To remove it, remove the three screws that hold it to the firewall and pull out the wiper motor and link as an assembly. Take off the clip which separates the link and the motor. Install in the reverse order of removal.

Instrument Cluster

Removal and Installation

In order to remove the instrument cluster, the center panel of the dash panel has to be removed. See "Radio Removal" for this procedure. Once the center panel is out, the instrument panel can be removed by detaching the screws which hold the cluster to the center panel.

Fuse Box Location

On earlier FF-1's, the fuse box is located on the left side of the engine compartment of the fender.

On later models, the fuse box is located on the right side wheel apron in the engine compartment.

TOYOTA

Index

INTRODUCTION

In 1933, the Toyoda Automatic Loom Works started an automobile division. Several models, mostly experimental, were produced between 1935 and 1937. Automobile production started on a large scale in 1937 when the Toyota Motor Co. Ltd. was founded. The name for the automobile company was changed from the family name, Toyoda, to Toyota, because a numerologist suggested that this would be a more auspicious name to use for this endeavor. It must have been; by 1947, Toyota had produced 100,000 vehicles. Today Toyota is Japan's largest producer of motor vehicles and ranks third largest in world production.

It was not until the late 1950s, that Toyota began importing cars to the United States. Public reception of the "Toyopet" was rather cool. The car was heavy and under-powered by U.S. standards. Several other models were imported, including the almost indestructible Land Cruiser. It was not until 1965, however, with the introduction of the Corona sedan, that Toyota enjoyed a real success on the U.S. market. Since that time, Toyota sales have risen at a steady rate, to make the Toyota the second largest-selling import in the U.S.

Continual product improvement, a good dealer network, and an ability to blanket the economy end of the market are responsible for this success. Today, Toyota produces a full range of models, from the economical Corolla 1200 to the luxurious new Corona Mark II, for the U.S. market. Toyota's primary emphasis has been on economy sedans but in 1971 the sporty Celica coupe was introduced, putting Toyota into the new "mini ponycar" business.

MODEL IDENTIFICATION

1968-69 Corolla 1100

1969-70 Corolla 1200

1970-71 Corolla 1200 and 1600

1972 Corolla 1200 and 1600

1973 Corolla 1600

1972 Carina

1973 Carina

1970-71 Corona 1900

1973 Corona 2000

1972 Mark II 2000

1971-72 Celica ST

1966-70 Corona

1972 Corona 2000

1969-71 Mark II 1900

1972-73 Mark II 6 cyl.

1973 Celica ST

1968-69 Crown 2300

1970-71 Crown 2300

1972 Crown 2600

1970-72 Hi-Lux

1966-73 Land Cruiser

1970-73 Land Cruiser station wagon

SERIAL NUMBER IDENTIFICATION

Vehicle

Prior to 1968 the vehicle identification number was stamped on a plate located in the engine compartment. The plate was usually located on the firewall.

After 1968 all models have the vehicle identification number (VIN) stamped on a plate which is attached to the left side of the instrument panel. This plate is visible through the windshield.

NOTE: *The plate in the engine compartment is also retained after 1968.*

The serial number consists of a series identification number (see chart below) followed by a six-digit production number.

Engine

The engine serial number consists of an engine series identification number, followed by a six-digit production number.

The location of this serial number varies from one engine type to another. Serial numbers may be found in the following locations:

1100 and 1200 cc (K-C and 3K-C)

The serial number on the K-C and 3K-C engine is stamped on the right side of the engine, below the spark plugs.

1600 cc(2T-C)

The serial number is stamped on the left side of this engine, behind the dipstick.

1900 cc (3R-B, 3R-C and 8R-C)

The serial number on these engines is embossed beside the fuel pump on the right side of the engine.

2000 cc(18R-C)

The serial number is stamped on the left side of the engine, behind the dipstick.

2300 and 2600 cc(2M and 4M)

The serial numbers on both of these engines are stamped on the right side of the cylinder block, below the oil filter.

Land Cruiser (F)

The serial number is located on the front, right side of the engine.

VEHICLE IDENTIFICATION

Model/Type	Year	Series Identification Number*
Corolla 1100 & 1200		
Sedan	1968-70 (early)	KE10L
Sprinter	1968-70 (early)	KE15L
Station Wagon	1968-70 (early)	KE16L
Corolla 1200		
Sedan	1970-73	KE20L
Coupe	1970-71	KE25L
Station Wagon	1970-71	KE26LV
Corolla 1600		
Sedan	1971-73	TE21L
Coupe	1971-73	TE27L
Station Wagon	1971-73	TE28LV
Carina	1972-73	TA12L
Corona		
Sedan	1966-70 (early)	RT43L
Hardtop	1967-70 (early)	RT52L
Corona 1900		
Sedan	1970 (early)-71	RT83L
Hardtop	1971	RT93L
Corona 2000		
Sedan	1972-73	RT85L
Hardtop	1972-73	RT95L
Station Wagon	1973	RT89L
Mark II 1900		
Sedan	1969-71	RT62L
Hardtop	1969-71	RT72L
Station Wagon	1969-71	RT78L

Model/Type	Year	Series Identification Number*
Mark II 2000		
Sedan	1972 (early)	RT63L
Hardtop	1972 (early)	RT73L
Station Wagon	1972 (early)	RT79L
Mark II/6		
Sedan	1972-73	MX12L
Hardtop	1972-73	MX22L
Station Wagon	1972-73	MX28L
Celica 1900 ST	1972	RA20L
Celica 2000 ST	1972-73	RA21L
Crown 2300		
Sedan	1968-71	MSS5L
Station Wagon	1968-71	MS53L
Crown 2600		
Sedan	1972	MS65L
Hardtop	1972	MS75L
Station Wagon	1972	MS63L
Hi-Lux 1900	1970-71	RN12L
Hi-Lux 2000	1972	RN14L
Hi-Lux		
Standard Wheelbase	1973	RN22L
Long Wheelbase	1973	RN27L
Land Cruiser		
2 door	1966-73	FJ40LV
Station Wagon	1966-69	FJ45LV
Station Wagon	1970-73	FJ55LG

* The suffixes L, V, KA, etc. may not appear in the serial number; a typical Toyota serial number would appear: MS55-132246

ENGINE IDENTIFICATION

Model	Year	Displacement Cu in. (cc)	Number of cylinders	Type	Engine Series Identification
Corolla					
1100	1968-69	65.7 (1077)	4	OHV	K-C
1200	1970-73	71.2 (1166)	4	OHV	3K-C
1600	1971-73	96.9 (1588)	4	OHV	2T-C
Carina	1972-73	96.9 (1588)	4	OHV	2T-C
Corona					
1900	1966-69	115.8 (1897)	4	OHV	3R-B & 3R-C
1900	1970-71	113.4 (1858)	4	OHC	8R-C
2000	1972-73	120.0 (1980)	4	OHC	18R-C
Mark II					
1900	1969-71	113.4 (1858)	4	OHC	8R-C
2000	1972	120.0 (1980)	4	OHC	18R-C
2300	1972 (late)	137.5 (2258)	6	OHC	2M
2600	1973	156.4 (2563)	6	OHC	4M
Celica					
1900	1971	113.4 (1858)	4	OHC	8R-C
2000	1972-73	120.0 (1980)	4	OHC	18R-C
Crown					
2300	1968-71	137.5 (2258)	6	OHC	2M
2600	1972	156.4 (2563)	6	OHC	4M
Hi-Lux					
1900	1970-71	113.4 (1858)	4	OHC	8R-C
2000	1972-73	120.0 (1980)	4	OHC	18R-C
Land Cruiser	1966-73	236.7 (3878)	6	OHV	F & FA

OHV—Overhead valve
OHC—Overhead cam

GENERAL ENGINE SPECIFICATIONS

Year	Engine Type	Engine Displacement Cu in. (cc)	Carburetor Type	Horsepower @ rpm ▲	Torque @ rpm (ft lbs) ▲	Bore x Stroke (in.)	Compression Ratio
1966-67	3R-B	115.8 (1897)	2-bbl	90@ @4600	110 @ 2600	3.46 x 3.07	8.0:1
	F	236.7 (3878)	1-bbl	145 @ 4000	217 @ 2000	3.54 x 4.00	7.8:1
1968-69	K-C	65.7 (1077)	2-bbl	60 @ 6000	61.5 @ 3800	2.95 x 2.40	9.0:1
	3R-C	115.8 (1897)	2-bbl	90 @ 4600	110 @ 2600	3.46 x 3.09	8.0:1
	8R-C①	113.4 (1858)	2-bbl	108 @ 5500	113 @ 3800	3.38 x 3.15	9.0:1
	2M	137.5 (2253)	2-bbl	115 @ 5200	117 @ 3600	2.96 x 3.35	9.0:1
	F	236.7 (3878)	2-bbl	115 @ 4000	230 @ 2000	3.54 x 4.00	7.8:1
1970-71	3K-C	71.8 (1166)	2-bbl	73 @ 6000	69.4 @ 4200	2.95 x 2.60	9.0:1
	2T-C②	96.9 (1588)	2-bbl	102 @ 6000	101 @ 3800	3.35 x 2.76	8.5:1
	8R-C	113.4 (1858)	2-bbl	108 @ 5500	113 @ 3800	3.38 x 3.15	9.0:1
	2M	137.5 (2253)	2-bbl	115 @ 5200	117 @ 3600	2.96 x 3.35	9.0:1
	F	236.7 (3878)	2-bbl	155 @ 4000	230 @ 2000	3.54 x 4.00	7.8:1
1972-73	3K-C	71.8 (1166)	2-bbl	65 @ 6000	67 @ 3800	2.95 x 2.60	9.0:1
	2T-C	96.9 (1588)	2-bbl	88 @ 6000	91.3 @ 3800	3.35 x 2.76	8.5:1
	18R-C	123.0 (1980)	2-bbl	97 @ 5500	106 @ 3600	3.48 x 3.15	8.5:1
	2M③	137.5 (2253)	2-bbl	109 @ 5200	120 @ 3600	2.95 x 3.35	8.5:1
	4M	156.4 (2563)	2-bbl	122 @ 5200	141 @ 3600	3.15 x 3.35	8.5:1
	F	236.7 (3878)	2-bbl	135 @ 4000	213 @ 2000	3.54 x 4.00	7.8:1

▲ Horsepower and torque ratings given in SAE net figures in 1972-73
① 8R-C engines were introduced in 1969
② 2T-C engines were introduced in 1971
③ Not available in 1973

Firing Orders

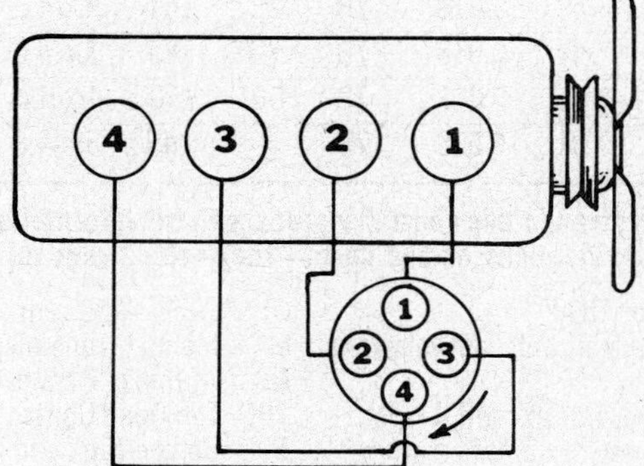

Four cylinder engines

2M and 4M engines

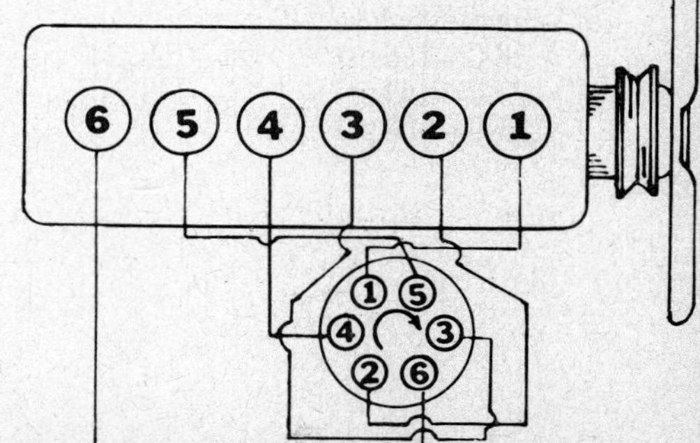

F engines

TUNE-UP SPECIFICATIONS

Year	Engine Type	Spark Plugs Type (ND)*	Spark Plugs Gap (in.)	Distributor Point Dwell (deg)	Distributor Point Gap (in.)	Ignition Timing (deg) ▲ MT	Ignition Timing (deg) ▲ AT	Compression Press.	Fuel Pump Press.	Idle Speed (rpm) ▲ MT	Idle Speed (rpm) ▲ AT	Valve Clearance (in.) Intake	Valve Clearance (in.) Exhaust
1966-67	3R-B	W200T30	0.031	52	0.018	12B	12B	156	3.0-4.5	550	550	0.008	0.014
	F	W175T6	0.035	41	0.018	7B	—	145	3.4-4.8	600	—	0.008	0.014
1968-69	K-C	W200T30	0.030	52	0.018	5A	—	171	3.0-4.5	650	—	0.008	0.014
	3R-C	W200T30	0.030	52	0.018	5B	5B	156	2.9-4.3	650	650	0.008	0.014
	8R-C	W200T30	0.030	52	0.018	TDC	TDC	164	2.8-4.3	650	650	0.008	0.014
	2M	W200T30	0.030	41	0.018	5B	5B	156	3.6-5.0	650	650	0.007	0.010
	F	W175T30	0.035	41	0.018	TDC	—	145	3.0-4.5	600	—	0.008	0.014
1970	3K-C	W20EP	0.031	52	0.018	5A	5A	171	2.8-4.3	650	650	0.008	0.012
	8R-C	W20EP	0.031	52	0.018	TDC	TDC	164	2.8-4.3	650	650	0.008	0.014
	2M	W20EP	0.031	41	0.018	TDC	TDC	156	3.6-5.0	650	650	0.007	0.010
	F	W17ES	0.036	41	0.018	7B	—	145	3.4-4.8	600	—	0.008	0.014
1971	3K-C	W20EP	0.031	52	0.018	5A	5A	171	2.8-4.3	650	650	0.008	0.012
	2T-C	W20EP	0.031	52	0.018	5B	5B	170	2.8-4.3	750	650	0.007	0.013
	3R-C	W20EP	0.031	52	0.018	10B	10B	146	2.8-4.3	650	650	0.008	0.014
	2M	W20EP	0.031	41	0.018	TDC	TDC	156	3.6-5.0	650	650	0.007	0.010
	F	W17ES	0.036	41	0.018	7B	—	145	3.4-4.8	600	—	0.008	0.014
1972-73	3K-C	W20EP	0.031	52	0.018	5B	—	171①	2.8-4.3	650	—	0.008	0.012
	2T-C	W20EP	0.031	52	0.018	5B	5B	170①	2.8-4.3	750	650	0.008	0.013
	18R-C	W20EP	0.031	52	0.018	7B	7B	164①	2.8-4.3	650	650	0.008	0.014
	2M	W16EP	0.030	41	0.018	7B	7B	149	3.4-4.6	700	600	0.007	0.010
	4M	W14EP	0.031	41	0.018	7B	5B	156①	4.2-5.4	700	650	0.007	0.010
	F	W17ES	0.036	41	0.018	7B	—	145①	3.4-4.8	600②	—	0.008	0.014

NOTE: If the information given in this chart disagrees with the information on the engine tune-up decal, use the specifications on the decal—they are current for the engine in your car.

* Nippondenso spark plugs are used as OEM
▲ With manual transmission in Neutral and automatic transmission in Drive (D)
** Difference between cylinders should not exceed 14 psi, however, look for uniformity among cylinders rather than specific pressures
‡ Valve clearances checked with engine HOT
① 1973 compression specifications:
3K-C—156 psi 4M—156 psi
2T-C—149 psi F—149 psi
18R-C—156 psi
② 1973—650 rpm
MT Manual transmission
AT Automatic transmission
TDC Top Dead Center
B Before top dead center
A After top dead center

CRANKSHAFT AND CONNECTING ROD SPECIFICATIONS

All measurements in inches.

Engine Type	CRANKSHAFT Main Brg. Journal Dia.	Main Brg. Oil Clearance	Shaft End-Play	Thrust on no.	CONNECTING ROD Journal Diameter	Oil Clearance	Side Clearance
K-C	1.9585-1.9685	0.0008-0.0016	0.0016-0.0087	3	1.6526-1.6535	0.0006-0.0016	0.0040-0.0080
3K-C	1.9675-1.9685	0.0005-0.0015	0.0020-0.0090	3	1.6525-1.6535	0.0006-0.0015	0.0040-0.0080
2T-C	2.2827-2.2834	0.0012-0.0024	0.0030-0.0070	3	1.8889-1.8898	0.0008-0.0020	0.0063-0.0102
3R-B, 3R-C	2.3634-2.3640	0.0008-0.0022	0.0020-0.0090	3	2.1648-2.1654	0.0016-0.0024	0.0067-0.0110
8R-C	2.3613-2.3622	0.0008-0.0020	0.0020-0.0100	3	2.0857-2.0866	0.0008-0.0020	0.0043-0.0097
18R-C	2.3613-2.3622	0.0008-0.0020	0.0008-0.0080	3	2.0857-2.0866	0.0010-0.0021	0.0060-0.0100
2M	2.3616-2.3622	0.0007-0.0017	0.0020-0.0017	4	2.0466-2.0472	0.0006-0.0020	0.0040-0.0100
4M	2.3617-2.3627	0.0012-0.0021	0.0020-0.0100	4	2.0463-2.0472	0.0008-0.0021	0.0020-0.0100
F	2.6366-2.6378	0.0012-0.0018	0.0024-0.0065	3	2.1252-2.1260	0.0008-0.0024	0.0040-0.0090

Dia. Diameter Brg. Bearing

PISTON AND RING SPECIFICATIONS

All measurements in inches

Engine Type	Piston Clearance 68°F	RING GAP Top Compression	Bottom Compression	Oil Control	RING SIDE CLEARANCE Top Compression	Bottom Compression	Oil Control
K-C and 3K-C	0.0010-0.0020	0.006-0.014	0.006-0.014	0.006-0.014	0.0011-0.0027	0.0007-0.0023	0.0006-0.0023
2T-C	0.0024-0.0031	0.008-0.016	0.004-0.012	0.004-0.012	0.0008-0.0024	0.0008-0.0024	0.0008-0.0024
3R-B and 3R-C	0.0012-0.0020	0.008-0.016	0.006-0.014	0.006-0.014	0.0012-0.0027	0.0012-0.0027	0.0010-0.0027
8R-C	0.0010-0.0020	0.004-0.012	0.004-0.012	0.004-0.012	0.0012-0.0028	0.0012-0.0028	0.0008-0.0028
18R-C	0.0020-0.0030	0.004-0.012	0.004-0.012	0.004-0.012	0.0012-0.0028	0.0012-0.0028	0.0008-0.0028
2M and 4M	0.0010-0.0020	0.006-0.014	0.006-0.014	0.008-0.020	0.0012-0.0028	0.0008-0.0024	N.A.
F	0.0012-0.0020	0.006-0.018	0.006-0.016	①	0.0016-0.0031	0.0016-0.0031	②

① Oil control gap:
Top—0.006-0.018 in.
Bottom—0.006-0.016 in.

N.A. Not Available

② Control clearance
Top—0.0016-0.0031 in.
Bottom—0.0016-0.0033 in.

VALVE SPECIFICATIONS

Engine Type	Seat Angle (deg)	Face Angle (deg)	SPRING TEST PRESSURE (lbs) Inner	Outer	SPRING INSTALLED HEIGHT (in.) Inner	Outer	STEM TO GUIDE CLEARANCE (in.) ▲ Intake	Exhaust	STEM DIAMETER (in.) Intake	Exhaust
K-C	45	45	—	70.1	—	1.512	0.0010-0.0020	0.0010-0.0030	0.3130	0.3130
3K-C	45	45	—	55.1	—	1.512	0.0010-0.0020	0.0020-0.0030	0.3140	0.3140
2T-C	45	45	—	58.4	—	1.484	0.0012-0.0022	0.0012-0.0024	0.3142	0.3140
3R-B and 3R-C	45	45	14.0	53.9	1.560	1.880	0.0016-0.0028	0.0016-0.0028	0.3140	0.3140
8R-C and 18R-C	45	45	15.2	50.6	1.480	1.640	0.0010-0.0022	0.0014-0.0030	0.3140	0.3136
2M	45	45	11.9	68.0①	1.535	1.654②	0.0006-0.0018	0.0014-0.0030	0.3153	0.3121
4M	45	45	25.7	63.1③	1.504	1.642④	0.0006-0.0018	0.0010-0.0024	0.3146	0.3140
F	45	45	—	132.0	—	1.324	0.0010-0.0026	0.0014-0.0028	0.3141	0.3137

▲ Valve guides are removable

① Exhaust valve spring test pressure: inner—11.5 lbs; outer —66.6 lbs

② Exhaust valve installed height: inner—1.535 in.; outer—1.661 in.

③ Exhaust valve spring test pressure: inner—24.6 lbs; outer —59.4 lbs

④ Exhaust valve installed height: inner—1.520 in.; outer—1.657 in.

TORQUE SPECIFICATIONS

All readings in ft lbs

Engine Type	Cylinder Head Bolts	Rod Bearing Bolts	Main Bearing Bolts	Crankshaft Pulley Bolt	Flywheel to Crankshaft Bolts	MANIFOLD Intake	MANIFOLD Exhaust
K-C and 3K-C	39.0-47.7	28.9-37.6	39.0-47.7	29.0-43.0	39.0-48.0	14.0-22.0①	
2T-C	52.0-63.5	28.9-36.1	52.0-63.5	28.9-43.3	41.9-47.7	7.2-11.6	7.2-11:6
3R-B and 3R-C	80.0-85.0	43.0-51.0	75.0-80.0	31.0-41.0	43.0-49.0	18.0-30.0	14.0-22.0
8R-C	75.0-85.0	42.0-48.0	72.0-80.0	43.0-51.0	42.0-49.0	20.0-25.0①	
18R-C	72.0-82.0	39.0-48.0	69.0-83.0	43.0-51.0	51.0-58.0	30.0-35.0①	
2M	②	25.0-30.0	72.0-79.0	43.0-51.0	41.0-46.0③	22.0-29.0④	18.0-25.0⑤
4M	⑥	30.0-36.0	72.0-78.0	69.0-76.0	41.0-46.0⑦	17.0-21.0④	12.0-17.0⑤
F	83.0-98.0	35.0-55.0	90.0-108.0⑧	—	43.0-51.0	14.0-22.0①	

① Intake and exhaust manifolds combined
② 8mm bolts—11-15 ft lbs
13mm bolts—54-61 ft lbs
③ Flex-plate (automatic) 14-22 ft lbs
④ Intake manifold stud bolt—14-18 ft lbs
⑤ Exhaust manifold stud bolt—6-7 ft lbs
⑥ 8mm bolts—7-12 ft lbs
10mm bolts—54-61 ft lbs
⑦ Flex-plate (automatic) 11-16 ft lbs
⑧ Rear bearing—76-94 ft lbs

Torque Sequences

Cylinder Head

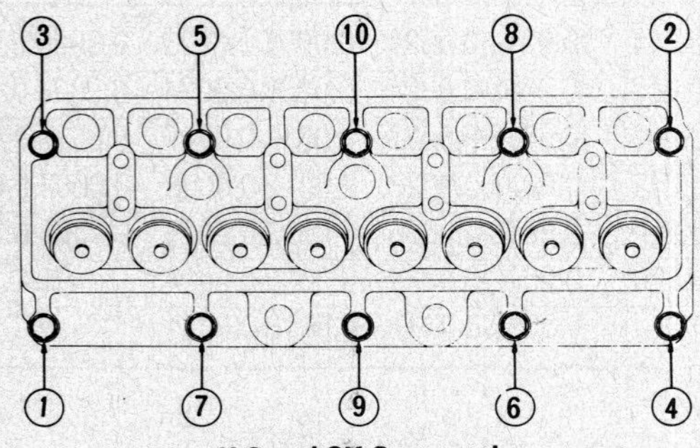

K-C and 3K-C removal

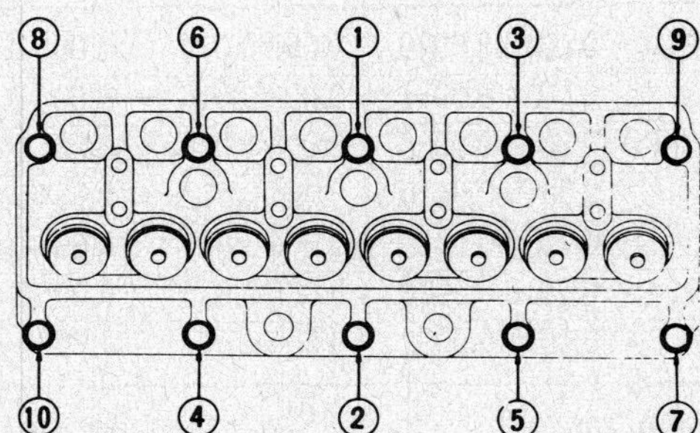

K-C and 3K-C installation

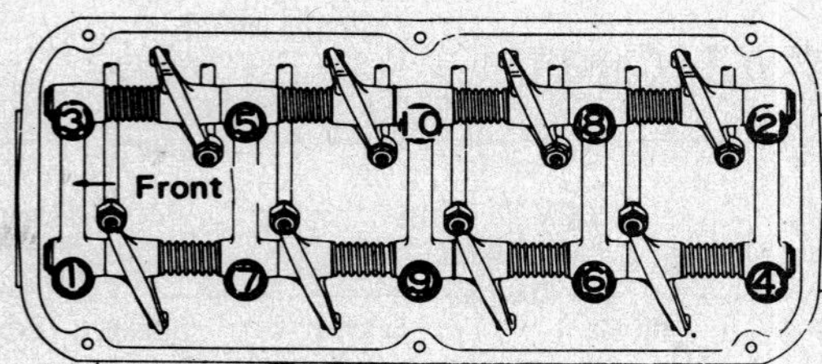

2T-C removal

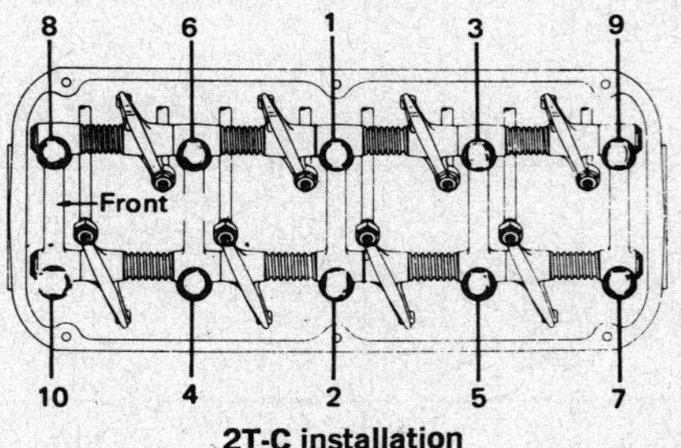

2T-C installation

3R-B and 3R-C removal

3R-B and 3R-C installation

8R-C and 18R-C removal

8R-C and 18R-C installation

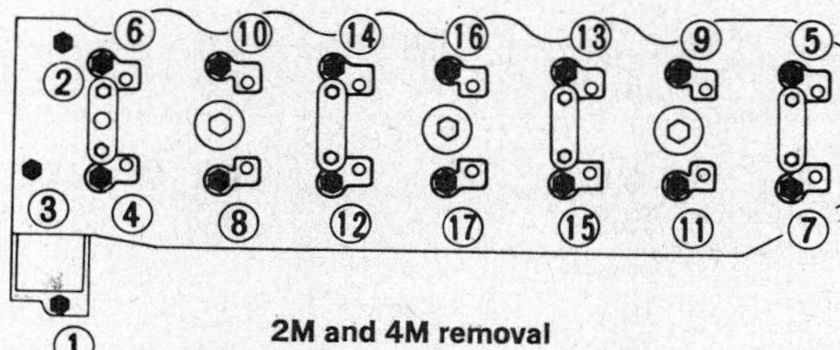

2M and 4M removal

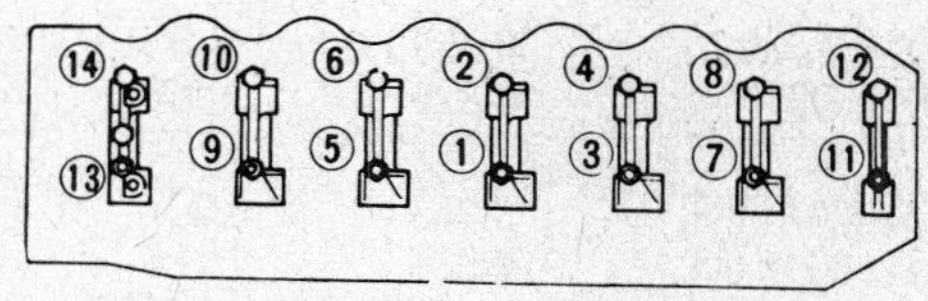

2M and 4M installation

F removal

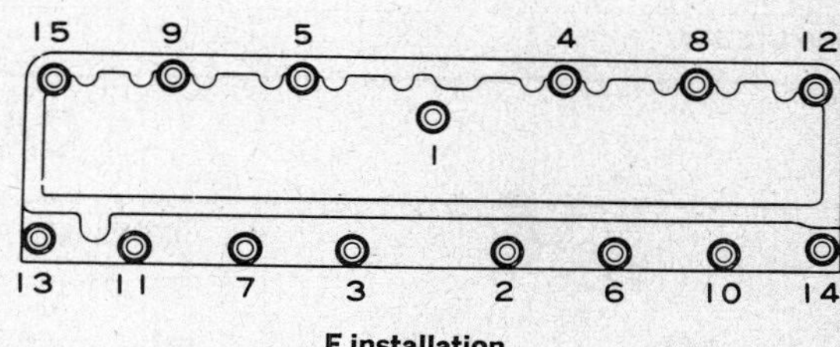

F installation

Rocker Arms

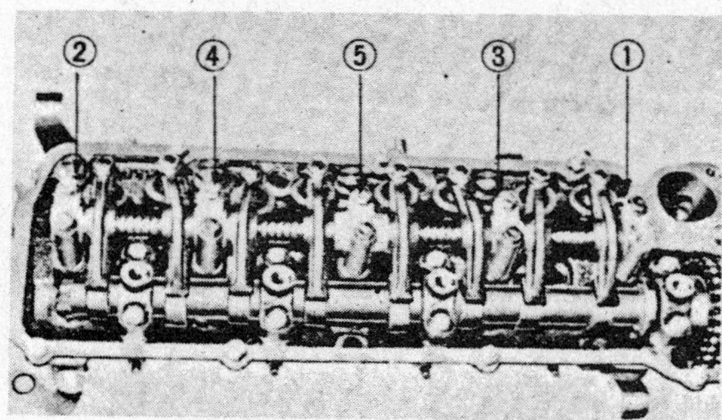

8R-C and 18R-C removal

8R-C and 18R-C installation

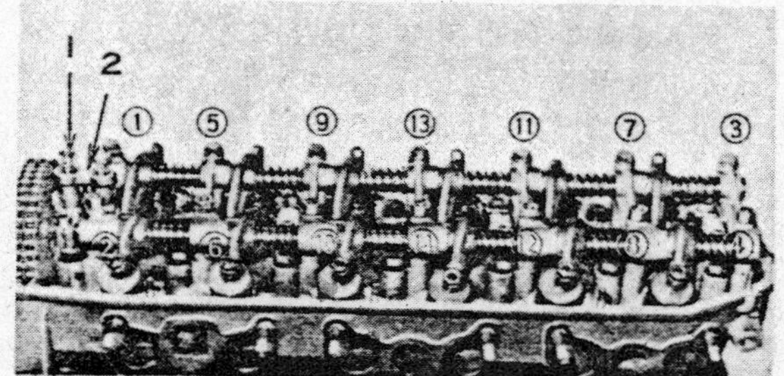

2M and 4M removal—remove the union bolt (1) and the union (2) first.

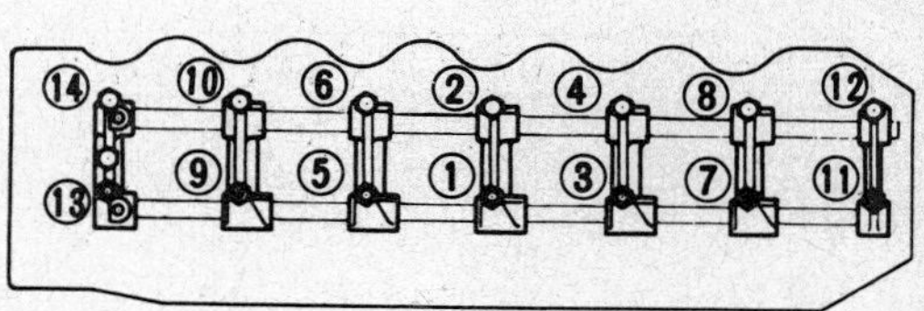

2M and 4M installation

BRAKE SPECIFICATIONS

All measurements are given in inches.

Model	Master Cylinder Bore	Wheel Cylinder or Caliper Piston Bore — Front Disc	Wheel Cylinder or Caliper Piston Bore — Front Drum	Wheel Cylinder or Caliper Piston Bore — Rear Drum	Brake Disc or Drum Diameter — Front Disc	Brake Disc or Drum Diameter — Front Drum	Brake Disc or Drum Diameter — Rear Drum	New Pad or Lining Thickness
Corolla								
1100	0.626	—	0.750	0.687	—	7.9	7.9	0.16
1200	0.626	1.750	0.750	0.687	7.9	7.9	7.9	0.16
1600	0.813	1.879	—	0.748	9.1	—	9.0	0.35
Carina and Celica	0.813	1.874	—	0.748	9.1	—	9.0	0.35
Corona								
RT40 Series	0.750	—	0.814	0.689	—	9.0	9.0	0.20
1900/2000	0.876	2.002	—	0.814	9.1	—	9.0	0.55
Mark II								
1900/2000 (4 cyl)	0.873	0.877	—	0.687	9.6	—	9.0	0.39
2300/2600 (6 cyl)	0.937	2.126	—	0.875	10.5	—	9.0	0.59
Crown								
2300	0.740	2.110	—	0.875	10.5	—	9.1	0.66
2600	0.937	2.126	—	0.750	10.5	—	9.1	0.59
Hi-Lux	1.001	—	1.123	1.000	—	9.1	9.1	0.19
Land Cruiser	0.997				—	11.4	11.4	0.26

CAPACITIES

Model	Year	Crankcase (qt) w/filter	Crankcase (qt) w/o filter	Transmission (qt) Manual	Transmission (qt) Automatic	Drive Axle (pt)	Fuel Tank (gal)	Cooling System w/heater (qt)
Corolla								
1100	1968-69	3.5	2.6	1.8	—	2.0	9.5	5.0
1200	1970-73	3.5	2.9	1.8	5.0	2.0	12.0①	5.6
1600	1971-73	4.2	3.3	1.6	5.0	2.0	12.0①	6.8
Carina								
1600	1972-73	4.2	3.3	1.6	5.0	2.0	13.2	7.2
Corona								
3R-B and 3R-C	1966-69	5.1	4.2	2.1	7.8	2.2	12.0	7.4
1900	1970-71	5.6	4.6	2.1	7.4	2.2	13.2	8.4
2000	1972-73	5.2	4.2	2.1	1.4	2.2	13.2	8.4
Mark II								
1900	1969-71	5.3	4.3	2.1	7.4	2.2	13.7	7.8
2000	1972 (early)	5.6	4.6	2.1	7.4	2.2	13.7	7.8
6 cyl	1972-73	5.6	4.6	1.8	6.8	2.6	15.9②	11.6
Celica								
1900	1971	5.6	4.6	2.1	—	2.0	13.0	8.4
2000	1972-73	5.6	4.6	2.1	7.4⑦	2.0	13.0	8.4
Crown								
2300	1968-71	5.6	4.6	2.1	6.8	2.6	17.2③	10.8
2600	1972	5.6	4.6	1.8	7.4	2.6	18.5④	11.6
Hi-Lux								
1900	1970-71	5.3	4.3	1.8	—	2.2	12.1	8.8
2000	1972-73	5.0	4.0	1.8	7.4	2.2	12.1	8.2
Land Cruiser								
2-dr	1970-73	9.0	7.4	1.8⑤	—	5.2⑥	18.4	17.7
4-dr	1970-73	9.0	7.4	1.8⑤	—	5.2⑥	23.8	17.7

① Station wagon—11.0 gal
② Station wagon—15.8 gal
③ Station wagon—15.8 gal
④ Station wagon—15.8 gal
⑤ Transfer case capacity—1.8 qts
⑥ Front and rear differential capacities are both the same
⑦ Automatic available in 1973

WHEEL ALIGNMENT

Model	CASTER Range (deg)	CASTER Pref Setting (deg)	CAMBER Range (deg)	CAMBER Pref Setting (deg)	Toe-in (in.)	Steering Axis Inclination	WHEEL PIVOT RATIO (deg) Inner Wheel	WHEEL PIVOT RATIO (deg) Outer Wheel
Corolla								
1100	½N-1P	½P	1½P-2½P	2P	0.08-0.24	6P-7P	37-38	32-33
1200	7½P-8½P	8½P	½P-1½P	½P	0.04-0.20	7½P-8½P	38½-41½	30-36
1600	7½P-8½P	8½P	½P-1½P	½P	0.04-0.20	7½P-8½P	38½-41½	27½-33½
Carina & Celica	½P-1½P	1P	0-1½P	1P	0.20-0.28	7½P	—	—
Corona	0-1P	½P	1P-2P	1½P	0.16-0.24①	7P	38½②	31②
Mark II/4	1P-2P	1½P	1P-2P	1P	0.16-0.24	7P	40	32½
Mark II/6	0-1P	½P	½P-1½P	1P	0.16-0.24	7P	36½	32½
Crown 2300	1N-0	½N	0-1P	½P	0.12-0.20	7½P	38	29½
Crown 2600	1N-½P	½N	0-1P	½P	0.12-0.20	7½P	38	29
Hi-Lux	1N-C	½N	½P-1½P	1P	0.24	7P	39	31½
Land Cruiser								
2 door	½P-1½P	1P	½P-1½P	1P	0.12-0.20	9½P	32	27
Wagon	½P-1½P	1P	½P-1½P	1P	0.12-0.20	9½P	30	23

P Positive
N Negative
① 1966-69 Corona—0.04-0.12 in.
② 1966-69 Corona: Inner—38°; Outer—30°

BATTERY AND STARTER SPECIFICATIONS

Engine Type	BATTERY Amp. Hour Capy.	BATTERY Volts	BATTERY Term. Grnd.	STARTERS Lock Test Amps	STARTERS Lock Test Volts	STARTERS Lock Test Torque (ft lbs)	STARTERS No-Load Test Amps	STARTERS No-Load Test Volts	STARTERS No-Load Test Rpm	Brush Minimum Tension (oz)	Brush Minimum Length (in.)
K-C and 3K-C	48④	12	Neg	450	8.5	8	55	11	3,500	21	0.51
2T-C	50	12	Neg	— Not Recommended —			— Not Recommended —			21	0.47
3R-B and 3K-C	50	12	Neg	550	7.7	10	45	11	6,000	21	0.47
8R-C and 18R-C	40①	12	Neg	550	7.7	10	45	11	6,000	21	0.47
2M	60②	12	Neg	600	7.0	13	50	11	5,000	21	0.47
4M	50③	12	Neg	600	7.0	13	50	11	5,000	21	0.47
F	50	12	Neg	430	7.3	11	45	11	3,500	21	0.51

① 50 AH—Celica and Hi-Lux
② 70 AH—Mark 11/6
③ 60 AH—with air conditioning
④ 32 AH—K-C engine
AH Amp Hour
Neg Negative

ALTERNATOR AND REGULATOR SPECIFICATIONS

	ALTERNATOR		REGULATOR						
				Field Relay			Regulator		
Engine Type	Manufacturer	Output (amps)	Manufacturer	Contact Spring Deflection (in.)	Point Gap (in.)	Volts to Close (in.)	Air Gap (in.)	Point Gap (in.)	Volts
K-C and 3K-C	Nippondenso	25	Nippondenso	0.008-0.024	0.016-0.047	4.5-5.8	0.012	0.010-0.018	13.8-14.8
2T-C	Nippondenso	40	Nippondenso	0.008-0.024	0.016-0.047	4.5-5.8	0.012	0.012-0.018	13.8-14.8
3R-B,3 R-C 8R-C and 18R-C	Nippondenso	40	Nippondenso	0.008-0.018	0.016-0.047	4.5-5.8	0.008	0.010-0.018	13.8-14.8
2M①	Nippondenso	40	Nippondenso	0.008-0.024	0.016-0.047	4.5-5.8	0.012	0.012-0.018	13.8-14.8
2M②	Nippondenso	45	Nippondenso	0.008-0.018	0.016-0.047	4.5-5.8	0.012	0.012-0.018	13.8-14.8
4M	Nippondenso	55	Nippondenso	0.008-0.024	0.016-0.047	4.5-5.8	0.012	0.008-0.024	13.8-14.8
F	Nippondenso	38	Nippondenso	—	—	4.5-5.8	—	0.001-0.018	13.6-14.8

① Crown—1968-71
② Mark II/6—1972

TIMING MARK LOCATIONS

Engine Type	Location	Type of mark
K-C, 3K-C and 2T-C	Crankshaft pulley	Notch and number scale
3R-B and 3R-C	Crankshaft pulley	Ball and pointer
8R-C and 18R-C	Crankshaft pulley	Pointer and painted slot
2M and 4M	Crankshaft pulley	Slot and number scale
F	Flywheel	Ball and pointer

AIR INJECTION SYSTEM DIAGNOSIS CHART

Problem	Cause	Cure
1. Noisy drive belt	1a Loose belt	1a Tighten belt
	1b Seized pump	1b Replace
2. Noisy pump	2a Leaking hose	2a Trace and fix leak
	2b Loose hose	2b Tighten hose clamp
	2c Hose contacting other parts	2c Reposition hose
	2d Diverter or check valve failure	2d Replace
	2e Pump mounting loose	2e Tighten securing bolts
	2g Defective pump	2g Replace
3. No air supply	3a Loose belt	3a Tighten belt
	3b Leak in hose or at fitting	3b Trace and fix leak
	3c Defective anti-backfire valve	3c Replace
	3d Defective check valve	3d Replace
	3e Defective pump	3e Replace
4. Exhaust backfire	4a Vacuum or air leaks	4a Trace and fix leak
	4b Defective anti-backfire valve	4b Replace
	4c Sticking choke	4c Service choke
	4d Choke setting rich	4d Adjust choke

EVAPORATIVE EMISSION CONTROL SYSTEM USAGE

Year	Model	Type of EEC system used	Gas Gap Type	Purge Control valve	Vacuum Switching valve	Thermal Expansion Tank and Fuel Tank
1970	Corolla	Case	Sealed①	Yes	No	Separate
	Corona	Case	Safety	No	Yes	Separate
	Mark II	Case	Safety	No	Yes	Separate
	Crown	Case	Safety	Yes	No	Separate
	Hi-Lux	Case	Sealed①	No	Yes	Separate
	Land Cruiser	Case	Sealed①	No	Yes	Separate
1971	Corolla	Case	Sealed①	Yes②	Yes③	Integral④
	Corona	Case	Safety	No	Yes	Separate
	Mark II	Case	Safety	No	Yes	Separate
	Celica	Case	Safety	No	Yes	Separate
	Crown	Case	Safety	Yes	No	Separate
	Hi-Lux	Case	Safety	No	Yes	Separate
	Land Cruiser	Case	Safety	No	Yes	Separate
1972	Corolla	Canister	Safety	No	Yes	Integral④
	All other Models	Canister	Safety	No	Yes	Separate
1973	All Models⑤	Canister	Safety	No	Yes	Integral

① Uses separate breather valve
② 3K-C engine only
③ 2T-C engine only
④ Station wagon uses thermal expansion tank
⑤ Mark II wagon uses separate thermal expansion tank

FLOAT LEVEL ADJUSTMENTS

Engine	Gauge Type	FLOAT RAISED Measure distance between:	Gap (in.)	Gauge Type	FLOAT LOWERED Measure distance between:	Gap (in.)
K-C and 3K-C	Special	Float end and air horn	0.260	Special	Lowest point of float and upper side of gauge	1.89
2T-C	Block	Float tip and air horn	0.138	Wire	Needle valve bushing pin and float lip	0.047
3R-B	Special	Float end and air horn	0.500	Special	Float end and air horn	1.00
3R-C	Special	Float end and air horn	0.366	Special	Float end and air horn	0.867
8R-C	Special	Float and air horn	0.370	Wire	Needle valve bushing pin and float tab	0.039
18R-C	Special	Float and air horn	0.200	Wire	Needle valve bushing pin and float tab	0.039
2M and 4M	Special	Float end and air horn	0.370	Special	Float end and air horn	0.910
F	Special	Float end and air horn gasket surface	0.230	Special	Float end and air horn gasket surface	0.800

FAST IDLE ADJUSTMENT

Engine	Throttle Valve to bore clearance (in.)	Primary throttle angle (deg)	To adjust fast idle:
K-C	0.040	26—from closed	Bend the fast idle lever
3K-C	0.040	—	Bend the fast idle lever
2T-C	0.032	—	Turn the fast idle adjusting screw
3R-B	0.020	—	Turn the fast idle adjusting screw
3R-C	0.040	12—from closed	Turn the fast idle adjusting screw
8R-C	0.029	11—from closed	Turn the fast idle adjusting screw
18R-C	0.041	13—from closed	Turn the fast idle adjusting screw
2M	—	24—from closed	Turn the fast idle adjusting screw
4M	—	16—from closed	Turn the fast idle adjusting screw
F	—	30—from closed	Bend the fast idle lever

— Not available

CHOKE UNLOADER ADJUSTMENT

Engine	CHOKE VALVE ANGLE (deg) Throttle valve fully closed	From closed to fully open	Throttle valve open (total)	To Adjust Bend:
2T-C	20	27	47	Fast idle cam follower or choke shaft lip
3R-B and 3R-C	30	20	50	Fast idle cam follower or choke shaft tab
8R-C	32	19	51	Fast idle cam follower or choke shaft tab
18R-C	—	27	—	Fast idle cam follower or choke shaft tab
2M and 4M	15	20	35	Fast idle lever

— Not available

CLUTCH TORQUE SPECIFICATIONS

Model	Release Fork (ft lbs)	Retracting Spring Bolts (ft lbs)	Clutch Cover-to-Flywheel Bolts (ft lbs)
Corolla 1100	—	3.0-50	7.0-11.0
Corolla 1200	13.7-22.4	—	10.9-15.9
Corolla 1600 and Carina	—	10.9-15.9	10.9-15.9
Corona	13.7-22.4	10.9-15.9	7.2-11.6
Mark II/4	14-22	—	11
Mark II/6	—	2.9-5.1	10.8-15.9
Crown 2300	—	3-5	6-9.5
Crown 2600	—	2.9-5.1	7.2-11.6
Hi-Lux	—	3-5	7-11
Land Cruiser	—	22-32	11-16

— Not available

CLUTCH PEDAL FREE-PLAY ADJUSTMENTS

Model	Master Cylinder piston to pushrod clearance (in.)	Release cylinder to release fork free-play (in.)	Pedal free-play (in.)
Corolla	0.02	1.00-1.40	1.00-1.80⑥
Carina	0.04-0.12	0.08-0.14	1.00-1.75
Corona RT40 series	④	0.15	0.98
Corona 1900 and 2000	0.02-0.12	0.08-0.14	1.00-1.75
Mark II/4	①	0.08-0.14	0.79-1.58
Mark II/6	0.02-0.12	0.08-0.12	1.20-1.80
Celica	0.04-0.12	0.08-0.14	1.00-1.75
Crown 2300	0.02-0.10	0.08-0.14	1.40-2.00
Crown 2600	0.02-0.12	0.08-0.14③	1.40-2.20
Hi-Lux	④	0.145	1.30
Land Cruiser—2-dr	⑤	0.120	1.00
Land Cruiser—Station Wagon	⑤	0.210	1.38

① Not adjustable
② Measured at clutch pedal
③ Adjustable type only
④ Adjust by feel
⑤ Adjust so that pushrod pin will fit through clevis
⑥ Corolla 1100—0.6-1.2 in.

REAR SUSPENSION TORQUE SPECIFICATIONS

(ft lbs)

Model	U-bolt Retaining nuts	Shock Absorber Retaining nuts	Shackle Retaining nuts	Bracket Pin
Corolla	22.0-32.0	25.0-40.0	14.5-21.5	14.5-21.5
Corona	29.0-39.8	25.0-40.0	—	—
Mark II/4—All and 6 Wagon	29.0-40.0①	25.0-40.0	—②	—③
Hi-Lux	47.0-65.0	25.0-40.0	54.0-79.0	54.0-79.0
Land Cruiser	50.0-70.0	25.0-40.0	36.0-58.0	36.0-58.0
Crown 2300—Wagon	62.0-84.0	25.0-40.0	36.0-50.0	36.0-50.0

① Mark II Station Wagon—47-65 ft lbs (4 cyl and 6 cyl)
② Mark II/6 Station Wagon—36.2-50.6 ft lbs
③ Mark II/6 Station Wagon—21.7-32.5 ft lbs
— Not available

SHOCK ABSORBER TIGHTENING TORQUE

Model	Upper Mounting (ft lbs)	Lower Mounting (ft lbs)
Corolla	—	25-40①
Carina	14-22	26-33
Corona	—	25-40
Mark II/4	—	25-40
Mark II/6		
Sedan and Coupe	14-22	26-33
Station Wagon	36-58	14-22
Crown 2300	11-16	22-23
Crown 2600		
Sedan and Coupe	11-16	22-33
Station Wagon	11-16	36-51
Hi-Lux	25-40	25-40
Land Cruiser	—	25-40

① Station wagon (KE16L)—11-15 ft lbs
— Not available

FRONT SPRING INSTALLATION SPECIFICATONS

Model	Replacement Strut Length (in.)	TORQUE SPECIFICATIONS (ft lbs) Ball Joint-to-Steering Knuckle	Strut-to-Control arm	Lower Control Arm-to-Member	Strut-to-Frame
Mark II/4	18.70	51-65	50-65	32-43	54-80
Mark II/6	14.16	51-65	51-65	65-87	43-54
Crown 2300	16.00	66-96	50-65	75-110	70-110
Crown 2600	16.14	65-94	50-65	72-108	69-108

STEERNG LINKAGE TORQUE SPECIFICATIONS

(ft lbs)

Model	Tie rod ends-to-knuckle arms	Pitman arm-to-sector shaft	Idler arm support-to-frame
Corolla 1100/1200	22-32	50-80	7-11
Corolla 1200/1600	36-51	36-58	22-32
Carina and Celica	36-51	72-101	25-36
Corona	36-51	80-101①	25-36
Mark II	36-51	80-101	29-40
Crown 2300	37-52	80-90	36-51
Crown 2600	54-80	80-101	36-51
Hi-Lux	36-51	80-90	25-36

① 1966-70 Corona—87 ft lbs

BRAKE DISC AND PAD SPECIFICATIONS

Model	New disc thickness	Disc service limit thickness	Run-out limit	Pad thickness limit
Corolla	—	0.35	0.006	0.22
Carina and Celica	0.39	0.35	0.006	0.22
Corona	0.39	0.35	0.006	0.35
Mark II/4	0.39	0.37	0.006	0.08
Mark II/6	0.49	0.45	0.006	0.28
Crown 2300	0.46	0.40	0.006	0.40
Crown 2600	0.49	0.45	0.006	0.27

— Not available

Wiring Diagrams

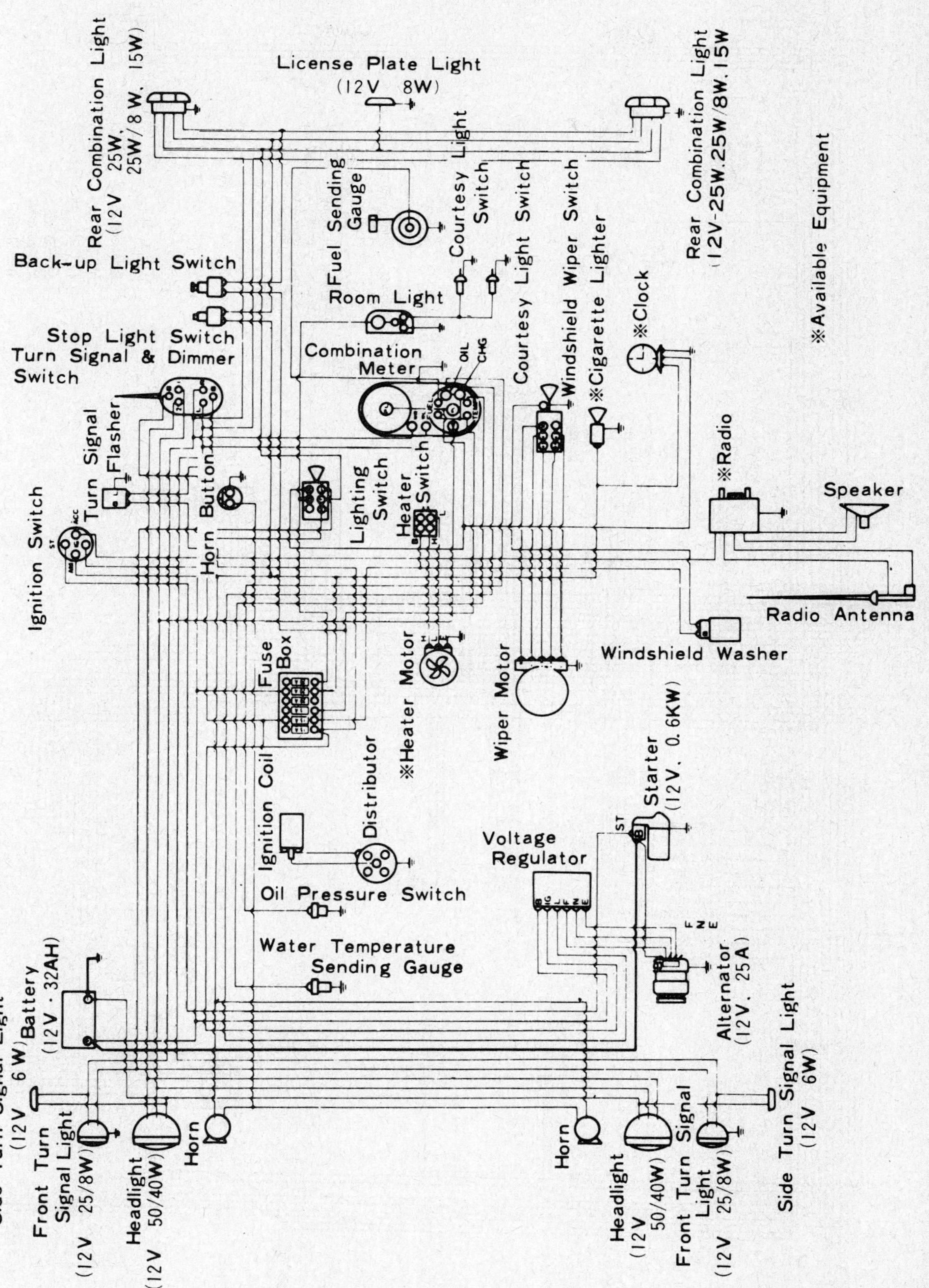

Corolla 1100 and 1200 1968-70 (early)

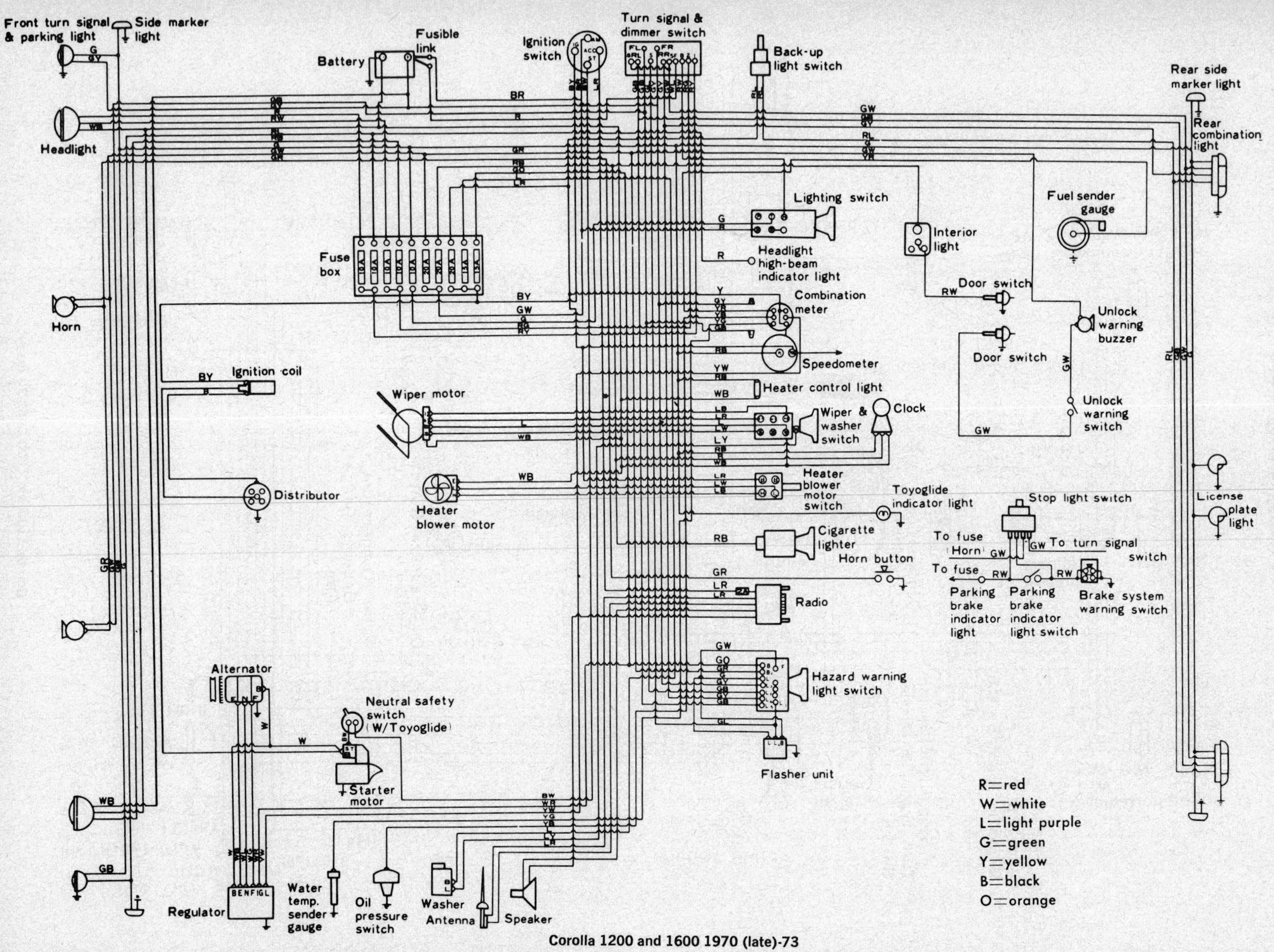

Corolla 1200 and 1600 1970 (late)-73

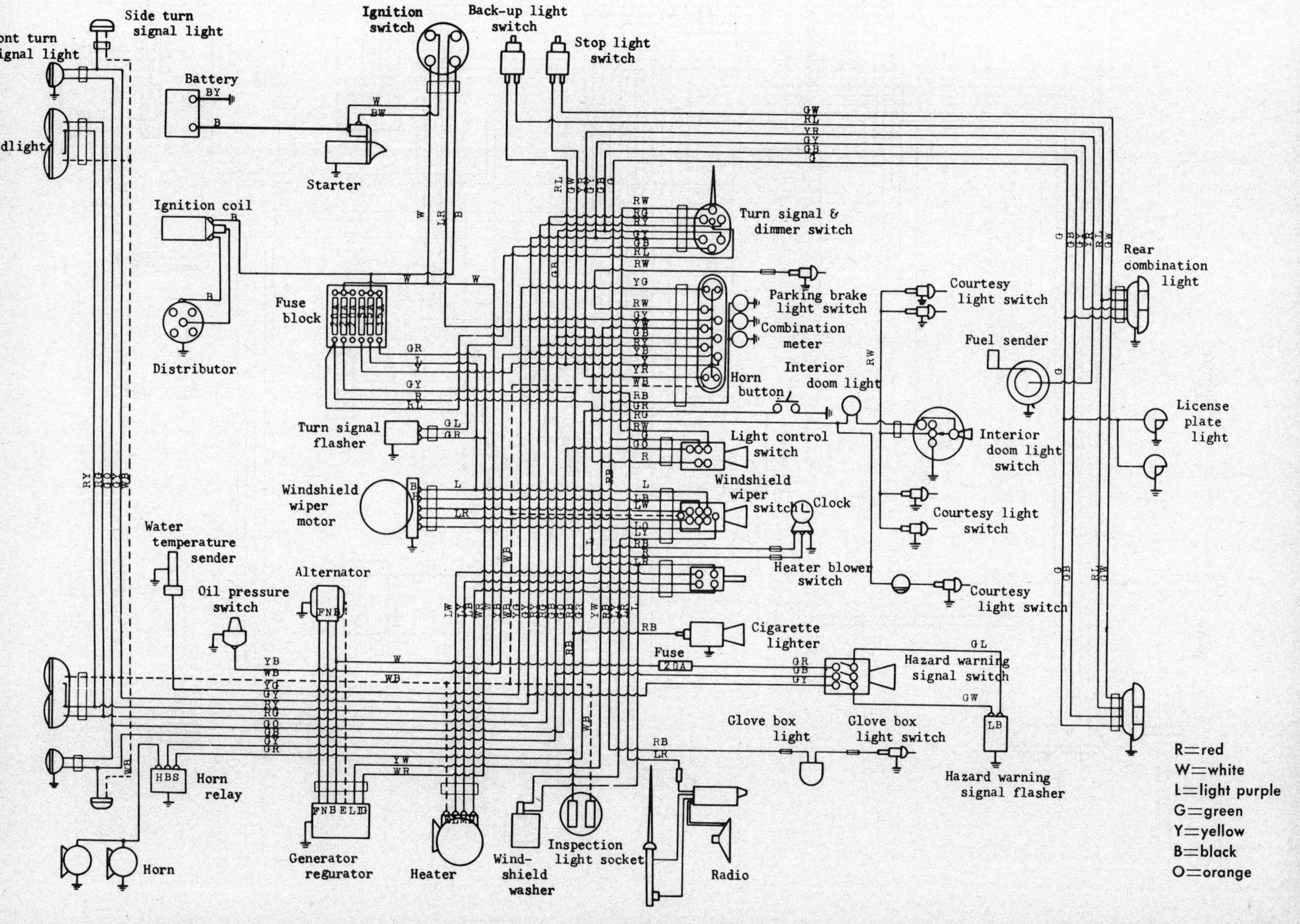

Corona 1966-70 (early)

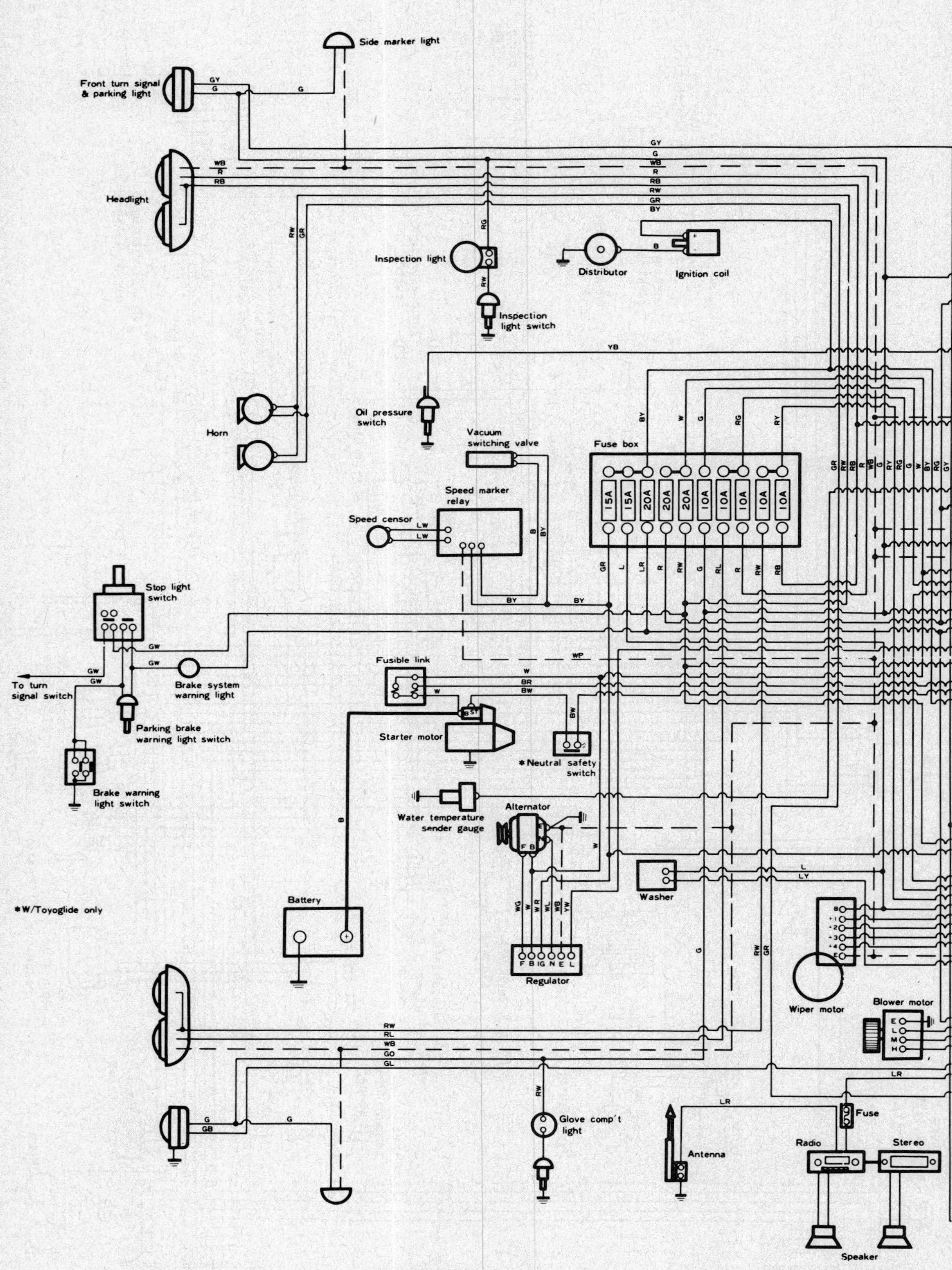

Corona 1970-73

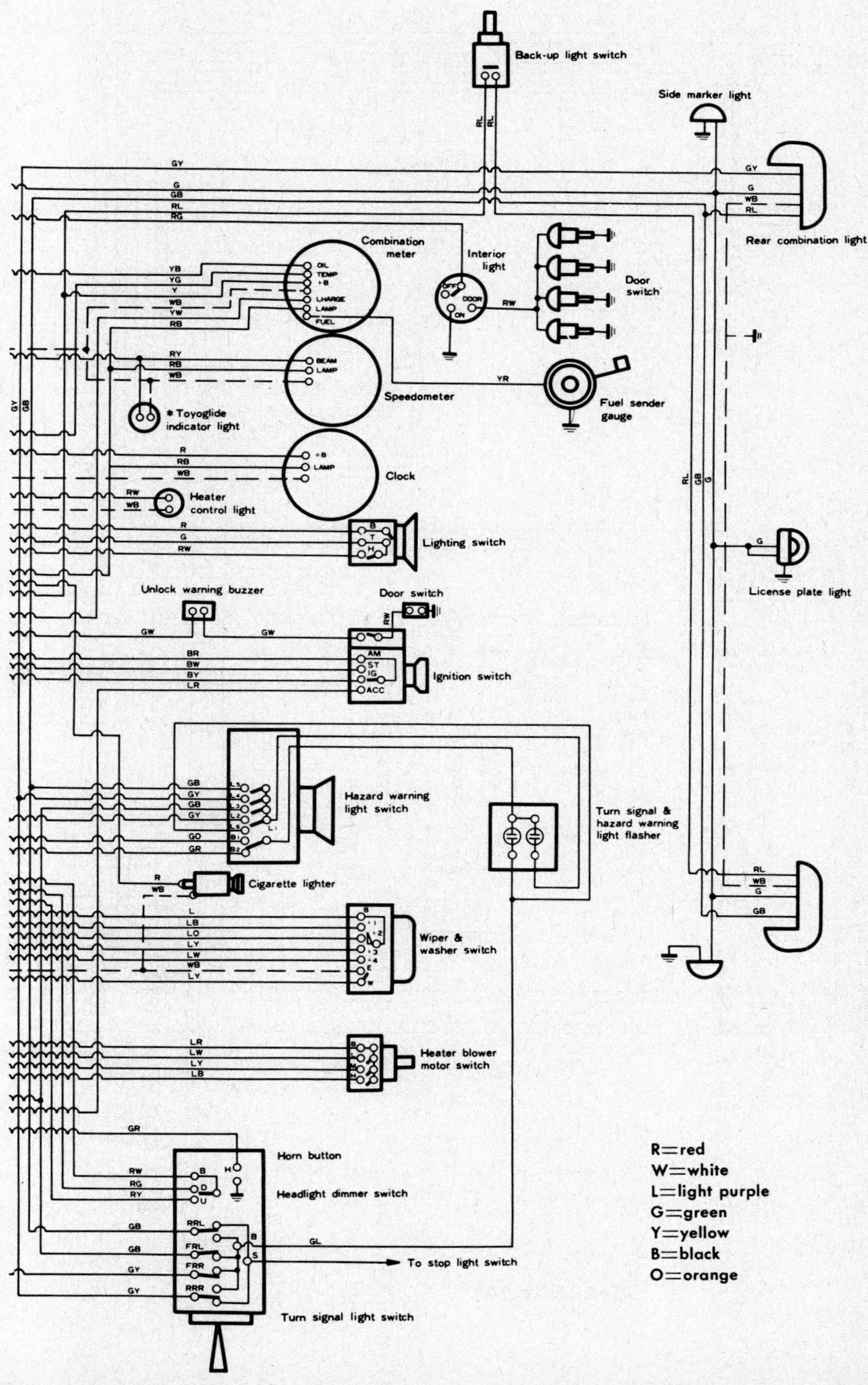

R=red
W=white
L=light purple
G=green
Y=yellow
B=black
O=orange

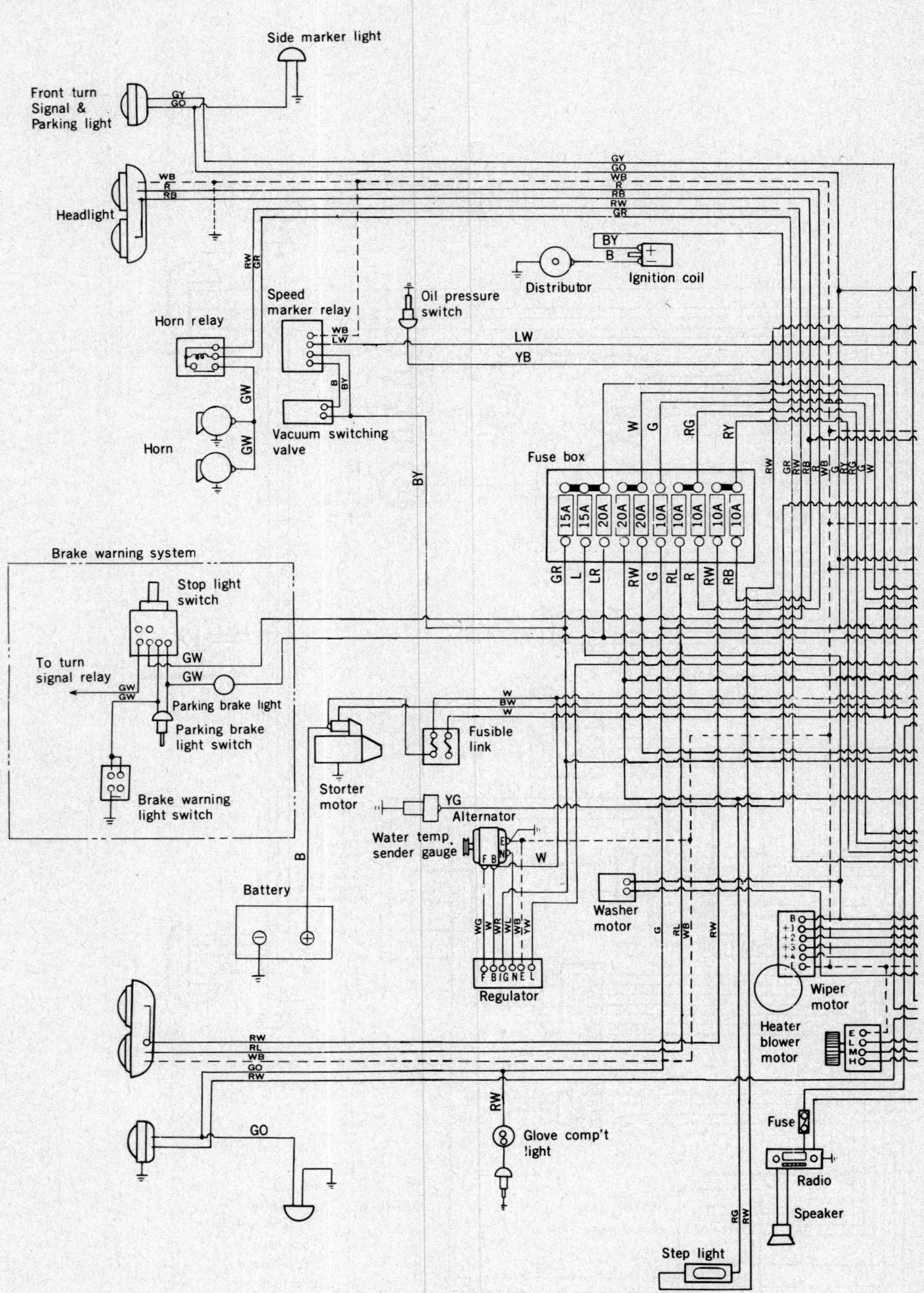

Mark II/4 1969-72

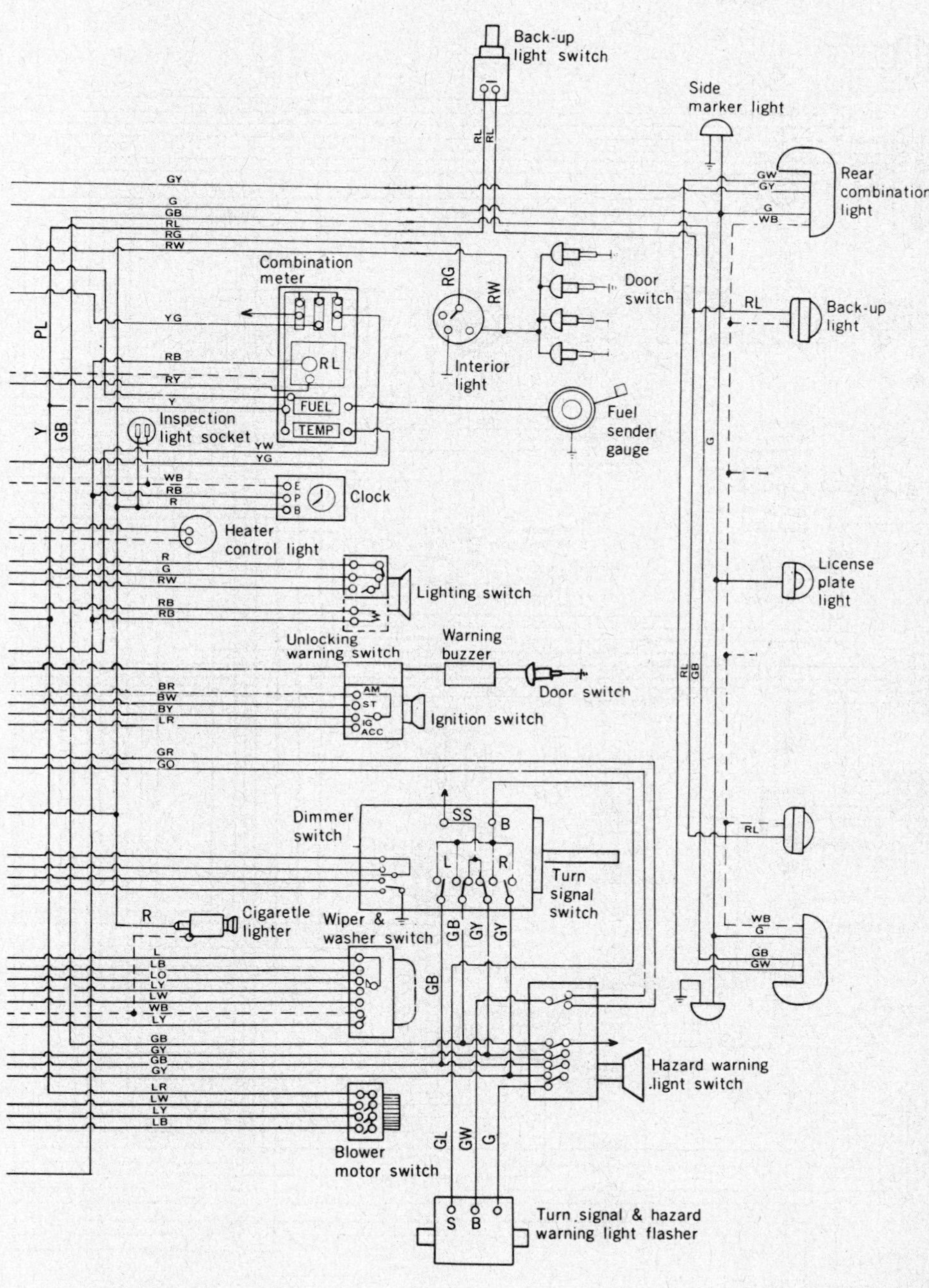

R=red
W=white
L=light purple
G=green
Y=yellow
B=black
O=orange

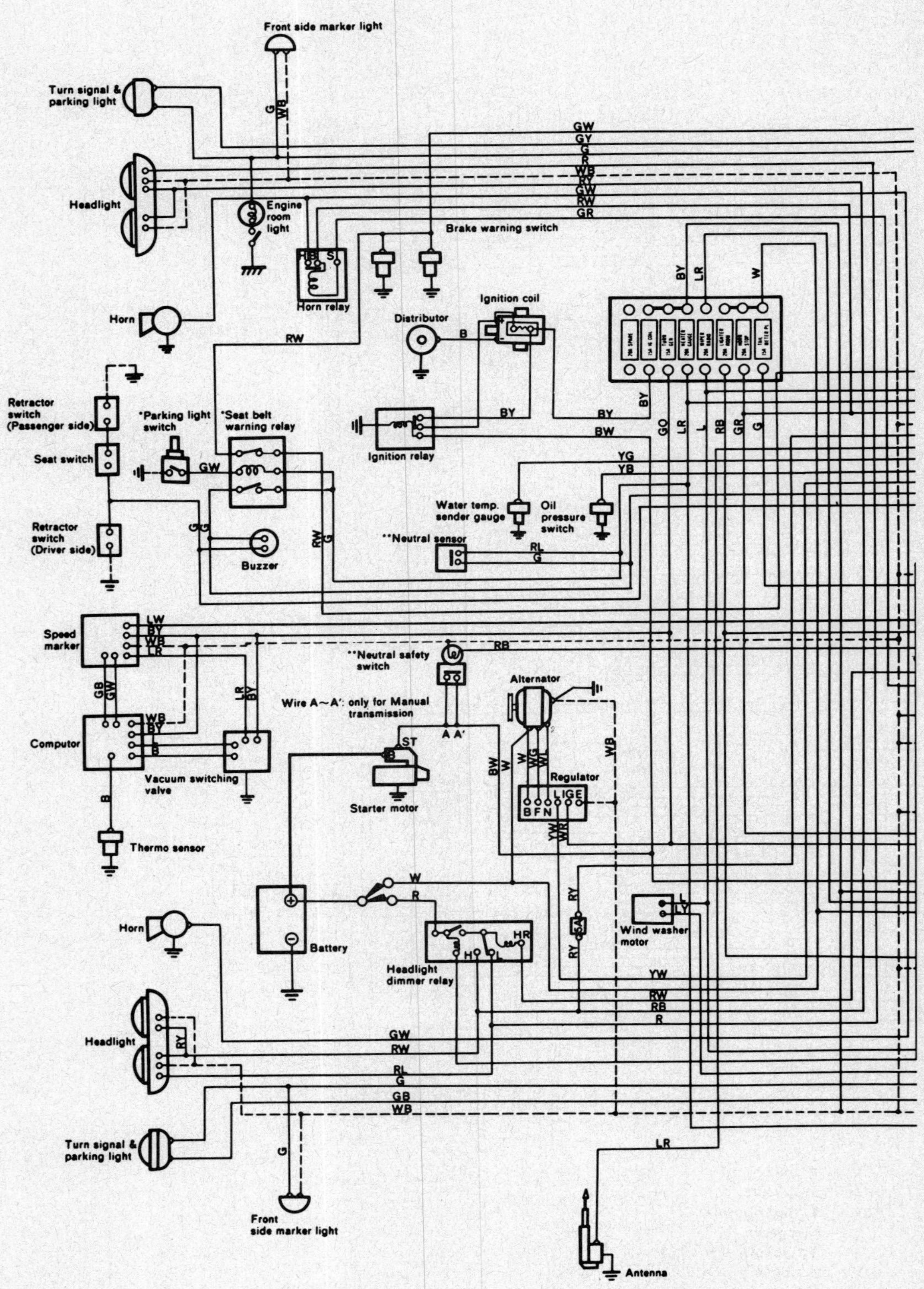

Mark II/6 1972-73

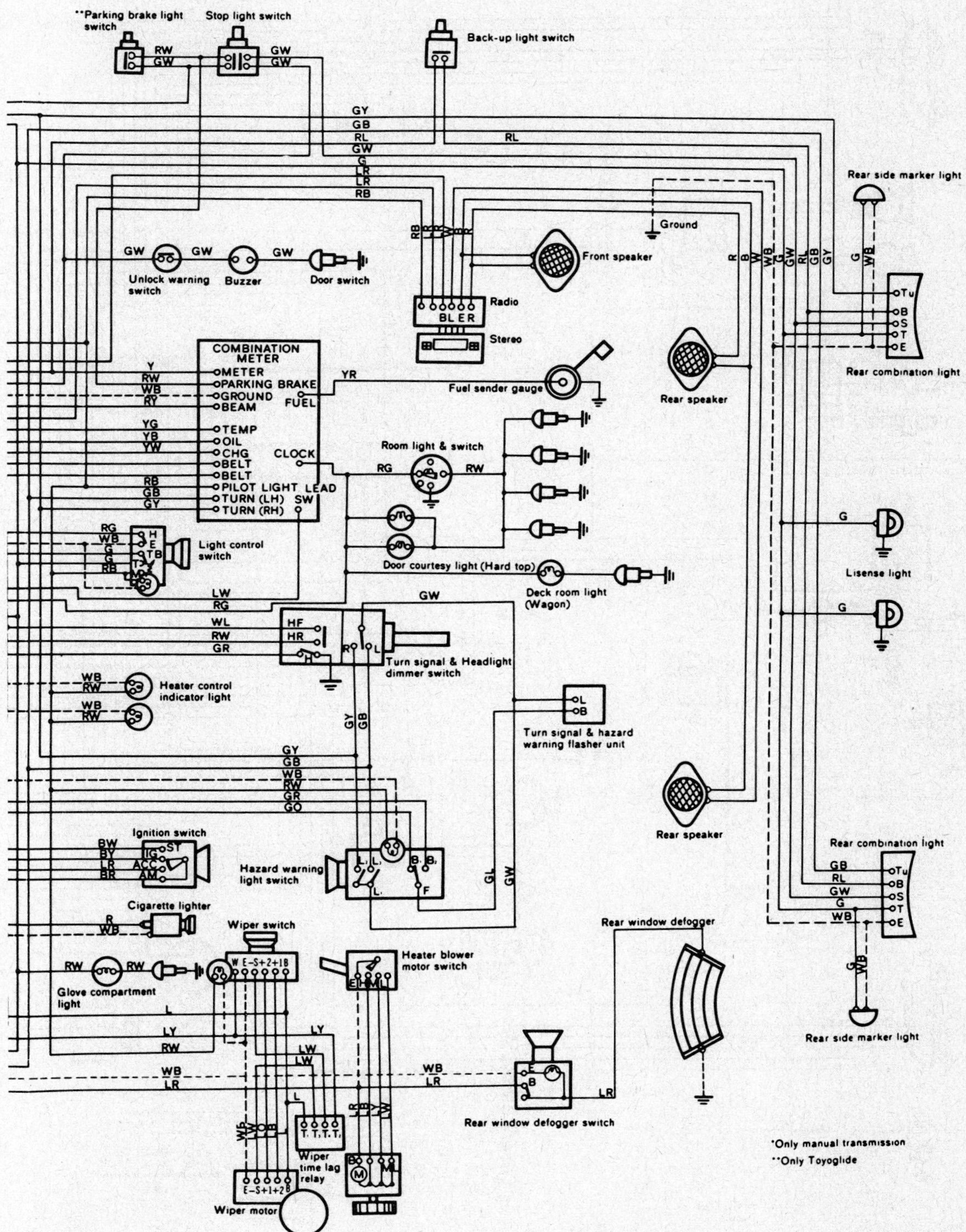

**Parking brake light switch
Stop light switch
Back-up light switch
Rear side marker light
Ground
Front speaker
Unlock warning switch
Buzzer
Door switch
Radio
Stereo
Rear combination light
COMBINATION METER
METER
PARKING BRAKE
GROUND
BEAM
FUEL
TEMP
OIL
CHG
BELT
BELT
PILOT LIGHT
TURN (LH)
TURN (RH)
CLOCK
LEAD
Fuel sender gauge
Rear speaker
Room light & switch
Light control switch
Door courtesy light (Hard top)
Deck room light (Wagon)
Lisense light
Turn signal & Headlight dimmer switch
Heater control indicator light
Turn signal & hazard warning flasher unit
Rear speaker
Ignition switch
Hazard warning light switch
Rear combination light
Cigarette lighter
Wiper switch
Rear window defogger
Heater blower motor switch
Glove compartment light
Rear side marker light
Rear window defogger switch
Wiper time lag relay
Wiper motor
*Only manual transmission
**Only Toyoglide

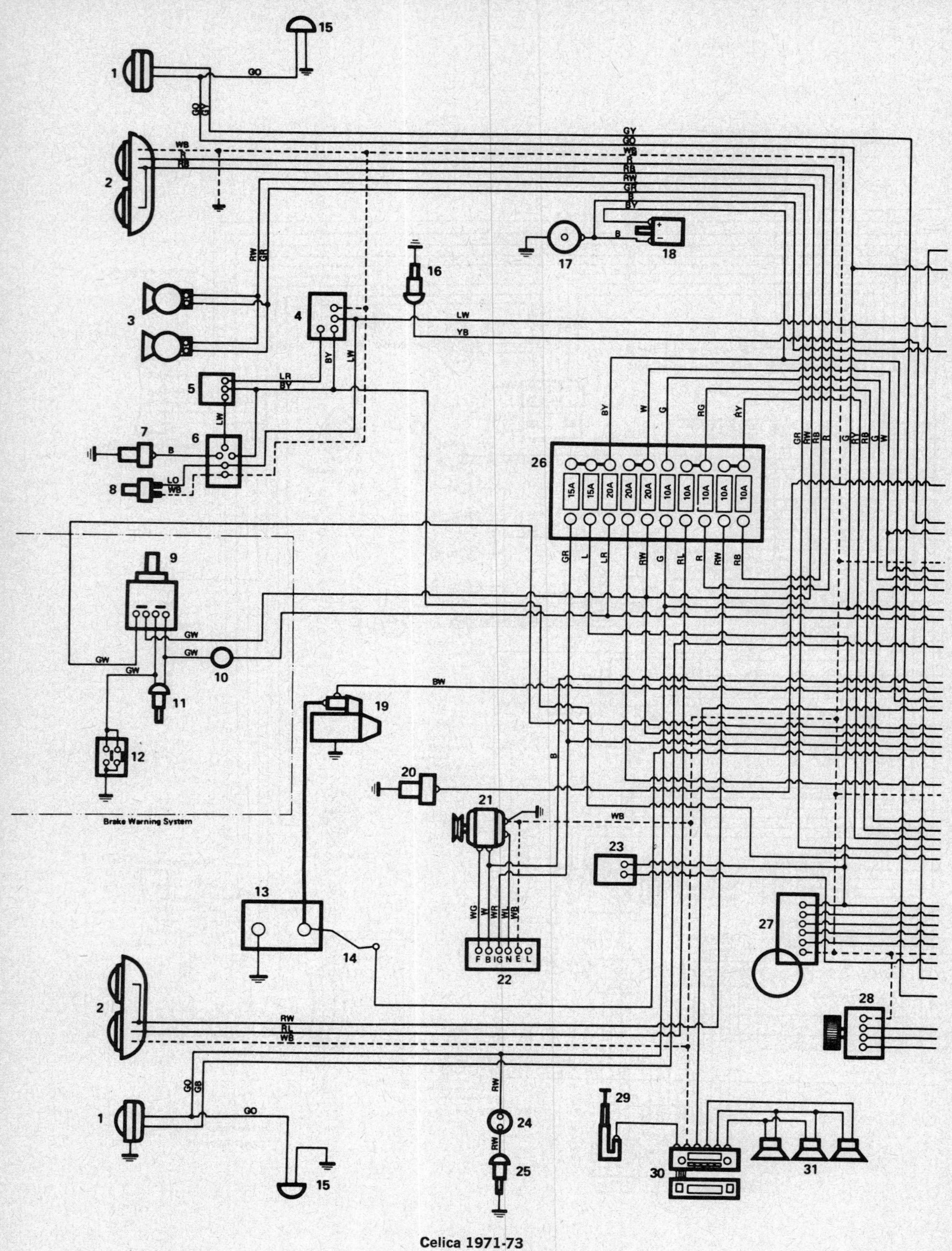

Celica 1971-73

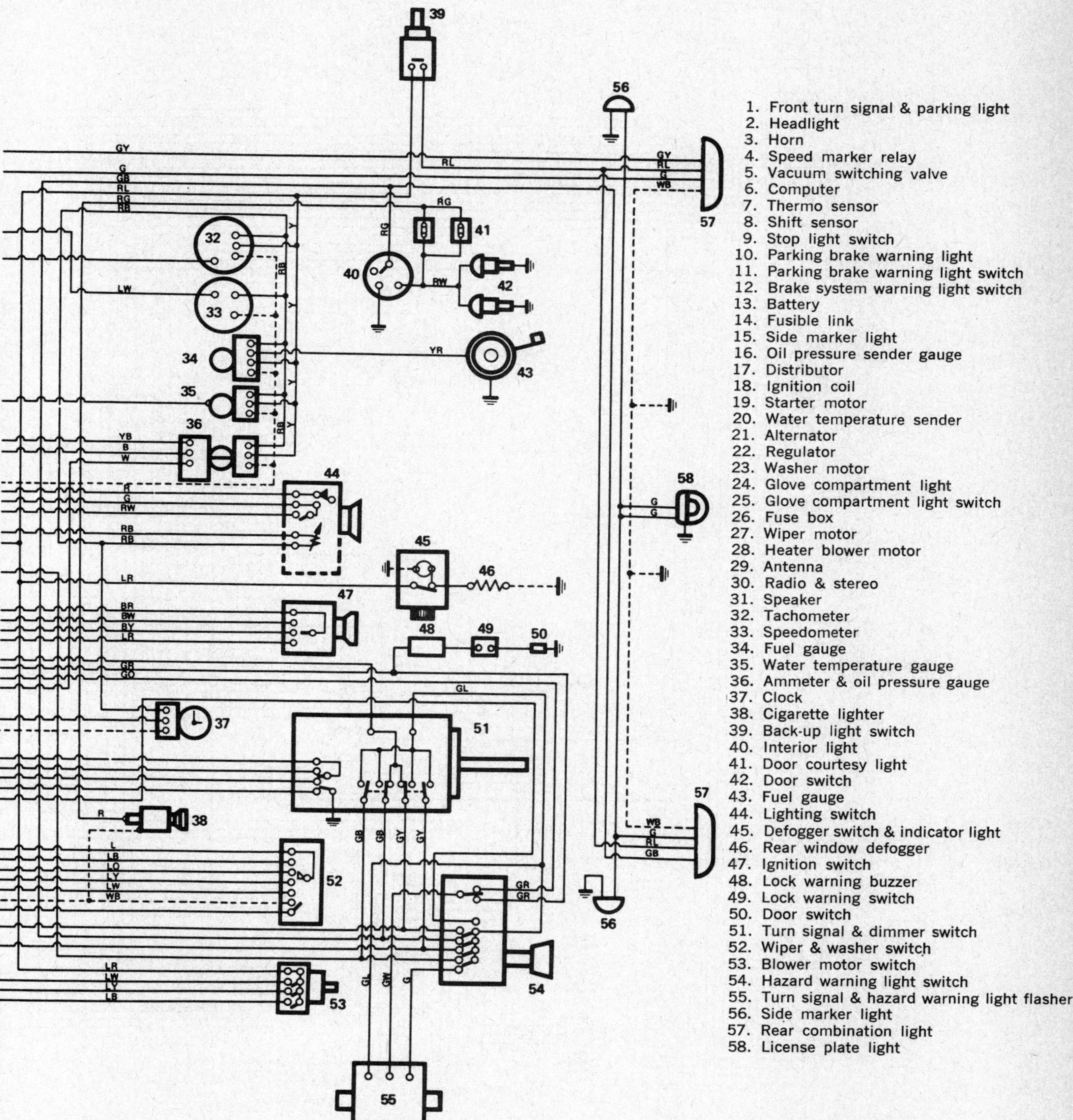

WIRING HARNESS COLOR CODES

The first alphabet indicates the basic color for the wire, and the second alphabet indicates the spiral line color.

R—red W—white L—light purple
G—green Y—yellow B—black
O—orange

Example: RG is for red and green line

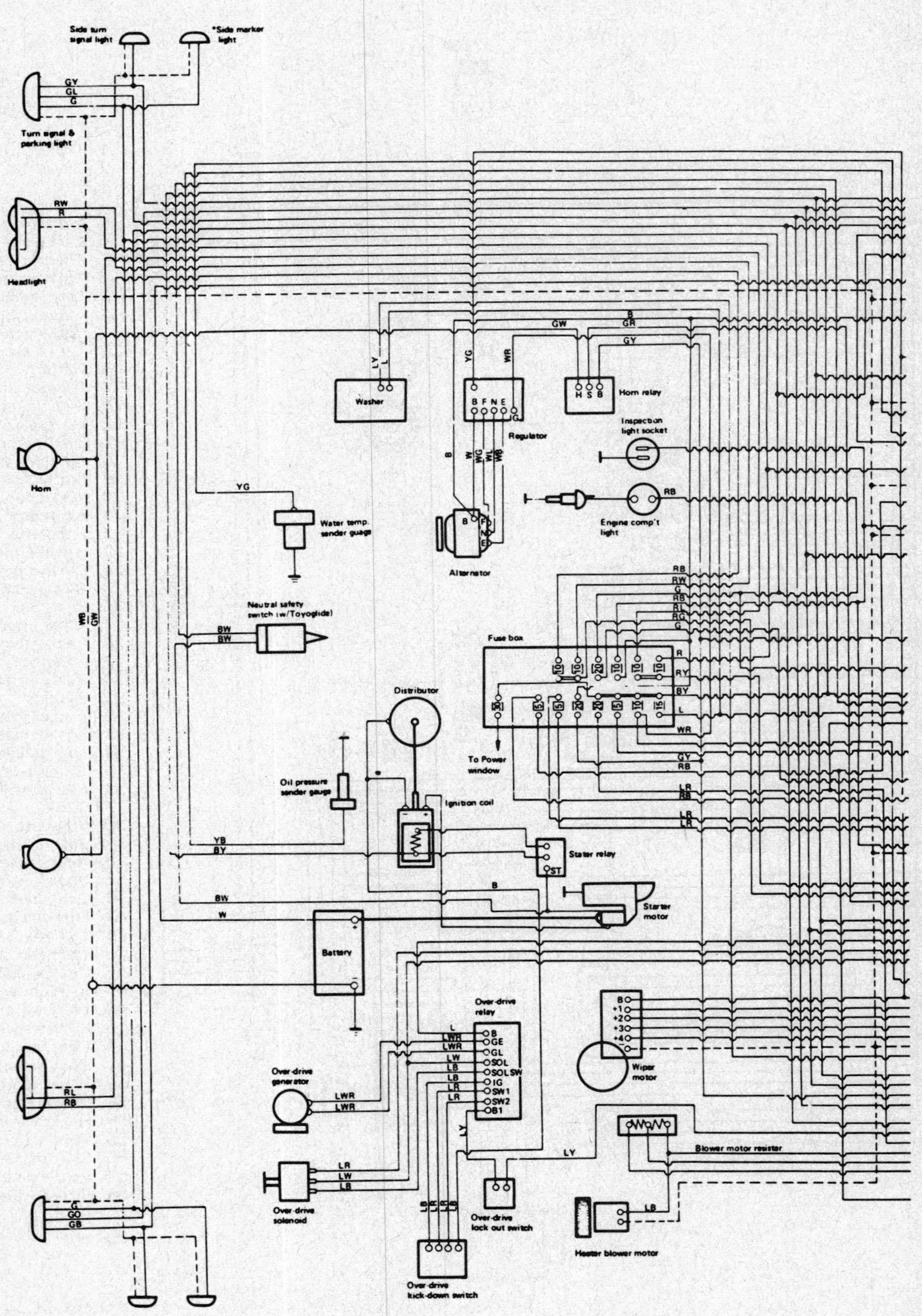

Crown 2300 1968-71

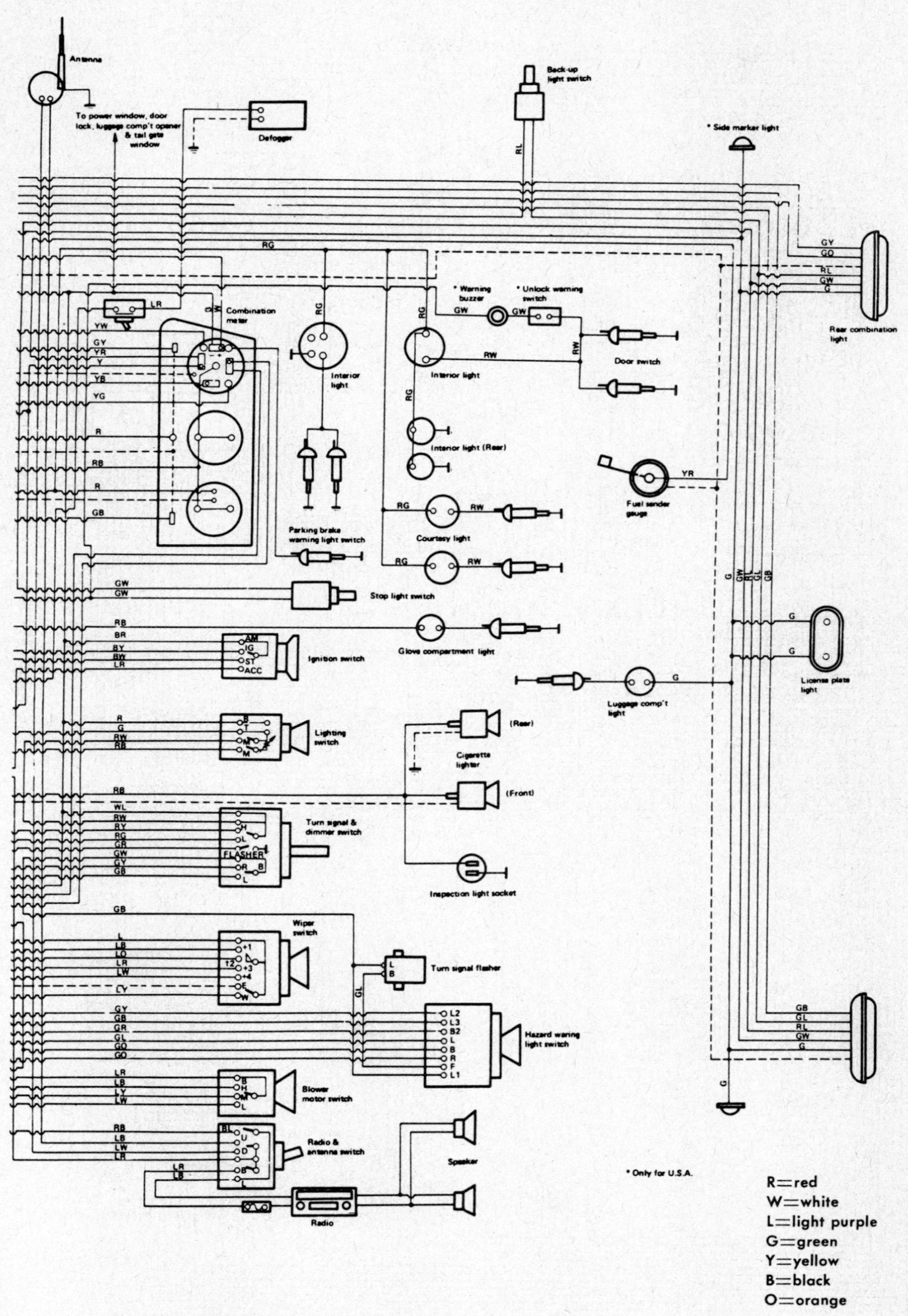

R=red
W=white
L=light purple
G=green
Y=yellow
B=black
O=orange

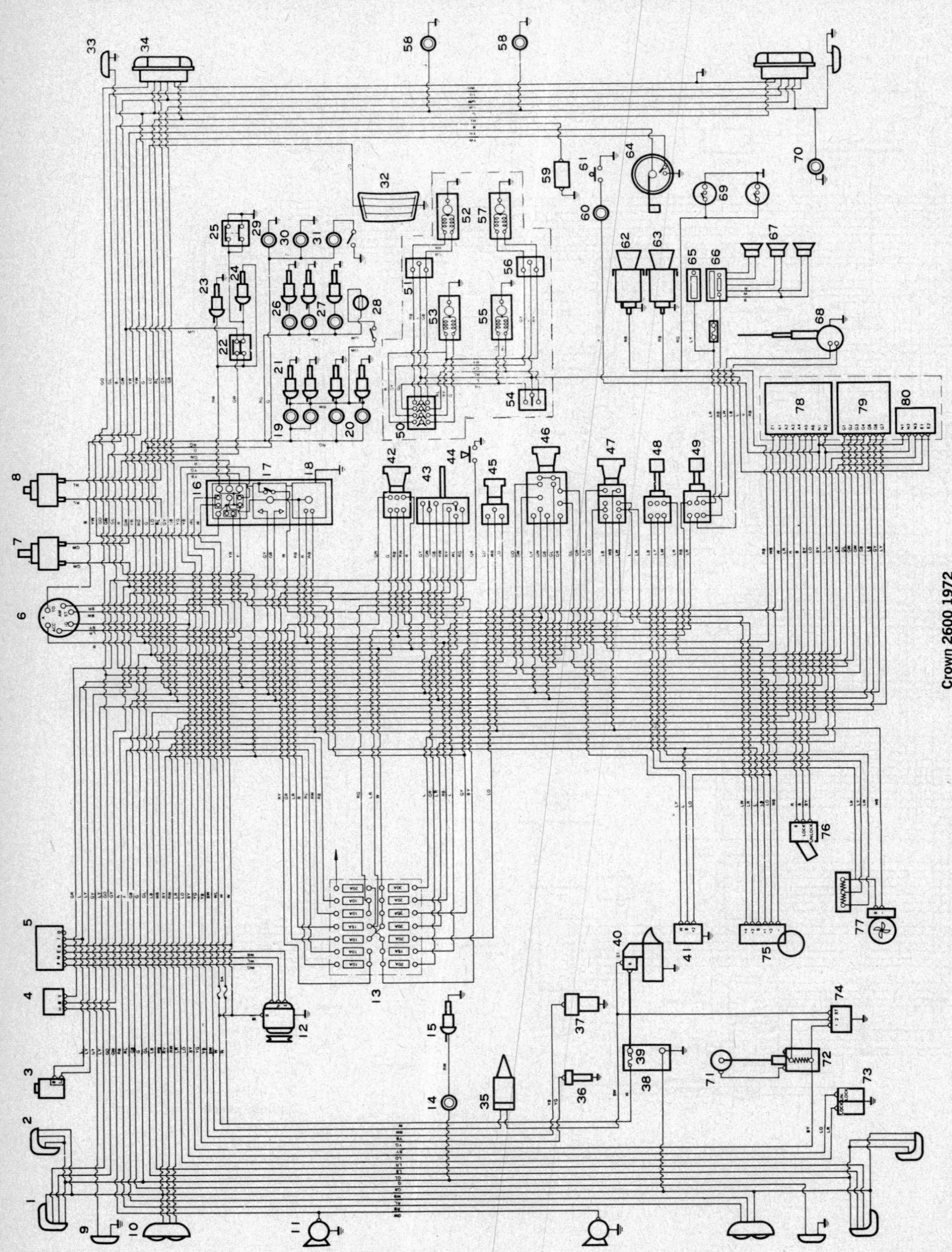
Crown 2600 1972

1. Clearance light
2. Clearance light**
3. Windshield washer
4. Horn relay
5. Regulator
6. Ignition switch
7. Stop light switch
8. Back-up light switch
9. Front turn signal
10. Headlight
11. Horn
12. Alternator
13. Fuse box
14. Engine compartment light
15. Engine hood switch
16. Combination gauge
17. Speedometer
18. Clock
19. Courtesy light
20. Interior light
21. Door switch (Hard-top)
22. Stop light switch
23. Parking brake
24. Brake warning test switch
25. Oil pressure switch
26. Door switch (Sedan)
27. Back door light
28. Unlock warning buzzer
29. Heater control indicator light
30. Toyoglide indicator light*
31. Glove compartment light
32. Rear window defogger
33. Rear side marker light**
34. Rear combination light
35. Neutral safety switch**
36. Water temperature sender gauge
37. Oil pressure switch
38. Battery
39. Fusible link
40. Starter motor
41. Windshield wiper relay
42. Lighting switch
43. Turn signal & dimmer switch
44. Horn button
45. Defogger timer switch
46. Hazard warning light switch
47. Windshield wiper switch
48. Heater blower motor switch
49. Radio & antenna switch
50. Power window master switch
51. Rear door switch
52. Rear window motor
53. Front window motor
54. Front door switch
55. Front window motor
56. Rear door switch
57. Rear window motor
58. License plate light
59. Luggage compartment lid opener
60. Back door indicator light
61. Door ajar switch
62. Cigarette lighter (Front)
63. Cigarette lighter (Rear)
64. Fuel gauge sender
65. Stereo system
66. Radio
67. Speaker
68. Antenna
69. Interior light (Rear)
70. Luggage compartment light
71. Distributor
72. Ignition coil
73. Vacuum solenoid valve
74. Starter relay
75. Wiper motor
76. Door lock control switch
77. Heater blower motor
78. Door control relay
79. Turn signal flasher & side turn signal relay
80. Main relay

* Toyoglide only.
** U.S. Specifications only.

WIRING HARNESS COLOR CODES

The first alphabet indicates the basic color for the wire, and the second alphabet indicates the spiral line color. R=red W=white L=light purple G=green Y=yellow B=black O=orange

Example: RG is for red and green line.

Crown 2600 1972

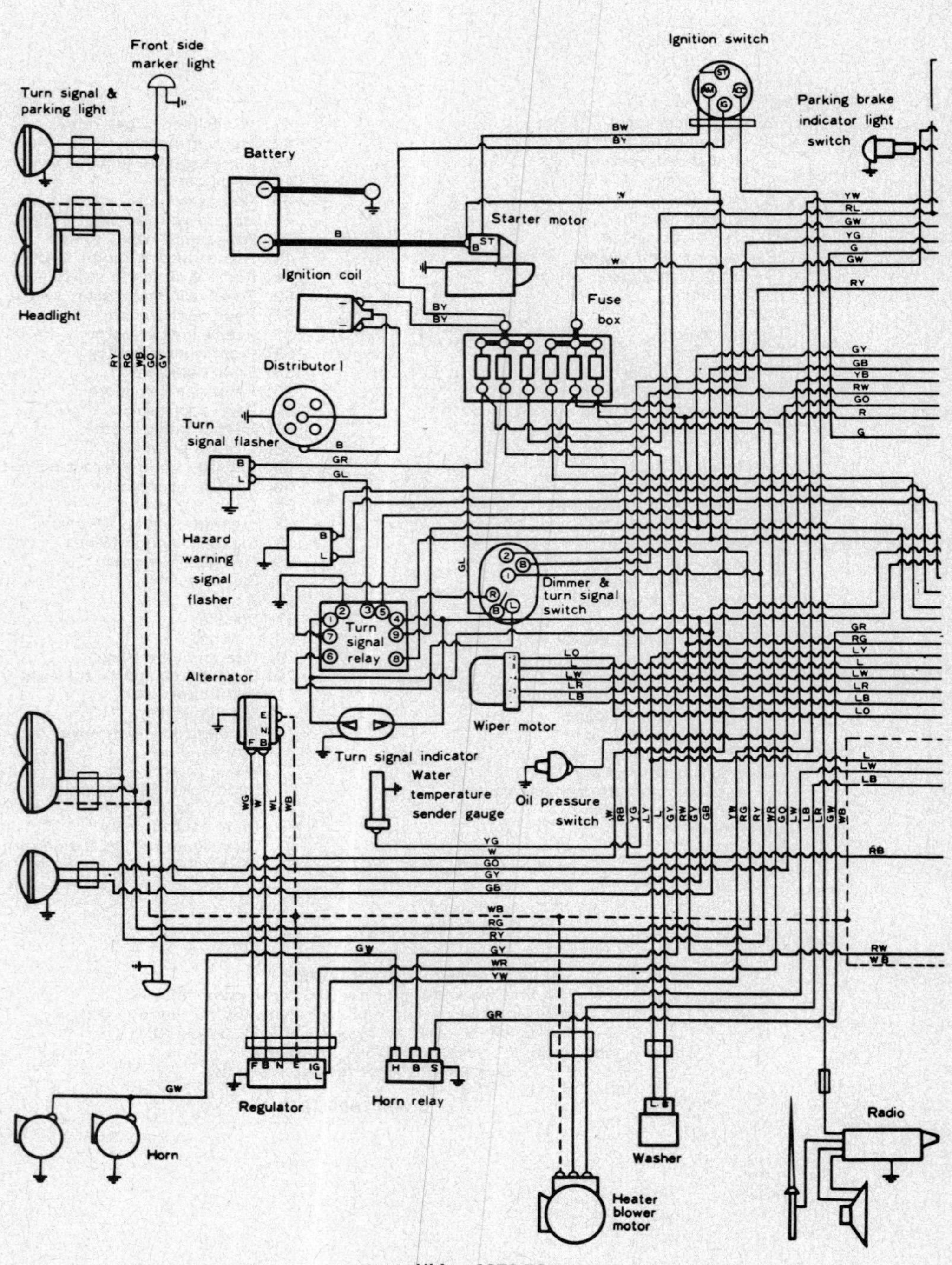

Hi-Lux 1970-72

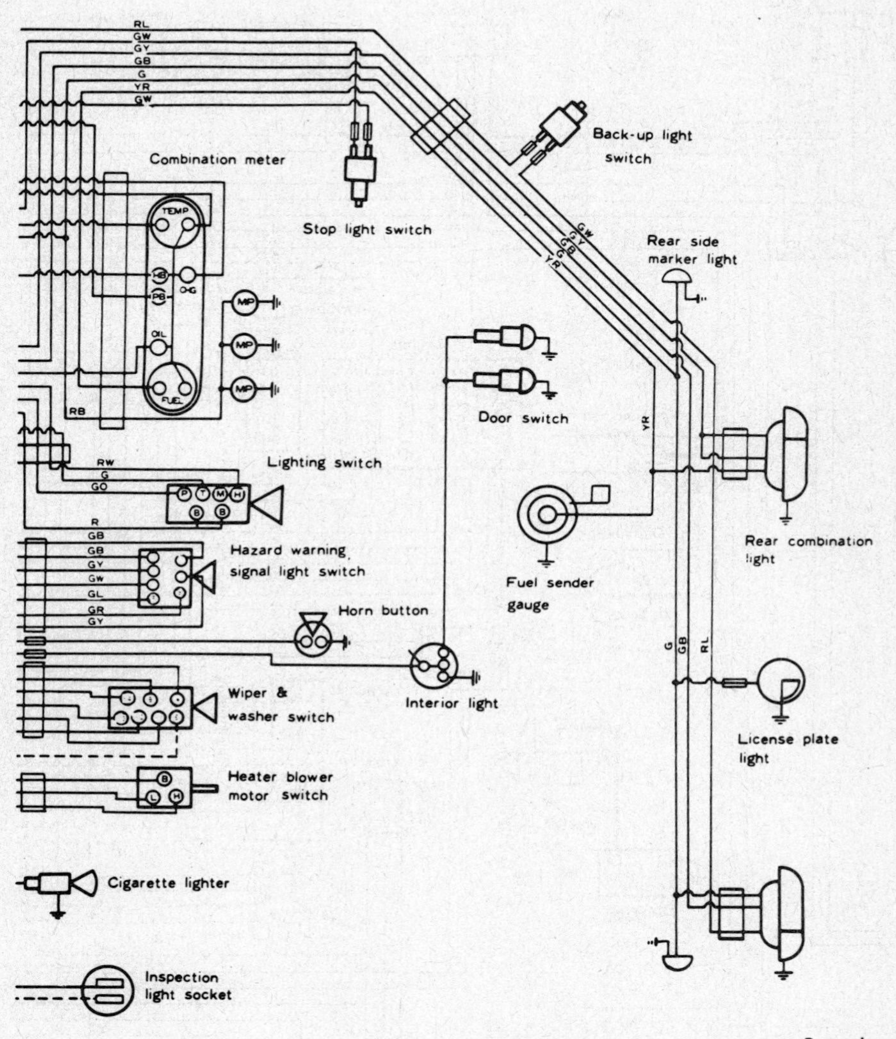

R=red
W=white
L=light purple
G=green
Y=yellow
B=black
O=orange

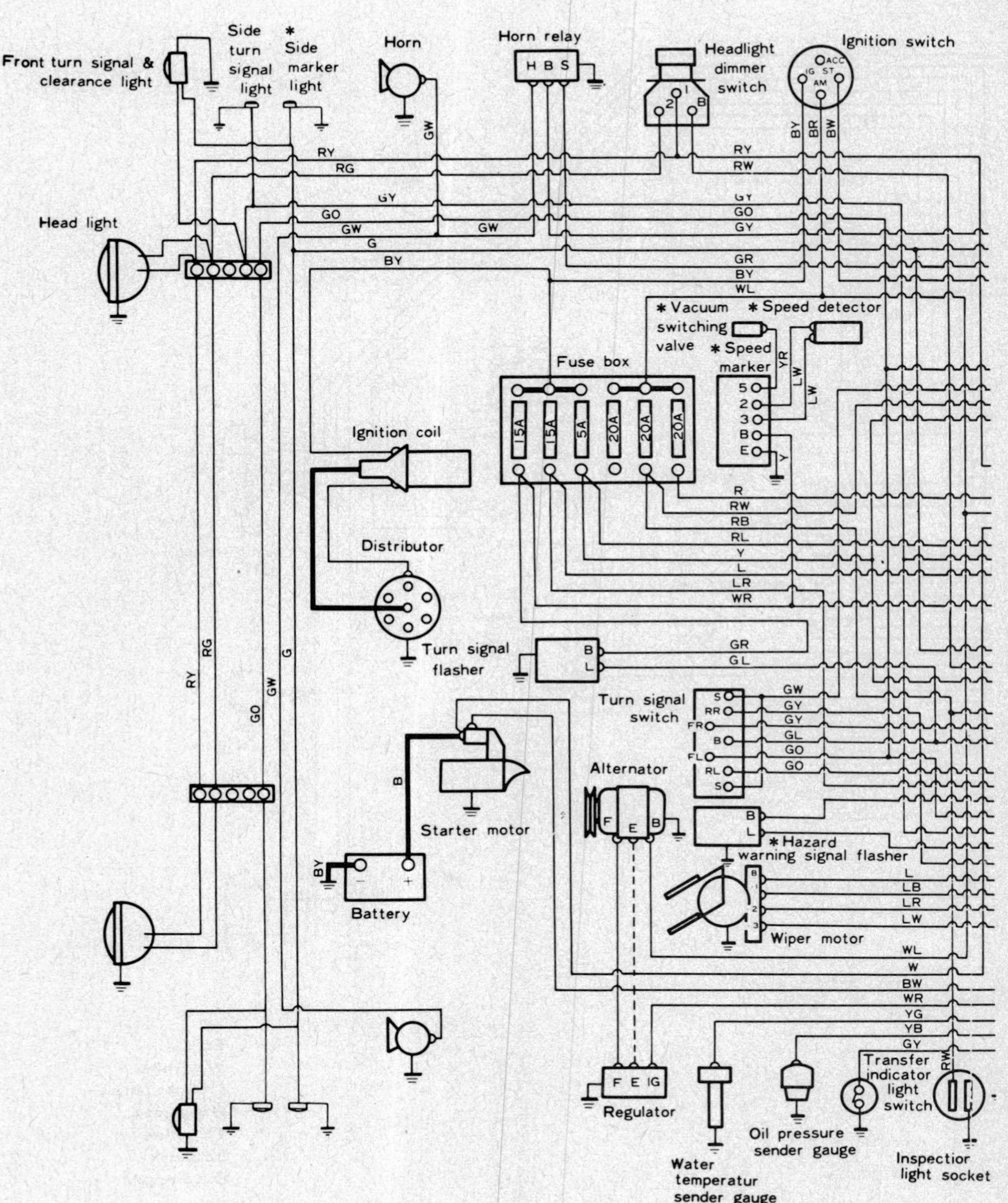

Land Cruiser 1966-73

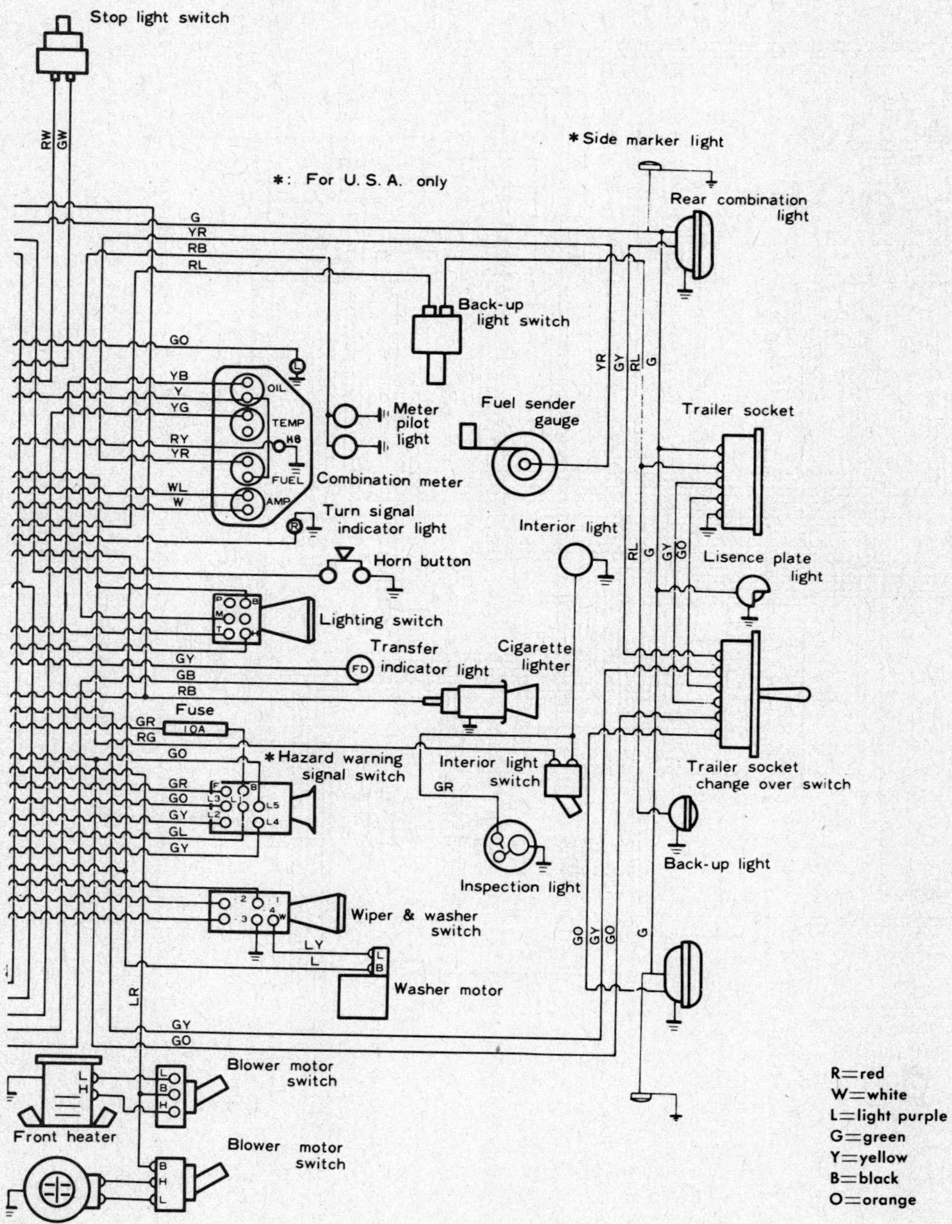

R=red
W=white
L=light purple
G=green
Y=yellow
B=black
O=orange

1. Front turn signal & parking light
2. Side turn signal light
3. Headlight
4. Horn
5. Oil pressure sender gauge
6. Slide turn signal relay*
7. Starter motor
8. Neutral safety switch
9. Water temperature sender
10. Alternator
11. Battery
12. Fusible link
13. Regulator
14. Distributor
15. Ignition coil
16. Fush box
17. Washer motor
18. Glove compartment light
19. Glove compartment switch
20. Wiper motor
21. Heater blower motor
22. Antenna
23. Radio & stereo
24. Speaker
25. Combination meter
26. Speedometer
27. Clock
28. Lighting switch
29. Ignition switch
30. Turn signal and dimmer
31. Cigarette lighter
32. Wiper & washer switch
33. Blower motor switch
34. Stop light switch
35. Back-up light switch
36. Interior light
37. Door switch
38. Parking brake warning light switch
39. Fuel gauge
40. Defogger switch & indicator light
41. Rear window defogger
42. Hazard warning light switch
43. Turn signal & hazard warning light flasher
44. Rear combination light
45. License plate light

* RHD cars only

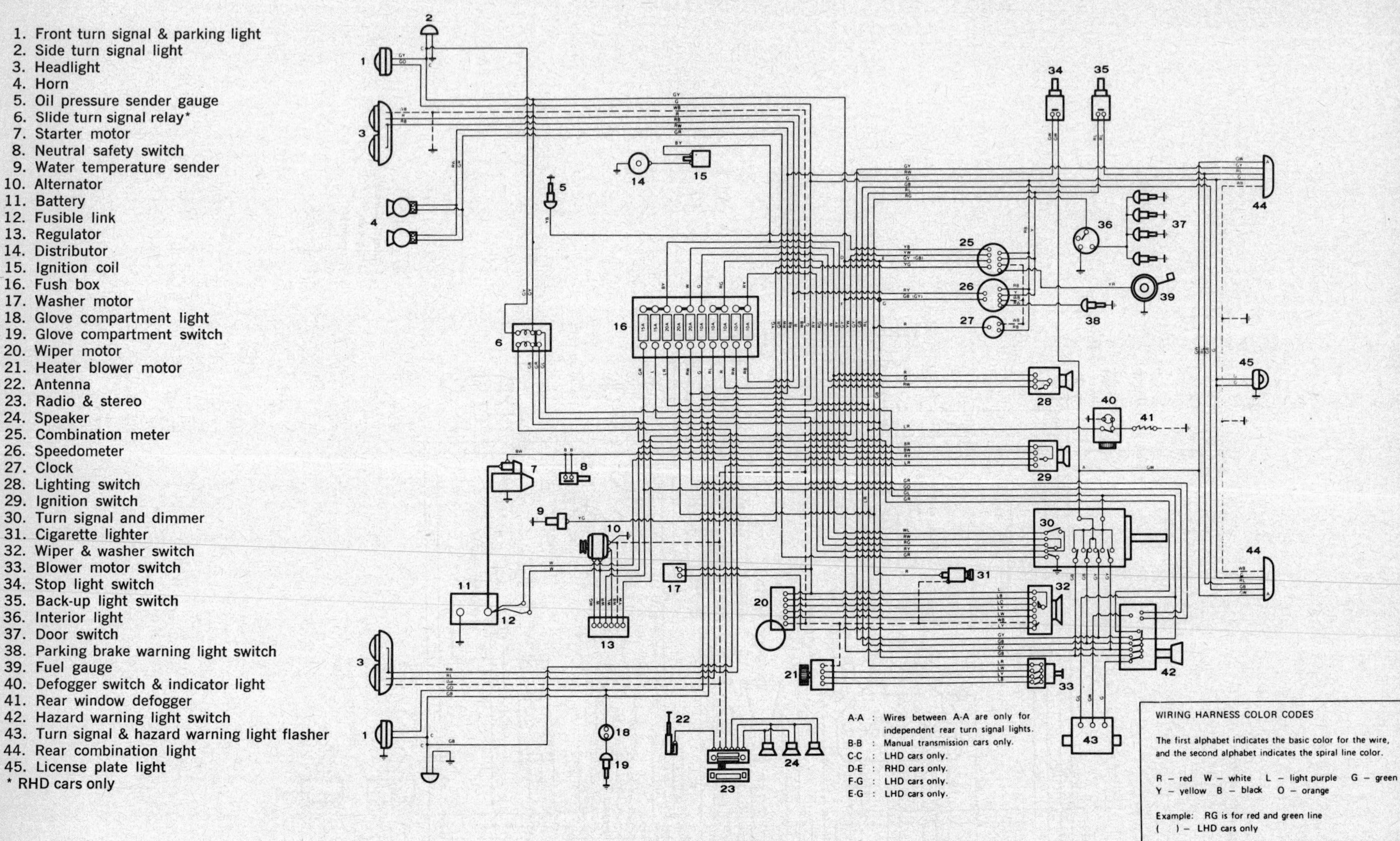

A-A : Wires between A-A are only for independent rear turn signal lights.
B-B : Manual transmission cars only.
C-C : LHD cars only.
D-E : RHD cars only.
F-G : LHD cars only.
E-G : LHD cars only.

WIRING HARNESS COLOR CODES

The first alphabet indicates the basic color for the wire, and the second alphabet indicates the spiral line color.

R – red W – white L – light purple G – green
Y – yellow B – black O – orange

Example: RG is for red and green line
( ) – LHD cars only

Carina 1972-73

TUNE-UP PROCEDURES

NOTE: *The procedures outlined below are the specific procedures for Toyota vehicles; general tune-up procedures may be found in the section at the end of this book.*

Spark Plugs

Check, clean, and adjust the spark plugs every 6,000 miles. Replace them every 12,000 miles.

Clean any foreign material from around the spark plugs before removing them. Use the spark plug wrench supplied in the tool kit.

NOTE: *Before removing the spark plugs, it is a good idea to label which wire goes to what plug.*

At the 6,000 mile check-up, clean any plugs which appear to be dirty and file their electrodes flat. Adjust the gap to the figure given in the "Tune-up Specifications" chart, above, using a wire feeler gauge.

NOTE: *Do not use a flat gauge; an inaccurate reading will result.*

Inspect the spark plug hole threads for rust and, if necessary, use a 14 mm plug tap to clean them.

Examine the condition of the spark plugs and check them against the diagnosis guide at the end of the book.

Lightly oil the threads and torque the plugs to 11–14 ft lbs. Use caution when tightening the plugs, as most Toyota models use aluminium heads.

Breaker Points and Condenser

Loosen the clips which attach the distributor cap to the distributor body and lift the cap straight up. Leave the leads connected to the cap. Remove the rotor and dust cover.

Clean the distributor cap and rotor with alcohol. Inspect them for cracks and other signs of wear or damage. Polish the points with a point file.

NOTE: *Do not use emery cloth or sandpaper; these may leave particles on the points, causing them to arc.*

If the points are badly pitted or worn, replace them as follows:

1. Unfasten the point lead connector.
2. Remove the point retaining clip and remove the point hold-down screw.
3. Remove the point set.
4. Installation is the reverse of removal.

After replacing the points, or as routine maintenance, adjust the points to the specifications given in the tune-up chart at the beginning of this section as follows:

1. Rotate the engine by hand or by using a remote starter switch, so that the rubbing block is on the high point of the cam lobe.
2. Insert a 0.018 in. feeler gauge between the points; a slight drag should be felt.
3. If no drag is felt or if the feeler gauge cannot be inserted at all, loosen, but do not remove, the point hold-down screw.
4. Insert a screwdriver into the adjustment slot. Rotate the screwdriver until the proper point gap is attained. The point gap is increased by rotating the screwdriver counterclockwise and decreased by rotating it clockwise.

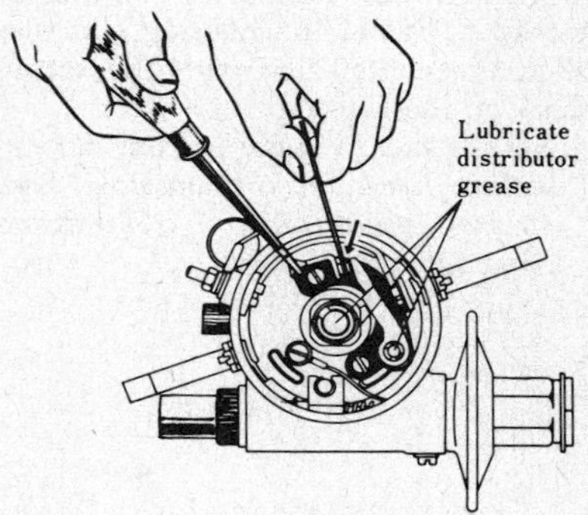

Adjustment of the points and lubrication of the distributor.

5. Tighten the point hold-down screw.

Lubricate the cam lobes, breaker arm, rubbing block, arm pivot, and distributor shaft with special high-temperature distributor grease.

Check the operation of the centrifugal advance mechanism by moving the rotor clockwise. Release the rotor; it should return to its original position. If it does not, check it for binding.

Check the vacuum advance unit by removing the cap and pressing in on the octane selector. Release the octane selector. It should snap back to its original position. Check for binding if it fails to do so.

Replace the condenser if it is suspect or as routine maintenance during the point replacement operation, in the following manner:

1. Remove the nut and washer from the condenser lead terminal.
2. Remove the condenser mounting screw and withdraw the condenser.
3. Installation is the reverse of removal.

NOTE: *The condenser is mounted on the outside of the distributor body on all models, except the Land Cruiser, which has it mounted inside the body.*

Install the dust cover, rotor, and the distributor cap on the distributor. Adjust the dwell and timing, as outlined below.

Dwell Angle

Connect a dwell/tachometer, in accordance with its manufacturer's instructions, between the distributor primary lead and a ground.

With the engine warmed up and running at the specified idle speed (see the tune-up chart, above), take a dwell reading.

If the point dwell is not within specifications, shut the engine off and adjust the point gap, as outlined above.

NOTE: *Increasing the point gap decreases the dwell angle and vice versa.*

Install the dust cover, rotor, and cap. Check the dwell reading again and adjust it, as required.

Ignition Timing

1. Warm up the engine. Connect a tachometer and check the engine idle speed to see that it is within specifications. Adjust it as outlined below if it is not.

If the timing mark is difficult to see, use chalk or a dab of paint to make it more visible.

2. Connect a timing light to the engine, as outlined in the instructions supplied by the manufacturer of the light.
3. Disconnect the vacuum line from the distributor vacuum unit.
4. Allow the engine to run at the specified idle speed with the gear shift in neutral for cars with manual transmissions, and in Drive (D) for cars with automatic transmissions.

CAUTION: *Be sure that the parking brake is firmly set and that the car is blocked, to prevent the car from rolling forward when Drive (D) gear is engaged.*

5. Point the timing light at the timing marks indicated in the chart below. With the engine at idle, timing should be at the specification given in the tune-up chart at the beginning of this section. If it is not, loosen the pinch bolt at the base and rotate the distributor to advance or retard the timing, as required.
6. Stop the engine and tighten the pinch bolt. Start the engine and recheck the timing.
7. Stop the engine and disconnect the timing light and the tachometer. Connect the vacuum line to the vacuum advance unit.

Timing Marks

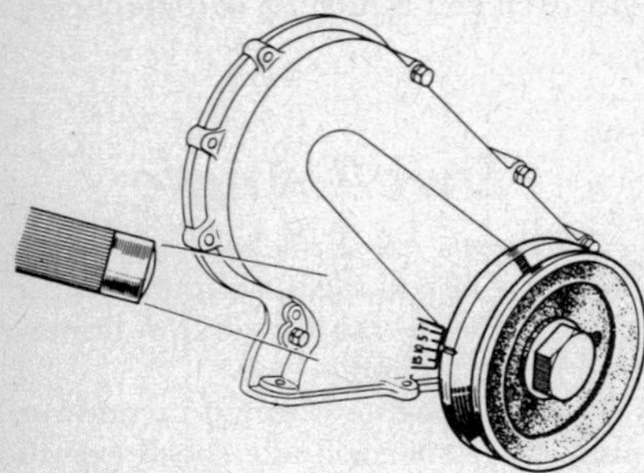

K-C, 3K-C and 2T-C

3R-B and 3R-C

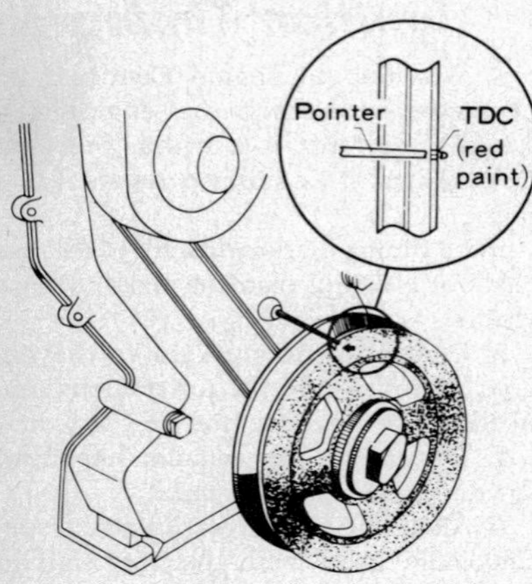

8R-C and 18R-C

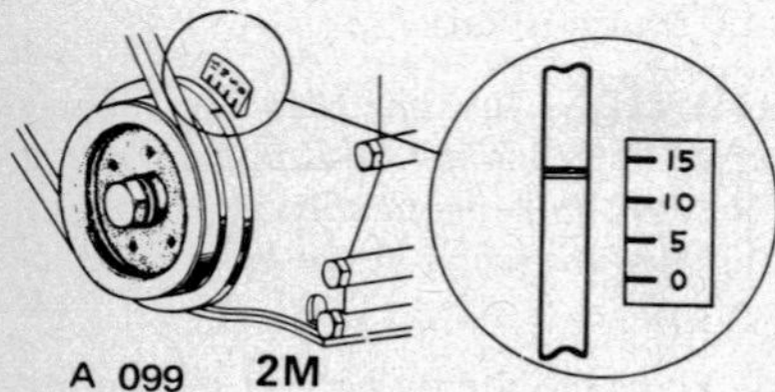

2M and 4M

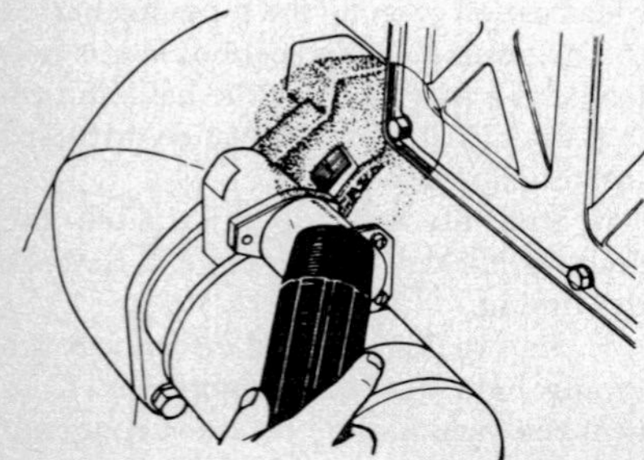

F engine

Octane Selector

The octane selector is used as a fine adjustment to match the vehicle's ignition timing to the grade of gasoline being used. It is located near the distributor vacuum unit, beneath a plastic dust cover. Normally the octane selector should not require adjustment, however, if necessary, adjustment is as follows:

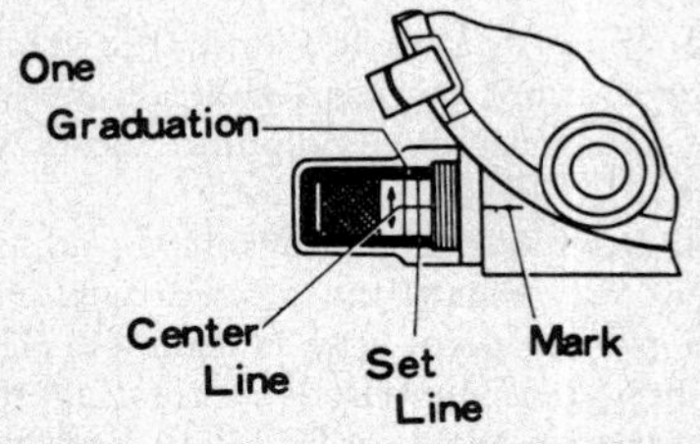

Passenger car and Hi-Lux octane selector

1. Align the setting line with the threaded end of the housing and then align the center line with the setting mark on the housing.

NOTE: *Land Cruiser models have no setting mark on the housing. Land Cruiser models made in 1973 do not have octane selectors.*

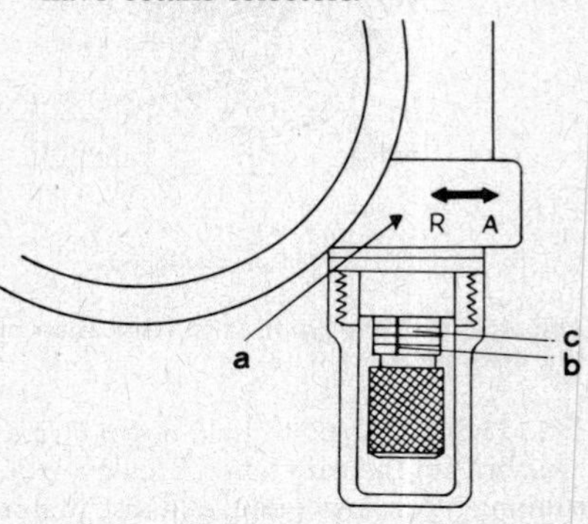

Land Cruiser octane selector (not used in 1973).
(a)—Adjustment scale
(b)—Center line
(c)—Setting line

2. Drive the car to the speed specified on the chart below, in high gear, on a level road.
3. Depress the accelerator pedal all the way to the floor. A slight "pinging" sound should be heard. As the car accelerates, the sound should gradually go away.
4. If the pinging sound is loud or if it fails to disappear as the vehicle speed increases, retard the timing by turning the knurled knob toward "R" (Retard).
5. If there is no pinging sound at all, advance the timing by turning the knob toward "A" (Advance).
6. When the adjustment is completed, replace the plastic dust cover.

NOTE: *One graduation of the octane selector is equal to about ten degrees of crankshaft angle.*

Octane Selector Test Speeds

Engine Type	Test Speed (mph)
3K-C	19-21
3R-B and 3R-C	12
2T-C, 8R-C and 18R-C	16-22
2M and 4M	25
F	20

Valve Lash

K-C, 3R-B, 3R-C, 3K-C and 2T-C Engines

1. Start the engine and allow it to reach normal operating temperature (165–185°F).
2. Stop the engine. Remove the air cleaner assembly, its hoses, and its bracket. Remove any other hoses, cables, etc. attached to the valve cover. Remove the valve cover.
3. Tighten the cylinder head bolts, in the proper sequence to the following values:

K-C and 3K-C—35–48 ft lbs
2T-C—52–63 ft lbs
3R-B and 3R-C—80 ft lbs

4. Next, on the K-C and 3K-C engines, tighten the valve rocker support bolts to 13–17 ft lbs. On 3R-B and 3R-C engines, tighten the rocker supports to 15 ft lbs.

CAUTION: *Tighten all of the above bolts in the proper sequence and in three stages.*

5. Install a suitable oil tray on the K-C or 3K-C engine, to prevent hot engine oil from being splashed out.

NOTE: *The tray may be ordered from a dealer or fabricated from sheet metal. (See illustration.)*

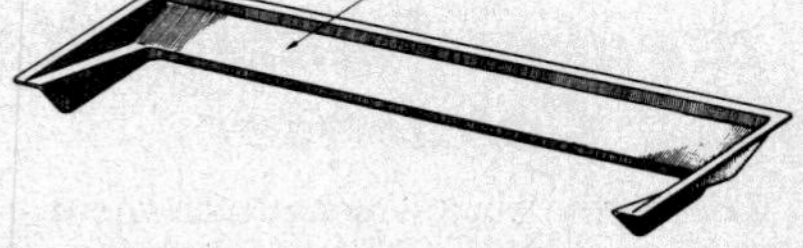

Special oil splash tray for K-C and 3K-C engines.

6. Start the engine. Check the clearance between the rocker arm and the valve stem with a feeler gauge, for each valve. The clearance specifications are given in the tune-up chart at the beginning of this section.
7. If the valves require adjustment, loosen the locknut and turn the adjustment screw to obtain the proper clearance.
8. Tighten the locknut. Check the valve clearance to be sure that it was not disturbed when the locknut was tightened.
9. When the valve inspection and adjustment are completed, replace the valve cover and all of the other compo-

nents which were removed.

8R-C and 18R-C Engines

1. Start the engine and allow it to reach normal operating temperature (above 175°F).

2. Stop the engine. Remove the air cleaner assembly, its hoses, and bracket. Remove any other cables, hoses, wires, etc. which are attached to the valve cover. Remove the valve cover.

3. Check the torque of the valve rocker shaft bolts and the camshaft bearing bolts; they should be 12–17 ft lbs.

4. Check the torque specification of the bearing cap union bolts. They should be torqued to 11–16 ft lbs.

5. Set the number one cylinder to TDC on its compression stroke. Remove the spark plug from the number one cylinder and place a finger over the hole. Crank the engine until a pressure is felt, then line the V-notch on the crankshaft pulley with the pointer on the timing chain cover. The number one cylinder is now at TDC.

NOTE: *Do not start the engine. Valve clearances are checked with the engine stopped to prevent hot oil from being splashed out by the timing chain.*

6. Check the clearances (see the tune-up chart) and adjust valves 1, 2, 3, and 5 to the proper specifications, if necessary.

NOTE: *The clearance is measured with a feeler gauge between the valve stem and the adjusting screw.*

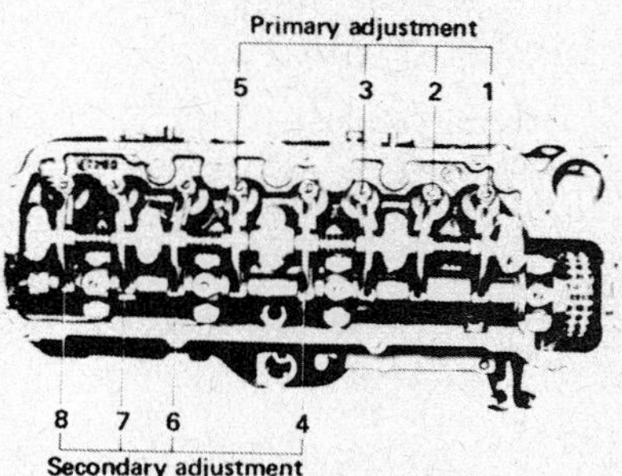

8R-C and 18R-C valve adjustment sequence.

7. To adjust the valve clearance, loosen the locknut and turn the adjusting screw until the specified clearance is obtained. Tighten the locknut and check the clearance again.

8. Crank the engine one revolution (360°) and perform steps 6 and 7 for valves 4, 6, 7, and 8 in the illustration.

9. Install the spark plug in the number one cylinder. Install the valve cover, air cleaner assembly, and any other components which were removed.

2M and 4M Engines

1. Allow the engine to reach normal operating temperature. Stop the engine.

2. Remove the air cleaner assembly, air cleaner bracket, spark plug cable guides, and any other components attached to the valve cover. Remove the valve cover.

3. Crank the engine until the number one cylinder is at TDC of its compression stroke. To determine this, remove the spark plug from the number one cylinder and place a screwdriver over the spark plug hole. Crank the engine until pressure is felt against the screwdriver and the slot in the crankshaft pulley aligns with the "O" (TDC) on the timing scale.

CAUTION: *Do not cover the spark plug hole with your finger when determining the compression stroke, as the proximity of the hole to the exhaust manifold could result in a severe burn.*

4. Check and adjust the clearance of the intake valves on 1, 2, and 4 cylinders and of the exhaust valves on 1, 3, and 5 cylinders.

5. Measure the clearance between the valve stem and the adjusting screw with a feeler gauge of the proper size. (See the specification chart at the beginning of this section.)

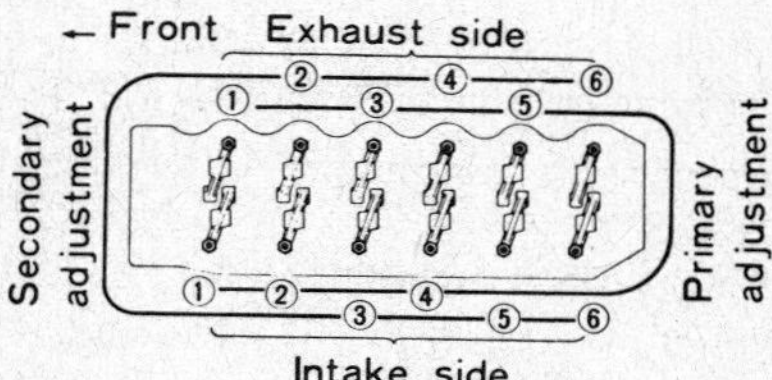

2M and 4M valve adjustment sequence

6. If the valves require adjustment, loosen the locknut and turn the adjusting screw until the proper clearancc is obtained. Tighten the locknut. Check the clearance again.

7. Crank the engine one revolution (360°) and repeat Steps 5 and 6 for the remaining valves.

8. Install the cylinder head cover, spark plug cable guides, air cleaner bracket, air cleaner assembly and any other components removed. Replace the number one spark plug as well.

F Engine

1. Warm the engine up to normal operating temperature (167–185°F).

2. Stop the engine. Remove the valve cover after removing the air cleaner assembly and any other components which might be in the way.

3. Tighten the cylinder head bolts to 83–98 ft lbs; the manifold retaining nuts to 14–22 ft lbs; and the rocker support nuts or bolts to 25–30 ft lbs (10 mm) and 14–22 ft lbs (8 mm).

NOTE: *See above for the proper tightening sequences. Tighten in three stages.*

4. Adjust the engine idle speed to 500 rpm.

5. Check the clearances between the rocker arm and the valve stem with a feeler gauge of the specified size. (See the tune-up chart.)

6. If the clearance is not according to specifications, loosen the locknut and turn the adjusting screw as required. Tighten the locknut and recheck the clearance.

7. When finished checking all of the valves, install the valve cover and any other components which were removed.

8. Adjust the idle speed to specification, as outlined in the appropriate section below.

Carburetor

NOTE: *See "Fuel System," above, for further carburetor adjustments.*

Idle Speed and Mixture

NOTE: *Perform the following adjustments with the air cleaner in place. While adjusting the idle speed and mixture the gear selector should be placed in Drive (D) range on models equipped with automatic transmissions. Be sure to block the front wheels.*

1. Run the engine until it reaches normal operating temperature. Stop the engine.

2. Connect a tachometer to the engine, as detailed in its manufacturer's instructions.

3. Remove the plug and install a vacuum gauge in the manifold vacuum port by using a suitable metric adaptor.

4. Start the engine and allow it to run at idle speed.

5. Turn the mixture screw in or out, until the engine runs smoothly at the lowest possible engine speed without stalling.

6. Turn the idle speed screw until the vacuum gauge indicates the highest specified reading (see the chart below) at the specified idle speed. (See the tune-up chart at the beginning of the section.)

7. On emission controlled engines, tighten the idle speed screw to the point just before the engine rpm and vacuum readings drop off.

8. Remove the tachometer and the vacuum gauge. Install the plug back in the manifold vacuum port. Road-test the vehicle.

Vacuum at Idle
(in. Hg)

Engine	Minimum vacuum gauge reading
KC, 3R-C, 3K-C and 2T-C	16.9
8R-C and 18R-C	15.7①
2M and 4M	15.7
F and 3R-B	18

① 18R-C engine/manual transmission—17.7 in. Hg

Carburetor Adjustments

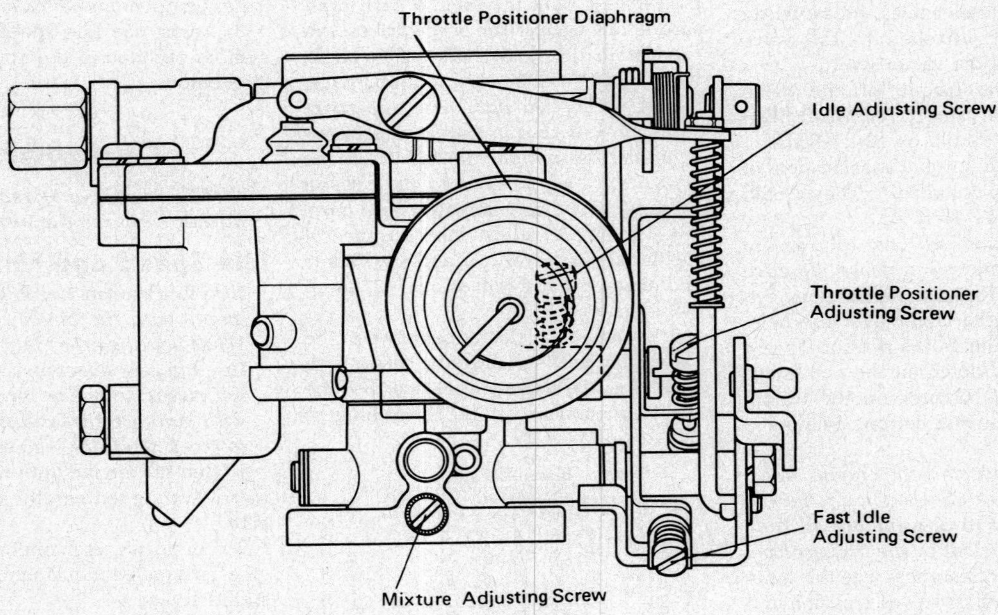

K-C and 3K-C

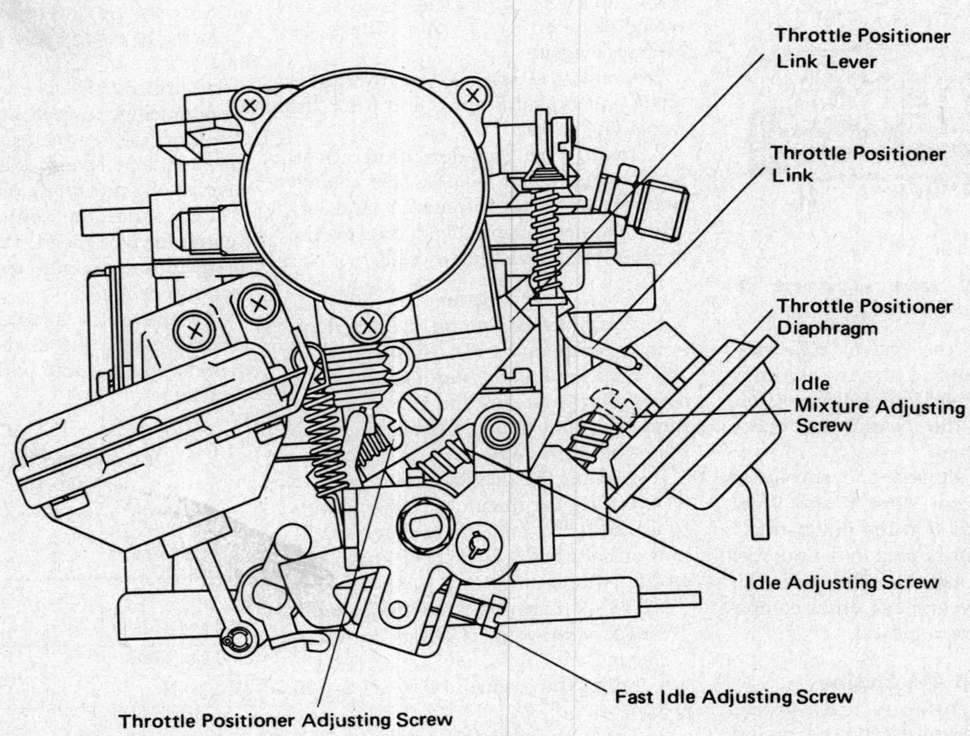

2T-C

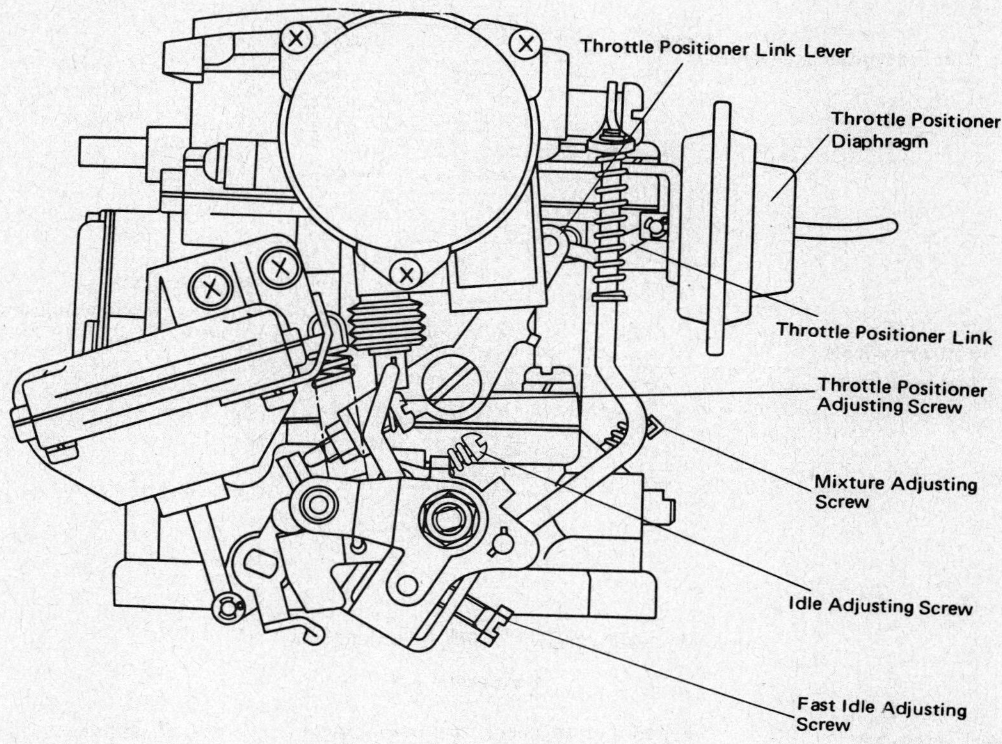

8R-C and 18R-C—3R series similar

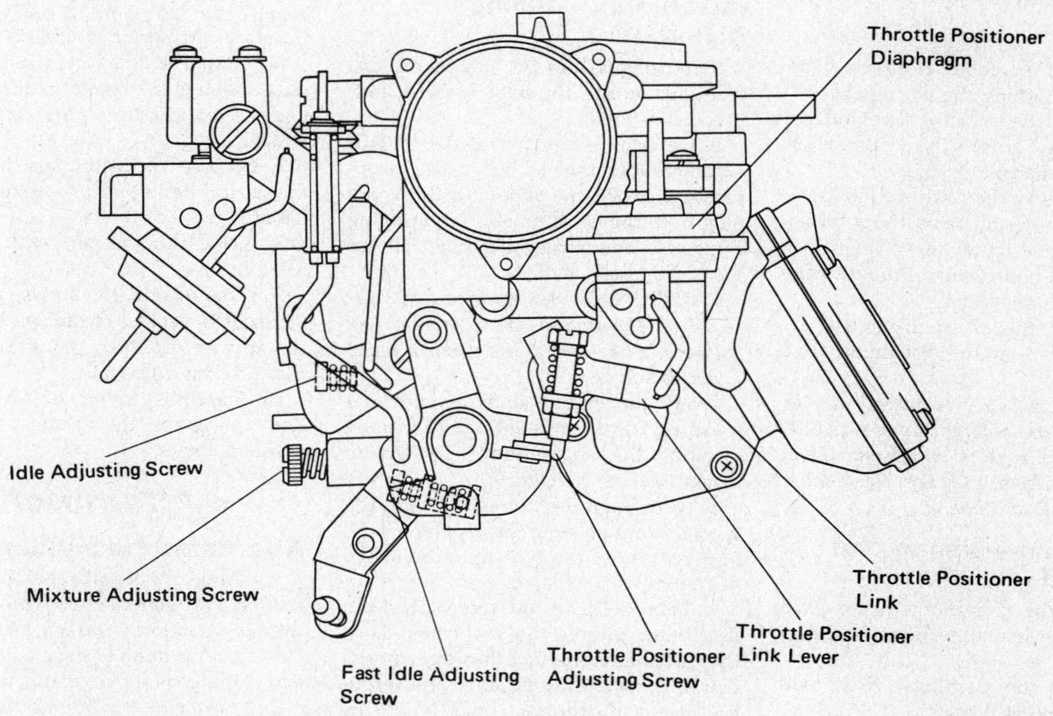

2M and 4M

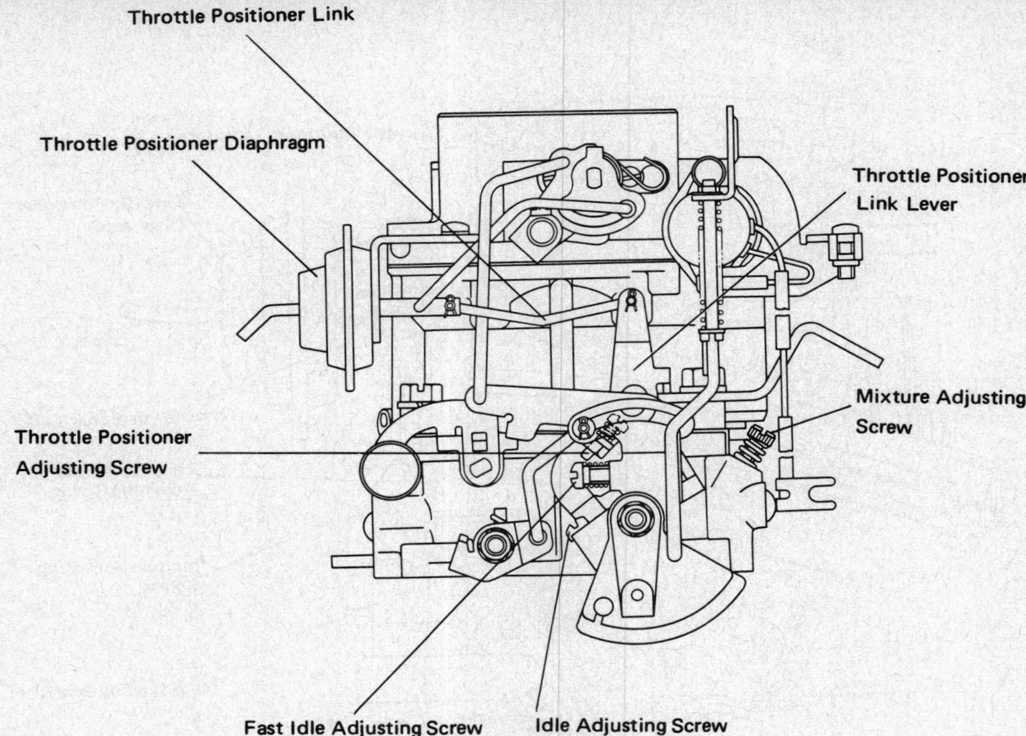

F engines

ENGINE ELECTRICAL

Distributor

Removal

1. Unfasten the cables from the spark plugs, after marking the wiring order.

2. Remove the primary wire and the vacuum line from the distributor. Remove the distributor cap.

3. Match-mark the distributor housing and the engine block; mark the rotor position in the distributor as well. This will aid in correct positioning of the distributor during installation.

4. Remove the clamp from the distributor. Withdraw the distributor from the block.

NOTE: *It is easier to install the distributor if the engine timing is not disturbed while it is removed. If the timing has been lost, see "Installation—Timing Lost," below.*

Installation—Timing Not Disturbed

1. Insert the distributor in the block and align the matchmarks made during removal.

2. Engage the distributor drive with the oil pump drive shaft.

3. Install the distributor clamp, cap, primary wire, and vacuum line.

4. Install the wires on the spark plugs. Remember to check the marks made during removal to be sure that the right wire goes to the right plug.

5. Start the engine. Check the timing and adjust the octane selector, as outlined.

Installation—Timing Disturbed

If the engine has been cranked, dismantled, or the timing otherwise lost, proceed as follows:

1. Determine top dead center (TDC) of the number one (no. 1) cylinder's compression stroke by removing the spark plug from the no. 1 cylinder and placing a finger or a compression gauge over the spark plug hole.

CAUTION: *On cars equipped with the 2M or 4M engine, use a screwdriver instead of a finger if the exhaust manifold is still hot.*

Crank the engine until compression pressure starts to build up. Continue cranking the engine until the timing marks indicate TDC (or 0°).

2. Next, align the timing marks to the specifications given in the "Ignition Timing" column of the tune-up chart at the beginning of the Toyota section.

3. Temporarily install the rotor in the distributor without the dust cover. Turn the distributor shaft so that the rotor is pointing toward the number one terminal in the distributor cap. The points should just be about to open.

4. Use a small screwdriver to align the slot on the distributor drive (oil pump driveshaft) with the key on the bottom of the distributor shaft.

5. Install the distributor in the block by rotating it slightly (no more than one gear tooth in either direction) until the driven gear meshes with the drive.

NOTE: *Oil the distributor spiral gear and the oil pump drive shaft end before distributor installation.*

6. Rotate the distributor, once it is installed, so that the points are just about to open. Temporarily tighten the pinch bolt.

7. Remove the rotor and install the dust cover. Replace the rotor and the distributor cap.

8. Install the primary wire and the vacuum line.

9. Install the no. 1 cylinder spark plug. Connect the cables to the spark plugs in the proper order by using the marks made during removal.

10. Start the engine. Adjust the ignition timing and the octane selector, as outlined above.

Alternator

Alternator Precautions

1. Always observe proper polarity of the battery connections; be especially careful when jump-starting the car.

2. Never ground or short out any alternator or alternator regulator terminals.

3. Never operate the alternator with any of its or the battery's leads disconnected.

4. Always remove the battery or dis-

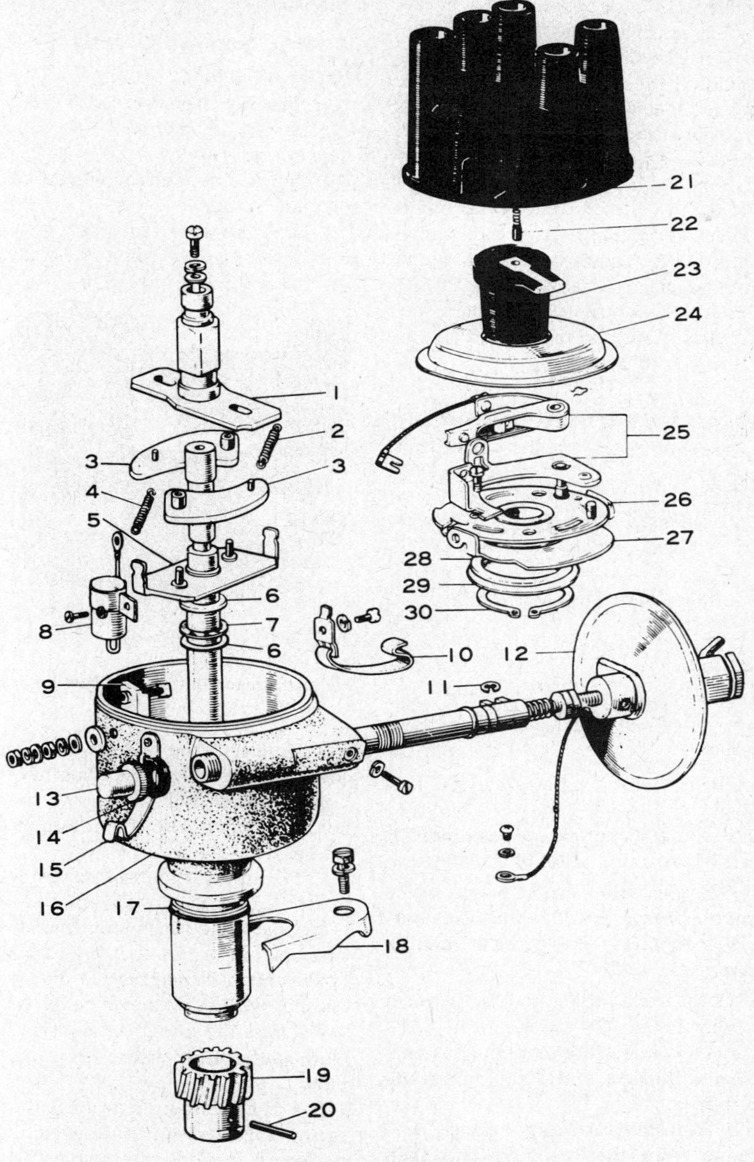

Distributor components

1. Cam
2. Governor spring
3. Governor weight
4. Governor spring
5. Distributor shaft
6. Metal washer
7. Bakelite washer
8. Condenser
9. Insulator
10. Cap spring clip
11. Snap ring
12. Vacuum advance unit
13. Octane selector assembly
14. Rubber washer
15. Cap spring clip
16. Distributor housing
17. O-ring
18. Distributor clamp
19. Spiral gear
20. Pin
21. Distributor cap
22. Spring
23. Rotor
24. Dust cover
25. Breaker point assembly
26. Movable plate
27. Stationary plate
28. Adjusting washer
29. Wave washer
30. Snap ring

connect its output lead while charging it.

5. Always disconnect the ground cable when replacing any electrical components.

6. Never subject the alternator to excessive heat or dampness if the engine is being steam-cleaned.

7. Never use arc-welding equipment with the alternator connected.

Removal and Installation

NOTE: *On some models the alternator is mounted very low on the engine. On these models it may be necessary to remove the gravel shield and work from underneath the car in order to gain access to the alternator.*

1. Unfasten the starter-to-battery cable at the battery end.

2. Remove the air cleaner, if necessary, to gain access to the alternator.

3. Unfasten the bolts which attach the adjusting link to the alternator. Remove the alternator drive belt.

4. Unfasten and tag the alternator wiring connections.

5. Remove the alternator attaching bolt and then withdraw the alternator from its bracket.

6. Installation is the reverse order of removal. After installing the alternator, adjust the belt tension as detailed in the following section.

Belt Tension Adjustment

Inspection and adjustment to the alternator drive belt should be performed every 3,000 miles or if the alternator has been removed.

1. Inspect the drive belt to see that it is not cracked or worn. Be sure that its surfaces are free of grease or oil.

2. Push down on the belt halfway between the fan and the alternator pulleys, with a force of about 22 lbs (24 lbs—3R-B and 3R-C engines). The belt should deflect ⅜–½ in.

NOTE: *On models with the 2M or 4M six-cylinder engines, push down on the belt with a pressure of 24 lbs halfway between the fan and the crankshaft pulleys.*

3. If the belt tension requires adjustment, loosen the adjusting link bolt and move the alternator until the proper belt tension is obtained.

CAUTION: *Do not overtighten the belt; damage to the alternator bearings could result.*

4. Tighten the adjusting link bolt.

Regulator

Removal and Installation

1. Unfasten the battery-to-starter cable at the battery end.

2. Disconnect the wiring harness connector from the regulator.

NOTE: *On Land Cruiser models, unfasten the leads from their screw terminals after noting their positions for installation.*

3. Unfasten the regulator securing bolts. Remove the regulator, complete with its condenser.

4. Installation is the reverse order of removal.

Voltage Adjustment

1. Connect a voltmeter to the battery terminals.

2. Start the engine and gradually increase its speed to about 1,500 rpm (2,000 rpm on Land Cruiser models).

3. At this speed, the voltage reading should fall within the range specified in the chart above.

4. If the voltage does not fall within the specifications, remove the cover from the regulator and adjust it by bending the adjusting arm.

5. Repeat steps 2 and 3; if the voltage cannot be brought to specification, proceed with the mechanical adjustments, outlined below.

Mechanical Adjustments

NOTE: *Perform the voltage adjustment outlined above, before beginning the mechanical adjustments.*

Field Relay

NOTE: *This adjustment does not apply to Land Cruiser models.*

1. Remove the cover from the regulator assembly.

2. Use a feeler gauge to check the amount that the contact spring is deflected while the armature is being depressed.

3. If the measurement is not within specifications (see the chart above), adjust the regulator by bending point holder P_2. *(See illustration.)*

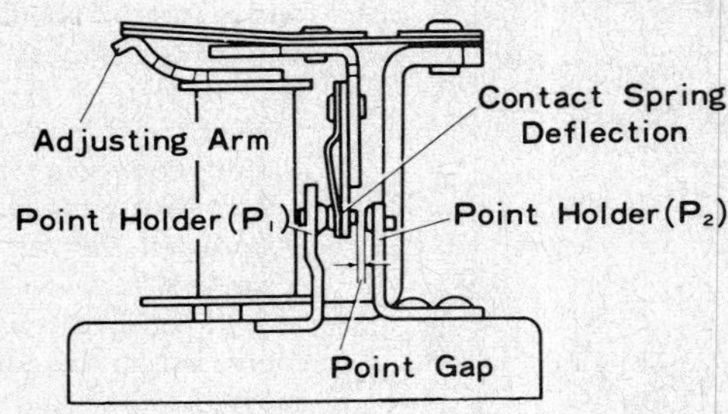

Field relay components

4. Check the point gap with a feeler gauge against the specifications in the chart.

5. Adjust the point gap, as required, by bending the point holder P_1. *(See illustration.)*

6. Clean off the points with emery cloth if they are dirty and wash them with solvent.

Voltage Regulator

NOTE: *Step 1 does not apply to Land Cruiser models.*

1. Use a feeler gauge to measure the air (armature) gap. If it is not within the specifications (see chart), adjust it by bending the *low*-speed point holder. (See illustration.)

2. Check the point gap with a feeler gauge. If it is not within specifications, adjust it by bending the *high*-speed point holder. (See illustration.) Clean the points with emery cloth and wash them off with solvent.

3. Check the amount of contact spring deflection while depressing the armature. The specification should be the same as that for the contact spring on the field relay. If the amount of deflection is not within specification, replace, do not adjust, the voltage regulator.

Go back and perform the steps outlined under "Voltage Adjustment," above. If the voltage cannot be brought within specifications, replace the voltage regulator. If the voltage still fails to come within specifications after regulator replacement, the alternator is probably defective and should be replaced.

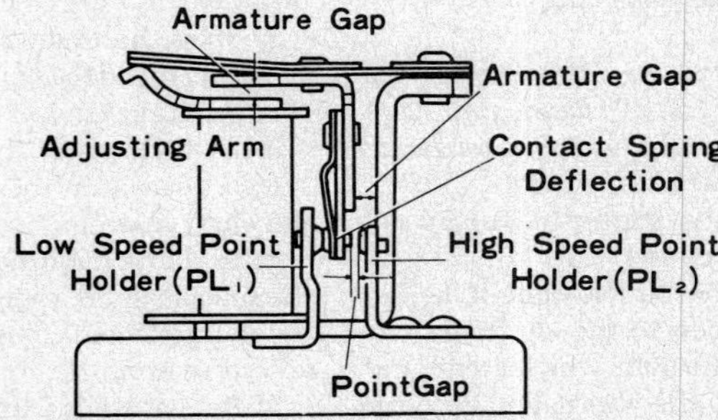

Voltage regulator components

Starter

Removal and Installation

1. Disconnect the cable which runs from the starter to the battery, at the battery end.

2. Remove the air cleaner assembly, if necessary, to gain access to the starter.

NOTE: *On some models with automatic transmissions, it may be necessary to unfasten the throttle linkage connecting rod.*

3. On Corolla 1200 models, perform the following:

a. Disconnect the manual choke cable and the accelerator cable from the carburetor.

b. Unfasten the front exhaust pipe flange from the manifold and then remove the complete manifold assembly. (See the appropriate section below for details.)

4. Disconnect all of the wiring at the starter.

5. Unfasten the starter securing nuts and withdraw the starter assembly toward the front of the car.

6. Installation is in the reverse order of removal.

Starter Solenoid and Brush Replacement

NOTE: *The starter must be removed from the car in order to perform this operation.*

1. Remove the field coil lead from the solenoid terminal.

2. Unfasten the solenoid retaining screws. Remove the solenoid by tilting it upward and withdrawing it.

Remove solenoid from starter in direction of arrow.

3. Unfasten the end frame bearing cover screws and remove the cover.

4. Unfasten and withdraw the thru-bolts. Remove the commutator end-frame.

5. Withdraw the brushes from their holder if they are to be replaced.

6. Check the brush length against the specification in the "Battery and Starter Specifications" chart, above. Replace the brushes with new ones if required.

7. Dress the new brushes with emery cloth so that they will make proper contact.

8. Use a spring scale to check the brush spring tension against the specification in the chart. Replace the springs if they do not meet specification.

Assembly is the reverse order of disassembly. Remember to pack the end bearing cover with multipurpose grease before installing it.

Battery

Removal and Installation

1. Unfasten the battery ground cable at the negative (-) battery terminal, *first.*

2. Next, unfasten the "hot" cable at the starter.

3. Loosen the hold-down clamps and remove the battery.

CAUTION: *Use care in handling the battery; remember, it is filled with a highly corrosive acid.*

4. Installation is the *exact* reverse of removal.

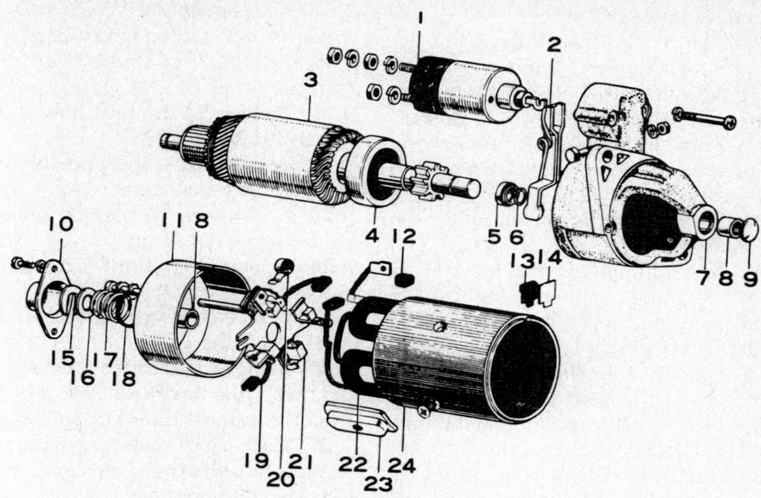

1. Solenoid
2. Engagement lever
3. Armature
4. Overrunning clutch
5. Clutch stop
6. Snap ring
7. Drive housing
8. Bushing
9. Bearing cover
10. Bearing cover
11. Commutator end frame
12. Rubber bushing
13. Rubber grommet
14. Plate
15. Lock plate
16. Washer
17. Brake spring
18. Gasket
19. Brush
20. Brush spring
21. Brush holder
22. Field coil
23. Pole shoes
24. Field yoke

Starter components

ENGINE MECHANICAL

Engine Removal and Installation

CAUTION: *Be sure that the car is supported securely, during engine removal.*

K-C and 3K-C Engines

1. Drain the entire cooling system.
2. Unfasten the cable which runs from the battery to the starter at the battery terminal.
3. Scribe marks on the hood and hinges to aid in hood alignment during assembly. Remove the hood.
4. Unfasten the headlight bezel retaining screws and remove the bezels. Remove the five radiator grille attachment screws and remove the grille.
5. Remove the hood lock assembly after detaching the release cable.
6. Unfasten the nuts from the horn retainers and disconnect the wiring. Withdraw the horn assembly.
7. Remove the air cleaner from its bracket after unfastening the hoses from it.
8. Remove the windshield washer tank from its bracket but first drain its contents into a clean container.
9. Remove both the upper and lower radiator hoses from the engine after loosening the hose clamps.

NOTE: *On models with automatic transmissions, disconnect the oil lines from the oil cooler.*

10. Detach the radiator mounting bolts and remove the radiator.
11. Remove the accelerator cable from its support on the cylinder head cover. Unfasten the cable at the carburetor throttle arm. Unfasten the choke cable from the carburetor.
12. Detach the water hose retainer from the cylinder head.
13. Disconnect the bypass and heater hoses at the water pump. Disconnect the other end of the heater hose from the water valve. Remove the heater control cable from the water valve.
14. Disconnect the wiring harness multiconnectors.
15. Detach the downpipe from the exhaust manifold.
16. Detach the wires from the water temperature and oil pressure sending units.
17. Remove the nut from the front left-hand engine mount.
18. Remove the fuel line from the fuel pump.
19. Detach the battery ground cable from the cylinder block.
20. Remove the nut from the front right-hand engine mount.
21. Remove the clip and detach the cable from the clutch release lever.
22. Remove the primary and high-tension wires from the coil.
23. Detach the back-up light switch wire at its connector on the right side of the extension housing.

The following steps apply to Corolla models with manual transmissions:

24. Remove the carpet from the transmission tunnel. Remove the boots from the shift lever.
25. Remove the snap-ring from the gearshift selector lever base. Withdraw the selector lever assembly.

The following steps apply to Corolla models with automatic transmissions:

26. Disconnect the accelerator linkage torque rod at the carburetor.
27. Disconnect the throttle linkage connecting rod from the bellcrank lever.
28. Drain the oil from the transmission oil pan.
29. Detach the transmission gear selector shift rod from the control shaft.

The following steps apply to Corollas with both manual and automatic transmissions:

30. Raise the rear wheels of the car. Support the car with jackstands.
31. Disconnect the driveshaft from the transmission.

NOTE: *Drain the oil from the manual transmission, first, to prevent it from leaking out.*

32. Detach the exhaust pipe support bracket from the extension housing.
33. Remove the insulator bolt from the rear engine mount.
34. Place a jack under the transmission and remove the four bolts from the rear (engine support) crossmember.
35. Install lifting hooks on the engine lifting brackets. Attach a suitable hoist.
36. Lift the engine slightly; then move it toward the front of the car. Bring the engine the rest of the way out at an angle.

Engine installation is the reverse order of removal. Adjust all transmission and carburetor linkages, as detailed in the appropriate section. Install and adjust the hood. Refill the engine, radiator, and transmission to capacity.

2T-C Engine

1. Drain the radiator, cooling system, transmission, and engine oil.
2. Disconnect the battery-to-starter cable at the positive battery terminal.
3. Scribe marks on the hood and its hinges to aid in alignment during installation.
4. Remove the hood supports from the body. Remove the hood.

NOTE: *Do not remove the supports from the hood.*

5. On Carina models, remove the headlight bezels. Disconnect the hood release cable then remove the grille, lower grille molding, hood lock base, and base support.

6. On Corolla models, perform steps 4–6 as detailed in the 3K-C engine removal section above.

7. Detach both the upper and lower hoses from the radiator. On cars with automatic transmissions, disconnect the lines from the oil cooler. Remove the radiator.

8. Unfasten the clamps and remove the heater and bypass hoses from the engine. Remove the heater control cable from the water valve.

9. Remove the wiring from the coolant temperature and oil pressure sending units.

10. Remove the air cleaner from its bracket, complete with its attendant hoses.

11. Unfasten the accelerator torque rod from the carburetor. On models equipped with automatic transmissions, remove the transmission linkage as well.

12. Remove the emission control system hoses and wiring, as necessary.

13. Remove the clutch hydraulic line support bracket.

14. Unfasten the high-tension and primary wires from the coil.

15. Mark the spark plug cables and remove them from the distributor.

16. Detach the right-hand front engine mount.

17. Remove the fuel line at the pump.

18. Detach the downpipe from the exhaust manifold.

19. Detach the left-hand front engine mount.

20. Disconnect all of the wiring harness multiconnectors.

21. On cars equipped with manual transmissions, remove the shift lever boot and the shift lever cap boot.

22. Unfasten the four gear selector lever cap retaining screws, remove the gasket and withdraw the gear selector lever assembly from the top of the transmission.

NOTE: *On all Carina models and on Corolla five-speed models, the floor console must be removed first.*

23. Lift the rear wheels of the car off the ground and support the car with jackstands.

24. On cars equipped with automatic transmissions, disconnect the gear selector control rod.

25. Detach the exhaust pipe support bracket.

26. Disconnect the driveshaft from the rear of the transmission.

27. Unfasten the speedometer cable from the transmission. Disconnect the wiring from the back-up light switch and the neutral safety switch (automatic only).

28. Detach the clutch release cylinder assembly, complete with hydraulic lines. Do not disconnect the lines.

29. Unbolt the rear support member mounting insulators.

30. Support the transmission and detach the rear support member retaining bolts. Withdraw the support member from under the car.

31. Install lifting hooks on the engine lifting brackets. Attach a suitable hoist to the engine.

32. Remove the jack from under the transmission.

33. Raise the engine and move it toward the front of the car. Use care to avoid damaging the components which remain on the car.

34. Support the engine on a workstand. Install the engine in the reverse order of removal. Adjust all of the linkages as detailed in the appropriate section. Install the hood and adjust it. Replenish the fluid levels in the engine, radiator, and transmission.

3R-B and 3R-C Engines

1. Drain the cooling system and the engine oil.

2. Unfasten the ground cable from the battery negative terminal.

3. Scribe alignment marks on the hood and hinges; then remove the hood.

4. Remove the air cleaner assembly and its related hoses.

5. Remove the grille and the upper radiator support.

6. Unfasten the clamps, and then remove the upper and lower radiator hoses.

7. On models equipped with automatic transmissions, remove the oil cooler-to-transmission lines.

8. Remove the accelerator linkage and fuel lines from the carburetor.

9. Disconnect the distributor high tension (coil) and primary leads.

10. Unfasten the battery-to-starter cable and the starter solenoid wire.

11. Remove the radiator complete with the fan shroud (see "Engine Cooling" below).

12. Unfasten the power brake unit vacuum line, if so equipped.

13. Unfasten clamps and remove the heater hoses. Remove the water valve.

14. Remove the clutch hydraulic lines from the mounting bracket. Do not disconnect the lines from the clutch release cylinder.

15. Disconnect the alternator multiconnector.

16. Unfasten the downpipe from the manifold flange.

17. Unfasten the nuts and bolts from the front engine mounts.

18. Unfasten the leads from the temperature and oil pressure gauge sending units.

19. Raise the car and support it with stands.

20. Remove the driveshaft yoke from the transmission.

NOTE: *Use an old U-joint yoke or a plastic bag, secured with rubber bands, to keep oil from leaking out of the transmission.*

21. Disconnect the shift linkage from the transmission.

22. Unfasten the speedometer cable from the transmission housing.

23. Disconnect the parking brake cable from the equalizer.

24. Remove the front exhaust pipe bracket.

25. Remove the gravel shields from underneath the car.

26. Remove the clutch release cylinder, with the hydraulic line attached, from the manual transmission.

27. Place a jack underneath the transmission to support it. Then remove the rear engine mountings.

28. Install lifting hooks on the engine hangers. Attach the hooks to a safe and suitable hoist.

29. Raise the engine/transmission assembly toward the front of the car, and then upward and out of the car.

Installation is the reverse order of removal. Adjust the various linkages outlined in the appropriate sections. Replenish the fluids in the engine, transmission and radiator. Perform an engine tune-up.

8R-C and 18R-C Engines

1. Perform steps 1–4 of the 2T-C engine removal procedure.

2. Remove the headlight bezel and the radiator grille.

3. Remove the fan shroud, the hood lock base and the base support.

4. Perform steps 7–20 of the 2T-C engine removal procedure.

Perform the following steps on 1971–73 models with manual transmissions:

5. Remove the center console if so equipped.

6. Remove the shift lever boot(s).

7. Unfasten the four shift lever cap retaining screws. Remove the cap and withdraw the shift lever assembly.

Perform the following steps on models equipped with automatic transmissions:

8. Remove the transmission selector linkage:

a. On models equipped with a floor-mounted selector, disconnect the control rod from the transmission.

b. On column-mounted gear selector models, remove the shifter rod.

9. Disconnect the neutral safety switch wiring connector.

Perform the following steps on all models:

10. Raise the rear of the vehicle with jacks and support it on jackstands.

11. Remove the retaining screws and remove the parking brake equalizer support bracket. Disconnect the cable which

runs between the lever and the equalizer.

12. Remove the speedometer cable from the transmission. Disconnect the back-up light wiring.

13. Detach the driveshaft from the rear of the transmission.

NOTE *If oil runs out of the transmission, an old U-joint yoke sleeve makes an excellent plug.*

14. On pre-1971 vehicles which are equipped with manual transmissions, unfasten the gearshift cross-shaft from the transmission.

15. Perform steps 28–34 of the 2T-C engine removal procedure.

Installation of the engine is the reverse order of removal. Refer to the appropriate chapters for transmission and carburetor adjustments. Replenish the engine oil, coolant, and transmission oil to the proper levels.

2M and 4M Engines

1. Disconnect the battery cables and remove the battery.

2. Scribe aligning marks on the hood and hinges to aid in their assembly. Remove the hood.

3. Remove the fan shroud and drain the cooling system.

4. Disconnect both the upper and lower radiator hoses. Unfasten the oil lines from the oil cooler on cars with automatic transmissions.

5. Detach the hose which runs to the thermal expansion tank at the tank. Remove the expansion tank from its mounting bracket.

6. Remove the radiator.

7. Disconnect the heater and bypass hoses from the engine.

8. Disconnect the oil pressure light sender wiring, the alternator multiconnector, and the back-up light switch wiring.

9. Unfasten the power brake unit vacuum lines.

10. Disconnect the engine oil cooler hoses at the oil filter, if so equipped.

11. Disconnect the power steering fluid cooler hose, if so equipped.

12. Remove the air cleaner assembly from its bracket, complete with hoses.

13. Detach the emission control system wires and hoses, as required.

14. Unfasten the distributor primary wire and the high tension wire from the coil.

15. Disconnect the wiring from the starter and temperature gauge sender.

16. Remove the fuel line from the fuel pump.

17. Disconnect the heater control cable from the water valve. Unfasten the heater control vacuum hose.

18. Remove the accelerator linkage from the carburetor.

19. Detach the clutch hydraulic line from its master cylinder connections (manual transmission only). Install a cap on the master cylinder fitting to keep the hydraulic fluid from running out.

20. Detach the pressure-feed lines from the steering gear housing on models equipped with power steering.

21. Raise both the front and the rear of the car with jacks. Support the car with jackstands.

22. Detach the exhaust pipe from the downpipe and remove the exhaust pipe hangers.

23. Disconnect the speedometer cable from the right side of the transmission.

The following steps apply to models with manual transmissions only:

24. On 1970–71 models, disconnect the shifter shaft from the transmission.

25. On 1972–73 models:

a. Remove the center console securing screws, the gearshift knob, the gearshift boot, and then unfasten the console wiring multiconnector. Lift the console over the gearshift lever.

b. Remove the four screws which attach the shift lever retainer to the shift tower and withdraw the shift lever assembly.

The following steps apply to models with automatic transmissions:

26. On models equipped with a floor-mounted gear selector, unfasten the connecting rod swivel nut and detach the control rod from the gear selector lever.

27. On models equipped with a column-mounted gear selector;

a. Disconnect the control rod and cross-shaft.

b. Remove both of the throttle link connecting rods.

28. Disconnect the parking brake lever rod, return spring, intermediate rod, and the cable from the equalizer.

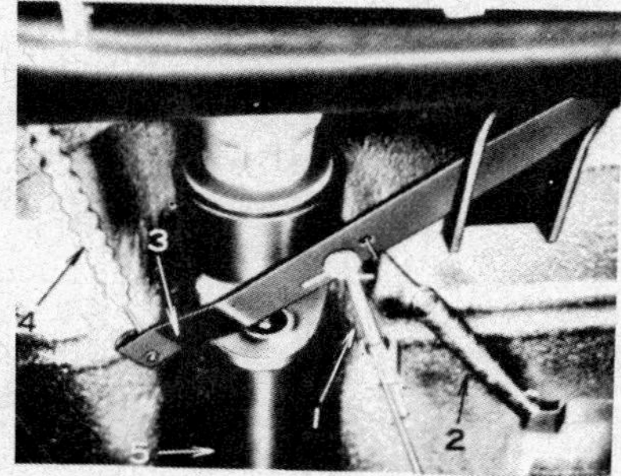

Components of the parking brake equalizer assembly—under-dash parking brake.

1. Pull rod
2. Return spring
3. Intermediate lever
4. Cable
5. Driveshaft

29. Disconnect the driveshaft from the end of the transmission.

NOTE: *If oil runs out from the transmission, an old U-joint yoke makes a good plug.*

30. Remove the left-hand gravel shield and then the front engine mounts.

31. Support the transmission with a jack.

32. Remove the rear engine mounts and the rear crossmember.

33. Attach a hoist to the engine and lift it up and forward, so that it clears the car.

Installation is in the reverse order of removal. Adjust the transmission and carburetor linkages, as detailed in the appropriate sections. Bleed the clutch as outlined below. Install the hood and adjust it. Replenish the fluid levels.

F Engine

1. Scribe marks on the hood and hinges to aid in alignment during installation. Remove the hinge bolts from the hood and then remove the hood.

2. Drain the cooling system and engine oil.

3. Unfasten the radiator grille mounting bolts and remove the grille.

NOTE: *On station wagon models, remove the parking light assembly and wiring first.*

4. Remove the hood latch support rod. Detach the hood latch assembly from the radiator upper bracket. Remove the bracket.

5. Disconnect the heater hose from the radiator.

6. Detach the upper radiator hose at the water outlet housing and the lower hose at water pump.

7. Remove the six bolts which secure the radiator and lift the radiator out of the vehicle.

8. Remove the heater hoses from the water valve and heater box. Disconnect the temperature control cable from the water valve.

9. Detach both of the battery cables and remove the battery.

10. Unfasten the wires from the starter solenoid terminal.

11. Detach the fuel lines from the pump and remove the fuel filter assembly.

12. Disconnect the primary wire from the ignition coil.

13. Detach both of the intermediate rods from the shifter shafts (column-shift models only).

14. Remove the air cleaner assembly complete with hoses, from its bracket.

15. Remove the emission control system cables and hoses as necessary.

16. Disconnect the alternator multiconnector.

17. Disconnect the hand throttle, accelerator, and choke linkages from the carburetor.

18. On Land Cruiser models with vacuum assisted 4WD engagement, remove the control unit vacuum hose from its manifold fitting.

19. Disconnect the oil pressure and water temperature gauge sender's wiring.

20. Unfasten the downpipe from the

exhaust manifold.

21. Detach the parking brake cable from the intermediate lever.

22. Unfasten the front driveshaft from the flange on the transfer case output shaft.

23. Remove both the left and right engine stone shields. Remove the transmission skid-plate.

24. Remove the cotter pin and disconnect both the high- and low-range shifter rods from their respective inner levers.

25. Remove the high/low range shifter link lever and the high/low shift rod.

26. Unfasten the clutch release fork spring. Remove the clutch release cylinder from its mounting bracket at the rear of the engine.

27. Unfasten the clamp screws and withdraw the vacuum lines from the transfer case control unit vacuum chamber (only on models with vacuum-assisted 4WD engagement).

28. Remove the 4WD indicator switch assembly.

29. Unfasten the speedometer cable from the transmission.

30. Disconnect the rear driveshaft from the transmission.

31. Detach the gearshift rod and gear selector rod from the shift outer lever and the gear selector outer lever, respectively.

32. Unfasten the nuts which secure the rear engine mounts to the frame.

33. Perform Step 32 to the front engine mounts.

34. Install lifting hooks on the engine lift-points. Connect a suitable (large) hoist to the hooks.

35. Lift the engine slightly and toward the front, so the engine/transmission assembly clears the front of the vehicle.

Engine removal is performed in the reverse order of its installation. Refill the engine with coolant and lubricant, as specified above. Check and adjust all linkages, as outlined in the appropriate section. Install the hood and align the matchmarks.

Cylinder Head

CAUTION: *Do not perform this operation on a warm engine. Remove the head bolts in the sequence illustrated under "Torque Sequences" and in several steps. Loosen the head bolts evenly, not one at a time. Keep the pushrods in their original order. Do not attempt to slide the cylinder head off of the block, as it is located with dowel pins. Lift the head straight up and off the block.*

Removal and Installation

K-C and 3K-C

1. Disconnect the battery and drain the cooling system.

2. Remove the air cleaner assembly from its bracket, complete with its attendant hoses.

3. Disconnect the hoses from the air injection system (1968–71) or the vacuum switching valve lines (1972–73).

4. Detach the accelerator cable from its support on the cylinder head cover and also from the carburetor throttle arm.

5. Remove the choke cable and fuel lines from the carburetor.

6. Remove the water hose bracket from the cylinder head cover.

7. Unfasten the water hose clamps and remove the hoses from the water pump and the water valve. Detach the heater temperature control cable from the water valve.

8. Disconnect the PCV line from the cylinder head cover.

9. Unbolt and remove the valve cover.

10. Remove the valve rocker support securing bolts and nuts. Lift out the valve rocker assembly.

11. Withdraw the pushrods from their bores.

12. Unfasten the hose clamps and remove the upper radiator hose from the water outlet.

13. Remove the wires from the spark plugs.

14. Disconnect the wiring and the fluid line from the windshield washer assembly. Remove the assembly.

NOTE: *Use a clean container to catch the fluid from the windshield washer reservoir when disconnecting its fluid line.*

15. Unfasten the exhaust pipe flange from the exhaust manifold.

16. Remove the head assembly retaining bolts and remove the head from the engine.

17. Place the cylinder head on *wooden* blocks to prevent damage to it.

Installation is essentially the reverse order of removal. Clean both the cylinder head and block gasket mounting surfaces.

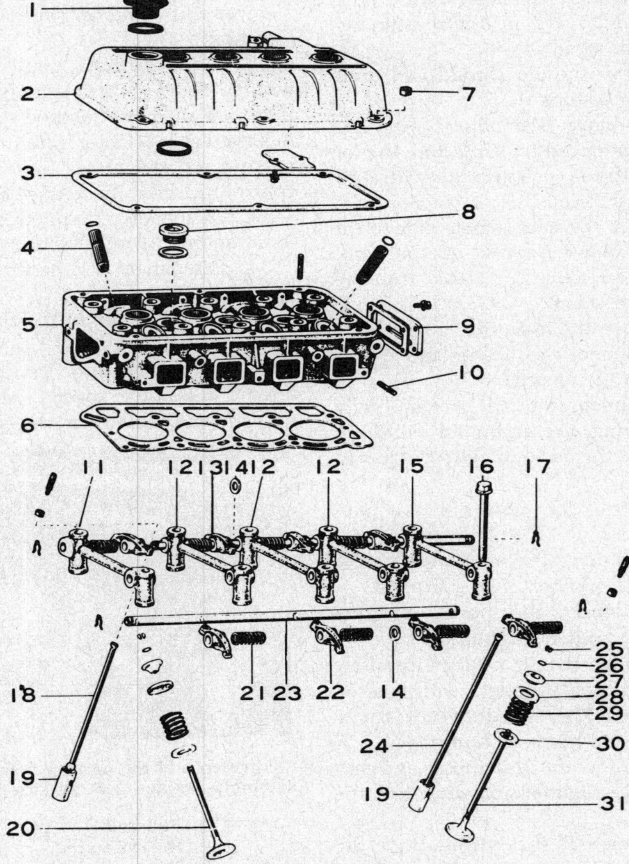

2T-C cylinder head components

1. Oil filler cap
2. Valve cover
3. Valve cover gasket
4. Valve guide (intake)
5. Cylinder head
6. Cylinder head gasket
7. Nut
8. Screw plug
9. Cylinder head rear cover
10. Stud
11. Valve rocker support
12. Valve rocker support
13. Valve rocker arm
14. Washer
15. Valve rocker support
16. Bolt
17. Retainer spring
18. Pushrod
19. Valve lifter
20. Intake valve
21. Compression spring
22. Valve rocker arm
23. Valve rocker shaft
24. Pushrod
25. Lock spring
26. O-ring
27. Valve spring retainer
28. Oil splash shield
29. Compression spring
30. Plate washer
31. Exhaust valve

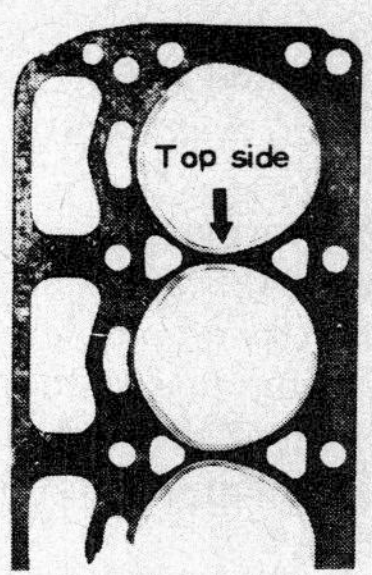

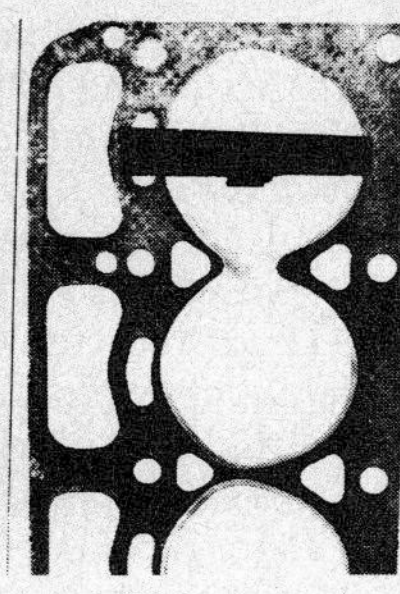

Identification of the top side of the K-C and 3K-C head gasket.

Always use a new head gasket.

NOTE: *Be sure that the top side of the gasket is facing upward. (See illustration.)*

When installing the head on the block, be sure to tighten the bolts in the sequence shown (see "Torque Sequences"), in several stages, to the torque specified in the "Torque Specifications" chart.

The valve rocker assembly nuts and bolts should be tightened to 13–16 ft lbs.

NOTE: *The valve clearance should be adjusted to specification with each piston at top dead center (TDC) of its compression stroke.*

2T-C Engine

1. Perform steps 1–2 of the 3K-C head removal procedure.
2. Disconnect the vacuum lines which run from the vacuum switching valve to the various emission control devices mounted on the cylinder head.
3. Disconnect the mixture control valve hose which runs to the intake manifold and remove the valve from its mounting bracket.
4. Perform step 7 of the K-C and 3K-C head removal procedure.
5. Detach the water temperature sender wiring.
6. Remove the choke stove pipe and its intake pipe.
7. Remove the PCV hose from the intake manifold.
8. Disconnect the fuel and vacuum lines from the carburetor.
9. Remove the clutch hydraulic line bracket from the cylinder head.
10. Raise the car and support it with jackstands. Unfasten the exhaust pipe clamp. Remove the exhaust manifold from the cylinder head. (See below.)
11. Remove the valve cover.
12. Remove the cylinder head bolts in the sequence illustrated under "Torque Sequences."
13. Perform steps 10–11 of the K-C and 3K-C cylinder head removal procedure.
14. Remove the cylinder head, complete with the intake manifold.
15. Separate the intake manifold from the cylinder head.

Install the cylinder head in the following order:

1. Clean the gasket mounting surfaces of the cylinder head and the block completely.

   NOTE: *Remove oil from the cylinder head bolt holes, if present.*
2. Place a *new* gasket on the block and install the head assembly.
3. Install the pushrods and the valve rocker assembly.
4. Tighten the cylinder head bolts *evenly*, in stages, as illustrated in the "Torque Sequence" diagrams. See the "Torque Specifications" chart, above, for the proper tightening torque.
5. Install the intake manifold, using a new gasket and tighten it to specifications.
6. The rest of the installation procedure is the reverse of removal. Remember to adjust the valve clearances.

3R-B and 3R-C Engines

1. Disconnect the battery and drain the cooling system.
2. Remove the air cleaner, complete with its attendant hoses.
3. Disconnect the air injection system hoses on 3R-C engines.
4. Detach the accelerator linkage and fuel lines from the carburetor. Remove the vacuum lines, as well.
5. Unfasten the water hose clamps, and remove the hose from the water pump and valve. Remove the water valve.
6. Remove the air pump, gulp valve, and air injection manifold from 3R-C engines.
7. Remove the distributor, complete with spark plug cables. Remove the high tension and primary cables.
8. Remove the spark plugs.
9. Remove the alternator drive belt, alternator and alternator mounting bracket.
10. Unfasten the automatic choke stove pipes and remove them.
11. Remove the carburetor, complete with heat insulator.
12. Remove the intake/exhaust combination manifold assembly, as detailed below.
13. Remove the oil pressure and water temperature wiring and senders. Detach the PCV line, water drain valve, and oil dipstick tube.
14. Remove the valve cover and gasket.
15. Remove the valve rocker support, complete with rocker arms and shaft.
16. Remove the push rod (side) covers and withdraw the push rods from their bores.
17. Remove the cylinder head bolts in several stages, and in the order illustrated under "Torque Sequences." Lift off the cylinder head and its gasket.
18. Place the cylinder head on wooden blocks, to prevent damage to it.

Cylinder head installation is performed in the reverse order of removal. Always use a new head gasket. Tighten the head bolts in the sequence shown under "Torque Sequences", and in several stages, to the proper specifications.

The valve rocker assembly securing bolts should be tightened to 15–18 ft lbs.

NOTE: *Remember to install the push rods in the same bores from which they were removed.*

Refill the cooling system, adjust the valves and check ignition timing after installation.

8R-C and 18R-C Engine

1. Perform steps 1–2 and then steps 4–8 of the K-C and 3K-C engine cylinder head removal procedure. Skip steps 3 and 5.
2. Remove the vacuum lines from the distributor vacuum unit. Remove the lines which run from the vacuum switching valve to the various emission contol system components on the cylinder head.
3. Remove the fuel and vacuum lines from the carburetor.
4. Remove the pipes from the automatic choke stove.
5. Unfasten the wires from the spark plugs. Remove the spark plugs.
6. Remove the cylinder head cover retaining bolts and withdraw the cover.

   NOTE: *Use a clean cloth, placed over the timing cover opening, to prevent anything from falling down into it.*
7. Remove the upper radiator hose from the cylinder head water outlet.
8. Remove the outlet elbow and thermostat.
9. Unfasten the downpipe clamp from the exhaust manifold. Remove the manifold from the head.
10. Remove the valve rocker assembly mounting bolts and the oil delivery pipes. Withdraw the valve rocker shaft assembly.

    CAUTION: *When removing the rocker shaft securing bolts, loosen them in two or three stages and in the proper sequence. (See torque sequences illustration.)*
11. Remove the timing gear from the camshaft. Support it so that the chain does not fall down into the cover.
12. Remove the camshaft bearing caps and withdraw the camshaft. Remove the camshaft bearings.

    NOTE: *Temporarily assemble the bearings and caps to keep them with their mates. Be sure to keep the bearings in proper order.*
13. Remove the gear from the timing chain. Support the timing chain so that it does not fall into the cover.
14. Loosen the head bolts in two or three stages; in the sequence illustrated. Lift the head assembly off the block.

Installation is performed in the following order:

1. Remove any water from the cylin-

der head bolt holes.

2. Clean the mating surfaces of the cylinder head and block. Use liquid sealer around the oil holes on the head and cylinder block. Do not get sealer in the holes.

3. Lower the cylinder head on to the block.

4. Tighten the cylinder head bolts in the proper sequence (see diagrams, above) and in three or four stages. Tighten them to the specifications given in the "Torque Specifications" chart above.

5. Install each lower bearing half into the seat from which it was removed.

6. Place the camshaft in the cylinder head.

7. Install each bearing into the cap from which it was removed.

8. Install the camshaft bearing caps on the head, in their numbered sequence, with the numbers facing forward. Tighten to 12–17 ft lbs.

9. First, check the camshaft bearing clearance and end-play, using Plastigage ®

NOTE: *This is checked in the same manner that connecting rod and crankshaft bearings are checked. For the procedure see "Engine Rebuilding".*

The oil clearance should be 0.001–0.-002 in.; the end-play should be 0.0017–0.0066 in.

10. Crank the engine so that no. 1 piston is at TDC of its compression stroke.

11. Align the mark on the timing chain with the dowel hole on the camshaft timing gear and the stamped mark on the camshaft.

NOTE: *All three marks should be aligned so that they are facing upward.*

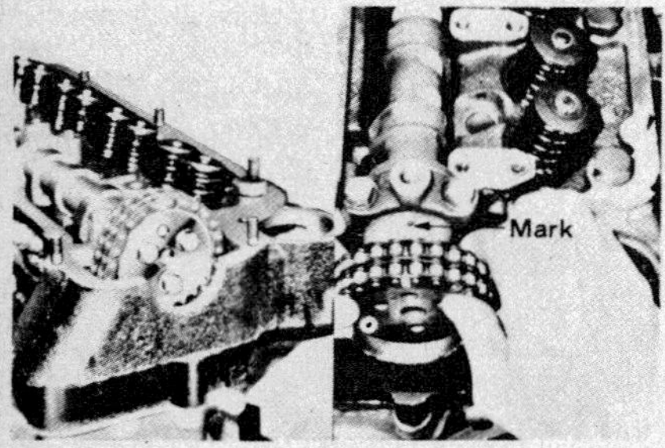

Alignment of marks on the 8R-C and 18R-C sprocket and timing chain

12. Install the valve rocker assembly. Tighten its securing bolts to 12–17 ft lbs, in the sequence illustrated, and in two or three stages.

13. Attach the oil delivery pipe to the valve rocker assembly and camshaft bearing caps. Tighten their securing bolts to 11–16 ft lbs.

14. Adjust the valve clearance as outlined above to the following *cold* specifications:

Intake—0.007 in.
Exhaust—0.013 in.

15. The rest of installation is performed in the reverse order of removal.

2M and 4M Engines

1. Perform steps 1–4 and 6–8 of the 3K-C cylinder head removal procedure. Skip step 5.

2. Remove the fuel and vacuum lines from the carburetor. Remove the carburetor.

3. Remove the spark plug wires from their supports on the cylinder head cover and from the spark plugs themselves.

4. Remove the distributor assembly.

5. Take off the automatic choke stove hoses.

6. Remove the exhaust manifold and the oil pressure light sender.

7. Remove the intake manifold assembly.

8. Unfasten the retaining bolts and remove the valve cover assembly.

NOTE: *Place a cloth over the timing gear to prevent anything from falling into the timing gear cover.*

9. Remove the valve rocker shaft assembly retaining bolts in the sequence illustrated. Loosen the bolts in two or three stages. Remove the rocker shaft assembly.

10. Remove the timing chain tensioner.

11. Straighten out the lockplate and unfasten the timing gear retaining bolt (left-hand thread). Withdraw the timing gear from the camshaft.

12. Perform steps 12–14 of the 8R-C and 18R-C cylinder head removal procedure.

Installation is performed in the following order:

1. Perform steps 1–10 of the 8R-C and 18R-C cylinder head removal procedure.

NOTE: *Apply liquid sealer around each cylinder block oil hole but be careful not to get any in the hole itself. Also, apply sealer to the timing chain cover and cylinder block.*

2. Align the V-notch on the camshaft with the 5/32 in. hole on the no. 1 camshaft bearing.

NOTE: *Be sure that the V-notch is also aligned with the mark on the timing chain cover.*

3. Install the camshaft timing gear, with the chain, on the end of the camshaft. Align the pin on the camshaft flange with the hole in the gear.

4. Install the timing gear bolt and lockplate. Fasten the bolt with the lockplate.

NOTE: *The bolt has a left-hand thread. Tighten it to 47–54 ft lbs.*

5. Install the chain tensioner, complete with shim. Tighten it to 22–29 ft lbs.

6. Turn the crankshaft two complete revolutions while checking to see that valve timing is correct. If, at the end of the two revolutions, the timing marks do not align, repeat Steps 2–4.

7. Apply pressure to the chain tensioner arm. If its movement is less than 3/16 in., add additional shims.

8. Install the valve rocker assembly and tighten the bolts to 22–29 ft lbs, in the sequence illustrated, and in three or four stages.

NOTE: *The stud bolt should only be tightened to 11–14 ft lbs.*

9. Install the union on the No. 1 rocker support and the No. 1 camshaft bearing cap. Tighten the union bolts to 6–9 ft lbs.

10. Adjust the valve clearance, as outlined above, to the following *cold* specifications:

Intake—0.006 in.
Exhaust—0.008 in.

11. The rest of the installation procedure is performed in the reverse order of removal.

F Engine

1. Perform steps 1–2 and 4–8 of the 3K-C cylinder head procedure. Skip step 3.

2. Disconnect the vacuum lines, which run from the vacuum switching valve, at the various components of the emission control system.

3. Drain the engine oil. Unfasten the oil lines from the oil filter and remove the filter assembly from the manifold.

4. Detach the vacuum valve solenoid wire from the coil.

5. Disconnect any remaining lines from the carburetor and remove the carburetor from the manifold.

6. Unfasten the alternator adjusting link and then remove the drivebelt and the alternator.

7. Disconnect the distributor vacuum line from the distributor. Remove the wire from its supports on the head.

8. Disconnect the carburetor fuel line from the fuel pump. Remove the line.

9. Disconnect the spark plug and coil cables, after marking their respective locations.

10. Unfasten the primary wire from

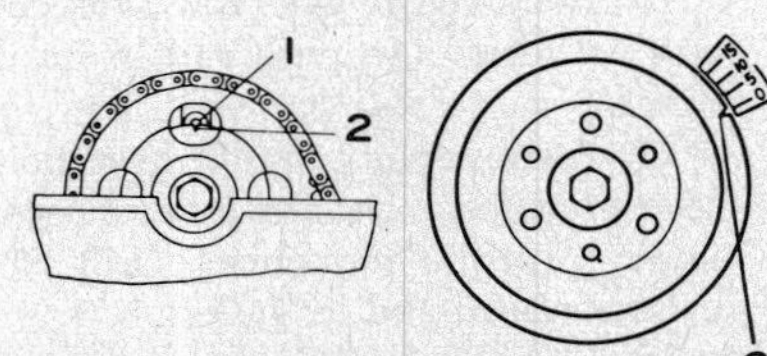

1. Valve timing mark (5/32 in. hole)
2. V-notch—camshaft flange
3. V-notch—crankshaft pulley

Alignment of the timing marks on the crankshaft and camshaft for 2M and 4M engines

the distributor. Remove the distributor clamp bolts and withdraw the distributor.

11. Remove the oil gauge sending unit.

12. Remove the coil from its bracket on the cylinder head.

13. Unfasten the fuel pump securing bolts and remove the pump.

14. Remove the oil filler tube clamping bolt from the valve lifter (side) cover. Drive the oil filler tube out of the cylinder block.

15. Remove the combination intake/exhaust manifold from the cylinder block. (See the appropriate section, below.)

16. Take off the cylinder head cover and its gasket.

17. Unfasten the oil delivery union, spring, and sleeve from the valve rocker shafts.

18. Unfasten the securing nuts and bolts from the valve rocker shaft supports. Withdraw the rocker assembly.

19. Withdraw the pushrods from their bores. Be sure to keep them in the same order in which they were removed.

20. Remove the valve lifter (side) cover and gasket.

21. Withdraw the valve lifters from the block.

NOTE: *The valve lifters should be kept, with their respective pushrods, in the sequence in which they were removed.*

22. Unfasten the oil delivery union from the oil feed pipe.

23. Loosen the cylinder head bolts in two or three stages and in the order illustrated above.

24. Lift off the cylinder head and the gasket.

Installation of the cylinder head is performed in the following order:

1. Clean the gasket mounting surfaces of both the cylinder head and block.

2. Place a *new* head gasket over the dowels on the block.

3. Lower the cylinder head on to the block with the air cleaner mounting bracket attached.

4. Tighten the bolts, in stages, and in the sequence illustrated, to the torque given in the "Torque Specifications" chart.

5. Install the oil feed pipe.

6. Place each valve lifter in the original position from which it came.

NOTE: *Do not interchange valve lifters.*

7. Perform step 6 for the pushrods, being careful to mate each pushrod with its original lifter.

8. Install the valve rocker assembly, oil delivery union, spring, and connecting sleeve in the head. Tighten the rocker assembly support nuts and bolts to the following torque specifications, in several stages:

10mm nuts and bolts—25–30 ft lbs
8mm bolts—14–22 ft lbs

9. Adjust the valves, as outlined above, to the following *cold* specifications (each piston TDC of its compression stroke):

Intake—0.0079 in.
Exhaust—0.0138 in.

NOTE: *Adjust the valve clearance again after the engine is assembled and warmed up.*

10. The rest of cylinder head installation is performed in the reverse order of the removal procedure.

Overhaul

NOTE: *General cylinder head overhaul procedures are given in the "Engine Rebuilding" section at the end of the book. The operations which differ greatly from those at the end of the book are detailed below.*

Valve Guide Replacement—2M, 4M, K-C and 3K-C Engines

1. Heat the cylinder head to 176–212°F, evenly, before beginning the replacement procedure.

2. Use a brass rod to break the valve guide off above its snap-ring. (See illustration.)

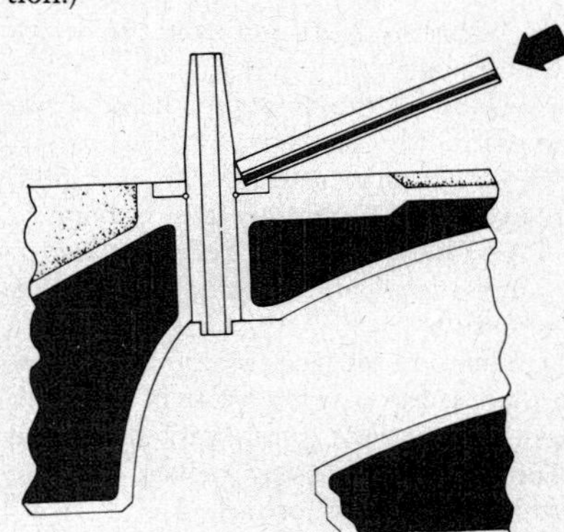

Use a brass drift to break off the valve guide.

3. Drive out the valve guide, toward the combustion chamber. Use a tool fabricated as described in "Engine Rebuilding," at the end of this book.

4. Install a snap-ring on the new valve guide. Apply liquid sealer. Drive in the valve guide until the snap-ring contacts the head. Use the tool described above.

5. Measure the guide bore; if the stem-to-guide clearance is below specification, ream it out, using a valve guide reamer.

Intake Manifold

Removal and Installation

2T-C Engine

1. Drain the cooling system.

2. Remove the air cleaner assembly, complete with hoses, from its bracket.

3. Remove the choke stove hoses, fuel lines, and vacuum lines from the carburetor. Unfasten the emission control system hoses and the accelerator linkage from it.

4. Unfasten the four nuts which secure the carburetor to the manifold and remove the carburetor.

5. Remove the mixture control valve line from its intake manifold fitting.

6. Disconnect the PCV hose.

7. Disconnect the water bypass hose from the intake manifold.

8. Unbolt and remove the manifold.

Installation is performed in the reverse order of removal. Remember to use *new* gaskets. Tighten the intake manifold bolts to the specifications given in the "Torque Specifications" chart.

NOTE: *Tighten the bolts, in several stages, working from the inside out.*

2M and 4M Engines

1. Drain the cooling system.

2. Remove the air cleaner assembly, complete with hoses, from its mounting bracket.

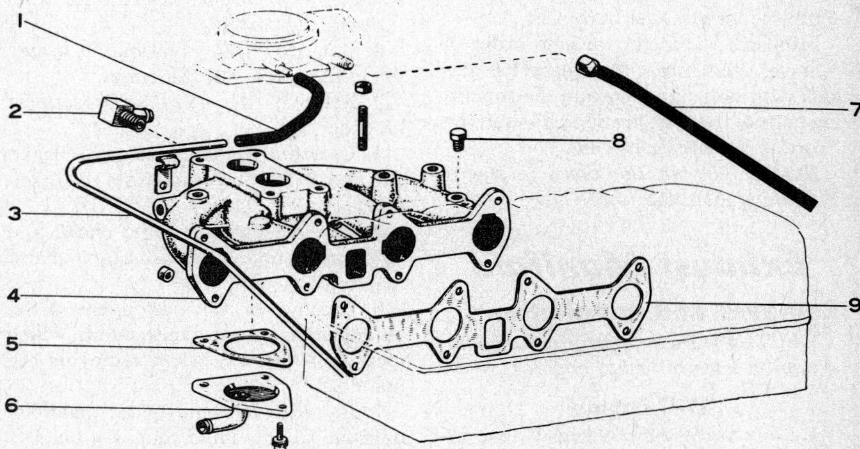

2T-C intake manifold assembly

1. Choke stove intake hose
2. Elbow
3. Choke stove intake
4. Intake manifold
5. Gasket
6. Water by-pass outlet
7. Choke stove outlet
8. Plug
9. Intake manifold gasket

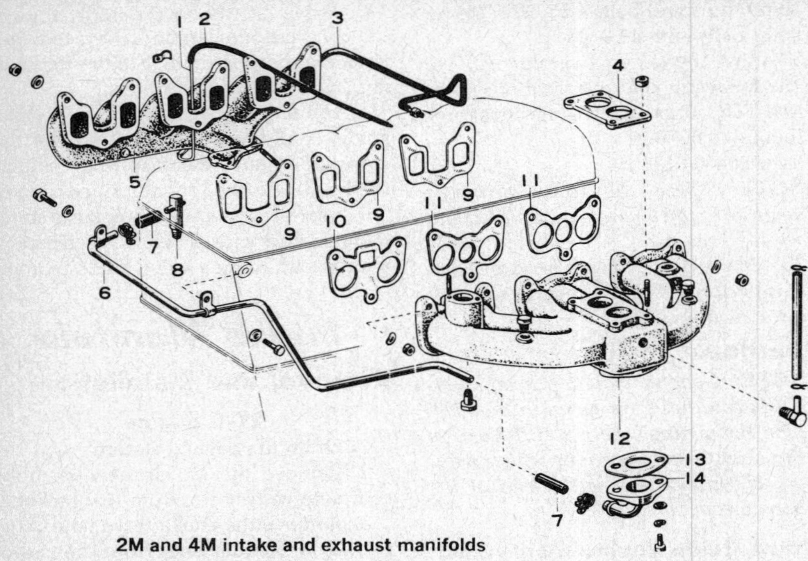

2M and 4M intake and exhaust manifolds

1. Automatic choke stove intake pipe
2. Automatic choke stove intake hose
3. Automatic choke stove outlet pipe
4. Carburetor heat insulator
5. Exhaust manifold
6. Water by-pass line
7. Water by-pass hose
8. Water hose joint
9. Exhaust manifold gasket
10. Intake manifold gasket (1)
11. Intake manifold gasket (2)
12. Intake manifold
13. Gasket
14. Water by-pass outlet

3. Remove the distributor cap.

4. Remove the upper radiator hose from the elbow.

5. Remove the wiring from the temperature gauge sending unit.

6. Remove the following from the carburetor: fuel lines; vacuum line; choke stove hoses; emission control system hoses; accelerator torque rod; and automatic transmission linkage (if so equipped).

7. Remove the emission control system lines and wiring from the manifold when equipped with a vacuum switching valve.

8. Remove the water bypass hose from the manifold.

9. Unbolt and remove the manifold, complete with the carburetor.

Installation is in the reverse order of removal. Remember to replace the gaskets with new ones. Torque the mounting bolts to the specifications given in the "Torque Specifications" chart.

NOTE: *Tighten the bolts, in stages, working from the inside out.*

Exhaust Manifold

Removal and Installation

CAUTION: *Do not perform this operation on a warm or hot engine.*

2T-C Engine

1. Detach the manifold heat stove intake pipe.

2. Unfasten the nut on the stove outlet pipe union.

3. Remove the wiring from the emission control system thermo sensor.

4. Unfasten the U-bolt from the downpipe bracket.

5. Unfasten the downpipe flange from the manifold.

6. In order to remove the manifold, unfasten the manifold retaining bolts.

CAUTION: *Remove the bolts in two or three stages and working from the inside out.*

Installation of the manifold is performed in the reverse order of removal. Remember to use a *new* gasket. See the "Torque Specifications" chart for the proper tightening torque.

2M and 4M Engines

1. Raise the front and the rear of the car and support it with jackstands.

CAUTION: *Be sure that the car is securely supported.*

2. Remove the right-hand gravel shield from beneath the engine.

3. Remove the downpipe support bracket.

4. Unfasten the bolts from the flange and detach the downpipe from the manifold.

5. Remove the automatic choke and air cleaner stove hoses from the exhaust manifold.

6. Remove, or move aside, any of the air injection system components which may be in the way when removing the manifold.

7. In order to remove the manifold, unfasten the manifold retaining bolts.

CAUTION: *Remove and tighten the bolts in two or three stages and, starting from the inside, working out.*

Installation is performed in the reverse order of removal. Always use a new gasket. Tighten the retaining bolts to the specifications given above in two or three stages.

Combination Manifold

Removal and Installation

CAUTION: *Do not perform this procedure on a warm engine.*

K-C, 3K-C, 3R-B, 3R-C and F Engines

1. Remove the air cleaner assembly, complete with hoses.

2. Disconnect the accelerator and choke linkages from the carburetor, as well as the fuel and vacuum lines. On F engines, remove the hand throttle linkage.

3. Remove, or move aside, any of the emission control system components which are in the way.

4. On F engines, disconnect the oil filter lines and remove the oil filter assembly from the intake manifold. Unfasten the solenoid valve wire from the ignition coil terminal.

5. Unfasten the retaining bolts and remove the carburetor from the manifold.

6. Loosen the manifold retaining nuts, working from the inside out, in two or three stages.

7. Remove the intake/exhaust manifold assembly from the cylinder head as a complete unit.

Installation is performed in the reverse order of removal. Always use *new* gaskets. Tighten the bolts, working from the inside out, to the specifications given in the "Torque Specifications" chart.

NOTE: *Tighten the bolts in two or three stages.*

8R-C and 18R-C Engines

1. Remove the air cleaner assembly, complete with hoses, from its mounting bracket.

2. Remove the fuel line, vacuum line, automatic choke stove hoses, PCV hose, and accelerator linkage from the carburetor.

3. Unfasten the carburetor securing nuts. Remove the torque rod support, carburetor, and heat insulator.

4. Use a jack to raise the front of the car. Support the car with jackstands.

CAUTION: *Be sure that the car is securely supported.*

5. Unfasten the bolts which attach the downpipe flange to the exhaust manifold.

6. In order to remove the manifold assembly, unfasten the manifold retaining bolts.

CAUTION: *Remove and tighten the bolts in two or three stages, working from the inside out.*

Installation is performed in the reverse order of removal. Always use *new* gas-

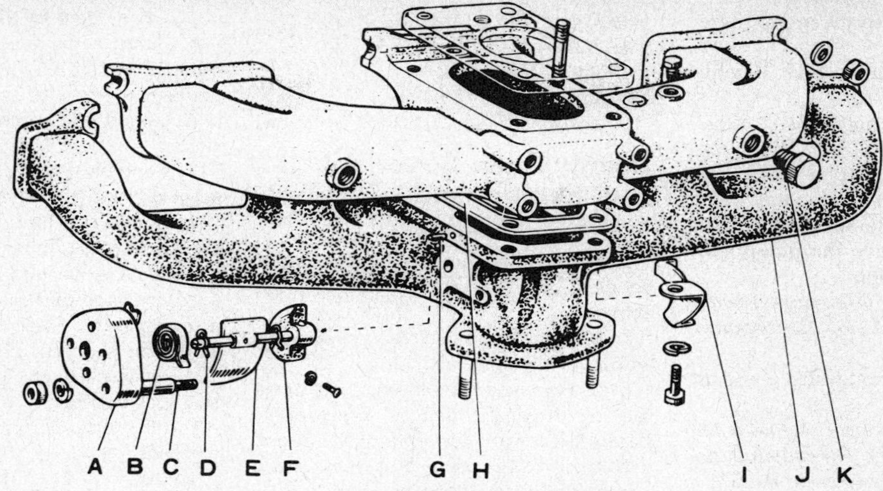

F engine combination manifold assembly

(a)—Heat control valve bimetal case
(b)—Valve coil
(c)—Bolt
(d)—Retaining spring
(e)—Heat control valve
(f)—Heat control valve shaft
(g)—Dowel
(i)—Counter weight stop
h)—Manifold gasket
(j)—Exhaust manifold
(k)—Screw plug

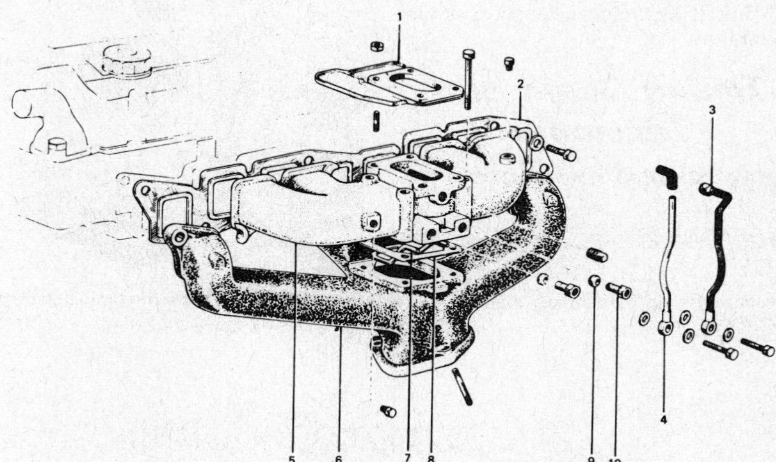

8R-C and 19R-C combination manifold assembly.

1. Heat insulator
2. Manifold gasket (manifold-to-car)
3. Choke stove outlet pipe
4. Choke stove intake pipe
5. Intake manifold
6. Exhaust manifold
7. Choke stove pipe
8. Manifold gasket (intake-to-exhaust)
9. Sleeve
10. Union

kets. Tighten the manifold securing bolts to the figure shown in the "Torque Specifications" chart, in the reverse sequence of removal.

Timing Gear Cover

Removal and Installation

3R-B, 3R-C, K-C, 3K-C, 2T-C, and F Engines

1. Drain the cooling system and the crankcase.

2. Disconnect the battery.

3. Remove the air cleaner assembly, complete with hoses, from its bracket.

4. Remove the hood latch as well as its brace and support (except on 1966–70 Corona models).

NOTE: *On 1966–70 Corona models, scribe aligning marks on the hood and hinges. Remove the hood.*

5. Remove the headlight bezels and grille assembly.

6. Unfasten the upper and lower radiator hose clamps and remove both of the hoses from the engine.

7. Unfasten the radiator securing bolts and remove the radiator.

NOTE: *Take off the shroud first, if so equipped.*

8. Loosen the drive belt adjusting link and remove the drive belt. Unfasten the alternator multiconnector, withdraw the retaining bolts, and remove the alternator.

9. Perform step 8 to the air injection pump, if so equipped. Disconnect the hoses from the pump before removing it.

10. Remove the fan and water pump as an assembly.

11. Unfasten the crankshaft pulley retaining bolt (except on 3R series and F engines). Remove the crankshaft pulley with a gear puller.

12. Remove the gravel shield from underneath the engine.

13. The following steps apply to the K-C and 3K-C engine only:

a. Remove the nuts and washers from both the right and left front engine mounts.

b. Detach the exhaust pipe flange from the exhaust manifold.

c. Slightly raise the front of the engine.

14. On Land Cruiser models, remove the front driveshaft.

15. On 2T-C engines, remove the right-hand brace plate.

16. Remove the front oil pan bolts, to gain access to the bottom of the timing chain cover.

NOTE: *It may be necessary to insert a thin knife between the pan and the gasket in order to break the pan loose. Use care not to damage the gasket.*

Installation is basically the reverse order of removal. There are, however, several points to remember:

1. Apply sealer to the two front corners of the 2T-C engine's oil pan gasket.

2. Tighten the crankshaft pulley to the figure given in the "Torque Specifications" chart above.

3. Adjust the drivebelts as outlined in the alternator service section above.

8R-C, 18R-C, 2M, and 4M Engines

1. Perform the cylinder head removal

procedure as detailed in the appropriate section above.

2. Remove the radiator. (See "Engine Cooling," below.)

3. Remove the alternator. (See "Alternator," above.)

4. On engines equipped with air pumps, unfasten the adjusting link bolts and the drivebelt. Remove the hoses from the pump; remove the pump and bracket from the engine.

NOTE: *If the car is equipped with power steering, see below for its pump removal procedure.*

5. Remove the fan and water pump as a complete assembly.

CAUTION: *To prevent the fluid from running out from the fan coupling, do not tip the assembly over on its side.*

6. Unfasten the crankshaft pulley securing bolt and remove the pulley with a gear puller.

CAUTION: *Do not remove the 10 mm bolt from its hole, if installed, as it is used for balancing.*

7. Loosen the bolts which secure the front of the oil pan, after draining the engine oil. Lower the front of the oil pan.

8. Remove the bolts which secure the timing chain cover. Withdraw the cover.

Installation is performed in the reverse order of removal. Apply sealer to the gaskets for both the timing chain cover and the oil pan.

NOTE: *The 2M and 4M engines use two gaskets on the timing chain cover.*

Tighten the timing chain cover bolts to the specifications below:

8R-C and 18R-C engines:
All bolts—11–15 ft lbs
2M and 4M engines:
8 mm bolts—7–12 ft lbs
10 mm bolts—14–22 ft lbs

Timing Chain Cover Oil Seal Replacement

All Engines

1. Remove the timing chain cover, as detailed in the appropriate section above.

2. Inspect the oil seal for signs of wear, leakage, or damage.

3. If worn, pry the old oil seal out, using a large flat-bladed screwdriver. Remove it toward the *front* of the cover.

NOTE: *Once the oil seal has been removed, it must be replaced with a new one.*

4. Use a socket, pipe, or block of wood and a hammer to drift the oil seal into place. Work from the *front* of the cover.

CAUTION: *Be extremely careful not to damage the seal or else it will leak.*

5. Install the timing chain cover as outlined above.

Timing Chain and Tensioner

Removal and Installation

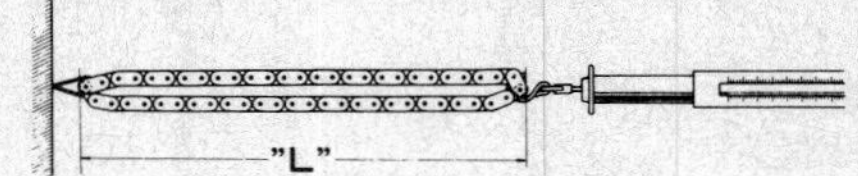

Measure timing chain stretch along "L"—K-C, 3K-C, and 2T-C

K-C and 3K-C Engines

1. Remove the timing chain cover as detailed in the appropriate section above.

2. Unbolt and remove the chain tensioner.

3. Remove the camshaft chain sprocket and then the chain itself.

4. Check the timing chain for wear, cracks, or loose links.

5. Secure one end of the chain to a fixed hook and pull on the other end with a spring scale. When the scale indicates 11 lbs, the chain should be no longer than 10.7 in. Replace the chain if it exceeds this specification.

Installation is performed in the following order:

1. Install the crankshaft chain sprocket. Align the sprocket O mark with the straight pin on the crankshaft, as illustrated.

2. Fit the timing chain on the crankshaft sprocket.

3. Align the mating marks on the tim-

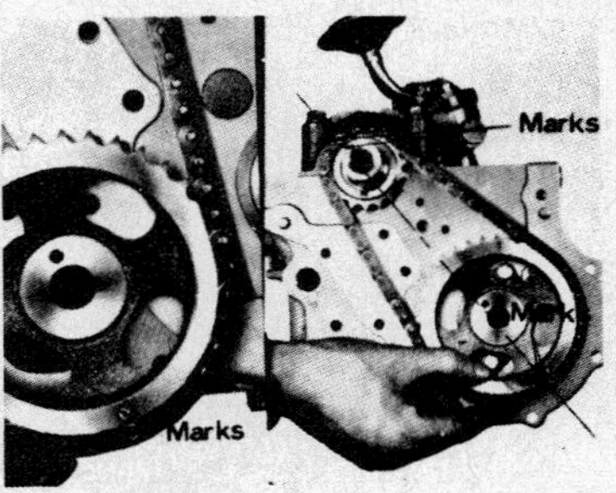

Aligning the marks on the timing chain and sprocket—K-C and 3K-C

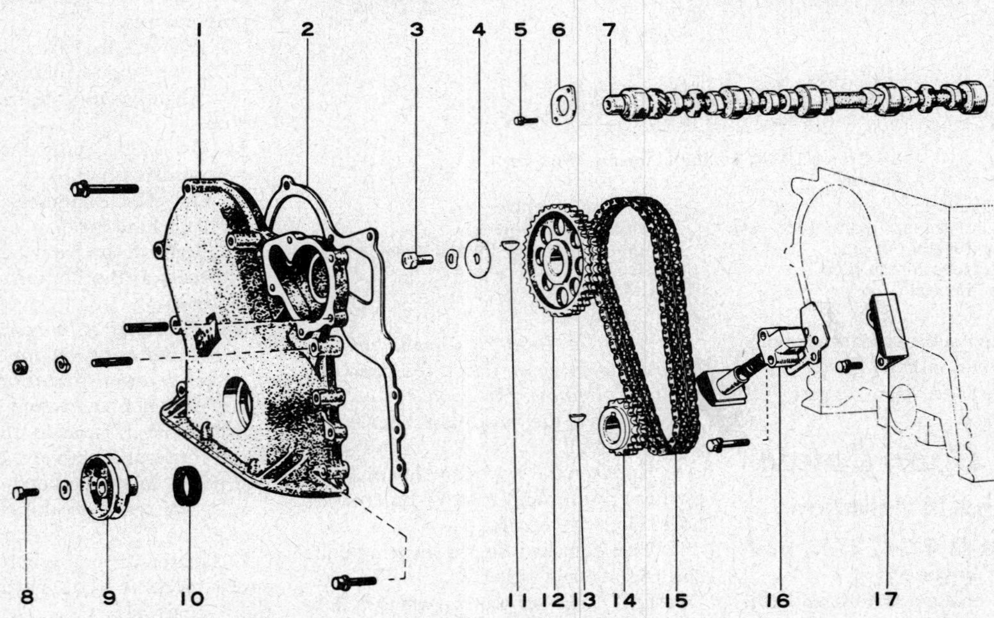

Timing chain covers, timing chain and camshaft—2T-C engine

1. Timing chain cover
2. Timing chain cover gasket
3. Bolt
4. Plate washer
5. Bolt
6. Plate
7. Camshaft
8. Bolt
9. Crankshaft pulley
10. Front oil seal
11. Woodruff key
12. Camshaft sprocket
13. Woodruff key
14. Crankshaft sprocket
15. Timing chain
16. Chain tensioner
17. Chain vibration damper

ing chain with the O-marks on both sprockets, as illustrated.

4. Align the camshaft sprocket O mark with the one on the crankshaft, as illustrated.

5. Tighten the camshaft timing sprocket securing bolt to 16–22 ft lbs.

6. Install the chain tensioner assembly and chain vibration damper. Tighten their bolts to 4–6 ft lbs.

7. Install the timing chain cover as detailed above.

2T-C Engine

1. Perform steps 1–3 of the K-C and 3K-C timing chain removal procedure.

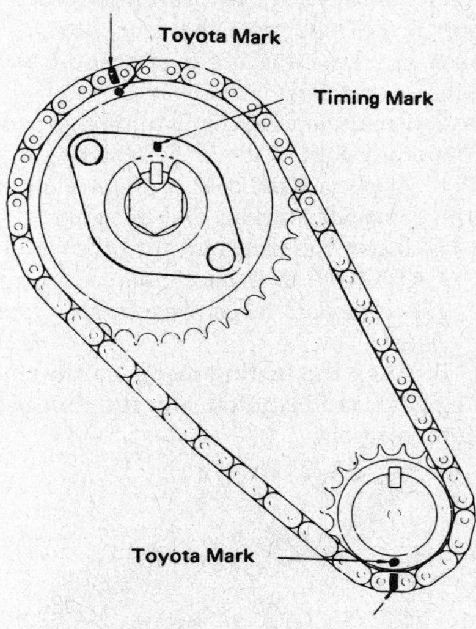

Proper alignment of the marks on 2T-C timing chain and sprocket

2. Perform steps 4–5 of the K-C and 3K-C timing chain removal procedure (chain inspection). The chain should stretch no more than 11.472 in. at 11 lbs on the spring scale.

Installation is performed in the following order:

1. Rotate the crankshaft so its key points straight up.

NOTE: *The no. 1 and no. 4 pistons should be at TDC.*

2. Rotate the camshaft so its key is aligned with the timing mark on the thrust plate.

3. Fit the chain on the camshaft and crankshaft timing sprockets so the marks on the timing chain align with the "Toyota" trademarks on each of the sprockets.

NOTE: *The above step is performed with the sprockets off the engine.*

4. Being careful to keep all the parts in proper alignment, fit the timing chain/-sprocket assembly to the engine. When assembled, the marks should align as in the illustration.

5. Torque the camshaft timing gear bolt to 50.6–79.6 ft lbs.

6. Fill the chain tensioner with engine oil and install it. Install the chain damper.

7. Install the timing chain cover as outlined above.

8R-C and 18R-C Engines

1. Remove the cylinder head and timing chain cover as detailed above.

2. Remove the timing chain (front) together with the camshaft drive sprocket.

3. Remove the crankshaft sprocket and oil pump jack shaft, complete with the pump drive chain (rear). Remove the chain vibration damper.

CAUTION: *Both timing chains are identical; tag them for proper identification during installation.*

4. Inspect the chains and sprockets for wear or damage. Clean the chains with solvent.

5. Use a vernier caliper to measure the amount of stretch of both chains. Measure any 17 links while pulling the chain that is being measured taut.

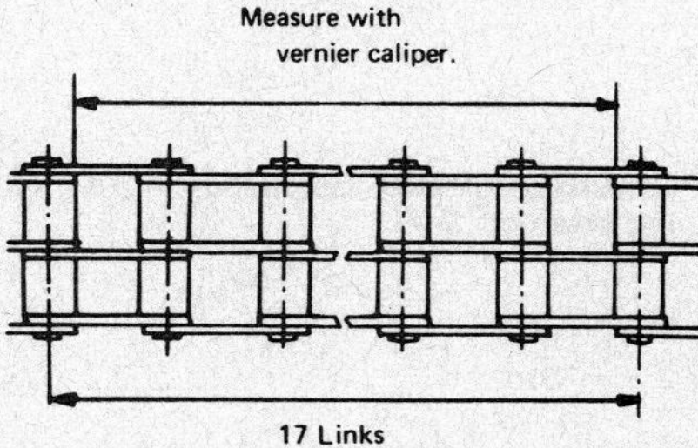

Timing chain stretch measurement—8R-C and 18R-C engines

6. Repeat step 5 at two other places on each chain. Replace either of the chains if any of the 17 link measurements exceed 5.792 in. or if the difference between the minimum and maximum readings is more than 0.0078 in., on any one chain.

7. Remove the plunger and spring from one of the chain tensioners. Inspect all of the parts of the tensioner for wear or damage. Fill it with oil and assemble it if it is not defective.

8. Repeat step 7 for the other tensioner.

CAUTION: *Do not mix the parts of the two chain tensioners together.*

Installation is performed in the following manner:

1. Position the No. 1 piston at TDC by having the crankshaft keyway point straight up (perpendicular to), toward the cylinder head.

2. Align the oil pump jackshaft, with its keyway pointing straight up as well.

3. Align the marks on the timing sprocket and the oil pump drive sprocket with each of the marks on the chain.

4. Install the chain and sprocket assembly over the keyways, while retaining alignment of the chain/sprocket timing marks.

CAUTION: *Use care not to disengage the welch plug at the rear of the oil pump drive shaft, by forcing the sprocket over its keyway.*

5. Install the oil pump drive chain vibration damper.

6. Install the gasket for the timing chain cover.

NOTE: *Use liquid sealer on the gasket before installation.*

7. Install both of the chain tensioners in their respective places, being careful not to mix them up. Tighten their securing bolts to 12–17 ft lbs.

CAUTION: *Use care when installing the chain tensioner bolts; they have oil holes tapped in them.*

8. Fit the camshaft drive sprocket over the keyway on the oil pump drive shaft. Tighten its securing nut to 58–72 ft lbs.

9. Install the camshaft drive chain over the camshaft drive sprocket. Align the mating marks on the chain and sprocket.

10. Apply tension to the chain by tying it to the chain tensioner. This will prevent it from falling back into the timing chain cover once it is installed.

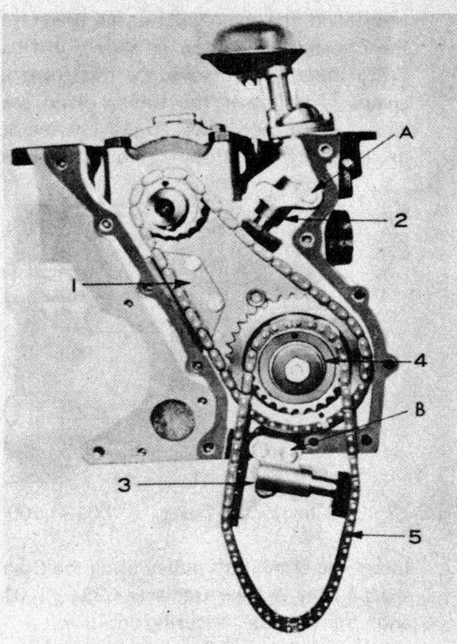

Installing the 8R-C and 18R-C timing chain

(a)—Chain tensioner bolt
(b)—Chain tensioner bolt
1. Chain vibration damper
2. Chain tensioner (oil pump drive chain)
3. Chain tensioner (Camshaft timing chain)
4. Camshaft drive sprocket
5. Camshaft timing chain

11. Install the timing chain cover and cylinder head as outlined above.

2M and 4M Engines

1. Remove the cylinder head and timing chain cover, as outlined above.

2. Remove the chain tensioner assembly (arm and gear).

3. Unfasten the bolts which retain the chain damper and damper guide and withdraw the damper and guide.

4. Remove the oil slinger from the crankshaft.

Removing the timing chain from the 2M or 4M engine.

1. Timing chain tensioner gear
2. Timing chain tensioner arm
3. Damper guide
4. Vibration damper
5. Vibration damper
6. Crankshaft oil slinger

5. Withdraw the timing chain.
6. Inspect the chain for wear or damage. Replace it if necessary.

Installation is performed in the following manner:

1. Position the no. 1 cylinder at TDC.
2. Position the crankshaft sprocket O mark downward, facing the oil pan.
3. Align the "Toyota" trademarks on the sprockets as illustrated.
4. Fit the tensioner gear assembly on the block.

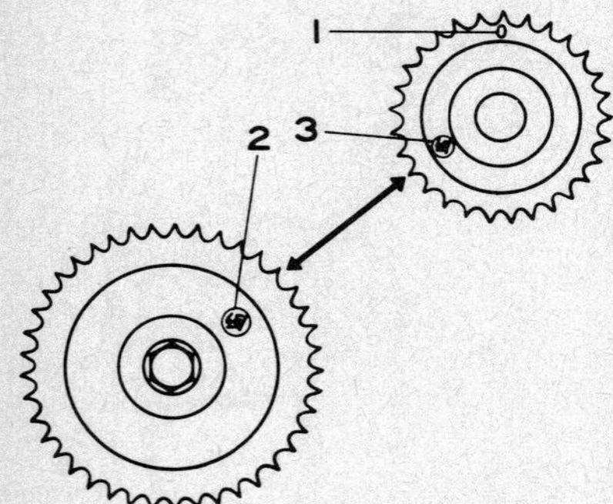

Proper alignment of the 2M or 4M timing marks.

1. Crankshaft sprocket O-mark
2. Camshaft sprocket "Toyota" mark
3. Crankshaft sprocket "Toyota" mark

NOTE: *Its dowel pin should be positioned 1.5 in. from the surface of the block.*

5. Install the chain over the two gears while maintaining tension.
6. Install both of the vibration dampers and the damper guide.
7. Fit the oil slinger to the crankshaft.
8. Tie the chain to the upper vibration damper, to keep it from falling into the chain cover, once the cover is installed.
9. Install the timing chain cover, as detailed above.
10. Perform the cylinder head installation procedure as detailed above.

NOTE: *If proper valve timing cannot be obtained, it is possible to adjust it by placing the camshaft slotted pin in the second or third hole on the camshaft timing gear, as required. If the timing is out by more than 15°, replace the chain and both of the sprockets.*

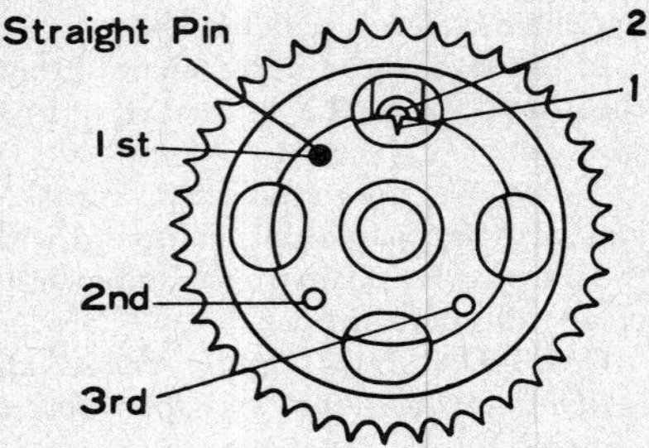

Camshaft sprocket showing normal timing

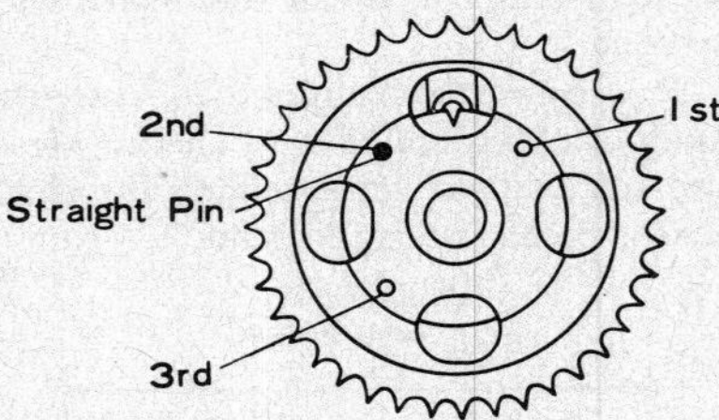

Camshaft sprocket installation—valve timing retarded 3-90.

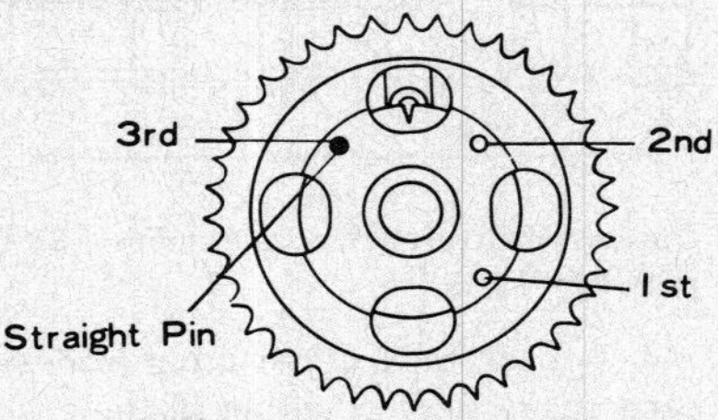

Camshaft sprocket installation—valve timing retarded 9-15°.

Timing Gears

Removal and Installation

3R-B and 3R-C Engines

NOTE: *This procedure contains camshaft removal and installation.*

1. Perform the cylinder head and timing chain cover removal procedures, as detailed above.
2. Unscrew the oil nozzle from the block.
3. Remove the camshaft thrust plate attaching bolts by working through the holes provided in the camshaft timing gear.
4. Withdraw the camshaft through the front of the cylinder block. Support it during removal so that its bearings or lobes are not damaged.
5. Check both of the timing gears for cracks, damage, wear or chips. Replace either or both of the gears, as necessary.
6. Check camshaft timing gear runout with a dial indicator. Replace the gear if runout exceeds 0.01 in.
7. Check the backlash between the timing gears with a feeler gauge. If it exceeds 0.012 in., replace the camshaft and/or the crankshaft timing gears.
8. If it is necessary to remove the camshaft timing gear, remove its securing bolt and washer. Use a gear puller to withdraw it from the camshaft.

NOTE: *Perform step 8, only if it is necessary to replace the camshaft timing gear.*

9. The crankshaft timing gear is to be removed in a similar manner, with a gear puller. Perform its removal only if the gear is to be replaced.

Installation is performed in the following manner:

1. Install the timing gear on the camshaft by installing the thrust plate and the key first. Then press the gear into place and install the washers and retaining bolt. Check end-play.
2. Press the crankshaft timing gear on the crankshaft, if it was removed.
3. Apply a light coat of engine oil on the camshaft journals and bearings.
4. Insert the camshaft into the block.

CAUTION: *Use care not to damage the camshaft lobes, bearings or journals.*

5. Align the mating marks on the timing gears as illustrated. Slip the camshaft into position.

Proper alignment of timing marks on the 3R-B and 3R-C engines.

6. Tighten the thrust plate securing bolts to 11–15 ft lbs.
7. Recheck timing gear backlash.
8. Screw the oil nozzle into the block with the oil hole pointing toward the gears. Lock it, by punching it in two places with a screwdriver, so that it will not loosen.
9. Install the timing gear cover and the cylinder head as outlined above.

F Engine

NOTE: *This procedure contains camshaft removal and installation.*

1. Perform the cylinder head and timing cover removal procedures, outlined above.
2. Slip the oil slinger off the crankshaft.
3. Remove the camshaft thrust plate retaining bolts by working through the holes provided in the camshaft timing gear.
4. Withdraw the camshaft through the front of the cylinder block. Support the

camshaft while removing it, so as not to damage its bearings or lobes.

NOTE: *The timing gear is a press-fit and cannot be removed without removing the camshaft.*

5. Inspect the crankshaft timing gear. Replace it if it has worn or damaged teeth.

6. To remove it, remove the sliding key from the crankshaft. Withdraw the timing gear with a gear puller.

Installation is performed in the following order:

1. Use a large piece of pipe to press the timing gear onto the crankshaft. Lightly and evenly tap the end of the pipe until the gear is in its original position.

2. Apply a coat of engine oil to the camshaft journals and bearings.

3. Insert the camshaft into the block.

CAUTION: *Use care not to damage the camshaft lobes, bearings, or journals.*

4. Align the mating marks on each of the gears as illustrated.

Alignment of the F engine timing marks

5. Slip the camshaft into position. Tighten the camshaft thrust plate bolts to 14.5 ft lbs.

6. Check the gear backlash with a feeler gauge, inserted between the crankshaft and the camshaft timing gears. The backlash should be no more than 0.002–0.005 in.; if it exceeds this, replace one or both of the gears, as required.

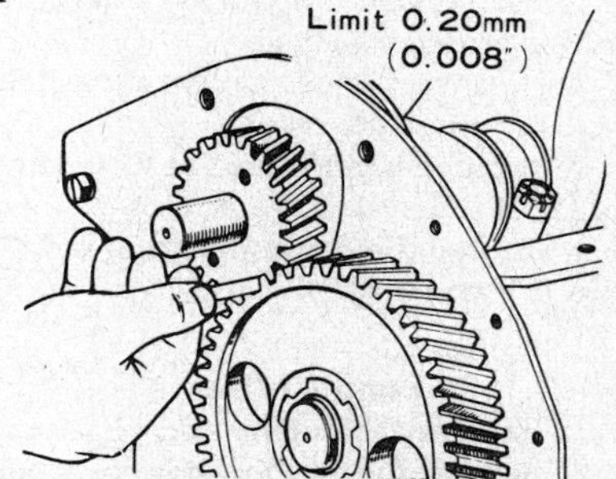

Checking timing gear backlash with a feeler gauge.

7. Check the gear run-out with a dial indicator. Run-out, for both gears, should not exceed 0.008 in.; if it does, replace the gear.

8. Install the oil nozzle, if it was removed, by screwing it in place with a screwdriver and punching it in two places, to secure it.

NOTE: *Be sure that the oil hole in the nozzle is pointed toward the timing gear before securing it.*

9. Install the oil slinger on the crankshaft.

10. Install the timing gear cover and cylinder head, as outlined above.

Camshaft

Removal and Installation

K-C and 3K-C Engines

1. Perform the timing chain cover and timing chain removal procedure, above.

2. Perform steps 1–11 of the K-C and 3K-C engine cylinder head removal procedure.

NOTE: *It is unnecessary to remove the cylinder head.*

3. Unfasten the spark plug wires and remove the spark plugs.

4. Remove the valve lifters in sequence.

NOTE: *Keep the valve lifters in their proper sequence, so that they go back into their original bores.*

5. If you have not already done so, disconnect the vacuum line and the primary wire from the distributor, loosen its clamping bolt, and remove it.

6. Detach the fuel lines from the fuel pump and remove the pump.

7. Remove the bolts which secure the camshaft thrust plate and then remove the thrust plate, itself.

8. Carefully remove the camshaft from the cylinder block.

CAUTION: *Use care not to damage the camshaft lobes, journals, or bearings.*

Installation of the camshaft is performed in the reverse order of removal. Coat the camshaft bearings and journals lightly with engine oil. The camshaft thrust plate attaching bolt should be tightened to 4–6 ft lbs.

2T-C Engine

1. Perform the cylinder head, timing chain cover, and timing chain removal procedures.

2. Unfasten the primary wire and vacuum lines from the distributor. Loosen its clamping bolt and withdraw it from the engine block.

3. Unfasten the lines from the fuel pump and remove the pump.

4. Remove the gear shifter shaft lever.

5. Use a jack to *lightly* support the transmission.

6. Remove the engine rear supporting crossmember.

7. Carefully lower the jack from beneath the transmission.

8. Unbolt and remove the camshaft thrust plate.

9. Ease out the camshaft, being careful not to damage the camshaft lobes or bearings.

Installation is performed in the reverse order of removal. Lubricate the camshaft journals and bearings lightly with engine oil prior to camshaft installation. Tighten the camshaft thrust plate attaching bolts to 7.2–11.6 ft lbs.

3R-B and 3R-C Engines

The procedure for removing the camshaft is given as part of the timing gear removal and installation procedure. If the camshaft is to be replaced, separate the gear from it as detailed in the timing gear removal section.

8R-C, 18R-C, 2M, and 4M Engines

All of these engines utilize a chain-driven overhead camshaft (OHC). Therefore, the procedure for removing the camshaft is given as part of the cylinder head removal procedure. Consult the appropriate section, above, for details.

NOTE: *It will not be necessary to completely remove the cylinder head in order to remove the camshaft. Therefore, proceed only as far as is necessary, to remove the camshaft, with the cylinder head removal procedure.*

F Engine

The procedure for removing the camshaft is given as part of the timing gear removal procedure, above; since the timing gear is press-fit onto the camshaft and cannot be removed separately from it.

Pistons and Connecting Rods

Removal and Installation

All Engines

See the procedures in the "Engine Rebuilding Section".

Piston and Ring Positioning

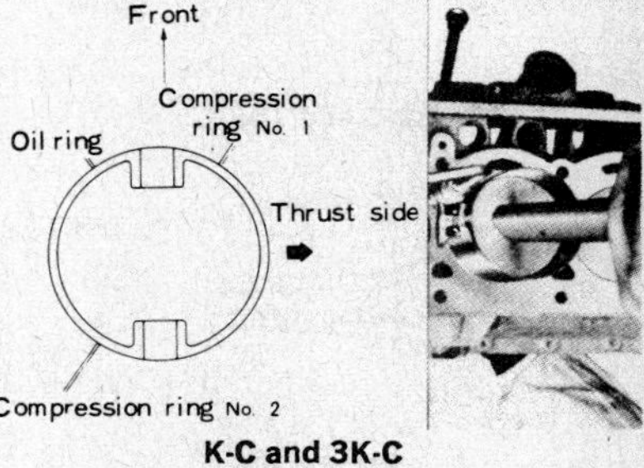

K-C and 3K-C

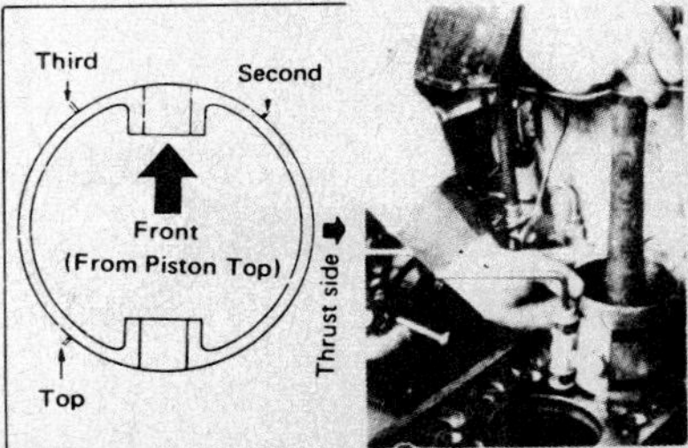

2T-C

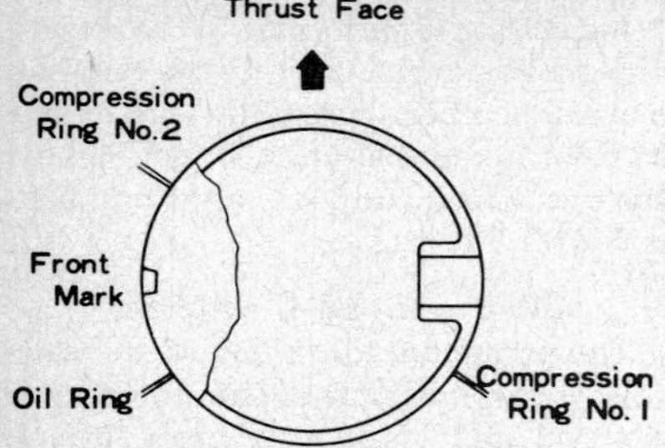

8R-C and 18R-C (2M and 4M are similar with no "front" mark).

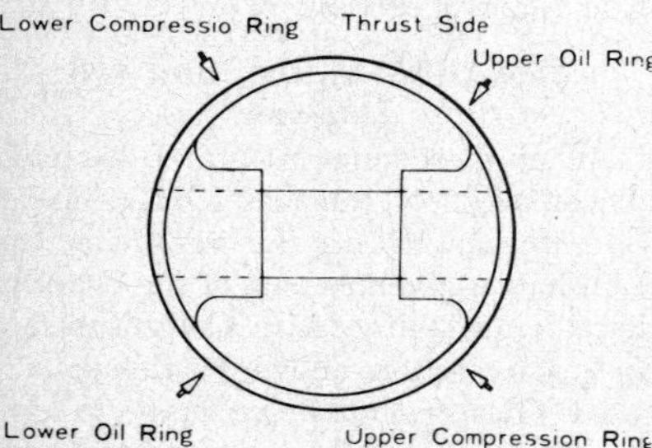

F engine

Piston and Connecting Rod Positioning

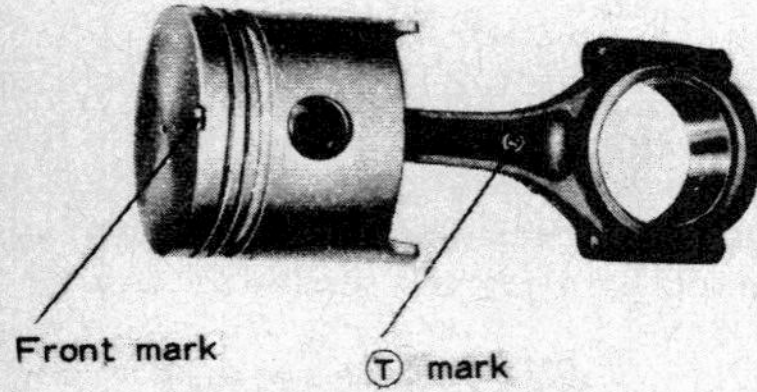

3R-B, 3R-C, K-C, 3K-C and 2TC

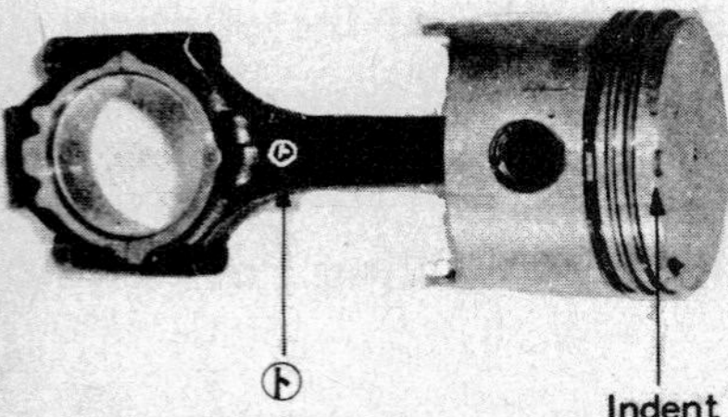

8R-C and 18R-C

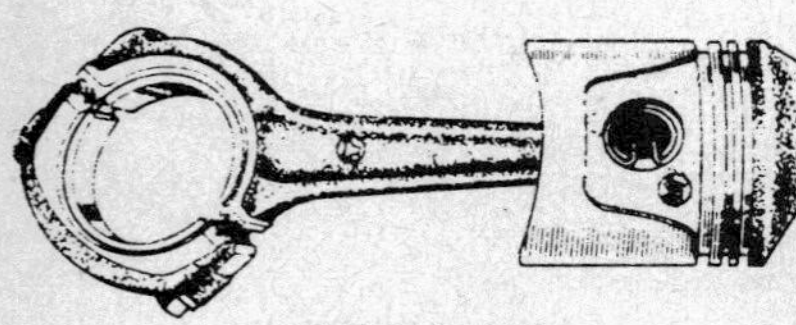

2M and 4M

F engine—piston marking

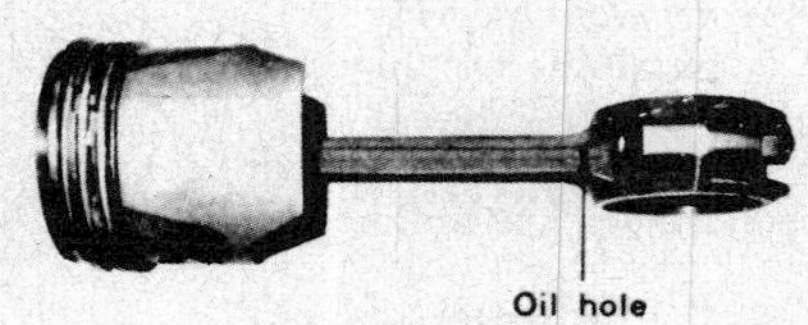

F engine—connecting rod oil hole

ENGINE LUBRICATION

Oil Pan

Removal and Installation

Corolla 1100, 1200 and 1600

1. Open the engine compartment hood.

NOTE: *Leave the hood open for the duration of this procedure.*

2. Raise the front end of the car and support it with jackstands.

CAUTION: *Be sure that the car is securely supported. Remember, you will be working underneath it.*

3. Remove the splash shield from underneath the engine.
4. Place a jack under the transmission to support it.
5. Unfasten the bolts which secure the engine rear supporting crossmember to the chassis.
6. Raise the jack under the transmission, *slightly.*
7. Unbolt the oil pan and work it out from underneath the engine.

NOTE: *If the oil pan does not come out easily, it may be necessary to unfasten the rear engine mounts from the crossmember.*

Installation is performed in the reverse order of removal. On Corolla models equipped with the 2T-C (1600cc) engine, apply liquid sealer to the four corners of the oil pan. Tighten the oil pan securing bolts to the following specifications:

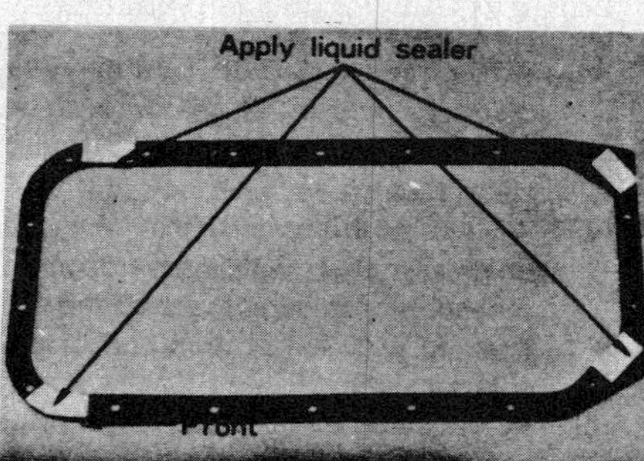

Apply sealer to the 2T-C oil pan gasket as shown.

K-C and 3K-C engines:
1.8–2.5 ft lbs
2T-C engine:
3.6–5.8 ft lbs

Carina, Corona, Mark II, Celica, and Hi-Lux

1. Drain the oil.
2. Raise the front end of the car with jacks and support it with jackstands.

CAUTION: *Be sure that the car is supported securely. Remember, you will be working underneath it.*

3. Detach the steering relay rod and the tie rods from the idler arm, pitman arm, and steering knuckles, as detailed below.
4. Remove the engine stiffening plates.
5. Remove the splash shields from underneath the engine.
6. Support the front of the engine with a jack and remove the front engine mount attaching bolts.
7. Raise the front of the engine *slightly* with the jack.

CAUTION: *Be sure that the hood is open before raising the front of the engine.*

8. Unbolt and withdraw the oil pan.

Installation is performed in the reverse order of removal. Apply liquid sealer to the four corners of the oil pan gasket used on 2T-C engines. Torque the oil pan securing bolts to the following specifications:

2T-C engine:
3.6–5.8 ft lbs
3R-B and 3R-C engines:
2.9–4.3 ft lbs
8R-C and 18R-C engines:
3.0–5.0 ft lbs

Crown 2300 and 2600

NOTE: *It is far easier to remove the engine on Crown models, in order to remove the oil pan, than to attempt to remove it with the engine installed in the car.*

1. Perform the 2M and 4M engine removal procedure above.
2. Remove the oil pan securing bolts and withdraw the oil pan.

Installation is performed in the reverse order of removal. Use a new oil pan gasket. Tighten the oil pan securing bolts to 3–5 ft lbs.

Land Cruiser

1. Remove the engine skid plates.
2. Remove the flywheel side cover and skid plate.
3. Unfasten the front driveshaft from the engine.
4. Drain the engine lubricant.
5. Remove the bolts which secure the oil pan; withdraw the pan and its gasket.

Installation is performed in the reverse order from removal. Always use a new pan gasket.

Rear Main Oil Seal

Replacement

All Engines

1. Remove the transmission as detailed below.
2. Remove the clutch cover assembly and flywheel. See below.
3. Remove the oil seal retaining plate, complete with the oil seal.
4. Use a screwdriver to pry the old seal from the retaining plate. Be careful not to damage the plate.
5. Install the new seal, carefully, by using a block of wood to drift it into place.

CAUTION: *Do not damage the seal; a leak will result.*

6. Lubricate the lips of the seal with multipurpose grease.

Installation is performed in the reverse order of removal.

Oil Pump

Removal and Installation

All Engines

1. Remove the oil pan, as outlined in the appropriate section above.
2. On passenger cars and High-Lux trucks, unbolt the oil pump securing bolts and remove it as an assembly.
3. On Land Cruiser models:
   a. Remove the oil strainer and unfasten the union nuts on the oil pump pipe.
   b. Remove the lock wire and unfasten the oil pump retaining bolt and pipe from the engine.

Installation is performed in the reverse order of the removal procedure.

ENGINE COOLING

Radiator

Removal and Installation

All Models

1. Drain the cooling system.
2. Unfasten the clamps and remove the radiator upper and lower hoses. If equipped with an automatic transmission, remove the oil cooler lines.
3. Detach the hood lock cable and remove the hood lock from the radiator upper support, except on pre-1970 Corona and all Celica models.

NOTE: *It may be necessary to remove the grille in order to gain access to the hood lock/radiator support assembly.*

4. Remove the fan shroud, if so equipped.
5. On models equipped with the 2M or 4M engines, disconnect the hose from the thermal expansion tank and remove the tank from its bracket.
6. Unbolt and remove the radiator upper support.
7. Unfasten the bolts and remove the radiator.

CAUTION: *Be careful not to damage the radiator fins on the cooling fan.*

Installation is performed in the reverse order of removal. Remember to check the transmission fluid level on cars with automatic transmissions.

Fill the radiator to the specified level.

Water Pump

Removal and Installation

All Engines

1. Drain the cooling system.
2. Unfasten the fan shroud securing bolts and remove the fan shroud, if so equipped.
3. Loosen the alternator adjusting link bolt and remove the drive belt.
4. Repeat step 3 for the air pump drive belt, if so equipped.
5. Detach the bypass and radiator hoses from the water pump.
6. Unfasten the water pump retaining bolts and remove the water pump and fan assembly, using care not to damage the radiator with the fan.

CAUTION: *If the fan is equipped with a fluid coupling, do not tip the fan/-pump assembly on its side, as the fluid will run out.*

Installation is performed in the reverse order of removal. Always use a new gasket between the pump body and its mounting. Remember to check for leaks after installation is completed.

Thermostat

Removal and Installation

All Engines

1. Drain the cooling system.
2. Unfasten the clamp and remove the upper radiator hose from the water outlet elbow.
3. Unbolt and remove the water outlet (thermostat housing).
4. Withdraw the thermostat.

Installation is performed in the reverse order of the removal procedure. Use a new gasket on the water outlet.

CAUTION: *Be sure that the thermostat is installed with the spring pointing down.*

EMISSION CONTROLS

Positive Crankcase Ventilation (PCV) System

A positive crankcase ventilation (PCV) system is used on all Toyotas sold in the United States. Blow-by gases are routed from the crankcase to the carburetor, where they are combined with the fuel/air mixture and burned during combustion.

A valve (PCV) is used in the line to prevent the gases in the crankcase from being ignited in case of a backfire. The amount of blow-by gases entering the mixture is also regulated by the PCV valve, which is spring-loaded and has a variable orifice.

The valve is either mounted on the valve cover or in the line which runs from the intake manifold to the crankcase.

The valve should be replaced at the following intervals:

1966–71 models—12,000mi/12mo
1972–73 models—24,000mi/24mo

Removal and Installation

Remove the PCV valve from the cylinder head cover on K-C, 3K-C, 8R-C, and 18R-C engines. Remove the hose from the valve.

On the remainder of the engines, remove the valve from the manifold-to-crankcase hose.

Installation is the reverse of removal.

Testing

Check the PCV system hoses and connections, to see that there are no leaks; then replace or tighten, as necessary.

To check the valve, remove it and blow through both of its ends (as illustrated). When blowing from the side which goes toward the intake manifold, very little air should pass through it. When blowing from the crankcase (valve cover) side, air should pass through freely.

Replace the valve with a new one, if the valve fails to function as outlined.

NOTE: *Do not attempt to clean or adjust the valve; replace it with a new one.*

Air Injection System

A belt-driven air pump supplies air to an injection manifold which has nozzles in each exhaust port. Injection of air at this point causes combustion of unburned hydrocarbons in the exhaust manifold rather than allowing them to escape into the atmosphere. An antibackfire valve controls the flow of air from the pump to prevent backfiring which results from an overly rich mixture under closed throttle conditions. There are two types of antibackfire valve used on Toyota models: 1968–71 models use "gulp" valves; 1972–73 models use "air bypass" valves.

A check valve prevents hot exhaust gas backflow into the pump and hoses, in case of a pump failure, or when the antibackfire valve is working.

Air injection systems are used on all 2M

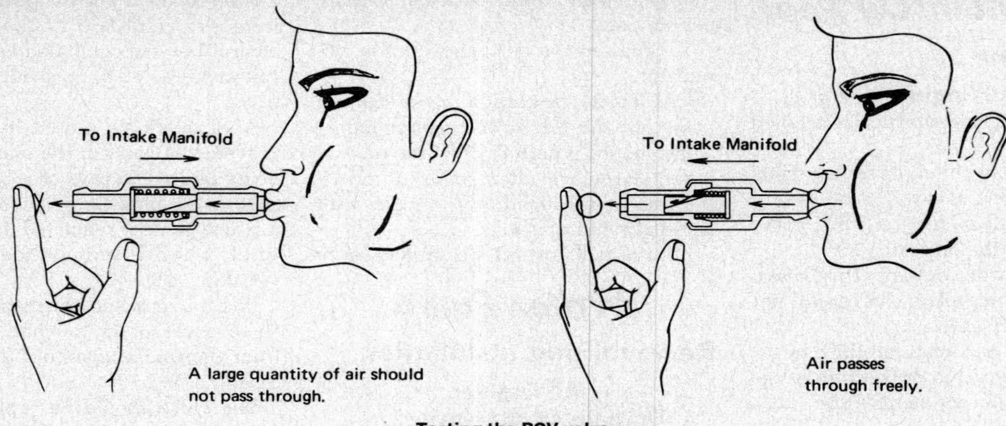

Testing the PCV valve

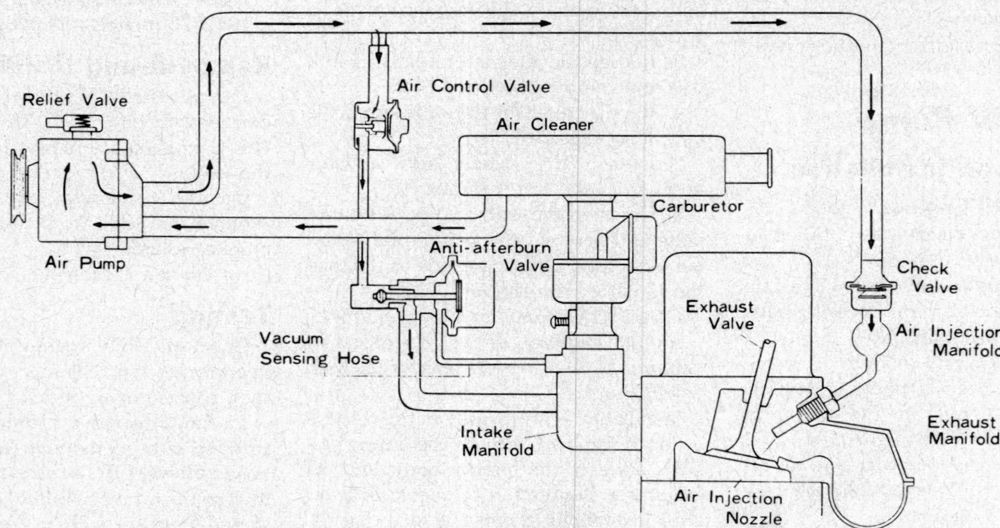

Schematic for the air injection system

and 4M engines, as well as on 1968–71 K-C, 3K-C and 3R-C engines. It is used on 1973 F engines, also.

Removal and Installation

Air Pump

1. Disconnect the air hoses from the pump.
2. Loosen the bolt on the adjusting link and remove the drive belt.
3. Remove the mounting bolts and withdraw the pump.

CAUTION: *Do not pry on the pump housing; it may be distorted.*

Installation is in the reverse order of removal. Adjust the drive belt tension after installation. Belt deflection should be ½–¾ in. with 22 lbs pressure.

Antibackfire Valve

1. Detach the air hoses from the valve.
2. Remove the valve securing bolt.
3. Withdraw the valve.

Installation is performed in the reverse order of removal.

Check Valve

1. Detach the intake hose from the valve.

Removing or installing the check valve

2. Use an open-end wrench to remove the valve from its mounting.

Installation is the reverse of removal.

Relief Valve

1. Remove the air pump from the car.
2. Support the pump so that it cannot rotate.

CAUTION: *Never clamp the pump in a vise; the aluminum case will be distorted.*

Removing the relief valve from the air pump.

3. Use a bridge to remove the relief valve from the top of the pump.
4. Position the new relief valve over the opening in the pump.

NOTE: *The air outlet should be pointing toward the left.*

5. Gently tap the relief valve home, using a block of wood and a hammer.
6. Install the pump on the engine, as outlined above.

Air Injection Manifold

1. Remove the check valve, as outlined above.

2. Loosen the air injection manifold attachment nuts and withdraw the manifold.

NOTE: *On 2M and 4M engines, it will first be necessary to remove the exhaust manifold.*

Installation is in the reverse order of removal.

Air Injection Nozzles

1. Remove the air injection manifold as outlined above.

2. Remove the cylinder head, as detailed in the appropriate section, above.

3. Place a new nozzle on the cylinder head.

4. Install the air injection manifold over it.

5. Install the cylinder head on the engine block.

Air Control Valve—3K-C and 3R-C Engines

The air control valve is used only on the 3K-C engine, and 3R-C engines with manual transmissions. It is removed by simply unfastening the hoses from it.

Testing

Air Pump

CAUTION: *Do not hammer, pry, or bend the pump housing while tightening the drive belt or testing the pump.*

Belt Tension and Air Leaks

1. Before proceeding with the tests, check the pump drive belt tension to see if it is within specifications. (See above.)

2. Turn the pump by hand. If it has seized, the belt will slip, making a noise. Disregard any chirping, squealing, or rolling sounds from inside the pump; these are normal when it is turned by hand.

3. Check the hoses and connections for leaks. Hissing or a blast of air is indicative of a leak. Soapy water, applied lightly around the area in question, is a good method for detecting leaks.

Air Output

1. Disconnect the air supply hose at the antibackfire valve.

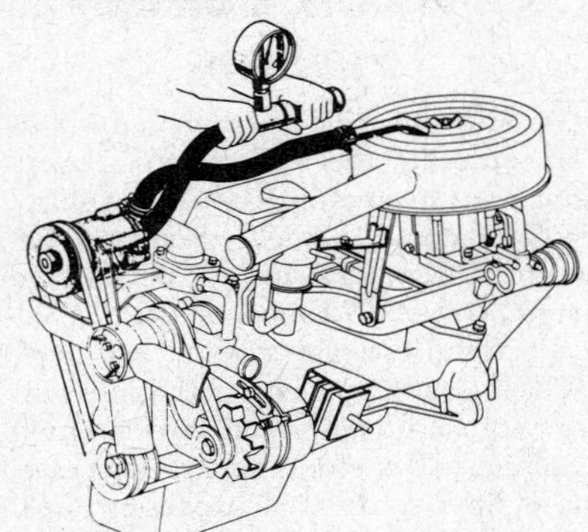

Checking the air pump output

2. Connect a vacuum gauge, using a suitable adaptor, to the air supply hose.

NOTE: *If there are two hoses, plug the second one.*

3. With the engine at normal operating temperature, increase the idle speed to 1,000–1,500 rpm and watch the vacuum gauge.

4. The air flow from the pump should be steady and fall between 2 and 6 psi. If it is unsteady or falls below this, the pump is defective and must be replaced.

Pump Noise Diagnosis

The air pump is normally noisy; as engine speed increases, the noise of the pump will rise in pitch. The rolling sound the pump bearings make is normal. But if this sound becomes objectionable at certain speeds, the pump is defective and will have to be replaced.

A continual hissing sound from the air pump pressure relief valve at idle, indicates a defective valve. Replace the relief valve.

If the pump rear bearing fails, a continual knocking sound will be heard.

Antibackfire Valve Tests

There are two different types of antibackfire valve used with air injection systems. A bypass valve is used on 1972–73 engines, while 1968–71 engines use a gulp type of antibackfire valve. Test procedures for both types are given below.

Gulp Valve

1. Detach the air supply hose which runs between the pump and the gulp valve.

2. Connect a tachometer and run the engine to 1,500–2,000 rpm.

3. Allow the throttle to snap closed. This should produce a loud sucking sound from the gulp valve.

4. Repeat this operation several times. If no sound is present, the valve is not working or else the vacuum connections are loose.

5. Check the vacuum connections. If they are secure, replace the gulp valve.

Bypass Valve

1. Detach the hose, which runs from the bypass valve to the check valve, at the bypass valve hose connection.

2. Connect a tachometer to the engine. With the engine running at normal idle speed, check to see that air is flowing from the bypass valve hose connection.

3. Speed up the engine so it is running at 1,500–2,000 rpm. Allow the throttle to

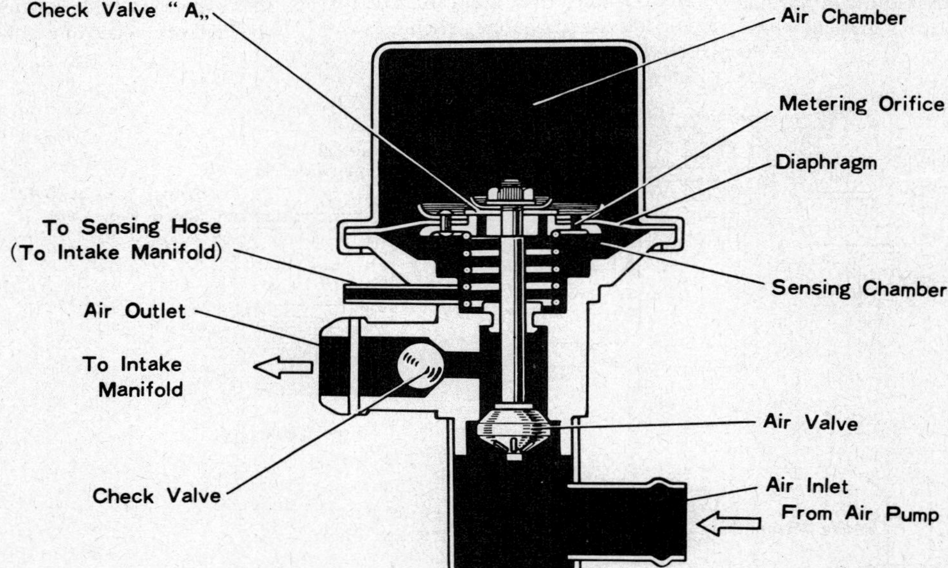

Sectional view of the gulp-type antibackfire valve.

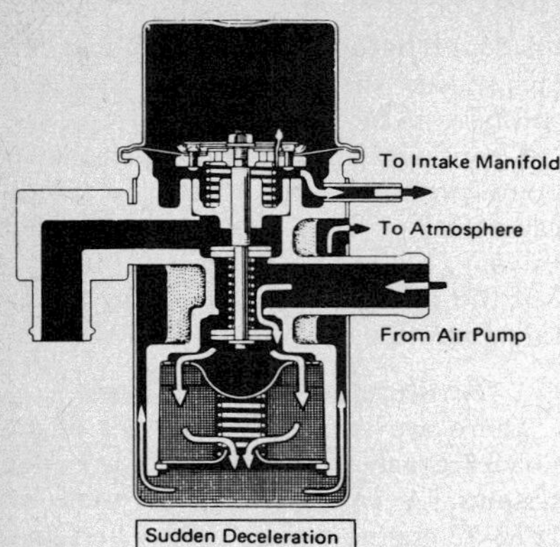

Sectional view of the by-pass antibackfire valve.

snap shut. The flow of air from the bypass valve at the check valve hose connection should stop momentarily and air should then flow from the exhaust port on the valve body or the silencer assembly.

4. Repeat step 3 several times. If the flow of air is not diverted into the atmosphere from the valve exhaust port or if it fails to stop flowing from the hose connection, check the vacuum lines and connections. If these are tight, the valve is defective and requires replacement.

5. A leaking diaphragm will cause the air to flow out both the hose connection and the exhaust port at the same time. If this happens, replace the valve.

Check Valve Test

1. Before starting the test, check all of the hoses and connections for leaks.

2. Detach the air supply hose from the check valve.

3. Insert a suitable probe into the check valve and depress the plate. Release it; the plate should return to its original position against the valve seat. If binding is evident, replace the valve.

4. With the engine running at normal operating temperature, gradually increase its speed to 1,500 rpm. Check for exhaust gas leakage. If any is present, replace the valve assembly.

NOTE: *Vibration and flutter of the check valve at idle speed is a normal condition and does not mean that the valve should be replaced.*

Evaporative Emission Control System

To prevent hydrocarbon emissions from entering the atmosphere, Toyota vehicles use evaporative emission control (EEC) systems. Models produced between 1970 and 1971 use a "case" storage system, while 1972 models use a "charcoal canister" storage system.

The major components of the case storage system are a purge control or vacuum switching valve, a fuel vapor storage case, an air filter, a thermal expansion tank, and a special fuel tank.

When the vehicle is stopped or the engine is running at a low speed, the purge control or vacuum switching valve is closed; fuel vapor travels only as far as the case where it is stored.

When the engine is running at a high speed (cruising speed), the purge control valve is opened by pressure from the air pump or else the vacuum switching valve opens—depending upon the type of emission control system used.

This allows the vapor stored in the case to be drawn into the intake manifold along with fresh air which is drawn in from the filter.

The charcoal canister storage system functions in a similar manner to the case system, except that the fuel vapors are stored in a canister filled with activated charcoal, rather than in a case, and that all models use a vacuum switching valve to purge the system. The air filter is not external as it is on the case system; rather it is an integral part of the charcoal canister.

Removal and Installation

Removal and installation of the various evaporative emission control system components consists of unfastening hoses, loosening securing screws, and removing the part which is to be replaced from its mounting bracket. Installation is the reverse of removal.

NOTE: *When replacing any EEC system hoses, always use hoses that are fuel-resistant or are marked "EVAP."*

Testing

EEC System Troubleshooting

There are several things which may be checked if a malfunction of the evaporative emission control system is suspected.

1. Leaks may be traced by using a hydrocarbon tester. Run the test probe along the lines and connections. The meter will indicate the presence of a leak by a high hydrocarbon (HC) reading. This method is much more accurate than visual inspection which would only indicate the presence of leaks large enough to pass liquid.

2. Leaks may be caused by any of the following:

a. Defective or worn hoses;

b. Disconnected or pinched hoses;

c. Improperly routed hoses;

d. A defective filler cap or safety valve (sealed cap system).

NOTE: *If it becomes necessary to replace any of the hoses used in the evaporative emission control system, use only hoses which are fuel-resistant or are marked "EVAP."*

3. If the fuel tank, storage case, or thermal expansion tank collapse, it may be the fault of clogged or pinched vent lines,

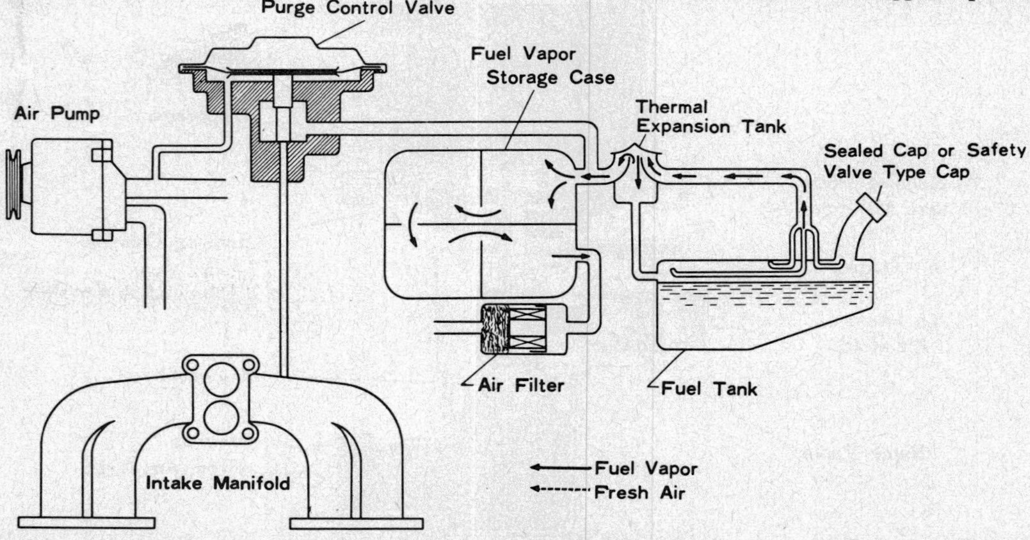

Schematic for the case storage system when used with air injection.

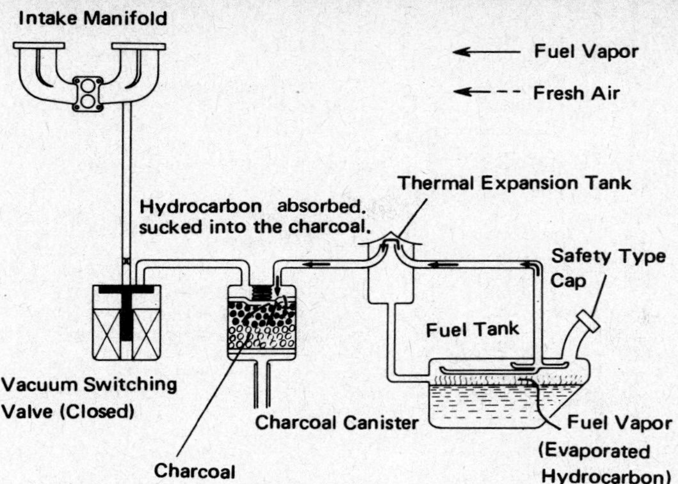

Schematic for charcoal storage system w/ thermal expansion tank.

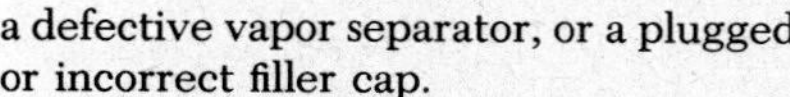

a defective vapor separator, or a plugged or incorrect filler cap.

4. To test the filler cap (if it is the safety valve type), clean it and place it against your mouth. Blow into the relief valve housing. If the cap passes pressure with light blowing or if it fails to release with hard blowing, it is defective and must be replaced.

NOTE: *Use the proper cap for the type of system used; either a sealed cap or safety valve cap, as required. See the chart at the end of this section for proper cap usage.*

Purge Control Valve

NOTE: *This valve is used only on 1970–71 engines which are also equipped with an air injection system.*

1. Disconnect the line which runs from the storage case to the valve, at the valve end.
2. Connect a tachometer to the engine in accordance with the manufacturer's instructions.
3. Start the engine and slowly increase its speed until the tachometer reads 2,-500 rpm (transmission in Neutral).
4. Place a finger over the hose fitting (storage-case-to-valve) on the valve.
5. If there is no suction, check the air pump for a malfunction. (See above.) If the air pump is not defective, replace the valve.

Check Valve—Corolla 1971–72 and A11 1973

NOTE: *The Mark II station wagon is the only model not equipped with a check valve for 1973.*

Rough idling when the gas tank is full is probably caused by a defective check valve. To test it, proceed as follows:

1. Run the engine at idle.
2. Clamp the hose between the vacuum switching valve and the charcoal canister or case.
3. If the engine idle becomes smooth, replace the check valve.

Carburetor Auxiliary Slow System

A carburetor auxiliary slow system is used on 1970–71 3K-C and 2M engines. It provides uniform combustion during deceleration. The components of the auxiliary slow system consist of a vacuum-operated valve, a fresh air intake, and a fuel line which is connected to the carburetor float chamber.

During deceleration, manifold vacuum acts on the valve which opens it, causing additional air/fuel mixture to flow into the intake manifold. The additional mixture aids in more complete combustion.

Removal and Installation

1. Remove the hoses from the auxiliary slow system unit.
2. Unfasten the recessed screws and withdraw the system as a complete unit.

Installation is performed in the reverse order of the above.

Testing

1. Start the engine, allow it to reach normal operating temperature, and run it at normal idle speed.
2. Remove the rubber cap from the diaphragm assembly and place your finger over the opening. There should be no suction at idle speed. If there is, the diaphragm is defective and the unit must be replaced.
3. Pinch the air intake hose which runs from the air cleaner to the auxiliary slow system. There should be no change in engine idle with the hose disconnected.
4. Disconnect the air intake hose at the auxiliary slow system. Race the engine. Place your finger over the air intake. Release the throttle; suction should be felt at the air intake.
5. If any of the tests indicate a defective auxiliary slow system, replace it as a unit. (See above.)

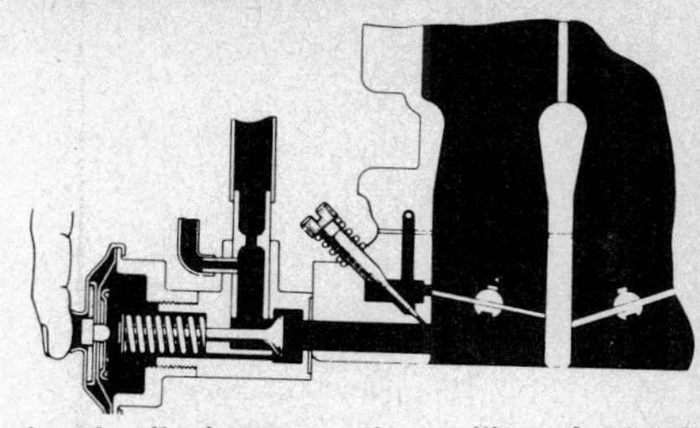

Testing the diaphragm on the auxiliary slow system

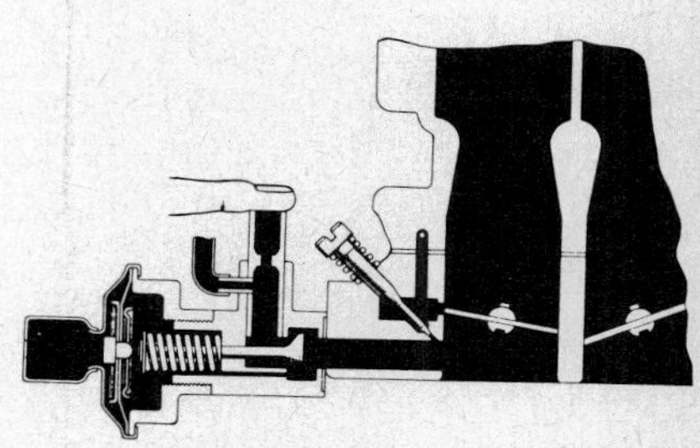

Place your finger over the air intake and race the engine.

Throttle Positioner

On Toyotas with an engine modification system, a throttle positioner is included to reduce exhaust emissions during deceleration. The positioner prevents the throttle from closing completely. Vacuum is reduced under the throttle valve which, in turn, acts on the retard chamber of the distributor vacuum unit. This compensates for the loss of engine braking caused by the partially opened throttle.

NOTE: *For a description of the operation of the dual-diaphragm distributor, see below.*

Once the vehicle drops below a predetermined speed, the vacuum switching valve provides vacuum to the throttle positioner diaphragm; the throttle positioner retracts allowing the throttle valve to close completely. The distributor also is returned to normal operation.

Adjustment

1. Start the engine and allow it to reach normal operating temperature.
2. Adjust the idle speed.

NOTE: *Leave the tachometer connected after completing the idle adjustments, as it will be needed in step 5, below.*

3. Detach the vacuum line from the positioner diaphragm unit and plug the line.
4. Accelerate the engine slightly to set the throttle positioner in place.
5. Check the engine speed with a tachometer when the throttle positioner is set.
6. If necessary, adjust the engine speed, with the throttle positioner adjusting screw, to the specifications given in the chart at the end of this section.

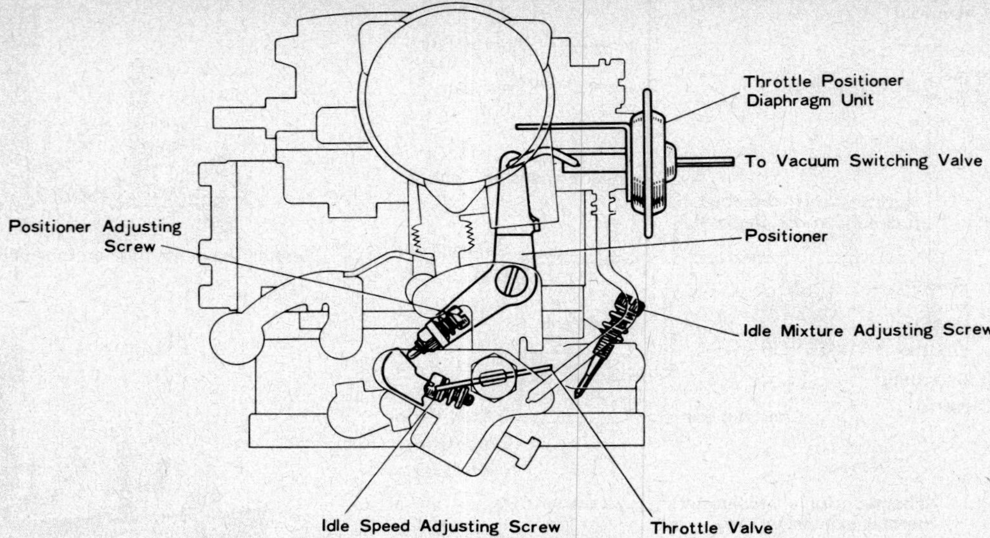

Components of the throttle positioner system.

7. Connect the vacuum hose to the positioner diaphragm.

8. The throttle lever should be freed from the positioner as soon as the vacuum hose is connected. Engine idle should return to normal.

9. If the throttle positioner fails to function properly, check its linkage, and vacuum diaphragm. If there are no defects in either of these, the fault probably lies in the vacuum switching valve or the speed marker unit.

NOTE: *Due to the complexity of these two components they require special test equipment.*

Throttle Positioner Settings
(rpm)

Year	Engine	Engine rpm (positioner set)
1970	8R-C	1,400
	F	1,400
1971	2T-C	1,400
	8R-C	1,400
	F	1,000
1972-73	3K-C	1,500
	2T-C	1,400
	18R-C	1,400
	2M & 4M	①
	F	1,200

① Manual transmission—1,300 rpm
Automatic transmission—1,200 rpm

Mixture Control Valve—2T-C Engines

The mixture control valve, used on all 2T-C engines, aids in combustion of unburned fuel during periods of deceleration. The mixture control valve is operated by the vacuum switching valve during periods of deceleration to admit additional fresh air into the intake manifold. The extra air allows more complete combustion of the fuel, thus reducing hydrocarbon emissions.

Removal and Installation

1. Unfasten the vacuum switching valve line from the mixture control valve.
2. Remove the intake manifold hose from the valve.
3. Remove the valve from its engine mounting.

Installation is performed in the reverse order of removal.

Testing

1. Start the engine and allow it to idle (warmed up).

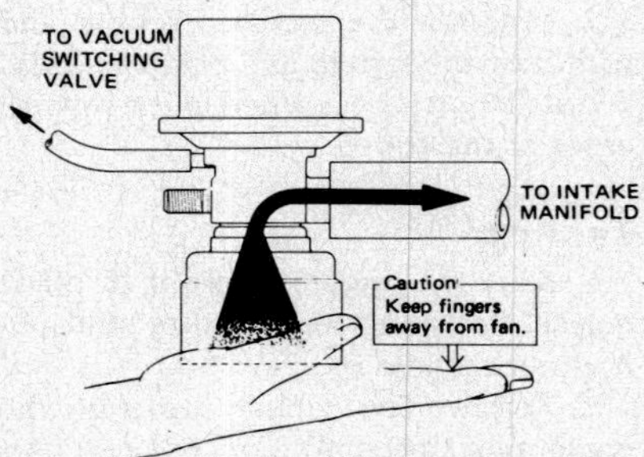

Checking the mixture control valve

2. Place your hand over the air intake at the bottom of the valve.

CAUTION: *Keep your fingers clear of the engine fan.*

3. Increase the engine speed and then release the throttle.
4. Suction should be felt at the air intake only while the engine is decelerating. Once the engine has returned to idle, no suction should be felt.

If the above test indicates a malfunction, proceed with the next step; if not, the mixture control valve is functioning properly and requires no further attention.

5. Disconnect the vacuum line from the mixture control valve. If suction can be felt underneath the valve with the engine at idle, the valve seat is defective and must be replaced.
6. Reconnect the vacuum line to the valve. Disconnect the other end of the line from the vacuum switching valve and place it in your mouth.
7. With the engine idling, suck on the end of the vacuum line to duplicate the action of the vacuum switching valve.
8. Suction at the valve air intake should only be felt for an instant. If air cannot be drawn into the valve at all, or if it is continually drawn in, replace the mixture control valve.

If the mixture control valve is functioning properly, and all of the hose and connections are in good working order, the vacuum switching valve is probably at fault.

NOTE: *Because the vacuum switching valve and related components are complex, special equipment is required to test them.*

Dual-Diaphragm Distributor

Some Toyota models are equipped with a dual-diaphragm distributor unit. This distributor has a retard diaphragm, as well as a diaphragm for advance. Retarding the timing helps to reduce exhaust emissions, as well as making up for the lack of engine braking on models equipped with a throttle positioner.

Testing

1. Connect a timing light to the engine. Check the ignition timing.

NOTE: *Before proceeding with the tests, disconnect any spark control de-*

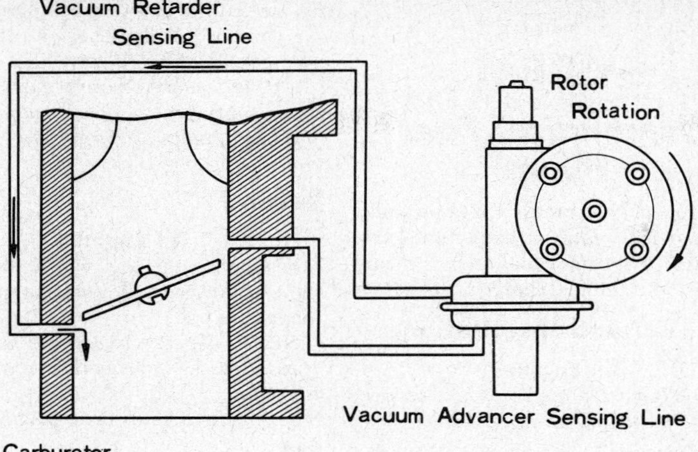

Dual-diaphragm distributor—without the vacuum switching valve.

vices, distributor vacuum valves, etc. If these are left connected, inaccurate results may be obtained.

2. Remove the retard hose from the distributor and plug it. Increase the engine speed. The timing should advance. If it fails to do so, then the vacuum unit is faulty and must be replaced.

3. Check the timing with the engine at normal idle speed. Unplug the retard hose and connect it to the vacuum unit. The timing should instantly be retarded from 4 to 10 degrees. If this does not occur, the retard diaphragm has a leak and the vacuum unit must be replaced.

Engine Modifications System

Toyota also uses an assortment of engine modifications to regulate exhaust emissions. Most of these devices fall into the category of engine vacuum controls. There are three principal components used on the engine modifications system, as well as a number of smaller parts. The three major components are: a speed sensor; a computer (speed marker); and a vacuum switching valve.

The vacuum switching valve and computer circuit operates most of the emission control components. Depending upon year and engine usage, the vacuum switching valve and computer may operate the purge control for the evaporative emission control system; the transmission controlled spark (TCS) or speed controlled spark (SCS); the dual-diaphragm distributor; and the throttle positioner systems.

The functions of the evaporative emission control system, the throttle positioner, and the dual-diaphragm distributor are described in detail in the sections above. However, a word is necessary about the functions of the TCS and SCS systems before discussing the operation of the vacuum switching valve/computer circuit.

The major difference between the transmission controlled spark and speed controlled spark systems is in the manner in which system operation is determined. Toyota TCS systems use a mechanical switch to determine which gear is selected; SCS systems use a speed sensor built into the speedometer cable.

Below a predetermined speed, or any gear other than fourth, the vacuum advance unit on the distributor is rendered inoperative or, on F engines, timing is retarded. By changing the distributor advance curve in this manner, it is possible to reduce emissions of oxides of nitrogen (NO_x).

NOTE: *Some engines are equipped with a thermo-sensor so that the TCS or SCS system only operates when the coolant temperature is 140°–212° F.*

Aside from determining the conditions outlined above, the vacuum switching valve computer circuit operates other devices in the emission control system.

The computer acts as a speed marker; at certain speeds it sends a signal to the vacuum switching valve which acts as a gate, opening and closing the emission control system vacuum circuits.

The vacuum switching valve on all 1970 and some 1971 engines is a simple affair; a single solenoid operates a valve that uncovers certain vacuum ports at the same time others are covered.

The valve used on all 1972—73, and some 1971 engines, contains several solenoid and valve assemblies so that differ-

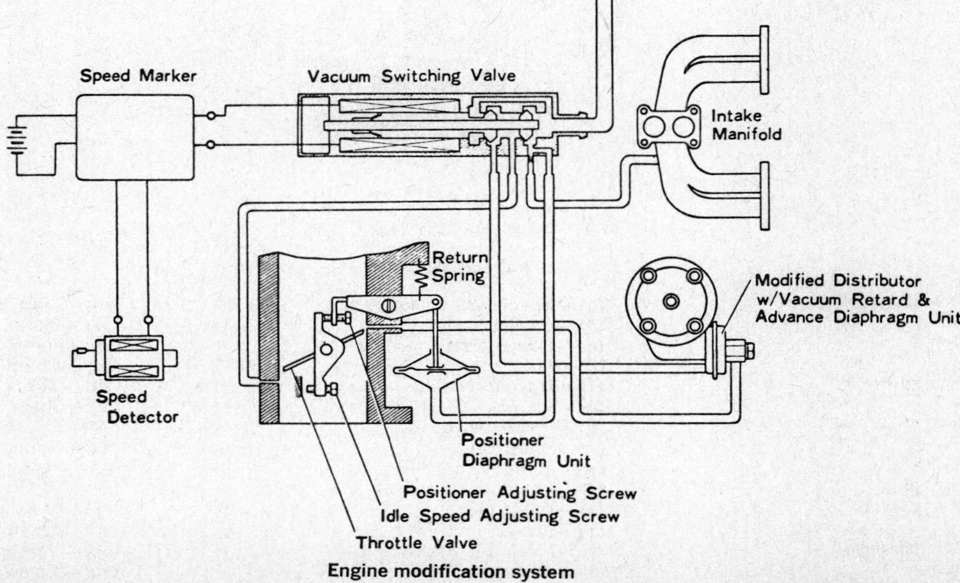

Engine modification system

ent combinations of opened and closed vacuum ports are possible. This allows greater flexibility of operation for the emission control system.

System Checks

Due to the complexity of the components involved, about the only engine modification system checks which can be made without the use of special test equipment, are the following:

1. Examine the vacuum lines to see that they are not clogged, pinched, or loose.
2. Check the electrical connections for tightness and corrosion.
3. Be sure that the vacuum sources for the vacuum switching valve are not plugged.
4. On models equipped with speed controlled spark, a broken speedometer cable could also render the system inoperative.

Beyond these checks, servicing the engine modifications system requires the use of special test equipment.

FUEL SYSTEM

Mechanical Fuel Pump

All Toyota vehicles use a mechanically operated fuel pump of diaphragm construction. A separate fuel filter is incorporated into the fuel line.

Removal and Installation

All Engines

CAUTION: *Do not smoke while performing fuel pump removal.*

1. Disconnect both of the fuel lines from the pump.
2. Unfasten the bolts which attach the fuel pump to the cylinder block.
3. Withdraw the pump assembly.

Installation is performed in the reverse order of removal. Always use a new gasket when installing the fuel pump. After the pump is installed check its discharge rate. See "Testing" below.

NOTE: *Failure to use a gasket of the correct thickness could result in an improper pump discharge rate.*

Testing

All Engines

1. Remove the line which runs from the carburetor to the fuel pump, at the fuel pump end.

NOTE: *Be sure that there is enough gasoline left to operate the engine briefly.*

2. Attach a pressure gauge to the pump outlet.
3. Run the engine and note the discharge pressure.

CAUTION: *Be careful to keep the open fuel line away from any of the car's ignition system components; a stray spark could ignite the fuel vapor*

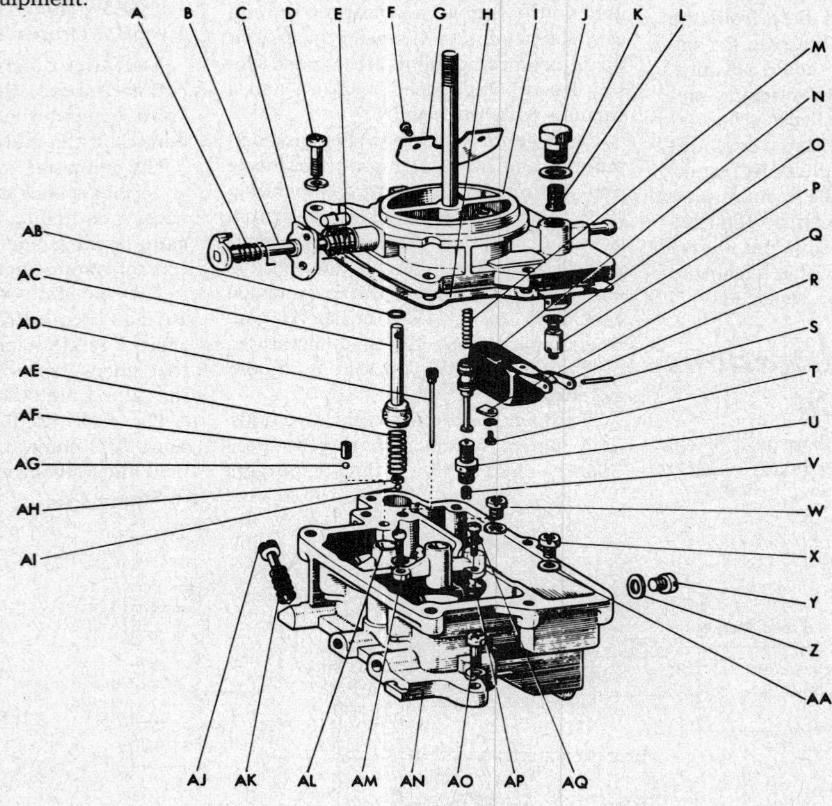

K-C and 3K-C

(a)—Choke valve relief spring
(b)—Choke shaft
(c)—Choke lever
(d)—Screw
(e)—Choke return spring
(f)—Screw
(g)—Choke valve
(h)—Air horn gasket
(i)—Air horn
(j)—Main passage plug
(k)—Inlet strainer gasket
(l)—Strainer
(m)—Power piston spring
(n)—Power piston
(o)—Needle valve seat gasket
(p)—Needle valve
(q)—Power piston stopper
(r)—Float
(s)—Float lever pin
(t)—Screw
(u)—Power valve
(v)—Power jet
(w)—Primary main jet
(x)—Secondary main jet
(y)—Drain plug
(z)—Gasket
(aa)—Main jet gasket
(ab)—O-ring
(ac)—Pump plunger
(ad)—Slow jet
(ae)—Pump damping spring
(af)—Pump discharge weight
(ag)—Check ball
(ah)—Check ball retainer
(ai)—Check ball
(aj)—Throttle adjusting screw
(ak)—Spring
(al)—Primary small venturi
(am)—Secondary small venturi
(an)—Main body
(ao)—Screw
(ap)—Venturi No. 1 gasket
(aq)—Screw

causing an explosion. Do not smoke while performing this test.

4. Check the pump discharge pressure against the specification given at the beginning of the section.

5. If the pump output is not up to specifications, replace the diaphragm spring or the entire pump assembly.

6. Reconnect the carburetor fuel line.

Carburetors

The carburetors used on Toyota models are conventional two-barrel, downdraft types similar to domestic carburetors.

NOTE: *Except for older Land Cruisers which use a single barrel downdraft carburetor.*

The main circuits are: *primary,* for normal operational requirments; *secondary,* to supply high-speed fuel needs; *float,* to supply fuel to the primary and secondary circuits; *accelerator,* to supply fuel for quick and safe acceleration; *choke,* for reliable starting in cold weather; and *power valve,* for fuel economy. Although slight differences in appearance may be noted, these carburetors are basically alike. Of course, different jets and settings are demanded by the different engines to which they are fitted.

Removal and Installation

All Engines

1. Remove the air cleaner housing, disconnect all air hoses from the air cleaner base, and disconnect the battery ground cable.

2. Disconnect the fuel line, choke pipe, and distributor vacuum line.

3. Remove the accelerator linkage. (With an automatic transmission, also remove the throttle rod to the transmission.)

NOTE: *On Land Cruiser models, disconnect the magnetic valve wire from the coil terminal.*

4. Remove the four nuts that secure the carburetor to the manifold and lift off the carburetor and gasket.

5. Cover the open manifold with a clean rag to prevent small objects from dropping into the engine.

Installation is performed in the reverse order of removal. After the engine is warmed up, check for fuel leaks and float level settings.

Overhaul

All Types

Efficient carburetion depends greatly on careful cleaning and inspection during overhaul since dirt, gum, water, or varnish in or on the carburetor parts are often responsible for poor performance.

Overhaul your carburetor in a clean, dust-free area. Carefully disassemble the carburetor, referring often to the exploded views. Keep all similar and look-alike parts segregated during disassembly and cleaning to avoid accidental interchange during assembly. Make a note of all jet sizes.

When the carburetor is disassembled, wash all parts (except diaphragms, electric choke units, pump plunger, and any other plastic, leather, fiber, or rubber parts) in clean carburetor solvent. Do not leave parts in the solvent any longer than is necessary to sufficiently loosen the deposits. Excessive cleaning may remove the special finish from the float bowl and choke valve bodies, leaving these parts unfit for service. Rinse all parts in clean solvent and blow them dry with compressed air or allow them to air dry. Wipe clean all cork, plastic, leather, and fiber parts with a clean, lint-free cloth.

Blow out all passages and jets with compressed air and be sure that there are no restrictions or blockages. Never use wire or similar tools to clean jets, fuel passages, or air bleeds. Clean all jets and valves separately to avoid accidental interchange.

Check all parts for wear or damage. If wear or damage is found, replace the defective parts. Especially check the following:

1. Check the float needle and seat for wear. If wear is found, replace the complete assembly.

2. Check the float hinge pin for wear and the float(s) for dents or distortion. Replace the float if fuel has leaked into it.

3. Check the throttle and choke shaft bores for wear or an out-of-round condition. Damage or wear to the throttle arm, shaft, or shaft bore will often require replacement of the throttle body. These parts require a close tolerance of fit; wear may allow air leakage, which could affect starting and idling.

NOTE: *Throttle shafts and bushings are not included in overhaul kits. They can be purchased separately.*

4. Inspect the idle mixture adjusting needles for burrs or grooves. Any such condition requires replacement of the needle, since you will not be able to obtain a satisfactory idle.

5. Test the accelerator pump check valves. They should pass air one way but not the other. Test for proper seating by blowing and sucking on the valve. Replace the valve if necessary. If the valve is satisfactory, wash the valve again to remove breath moisture.

6. Check the bowl cover for warped surfaces with a straightedge.

7. Closely inspect the valves and seats for wear and damage, replacing as necessary.

8. After the carburetor is assembled, check the choke valve for freedom of operation.

Carburetor overhaul kits are recommended for each overhaul. These kits contain all gaskets and new parts to replace those that deteriorate most rapidly. Failure to replace all parts supplied with the kit (especially gaskets) can result in poor performance later.

Some carburetor manufacturers supply overhaul kits of three basic types: minor repair; major repair; and gasket kits. Basically, they contain the following:

Minor Repair Kits:
- All gaskets
- Float needle valve
- Volume control screw
- All diaphragms
- Spring for the pump diaphragm

Major Repair Kits:
- All jets and gaskets
- All diaphragms
- Float needle valve
- Volume control screw
- Pump ball valve
- Main jet carrier
- Float
- Complete intermediate rod
- Intermediate pump lever
- Complete injector tube
- Some cover hold-down screws and washers

Gasket Kits:
- All gaskets

After cleaning and checking all components, reassemble the carburetor, using new parts and referring to the exploded view. When reassembling, make sure that all screws and jets are tight in their seats, but do not overtighten, as the tips will be distorted. Tighten all screws gradually, in rotation. Do not tighten needle valves into their seats; uneven jetting will result. Always use new gaskets. Be sure to adjust the float level when reassembling.

Float Level Adjustment

Float level adjustments are unnecessary on models equipped with a carburetor sight glass, if the fuel level falls within the lines when the engine is running.

There are two float level adjustments which may be made on Toyota carburetors. One is with the air horn inverted, so that the float is in a fully *raised* position; the other is with the air horn in an upright position, so that the float falls to the bottom of its travel.

The float level is either measured with a special carburetor float level gauge, which comes with a rebuilding kit, or with a standard wire gauge.

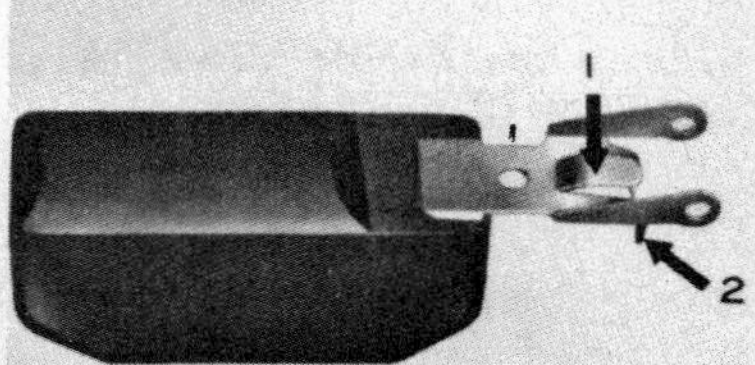

To adjust the float level, bend the upper tab (1) or the lower tab (2).

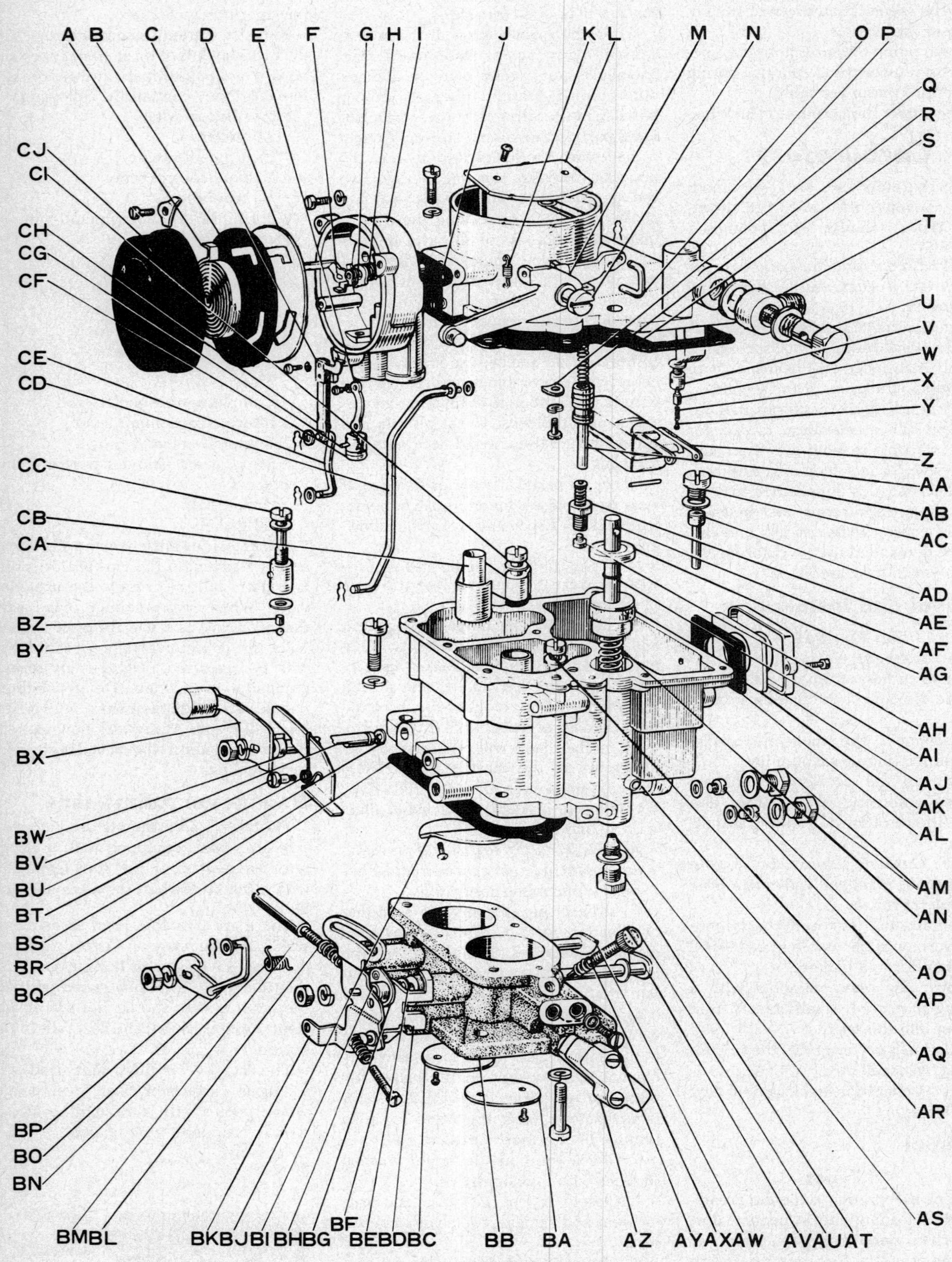

3R-B and 3R-C—2T-C, 8R-C and 18R-C similar.

(a)—Thermostat bimetal
(b)—Coil housing gasket
(c)—Fast idle cam follower
(d)—Coil housing plate
(e)—Piston connector
(f)—Choke shaft
(g)—Fast idle cam
(h)—Fast idle cam spring
(i)—Thermostat case
(k—Pump arm spring
(j)—Thermostat case gasket
(l)—Choke valve
(m)—Pump lever
(n)—Pump arm securing screw
(o)—Pump connecting link
(p)—Air horn
(q)—Power piston stopper
(r)—Power piston spring
(s)—Air horn gasket
(t)—Union nipple
(u)—Plug with strainer
(v)—Needle valve seat
(w)—Needle valve
(x)—Needle valve spring
(y)—Needle valve push pin
(z)—Float
(aa)—Power piston
(ab)—Slow circuit plug
(ac)—Float lever pin
(ad)—Slow jet
(ae)—Power valve
(af)—Pump plunger
(ag)—Plunger guide
(ah)—Power jet
(ai)—O-ring
(aj)—Level gauge clamp
(ak)—Level gauge glass
(al)—Gasket
(am)—Main passage plug
(an)—Pump damping spring
(ao)—Primary main jet
(ap)—Secondary main jet
(aq)—Primary air bleeder
(ar)—Body
(as)—Discharge check valve
(at)—Main passage plug
(au)—Idle adjusting screw
(av)—Primary throttle shaft
(aw)—Secondary throttle shaft
(ax)—Spring
(ay)—Main passage plug
(az)—Thermostatic valve
(ba)—Primary throttle valve
(bb)—Flange
(bc)—Secondary throttle valve
(bd)—Fast idle adjusting lever
(be)—Retaining ring
(bf)—Fast idle adjusting bolt
(bg)—Fast idle lever
(bh)—Spring
(bi)—Throttle lever collar
(bj)—High speed valve
(bk)—Primary throttle arm
(bl)—Spring
(bm)—Thoottle adjusting screw
(bn)—Secondary throttle back spring
(bo)—Throttle shaft link
(bp)—Secondary throttle lever
(bq)—Gasket
(br)—High speed valve stop lever
(bs)—Retaining ring
(bt)—High speed valve stop lever spring
(bu)—Stop lever securing screw
(bv)—High speed valve shaft
(bw)—High speed valve stopper
(bx)—High speed valve weight
(by)—Check ball
(bz)—Weight
(ca)—Pump jet
(cb)—Secondary small venturi
(cc)—Pump jet screw
(cd)—Pump connecting rod
(ce)—Connecting rod
(cf)—Vacuum piston
(cg)—Piston pin
(ch)—Sliding rod
(ci)—Primary main air bleeder
(cj)—Coil housing

3R-B and 3R-C—2T-C, 8R-C and 18R-C similar.

1. Coil housing
2. Thermostatic bimetal coil
3. Coil housing gasket
4. Coil housing plate
5. Pump damping spring
6. Pump lever
7. Pump lever set screw
8. Back spring support
9. Choke shaft
10. Choke lever link
11. Fast idle cam lever
12. Thermostat case
13. Air horn
14. Choke valve
15. Union fitting gasket
16. Union fitting
17. Pump connecting link
18. Piston pin
19. Piston connector
20. Vacuum piston
21. Discharge weight stop
22. Pump discharge weight
23. Steel ball
24. Boot
25. Plunger return spring
26. Pump plunger
27. Primary slow jet
28. Power piston spring
29. Power piston
30. Power piston stopper
31. Needle valve
32. Float lever pin
33. Float
34. Secondary slow jet
35. Air horn gasket
36. Nut plug
37. Steel ball
38. Power valve
39. Power jet
40. Fuel hose
41. Thermostatic valve
42. Bracket
43. Primary throttle return spring
44. Fast idle cam
45. Lever return spring
46. Dash pot lever
47. Fast idle adjusting screw
48. Primary throttle lever
49. Fast idle adjusting lever
50. Throttle valve adjusting shim
51. Primary throttle shaft
52. Idle mixture adjusting screw
53. Adjusting screw spring
54. Idle speed adjusting screw
55. Adjusting screw spring
56. Nut plug
57. Pump jet plug
58. Primary small venturi
59. Secondary small venturi
60. Level gauge gasket
61. Level gauge glass
62. Level gauge clamp
63. Dash pot
64. Boot
65. Diaphragm housing cap gasket
66. Diaphragm relief lever
67. Diaphragm relief spring
68. Collar
69. Secondary throttle shaft
70. Diaphragm housing
71. Diaphragm housing gasket
72. Diaphragm rod
73. Diaphragm spring
74. Diaphragm cap gasket
75. Diaphragm housing cap
76. Primary throttle valve
77. Secondary throttle valve
78. Venturi gasket
79. Carburetor body
80. Secondary main jet
81. Main passage plug
82. Primary main jet
83. First kick lever
84. Throttle shaft link
85. Secondary throttle return spring
86. Second kick lever
87. Second kick arm

2M and 4M

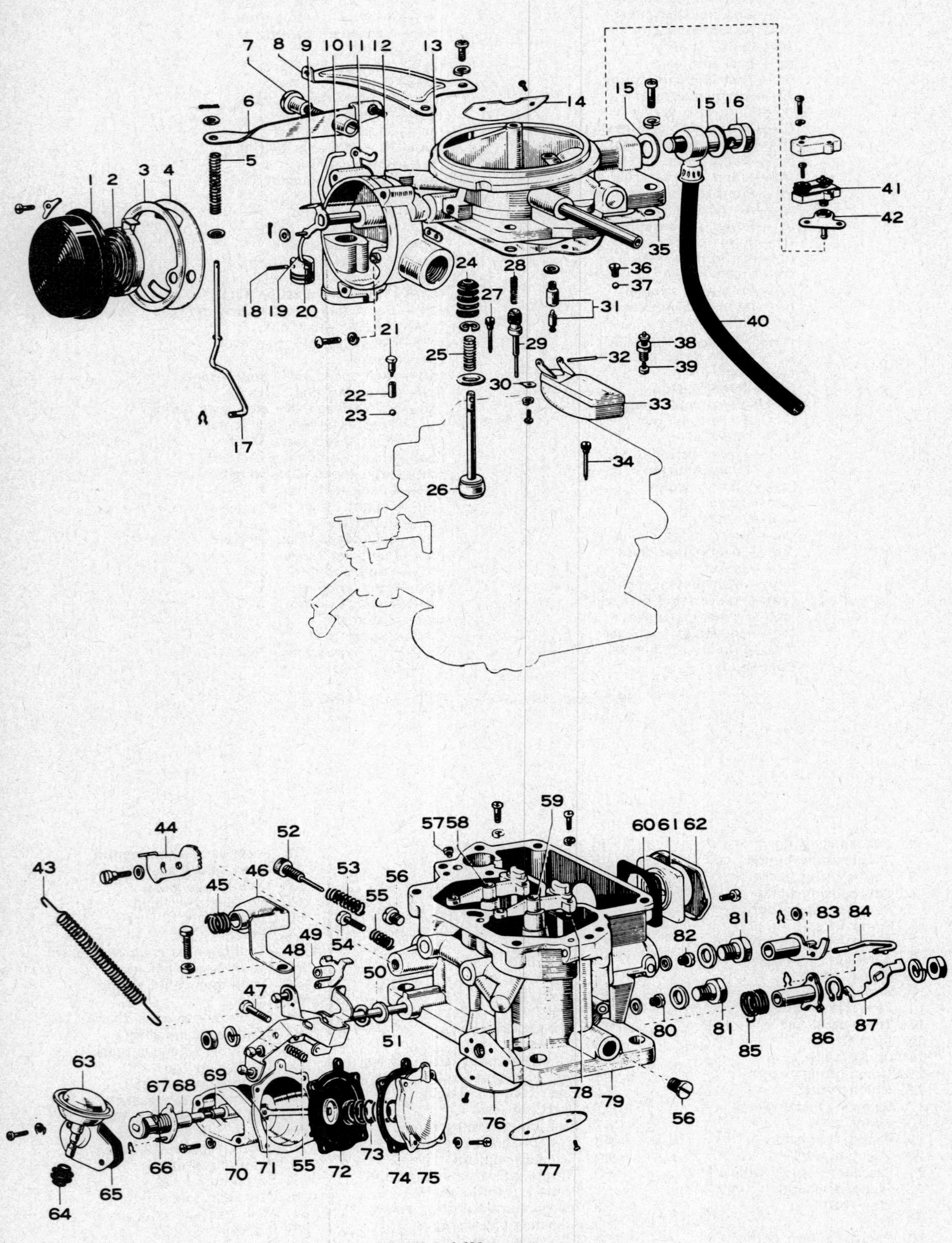
1
2
3
4
5
6
7
8
9
10
11
12
13
14
15
15
16
17
18
19
20
21
22
23
24
25
26
27
28
29
30
31
32
33
34
35
36
37
38
39
40
41
42
43
44
45
46
47
48
49
50
51
52
53
54
55
55
56
56
57
58
59
60
61
62
63
64
65
66
67
68
69
70
71
72
73
74
75
76
77
78
79
80
81
81
82
83
84
85
86
87

2M and 4M

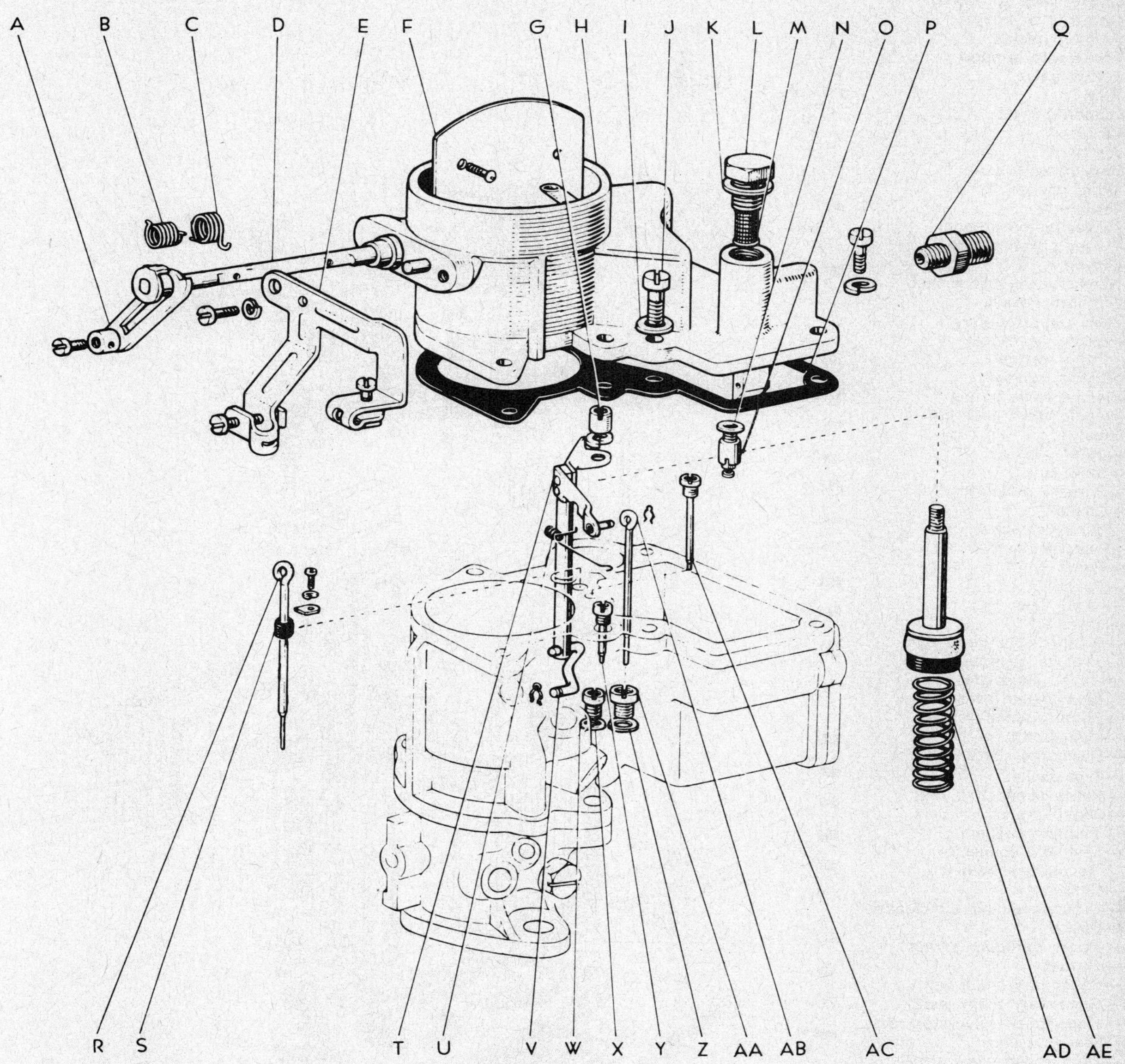

F engine—1-bbl

(a)—Choke lever
(b)—Choke valve relief spring
(c)—Choke valve spring
(d)—Choke shaft
(e)—Choke wire support
(f)—Choke valve
(g)—Pump plunger attaching nut
(h)—Air-horn
(i)—Idle circuit
(j)—Idle circuit
(k)—Intake strainer gasket
(l)—Main plug circuit
(m)—Strainer
(n)—Needle valve seat gasket
(o)—Needle valve sub-assembly
(p)—Air-horn gasket
(q)—Fitting
(r)—Step-up-rod (spare)
(s)—Rod support seal
(t)—Lifter rod
(u)—Step-up-rod spring
(v)—Throttle connecting link
(w)—Main jet gasket
(x)—Main jet
(y)—Main air bleeder
(z)—Step-up-rod jet gasket
(aa)—Step-up-rod jet
(ab)—Step-up-rod
(ac)—Idle jet
(ad)—Pump spring
(ae)—Pump plunger

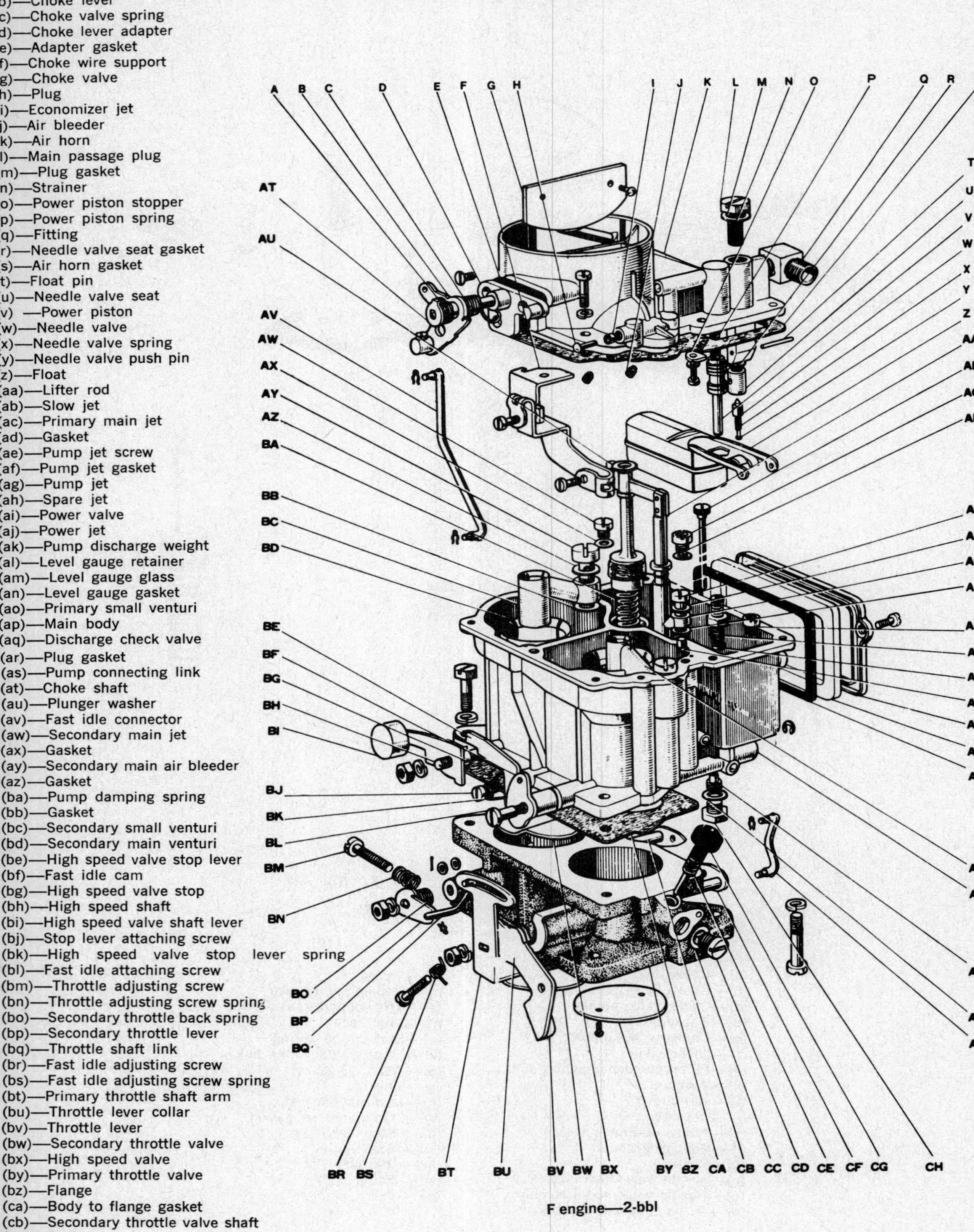

(a)—Choke valve relief spring
(b)—Choke lever
(c)—Choke valve spring
(d)—Choke lever adapter
(e)—Adapter gasket
(f)—Choke wire support
(g)—Choke valve
(h)—Plug
(i)—Economizer jet
(j)—Air bleeder
(k)—Air horn
(l)—Main passage plug
(m)—Plug gasket
(n)—Strainer
(o)—Power piston stopper
(p)—Power piston spring
(q)—Fitting
(r)—Needle valve seat gasket
(s)—Air horn gasket
(t)—Float pin
(u)—Needle valve seat
(v) —Power piston
(w)—Needle valve
(x)—Needle valve spring
(y)—Needle valve push pin
(z)—Float
(aa)—Lifter rod
(ab)—Slow jet
(ac)—Primary main jet
(ad)—Gasket
(ae)—Pump jet screw
(af)—Pump jet gasket
(ag)—Pump jet
(ah)—Spare jet
(ai)—Power valve
(aj)—Power jet
(ak)—Pump discharge weight
(al)—Level gauge retainer
(am)—Level gauge glass
(an)—Level gauge gasket
(ao)—Primary small venturi
(ap)—Main body
(aq)—Discharge check valve
(ar)—Plug gasket
(as)—Pump connecting link
(at)—Choke shaft
(au)—Plunger washer
(av)—Fast idle connector
(aw)—Secondary main jet
(ax)—Gasket
(ay)—Secondary main air bleeder
(az)—Gasket
(ba)—Pump damping spring
(bb)—Gasket
(bc)—Secondary small venturi
(bd)—Secondary main venturi
(be)—High speed valve stop lever
(bf)—Fast idle cam
(bg)—High speed valve stop
(bh)—High speed shaft
(bi)—High speed valve shaft lever
(bj)—Stop lever attaching screw
(bk)—High speed valve stop lever spring
(bl)—Fast idle attaching screw
(bm)—Throttle adjusting screw
(bn)—Throttle adjusting screw spring
(bo)—Secondary throttle back spring
(bp)—Secondary throttle lever
(bq)—Throttle shaft link
(br)—Fast idle adjusting screw
(bs)—Fast idle adjusting screw spring
(bt)—Primary throttle shaft arm
(bu)—Throttle lever collar
(bv)—Throttle lever
(bw)—Secondary throttle valve
(bx)—High speed valve
(by)—Primary throttle valve
(bz)—Flange
(ca)—Body to flange gasket
(cb)—Secondary throttle valve shaft
(cc)—Gasket
(cd)—Idle port plug
(ce)—Idle adjusting screw spring
(cf)—Primary throttle valve shaft
(cg)—Idle adjusting screw
(ch)—Plug

F engine—2-bbl

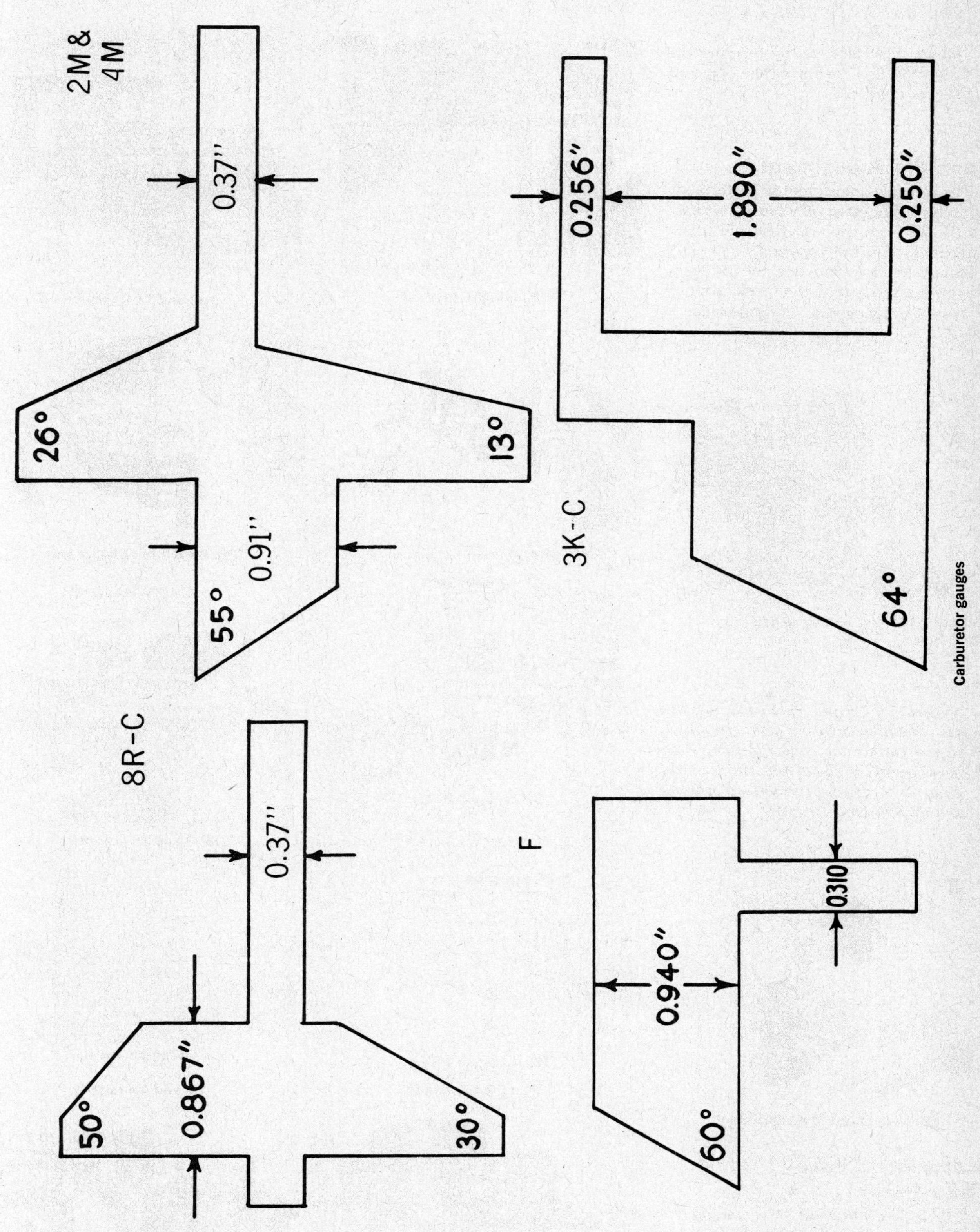

Carburetor gauges

NOTE: *Gap specifications are also given so that a float level gauge may be fabricated. Several different gauges are illustrated below.*

Adjust the float level by bending the tabs on the float levers, either upper or lower, as required.

Fast Idle Adjustment

The fast idle adjustment is performed with the choke valve fully *closed,* except on the 2T-C engine which should have the choke valve fully *opened.*

Adjust the gap between the throttle valve edge and bore to the specifications. Use a wire gauge to determine the gap.

Adjusting the fast idle by bending the linkage.

NOTE: *The throttle valve opening angle is measured with a gauge supplied in the carburetor rebuilding kit. It is also possible to make one out of cardboard by using a protractor to obtain the correct angle.*

Screw-type fast idle adjustment

Automatic Choke Adjustment

NOTE: *The automatic choke should be adjusted with the carburetor installed and the engine running.*

1. Check to see that the choke valve will close from fully opened when the coil housing is turned counterclockwise (2M and 4M engines—clockwise).

Measuring the Float Level

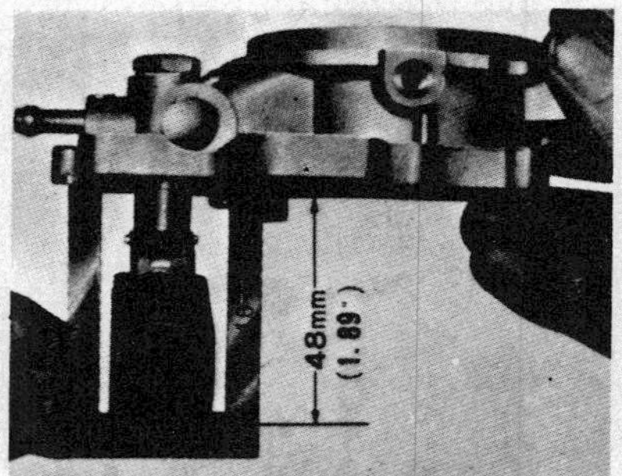

K-C and 3K-C lowered

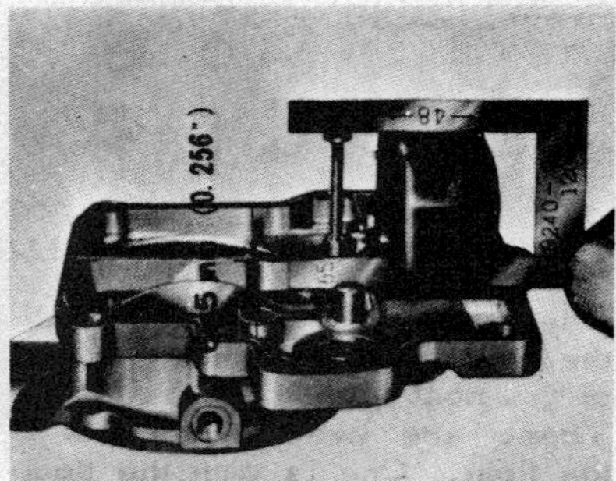

K-C and 3K-C raised

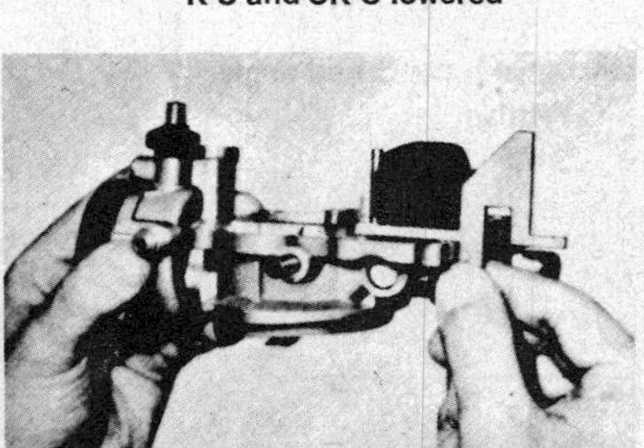

2T-C, 8R-C and 18R-C lowered

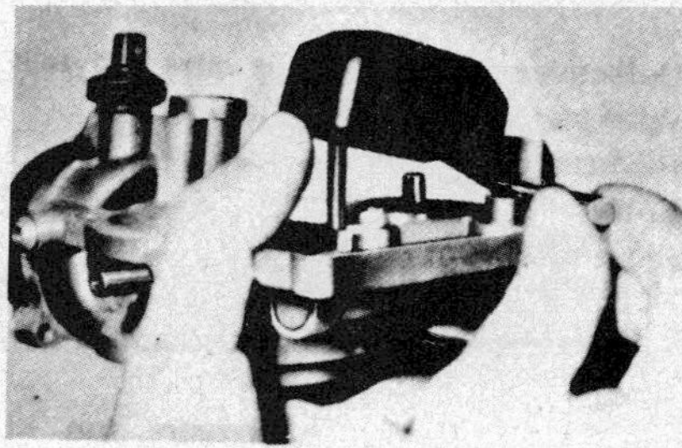

2T-C, 8R-C and 18R-C raised

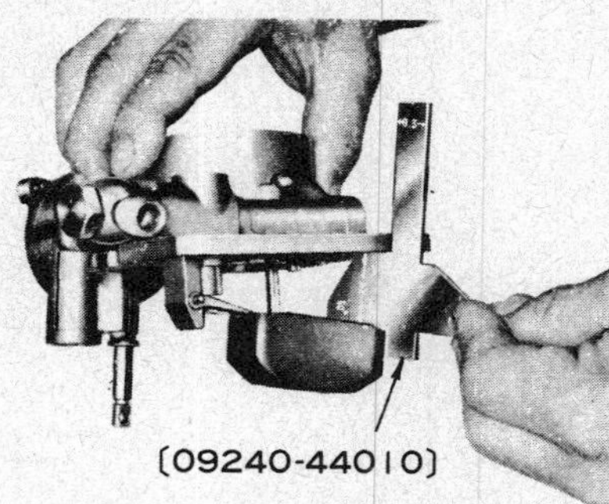

3R-B and 3R-C lowered

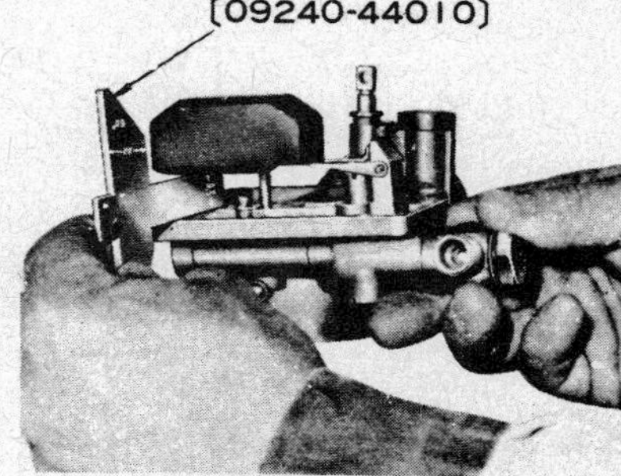

3R-B and 3R-C raised

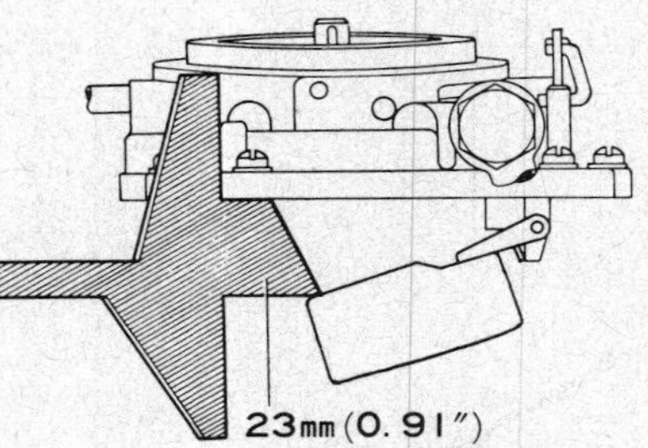

2M and 4M lowered

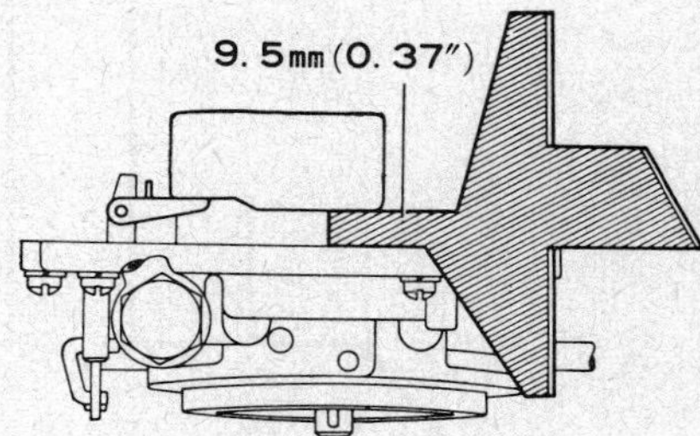

2M and 4M raised

F engine lowered

F engine raised

2. Align the mark on the coil housing with the center line on the thermostat case. In this position, the choke valve should be fully closed when the ambient temperature is 77°F.

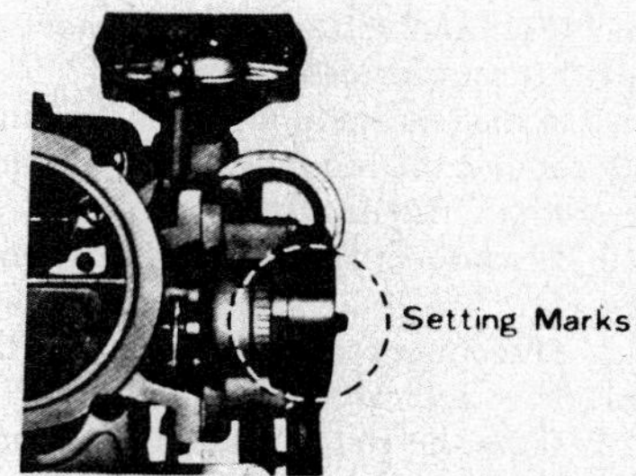

Align the setting marks on the choke housing.

3. If necessary, adjust the mixture by turning the coil housing. If the mixture is too *rich,* rotate the housing *clockwise;* if too *lean,* rotate the housing *counterclockwise.* On models equipped with the 2M and 4M engines, rotate the housing in exactly the reverse direction of the above.

NOTE: *Each graduation on the thermostat case is equivalent to 9°F.*

Unloader Adjustment

Make the unloader adjustment with the primary valve fully opened. The total angle of the choke valve opening, in the chart, is measured with either a special gauge, supplied in the carburetor rebuilding kit, or a gauge of the proper angle fabricated from cardboard.

Reloader Adjustment

8R-C Engine

A reloader is used on the 8R-C engine to prevent the throttle valve from opening during automatic choke operation.

1. When the choke valve is opened 45° from the closed position, the reloader lever should disengage from its stop.

NOTE: *Angle "A", in the illustration, should be 20° when measured with a gauge.*

2. To adjust, bend the portion of the linkage where angle "A" was measured.

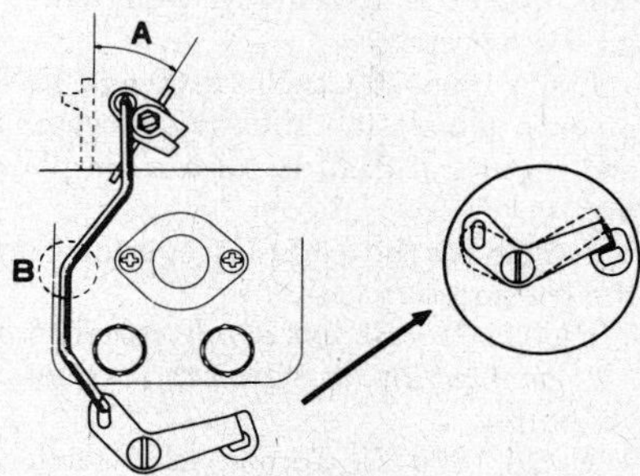

Measure the angle at "A" (20 degrees)

3. When the primary throttle valve is fully opened, with the reloader in operating position, the clearance between the secondary throttle valve edge and bore should be 0.014–0.030 in. Measure the clearance with a wire gauge and bend the reloader tab to adjust it.

4. Fully open the choke valve by hand; the reloader lever should be disengaged from its stop by the weight on its link.

MANUAL TRANSMISSION

Removal and Installation

Corolla and Carina

Working from inside of the car, perform the following:

1. Place the gear selector in Neutral. Remove the center console, if so equipped.
2. Remove the trim boot at the base of the shift lever and the boot underneath it on the shift tower.
3. On Corolla 1100 and 1200 models only:
   a. Unfasten the snap-ring from the base of the shift lever. On 1968–70 models, press down and turn the lever counterclockwise.
   b. Withdraw the conical spring and the shift lever itself.
4. On Corolla 1600 and Carina models only:
   a. Unfasten the four shift lever plate retaining screws.
   b. Withdraw the shift lever assembly.
   c. Remove the gasket.

NOTE: *Cover the hole with a clean cloth to prevent anything from falling into the transmission case.*

Working in the engine compartment perform the following:

5. Drain the cooling system and disconnect the cable from the positive side of the battery.
6. Remove the radiator hoses.
7. On Corolla 1100 and 1200 models, only:
   a. Unfasten the back-up lamp switch connector.
   b. Remove the engine fan.
8. On Corolla 1600 and Carina models, only:
   a. Remove the air cleaner, complete with hoses.
   b. Unfasten the accelerator torque rod at the carburetor.
   c. Remove the clutch hydraulic line support bracket.
   d. Remove the starter assembly from the left side of the engine.
   e. Remove the upper left-hand clutch housing bolt, from the flat at the top of the clutch housing.

Working from beneath the car:

CAUTION: *Be sure that the car is securely supported with jackstands. Remember, you will be working underneath it.*

9. Drain the transmission oil.
10. Detach the exhaust pipe from the manifold and remove the exhaust pipe support bracket.
11. Remove the driveshaft.

NOTE: *It will be necessary to plug the opening in the end of the transmission with an old yoke or, if none is available, cover it with a plastic bag secured by a rubber band.*

12. Unfasten the speedometer cable from the right side of the transmission.
13. On Corolla 1600 and Carina models, only:
   a. Remove the clutch release cylinder assembly from the transmission and tie it aside, so that it is out of the way.
   b. Unplug the back-up lamp switch connector.
14. Support the front of the transmission with a jack.
15. Unfasten the engine rear mounts. (See the engine removal section.) Remove the rear crossmember.
16. Remove the jack from under the transmission.
17. On Corolla 1600 and Carina models, unbolt the clutch housing from the engine and withdraw the transmission assembly.

NOTE: *Remove the brace, if so equipped.*

18. Perform the following on Corolla 1100 and 1200 models, before removing the transmission:
   a. Remove the cotter pin from the clutch release linkage.
   b. Remove the clutch release cable.
   c. Remove the stiffener plate, if so equipped.
   d. Unbolt the clutch housing from the engine by removing the bolts in the order illustrated.

Installation is performed in the reverse order of removal, but remember to perform the following during installation.

Apply a light coating of multipurpose grease to the input shaft end, input shaft spline, clutch release bearing, and driveshaft end. On Corolla 1100 and 1200 models, apply multipurpose grease to the ball on the end of the gearshift lever assembly; and to the clutch release cable end.

On Corolla 1100 and 1200 models, install the clutch housing-to-engine bolts in two or three stages, and in the order shown.

After installation:

1. Fill the transmission and cooling system. (See "Capacities" above.)
2. Adjust the clutch as detailed below.
3. Check to see that the back-up lamps function when Reverse is selected.

Corona, Mark II/4, and Hi-Lux

Working under the hood, perform the following:

1. Unfasten the cable from the positive battery terminal.
2. Remove the accelerator torque rod from its valve cover mounting.
3. Separate the downpipe from the flange and remove the flange. Remove the exhaust pipe bracket.

Raise the car with a jack and support it with jackstands.

CAUTION: *Be sure that the car is securely supported. Remember, you will be working underneath it.*

Working beneath the car, perform the following:

4. Remove the parking brake equalizer support bracket.
5. Unfasten the speedometer cable and back-up lamp wiring harness from the transmission.
6. Remove the control shaft lever retainer.
7. Remove the clutch release cylinder from the transmission and set it up, out of the way.

NOTE: *Do not disconnect the hydraulic line from the release cylinder.*

8. Drain the transmission oil.
9. Remove the driveshaft.

NOTE: *To prevent oil from draining out of the transmission, install a spare U-joint or, if none is available, cover the opening with a plastic bag secured by a rubber band.*

10. Support the transmission with a jack.
11. Unfasten the rear engine mounts and remove the engine rear supporting crossmember. (See the engine removal section.)
12. Lower the jack.
13. Unfasten the bolts which secure the clutch housing to the cylinder block.
14. Remove the transmission toward the rear of the car.

Installation is performed in the reverse order of removal. See the notes at the end of the Corolla and Carina transmission installation section for details which require attention during installation.

NOTE: *Use a clutch guide tool, of the proper size, during installation, to locate the clutch disc.*

Celica, Mark II/6, and Crown 2600

Perform the removal procedures as outlined for the Corolla 1600 and Carina. In addition, perform the following:

1. Working under the hood, remove the accelerator connecting rod from the linkage.
2. With the car jacked up and supported:
   a. Remove the left-hand, rear stone shield before removing the clutch release cylinder.
   b. Remove the flywheel housing lower cover and its braces.

Installation is performed in the reverse order of removal.

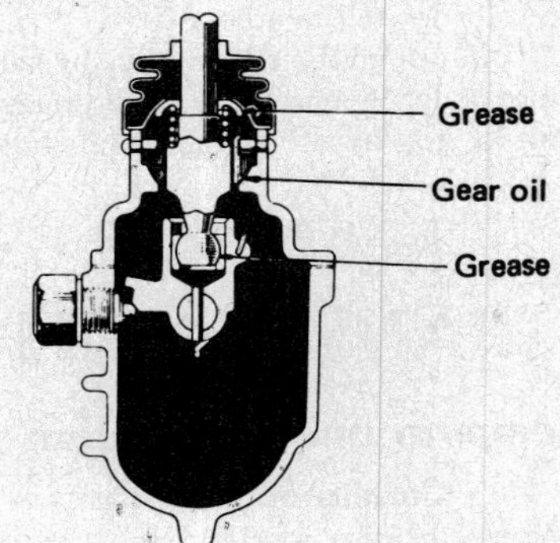

Floor shift lever lubrication points—Celica, Mark II/6 and Crown 2600.

NOTE: *Use a clutch guide tool, during installation, to locate the clutch disc.*

Crown 2300

Perform the removal procedure as outlined for the Corona, Mark II/4, and Hi-Lux, above. In addition, perform the following steps:

1. Working under the hood:
   a. Disconnect the radiator hoses after draining the cooling system.
   b. Remove the air cleaner assembly complete with hoses.
   c. Disconnect the connecting rod from the accelerator linkage, before removing the torque rod.
2. With car jacked-up and supported as above, perform the following:
   a. Disconnect the starter wiring and remove the starter.
   b. Remove the right-hand engine stone shield before disconnecting the exhaust pipe from the manifold.
   c. Detach the parking brake operating lever from the intermediate lever. Remove the return spring and the intermediate lever from its support bracket. Unfasten the parking brake cable.
   d. Jack up the front of the engine—once the jack has been removed from the transmission—to facilitate transmission removal.

Installation is performed in the reverse order of removal.

Land Cruiser

1. Raise the vehicle and support it with jackstands.

CAUTION: *Be sure that the vehicle is securely supported. Remember you will be working underneath it.*

2. Remove the transmission skid plate.
3. Drain the transmission and transfer case.
4. On two-door models only:
   a. Remove the passenger seat.
   b. Remove the fuel tank (only if it is under the passenger seat).
5. Remove the transmission cover.
6. Detach the parking brake cable from the end of the parking brake lever.
7. Disconnect the speedometer cable from the transmission.
8. Loosen the clamps and disconnect the hoses from the transfer case (vacuum-operated transfer case only).
9. On models equipped with a column shift, remove the rod pins and cotter pins, then detach the intermediate rods.
10. Disconnect the high and low shift rods.
11. Disconnect the wires from the front drive indicator light switch.
12. Raise the transmission with a jack.
13. Disconnect both front and rear U-joint yokes from the transfer case.
14. Remove the clutch housing skid plate.
15. Unfasten the bolts which attach the transmission to the transfer case.
16. Slide the transmission toward the rear of the vehicle so that the input shaft clears the clutch housing.
17. Remove the transmission transfer case assembly from under the vehicle, complete with the parking brake assembly.

Installation is performed in the reverse order of removal. Tighten the transmission mounting bolts to 52–57 ft lbs. Refill the transmission, and check the clutch linkage and shift linkage operation, after installation.

Overhaul

Corolla 1100 and 1200

1. Drain the lubricant from the transmission, if you have not already done so. Clean off the magnetic plug.
2. Unfasten the lead from the back-up light switch.
3. Remove the tension spring from the clutch release fork. Unfasten the throw-out bearing hub clips and the release fork boot.
4. Withdraw the clutch fork and the release hub.
5. Unfasten the oil pan retaining nuts, and remove the pan complete with its gasket.
6. Remove the speedometer shaft sleeve and the driven gear from the extension housing.
7. On 1968–70 Corolla 1100 and 1200 models, unbolt the shift lever retainer and remove it from the extension housing.
8. Remove the extension housing from the transmission case.

CAUTION: *Be extremely careful not to damage the oil seal on the extension housing.*

9. On 1970–73 Corolla 1200 models, perform the following:
   a. Remove the shift lever retainer by pulling the selector shaft toward the front of the extension housing while sliding the retainer toward the rear of

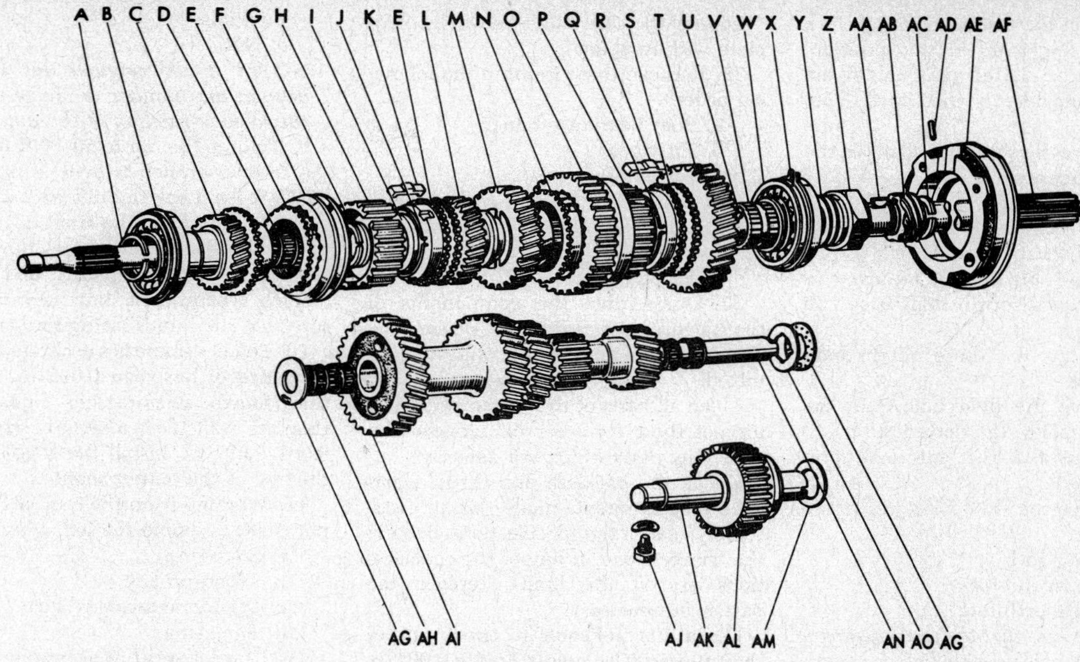

Corolla 1100 and 1200 transmission components.

(a)—Shaft snap-ring
(b)—Bearing (transmission front)
(c)—Input shaft
(d)—Needle roller bearing
(e)—Synchronizer ring No. 3
(f)—Transmission hub sleeve
(g)—Shaft snap-ring
(h)—Transmission clutch hub No. 2
(i)—Clutch hub spacer
(j)—Synchromesh shifting key spring No. 2
(k)—Synchromesh shifting key No. 2
(l)—Side gear
(m)—Second gear
(n)—Synchronizer ring No. 2
(o)—Reverse gear
(p)—Transmission clutch hub No. 1
(q)—Synchromesh shifting key spring No. 1
(r)—Synchromesh shifting key No. 1
(s)—Synchronizer ring No. 1
(t)—First gear
(u)—Ball
(v)—First gear bushing
(w)—Bearing (transmission rear)
(x)—Shaft snap-ring
(y)—Shim
(z)—Nut
(aa)—Woodruff key
(ab)—Speedometer drive gear
(ac)—Shaft snap-ring
(ad)—Slotted split pin
(ae)—Output shaft rear retainer
(af)—Output shaft
(ag)—Countergear thrust washer (case side)
(ah)—Needle roller bearing
(ai)—Countergear
(aj)—Shaft retaining bolt
(ak)—Reverse idler gear shaft
(al)—Reverse idler gear
(am)—Spacer
(an)—Counter shaft
(ao)—Countergear thrust washer (gear side)

1970-73 Corolla shift lever retainer removal.

the housing.

b. Drive out the roll pin which secures the shift housing to the selector shaft and remove the housing.

c. Withdraw the selector shaft, as well as its support and gasket.

10. Remove the countershaft cover and the front bearing retainer, complete with gaskets.

CAUTION: *Be careful not to damage the front bearing oil seal.*

11. Evenly loosen the five nuts which attach the transmission case cover. Withdraw the cover, gasket, and three detent springs.

CAUTION: *Be careful not to lose the three detent balls, as the springs keep them under compression.*

12. Remove the securing bolt and withdraw the reverse idler gear shaft from the transmission case.

13. Remove the idler gear and the spacer, if installed.

14. Measure gear backlash:

a. Mount a dial indicator, so that its plunger makes contact with the countergear teeth at right angles.

b. With a screwdriver, lock each gear, in turn, to the output shaft so that it cannot move.

c. Rock the countershaft back and forth and note the reading on the dial indicator for each gear.

d. The specifications for each gear follow:

Gear Backlash

Gear	BACKLASH Specified	Limit
Input shaft	0.004	0.008
Ist, 2nd and 3rd gears	0.004	0.008
Reverse	0.006	0.012
Reverse idler	0.007	0.012

15. Measure the countergear thrust clearance with a feeler gauge.

16. Use a brass drift to drive the countershaft out toward the rear of the gearbox.

17. Remove the countergear and the thrust washers from the shaft.

18. Remove the four needle bearings from the countershaft. Be careful not to drop them.

19. Engage Reverse and Second gears,

by pushing on the first/second shift fork shaft. With the gears in this position, drive the three slotted pins out of the shift forks and detents with an 0.18 in. punch.

20. Remove the shift fork shafts in the following sequence:

a. Reverse shaft
b. First/second shaft
c. Third/fourth shaft

The interlock pin may be removed by shaking the third/fourth shaft back and forth.

21. Withdraw the three detent balls from the case.

22. Remove the plug bolt from the housing (just below the slotted pin holes) and take out the two interlock pins (1970–73 only).

23. Remove the shift forks in the following order:

a. Reverse fork
b. First/second fork
c. Third/fourth fork

NOTE: *Be sure that the transmission is shifted into second gear before removing the first/second shift fork.*

24. Carefully remove the output shaft assembly from the rear of the transmission case.

25. Remove the roller bearings and fourth gear synchronizer ring from the input shaft. Use a soft brass drift to drive the input shaft toward the front of the transmission.

26. Measure the thrust clearance of the third, second and first gears with a feeler gauge.

Thrust Clearance
(in.)

Gear	Range	Limit
Third	0.004-0.010	0.020
Second	0.006-0.012	0.020
First	0.004-0.012	0.020
Countergear	0.002-0.010	0.020

27. Remove the snap-ring from the output shaft. Remove the third and fourth synchronizer assembly, clutch, hub spacer and third gear.

NOTE: *Be careful not to mix up the third and fourth gear synchronizer rings. Label them as they are removed.*

28. Remove the snap-ring which retains the speedometer drive gear. Withdraw the drive gear from the input shaft.

29. Remove the woodruff key.

30. Use a punch to straighten out the punched portion of the nut. Be careful not to damage the threaded portion of the output shaft.

31. Support the input shaft by placing reverse gear in a vise.

CAUTION: *Use aluminum plates to protect the gear teeth.*

Loosen the nut and remove it, complete with its shims.

32. Remove these items in the following order:

a. Rear bearing retainer
b. First gear
c. Second gear
d. Ball
e. First/second gear synchronizer
f. Synchronizer rings
g. Second gear

33. Disassemble the components of the synchronizer assemblies. Be sure the components of the two assemblies are not mixed.

Clean all parts of the transmission and inspect them for wear or damage. Replace any parts which are defective.

Check the backlash and thrust clearance measurements made during disassembly against the specifications given in the charts above. If any of the specifications exceed the limits, replace the part(s), as necessary.

Use a dial indicator to check output shaft runout. The runout limit is 0.001 in.

Replace the front bearing, if it is rough or noisy, using a drift and press. Replace the bearing snap-ring with one of the following to obtain the *minimum* thrust clearance:

0.091–0.095 in.
0.097–0.101 in.

Transmission assembly is performed in the following order:

NOTE: *Always use new gaskets (apply liquid sealer) and snap-rings.*

1. Apply a thin coat of gear oil to all of the rotating surfaces prior to assembly.

2. Assemble the components of the third/fourth gear synchronizer hub:

a. Install the key springs in the clutch hub.
b. Place the three shifting keys into the hub slots.
c. Install the second clutch hub into the sleeve.

NOTE: *Keep the open end of the key springs 120 degrees apart. By doing this, spring tension is kept uniform.*

3. Assemble the second/third synchronizer hub in the same manner detailed in step 2.

4. Install the second gear and its synchronizer ring, working from the back end of the output shaft. Be sure that the synchronizer is facing the proper direction. Do not mix the rings for the different gears.

5. Fit the first and second gear synchronizer hub on the output shaft, being careful to align its keys with the slots on the synchronizer ring.

6. Install first gear, complete with its synchronizer ring, bushing, and ball on the output shaft.

7. Attach the following to the output shaft:

a. Rear bearing
b. Shims
c. Nut

NOTE: *If the original nut is used, change the number of shims to alter the locking position of the nut.*

8. Tighten the nut to 60–80 ft lbs, or if the torque wrench is over 20 in. long, 50–70 ft lbs. Lock the nut with a chisel.

9. Working from the front of the output shaft, install third gear, third gear synchronizer ring, spacer, and third-/fourth synchronizer hub assembly. Be sure that the hub is facing forward.

10. Select a snap-ring to obtain a thrust clearance of less than 0.002 in. for the third/fourth synchronizer hub. Snap-rings are available in a range of sizes from 0.081–0.097 in. Install the snap-ring on the end of the output shaft.

11. Working from the rear of the output shaft, assemble the following:

a. Snap-ring
b. Woodruff key
c. Speedometer drive gear
d. Snap-ring

12. Check the thrust clearance of each gear.

13. Fit the input shaft into the transmission case with a piece of pipe which is large enough so that it drives the bearing into place, but does not damage the shaft.

14. Select the proper gasket for the bearing retainer:

a. If the transmission case sticks out beyond the bearing installation surface, use a gasket with a thickness of 0.01 in.
b. If the bearing installation surface protrudes beyond the transmission case, use a gasket with a thickness of 0.02 in.
c. Apply liquid sealer to both sides of the gasket.

15. Apply grease to the lip of the bearing retainer oil seal.

16. Mount the bearing retainer and gasket in the transmission case and tighten its securing bolts to 7–12 ft lbs.

17. Fit the needle bearing and the synchronizer ring onto the output shaft.

18. Slide the output shaft into the transmission case, carefully. Be sure to align the slotted pin on the bearing retainer with the grooves on the transmission case, and the notches on the ring with the proper shift keys.

19. Engage reverse gear with the second gear, then install the first/second shift fork in the groove on reverse gear. Rotate the fork half a turn around the gear.

20. Working from the rear of the transmission case, fit the first/second shift fork shaft into the case and then into the shift fork.

21. Fit the third/fourth shift fork into the groove on the clutch hub sleeve and rotate it one half turn around the sleeve.

22. Install the third/fourth shift fork

shaft in the same manner outlined in step 20.

23. Engage the reverse shift fork with the center of the reverse shift arm. Fasten it with the E-ring. Fit the shaft into the transmission case and then into the fork, itself.

24. Align the slotted spring pin hole in each shift fork with the corresponding hole on each shaft.

NOTE: *Grease the pins, prior to installation.*

25. If the transmission is equipped with a pin installation hole, apply seal packing on the threads of the plug bolt and screw the bolt into the hole.

26. Install the needle roller bearings in countergear set. Be sure to grease the rollers first.

27. Install the front thrust washer in the recess on the transmission case. Install the rear gearset thrust washer and the rear case thrust washer in the recess located at the rear of the transmission case.

NOTE: *The washer which abuts the case goes into the recess first. Be sure that the embossed portion of each washer fits snugly in the case.*

28. Place the countergear into the transmission case. Measure the countergear thrust clearance with a feeler gauge; it should be 0.002–0.010 in. The thrust washer which abuts the case is available in several sizes, ranging from 0.051 to 0.-063 in., to adjust countergear thrust clearance to specifications.

29. Working from the rear of the transmission case, insert the countershaft.

NOTE: *The slot in the end of the shaft should be in a horizontal position.*

30. Install the countershaft front end cover and gasket. Tighten the securing bolts to 7–12 ft lbs.

31. Fit the groove in the reverse idler gear over the pin on the reverse shift arm. Place the gear and reverse idler shaft in the transmission case, with the shaft retaining boss facing upward.

32. Check the clearance between the reverse idler gear and the countergear end teeth when the reverse idler gear is pulled fully to the rear. If the clearance is less than 0.02 in., insert a spacer on the rear side of the reverse idler gear.

33. Align the boss on the reverse idler gear shaft with the retaining bolt boss. Tighten the retaining bolt to the following specifications:

1968–70(early)—9.5–13 ft lbs
1970(late)–73—7–12 ft lbs

34. Drop the three detent balls and their compression springs into the three holes provided on the transmission case.

35. Fit the case cover and gasket over the holes. Tighten the cover securing bolts to 3–7 ft lbs.

36. Adjust the reverse shift arm pivot in the following manner:

a. Position the gears in neutral.

b. Unscrew the pivot out all of the way.

c. Adjust the clearance between the reverse idler gear teeth and the rear teeth of the countergear, so that it is 0.06 in. Adjust by turning the pivot.

d. Check the clearance between the bottom of the reverse idler gear groove and the reverse shift arm. It should be 0.02–0.06 in.

e. Adjust the pivot until both clearances are obtained.

f. Lock the pivot with the locknut and recheck both clearances.

NOTE: *Be sure that the reverse idler gear does not contact the reverse gear when the transmission is in First gear.*

37. Perform the following steps on late 1970–73 transmission extension housings:

a. Install the support and gasket for the selector shaft through the hole in the support. Coat both sides of the gasket with sealer.

b. Fit the selector shaft through the hole in the support.

c. Attach the shift lever housing on the selector shaft, so that the pin hole is on the left side.

d. Drive the slotted pin into the shift lever housing with a brass drift.

e. Push in on the selector shaft and slide the shift lever retainer gasket and the retainer forward into place on the extension housing.

NOTE: *Apply sealer to both sides of the retainer gasket, before installation.*

f. Tighten the shift lever retainer bolts to 11–16 ft lbs.

38. Coat the extension housing oil seal lips with grease and coat the extension housing gasket with sealer on both sides.

39. Attach the extension housing to the transmission case, using care not to damage the oil seal. Tighten the housing securing bolts to the following specifications:

1968–70(early)—15–22 ft lbs
1970(late)–73—22–33 ft lbs

40. Install the back-up light switch, if it was removed, in the following order:

a. Grease the reverse restricter pin and insert it into the extension housing.

b. Insert the compression spring, followed by the straight pin, into the housing.

c. Screw the back-up light switch into the housing and tighten it to 22–36 ft lbs.

41. Coat the speedometer gear with gear oil. Install the speedometer shaft sleeve and the gear in the extension housing.

42. Perform the following steps in the 1968–70 (early) 1100 and 1200 models:

a. Coat the shift interlock plate moving surfaces with grease.

b. Attach the interlock to the shift lever retainer.

c. Position the three shift fork shafts in neutral and attach the shift lever retainer to the extension housing.

43. Position the embossed portion of the transmission oil pan gasket on the left-hand rear side of the case. Tighten the securing nuts to 4.5–5.0 ft lbs.

44. Install the drain plug and gasket on the oil pan. Tighten the plug to 27–31 ft lbs.

45. Coat the portions of the clutch release hub and fork which contact each other, with grease. Grease the inner surface of the clutch release hub.

46. Fit the boot over the release fork.

47. Install the release fork and hub. Tighten the fork securing bolt to 14–22 ft lbs.

48. Fit the release fork tension spring in place.

49. Connect the back-up light switch wiring.

50. Install the transmission in the car as outlined above.

Corolla 1600 and Carina

CAUTION: *The clutch housing, split transmission case, and extension housing are all made of aluminum. Care should be taken not to strip the threads and not to damage the machined surfaces of these components.*

1. Drain the oil from the transmission, if you have not done so during removal.

2. Remove the bolts which secure the clutch housing and withdraw the housing, with the bearing retainer, release bearing, and release fork still attached.

NOTE: *Use care not to lose the two conical springs from the bearings.*

3. Remove the bolt and withdraw the speedometer shaft sleeve and driven gear from the extension housing.

4. Remove the six bolts which retain the extension housing and separate the housing from the case.

CAUTION: *Be careful not to damage the extension housing oil seal.*

5. Remove the back-up light switch, spring and ball from the transmission case.

6. Unfasten the 14 bolts which secure the transmission case halves. Using a *wooden* mallet, tap the protrusion on the right-hand side of the case.

CAUTION: *Do not separate the halves of the case by prying them apart.*

7. Measure gear backlash, as detailed in step 14 of the Corolla 1100 and 1200 transmission overhaul procedure. Make a note of the values obtained. The backlash for all gears should be 0.004–0.008 in. and the wear limit should be 0.016 in.

8. Lift the countergear set out of the right-hand half of the case.

9. Use a magnet to remove the ball from the second countergear bearing.

10. Withdraw the input and the output shafts as a unit.

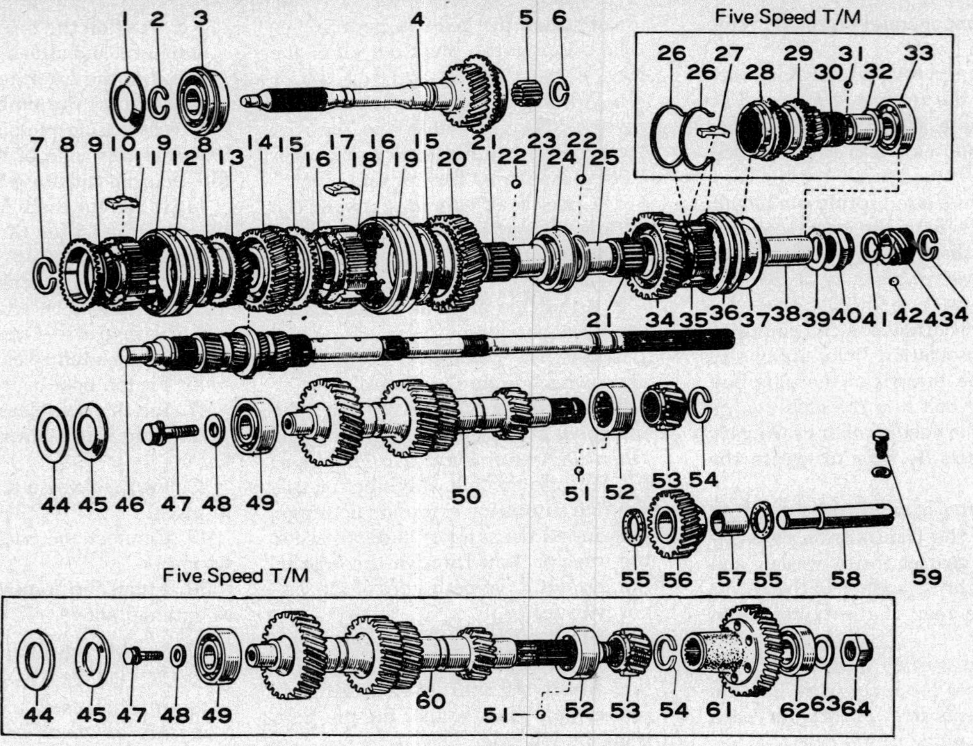

Corolla and Carina four and five-speed transmission components.

1. Conical spring
2. Shaft snap-ring
3. Ball bearing
4. Input shaft
5. Roller
6. Snap-ring
7. Shaft snap-ring
8. Synchronizer ring
9. Shift-key spring
10. Shift-key
11. Clutch hub
12. Hub sleeve
13. Third gear assembly
14. Second gear assembly
15. Synchronizer ring
16. Shift-key spring
17. Shift-key
18. Clutch hub
19. Hub sleeve
20. First gear assembly
21. Needle roller bearing
22. Ball
23. First gear bushing
24. Ball bearing
25. Reverse gear bushing
26. Shift-key spring*
27. Shift-key*
28. Synchronizer ring*
29. Fifth gear assembly*
30. Needle roller bearing*
31. Ball*
32. Fifth gear bushing*
33. Ball bearing*
34. Reverse gear
35. Clutch hub
36. Hub sleeve
37. Spacer
38. Spacer (long)
39. Shim
40. Nut
41. Shaft snap-ring
42. Ball
43. Speedometer drive gear
44. Shim
45. Conical spring
46. Output shaft
47. Bolt and washer
48. Plate washer
49. Ball bearing
50. Countergear
51. Ball
52. Roller bearing
53. Reverse countergear
54. Snap-ring
55. Thrust washer—reverse idler gear
56. Reverse idler gear
57. Bushing
58. Reverse idler gear shaft
59. Shaft retaining bolt
60. Countergear*
61. Fifth-speed countergear*
62. Ball bearing*
63. Shim*
64. Nut*

* Five-speed transmission only

11. Use a punch to drive the three slotted spring pins out of the shift forks and shift fork shafts.

NOTE: *The slotted pin cannot always be fully removed from the first/second shift fork; however, the shift fork can still be withdrawn. Do not try to force the pin out, as damage to the transmission case could result.*

12. Remove the case cover and withdraw the three detent balls and springs.

13. Remove the shift fork shafts in the following order:
   a. First/second shaft
   b. Pin
   c. Reverse shift fork shaft
   d. Third/fourth shaft
   e. Pin

14. Measure the thrust of the reverse idler gear with a feeler gauge. The specified clearance is 0.002–0.020 in. and the wear limit is 0.039 in.

15. Unfasten the idler shaft retaining bolt and withdraw the shaft. Remove the gear and washer.

16. Measure the thrust clearance of the gears on the output shaft and make a note of their values.

Thrust Clearance Specifications

Gear	Specified	Wear Limit
First	0.006-0.010	0.020
Second	0.006-0.010	0.020
Third	0.006-0.012	0.024
Reverse	0.008-0.012	0.024
Fifth①	0.006-0.010	0.020

① Optional

17. Disassemble the components of the output shaft in a similar manner to that outlined in steps 27–33 of the Corolla 1100 and 1200 overhaul (disassembly) procedure. Remember that five-speed transmissions have an extra gearset and related parts.

Clean all of the parts of the transmission and check them for wear or damage. Replace any defective parts.

Check the backlash and thrust clearance measurements made during disassembly against the specifications given in the charts above. If any of the specifications exceed the wear limits, replace the part(s) as necessary.

Use a dial indicator to check output shaft runout. The runout limit is 0.0012 in.; replace the shaft if it exceeds this.

Replace the front bearing, if it is rough or noisy. Use a drift and a press. Remove the snap-ring first.

For bearing installation, replacement snap-rings are available in a range of sizes (0.0925–0.1024 in.) to obtain *minimum* axial play between the input shaft and the bearing.

Assembly is performed in the following manner:

NOTE: Always use new gaskets and snap-rings. Apply gear lubricant to all sliding contact surfaces, gears, bushings and bearings.

1. Assemble the components of the synchronizer hubs, and the output shaft, as detailed in steps 2–6 of the Corolla 1100 and 1200 assembly procedures, above.
2. Install the rear bushing on the output shaft, being careful to install it in the proper direction.
3. Fit the ball into the groove of the bushing and slide the bushing over the shaft.
4. Install the needle roller bearing, reverse gear, the ball and the reverse gear synchronizer hub.
5. Install the following items on the output shaft of the four-speed transmission, in the order indicated:
   a. Large-diameter reverse gear spacer
   b. Long spacer
   c. Shims
6. Install the following items on the output shaft of the five-speed transmission in the order indicated:
   a. Ball
   b. Fifth gear synchronizer ring
   c. Fifth gear
   d. Needle roller bearing
   e. Bushing
   f. Rear support ball bearing
7. Install the shims and the nut on the end of the output shaft. Tighten it to 33–54 ft lbs and lock it with a chisel.

NOTE: *If the original nut is being used, change the number of shims to alter the locking portion of the nut.*

8. Check the thrust clearance of each gear.
9. Perform steps 9–12 of the Corolla 1100 and 1200 transmission assembly procedure.
10. Apply multipurpose grease on the end of the third/fourth gearshift fork shaft and install the shift fork. Install the fork and shaft assembly in the transmission case.
11. Insert the straight pins in the grooves on either side of the third/fourth shift shaft, after applying multipurpose grease to the pins.
12. Assemble the first/second gearshift shaft and fork and install it as outlined in step 10.
13. Perform step 10 for the reverse shift fork shaft, also.

NOTE: *Check to see that the shafts interlock properly.*

14. Insert the three detent balls, followed by their springs, into their respective bores.
15. Place the cover gasket on the case and then install the cover over it.
16. Tighten the cover retaining bolts to 8–11 ft lbs, carefully, as the case is made out of aluminum.
17. Use a punch to drive a slotted spring pin into each shift fork to secure it.
18. Fasten the input and output shafts together.
19. Install the shift forks into their respective grooves on the input/output shaft assembly.
20. Install the shaft assembly in the right-hand half of the transmission case, so that the snap-ring is positioned firmly against the front surface of the transmission case.
21. Apply grease to the countergear rear bearing lock ball. Insert the ball into the hole in the rear bearing outer race.
22. Place the countergear assembly into the right-hand half of the transmission case. Mate the lock ball with the hole in the transmission case. Place the bearing snap-ring firmly against the front surface of the transmission case.
23. Check the operation of the gear train for smoothness and measure the gear backlash again.
24. Apply grease to the reverse idler shaft, washers and case sliding contact surfaces. Install the reverse idler gear.
25. Fit the washers, so that their protrusions align with the grooves in the transmission case.
26. Install the shaft into the case and through the gears and washers.
27. Align the grooves in the idler shaft with the hole in the shaft boss. Install the retaining bolt and washer into the boss. Torque the bolt to 9.4–13.0 ft lbs.
28. Apply a light coating of liquid sealer over the joint surfaces of the transmission case halves.

CAUTION: *Do not apply sealer to the ½ in. hole for the back-up light switch.*

29. Align the transmission case locating pins with their holes and assemble the halves of the case.
30. Install the bolts and tighten them evenly, in two or three stages, to 10.9–14.5 ft lbs. Remember, the case is aluminium, do not overtighten the bolts.

NOTE: *There are four different bolt lengths, do not install the wrong bolt in the wrong hole. See the illustration for the correct installing position.*

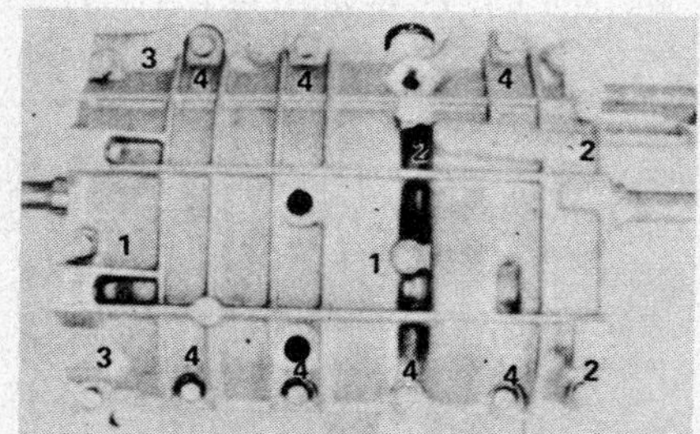

The split case transmission uses four different bolt lengths. Be careful not to mix them.

1. 3.55 in.
2. 2.76 in.
3. 1.77 in.
4. 1.26 in.

31. Insert the ball, spring, and washer in the back-up light switch hole. Screw in the switch assembly and tighten it to 22–36 ft lbs.
32. Fit the gasket and bolt the extension housing to the rear of the transmission. Tighten the bolts evenly, in two or three stages, to 22–33 ft lbs. Do not overtighten.

CAUTION: *Be careful not to damage the extension housing oil seal.*

33. Install the speedometer shaft sleeve and drive gear into the extension housing. Tighten to 36–61 in. lbs.
34. Apply grease to the conical springs. Install one spring over the input shaft bearing and the other over the countershaft bearing. Install the spacer over the countershaft bearing spring, after coating the spacer with grease.
35. Install the gasket and the clutch housing. Tighten the clutch housing securing bolts, evenly and in two or three stages, to 22–33 ft lbs. Do not overtighten.

Corona, Mark II, Crown 2300 and Hi-Lux—Side Cover

1. Remove the clutch release fork and the release bearing hub assembly. Remove the clutch housing from the gear case.
2. Remove the front bearing retainer and transmission case cover assembly.
3. Before removing the internal parts, check the countergear thrust clearance with a feeler gauge, record the reading, then pick the proper adjusting gear side thrust washer to obtain the specified clearance of 0.002–0.006 in.
4. Remove the bolts which retain the extension housing to the transmission case. Turn and align the cut portion of the extension housing with the countershaft.
5. Use a dummy shaft and drive out the countershaft and the woodruff key to the rear. Remove the extension housing, the output shaft, and the gear assembly.
6. Remove the input shaft with the bearing.
7. Take the countergear assembly and the thrust washers out of the transmission case. Remove the dummy shaft, roller bearings, and the spacer from the countergear.
8. Using a brass rod, gently tap the reverse idler gear shaft toward the rear and remove it. Remove the reverse idler gear.
9. Check and record the following clearances; first gear thrust clearance, third gear thrust clearance, second gear thrust clearance, and clearance between snap-ring and clutch hub.
10. Remove the shaft snap-ring at the front end of the output shaft. Slide the synchronizer unit, synchronizer ring, third gear, third gear bushing, thrust

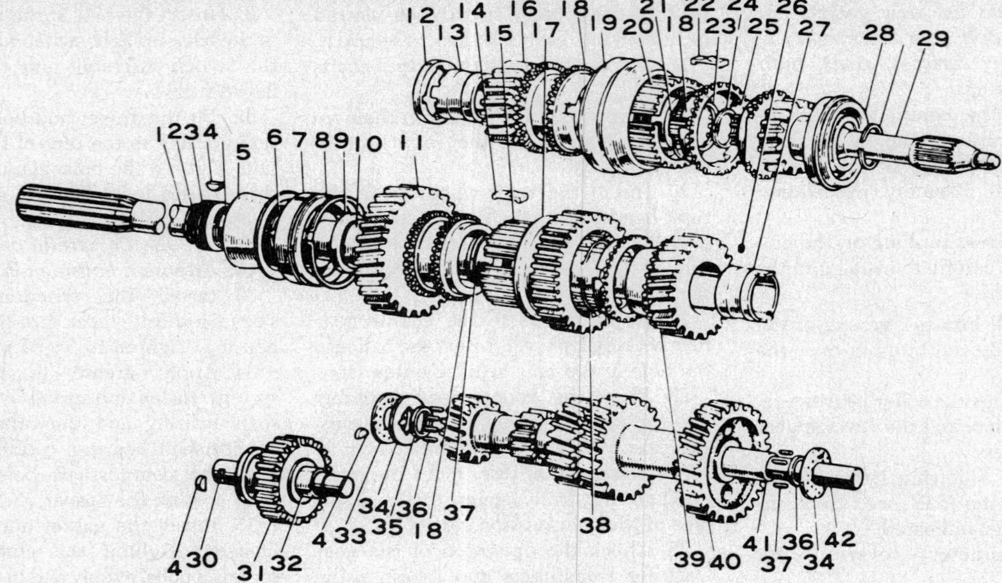

Transmission components for the Corona, Mark II, Crown and Hi-Lux—side cover type.

1. Output shaft
2. Shaft snap-ring
3. Speedometer drive gear
4. Woodruff key
5. Extension housing baffle
6. Shaft snap-ring
7. Radial ball bearing
8. Shaft snap-ring
9. Spacer
10. Bi-metal formed bushing
11. First gear
12. Second & Third gear thrust washer
13. Third gear bushing
14. Synchromesh shifting key No. 1
15. Transmission clutch hub No. 1
16. Third gear
17. Reverse gear
18. Synchronizer ring
19. Transmission sleeve
20. Transmission clutch hub No. 2
21. Synchromesh shifting key spring
22. Synchromesh shifting key No. 2
23. Shaft snap-ring
24. Hole snap-ring
25. Roller
26. Straight pin
28. Bushing
27. Second gear bushing
29. Input shaft
30. Reverse idler gear shaft
31. Reverse idler gear
32. Bi-metal formed bushing
33. Counter gear case side thrust washer
34. Counter gear side thrust washer
35. Spacer
36. Roller
37. Shaft snap-ring
38. Synchromesh shifting key spring
39. Second gear
40. Countergear
41. Tube
42. Countershaft

washer, second gear bushing, second gear, synchronizer ring, clutch hub and reverse gear assembly and the synchronizer ring, out of the output shaft.

11. Remove the lock plate and speedometer driven gear assembly from the extension housing.

12. Expand the shaft snap-ring on the output shaft rear bearing with a snap-ring expander. Drive the output shaft out of the extension housing with a mallet.

13. Check and record the output shaft rear bearing thrust clearance. Remove the shaft snap-ring and speedometer drive gear, the woodruff key, and oil baffle.

14. Remove the shaft snap-rings. Place the first gear on vise anvils, and press out first gear, spacer, and the bearing from the output shaft.

15. Loosen and remove the backup light switch. Move the third and fourth shift fork into the fourth speed position (to the front).

16. Using a long drift punch, drive out the slotted spring pin which connects the shift fork to the shift fork shaft.

17. Slide the shift fork shaft out of the rear of the case cover gradually, preventing the lock ball from popping out under spring tension. Remove the lock ball, spring and the two interlock pins from the case cover.

18. Drive the slotted spring pin out of the first and second shift fork and the shift fork shaft in the same manner. Remove the shift fork shaft and the shift fork, then remove the lock ball and the spring from the case cover.

19. Remove the shift arm pivot locknut. Remove the shift arm from the case cover. Drive out the slotted spring pin, and remove the reverse shift head and the shift fork shaft. Remove the lock ball and the spring. Remove the selector outer lever and the selector lever shaft.

20. Remove the shift lever shaft lockbolt, slide out the shift lever shaft from the case cover. Be careful to prevent the lock ball from popping out under spring tension.

21. Remove the sliding shift lever, lock ball and spring. Remove the wire and shift lever lockbolt.

22. Remove the shift and selector lever shaft toward the rear side of the case.

Wash all disassembled parts thoroughly. Check the transmission case, case cover and the extension housing for cracks; check the bearing fitting portions and gasket surfaces for burrs and nicks.

Check the output shaft splines, snapring grooves, bearing contact surfaces, bearing fitting portions and oil seal lip contact surface for wear, scores, or damage. Check the output shaft for runout. If the runout exceeds 0.0012 in. replace the shaft. To measure runout, place a dial indicator on the center point of the shaft and rotate the shaft slowly to read the maximum and minimum values. The runout equals the maximum value minus the minimum value divided by two.

Check the bearings for roughness and wear. Check for noise or damage by rotating the bearing after applying a few drops of oil. To remove the input shaft bearing, remove the shaft snap-ring with a snap-ring expander, then remove the bearing from the input shaft with a puller. Check the bushings and the bearing rollers for abnormal wear. If the wear is excessive, replace the bushing/s or the bearing rollers.

Inspect the extension housing bushing for wear or scoring. To replace the bushing, press the bushing out of the extension housing to the front side. To install, align the oil grooves of the bushing and the extension housing, and press the bushing into the housing. After installing the bushing, ream the bushing to fit the outer diameter of the universal joint sleeve yoke.

Specified Gear Backlash

Input shaft gear to countergear: 0.004 in.

Third gear to countergear: 0.004 in.

Second gear to countergear: 0.004 in.

First gear to countergear: 0.004 in.

Reverse idler gear to countergear: 0.005 in.

Reverse idler gear to reverse gear: 0.005 in.

Assembly is performed in the following order:

NOTE: *Always install new gaskets, apply liquid sealer or gasket cement when assembling. Apply a thin coating of transmission lubricant on all parts before installation. Thrust clearances of gears and bearings are important factors for smooth gear shifting. Therefore, select and assemble thrust washers, snap-rings and spacers of proper thickness.*

1. Slide the first gear onto the output shaft with the synchronizer gear toward the front of the shaft. Install the spacer, and press the bearing onto the output shaft with the snap-ring groove on the bearing toward the front of the shaft.

2. Check the first gear thrust clearance, and if necessary, select and install a thicker first gear spacer to obtain the following clearance. First gear thrust clearance: 0.004–0.008 in. A first gear spacer, 0.209–0.211 in. thick is available.

3. After installing the first gear spacer, make sure that first gear will rotate smoothly. Checking the first gear thrust clearance must be performed with the rear bearing snap-ring installed.

4. Check the clearance between the rear bearing and the snap-ring, and if necessary select and install a thicker snap-ring to obtain an output shaft rear bearing thrust clearance of 0–0.002 in. Six thicknesses of rear bearing snap-rings are available.

5. Check the clearance between the second gear and second and third gear thrust washer while pressing the third gear bushing against the second gear, and if necessary, file off the rear end of the second gear bushing with sand paper on the surface plate to obtain a second gear thrust clearance of 0.004–0.008 in. Five thicknesses of second and third gear thrust washers are available. A second gear bushing 1.264–1.265 in. long is available.

6. Check the clearance between the third gear and second and third gear thrust washer while pressing the clutch hub against the third gear, and if necessary, file off the front end of the third gear bushing as well as the second gear bushing to obtain 0.004–0.008 in. third gear thrust clearance. A third gear bushing 1.382–1.384 in. long is available. Make sure that gears rotate smoothly while pressing the clutch hub against third gear.

7. Check the clearance between the front end snap-ring and the clutch hub. If necessary, use a thicker front end snap-ring to obtain 0–0.002 in. clearance between the snap-ring and clutch hub.

8. If specified clearance cannot be obtained by installing a snap-ring, select and install a thicker second and third gear thrust washer, then install a front end snap-ring of proper thickness. Front end snap-rings are available in ten thicknesses.

9. Install the oil baffle and the shaft snap-ring. Install the Woodruff key into the key groove of the output shaft.

10. Slide the speedometer drive gear onto the output shaft, then install the shaft snap-ring and secure the gear.

11. Install the shaft snap-ring into the groove of the extension housing front end. Expand the shaft snap-ring with a snap-ring expander, then assemble the output shaft into the extension housing.

12. When assembling the output shaft, install the universal joint sleeve yoke temporarily onto the output shaft rear end to prevent damaging the extension housing bushing and the oil seal, and to properly center the output shaft.

13. Assemble the synchronizer unit by installing the two shifting springs onto the clutch hub with open ends of the springs 120° apart, so that the spring tension on each shifting key will be uniform.

14. Place the three shifting keys into the clutch hub key slots and onto the shifting springs.

CAUTION: *There are two kinds of shifting keys in this transmission. The keys with the shorter straddle length should be installed on the third and fourth synchronizer unit.*

15. Next, slide the hub sleeve onto the clutch hub. The clutch hubs and the hub sleeve of the reverse gear are matched, and should be kept together as an assembly for smooth operation.

16. Assemble the first and second synchronizer unit in the same manner as described.

17. Install the synchronizer ring, reverse gear, and synchronizer ring onto the output shaft. Align the cut portions of the synchronizer rings with the shifting keys on the clutch hub.

18. Slide the second gear bushing onto the output shaft, and align the bushing groove with the straight pin on the output shaft.

19. Install the second gear onto the bushing of the output shaft.

20. Install the second and third gear thrust washer, and align the indents of the thrust washer and the claws of the bushing.

21. Install the third gear bushing, third gear, synchronizer ring and the third and fourth synchronizer unit onto the output shaft.

22. Install the shaft snap-ring onto the output shaft.

23. Check the first gear, second gear and the third gear on the output shaft for smooth rotation, and also check the synchronizer units for smooth movement.

24. Press the bearing onto the input shaft with the snap-ring on the bearing toward the front.

25. Select and install the proper shaft snap-ring to obtain minimum thrust play on the input shaft. Shaft snap-rings are available in two sizes; No. 1 is 0.096–0.102 in. thick, No. 2 is 0.091–0.095 in. thick.

26. Coat the bearing rollers with grease, and coat the bore of the input shaft gear. Install the bearing rollers into the bore, then install the hole snap-ring.

27. Position the reverse idler gear into the transmission case with the shift fork groove toward the rear. Align the key groove of the reverse idler gear shaft and the cut portion of the transmission case, and drive the shaft through the gear and into the transmission case.

28. Secure the shaft by installing the Woodruff key. Install the collar into the countergear, then install the two needle roller bearings into both sides of the countergear.

29. Insert the dummy shaft into the countergear. Position the countergear assembly, case side thrust washers and the proper adjusting gear side thrust washer which was determined when disassembling the transmission, onto the bottom of the transmission case.

30. Countergear thrust clearance is 0.002–0.006 in. Side thrust washers are available in fourteen sizes. After installing the side thrust washer, make sure that the countergear rotates smoothly.

31. Install the input shaft assembly onto the transmission case.

32. Install the output shaft and gears, and the extension housing assembly with the gasket, onto the transmission case. Turn and align the cut portion of the extension housing with the countershaft bore of the transmission.

33. Next, align the bores of the transmission case and the countergear. Install the countershaft from the rear of the transmission case. Secure the countershaft by installing the woodruff key onto the end of the shaft.

34. Tighten the extension housing retaining bolts to 22–33 ft lbs.

35. Install the speedometer driven gear into the extension housing, and secure the driven gear sleeve with the lock plate.

36. Install the front bearing retainer with the gasket. Apply liquid sealer on the threads of the bolts, and torque the front bearing retainer attaching bolts to 3–5 ft lbs.

37. Install the clutch housing onto the transmission case. Lubricate the clutch release bearing hub bore with multipurpose grease, and install the clutch release fork and hub assembly onto the transmission case.

38. To assemble the transmission case cover, install the shift arm pivot onto the reverse shift arm, and insert into the case.

39. Assemble the shift and selector lever shaft together with the shift and selector lever, and secure the bolt with a wire.

40. Insert the reverse shift fork shaft compression spring and lock ball into the case, and insert the fork shaft from the rear side, then secure the shift head with a new slotted spring pin.

41. Align the fork shaft positioning groove with the shift interlock pin groove.

42. Align the reverse shift arm knob with the reverse shift fork shaft, and install the O-ring, washer and nut onto the shift arm pivot. Insert the shift interlock pin into the rear side of the case cover and the compression spring and lock ball into the front side, and assemble the shift fork together with the first and second shift fork shaft. Secure the shift fork with a new slotted spring pin.

43. Align the shift fork shaft positioning groove with the shift interlock pin groove. Insert the two shift interlock pins into the front side of the case cover.

44. Insert the compression spring and the lock ball, and assemble the shift fork together with the third and fourth shift fork shaft, then secure the shift fork with a new slotted spring pin.

45. Install the lock ball, compression spring and reverse restricting ball holder.

46. Check all shift forks for smooth movement.

47. Install the back-up light switch on the case cover.

48. Align each shift fork and the reverse shift arm with the respective gears, and install the transmission case cover, with the gasket, onto the transmission. Torque the case cover retaining bolts to 11–16 ft lbs.

49. To adjust the shift arm pivot, loosen the locknut on the shift arm pivot, turn the shift arm pivot clockwise until friction is felt, when the reverse idler gear contacts with the first gear and/or the countergear.

50. Next from this position, turn the shift arm pivot counterclockwise approximately 90 degrees. Tighten the pivot locknut securely.

51. With the input shaft rotating, make sure that there is no noise and that the reverse idler gear does not contact other gears in the transmission.

52. If no friction is felt when the shift arm pivot is turned clockwise, set the pivot line mark at 60 degrees rearward from its horizontal position to the case cover surface.

53. If necessary, replace the oil seal in the extension housing after assembling the transmission using the oil seal puller, and pull out the oil seal together with the dust seal.

Corona, Mark II, Celica, Crown 2600 and Hi-Lux—Internal Linkage

1. Drain the oil from the transmission, if you have not already done so.

2. Unbolt and remove the clutch housing from the transmission case, with the release fork, bearing and hub still attached.

3. Unbolt the back-up light switch. Remove the reverse restrictor pin and the speedometer driven gear.

4. Remove the gearshift lever retainer.

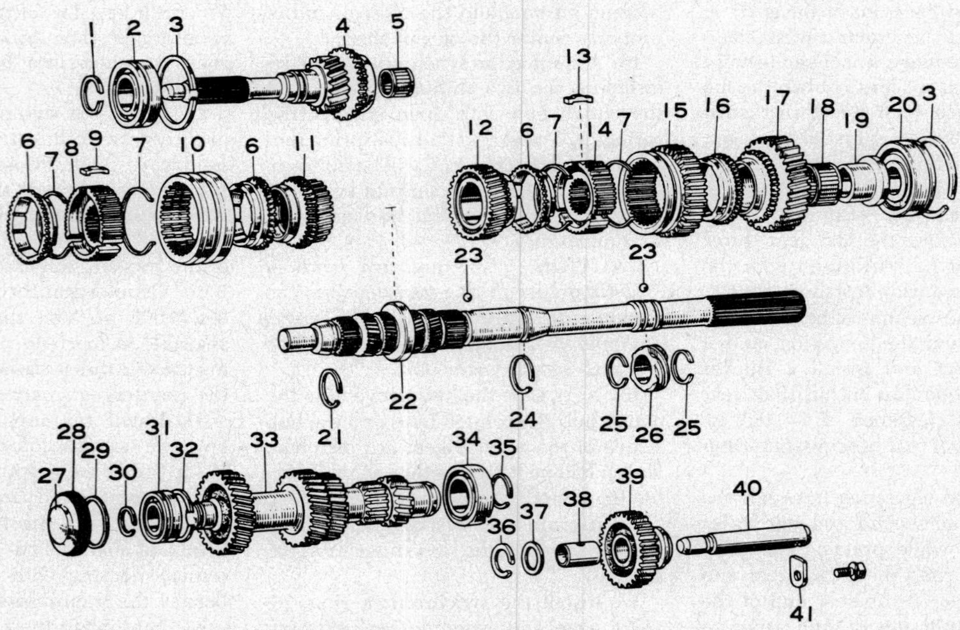

Transmission components for the Corona, Mark II, Celica, Crown and Hi-Lux—enclosed linkage type.

1. Shaft snap-ring
2. Radial ball bearing
3. Shaft snap-ring
4. Input shaft assembly
5. Needle roller bearing
6. Synchronizer ring
7. Shift-key spring
8. Clutch hub
9. Shift-key
10. Hub spring
11. Third gear assembly
12. Second gear assembly
13. Shift-key
14. Clutch hub
15. Reverse gear
16. Synchronizer ring
17. First gear assembly
18. Needle roller bearing
19. First gear bearing inner race
20. Radial ball bearing
21. Shaft snap-ring
22. Output shaft
23. Reverse shaft restricter ball
24. Shaft snap-ring
25. Shaft snap-ring
26. Speedometer drive gear
27. Countershaft end cover—front
28. Countershaft end cover—rear
29. Spacer
30. Snap-ring
31. Radial ball bearing
32. Snap-ring
33. Countergear
34. Radial ball bearing
35. Shaft snap-ring
36. Shaft snap-ring
37. Spacer
38. Bushing
39. Reverse idler gear
40. Reverse idler shaft
41. Reverse idler shaft stop

5. Rotate the shift rod housing counterclockwise (viewed from behind) and then disconnect the rod from the shift fork shafts.

6. Unbolt and remove the extension housing.

7. Drive out the slotted pin and separate the shift rod, housing and spring.

8. Unbolt and remove the front bearing retainer.

9. Take off both of the front countershaft covers, as well as the spacer.

10. Using an expander, remove the snap-rings from the input and countershaft bearings.

11. Remove the rear cover from the transmission case, by unfastening the bolts which secure it.

NOTE: *Use a hammer and a wooden drift to break the rear cover free of the case, if necessary.*

12. When removing the rear cover leave all of the gears and other parts attached. Mount the cover in a vise.

CAUTION: *Use a copper sheet and clamp the rear cover in the vise at the crosshatched area, to prevent damage to its joining surfaces.*

13. Withdraw the speedometer driven gear from the output shaft, using care not to lose its lockball.

14. Punch the slotted pin out of the reverse shift arm bracket bolt and remove the bracket, complete with the shift arm.

15. Remove the reverse idler shaft stop and withdraw the idler gear and shaft assembly away from the rear cover.

16. Unbolt and remove the output shaft rear bearing retainer.

17. Remove the screwplug and spring from each shift fork and shaft.

18. Drive the slotted interlock pins out of each shaft. Be careful not to lose the balls.

19. Remove the shift fork shafts in the following order:

a. Reverse
b. First/second
c. Third/fourth

Once the shafts have been removed, slide the shift forks off them.

20. Remove the snap-ring from the output shaft rear bearing. Push the output shaft and countershaft out, working from the rear side of the cover. Once the shafts are started, grasp them carefully and pull them forward as an assembly.

CAUTION: *Do not drop either of the shafts while removing them.*

21. Separate the input shaft and the front synchronizer ring from the output shaft.

22. Use an expander to remove the snap-ring and remove the hub and synchronizer ring, followed by third gear.

23. Remove the rear bearing snap-ring and press off the rear bearing.

24. Remove the following items from the output shaft, in the order listed:

a. First gear
b. Roller bearing with inner race

NOTE: *Do not lose the lockballs from the inner race.*

c. Synchronizer ring
d. Reverse gear
e. Clutch hub
f. Second gear
g. Synchronizer ring

Clean all of the parts and inspect them for wear or damage. Replace any parts which are defective.

Use a dial indicator to check output shaft runout, which is measured at the rear bearing installation point. Runout should not exceed 0.001 in. Replace the output shaft, if it does.

Replace the input shaft bearing only if it is rough or noisy. Remove the snap-ring and press the bearing off the shaft. When installing a new bearing, use a snap-ring to obtain *minimum* thrust clearance. Snap-rings are available in six sizes, ranging from 0.081–0.93in.

Installation is performed in the following order:

1. Apply a thin coating of gear oil to all rotating or sliding surfaces, prior to assembly.

2. Perform steps 2–3 of the Corolla 1100 and 1200 transmission assembly procedure, above.

3. Assemble the synchronizer ring to third gear, and fit both of them on the output shaft.

4. Insert the third/fourth synchronizer hub on the output shaft, until it contacts the shoulder of the shaft.

NOTE: *If the hub is tight on the shaft, lightly tap it home with a wooden mallet.*

5. Select a snap-ring to provide 0.002 in. axial play for the synchronizer hub and fit it onto the shaft. Snap-rings are available in a range of four sizes between 0.071–0.079 in.

6. Measure third gear thrust clearance with a feeler gauge. The clearance should be 0.004–0.010 in. Replace third gear if the clearance exceeds the limit of 0.010 in.

7. Fit the synchronizer ring for second gear to the gear and install the assembly on the output shaft.

8. Fit the reverse gear over its clutch hub. Examine them to see that they are properly positioned and slide smoothly.

9. Install the reverse gear and hub on the output shaft so that they contact the shoulder.

10. Measure second gear thrust clearance; it should be between 0.004–0.010 in. Replace the gear if the clearance is more than 0.010 in.

11. Coat the locking ball with grease. Insert it, and the roller bearing inner race, on the output shaft.

NOTE: *Be sure that the locking ball does not protrude from the shaft.*

12. Assemble first gear with its synchronizer ring, bearing and bearing inner race. Install them on the output shaft, so that the end of the inner race contacts the clutch hub and the groove on the inner race aligns with the locking ball.

13. Press the rear bearing onto the output shaft.

14. Measure first gear thrust clearance; it should be 0.004–0.010 in. Replace the gear if the clearance exceeds 0.010 in.

15. Select a snap-ring for the rear output shaft bearing that will provide 0.002 in. axial play for it. Snap-rings are available in six sizes, ranging between 0.081–0.093 in.

16. Use a press to insert the straight pin into the rear cover, until it protrudes ¼–5/16 in. from the cover front side.

17. Clamp the rear cover in a vise, as detailed in step 12 of the disassembly procedure.

18. Coat the roller bearing with grease and fit it over the input shaft.

19. Apply gear oil to the front synchronizer ring on the output shaft.

20. Assemble the output shaft and the input shaft.

21. Assemble the output shaft and countergear, then fit them through the holes in the rear cover. Push them in until the snap-ring sticks out beyond the rear cover. Install the snap-ring and then push the shafts back until the snap-ring is flush with the rear cover surface.

22. Fit the shaft through the reverse idler gear. Insert the end of the shaft into the end of the rear cover.

23. Install the spacer on the idler shaft and secure it with a snap-ring.

24. Install the idler shaft stop.

25. Fit the first/second and third-/fourth shift forks into the grooves on the hub sleeves, so that the longer parts of their bosses face each other.

26. Assemble the ends of the three shift fork shafts and insert them into the rear cover. Install the interlock pins, after coating them with grease.

27. Fit the shafts through the forks and drive in the slotted spring pins to secure them.

28. Insert the lockballs, followed by their springs. Tighten their plugs to 14–22 ft lbs.

29. Install the output shaft rear bearing retainer and tighten its attaching bolts to 11–16 ft lbs.

NOTE: *There should be zero clearance between the rear bearing snap-ring and the surface of the rear cover.*

30. Assemble the reverse shift arm to its bracket. Finger-tighten the pivot bolt. Install the assembly on the rear cover.

31. Drive the slotted mounting pin in, so that it protrudes 0.08–0.16 in. beyond the rear cover. Tighten the securing bolts to 11–16 ft lbs.

32. Shift the gears so that Reverse is selected. Check the gear contact. If the gears are meshing properly, the front face of the idler gear will align with the front face of the reverse gear.

33. If necessary, adjust the gear mesh at the pivot.

NOTE: *When the gears are meshing properly, the slot in the pivot should be perpendicular to the rear cover.*

34. Tighten the pivot nut to 7–12 ft lbs and install the lockpin. Be careful not to change gear contact.

35. Install the shift rod from the front end of the extension housing. Fit the spring and housing onto the end of the shift rod. Secure them with a slotted pin.

36. Clean the gasket surfaces of the rear cover and transmission case. Place a new gasket over the end of the transmission case and fit the rear cover assembly into the case.

37. Install the input shaft and countergear front bearing snap-rings.

38. Install the extension housing and gasket over the rear cover, after cleaning both gasket mounting surfaces.

NOTE: *Coat the bushing bore with grease.*

39. Screw the securing bolts through the extension housing, the rear cover and into the transmission case. Tighten the bolts to 22–29 ft lbs.

40. Install the reverse restrictor pin and gasket. Tighten it to 22–29 ft lbs.

41. Push the countergear rearward, as far as it will go and measure the distance (E) in the illustration. Select a spacer to yield the *minimum* clearance which is closest to the measurement obtained. Spacers are available in four sizes, ranging between 0.081 and 0.102 in.

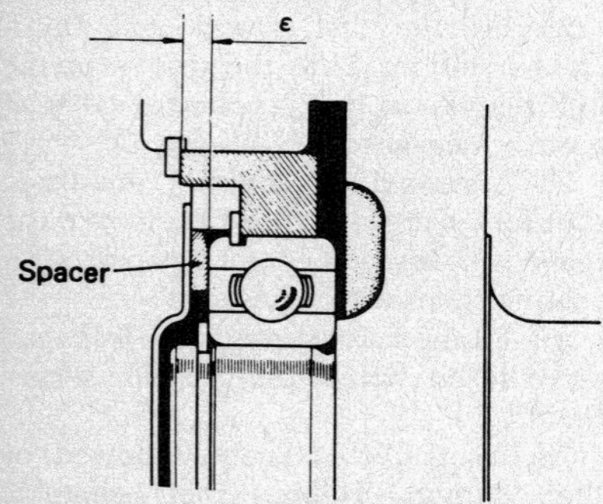

Measure the distance (E) to obtain the proper countergear spacer size.

42. Install the spacer and then the countershaft end covers.

43. Align the front bearing retainer gasket with the oil holes. Fit the bearing retainer over the gasket and tighten its securing bolts to 4.3–6.5 ft lbs evenly, in two or three stages.

44. Bolt the clutch housing onto the front of the transmission case, evenly, in two or three stages, to 36–50 ft lbs.

45. Attach the shift lever retainer to the extension housing by securing it with its bolts. Tighten the bolts to 11–16 ft lbs.

46. Install the speedometer driven gear and secure it with its lockplate. Tighten it to 7.2–11.6 ft lbs.

47. Install the components of the back-up light switch in the reverse order of their removal. Tighten the switch to 27–33 ft lbs.

48. Install the drain plug and its gasket. Tighten the plug to 27–33 ft lbs.

Shift Linkage Adjustment

Land Cruiser—Column Shift

Shift lever adjustment:

The only adjustments which may be performed on the column shift linkages are for the length of the column-to-rods. Adjust these so that the transmission operates smoothly and so that the gear selector is neutral.

Transfer case selector adjustment:

The transfer case shift linkage is adjusted by adjusting the length of the high/low range intermediate rod and the bellcrank-to-transfer case shift rod. To adjust them, proceed in the following manner:

1. Disconnect the shift rods at the high/low range shift link lever and bellcrank respectively.

2. Push the high/low range shift lever under the dash into the high (H) position. Set the outer shift lever on the transfer

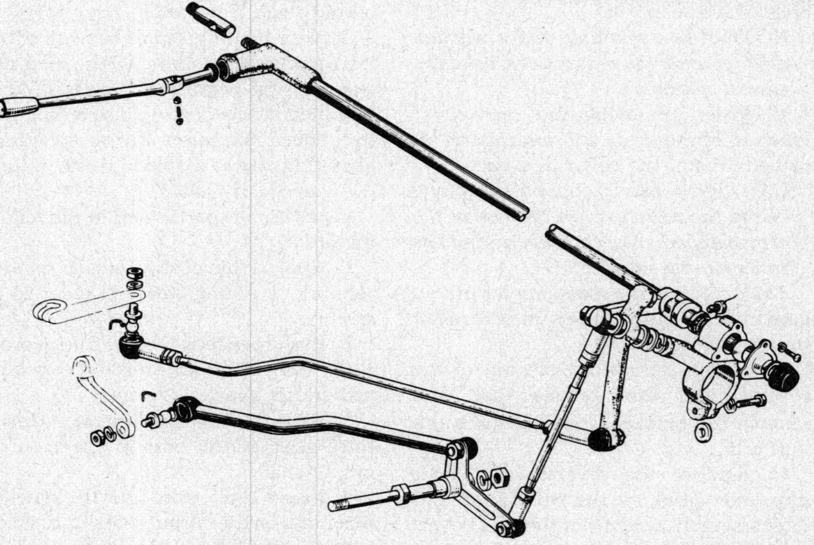

Two-door Land Cruiser transmission linkage.

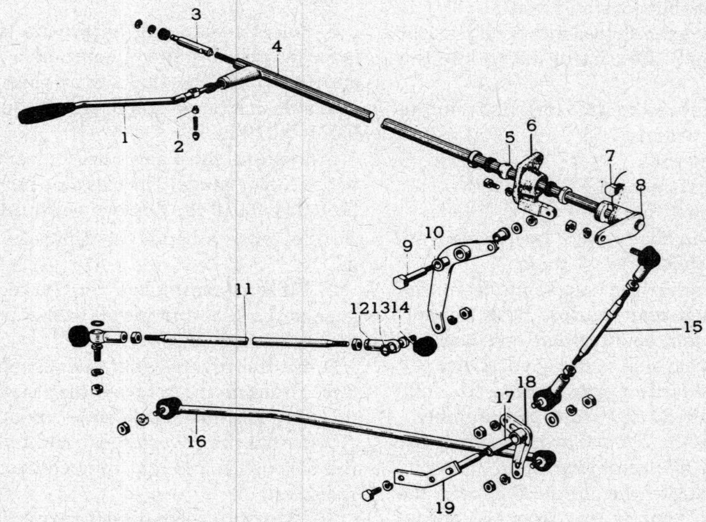

Land Cruiser station wagon shift linkage.

1. Gear selector lever
2. Pin
3. Control shaft—upper end
4. Control shaft
5. Control shaft bushing
6. Control shaft bracket
7. Lock bolt
8. Control shaft lever
9. Selector shaft
10. Bushing
11. Gear selecting rod
12. Connecting rod end
13. Snap ring
14. Dust cap
15. Intermediate rod
16. Gear shifting rod
17. Bushing
18. Bell crank
19. Support

case in the high position, also.

3. Adjust the length of the high/low range intermediate rod and bellcrank-to-transfer case shift rod by turning the rod

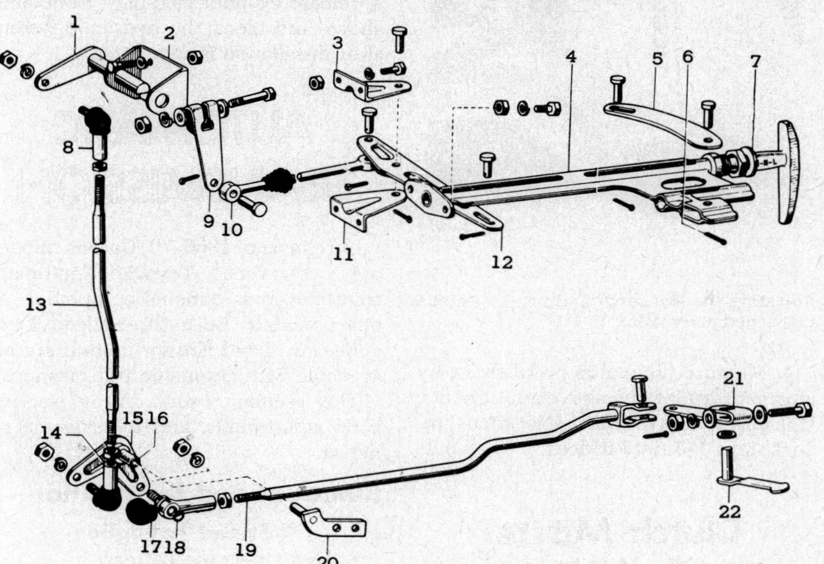

Transfer case shift linkage station wagon

1. High/low shift link
2. Shift link bracket
3. Bracket
4. Shift lever housing
5. Lever
6. Cotter pin
7. Transfer range selector lever
8. Connecting rod end—upper
9. Shift link lever
10. High/low shift intermediate rod
11. Bracket
12. Front drive engagement lever
13. High/low connecting rod
14. Connecting rod end—lower
15. Bell crank
16. Bushing
17. Dust cap
18. Snap ring
19. High/low shift rod
20. Support
21. Transfer case high/low shift lever
22. Lever

ends until they connect properly.

4. After installing the rods, move the transfer case shift lever through the ranges to see that each range is properly selected.

Floor Shifter Adjustment

All Toyota models equipped with a floor shifter have internally-mounted shift linkages. On older models, the linkage is contained in the side cover which is bolted on the transmission case. Newer cars have the shift linkage mounted in the top of the transmission case itself.

No external adjustment is needed or possible.

CLUTCH

The clutch is a single-plate, dry disc type. Some early models, and all Land Cruisers, use a coil-spring pressure plate. Later models use a diaphragm-spring pressure plate. Clutch release bearings are sealed ball bearing units which need no lubrication and should never be washed in any kind of solvent. All clutches, except those on the Corolla 1200 series, are hydraulically operated.

Removal and Installation

CAUTION: *Do not allow grease or oil to get on any of the disc, pressure plate, or flywheel surfaces.*

1. Remove the transmission from the car as detailed above.

2. Remove the clutch cover and disc from the bellhousing.

3. Unfasten the release fork bearing clips. Withdraw the release bearing hub, complete with the release bearing.

4. Remove the tension spring from the clutch linkage.

5. Remove the release fork and support.

6. Punch matchmarks on the clutch cover and the pressure plate so the pressure plate can be returned to its original position during installation.

7. Slowly unfasten the screws which attach the retracting springs.

NOTE: *If the screws are released too fast, the clutch assembly will fly apart, causing possible injury or loss of parts.*

8. Separate the pressure plate from the clutch cover/spring assembly.

Inspect the parts for wear or deterioration. Replace parts as required.

Installation is performed in the reverse order of removal. Several points should be noted, however:

1. Be sure to align the matchmarks on the clutch cover and pressure plate which were made during disassembly.

2. Apply a thin coating of multipurpose grease to the release bearing hub and release fork contact points. Also, pack the groove inside the clutch hub with multipurpose grease.

3. Center the clutch disc by using a clutch pilot tool or an old input shaft. Insert the pilot into the end of the input shaft front bearing and bolt the clutch to the flywheel.

NOTE: *Bolt the clutch assembly to the flywheel in two or three stages, evenly.*

4. Adjust the clutch as outlined below.

Pedal Height Adjustment

Adjust the pedal height to the specification given in the chart below, by rotating the pedal stop (nut).

Pedal Height Specifications

Pedal Height Specifications

Model	Height (in.)	Measure between:
Corolla 1100	5.5-5.9	Pedal pad and floor mat
Corolla 1200	2.2①	Pedal pad and floor mat
Corolla 1600	2.8①	Pedal pad and floor mat
Carina	6.3	Pedal pad and floor mat
Corona	5.7-6.1	Pedal pad and floor mat
Mark II/4	6.0-6.2	Pedal pad and top of floor panel
Mark II/6	6.2-6.6	Pedal pad and asphalt seat
Celica	6.3	Pedal pad and floor mat
Crown 2300	5.7	Pedal pad and floor
Crown 2600	6.8	Pedal pad and asphalt seat
Hi-Lux	6.0	Pedal pad and floor
Land Cruiser 2-dr	6.7	Pedal pad and firewall
Station Wagon	9.6	Pedal pad and firewall

① Pedal depressed

Free-Play Adjustment

Corolla 1100 and 1200

1. Pull on the clutch release cable at the clutch support flange until a resistance is felt when the release bearing contacts the clutch diaphragm spring.

2. Holding the cable in this position, measure the distance between the E-ring and the end of the wire support flange. The distance should be 5–6 threads.

3. If adjustment is required, change the position of the E-ring.

4. After completing the adjustment,

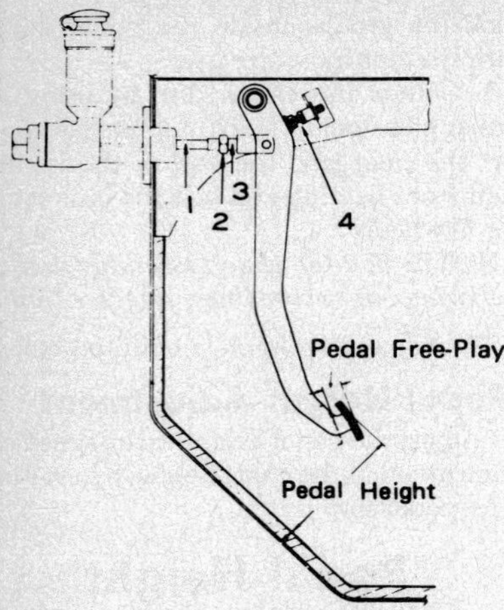

Clutch pedal adjustments

1. Master cylinder push rod
2. Push rod locknut
3. Clevis
4. Pedal stop (bolt)

check the clutch pedal free-play which should be 0.8–1.4 in. after the pedal is depressed several times.

All—Except Corolla 1100 and 1200

1. Adjust the clearance between the master cylinder piston and the pushrod to the specifications. Loosen the pushrod locknut and rotate the pushrod while depressing the clutch pedal lightly with your finger.
2. Tighten the locknut when finished the adjustment.
3. Adjust the release cylinder free-play by loosening the release pushrod locknut and rotating the pushrod.

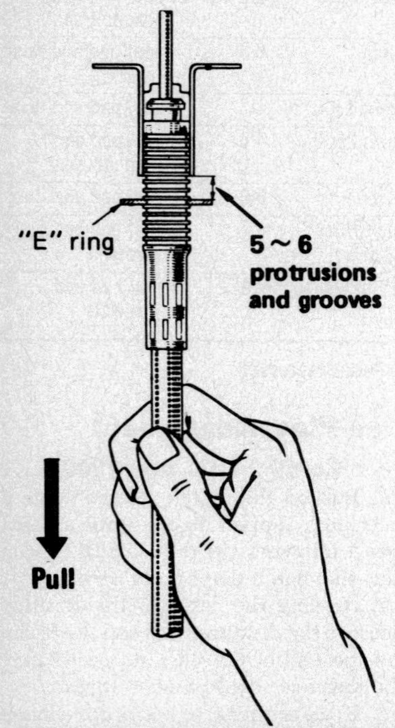

Clutch release cable adjustment—Corolla 1100 and 1200.

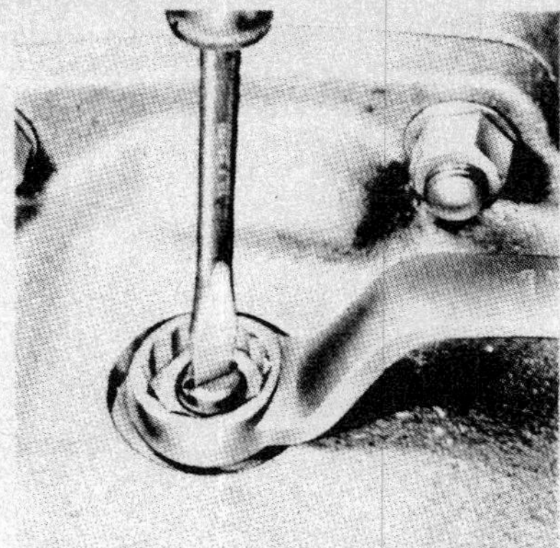

Adjusting the low servo and band—Corolla two-speed automatic.

4. Measure the clutch pedal free-play after performing the above adjustments. If it fails to fall within specifications, repeat steps 1–3 until it does.

Clutch Master Cylinder

Removal and Installation

All Models

CAUTION: *Do not spill brake fluid on the painted surfaces of the vehicle.*

1. Remove the clevis pin.
2. Detach the hydraulic line from the tube.
3. Unfasten the bolts which secure the master cylinder to the firewall. Withdraw the assembly.

Installation is performed in the reverse order of removal. Bleed the system as detailed below. Adjust the clutch pedal height and free-play as detailed above.

Clutch Release Cylinder

Removal and Installation

All Models

1. Plug the master cylinder cap to prevent fluid leakage.
2. Raise the front of the vehicle and support it with jackstands.

CAUTION: *Be sure that the vehicle is securely supported. Remember, you will be working underneath it.*

3. Remove the gravel shield, if necessary, to gain access to the release cylinder.
4. Unfasten the clutch fork return spring at the fork.
5. Detach the hydraulic line from the release cylinder.
6. Screw the release cylinder push rod in.
7. Loosen and remove the securing nuts from the release cylinder. Remove the cylinder.

Installation is performed in the reverse order of removal. Adjust the release fork-to-release cylinder free-play, as detailed above, and bleed the hydraulic system, after installation is completed.

AUTOMATIC TRANSMISSION

Corolla and 1966–70 Corona models use a two-speed Toyoglide automatic transmission as optional equipment. All other models use a three-speed Toyoglide unit. Land Cruiser models are not available with automatic transmissions.

This section covers routine service, basic adjustments, and transmission removal.

Removal and Installation

2-Speed Toyoglide

1. Disconnect the battery.
2. Drain all coolant from the engine and disconnect the radiator inlet hose.
3. Disconnect the throttle link from the carburetor bell-crank (remove the air filter if necessary).
4. Remove the exhaust pipe flange nuts, then jack up the car and support it on stands.
5. Drain the transmission oil, remove the drive shaft and remove the exhaust pipe bracket from the transmission case.
6. Disconnect the exhaust pipe and transmission shift rod from the control shaft.
7. Disconnect the throttle link rod from the throttle valve lever, then disconnect the speedometer drive cable.
8. Remove the four bolts from the rear support and take off the crossmember. (Support the transmission with a suitable jack.)
9. Remove the clamp from the two oil cooler lines and disconnect both lines, then remove the seven bolts that hold the transmission case to the bellhousing.
10. Withdraw the transmission slowly so as not to damage the oil seal.

CAUTION: *There will be some oil in the converter, so be prepared with a drain pan.*

Installation

Reverse the order of the removal procedures, with the following precautions.

1. Do not extend the crankshaft locating dowel more than 0.315 in. from the end.
2. Tighten the drive plate to 45–47 ft lbs.
3. When installing the torque converter position the drive plate as it was during removal.

4. Tighten the drive plate to the pump impeller front disc to 7.5–9.5 ft lbs. First tighten the eight bolts finger tight, then to the specified torque.

5. When installing the transmission, align the pump drive keys of the pump impeller with the key holes of the pump drive gear.

6. After installing the transmission, adjust the throttle link connecting rod, and the selector lever. (See "Adjustment".)

7. Fill the transmission with automatic transmission fluid, and then start the engine. Run the engine at idle speed, with the selector lever at N (Neutral). Add fluid gradually up to the F line of the level gauge. After warming the engine, fill the transmission with automatic transmission fluid.

8. Adjust the engine idle to 600 rpm, with the selector at N (Neutral).

9. Road test the vehicle. With the selector lever at D (Drive), check the point at which the transmission shifts. Check for shock, noise and slippage, with the selector lever in all positions. Check for leakage from the transmission.

Torque Specifications

Drive plate to crankshaft: 33–39 ft lbs

Drive plate to torque converter: 8–11 ft lbs

Transmission housing to engine: 37–50 ft lbs

Transmission housing to case: 14–22 ft lbs

3-Speed Toyoglide

1. Disconnect the battery.

2. Remove the air cleaner and disconnect the accelerator torque link or the cable.

3. Disconnect the throttle link rod at the carburetor side, then disconnect the back-up light wiring at the firewall (on early models).

4. Jack up the car and support it on stands, then drain the transmission oil. (Use a clean receptacle so that the oil can be checked for color, smell and foreign matter.)

5. Disconnect all shift linkage.

6. On early models, remove the cross shaft from the frame.

7. Disconnect the throttle link rod at the transmission side and remove the speedometer cable, oil cooler lines and parking brake equalizer bracket.

8. Loosen the exhaust flange nuts and remove the exhaust pipe clamp and bracket.

9. Remove the drive shaft and the rear mounting bracket, then lower the rear end of the transmission carefully.

10. Support the engine with a suitable jack stand and remove the seven bolts that hold the transmission to the engine.

Reverse the order of the removal procedures with the following precautions.

1. Install the drive plate and ring gear, tighten the attaching bolts to 37–43 ft lbs.

2. After assembling the torque converter to the transmission, check the clearance, it should be about 0.59 in.

3. Before installing the transmission, install the oil pump locator pin on the torque converter to facilitate installation.

4. While rotating the crankshaft, tighten the converter attaching bolts, a little at a time.

5. After installing the throttle connecting second rod, make sure the throttle valve lever indicator aligns with the mark on the transmission with the carburetor throttle valve fully opened. If required, adjust the rod.

6. To install the transmission control rod correctly, move the transmission lever to N (Neutral), and the selector lever to Neutral. Fill the transmission with automatic transmission fluid (Type F only), then start the engine. Run the engine at idle speed and apply the brakes while moving the selector lever through all positions, then return it to Neutral.

7. After warming the engine, move the selector lever through all positions, then back to Neutral, and check the fluid level. Fill as necessary.

8. Adjust the engine idle to 550–650 rpm with the selector lever at Drive. Road test the vehicle.

9. With the selector lever at 2 or Drive, check the point at which the transmission shifts. Check for shock, noise and slipping with the selector lever in all positions. Check for leaks from the transmission.

Pan Removal

1. Unfasten the oil plug and drain the fluid from the transmission.

2. Unfasten the pan securing bolts.

3. Withdraw the pan.

Installation is performed in the reverse order of removal. Torque the pan securing bolts to 4–6 ft lbs. Refill the transmission with fluid as outlined above.

Low Servo and Band Adjustment

2 Speed

The low servo and band adjusting bolt is located on the outside of the transmission case, so it is unnecessary to remove the oil pan in order to perform the adjustment.

1. Loosen the locknut on the adjusting bolt.

2. Tighten the bolt until it is bottomed.

3. Back off 3½ turns (3 turns—Corona) and hold the adjusting bolt securely while tightening the locknut.

Front Band Adjustment

3 Speed

1. Remove the oil pan as outlined above.

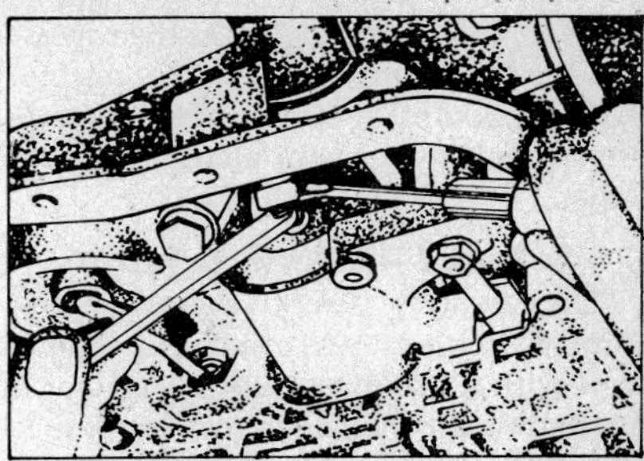

Adjusting the three-speed transmission front band.

2. Pry the band engagement lever toward the band with a screwdriver.

3. The gap between the end of the piston rod and the engagement bolt should be 0.138 in.

4. If the gap does not meet the specification, adjust it by turning the engagement bolt.

5. Install the oil pan and refill the transmission as outlined above.

Rear Band Adjustment

3 Speed

The rear band adjusting bolt is located on the outside of the case, so it is not necessary to remove the oil pan in order to adjust the band.

1. Loosen the adjusting bolt locknut and fully screw in the adjusting bolt.

2. Loosen the adjusting bolt one turn.

3. Tighten the locknut while holding the bolt so that it cannot turn.

Neutral Safety Switch Adjustment

Corolla—1968–70 and Corona—1966–70

1. Remove the shift quadrant housing.

2. Place the gear selector in Neutral, then loosen the switch locknut.

3. Adjust the length of the control rod, so that the shift lever pin rests firmly against the neutral detent on the shift plate.

4. Tighten the locknut.

5. Check to see that the back-up lights operate only when Reverse is selected and that the engine starts only in Neutral or Park.

6. Install the shift quadrant housing.

Corolla—1970 (late)–1973

The neutral safety switch used on 1970–73 Corolla models is not adjustable. If it malfunctions, it must be replaced. To do so, proceed in the following manner:

1. Remove the center console.

2. Unfasten and remove the three screws which secure the transmission selector assembly.

3. Disconnect the neutral safety switch multiconnector.

4. Slightly lift the transmission selector assembly and unfasten the two neutral safety switch attaching screws.

5. Withdraw the switch.

Installation is performed in the reverse order of removal. Position the selector lever in Neutral and install the switch so that installation marks align with each other.

3 Speed—Column Selector

The neutral safety switch/reverse lamp switch on the Toyoglide transmission with a column-mounted selector is located under the hood on the shift linkage. If the switch is not functioning properly, adjust as follows:

1. Loosen the switch securing bolt.
2. Move the switch so that its arm just contacts the control shaft lever when the gear selector is in Drive position.

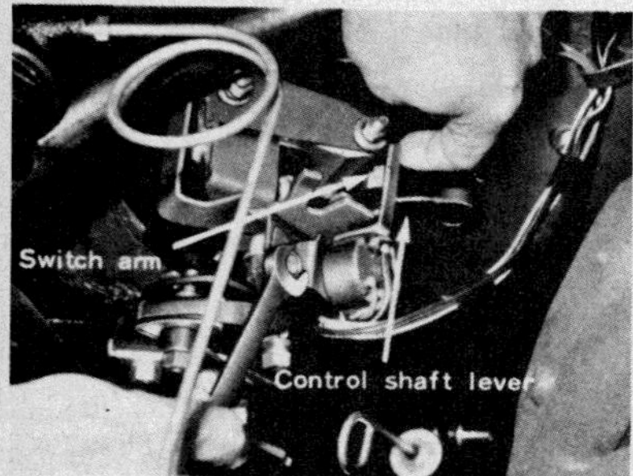

Adjusting the neutral safety switch on models wih three-speed Toyoguide and a column-mounted shift.

3. Tighten the switch securing bolt.
4. Check the operation of the switch; the car should start only in Park or Neutral and the back-up lamps should come on only when Reverse is selected.
5. If the switch cannot be adjusted so that it functions properly, replace it. Perform the adjustment as outlined above.

3 Speed—Console Shift

Models with a console-mounted selector have the neutral safety switch on the linkage located beneath the console. To adjust it, proceed in the following manner:

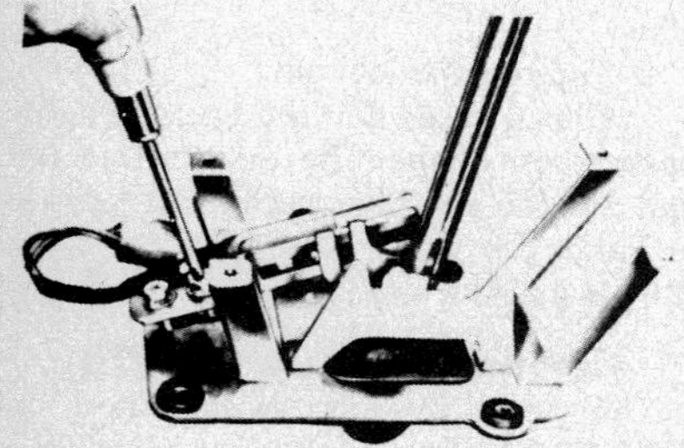

Adjusting the neutral safety switch on models with three-speed Toyoglide and a floor-mounted shift.

1. Remove the screws which secure the center console.
2. Unfasten the console multiconnector, if so equipped, and completely remove the console.
3. Adjust the switch in the manner outlined in the column selector section, above.
4. Install the console in the reverse order of removal after completion of the switch adjustment.

Shift Linkage Adjustment

The transmission should be engaged, in the gear selected as indicated on the shift quadrant. If it is not, then adjust the linkage as follows:

1. Check all of the shift linkage bushings for wear. Replace any worn bushings.
2. Loosen the connecting rod swivel locknut.
3. Move the selector lever and check movement of the pointer in the shift quadrant.
4. When the control shaft is set in the neutral position the quadrant pointer should indicate "N" (Neutral), as well.

Steps 5–7 apply only to cars equipped with column-mounted gear selectors.

5. If the pointer does not indicate Neutral, then check the drive cord adjustment.
6. Remove the steering column shroud.
7. Turn the drive cord adjuster with a phillips screwdriver until the pointer indicates Neutral.

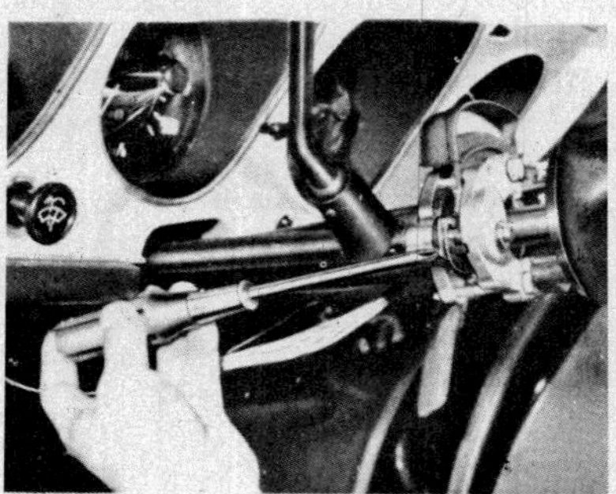

Adjusting the column-shift indicator drive cord.

Steps 8–10 apply to both column-mounted and floor-mounted selectors:

8. Position the manual valve lever on the transmission so that it is in the Neutral position.
9. Lock the connecting rod swivel with the locknut so that the pointer, selector, and manual valve lever are all positioned in Neutral.
10. Check the operation of the gear selector by moving it through all ranges.

Throttle Linkage Adjustment

2 Speed

1. Loosen the locknuts on the throttle linkage connecting rod turnbuckle.
2. Have an assistant depress the accelerator pedal fully.
3. Hold the throttle butterfly in the fully opened position.
4. Adjust the length of the rod so that the pointer lines up with the mark on the transmission case.
5. Tighten the locknut.

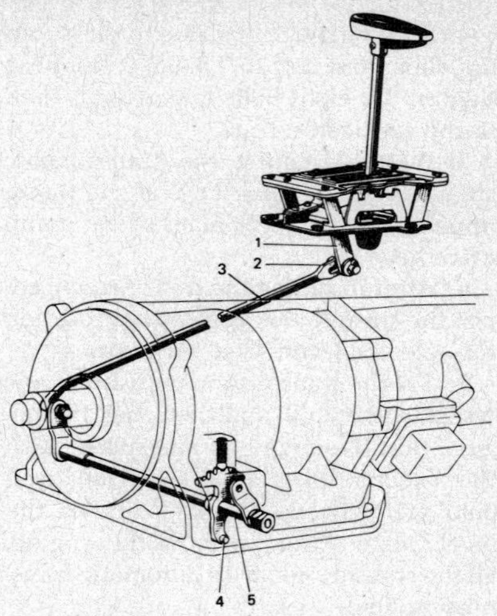

Floor-shift linkage components

1. Gear selector lever
2. Intermediate rod
3. Control rod
4. Manual valve lever
5. Shaft

3 Speed

1. Loosen the locknut at each end of the linkage adjusting turnbuckle.

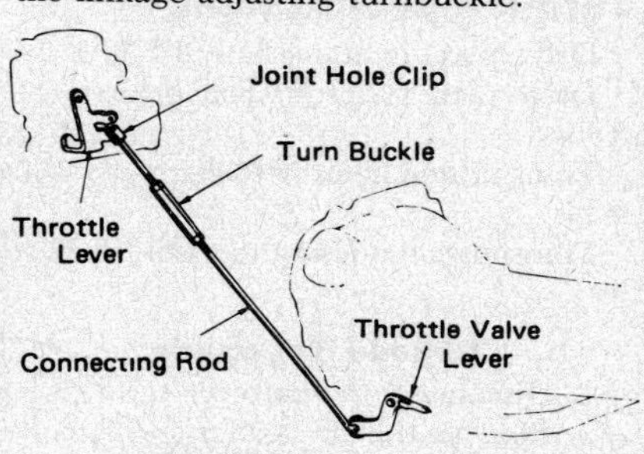

Throttle linkage components

2. Detach the throttle linkage connecting rod from the carburetor.
3. Align the pointer on the throttle valve lever with the mark stamped on the transmission case.
4. Rotate the turnbuckle so that the end of the throttle linkage rod and the carburetor throttle lever are aligned.

NOTE: *The carburetor throttle valve must be fully opened during this adjustment.*

5. Tighten the turnbuckle locknuts and reconnect the throttle rod to the carburetor.

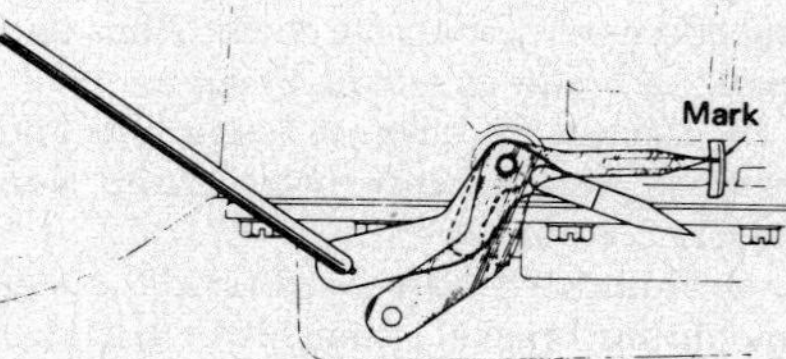

Throttle linkage aligning marks

6. Open the throttle valve and check the pointer alignment with the mark on the transmission case.
7. Road-test the car. If the transmission "hunts," i.e, keeps shifting rapidly

back and forth between gears at certain speeds or if it fails to downshift properly when going up hills, repeat the throttle linkage adjustment.

DRIVE AXLES

Driveshaft and U-Joints

Removal and Installation

Passenger Cars and Hi-Lux

1. Raise the rear of the car with jacks and support the rear axle housing with jackstands.

CAUTION: *Be sure that the car is securely supported. Remember, you will be working underneath it.*

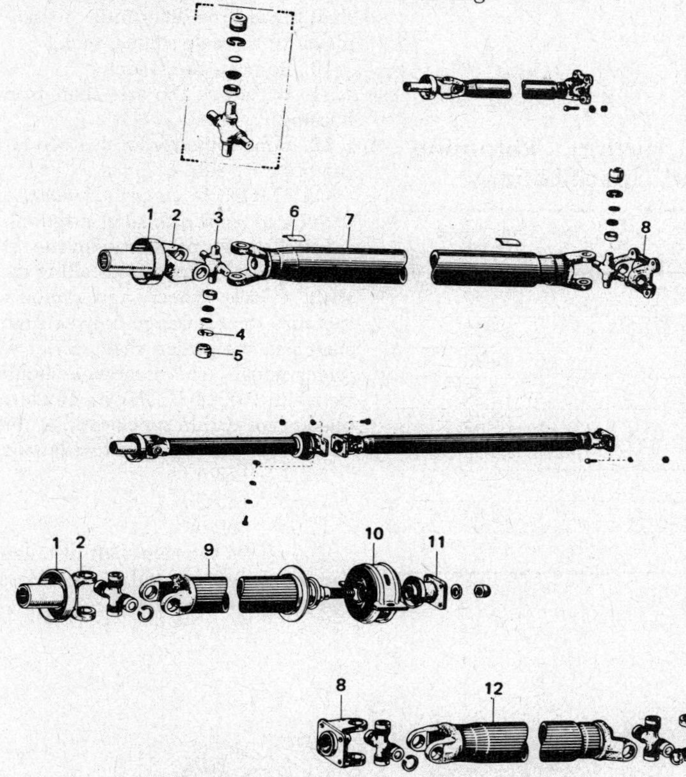

Driveshaft components—the upper illustration shows a single piece driveshaft.

1. Transmission end of driveshaft
2. U-joint yoke and sleeve
3. U-joint spider
4. Snap ring
5. U-joint spider bearing
6. Balancing weight
7. Driveshaft
8. U-joint yoke flange
9. Intermediate driveshaft assembly
10. Center bearing support
11. U-joint flange assembly
12. Driveshaft

2. Unfasten the bolts which attach the driveshaft universal joint yoke flange to the mounting flange on the differential drive pinion.

3. On models equipped with three universal joints, perform the following:

a. Withdraw the driveshaft subassembly from the U-joint sleeve yoke.

b. Unfasten the center support bearing from its bracket.

4. Remove the driveshaft end from the transmission.

5. Install an old U-joint yoke in the transmission or, if none is available, use a plastic bag secured with a rubber band over the hole to keep the transmission oil from running out.

6. Withdraw the driveshaft from beneath the vehicle.

Installation is performed in the following order:

1. Apply multipurpose gease on the section of the U-joint sleeve which is to be inserted into the transmission.

2. Insert the driveshaft sleeve into the transmission.

CAUTION: *Be careful not to damage any of the seals.*

3. For models equipped with three U-joints and center bearings, perform the following:

Two-piece driveshaft only

a. Adjust the center bearing clearance with no load placed on the driveline components; the top of the rubber center cushion should be 0.04 in. *behind* the center of the elongated bolt hole.

b. Install the center bearing assembly.

NOTE: *Use the same number of washers on the center bearing bracket as were removed.*

c. On Hi-Lux models, match the arrow marks on the driveshaft and grease fittings.

4. Secure the U-joint flange to the differential pinion flange with the mounting bolts.

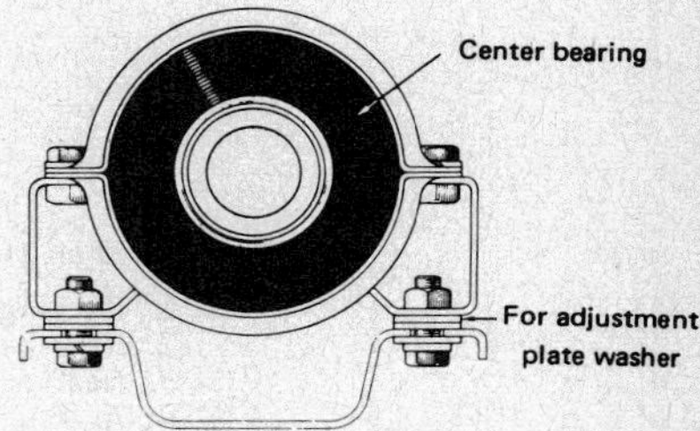

Center bearing adjustment

CAUTION: *Be sure that the bolts are of the same type as those removed and that they are tightened securely.*

5. Remove the jackstands and lower the vehicle.

Land Cruiser

Land Cruiser models are equipped with two driveshafts; one runs from the transfer case to the rear differential and the other from the transfer case to the front differential. Removal and installation of both driveshafts is performed in the same manner.

1. Raise the vehicle and support it with jackstands.

CAUTION: *Be sure that the vehicle is securely supported. Remember, you will be working underneath it.*

2. Unfasten the bolts which secure the universal joint flange to the differential pinion flange.

3. Perform step 2 for the U-joint-to-transfer case flange bolts.

4. Withdraw the driveshaft from beneath the vehicle.

Installation is performed in the reverse order of removal.

NOTE: *Lubricate the U-joints and sliding joints with multipurpose grease before installation.*

Axle Shafts

Removal and Installation

Passenger Cars and Hi-Lux

1. Raise the rear of the car and support it securely by using jackstands.
2. Drain the oil from the axle housing.
3. Remove the wheel disc, unfasten the lug nuts, and remove the wheel.
4. Punch matchmarks on the brake drum and the axle shaft to maintain rotational balance.
5. Remove the brake drum and related components, as detailed below.
6. Remove the rear bearing retaining nut.
7. Remove the backing plate attachment nuts through the access holes in the rear axle shaft flange.

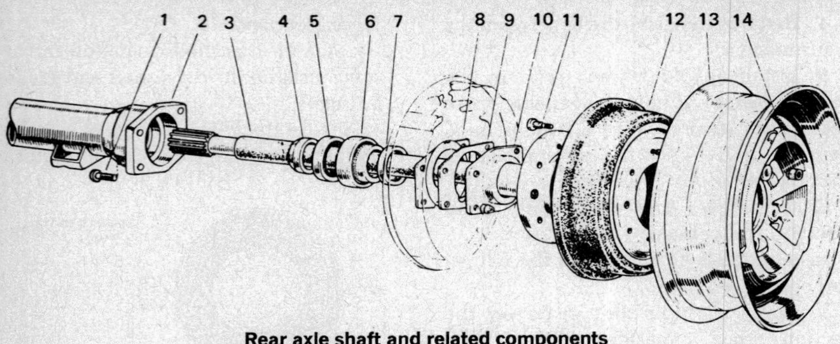

Rear axle shaft and related components

1. Backing plate set bolt
2. Rear axle housing
3. Rear axle shaft
4. Axle bearing inner retainer
5. Oil seal
6. Bearing
7. Spacer
8. Axle housing end gasket
9. Bearing retainer gasket
10. Axle bearing inner retainer
11. Hub bolt
12. Brake drum assembly
13. Wheel
14. Hub nut

8. Use a slide hammer with a suitable adapter to withdraw the axle shaft from its housing.

CAUTION: *Use care not to damage the oil seal when removing the axle shaft.*

9. Repeat the procedure for the axle shaft on the opposite side.

CAUTION: *Be careful not to mix the components of the two sides.*

Installation is performed in the reverse order of removal. Coat the lips of the rear housing oil seal with multipurpose grease prior to installation of the rear axle shaft. Torque the bearing retaining nut to the specifications given in the chart below.

NOTE: *Always use new nuts, as they are the self-locking type.*

Axle Bearing Retaining Nut Specifications

Model	Torque range (ft lbs)
Corolla 1100/1200	15-22
Corolla 1200/1600	26-38
Carina	26-38
Corona	29-36
Mark II/4	29-26
Mark II/6	43-52
Crown 2300	—
Crown 2600	29-40
Hi-Lux	—

— Not available

Land Cruiser

1. Remove the hub cap and loosen the wheel nuts.

2. Raise the rear axle housing with a jack and support the rear of the vehicle with jackstands.

CAUTION: *Be sure that the vehicle is securely supported. Remember, you will be working underneath it.*

3. Drain the oil from the differential.

4. Remove the wheel nuts and take off the wheels.

5. Remove the brake drum and related parts, as detailed below.

6. Remove the cover from the back of the differential housing.

7. Remove the pin from the differential pinion shaft.

8. Withdraw the pinion shaft and its spacer from the case.

9. Use a mallet to *tap* the rear axle shaft toward the differential, to aid in removal of the axle shaft C-lock.

10. Remove the C-lock.

11. Withdraw the axle shaft from the housing.

12. Repeat the removal procedure for the opposite side.

CAUTION: *Do not mix the parts of the left and right axle shaft assemblies.*

Installation is performed in the reverse order of removal. After installing the axle shaft, C-lock, spacer, and pinion shaft, measure the clearance between the axle shaft and the pinion shaft spacer with a feeler gauge. The clearance should fall between 0.0024–0.0181 in. If the clearance is not within specifications, use one of the following spacers to adjust it:

1.172–1.173 in.
1.188–1.189 in.
1.204–1.205 in.

The rest of the axle shaft installation is the reverse of removal. Remember to fill the axle with lubricant.

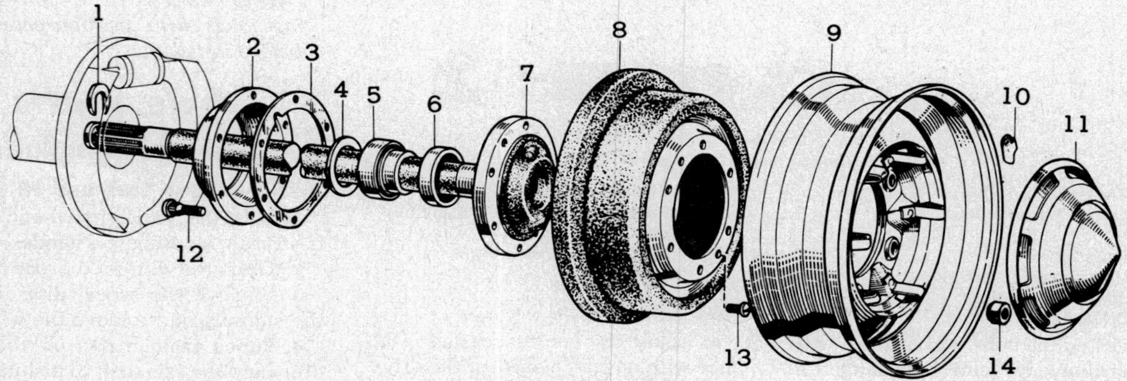

Land Cruiser rear axle components

1. Rear axle shaft lock
2. Brake drum oil deflector
3. Gasket
4. Spacer
5. Wheel bearing
6. Oil seal
7. Axle shaft
8. Brake drum
9. Wheel
10. Wheel balancing weight
11. Hub cap
12. Hub bolt
13. Brake drum set bolt
14. Lug nut

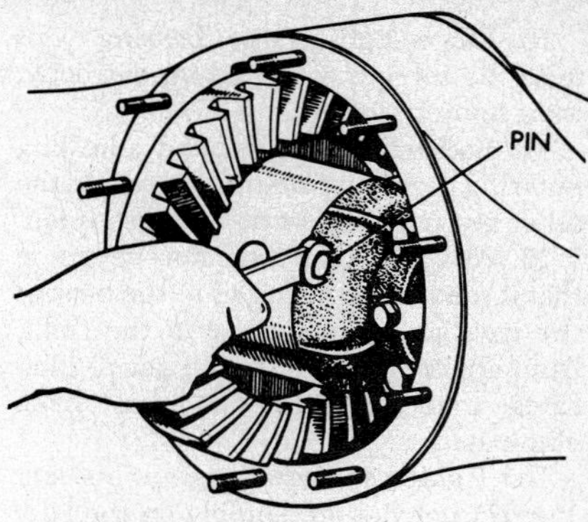

Pinion shaft pin removal on Land Cruiser models.

Differential

Removal and Installation

NOTE: *Rear axle servicing is a complex operation. Repair should not be attempted unless the special tools and knowledge required are readily available.*

Rear Carrier—All Models

1. Remove the axle shafts, as detailed in the appropriate section above.
2. Disconnect the driveshaft from the pinion shaft flange.
3. Unfasten the carrier securing nuts and remove the carrier assembly.

Installation is performed in the reverse order of removal. Be sure to apply liquid sealer to both the carrier gasket and the lower carrier securing nuts.

Front Carrier—Land Cruiser

1. Remove the wheel covers and loosen the lug nuts.
2. Jack the front axle housing up and support it with jackstands.

CAUTION: *Be sure that the vehicle is securely supported. Remember, you will be working underneath it.*

3. Remove the lug nuts and the wheels.
4. Unfasten the bolts and disconnect the front driveshaft from the flange on the differential.
5. Drain the lubricant from the differential.
6. Remove the axle outer shaft flange cap. Unfasten the snap-ring from the shaft.
7. Unfasten the securing bolts from the axle shaft outer flange. Withdraw the flange by screwing service bolts into it alternately. Do not pry it off.
8. Straighten the lockwasher and remove the adjusting nuts with a hub nut wrench.
9. Remove the brake drum and front axle hub as an assembly.
10. Cut the lockwire and remove it. Unfasten the backing plate retaining bolts from the steering knuckle and wire the backing plate up to the front spring.

NOTE: *Do not remove the hydaulic brake line from the backing plate.*

11. Remove the spindle and gasket from the steering knuckle. Withdraw the outer shaft, front ball joint and axle inner shaft.
12. Unfasten the differential carrier retaining nuts and remove the carrier inner shaft.

Reverse the removal procedure for installation. Note the following, however:

Replace all lockwashers and gaskets with new ones. Apply liquid sealer to the carrier gasket and tighten the carrier retaining nuts to 29–40 ft lbs. Adjust the front wheel bearing preload, as detailed

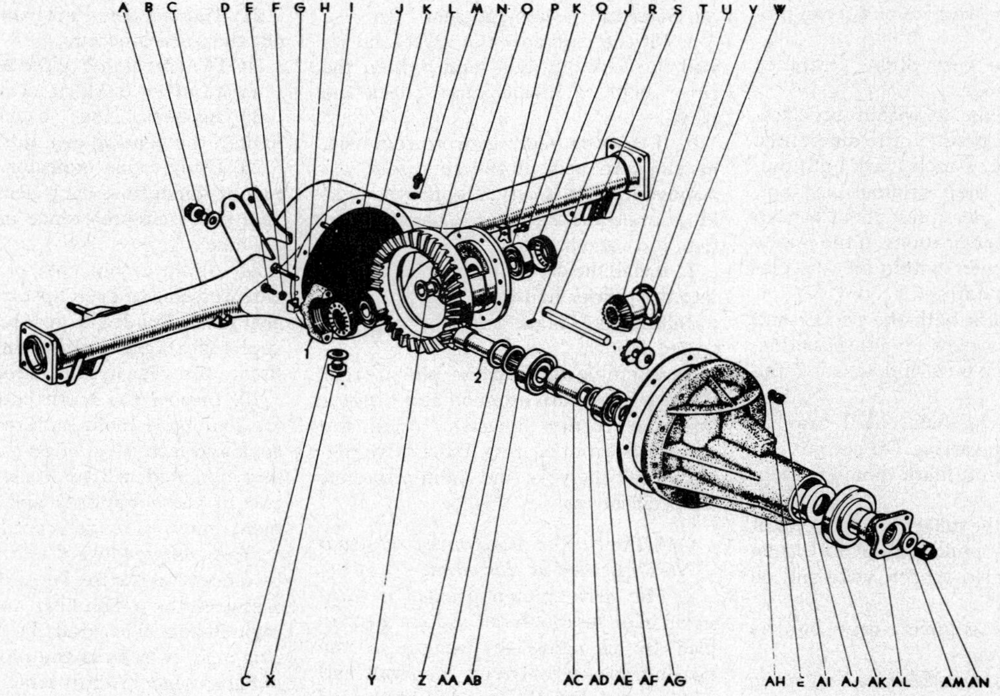

Differential components

(a)—Housing assembly
(b)—Filler plug
(c)—Gasket
(d)—Bolt
(e)—Lock washer
(f)—Hexagon bolt
(g)—Bearing adjusting nut lock
(h)—Lockwasher
(i)—Stud
(j)—Bearing adjusting nut
(k)—Bearing
(l)—Breather plug
(m)—Lockwasher
(n)—Ring gear and drive pinion 1 and 2
(o)—Case
(p)—Lockplate
(q)—Bolt
(r)—Lockpin
(s)—Pinion shaft
(t)—Side gear
(u)—Thrust washer
(v)—Pinion
(w)—Thrust washer
(x)—Drain plug
(y)—Oil reservoir
(z)—Spacer
(aa)—Shim
(ab)—Bearing
(ac)—Spacer
(ad)—Shim
(ae)—Bearing
(af)—Oil slinger
(ag)—Gasket
(ah)—Carrier
(ai)—Nut
(aj)—Oil seal
(ak)—Dust deflector
(al)—Universal joint flange
(am)—Flat washer
(an)—Nut

in the appropriate section below. Remember to fill the axle housing with SAE 90 gear lubricant.

Overhaul

1. Thoroughly wash and rinse the carrier and blow dry with compressed air.
2. Securely clamp the carrier in a vise or suitable stand.
3. Apply a light coating of mechanic's blue (or lipstick) to the teeth of the ring gear.
4. Applying a slight drag on the ring gear to avoid backlash, rotate the pinion in a smooth and continuous manner to obtain a good tooth pattern on the ring gear.
5. Next, attach a dial indicator gauge to the carrier base and check the ring gear backlash.
6. Also check ring gear runout at this time. If the tooth pattern obtained is correct, and the backlash and runout are within limits, any gear noise must come from the side gears.
7. With the dial indicator gauge set up on the carrier, check the backlash between the pinion gears and side gears. Excessive backlash usually is due to either worn thrust washers or a worn pinion shaft.
8. Check side gear thrust clearance with a feeler gauge.
9. If everything is within specifications, test the preload on the differential drive pinion nut. Punch mark both pinion and nut in their original positions, then loosen the pinion nut about ½ turn and torque to specifications. If the punch marks line up again (within 60°) the pinion preload was correct.
10. Punch mark both the carrier and the side bearing caps for identification, remove the lock-nuts and take off the caps.
11. Remove the differential case assembly from the carrier. Do not mix the bearing cups; paint mark them for identification.
12. Remove the differential pinion nut (do not let the pinion drop out), then remove the pinion spacer, yoke and oil seal.
13. With a brass punch, drive out the pinion bearing cups.

NOTE: *This should be done only when the bearings are to be replaced.*

14. Press or pull off the drive pinion rear bearing. Avoid damaging the flat spacer behind the bearing.
15. Measure the spacer thickness and note the measurement for future use. Remove both side bearings from the differential case and mark them "L" and "R" for identification.

NOTE: *Remove side bearings only if they must be replaced.*

16. Punch mark the differential case and cover, then remove the cover bolts and the cover (where fitted).
17. Remove the shaft and pinions, the side gears and all thrust washers.

NOTE: *Some differential types have four spider pinion gears; punch mark the gears before removal so they can be correctly reinstalled.*

Check all bearing cones and cups for wear. Inspect the tooth surfaces of all gears carefully and inspect all thrust washers for wear and signs of slipping in their seats. Check all gear shafts for scoring, wear or distortion. Finally, inspect the case and carrier housing for cracks or other damage. Also check the case for signs of wear at the side gear bores, bearing cap and mounting hubs.

Assembly is performed in the following order:

1. Wash and clean all parts before installation.
2. Lightly oil all bearings and gear shafts, except the ring gear and drive pinion teeth.
3. Place the side gears and the pinion gears, with their thrust washers, into the differential case.
4. Insert the shaft and align the lock pin holes in the case and shaft.
5. Fit the case cover in place and install the lock pin (bolt) and tighten the cover bolts to specification; check the play.
6. If the side bearings were removed, install them now. If the ring gear was removed, install it now. Tighten the bolts in symmetrical sequence to avoid distortion and runout.
7. Install the drive pinion bearing cups into the carrier housing, using a suitable installing tool. Make sure the cups are seated solidly.
8. Assemble the drive pinion rear bearing to the drive pinion and insert it into the carrier housing. Install the spacer and front bearing to the drive pinion; install the yoke and tighten the nut to specifications.

CAUTION: *The drive pinion oil seal is NOT installed at this point.*

9. The drive pinion preload is measured in in. lbs (not ft lbs). Adjust the preload by changing the length of the bearing spacer (between the front and rear bearings) until the required preload is obtained.
10. Place the previously assembled differential case into position in the bearing hubs and put the caps into position as marked (L and R).
11. Set the case so that there will be the least amount of backlash between the ring gear and pinion (in order to save time adjusting).
12. Install the adjusting nuts (also marked L and R) and take care not to cross-thread them.
13. Finger-tighten the bearing caps until the threads are lined up correctly, then tighten slowly.
14. Back off the right-hand adjusting nut (ring gear teeth side) and screw in the other nut until almost no backlash is felt.
15. Attach a dial indicator gauge so that it reads at right angles to the back of the ring gear, then screw in the right-hand adjusting nut until the gauge indicates that all side play has been eliminated.
16. Tighten the adjusting nut another 1 or 1½ notches (depending on the fit of the lock tabs).
17. Recheck the preload on the drive pinion as before; this time the specifications are different (see table).
18. If too loose, readjust the side bearing preload; if too tight, adjust the ring gear backlash.
19. Install the dial indicator gauge so that it contacts the ring gear teeth at right angles. Adjust the backlash to specifications.
20. If too great, adjust by loosening the bearing cap bolts slightly and screwing the right-hand adjusting nut (ring gear teeth side) out about two notches.
21. Tighten the left-hand adjusting nut the same amount.

NOTE: *One notch of the adjusting nut equals about 0.002 in. of backlash.*

22. Recheck the backlash, then tighten the bearing cap nuts.
23. Using a dial indicator recheck all runout dimensions (ring gear back, ring gear outer circumference and differential case).
24. Apply a thin coat of mechanic's blue, red lead or even lipstick to the ring gear teeth. Rotate the gear several times, applying a light drag to the ring gear. Rotate the gear in both directions.
25. Inspect the tooth pattern. There are four basic tooth patterns: heel, toe, flank and face. Most often the tooth pattern obtained will be a combination of two of these patterns and the adjustments must be made accordingly.

Heel contact Move the drive pinion in by increasing the thickness of the spacer (between the pinion head and rear bearing). Readjust backlash by moving the ring gear away from the pinion.

Face contact Adjust same as above.

Toe contact Adjust by moving the drive pinion out by reducing the thickness of the spacer. Readjust backlash.

Flank contact Adjust same as toe contact.

Continue assembling as follows:

25. Remove the drive pinion nut and install the seal into the differential carrier housing, then install the oil slinger, dust shield and yoke and retorque the pinion nut as specified.
26. Install the differential carrier assembly into the axle housing.

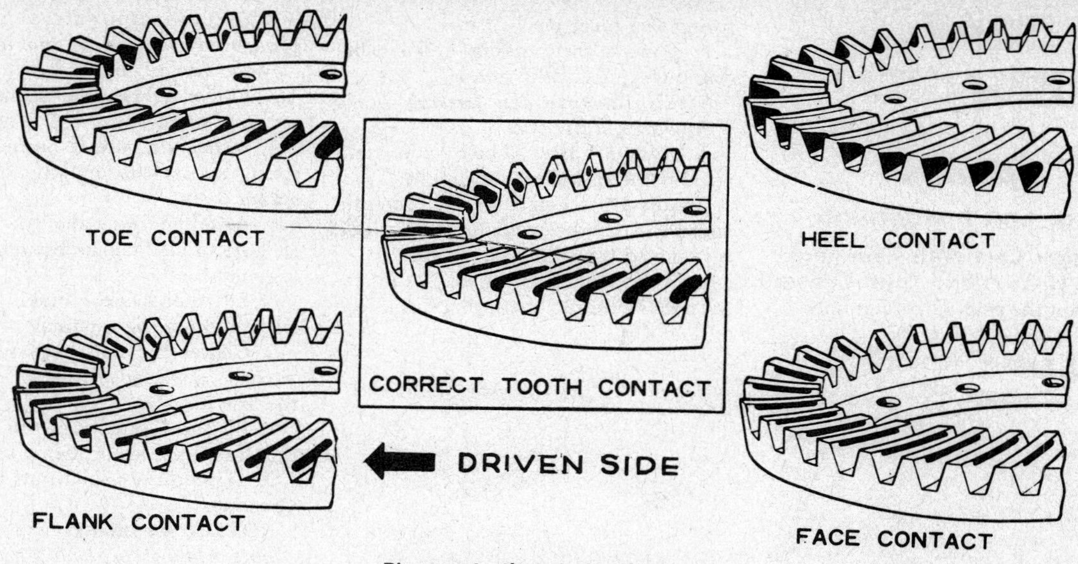

Ring gear tooth contact pattern

DIFFERENTIAL SPECIFICATIONS

Model	BACKLASH (in.)		Runout (in.)	TORQUE (ft lbs)		PINION BEARING PRELOAD① (in. lbs)	
	Ring gear and pinion	Side gears	Ring gear	Side bearing cap	Differential pinion nut	New	Old
Corolla 1100/1200	0.004-0.006	0.001-0.006	0.0016	40-47	95-110	3-5	1-3
Corolla 1600	0.004-0.006	0.0008-0.0060	0.0016	40-47	123-145	4-5	3
Carina & Celica	0.005-0.007	0.003-0.008	0.0016	36-50	123-145	4-5	2-3
Corona RT40 series	0.005-0.007	0.002-0.008	0.0016	37-52	125-130	7-9	5-7
Corona 1900/2000	0.005-0.007	0.0008-0.0080	0.0020	36-51	123-145	4-8	1-2
Mark II 1900/2000	0.005-0.007	—	0.0020	36-51	123-145	4-6	1-3
Mark II 6-cyl	0.005-0.007	0.002-0.008	0.0030	51-65	80-145	7-10	2-4
Crown 2300	0.005-0.007	—	0.0020	50-70	115-145	12-15	5-8
Crown 2600	0.006-0.007	0.002-0.008	0.0030	51-65	80-145	16-23	4-10
Hi-Lux 1900/200	0.005-0.007	0.002-0.008	0.0020	51-65	120-152	17-23	4-13
Land Cruiser	0.006-0.008	—	0.0040	65-80	145-175	12-15	5-8

① Without oil seal and differential gears installed

REAR SUSPENSION

Springs

Removal and Installation

Passenger Cars with Rear Leaf Springs. Hi-Lux, and Land Cruiser

1. Loosen the rear wheel lug nuts.

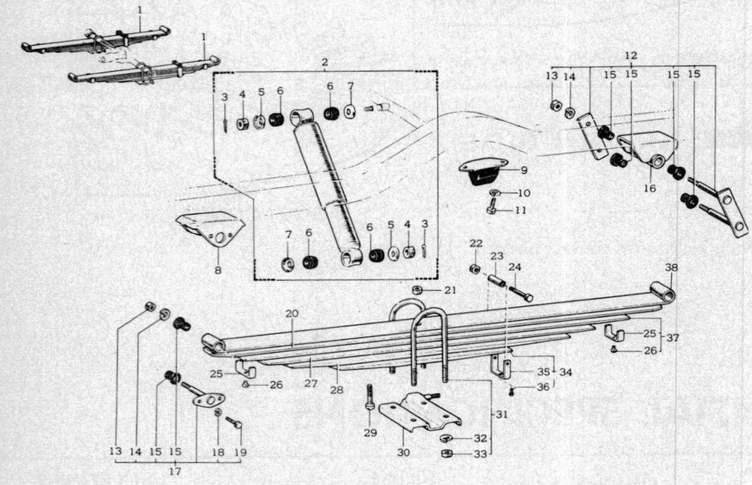

Components of the Hi-Lux rear suspension —other vehicles with leaf springs similar.

1. Rear spring
2. Rear shock absorber
3. Cotter pin
4. Castle pin
5. Shock absorber cushion washer
6. Bushing
7. Shock absorber cushion washer
8. Spring bracket
9. Rear spring bumper
10. Spring washer
11. Bolt
12. Rear spring shackle
13. Nut
14. Spring washer
15. Bushing
16. Spring bracket
17. Rear spring hanger pin
18. Spring washer
19. Bolt
20. Rear spring leaf
21. Nut
22. Nut
23. Rear spring clip bolt
24. Clip bolt
25. Rear spring clip
26. Round rivet
27. Rear spring leaf
28. Rear spring leaf No. 5
29. Rear spring center bolt
30. U-bolt seat
31. U-bolt
32. Spring washer
33. Nut
34. Rear spring leaf
35. Rear spring clip
36. Round rivet
37. Rear spring leaf
38. Rear spring leaf
39. Bumper block spacer

2. Raise the rear of the vehicle. Support the frame and rear axle housing with stands.

CAUTION: *Be sure that the vehicle is securely supported. Remember; you will be working underneath it.*

3. Remove the lug nuts and the wheel.
4. Remove the cotter pin, nut, and washer from the lower end of the shock absorber.
5. On Land Cruiser models, perform the following:

a. Remove the cotter pins and nuts from the lower end of the stabilizer link.

b. Detach the link from the axle housing.

6. Detach the shock absorber from the spring seat pivot pin.
7. Remove the parking brake cable clamp (except Land Cruiser).

NOTE: *Remove the parking brake equalizer, if necessary.*

8. Unfasten the U-bolt nuts and remove the spring seat assemblies.
9. Adjust the height of the rear axle housing so that the weight of the rear axle is removed from the rear springs.
10. Unfasten the spring shackle retaining nuts. Withdraw the spring shackle inner plate. Carefully pry out the spring shackle with a bar.
11. Remove the spring bracket pin from the front end of the spring hanger and remove the rubber bushings.
12. Remove the spring.

CAUTION: *Use care not to damage the hydraulic brake line or the parking brake cable.*

Installation is performed in the following order:

1. Install the rubber bushings in the eye of the spring.
2. Align the eye of the spring with the spring hanger bracket and drive the pin through the bracket holes and rubber bushings.

NOTE: *Use soapy water as lubricant, if necessary, to aid in pin installation. Never use oil or grease.*

3. Finger-tighten the spring hanger nuts and/or bolts.
4. Install the rubber bushings in the spring eye at the opposite end of the spring.
5. Raise the free end of the spring. Install the spring shackle through the bushings and the bracket.
6. Fit the shackle inner plate and finger-tighten the retaining nuts.
7. Center the bolt head in the hole which is provided in the spring seat on the axle housing.
8. Fit the U-bolts over the axle housing. Install the lower spring seat.
9. Tighten the U-bolt nuts to the specifications.

NOTE: *Some models have two sets of nuts, while others have a nut and lockwasher.*

10. Install the parking brake cable clamp. Install the equalizer, if it was removed.
11. On passenger cars:

a. Install the shock absorber end at the spring seat. Tighten the nuts to the specified torque.

b. Install the wheel and lug nuts. Lower the car to the ground.

c. Bounce the car several times.

d. Tighten the spring bracket pins and shackles.

e. Repeat step b, and check all of the torque specifications again.

12. Hi-Lux and Land Cruiser:

a. Raise the rear axle with the jack so that the stands no longer support the frame.

b. Tighten the hanger pin and shackle nuts to the specifications.

c. Install the shock absorber bushings and washers. Tighten to specifications and install the cotter pins.

d. Install the stabilizer link and hand-tighten its retaining nuts (Land Cruiser).

e. Install the wheels, remove the stands, and lower the vehicle to the ground.

f. Tighten the stabilizer link bolts, bounce the vehicle, and tighten them again (Land Cruiser).

Passenger Cars with Coil Spring Rear Suspensions

1. Remove the hubcap and loosen the lug nuts.
2. Jack up the rear axle housing and support the frame with jackstands. Leave the jack in place under the rear axle housing.

CAUTION: *Support the car securely. Remember; you will be working underneath it.*

3. Remove the lug nuts and wheel.

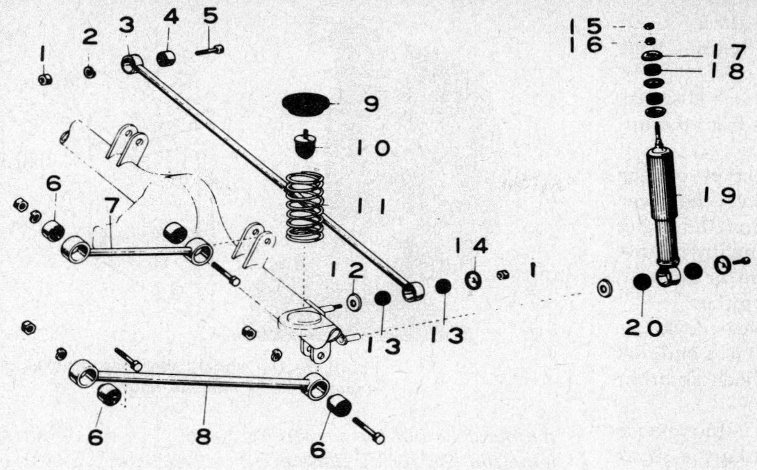

Celica and Carina rear suspension—Crown similar.

1. Nut
2. Washer
3. Lateral control rod
4. Bushing
5. Bolt
6. Bushing
7. Upper control arm
8. Lower control arm
9. Spring insulator
10. Spring bumper
11. Coil spring
12. Washer
13. Bushing
14. Washer
15. Nut
16. Nut
17. Washer
18. Bushing
19. Shock absorber
20. Bushing

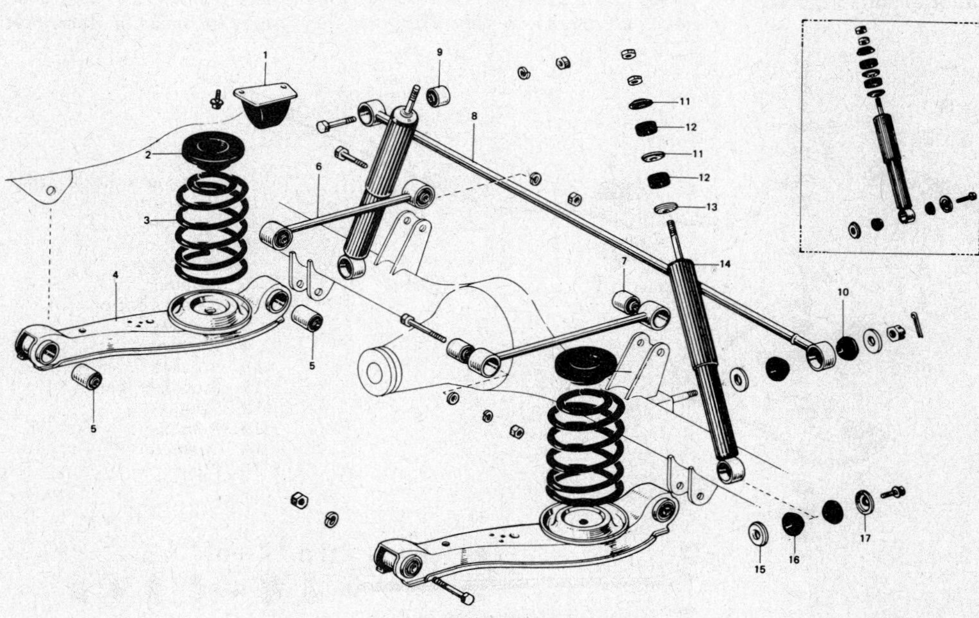

Mark II/6 rear suspension.

1. Bumper
2. Spring insulator
3. Coil spring
4. Lower control arm
5. Bushing
6. Upper control arm
7. Bushing
8. Bushing
9. Lateral control rod
10. Bushing
11. Retainer
12. Cushion
13. Retainer
14. Shock absorber
15. Washer
16. Bushing
17. Washer

4. Unfasten the lower shock absorber end.

5. Slowly lower the jack under the rear axle housing until the axle is at the bottom of its travel.

6. Withdraw the coil spring, complete with its insulator.

Inspect the coil spring and insulator for wear, cracks, or weakness; replace either or both, as necessary.

Installation is performed in the reverse order of removal. Tighten the lower shock absorber mounting to the specifications

Rear Shock Absorbers

Removal and Installation

1. Jack up the rear end of the vehicle. **CAUTION:** *Be sure that the vehicle is securely supported. Remember; you*

will be working underneath it.

2. Support the rear axle housing with jackstands.

3. Unfasten the upper shock absorber retaining nuts and/or bolts from the upper frame member.

4. Depending upon the type of rear springs used, either disconnect the lower end of the shock absorber from the spring seat, or the rear axle housing, by removing its cotter pins, nuts, and/or bolts.

5. Remove the shock absorber.

Inspect the shock for wear, leaks, or other signs of damage. Test it as outlined in the front suspension shock absorber section.

Installation is performed in the reverse order from removal. Tighten the shock absorber securing nuts and bolts.

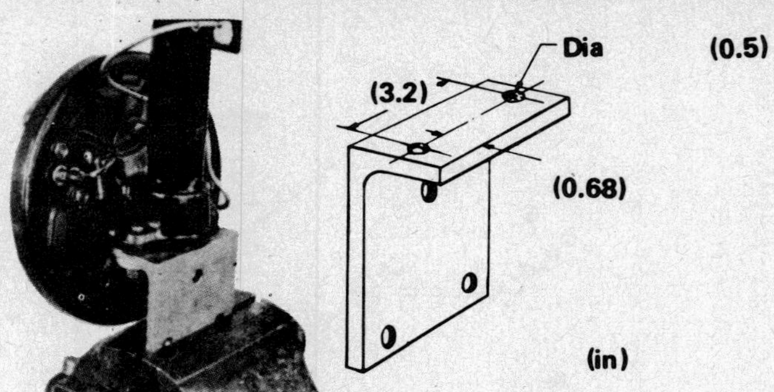

Fabricate the shock absorber bracket and mount it in a vise as shown.

FRONT SUSPENSION

Springs

Removal and Installation

Corolla, Carina and Celica

1. Remove the hubcap and loosen the lug nuts.

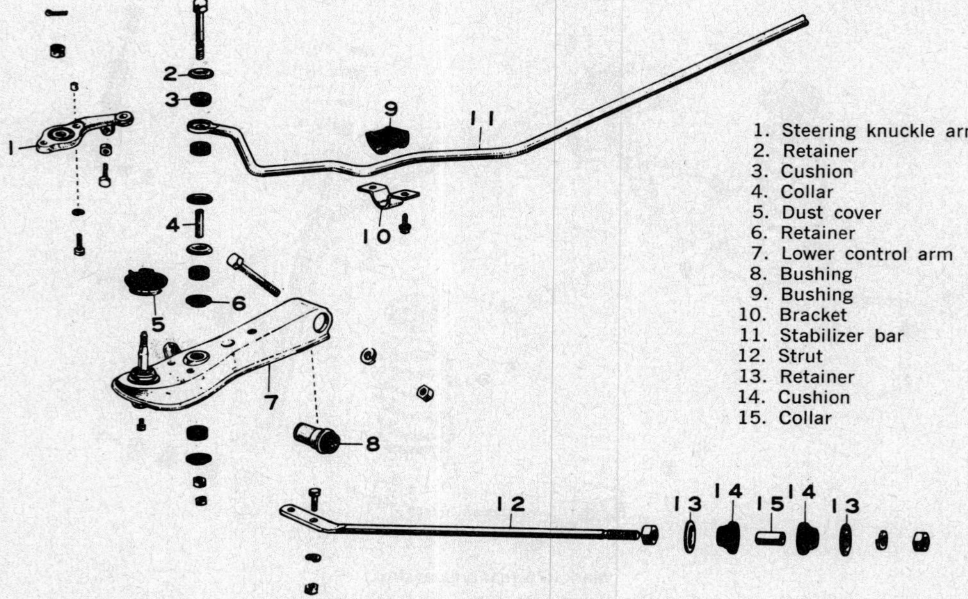

The components of the MacPherson strut front suspension—Corolla, Carina and Celica.

2. Raise the front of the car and support it, on the chassis jacking plates provided, with jackstands.

CAUTION: *Do not support the weight of the car on the suspension arm; the arm will deform under its weight.*

3. Unfasten the lug nuts and remove the wheel.

NOTE: *On 1969–70 Corolla models having a transverse leaf spring, raise the outer end of the suspension to release the leaf spring tension.*

4. Detach the front brake line from its clamp.

5. Remove the brake drum, or the caliper and wire it out of the way.

6. Unfasten the three nuts which secure the upper shock absorber mounting plate to the top of the wheel arch.

7. Remove the two bolts which attach the shock absorber lower end to the steering knuckle lower arm.

NOTE: *Press down on the suspension lower arm, in order to remove the shock absorber assembly. This must be done to clear the collars on the steering knuckle arm bolt holes when removing the shock/spring assembly.*

8. Fabricate the shock absorber/-spring assembly mounting stand, as illustrated. Bolt the assembly on the stand and mount the stand on a vise.

9. Use a coil spring compressor to compress the spring until it can be moved freely.

10. Remove the bearing dust cap from the top of the shock absorber assembly.

11. Use a spanner or a large open-end wrench to keep the upper spring seat from turning and unfasten the 10 mm nut at the top of the shock absorber assembly.

CAUTION: *Do not use an impact wrench when loosening the nut.*

12. Remove the components from the top of the shock and withdraw the spring in its compressed state.

Check the spring for cracks and weakness. Check the dust seals and spring seats for wear or deterioration. Replace parts, as necessary.

Installation is performed in the reverse order of removal. Be sure to note the following, however:

1. Align the hole in the upper suspension support with the shock absorber piston rod end, so that they fit properly.

2. Always use a *new* nut and nylon washer on the shock absorber piston rod end when securing it to the upper sus-

pension support. Torque the nut to 29–40 ft lbs.

CAUTION: *Do not use an impact wrench to tighten the nut.*

3. Coat the suspension support bearing with multipurpose grease prior to installation. Pack the space in the upper support with multipurpose grease, also, after installation.

4. Tighten the suspension support-to-wheel arch bolts to the following specification:

Corolla—10.9–15.9 ft lbs
Carina and Celica—14.0–23.0 ft lbs

5. Tighten the shock absorber-to-steering knuckle arm bolts to the following specifications.

Corolla—50–65 ft lbs
Carina and Celica—58–87 ft lbs

6. Adjust the front wheel bearing preload as outlined below.

7. Bleed the brake system.

Corona

1. Remove the hubcap and loosen the nuts.

2. Raise the front of the car and support it by using jackstands.

CAUTION: *Be sure that the car is securely supported. Remember; you will be working underneath it.*

3. Remove the lug nuts and the wheel.

4. Remove the shock absorber as detailed in the appropriate section below.

5. Remove the dust cover.

6. Install a coil spring compressor and compress the spring until there is no load on it.

7. Unfasten the lower ball joint retaining bolts and withdraw the ball joint, complete with the steering knuckle, from the lower control arm.

8. Slowly and carefully loosen the spring compressor and remove the spring.

Inspect the spring, ball joint, and related components for wear or damage. Replace any parts necessary.

Installation is performed in the reverse order of removal.

If the spring is being replaced with a new one, be sure to purchase one of the correct load tolerance for your Corona.

NOTE: *The coil springs are not interchangeable from the right side to the left side.*

The ball joint/steering knuckle assembly securing bolts should be tightened to the following specifications:

12 mm bolts—58–83 ft lbs
8 mm bolts—11–16 ft lbs

After completing installation of the coil spring, check to see that it is properly seated in the lower suspension arm. Check front end alignment. (See below.)

Mark II and Crown

1. Perform steps 1–3 of the Corona coil spring removal and installation procedure. Be sure to observe the **"Caution."**

2. Unfasten the stabilizer bar.

3. Measure the distance between the serrated bolt holes on the front side of the torque strut and the attachment nut on the rear side to aid in installation. (See illustration.) Remove the strut.

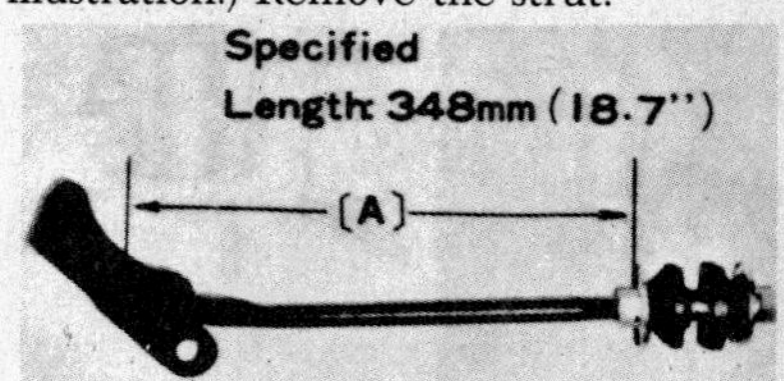

Measure distance (A) before removing the strut.

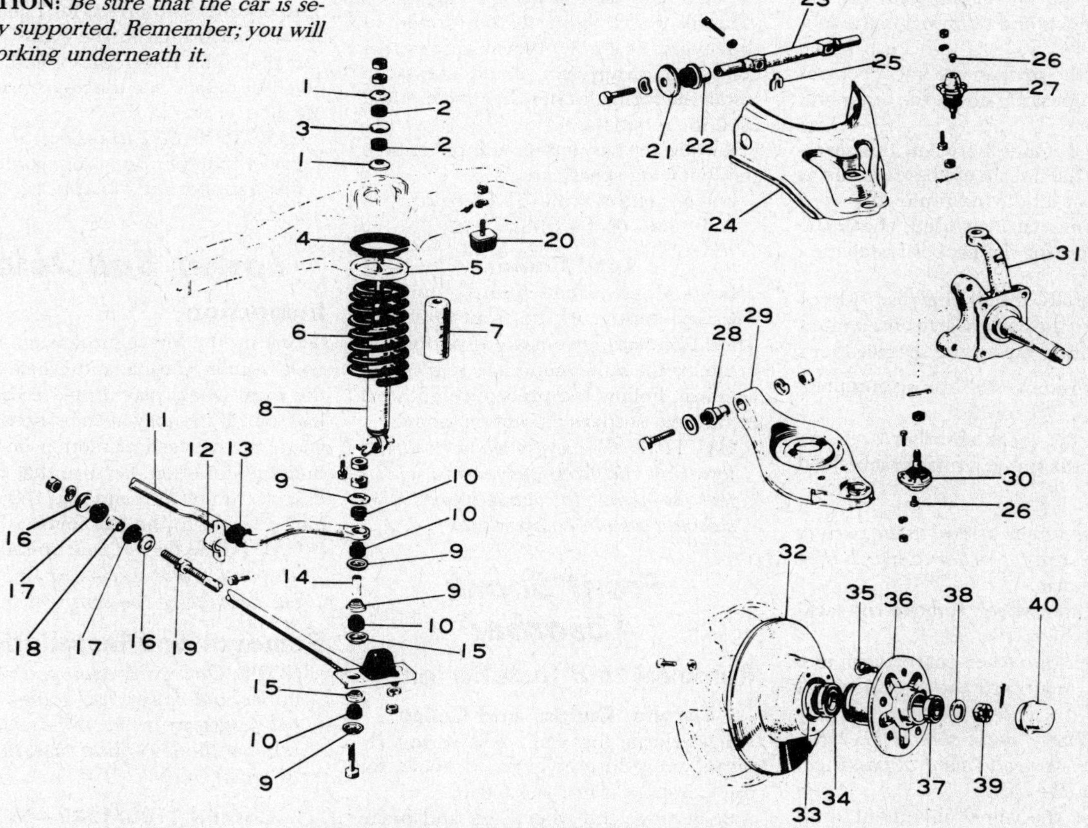

Components of the Crown front suspension —Mark II similar.

1. Washer
2. Cushion
3. Retainer
4. Insulator
5. Spacer
6. Coil spring
7. Dust cover
8. Shock absorber
9. Retainer
10. Cushion
11. Stabilizer bar
12. Bracket
13. Bushing
14. Collar
15. Retainer
16. Retainer
17. Cushion
18. Collar
19. Strut
20. Bumper
21. Retainer
22. Bushing
23. Shaft
24. Upper control arm
25. Camber adjusting shim
26. Plug
27. Upper ball joint
28. Bushing
29. Lower control arm
30. Lower ball joint
31. Steering knuckle
32. Brake disc
33. Oil seal
34. Roller bearing
35. Hub bolt
36. Axle hub
37. Roller bearing
38. Washer
39. Wheel adjusting nut
40. Hub cap

4. On Crown models, disconnect the brake line.

5. Remove the shock absorber, as detailed in the appropriate section below.

6. Install the coil spring compressor on the third coil from the bottom. Tighten the compressor until the load is removed from the spring.

7. Remove the lower ball joint with a ball joint puller.

8. Unbolt and remove the lower control arm.

9. Carefully and slowly remove the spring compressor and withdraw the spring.

Inspect the components of the suspension which were removed for signs of wear or damage. Replace parts as required.

Installation is performed in the following order:

1. Install the lower control arm but do not fully tighten the mounting bolts.

2. Compress the spring with the spring compressor and install the spring.

NOTE: *Keep the spring compressed after installation.*

3. Install the lower ball joint on the steering knuckle and tighten it to the specifications.

4. Install the strut on the lower control arm and temporarily install the other end on the frame.

   a. The distance between the serrations and the nut should be the same as that measured during removal.

   b. If a new strut is used, check the chart below for the proper installation distance.

   c. Carefully install the rear side of the strut to the control arm and tighten the mounting nut to the specifications.

5. Slowly remove the spring compressor from the coil spring.

6. Install the shock absorber.

7. Install the stabilizer bar bracket and the bar.

NOTE: *Be sure to assemble the parts of the bracket in the order in which they were removed.*

8. Install the wheel, remove the jackstands, and lower the car.

9. Tighten the lower control arm and strut front mount to the specifications.

NOTE: *These parts should be tightened with the equivalent of passenger weight in the car.*

10. Check the wheel alignment, after completing installation. (See below.)

Hi-Lux

1. Remove the hubcap and loosen the lug nuts.

2. Raise the front end of the truck and support the front suspension crossmember with jackstands.

CAUTION: *Be sure that the vehicle is securely supported. Remember; you will be working underneath it.*

3. Remove the lug nuts and the wheel.

4. Remove the stabilizer bar connecting bolts and remove the bracket parts, being careful to note their removal sequence in order to aid in installation.

5. Remove the tie rod cotter pin and nut. Use a puller to remove the end of the tie rod from the knuckle arm.

6. Remove the shock absorber, as detailed in the appropriate section below.

7. Raise the lower control arm, using a jack, so that the arm is free of the steering knuckle.

8. Loosen the ball joint attachment nut and remove the ball joint puller.

9. Slowly lower the jack underneath the control arm.

CAUTION: *If the jack is lowered too fast, the spring could suddenly release, causing damage or injury.*

10. Remove the coil spring and its insulator from underneath the truck.

Inspect the coil spring, its insulator, and bumper for cracks, wear, or damage. Replace parts as necessary.

Installation is basically performed in the reverse order of removal. However, a coil spring compressor should be used to install the spring, rather than the method used for removing it.

Torque the suspension components to the following specifications:

Lower control arm—51–65 ft lbs
Ball joint—65–94 ft lbs

Land Cruiser

Land Cruiser models are equipped with leaf springs in the front and rear. Thus, front spring removal is performed in almost the same manner as rear spring removal. Follow the procedure outlined in the rear suspension section, above.

CAUTION: *Be careful when raising or lowering the front suspension with a jack, so as not to damage any of the steering system components.*

Front Shock Absorber

Removal and Installation

Corolla, Carina, and Celica

1. Perform the front coil spring removal procedure as outlined above for the Corolla, Carina, and Celica.

2. Remove the wheel hub and brake drum or disc as outlined in below.

Inspect the shock absorber and test it as outlined below. Inspect the other parts of the front suspension system which were removed.

Installation is performed in the reverse order of removal. See the notes at the end of coil spring installation for specific details and torque specifications.

Corona, Mark II, Crown, and Hi-Lux

1. Remove the hubcap and loosen the lug nuts.

2. Raise the front of the car and support it with jackstands.

CAUTION: *Be sure that the vehicle is supported securely. Remember; you will be working underneath it.*

3. Remove the lug nuts and the wheel.

4. Unfasten the double nuts at the top end of the shock absorber. Remove the cushions and cushion retainers.

5. Remove the two bolts which secure the lower end of the shock absorber to the lower control arm.

6. Remove the shock absorber.

Inspect and test the shock as detailed below.

Installation of the shock is performed in the reverse order of removal. Tighten the securing nuts and bolts to the following specifications:

Upper securing nuts—14–22 ft lbs
Lower mounting bolts—11–16 ft lbs

Land Cruiser

Removal and installation procedures of the front shock absorbers for Land Cruisers are performed in the same order as rear shock absorber removal and installation. For details, see the appropriate section above.

CAUTION: *Be careful not to damage any of the steering system components when supporting the axle housing with a jack.*

Lower Ball Joints

Inspection

Jack up the lower suspension arm (except Corolla, Carina, and Celica). Check the front wheel play. Replace the lower ball joint if the play at the wheel rim exceeds 0.1 in. vertical motion or 0.25 in. horizontal motion. Be sure that the dust covers are not torn and that they are securely glued to the ball joints.

CAUTION: *Do not jack up the control arm on Corolla, Carina, or Celica models; damage to the arm will result.*

Removal and Installation

NOTE: *On models equipped with both upper and lower ball joints—if both ball joints are to be removed, always remove the lower and then the upper ball joint.*

Corolla 1100/1200—With Transverse Leaf Spring

1. Remove the wheel, brake drum, and backing plate.

2. Disconnect the lower arm assembly. Remove the cotter pin and nut from the ball joint stud.

3. Using an appropriate tool, remove the knuckle arm from the ball joint. Pry off the ball joint dust cover.

4. With the aid of a press, remove the ball joint from the suspension arm.

To install the ball joints, reverse the removal procedures. Be sure to lubricate ball joints with a molybdenum disulphide lithium base grease. Do not use any other type.

Torque Specifications

Knuckle arm to ball joint: 36–53 ft lbs
Crossmember to frame: 30–40 ft lbs
Lower arm bushing: 30–40 ft lbs
Lower arm shaft to front crossmember: 50–60 ft lbs
Front spring bushing to suspension arm: 11–16 ft lbs
Knuckle arm to shock absorber: 15–22 ft lbs
Tierod end to steering knuckle: 22–32 ft lbs
Hub nut: 65–85 ft lbs

Corolla 1200/1600, Carina, and Celica

The ball joint and control arm cannot be separated from each other. If one fails, then both must be replaced as an assembly, in the following manner:

1. Perform steps 1–7 of the Corolla, Carina, and Celica front coil spring removal procedure. Skip step 6.
2. Remove the stabilizer bar securing bolts.
3. Unfasten the torque strut mounting bolts.
4. Remove the control arm mounting bolt and detach the arm from the front suspension member.
5. Remove the steering knuckle arm from the control arm with a ball joint puller.

Inspect the suspension components, which were removed for wear or damage. Replace any parts, as required.

Installation is performed in the reverse order of removal. Note the following, however:

1. When installing the control arm on the suspension member, tighten the bolts partially at first.
2. Complete the assembly procedure and lower the car to the ground.
3. Bounce the front of the car several times. Allow the suspension to settle, then tighten the lower control arm bolts to 51–65 ft lbs.

CAUTION: *Use only the bolt which was designed to fit the lower control arm. If a replacement is necessary, see an authorized dealer for the proper part.*

4. Remember to lubricate the ball joint. Check front-end alignment. (See below.)

Torque Specifications

Part(s)	Torque (ft lbs)
Control arm-to-strut	29-40
Stabilizer bar (upper nut)	10-16
Stabilizer bar (lower nut)	7-12
Ball joint-to-knuckle arm	36-51
Knuckle arm-to-shock	51-65

Corona

1. Remove the hubcap and loosen the lug nuts.
2. Raise the front of the car and support it with jackstands.

CAUTION: *Be sure that the car is securely supported. Remember; you will be working underneath it.*

3. Remove the lug nuts and the wheel.
4. Remove the cotter pin and the castellated nut from the ball joint.
5. Use a ball joint puller to detach the lower ball joint from the steering knuckle.
6. Remove the securing bolt and withdraw the ball joint.

Installation is performed in the reverse order of removal. Use the torque specifications in the chart below. Lubricate the ball joint and check alignment as outlined below.

Torque Specifications

Part(s)	Torque (ft lbs)
Ball joint-to-control arm	
12 mm bolt	58-83
8 mm bolt	11-16
Ball joint-to-steering knuckle	51-65

Mark II and Crown

Perform steps 1–7 of the Mark II and Crown coil spring removal procedure. Skip step 3.

Installation is performed by starting with step 3 of the Mark II and Crown coil spring installation procedure. When step 3 is completed, go on to steps 5–10. Lubricate the ball joints and check alignment. (See below.)

Hi-Lux

Perform steps 1–8 of the Hi-Lux coil spring removal procedure. Skip step 6.

Installation is performed in the reverse order of removal. Lubricate the ball joint. Check front end alignment. (See below.)

Upper Ball Joint

Inspection

Disconnect the ball joint from the steering knuckle and check free-play by hand. Replace the ball joint, if it is noticeably loose.

Removal and Installation

NOTE: *On models equipped with both upper and lower ball joints—if both are to be removed, always remove the lower one first.*

Corona

1. Perform steps 1–5 of the Corona lower ball joint removal procedure.
2. Suspend the steering knuckle with a wire.
3. Use an open-end wrench to remove the upper ball joint.

Installation is performed in the reverse order from removal. Note the following:

1. Install the upper ball joint dust cover with the escape valve toward the rear.
2. Use sealer on the dust cover before installing it.
3. Tighten the upper ball joint-to-steering knuckle bolt to 29–40 ft lbs.

Mark II and Crown

1. Remove the wheel cover and loosen the lug nut.
2. Raise the front of the car and support it with jackstands.

CAUTION: *Be sure that the car is securely supported. Remember; you will be working underneath it.*

3. Remove the lug nuts and the wheel.
4. Place a jack beneath the lower control arm spring seat. Raise the jack until the spring bumper separates from the frame.
5. Detach the flexible hose from the dust cover.
6. Using a ball joint puller, remove the upper ball joint from the steering knuckle.
7. Use an open-end wrench to remove the ball joint from the upper control arm.

Installation is performed in the reverse order of removal. Tighten the components to the specifications given in the chart below. Lubricate the ball joint. Check front wheel alignment. (See below.) Remember to bleed the air from the flexible hose.

Torque Specifications

Model	UPPER BALL JOINT-TO- Knuckle	Arm
Mark II/4	40-50	15-22
Mark II/6	40-51	15-22
Crown 2300	66-96	11-16
Crown 2600	65-94	11-16

Hi-Lux

Remove and install the upper ball joint in the same manner as outlined for the lower ball joint.

Front-End Alignment

Front-end alignment measurements require the use of special equipment.

Before measuring alignment or attempting to adjust it, always check the following points:

1. Be sure that the tires are properly inflated.
2. See that the wheels are properly balanced.
3. Check the ball joints to determine if they are worn or loose.
4. Check front wheel bearing adjustment.
5. Be sure that the car is on a level surface.
6. Check all suspension parts for tightness.

Caster and Camber Adjustments

NOTE: *The MacPherson strut front suspension used on the Corolla, Carina, and Celica models cannot be adjusted for caster or camber. If measurements indicate that the suspension is out of alignment, the damaged part must be found and replaced. The same thing is true for Land Cruiser models, all of which use a solid front axle.*

Measure the caster and camber angles. Check them against the specifications given in the chart at the beginning of this section. If they are not within specifications, adjust them by adding or subtracting the shims on the mounting bolts between the upper control arm and the suspension member:

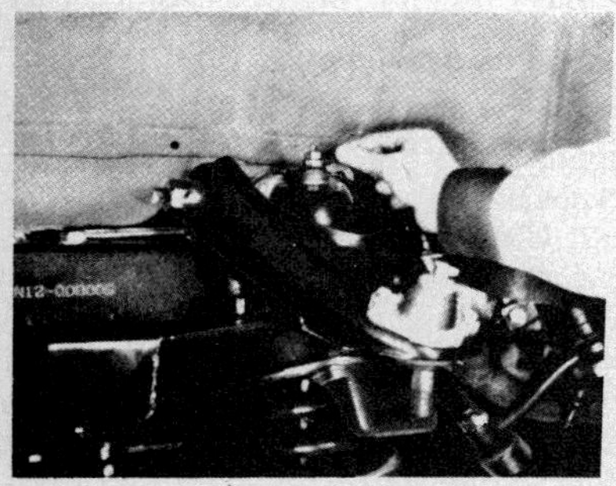

Remoming camber adjustment shims

1. To *increase* camber, *remove* shims equally from both of the control shaft mounting bolts. Do the reverse to decrease camber.
2. To *increase* caster, add camber adjusting shims to the *rear* mounting bolt, or remove them from the front mounting bolt. Do the reverse to decrease caster.

NOTE: *Caster and camber adjustments should always be performed in a single operation.*

Toe-in Adjustment

Measure the toe-in. Adjust it, if necessary, by loosening the tie rod end clamping bolts and rotating the tie rod adjusting tubes. Tighten the clamping bolts when finished.

NOTE: *Both tie rod ends should be the same length. If they are not, perform the adjustment until the toe-in is within specifications and the tie rod ends are equal in length.*

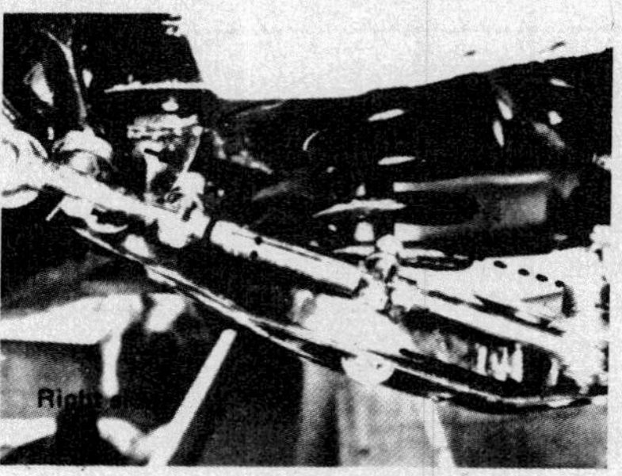

Tie rod adjustment

STEERING

Steering Wheel

Removal and Installation

Three-Spoke

CAUTION: *Do not attempt to remove or install the steering wheel by hammering on it. Damage to the energy-absorbing steering column could result.*

1. Unfasten the horn and turn signal multiconnector(s) at the base of the steering column shroud.
2. Loosen the trim pad retaining screws from the back side of the steering wheel.
3. Lift the trim pad and horn button assembly(ies) from the wheel.
4. Remove the steering wheel hub retaining nut.
5. Scratch matchmarks on the hub and shaft to aid in correct installation.
6. Use a steering wheel puller to remove the steering wheel.

Installation is performed in the reverse order of removal. Tighten the wheel retaining nut to 15–22 ft lbs, except for the Mark II/6, which should be tightened to 22–29 ft lbs.

Two-Spoke

The two-spoke steering wheel is removed in the same manner as the three-spoke, except that the trim pad should be pried off with a screwdriver. Remove the pad by lifting it toward the top of the wheel.

Power Steering Pump

Removal and Installation

1. Remove the fan shroud.
2. Unfasten the nut from the center of the pump pulley.

NOTE: *Use the drive belt as a brake to keep the pulley from rotating.*

3. Withdraw the drive belt.
4. Remove the pulley and the Woodruff key from the pump shaft.
5. Detach the intake and outlet hoses from the pump reservoir.

NOTE: *Tie the hose ends up high so the fluid cannot flow out of them. Drain or plug the pump tp prevent fluid leakage.*

6. Remove the bolt from the rear mounting brace.
7. Remove the front bracket bolts and withdraw the pump.

Installation is performed in the reverse order of removal. Note the following, however:

1. Tighten the pump pulley mounting bolt to 25–39 ft lbs.
2. Adjust the pump drive belt tension. The belt should deflect 0.31–0.39 in. when 22 lbs pressure is applied midway between the air pump and the power steering pump.
3. Fill the reservoir with "Dexron"® automatic transmission fluid. Bleed the air from the system, as detailed below.

Bleeding

1. Raise the front of the car and support it securely with jackstands.
2. Fill the pump reservoir with "Dexron"® automatic transmission fluid.
3. Rotate the steering wheel from lock to lock several times. Add fluid as necessary.
4. With the steering wheel turned fully to one lock, crank the starter while watching the fluid level in the reservoir.

NOTE: *Do not start the engine. Operate the starter with a remote starter switch or have an assistant do it from inside of the car. Do not run the starter for prolonged periods.*

5. Repeat step 4 with the steering wheel turned to the opposite lock.
6. Start the engine. With the engine idling, turn the steering wheel from lock to lock two or three times.
7. Lower the front of the car and repeat step 6.
8. Center the wheel at the midpoint of its travel. Stop the engine.
9. The fluid level should not have risen more than 0.2 in. If it does, repeat step 7.
10. Check for fluid leakage.

Steering Linkage

Removal and Installation

Passenger Cars and Hi-Lux

1. Raise the front of the vehicle and support it with jackstands.

CAUTION: *Be sure that the vehicle is securely supported. Do not support it by the lower control arms.*

2. Remove the gravel shields if they prevent access to the steering linkage.
3. Unfasten the nut and, using a puller, disconnect the pitman arm from the sector shaft.

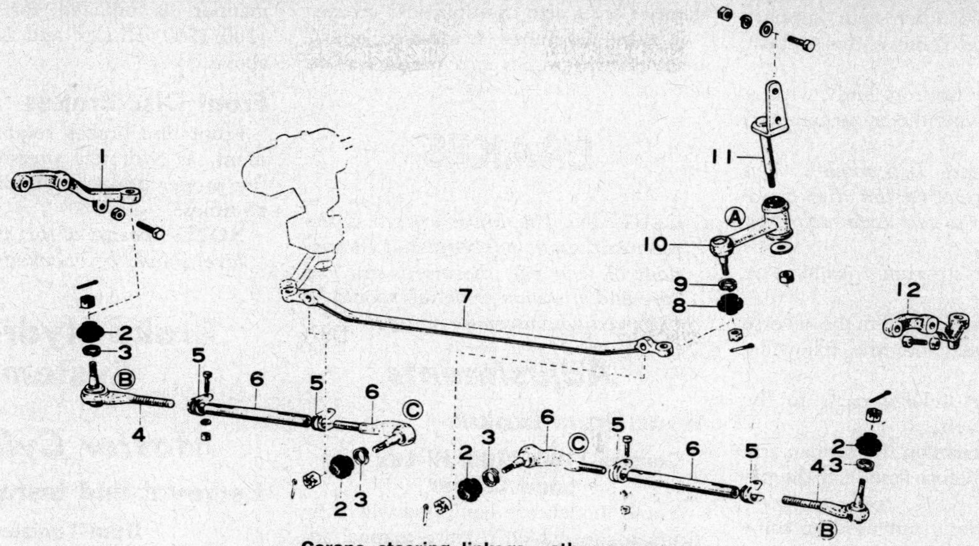

Corona steering linkage—other passenger cars similar.

1. Steering knuckle arm—right-hand
2. Dust seal
3. Clip
4. Tie rod end
5. Tie rod end clamp
6. Tie rod adjusting tube
7. Steering relay rod
8. Dust seal
9. Lock ring
10. Steering idler arm
11. Idler arm support
12. Steering knukle arm—left-hand

(a)—Idler arm assembly
(b)—Tie rod end assembly
(c)—Tie rod adjusting tube

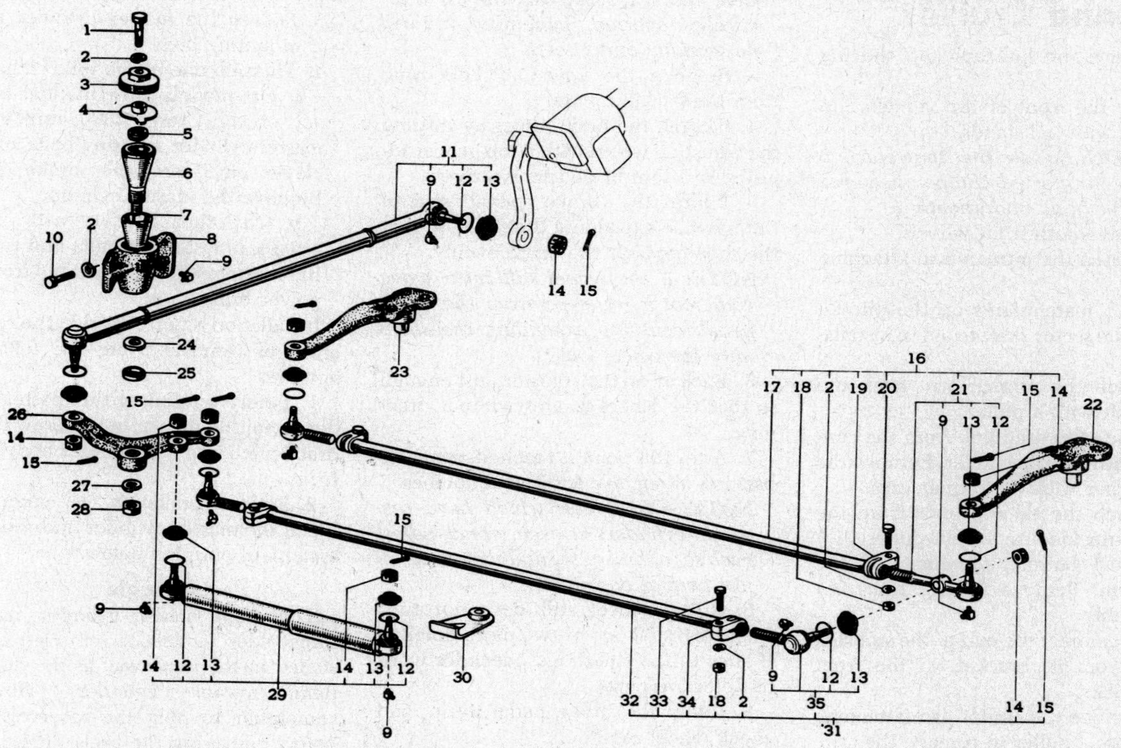

Components of the Land Cruiser steering linkage.

1. Bolt
2. Lock washer
3. Center arm shaft nut
4. Center arm nut lock plate
5. Compression spring
6. Center arm shaft
7. Shaft bushing
8. Center arm bracket
9. Grease fitting
10. Bolt
11. Steering drag link assmebly
12. Set ring
13. Joint dust seal
14. Lock nut
15. Cotter pin
16. Tie-rod assembly
17. Steering tie-rod
18. Lock nut
19. Tie-rod end clamp
20. Bolt
21. Tie-rod end assembly
22. Steering knuckle arm
23. Steering knuckel arm
24. Dust seal
25. Center arm dust lower seal
26. Steering center arm
27. Lock washer
28. Nut
29. Steering damper
30. Damper bracket
31. Steering relay rod assembly
32. Steering relay rod
33. Bolt
34. Tie-rod end clamp
35. Relay rod end assembly

4. Unfasten the idler arm support securing bolts and remove the support from the frame.

5. Detach the tie rod ends with a puller after removing the cotter pins and castellated nuts.

NOTE: *On Mark II/6 models, it is necessary to remove the disc brake caliper in order to gain access to the tie rod ends.*

6. Remove the steering linkage as an assembly.

Installation is performed in the reverse order of removal. Note the following, however:

1. Tighten the linkage parts to the torque figures given.
2. Align the marks on the pitman arm and sector shaft before installing the pitman arm.
3. The self-locking nut used on some models, on the idler arm, may be reused if it cannot be turned by hand when fitted to the bolt.
4. Adjust the toe-in to specifications (see above) after completing the steering linkage installation procedure.

Land Cruiser

1. Remove the hubcaps and the lug nuts.
2. Raise the front of the vehicle and support it with jackstands.

CAUTION: *Be sure that the vehicle is securely supported. Remember; you will be working underneath it.*

3. Remove both front wheels.
4. Unfasten the pitman arm attaching nut.
5. Punch matchmarks on the pitman arm and the sector shaft to aid in installation.
6. Detach the pitman arm from the sector shaft with a puller.
7. Detach the drag link from the center arm with a tie rod puller. Remove the link together with the pitman arm.
8. Detach the tie rod ends from the steering knuckle arm with a puller.
9. Detach the relay rod ends from the center arm. Remove the tie rod/relay rod assembly.
10. Disconnect the end of the steering damper from its bracket on the front crossmember.
11. Remove the center arm attaching nut and use a puller to remove the arm, complete with the damper.
12. Remove the skid plate and then remove the center arm bracket from the frame.

Installation is performed in the reverse order of removal. Note the following, however:

1. Align the matchmarks, which were made during removal, on the pitman arm and the sector shaft. Tighten the mounting bolt to 120–140 ft lbs.
2. Lubricate all of the rod ends and damper ends with multipurpose grease.
3. After the linkage is installed, adjust toe-in to the proper specifications. (See above.)

BRAKES

CAUTION: *The brake system is the most important safety-related component of your car; therefore, extreme care and attention to details should be observed whenever servicing it.*

Adjustments

Rear Drum Brakes

Corolla 1100/1200, Hi-Lux and Land Cruiser

These models are equipped with rear drum brakes which require manual adjustment. Perform the adjustment in the following order:

1. Chock the front wheels and fully release the parking brake.
2. Raise the rear of the car and support it with jackstands.

CAUTION: *Be sure that the car is securely supported. Remember, you will be working underneath it.*

3. Remove the adjusting hole plug from the backing plate.
4. Expand the brake shoes by turning the adjusting wheel with a star-wheel adjuster or a thin-bladed screwdriver.
5. Pump the brake pedal several times, while expanding the shoes, so that the shoe contacts the drum evenly.

NOTE: *If the wheel still turns when your foot is removed from the brake pedal, continue expanding the shoes until the wheel locks.*

6. Back off on the adjuster, just enough so that the wheel rotates without dragging.
7. After this point is reached, continue backing off for *five* additional notches.

NOTE: *On models which have two wheel cylinders at each wheel, adjust each set of brakes separately; never adjust both at once.*

8. If the wheel still does not turn freely, back off one or two more notches. If after this, it still drags, check for worn or defective parts.
9. Pump the brake pedal again, and check wheel rotation.
10. Reverse steps 1–3.

Passenger Cars—Except Corolla 1100 and 1200

These models are equipped with self-adjusting rear drum brakes. No adjustment is possible or necessary.

Front Drum Brakes

Corolla 1100/1200, Hi-Lux and Land Cruiser

Perform the adjustment in the same manner as detailed for the Corolla 1100/1200, Hi-Lux and Land Cruiser, above.

Front Disc Brakes

Front disc brakes require no adjustment, as hydraulic pressure maintains the proper brake pad-to-disc contact at all times.

NOTE: *Because of this, the brake fluid level should be checked regularly.*

Brake Hydraulic System

Master Cylinder

Removal and Installation

Dual-Tandem

CAUTION: *Be careful not to spill brake fluid on the painted surfaces of the vehicle: it will damage the paint.*

1. Unfasten the hydraulic lines from the master cylinder.
2. Detach the hydraulic fluid pressure differential switch wiring connectors.
3. Loosen the master cylinder reservoir mounting bolt.
4. Then do one of the following:
   a. On models with manual brakes and on the Crown 2300, remove the master cylinder securing bolts and the clevis pin from the brake pedal. Remove the master cylinder.
   b. On other models with power brakes, unfasten the nuts and remove the master cylinder assembly from the power brake unit.

Installation is performed in the reverse order of removal. Note the following, however:

1. Before tightening the master cylinder mounting nuts or bolts, screw the hydraulic line into the cylinder body, a few turns.
2. After installation is completed, bleed the master cylinder and the brake system, as outlined below.

Single

The single master cylinder, used on some older models, is removed and installed in the same way as the dual-tandem master cylinder. However, remember to plug the reservoir inlet, before removing the brake line, to prevent fluid leakage.

Overhaul

1. Remove the reservoir caps and floats and unscrew the bolts that hold the reservoir to the main body.
2. Remove warning switches (where fitted), then remove from the rear of the cylinder, in order: boot and snap-ring, stop plate (washer), piston No. 1 with spacer, cylinder cup, spring retainer and spring.

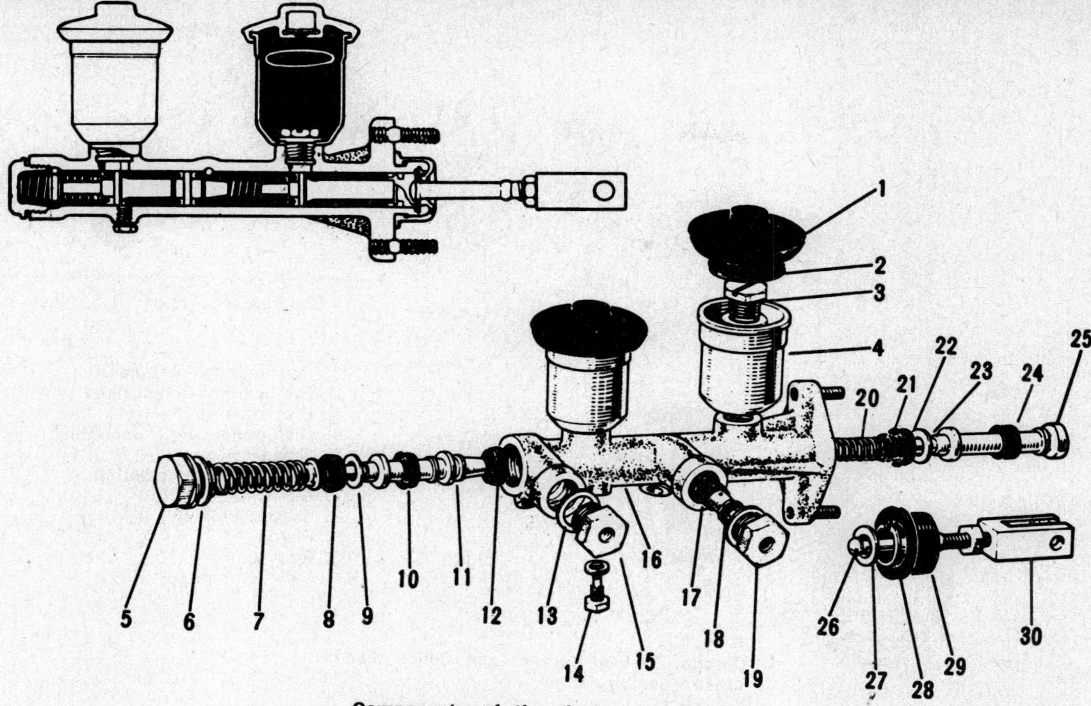

Components of the dual-tandem master cylinder.

1. Reservoir filler cap
2. Reservoir float
3. Reservoir set bolt
4. Master cylinder reservoir
5. Master cylinder plug
6. Gasket
7. Compression spring
8. Cylinder cup
9. Piston cup spacer
10. Cylinder cup
11. Master cylinder piston No. 2
12. Cylinder cup
13. Gasket
14. Piston stop bolt
15. Valve plug
16. Tandem master cylinder body
17. Compression spring
18. Master cylinder outlet check valve
19. Valve plug
20. Compression
21. Piston return spring retainer
22. Cylinder cup
23. Master cylinder piston cup spacer
24. Cylinder cup
25. Master cylinder piston No. 1
26. Master cylinder pushrod
27. Master cylinder piston stop plate
28. Hole snap-ring
29. Master cylinder boot
30. Master cylinder pusrod clevis

3. Remove the end plug and gasket from the front of the cylinder, then remove the front piston stop bolt from underneath. Pull out the spring and its retainer, piston No. 2, the spacer and the cylinder cup.

4. Remove the two outlet fittings, washers, check valves and springs.

5. Remove the piston cups from their seats on the pistons only if they are to be replaced.

After washing all parts in brake fluid, dry with compressed air. Inspect the cylinder bore for wear, scuff marks or nicks. Cylinders may be honed slightly, but the limit is 0.006 in. In view of the importance of the master cylinder, it is recommended that it be replaced rather than overhauled.

Reverse the sequence of disassembly. Absolute cleanliness is important, and all parts must be coated with clean brake fluid. Bleed the master cylinder and make sure all lines are tightened correctly and do not leak. Use fluid that meets specifications (for standard brakes) and use the special disc brake fluid for disc brake equipped cars.

Bleeding

CAUTION: *Do not reuse brake fluid which has been bled from the brake system.*

1. Insert a clear vinyl tube into the bleeder plug on the master cylinder or the wheel cylinders.

NOTE: *If the master cylinder has been overhauled or if air is present in it, start the bleeding procedure with the master cylinder. Otherwise, (and after bleeding the master cylinder) start with the wheel cylinder which is farthest from the master cylinder.*

2. Insert the other end of the tube into a jar which is half filled with brake fluid.

3. Slowly depress the brake pedal (have an assistant do it) and turn the bleeder plug 1/3–½ of a turn at the same time.

NOTE: *If the brake pedal is depressed too fast, small air bubbles will form in the brake fluid which will be very difficult to remove.*

4. Bleed the cylinder before hydraulic pressure decreases in the cylinder.

5. Repeat this procedure until the air bubbles are removed and then go on to the next wheel cylinder.

CAUTION: *Replenish the brake fluid in the master cylinder reservoir, so that it does not run out during bleeding.*

FRONT DISC BRAKES

Disc Brake Pads

Removal and Installation

Corolla, Carina, Corona and Celica

1. Remove the hub cap and loosen the lug nuts.

2. Raise the front of the vehicle with a jack and support it with stands on the chassis pads provided.

CAUTION: *Be sure that the car is securely supported. Do not support Corolla, Carina or Celica models by the lower control arm.*

3. Remove the lug nuts and the wheel.

4. Unfasten the four clips which secure the caliper guides and remove the

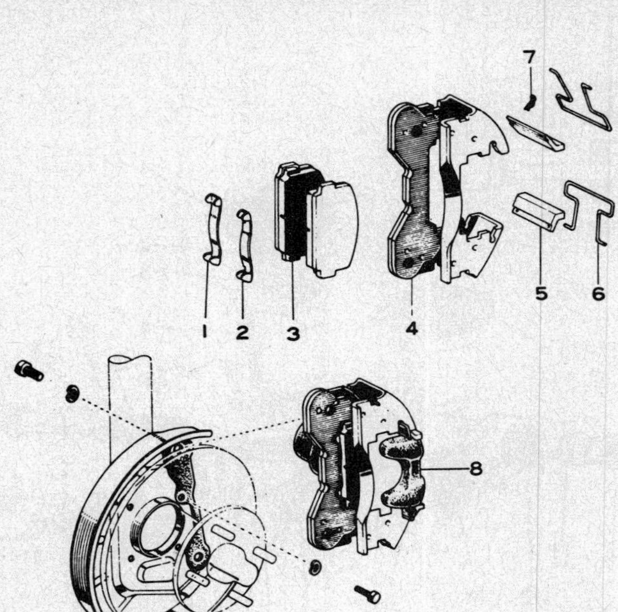

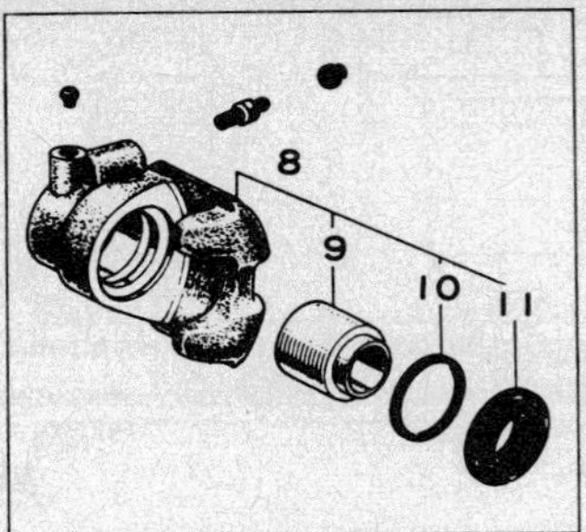

Disc brake cylinder

1. Pad support—left-hand
2. Pad support—right-hand
3. Disc brake pad
4. Disc brake caliper mounting
5. Guide
6. Cylinder support spring
7. Clip
8. Caliper assembly
9. Piston
10. Ring
11. Cylinder boot

Corolla, Carina, Corona, and Celica disc brake assembly.

guides.

5. Detach the flexible line from the caliper.

NOTE: *Be sure that the master cylinder is closed to prevent brake fluid from leaking out.*

6. Remove the caliper assembly.
7. Remove the pads.

Inspect the pads for wear. If the grooves are worn out of the pads, they must be replaced. Check pad thickness against the specifications given in the chart section for wear or deformity.

Installation is performed in the following order:

1. Clean the exposed portions of the piston;

2. Carefully insert the piston in its caliper. If the piston is difficult to install, loosen the bleeder plug.

3. Insert the brake pads.

CAUTION: *Replace the pads on one side at a time, to prevent the opposite piston from falling out.*

4. Install the caliper assembly, the guides and the clips.

5. Bleed the brake line, as detailed above, and lower the vehicle.

Mark II and Crown

1. Perform steps 1–3 of the disc brake pad removal procedure immediately above. Be sure to note the "**Caution**".
2. Remove the clips and the pins (which have the holes).
3. Withdraw the anti-squeal shims and the pads.
4. Check pad thickness against the specifications given .

Install the pads in the following order:

1. Clean the back of the pistons, cylinder boots and the caliper surfaces which contact the brake pads.
2. Fit the pads and anti-squeal shims into the caliper.

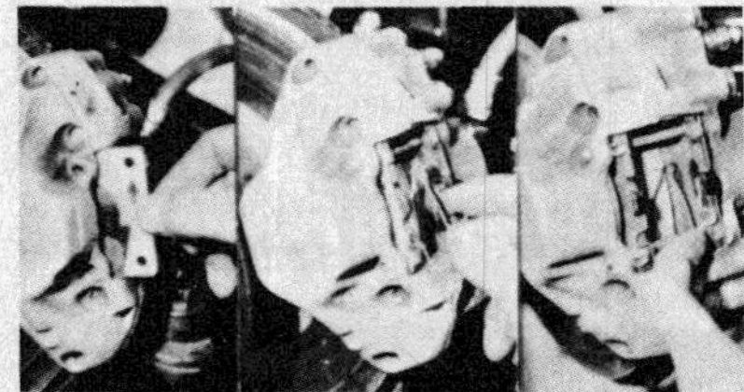

Mark II and Crown disc brake pad installation sequence.

NOTE: *Install the shims with their arrows pointing toward the rotational direction of the disc.*

3. Install the spring so that it presses correctly against the pads.
4. After completing installation, depress the brake pedal several times before lowering the car. This will provide proper operating clearance for the wheel cylinder components.
5. Install the wheel and lower the car.

Disc Brake Calipers

Removal and Installation

Corolla, Carina, Corona and Celica

Caliper removal and installation for these models is given as part of the brake pad removal and installation procedure. Consult the appropriate section above for details.

Mark II and Crown

CAUTION: *Do not unfasten the bridge bolt and separate the caliper halves.*

1. Remove the wheel covers and loosen the lug nuts.
2. Raise the front of the car and support it with jackstands.

CAUTION: *Be sure that the car is supported securely.*

3. Remove the lug nuts and the wheel.
4. Plug the master cylinder inlet, so that the brake fluid will not run out when the hydraulic line is disconnected.
5. Remove the hydraulic line from the caliper by unfastening the union bolt.
6. Remove the lockwire and unfasten the caliper securing bolts. Withdraw the caliper assembly.

NOTE: *Shims are installed between the caliper mounting points and its body to center the caliper over the disc. Count the number of shims at each mounting point. Use care not to mix the shims from the upper and lower mounting points.*

Installation is performed in the following order:

1. If the brake disc was not removed or if the caliper was not replaced, use exactly the same number of shims as were removed.

CAUTION: *Do not mix the shims from the upper and lower mounting points.*

2. If the brake disc was removed or if the caliper was replaced, adjust the number of shims used, so that the caliper assembly is centered over the disc.
3. Tighten the caliper securing bolts to the following specifications:

Mark II/4—72–87 ft lbs
Mark II/6—67-87 ft lbs
Crown 2300—73–88 ft lbs
Crown 2600—67–87 ft lbs

4. Install the lockwire on the caliper securing bolts.
5. Connect the hydraulic line to the caliper.
6. Bleed the hydraulic system, as detailed above and check it for leaks.

Brake Disc

Removal and Installation

All Models

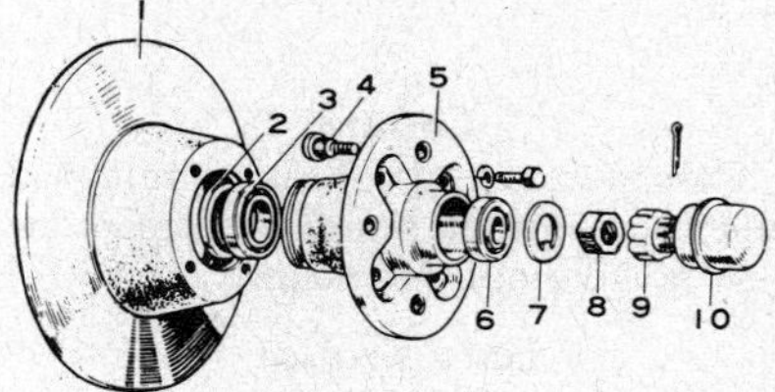

Brake disc and hub assembly

1. Disc
2. Oil seal
3. Tapered roller bearing
4. Hub bolt
5. Hub
6. Tapered roller bearing
7. Washer
8. Nut
9. Adjusting lock cap
10. Grease cap

1. Remove the brake pads and the caliper, as detailed in the appropriate section above.
2. On Corolla, Carina, Corona and Celica models only:
   a. Loosen the bolts which secure the caliper mounting bracket.
   b. Withdraw the bracket, complete with the caliper support plates and springs attached.
3. Check the disc run-out, as detailed below, at this point. Make a note of the results for use during installation.
4. Remove the grease cap from the hub. Remove the cotter pin and the castellated nut.
5. Remove the wheel hub with the brake disc attached.

Perform the disc inspection procedure, as outlined in the section below.

Installation is performed in the following order:

1. Coat the hub oil seal lip with multipurpose grease and install the disc/hub assembly.
2. Adjust the wheel bearing preload, as detailed below.
3. Measure the disc run-out (see below). Check it against the specifications in the chart and against the figures noted during removal.

NOTE: *If the wheel bearing nut is improperly tightened, disc run-out will be affected.*

4. On Corolla, Carina, Corona and Celica models only:
   a. Install the caliper support, complete with springs. Tighten the securing nuts to the following torque specifications:
   Corolla, Carina and Celica—20–40 ft lbs
   Corona—65–87 ft lbs
   CAUTION: *Be careful not to distort the support springs during installation.*
   b. Install the support plates and the brake pads in the same positions from which they were removed.
   NOTE: *Install the pad support plate with the arrow pointing in the same direction as when it was removed.*
5. Install the remainder of the components as outlined in the appropriate section, above.
6. Bleed the brake system.
7. Road test the car. Check the rolling resistance of the wheel (see below).

Inspection

Examine the disc. If it is worn, warped or scored, it must be replaced.

Check the thickness of the disc against the specifications given in the chart below. If it is below specifications, replace it. Use a micrometer to measure the thickness. Disc run-out should be measured *before* the disc is removed and again. *after* the disc is installed. Use a dial indicator mounted on a stand to determine run-out. If run-out exceeds 0.006 in. (all models), replace the disc.

NOTE: *Be sure that the wheel bearing nut is properly tightened. If it is not, an inaccurate run-out reading may be obtained. If different run-out readings are obtained with the same disc, between removal and installation, this is probably the cause.*

Wheel Bearings

Removal and Installation

1. Remove the disc/hub assembly, as detailed above.
2. If either the disc or the entire hub assembly is to be replaced, unbolt the hub from the disc.

NOTE: *If only the bearings are to be replaced, do not separate the disc and hub.*

3. Using a brass rod as a drift, tap the inner bearing cone out. Remove the oil seal and the inner bearing.

NOTE: *Throw the old oil seal away.*

4. Drift out the inner bearing cup.
5. Drift out the outer bearing cup.

Inspect the bearings and the hub for signs of wear or damage. Replace components, as necessary.

Installation is performed in the following order:

1. Install the inner bearing cup and then the outer bearing cup, by drifting them into place.

CAUTION: *Use care not to cock the bearing cups in the hub.*

2. Pack the bearings, hub inner well and grease cap with multipurpose grease.
3. Install the inner bearing into the hub.
4. Carefully install a new oil seal with a soft drift.
5. Install the hub on the spindle. Be sure to install all of the washers and nuts which were removed.
6. Adjust the bearing preload, as detailed below.
7. Install the caliper assembly, as detailed above.

Preload Adjustment

1. With the front hub/disc assembly installed, tighten the castellated nut to the torque figure specified in the chart below.
2. Rotate the disc back and forth, two or three times, to allow the bearing to seat properly.
3. Loosen the castellated nut until it is only finger-tight.
4. Tighten the nut firmly, using a box wrench.

Measuring wheel bearing preload with a spring scale.

5. Measure the bearing preload with a spring scale attached to a wheel mounting stud. Check it against the specifications given in the chart below.
6. Install the cotter pin.

NOTE: *If the hole does not align with the nut (or cap) holes, tighten the nut slightly until it does.*

7. Finish installing the brake components and the wheel.

Preload Specifications

Model	Initial torque setting (ft lbs)	Preload (oz)
Corolla	19-23	6-13
Carina and Celica	19-24	10-22
Corona	19-26	10-22
Mark II	19-23	10-22
Crown 2300	22	12-38
Crown 2600	22	12-30

FRONT DRUM BRAKES

Brake Drums

Removal and Installation

Corolla 1100/1200, Corona, Hi-Lux and Land Cruiser

1. Remove the hub cap and loosen the lug nuts.
2. Raise the front of the vehicle and support it with jackstands.

CAUTION: *Support the vehicle securely.*

3. Remove the lug nuts and the wheel.
4. On Corona, Corolla and Hi-Lux models:
   a. Remove the axle hub grease cap.
   b. Remove the cotter pin and claw washer.
   c. Unfasten the nut and withdraw the drum, complete with the hub.
5. On Land Cruiser models:
   a. Unfasten the brake drum retaining screws.
   b. Tap the drum lightly with a mallet to free it.

CAUTION: *Do not depress the brake pedal once the drum has been removed.*

Inspect the brake drum as detailed in the section below.

Installation is performed in the reverse order of removal. On Corolla, Corona and Hi-Lux models adjust the wheel bearing preload (see below).

Inspection

1. Clean the drum.
2. Inspect the drum for scoring, cracks, grooves, and out of roundness. Replace or turn the drum, as required.
3. Light scoring may be removed by dressing the drum with *fine* emery cloth.
4. Heavy scoring will require the use of a brake drum lathe to turn the drum. The service limits of the drum inside diameter are as follows:

Hi-Lux—9.134 in.
Land Cruiser—11.540 in.
Corolla—7.950 in.
Corona—9.080 in.

Brake Shoes

Removal and Installation

Hi-Lux and Corolla 1100/1200

1. Remove the drum, as outlined above.
2. Remove the following parts in the order listed:
   a. Shoe retaining spring pins
   b. Shoe retaining springs
   c. Shoe tension (return) springs
   d. Shoes

NOTE: *Use a brake shoe removal tool to aid in removal of the tension springs.*

3. After removal, keep the brake shoes in their proper order.

CAUTION: *Be careful to keep oil or grease from contacting the lining surface.*

Inspect the brake shoes for wear, rust or damage. Inspect the brake linings for wear. The shoes should be relined if the lining thickness is less than 0.06 in.

Inspect the tension spring for deformation or weakness.

Installation is performed in the following order:

1. Coat all of the points where the brake shoes make contact with other brake assembly parts, with grease.

CAUTION: *Be careful not to get grease on the surface of the lining.*

2. Fit the upper and lower shoes into the grooves on the wheel cylinders and adjusting bolts. Install the spring pins in the shoes and then attach the retaining springs.
3. Hook the brake shoe tension springs on the upper and lower shoes with the aid of the tool used during removal.
4. Install the drum as outlined above.

Corona

Corona front brake shoes are removed and installed in the same order as Corona rear brake shoes. See below.

Land Cruiser

1. Remove the brake drum, as outlined above.
2. Remove the upper shoe by pulling out the end, while applying an upward force on it.
3. Depress the lower shoe and repeat the removal procedure for it.

CAUTION: *Do not interchange the upper and lower shoes. Do not allow grease to contact the lining surface.*

Inspect the shoes for wear, rust or damage. Check the linings for wear. The service limit of lining thickness is 0.16 in.; have the shoes relined if it is less.

Inspect the springs for weakness and deformation.

Installation is performed in the following order:

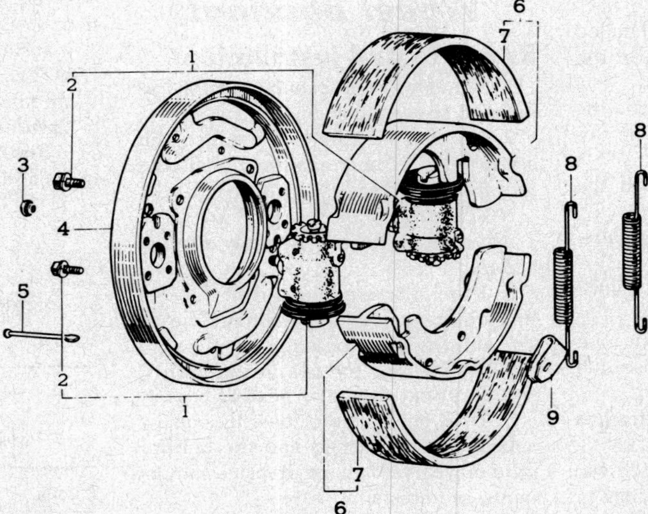

Hi-Lux front drum brake—Land Cruiser similar.

1. Front brake
2. Bolt
3. Shoe adjusting hole plug
4. Front brake backing plate
5. Shoe hold down spring pin
6. Brake shoe assembly
7. Brake shoe lining
8. Tension spring
9. Shoe hold down spring

1. Grease all points at which the brake shoe makes contact with other brake components.

CAUTION: *Do not allow grease to contact the lining surface.*

2. Fit the ends of the lower brake shoe into the grooves on the wheel cylinder piston and the adjusting bolt.

3. Push up on the upper brake shoe and fit it into the grooves on the piston and the adjusting bolt.

4. Hook the return springs on the brake shoes.

5. Install the brake drum, as outlined above.

Wheel Cylinders

Removal and Installation

Corolla, Corona, Hi-Lux and Land Cruiser

1. Perform the brake drum and brake shoe removal procedures, as outlined above.

2. Plug the master cylinder reservoir inlet, to prevent fluid from leaking out.

3. Remove the hydraulic lines from the wheel cylinders by unfastening the union bolt.

4. Remove the wheel cylinder attachment screws and withdraw the wheel cylinders.

CAUTION: *Do not mix the right and left wheel cylinders.*

To install the wheel cylinders, proceed in the following manner:

1. Use the attaching screws to install the wheel cylinder to the backing plate.

NOTE: *The wheel cylinder adjusting nut and bolt on the right side of the brake have left-hand threads; while those on the left side have right-hand threads. Be careful not to mix them.*

2. Connect the hydraulic lines to the wheel cylinders.

CAUTION: *Use care to see that the hydraulic line is not twisted.*

General Overhaul

Remove the boots, pistons and the cups and closely inspect the bores for signs of wear, scoring and/or scuffing. When in doubt, replace or hone the wheel cylinders with a special brake hone, using clean brake fluid as lubricant. Wash residue from the bores using clean fluid; never use oil or any other solvent on any brake components. Blow dry with air and install with fresh brake fluid. The general limit for a honed cylinder is 0.005 in. oversize. (Do not try to save money by reusing brake components such as cylinders and cups.) The self-adjuster screws should be taken apart and all dirt and rust removed with a wire brush. Lightly coat with Lubriplate before assembly; components should turn freely.

3. Install the brake drum and shoes, as outlined above. Bleed the brake system.

Wheel Bearings

Removal and Installation

Corolla, Corona and Hi-Lux

1. Perform the brake drum removal procedure, as outlined above. Do not separate the drum from the hub, unless either one is to be replaced.

NOTE: *The outer bearing comes off with the brake drum.*

2. Use a puller to remove the inner bearing and the steering knuckle grease retainer.

3. Use a brass drift to remove the bearing cups from the axle hub.

Check the bearings for worn or pitted rollers. Examine the cup for signs of wear or damage. Inspect the hub itself, for defects.

Installation and packing are performed in the following order:

1. Use the brass drift to install the bearing cups in the hub.

CAUTION: *Be careful not to cock the bearing cups in the hub.*

2. Coat both the inner and outer bearings with multipurpose grease. Work the grease into the roller cages.

3. Drift the inner bearing and the steering knuckle grease retainer on the spindle.

4. Clean all of the old grease out of hub. Pack the inside of the hub with multipurpose grease.

5. Install the hub and brake drum assembly over the steering knuckle.

6. Install the outer bearing in the axle hub and adjust the preload, as detailed below.

7. Pack the grease cap with multipurpose grease and fit it over the hub.

8. Check and adjust the brake shoe clearance (see above). Lower the vehicle.

Land Cruiser

1. Perform steps 1–3 of the front brake drum removal procedure.

2. Remove the cap from the axle shaft outer flange. Remove the snap-ring from the shaft.

3. Remove the bolts which secure the axle shaft outer flange to the hub.

4. Install the two service bolts into the holes provided in the flange. Tighten the bolts evenly in order to loosen the flange. Withdraw the flange, complete with gasket.

CAUTION: *Never remove the flange by prying it off; oil leaks will result.*

5. Remove the set screws and withdraw the brake drum.

6. Straighten out the lockwasher and remove the adjusting nut, using a spindle nut wrench.

CAUTION: *Do not use a hammer and chisel to remove the nut.*

7. Remove the hub assembly, complete with the claw washer, bearings and oil seal.

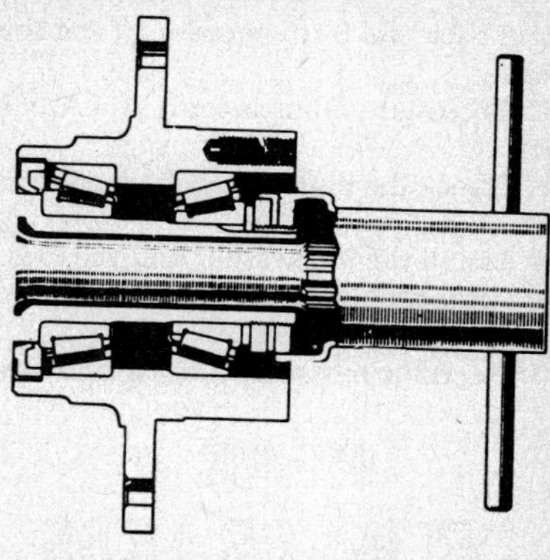

Removing the bearing adjustment nut from the Land Cruiser.

NOTE: *If the bearings or cups are difficult to remove, use a puller.*

Installation and packing are performed in the following order:

1. Install the oil seal and the inner bearing cone.

2. Pack the hub with multipurpose grease, after assembling both inner and outer bearing cups to it.

3. Assemble the axle hub and brake drum.

4. Install the hub/drum assembly over the spindle then install the outer bearing.

5. Install the claw washer and adjusting nut with the spindle nut wrench.

6. Adjust the bearing preload, as detailed below, then install the locknut and washer.

7. Install the axle shaft flange and gasket. Tighten the retaining bolts to 11–16 ft lbs.

8. Install the bolt on the end of the outer shaft. Pull out on the shaft while installing the snap-ring.

9. Install the flange cap.

10. Install the wheel and the hub cap Lower the vehicle.

Preload Adjustment

Corolla, Corona and Hi-Lux

1. Fit the claw washer and tighten the retaining nut to 34 ft lbs—Hi-Lux, or to 19–23 ft lbs—Corolla and Corona.

2. Rotate the axle hub back and forth to set the bearings.

3. Retorque the bearing nut to the proper specification above. Loosen the nut 1/6–1/3 of a turn, so that the cotter pin can be inserted through the castellated nut and into the spindle.

4. Install the front wheel and the lug nuts.

5. Check the wheel for free rotation. Check the axial play of the wheel by shaking it back and forth; the bearing free play should feel like it is about zero.

6. Install a *new* cotter pin and lock the retaining nut.

Land Cruiser

1. After tightening the adjusting nut with the spindle nut wrench, rotate the

wheel back and forth in order to seat the bearing.

2. Loosen the adjusting nut ⅛–1/6 of a turn.

3. Check the brake drum for free rotation.

4. Install the lockwasher and the locknut. Use the spindle nut wrench to tighten the locknut.

5. Bend the tabs on the lockwasher up.

REAR DRUM BRAKES

Brake Drums

Removal and Installation

All Models

The rear brake drum removal and installation procedure for all models is performed in the same manner as that for the Land Cruiser front brake drum.

NOTE: *Release the parking brake before attempting rear drum removal. Do not depress the brake pedal, once the drum has been removed.*

Inspection

Inspection for the rear brake drum is performed in the same way as that for the front brake drum (see above).

The service limits for the inside diameter of the rear drums are as follows:

Model	Inside diameter limit (in.)
Corolla	7.95
Carina and Celica	9.08
Corona	9.09
Mark II (all)	9.08
Crown 2300	9.13
Crown 2600	10.08
Hi-Lux	9.13
Land Cruiser	11.54

Brake Shoes

Removal and Installation

Corolla, Carina, Celica and Crown

1. Perform the brake drum removal procedure, as detailed for the Land Cruiser front brakes, above.

2. Unhook the shoe tension springs from the shoes with the aid of a brake spring removing tool.

3. Remove the brake shoe securing springs.

4. Disconnect the parking brake cable at the parking brake shoe lever.

5. Withdraw the shoes, complete with the parking brake shoe lever.

6. Unfasten the C-clip and remove the adjuster assembly from the shoes.

Inspect the shoes for wear and scoring. Have the linings replaced if their thickness is less than 0.04 in. (0.06 in.—Crown).

Check the tension springs to see if they are weak, distorted or rusted.

Inspect the teeth on the automatic adjuster wheel for chipping or other damage.

Installation is performed in the following order:

NOTE: *Grease the point of the shoe which slides against the backing plate. Do not get grease on the linings.*

1. Attach the parking brake shoe lever and the automatic adjuster lever to the rear of the shoe from which they were removed.

2. Fasten the parking brake cable to the lever on the brake shoe.

3. Install the automatic adjuster and fit the tension spring on the adjuster lever.

4. Install the securing spring on the *rear* shoe and then install the securing spring on the *front* shoe.

NOTE: *The tension spring should be installed on the anchor before performing step 4.*

5. Hook one end of the tension spring over the rear shoe, with the tool used during removal; then hook the other end over the front shoe.

CAUTION: *Be sure that the wheel cylinder boots are not being pinched by the ends of the shoes.*

6. Test the automatic adjuster by operating the parking brake shoe lever.

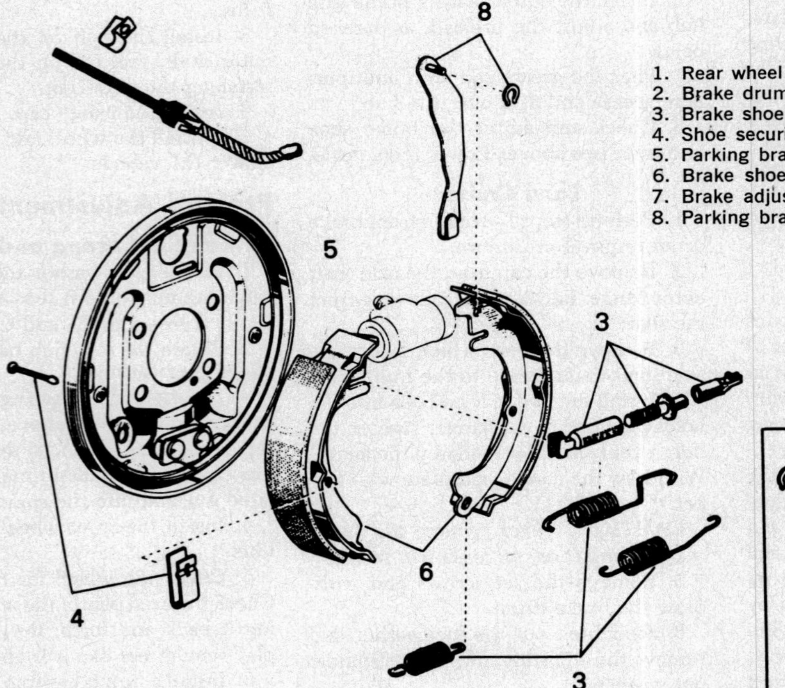

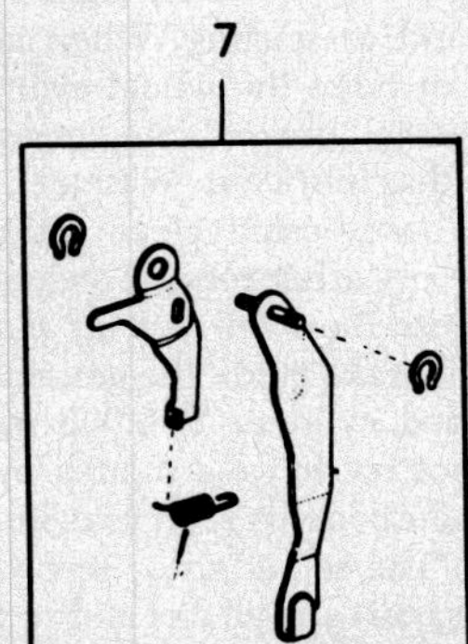

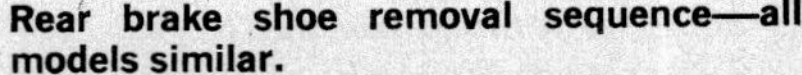
Rear brake shoe removal sequence—all models similar.

7. Install the brake drum and adjust the brakes as detailed above.

Corona and Mark II

NOTE: *This procedure is also used to remove and install the front brake shoes on Corona models with front drum brakes.*

1. Remove the brake drum by performing the procedure detailed for the Land Cruiser front brake drum.
2. Remove the tension springs from the trailing (rear) shoe with the aid of a brake return spring removal tool.
3. Press down on the brake adjuster ratchet and move the shoe adjusting lever forward, to the center of the drum.
4. Remove the securing spring and remove the leading (front) shoe with the tension spring attached.
5. Disconnect the trailing shoe from the parking brake cable (rear brakes only) and remove the shoe retaining spring. Withdraw the shoe.

CAUTION: *Use care not to get grease on the lining surface.*

Inspect all of the parts removed for wear or damage. Check the lining thickness; it should be no less than 0.06 in. If it is less than this have the brakes relined.

Installation is performed in the following order:

1. Install the adjusting lever and ratchet on to the leading shoe. Attach the parking brake cable to the trailing shoe.

NOTE: *Use a new retaining clip.*

2. Apply non-melting lubricant to the shoe parts which contact other components of the brake.

CAUTION: *Do not allow lubricant to get on the surface of the brake lining.*

3. Install the parking brake strut on the trailing shoe with its retaining spring (rear brakes only).
4. Attach the parking brake cable to the lever (rear brakes only).
5. Fasten the trailing shoe with its securing spring.
6. Push the adjusting lever toward the center of the brake and install it with the tension spring. Fasten the shoe retaining spring.

NOTE: *The longer hook of the tension spring attaches to the leading shoe.*

7. Push the adjusting ratchet downward, while returning the lever, so that it contacts the rim of the shoe.
8. Install the retaining spring.
9. Attach the tension spring to the shoes with the tool used during removal.
10. Install the drum and adjust the brakes, as detailed above.

Land Cruiser and Hi-Lux

Land Cruiser rear brake shoe removal and installation procedures are identical to those for Land Cruiser front brake shoes.

The procedure for the Hi-Lux is also similar to the Land Cruiser front shoe removal procedure, except for the following points:

1. Remove and install the parking brake strut and springs along with the front shoe.
2. Disconnect the parking brake cable from the shoe lever. Remember to connect it during installation.
3. Remove and install the rear shoe complete with the parking brake shoe lever.

The service limits of the brake lining thickness, are as follows:

Hi-Lux—0.06 in.

Land Cruiser—0.16 in.

The brakes must be relined if the lining thickness falls below these specifications.

Wheel Cylinders

Removal and Installation

Passenger Cars and Hi-Lux

1. Plug the master cylinder inlet to prevent hydraulic fluid from leaking.
2. Remove the brake drums and shoes as detailed in the appropriate section above.
3. Working from behind the backing plate, disconnect the hydraulic line from the wheel cylinder.
4. Unfasten the screws retaining the wheel cylinder and withdraw the cylinder.

Installation is performed in the reverse order of removal. However, once the hydraulic line has been disconnected from the wheel cylinder, the union seat must be replaced. To replace the seat, proceed in the following manner:

NOTE: *This procedure is not required on Crown and Hi-Lux models.*

1. Use a screw extractor with a diameter of 0.1 in. and having reverse threads, to remove the union seat from the wheel cylinder.
2. Drive in the new union seat with a 5/16 in. bar, used as a drift.

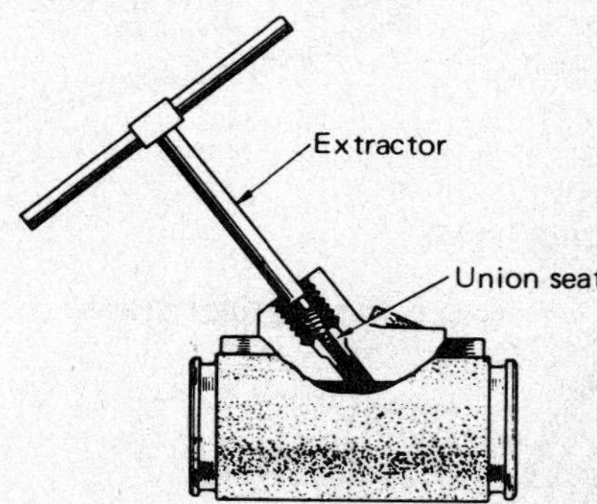

Replacing the wheel cylinder union seat

Remember to bleed the brake system after completing wheel cylinder, brake shoe and drum installation (see above).

Land Cruiser

The front brake wheel cylinder removal procedure is performed in the same manner as the procedure for the Hi-Lux and Land Cruiser rear brakes. For details see the section above which deals with these vehicles.

Overhaul

See "General Overhaul" in the front brake section, for a description of wheel cylinder overhaul procedures.

PARKING BRAKE

Adjustments

Floor-Mounted Lever

Corolla, Carina and Celica

NOTE: *On Corolla 1100 and 1200 models, the rear brake shoes must be adjusted before performing this procedure. See the section on brake adjustments at the beginning of this chapter for details.*

1. Slowly pull the parking brake lever upward, without depressing the button on the end of it, and while counting the number of notches required until the parking brake is applied.

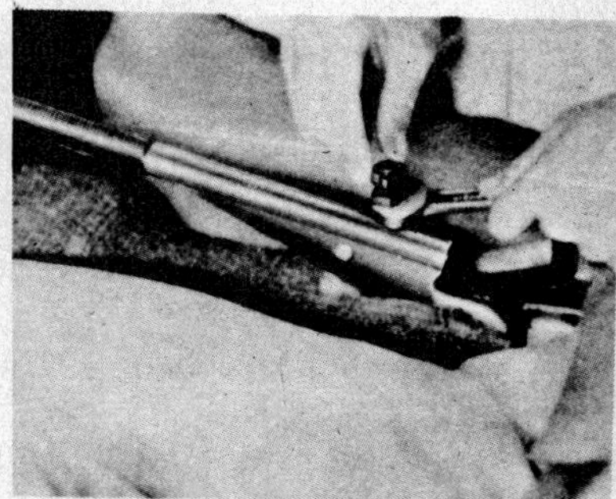

Adjusting the floor-mounted parking brake lever.

NOTE: *Two "clicks" are equal to one notch.*

2. Check the number of notches against the specifications given in the chart below.
3. If the brake requires adjustment, loosen the cable adjusting nut cap which is located at the rear of the parking brake lever. Hold the cap with an open-end wrench.
4. Take up the slack in the parking brake cable by rotating the adjusting nut with another open-end wrench.
   a. If the number of notches is *less* than specified, turn the nut *counterclockwise.*
   b. If the number of notches is *more* than specified, turn the nut *clockwise.*
5. Tighten the adjusting cap, using care not to disturb the setting of the adjusting nut.
6. Check the rotation of the rear wheels to be sure that the brakes are not dragging.

Parking Brake Adjustment

Model	Range of adjustment (notches)
Corolla 1200	7-8
Corolla 1600	5-8
Carina	3-7
Celica	3-7

NOTE: Each notch equals two clicks.

Dash-Mounted Lever

Corona, Mark II, Crown and Hi-Lux

NOTE: *On Hi-Lux models, adjust the rear brake shoes, as detailed at the beginning of this chapter, before attempting to adjust the parking brake.*

1. Loosen the parking brake warning light switch bracket.
2. Push the parking brake lever in until it is stopped by the pawl.

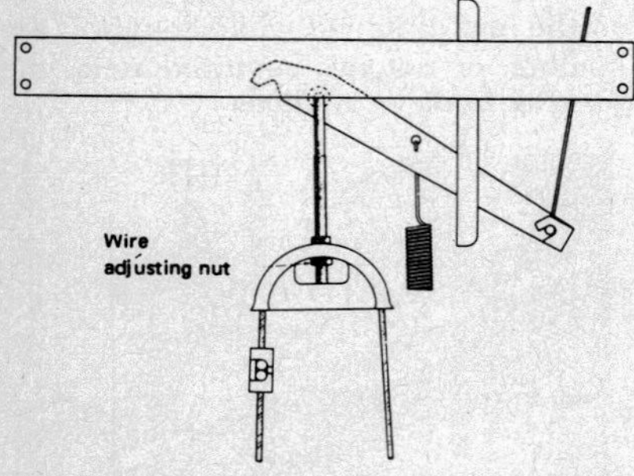

Adjusting the dash mounted parking brake from underneath the car.

3. Move the switch so that it will be "off" at this position but "on" when the handle is pulled out.
4. Tighten the switch bracket and push the brake lever in again.
5. Working from underneath the vehicle, loosen the locknut on the parking brake cable equalizer.
6. Screw the adjusting nut *in,* just enough so that the brake cables have no slack.
7. Hold the adjusting nut in this position while tightening the locknut.
8. Check the rotation of the rear wheels to make sure that the brakes are not dragging.
9. Pull out on the parking brake lever, and count the number of notches needed to apply the parking brake. Check the number against the figures given in the chart below.

Parking Brake Adjustment

Model	Adjusting Range (notches)
Corona	7-12
Mark II/4	5-9
Mark II/6	8-10
Crown 2300	5-9
Crown 2600	8-11
Hi-Lux	6-9

Land Cruiser

Land Cruiser models use a separate drum brake assembly, operating on the driveshaft, to serve as a parking brake. Adjust it as follows:

1. Push the parking brake lever all the way in, so that the brake is relesed.
2. Raise the rear of the vehicle and support it with jackstands.

CAUTION: *Be sure that the vehicle is securely supported. Remember, you will be working beneath it.*

3. Turn the parking brake adjustment shaft, which is located at the bottom of the parking brake backing plate, counterclockwise until the shoes seat against the drum.
4. Back the adjuster off one notch.
5. Apply the parking brake; the drum should be locked. Release the brake; the drum should rotate freely.

NOTE: *If the drum does not rotate freely with the brake off, loosen the adjuster one more notch.*

6. Adjust the turnbuckles on the parking brake intermediate levers and the adjusting nuts on the end of the parking brake cables, so that 6–9 notches are required to apply the parking brake.

CHASSIS ELECTRICAL

Windshield Wiper Motor

Removal and Installation

Corolla

1. Disconnect the car battery.
2. Unfasten the wiper motor connection.
3. Detach the wiper motor from the linkage by prying it with a screwdriver.

NOTE: *It may be necessary to remove the defroster nozzle to gain access to the motor.*

4. Remove the package tray.
5. Unfasten the three wiper motor securing nuts and withdraw the motor from inside the car.

Installation is performed in the reverse order of removal.

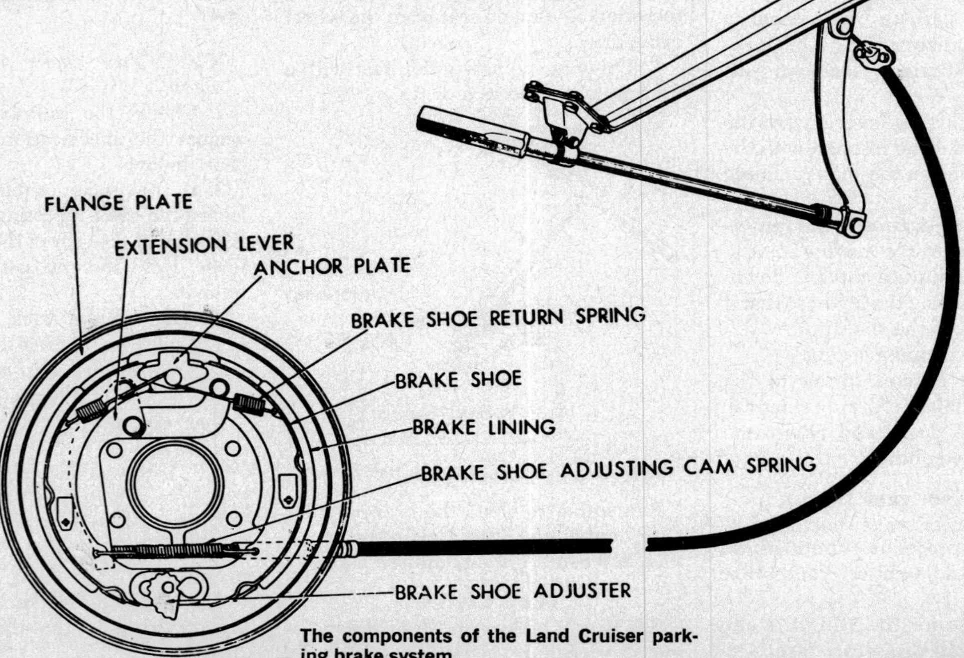

The components of the Land Cruiser parking brake system.

Carina, Corona and Crown

1. Disconnect the wiper motor multiconnector.

2. Remove the service cover and loosen the wiper motor securing bolts.

3. Use a screwdriver to separate the wiper link-to-motor connection.

CAUTION: *Be careful not to bend the linkage.*

4. Withdraw the wiper motor assembly.

Installation is performed in the reverse order of removal.

Celica and Mark II/4

1. Remove the access hole cover.

2. Separate the wiper link from the motor by prying gently with a screwdriver.

3. Remove the left and right cowl ventilators by lifting their inner clips.

4. Remove the wiper arms and the linkage mounting nuts. Push the linkage pivot ports into the ventilators.

5. Loosen the wiper link connectors at their ends and with the linkage from the cowl ventilator.

6. Start the wiper motor and turn the ignition key off when the crank is at the position illustrated.

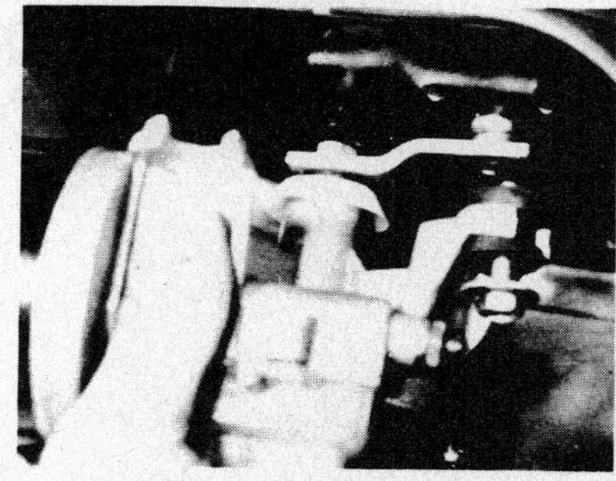

Remove the wiper motor with the crank in this position—Celica and Mark II/4.

NOTE: *The wiper motor is difficult to remove when it is in the parked position. If the motor is turned off at the wiper switch, it will automatically return to this position.*

7. Unfasten the multiconnector.

8. Loosen the motor securing bolts and withdraw the motor.

Installation is performed in the reverse order of removal. Be sure to install the wiper motor with it returned to the park position by connecting the multiconnector and operating the wiper control switch. Assemble the crank as illustrated below.

Mark II/6 1972-73

1. Remove the cover from the service hole.

2. Set the wiper crank at 180° from park, by turning the wiper switch on and then turning the ignition switch off, once the desired position is reached.

3. Separate the link from the motor crank with a screwdriver.

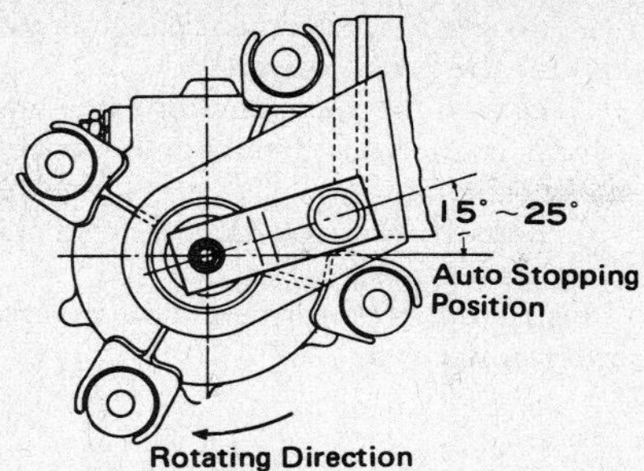

Install the wiper motor with the crank in this position—Celica and Mark II/4.

4. Disconnect the wiper motor multiconnector.

5. Unfasten the wiper motor securing bolts and withdraw the motor.

Installation is performed in the reverse order of removal.

Land Cruiser

1. Detach the wiper link from the motor with a screwdriver.

2. Unfasten the two bracket securing bolts at the rear of the motor.

3. Disconnect the wiper motor wiring.

4. Unfasten the wiper motor attachment screws and withdraw the motor.

Installation is performed in the reverse order of removal.

Instrument Cluster

Removal and Installation

Corolla and Corona (1966-70)

1. Disconnect the battery.

2. Detach the speedometer cable from the speedometer.

3. Remove the center and right-hand trim moldings from the instrument panel. (1970-73).

4. Unfasten the instrument cluster and panel molding retainer screw.

5. Remove the two nuts which secure the instrument cluster from behind (1970-73).

6. Pull the cluster out slightly and disconnect the wiring.

7. Remove the cluster assembly completely.

CAUTION: *Be careful not to scratch the steering column cover.*

Installation is performed in the reverse order of removal.

Carina

1. Remove the glove box door and withdraw the glove box slightly.

2. Disconnect the inspection lamp socket and glove box light wiring.

3. Remove the glove box completely.

4. Unfasten the cigarette lighter wiring and remove the ash tray.

5. Unfasten the lower crash pad screws and remove the crash pad.

NOTE: *It may be necessary to unfasten the attachment screws and lower the steering column. Be careful, the column is the collapsible type.*

6. Loosen the radio rear attachment screws and detach the heater cable at the heater.

7. Unfasten the instrument retaining screws and tilt the panel toward the rear.

8. Detach the speedometer cable and the wiring multiconnectors. Remove the cluster assembly.

Installation is performed in the reverse order of removal.

Corona 1970-73

1. Disconnect the battery.

2. Remove the fuse block attachment bolts.

3. Remove the parking brake bracket.

4. Detach the fuel gauge/warning light pod wiring harness and remove its mounting screws. Pull out the pod.

5. Perform step 4 for the clock.

6. Disconnect the speedometer wiring harness and cable.

7. Unfasten the wiring harness clamp then push the harness toward the front.

8. Loosen the speedometer attachment screws and remove the speedometer.

NOTE: *Cover the lens with a cloth during removal.*

Installation is performed in the reverse order of removal.

Mark II/4

1. Disconnect the battery.

2. Remove the package shelf from beneath the dashboard.

3. Remove the fuse block bracket.

4. Remove the lower left-side crash pad and the left-hand trim molding.

5. Unfasten the instrument cluster securing screws and tip the cluster slightly forward.

6. Detach the cluster wiring harness and the speedometer cable. Remove the cluster.

NOTE: *If the car is not equipped with a radio, it is much easier to remove the glove box and then remove the instrument cluster through the opening.*

Installation is performed in the reverse order of removal.

Mark II/6

1. Remove the housing from the steering column.

2. Remove the control knobs from the heater and radio.

3. Loosen the heater control floodlight and pull it out slightly.

4. Remove the nine screws which attach the cluster surround.

5. Push the upper crash pad away from the surround and slightly pull out the surround.

6. Remove the heater control floodlight from the surround.

7. Remove the surround toward the right.
8. Remove the instrument panel lower garnish moldings. Remove the ash tray.
9. Remove the heater control assembly.
10. Unfasten the dash side ventilator mounting screws.
11. Remove the radio and tape deck, if so equipped.
12. Remove the heater control bracket.
13. Remove the six cluster securing bolts and lift it out slightly.
14. Detach the speedometer cable and all of the wiring harnesses. Remove the cluster.

Installation is performed in the reverse order of removal.

NOTE: *Have the heater control floodlight installed in the cluster surround prior to its installation.*

Celica and Crown 2300

1. Disconnect the battery.
2. Detach the heater control cables at the heater box.
3. Loosen the steering column clamping nuts and lower the column.

CAUTION: *Be careful when handling the column; it is the collapsible type. Cover the column shroud with a cloth to protect it.*

4. Loosen the instrument panel screws and tilt the panel forward.
5. Detach the speedometer cable and wiring connectors. Remove the entire panel assembly.
6. Remove the instruments from the panel as required.

Installation is performed in the reverse order of removal.

Crown 2600

1. Disconnect the battery.
2. Remove the air duct from the center air outlet.
3. Remove the radio surround from the center instrument panel.
4. Remove the radio. (See above.)
5. Unfasten the screws and remove the instrument cluster surround. Remove the cluster housing.
6. Detach the speedometer drive cable and wiring connectors by reaching through the radio opening.
7. Withdraw the instrument cluster.

Installation is performed in the reverse order of removal.

Land Cruiser and Hi-Lux

1. Working from underneath the dashboard, disconnect the speedometer cable.
2. Remove the instrument cluster retaining screws. Pull the cluster part of the way out of the panel.
3. Detach the wiring connectors and light bulbs from the cluster.
4. Remove the instrument cluster from the panel.

NOTE: *On Hi-Lux and Land Cruiser station wagon models, it will be necessary to unfasten the steering column clamping bolts and lower the column in order to remove the cluster.*

Installation is performed in the reverse order of removal.

Fuses and Fusible Links

The fuse box is located on the left-hand side, underneath the dashboard, on all models except the Crown 2600. On the Crown 2600, the fuse box is located behind a door on the driver's-side kick panel.

All models are equipped with fusible links on the battery cables running from the positive (+) battery terminal.

TRIUMPH

Index

INTRODUCTION

The Triumph Spitfire Mk III was introduced in 1968 to supersede the Mk II. It featured a slightly larger 1296 cc engine and is recognizable by higher bumpers and a one-piece grille.

In 1971, the Spitfire Mk IV was introduced. The rear suspension was modified to limit the rear roll center and the engine was strengthened by the addition of larger rod bearings and journals. A new, all-synchromesh four-speed transmission became standard equipment on the Mk IV. The Mk IV is readily identifiable by its redesigned, Stag-like rear end.

For 1973, the Spitfire engine displacement has been increased to 1493 cc, hence the Spitfire 1500. To accommodate the increased torque of the engine, the clutch diameter was increased to 7 ¼ in.

The GT6+ was introduced in 1969 to replace the GT6 Mk I. The GT6+ dropped the swing axle rear suspension that had been used on the Mk I in favor of a fully independent rear suspension. The GT6+ is readily identifiable by its higher bumpers and one-piece grille.

In 1971, the GT6 Mk III was introduced, retaining the same basic 1998 cc six cylinder engine and fastback/hatchback theme of the GT6+. The GT6 Mk III can be identified by its redesigned rear end treatment and large horizontal tail lights.

The TR-250 was introduced in 1968 to replace the TR-4A. The TR-250 incorporated the basic styling and independent rear suspension of the TR-4A IRS with a 2498 cc six cylinder engine.

The following year, the TR-6 was introduced, superseding the TR-250. The TR-6 is mechanically identical to the TR-250, except for the addition of a front anti-roll bar and wider wheels. The TR-6 is identifiable by its full width horizontal grille and its Kammback tail end treatment.

MODEL IDENTIFICATION

1968-70 Spitfire Mk. III

1971-72 Spitfire Mk. IV,
1973 Spitfire 1500

1969-70 GT6 +

1971-73 GT 6 Mk. III

1968 TR 250

1969-73 TR-6

SERIAL NUMBER IDENTIFICATION

Chassis Number

All 1968 and later Triumphs have the chassis number (commission number) stamped on a plate adjacent to the driver's door striker plate and on another small plate visible through the windshield.

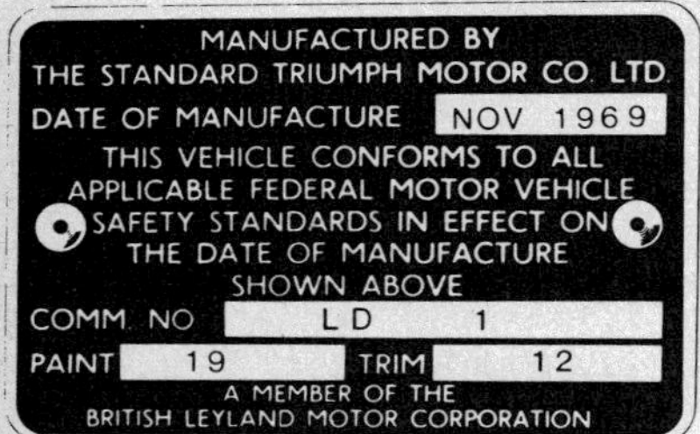

Chassis number plate

Chassis number plate location

Engine Number

The engine number is stamped on the left side of the engine block on all models.

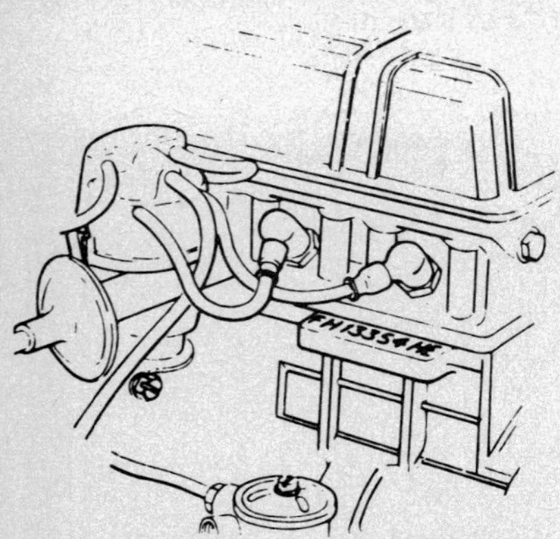

Engine number location

Transmission Number

The transmission number is stamped on the left side of the clutch housing (TR models), or on the top right side of the transmission case (GT6 and Spitfire models).

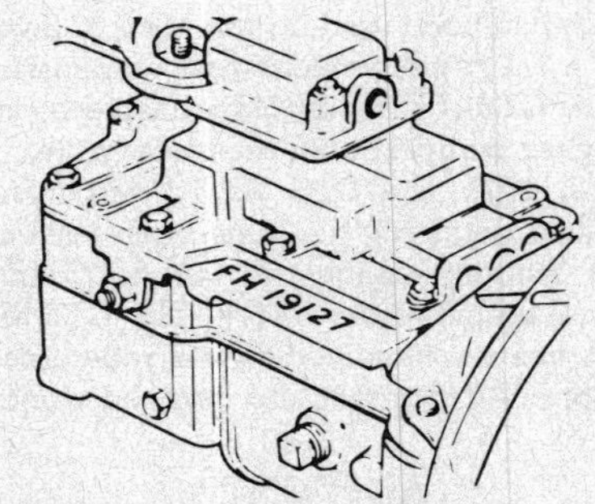

Transmission number location—Spitfire, GT-6 shown; TR-250, TR-6 similar.

Rear Axle Number

The rear axle number is stamped on the housing flange on all models.

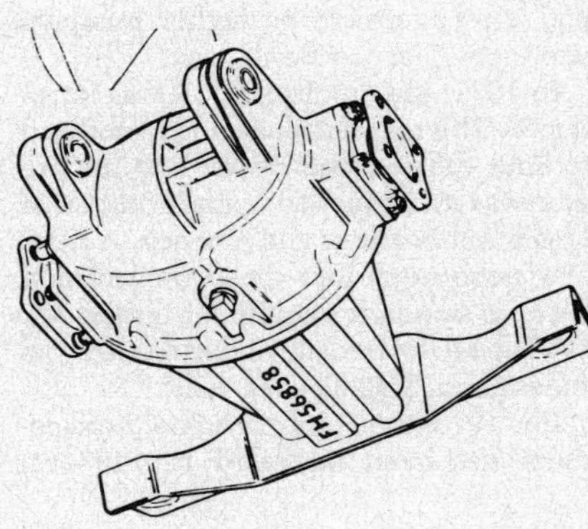

Rear axle number location—Spitfire, GT6 shown; TR series similar.

CHASSIS NUMBER CHART

Model	Year	Starting Chassis Number
Spitfire Mk III	1968	FD 7796
	1969	N.A.
	1970	FDU 75000
Spitfire Mk IV	1971	FK 1
	1972	FK 25001
Spitfire 1500	1973	FM 1U
GT6+	1969	N.A.
	1970	KC 75000
GT6 Mk III	1971	KF 1
	1972	KF 10001
	1973	KF 20001
TR-250	1968	CK 1L (convertible), and CN 1L (hdt)
TR-6	1969	CC 25000
	1970	CC 50000
	1971	CC 58298
	1972	CC 75001
	1973	CF 1

N.A. Not available

GENERAL ENGINE SPECIFICATIONS

Year & Model	Engine Displace. Cu in (cc)	Carburetor Type	Horsepower @ rpm	Torque @ rpm (ft lbs)	Bore x Stroke (in.)	Compression Ratio	Oil Pressure @ rpm (psi)
1968-70 Spitfire Mk III	79.2 (1296)	Twin horizontal① SU HS2	68 @ 5500	73.3 @ 3000	2.900 x 2.992	8.5:1	40-60 max
1971 Spitfire Mk IV	79.2 (1296)	Single horizontal Zenith-Stromberg 150 CDSE	58 @ 5200	71.6 @ 3000	2.900 x 2.992	9.0:1	40-60 max
1972 Spitfire Mk IV	79.2 (1296)	Single horizontal Zenith-Stromberg 150 CDSE	48 @ 5500	60.8 @ 2900	2.900 x 2.992	8.0:1	40-60 max
1973 Spitfire 1500	91.0 (1493)	Single horizontal Zenith-Stromberg 150 CDSE	57 @ 5000	71 @ 3000	2.900 x 3.440	7.5:1	40-60 max
1969-70 GT6+	122.0 (1998)	Twin horizontal Zenith-Stromberg 150 CDSE	95 @ 4700	117 @ 3400	2.940 x 2.992	9.25:1	45-55 max
1971 GT6 Mk III	122.0 (1998)	Twin horizontal Zenith-Stromberg 150 CDSE	90 @ 4700	116 @ 3400	2.940 x 2.992	9.25:1	45-55 max
1972-73 GT6 Mk III	122.0 (1998)	Twin horizontal Zenith-Stromberg 150 CDSE	79 @ 4900	97 @ 2900	2.940 x 2.992	8.0:1	45-55 max
1968 TR-250	152.0 (2498)	Twin horizontal Zenith-Stromberg 175 CDSE	111 @ 4500	152 @ 3000	2.940 x 3.740	8.5:1	70 max
1966-67 TR-6	152.0 (2498)	Twin horizontal Zenith-Stromberg 175 CDSE	104 @ 4500	142 @ 3000	2.940 x 3.740	8.6:1	70 max
1972-73 TR-6	152.0 (2498)	Twin horizontal Zenith-Stromberg 175 CDSE	106 @ 4900	133 @ 3000	2.940 x 3.740	7.75:1	70 max

① 1970 Spitfire MK 111 uses a single horizontal Zenith-Stromberg 150 CDSE carburetor

Firing Order

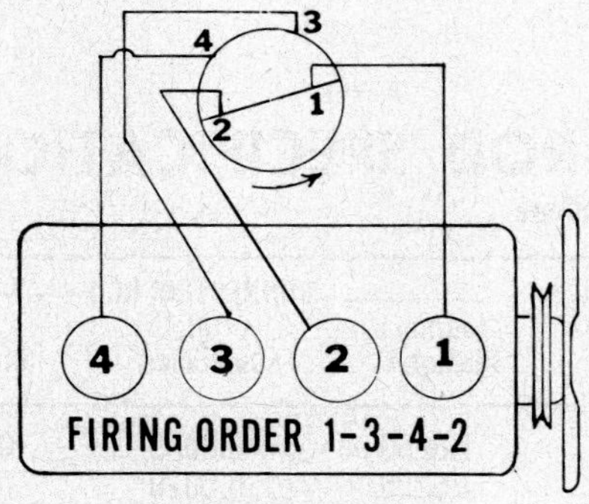

Four-cylinder engine

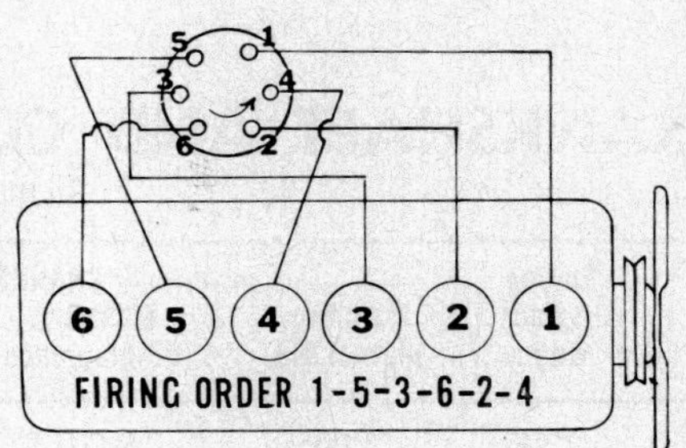

Six-cylinder engine

TUNE-UP SPECIFICATIONS

When analyzing compression test results, look for uniformity among cylinders, rather than specific pressures.

Year and Model	Engine (cc)	SPARK PLUGS Type	Gap (in.)	DISTRIBUTOR Point Dwell (deg)	Point Gap (in.)	STATIC Ignition Timing (deg) MT	Intake Valve Opens (deg)	IDLE SPEED (rpm) MT	VALVE CLEARANCE (in.) In	Ex
1968-70 Spitfire Mk III	1296	UN-12Y	0.025	38-40	0.014-0.016	6BTDC ①	10BTDC	800-850	0.010	0.010
1971-72 Spitfire Mk IV	1296	UN-12Y	0.025	38-40	0.014-0.016	6ATDC ①②	③	800-850	0.010	0.010
1973 Spitfire 1500	1493	UN-12Y	0.025	38-40	0.014-0.016	8BTDC ①	18BTDC	800-850	0.010	0.010
1969-70 GT6+	1998	UN-12Y	0.025	40-42	0.014-0.016	6BTDC ④	10BTDC	800-850	0.010	0.010
1971-72 GT6 Mk III	1998	UN-12Y	0.025	40-42	0.014-0.016	6BTDC ④	10BTDC	800-850	0.010	0.010
1973 GT6 Mk III	1998	UN-12Y	0.025	40-42	0.014-0.016	12BTDC ④	18BTDC	800-850	0.010	0.010
1968 TR-250	2498	UN-12Y	0.025	32-38	0.014-0.016	10BTDC ④	10BTDC	800-850	0.010	0.010
1969-72 TR-6	2498	UN-12Y	0.025	34-37	0.014-0.016	10BTDC ④	10BTDC	800-850	0.010	0.010
1973 TR-6	2498	UN-12Y	0.025	34-37	0.014-0.016	12BTDC ④	10BTDC	800-850	0.010	0.010

① Dynamic timing—2ATDC @ 800-850 rpm
② After engine no. FK25000-8BTDC
③ Below engine no. FK25001-10BTDC
After engine no. FK25000-18BTDC
④ Dynamic timing—4ATDC @ 800-850 rpm

NOTE: All models exported to the United States since Jan. 1, 1968 have been modified to comply with federal exhaust emission standards. Particular care must be taken to follow the ignition timing and carburetor tuning instructions exactly to ensure reliable and sufficient engine performance, as well as a safe and legal level of emissions. If the figures in the tune-up chart do not agree with those on the engine compartment sticker, use the sticker figures.

CRANKSHAFT AND CONNECTING ROD SPECIFICATIONS

All measurements are given in inches

Year	Engine Displace. Cu In.	CRANKSHAFT Main Brg. Journal Dia.	Main Brg. Oil Clearance	Shaft End-Play	Thrust on No.	CONNECTING ROD Journal Diameter	Oil Clearance	Side Clearance
1968-72	1296	2.0005-2.0010	0.0010-0.0020	0.004-0.008	3	1.6250-1.6255	0.0005-0.0020	0.0105-0.0126
1973	1493	—	—	—	3	—	—	—
1969-73	1998	2.0005-2.0010	0.0012-0.0020	0.006-0.008	4	1.8750-1.8755	0.0010-0.0027	0.0086-0.0125
1968-73	2498	2.3110-2.3115	0.0015-0.0025	0.006-0.008	4	1.8750-1.8755	0.0010-0.0027	0.0070-0.0140

— Not Available

PISTON AND RING SPECIFICATIONS

All measurements in inches

Year	Engine Displace. Cu in.	PISTON CLEARANCE Crown	Skirt	RING GAP Top Compression	Bottom Compression	Oil Control	RING SIDE CLEARANCE Top Compression	Bottom Compression	Oil Control
1968-70	1296	①	②	0.012-0.022	0.012-0.022	0.012-0.022	0.0015-0.0035	0.0015-0.0035	0.0018-0.0048
1971-72	1296	③	④	0.012-0.022	0.012-0.022	(ends butt)	0.0020-0.0025	0.0020-0.0025	0.0028-0.0038
1973	1493	—	—	—	—	—	—	—	—
1969-73	1998	0.0035-0.0042	0.0017-0.0024	0.008-0.013	0.008-0.013	0.008-0.0013	0.0019-0.0035	0.0019-0.0035	0.0007-0.0027
1968	2498	0.0035-0.0042	0.0017-0.0024	0.008-0.013	0.008-0.013	0.008-0.0013	0.0019-0.0035	0.0019-0.0035	0.0007-0.0027
1969-73	2498	0.0038-0.0045	0.0021-0.0028	0.012-0.017	0.008-0.013	⑤	0.0010-0.0030	0.0010-0.0030	0.0010-0.0030

① Grade F-0.019-0.025
Grade G-0.020-0.026
② Grade F-0.0009-0.0024
Grade G-0.0014-0.0023
③ Grade F-0.020-0.024
Grade G-0.0205-0.0260
— Not Available

④ Grade F-0.0014-0.0019
Grade G-0.0013-0.0028
⑤ Plain oil rings-0.015-0.055
Scraper oil ring-(ends butt)

VALVE SPECIFICATIONS

Year	Engine Displace. (cc)	Seat Angle (deg)	Face Angle (deg)	Spring Test Pressure (lbs @ in.)	Spring (in.) Free Length	STEM TO GUIDE CLEARANCE (in.) Intake	Exhaust	STEM DIAMETER (in.) Intake	Exhaust
1968-72	1296	44.5	45	27-30 @ 1.36	1.61	0.0008-0.0023	0.0015-0.0030	0.3107-0.3112	0.3100-0.3105
1973	1493	44.5	45	—	—	—	—	—	—
1969-73	1998	44.5	45	①	②	0.0008-0.0023	0.0015-0.0030	0.3107-0.3112	0.3100-0.3105
1968-73	2498	44.5	45	—	1.59③	0.0008-0.0023	0.0015-0.0030	0.3107-0.3112	0.3100-0.3105

① Inner—11-14 @ 1.14
Outer—27-30 @ 1.386
② Inner—1.56
Outer—1.61
— Not Available

③ Vehicles with inner and outer valve springs
Inner—1.56
Outer—1.57

TORQUE SPECIFICATIONS

All readings in ft lbs

Year	Engine Displace. (cc)	Cylinder Head Bolts	Rod Bearing Bolts	Main Bearing Bolts	Crankshaft Pulley Bolt	Flywheel To Crankshaft Bolts	MANIFOLD Intake	Exhaust	Spark Plug
1968-72	1296	42-46	38-42	50-55	90-110	①	25-25	20-25	14-20
1973	1493	42-46	38-42	50-55	90-110	35-40	25-25	20-25	14-20
1969-73	1998	65-70	38-42	55-60	90-100	42-46	14-16②	20-22	14-16
1968-73	2498	65-70	38-42	55-60	90-100	55-60	③④	③④	14-16

① Black parkerized bolt—42-50 ft ibs
Bright cadmium plated bolt—35-40 ft lbs
② Exhaust/intake attaching bolt—20-22 ft lbs

③ TR-250; studs—24-26 ft lbs, bolts—18-20 ft lbs
④ TR-6; outer (2)—12-14 ft lbs, inner—16-18 ft lbs

Torque Sequences

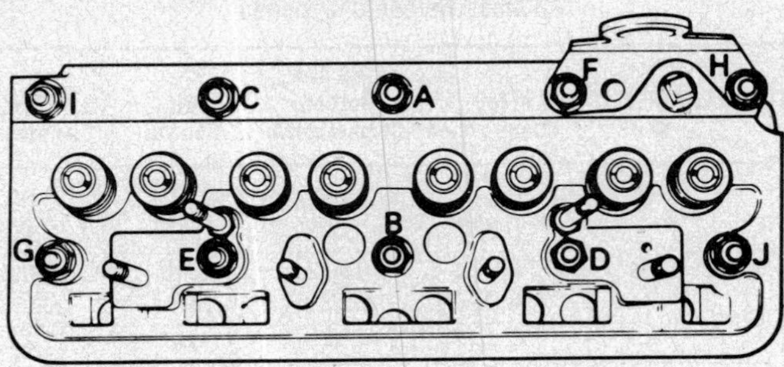

Cylinder head—four cylinder engine

Cylinder head—six cylinder engine

CAPACITIES

Year	Model	Engine Displace. Cu in. (cc)	ENGINE CRANKCASE (qts) With Filter	Without Filter	Trans-mission (pts) Manual 4-spd over drive	Drive Axle (pts)	Gasoline Tank (gals)	Cooling System (qts) W/C AC
1968-70	Spitfire Mk III	1296	4.8	4.2	1.8(2.8)	1.2	9.9	4.8
1971-72	Spitfire Mk IV	1296	4.8	4.2	1.8(3.0)	1.2	①	4.8
1973	Spitfire Mk 1V (1500)	1493	4.8	4.2	1.8(3.0)	1.2	8.7	4.8
1969-70	GT6+	1998	—	4.8	1.8(2.8)	1.2	11.7	6.6
1971-73	GT6 Mk III	1998	—	4.8	1.8(3.0)	1.2	11.7	6.6
1968	TR-250	2498	—	4.8	2.4(4.2)	1.8	13.5	6.6
1969-73	TR-6	2498	—	4.8	2.4(4.2)	3.0	13.5	6.6

① 1971—9.9
1972—8.7
— Not Available

BATTERY AND STARTER SPECIFICATIONS

Year	Engine Displace. (cc)	BATTERY Ampere Hour Capacity	Volts	Term. Ground	STARTERS Manu-facturer	Lock Test Amps.	Lock Test Volts	Torque (ft lbs)	No-Load Test Amps.	No-Load Test Volts	No-Load Test RPM	Brush Spring Tension (oz)
1968-70	1296	43	12	Neg	Lucas M35G	420-440	7.3-7.9	10.0	45	12	7400-8500	32-34
1971-72	1296	40	12	Neg	Lucas M35J	350-375	—	7.0	65	12	8000-10000	28
1973	1493	40	12	Neg	Lucas M35J	350-375	—	7.0	65	12	8000-10000	28
1969-70	1998	56	12	Neg	Lucas M35G	370	7.5-7.9	8.2	60	12	8000-11000	30-34
1971-73	1998	56	12	Neg	Lucas #25149	—	—	—	—	12	—	—
1968-72	2498	57(60)	12	Neg	Lucas M418G	465	7.0	15.0	80	12	5500-8000	36
1973	2498	57	12	Neg	Lucas M100	—	—	—	—	12	—	—

— Not Available

WHEEL ALIGNMENT

All models are measured in the unladen position

Year	Model	FRONT SUSPENSION Caster Pref Setting (deg) ±0.5°	Camber Pref Setting (deg) ±0.5°	Toe-in (in.)	Steering Axis Inclination (deg.)	REAR SUSPENSION Camber (deg.)	Rear Wheel Alignment (in.)
1968-70	Spitfire Mk III	3.5P	3P	1/16-1/8	5.75	0.5P	1/16-1/8 (TO)①
1971-73	Spitfire Mk 1V, 1500	4.0P	3P	1/16-1/8	5.75	1.0N①	1/32-3/32 (TO)①
1969-73	GT6+, GT6 Mk III	3.5P	2.75P	1/16-1/8	6.00	0	0 ± 1/32
1968	TR-250	2.75P	0.5P	1/16-1/8	8.50	0.5P	0-1/16 (TI)
1969-73	TR-6	2.75P	0.25P	1/16-1/8	8.75	0.5P	0-1/16 (TI)

P—Positive N—Negative
(TI)—Toe-in (TO)—Toe-out
① When checking rear suspension camber and rear wheel alignment, swivel plates must be used. Without the use of the swivel plates, side thrust may vary the readings approximately 15 per cent.

BRAKE SPECIFICATIONS

All measurements are given in inches

Year	Model	BRAKE DISC OR DRUM DIAMETER Front Disc	Rear Drum	Manufacturer's Recommended Minimum Lining Thickness (in.) Disc	Drum
All	Spitfire	9.0	7.0	1/8	1/16
All	GT6	9.7	8.0	1/8	1/16
All	TR-250, TR-6	10.9	9.0	1/8	1/16

NOTE: Due to variations in state inspection laws, the minimum allowable thickness may be greater than that stated by the manufacturer.

Wiring Diagrams

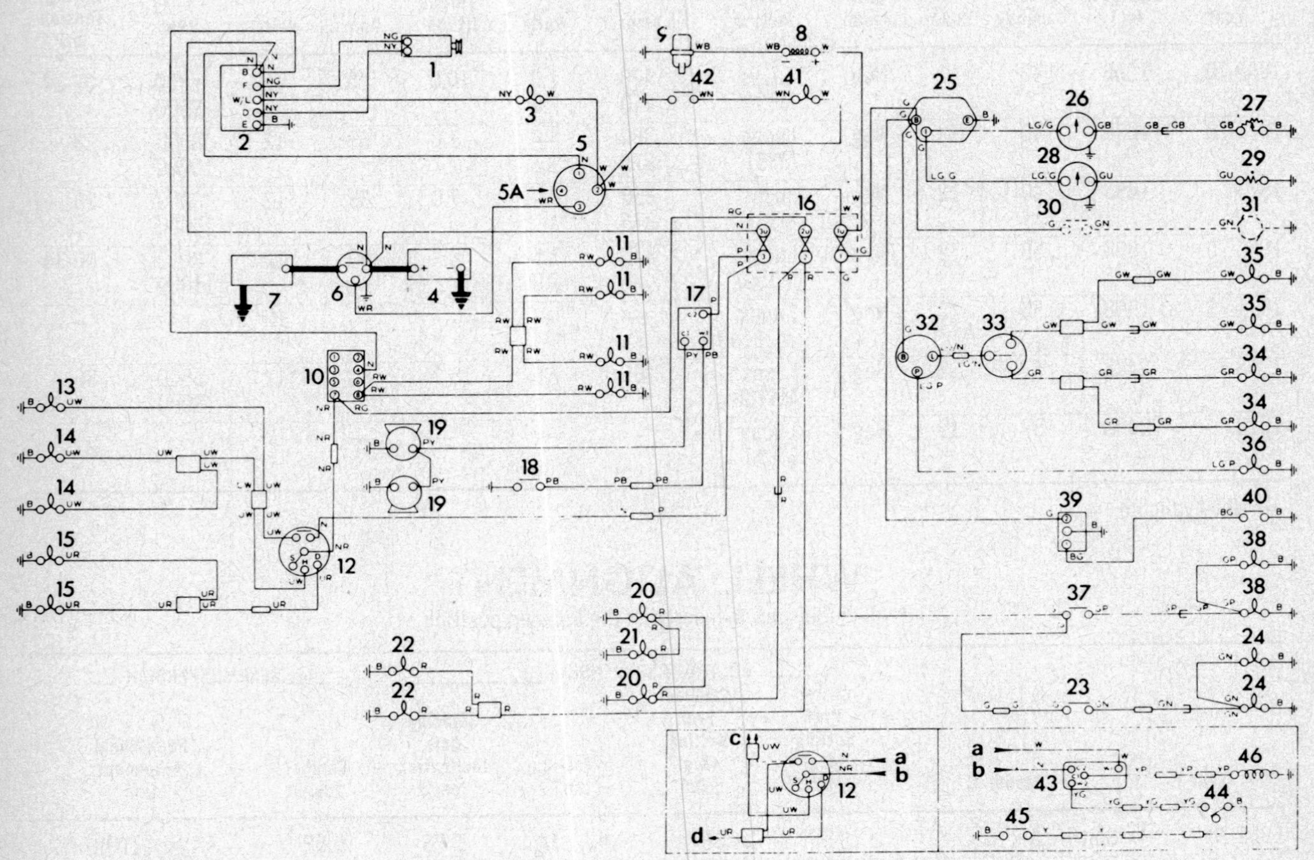

1968-70 Spitfire Mk. III

1. Generator
2. Voltage regulator
3. Ignition warning light
4. Battery
5. Ignition/starter switch
5a. Ignition/starter switch—radio supply position
6. Starter solenoid
7. Starter motor
8. Ignition coil
9. Ignition distributor
10. Master light switch
11. Instrument illumination
12. Lights selector switch
13. High beam warning light
14. High beam
15. Low beam
16. Fuse assembly
17. Horn relay
18. Horn button
19. Horn
20. Tail lamp
21. Plate illumination lamp
22. Front parking lamp
23. Backup lamp switch
24. Backup lamp
25. Voltage stabilizer
26. Fuel indicator
27. Fuel tank unit
28. Temperature indicator
29. Temperature transmitter
30. Heater switch
31. Heater motor
32. Flasher unit
33. Direction indicator switch
34. L.H. direction indicator lamp
35. R. H. direction indicator lamp
36. Direction indicator warning light
37. Stop lamp switch
38. Stop lamp
39. Windshield wiper motor
40. Windshield wiper switch
41. Oil pressure warning light
42. Oil pressure switch

OVERDRIVE (OPTIONAL)

43. Overdrive relay
44. Overdrive column switch
45. Overdrive transmission switch
46. Overdrive solenoid

a. From ignition starter switch—connector 2
b. From ignition starter switch—connector 1

CABLE COLOR CODE

N	Brown
U	Blue
R	Red
P	Purple
G	Green
LG	Light Green
W	White
Y	Yellow
B	Black

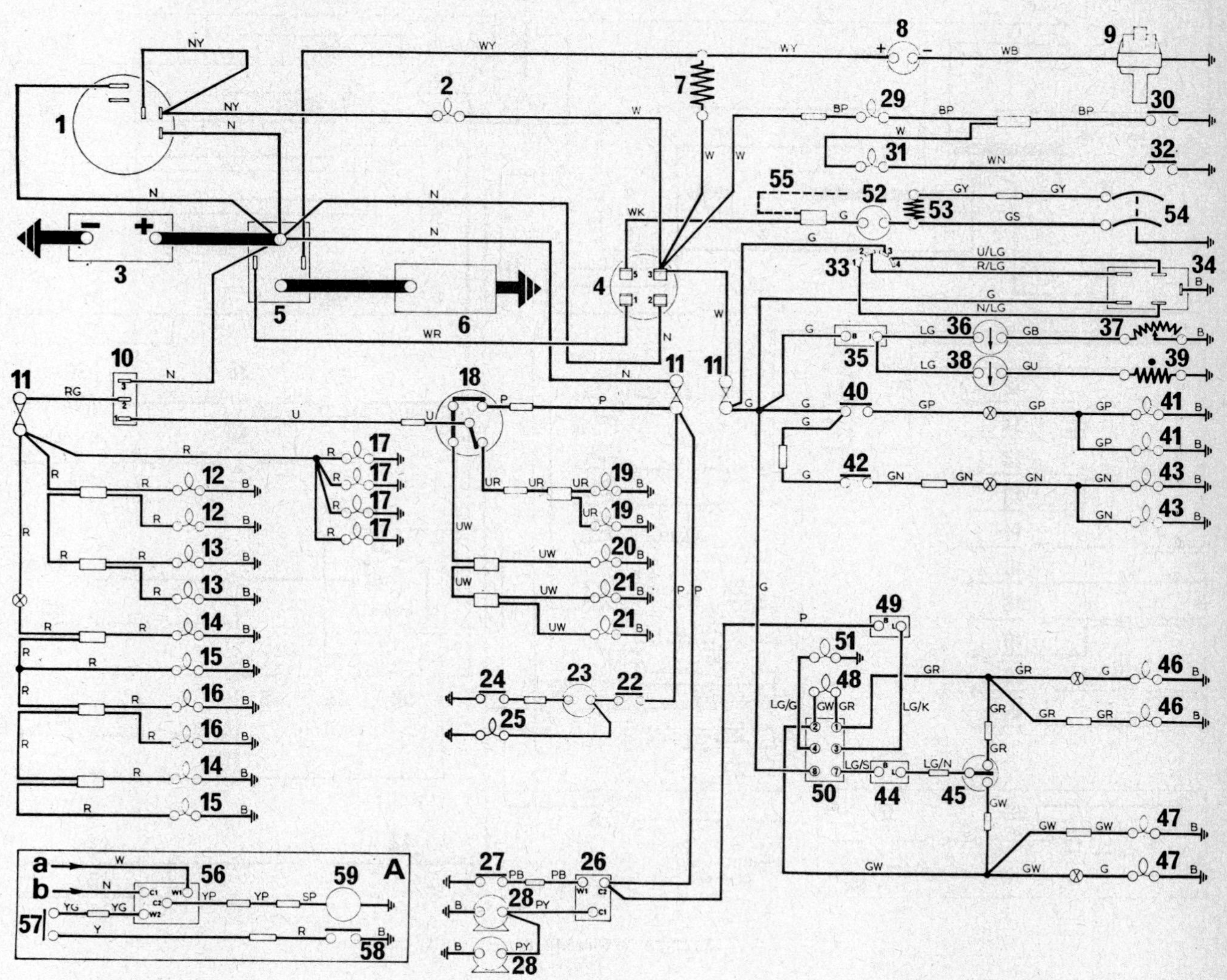

1971 Spitfire Mk. IV

1. Alternator
2. Ignition warning light
3. Battery
4. Ignition starter switch
5. Starter solenoid
6. Starter motor
7. Ballast resistor
8. Ignition coil—6 volt
9. Ignition distributor
10. Master light switch
11. Fuse
12. Front parking lamp
13. Front marker lamp
14. Rear marker lamp
15. Tail lamp
16. Plate illumination lamp
17. Instrument illumination
18. Column light switch
19. Low beam
20. High beam warning light
21. High beam
22. Door switch
23. Key warning buzzer
24. Key switch
25. Courtesy light
26. Horn relay
27. Horn button
28. Horn
29. Brake warning light
30. Brake line failure switch
31. Oil pressure warning light
32. Oil pressure switch
33. Windshield wiper switch
34. Windshield wiper motor
35. Voltage stabilizer
36. Fuel indicator
37. Fuel tank unit
38. Temperature indicator
39. Temperature transmitter
40. Stop lamp switch
41. Stop lamp
42. Backup lamp switch
43. Backup lamp
44. Turn signal flasher unit
45. Turn signal switch
46. L.H. flasher lamp
47. R.H. flasher lamp
48. Turn signal warning light
49. Hazard flasher unit
50. Hazard switch
51. Hazard warning light
52. Heater motor
53. Heater switch
54. Radio

A. Overdrive (optional extra)

55. Overdrive relay
56. Overdrive transmission switch
57. Overdrive gear lever switch

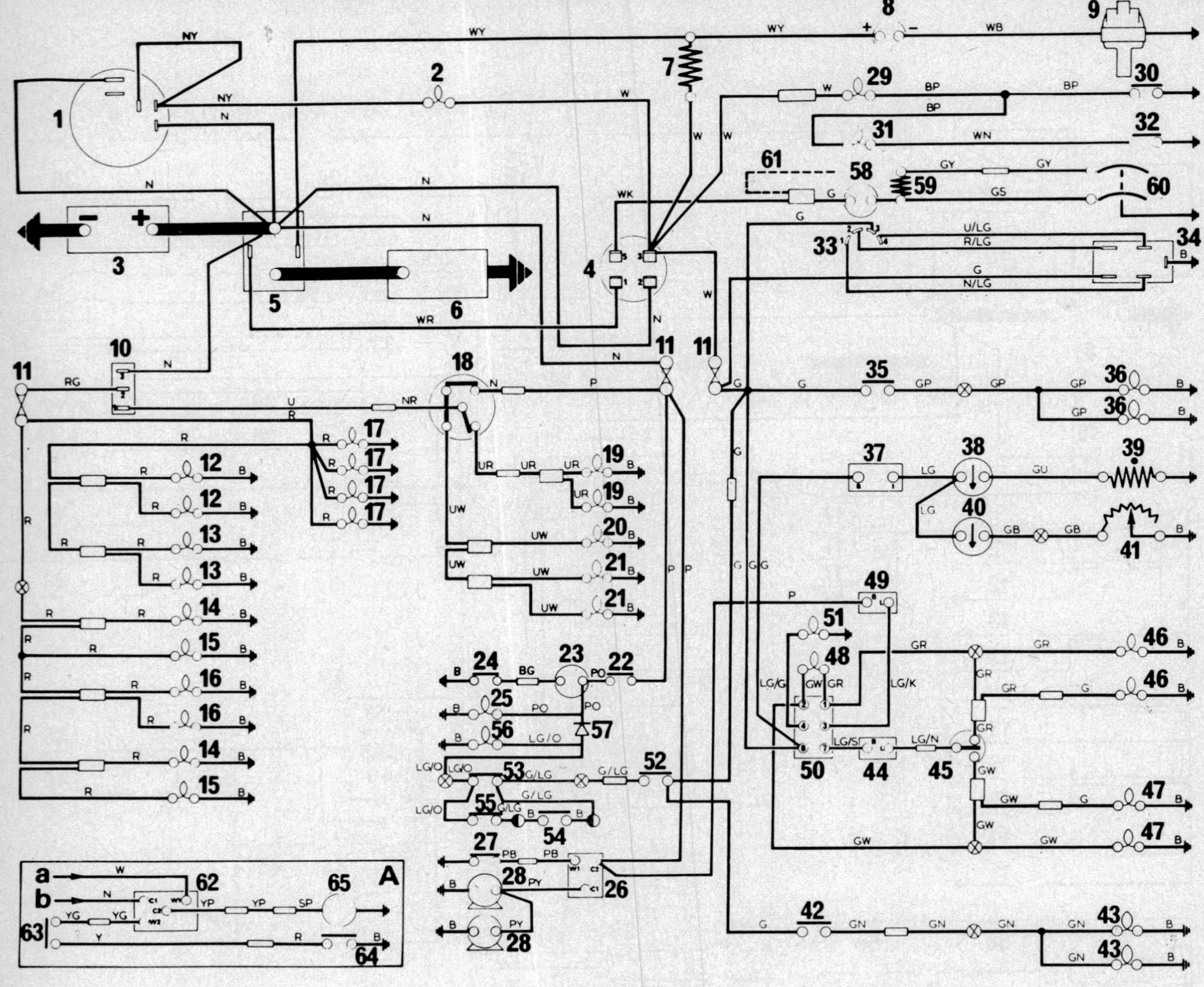

1972-73 Spitfire Mk. IV

1. Alternator
2. Ignition warning light
3. Battery
4. Ignition/starter switch
5. Starter solenoid
6. Starter motor
7. Ballast resistor
8. Ignition coil—6 volt
9. Ignition distributor
10. Master light switch
11. Fuse
12. Front parking lamp
13. Front marker lamp
14. Rear marker lamp
15. Tail lamp
16. Plate illumination lamp
17. Instrument illumination
18. Column light switch
19. Low beam
20. High beam warning light
21. High beam
22. Door switch
23. Buzzer
24. Key switch
25. Key light
26. Horn relay
27. Horn button
28. Horn
29. Brake warning light
30. Brake line failure switch
31. Oil pressure warning light
32. Oil pressure switch
33. Windshield wiper switch
34. Windshield wiper motor
35. Stop lamp switch
36. Stop lamp
37. Voltage stabilizer
38. Temperature indicator
39. Temperature transmitter
40. Fuel indicator
41. Fuel tank unit
42. Reverse lamp switch
43. Reverse lamp
44. Turn signal flasher unit
45. Turn signal switch
46. L.H. flasher lamp
47. R.H. flasher lamp
48. Turn signal warning light
49. Hazard flasher unit
50. Hazard switch
51. Hazard warning light
52. Belt warning transmission switch
53. Drivers belt switch
54. Passengers seat switch
55. Passengers belt switch
56. Belt warning light
57. Diode
58. Heater motor
59. Heater rheostat
60. Heater switch
61. Radio facility

A. Overdrive (optional extra)

62. Overdrive relay
63. Overdrive transmission switch
64. Overdrive gear lever switch
65. Overdrive solenoid

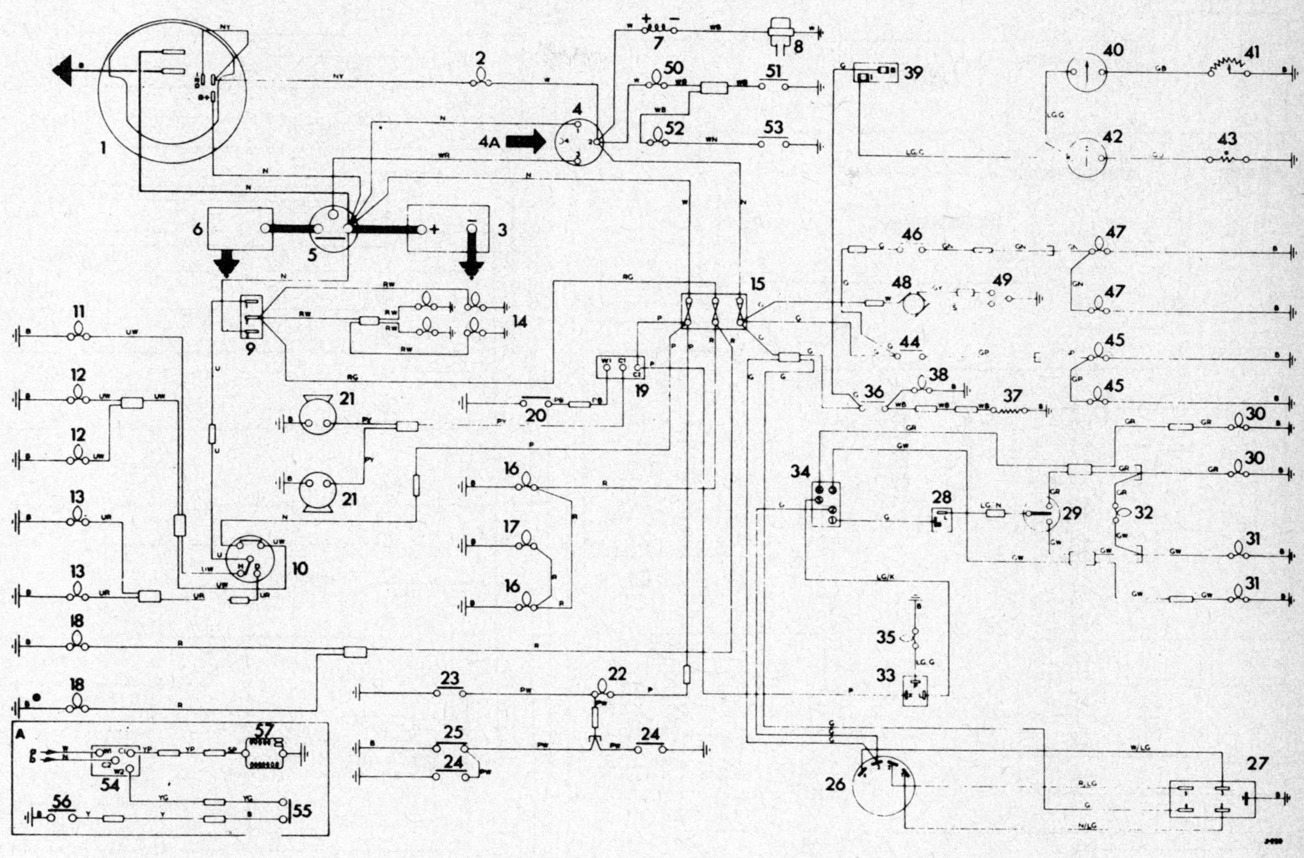

1969-70 GT6+

1. Alternator
2. Ignition warning light
3. Battery
4. Ignition/starter switch
4A. Ignition/starter switch—radio supply connector
5. Starter solenoid
6. Starter motor
7. Ignition coil
8. Ignition distributor
9. Master light switch
10. Column light switch
11. High beam warning light
12. High beam
13. Low beam
14. Instrument illumination
15. Fuse assembly
16. Tail lamp
17. Plate illumination lamp
18. Front parking lamp
19. Horn relay
20. Horn button
21. Horn
22. Interior lamp
23. Interior lamp tailgate switch
24. Interior lamp door switch
25. Interior lamp instrument panel switch
26. Windshield wiper switch
27. Windshield wiper motor
28. Turn signal flasher unit
29. Turn signal flasher switch
30. L.H. Flasher lamp
31. R.H. Flasher lamp
32. Turn signal warning light
33. Hazard flasher unit
34. Hazard switch
35. Hazard warning light
36. Heated rear window switch
37. Heated rear window
38. Heated rear window warning light
39. Voltage stabilizer
40. Fuel indicator
41. Fuel tank unit
42. Temperature indicator
43. Temperature transmitter
44. Stop lamp switch
45. Stop lamp
46. Backup lamp switch
47. Backup lamp
48. Heater motor
49. Heater switch
50. Brake line failure warning light
51. Brake line failure switch
52. Oil pressure warning light
53. Oil pressure switch
A. Overdrive (optional extra)
54. Overdrive relay
55. Overdrive column switch
56. Overdrive transmission switch
57. Overdrive solenoid

(a)—From ignition/starter switch—connector 2
(b)—From ignition/starter switch—connector 1

COLOR CODE

N	Brown
U	Blue
R	Red
P	Purple
G	Green
LG	Light Green
W	White
Y	Yellow
B	Black
S	Slate

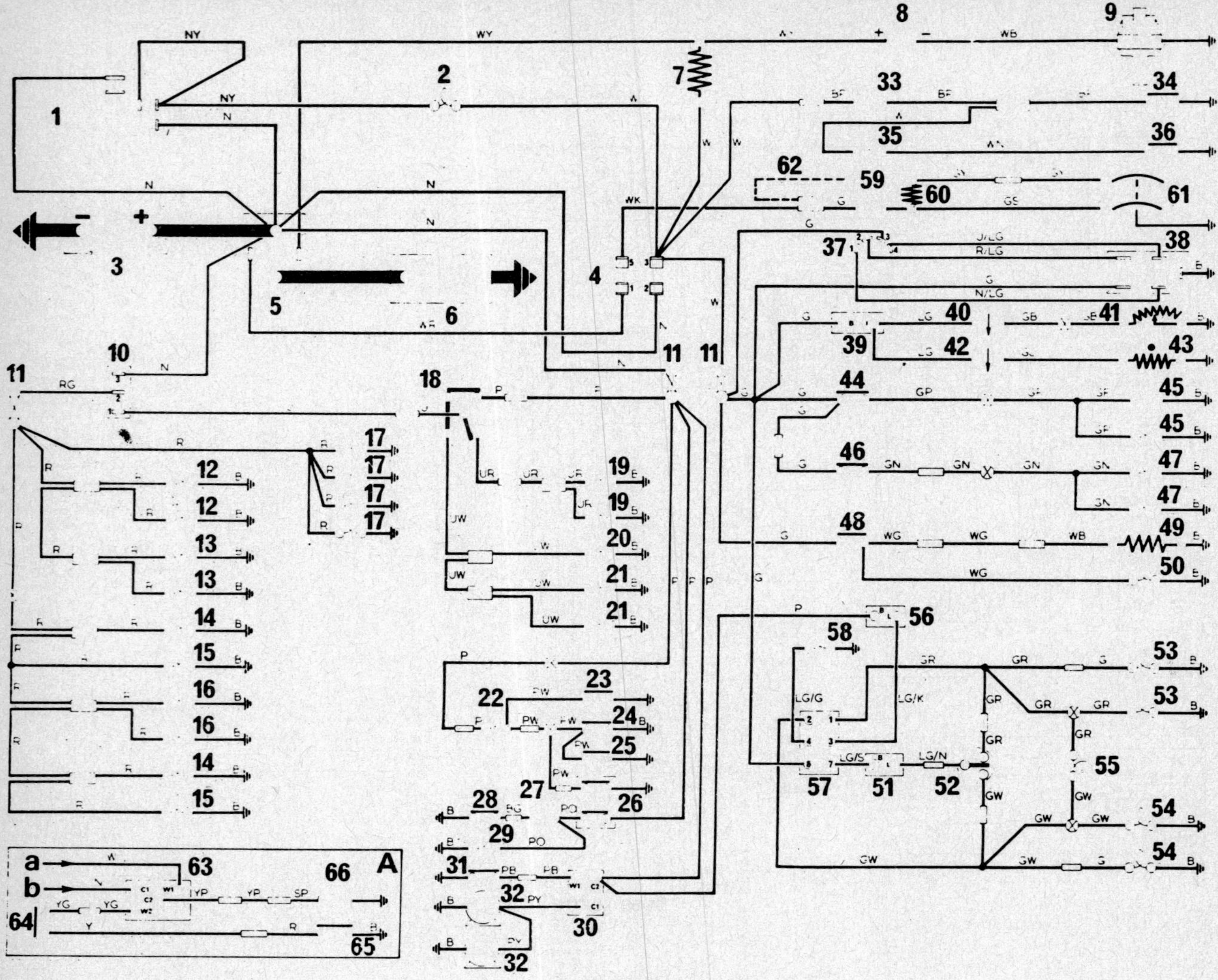

1971-73 GT6 Mk. III

1. Alternator
2. Ignition warning light
3. Battery
4. Ignition/starter switch
5. Starter solenoid
6. Starter motor
7. Ballast resistor
8. Ignition coil—6 volt
9. Ignition distributor
10. Master light switch
11. Fuse
12. Front parking lamp
13. Front marker lamp
14. Rear marker lamp
15. Tail lamp
16. Plate illumination lamp
17. Instrument illumination
18. Column light switch
19. Low beam
20. High beam warning light
21. High beam
22. Interior lamp
23. Tailgate switch
24. Instrument panel switch
25. R.H. door switch
26. L.H. door switch
27. Key warning buzzer
28. Key switch
29. Key courtesy light
30. Horn relay
31. Horn button
32. Horn
33. Brake warning light
34. Brake line failure switch
35. Oil pressure warning light
36. Oil pressure switch
37. Windshield wiper switch
38. Windshield wiper motor
39. Voltage stabilizer
40. Fuel indicator
41. Fuel tank unit
42. Temperature indicator
43. Temperature transmitter
44. Stop lamp switch
45. Stop lamp
46. Backup lamp switch
47. Backup lamp
48. Heated rear window switch
49. Heated rear window
50. Heated rear window warning light
51. Turn signal flasher unit
52. Turn signal switch
53. L.H. flasher lamp
54. R.H. flasher lamp
55. Turn signal warning light
56. Hazard flasher unit
57. Hazard switch
58. Hazard warning light
59. Heater motor
60. Heater rheostat
61. Heater switch
62. Radio

A. Overdrive (optional extra)

63. Overdrive relay
64. Overdrive transmission switch
65. Overdrive gear lever switch
66. Overdrive solenoid

(a)—From ignition/starter switch—terminal 3

(b)—From ignition/starter switch—terminal 2

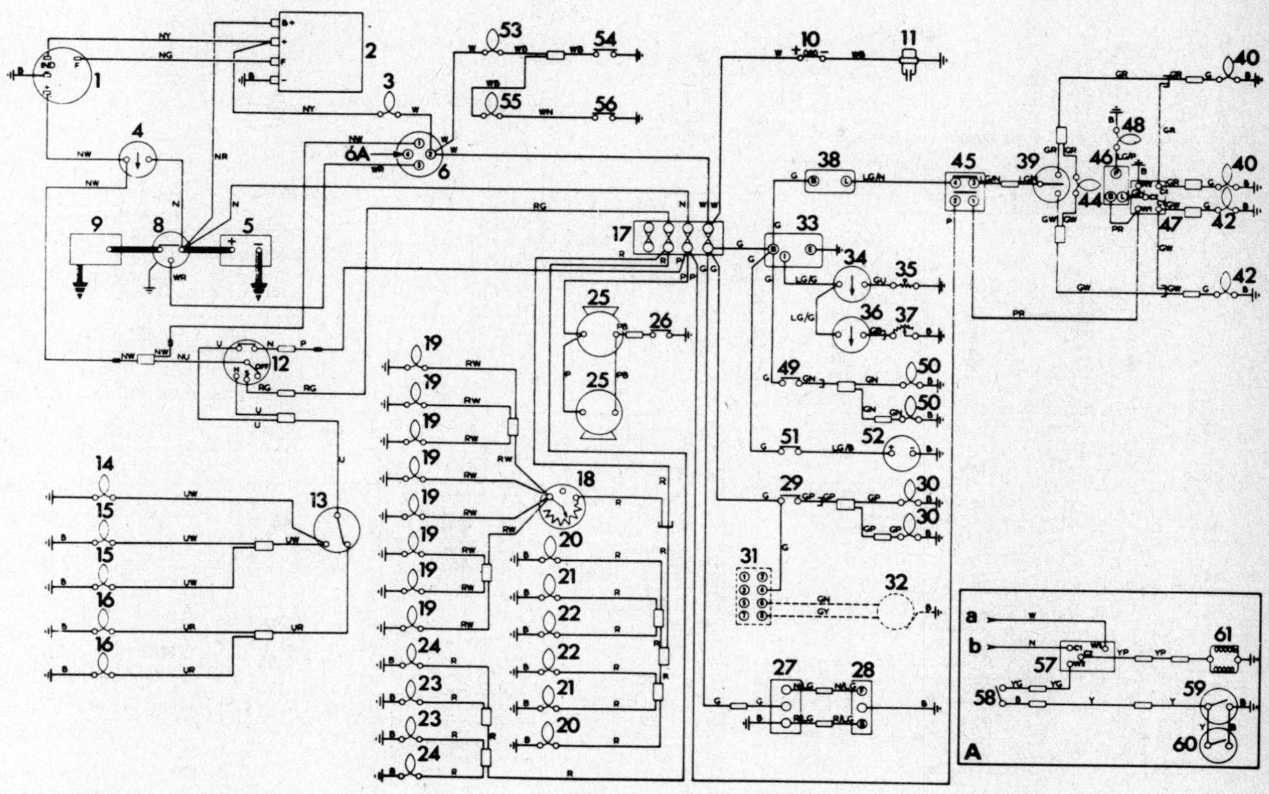

1968 TR-250

1. Alternator
2. Alternator voltage regulator
3. Ignition warning light
4. Ammeter
5. Battery
6. Ignition/starter switch
6a. Ignition/starter switch—radio supply connector
8. Starter solenoid
9. Starter motor
10. Ignition coil
11. Ignition distributor
12. Column light switch
13. Dimmer switch
14. High beam warning light
15. Dimmer beam
16. Low beam
17. Fuse box
18. Panel rheostat
19. Instrument illumination
20. Rear marker lamp
21. Tail lamp
22. Plate illumination lamp
23. Front parking lamp
24. Front marker lamp
25. Horn
26. Horn button
27. Windshield wiper motor
28. Windshield wiper switch
29. Stop lamp switch
30. Stop lamp
31. Heater motor
32. Heater motor
33. Voltage stablizer
34. Temperature indicator
35. Temperature transmitter
36. Fuel indicator
37. Fuel tank unit
38. Flasher unit
39. Flasher switch
40. L.H. flasher lamp
42. R.H. flasher lamp
44. Flasher warning light
45. Hazard switch
46. Hazard flasher unit
47. Hazard relay
48. Hazard warning light
49. Backup lamp switch
50. Backup lamp
51. Windshield washer switch
52. Windshield washer motor
53. Brake pressure differential warning light
54. Brake pressure differential switch
55. Oil pressure warning light
56. Oil pressure switch

A. Overdrive (optional extra)

57. Overdrive relay
58. Overdrive column switch
59. Overdrive transmission switch—2nd gear ON
60. Overdrive transmission switch—3rd and 4th gear ON
61. Overdrive solenoid

(a)—From fuse box

(b)—From fuse box

COLOR CODE

N	Brown
U	Blue
P	Purple
G	Green
LG	Light Green
W	White
Y	Yellow
S	Slate
B	Black

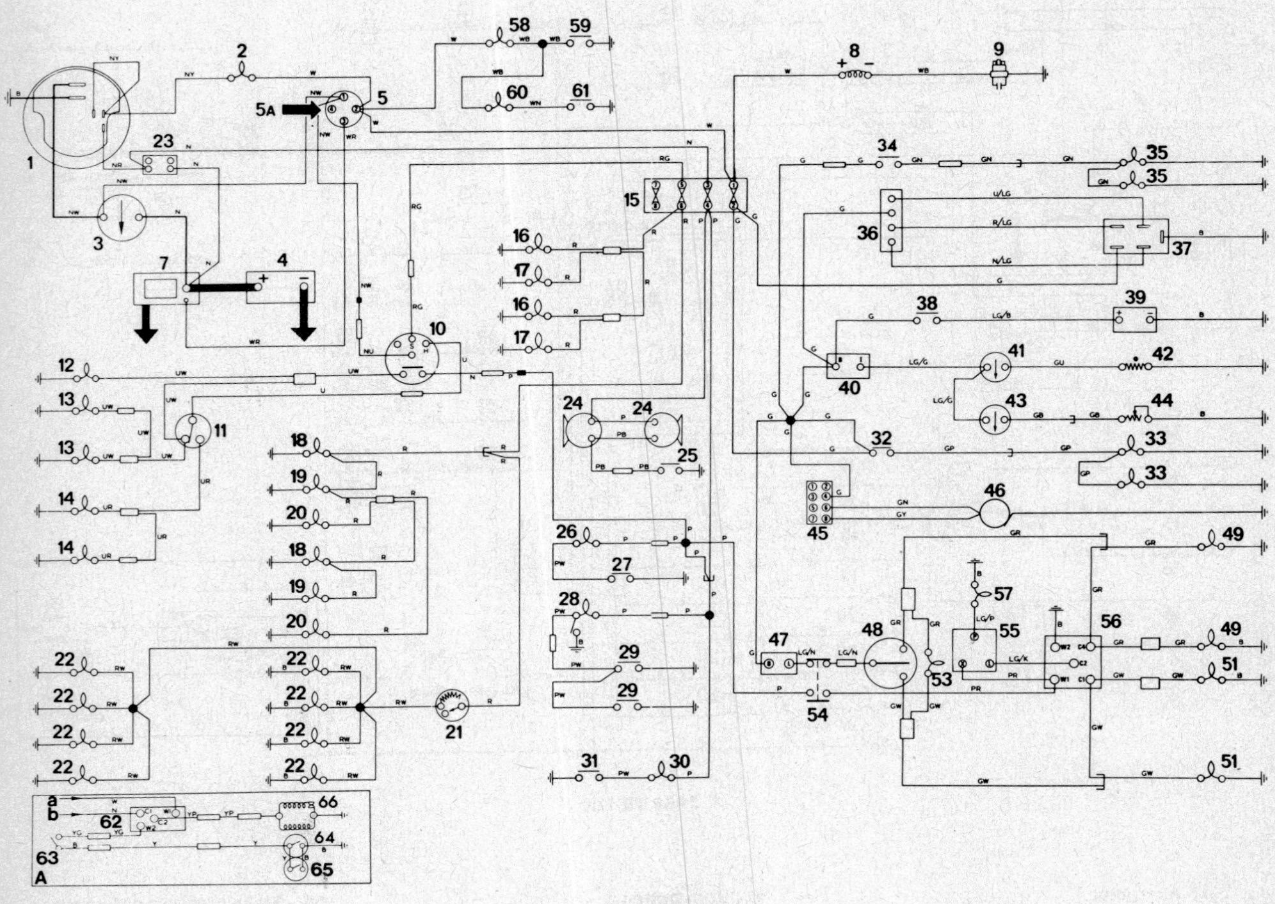

1969-73 TR-6

1. Alternator
2. Ignition warning light
3. Ammeter
4. Battery
5. Ignition/starter switch

5a. Ignition/starter switch radio supply connector

7. Starter motor
8. Ignition coil
9. Ignition distributor
10. Column light switch
11. Dimmer switch
12. High beam warning light
14. Low beam
15. Fuse box
16. Front parking lamp
17. Front marker lamp
18. Rear marker lamp
19. Tail lamp
20. Plate illumination lamp
21. Panel rheostat
22. Instrument illumination
23. Connector block
24. Horn
25. Horn button
26. Glove compartment illumination
27. Glove compartment illumination switch
28. Transmission tunnel lamp
29. Transmission tunnel lamp door switch
30. Trunk lamp
31. Trunk lamp switch
32. Stop lamp switch
33. Stop lamp
34. Backup lamp switch
35. Backup lamp
36. Windshield wiper switch
37. Windshield wiper motor
38. Windshield washer switch
39. Windshield washer pump
40. Voltage stabilizer
41. Temperature indicator
42. Temperature transmitter
43. Fuel indicator
44. Fuel tank unit
45. Heater switch
46. Heater motor
47. Turn signal flasher unit
48. Turn signal switch
49. L.H. flasher lamp
51. R.H. flasher lamp
53. Turn signal warning light
54. Hazard switch
55. Hazard flasher unit
56. Hazard relay
57. Hazard warning light
58. Brake line failure warning light
59. Brake line failure switch
60. Oil pressure warning light
61. Oil pressure switch

A. Overdrive (optional extra)

62. Overdrive relay
63. Overdrive column switch
64. Overdrive transmission switch 2nd gear ON
65. Overdrive transmission switch 3rd and 4th gear ON
66. Overdrive solenoid

(a)—From fuse box
(b)—From fuse box

COLOR CODE

N Brown
U Blue
R Red
P Purple
G Green
LG Light Green
W White
Y Yellow
S Slate
B Black

TUNE-UP PROCEDURES

Spark Plugs

Removal and Installation

Every six months or 6,000 miles, the spark plugs should be removed for inspection. At this time they should be cleaned and regapped. At 12 month or 12,000 mile intervals, the plugs should be replaced.

Prior to removal, number each spark plug with a piece of masking tape bearing the cylinder number. Remove each spark plug wire by grasping its rubber boot and twisting slightly to free the wire from the plug. Using a 13/16 in. spark plug socket, turn the plugs counterclockwise to remove them. Do not allow any foreign matter to enter the cylinders through the spark plug holes.

Consult the spark plug inspection chart in the "Troubleshooting" section. If the plugs are to be reused, check the porcelain insulator for cracks and the electrodes for excessive wear. Replace the entire set if one plug is damaged. Clean the reusable plugs with a stiff wire brush, or in a sandblasting machine. Uneven wear of the center or ground electrode may be corrected by leveling off the unevenly worn section with a file. The gap must be checked with a feeler gauge. With the ground electrode positioned parallel to the center electrode, a 0.025 in. wire gauge must pass through the opening with a slight drag. If the air gap between the two electrodes is not correct, the ground electrode must be bent to bring it to specifications.

After the plugs are gapped correctly, they may be inserted into their holes and hand tightened. Be careful not to cross-thread the plugs. Torque the plugs to their proper specification. Install each numbered plug wire onto its respective plug.

Breaker Points and Condenser

Removal and Installation

Remove the distributor cap and rotor, noting their position. Inspect the contacts and replace the points if the contacts are blackened, pitted or worn excessively, if the breaker arm has lost its tension, or if the fiber rubbing block has become worn or loose. Points that appear light gray in color may be cleaned with a point file.

To replace the points and condenser, disconnect the electrical leads at the primary connection, remove the lock screw for the points and lift them straight up. Loosen the condenser retaining bracket and slide out the condenser. While the points are out, lubricate the breaker cam with a very light coating of silicone based grease. Clean the distributor base plate with alcohol to free it of any oil film that might impede completion of the ground circuit. Also clean the contact point surfaces with the solvent. Install the new points and condenser and tighten their retaining screws. Connect the electrical leads for both at the primary connection. If the point contacts are not aligned, bend the stationary arm to suit.

To gap the contact points, turn the engine until the rubbing block on the point assembly is resting on the high point of the cam lobe. Loosen the point hold-down screw slightly and insert a feeler gauge of the specified thickness (0.014–0.016 in.) between the point contacts. Fine adjustment is made either by inserting a screwdriver into the eccentric adjusting slot on the stationary arm (late distributors) or by turning the eccentric adjusting screw on the stationary arm (early distributors). When the feeler gauge passes between the point contacts with a slight drag, tighten the hold-down screw without disturbing the setting.

Adjusting point gap—GT6+, Spitfire Mk. III.

1. Hold-down screw
2. Eccentric adjusting screw

If a dwell meter is available, proceed to "Dwell Angle Setting". If the meter is not available, install the rotor and cap, and proceed to "Ignition Timing Adjustment".

Dwell Angle Setting

The dwell angle is the number of degrees of distributor cam rotation through which the breaker points remain fully closed (conducting electricity). Increasing the point gap decreases dwell, while decreasing the point gap increases dwell.

Connect the positive wire of the meter to the distributor primary wire connection on the positive side of the coil, and the negative wire of the meter to a good ground on the engine (e.g. thermostat housing nut).

The dwell angle may be checked either with the engine running or with the cap and rotor removed and the engine cranking at starter speed. The meter gives a constant reading with the engine running. With the engine cranking, the reading will fluctuate between zero degrees dwell and the maximum figure for that angle. While cranking, the maximum figure is the correct one. Never attempt to change dwell angle while the ignition is on, as touching the point contacts or the primary wire connection with a metal screwdriver may result in a 12 volt shock.

To change dwell angle, loosen the point hold-down screw slightly and make the approximate correction. Tighten the hold-down screw and test the dwell with the engine cranking. If the dwell appears to be correct, install the rotor and distributor cap and test the dwell with the engine running. Take the engine through its entire rpm range and observe the dwell meter. The dwell should remain within specifications at all times. Great fluctuation of dwell at different engine speeds indicates worn distributor parts.

Following the dwell angle adjustment, the ignition timing must be checked. A 1° increase in dwell results in the ignition timing being retarded 2° and vice-versa.

Ignition Timing

Preliminary Setting-Disturbed Engine

This procedure is used to obtain a rough initial timing setting when the distributor has been removed.

Spitfire

1. Set No. 1 cylinder on TDC of its compression stroke. Set the points to the specified gap.
2. Place the distributor and bracket in the cylinder block. Be sure the distributor gear is engaged.
3. On models with emission controls, start the engine and accelerate to 800–850 rpm. Set the final ignition timing.

GT6+, GT6 MK III

1. Place the distributor in the engine. Be sure the gears are engaged. Set the points to the specified gap and loosely tighten the pinch bolt.
2. Rotate the crankshaft clockwise to 13° BTDC with No. 1 cylinder on its compression stroke. The rotor should be as shown.

   CAUTION: *Be sure not to rotate the engine counter-clockwise.* Set the vacuum unit at mid scale.
3. Connect a 12 volt test light. Rotate the distributor until the points open (light goes out). Tighten down the distributor. With the light still attached, rotate the engine until No. 6 cylinder comes up on its compression stroke. Note the crank-

GT6 distributor in firing position for No. 1 cylinder.

shaft pulley position when the light goes out. Again rotate the engine to TDC on No. 1. Note the pulley position as above. Both readings should be 13° BTDC.

4. Tighten the distributor.

TR-250, TR-6

1. Place No. 1 cylinder at 10° BTDC on its compression stroke. If there is no timing mark or pointer, place No. 1 cylinder at TDC and turn the engine backward slightly. Adjust the points to specifications. Insert the distributor. Be sure the gears are in mesh. Snug down the clamp bracket.

2. Loosen the pinch bolt (1). Align the distributor as shown. Rotate the distributor clockwise. When the points are seen to open, stop. Tighten the pinch bolt. The rotor (3) should be opposite the distributor terminal No. 1 primary wire.

3. Finalize timing with the timing light.

TR-6, TR-250 distributor alignment

Final Ignition Timing

Spitfire Mk III, Mk IV, and 1500

The Spitfire Mk III has two timing marks. When number one piston is at

Timing marks—Spitfire Mk. III

A. Pointer
B. 2° ATDC dynamic timing mark
C. TDC static timing mark

TDC, a *hole* on the inside face of the crankshaft pulley lines up with the pointer on the timing cover. When number one piston is 2° past TDC (i.e., 2° ATDC), the timing cover pointer aligns with a *mark* across the periphery of the crankshaft pulley. Spitfire Mk III timing specs are 6° ATDC (static) and 2° ATDC (stroboscopic). With the vacuum lines disconnected and plugged, time the engine with a strobe light at the idling speed of 800–850 RPM. During the initial static adjustment, the micrometer adjustor on the distributor should be set in the middle of its range. After the clamp bolt has been tightened, the timing should be rechecked. The Spitfire Mk IV and 1500 are provided with a scale, and are adjusted in the same manner to the settings in the Tune-up Chart.

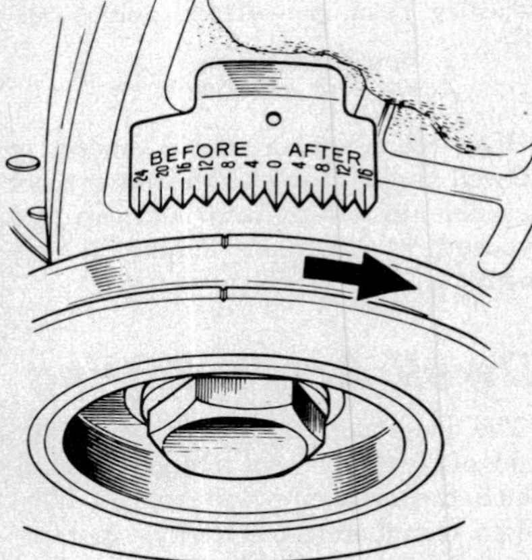

Timing marks—Spitfire Mk. IV, 1500

GT6+, GT6 Mk III

GT6 models with emission control systems require a stroboscopic ignition timing setting for greater accuracy. On earlier models, there is no scale provided on the crankshaft pulley, necessitating the measurement of the advance and retard distances along the periphery of the pulley. When number one piston is at TDC, the timing cover pointer will line up with a white mark on the periphery of the crankshaft pulley. Set 1969–72 GT6 models at 6° BTDC static timing and 4° ATDC at 800–850 rpm using a timing light. 1973 models are provided with a scale and are adjusted to a static setting of 12° BTDC. The 6° BTDC timing point (static setting) is determined by measuring 0.3 in. to the right of the TDC mark already provided. Likewise, the 4° ATDC (*after* TDC) mark is determined by measuring 0.2 in. to the left of the TDC mark on the crankshaft pulley. Later models are provided with a scale that eliminates the necessity of the preceding measurements. Remember to disconnect and plug the vacuum lines prior to adjusting the timing.

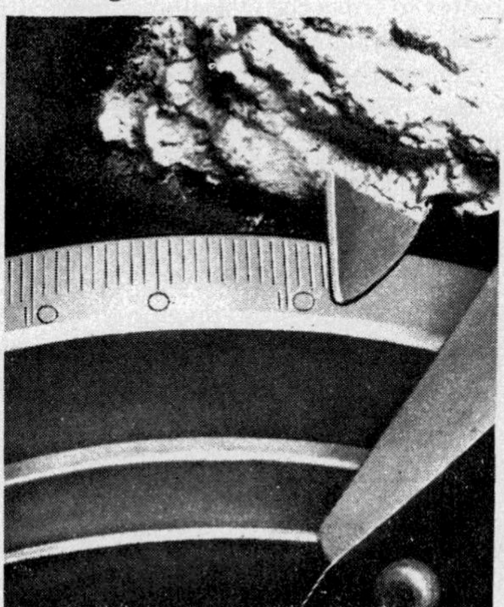

Timing marks—GT6 models, TR-6 similar

TR-250, TR-6

Ignition timing for 1968–72 models is 10° BTDC (static) and 4° ATDC (stroboscopic, at 800–850 rpm) with all vacuum lines disconnected and plugged. For 1973, the static setting has been changed to 12° BTDC. In the case of the TR-250, it may be necessary to measure the distances from the TDC point and mark accordingly. On the TR-250 crankshaft pulley, 10° BTDC is 0.57 in. to the right of the TDC mark, while 4° ATDC is 0.23 in. to the left of TDC. As with the GT6, timing scales are provided on more recent models.

Valve Lash Adjustment

If valve clearances in the Triumph engine are too small, the valves may be seriously damaged by warping or burning, and compression will eventually suffer from lack of proper valve sealing. If the valves are open too long, they will not have sufficient opportunity to rest against their seats, and hence cannot transfer their intense heat to the cylinder head. On the other hand, if valve clearance is too great, the result will be rough running, loss of power, and excessive wear of the valve train components. While no error is excusable, it is best that any errors made be in the direction of too large a clearance, for this at least will prevent the valves from burning.

Valve clearances for the Triumph should be 0.010 in. (0.254 mm.) with the engine cold. For the four-cylinder engines, adjust the valves as follows: turn the crankshaft until the valve to be adjusted is fully open, then rotate the crankshaft one more revolution to be sure that the valve will be fully closed. Loosen the locking nut and adjust the screw until a 0.010 in. (0.254 mm.) feeler gauge will just fit between the valve stem and the rocker arm. Tighten the locking nut and recheck the clearance to see that it has not changed. If the screw is not held with a screwdriver while the nut is being locked, it will tend to turn with the nut and leave the valve with too little clearance. Adjust all eight rocker arms in the preceding manner.

Adjusting valve lash

For the six-cylinder engines, the following sequence of valve clearance adjustments is recommended. Turn the engine clockwise and adjust as follows:

Adjust These Valves	When These Are Fully Open
1 and 3	10 and 12
8 and 11	2 and 5
4 and 6	7 and 9
10 and 12	1 and 3
2 and 5	8 and 11
7 and 9	4 and 6

Carburetor

Tuning and Adjustment

SU HS2

Before tuning the carburetors, make sure that all other engine adjustments, and the engine itself, are up to specifications. Carburetor tuning will only be as good as the engine adjustments that precede it.

The S.U. emission control carburetors on the Spitfire Mk III incorporate a number of changes from the previous S.U. units. A new needle is used to provide a leaner mixture. Jet adjustment restrictors are installed in each carburetor to restrict the range of adjustment of the mixture strength. After the correct mixture has been set at the factory, the restrictor is locked to prevent further enrichment; subsequent adjustment within the range of the restrictor will only lean the mixture. A modified piston damper is installed to provide a more immediate effect on the piston, thereby maintaining acceleration efficiency with the leaner needle. A throttle disc poppet valve is added to supplement the volume of fuel-air mixture when the vehicle is overrunning the engine with the throttle closed.

Loosen both clamping bolts on the throttle coupling and unscrew both fast-idle screws until they are clear of their respective cams. Disconnect the jet control interconnection by loosening the clamping bolts. Disconnect the choke cable. Close the throttles by unscrewing the throttle adjusting screws fully, then open slightly by screwing each adjustment screw one-half turn in the open direction. Be sure that the carburetor piston dampers are filled up.

To stabilize engine temperature and air-fuel mixture requirements, observe the following *tuning conditions.*

Run the engine at a fast idle until normal operating temperature is reached. Ideal ambient temperature is between 60° and 80° F. The engine should be run for at least five minutes after the thermostat has opened. Run the engine for one-half minute at 2,500 rpm under no-load conditions. Start tuning adjustments and carry them out in the shortest possible time. If the time exceeds three minutes, run the engine once again at 2,500 rpm for one-half minute. Repeat this cleaning operation at three-minute intervals until tuning is completed. With this in mind, proceed as follows:

Adjust each throttle screw by the same amount to obtain the correct idle speed (800–850 rpm for Spitfire Mk III). Using a Uni-Syn or other suitable air-flow meter, balance the carburetors while maintaining the given idle speed.

Adjust the mixture setting:

NOTE: *Each time the jet adjusting nut is moved, tap the neck of the suction chamber lightly with a screwdriver handle.* Turn each jet adjusting nut up (to lean) or down (to enrich) until the engine is running as fast as possible. Turn both adjusting nuts very slowly up to lean the mixture until the engine speed just starts to drop, then turn both adjusting nuts down by one-half flat to enrich the mixture. Adjust the idle speed, if necessary, ensuring that both carburetors remain balanced. Using an exhaust gas analyzer (carbon monoxide meter or air/fuel ratio meter), make sure that the percentage of CO or the air/fuel ratio is within the following limits:

Idle CO level, engine warm: 3.5–4.5%
Equiv. air/fuel ratio at idle: 13:1

If the meter reading falls outside the above limits, both adjusting nuts will have to be turned just enough to bring the reading within the limits. Holding the jet adjusting nut of each carburetor, rotate each adjustment restrictor until the vertical tag contacts the carburetor body on the left side as seen from the air cleaner flange. Bend the tag of the adjustment restrictor so that the restrictor locks to the nut.

NOTE: *The preceding applies only if, for reasons such as carburetor replacement or reconditioning, new jet adjustment restrictors are being installed.*

Set the throttle interconnection clamping levers so that there is 0.015 in. (0.38 mm.) clearance between the actuating pins and the lower edge of the fork. There should be a total of 1/32 in. end play between the interconnecting clamping levers and the throttle nuts. With both jet levers pressed to their lowest position, adjust the jet interconnection lever clamping bolts so that the jets begin to open at the same time. With the engine running at 1,500 rpm, use the air-flow meter to ensure that the carburetors are balanced. Reconnect the choke cable so that it has about 1/16 in. free movement before it begins to displace the jet levers. With the choke pulled out until the carburetor jets are about to drop, use the balancing meter to maintain equal adjustment while turning the fast idle screws to obtain the proper hot fast-idle speed—1,100 rpm.

Idle Speed and Mixture Adjustment

Zenith-Stromberg 175 CDSE

These carburetors are used on the TR-250 and TR-6. The letter E signifies that these are emission control carburetors.

Permissible adjustments are limited to the following: (1) idle speed (2) idle emission (controlled by trimming screw), and (3) fast idle. Idle speed is adjusted in the normal manner, which requires the use of a suitable air-flow meter to maintain the balance between the carburetors. The purpose of the idle trimming screw is to provide a very fine degree of adjustment to compensate for the difference between a new, stiff engine and one that has been broken in. It is not an idle mixture adjusting screw, as the amount of adjustment it provides is minimal and can only be detected by means of a CO or air/fuel meter.

In setting the fast idle, ensure that the choke lever on each carburetor is against its stop when the choke control is pushed fully in. If necessary, the cables should be adjusted. Pull the choke control out so that the cable pivot lines up with the center of the fast-idle screw and the center of the cam pivot point. Loosen the locknuts and unscrew both idle screws until each is just contacting the cam. Start the engine and, while it is cold (68°–86° F), adjust the fast-idle screws an equal amount to provide an engine speed of 1,100 rpm. Tighten the locknuts and recheck the fast-idle speed.

Carburetor settings for the TR-250 and 1969 TR-6 are as follows:

Idle CO level: 2.5–3.5% (warm engine)

Equivalent air/fuel ratio: 13.5:1

Carburetor settings for the 1970–73 TR-6 settings are as follows:

Idle CO level: 0.5–2.5% (warm engine)

Equivalent air/fuel ratio: 14.4:1–13.6:1

Zenith-Stromberg 150 CDSE

There are only three permissible adjustments to this unit. They are:

1. Idle speed—screw adjustment
2. Idle emission—to be used only with a fuel/air ratio measuring device.
3. Fast idle—simple screw adjustment.

Settings are as follow:

1969 GT6+;

Idle CO level: 2.5–3.5% (warm engine)

Equivalent air/fuel ratio: 13.5:1

1970 Spitfire Mk III, 1971 Spitfire Mk IV;

Idle CO level: 1.0–3.5% (warm engine)

Equivalent air/fuel ratio: 14.2:1–13.2:1

1970 GT6+, 1971–73 GT6 Mk III, 1972–73 Spitfire Mk IV;

Idle CO level: 0.5–2.5% (warm engine)

Equivalent air/fuel ratio: 14.4:1–13.6:1

ENGINE ELECTRICAL

All Spitfire Mk III, Spitfire Mk IV, GT6+, GT6 Mk III, TR-250, and TR-6 models employ a 12 V, negative ground electrical system consisting of a battery, alternator (or generator) and voltage regulator, starter motor, ignition system, lighting system, accessories, and signaling and instrumentation components.

Distributor

Spitfire and GT6 models use a Delco-Remy distributor. TR-250 and TR-6 models use a Lucas distributor. Removal and installation procedures for both are the same.

Removal and Installation

1. Detach the spring clips and remove the distributor cap, low tension wire, and vacuum connection. Remove the tachometer drive.
2. Release the clamping plate and withdraw the distributor assembly.

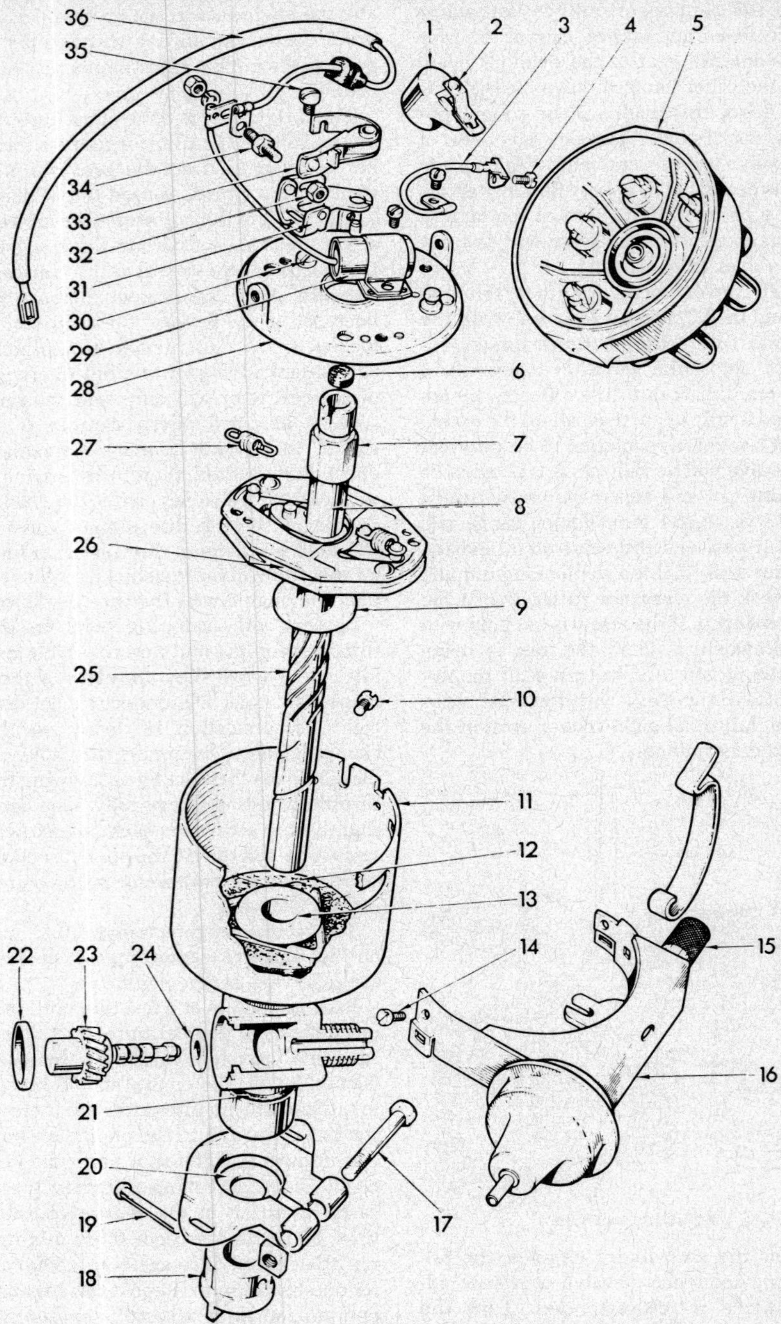

Delco-Remy distributor disassembled—GT6 series, Spitfire similar

1. Rotor
2. Rotor contact
3. Mounting plate lead
4. Side screw
5. Cap
6. Oil retaining felt
7. Cam
8. Cam spindle
9. Upper thrust washer
10. Short side screw
11. Housing
12. Oil retaining felt
13. Upper sintered iron bearing
14. Side screw
15. Vernier adjustment knob
16. Vacuum advance mechanism
17. Clamp bolt
18. Coupling
19. Coupling pin
20. Lower thrust washer
21. Rubber O-ring
22. Staked plug
23. Tachometer drive gear
24. Thrust washer
25. Shaft and centrifugal advance mechanism unit
26. Weight
27. Control spring
28. Mounting plate
29. Condenser
30. Eccentric screw
31. Fixed contact
32. Terminal stud inner nut
33. Moving contact
34. Terminal stud
35. Lock screw
36. Low tension wire

NOTE: *Do not loosen the pinch bolt unless the ignition timing is to be reset, and note the position of the rotor prior to removal of the assembly.*

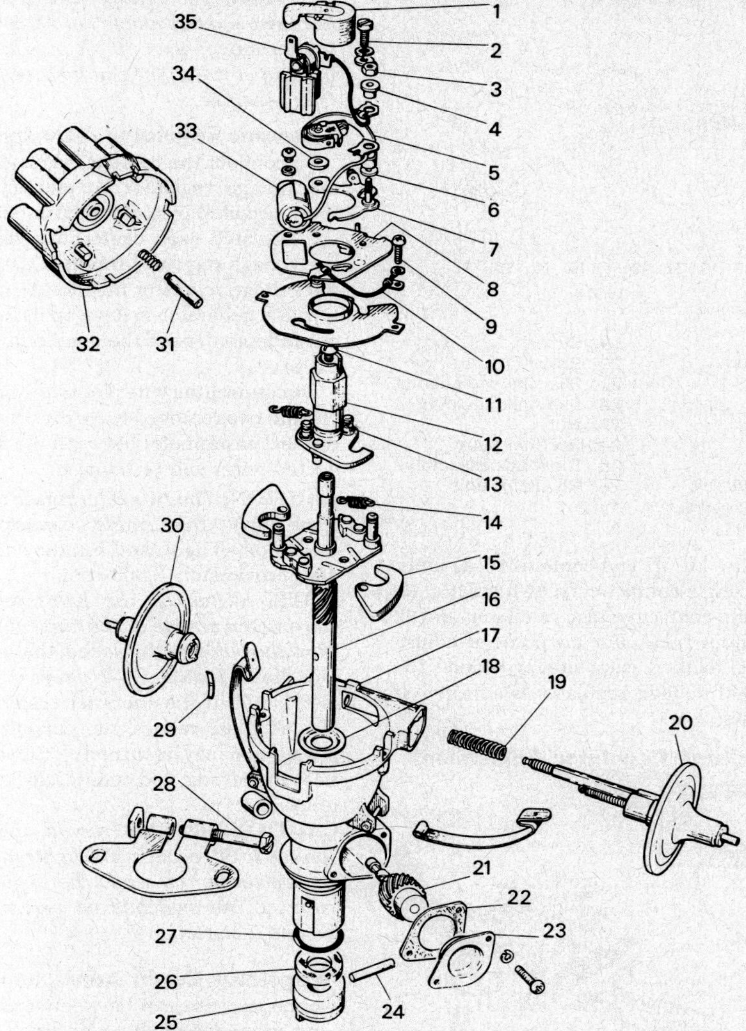

Lucas dual diaphragm distributor disassembled—TR-250, TR-6

1. Rotor
2. Lock screw
3. Nut
4. Insulation piece
5. Moving contact
6. Small insulation washer
7. Fixed contact
8. Moving plate
9. Side screw
10. Moving plate ground lead
11. Cam spindle screw
12. Cam
13. Cam spindle
14. Control spring
15. Weight
16. Shaft and action plate
17. Body
18. Spacer collar
19. Spring
20. Vacuum advance unit
21. Tachometer drive gear
22. Gasket
23. Cover
24. Driving dog pin
25. Driving dog
26. Thrust washer
27. Rubber O-ring
28. Clamp bolt
29. Retaining spring
30. Retard unit
31. High tension carbon brush
32. Cover
33. Condenser
34. Large insulation washer
35. Terminal block

3. If the pinch bolt has not been loosened, replace the distributor by reversing the installation procedure, and rotate the distributor rotor until it properly engages the driving shaft, then secure the clamping plate.

Charging System

Mark III Spitfires are equipped with a 22 amp Lucas C40–1 generator and Lucas RB–340 voltage regulator. The TR-250 uses a 28 amp Lucas 15 AC alternator with a Lucas 4TR regulator. The 1971–72 Mark IV Spitfire, 1969–70 GT6+, 1971–72 Mark III GT6, and 1969–71 TR-6 all utilize a 28 amp Lucas 15 ACR alternator with integral voltage regulator. 1973 Mark IV Spitfires and Mark III GT6's use a similar 34 amp 16 ACR integral alternator-regulator, and 1972–73 TR-6's use a 36 amp 17 ACR integral alternator-regulator.

Alternator (Generator) Removal and Installation

All Models

1. Disconnect the electrical leads, taking note of their placement.
2. Loosen the main mounting bolt and the adjustment bracket bolts.
3. Push the alternator (generator) toward the engine and remove the drive belt from the pulley.
4. Remove the outer adjustment bracket bolt and, supporting the weight of the unit, remove the main mounting bolt and spacer.
5. Reverse the above procedure to install, taking care to properly tension the drive belt.

Alternator Precautions

Several precautions must be observed when performing work on alternator equipment.

1. If the battery is removed for any reason, make sure that it is reconnected with the correct polarity. Reversing the battery connections may result in damage to the one-way rectifiers.
2. Never operate the alternator with the main circuit broken. Make sure that the battery, alternator, and regulator leads are not disconnected while the engine is running.
3. Never attempt to polarize an alternator.
4. When charging a battery that is installed in the vehicle, disconnect the negative battery cable.
5. When utilizing a booster battery as a starting aid, always connect it in parallel; negative to negative, and positive to positive.

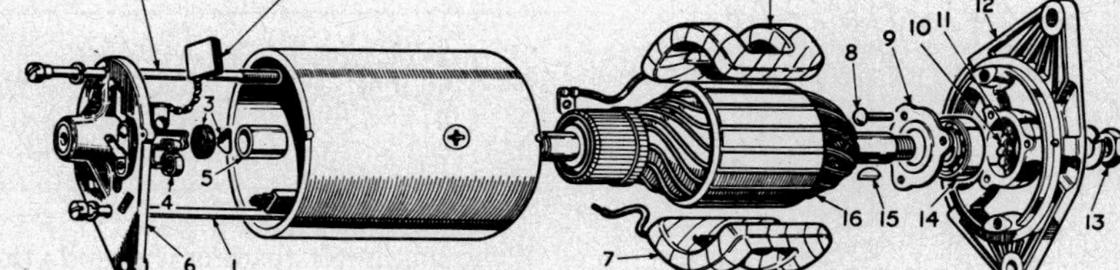

Lucas C40-1 generator disassembled

1. Bolts
2. Brush
3. Felt ring and aluminum sealing disc
4. Brush spring
5. Bearing bushing
6. Commutator end bracket
7. Field coils
8. Rivet
9. Bearing retainer plate
10. Corrugated washer
11. Felt washer
12. Driving end bracket
13. Pulley retainer nut
14. Bearing
15. Woodruff key
16. Armature

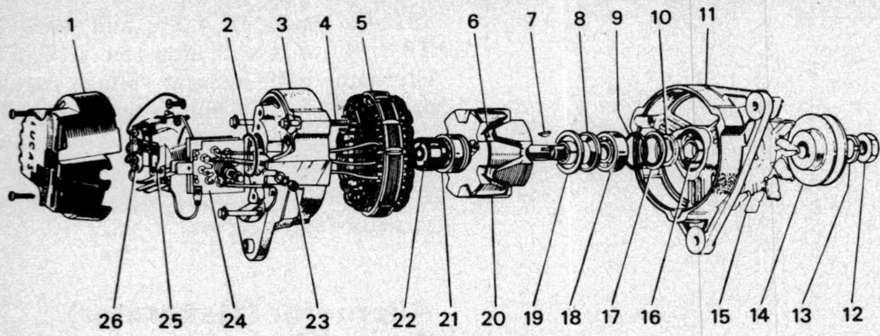

Lucas 15 ACR alternator disassembled

1. Moulded cover
2. Rubber O-ring
3. Slip ring end bracket
4. Through bolt
5. Stator windings
6. Field winding
7. Key
8. Bearing retaining plate
9. Pressure ring
10. Felt ring
11. Drive end bracket
12. Nut
13. Spring washer
14. Pulley
15. Fan
16. Spacer
17. Pressure ring and felt ring retaining plate
18. Drive end bearing
19. Circlip
20. Rotor
21. Slip ring end bearing
22. Slip ring moulding
23. Nut
24. Rectifier pack
25. Brushbox assembly
26. Regulator unit

6. When arc welding is to be performed on any part of the vehicle, disconnect the negative battery cable, disconnect the alternator leads, and unplug the voltage regulator.

Drive Belt Adjustment

Check the drive belt for cracks and wear. Replace it if its condition is questionable. The belt should be adjusted so that it is possible to depress the belt approximately ¾ in. between the pulleys of the longest run. To adjust, loosen the adjusting bolt and alternator (generator) mounting bolt, then pivot the alternator (generator) until the belt has the correct amount of free movement. Tighten the bolts in this position.

NOTE: *Do not use a metal pry bar against the aluminum alternator housing to tension the belt.*

Voltage Regulator

The AC voltage regulators are non-adjustable and must be replaced as a unit.

The RB-340 Voltage Regulator

This voltage regulator is used in the Spitfire, Mk III and contains three units: (1) a single-contact current regulator, (2) a single-contact voltage regulator, and (3) a cut-out relay. For purposes of adjustment, toothed cams are provided. The RB-340 voltage regulator is adjusted as follows:

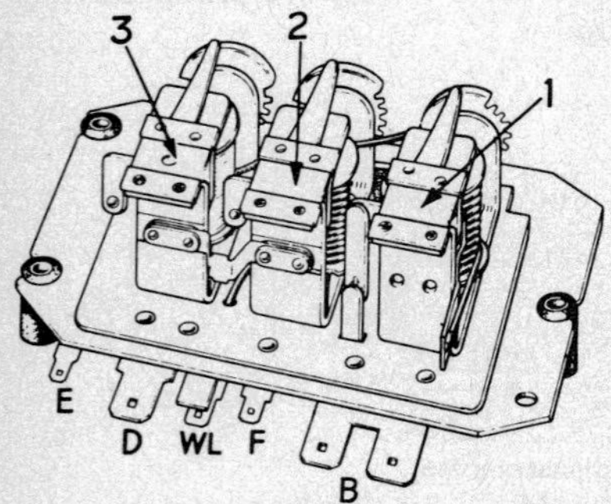

Lucas RB 340 DC voltage regulator

1. Cut-out relay
2. Current regulator
3. Voltage regulator

Voltage Regulator Adjustment

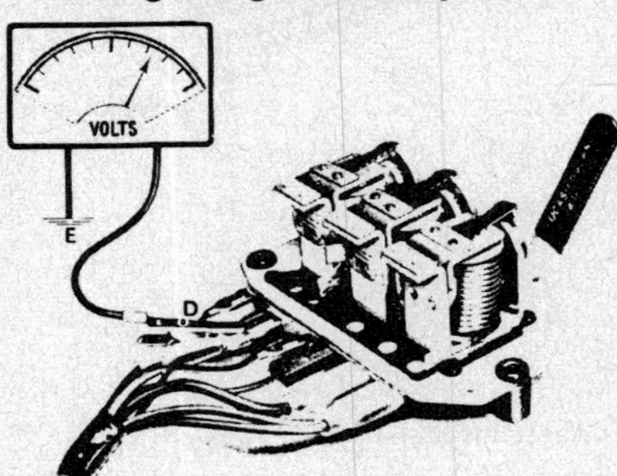

RB 340 test circuit—voltage setting adjustment, cut-in voltage adjustment.

Disconnect the wires from the control box terminal B and connect a voltmeter between terminal D and ground. Connect the two removed wires with a suitable clip. Increase the engine speed until the generator speed is approximately 3,000 rpm and note the reading on the voltmeter, which should be as follows:

Temperature	Voltage Range
50° F	14.9-15.5
68° F	14.7-15.3
86° F	14.5-15.1
104° F	14.3-14.9

If the voltmeter reading is outside the range specified, rotate the voltage adjustment cam clockwise to raise the voltage reading, and counterclockwise to lower it. After adjusting the voltage, stop the engine, restart, and repeat the measurement procedure.

CAUTION: *The voltage regulator adjustment and test should not be carried out for longer than 30 seconds or the heating of the shunt coil will result in false readings.*

Current Regulator Adjustment

To conduct the current regulator test, the voltage regulator contact must be short-circuited by a clip placed between the insulated fixed contact bracket and the voltage regulator frame. This makes the voltage regulator inoperative and allows the generator to develop its full output independent of the condition of the battery.

Disconnect the wires from terminals B, clip the two removed wires together, and connect an ammeter between the disconnected wires and terminal B.

CAUTION: *The two B terminals must have only this single connection.* Switch on all lights and run the engine at approximately 3,300 rpm.

NOTE: *Switch on the lights before starting the engine or the current may blow the bulbs.* At this speed, the ammeter should register 20–24 amps for the C40-1 unit. If the ammeter reading is outside these ranges, the current adjusting cam may be turned clockwise to raise the setting, and counterclockwise to lower it.

CAUTION: *This test should also be limited to 30 seconds. The lights should not be turned on while the engine is running, but switched on before the engine is started.*

Regulator Cut-in Adjustment

Connect a voltmeter between terminal D and ground. Switch on all lights and start the engine, slowly increasing its speed. While the engine is gradually accelerated, observe the voltmeter. The voltage should rise steadily and then drop slightly when the contacts close. The cut-in voltage is the figure reached just before the voltmeter pointer drops. If the headlights are turned on, the drop will be easier to spot. If the cut-in voltage is outside of the limits 12.7–13.3 volts, adjust by turning the adjusting cam clockwise to raise and counterclockwise to lower the setting. After each adjustment, repeat the test and complete within 30 seconds each time. After removing the voltmeter and replacing all disturbed components, check the drop-off voltage as follows:

Remove the wires from terminal B of the control box and connect them together. Connect a voltmeter between terminal B and ground. Start the engine and increase its speed until the cut-in speed is exceeded, then slowly decelerate the engine and observe the voltmeter needle. When the contacts open, the needle should drop to zero—this should happen between 9.5 and 11.0 volts. If adjustment is required, this is done by

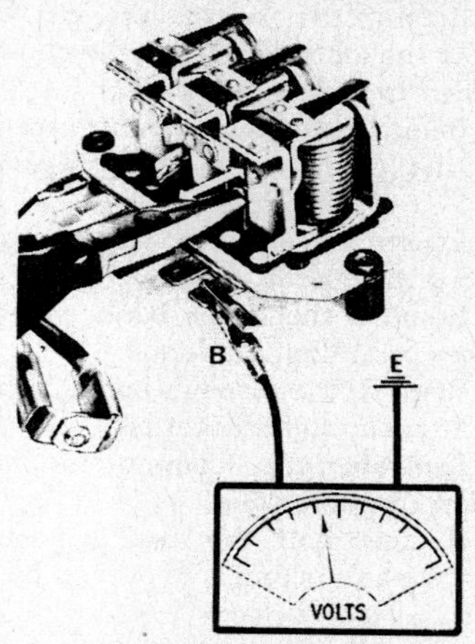

RB 340 test circuit—drop off setting adjustment.

slightly bending the fixed contact. Closing the gap will raise the drop-off voltage, while opening it will reduce the voltage.

The Lucas 4TR Voltage Regulator

The 4TR voltage regulator is used on the TR-250 which is equipped with an alternator in place of a DC generator. Because of this, the 4TR does not have a current regulator as alternators have inherent self-regulating current characteristics, and it does not have a cutout since diodes incorporated in the alternator perform this function. The only maintenance required is ensuring that the contacts, the multi-socket connector, and the cover remain clean and dry.

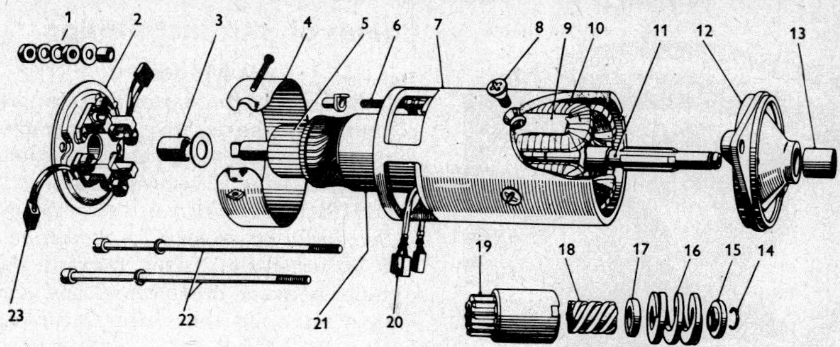

Lucas M35G starter disassembled—M35J similar.

1. Terminal post nuts and washers
2. Commutator end bracket
3. Commutator end bracket bearing bushing
4. Cover band
5. Commutator
6. Terminal post
7. Yoke
8. Pole shoe screw
9. Pole shoe
10. Field winding
11. Shaft
12. Drive end bracket
13. Drive end bracket bearing bushing
14. Ring
15. Shaft collar
16. Main spring
17. Buffer washer
18. Screwed sleeve
19. Pinion and barrel
20. Field winding brush
21. Armature
22. Through bolts
23. Ground brush

Starter

The Spitfire Mk III and GT6+ use a Lucas M35G starter with remote solenoid. The Spitfire Mk IV uses a similar Lucas M35J starter with remote solenoid. The GT6 Mk III is equipped with a Lucas #25149 starter. The TR-250 and 1969–72 TR-6 utilize a Lucas M418G starter with integral solenoid. The 1973 TR-6 employs a similar Lucas M100 starter with integral solenoid.

1. Cover band
2. Motor lead
3. 'STA' terminal
4. Solenoid battery terminal
5. Contact assembly spring
6. Contact assembly
7. Hold in winding
8. Pull in winding
9. Plunger
10. Outer engaging spring
11. Inner engaging spring
12. Return spring
13. Lost motion spring
14. Rubber moulding
15. Engaging lever
16. Eccentric pin
17. Fixing bracket
18. Fixing bracket bearing bush
19. Thrust washer
20. Jump ring
21. Thrust collar starter drive—
22. Pinion
23. Pinion bearing
24. Roller clutch action
25. Drive sleeve
26. Distance piece
27. Drive operating plate
28. Field winding
29. Pole shoe
30. Pole shoe screw
31. Yoke
32. Armature
33. Insulation strip
34. Commutator
35. Brush
36. Steel thrust washer
37. Fabric thrust washer
38. Commutator end bracket
39. Commutator end bracket bearing bushing

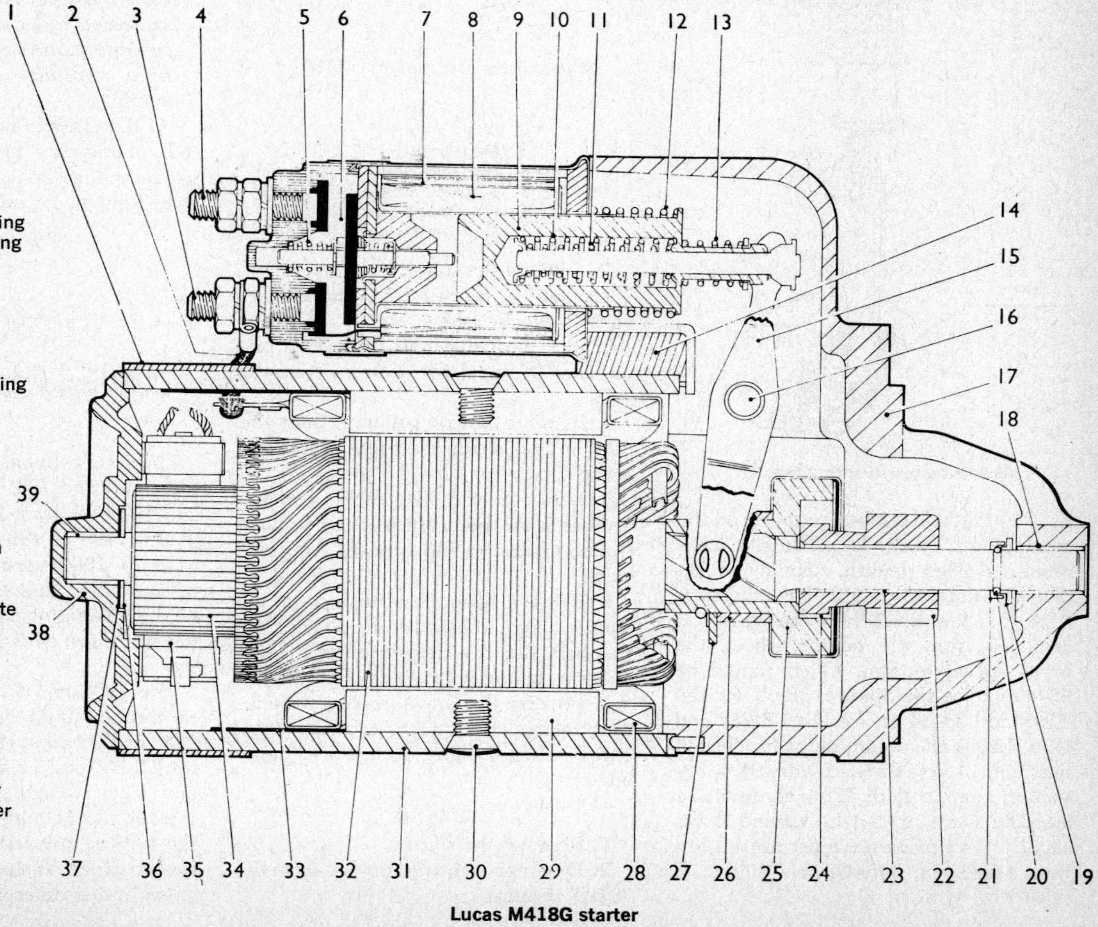

Lucas M418G starter

Typical remote starter solenoid

Starter Maintenance

The only maintenance normally required on starters is an occasional cleaning and checking of the brushes and commutator. To accomplish this, remove the starter motor, take off the metal band cover, and make sure that the brushes move freely in the brush holders by pulling gently on the flexible connection. If a brush has a tendency to stick, remove it from its holder and clean its sides with a cloth soaked in a safe solvent. Replace the brushes in their original positions.

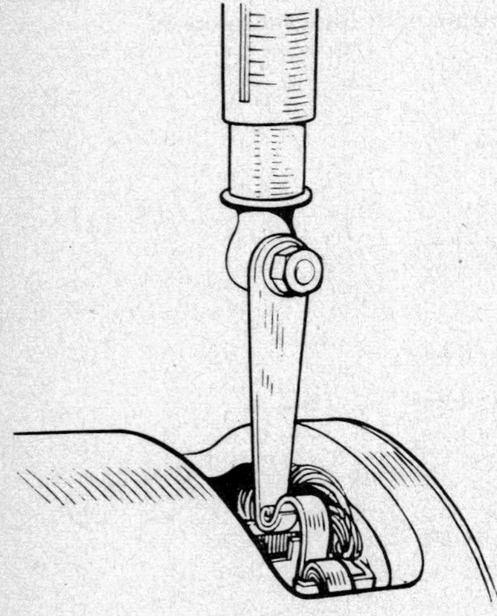

Measuring brush spring tension

Brushes that will not bed properly on the commutator, or are less than the minimum specified length, should be replaced. Minimum length for brushes is 5/16 in. (8 mm.). While the starter is removed from the engine, check the brush spring tension, which should be 32–40 oz. for the Spitfire, 36 oz. for the TR-6, and 30–34 oz. for the TR-250 and GT6. Check the commutator for cleanliness and, if necessary, clean with a solvent moistened cloth. If the commutator is badly worn, it can be turned down slightly. The diameter must not be less than 1 9/32 in. (M35G) or 1 17/32 in. (M418G).

Removal and Installation

All Models

1. Removal of the starter requires disconnecting of the negative battery cable, disconnecting all terminal connections and withdrawing all securing bolts.

   CAUTION: *The starter is very heavy. Be careful not to drop or damage it.*

2. To install the starter, measure the distance between the flywheel ring gear (pinion side) and the starter mounting face.
3. In addition, measure the distance from the starter face to the pinion end. End clearance from the starter pinion to the flywheel ring gear should be 3/32 to 5/32 in. (shims are available).
4. Connect all cables. Be sure the battery lead is connected last.

Starter Drive Replacement

M35G, M35J

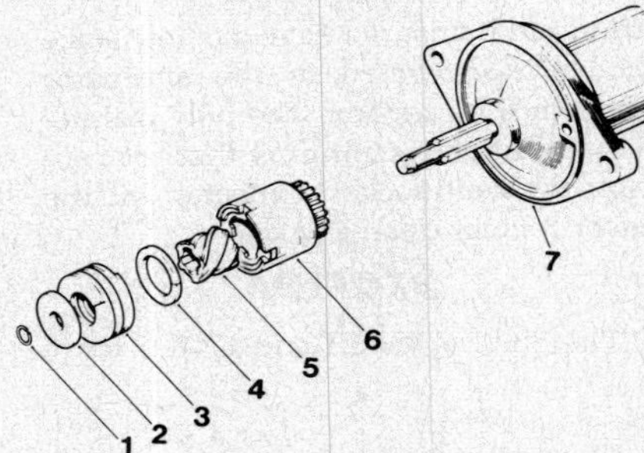

Starter drive components—M35J

1. Jump ring
2. Shaft collar
3. Main spring
4. Buffer washer
5. Screwed sleeve
6. Pinion and barrel
7. Drive end bracket

1. Remove the starter.
2. Remove the two drive end bracket bolts and lockwashers.
3. Pull the drive end bracket, armature, and inertia drive assembly from the yoke.
4. Remove the four retaining bolts and position to one side the commutator end bracket.
5. Lift out the two field winding brushes from the brush box and remove the commutator end bracket from the yoke.
6. Using a hand press, compress the main spring and ease the snap-ring from the shaft. Remove the starter drive components, taking note of their placement.
7. Reverse the above procedure to install, taking care to lubricate the drive end bracket bushing with 10W engine oil.

M418G

1. Remove the starter.
2. Disconnect the motor lead from the "STA" terminal.
3. Remove the two retaining nuts and pull out the solenoid, leaving the plunger attached to the engaging lever.
4. Remove the plunger return spring, then the plunger, from the engaging lever.
5. Loosen the locknut. Unscrew and pull out the eccentric pin.
6. Remove the cover band and the brushes from their holders.
7. Remove the through bolts. Lightly rap the mounting bracket lugs.
8. Separate the commutator end bracket from the yoke.
9. Remove both the steel and fabric thrust washers taking note of their placement.
10. Remove the rubber molding. Pull out the armature and starter drive assembly.
11. Remove the engaging lever and thrust washer.
12. Using a tube with an internal diameter of ⅝ in., place the tube over the shaft end and force the thrust collar of the snap ring toward the starter drive.
13. Remove the snap-ring from the shaft groove.
14. Remove the thrust collar and the starter drive. Replace the entire drive assembly if the roller clutch is defective.

    CAUTION: *Do not wash the starter drive in gasolene or paraffin, as this will remove the permanent lubricant from the sealed roller clutch. Use instead a gasolene moistened cloth to clean the drive, carefully avoiding the roller clutch.*

15. Reverse the above procedure to install, taking care to lubricate the drive sleeve splines and pinion bearing with Shell Retinax grease or its equivalent.

ENGINE MECHANICAL

The four cylinder Spitfire engine displaces 1296 cc (79.2 cu in.) in the Mark III and 1971–72 Mark IV versions, and displaces 1493 cc (91 cu in.) in the 1973 Mark IV (1500) version. The 1493 cc unit is essentially a stroked version of the 1296 cc unit, resulting in higher torque and lower exhaust emissions over the smaller unit.

The 1998 cc (122 cu in.) six cylinder powerplant used in the GT6, and the 2498 cc (152 cu in.) six employed both in the TR-250 and TR-6 share the same bore and block design. The 2498 cc unit's greater power and torque over that of the 1998 cc unit arises out of its 0.748 in. longer stroke, as well as carburetion and valve timing differences.

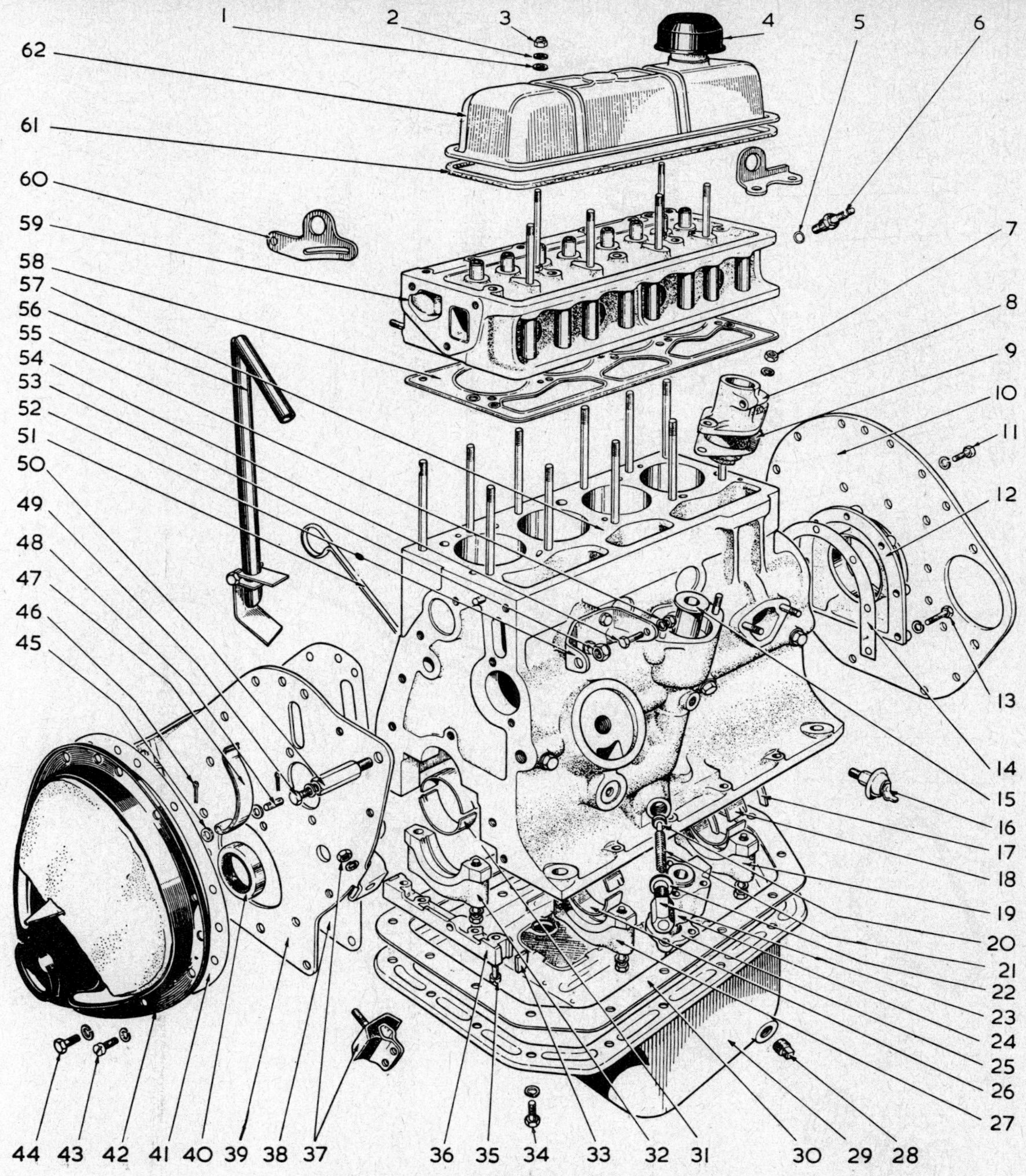

Stationary components of four cylinder Spitfire engine

1. Fiber washer
2. Plain washer
3. Nyloc nut
4. Filler cap
5. Copper/asbestos washer
6. Spark plug
7. Nut
8. Adaptor
9. Gasket
10. Rear engine plate
11. Bolt
12. Rear oil seal
13. Bolt
14. Gasket
15. Oil pump drive shaft bushing
16. Oil pressure switch
17. Crankshaft thrust washer
18. Rear bearing shell
19. Rear bearing cap
20. Relief valve
21. Spring
22. Copper washer
23. Cap nut
24. Oil pump body
25. Oil pump end plate
26. Center bearing shell
27. Center main bearing cap
28. Drain plug
29. Oil pan
30. Oil pan gasket
31. Front bearing shell
32. Front main bearing cap
33. Sealing wedges
34. Sump bolt
35. Slotted screw
36. Front sealing block
37. Front engine mounting
38. Gasket
39. Front engine plate
40. Oil seal
41. Gasket
42. Front timing cover
43. Slotted setscrew
44. Bolt
45. Plain washer
46. Cotter pin
47. Chain tensioner
48. Pivot pin
49. Bolt
50. Generator pedestal
51. Dipstick
52. Bracket
53. Nyloc nut
54. Bolt
55. Nyloc nut
56. Breather pipe
57. Cylinder block
58. Cylinder head gasket
59. Cylinder head
60. Generator adjusting link
61. Rocker cover gasket
62. Rocker cover

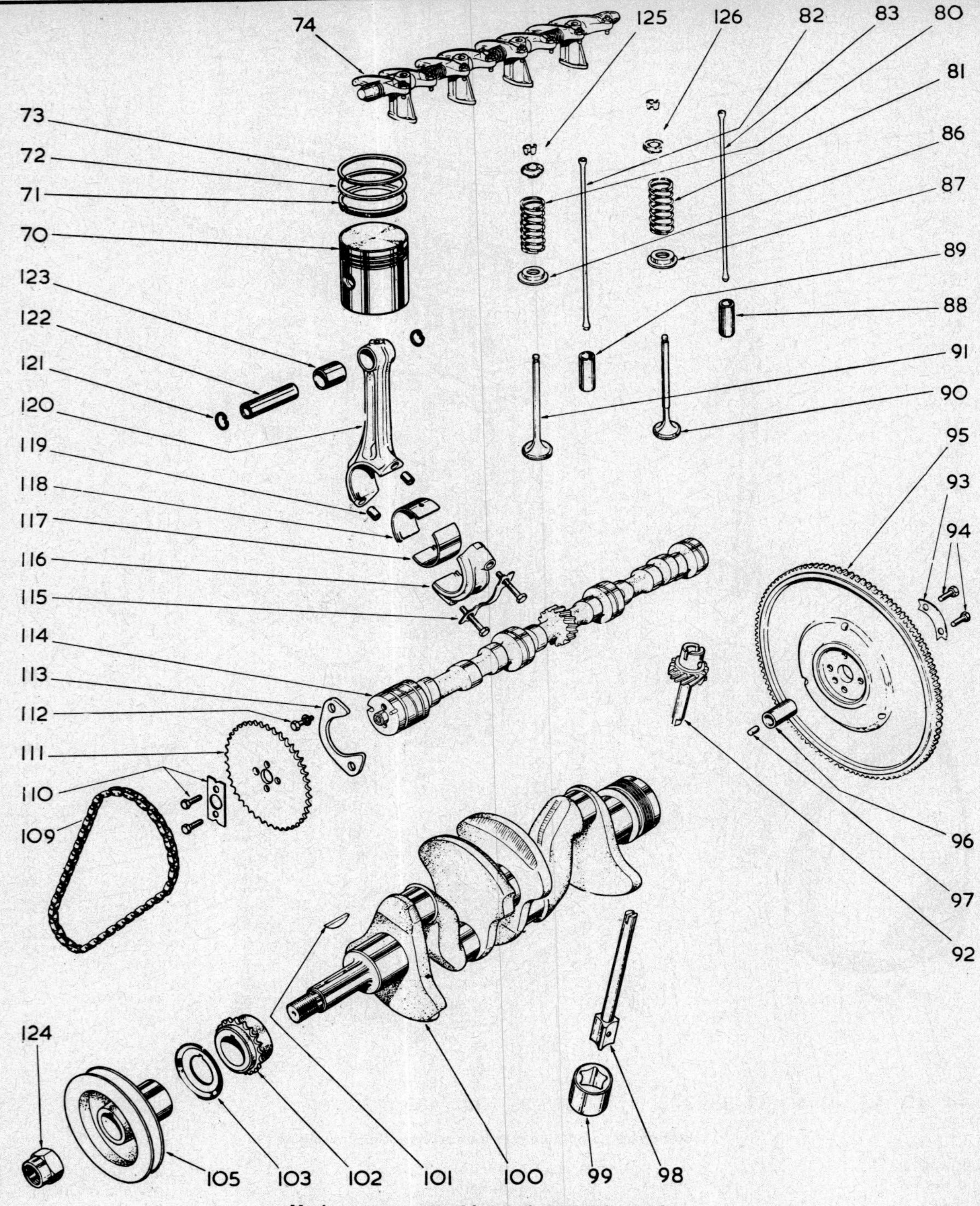

Moving components of four cylinder Spitfire engine

70. Piston
71. Oil control ring
72. Taper compression ring
73. Plain compression ring
74. Rocker assembly
80. Spring—outer
81. Spring—inner
82. Pushrod
83. Pushrod
86. Spring seats
87. Spring seats
88. Tappet
89. Tappet
90. Exhaust valve
91. Intake valve
92. Distributor and oil pump drive gear
93. Lock tab
94. Bolt
95. Flywheel
96. Bush
97. Dowel
98. Inner rotor and spindle
99. Outer rotor
100. Crankshaft
101. Key
102. Sprocket
103. Slinger
105. Crankshaft pulley
109. Timing chain
110. Bolts and lock tab
111. Camshaft sprocket
112. Bolt
113. Keeper plate
114. Camshaft
115. Bolt and locktab
116. Con-rod cap
117. Con-rod bearing shell—lower
118. Con-rod bearing shell—upper
119. Dowels
120. Con-rod
121. Circlip
122. Piston pin
123. Piston pin bushing
124. Nut
125. Retainer and keeper
126. Retainer and keeper

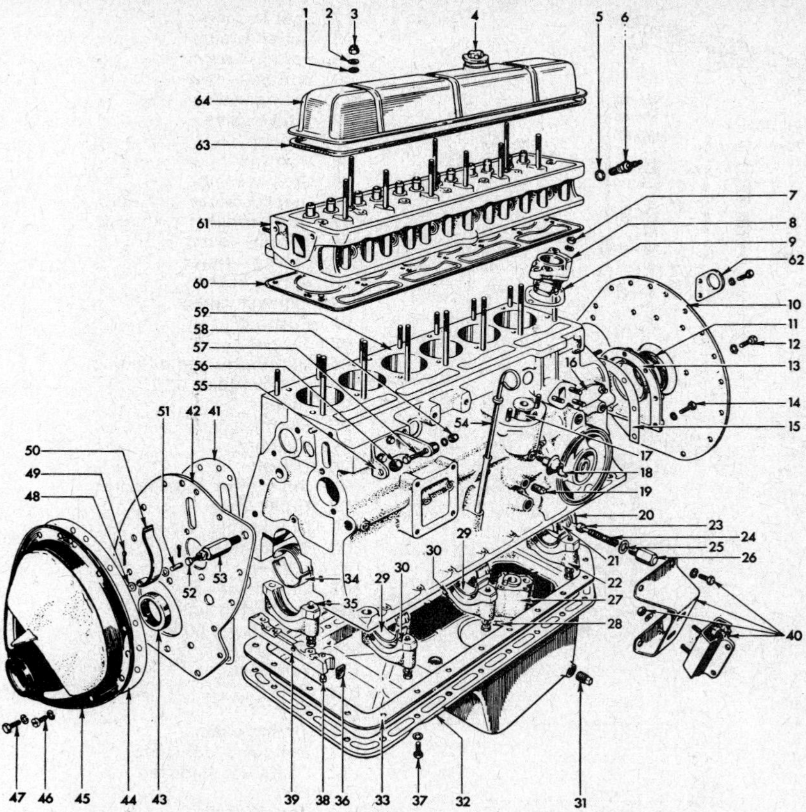

Stationary components of six cylinder GT6 engine—TR-250, TR-6 units similar

1. Fiber washer
2. Plain washer
3. Nyloc nut
4. Filler cap
5. Copper/asbestos washer
6. Spark plug
7. Nut
8. Adaptor
9. Gasket
10. Rear engine plate
11. Rear oil seal
12. Bolt
13. Rear oil seal housing
14. Bolt
15. Gasket
16. Banking plate
17. Oil pump drive shaft bushing
18. Oil pressure switch
19. Plug
20. Crankshaft thrust washer
21. Rear bearing shell
22. Rear bearing cap
23. Relief valve
24. Spring
25. Copper washer
26. Cap nut
27. Oil pump body
28. Oil pump end plate
29. Center bearing shell
30. Center main bearing cap
31. Drain plug
32. Oil pan
33. Oil pan gasket
34. Front bearing shell
35. Front main bearing cap
36. Sealing wedges
37. Oil pan bolt
38. Slotted screw
39. Front sealing block
40. Front engine mounting
41. Gasket
42. Front engine plate
43. Oil seal
44. Gasket
45. Front timing cover
46. Slotted setscrew
47. Bolt
48. Plain washer
49. Cotter pin
50. Chain tensioner
51. Pivot pin
52. Bolt
53. Generator pedestal
54. Dipstick
55. Bracket
56. Nyloc nut
57. Bolt
58. Nyloc nut
59. Cylinder block
60. Cylinder head gasket
61. Cylinder head
62. Lifting eye
63. Rocker cover gasket
64. Rocker cover

Engine Removal and Installation

Spitfire

Remove the engine and transmission of the Spitfire as follows:

1. Drain the cooling system, engine and transmission.

2. Disconnect the battery and remove the hood.

3. Disconnect and plug the fuel inlet line.

4. Remove the air cleaners, choke and throttle controls, starter motor cable, heater hoses, and the exhaust pipe flange and bracket to the clutch housing.

5. Remove the radiator and hoses and disconnect the coil cables, oil pressure switch cable, generator alternator cables, ground strap, fuel connector to the pump, and tachometer cable.

6. Remove the front seats and carpeting, transmission cover attaching screws, dashboard support bracket and transmission cover.

7. Disconnect the speedometer cable, clutch slave cylinder, overdrive solenoid wires (if installed), and the front end of the driveshaft.

8. Remove the transmission gear shift extension, installing a cardboard cover in its place.

9. With the engine supported by a hoist attached to the lifting eyes, release the front and rear engine mountings and lift the engine and transmission assembly until the oil pan clears the chassis crossmember. Lift the assembly and push it forward until the transmission is clear of the vehicle.

10. To install the engine, reverse the above procedure.

GT6

1. Disconnect the battery, drain the cooling system, transmission, and engine sump, and remove the air cleaner.

2. Remove the front hood assembly and radiator components.

3. Remove the front support members at the side of the engine by removing the three bolts at the front and two bolts at the rear.

4. Remove the seat cushions, seats, dashboard support bracket, safety belt anchor bolts, transmission tunnel screws, gear-shift lever knob, and carpeting.

5. Remove the 12 screws and plates and lift off the transmission cover.

6. Disconnect the driveshaft from the transmission drive flange and detach the slave cylinder, speedometer drive cable, and exhaust pipe attachment.

7. With first gear selected, remove the transmission top cover and extension assemblies. Place a cardboard cover over the transmission opening.

8. Remove the rear transmission mounting bracket nuts and release the mounting bracket. Place a jack under the oil pan in order to support the engine.

9. Remove the fuel line from the fuel pump, disconnect the tachometer drive cable from the distributor, and release the oil pressure switch and alternator wires. Remove the ignition lead wire from the coil.

10. Disconnect the heater hoses and remove the cable from the heater control valve. Disconnect the choke and throttle controls, the electrical connection to the starter motor, and the ground strap from the bellhousing.

11. Release the wire from the temperature sending unit at the thermostat housing. Disconnect the front exhaust pipe from the manifold flange and transmission, and remove the ground strap from the front engine plate.

12. Supporting the weight of the engine with a hoist, remove the nuts, bolts and shims from the engine mountings and raise the engine sufficiently to enable the positioning of a brake line protection plate (a special plate designed to protect the vulnerable brake line at the front from damage when the engine and transmission are removed). If this special tool is not available, a suitable substitute may be fabricated according to the dimensions and material described in the accompanying diagram. Raise the engine,

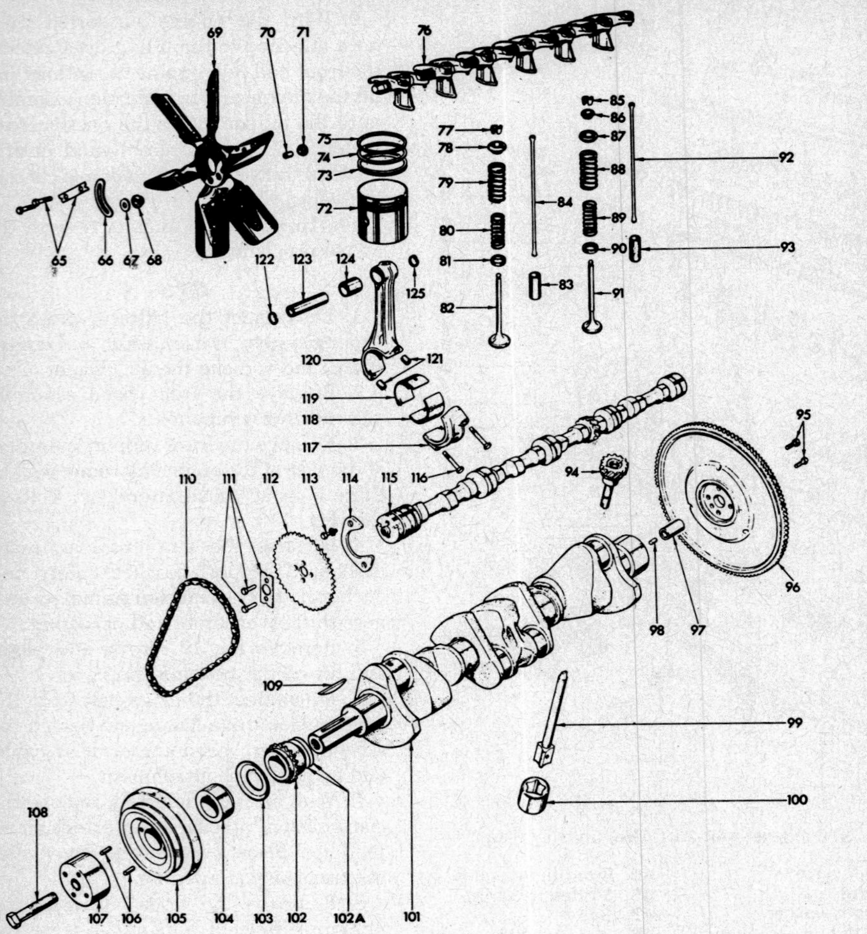

65. Bolts and lock tabs
66. Balance weight
67. Washer
68. Rubber bushing
69. Fan assembly
70. Steel bushing
71. Rubber bushing
72. Piston
73. Oil control ring
74. Tapered compression ring
75. Plain compression ring
76. Rocker shaft assembly
77. Split keepers
78. Collar retainer
79. Spring—outer
80. Spring—inner
81. Spring seats
82. Intake valve
83. Tappet
84. Pushrod
85. Split keepers
86. Inner retainer (exhaust)
87. Outer retainer (exhaust)
88. Spring—outer
89. Spring—inner
90. Spring seats
91. Exhaust valve)
92. Pushrod
93. Tappet
94. Distributor and oil pump drive gear
95. Bolts
96. Flywheel
97. Bushing
98. Dowel
99. Inner rotor and spindle
100. Outer rotor
101. Crankshaft
102. Sprocket
102A. Shim
103. Oil slinger
104. Seal extension
105. Crankshaft pulley
106. Dowels
107. Fan boss
108. Bolt
109. Key
110. Timing chain
111. Bolts and lock plate
112. Camshaft sprocket
113. Bolt
114. Keeper plate
115. Camshaft
116. Bolt
117. Con-rod cap
118. Con-rod bearing shell—lower
119. Con-rod bearing shell—upper
120. Con-rod
121. Dowels
122. Circlip
123. Piston pin
124. Piston pin bushing
125. Circlip

Moving components of six cylinder GT6 engine—TR-250, TR-6 units similar

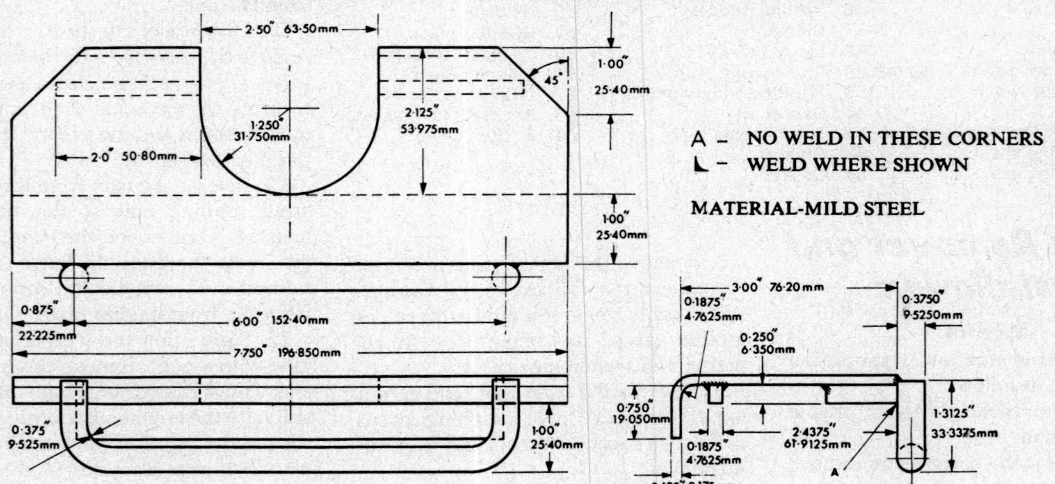

GT 6 brake line protection plate details

at the same time tilting it to the rear and pulling it forward, and maneuver the engine-transmission assembly from the car.

13. In replacing the engine and transmission, the assembly is hoisted into position and suspended while the front and rear mountings are secured to the frame.

TR-250, TR-6

The six-cylinder engine is removed usually along with the transmission.

1. Disconnect the battery and remove it from the car. Remove the front hood.

2. With the heater set to the HOT position and the radiator cap removed, drain

the cooling system via the cylinder block and radiator taps.

3. Disconnect the choke control cables, the throttle linkage at the cross-shaft lever, and the fuel supply line. Release the radiator overflow at the filler cap, the radiator hoses, the heater hoses, and the heater valve control cable.

4. Remove the electrical connections of the starter motor solenoid, positive lead to coil, alternator, oil switch, ground strap, and water temperature sending unit.

5. Disconnect the oil pressure pipe at the crankcase, the tachometer drive at the distributor, the brake servo pipe and clip, the ignition advance and retard lines, and the breather pipe from the air cleaner.

6. Remove the radiator air deflector attachments, air deflector, radiator support struts, and lift out the radiator. Remove the tubular crossmember beneath the radiator.

7. Remove the air cleaner, the U-clamps attaching the steering box to the chassis, and the exhaust pipe from the exhaust manifold flange.

8. From within the car, remove the driver's and passenger's seats, console, carpeting, and the bolts which secure the transmission cover. Remove the gearshift lever knob and rubber boot and withdraw the transmission cover from the right side of the car.

9. Disconnect the backup light connection and the overdrive relay leads (if installed).

10. Disconnect the driveshaft at the transmission flange, the exhaust bracket at the transmission mounting, and the clutch slave cylinder bracket from the bellhousing. Remove the pin from the slave cylinder actuating rod.

11. Loosen the bolts which secure the transmission rear mounting and support bracket. Disconnect the speedometer cable and remove the transmission cover.

12. With a hoisting cable attached to the engine lifting eyes, support the weight of the transmission rear extension and remove the engine front mounting next to the steering linkage and remove the two securing bolts from the opposite mount. Remove the transmission mounting and support plate, and maneuver the engine-transmission assembly clear of the car.

NOTE: *The engine may be removed alone leaving the transmission in place, although this is not recommended. To remove the engine alone, proceed as above until the transmission cover is removed. Then support the transmission and attach the hoist to the lifting eyes. Disconnect the clutch housing from the engine and remove the starter motor. Support the engine using the hoist and remove the engine mounting brackets. Raise the front of the engine, pull it forward and lift it clear of the body.*

13. To install the engine reverse the above procedure.

NOTE: *Do not allow the weight of the engine and transmission to rest on the transmission input shaft.*

Cylinder Head

Removal and Installation

All Models

1. Disconnect the battery, drain the cooling system, and disconnect the cable of the cylinder head.

2. Remove the air cleaner(s) and the intake and exhaust manifolds.

3. Loosen the generator mounting bolts, pivot the generator toward the cylinder head and detach the belt from the water pump pulley. Remove the bolts which secure the water pump to the cylinder head and remove the pump.

4. Remove the rocker arm cover, the rocker assembly, and the pushrods. Be sure that all electrical and hose connections to the cylinder head have been disconnected. Remove the spark plugs.

5. Loosen and remove the cylinder head nuts in reverse order of the tightening sequence shown for each model. Lift off the cylinder head.

NOTE: *If the cylinder head does not lift readily, tap each side with a hammer, using a short piece of wood to help absorb the shock. Another method is to reinsert the spark plugs and crank the engine with the starter, using the engine's own compression pressure to supply the force needed to break the seal.*

6. Before replacing the cylinder head, be sure that the gasket surfaces of the head and block are perfectly clean and smooth. If any dirt is present, the gasket may leak when the head is installed. Check for the presence of dirt or carbon particles in the stud passages in the head. Also, inspect the valves and guides for wear and damage. Check valve stems for wear and distortion. Any valve with a head thickness less than 1/32 in. (0.8 mm.) at the seat edge should be replaced. Valve guide wear may be checked by inserting a new valve into the guide, lifting it ⅛ in. (3.2 mm.) from its seat, and moving it sideways, as shown in the accompanying illustration. If the movement of the valve head across the seat exceeds 0.020 in. (0.5 mm.), the guide should be replaced. Valve guides must protrude above the top face of the cylinder head as follows:

TR-250, GT6, Spitfire: 0.749–0.751 in. (19.025–19.075 mm)

TR-6: 0.63 in. (16 mm)

7. Upon replacing the head gasket, note its markings and position it accordingly. After slipping the head gasket over the studs, lower the cylinder head into position. Tighten the cylinder head nuts finger tight, then gradually tighten them in the proper order.

8. Replace the valve rocker arm assembly and reverse the cylinder head removal sequence covered previously. Check the valve clearances before running the engine, then again after a brief running period when normal temperature is reached. Make a third check after a few hundred miles and at this time check the cylinder head nuts for tightness and tighten them to the specified torque. Although tightening down the cylinder head nuts will affect valve clearances slightly, the differences will not usually be enough to warrant resetting the valves. However, the clearances should be checked.

Upper Cylinder Area Cleaning

Clean, or decarbonize, the upper cylinder area as follows: Remove the cylinder head, valves, and head gasket. Plug the water passages with clean rags. In the absence of special equipment, use a blunt scraper to clean the carbon deposits from the piston crowns, cylinder block, and cylinder head. Allow a ring of carbon to remain around the periphery of the piston crown, and around the top of the cylinder bore. To facilitate this, place an old piston ring in the bore so that it rests on top of the piston.

Clean and gap the spark plugs. Clean carbon deposits from the valve stems, valve ports, and combustion chamber surfaces. Use compressed air after cleaning to remove any remaining particles. Next, clean all components thoroughly with kerosene and permit to dry before reassembly. Replace the cylinder head and gasket as described in the preceding section.

Cylinder Head Overhaul

See "Engine Rebuilding" section.

Rocker Shaft

Removal and Installation

All Models

1. Disconnect the negative battery cable.

2. Disconnect any positive crankcase ventilation hoses and retaining clips for vacuum hoses from the rocker cover.

3. Remove the rocker cover retaining screws and lift off the rocker cover and gasket.

4. Evenly loosen, a few turns at a time in rotation, the 4 nuts (four cylinder) or 6 nuts (six cylinder) with washers which secure the rocker shaft pedestals to the cylinder head, and lift off the rocker shaft

assembly.

5. Prior to installation, loosen the locknuts and back off the tappet adjusting nuts a few turns to avoid bending the pushrods when tightening the rocker shaft nuts.

6. Position the rocker shaft assembly on the cylinder head, making sure that the pushrods seat correctly on their balls and that the adjusting screws are located correctly. Hand tighten the rocker assembly nuts a few turns.

7. Evenly tighten the rocker shaft pedestal nuts in an order (from the front) of 3–2–4–1 to a torque of 26–32 ft lbs for 4-cylinder Spitfire engines, and in an order of 4–3–5–2–6–1 to 24–26 ft lbs for 6-cylinder GT6 series, TR-250, and TR-6 engines.

8. Connect the negative battery cable.

Intake Manifold

Removal and Installation

All Models

1. Disconnect the negative battery cable.

2. Drain the cooling system.

3. Remove the air cleaner. Disconnect the throttle linkage spring and disconnect the choke cable(s) from the carburetor(s).

4. Disconnect the vacuum lines, the fuel lines, and the water hoses from the induction assembly.

5. Unscrew the nuts (or bolts) and remove the clamps which retain the manifold to the cylinder head and to the exhaust manifold (if so equipped). Remove the manifold.

NOTE: *If the intake manifold gasket is in need of replacement, the exhaust manifold must be removed first.*

6. To install, reverse the above procedure taking care to torque the nuts (or bolts) to specifications.

7. Connect the negative battery cable.

Exhaust Manifold

Removal and Installation

All Models

1. Remove the intake manifold.

2. Remove the nuts which retain the exhaust manifold to the exhaust pipe and discard the old gasket.

3. Remove the nuts (or bolts) which retain the manifold to the cylinder head. Remove the manifold and discard the old gasket.

4. To install, reverse the above procedure taking care to use new gaskets and to torque the nuts (or bolts) to specifications.

Timing Gear Cover

Removal and Installation

Spitfire

1. Remove the drive belt.

2. Remove the four bolts which retain the fan to the water pump pulley and remove the fan.

3. Remove the crankshaft damper nut (accessible from below).

NOTE: *It may be necessary to block the flywheel to stop the crankshaft from turning. Replace the nut loosely and pull off the damper with a gear puller.*

4. Remove the five screws, six bolts, and one nut which retain the timing gear cover to the engine. Lift off the cover with its gasket, taking care not to damage the seal.

4. To install, reverse the above procedure taking care to install a new gasket on the cover dowels. To ease installation of the cover, hold the chain tensioner back with a bent length of rod until the tensioner clears the chain. When installing the pulley, take care to position the drive key between the pulley and the crankshaft spindle. Tighten the nut to specifications. Readjust the drive belt tension.

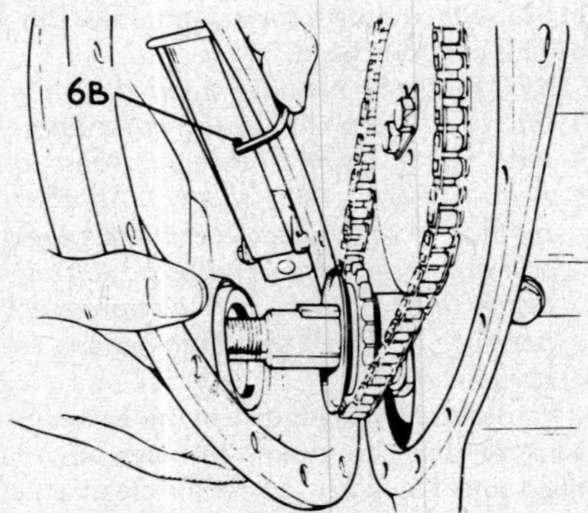

Installing timing chain cover holding tensioner back with bent rod (6B).

GT6 series, TR-250, TR-6

1. Drain the cooling system. Drain the engine sump. Disconnect the overflow pipe and tank, if so equipped.

2. Remove the radiator support(s), radiator valance(s), and radiator.

3. Remove the fan, cross tube and drive belt.

4. On the TR-250 and TR-6, remove the U-bolts from the steering rack and ease the rack forward.

5. Remove the fan adaptor. Using a gear puller, remove the crankshaft pulley.

6. Remove the nuts, bolts and screws which retain the timing cover to the engine, and remove the cover, gasket, and spacer.

7. To install, reverse the above procedure using a new cover gasket. To ease installation, hold the chain tensioner back with a bent length of rod until the tensioner clears the chain. Readjust the drive belt tension.

Oil Seal Replacement

All Models

1. Remove the timing gear cover.

2. Tap out the old seal taking care not to damage the sealing surfaces of the cover.

3. Smear the new seal with engine oil and, making sure that the cavity face of the seal faces the engine, install it into the cover using a drift or wooden block.

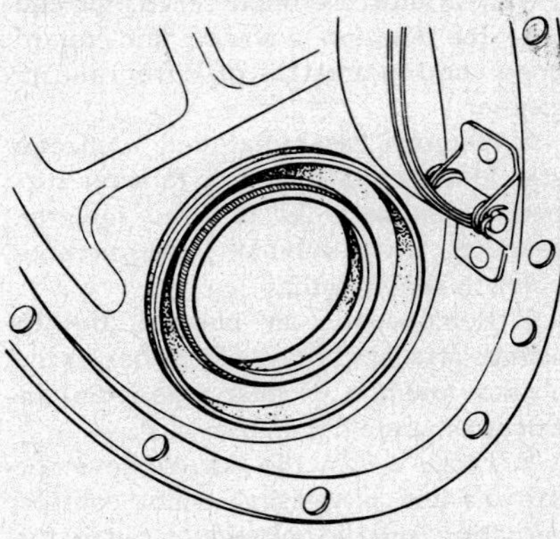
Oil seal installation

4. Install the timing gear cover as outlined under the applicable "Timing Gear Cover Removal and Installation" procedure.

Timing Chain

The Spitfire four cylinder and the GT6 six cylinder engines use a single width timing chain whereas the TR-250 and TR-6 six cylinder engines use a duplex timing chain. Removal and installation procedures are the same for both.

Removal and Installation

All Models

1. Remove the timing gear cover as outlined in the applicable "Timing Gear Cover Removal and Installation" procedure.

2. Remove the oil thrower.

3. Check timing chain wear by placing a straight edge along the slack length of chain. If the free-play "A" between the straight edge and the chain, at a point midway between the two sprockets, exceeds 0.4 in., the chain must be discarded and replaced.

4. Rotate the crankshaft until the crankshaft key is at 12 o'clock and the sprocket dots align.

5. Pry back the locking tabs and remove the bolts which retain the camshaft sprocket to the camshaft.

6. Taking care not to disturb the crankshaft or camshaft, remove both sprockets with the timing chain.

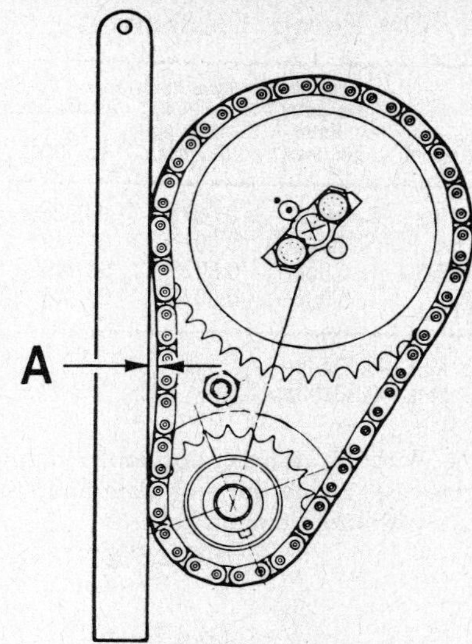

Checking timing chain slack

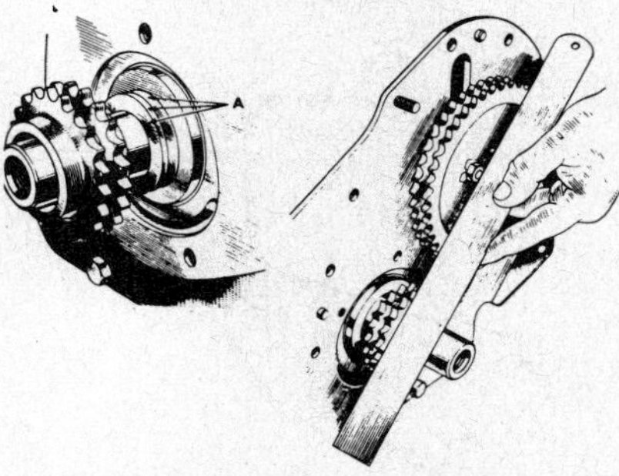

Checking sprocket alignment (right), correcting alignment with shims (A) (left).

7. To check alignment of the sprockets, remove the crankshaft drive key and temporarily install both sprockets. Place a straight edge across the teeth of both sprockets. Correct any misalignment by placing shims behind the crankshaft sprocket.

8. After checking the alignment, remove the sprockets, install the crankshaft drive key, and place the sprocket and chain assembly into position—aligned dot to dot, or line to line. Install the camshaft sprocket retaining bolts using a new lockplate.

Relative position of timing marks on sprockets.

A. Scribed alignment marks
B. Punch mark opposite camshaft groove

9. Install the oil thrower.

10. Install the timing gear cover as outlined in the applicable "Timing Gear Cover Removal and Installation" procedure.

Timing Chain Tensioner Adjustment

The tensioner is non-adjustable. If the chain is not tensioned properly and is not stretched, the tensioner must be replaced. To remove the tensioner, remove the timing chain cover as previously described. Spread the tensioner blades apart and slide the tensioner off the anchor pin.

Installation is the reverse of removal. Make sure that the convex surface of the tensioner faces the timing chain.

Camshaft

Removal and Installation

All Models

1. Disconnect the negative battery cable.
2. Drain the cooling system. Remove the radiator valence(s) and the radiator. On TR-250 and TR-6 models, remove the radiator grille. On GT6 models, remove the hood.
3. Remove the timing cover as outlined in the applicable "Timing Cover Removal and Installation" procedure.
4. Remove the timing chain and camshaft sprocket. Remove the fuel pump, the distributor driveshaft, and gear.
5. Remove the cylinder head as outlined under "Cylinder Head Removal and Installation". Take out the pushrods and lifters, keeping them in the order of their removal.
6. Remove the camshaft keeper plate and carefully slide the camshaft forward and out.
7. To install, reverse the above procedure. Keep the camshaft end play to 0.-004–0.008 in. Adjust the valve timing.

Pistons and Connecting Rods

Removal and Installation

All Models

1. Disconnect the negative battery cable.
2. Position the car on a ramp or over a pit.
3. Drain the cooling system and engine sump.
4. Remove the cylinder head as outlined under "Cylinder Head Removal and Installation".
5. Remove the oil pan as outlined under "Oil Pan Removal and Installation". Check the identification marks on the connecting rods and bearing caps. Mark, if necessary.

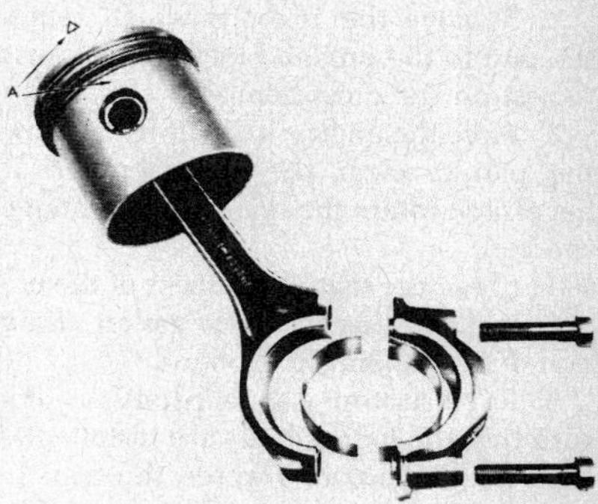

Piston and connecting rod assembly showing positioning arrow.

6. On Spitfire models, remove the oil pump strainer and rotate the crankshaft until Nos. 1 and 4 connecting rod bearing bolts are brought to an accessible position. Remove the bolts, then rotate the crankshaft until Nos. 2 and 3 bearing bolts are accessible and remove them.
7. On six-cylinder models, bring each pair of pistons (1 and 6, 2 and 5, 3 and 4) to the bottom of their stroke and remove the connecting rod bearing bolts.
8. Remove the bearing caps and the lower half bearing shells. Do not intermix shells.
9. Push each piston and connecting rod assembly upward out of the bore. Identify each assembly for installation. Use a ridge reamer, if necessary, to remove the carbon ridge from the top of the bore. Do not attempt to force the piston past the ridge.
10. After smearing the mating surfaces of the crankshaft, bearing shells, pistons, and cylinder bores with clean engine oil, install the piston and connecting rod assemblies into their bores from the top. Use a piston ring compressor and make sure that the arrow stamped on the pistons is facing forward. The piston ring gaps should be staggered, avoiding a gap on the thrust side of the piston. The open side of the connecting rod bearing should be facing the non-thrust side of the cylinder bore.
11. If the upper bearing shells were removed, install them in the connecting rod before it contacts the crankshaft. Make sure that the connecting rod bolt bushes are positioned correctly.
12. Install the lower bearing shells and caps with new bolts and torque them to specifications.
13. Reverse steps 1–5 to install.

ENGINE LUBRICATION

Oil Pan

Removal and Installation

Spitfire

1. Drain the engine oil.
2. Remove the 16 bolts which retain the pan to the engine block and allow it to rest on the crossmember.
3. Raise the engine sufficiently to allow the pan to clear the crossmember. If necessary, rotate the crankshaft. Remove the pan.
4. Clean the mating surfaces of the engine and pan. Install a new gasket, using non-drying sealing compound.
5. Reverse steps 1–3 to install, making sure that the longer bolts are installed at the rear of the pan. Tighten the bolts to specifications.

GT6

1. Disconnect the negative battery cable.
2. Drain the engine oil. Drain the cooling system. Disconnect the radiator hoses.
3. Lift the engine a few inches with a hoist. Loosen the right side engine mount bolts, and remove the bolts for the left mount.
4. Remove the oil pan bolts. Lever the engine rearward sufficiently to allow the pan to clear the crossmember. Remove the pan.
5. Clean the mating surfaces of the pan and engine. Install a new gasket, using non-drying sealing compound.
6. Reverse steps 1–4 to install. Torque the pan bolts to specifications.

TR-250, TR-6

1. Disconnect the negative battery cable.
2. Drain the engine oil. Remove the dipstick.
3. Remove the oil pan bolts, and lower out the pan.
4. Using a new gasket and non-drying sealing compound, position the oil pan to the engine and install the retaining bolts. Torque the bolts to specifications.
5. Fill the crankcase to capacity with the proper grade of oil. Install the dipstick.
6. Connect the negative battery cable.

Rear Main Oil Seal Replacement

All Models

1. Remove the transmission as outlined in the applicable "Transmission Removal and Installation" procedure.
2. Remove the flywheel. Remove the engine rear transmission adapter plate.
3. On the GT6, lift the engine sufficiently to provide access to the rear main seal retaining bolts.

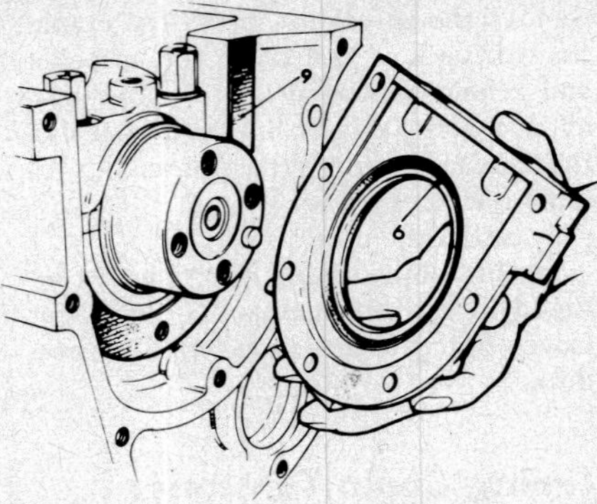

Rear main oil seal correctly positioned in housing.

4. Remove the bolts which retain the oil seal housing to the crankcase and oil pan.
5. Taking care not to damage the oil pan gasket, remove the oil seal housing with gasket (9). Press out the old seal (6).
6. Smear the outside diameter of the new oil seal (6) with grease and press it into the housing, lip toward the crankshaft.
7. Coat the crankcase face with sealing compound and smear the crankshaft with oil.
8. Using a new gasket (9), install the seal housing and hand-tighten the retaining bolts.
9. Position the housing to the crankcase face using a centering sleeve. After the housing is centered, tighten the bolts to specifications.
10. Reverse steps 1–3 to install.

Oil Pump

Removal and Installation

All Models

The oil pump is an eccentric rotor type and consists of: the body, the driving spindle inner rotor, the outer rotor, the cover, and the main body.

1. To remove the oil pump, remove the dipstick, drain the oil pan, remove the oil pan and remove the bolts which secure the oil pump to the crankcase. Clean all components.
2. With the oil pump assembled except for the top cover, measure the clearances between the inner and outer rotors, the outer rotor and the pump housing, and the inner rotor and the face of the pump housing as shown in the accompanying figures. Clearances should fall within the clearances in the table. In case of excessive clearances replace worn or damaged parts.

3. When assembling the oil pump, replace worn components and install the inner rotor in the pump housing, followed by the outer rotor, with its chamfered face leading.

Oil Pump Clearances

Model	Inner Rotor to Outer Rotor (in. max.)	Outer Rotor to Pump Housing (in. max.)	Innter Rotor to Housing Face (in. max.)
Spitfire	0.010	0.0075	0.0035②
GT6	0.004①	0.0075	0.0040
TR-250	0.004①	0.0075	0.0040
TR-6	0.004①	0.0075	0.0040

① Min.—0.001 in.
② Min.—0.0015 in.

4. With the assembly positioned in the crankcase, attach the end plate and secure with the retaining bolts.

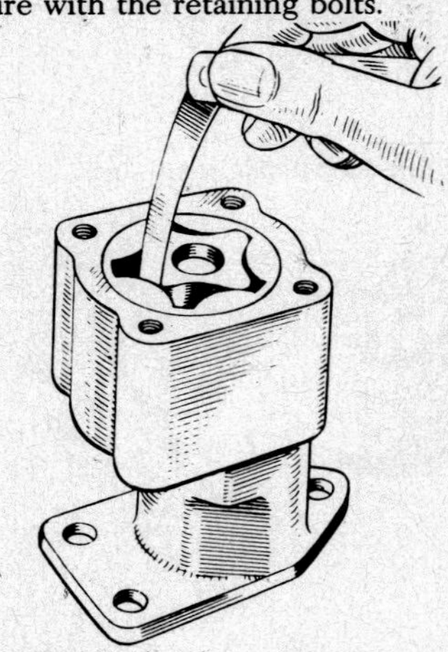

Measuring oil pump inner rotor to outer rotor clearance.

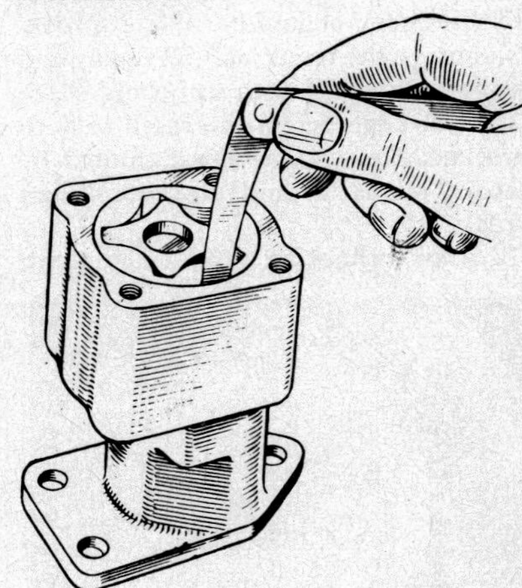

Measuring oil pump outer rotor to pump housing clearance.

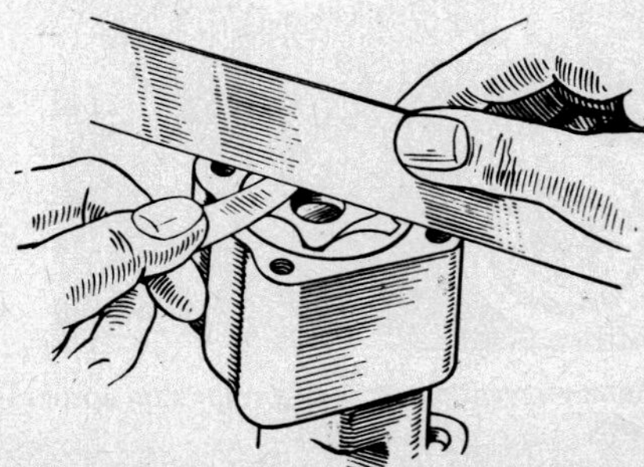

Measuring oil pump rotor end clearance

ENGINE COOLING

Radiator

Removal and Installation

All Models

1. Drain the cooling system by opening the engine block drain cock and the radiator drain cock or by disconnecting the lower radiator hose.
2. On GT6 models, remove the air duct. On TR-250 and TR-6 models, remove the radiator valance and position the stay rods to one side.
3. Disconnect the remaining radiator hoses. Disconnect the overflow hose to the expansion tank.
4. Remove the radiator retaining bolts and lift out the radiator.
5. Reverse the above procedure to install, making sure that the cooling system is filled to the proper level with a 50% water, 50% ethylene glycol solution.

Water Pump

Removal and Installation

All Models

1. Disconnect the battery, drain the cooling system, loosen the generator (alternator) mounting bolts and remove the fan belt.
2. Disconnect the radiator and water hoses at the thermostat housing and water pump, and disconnect the fuel supply line at the carburetors and fuel pump.
3. Remove the temperature transmitter connection and the three bolts which secure the water pump to the cylinder head.
4. Remove the water pump.
5. When replacing the pump, be sure that the cylinder head and pump mating surfaces are clean and install a new gasket.

Thermostat

All thermostats are pre-set by the manufacturer; no adjustment is necessary. Servicing is by replacement only. If a thermostat malfunction is suspected, it may be tested by placing the thermostat in water of specific temperature and watching to see if unit functions at the temperature marked on the thermostat flange.

Removal and Installation

Empty the cooling system and remove the outlet hose. Lift out the thermostat. To replace, reverse the above procedure. Be sure to replace the old gasket with a new one.

EMISSION CONTROLS

With the advent of emission control laws, Triumphs were modified to comply. Due to the strictness of these laws, exhaust emission control systems should not be modified in any way. What follows is a brief rundown on the various modifications made to meet smog control specifications.

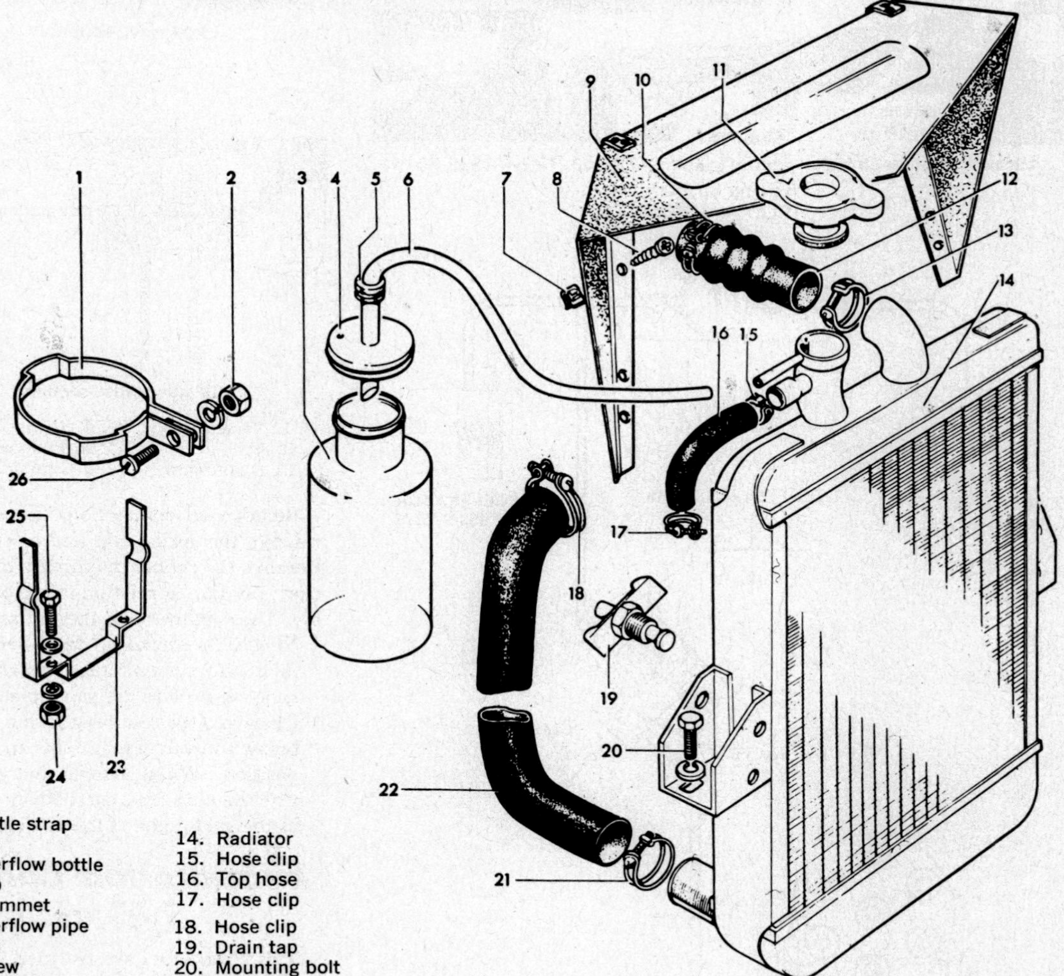

1. Bottle strap
2. Nut
3. Overflow bottle
4. Cap
5. Grommet
6. Overflow pipe
7. Nut
8. Screw
9. Air duct
10. Hose clip (top hose)
11. Radiator cap
12. Top hose (convoluted)
13. Hose clip (top hose)
14. Radiator
15. Hose clip
16. Top hose
17. Hose clip
18. Hose clip
19. Drain tap
20. Mounting bolt
21. Hose clip
22. Bottom hose
23. Bracket
24. Nut
25. Bolt
26. Screw

Typical radiator assembly—GT6 shown

Carburetors

These are the main components of the emission control system. Generally, they were modified by using leaner jets and mixture. In the case of the Spitfire MK IV, a change was made from dual S.U. HS2 carburetors to a single Stromberg 150 CDSE. The tuning of carburetors to meet emission standards has, in general, reduced power considerably. Servicing procedures will be found in the "Carburetor" section.

Distributors

All current models are now equipped with a vacuum retard unit. This assembly retards the spark during idling and deceleration, thereby reducing exhaust emissions.

Cylinder Head and Camshaft

These have been modified for cleaner burning in the case of the former and lower emissions at idle in the case of the latter. (The camshaft accomplishes this by reduced overlap.)

PCV Valve

The crankcase vent valve has been used for several years and remains virtually unchanged. This component requires the following service at 12,000 mile intervals:

PCV valve assembly

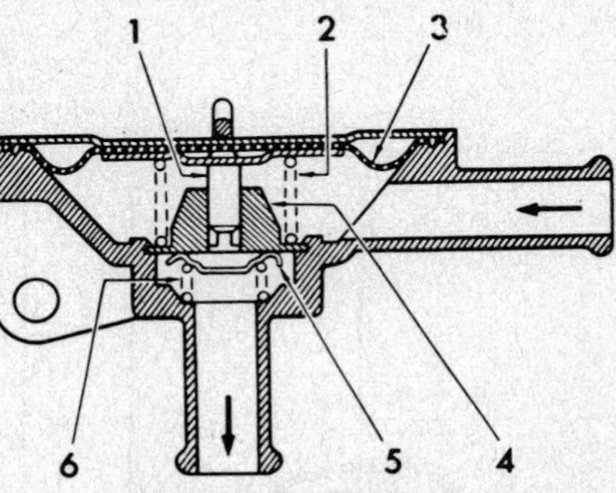

PCV valve cross-section

1. Valve pin
2. Spring
3. Diaphragm
4. Orifice plate
5. Plate valve
6. Spring

Remove all connections. Loosen and remove the spring clip and cover plate. Remove the rubber diaphragm noting its exact position in relation to top of assembly. Thoroughly clean the entire unit.

NOTE: *Be certain all parts are cleaned in a safe solvent and are absolutely spotless.* Be sure the valve plate moves freely and the retaining spring (located below the valve) maintains an upward position. When reassembling, make sure the plunger is correctly positioned in the mid-point of the orifice plate.

Evaporation Control System

This closed fuel system used on 1970 and later models sold in the U.S.A. prevents gasoline from escaping into the atmosphere. The following maintenance is required every 12,000 miles:

Remove all tubes from the canister top.

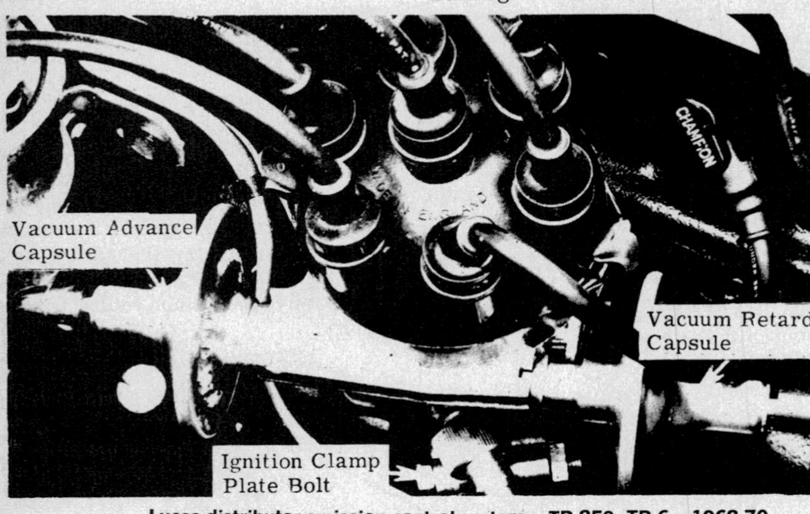

Lucas distributor emission control system—TR-250, TR-6—1968-70

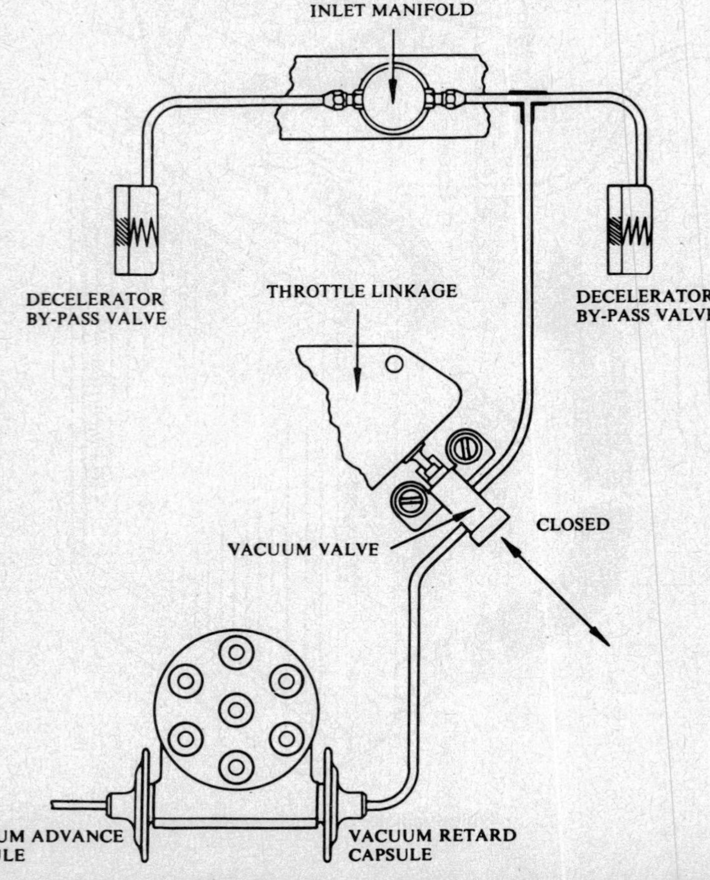

Emission control vacuum circuit schematic—TR-250, TR-6—1968-70

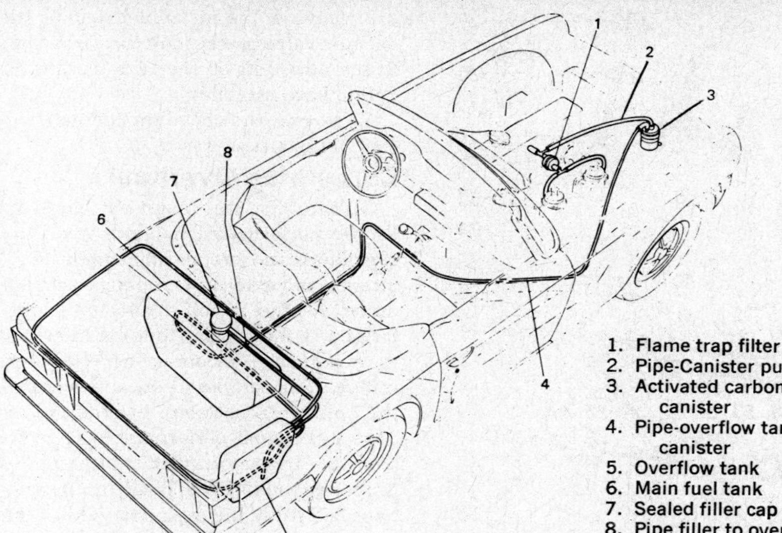

1. Flame trap filter
2. Pipe-Canister purge
3. Activated carbon canister
4. Pipe-overflow tank to canister
5. Overflow tank
6. Main fuel tank
7. Sealed filler cap
8. Pipe filler to overflow tank

Typical evaporation control system— 1970-71 TR-6 shown

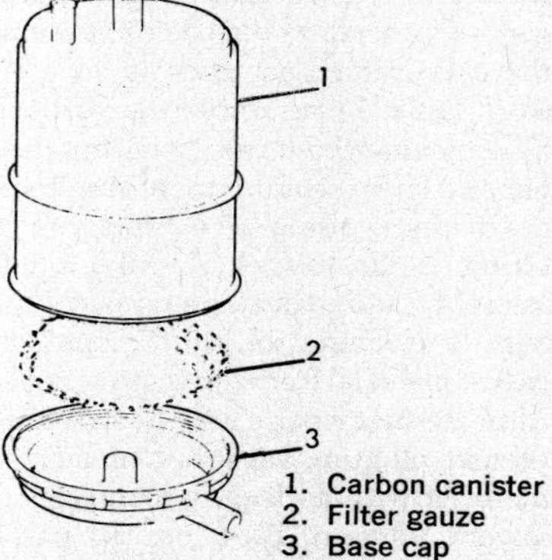

1. Carbon canister
2. Filter gauze
3. Base cap

Evaporation control system carbon canister.

Loosen all attachments and lift from the bracket. Loosen the base cover and remove; lift out the filter gauze and replace. Clean the base and replace it. Make certain all lines are not bent or rubbing.

The entire canister is replaced at 48,000 mile intervals on 1970-72 models, and at 24,000 mile intervals on 1973 models.

FUEL SYSTEM

Fuel Pump

All models are equipped with an AC mechanical diaphragm type fuel pump located on the left side of the engine.

Removal and Installation

To remove the fuel pump, disconnect the fuel inlet and outlet lines.

NOTE: *Gasoline will spill on the engine unless precautions are taken.* Unscrew the attaching nuts. The pump will now be free.

When installing, make sure that the pump lever (rocker arm) is positioned correctly above its lobe on the cam.

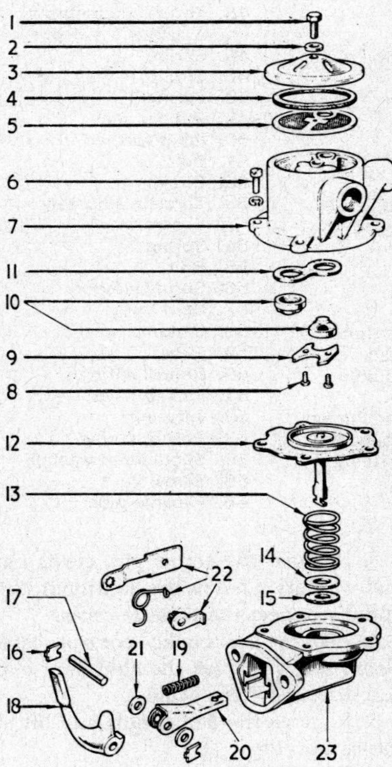

Spitfire fuel pump assembly

1. Retaining screw
2. Washer
3. Cover
4. Joint
5. Gauze
6. Screw
7. Body
8. Screws
9. Retainer
10. Valves
11. Upper retainer
12. Diaphragm assembly
13. Spring
14. Washer
15. Washer
16. Retainer
17. Spindle
18. Operating lever
19. Return spring
20. Operating fork
21. Distance washer
22. Priming lever assembly
23. Lower body

Fuel Pump Disassembly

The mechanical fuel pumps shown in this section are disassembled in numerical order of their numbered components. When removing the diaphragm assembly, turn the assembly 90° counterclockwise before lifting it out of engagement with the link lever. When replacing the inlet and outlet valve assemblies, be sure that the valves are pointed in the proper directions. Fuel pump delivery pressure should be 1 ½-2 ½ pounds per square inch (psi).

CAUTION: *Be certain the fuel lines are snug to the pump, but do not overtighten them.*

Fuel Pump Cleaning

Every 12,000 miles the fuel pump should be serviced. This may be accomplished by:

1. Removing the top bolt and domed cover.

2. Removing the gauze filter and thoroughly washing in a safe solvent (denatured alcohol).

3. Cleaning the sediment in the fuel bowl with a small screw driver. The preferred method for removing loosened sediment is compressed air. Wipe out the interior of the fuel bowl with a soft, clean rag.

CAUTION: *The interior of the fuel bowl must be absolutely free of grease or lint.*

4. Renewing the cork gasket if cracked or brittle. Fuel pump parts are delicate; use caution. When reassembling, be sure the filter gauze is facing down.

Carburetors

1968–69 Spitfire Mk III models are equipped with twin SU HS2 carburetors. 1970 Mk III models, as well as all Spitfire Mk IV models (including 1973 1500), are equipped with a single Zenith-Stromberg 150 CDSE unit. All GT6+ and GT6 MK III models use twin 150 CDSE units. The TR-250 and TR-6 utilize a pair of Zenith-Stromberg 175 CDSE carburetors. All carburetors are installed horizontally.

Both the SU and the Zenith-Stromberg units are variable venturi, air valve types and have a relatively simple construction. The Zenith-Stromberg units differ slightly in that they are equipped with a vacuum diaphragm.

The mixture of air and fuel is determined by the position of the tapered needle in its jet. The carburetor piston, to which the needle is attached, moves the needle along its vertical path according to the vacuum present at the top of the piston. As the vacuum (and engine speed) increases, the piston rises and exposes a smaller cross section of the needle to the jet, thereby enriching the mixture.

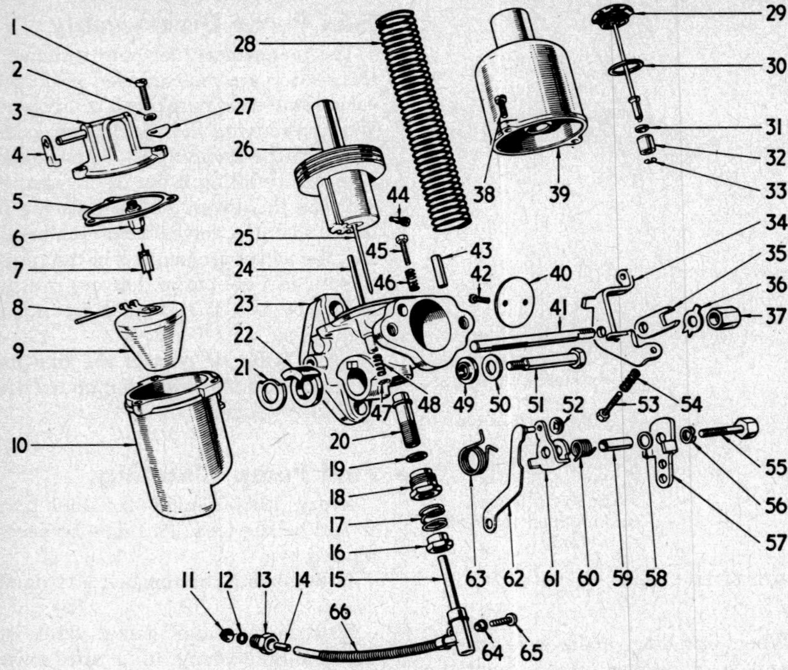

SU HS2 carburetor assembly

1. Screw
2. Spring washer
3. Float chamber lid
4. Breather hole shroud
5. Gasket
6. Needle valve body
7. Needle valve
8. Float spindle
9. Float
10. Float chamber
11. Cup
12. Washer
13. Union nut
14. Sleeve
15. Jet
16. Adjusting nut
17. Spring
18. Gland nut
19. Washer
20. Jet holder
21. Washer
22. Rubber seal
23. Main body
24. Lifting pin
25. Needle
26. Piston
27. Identification plate
28. Spring
29. Cap
30. Washer
31. Washer
32. Piston
33. Circlip
34. Throttle adjusting bracket
35. Throttle fork
36. Lock tab
37. Nut
38. Screw
39. Vacuum chamber
40. Throttle disc
41. Throttle spindle
42. Screw
43. Mixture enrichment cable abutment
44. Needle retaining screw
45. Throttle adjusting screw
46. Spring
47. Circlip
48. Spring
49. Rubber seal
50. Plain washer
51. Bolt
52. Circlip
53. Throttle adjusting screw
54. Spring
55. Bolt
56. Spring washer
57. Cam lever
58. Distance washer
59. Tube
60. Return spring
61. Pick-up lever
62. Jet lever
63. Return spring
64. Shouldered washer
65. Screw
66. Flexible pipe

Removal and Installation

Twin SU HS2

1. Remove the air cleaners.

2. Disconnect the choke cable, throttle control rod, throttle return springs, and the fuel feed pipes.

3. Remove the flange nuts and lift off the twin carburetor and linkage assembly.

4. To install, reverse the above procedure, taking care to use new carburetor-to-manifold gaskets.

Single Zenith-Stromberg 150 CDSE

1. Remove the air cleaner.

2. Disconnect the fuel feed pipe, the distributor vacuum hose, the positive crankcase ventilation hose, and the throttle return spring.

3. Remove the cotter pin, clevis pin, and washers. Loosen the abutment nuts and disconnect the throttle cable.

4. Loosen the choke control cable clamp screw, pry off the abutment clip, and disconnect the cable.

5. Remove the flange nuts and lift off the carburetor.

6. To install, reverse the above procedure, using a new gasket.

Twin Zenith-Stromberg 150 CDSE, 175 CDSE

1. Remove the air cleaner.

2. Disconnect the vacuum valve lines at each carburetor and from both sides of the vacuum valve. Disconnect the distributor vacuum hose, both fuel feed pipes, the accelerator control rod (from the firewall side of the rear carburetor), and both choke cables.

3. Remove the nut which retains the vacuum valve bracket and the carburetor flange nuts. Lift off the twin carburetor and linkage assembly.

4. Reverse the above procedure to install, using a new gasket.

Carburetor Overhaul

Carburetors are relatively complex. Proper performance depends upon the cleanliness and proper adjustment of all internal and external components. In addition to the usual adjustments performed at the regular tune-up intervals, it eventually becomes necessary to remove, disassemble, clean, and overhaul the entire carburetor(s), in order to restore its original performance. To overhaul a carburetor, first purchase the proper rebuilding kit. Read the instructions and study the exploded view of the carburetor thoroughly prior to the actual removal and disassembly.

After reading the detailed carburetor rebuilding instructions, the following general procedure may be used. Remove the carburetor and place it on a clean work table. Disassemble the carburetor by removing the screws securing the upper and lower sections together. Remove the damping piston, air valve, spring, metering needle, fuel jet (SU only), and float assembly, and soak all metal parts in carburetor cleaning solvent. Scrape all old gasket material from the mating surfaces. After the metal parts have been soaked to remove all gum, varnish, and dirt, rinse them off with a clean, uncontaminated, solvent solution. Blow out all passages with compressed air and allow them to air dry. Do not use drills or wire to clean the passages. Check the throttle shaft and choke disc for excessive wear. Inspect the float hinge pins for distortion. All non-metal parts that are not being replaced should be wiped clean with a lint-free cloth. After all of the parts have been sufficiently cleaned or replaced, assemble the carburetor using new gaskets and seals, and, on Stromberg carburetors, a new air valve diaphragm. If any of the replacement seals in the SU carburetor are cork, they must first be soaked in penetrating oil for a minimum of a half hour to avoid splitting during installation. Assemble the float chamber and adjust the float height. Assemble the air valve, spring, and metering needle into the upper housing. Join the upper and lower housing together, taking care to properly align the metering needle and fuel jet. When the jet and needle are installed correctly, the air valve should drop to the bridge with a distinctive click. Any binding of these two parts will result in poor carburetor performance. Install the damping piston. Install the carburetor on its manifold with a new gasket. Adjust the choke and throttle linkage, and the idle speed and mixture.

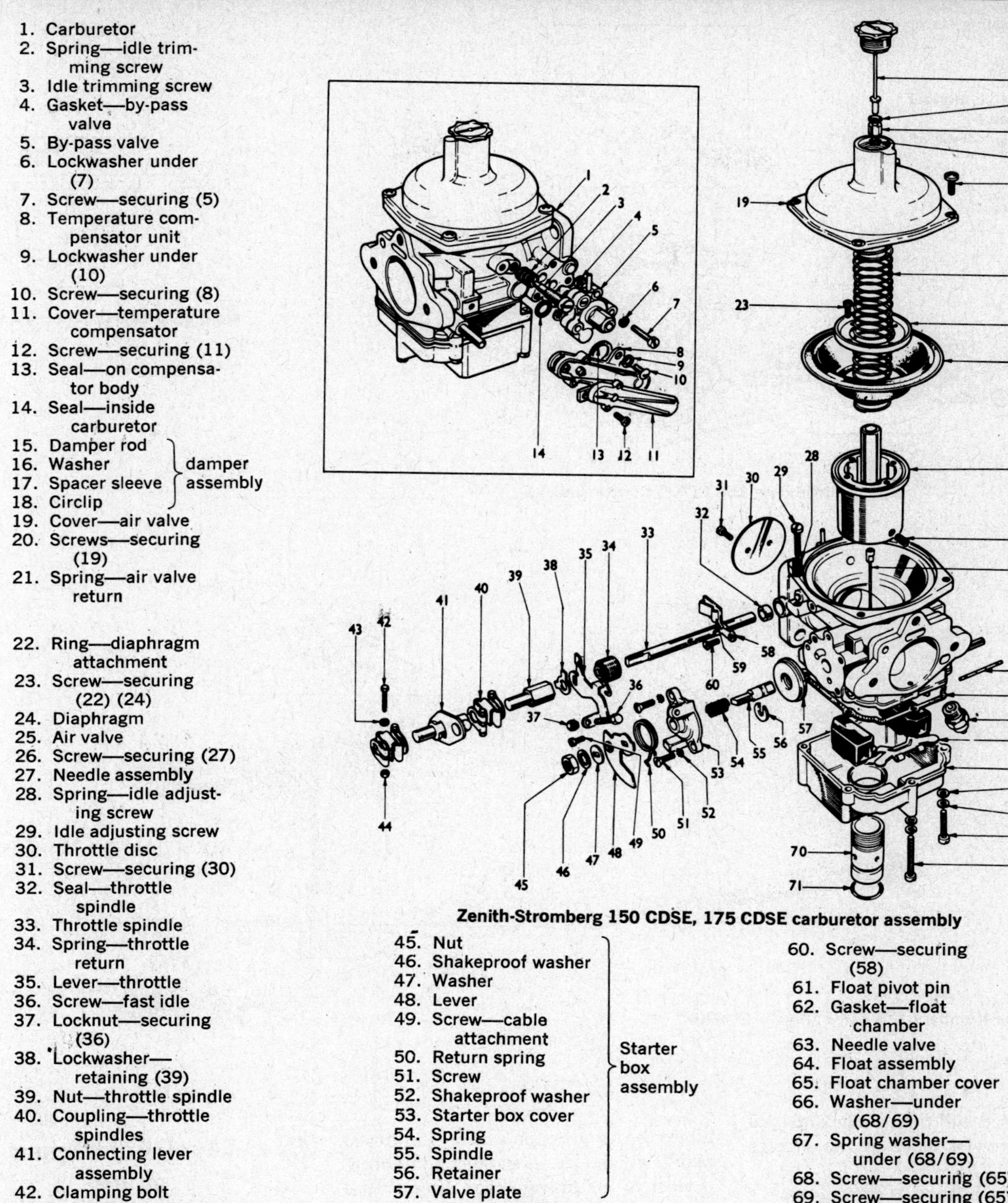

Zenith-Stromberg 150 CDSE, 175 CDSE carburetor assembly

1. Carburetor
2. Spring—idle trimming screw
3. Idle trimming screw
4. Gasket—by-pass valve
5. By-pass valve
6. Lockwasher under (7)
7. Screw—securing (5)
8. Temperature compensator unit
9. Lockwasher under (10)
10. Screw—securing (8)
11. Cover—temperature compensator
12. Screw—securing (11)
13. Seal—on compensator body
14. Seal—inside carburetor
15. Damper rod (damper assembly)
16. Washer (damper assembly)
17. Spacer sleeve (damper assembly)
18. Circlip (damper assembly)
19. Cover—air valve
20. Screws—securing (19)
21. Spring—air valve return
22. Ring—diaphragm attachment
23. Screw—securing (22) (24)
24. Diaphragm
25. Air valve
26. Screw—securing (27)
27. Needle assembly
28. Spring—idle adjusting screw
29. Idle adjusting screw
30. Throttle disc
31. Screw—securing (30)
32. Seal—throttle spindle
33. Throttle spindle
34. Spring—throttle return
35. Lever—throttle
36. Screw—fast idle
37. Locknut—securing (36)
38. Lockwasher—retaining (39)
39. Nut—throttle spindle
40. Coupling—throttle spindles
41. Connecting lever assembly
42. Clamping bolt
43. Washer—under (42)
44. Nut—securing (42)
45. Nut (Starter box assembly)
46. Shakeproof washer (Starter box assembly)
47. Washer (Starter box assembly)
48. Lever (Starter box assembly)
49. Screw—cable attachment (Starter box assembly)
50. Return spring (Starter box assembly)
51. Screw (Starter box assembly)
52. Shakeproof washer (Starter box assembly)
53. Starter box cover (Starter box assembly)
54. Spring (Starter box assembly)
55. Spindle (Starter box assembly)
56. Retainer (Starter box assembly)
57. Valve plate (Starter box assembly)
58. Cable abutment bracket
59. Spring clip
60. Screw—securing (58)
61. Float pivot pin
62. Gasket—float chamber
63. Needle valve
64. Float assembly
65. Float chamber cover
66. Washer—under (68/69)
67. Spring washer—under (68/69)
68. Screw—securing (65)
69. Screw—securing (65)
70. Plug
71. Rubber O-ring—for (70)

Throttle Linkage Adjustment

Twin SU HS2

1. Remove the air cleaners.

2. Loosen the clamping bolts on the throttle spindle connections. Fully close the throttles by unscrewing the idling adjustment screws, then open them evenly 1 ½ turns.

3. Insert a 0.015 in. feeler gauge between the lever and the lower arm of the throttle lever fork. Move the throttle shaft lever of each carburetor down until the lever pin lightly contacts the feeler gauge. Tighten the clamp bolts in this position. The pins on the throttle shafts should now have clearance in the forks.

4. Install the air cleaners.

Single Zenith-Stromberg 150 CDSE

1. Remove the air cleaner.

2. Loosen the throttle cable abutment nuts. Loosen the fast idle screw to obtain maximum cam clearance. Fully close the throttle by unscrewing the idling screw. Open the throttle by turning the screw 1 ½ turns clockwise.

3. Loosen the locknut and set the linkage adjusting screw until the clevis pin is moved to the engine side of the slots in the linkage straps; then tighten the locknut.

NOTE: *It is necessary to have free play in the linkage to allow for a fast idle setting without interfering with the closed position of the throttle.*

4. Tighten the cable abutment nuts so that the cable has no play and is not taut.

5. Install the air cleaner.

Twin Zenith-Stromberg 150 CDSE

1. Loosen the spring coupling bolts on both carburetor ends.

2. Fully close the throttles by unscrewing the idling screws, then open them evenly 1 ½ turns. Make sure that the

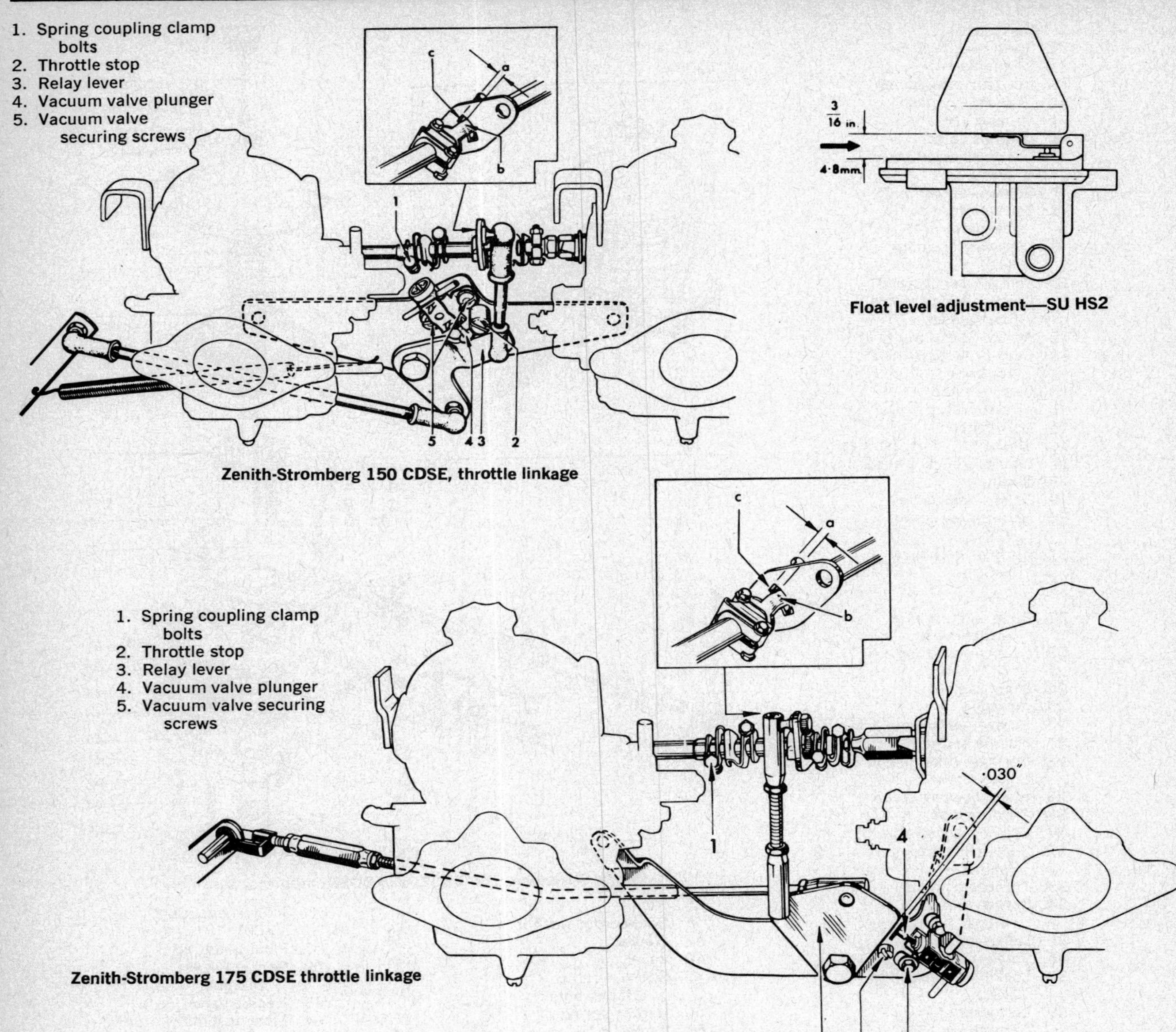

Zenith-Stromberg 150 CDSE, throttle linkage

Float level adjustment—SU HS2

Zenith-Stromberg 175 CDSE throttle linkage

choke is closed and that the fast idle adjustment screw is clear of the linkage cam.

3. With the linkage as shown, place a 1/16 in. drill bit in space (a) between the lever tongue (b) and the lever slot edge. With the bit in position, put pressure on the stop cam and tighten the spring bolts. Remove the drill bit.

4. Loosen the vacuum valve screws. Adjust the valve to provide a 0.030 in. clearance between the valve and the lever.

5. Position the linkage so that the tongue (b) rests in the lever slot. With the throttle at the point of opening, the valve should be fully closed.

Twin Zenith-Stromberg 175 CDSE

1. Loosen the bolts on the spring couplings (both carburetor ends).

2. Adjust the slow idle screw to the fully closed position (both). At this point, rotate the screws open exactly 1 ½ turns. Make sure the fast idle adjustment screw is clear of the linkage cam. Be sure the choke linkage is fully closed.

3. Start and warm the engine to operating temperature. Adjust the slow idle screw to set both carburetors to the correct speed. Stop the engine.

4. With the linkage as shown, place a 3/32 in. drill bit in space (a). Be sure it is in the space between the lever tongue (b) and the lever slot edge. With the bit in position put pressure on the stop cam and tighten the spring bolts. Remove the bit.

5. Place the relay lever against the stop screw. Loosen the vacuum valve screws. Adjust the valve to 0.030 in. clearance (between the valve and the lever).

6. Move the linkage until the tongue (b) nests in the lever slot. The valve should be fully closed (the throttle should be at the point of opening).

Float Level Adjustment

SU HS2

1. Disconnect the fuel line from the float chamber lid. Remove the screws which retain the lid to the float chamber.

2. Lift out and invert the float chamber lid. With the needle valve held in the closed position, and the float hanging free, the gap between the float lever and the rim of the float chamber lid should be 3/16 in.

3. After adjusting the float level, install the lid and connect the fuel line.

Zenith-Stromberg 150 CDSE, 175 CDSE

1. Remove the carburetor(s) from the manifold as outlined in the applicable "Carburetor Removal and Installation" procedure.

2. Unscrew the cap(s) and drain the oil

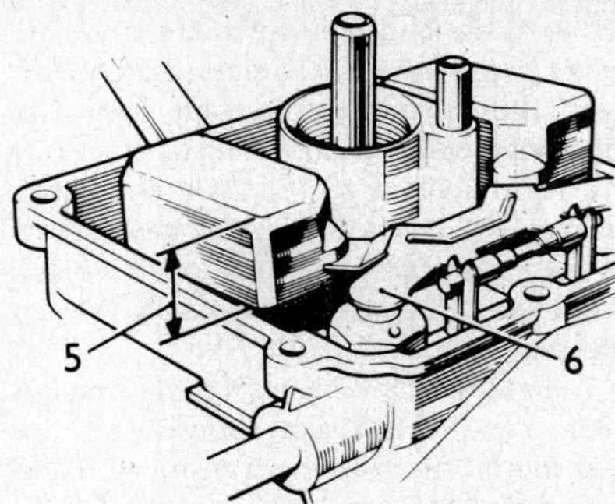

Float level adjustment—Zenith-Stromberg 150 CDSE, 175 CDSE.

from the damping cylinder(s). Drain the fuel from the float chamber(s).

3. With the carburetor inverted and the float chamber cover removed, make sure that the distance (5) between the highest point of the floats and the carburetor body is 0.625–0.672 in.

4. To adjust, bend the float tag (6) which contacts the needle of the valve assembly. To lower the fuel level, a thin washer may be inserted beneath the needle valve assembly.

5. Install the float chamber cover with a new gasket. Fill the damping cylinder(s) to ¼ in. from the top with Type A automatic transmission fluid and install the cap(s).

6. Install the carburetor(s) as outlined in the applicable "Carburetor Removal and Installation" procedure.

Fast Idle and Choke Adjustment

Twin SU HS2

Make sure that the jet control linkage has approximately 1/16 in. free travel before it begins to pull on the jet levers. Set the choke control knob as far out as possible before lowering the jets. Start the engine and adjust the fast idle screws to 1100 rpm with the engine hot.

Single Zenith-Stromberg 150 CDSE

Push the choke control knob fully in and make sure that the cam is positioned against its stop. With the choke cable properly tensioned (not too tight, no slack), adjust the gap (A) between the fast idle screw and the cam to 0.020–0.025 in. Start the engine and pull out the choke control knob until the cam pivot, cable clamp screw, and fast idle screw are in alignment (see illustration). Adjust the fast idle screw to an engine speed of 1100–1300 rpm with the engine hot and the air cleaner installed.

Twin Zenith-Stromberg 150 CDSE, 175 CDSE

Make sure that with the choke control knob pushed fully in, the choke lever on each carburetor is against its stop. Adjust the tension of the choke cables as necessary. Pull out the choke control knob until the cable pivot aligns with the center of the fast idle screw and the center of the cam pivot point. Loosen the locknuts and unscrew both idle screws until each is just contacting the cam. Start the engine and, while it is cold (68–86°F), adjust the fast idle scews an equal amount to 1100 rpm. Tighten the locknuts and recheck the fast idle speed.

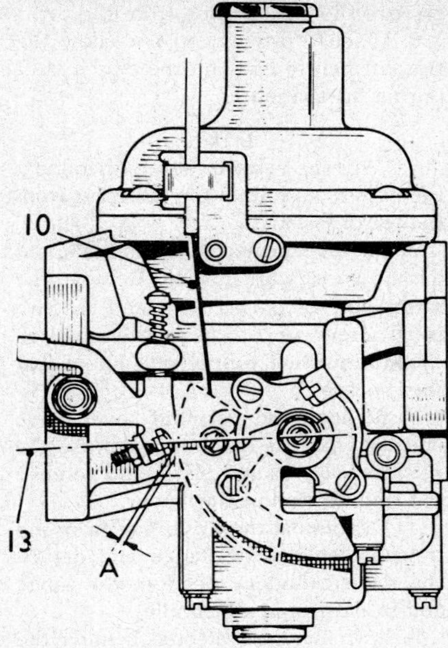

Fast idle adjustment—single Zenith-Stromberg 150 CDSE.

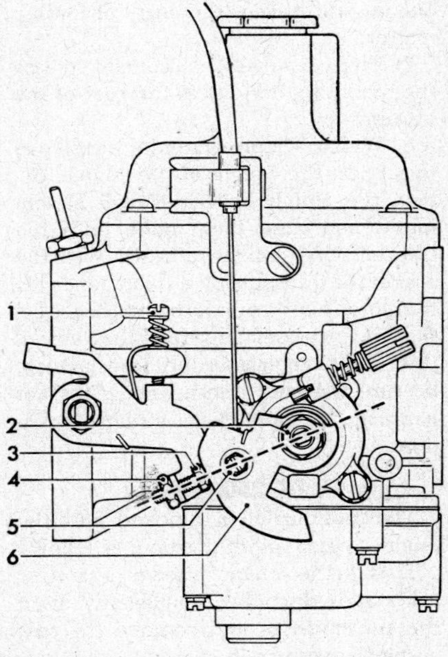

Fast idle adjustment—twin Zenith-Stromberg 150 CDSE, 175 CDSE.

1. Idling screw
2. Starter box
3. Fast-idle screw
4. Locknut
5. Cable trunnion
6. Cam lever

Centering the Jet

SU HS2

NOTE: *When performing the centering operation, be careful not to bend the needle.* If the jet is correctly centered, the piston should fall freely and hit the jet bridge with a metallic click when the jet adjusting nut is in its uppermost position. If the metallic click is audible only when the jet is in its lowest position, the jet must be centralized.

1. With the jet in its uppermost position (do not force the jet upward if it is impeded by the piston needle; temporarily remove the piston), loosen the jet locking nut and move the jet assembly laterally until the jet is concentric with the needle.

2. Tighten the locking nut. The piston should now be able to fall freely and hit the jet bridge with a metallic click.

3. Check the centering of the jet by noting the difference in sound when: (1) the piston drops onto the jet when the jet is in its highest position, and (2) when the piston is dropped when the jet is in its lowest position. If there is any difference in sound between conditions (1) and (2), the adjustment process will have to be repeated.

4. When the operation is completed, top up the dampers and adjust the mixture setting of the carburetors.

Zenith-Stromberg 150 CDSE, 175 CDSE

Ascertain that the air valve moves freely by raising and allowing the valve to fall. Slow action may indicate the need for cleaning by removing and cleansing both the bore and the air valve with solvent.

If the jet is not centralized, it may be corrected as follows:

1. Raise the air valve and tighten the jet bushing screw. Tighten the orifice adjusting screw until it is just above the bridge.

2. Loosen the jet bushing screw to release the orifice bushing. Permit the air valve to drop. This will align the bushing. Tighten the bushing screw to secure the bushing and recheck. Repeat until the piston falls freely.

3. Move the adjusting screw until it barely touches the air valve underside when resting on the bridge. Three turns from this position (loose) gives a reasonable figure to use when synchronizing dual carburetors.

Suction Chamber and Piston Cleaning

SU HS2

Clean the suction chamber and piston of an S.U. carburetor at intervals of no greater than 12 months or 12,000 miles and also if the carburetor has been disassembled for any reason.

1. Remove the three screws that hold the suction chamber and remove the chamber and piston. Be careful of the needle at the end of the piston, for it is easily bent.

2. Clean the suction chamber and piston with a solvent-moistened rag and then reassemble with a few drops of oil on the piston rod only. Do not use any form of abrasive or metal cleaner to clean these parts. If the needle is bent or loose, it will have to be replaced or repositioned. Removal of the needle involves only the withdrawal of the setscrew.

3. When a needle is installed in the piston, it is important that it be positioned with the lower edge of the groove flush with the base of the piston.

MANUAL TRANSMISSION

All Triumph Spitfire, GT6, TR-250, and TR-6 models are fitted with a four-speed manual transmission. On all models, except the Spitfire Mk III and preceding Spitfires, all four forward speeds are equipped with synchromesh engagement. The Spitfire Mk III has synchromesh on Second, Third, and Fourth gears only.

Removal and Installation

Spitfire

1. With the vehicle suitably supported on a ramp or stands, disconnect the battery, drain the transmission, and remove the front seats and carpets. Remove the dashboard support beneath the instruments and disconnect the tachometer drive cable.

2. Remove the gearshift lever knob and rubber boot. Remove the screws and fasteners and lift off the transmission cover. Remove the securing nuts and pin and release the clutch slave cylinder, allowing it to hang on its pipe.

3. Remove the retaining bolts and remove the driveshaft.

4. Release the front exhaust pipe at its manifold and clutch housing. Remove the starter motor and remove the speedometer drive cable from the transmission extension.

5. Remove the retaining nuts, lift off the transmission gearshift extension, and temporarily install a cardboard cover to prevent the entry of foreign matter.

6. Remove the nuts which attach the rear transmission mountings to the body crossmember, and jack up the engine until the transmission extension clears the mounting bracket. Then remove the rear mountings.

7. Release the bolts which secure the clutch housing flange to the engine, and remove the transmission from the car.

8. When replacing, do not allow the transmission to hang on the clutch shaft during installation.

GT6

1. With the vehicle raised, disconnect the battery and drain the lubricant from the transmission.

2. Remove the seat cushions, seats, and dashboard support bracket. Remove the safety belt anchoring bolts and the two small screws next to each, then take off the transmission tunnel side liners that they secure.

3. Remove the gearshift lever knob and take out the carpeting. Release the retaining screws and plates and remove the transmission center cover.

4. Disconnect the driveshaft from the transmission driving flange and detach the slave cylinder, speedometer cable, and exhaust pipe attachment.

5. With first gear selected, remove the transmission top cover and extension assemblies.

6. Fit a cardboard cover over the opening to prevent the entry of foreign matter.

7. From beneath the vehicle, release the mounting bracket at the rear of the transmission.

8. With a jack placed under the oil pan to support the weight of the engine, detach the clutch housing flange attachments and raise the engine until the transmission can be withdrawn. With the rear of the transmission raised, maneuver the clutch housing underneath the parcel shelf at the passenger side of the vehicle.

9. When replacing the transmission, be sure that the transmission does not hang on the input shaft during installation.

TR-250, TR-6

The transmission is removed, with the engine remaining in position, as follows:

1. With the vehicle raised on a ramp or axle stands, disconnect the battery, drain the transmission, and remove the seat cushions and carpets.

2. Disconnect the cables from the heater control switch, the control cable from the heater unit, and the lower left control cable from the center control panel. Remove the dashboard support, which is secured by two bolts at the top and two bolts at each side of the bottom. Remove the headlight dimmer switch, leaving the electrical connections attached.

3. Remove the bolts and washers which secure the center floor cover and remove the cover.

4. Disconnect and remove the driveshaft.

5. Remove the retaining pin and bolts and remove the clutch slave cylinder, allowing it to hang by its flexible hose. Remove the clutch cover plate from the lower part of the clutch housing. Disconnect the speedometer cable and the overdrive connections (if installed).

6. With a block of wood protecting the oil pan, use a jack to support the weight of the engine and transmission. The jack should be placed as far as possible toward the rear of the oil pan.

7. Release the exhaust pipe bracket next to the hand brake, then detach the rear mounting from the transmission and crossmember.

8. Raise the engine and transmission, then remove the crossmember by sliding it forward.

9. Remove the bolts, nuts, and washers which attach the clutch housing flange to the engine.

10. Withdraw the transmission to the rear until it is clear of the clutch, then maneuver the clutch housing to the right and the rear section to the left, at the same time tilting the transmission case so that the clutch operating lever will clear the opening in the floor. Lift the transmission from the car.

11. Replacement is the reverse of the preceding, except it is important that the transmission not be allowed to hang on the clutch shaft while it is being attached to the engine. Fill the transmission with lubricant of the proper type and viscosity.

Overhaul

Spitfire Mk III

Disassembly

Disassemble the top cover as follows: Withdraw the retaining bolts and lift off the top cover and gasket. Remove the retaining nuts and washers and lift off the gearshift extension and gasket. Remove the nut and bolt to detach the shaft from the gearshift lever. Remove the gearshift lever knob. Remove the cap at the bottom of the gearshift lever and lift the lever assembly from the extension and remove the cups and the outer spring. Remove the snap ring from the lever and remove the inner spring and nylon ball. Remove the retaining screws and detach the reverse stop plate. Remove the reverse stop bolt from the gearshift lever. Withdraw the threaded, tapered locking pin and extract the shaft from the extension case and selector. Remove the rubber O-rings from the extension case bore. Remove the locking nut and remove the pivot bolt from the coupling fork. Withdraw the shaft and fiber washers from the coupling. Remove the hollow spring steel pin and detach the coupling fork from the shaft. Disassemble the selector shaft and fork assemblies by driving out the plugs with a ⅛ in. (3.17 mm.) punch, taking care to see that the selector shafts are clear. Remove the threaded, tapered

1. Knob
2. Locknut
3. Gearshift lever
4. Cover
5. Shield
6. Plate
7. Spring
8. Circlip
9. Spring
10. Nylon ball
11. Stepped nylon washer
12. Bushing
13. Washer
14. Lever end
15. Reverse stop pin
16. Locknut
17. Bolt
18. Welch plug
19. Gasket
20. Spring
21. Plunger
22. Taper locking pin
23. 1st/2nd selector shaft
24. 3rd/top selector shaft
25. Reverse selector shaft
26. Interlock ball
27. Nut
28. Rubber O-ring
29. Top cover
30. Gasket
31. Selector ball-end
32. Bolt
33. Dowel
34. Washer
35. Bonded rubber bushing
36. Gearshift extension
37. Reverse stop
38. Bolt
39. Nyloc nut
40. Screw
41. Pin
42. Remote control shaft (front)
43. Taper locking pin
44. Fork
45. Nut
46. Remote control shaft (rear)
47. Bolt
48. 1st/2nd selector fork
49. Reverse selector
50. Interlock ball
51. Interlock plunger
52. Top/3rd selector fork
53. Taper locking pin
54. Clutch housing
55. Pin
56. Clutch release mechanism
57. Bolt
58. Plain washer
59. Bolt
60. Gasket
61. Dowel
62. Rear extension
63. Rubber O-ring
64. Peg bolt
65. Speedometer drive gear housing
66. Speedometer drive gear
67. Extension ball race
68. Oil seal
69. Gearbox mounting rubber
70. Mounting bracket
71. Nut
72. Bolt
73. Gasket
74. Clutch slave cylinder bracket
75. Sump plug
76. Speedometer driving gear
77. Circlip
78. Space washer
79. Ball race
80. 1st speed gear
81. Spring
82. Shim
83. Synchromesh ball
84. Plunger
85. Ball
86. 2nd speed synchro hub
87. 2nd speed synchro cup
88. Thrust washer
89. 2nd speed mainshaft gear
90. Thrust washer
91. Bushings
92. 3rd speed mainshaft gear
93. Thrust washer
94. Circlip
95. 3rd/top synchro sleeve
96. 3rd speed synchro cup
97. 3rd/top inner synchro hub
98. Top synchro cup
99. Circlip
100. Spacer washer
101. Circlip
102. Ball race
103. Oil deflector
104. Input shaft
105. Needle roller bearing
106. Mainshaft
107. Spacer washer
108. Driving flange
109. Spring washer
110. Nut
111. Countershaft
113. Peg bolt
114. Spring washer
115. Rear fixed thrust washer
116. Rear rotating thrust washer
116. Rear rotating thrust washer
117. Countershaft gear cluster
118. Countershaft bushing
119. Front fixed thrust washer
120. Reverse gear bushing
121. Reverse gear
122. Reverse gear actuator
123. Actuator pilot
124. Plain washer
125. Nyloc nut
126. Reverse gear shaft
127. Reverse shaft retaining bolt
128. Spring washer

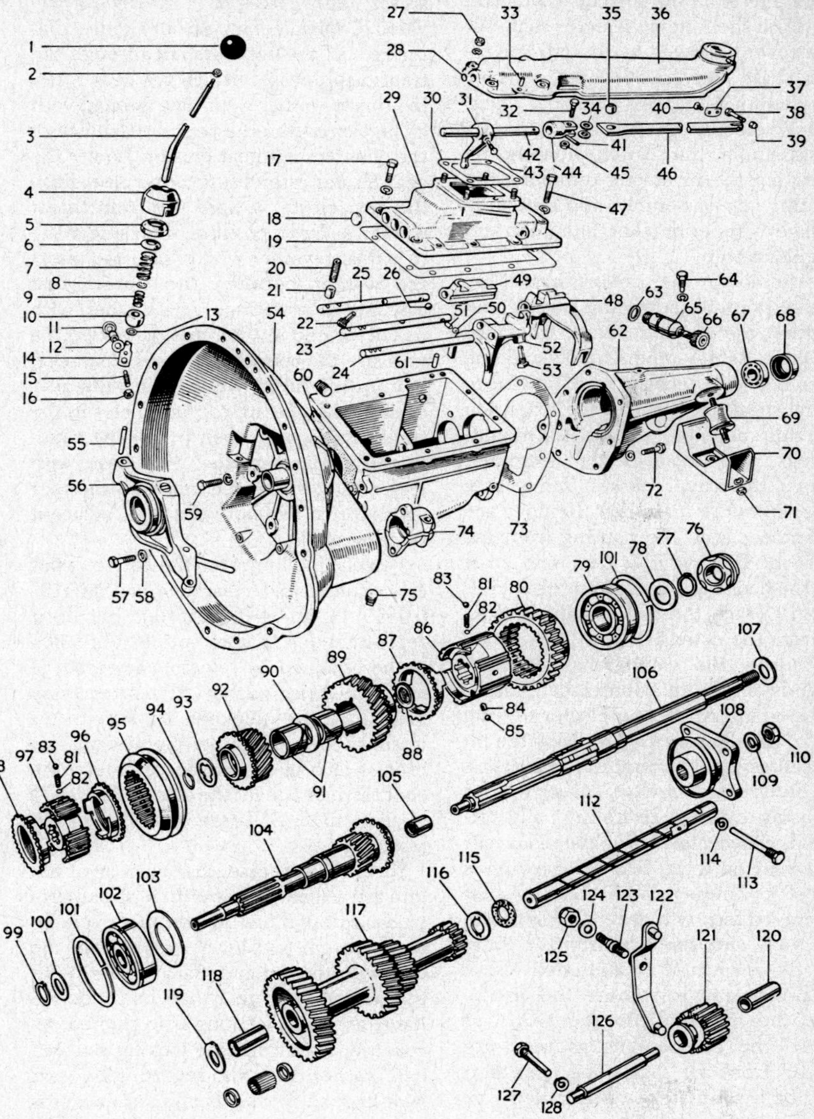

Spitfire Mk III transmission disassembled

locking pins from the selector shafts and forks. Push the reverse selector shaft out of the cover, followed by the 1st/2nd selector shaft and the 3rd/4th selector shaft. Remove the two interlock balls, plunger, selector plungers and springs.

Disassemble the clutch housing by driving out the pivot pin, removing the operating lever assembly, and removing the slave cylinder bracket, four bolts and Wedgelock bolt.

Disassemble the rear extension: Remove the nut and spring washer and withdraw the driving flange from the mainshaft. Remove the six bolts and one longer bolt that secure the extension to the transmission. Remove the extension by pulling and lightly tapping the mounting lugs with a soft-headed hammer. Remove the paper gasket and spacer washer from the mainshaft. Remove the bolt and separate the housing from the extension. Remove the gear and shaft from the housing and take out the rubber O-ring. Detach the ball bearing and oil seal from the extension.

Withdraw the countershaft locating bolt and remove the countershaft, allowing the countershaft gear cluster to drop clear of the mainshaft. Withdraw the input shaft assembly from the transmission case. Remove the circlips, spacer washer and, using a press, extract the ball bearing and oil deflector. Drive the mainshaft to the rear until the rear ball bearing is clear of its housing. With the mainshaft assembly tilted, withdraw the synchronizer unit and the synchronizer cups. With the mainshaft repositioned, use a special extractor to remove the circlip. Drive the mainshaft to the rear and remove the components as they are released from the shaft. The mainshaft may be completely dismantled by removing the nylon speedometer driving gear, circlips, spacer washer and ball bearing.

Withdraw the reverse idler gear to the rear and remove the retaining bolt and the reverse idler gear shaft. Remove the rear thrust washer, lift the gear cluster from the case, and remove the front thrust washer and the rear rotating thrust washer. Remove the nut and remove the operating lever and pivot pin.

Disassemble the synchronizer units by withdrawing their outer sleeves. Because these sleeves retain the spring-loaded balls, perform this operation with the synchronizer units in a small container so that the balls are not lost. In addition to the synchronizer balls and springs, the 2nd gear synchronizer unit is provided with an interlock ball and plunger.

Assembly

Smear the steel face of the front countershaft thrust washer with grease and locate the washer in the transmission case so that its bronze face is toward the gear and its tag is engaged in the recess provided. Centralize the washer by inserting the rear of the countershaft through the transmission case. Attach the rear rotating thrust washer in similar fashion, with its tags engaging the rear slotted face of the countershaft gear cluster. Lower the gear cluster assembly into the case. Push the gear cluster toward the front thrust washer as far as possible, then smear the rear thrust washer with grease and insert the washer between the transmission case and the rotating thrust washer, with its tag located in the recess provided. To measure the countershaft end clearance, line up the thrust washers and the gear cluster with the appropriate holes in the transmission case, then install the countershaft. Measure the end float with feeler gauges inserted between the rear fixed thrust washer and the adjacent rotating washer.

Permissible limits for the countershaft cluster gear end clearance are 0.0015–0.0125 in. (0.04–0.31 mm.), but it is recommended that an end float of 0.006 in. be obtained by selective assembly of available thrust washers. If it is necessary to reduce the thickness of any thrust washer, do not remove metal from the bronze face of the washer. Remove the countershaft and let the cluster gear drop to allow the installation of the mainshaft assembly.

Screw the reverse idler gear pivot pin into the selector lever until a thread protrudes through the boss on the lever. Secure the pin and lever assembly in the case with the nut and plain washer. With the reverse idler gear shaft positioned in the case and its locating hole aligned, secure the shaft with the locking pin and lock washer. Slide the reverse idler gear over its shaft so that its annular groove is engaged with the pin attached to the lower end of the operating lever.

Assemble the 3rd/4th synchronizer unit by installing the springs, balls and shims to the hub and adding the outer sleeve. Repeat the preceding with the 2nd gear synchronizer unit. Test the axial release load of the synchronizer units. Axial release should occur at 19–21 lbs. Adjust release by altering the number of shims beneath each synchronizer spring until the correct loading is achieved.

Measure the end clearance of each mainshaft gear on its respective bushing. End clearance on the bushing should be 0.002–0.006 in. (0.05–0.1524 mm.) for both gears. Float may be increased by installing a new bushing and decreased by reducing the housing length.

NOTE: *Reduction of bushing length will increase the end clearance of the bushings on the mainshaft.* Check the overall end clearance of the bushings on the mainshaft as follows: With the thrust washer, bushing, washer, bushing and thrust washer assembled to the mainshaft, secure the assembly with a discarded half-circlip and measure the total end clearance of the bushings and thrust washers on the mainshaft. If necessary, adjust the end clearance to the recommended 0.004–0.010 in. (0.-1016–0.254 mm.) by the selective use of thrust washers of various thicknesses.

Assemble the mainshaft as follows: With the circlip groove to the rear, press the ball bearing onto the mainshaft. Install the spacer washer and circlip, ensuring that the circlip is correctly located in the groove of the mainshaft. Press the speedometer drive gear onto the mainshaft and install the large circlip into the groove of the ball bearing. Insert the mainshaft through the transmission case and install the components to the shaft in the following order (see accompanying illustration): 2nd gear synchronizer unit assembly, with gear portion forward (be sure that the interlock plug and ball are located correctly in the unit), 2nd gear synchronizer cup (be sure that the three lugs are located in the synchronizer hub), rear thrust washer, with scrolled face forward, and 2nd gear and bushing. Install the center thrust washer, 3rd gear and bushing, and the front thrust washer, with its scrolled face to the rear. Install the circlip. With the longer boss of the inner synchronizer member forward, slide the 3rd/4th synchronizer unit, baulk rings attached, over the mainshaft and drive the rear ball race into its housing.

Assemble the input shaft as follows:

NOTE: *It is not possible to remove the needle roller bearing and its replacement necessitates replacement of the input shaft.* Smear the oil deflector plate with grease and position it on the input shaft. Without disturbing the position of the plate, press the ball bearing onto the shaft. Secure the ball bearing with the spacer washer and circlip, ensuring that the latter is correctly located in the groove of the shaft. With the large circlip on the ball bearing outer race and the synchronizer cup over its cone on the input shaft, insert the assembly, simultaneously locating the baulk ring lugs into their respective slots in the synchronizer hub.

Line up the thrust washers and the countershaft gear cluster by pushing a 0.-655 in. (16.64 mm.) diameter rod, tapered at one end, through the case and countershaft assembly. Push the countershaft through the case and countershaft assembly, forcing out the pilot rod. Be sure to maintain contact between the two shafts when the pilot rod is being driven out. Secure the countershaft by locking pin holes, inserting the locking pin and securing with the lockwasher.

Assemble the rear extension: Drive the ball bearing into its bore in the rear of the housing and insert the oil seal, with its sealing lip facing forward. Lubricate the speedometer drive shaft and insert it into its housing. The rubber O-ring should be replaced if it is worn or damaged. With the drive gear assembly inserted into the rear extension, line up the location hole with the corresponding hole in the extension. Insert the retaining bolt and tighten. Install the spacer washer over the end of the mainshaft. Smear the gasket with grease and locate it on the rear face of the transmission case. Drive the rear ball bearing over the mainshaft, install the extension and secure it with the retaining bolts and locking washers. Install the driving flange, washer and nut and tighten to a torque of 6–8 ft lbs. To reassemble the clutch housing and release mechanism, reverse the removal procedure, except for the installation of a new copperplated steel washer beneath the lower bolt to prevent oil leakage.

Assemble the top cover as follows: Insert the plungers and springs into the cover and slide the 3rd/4th selector shaft into the front end of the cover. While the 3rd/4th shaft is being pushed into position, depress the selector plunger to enable the shaft to pass over it and through

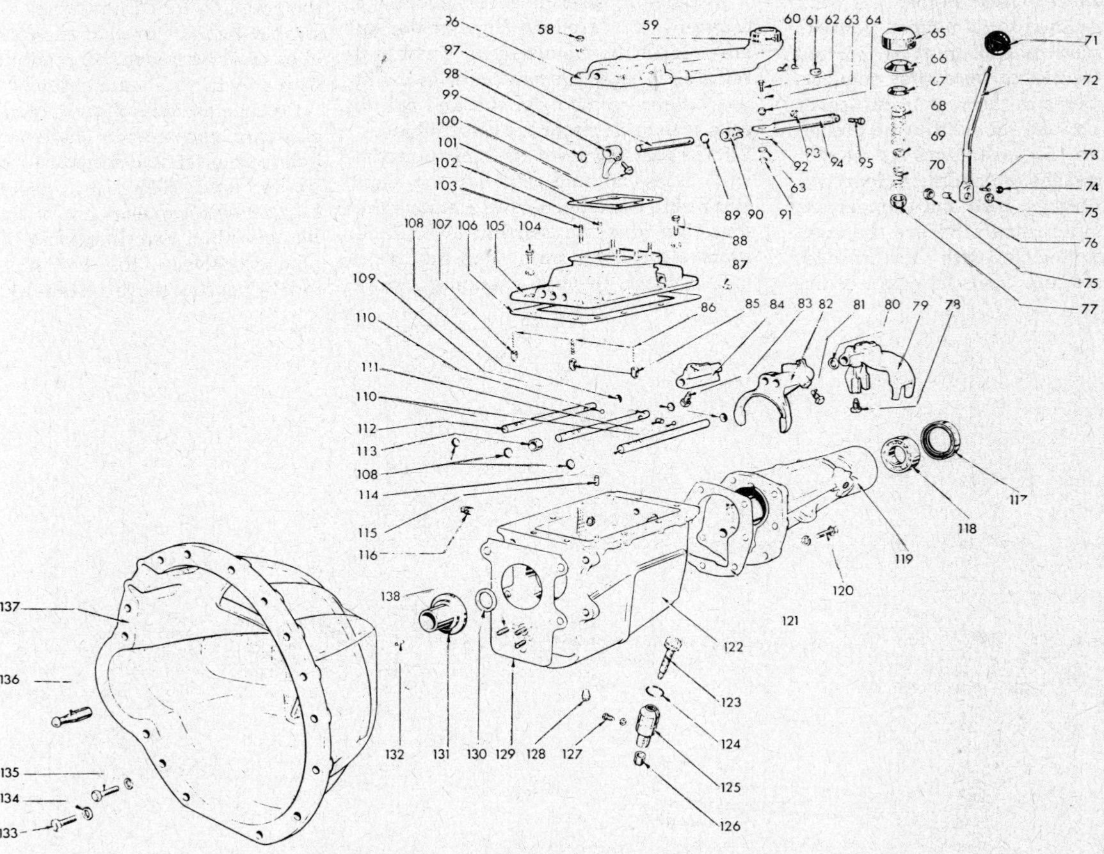

GT6 series transmission stationary components disassembled

58. Nut
59. Locating pin
60. Screws
61. Reverse stop plate
62. Pivot bolt
63. Fiber washers
64. Bushing
65. Cap
66. Cup
67. Cup
68. Spring
69. Snap ring
70. Spring
71. Knob
72. Gear lever
73. Reverse stop bolt
74. Locknut
75. Nylon bushings
76. Spacer tube
77. Nylon ball
78. Taper locking pin
79. 1st/2nd selector fork
80. Spacer washer
81. Taper locking pin
82. 3rd/top selector fork
83. Taper locking pin
84. Reverse selector
85. Detent plungers
86. Springs
87. Plug
88. Bolt
89. Rubber O-ring
90. Coupling fork
91. Nyloc nut
92. Hollow pin
93. Nyloc nut
94. Gear lever shaft
95. Setscrew
96. Top cover extension housing
97. Gear lever shaft
98. Selector
99. Rubber O-ring
100. Taper locking pin
101. Gasket
102. Dowel
103. Stud
104. Bolt
105. Top cover housing
106. Gasket
107. Detent plunger
108. Plugs
109. 1st/2nd selector shaft
110. Interlock balls
111. Interlock plunger
112. Reverse selector shaft
113. Sleeve
114. 3rd/Top selector shaft
115. Dowel
116. Filler/level plug
117. Oil seal
118. Rear ballrace
119. Rear extension
120. Bolt
121. Gasket
122. Gear casing
123. Speedometer
123. Speedometer driven gear
124. Rubber O-ring
125. Bearing
126. Oil seal
127. Locating bolt
128. Drain plug
129. Gasket
130. Oil seal
131. Oil seal housing
132. Pin
133. Bolt
134. Copper washer
135. Bolt
136. Pivot pin
137. Clutch housing
138. Springs

the appropriate selector fork. Continue to insert the shaft until its middle indentation engages the plunger. This will be the neutral position. Repeat the preceding procedure with the reverse shaft and selector until it has also reached the neutral position. With the interlock plunger inserted into the 1st/2nd gear shaft, assemble these and the selector fork into the cover in similar fashion, except that the shaft will also pass through the 3rd/4th selector fork. Before the shaft has been pushed to its neutral position, the two interlock balls must be inserted into the transverse bore that connects the shaft bores at the rear of the cover casting. The shaft should then be pushed further into the cover until its selector plunger engages the middle indentation and the interlock balls and plunger are retained by the shafts. Secure the forks and reverse selector with the threaded, tapered lockpins. Coat the edges of the plugs with sealing compound and drive these into the ends of the selector shaft bores. With all selectors and gears in the neutral position, install the gasket and top cover assembly over the two dowels on the transmission and secure with the retaining bolts and lock washers, with the longer bolts at the rear.

GT6+, GT6 Mk III

Disassembly

Disassembly procedure for the GT-6 transmission is as follows: Remove the top cover from the transmission. Twist and release the cap at the base of the gearshift lever. Remove the nyloc nut and bolt to release the shaft from the gearshift lever. Lift the gearshift lever assembly from the rear extension and remove the cups along with the outer spring. Remove the snap ring from the gearshift lever, then remove the inner spring and the nylon ball. Remove the two retaining screws and take off the reverse stop plate. Remove the reverse stop bolt from the gearshift lever. Remove the threaded and tapered locking pin and extract the shaft from the extension housing and selector. Remove the rubber O-rings from the bores of the extension housing. Remove the retaining nut and withdraw the pivot bolt from the coupling fork. Extract the shaft and fiber washers from the coupling. Remove the steel pin, releasing the coupling fork from the shaft. Disassemble the selector shaft and fork assemblies by driving out the retaining plugs with a ⅛ in. (3.17 mm.) punch.

Remove the threaded, tapered locking pins from the selector shafts and forks. Release the 1st/2nd selector fork, spacer washer and sleeve by pushing the 1st/2nd selector shaft out of the cover. Remove the two interlock balls and plunger. Release the 3rd/4th selector fork by pushing the 3rd/4th selector shaft

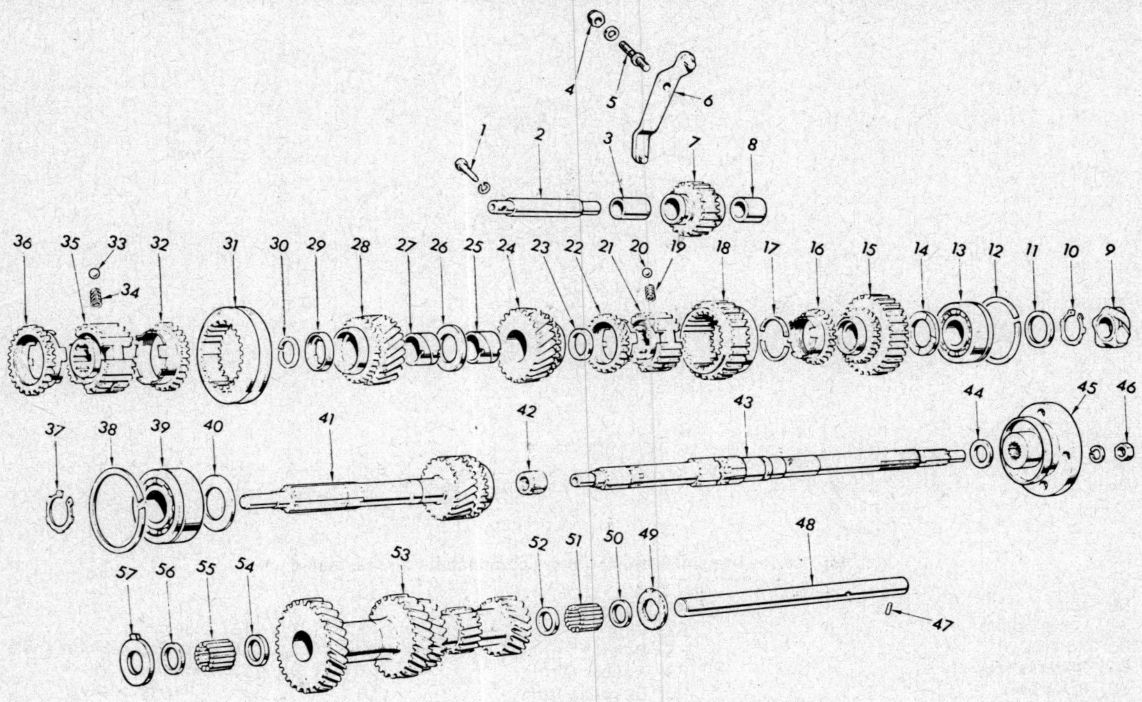

GT6 series transmission working components disassembled

1. Locating ball
2. Reverse idler spindle
4. Nyloc nut
5. Pivot pin
6. Reverse actuator
7. Reverse idler gear
8. Spacer tube
9. Speedometer driven gear
10. Circlip
11. Washer
12. Snap ring
13. Center ballrace
14. Thrust washer
15. 1st speed gear
16. Baulk ring
17. Split collars
18. 1st/2nd synchro sleeve
19. Spring
20. Ball
21. 1st/2nd synchro hub
22. Baulk ring
23. Thrust washer
24. 2nd speed gear
25. 2nd gear bushing
26. Thrust washer
27. 3rd gear bushing
28. 3rd speed gear
29. Circlip washer
30. Circlip
31. 3rd/Top synchro sleeve
32. Baulk ring
33. Ball
34. Spring
35. 3rd/Top synchro hub
36. Baulk ring
37. Circlip
38. Snap ring
39. Front ballrace
40. Oil thrower
41. Input shaft
42. Roller bearing
43. Mainshaft
44. Thrust washer
45. Coupling flange
46. Nut
47. Pin
48. Countershaft spindle
49. Rear thrust washer
50. Retaining ring
51. Needle rollers
52. Retaining ring
53. Countershaft gear cluster
54. Retaining ring
55. Needle rollers
56. Retaining ring
57. Front thrust washer

out of the cover. Release the reverse selector by pushing the reverse selector shaft out of the cover. Remove the detent plungers and springs from the cover.

Disassemble the clutch housing: Remove the release lever from its pivot pin and remove the lever and bearing. Remove the retaining bolts, releasing the clutch housing, and remove the springs.

Disassemble the rear extension: Remove the retaining nut and extract the driving flange from the mainshaft. Remove the retaining bolts and carefully withdraw the extension from the transmission. The operation may be facilitated by lightly tapping the mounting lugs with a soft-headed hammer. Remove the paper washer and spacer washer from the mainshaft. Remove the bolt and extract the reverse spindle and spacer tube. If necessary, withdraw the ball bearing and oil seal from the extension.

Withdraw the countershaft, retaining the needle roller bearings. Using a special tool, withdraw the input shaft assembly from the transmission case. Shake out the roller bearing and remove the baulk ring. Remove the circlip and snap ring and use the special tool and adaptor to extract the ball race and oil thrower. With an abutment plate installed, remove the snap ring, circlip, and spacer washer. Withdraw the ball bearing and speedometer gear, using the special tool and adaptors used for the first ball race. Remove the abutment plate, tilt the mainshaft assembly and maneuver it from the transmission case.

Disassemble the mainshaft as follows: Remove the 3rd/4th synchronizer unit, 3rd gear baulk ring, thrust washer, 1st gear and 1st gear baulk ring. Remove the circlip, washer, 3rd gear, bushing, thrust washer, 2nd gear, bushing, thrust washer, 2nd gear baulk ring, 1st/2nd synchronizer unit, and split collars. Disassemble each synchronizer unit by pressing the hub through the sleeve. During this operation, the synchronizer unit should be placed in a suitable container to prevent the loss of the spring-loaded balls. Withdraw the countershaft assembly from the case and lift out the thrust washers. The countershaft may be further disassembled by removing the needle rollers and the retaining rings. Disassemble the reverse idler gear and actuator by taking out the idler gear, removing the securing nut, and removing the actuator and pivot pin.

Assembly

Replace the needle rollers, smearing them with grease, and insert the retaining tube. With the steel face of the front thrust washer smeared with grease, locate the washer in the transmission case. The tag should engage the recess provided. Insert the end of the countershaft spindle through the case to centralize the thrust washer. With the countershaft gear cluster assembly lowered into the case, install the rear thrust washer and insert the spindle. Measure the end clearance of the countershaft and adjust if necessary to 0.007–0.013 in. (0.178–0.330 mm) by using thrust washers of selected thickness. If the thickness of a thrust washer must be reduced, do not remove metal from the bronze face. Insert the needle roller retaining tube and remove the countershaft spindle. Allow the gear cluster assembly to drop to the bottom of the transmission case.

Determining required thickness of mainshaft circlip washer.

Assemble the reverse idle gear mechanism by screwing the pivot pin into the actuator until a thread protrudes through the boss of the lever. Install it into the transmission case and secure it with a nut and washer. Position the reverse idler gear in the case. Install the synchronizer springs and balls to the 3rd/4th synchronizer hub and install the outer sleeve. Repeat the preceding with the 1st/2nd synchronizer unit and test the axial release loads, which should be between 19 and 21 pounds for each unit. The axial release load may be adjusted by the installation of new springs or the addition/-subtraction of shims to/from the position beneath each synchronizer spring.

Measure the end clearance of each mainshaft gear on its respective bushing. Correct end clearance is 0.002–0.006 in. (0.05–0.15 mm.). End clearance may be increased by the installation of a new bushing and decreased by the reduction of the length of the bushing.

NOTE: *The reduction of bushing length will increase the end clearance of the bushings on the mainshaft.* Install the thrust washer, bushing, thrust washer, bushing and washer to the mainshaft. With the assembly secured with half a circlip, measure the total end clearance of the bushings and thrust washers on the mainshaft. The end clearance may be adjusted to the correct range of 0.004–0.010 in. (0.10–0.25 mm.) through the use of thrust washers of various thicknesses.

Determine the required thickness of the circlip washer by installing the split collars, 1st gear thrust washer, bearing inner race or spacer tube, spacer washer and half a circlip to the mainshaft, then insert a feeler gauge as shown in the illustration. Use washers of proper thickness to obtain the correct clearance of 0.000–0.002 in. (00–0.50 mm.).

Proper positioning of 4th gear baulk ring (36) in 3rd/4th synchronizer unit.

Install the following components on the mainshaft: 1st/2nd synchronizer unit, 2nd gear baulk ring, thrust washer, 2nd gear bushing, 2nd gear, thrust washer, 3rd gear bushing, 3rd gear, and washer. Use a special tool to install the circlip, and install the 3rd/4th synchronizer unit, split collars, 1st gear baulk ring, and 1st gear. Position the mainshaft assembly in the transmission case, install an abutment plate tool or its equivalent, and install the thrust washer.

With the transmission positioned vertically, and the abutment plate held in a vise, install the snap ring to the ball bearing and position the ball bearing over the mainshaft. Being sure that the mainshaft is correctly located in the abutment plate, drive the ball bearing into position, using the special tool and adaptor or their equivalents. Install the speedometer drive gear and remove the abutment plate from the transmission.

Replacement of interlock balls to top cover

Assemble the input shaft components: Position the 4th gear baulk ring into the 3rd/4th synchronizer unit, as shown in the illustration. Using the special tool and adaptor or their equivalents, press the ball bearing and oil thrower onto the input shaft and secure the ball bearing with the circlip. Install the snap ring onto the ball bearing and place the roller bearing in the bore of the input shaft. Ensuring that the baulk ring is correctly located, drive the input shaft assembly into the transmission case. Assemble the countershaft by inverting the transmission, lining up the countershaft thrust washers and gear cluster, and inserting the spindle from the rear. With the reverse idler gear correctly positioned, insert the spindle and install the spacer tube.

Assemble the rear extension: Replace the ball bearing and seal to the rear extension. Install a new gasket at the rear of the transmission and place the washer over the end of the mainshaft. Install the rear extension assembly and secure it with bolts. Replace and secure the driving flange. Torque the nut to 90–100 ft lbs. Assemble the bearing, oil seal, O-rings and driven gear and install the assembly to the extension housing, securing it with the bolt. Insert the three springs into their holes in the front face of the transmission case. Replace, if necessary, the oil seal in the clutch housing and install a new gasket to the front face of the transmission. Secure the clutch housing with bolts and washers. Replace the clutch throw-out bearing and sleeve and the release lever.

Reassemble the top cover as follows: Insert the plungers and springs into the cover and slide the 3rd/4th selector shaft into the front end of the cover. While the shaft is being slid into position, press down on the selector plunger so that the shaft will be able to pass over it and through the selector fork. The shaft should be inserted until its middle indentation engages the plunger, achieving the neutral position. Repeat the above procedure with the reverse shaft and selector. With the interlock plunger inserted into the 1st/2nd selector shaft, install the selector fork, sleeve and washer into the cover in similar fashion, ensuring that the shaft also passes through the 3rd/4th selector fork. Before the 1st/2nd selector shaft is pushed to its neutral position, insert the two interlock balls into the transverse bore which connects the shaft bores at the rear of the casting (see accompanying illustration) and then push the shaft further into the cover until the selector plunger engages the middle indentation and the balls and plunger are retained by the shafts. Use new tapered locking pins to secure the selector and forks to the shafts. Use sealing compound around the edges of the plugs before driving them into the ends of the selector shaft bores. Use a new pin to secure the fork to the shaft. If necessary, replace the "Metalistik" bushing in the shaft. Using new fiber washers, secure the shaft to the fork with the bolt and nut. Install new O-rings to the case and install the shaft through the bores of the case and through the selector. Use a new tapered locking pin when securing the selector to the shaft. Install the reverse stop bolt, locknut, nylon ball, spring and snap ring to the gear shift lever. Install the reverse stop plate to the cover and secure with the retaining screws. With the gearshift lever assembly positioned in the cover, install two new bushings to the lever, install the spacer tube, and secure the lever to the shaft with the retaining bolt and

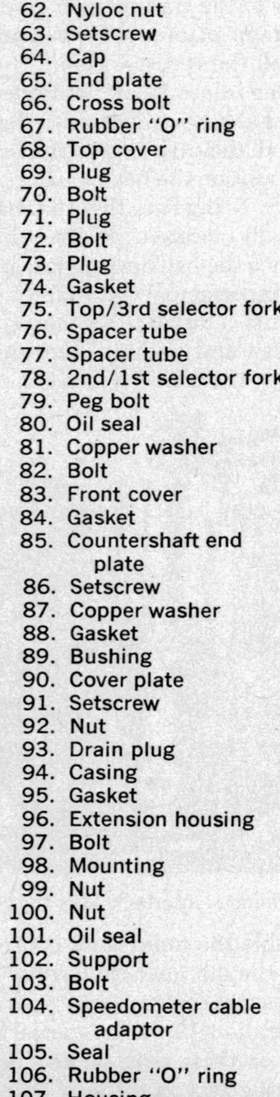

60. Knob
61. Setscrew
62. Nyloc nut
63. Setscrew
64. Cap
65. End plate
66. Cross bolt
67. Rubber "O" ring
68. Top cover
69. Plug
70. Bolt
71. Plug
72. Bolt
73. Plug
74. Gasket
75. Top/3rd selector fork
76. Spacer tube
77. Spacer tube
78. 2nd/1st selector fork
79. Peg bolt
80. Oil seal
81. Copper washer
82. Bolt
83. Front cover
84. Gasket
85. Countershaft end plate
86. Setscrew
87. Copper washer
88. Gasket
89. Bushing
90. Cover plate
91. Setscrew
92. Nut
93. Drain plug
94. Casing
95. Gasket
96. Extension housing
97. Bolt
98. Mounting
99. Nut
100. Nut
101. Oil seal
102. Support
103. Bolt
104. Speedometer cable adaptor
105. Seal
106. Rubber "O" ring
107. Housing
108. Peg bolt

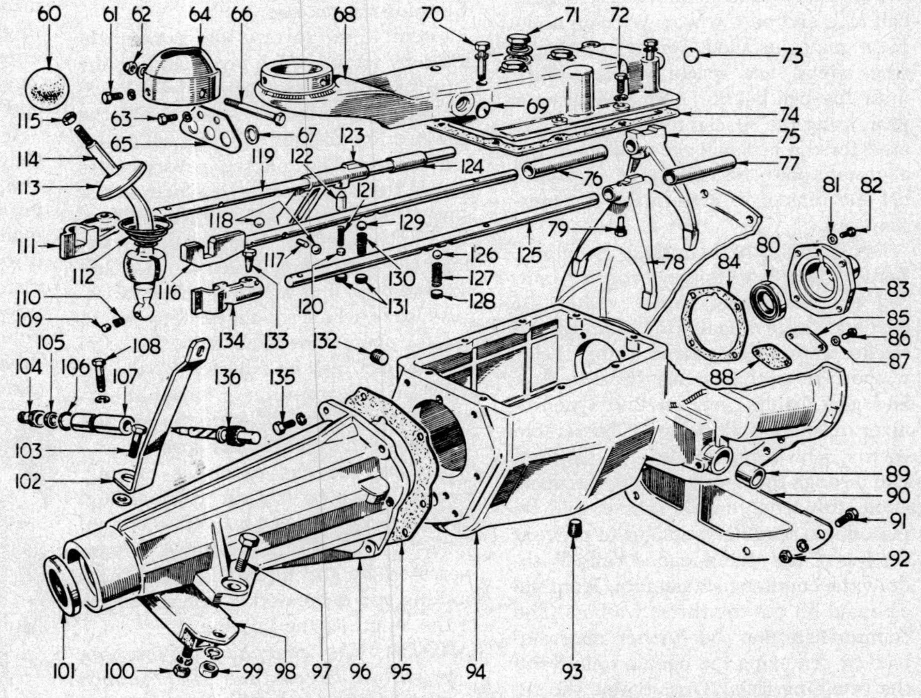

TR-250, TR-6 transmission stationary components disassembled

109. Plunger—anti-rattle
110. Spring
111. Selector—reverse
112. Spring
113. Cap disc
114. Lever
115. Nut
116. Top/3rd selector shaft
117. Interlock plunger
118. Balls—interlock
119. Reverse selector shaft
120. Shim
121. Spring
122. Plunger
123. Reverse actuator
124. Spacer
125. 2nd/1st selector shaft
126. Ball—detent
127. Spring
128. Plug
129. Ball—detent
130. Spring
131. Plug
132. Level/filler plug
133. Peg bolt
134. Selector 1st/2nd
135. Bolt
136. Speedo drive gear

nut. Install the spring, cups, and cap over the gearshift lever. Adjust the reverse stop plate and bolt with the gearshift lever in the neutral position of the 1st/2nd gate. The clearance between the reverse stop plate and bolt should be, as shown in the diagram, 0.010–0.050 in (0.-26–1.27 mm). Reinstall the top cover on the transmission.

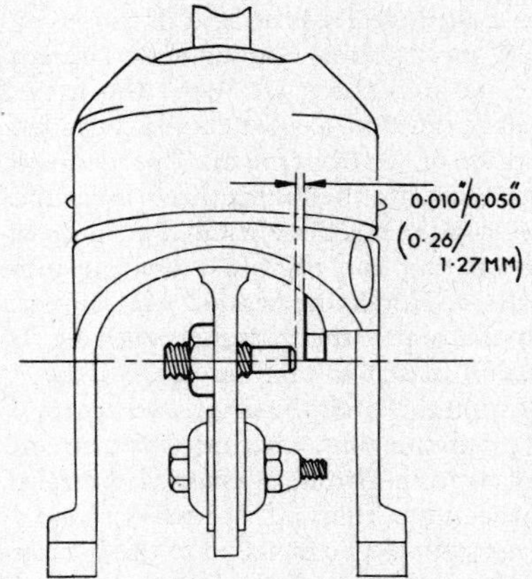

Correct clearance between reverse stop plate and bolt.

TR-250, TR-6

Disassembly

Disassemble the top cover as follows: Remove the bolts, washers, top cover, and paper gasket. Remove the nut, cross pin, cover, and withdraw the gear shift lever assembly from the top cover. With the cover inverted, remove the plugs, spacer, springs, plunger, and balls. Detach the peg bolts. With the selector shafts in the neutral position, withdraw the 3rd/4th gear selector shaft, being careful to remove the interlock plunger and balls as they are released. Remove the 3rd/4th selector fork and spacer tube from the top cover. Repeat the preceding operation for the 1st/2nd and reverse gear selector shafts. Remove the retaining screws and take out the retaining plate. Remove the sealing rings from their recesses. If necessary, remove the peg bolts and remove the selectors from their shafts.

Disassemble the front cover: Remove the tapered bolt, bolt, and spring washer.

NOTE: *See accompanying illustration for components.* Withdraw the cross-shaft along with the release spring, release bearing, sleeve and fork. Remove the retaining bolts and remove the front cover, bolts, and plate.

Disassemble the rear extension: Remove the peg bolt and withdraw the speedometer drive gear assembly. Remove the cotter pin, slotted nut, and withdraw the flange. Remove the retaining bolts and detach the rear extension, using an extractor.

Remove the countershaft and reverse pinion shaft by removing the retaining screw and plate. Withdraw the input shaft assembly from the transmission. Remove the circlips, spacer washer, and withdraw the bearing. Detach the disc and, if necessary, remove the needle roller bearing.

Remove the circlip, spacer washer, and circlip, and remove the mainshaft rear bearing. After maneuvering the mainshaft assembly through the transmission top cover opening, lift out the countershaft assembly, thrust washers, and reverse gear. Remove the countershaft gears from the hub and, if necessary, remove the needle roller assemblies from the hub bore. Remove the circlip by driving a special tool beneath the circlip and then levering the 3rd gear forward to remove the circlip from its groove. Remove all mainshaft components, and remove the 1st/2nd and 3rd/4th synchronizer inner hubs from the outer sleeves (being careful to catch the springs and balls).

After disassembly is completed, clean all components and inspect for wear. The transmission case should be washed with

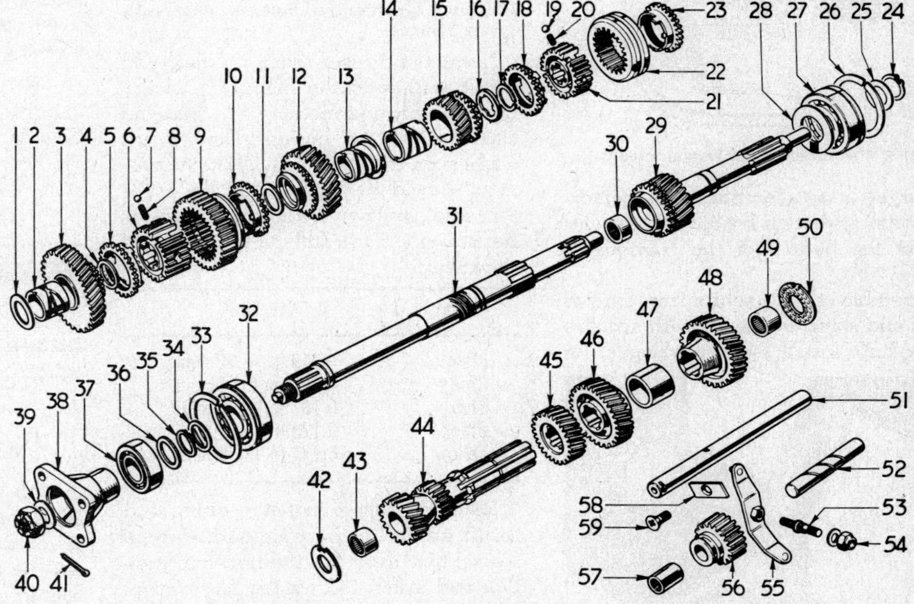

TR-250, TR-6 transmission working components disassembled

1. Thrust washer
2. Bushing—1st speed gear
3. 1st speed gear
4. Thrust washer
5. 1st speed synchro cup
6. 1st/2nd speed synchro hub
7. Synchro ball
8. Spring
9. Reverse mainshaft gear and synchro outer sleeve
10. 2nd speed synchro cup
11. Thrust washer
12. 2nd speed gear
13. Bushing—2nd speed gear
14. Bushing—3rd speed gear
15. 3rd speed gear
16. Thrust washer
17. Circlip
18. 3rd speed synchro cup
19. Synchro ball
20. Spring
21. 3rd/top synchro hub
22. Synchro sleeve
23. Top gear synchro cup
24. Circlip
25. Spacer washer
26. Circlip
27. Ball race
28. Oil deflector plate
29. Input shaft
30. Needle roller bearing
31. Mainshaft
32. Ball race
33. Circlip
34. Spacer washer
35. Circlip
36. Spacer washer
37. Rear ball race
38. Flange
39. Plain washer
40. Slotted nut
41. Cotter pin
42. Rear thrust washer
43. Needle roller bearing
44. Countershaft hub
45. 2nd speed countershaft gear
46. 3rd speed countershaft gear
47. Spacer piece
48. Countershaft gear
49. Needle roller bearing
50. Front thrust washer
51. Countershaft
52. Reverse gear shaft
53. Pivot stud
54. Nyloc nut and washer
55. Reverse gear operating lever
56. Reverse gear
57. Reverse gear bushing
58. Locating plate
59. Screw

solvent and inspected for cracks and burrs. All items that have doubtful potential for reuse should be replaced.

Assembly

Install the reverse gear in the transmission, with the selector groove to the rear. Install the reverse gear shaft, securing it with string to prevent it from sliding into the transmission. Use a stepped drift to drive a new needle roller bearing (with lettered face outward) into each end of the countershaft hub. Install the gears, spacer, and gear to the countershaft hub. Using grease to retain the countershaft thrust washers, install the washers into the transmission and lower the gear cluster into position. With the countershaft temporarily installed, measure the cluster gear end float, which should be 0.-007–0.012 in. (0.1778–0.3048 mm). End clearance may be adjusted to within this range through the use of thrust washers

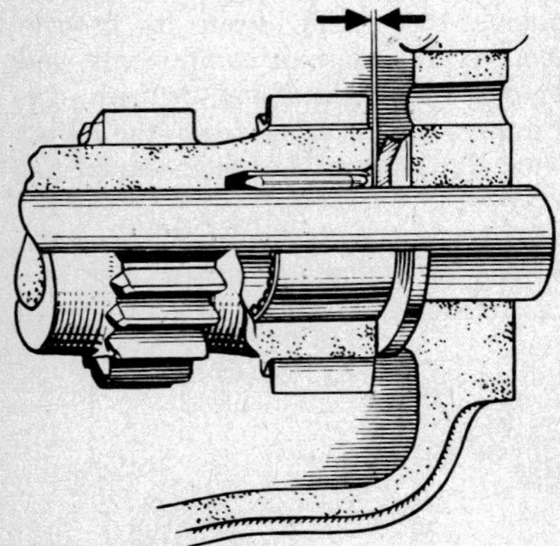

Countershaft rear thrust washer clearance

of larger or smaller thickness. Remove the countershaft and drop the gear cluster to the bottom of the transmission case.

Assemble the synchronizer springs, balls and shims to the 3rd/4th synchronizer hub. Install the outer sleeve. Re-

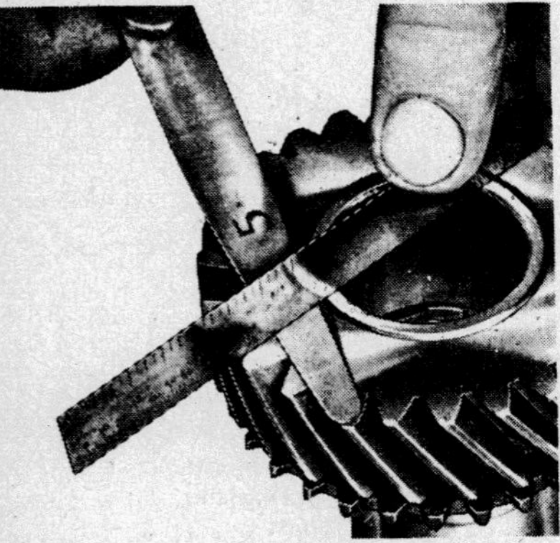

Measuring end clearance of countershaft gears.

peat the preceding operations with the 1st/2nd synchronizer unit. Check the axial release loads, as illustrated in the accompanying diagram. The points of release should be as follows:

3rd/4th: 19–21 lbs
1st/2nd: 25–27 lbs

If the actual release loads observed are greater or less than those specified above, the correct loading may be achieved by adjusting the number of shims beneath each synchronizer spring.

Using a straightedge and a feeler gauge, measure the end clearance of each mainshaft gear on its bushing, as shown in the accompanying illustration. The end clearance measured should be 0.004–0.006 in. (0.1–0.15 mm.), and may be increased by installing a new bushing and decreased by reducing bushing length. In the preceding adjustments, take care, as reduction of bushing length will cause the end clearance of the bushings on the mainshaft to increase.

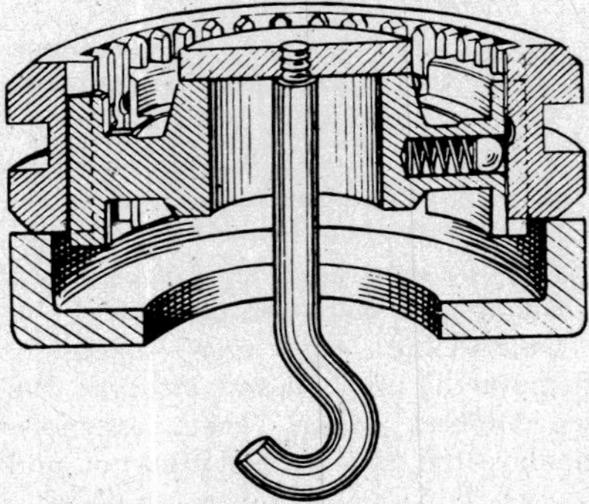

Checking synchronizer release load with spring balance.

Install the thrust washer, bushings and thrust washer to the mainshaft, secure the assembly and measure the total end clearance of the bushings and thrust washers on the mainshaft. This measurement should be 0.003–0.009 in. (0.08–0.23 mm), and may be adjusted by using thrust washers available in the following thicknesses:

Color	Thickness
Plain	0.119 in. (3.02 mm)
Green	0.122 in. (3.10 mm)
Blue	0.125 in. (3.18 mm)
Orange	0.128 in. (3.25 mm)
Yellow	0.133 in. (3.38 mm)

Install the thrust washer, bushing, and thrust washer to the mainshaft. Using a special tool, assemble the race into position and install the washer and circlip. The race should be driven toward the rear to ensure that it is firmly against the circlip. Measure the 1st gear end clearance by gauging the distance between the washer and bushing. The end clearance should be 0.003–0.009 in. (0.08–0.23 mm.) and is adjustable by use of the various thrust washers described above. Prior to final assembly, all components should be removed from the mainshaft.

Assemble the mainshaft as follows: With the components placed in their proper relative positions, install them in the following order: thrust washer, gear and bushing, gear and bushing, thrust washer, a new circlip, 3rd/4th synchronizer unit with baulk ring at each side. Install a baulk ring to each side of the 1st/2nd synchronizer unit, slide the unit over the rear of the mainshaft and onto the larger splines. Install the washer, gear and bushing, and washer to the rear of the mainshaft. Pass the rear of the mainshaft through the rear bearing housing and position the shaft. With the mainshaft in position, a special tool is installed in place of the front cover. This tool consists of a plate that holds the front of the mainshaft in position. Install the circlip to the bearing and drive the bearing into position. Install the washer and circlip. Tap the rear of the mainshaft with a soft-headed mallet to take up the clearance between the circlip, washer, and bearing.

Install the disc, bearing (with circlip groove to the front), washer, and circlip to the input shaft. If necessary, a new bearing should be installed to the bore of the input shaft, with the lettered face of the bearing facing outward. Install the circlip to the bearing and install the assembly. Install the front cover as follows: With the lip of the seal toward the gears, use a special tool to drive a new seal into the front cover. With a seal protector protecting the oil seal, install the gasket and cover and secure with the retaining washers and bolts.

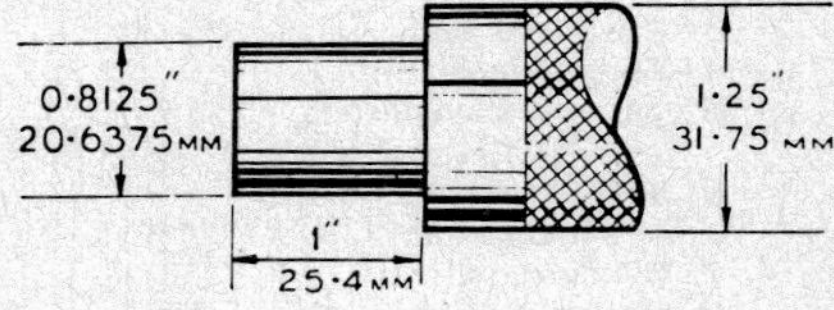

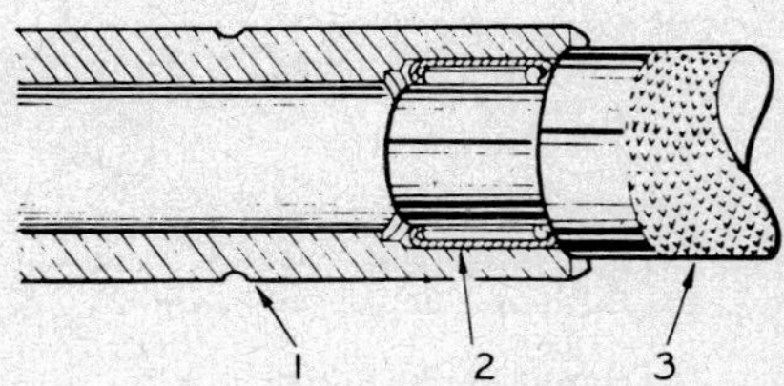

Countershaft bearing tool.

With a tapered pilot tool inserted to align the countershaft gears and thrust washers, insert the countershaft, pushing out the pilot tool. With the ends of the countershaft and reverse gear shafts engaged at the retaining plate, secure with the Phillips head screw. Install and secure the countershaft cover gasket and cover plate.

Assemble the rear extension as follows: Install a new gasket and the rear extension to the transmission and secure with the retaining bolts. Install a spacer washer to the mainshaft and drive the extension ball bearing into position. With its sealing face forward, install a new oil seal. With the driving flange positioned on the mainshaft, install the washer and slotted nut. Tighten the nut to a torque of 80–120 ft lbs and install a new cotter pin. Install the speedometer drive gear assembly, and secure with a retaining bolt.

Reassemble the top cover: Install the selectors to their shafts and secure with the retaining bolts. Install new O-rings to the recesses in the rear of the top cover and install the retaining plate and secure it. With the interlock plunger positioned in the 3d/4th selector shaft, insert the shaft into the top cover. Install the selector fork, spacer tube, and retaining bolt. Install the interlock ball between the bores of the reverse and 3rd/4th selector shafts, using grease to retain the ball. Slide the reverse selector shaft into the top cover and engage it with the reverse selector fork and distance tube. Install the retaining bolt to the selector fork. With the reverse and 3rd/4th selector shafts in the neutral position, install the other interlock ball, using grease to retain it.

Install the 1st/2nd selector shaft into the top cover, inserting the shaft through the 1st/2nd selector fork and spacer tube. Install the balls and long springs to the 1st/2nd and 3rd/4th selector shaft detents. The springs may be retained by screwing the plugs so that they are flush with the machined lower face of the top cover.

NOTE: *From transmission number CT.9899, the 3rd/4th selector shaft ball and long spring have been replaced by a plunger and short spring identical to those of the reverse selector shaft.*

Install the plunger, short spring, and shim to the reverse selector shaft detent, and use the plug to retain the assembly. Use a spring balance to check the selector shaft release loads, which should be as follows:

Selector Shaft	Release Load
1st/2nd	32-34 lbs
3rd/4th	26-28 lbs
Reverse	26-28 lbs

If necessary, the spring loads may be adjusted by grinding the end of the spring (to reduce the release load) or by installing shims between the spring and plunger (to increase the load).

Replace the spring and plunger to the gearshift lever. Assemble the gearshift lever, spring and plate to the top cover, pressing the plunger with a screwdriver as the end of the gearshift lever engages the selectors. Retain the gearshift lever with the cap, cross pin, and nut. Install a new gasket and replace the top cover assembly to the transmission. Be sure that the reverse selector fork engages the actuating lever. Install the strap beneath the head of the rear mounting bolt.

NOTE: *With the modified gearshift lever installed in TR-250 and TR-6 models, the position of the gearshift lever is adjusted as follows: With the gearshift lever positioned into the 1st and 2nd gate, screw the locating pin clockwise until it just causes the gearshift lever to move, then turn the locating pin one-half turn in the counterclockwise direction and tighten the locknut. Move the gearshift lever into the reverse gate position and adjust the other locating pin in the same manner.*

CLUTCH

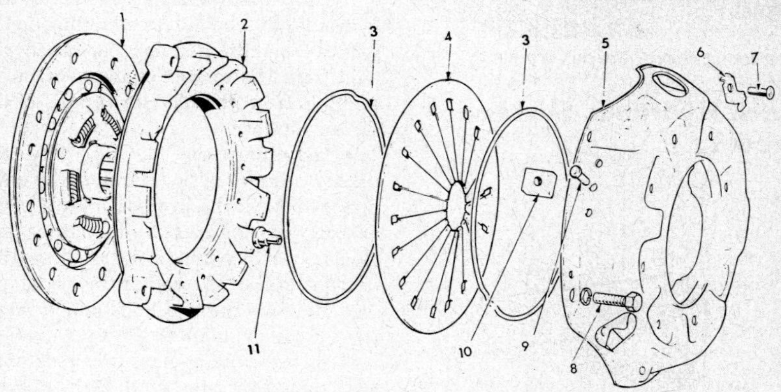

GT6 series clutch components

1. Driven plate
2. Pressure plate
3. Fulcrum ring
4. Diaphragm spring
5. Cover pressing
6. Retractor clip
7. Rivet
8. Setscrew
9. Rivet
10. Balance weight
11. Rivet

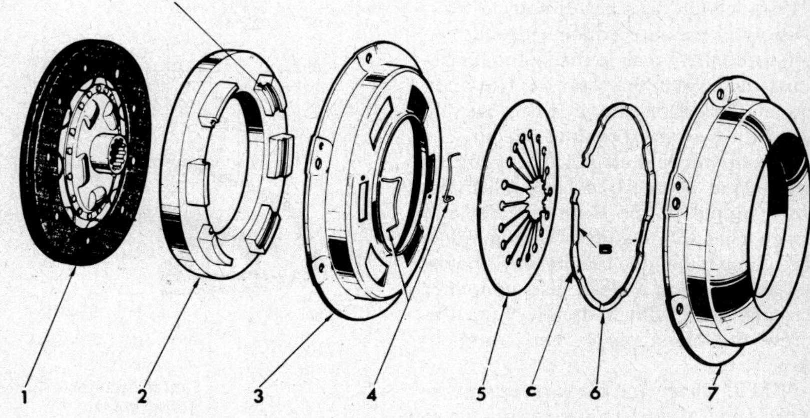

TR-250, TR-6 clutch components

1. Driven plate
2. Pressure plate
3. Inner cover
4. Spring clips
5. Diaphragm spring
6. Circlip
7. Outer cover

The clutch is a single-plate, diaphragm-spring type and is operated hydraulically. Depression of the clutch pedal causes fluid pressure to be transmitted through the clutch master cylinder to the slave cylinder mounted on the clutch housing. At the slave cylinder, the pressure is transformed to mechanical force at the pushrod, which in turn causes the clutch withdrawal lever to pivot, and the clutch to release.

All Spitfire Mk III models and 1971–72 Mk IV models are equipped with a 6 ½ in. diameter clutch. For 1973, the clutch diameter of the Spitfire Mk IV (1500) has been increased to 7 ¼ in. All GT6+, GT6 Mk III, TR-250, and TR-6 models are equipped with an 8 ½ in. clutch.

Removal and Installation

All Models

The clutch may be removed with the engine still in the car.

1. Remove the transmission as outlined in the applicable "Transmission Removal and Installation" procedure.
2. In rotation, progressively loosen the bolts which retain the clutch assembly to the flywheel.
3. Lift off the clutch cover assembly (cover, diaphragm, driving plate, and pressure plate) and pull off the driven plate.
4. Reverse the above procedure to install, taking care to center the driven

plate with a centering mandrel or dummy shaft.

Centering clutch with dummy shaft

Clutch Hydraulic System Bleeding

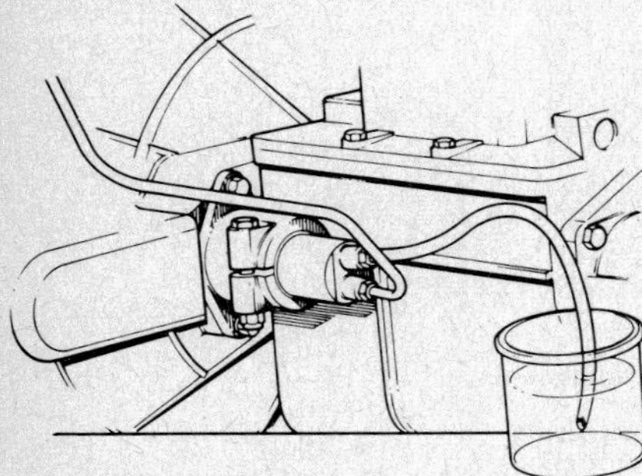

Clutch hydraulic system bleeding—Spitfire shown.

If the clutch does not disengage fully, possibly air has entered the hydraulic system through a break in the system or because the level in the reservoir has fallen too low. In either case, it is necessary to bleed the system to remove the air.

Top up the clutch fluid reservoir to within ¼ in. of the FULL level. Clean the bleed nipple on the slave cylinder and attach to it a short length of tubing. Allow the tubing to hang so that its end is below the fluid level in a clean glass container partially filled with hydraulic fluid. Unscrew the bleed nipple one complete turn.

NOTE: *During the bleeding operation, the level of fluid in the reservoir will fall quickly. Constantly add new fluid to ensure that the reservoir is always at least half filled with fluid. If the reservoir should empty during the bleeding operation, air will be drawn into the system and the entire procedure will have to be repeated.*

Depress the clutch pedal fully and allow it to return normally. Repeat this operation, allowing a slight pause between each depression of the pedal. Note the appearance of the fluid being discharged into the glass container. When no bubbles are observed, hold the clutch pedal down on the following depression. While the pedal is held down, tighten the bleed screw and remove the tubing from the nipple. Top up the master cylinder reservoir with hydraulic fluid and road test the car. After the bleeding operation has been completed, store left-over fluid in a sealed container. Exposure to the atmosphere will cause the hydraulic fluid to deteriorate.

Clutch Master Cylinder

Removal and Installation

All Models

1. Using absorbent rags to prevent the hydraulic clutch fluid from spilling on the paintwork, either siphon or drain the fluid from the master cylinder or pump the fluid from the bleeder nipple on the slave cylinder.
2. Disconnect the fluid pipe from the master cylinder outlet and plug the ends.
3. Pull back the protective dust cover and remove the cotter pin, washer, and clevis pin which retain the master cylinder pushrod to the top of the pedal.
4. Remove the two bolts which retain the master cylinder to the firewall.
5. Reverse the above procedure to install, taking care to bleed the clutch hydraulic system prior to installation.

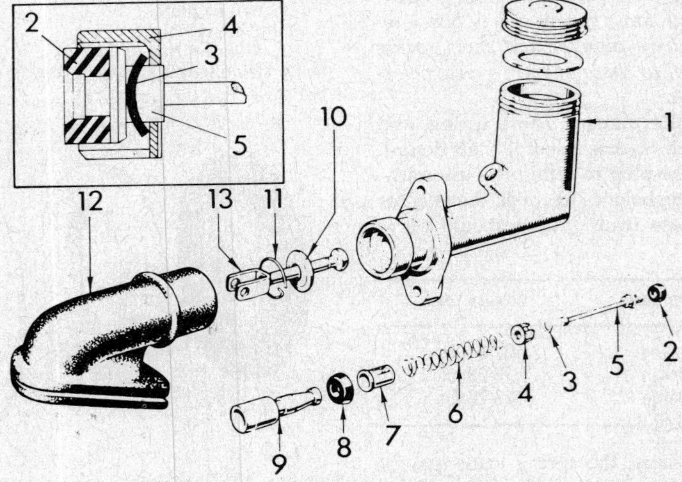

Clutch master cylinder disassembled—GT6 series shown.

1. Master cylinder body
2. Seal (valve)
3. Spring (valve seal)
4. Distance piece
5. Valve
6. Plunger return spring
7. Retainer
8. Seal (plunger)
9. Plunger
10. Abutment plate
11. Circlip
12. Dust excluder
13. Push-rod

Overhaul

1. Remove the master cylinder as outlined under "Clutch Master Cylinder Removal and Installation".
2. Pull back the rubber dust cover. Lightly press in the pushrod and, with a pair of needle nose pliers, remove the circlip and withdraw the pushrod and washer.
3. Connect a compressed air line to the outlet connection and, using light pressure, force out the internal parts.
4. Lift the leaf on the spring retainer and pull it free of the plunger.
5. Compress the return spring and slide the valve stem sideways through the larger offset hole of the retainer. Remove the spring, spacer, and spring washer from the valve shank.
6. Using fingers only, remove the two rubber seals and discard them. Replace with new seals. Clean all parts in methylated alcohol or in clean hydraulic fluid meeting SAE 70 R3 specifications. Lay all metal parts out to dry on a clean sheet of paper. Check the cylinder bore for pitting or scoring.
7. Reverse the above procedure to install, taking care to dip each internal part in hydraulic fluid prior to installation. Make sure that the rubber seals are installed with the lips facing the bore.

Clutch Slave Cylinder

Removal and Installation

All Models

1. On GT6 models, remove the transmission cover to gain access to the cylinder.
2. Drain the clutch hydraulic system by opening the slave cylinder bleeder nipple ½ turn and pumping on the clutch pedal.
3. Disconnect the hydraulic pipe, taking care not to bend it, and push it clear

of the cylinder.

4. Remove the nuts and bolts which retain the cylinder to its bracket on the bellhousing. Remove the dust cover and pull the cylinder forward to clear it from the pushrod. Leave the pushrod attached to the operating shaft lever.

5. Reverse the above procedure to install, taking care to bleed the hydraulic system.

Overhaul

1. Remove the slave cylinder as outlined under "Slave Cylinder Removal and Installation".

2. Remove the rubber dust cover. Depress the piston and, using a pair of needle nose pliers, remove the circlip from the bore.

3. If the internal parts cannot be shaken out, use low pressure compressed air injected into the inlet port to force them out.

4. Remove and discard the rubber seal. Remove the return spring.

5. Clean all metal parts in methylated alcohol or in clean hydraulic fluid meeting SAE 70 R3 specifications. Lay out the parts to dry on a clean sheet of paper. Replace the cylinder body if its bore is pitted or scored. Lubricate the bore and dip each internal part in clean hydraulic fluid.

6. To assemble, insert the internal parts into the cylinder bore, using a new rubber seal. Be careful not to bend back the lips of the seal when installing in the bore. Retain the parts in the bore with the circlip.

7. Install the cylinder as outlined under "Slave Cylinder Removal and Installation".

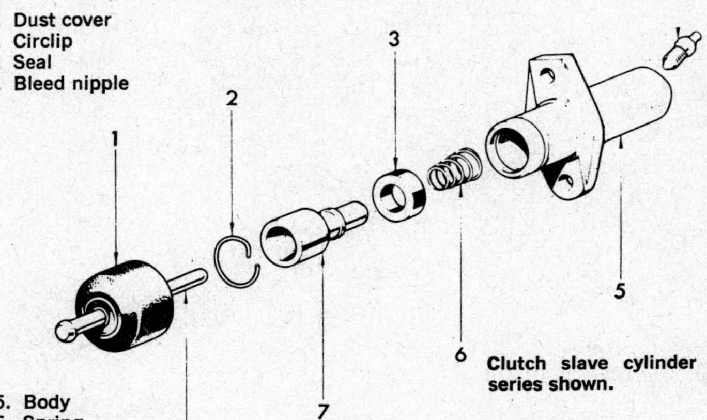

Clutch slave cylinder disassembled—GT6 series shown.

DRIVE AXLES

All current production Triumphs are equipped with differentials that use hypoid bevel gears which drive the rear wheels through a pair of inner and outer axle shafts connected by means of splined couplings, universal joints, and rotoflex couplings (GT6 only).

Driveshaft and U-Joints

Removal and Installation

All Models

1. Place the vehicle on jackstands. Remove the dashboard supports and the transmission cover.

2. Remove the attaching nuts. Gently angle the transmission/engine forward to remove the driveshaft. Remove the shaft to the rear. Models with sliding splines do not require movement of the engine/-transmission assembly.

3. To replace, reverse the above procedure. If the original nuts cannot be replaced with finger pressure, they must be replaced with new nyloc nuts.

U-Joint Overhaul

All Models

Disassembly

1. Remove the snap-ring from the forked end of the shaft. Tap the lug until the bearing cup is seen to protrude. Remove the cup with pliers.

2. Repeat the operation on the reverse side.

3. Remove the flange.

4. Remove all remaining snap-ring Rest the shaft on a block and gently tap out the remaining components.

Assembly

1. Place sealing compound on the shoulders of the new spider journals.

2. Fit oil seal retainers over the trunn-

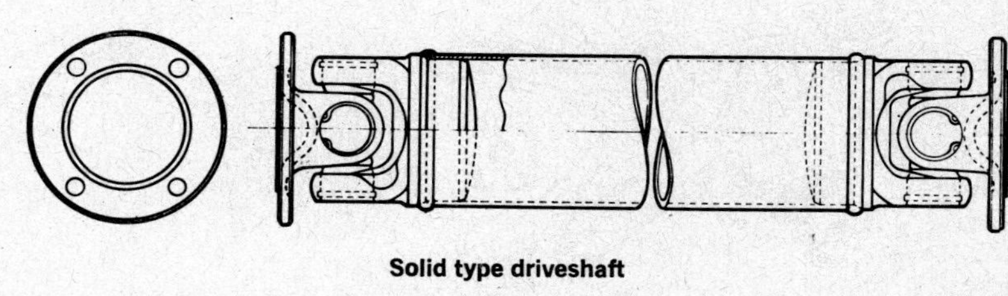
Solid type driveshaft

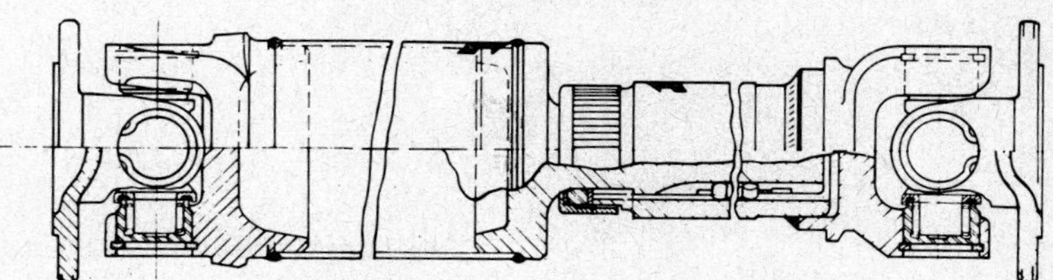
Sliding spline type driveshaft

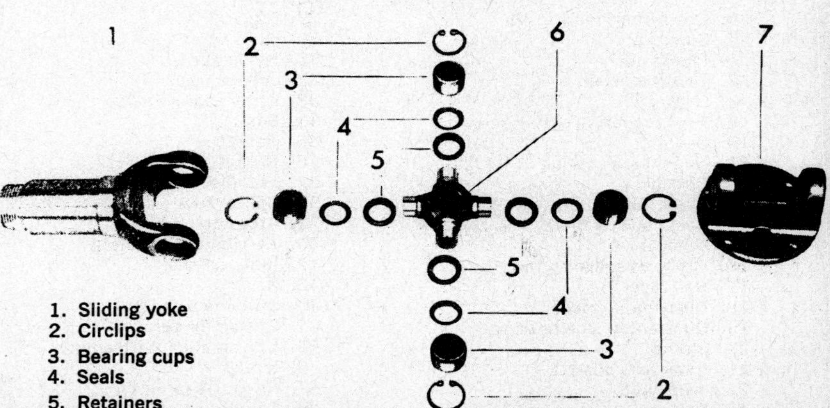

Universal joint disassembled

Replacing bearing cups

ions with a tubular drift. Fit the oil seals.

3. Place the trunnion into the bearing holes and fit the bearing caps and snap-rings. Make sure they are properly seated.

4. Fit the spider with the lubrication nipple toward the driveshaft. Place the other trunnion through the bearing holes in the forked end of the driveshaft and fit the cups and snap-rings.

5. Repeat the procedure on the second universal joint.

CAUTION: *Do not disassemble the sliding yoke for any reason.*

Outer Axle Shaft and Hub Assembly

Removal and Installation

All Models

1. Place the vehicle on jack stands; remove the wheel and backing plate.

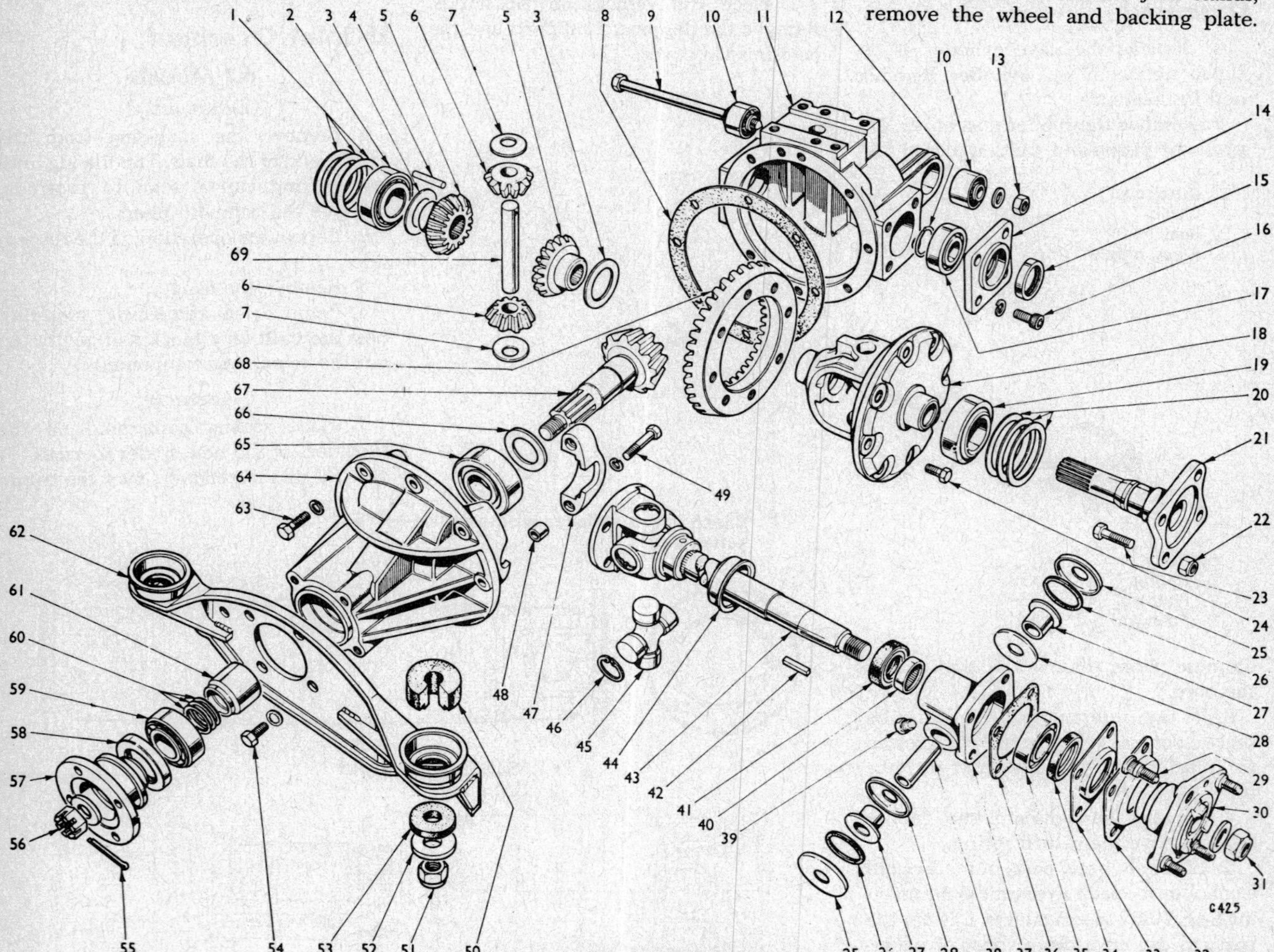

Rear axle disassembled—Spitfire, GT6

1. Shims
2. Differential side bearing
3. Thrust washer
4. Cross-shaft locking pin
5. Sun gear
6. Planet gear
7. Thrust washer
8. Gasket
9. Rear mounting bolt
10. Bushing
11. Hypoid rear casing
12. Circlip
13. Nyloc nut
14. Seal housing plate
15. Oil seal
16. Hexagon socket screw
17. Ball race
18. Differential carrier
19. Differential side bearing
20. Shims
21. Inner axle shaft
22. Nyloc nut
23. Bolt
24. Bolt
25. Shim
26. Rubber sealing ring
27. Nylon bushing
28. Shim
29. Stud
30. Hub
31. Nyloc nut
32. Grease trap
33. Outer seal housing
34. Seal
35. Ballrace
36. Gasket
37. Trunnion housing
38. Spacer tube
39. Grease plug
40. Needle roller bearing
41. Inner oil seal
42. Key
43. Outer axle shaft
44. Grease flinger
45. Universal joint assembly
46. Circlip
47. Bearing cap
48. Tubular dowel
49. Bolt
50. Mounting rubber
51. Nyloc nut
52. Plain washer
53. Rubber pad
54. Bolt
55. Cotter pin
56. Slotted nut
57. Coupling flange
58. Oil seal
59. Pinion tail bearing
60. Shims
61. Spacer
62. Mounting plate
63. Bolt
64. Hypoid nose piece casing
65. Pinion head bearing
66. Spacer
67. Pinion
68. Ring gear
69. Cross-shaft
70. Bolt
71. Lockplate
72. Brake backplate
73. Bolt
74. Nyloc nut
75. Vertical link

Remove the brake hose, attaching bracket, and brake line. Disconnect the handbrake from the attaching lever.

2. Relieve the shock absorber of load by use of a jack.

3. Remove the bolt to release the radius arm.

4. Remove the universal joint coupling bolts.

5. Remove the nut and washer from the lower attaching eye; pull the shock clear. Remove the jack.

6. While supporting the brake drum by hand, remove the spring eye nuts. The hub and axle shafts are now free.

7. To install, refit the vertical link to the spring attaching eye; leave the nut loose.

8. Using caution, jack up the vertical link and affix the extended shock absorber to the lower attaching bracket. Refit the radius arm to the link; secure in position.

9. Fasten the inner and outer axle shafts together. Place a load of 300 lbs in the front seats. Tighten the securing nut to the vertical link.

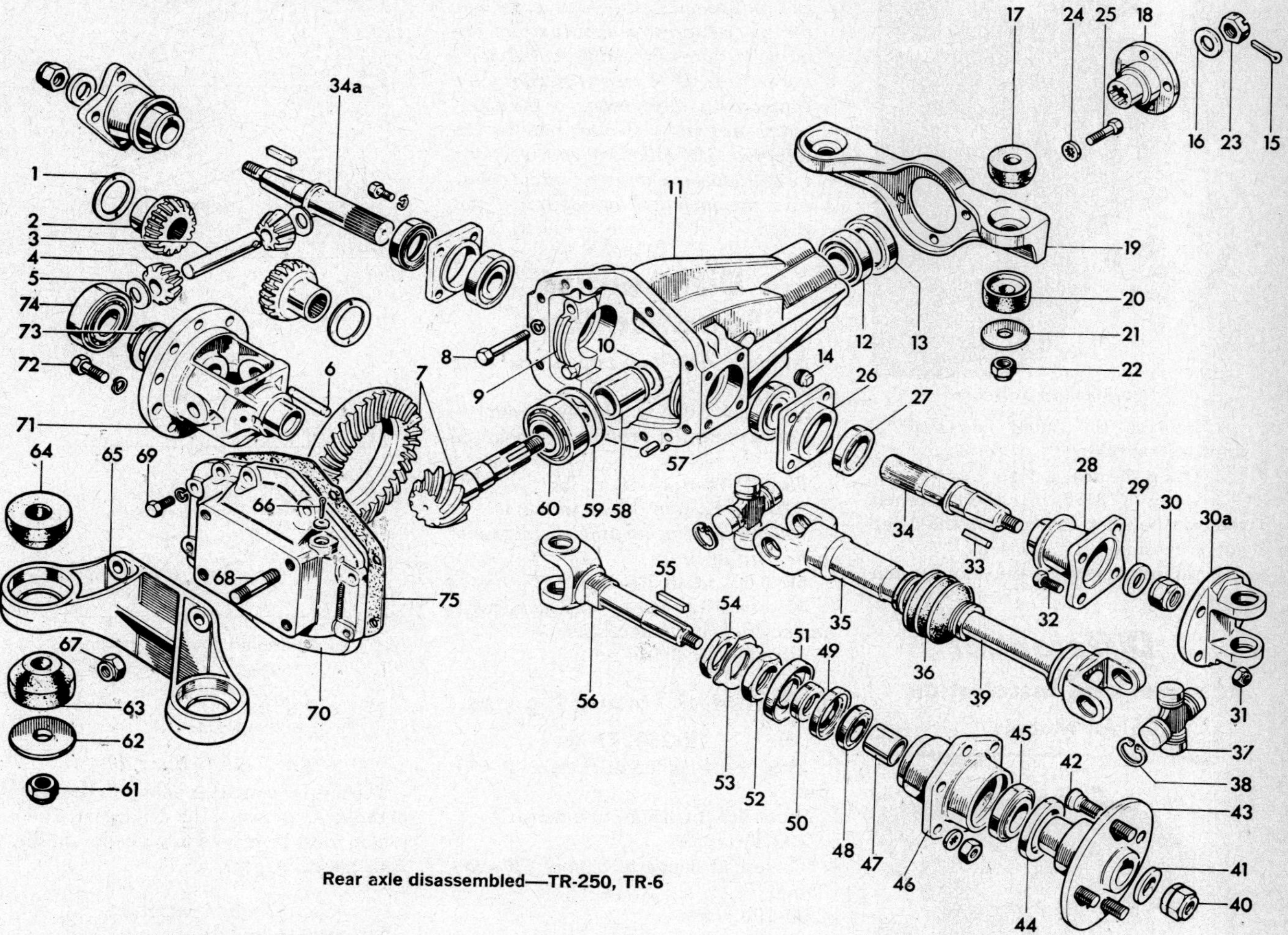

Rear axle disassembled—TR-250, TR-6

1. Thrust washer—sun gear
2. Sun gear
3. Cross shaft
4. Planet gear
5. Thrust washer—planet gear
6. Locking pin—cross shaft
7. Ring gear and pinion
8. Bolt, bearing cap
9. Bearing cap
10. Shim, pinion pre-loading
11. Axle casing
12. Tail bearing, pinion
13. Oil seal, pinion
14. Filler plug—oil level
15. Cotter pin
16. Washer
17. Rubber buffer, upper
18. Companion flange
19. Mounting, front
20. Rubber buffer, lower
21. Backing plate
22. Nyloc nut
23. Slotted nut
24. Lockwasher
25. Bolt
26. Bearing retainer
27. Oil seal
28. Flange
29. Washer
30. Nut
30a. Yoke
31. Nut
32. Bolt
33. Key
34. Axle shaft, inner, short
34a Axle shaft, inner, long
35. Axle shaft, fixed, outer
36. Seal
37. Universal spider
38. Circlip
39. Axle shaft, sliding, outer
40. Nut
41. Washer
42. Wheel stud
43. Hub
44. Oil seal
45. Hub bearing, outer
46. Bearing housing
47. Bearing spacer, collapsible
48. Hub bearing, inner
49. Oil seal
50. Bearing spacer
51. Stone guard
52. Adjusting nut
53. Tab washer
54. Locknut
55. Key
56. Stub shaft
57. Bearing, inner axle shaft
58. Spacer, pinion bearing
59. Shim, pinion locating
60. Head bearing, pinion
61. Nut
62. Backing plate
63. Buffer, lower
64. Buffer, upper
65. Mounting, rear
66. Cotter pin—breather
67. Nut
68. Stud
69. Bolt
70. Rear cover
71. Differential cage
72. Bolt
73. Shim, pre-load
74. Bearing, differential cage
75. Gasket, rear cover

10. Reverse the removal procedures to complete installation.

Inner Axle Shaft

Removal and Installation

All Models

Removing inner axle shaft

1. Remove the outer axle shaft as previously described.
2. Drain the rear axle.
3. Using a 3/16 in. Allen wrench, remove the Allen screws from the differential housing.
4. To install, reverse the above procedure.

Differential

Removal and Installation

All Models

Luggage compartment floor panel removed showing rear leaf spring mounting bolts—Spitfire, GT6.

1. Place the vehicle on jackstands and drain the rear axle. Remove the wheels and backing plate.
2. Place supports under the vertical links to remove the load from the shock absorbers. Remove the shock absorbers.
3. Remove the resonator and tailpipe.
4. Disconnect the driveshaft.
5. Remove the luggage compartment floor panel; remove the spring access plate. Unscrew the nuts and remove the rear spring attachments.
6. With an assistant supporting the weight of the unit, cautiously release the front mounts. Remove the unit forward and down.
7. To reassemble, reverse the above procedures. Be sure to readjust the brakes.

Overhaul

NOTE: *Unless one has the experience and the special factory tools, especially the special spreader tool used by Triumph to spread the differential housing sufficiently to free the differential components, the overhaul of the differential assembly should not be attempted. The following specifications, torque figures, and tooth contact conditions are included for reference purposes.*

Differential Specifications

Backlash between pinion and ring gears:
All: 0.004–0.006 in. (0.10–0.15 mm)
Pinion bearing preload, without oil seal:
TR-250, TR-6: 15–18 in. lbs
GT6 and Spitfire: 12–16 in. lbs
Differential bearing preload, measured over both bearings:
All: 0.003 in. (0.076 mm)
Maximum run-out of ring gear, when bolted to differential carrier:
All: 0.003 in. (0.076 mm)

Differential Torque Figures

TR-250, TR-6

Ring gear to differential case: 40–45 ft lbs
Inner driving flange to inner axle: 100–110 ft lbs
Driveshaft flange to pinion; TR—250, TR—6:
90–100 ft lbs

GT6, Spitfire

Hypoid pinion flange attachment:
(GT6) 90–100 ft lbs
(Spitfire) 70–85 ft lbs
Rear hub to axle shaft: 100–110 ft lbs

Differential Tooth Contact Conditions

By painting about ten teeth of the ring gear with special paint, then moving the pinion into mesh with the painted teeth, it is possible to obtain a good impression of how the teeth are making contact. The following tooth contact conditions, along with their remedies, are keyed to the accompanying diagrams:

Ideal Contact (a):

The area of contact is distributed evenly over the tooth profile, and is closer to the toe than to the heel.

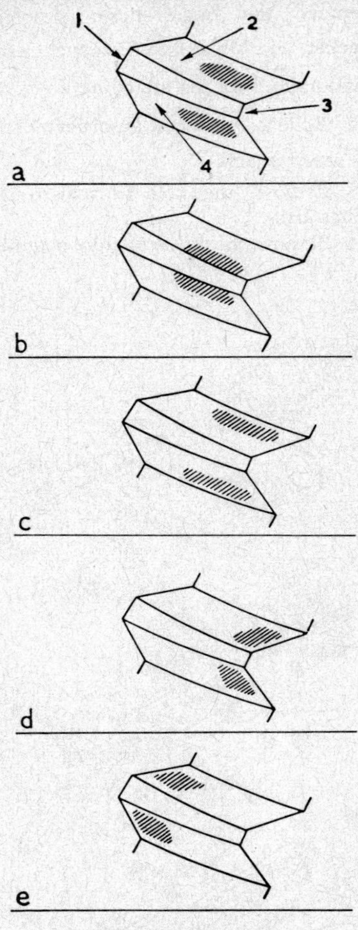

Gear tooth markings
1. Heel
2. Coasting side
3. Toe
4. Drive side

High Tooth Contact (b):

The area of contact is heavy on the top of the tooth profile of the drive gear. The pinion must be moved into deeper mesh with the drive gear.

Low Tooth Contact (c):

The contact area is heavy in the root of the drive gear tooth profile, and the pinion gear is meshed too deeply with the drive gear. The pinion must be moved away.

Toe Contact (d):

The contact area is concentrated at the small end of the driven tooth. To correct, the ring gear must be moved out of mesh by increasing the backlash.

Heel Contact (e):

The contact area is concentrated at the large end of the driven tooth. To correct, the ring gear must be moved into closer mesh with the pinion by decreasing the backlash.

CAUTION: *When decreasing the backlash, be sure to maintain the minimum backlash of 0.004 in. (0.10 mm).*

REAR SUSPENSION

All current production Triumphs are equipped with independent rear suspension. Spitfire Mk III models utilize swing axles with a transverse leaf spring and radius rods. Spitfire Mk IV models also use swing axles, but have modified the leaf spring to a centrally pivoted, rate-compensating unit with the center leaf clamped to the differential housing. This creates a lower rear roll center, less camber change, and more predictable handling. All GT6+ and GT6 Mk III models use a fully independent, parallel guidance system with reversed wishbones, radius rods, and a transverse leaf spring. The TR-250 and TR-6 models utilize a fully independent system also but with semi-trailing arms and a pair of coil springs.

All Spitfire Mk III and IV models, as well as all GT6+ and GT6 Mk III models are equipped with telescopic shock absorbers, whereas the TR-250 and TR-6 use lever (piston) types.

Transverse Leaf Spring

Removal and Installation

1. Disconnect the brake lines (be careful not to spill fluid) and the chassis bracket. Disconnect the handbrake.
2. Jack up the suspension vertical link. Disconnect the axle shaft and couplings.
3. On late GT6's, remove the radius arm mounting bolts from the chassis. Remove the shock absorber and lower vertical link.
4. While supporting the vertical link, remove the eye bolt from the spring eye. Remove the luggage floor plate and slide the spring from the vehicle.
5. To replace the spring: align the spring in the recess in the differential casing. Make sure the bolt is in the correct hole. (The spring is marked Front to indicate the proper position.)
6. Replace the studs in the casing. Make sure the shorter threaded end is down. Replace the spring clamp plate and fasten down. Refit the luggage floor plate. Use the appropriate body sealer.
7. Fasten the vertical link to the spring eyes. Do not tighten the spring eye nut. (Refit the radius arms at this point, if required.)
8. Raise the vertical link and refit the shock absorber. Refit the axle shaft attachments. Refit the handbrake brake lines.

CAUTION: *Do not forget to adjust and bleed the brakes.*

9. Place the floor jack under the differential, remove the jackstands and, with

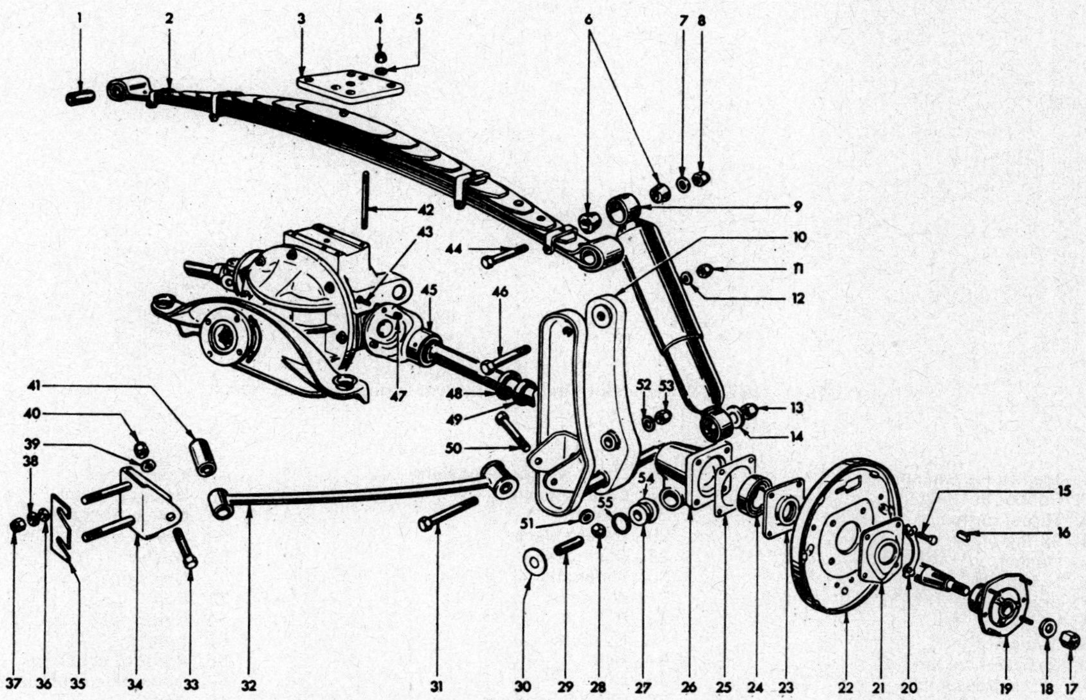

Spitfire MK III swing axle rear suspension—MK IV, 1500 similar

1. Spring eye bushing
2. Spring
3. Spring clamp plate
4. Nut
5. Washer
6. Rubber bushing
7. Washer
8. Nut
9. Shock absorber
10. Vertical link
11. Nut
12. Washer
13. Nut
14. Washer
15. Bolt
16. Key
17. Nut
18. Washer
19. Hub
20. Locktab
21. Grease retainer
22. Brake backplate
23. Seal housing
24. Bearing
25. Gasket
26. Trunnion housing
27. Nylon bushing
28. Nut
29. Steel bushing
30. Dust seal
31. Bolt
32. Radius arm
33. Bolt
34. Radius arm bracket
35. Shim
36. Washer
37. Nut
38. Washer
39. Washer
40. Nut
41. Rubber bushing
42. Stud
43. Bolt
44. Bolt
45. Axle shaft coupling
46. Bolt
47. Nut
48. Flinger
49. Seal
50. Bolt
51. Washer
52. Washer
53. Nut
54. Dust seal
55. Rubber ring

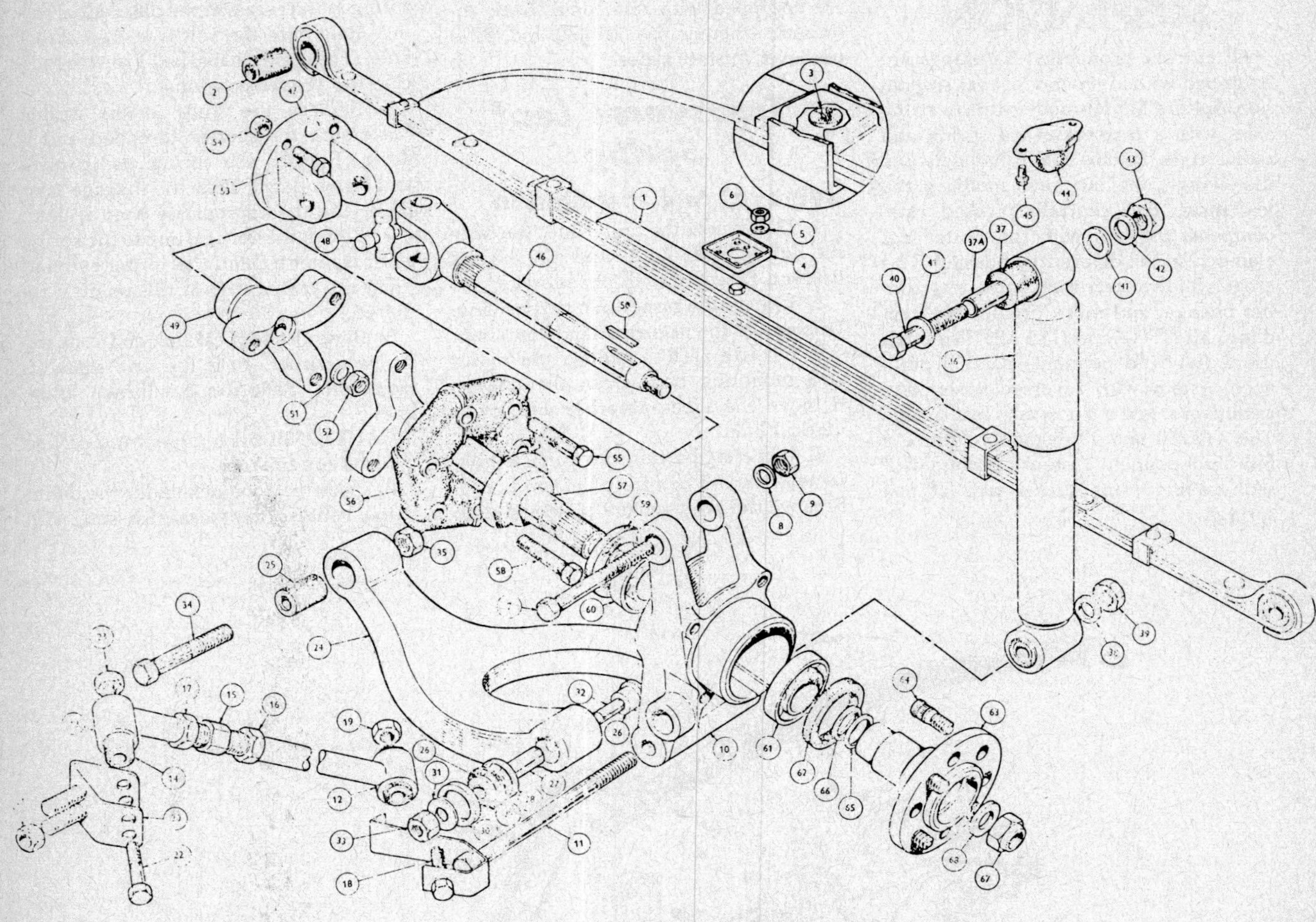

GT6+, 1971-72 GT6 Mk III independent leaf spring rear suspension

1. Transverse leaf spring
2. Rubber bushing
3. Thrust button
4. Spring plate
5. Washer
6. Nyloc nut
7. Bolt
8. Washer
9. Nyloc nut
10. Rear vertical link
11. Bracket assembly
12. Radius arm rear eye
13. Radius arm front eye
14. Rubber bushing
15. Radius arm adjuster
16. Locknut
17. Locknut
18. Bolt
19. Nut
20. Mounting bracket assembly
21. Nyloc nut
22. Bolt
23. Nyloc nut
24. Lower wishbone assembly
25. Lower wishbone bushing
26. Outer bushing
27. Spacer
28. Water shield
29. Dust shield
30. Water shield
31. Washer
32. Bolt
33. Nyloc nut
34. Bolt
35. Nut
36. Shock absorber
37. Rubber bushing

37a. Sleeve

38. Washer
39. Nyloc nut
40. Bolt
41. Washer
42. Washer
43. Nyloc nut
44. Rubber bumper
45. Screw
46. Intermediate axle shaft assembly
47. Yoke flange
48. Universal joint
49. Driven flange
50. Key
51. Washer
52. Nyloc nut
53. Bolt
54. Nyloc nut
55. Bolt
56. Rotoflex coupling
57. Outer axle shaft assembly
58. Bolt
59. Inner oil seal
60. Inner bearing
61. Outer bearing
62. Outer oil seal
63. Rear hub
64. Stud
65. Adjusting spacer
66. Shim
67. Nyloc nut
68. Washer

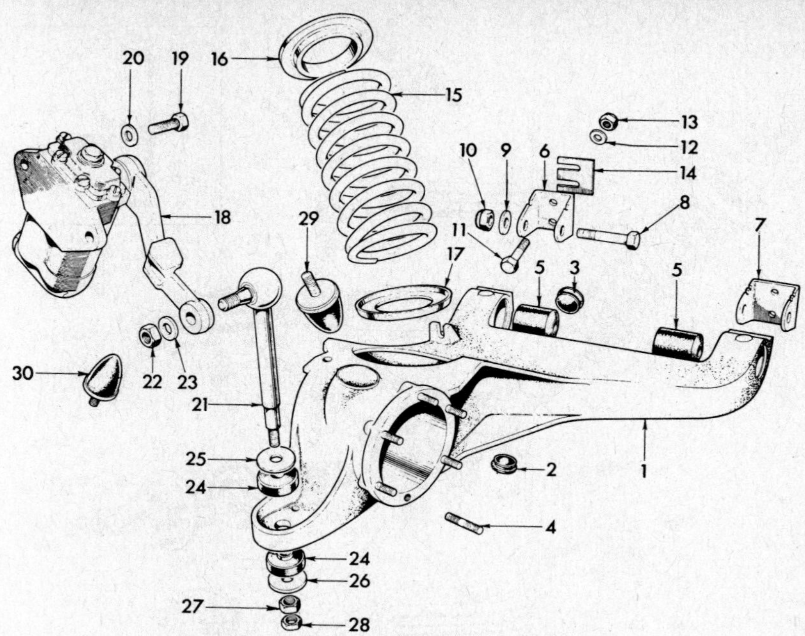

TR-250, TR-6 independent coil spring rear suspension

1. Suspension arm
2. Rubber plug
3. Rubber plug
4. Stud
5. Metalastik bushing
6. Fulcrum bracket, inner
7. Fulcrum bracket, outer
8. Bolt
9. Plain washer
10. Nyloc nut
11. Bolt
12. Plain washer
13. Nyloc nut
14. Shim
15. Road spring
16. Rubber insulator
17. Rubber insulator
18. Shock absorber arm
19. Bolt
20. Washer
21. Shock absorber link
22. Nut
23. Washer
24. Rubber buffer
25. Backing plate
26. Backing plate
27. Nut
28. Locknut
29. Bump stop
30. Rebound rubber

the vertical link raised to the proper height, load the car to the static (300 lbs) setting. At this point tighten the spring eye nuts.

Coil Spring

Removal and Installation

1. Place the car on jackstands and position a floor jack under the differential. Push up the suspension arm with the jack under the spring well.

2. Remove the wheel, disconnect the driveshaft, remove the shock absorber.

3. Being careful to avoid placing stress on the brake line, lower the suspension arm until the spring is free.

4. Reverse the procedure to install.

Rear Shock Absorber

Removal and Installation

Spitfire, GT6

1. Block the front wheels. Jack up the rear of the car and support the chassis on jackstands.

2. Remove the applicable wheel and tire assembly. Unload the shock absorber by placing a jack beneath the vertical link.

3. Remove the nut and washer which retain the lower end of the shock absorber to the vertical link, then remove the upper nut and washer. Pull the shock clear of its attachments.

4. Keeping the shock vertical, pump it several times to force any trapped air in the unit into the upper chamber. Discard the shock if it offers inconsistent resistance, or if it seizes in its bore and is difficult to move in either direction.

5. Reverse the above procedure to install.

TR-250, TR-6

1. Block the front wheels. Jack up the rear of the car and support the chassis on jackstands.

2. Remove the applicable wheel and tire assembly.

3. Loosen and remove the locknut and nut which retain the shock absorber link to the suspension arm.

4. Lift the shock absorber arm and remove the link from the suspension arm, taking care not to misplace the two rubber buffers and buffer backing plates. Remove the two bolts and washers which retain the shock absorber to the chassis and lift out the shock absorber and link assembly.

5. Clean away any dirt from the filler plug hole. Keeping the shock vertical, unscrew the filler plug and check the level of the fluid. Top-up to the bottom of the filler plug hole with the recommended shock absorber fluid.

CAUTION: *Do not overfill the shock as the air space above the fluid is required for the proper operation of the unit. Move the shock absorber arm (lever) up and down a few times to force trapped air to the top of the unit. Recheck the fluid level. Replace the filler plug. Keeping the unit vertical, pump it several times. Discard the unit if it offers pockets of no resistance or if it becomes extremely difficult to move.*

6. If the shock absorber proves satisfactory, install it by reversing the above procedure. If the shock is in need of replacement, transfer the link from the old unit to the new one. To remove the link from the shock absorber arm, remove the nut and washer and carefully press the threaded portion of the link from the arm.

NOTE: *Do not use a hammer to force out the link as this may result in damage to the threads.*

Rear Suspension Adjustments

Because special equipment is required to properly adjust the rear suspension alignment, it is not advised that the owner attempt this operation. The following information is included for reference purposes.

Camber

Rear suspension camber angle is non-adjustable. If the camber angle is not within the specifications given in the Wheel Alignment Table, this indicates a weak or incorrectly set spring or excessive wear in the vertical link bushings (Spitfire, GT6) or in the suspension arm bushings (TR-250, TR-6).

Toe-in/Toe-out

Rear wheel toe-in/toe-out is adjustable by means of shims. Toe-in/toe-out dimensions are influenced by vehicle load, rear spring rate, and wear factors in the vertical link linkage (Spitfire, GT6) or in the suspension arm linkage (TR-250, TR-6). Unlike the front wheels, each rear wheel may be adjusted independently. Adding shims increases toe-out while removing shims decreases toe-out.

FRONT SUSPENSION

The front suspension is fully independent and consists of upper and lower control arms at each side which hold the spindles, coil springs, and hydraulic shock absorbers. The front wheel bearings are a tapered roller design.

Front Spring and Shock Absorber Assembly

Removal and Installation

Spitfire, GT6

1. Jack up the front of the car and support the chassis on jackstands.
2. Remove the applicable front wheel and tire assembly.
3. Loosen the bolt and nut which retain the steering trunnion to the lower control arm.
4. Remove the lower bolt, nut, and washer from the shock absorber.
5. Remove the three nuts which retain the front spring pad to its bracket.
6. Free the shock absorber from the lower control arm and remove the spring and shock absorber assembly.
7. Reverse the above procedure to install, taking care not to torque the shock absorber bolts and steering trunnion bolts to their final figure until the suspension is loaded to its normal working position.

Disassembly

Spitfire, GT6

1. Remove the spring and shock absorber assembly as previously described.
2. Using a spring compressor, relieve the load on the upper nuts of the shock absorber by compressing the spring as far as possible.
3. Remove the locknut and nut which retain the shock absorber rod to its mounting flange. Remove the mounting rubbers, mounting rubber seats, and mounting flange from the shock.
4. Carefully release the spring compressor and remove the assembly from the tool.
5. Remove the shock absorber from the spring.
6. Inspect the shock absorber for a damaged or dented body, bent piston rod, loosened mounting, or fluid leakage. Also make sure that the unit offers resistance in one or both directions, does not offer excessive resistance (indicating seizing), or does not offer a pocket of no resistance when reversing direction.

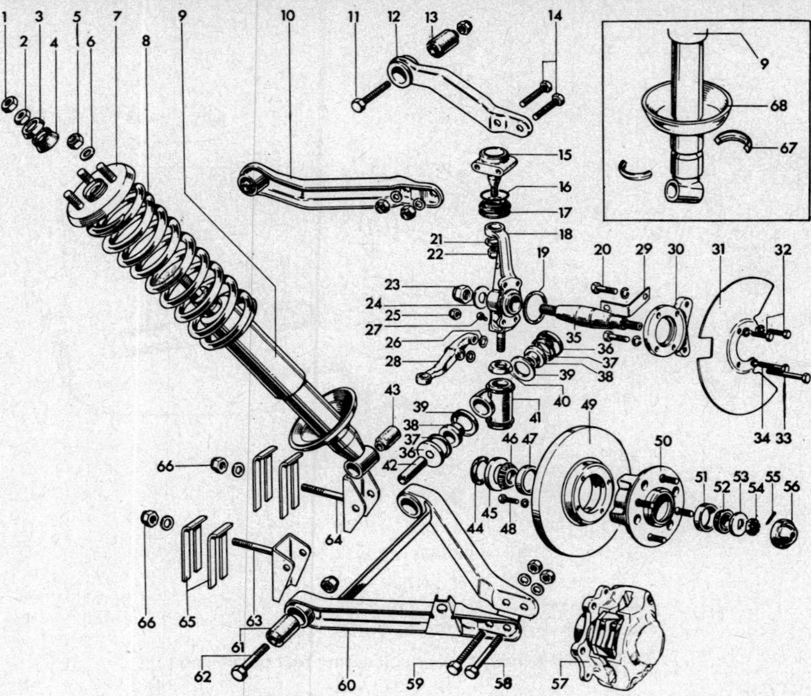

Front suspension assembly—Spitfire, GT6

1. Nut
2. Nut
3. Washer
4. Mounting rubber
5. Nut
6. Washer
7. Upper spring pan
8. Road spring
9. Shock absorber
10. Top control arm
11. Fulcrum bolt
12. Top control arm
13. Fulcrum bushing
14. Bolt
15. Ball joint
16. Retainer
17. Rubber seal
18. Vertical link
19. Rubber seal
20. Bolt
21. Washer
22. Nut
23. Nut
24. Washer
25. Nut
26. Spacer
27. Plug
28. Steering arm
29. Bracket
30. Caliper bracket
31. Dust shield
32. Bolt
33. Bolt
34. Bolt
35. Spindle
36. Dust seal
37. Rubber ring
38. Nylon bushing
39. Dust seal
40. Rubber seal
41. Trunnion
42. Bushing
43. Fulcrum bushing
44. Felt seal
45. Seal holder
46. Inner race
47. Outer track
48. Bolt
49. Brake disc
50. Hub
51. Outer track
52. Inner race
53. Washer
54. Nut
55. Cotter pin
56. Grease cap
57. Brake caliper
58. Trunnion bolt
59. Shock absorber bolt
60. Lower control arm
61. Fulcrum bushing
62. Bolt
63. Front fulcrum bracket
64. Rear fulcrum bracket
65. Shim
66. Nut
67. Keeper
68. Lower spring pan

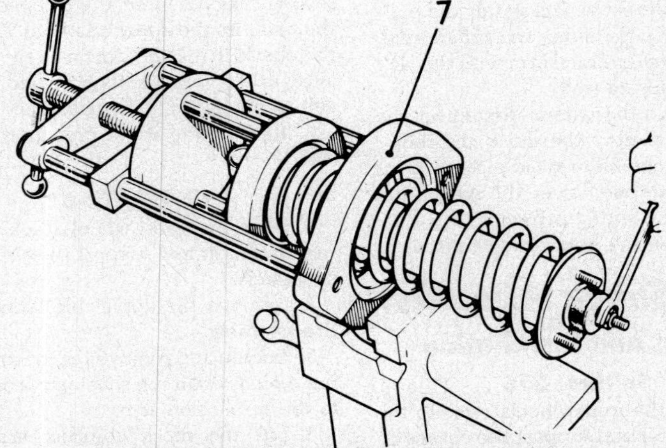

Disassembling front spring and shock absorber assembly using spring compressor (7).

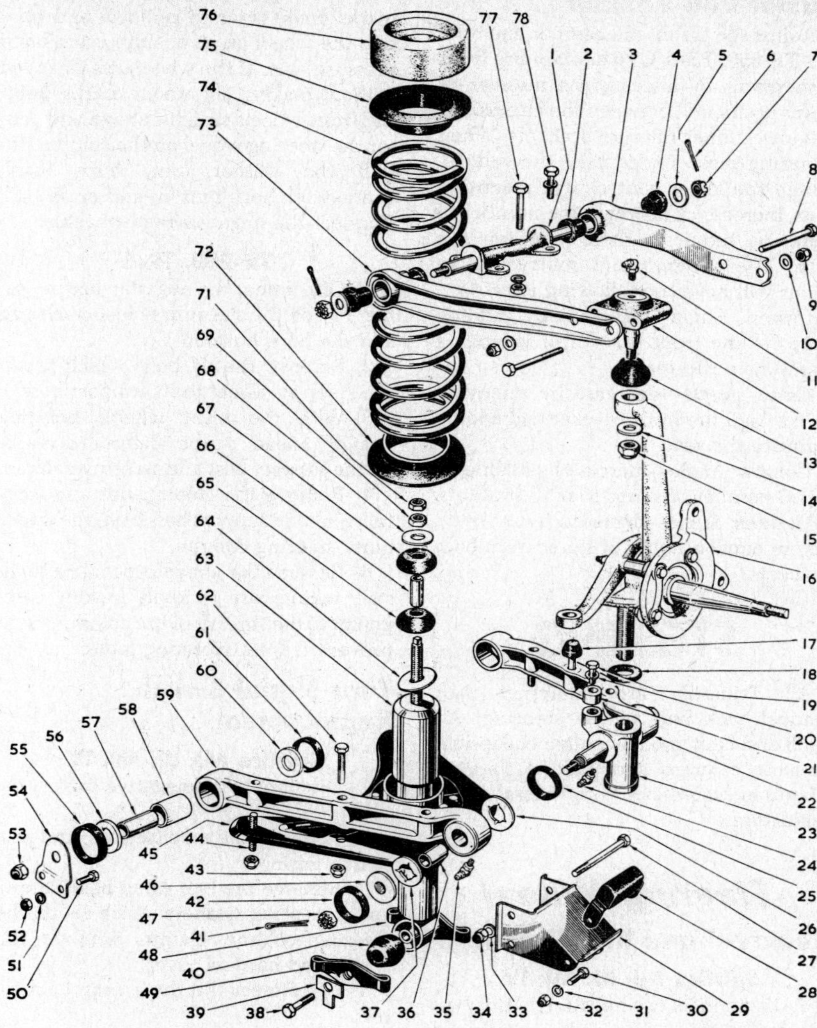

Front suspension assembly—TR-250, TR-6

1. Upper inner fulcrum
2. Rubber bushing
3. Upper control arm—rear
4. Rubber bushing
5. Washer
6. Cotter pin
7. Slotted nut
8. Bolt
9. Nyloc nut
10. Plain washer
11. Grease nipple
12. Upper ball joint
13. Rubber seal
14. Plain washer
15. Nyloc nut
16. Caliper bracket and vertical link
17. Bump rubber
18. Rubber seal
19. Bolt
20. Spring washer
21. Lock stop collar
22. Lower control arm—rear
23. Lower trunnion bracket
24. Grease nipple
25. Rubber seal
26. Thrust washer
27. Bolt
28. Rebound rubber
29. Bracket
30. Bolt
31. Spring washer
32. Nyloc nut
33. Plain washer
34. Nyloc nut
35. Grease nipple
36. Bushing—nylon
37. Thrust washer
38. Bolt
39. Tab washer
40. Rubber bushing
41. Cotter pin
42. Rubber seal
43. Nyloc nut
44. Stud
45. Spring pan
46. Serrated washer
47. Slotted nut
48. Shock absorber attachment bracket—rear
49. Shock absorber attachment bracket—front
50. Bolt
51. Spring washer
52. Nut
53. Nyloc nut
54. Fulcrum bracket
55. Rubber seal
56. Thrust washer
57. Steel sleeve
58. Nylon bushing
59. Lower control arm—front
60. Thrust washer
61. Rubber seal
62. Bolt
63. Shock absorber
64. Washer
65. Rubber bushing
66. Sleeve
67. Rubber bushing
68. Washer
69. Nut
71. Locknut
72. Rubber collar
73. Upper control arm—front
74. Spring
75. Rubber collar
76. Spacer
77. Bolt
78. Bolt

Replace the shock if any of the above conditions are present. Also, check the front spring for cracks or sagging.

7. Reverse the above procedure to install.

Front Shock Absorber

Removal and Installation

TR-250, TR-6

1. Jack up the front of the car and support the chassis on jackstands.
2. Remove the applicable wheel and tire assembly.
3. Remove the four nuts and washers which retain the shock absorber to its lower attachment plate and remove the plate.
4. Remove the locknut from the top of the shock absorber. Holding the shock, remove the other nut which retains the unit in the shock tower and slide the shock down and out.
5. Remove the rubber bushing and the inner washer from the top of the shock. Remove the bolts which retain the lower attaching points to the bottom of the shock.
6. Inspect the shock absorber for road damage, leakage, and proper resistance.
7. Reverse the above procedure to install, taking care to replace any worn rubber bushings. Pump the shock a few times to force any trapped air to the upper section, and keep the unit vertical during installation.

Front Spring

Removal and Installation

TR-250, TR-6

1. Remove the shock absorber as outlined under "Shock Absorber Removal and Installation".
2. Jack up the lower control arm until it is clear of the rebound stop. Disconnect the rebound stop and bracket assembly and lower the suspension. Remove the jack.
3. Pass the spring compressor (Triumph no. S.112A) up through the spring pan, the spring, and the suspension turret, locking the tool at the top. Install the adapter plate (Triumph no. S.112A.1A) and winding nut of the tool below the spring pan, allowing the shock absorber lower attachment bolts to seat in the clearance holes provided in the shock.
4. Compress the spring until the lower control arm assembly is horizontal. Position a wooden block between the top of the turret and the upper control arm assembly for support.
5. Remove the bolt and nuts which retain the front lower control arm to the spring pan. Remove the bump rubber. Replace the front lower control arm-to-

spring pan bolt and bump rubber with 3/8 x 6 in. guide rods.

6. Carefully release the spring compressor, allowing the spring pan to slide down the guide rods, until the spring is loose. Disassemble the compressor and remove the spring pan, rubber collars, front spring, and spacer (distance piece). Remove the four shock absorber lower attachment bolts.

7. Inspect the spring for cracks and sagging.

8. Reverse the above procedure to install, taking care to install new rubber collars and a new rebound rubber if any are cracked or worn.

Ball Joint

Removal and Installation

All Models

1. Before starting work, be sure the handbrake is on.

2. Remove the ball joint stud washer and nut. Using a ball joint separator, pull the ball joint from the vertical link.

3. Loosen and remove the bolts holding the ball joint to the upper A-arm.

CAUTION: *When removing the ball joints, the hub assembly must be supported.*

4. To replace: Make sure all parts are thoroughly cleaned. Attach the ball joint to the upper A-arm. Tighten the bolts.

5. Place the ball joint stud into the vertical link and tighten the nut and washer. Replace the stud nut with a new nyloc nut. Tighten all remaining bolts.

Front End Alignment

The following suspension geometry angles and measurements apply to cars that are static laden, i.e. with the vehicle stationary, steering centered, and a 150 lb. weight (or its equivalent) on each front seat.

Toe-in

With the steering centralized, measure the toe-in. If adjustment is required, loosen the tie-rod end locknuts and the outer clip of the rubber seals. Rotate the tie-rod ends until the correct alignment is obtained. Note the reading and move the vehicle forward until the wheels rotate one-half turn, then take a second reading. This procedure allows for wheel rim runout. Adjust the tie-rods to the mean of the two readings for greater accuracy. After adjustment, tighten the tie-rod locknuts and rubber seal clips.

NOTE: *When checking toe-in or other suspension geometry, the vehicle should be static laden, on a smooth and level surface, and should have the tires inflated to the correct pressure.*

Caster and Camber

Adjust the caster and camber angles of the TR-250, TR-6, GT6 and Spitfire front suspensions by altering the number of shims positioned between the chassis and the lower inner fulcrum brackets. When adjusting these angles, raise the vehicle, loosen the lower control arm mounting nuts, increase or decrease the number of shims as required, then retighten the nuts. The addition and subtraction of shims will have the following effects:

Caster Angle—increase by adding shims to the front bracket or removing shims from the rear.

Caster Angle—decrease by removing shims from the front bracket and adding shims to the rear.

Camber Angle—increase by adding an equal number of shims to both brackets.

Camber Angle—decrease by subtracting an equal number of shims from both brackets.

STEERING

All Triumphs are equipped with manual rack and pinion steering. All 1968 and later models utilize collapsible steering columns and padded steering wheels in accordance with federal safety regulations.

Steering Wheel

Removal and Installation

Spitfire Mk III, Mk IV

1. Disconnect the negative battery cable. Pry off the steering wheel crash pad and the horn button.

2. Remove the horn brush connection.

3. Remove the nut and washer which retain the wheel to the steering column.

4. Scribe alignment marks on the steering wheel and column.

5. Being careful not to jar the collapsible column, install a steering wheel puller and remove the wheel.

CAUTION: *The use of a knock-off type puller may damage the column.*

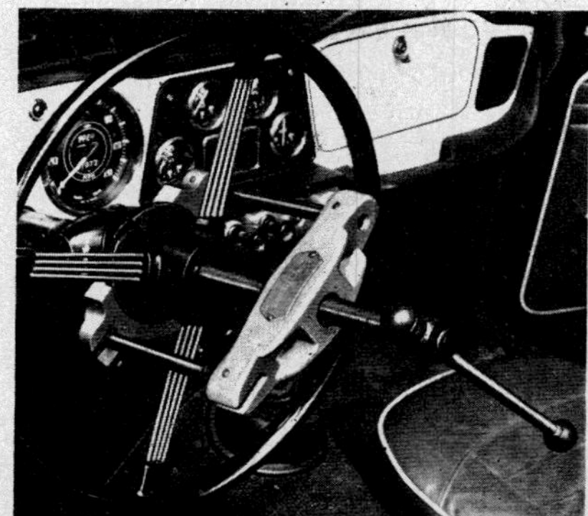

Removing steering wheel with puller

6. To install, line up the alignment marks made prior to removal and position the wheel on its column using hand pressure only. If the wheel was removed without making alignment marks, point the front wheels straight ahead and center the steering wheel on the column. Install the washer, nut, horn brush connection, horn button, and crash pad. Connect the negative battery cable.

TR-250, TR-6

1. Disconnect the negative battery cable. Pry off the steering wheel crash pad and the horn button.

2. Remove the six bolts which retain the steering wheel to its support boss.

3. With the front wheels pointing straight ahead, scribe alignment marks on the support boss and steering column.

4. Remove the column nut and carefully pull the support boss from the upper inner steering column.

5. Reverse the above procedure to install, taking care to apply locking compound to the threads of the column nut to prevent it from vibrating loose.

Turn Signal Switch Replacement

Spitfire Mk III, Mk IV

1. Disconnect the negative battery cable.

2. Remove the two screws and the switch fairings.

3. Remove the two Allen head screws and the spring washers which retain the steering column clamp. Remove the clamp and harness cover.

4. Disconnect the three snap connectors.

5. Remove the two screws and spring washers.

6. Carefully lift out the switch with its electrical leads.

7. Reverse the above procedures to install.

Steering Column

Removal and Installation

Spitfire Mk III, Mk IV

1. Disconnect the negative battery cable. Make sure the front wheels are pointing straight ahead.

2. Remove the driver's side package shelf.

3. Remove the pinch bolt which retains the steering column housing to the flexible coupling.

4. Remove the nuts, spring, and washers from the two bolts which retain the steering column forward bracket.

5. Lift out the forward support housing with felt liner.

6. Disconnect and label the electrical connectors for the horn, turn signals, and lights. On 1969 and later models, disconnect the electrical plug from the steering column lock.

7. Remove the two cap screws which retain the column rear bracket. Remove the clamp halves and the upper plate.

8. Remove the steering column and tie bar assembly.

9. Reverse the above procedures to install, making sure that the front wheels are pointing straight ahead and the steering wheel is properly centered.

GT6+, GT6 Mk III

1. Disconnect the negative battery cable. Make sure that the front wheels are pointing straight ahead.

2. Remove the nut and bolt which retain the coupling to the lower steering column.

3. Disconnect and label the electrical connectors from the steering head beneath the dash.

4. Support the weight of the column, and remove the lower outer column support clamp nuts and bolts, and remove the nuts and bolts for the bottom half of the upper clamp.

5. Remove the steering column assembly up and out of the car.

6. To install, loosen the impact clamp locknut and, using an Allen key, unscrew the adjusting screw two complete turns.

7. Place the steering column assembly in position, loosely retained by the upper and lower clamps (with felt inserts).

8. Point the front wheels straight ahead and center the steering wheel. Connect the lower steering column to its flexible coupling and install the nut and bolt.

9. Adjust the steering wheel to its desired height, then tighten the upper and lower clamp bolts and nuts.

CAUTION: *Do not adjust the column at the bottom of its range of movement, as this will limit the telescoping feature of the column in a frontal collision.*

10. Tighten the impact clamp adjusting screw with an Allen key, and then tighten its locknut.

11. Reconnect the electrical connectors. Connect the negative battery cable.

12. Before driving the car, make sure that the steering moves freely from lock to lock.

TR-250, TR-6

1. Disconnect the negative battery cable. Make sure that the front wheels are pointing straight ahead.

2. Disconnect and label the electrical connectors from the steering column.

3. Remove the bolt which retains the lower all-metal coupling to the steering rack unit pinion. Remove the bolts and separate the impact clamp halves. Using an Allen key, remove the adjusting screw and locknut assembly from the impact clamp lower half.

4. Push the intermediate column upward inside the inner column so that the lower coupling disengages from the rack unit pinion. Position the coupling to one side and pull out the intermediate shaft, complete with both steering couplings and the lower column from the upper inner steering column. Remove the nylon washer.

5. Working beneath the dash, remove the nuts and bolts which retain the intermediate clamp and its felt to the column. Also remove the bracket (stay) and upper outer clamp half with its felt.

6. Remove the steering column assembly out through its grommet and the opening in the dash.

7. To install, place the steering column assembly in position, loosely retained by the clamps (with felt inserts) and the brackets (stays).

8. Loosen the impact clamp locknut and, using an Allen key, unscrew the adjusting screw two turns. Rotate the lower column to align its flat surface with the slot in the upper steering column. Install the two halves of the impact clamp in place with the two bolts and washers.

9. Push the lower column into the upper inner column. Point the front wheels straight ahead and center the steering wheel. Connect the lower column to its flexible coupling and install the nut and bolt.

10. Adjust the steering wheel to its desired height, then tighten the clamp bolts and nuts.

11. Tighten the impact clamp adjusting screw with an Allen key, and then tighten its locknut.

12. Reconnect the electrical connectors. Connect the negative battery cable.

13. Before driving the car, make sure that the steering moves freely from lock to lock.

Steering Column Ignition Lock Switch

Removal and Installation

1969–70 Spitfire Mk III, All Spitfire Mk IV

1. Remove the steering column as outlined under "Steering Column Removal and Installation".

2. Remove the two nuts and washers which retain the steering lock shroud and remove the shroud and steering column tie-bar.

3. Using a center punch, mark the center of the bolt heads of the two shear-off bolts used to retain the steering lock clamp bracket.

4. Either unscrew the shear-off bolts with a small chisel, or drill into the bolt heads and remove the bolts with an easy-out.

5. Remove the lock switch.

6. To install, position the lock switch to the column so that the switch dowel locates in the column drilling.

7. Install the steering lock shroud using two new shear-off bolts.

8. Evenly tighten the bolts until the heads shear.

9. Install the steering column as outlined under "Steering Column Removal and Installation".

Manual Steering Gear

Adjustment

The steering gear is the direct-acting rack and pinion type in which motion is transmitted from the steering wheel column through a pinion to the steering rack. First, adjust the end clearance of the pinion shaft. This should be as little as possible with the pinion still able to rotate freely. There are shims available in thicknesses of 0.004 in. (0.102 mm.) and 0.010 in. (0.254 mm.) to obtain minimal end clearance with free rotation. The second adjustment involves the damper cap. With the pressure pad and cap nut installed to the rack tube, tighten the cap nut to eliminate all end clearance. Measure, with a feeler gauge, the clearance between the nut and the housing, as shown in the accompanying illustration. Put together a shim package that is equal to the clearance between the cap nut and the housing plus 0.004 in. (0.1 mm.) (i.e., pack-clearance + 0.004 in.). Pack the unit with grease and install the cap nut, shim pack, spring, and pressure pad to the housing and tighten the cap nut. When the cap nut is correctly adjusted, a force of 2 lbs on a radius of 8 in. (20.3 cm) is required to rotate the pinion shaft. Check the unit and readjust if necessary by adding or subtracting shims from beneath the cap nut.

Measuring clearance between cap nut and housing.

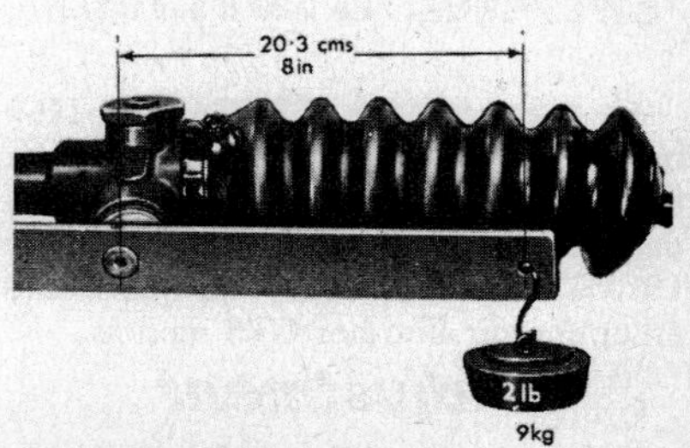

Measuring load required to turn pinion

Removal

1. Place the vehicle on jack stands and remove the front wheels. Empty the cooling system and remove the bottom radiator hose.
2. Loosen and remove the bolt from the steering shaft coupling. Remove the steering rod end nuts. Pull the ball joints from the tie rod lever.
3. Remove: nuts, U-bolts, and shims. Pull the steering unit forward. Remove the unit by pulling it through the wheel-well.

Disassembly

1. Pinch the wire clips and slide bellows toward the ball joints.
2. Remove the outer tie rods from the rack. Remove the spring, washer and nut and washer assembly from the rack end. Remove the nuts from the rack ends.
3. Loosen the cap and remove the spring, shims, and pad.
4. Remove the circlips and pull out the pinion assembly. Be sure not to lose the peg. Remove the ring, shim, bushings, and thrust washer. Detach the rubber O-ring.
5. Pull the rack from the tube. Remove the remaining parts from the housing.

Assembly

To reassemble the steering gear, reverse the above procedure. Be careful to note the steering adjustments.

Installation

1. Count the number of pinion shaft turns required to move the gear from lock to lock. Return the shaft to the central position and move the steering wheel to straight ahead. Fit the steering unit by placing the splined pinion shaft into the splined coupling.
2. Place the aluminum packing pieces behind the rack and the two front aluminum packing blocks into the dowels. These fit into holes in the rack tube.
3. Replace the U-bolts and nuts. Replace the unit in the car.
4. Place the taper pins of the tie rod ball joints into the steering levers and insert the steering washers and nuts. Replace the bolt and nut.

CAUTION: *Check the front end alignment.*

BRAKE SYSTEMS

All Spitfire, GT6, TR-250 and TR-6 models are equipped with disc front and drum rear brakes. Power assist is standard on the TR-250 and TR-6, as well as 1973 GT6 Mk III models, and available as an option on all other GT6 models.

Adjustment

Disc brakes are inherently self-adjusting and therefore require no adjustments between pad changes. To adjust the rear drum brakes, the following procedure is used.

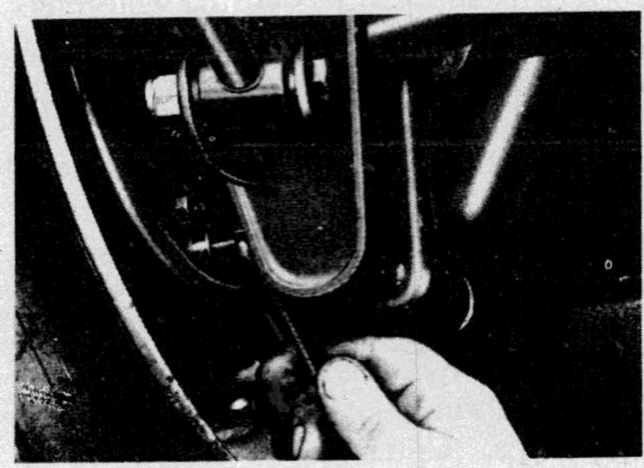

Adjusting rear drum brakes

1. Block the front wheels. Release the handbrake. Raise the rear of the car so that both rear wheels clear the ground. Install jackstands.
2. Turn the square-ended adjuster on the rear of the backing plate clockwise until the wheel is locked.
3. Back-off the adjuster a notch at a time until the wheel may spin freely when turned with one hand.
4. Adjust the remaining rear brake following steps 2 and 3.
5. Lower the car and remove the jack.

HYDRAULIC SYSTEM

All Triumphs are equipped with four wheel hydraulic brakes. Since 1967, models destined for export to the U.S. have utilized a dual hydraulic brake circuit, each independent of the other, incorporating a tandem master cylinder and a pressure differential warning valve. One circuit services the front brakes and the other, the rear brakes. In case of a leak or other hydraulic failure, ½ braking efficiency will still be maintained. A brake system failure will decentralize the pressure differential warning valve, actuating a warning light on the dash.

Master Cylinder

Removal and Installation

All Models

1. Remove both brake lines. Be careful not to let fluid drip out.
2. Pull out the rubber dust cover. Remove the clevis pin. (This is secured by a cotter or split type pin.)
3. Remove the master cylinder attaching bolts and lift off the cylinder.
4. Reverse the above procedure to install. Bleed the brake system.

Overhaul

1. Remove the master cylinder.
2. Drain the master cylinder and discard the old fluid. Remove the screws which hold the reservoir to the body.
3. Press down on the pushrod, remove the circlip, and pull out the pushrod, abutment plate, and circlip. Using an Allen wrench, remove the tipping valve nut and lift out the seal.
4. Depress the plunger and remove the tipping valve. Lightly shake the body to remove the internal parts. Pull the intermediate spring and plunger apart.

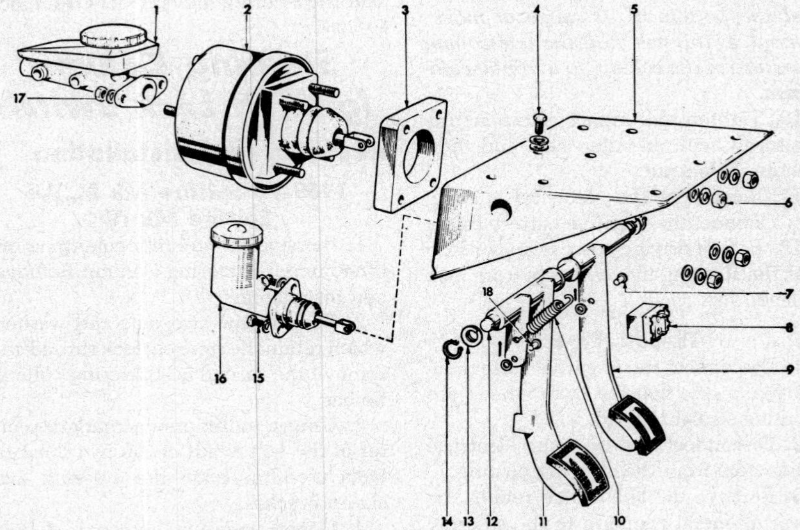

TR-250, TR-6 master cylinders—servo, pedal box layout

1. Brake master cylinder
2. Vacuum booster
3. Spacer
4. Bolt
5. Pedal box
6. Nut
7. Clevis pin—brake
8. Stop light switch
9. Brake pedal
10. Clutch pedal pull-off spring
11. Clutch pedal
12. Pedal fulcrum shaft
13. Spring washer
14. Circlip
15. Bolt
16. Clutch master cylinder
17. Nut
18. Clevis pin—clutch

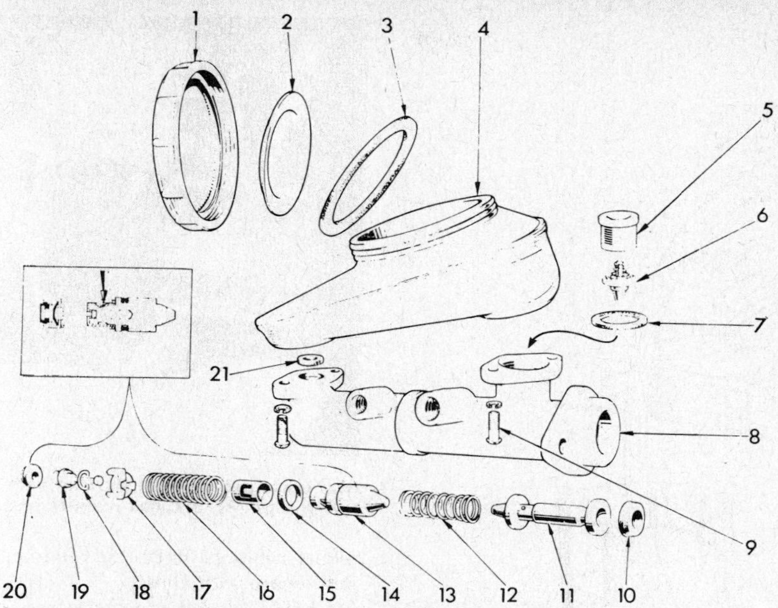

Tandem master cylinder disassembled—TR-250, TR-6

1. Cap
2. Baffle plate
3. Seal
4. Reservoir
5. Tipping valve securing nut
6. Tipping valve
7. Seal—reservoir to body
8. Body
9. Screw—reservoir to body
10. Seal
11. Primary plunger
12. Intermediate spring
13. Secondary plunger
14. Seal
15. Spring retainer
16. Secondary spring
17. Valve spacer
18. Spring washer
19. Valve
20. Seal
21. Seal—reservoir to body

5. Raise the leaf spring of the spring retainer and lift out the valve assembly from the plunger. Remove the spring, valve spacer, and washer spring from the valve stem.

6. Next, take the valve seal from the valve head end. Remove the seals from both plungers. Take the baffle and cap washer from the cap.

7. Replace all seals with new ones from the rebuilding kit. Thoroughly clean all other parts in clean brake fluid. Check the cylinder bore for any imperfections or coarseness. If any doubt exists as to condition, replace the cylinder.

8. Before assembling, lubricate all parts with clean brake fluid. Place seals on the plungers.

9. Place the valve seals, smaller end leading, on the valve head. Place the spring washer on the stem of the valve. It must be positioned with the flare away from the stem shoulder. Next, fit the valve spacer, legs leading.

10. Place the retainer on the stem, keyway first. Put the spring over the retainer; position the assembly on the plunger.

11. Compress the spring while the retainer is pushed behind the plunger head. To accomplish this, place the subassembly in a vise and place clean paper between each subassembly end and the vise jaws to prevent contamination.

12. Close the vise until the spring is nearly coil bound. Using a small screwdriver, press the spring retainer against the secondary plunger. Using needle nose pliers, depress the spring retainer leaf behind the plunger head. Be certain the retainer lead is properly aligned (straight) and is firmly located behind the plunger.

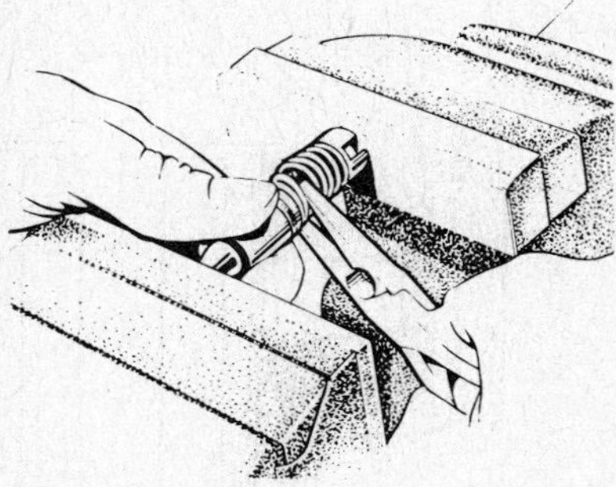

Pushing spring retainer behind plunger head.

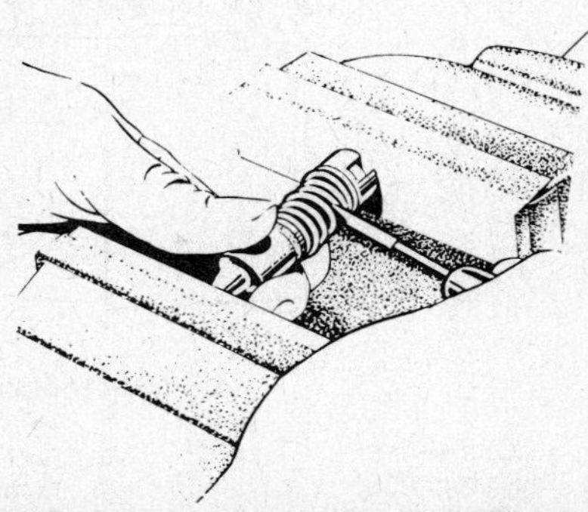

Depressing spring against secondary plunger.

13. Place the spring between the plungers. Lubricate the plunger seals and the bore of the cylinder with clean brake fluid.

14. Fit the plunger assembly in the bore. Make sure the valve end is leading. Use caution to avoid seal damage. Press the plunger down into the bore and put in the tipping valve. Tighten the seal to 35–40 ft lbs.

15. Reassemble the cap washer and baffle to the cap. Place the cap on the reservoir. Assembly is now complete.

16. Install the master cylinder.

Hydraulic System Bleeding

For those recent models equipped with a dual braking system (one system serves the front brakes, the other serves the rear), proceed as follows: In bleeding the rear brakes, turn the brake adjusters so that the shoes are locked against the drums. Note that the front brakes must be bled as one system, and the rear brakes as another. Attach a tube to the system bleed nipple that is farthest from the master cylinder, allowing the other end of the tube to hang submerged in a jar containing a small amount of clean brake fluid. Unscrew the bleed nipple about half a turn to allow the fluid to be pumped out. Press the brake pedal *lightly* without pushing through to the end of the stroke. If the pedal is pushed heavily or fully through its stroke, the pressure differential switch could be actuated, causing the brake warning light to glow brightly until the actuating piston is recentralized. Pausing between each depression of the pedal, pump until no bubbles can be seen in the fluid being pumped into the jar. With the pedal depressed, tighten the bleed nipple and repeat on the other brake of the system.

If, by mistake, the brake warning light piston has been pushed off center, causing the brake warning light to glow, the following procedure will have to be followed to recentralize the piston: Attach a

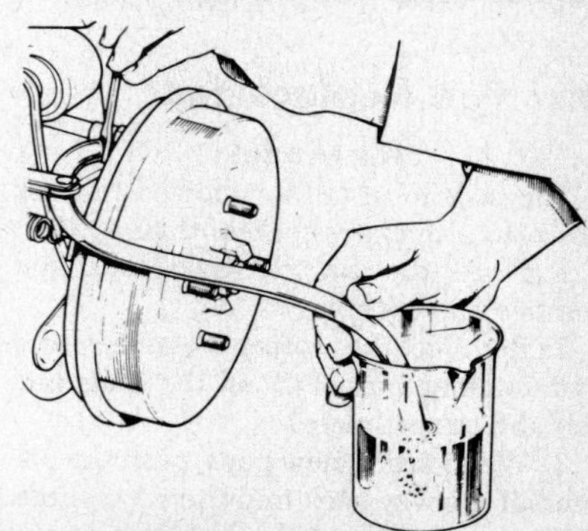

Bleeding rear drum brake

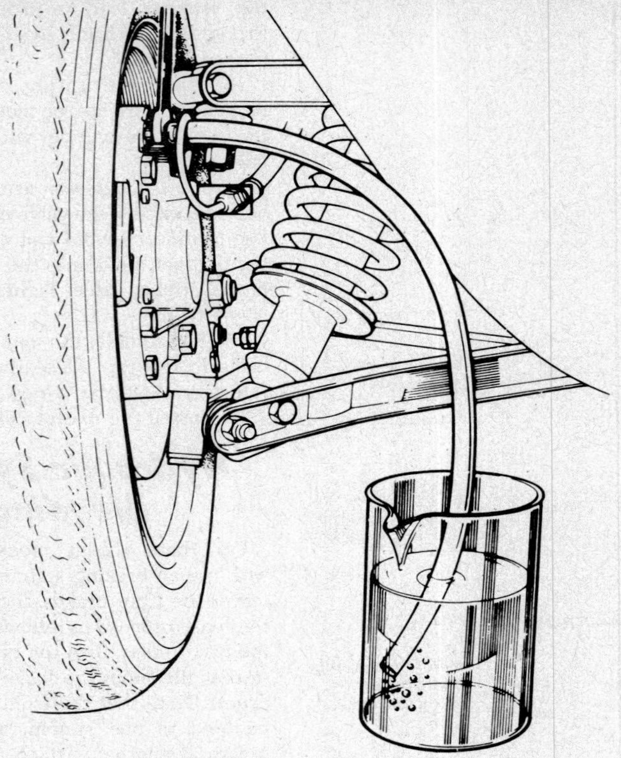

Bleeding front disc brake

rubber tube to a bleed nipple at the opposite end of the car to that which was being bled when the piston was actuated. Open the bleed screw and turn the ignition to the ON position without starting the engine. The brake warning light will glow, but the oil pressure warning light will be out. Push steadily on the brake pedal until the brake light dims and the oil light glows. As the piston returns to mid-position, a click will be felt on the pedal.

NOTE: *If the pedal is pushed too hard, the piston will move over to the other side, necessitating the repeat of the preceding operations at the other end of the car.* Tighten the bleed screw.

FRONT DISC BRAKES

Disc Pad Replacement

All Models

The pads must not be allowed to wear down to a thickness of less than ⅛ in.

1. Place the car on jackstands and remove the wheels.
2. Remove the spring retainers and pad retainer pins. Lift off the pads and the anti squeal plates.
3. When fitting new pads, push the pistons all the way back into their cylinders. Place new pads and squeal plates on the wheel; place the arrow in the direction of

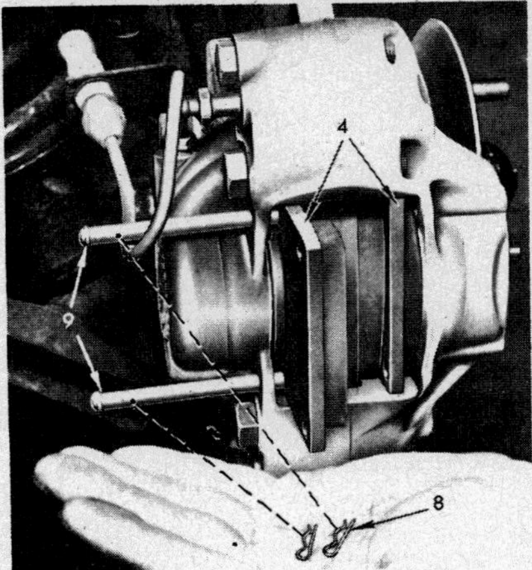

Disc brake pad removal showing pads (4), spring clips (8), and pad retainer pins (9).

wheel rotation. Refit the retainer pins and secure with clips.

CAUTION: *Be sure the master cylinder is full and that the system is bled and leakproof.*

Caliper Overhaul

Replacing Piston Seals

1. Remove the line and the locknut at the supporting bracket. Remove the flexible hose.

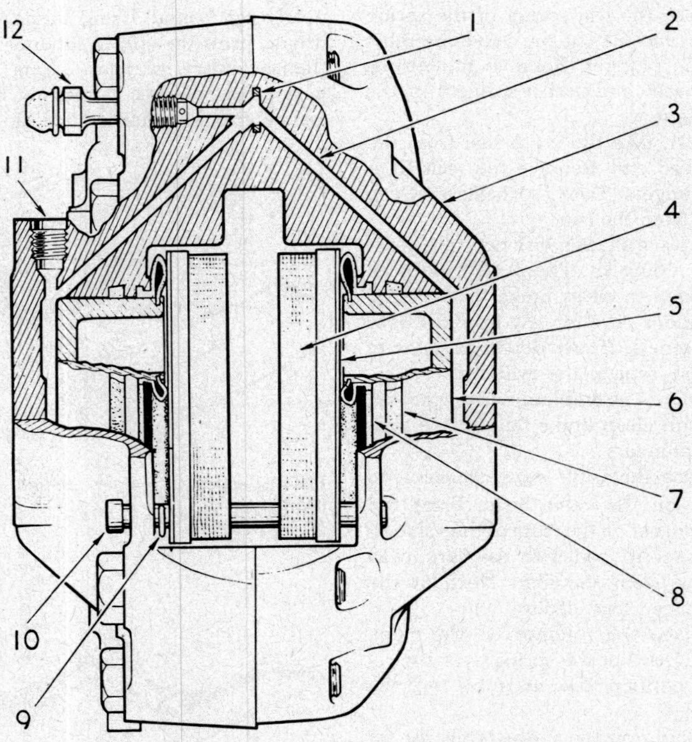

Disc caliper assembly cross-section

1. Rubber O-ring
2. Fluid transfer channels
3. Caliper body
4. Brake pad
5. Anti-squeal plate
6. Piston
7. Piston sealing ring
8. Dust cover
9. Retaining clip
10. Retaining pin
11. Flexible hose connection
12. Bleed nipple

2. Remove the bolts which hold the caliper to the support bracket; lift off the caliper and take out the pistons.

3. Remove the rubber seals from the recess. Replace all the components as needed; thoroughly clean all others. Oil all the parts and the bore with brake fluid.

4. Place the piston seal in the cylinder recess. Locate the lips (projecting) of the dust cover in the cylinder recess. Place the closed end of the piston into the cylinder.

CAUTION: *Do not harm the polished surface.* Insert the piston to the furthest extent and engage the outer lip of the dust cover with the piston recess.

5. Place the caliper over the disc; place shims between the mounting bracket and the calipers.

6. Replace all hoses and bleed the system.

Brake Disc (Rotor)

Removal and Installation

All Models

1. Loosen and remove the disc caliper assembly.

2. Remove the grease cap with a screwdriver. Remove the cotter pin, nut, and washer. Pull out the hub with the outer race and part of the inner race.

3. Remove the brake disc from the hub assembly.

NOTE: *Bearings, if needed, should only be fitted as a complete set.*

4. Place the outer bearing rings (taper outward) into the proper position.

5. Replace the discs. Secure with washers and bolts. Put the inner races together and fit the hub with the disc to the stub axle.

6. Put on the washer and slotted nut while rotating the hub; finger tighten only. Loosen the nut to the closest cotter pin hole and mark the position by center punching the end of the stub axle and nut. Hub end float should be 0.003–0.005 in.

If loosening the nut gives excessive float, remove the nut and file the rear face. This will correct the problem. Remove the nut, washer, hub, and races. Pack the hub with the appropriate grease.

Place the new hub seal in the seal retainer. Use joining compound. Allow to dry. Then saturate the seal in engine oil and squeeze out the excess. Place the races and seal retainer on the hub. Be sure the seal faces inward.

Replace the hub assembly to the axle. Refit the washer and nut. Tighten the nut until the punch marks correspond; secure the nuts with a new cotter pin. Refit the remaining parts. Be sure to replace any shims.

Wheel Bearing Adjustment

The end float of the front wheel bear-

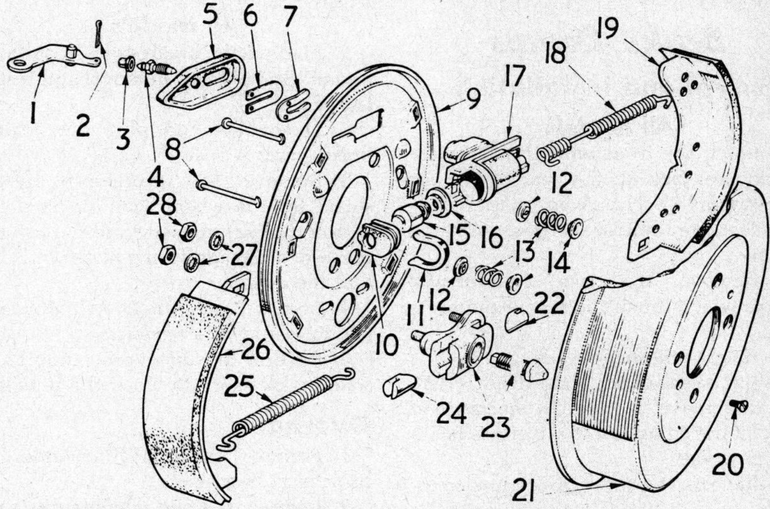

Rear drum brake disassembled—Spitfire, GT6 shown; TR-250, TR-6 similar

1. Handbrake lever
2. Cotter pin
3. Dust cap
4. Bleed nipple
5. Dust excluder
6. Retaining clip
7. Retaining clip
8. Steady pins
9. Backplate
10. Dust excluder
11. Clip
12. Steady pin cups
13. Springs
14. Steady pin cups
15. Piston
16. Seal
17. Wheel cylinder
18. Return spring
19. Brake shoe
20. Countersunk screw
21. Brake drum
22. Adjuster tappet
23. Adjuster wedge and body
24. Adjuster tappet
25. Return spring
26. Brake shoe
27. Shakeproof washers
28. Nuts

1. Bolt
2. Spring washer
3. Nyloc nut
4. Plain washer
5. Dust shield
6. Stub axle
7. Caliper bracket
8. Tab plate
9. Bolt
10. Felt seal
11. Seal retainer
12. Bolt
13. Spring washer
14. Inner tapered race
15. Disc
16. Hub
17. Outer tapered race
18. Washer
19. Slotted nut
20. Cotter pin
21. Hub cap
22. Bolt
23. Bolt
24. Caliper unit
25. Vertical link
26. Plain washer
27. Nyloc nut
28. Distance pieces
29. Steering arm
30. Nyloc nut

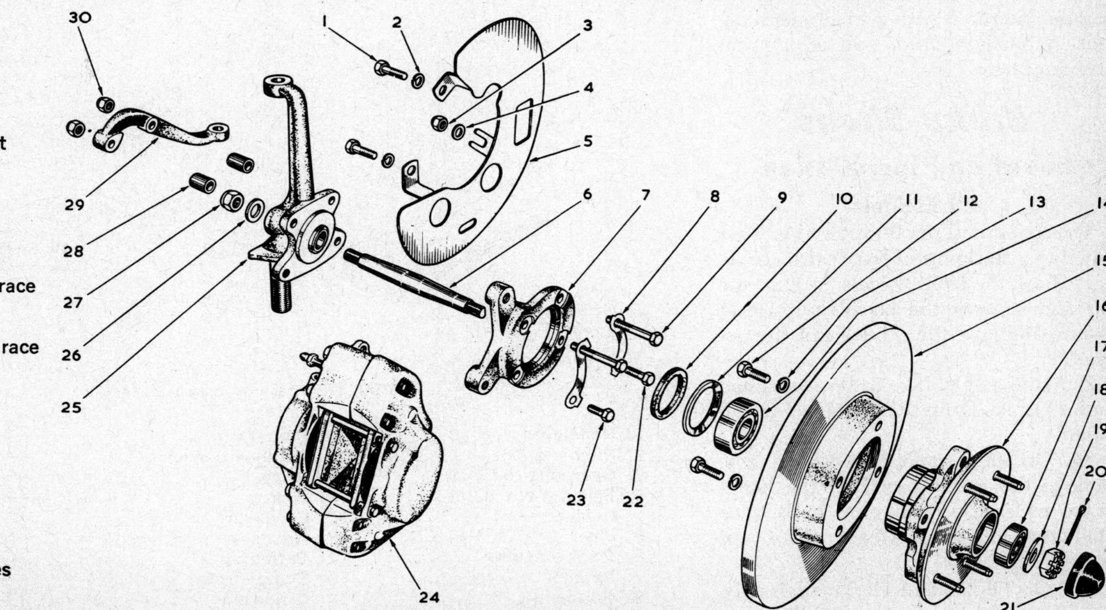

Disc and hub assembly

ings should be 0.003–0.005 in. and may be checked by a suitable dial gauge. The front wheel hub nut is provided with slots to accompany a securing cotter pin. In the event that a suitable gauge is not available, proceed as follows: While rotating the hub, tighten the nut only sufficiently to remove looseness (5 ft lbs), then loosen the nut by one flat and secure it with a new cotter pin.

REAR DRUM BRAKES

Brake Drums

Removal and Installation

All Models

1. Block the front wheels. Apply the handbrake. Jack up the rear of the car and support the chassis on jackstands.
2. Remove the rear wheel and tire assembly.
3. Remove the two countersunk screws which retain the rear drum to its hub.
4. Release the handbrake.
5. Lift off the drum. If the drum is difficult to remove, it may be necessary to back off the adjuster a few turns to facilitate removal.
6. Reverse the above procedure to install.

Inspection

Check the working surface of the drum for scoring. Minor scoring may be removed by having the drum turned on an arbor in a lathe, but deeper scoring may require replacement of the drum.

Check the drum for cracks and replace it if any are evident. A good way to check this is to hang the drum by a wooden handle and tap it with a small metal object. A cracked drum will emit a flat sounding note.

Brake Shoes

Removal and Installation

All Models

The shoes must not be allowed to wear down to a thickness of less than 1/16 in.

1. Block the front wheels. Jack up the car and support the chassis with jackstands. Remove the wheel and tire assembly.
2. Remove the brake drum as outlined under "Brake Drum Removal and Installation".

3A. On Spitfire and GT6 models only, remove the cotter pin from the handbrake lever. Also remove the brake shoe hold-down pins (shoe-steady pins), caps and springs.

3B. On TR-250 and TR-6 models only, remove the spring clips, rotate the shoe-steady pins 90° and remove the pins.

4. Release the lower end of one shoe from the adjuster. Then release the upper end of the same shoe from the wheel cylinder.
5. Remove the brake shoe return springs, and lift off the shoes.
6. Reverse the above procedure to install, taking care to mount the shoe return springs inboard.

Rear Wheel Cylinder

Removal and Installation

All Models

1. Remove the brake shoes as outlined under "Brake Shoes Removal and Installation".
2. Disconnect and plug the flexible brake hose.
3. Remove the protective rubber shield for the wheel cylinder from the rear of the backing plate and remove the horseshoe clip and spring plate which retain the cylinder.
4. Remove the wheel cylinder and handbrake lever assembly.
5. Reverse the above procedure to install, making sure to bleed the brakes.

Overhaul

1. Remove the wheel cylinder as previously described.
2. Remove the clip which retains the rubber boot to the cylinder body.
3. Remove the piston, rubber boot, and seal assembly from the cylinder body. Discard the old boot and seal.
4. Clean the piston and body in methylated alcohol or clean brake fluid meeting SAE 70 R3 specifications. Replace the piston or body if either is corroded or scored.
5. Dip the cylinder bore, the piston, and a new seal in clean brake fluid and insert the piston and seal assembly in the bore.
6. Install the rubber boot and its retaining clip on the cylinder.
7. Install the wheel cylinder as previously described.

PARKING BRAKE

Cable Adjustment

Adjust as follows: Lift the rear wheels from the ground. Lock the brake drums by screwing each adjuster in to its fullest extent. Remove the spring and clevis pin. Adjust the clevis at each cable end by equal amounts to reduce play in the cable. The cable is overly tightened when the clevis pin cannot be inserted without straining the cables. Secure the clevis pin, hook up spring and adjust the cable brackets to give slight spring tension.

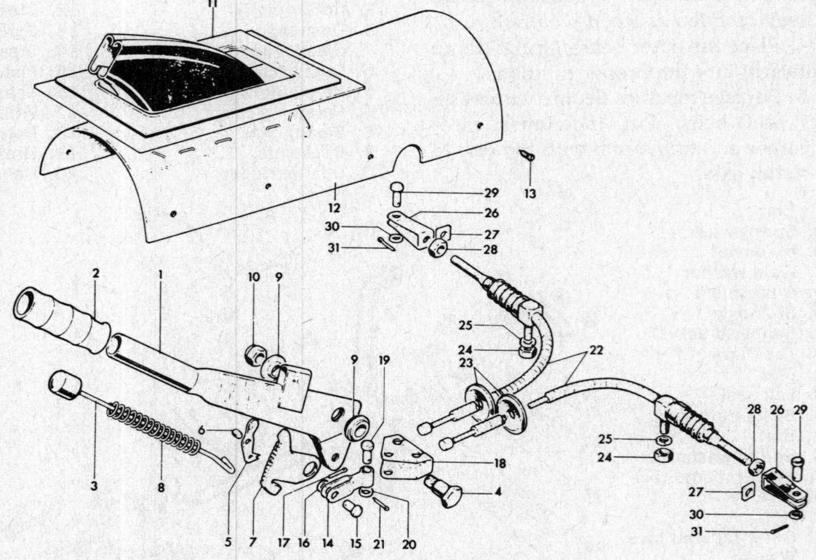

TR-250, TR-6 parking brake assembly

1. Handlever
2. Rubber grip
3. Operating rod, pawl
4. Fulcrum pin, handlever
5. Pawl
6. Pivot pin, pawl
7. Ratchet
8. Spring
9. Nylon washer
10. Nyloc nut
11. Carpet trim
12. Cardboard cover
13. Screw
14. Link
15. Clevis pin
16. Washer
17. Cotter pin
18. Compensator
19. Clevis pin
20. Washer
21. Cotter pin
22. Cable assembly
23. Rubber grommet
24. Nut
25. Lockwasher
26. Fork end
27. Nut
28. Locknut
29. Clevis pin
30. Washer
31. Cotter pin

CHASSIS ELECTRICAL

Heater Assembly

Removal and Installation

All Models

1. Disconnect the battery and empty the cooling system.
2. Remove the heater hoses. Remove the screws which hold the water valve mounting bracket to the dash shelf. Push the bracket and valve assembly away from the dash.
3. Inside the car, remove the dashboard support bracket. Remove the passenger and driver's side parcel shelf. Take off the bracket which holds the choke and heater cable.
4. Disconnect the tachometer and speedometer cables from the back of the gauges. Pull the cables into the engine compartment. Be careful not to damage the cables or the grommet.
5. Remove the bolts which attach the heater box to the dash. Plug the heater lines to insure against water spillage. Lift out the heater.
6. To replace the heater, reverse the above procedure.

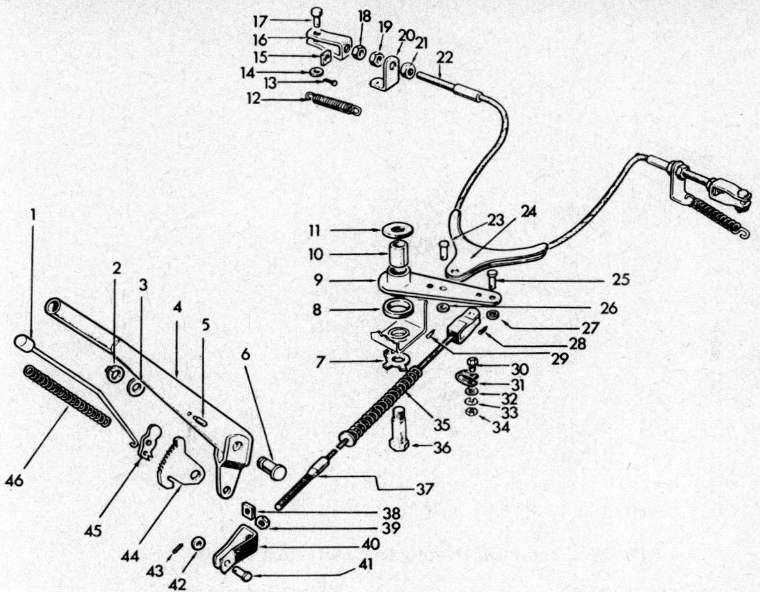

Spitfire, GT6 parking brake assembly

1. Pawl release rod
2. Circlip
3. Plain washer
4. Handbrake lever
5. Pawl pivot pin
6. Pivot pin
7. Lock plate
8. Rubber seal
9. Relay lever
10. Bushing
11. Felt seal
12. Pull-off spring
13. Cotter pin
14. Plain washer
15. Square nut
16. Clevis
17. Clevis pin
18. Locknut
19. Adjusting nut
20. Adjustable spring anchor
21. Lock nut
22. Secondary cable
23. Clevis pin
24. Compensator sector
25. Clevis pin
26. Plain washer
27. Plain washer
28. Cotter pin
29. Cotter pin
30. Clamp bolt
31. Clamp
32. Plain washer
33. Spring washer
34. Nut
35. Spring
36. Pivot bolt
37. Primary cable
38. Square nut
39. Locknut
40. Clevis
41. Clevis pin
42. Plain washer
43. Cotter pin
44. Ratchet
45. Pawl
46. Pawl spring

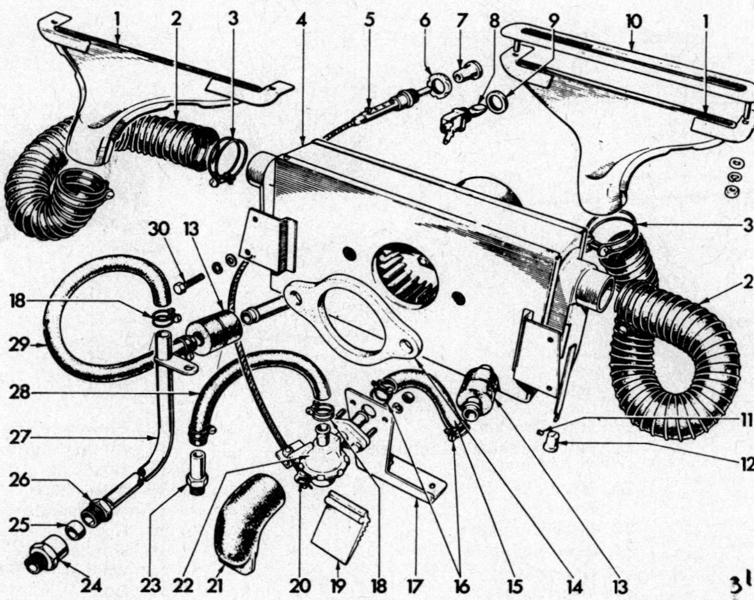

1. Defroster nozzle
2. Air hose
3. Hose clip
4. Heater unit
5. Heat control assembly
6. Bezel
7. Control knob
8. Blower switch
9. Bezel
10. Demister finisher
11. Screw
12. Flap knob
13. Sponge packing
14. Sealing ring
15. Water hose
16. Hose clip
17. Mounting bracket
18. Hose clip
19. Drain flap (from April 1964)
20. Water valve lever
21. Drain elbow (up to April 1964)
22. Water control valve
23. Adapter—cylinder head
24. Adapter—water pump
25. Sealing ring
26. Nut
27. Water return pipe
28. Water hose
29. Water hose
30. Bolt—heater attachment

Typical Spitfire heater assembly

1. Demister outlet—capping
2. Grub screw—knob
3. Knob assembly
4. Spacer—control lever
5. Lever control—water valve
6. Trunnion—cable attachment
7. Screw—cable attachment
8. Spacer—control lever
9. Setscrew—lever control attachment
10. Lever control—ventilator and heater motor
11. Spacer—control lever
12. Trunnion } Cable
13. Screw } attachment
14. Pull boast—label
15. Knob assembly
16. Setscrew—heater attachment
17. Demister nozzle
18. Hose demister
19. Heater unit assembly
20. Hose "Y" piece to foot level vent
21. Hose clip
22. Hose "Y" piece to facia level vent
23. "Y" piece
24. Hose clip
25. Clip "Y" piece retainer
26. Fix nut
27. Bracket "Y" piece clip
28. Fix nut
29. Setscrew—bracket attachment
30. Seal—inlet and outlet pipes
31. Hose—water to valve heater
32. Screw } Cable to
33. Trunnion } water valve

GT6 MK. 2 and Plus, Heating and ventilating details

34. Water control valve
35. Seal—heater blower
36. Hose—water return
37. Hose clip
38. Hose—heater to "Y" piece
39. Seal—inlet and outlet pipes
40. Hose clip
41. Trunnion } Cable
42. Screw } attachment
43. Hose—heater to "Y" piece
44. Setscrew—cable clamp attachment
45. Cable clamp
46. "Y" piece
47. Hose "Y" piece to face level vent
48. Hose "Y" piece to face level vent
49. Hose—demister
50. Setscrew—lever control attachment
51. Hose clip
52. Nut—demister nozzle attachment

Typical TR-250, TR-6 heater assembly

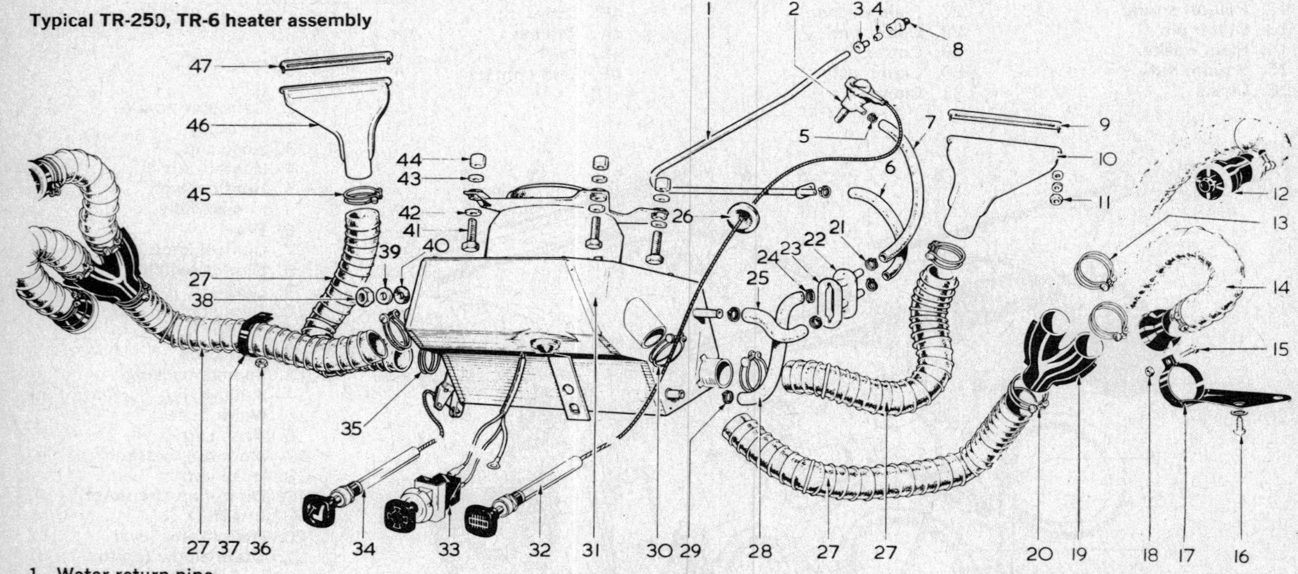

1. Water return pipe
2. Water control valve
3. Nut
4. Olive
5. Clip
6. Hose
7. Hose
8. Adaptor
9. Finisher
10. Air duct
11. Nut—duct attachment
12. Air vent
13. Hose clip
14. Ventilation hose
15. Setscrew—hose attachment
16. Screw—bracket attachment
17. Hose bracket
18. Nut—bracket attachment
19. Tube "Y" piece
20. Hose clip
21. Hose clip
22. Firewall adaptor
23. Seal—adaptor
24. Hose clip
25. Water hose
26. Control cable grommet
27. Ventilation hose
28. Water hose
29. Hose clip
30. Hose clip
31. Heater unit
32. Heat control
33. Blower switch
34. Air distribution control
35. Hose clip
36. Nut—hose
37. Hose support clip
38. Nut
39. Washer } Heater unit to
40. Washer } dash panel
41. Bolt
42. Washer } Heater unit to
43. Washer } scuttle top panel
44. Spacer
45. Hose clip
46. Air duct
47. Finisher

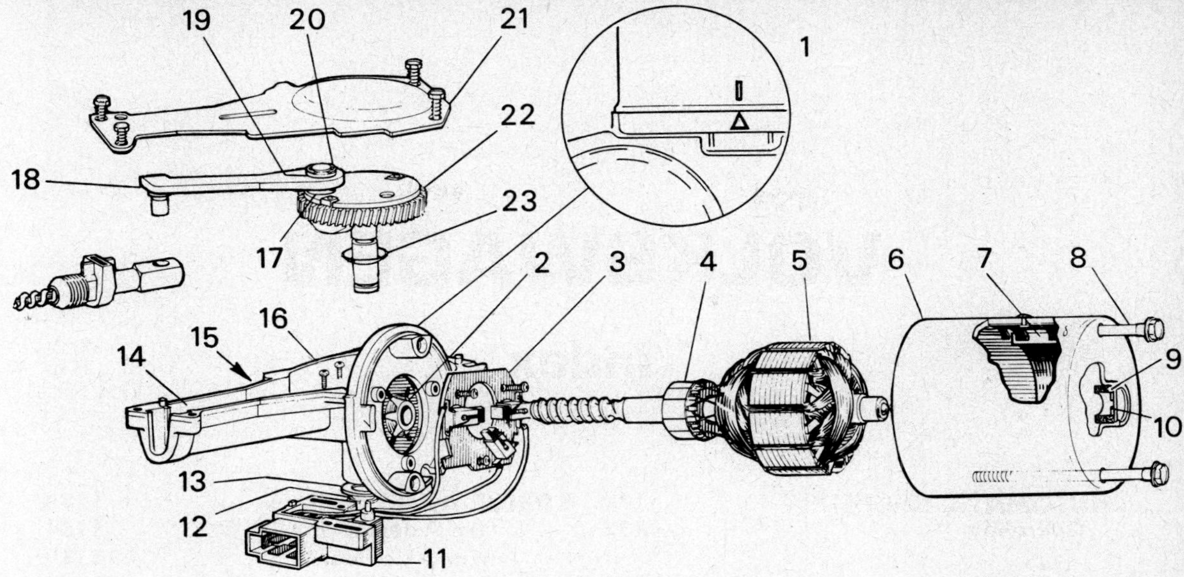

Wiper motor disassembled

1. Aligning marks
2. Self aligning bearing
3. Brush assembly
4. Commutator
5. Armature
6. Cover
7. Permanent magnet
8. Through bolt
9. Cover bearing
10. Felt washer
11. Limit switch unit
12. Final gear shaft spring clip
13. Washer
14. Crosshead guide channel
15. Thrust screw (non adjustable) or Thrust screw and lock nut (adjustable)
16. Gearbox
17. Washer
18. Connecting rod
19. Washer
20. Crank pin spring clip
21. Gearbox cover
22. Final gear
23. Dished washer

Blower Motor

Removal and Installation

All Models

1. Remove the heater.
2. Remove the screws which secure the inner and outer heater assembly.
3. Loosen the large nut in the center of the impeller. Remove the impeller from the shaft. Remove the exposed nut and lift out the motor.
4. To replace, reverse the above procedure.

Windshield Wipers

The windshield wiper mechanism used on all models consists of a dual speed electric motor connected to a cable rack mechanism. A small gearbox unit is also employed.

Removal and Installation

All Models

1. Remove all electrical connections.
2. Make a mark on the domed cover and gearbox cover. Remove the four hold down screws. Move the gearbox and cover clear. Remove the exposed spring clip by pulling it sideways.
3. Take off the moving contact limiting switch. Remove the connecting rod.
4. Take the mounting bracket from the firewall. Move the unit to allow the vacuum assembly to be released. Remove the mounting bracket.
5. Reverse the above procedure to install.

Adjusting Wiper Stop (Park Position)

Loosen the four holding screws and rotate the domed cover. Rotate the cover either way until the desired stop position is achieved. Replace the cover and tighten down.

Fuses

A fuse that is burned out may be suspected when all electrical components in the particular circuit refuse to operate. A blown fuse may be identified by merely looking at the glass enclosed metal strip. If it is separated or burned, it must be replaced.

NOTE: *It is imperative that a fuse be replaced by one of the same amperage.* If a fuse is replaced and immediately fails, the source of the trouble should be found before the vehicle is operated. Otherwise, serious and costly damage may result.

TR-250, TR-6

The fusebox is located on the left side of the inner fender panel at the rear of the engine compartment. It contains three 35 amp operating fuses, one fuse for a possible accessory circuit, and two spares.

Fuse one (brown leads) protects the headlamp flasher, dash warning lights, and horn. Fuse two (red/green leads) protects the tail lights, front parking and marker lamp circuits, rear marker, dash board, and license plate lamps. Fuse three (white leads) protects all other electrical components.

GT6, GT6 MKIII

This unit contains three operating fuses of 35 amp capacity and provision for two spares. Brown leads denote the fuse which protects the following: horns, dash warning lights, headlamp flasher and the interior light. The fuse fed by a red and green wire protects the tail lamps, license plate, and front parking lights. The fuse fed by a white wire protects everything not specifically listed above.

Spitfire

The fuse box for all Spitfire models is located under the dashboard on the left side. The unit contains two 35 amp fuses. In addition, an inline fuse of the same rating is located adjacent to the main unit and protects the headlights and horn. Fuse one may be identified by red and green leads. It protects the tail and front parking lights. Fuse two can be readily distinguished by its white cable leads. It protects all instruments and accessory equipment.

VOLKSWAGEN

Index

VEHICLE IDENTIFICATION—TYPES 1, 2, AND 3

	SAE Output	from Chassis No.	from Date	to Chassis No.	to Date
Volkswagen 1600	66 bhp	0 221975	Aug. 1963	0 483 592	July 1964
		315 000 001	Aug. 1964	315 220 883	July 1965
		316 000 001	Aug. 1965	316 316 238	July 1966
		317 000 001	Aug. 1966	317 233 853	July 1967
		318 000 002	Aug. 1967	318 235 387	July 1968
		319 000 002	Aug. 1968	319 264 032	July 1969
		310 2000 002	Aug. 1969		
VEHICLE, TYPE 4					
Volkswagen 411	85 bhp		Aug. 1970		

ENGINE IDENTIFICATION

Common Designation	Number Of Cylinders	CC Displacement (cu in.)	Type Engine	Type Vehicle	Engine Code Letter	Year
—	4	1,131 (69.02)	Upright fan	1	—	To December, 1953
1,200	4	1,192 (72.74)	Upright fan	1,2	A	To July, 1960
1,200	4	1,192 (72.74)	Upright fan	1,2	D	From August, 1960
1,300	4	1,285 (78.4)	Upright fan	1,2	F	From August, 1965
1,500	4	1,493 (91.1)	Upright fan	1,2	H	From August, 1967①
1,600	4	1,584 (96.6)	Upright fan	1,2	B	From August, 1969②
1,500	4	1,493 (91.1)	Upright fan	2	G	To July, 1965
1,500	4	1,493 (91.1)	Suitcase engine	3	K	To July, 1965③ From August, 1965④
1,500S	4	1,493 (91.1)	Suitcase engine	3 1500S	R	To July, 1965
1,600	4	1,584 (96.6)	Suitcase engine	3	T	From August, 1965
1,600	4	1,584 (96.6)	Suitcase engine	3 injected	U	From August, 1967
1,600	4	1,584 (96.6)	Upright fan	1,2	AD	From August, 1970
1,700	4	1,679	Suitcase engine	4 injected	W	From August, 1970
1,700	4	1,679	Suitcase engine	2	CB	From August, 1971
1,600	4	1,584	Upright fan	1,2	AE	From August, 1970
1,600	4	1,584	Upright fan	1	AH	From August, 1971
1,600	4	1,584	Suitcase engine	3	X	From August, 1971

① Type 2 from August, 1965
② Type 2 from August, 1967
③ High compression
④ Low compression

GENERAL ENGINE SPECIFICATIONS

Engine Code①	CC Displacement (cu in.)	Carburetor	Developed Horsepower (SAE) @ rpm	Developed Torque (ft lbs) @ rpm	Bore x Stroke (in.)	Compression Ratio	Normal Oil Pressure (psi) @ 2,500 rpm
—	1,131 (69.02)	Single-barrel downdraft	25 @ 3,300	51 @ 2,000	2.953 x 2.520	5.8:1	42⑤
A	1,192 (72.74)	Single-barrel downdraft	36 @ 3,700	60 @ 2,400	3.03 x 2.52	6.6:1	42⑤
D	1,192 (72.74)	Single-barrel downdraft	41.5 @ 3,900	65 @ 2,400	3.03 x 2.52	7.0:1	42⑤
F	1,285 (78.4)	Single-barrel downdraft	50 @ 4,600	69 @ 2,600	3.03 x 2.72	7.3:1	42⑤
H	1,493 (91.1)	Single-barrel downdraft	53 @ 4,200	78 @ 2,600	3.27 x 2.72	7.5:1	42⑤
B	1,584 (96.6)	Single-barrel downdraft	57 @ 4,400	113 @ 3,000②	3.36 x 2.72	7.5:1③	42⑤
G	1,493 (91.1)	Single-barrel downdraft	51 @ 4,000	74 @ 2,600	3.27 x 2.72	7.8:1	42⑤
K	1,493 (91.1)	Single-barrel downdraft	54 @ 4,200	84 @ 2,800	3.27 x 2.72	7.8:1④	42⑤
R	1,493 (91.1)	Two single-barrel downdraft	66 @ 4,800	84 @ 3,000	3.27 x 2.72	8.5:1	42⑤
T	1,584 (96.6)	Two single-barrel downdraft	65 @ 4,600	87 @ 2,800	3.36 x 2.72	7.5:1	42⑤
U	1,584 (96.6)	Electronic fuel injection	65 @ 4,600	87 @ 2,800	3.36 x 2.72	7.7:1	42⑤
AD	1,584 (96.6)	Single-barrel downdraft	60 @ 4,400	81.6 @ 3,000	3.36 x 2.72	7.5:1	42⑤
W	1,679	Electronic fuel injection	85 @ 5,000	99.5 @ 3,500	3.54 x 2.60	8.2:1	42
X	1,584	Electronic fuel injection	65 @ 4,600	86.8 @ 2,800	3.36 x 2.72	7.3:1	42⑤
CB	1,679	Two single-barrel downdraft	74 @ 5,000	88 @ 2,800	3.54 x 2.60	7.3:1	42⑤
AE	1,584	Single-barrel downdraft	60 @ 4,400	81.7 @ 3,000	3.36 x 2.72	7.5:1	42⑤
AH	1,584	Single-barrel downdraft	60 @ 4,400	78.8 @ 2,600	3.36 x 2.72	7.3:1	42⑤

① See Engine Identification Chart for explanation of codes
② Type 2—82 @ 3,000
③ Type 2—7.7:1
④ To July 1965; 7.5:1 from August 1965
⑤ Minimum—28 @ 2,500 rpm, 7 @ idle rpm

ENGINE REBUILDING SPECIFICATIONS FROM 1971 TO 1972

Engines	Bore (in.)	Number of Oversizes	1st O/S (in.)	2nd O/S (in.)	Piston to Cylinder Clearance (in.)	Wrist Pin Diameter (in.)	Ring Specifications: Side Clearance (in.) Top Ring	Side Clearance (in.) 2nd Ring	Side Clearance (in.) Oil Ring	End Gap (in.) Top Ring	End Gap (in.) 2nd Ring	End Gap (in.) Oil Ring
Type 1 Type 2, 1600 engine Type 3, 1600 engine	3.366①	2	.020	.040	.0016-.0023	.8658-.8661	.0027-.0039	.0016-.0027	.0011-.0019	.012-.018	.012-.018	.010-.016
Type 2, 1700 engine Type 4	3.543①	2	.020	.040	.0016-.0023	.9445-.9448	.0023-.0035	.0016-.0027	.0008-.0019	.014-.021	.012-.014	.010-.016

① All pistons, rings, and cylinders are matched and color-coded blue, pink and green. This figure is the nominal size for the standard bore, with a pink color code. To get the blue color code, subtract .01 in. To get the green color code, add .01 in.

Type 1 Engine number location

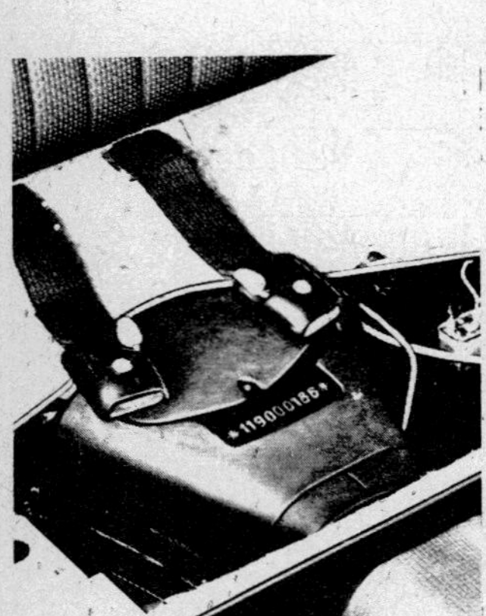
Type 1 chassis number location

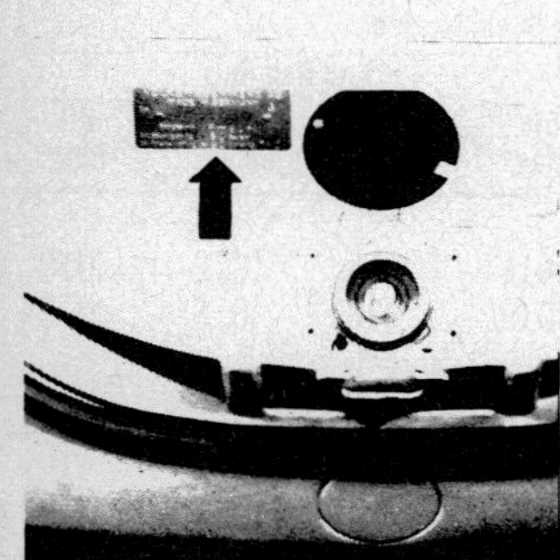
Type 1 identification plate location

VEHICLE IDENTIFICATION—TYPES 1, 2, AND 3

	SAE Output	from Chassis No.	from Date	to Chassis No.	to Date
VEHICLE, TYPE 1					
Standard Sedan	36 bhp	1-0575 415	Dec. 1953	6 502 399	July 1964
Standard Sedan, Sedan A	36 bhp	115 000 001	Aug. 1964	115 979 202	July 1965
Deluxe Sedan Karmann Ghia Models VW Convertible	36 bhp	1-0575 415	Dec. 1953	3192 506	July 1960
	42 bhp	3192 507	Aug. 1960	6 502 399	July 1964
		115 000 001	Aug. 1964	115 979 202	July 1965
1200A	42 bhp	116 000 001	Aug. 1965	1161 021 297	July 1966
VW 1200	42 bhp	117 483 306	Jan. 1967	117 844 900	July 1967
		118 000 001	Aug. 1967	1181 061 095	July 1968
		119 000 001	Aug. 1968	1191 093 701	July 1969
		110 2000 001	Aug. 1969		
VW 1300 Sedan Karmann Ghia Models VW Convertible	50 bhp	116 000 001	Aug. 1965	1161 021 298	July 1966
VW 1300 A	50 bhp	117 000 001	Aug. 1966	117 403 305	Jan. 1967
VW 1300 Sedan	50 bhp	117 000 001	Aug. 1966	117 844 901	July 1967
		118 000 001	Aug. 1967	1181 016 096	July 1968
		119 000 002	Aug. 1968	1191 093 702	July 1969
		110 2000 002	Aug. 1969		
VW 1500 Sedan Karmann Ghia Models VW Convertible	53 bhp	117 000 001	Aug. 1966	117 844 902	July 1967
		118 000 001	Aug. 1967	118 1016 097	July 1968
		119 000 003	Aug. 1968	119 1093 703	July 1969
		110 2000 003	Aug. 1969		
	57 bhp	110 2000 004	Aug. 1969		
VW 1600 Sedan Karmann Ghia Models VW Convertible	57 bhp		1970		
VW 1600 Sedan Super Beetle Karmann Ghia Models VW Convertible	60 bhp		1971		
VEHICLE, TYPE 2					
Transporter 1200	36 bhp	20-069 409	Dec. 1953	614 455	May 1960
	42 bhp	614 456	June 1960	1 328 271	July 1964
		215 000 001	Aug. 1964	215 036 378	Sept. 1964
Transporter 1500	51 bhp	1041 014	Jan. 1963	1 328 271	July 1964
		215 000 001	Aug. 1964	215 176 339	July 1965
	53 bhp	216 000 001	Aug. 1965	216 179 668	July 1966
		217 000 001	Aug. 1966	217 148 459	July 1967
Transporter 1600	57 bhp	218 000 001	Aug. 1967	218 202 251	July 1968
		219 000 001	Aug. 1968	219 238 131	July 1969
		210 2000 001	Aug. 1969		
	60 bhp		1971		
VEHICLE, TYPE 3					
Volkswagen 1500	54 bhp	0 000 001	Apr. 1961	0 483 592	July 1964
		315 000 001	Aug. 1964	315 220 883	July 1965
		316 000 001	Aug. 1965	316 316 237	July 1966
		317 000 001	Aug. 1966	317 283 852	July 1967
		318 000 001	Aug. 1967	318 235 387	July 1968
		319 000 001	Aug. 1968	319 264 031	July 1969
		310 2000 002	Aug. 1969		

ENGINE REBUILDING SPECIFICATIONS TO 1970—CRANKSHAFT

Engine	Main Bearing Journals (in.) — Journal Diameter — Journal 1, 2, 3		Journal 4		Oil Clearance — Journal 1-4		Shaft End-Play	Thrust On No.	Connecting Rod Journals (in.) — Journal Diameter		Oil Clearance	End-Play	Max Journal Out-of-Round (in.)
36 hp,	Std	1.9681, 1.9675	Std	1.5748, 1.5742	.002-	.002-	.0027-	1 (at	Std	1.9861, 1.9675	.0008-	.0067-	
A engine-	1st U/S	1.9583, 1.9577	1st U/S	1.5650, 1.5643	.004	.004	.005	flywheel)	1st U/S	1.9583, 1.9577	.0024	.016	.001
type 1,	2nd U/S	1.9484, 1.9478	2nd U/S	1.5551, 1.5545					2nd U/S	1.9484, 1.9478			
Type 2	3rd U/S	1.9386, 1.9380	3rd U/S	1.5453, 1.5446					3rd U/S	1.9386, 1.9380			
engine-													
before													
May, 1959③													
All	Std	2.1648, 2.1642	Std	1.5748, 1.5742	②	.002-	.0027-	1 (at	Std	2.1650, 2.1645	.0008-	.004-	
later	1st U/S	2.1551, 2.1544	1st U/S	1.5650, 1.5643		.004	.005	flywheel)	1st U/S	2.1553, 2.1544	.003④	.016	.001
engines to	2nd U/S	2.1453, 2.1445	2nd U/S	1.5551, 1.5545					2nd U/S	2.1455, 2.1448			
1970①	3rd U/S	2.1353, 2.1347	3rd U/S	1.5452, 1.5446					3rd U/S	2.1355, 2.1350			

NOTE: The crankshaft of type 1/1,200 cc engines may be reground only twice

U/S undersize

① Including modified 36 hp type 2 engine from May, 1959 (chassis 469477, engine 3400000)

② Bearings No. 1 and 3 from August, 1965: .0016-.004 in. Bearings No. 1, 2, 3; to engine 3520332: .0016-.0035 in. ① to engine 3472699: .001-.0035 in. ① Steel-backed bearing No. 2 from August, 1965 and all other steel-backed bearings (used in cold countries): .001-.0035 in.

③ Also 25 hp

④ All 1,500 and 1,600 cc: .0008 in.

ENGINE REBUILDING SPECIFICATIONS FROM 1971 TO 1972—CRANKSHAFT

Engines	Undersizes① 1st U/S (in.)	2nd U/S (in.)	3rd U/S (in.)	Main Bearing Journal Dia Standard — Journals 1, 2, 3 (in.)	Journal 4 (in.)	Crank-shaft End-play (in.)	Connecting Rod Journals — Journal Dia Standard (in.)	End-play (in.)
Type 1 Type 2 Type 3, 1600 engine	.010	.020	.030	2.1640- 2.1648	1.5739- 1.5748	.0027- .005	2.1644- 2.1653	.004- .016
Type 2, 1700 engine Type 4	.010	.020	.030	2.3609- 2.3617	1.5739- 1.5748	.0027- .005	2.1644- 2.1653	.004- .016

① Undersizes applicable to main bearing and connecting rod journal

ENGINE REBUILDING SPECIFICATIONS TO 1970—PISTONS, CYLINDERS, AND RINGS

Engines to 1970	Color Coding ③	CYLINDERS — Cylinder Diameter (mm) — Std	1st O/S	2nd O/S	PISTONS — Piston Diameter (mm) — Std	1st O/S	2nd O/S	Wrist Pin ② Diameter (in.) — No Mark	Green	RINGS — Side Clearance (in.) — Top	2nd	Oil Scraper	End Gap (in.) — Top 2nd	Oil Scraper
1,131, 1,200, and 1,300 cc	B P G	76.99 77.00 77.01	77.49 77.50 77.51	77.99 78.00 78.01	76.95 76.96 76.97	77.45 77.46 77.47	77.95 77.96 77.97	19.996- 20.00①	20.001- 20.004①	.002- .0027	.002- .0027	.001- .002	.012- .018	.010- .016
1,500 cc	B P G	82.99 83.00 83.01	83.49 83.50 83.51	83.99 84.00 84.01	82.95 82.96 82.97	83.45 83.46 83.47	83.95 83.96 83.97	21.996- 22.000	22.001- 22.004	.0027- .0035	.002- .0027	.001- .002	.012- .018	.010- .016
1,600 cc	B P G	85.49 85.50 85.51	85.99 86.00 86.01	86.49 86.50 86.51	85.45 85.46 85.47	85.95 85.96 85.97	86.45 86.46 86.47	21.996- 22.000	22.001- 22.004	.0027- .0035	.002- .0027	.001- .002	.012- .018	.010- .016

O/S Oversize

① Pin diameter given applies to 1,131 and 1,200 cc engines only. Pins for the 1,300 cc engine are the same as for the 1,500 and 1,600

② Pin should be light push fit in piston. Piston pin to connecting rod clearance: .0004-.001 in.-maximum-.002 in.

③ Color coding of cylinders and matching pistons: B—blue; P—pink; G—Green

ENGINE REBUILDING SPECIFICATIONS—VALVES

Engine	Seat Angle (deg)	Valve Seat Width (in.) Intake	Valve Seat Width (in.) Exhaust	Spring Pressure (lbs @ in.)	Stem (in.) Diameter Intake	Stem (in.) Diameter Exhaust	Stem-to-Guide Rock (in.) Intake	Stem-to-Guide Rock (in.) Exhaust	Valve Guide Remove-able
25 hp, 36 hp, A engine-Type 1, and Type 2 engine-before May, 1959	45	.05-.09		73.5 ± 3.7 @ 1.1	.2739-.2736	.2736-.2732	.011-.012		With Special Equipment
All Later Engines to 1970	45	.05-.09		①	.3130-.3126	.3118-.3114	.008-.009	.011-.012	With Special Equipment

①

Engine Code	To Engine No.	Spring Pressure
G	0627578	96.4 ± 6.6 @ 1.32 in.
K, R, T	0663330	
D	6805938 (type 2) 6850939 (type 1) 0042987	102.0 ± 5.0 @ 1.35 in.
K Engines with progressively wound springs		126.0 ± 8.8 @ 1.22 in.

NOTE: Cylinder head combustion chamber volumes are as follows:

Engine	Volume (cc)
A	45.5-47.0
D	43.0-45.0
F	44.0-46.0
All 1,500 and 1,600 cc	48.0-50.0

ENGINE REBUILDING SPECIFICATIONS 1971-72—VALVES

Engine	Seat Angle (deg)	Valve Seat Width (in.) Intake	Valve Seat Width (in.) Exhaust	Spring Pressure (lbs @ in.)	Stem (in.) Diameter Intake	Stem (in.) Diameter Exhaust	Stem-to-Guide Rock (in.) Intake	Stem-to-Guide Rock (in.) Exhaust	Valve Guide Remove-able
Type 1 Type 2 1,600 Type 3 1,600	45	.05-.10		117.2-134.8	.3125-.3129	.3125-.3117	.009-.010		With Special Equipment
Type 2 1,700 Type 4 1,700	Intake 30 Exhaust 45	.07-.08	.078-.098	168-186	.3125-.3129	.3507-.3511	.018 (new)		With Special Equipment

ELECTRICAL SPECIFICATIONS 1971-1972— GENERATOR AND REGULATOR

	GENERATOR		REGULATOR	
	Max Output	Average Regulating Voltage	Cut-In Voltage (volts)	Voltage Setting (no load)
Type 1, 2, and 3	30 amps	14V @ 2000 rpm	12.4-13.1	13.5-14.5

	ALTERNATOR		REGULATOR	
	Max Output	Average Regulating Voltage	Cut-In Speed	Output
Type 2/1700 Type 4	55 amps	14V @ 2000 rpm	1000 rpm	10 amps @ 1350 rpm 36 amps @ 2200 rpm 55 amps @ 6000 rpm

ELECTRICAL SPECIFICATIONS— GENERATOR AND REGULATOR

Generator				Regulator		
Part Number	Brush Spring Pressure (oz)	Field Resistance (ohms)	Max Output	Part Number	Cut-in Voltage	Voltage Setting (No Load)
25 hp Bosch RED 130/ 6-2600 AL 16	16-21	1.20-1.32	NA	Bosch RS/G130/ 6/11 (on generator)	NA	7.3-8.6
36 hp 1,200 cc Bosch LJ/ REF 160/ 2500 L4	16-21	1.20-1.32	NA	Bosch RS/TA 160/ 6/A1 (on generator)	5.5-6.3	7.3-8.6
36 hp 1,200 cc Bosch LJ/ REF 160/6/ 2500 L17	16-21	1.20-1.32	NA	Bosch RS/TAA 160/ 6/1 (on generator)	6.4-6.7	7.4-8.1
40 hp 1,200 cc Bosch 111 903 021 G	16-21	1.20-1.32	270 Watts	Bosch RS/TAA 180/ 6/A4	6.2-6.8	7.3-8.0
40 hp 1,200 cc VW 113 903 021 C	16-21	1.20-1.32	270 Watts	VW 113 903 801 C	6.4-6.7	7.4-8.1
Late 1,200 and 1,300 cc Bosch 113 903 021 H	16-21	1.20-1.32	NA	Bosch 113 903 801F	6.2-6.8	7.4-8.1
Late 1,200 and 1,300 cc VW 111 903 021 J	16-21	1.20-1.32	NA	VW 113 903 801G	6.4-6.7	7.4-8.1
Karmann Ghia 1,300 and Type 1 1,500 Bosch 131 903 021	16-21	NA	30 Amps	Bosch 131 903 801	6.2-6.8	7.3-8.0
Bosch 450 M 12/ 3700-14 38A 32 (12 Volt)	16-21	NA	38 Amps	Bosch UA 14 V 38A	12.5-13.2	13.5-14.5
Bosch E(L) 14V 38A 32, EG (R) 14V 38A 32 (12 Volt)	16-21	NA	38 Amps	Bosch RS/VA 14V 38A	12.4-13.1	13.6-14.4
Bosch G(L) 14V 30A 20	16-21	NA	30 Amps	Bosch RS/VA 14V 30A	12.4-13.1	13.6-14.4

NA Information not available

ELECTRICAL SPECIFICATIONS—BATTERY AND STARTER

Model	BATTERY			STARTER						
	Capacity (Amp Hours)	Volts	Grounded Terminal	Model	Lock Test Amps	Lock Test Volts	Lock Test Torque (ft lbs)	No Load Test Amps	No Load Test Volts	No Load Test rpm
Type 1 up to Chassis No. 929745	70	6	Neg	25, 36 hp Bosch EED 0.4/6L/4	500	3.5	NA	80	5.5	5,400
Type 1 from Chassis No. 929746	66	6	Neg	40 hp 1,200 cc Bosch EEF 0.5/6L/1	450-520	3.5	8.0	60-80	5.5	5,500-7,300
Type 1 from Chassis No. 118000001①	36	12	Neg	40 hp 1,200 and 1,300 cc-VW 113 911 021 A	450-520	3.5	8.0	60-80	5.5	5,500-7,300
Type 2 up to Chassis No. 117901	84	6	Neg	40 hp 1,200 and 1,300 cc-Bosch 113 911 021 B	450-520	3.5	8.0	60-80	5.5	5,500-7,300
Type 2 from Chassis No. 117902	77	6	Neg	Bosch AL/EEF 0.8/12L1 (12 Volt)	250-285	6.0	6.5 8.2	38-45	12	6,400-7,900
Type 2 from Chassis No. 217000001	45	12	Neg	1,500 cc-111 911 021 G (12 Volt)②	250-285	NA	NA	38-45	12	7,150
Type 3 from Chassis No. 0000001	77	6	Neg	—	—	—	—	—	—	—
Type 3 from Chassis No. 317000001	36	12	Neg	—	—	—	—	—	—	—
Type 1, 2, 3, 4 from 1971 to 1972	45	12	Neg	311 911 023B	220-260	6.0	—	35-45	12	7,400-9,100
				111 911 023A	270-290	6.0	—	25-40	12	6,200-7,800
				003 911 023A	250-300	6.0	—	35-50	12	6,400-7,600

① Excluding VW 1,200, Type 1

② Test figures for 6 Volt units on 1,500 cc engines should be the same as for previous 6 volt units

NA Not available

TUNE-UP SPECIFICATIONS

Year	Engine Code,⑨ SAE HP Rating Displacement	Spark Plugs: Make, Type⑧	Spark Plugs: Gap (in.)	Distributor: Approx Point Dwell (deg)	Distributor: Point Gap (in.)	Basic Ignition Timing (deg)	Cranking Comp. Pressure (psi)	Valves: Clearance (in.) Intake	Valves: Clearance (in.) Exhaust	Valves: Intake Opens (deg)①	Idle Speed (rpm)
To Dec., 1953	25 hp, 1,100	Bosch W175T1, Champion L-10	.026	50	.016	5 BTDC	85-107	.004	.004	2½ BTDC	550
To July, 1960	A, 36 hp, 1,200	Bosch W175T1, Champion L-10	.026	50	.016	7.5 BTDC	100-114	.004	.004	2½ BTDC	550
From Aug., 1960	D, 42 hp, 1,200	Bosch W175T1, Champion L-87Y	.026	50	.016	10 BTDC	100-128	.004 ②	.004 ②	6 BTDC	550
From Aug., 1965	F, 50 hp, 1,300	Bosch W175T1, Champion L-87Y	.028	50	.016	7.5 BTDC	107-135	.004	.004	7½ BTDC	550
From Aug., 1965-Type 2, From Aug., 1967-Type 1	H, 53 hp, 1,500	Bosch③ W175T1, Champion L-87Y	.028	42-58	.016	7.5 BTDC④	114-142	.004	.004	7½ BTDC	550⑤
From Aug., 1969-Type 1, From Aug., 1967-Type 2	B, 57 hp, 1,600	Bosch W145T1	.026	47-53	.016	TDC	114-142	.004	.004	7½ BTDC	850
To July 1963	G, 51 hp, 1,500	Bosch W145T1	.028	42-58	.016	10 BTDC	121-142	.004 ②	.004 ②	7½ BTDC	550
From Aug., 1970	W, 85 hp, 1,700	Bosch W175T2	.028	44-50	.016	27 BTDC⑩ At 3500 rpm	128-156	.006	.006	12 BTDC	900
From Aug., 1971	X, 65 hp, 1,600	Champion L-88A, Bosch W145T1	.028	44-50	.016	TDC⑩	128-156	.004	.004	7½ BTDC	850
From Aug., 1971	CB, 74 hp, 1,700	Champion L-88A, Bosch W145T1	.028	44-50	.016	5 ATDC⑪	128-156	.004	.004	7½ BTDC	850

① With valve clearance of .04 in. (This clearance is used for checking valve timing only)

② Before 1965, some 1,200 and 1,500 cc engines used long rocker arm mounting studs which pass through the full thickness of the cylinder head. Valve clearances on engines with long studs must be set at .008 in. (intake), and .012 in. (exhaust). These engines are:

Engine Code	Up to Engine No.
D	9205699
G	0710799
K	0672748
R	0672297

Some of these engines have had short studs installed in one or both heads. In this case, the valves are set at .004 in. (intake and exhaust); The only sure way to determine what clearance to use on these engines is by a sticker on the engine, or by feeling the stud ends between the pushrod tubes under the engine.

③ Type 1—Bosch W145T1

④ Type 1 with throttle positioner—TDC

⑤ Type 1—850 rpm

⑥ High compression

⑦ Low compression

⑧ The Bosch W175T1 plug can be used to replace the W145T1 for sustained high speeds

⑨ See Engine Identification Chart for explanation of codes

⑩ Vacuum hoses off

⑪ Vacuum hoses on

NOTE: If any of this tune-up information conflicts with the information on the engine sticker(s), use the sticker figures

TUNE-UP SPECIFICATIONS • Continued

Year	Engine Code,⑨ SAE HP Rating Displacement	SPARK PLUGS: Make, Type⑧	SPARK PLUGS: Gap (in.)	DISTRIBUTOR: Approx Point Dwell (deg)	DISTRIBUTOR: Point Gap (in.)	Basic Ignition Timing (deg)	Cranking Comp. Pressure (psi)	VALVES: Clearance (in.) Intake	VALVES: Clearance (in.) Exhaust	VALVES: Intake Opens (deg)①	Idle Speed (rpm)
From Aug., 1970	AE, 60 hp, 1,600	Champion L-88A, Bosch W145T1	.028	44-55	.016	5 ATDC⑪	128-156	.004	.004	7½ BTDC	850
From Aug., 1971	AH, 60 hp, 1,600	Champion L-88A, Bosch W145T1	.028	44-55	.016	5 ATDC⑪	128-156	.004	.004	7½ BTDC	850
To July, 1965⑥ From Aug., 1965⑦	K, 54 hp, 1,500	Bosch W175T1	.026	50	.016	10 BTDC⑥ 7.5 BTDC⑦	121-142 ⑥ 114-142 ⑦	.004 ②	.004 ②	7½ BTDC	550
To July, 1965	R, 66 hp, 1,500S	Bosch W175T1	.026	50	.016	10 BTDC	135-164	.004 ②	.004 ②	7½ BTDC	750
From Aug., 1965	T, 65 hp, 1,600	Bosch W175T1	.028	50	.016	7.5 BTDC	114-142	.004	.004	7½ BTDC	750
From Aug., 1967, Injected	U, 65 hp, 1,600	Bosch W175T1	.028	47-53	.016	TDC	114-142	.004	.004	7½ BTDC	850
From Aug., 1970	AD, 60 hp, 1,600	Bosch W145T1	.028	44-50	.016	5 ATDC	114-142	.004	.004	7½ BTDC	850

TORQUE SPECIFICATIONS
TRANSMISSION AND REAR AXLE

Fastener	Size Thread	Torque (ft lbs)
Transmission and Rear Axle (Standard and Partly Synchronized Transmission) Type 1 and 2		
Transmission housing nuts and bolts①	M 8 x 1.25	14
Oil drain plug	M 18 x 1.5	22-29
Oil filler plug	M 24 x 1.5	14
Axle shaft nut	M 24 x 1.5	217
Transmission carrier-to-frame	M 18 x 1.5	166
Spring plate nuts/bolts	M 12 x 1.5	72
Transmission and Rear Axle (fully synchronized) all Types		
Axle tube retainer nuts	M 8 x 1.25	14
Rear wheel bearing retainer screws	M 10 x 1.5	43
Oil drain plug	M 24 x 1.5	14
Oil filler plug		
Rear axle shaft nut (Types 1 and 3)	M 24 x 1.5	217
Nut on driven shaft (Type 2 from August 1963)	M 30 x 1.5	108
Nut on rear axle driven shaft (Type 2) up to Chassis No. 1144302	M 24 x 1.5	217②
from Chassis No. 1144303	M 30 x 1.5	217②
Transmission carrier on frame	M 18 x1 .5	166
Spring plate/ reduction gear housing screw (Type 2)	M 12 x 1.5	72-87

Fastener	Size Thread	Torque (ft lbs)
Additional torques for transmission and rear axle (Stick-shift automatic)		
Temperature switch/Selector switch/Starter inhibtor switch	M 14 x 1.5	18
Converter to drive plate screws	M 8 x 1.25	18
Retaining nut for taper roller bearing	M 80 x 1	159
Nut for converter housing	M 8 x 1.25	14
Screw for one-way clutch support	M 6 x 1	11③
Screw for clutch	M 6 x 1	11
Lockscrew	M 8 x 1.25	7
Clamp screw for clutch lever	M 8 x 1.25	18
Screw for transmission oil pan and lockplate	M 7 x 1.25	7
Union for oil pressure line	M 12 x 1.5	25
Union for oil return line	M 14 x 1.5	25
Screw for drive shaft	M 8 x 1.25	25
Fitted screw in diagonal arm	M 14 x 1.5	87

① Note tightening sequence
② If cotter pin holes are not in line, tighten to a maximum of 250 ft lbs. If hole is still not in line, fit a different nut
③ Use new screws
④ Tighten to 32 ft lbs first, slacken off, and tighten to 22 ft lbs
⑤ With reinforced spacer sleeve: at least 253 ft lbs then turn on to cotter pin hole

TORQUE SPECIFICATIONS— TRANSMISSION AND REAR AXLE

Fastener	Thread Size	Torque (ft lbs)
Transmission and Rear Axle (fully synchronized) Type 2 from Chassis No. 218 000-001		
Double taper roller bearing retainer	M 9 x 1.25	22④
Final drive side covers	M 8 x 1.25	14
Brake backplate-to-housing	M 8	18
Brake backplate-to-housing	M 10	25
Slotted nut on rear wheel shaft	M 30 x 1.5	230-253⑤
Joint-to-flange (socket head screw)	M 8	25
Control arm-to-frame	M 12 x 1.5	58
Cover/spring plate mounting	M 10	32
Control arm-to-bearing housing	M 14 x 1.5	94
Shock absorber-to-frame and bearing housing	M 12 x 1.5	43

TORQUE SPECIFICATIONS— FRONT AXLE AND STEERING GEAR

Fastener	Thread Size	Torque (ft lbs)
TYPE 1 FRONT AXLE		
Front axle-to-frame	M 12 x 1.5	22-25
Shock absorber screw on side plate	M 12 x 1.5	36
Shock absorber nut on side plate	M 10	14
Shock absorber nut on lower tension arm	M 10	22-25
Hexagon nuts for steering ball joints⑤	M 12 x 1.5 or M 10 x 1	36-50 29-36
Inner wheel bearing nut	M 18 x 1.5	29①
Locknut for wheel bearing	M 18 x 1.5	50①
Socket head screw in clamp nut	M 7 M 12 x 1.5	7—max 9②
Slotted nut on tie rod	M 10 x 1	22③
Steering damper nut on tie rod⑤	M 10 x 1 M 10 x 1	18③ 18
Steering damper screw on axle tube	M 10	29-32
Setscrew for torsion bars	M 14 x 1.5	29-36
Locknut for setscrew	M 14 x 1.5	29-36
Caliper to steering knuckle	M 10	36
Clamping screw link pin to torsion arm	M 10	32
Screw for front axle support/front axle	M 12 x 1.5	40-43
Screw for front axle/frame	M 10	40-43
TYPE 2 FRONT AXLE		
Front axle/frame bolts (side member)	M 12 x 1.5	65-90
Shock absorber nut and bolt	M 12 x 1.5	36
upper (from Chassis No. 971550)	M 10	29-32
Shock absorber securing bolt, upper (up to Chassis No. 971549)	M 12 x 1.5	25-32
Shock absorber securing nut, lower	M 10	18-22
Steering knuckle/torsion arm (link pin bolts)	M 10	29-32
Ball joints-to-steering knuckle⑤	M 18 x 1.5	72
Inner wheel bearing nut	M 18 x 1 or M 22 x 1.5	25④
Wheel bearing locknut	M 18 x 1 or M 22 x 1.5	50④
Tie rod and draglink nuts	M 12 x 1.5 M 10 x 1	22③ 18③
TYPES 1 and 3 STEERING GEAR		
Steering gear-to-axle Type 1	M 10	18-22
Steering gear-to-axle Type 3	M 10	18-22
Locknut for roller shaft adjusting screw	M 10 x 1	18
Steering gear cover screws	M 8 x 1.25	14-18
Screw securing drop arm to roller shaft	M 12 x 1.5	50
Steering wheel nut	M 18 x 1.5	36
Locknut for steering worm adjustment screw	M 35 x 1.5	36-43
Hex bolt for steering coupling-to-steering worm	M 8	14-18
Hex nut flange-to-coupling disc	M 8	11
Fillister head screw for self-cancelling ring on steering wheel	AM 3.5	3.6
Locknut for tapered ring-to-tie rod	M 14 x 1.5	18
Clamping screw for tie rod retaining clip	M 8 x 1	11
Hex bolt for steering column mounting plate-to-instrument panel	M 8	11
Screw for retainer eccentric bearing	M 8	11
TYPE 2 STEERING GEAR		
Bracket-to-frame screws	M 10 x 22	29-32
Steering boss to bracket	M 10 x 40	25-36
Drop arm nut	M 20 x 1.5	58-80
Swing lever pinch bolt (from Chassis No. 20-117 901)	M 12 x 1.5	43
Upper and lower steering arm bolts (up to Chassis No. 20-117 901)	M 12 x 1.5	47-54
Steering wheel nut	M 16 x 1.5	18-22
Hex nut for flange-to-steering worm	M 8	14
Castellated nut for coupling disc-to-flange	M 8	11
Cheese-head screw for steering column cap-to-floor plate	M 6	3.6
Steering gear case cover bolt	M 8	18
Steering gear and cover bolt	M 6	11

① Tighten inner nut to 29 ft lbs first, fit new lock plate, and slacken nut 72° (distance from one wheel bolt hole in drum to next). Tighten outer nut to 50 ft lbs

② Tighten nut while turning the wheel. Slacken the nut until the specified axial play of .03-.12mm (.001-.005 in.) is obtained. If front axle tends to be noisy, keep play to lower limit (.03-.06mm). When play is correct, tighten socket head screw to the correct torque

③ Turn on to cotter pin hole

④ Tighten inner nut to 25 ft lbs first, while turning the wheel. Then fit a new lockplate and slacken the nut until the specified axial play of .03-.12mm (.001-.005 in.) is obtained. If front axle tends to be noisy, keep play to lower limit (.03-.06mm). When play is correct, tighten outer locknut to 50 ft lbs

⑤ Always use new self-locking nuts after removal

⑥ Tighten clamp screw to 29 ft lbs first, then tighten adjusting screw to 7 ft lbs and lock it

TORQUE SPECIFICATIONS—FRONT AXLE AND STEERING GEAR

Fastener	Thread Size	Torque (ft lbs)
Steering damper/frame bolt and nut (up to Chassis No. 851 389)	M 10 x 45	32
Steering damper/axle tube screw (from Chassis No. 851 390)	M 10 x 40	29-32
Steering damper/swing lever screw	M 10 x 72	29-32
Setscrew for torsion bars	M 14 x 1.5	29
Locknut for setscrew	M 14 x 1.5	29
Stabilizer to torsion arm	M 10	25-36
	M 8	18
Screw for brake back-plate to steering knuckle	M 10	36-43
Clamping screw for link pins to torsion bar	M 10	29-36
TYPE 3 FRONT AXLE		
Front axle securing bolts		
a—upper and lower	M 10	22
b—center	M 10	29
Grub screw securing torsion bars	M 14 x 1.5	22
Grub screw securing stabilizer	M 14 x 1.5	32-40
Locknut for grub screw	M 14 x 1.5	29
Torsion bar to axle beam screws	M 10	29
Clamp screw stabilizer	M 10	29
Adjusting screw for stabilizer	M 8	7⑥
Shock absorber-to-axle beam screws	M 12 x 1.5	22-25
Shock absorber nut on torsion arm	M 10	22-25
Steering arm on steering knuckle	M 10 x 1	40
Nuts for upper and lower ball joints	M 20 x 1.5 or M 18 x 1.5	80
Clamp screws for upper and lower ball joints	M 10 x 40	40
up to Chassis No. 0273513 (October 1963)	M 8 x 40	25
Socket head screw in split nut	M 7	7—max 9
Inner wheel bearing nut up to Chassis No. 315 220 883	M 16 x 1.5	11②
Wheel bearing locknut	M 16 x 1.5	50②
Tie rod nuts	M 12 x 1.5	22④
	M 10 x 1	18④
Steering damper screw on axle	M 10	29-32
Steering damper nut on drop arm	M 10	18

TORQUE SPECIFICATIONS—BRAKES AND WHEELS

Fastener	Thread Size	Torque (ft lbs)
BRAKES, TYPE 1		
Master cylinder-to-frame	M 8	14-22
Screws for bearing cover/backplate/bearing flange	M 10	40-47
Backplate/steering knuckle screws	M 10	36
Brake hose unions	M 10 x 1	11-14
Brake pipe unions	M 10 x 1	11-14
Stoplight switch	M 10 x 1	11-14
Wheel cylinder-to-backplate	M 8	14-22
Caliper-to-steering knuckle	M 10	36
Residual pressure valve in tandem master cylinder	M 12 x 1	14
BRAKES TYPE 2		
Screws for bearing cover-to-rear brake backplate	M 10	40-43
Brake backplate/wheel cylinder front	M 10	40-43
Brake hose unions	M 10 x 1	11-14
Brake pipe unions	M 10 x 1	11-14
Stoplight switch	M 10 x 1	11-14
Tandem master cyinder-to-brake servo	M 8	9
Brake servo-to-retaining plate/front axle	M 8	9
BRAKES TYPE 3		
Master cylinder-to-frame	M 8	14-22
Screws for bearing cover/backplate rear	M 10 x 1.5	40-47
Wheel cylinders		
a—rear on backplate	M 8	18
b—front on backplate/steering knuckle	M 10 x 1	32
Disc brake caliper housing-to-steering knuckle	M 10	43
Brake hose at		
a—brake pipe	M 10 x 1	11-14
b—wheel cylinder	M 10 x 1	11-14
c—disc brake caliper housing	M 10 x 1	11
Stoplight switch	M 10 x 1	11-14
WHEELS		
Wheel bolts		
Type 1	M 12 x 1.5	72
from August 1965 (four-hole wheel)①	M 14 x 1.5	108
Type 2	M 14 x 1.5	94
Type 3	M 12 x 1.5	72
from August 1965 (four-hole wheel)	M 14 x 1.5	108

① Only on vehicles with disc brakes. For all from Chassis No. 118 000 001

TORQUE SPECIFICATIONS—ENGINE

Fastener	Thread Size	Torque (ft lbs)
ALL ENGINES		
1-Nuts for crankcase halves	M 12 x 1.5	25①
2-Screws and nuts for crankcase halves⑥	M 8	14
3-Cylinder head nuts②	M 10	23
4-Rocker shaft nuts⑦	M 8	14-18
5-Flywheel gland nut	M 28 x 1.5	217
6-Connecting rod bolts and nuts	M 9 x 1	22-25④
7-Special nut for fan	M 12 x 1.5	40-47
8-Generator pulley nut	M 12 x 1.5	40-47
9-Crankshaft pulley bolt	M 20 x 1.5	29-36
10-Spark plugs	M 14 x 1.25	22-29
11-Oil drain plug	M 14 x 1.5	25⑧
12-Clutch-to-flywheel	M 8 x 1.5	18
13-Self-locking nuts for engine carrier to the crankcase	M 8	18⑤
14-Nuts for oil pump	M 8	14
15-Cap nut for oil filter cover	M 6	5
16-Nuts for engine mounting	M 10	22
17-Screws for converter-to-drive plate	M 8	18

TORQUE SPECIFICATIONS—ENGINE

Fastener	Thread Size	Torque (ft lbs)
25 and 36 hp—EXCEPTIONS		
1-Nuts for crankcase halves	M 10	22
3-Cylinder head nuts②	M 10	26-27
11-Oil drain plug③	M 18 x 1.5	22-29
13-Insert for spark plug	M 18 x 1.5	50-54
TYPE 3—EXCEPTIONS		
8-Generator pulley nut	M 12 x 1.5	40-47
9-Special bolt for fan and crankshaft pulley	M 20 x 1.5	94-108
17-Screws for converter-to-drive plate	M 8	14
19-Self-locking nuts for engine carrier to body	M 8	18⑤

① For cap nuts: 18 ft lbs
② See tightening sequences
③ As above from August 1959
④ Contact surfaces oiled 1,300 cc and earlier—28-36 ft lbs
⑤ Renew
⑥ Type 1, 2, 3/1600 1971-72 Nonsealing nuts 14, sealing nuts 18, Type 2/1700 and Type 4 sealing nuts 23 ft lbs
⑦ Type 2/1700, Type 4 1971-72 11 ft lbs
⑧ Type 2/1700, Type 4 1971-72 16 ft lbs

BRAKE SPECIFICATIONS

Vehicle	Model	TYPE		BRAKE CYLINDER BORE (in.)			BRAKE DRUM OR DISC DIAMETER (in.)	
		Front	Rear	Master Cylinder	Wheel Cylinder Front	Wheel Cylinder Rear	Front	Rear
Type 1	25 hp, 36 hp 1,200 cc	Drum①	Drum	.750	.750	.690	9.05 ±.008	9.05 ±.008
	40 hp 1,200 and 1,300 cc	Drum	Drum	.687	.874	.750	9.059 ±.008	9.055 ±.008
	1,500 and 1,600 cc Single Master Cylinder	Drum	Drum	.687	.875	.687	9.059 ±.008	9.055 ±.008
	1,500 and 1,600 cc-Tandem Master Cylinder	Drum	Drum	.750	.875	.687	9.059 ±.008	9.055 ±.008
	1971 Models	Drum	Drum	.750	.94	.690	9.76	9.06
	Karmann Ghia	Disc	Drum	NA	1.574	.687	10.9	NA
	Karmann Ghia, 1971-72	Disc	Drum	.750	1.575②	.687	10.9	9.06
	1972 Models	Drum	Drum	.750	.938	.687	9.768 ±.008	9.06 ±.008
Type 2	Tandem Master Cylinder	Drum	Drum	.875	1.00	.875	9.843 ±.008	9.843 ±.008
	1971-72 Models	Disc	Drum	.938	2.126	.875	10.9	9.92
Type 3	Tandem Master Cylinder	Disc	Drum	.750	1.653	.875	10.9	9.768 ±.008
	1971 Models	Disc	Drum	.813	NA	.875	10.9	9.92
	1972 Models	Disc	Drum	.750	1.654	.874	—	9.768 ±.008
Type 4	1971-72 Models	Disc	Drum	.750	1.654	.874	—	9.768 ±.008

① Some early models have mechanical brakes
② After ch. no. 142 2000001 Dia is 1.654 in.

CHASSIS AND WHEEL ALIGNMENT SPECIFICATIONS

Vehicle	Model	CHASSIS (in.)			WHEEL ALIGNMENT						
		Wheel-base	Track Front	Track Rear	Caster (deg or in.)	Camber (deg)	Toe-in (in or deg) ④	King Pin Inclination (deg)	Rear Wheel Camber (deg)	Wheel Pivot Ratio (deg) Inner Wheel	Wheel Pivot Ratio (deg) Outer Wheel
Type 1	25 hp and 36 hp 1,200 cc	94.5	51	49.2	2°30′ ± 30′	0°40′ ± 30′	.04-.12	4°20′	NA	NA	NA
	42 hp 1,200 cc	94.5	51.4	50.7	2° ± 15′	0°40′ ± 30′	.08-.16	4°20′	3° ± 30′	34	28
	42 hp 1,200 and 1,300 cc-after August, 1965	94.5	51.4	51.2	2° ± 15′	0°30′ ± 15′	.08-.16	4°20′	3° ± 30′①	34	28
	1,500 cc-Swing Axles	94.5	51.4	53.5	2° ± 15′	0°30′ ± 15′	.08-.18	4°20′	1° ± 1°①	34	28
	1,500 cc and 1,600 cc-Double Jointed Rear Axles	94.5	51.57	NA	3°30′ ±1°	30′ ± 20′	30′ ± 15′	5°	− 1°20′ ± 40′	34 ± 2	28-1
	1971-72 Beetle Torsion Bar Front Suspension	94.5	51.6	53.1	3°20′ ±1°	0°30′ ± 20′	30′ ± 15′	NA	1° ± 1°	—	—
	1971-72 Super Beetle with Strut Suspension	95.3	54.1	53.1	2° ± 35′	1°20′ ± 40′	30′ ± 10′	NA	− 1°20′ ± 40′	—	—
Type 2	Pre-1968-Swing Axles	94.5	54.1	53.5	3° ± 40′	40′ ± 30′	± .04 (5′ ± 10′)	NA	3° ± 30′②	NA	NA
	1968-70 Double-Jointed Rear Axles	94.5	54.5	56.2	3° ± 40′	40′ ± 15′	10′ ± 10′	5°	− 50′ ± 30′	32	24
	1971-72	94.5	54.5	56.6	3° ± 40′	40′ ± 20′	15′± 15′	NA	− 50′ ± 30′	—	—
Type 3	With Swing Axles	94.5	51.58	52.99	4° ± 40′	1°20′ ± 20′	40′ ± 5′	NA	2°30′ ± 1°③	NA	NA
	With Double Jointed Rear Axles	94.5	51.58	53.14	4° ± 40′	1°20′ ± 20′	40′ ± 15′	5°10′	− 1°20′ ± 40′	30	27-1
	1971-72	94.5	51.6	53.1	4° ± 40′	1°20′ ± 20′	40′ ± 15′	NA	− 1°20′ ± 40′	—	—
Type 4	1971-72	98.4	54.7	52.8	1°10′ ± 35′	1°10′ + 25′ − 30′	20′ ± 15′	NA	− 1° ± 30′	—	—

NA Information not available

① 1967 sedan: 1° ± 1°
1967 Karmann Ghia and VW convertible: 15′ ± 1°

② After chassis No. 117 901:
Van: 4° ± 30′
Kombi: 3°30′ ± 30′
Bus: 3° ± 30′

③ 1967 and later Notchback and Type 3 Karmann Ghia: 1°45′ ± 1°

④

Size Wheel	10′ toe-in equals:
14 in.	.043 in.
15 in.	.047 in.
16 in.	.051 in.

CARBURETOR SPECIFICATIONS—TYPES 1 AND 2

Vehicle	Engine	Car-buretor	Venturi (mm dia)	Main Jet	Air Correction Jet	Pilot Jet	Pilot Jet Air Bleed or Pilot Air Jet (mm dia)	Pump Fuel Jet	Pump Air Correction Jet	Power Fuel Jet (mm dia)	Emulsion Tube	Float Needle Valve (mm dia)	Float Needle Valve Washer (mm)	Float Weight (g)	Accel Pump Cap (cc Stroke)
Type 1	1,131 cc 25 hp	Solex 28 PCI	20	105	190	50	.8	50	2.0	—	10	1.5	—	12.5	—
Type 1	1,200 cc 36 hp from No. 695282	Solex 28 PCI	21.5	122.5	200	g50	.8	50	2.0	—	29⑧	1.5	—	5.7	.4-.6
Type 1	1,200 cc 36 hp from No. 849905	Solex 28 PCI	21.5	117.5	195	g50	.8	50	2.0	—	29⑧	1.5	—	5.7	.4-.6
Kar-mann Ghia-Type 1	1,200 cc 36 hp from No. 1118403	Solex 28 PCI	21.5	117.5	180	g50	.8	50	2.0	—	29⑧	1.5	—	5.7	.4-.6
Type 2	1,200 cc 36 hp from No. 991590	Solex 28 PCI													
Type 1 & 2	1,200 cc 42 hp from No. 5000 001	Solex 28 PICT(-1)	22.5	122.5	130Y/ 140Z/ 135Z/	g55	2.0	.5	—	1.0/75	①	1.5	—	5.7	1.1-1.4/ .8-1.0
Type 2	1,500 cc 51 hp from No. 0143543	Solex 28 PICT-2	22.5	115	145Y/ 150Z/	g45	1.55	.5	—	.7	①	1.5	—	5.7	1.1-1.4/ 1.2-1.3
Type 1	1,300 cc 50 hp from No. F0 000 001	Solex 30 PICT-1	24.0	125	125Z ②	g55	150	50	—	— ③	①	1.5	—	5.7	1.3-1.6
Type 2	1,500 cc 53 hp from No. H0000001	Solex 30 PICT-1	24.0	115	135Z	g60	150	50	—	75	①	1.5	—	5.7	1.3-1.6
Type 1 & 2	1,600 cc 57 hp from No. B0000001	Solex 30 PICT-1	24.0	120	135Z	55	140	50	—	50	①	1.5	—	5.7	1.3-1.6
Type 1	1,300 cc 50 hp Automatic from No. F1462682	Solex 30 PICT-2	24.0	x120	170Z	55	140	50	—	50	①	1.5	—	8.5	1.3-1.6
Type 1	1,500 cc 53 hp Automatic from No. H0879927	Solex 30 PICT-2	24.0	x120	125Z ④	55	140	50	—	50	①	1.5	—	8.5	1.3-1.6/ 1.05-1.35
Type 1	1,500 cc 53 hp from No. H0204001	Solex 30 PICT-2	24.0	x120	125Z ④	g55	150 ⑤	50	—	50	①	1.5	—	5.7 ⑥	1.3-1.6/ 1.05-1.35

① Fixed to air correction jet
② Karmann Ghia—170Z
③ Karmann Ghia—75
④ Karmann Ghia—135Z
⑤ From engine No. H087400—140
⑥ From No. H0874200—8.5
⑦ With emission control
⑧ Emulsion tube carrier dia (mm)—5.0

CARBURETOR SPECIFICATIONS—TYPES 1 AND 2

Vehicle	Engine	Carburetor	Venturi (mm dia)	Main Jet	Air Correction Jet	Pilot Jet	Pilot Jet Air Bleed or Pilot Air Jet (mm dia)	Pump Fuel Jet	Pump Air Correction Jet	Power Fuel Jet (mm dia)	Emulsion Tube	Float Needle Valve (mm dia)	Float Needle Valve Washer (mm)	Float Weight (g)	Accel Pump Cap (cc Stroke)
Type 1 & 2	1,500 cc 53 hp⑦ from No. H5000001	Solex 30 PICT-2	24.0	x116	125Z	55	140/ 135	50	—	60	①	1.5	—	8.5	1.3-1.6/ 1.05-1.35
Type 1 & 2	1,600 cc 57 hp from No. B5000001	Solex 30 PICT-2	24.0	x116	125Z	55	140	50	—	60	①	1.5	—	8.5	1.3-1.6
Type 1	1,600 cc 57 hp from No. B6000001	Solex 30 PICT-3	24.0	x122.5	125Z	65	135	—	—	100	①	1.5	1.5	8.5	1.2-1.35
Type 1	1,600 cc 57 hp Automatic from No. B6000002	Solex 30 PICT-3	24.0	x112.5	125Z	65	135	—	—	100	①	1.5	1.5	8.5	1.2-1.35
Type 1	1,600 cc 57 hp from No. B5116437	Solex 30 PICT-3													
Type 1	1,600 cc 60 hp AE 1971-72 Models	Solex 34 PICT-3	26.0	130	75Z	60	147.5	—	—	100	—	1.5	.5	8.5	—
Type 1	1971-72 AH	Solex 34 PICT-3	26.0	127.5x 130	75Z 80Z	55	147.5	—	—	100	—	1.5	.5	8.5	1.3-1.6
Type 2	1,600 cc 1971-72 AE	Solex 34 PICT-3	26.0 26.0	125	60Z	60	147.5	—	—	95	—	1.5	.5	8.5	1.45-1.75
Type 2	1,700 cc 1971-72 CE	Solex 34 PDSIT-2(-3)	26.0	137.5	155/ 050	55	120	—	—	—	—	1.2	.5	7.0	.7 ± 15

CARBURETOR SPECIFICATIONS—TYPE 3

Vehicle	Engine	Carburetor	Venturi (mm dia)	Main Jet	Air Correction Jet	Pilot Jet	Idling Air Drilling	Pump Injector Tube (mm dia)	Power Fuel Jet (mm dia)	Emulsion Tube (No.)	Float Needle Valve (mm dia)	Float Needle Valve Washer (mm)	Float Weight (g)	Accel Pump Cap (cc Stroke)	Throttle Valve Gap (mm)
Type 3 Single Carburetor	From No. 0 000 001	Solex 32 PHN	23.5	137.5	125	g45 g50	—	.8	1.05	48	1.5	—	12.5	.9-1.2/ 1.2-1.5	.8-.9
	From No. 0 084 752	Solex 32 PHN-1	23.5	132.5	115	g45	—	.8	.7	48	1.5	—	12.5	.9-1.2	.8-.9
	From No. 0220137	Solex 32 PHN-1	23.5	127.5	115	g45	—	.8	.7	48	1.5	—	12.5	.9-1.2	.8-.9
	From No. 0319841	Solex 32 PHN	23.5	130.0	115	g50	—	.7	.7	48	1.5	—	12.5	.8-1.0	.8-.9
	From No. K0150001	Solex 32 PHN	23.5	130.0	115	—	1.4	.7	.7	48	1.5	—	12.5	.8-1.0	.8-.9

① 2 - Left carburetor, with distributor vacuum connection
3 - Right carburetor

② Return valve for accelerator pump - .3

CARBURETOR SPECIFICATIONS—TYPE 3

Vehicle	Engine	Carburetor	Venturi (mm dia)	Main Jet	Air Correction Jet	Pilot Jet	Idling Air Drilling	Pump Injector Tube (mm dia)	Power Fuel Jet (mm dia)	Emulsion Tube (No.)	Float Needle Valve (mm dia)	Float Needle Valve Washer (mm)	Float Weight (g)	Accel Pump Cap (cc Stroke)	Throttle Valve Gap (mm)
Type 3 Dual Carbu-retors	1,500 cc From No. 0255001	Solex 32 PDSIT-2(-3)①	21.5	x125	180	g45	—	.5 (12 mm)	.9 (9.5 mm)	—	1.2	—	7.3	.35-.55	.60-.65
	1,500 cc From No. 0633331	Solex 32 PDSIT-2(-3)①	23	x135	180	g45	—	.5 (15 mm)	.8 (10.5 mm)	—	1.2	1.5	7.3	.35-.55	.60-.65
	1,600 cc From No. T0000001	Solex 32 PDSIT-2(-3)①	23	x130	240	g45	—	50 (12 mm)	80 (15 mm)	—	1.2	1.5	7.3	.35-.55	.60-.65
	1,600 cc From No. T0244544	Solex 32 PDSIT-2 (Left)	24	x132.5	150	g50	—	.5 (9 mm)	—	—	1.2	.5	7.3	.35-.55	.60-.65
		Solex 32 PDSIT-3 (Right)	24	x130	120	g50	—	.5 (9 mm)	—	—	1.2	.5	7.3	.35-.55	.60-.65
	1,600 cc From No. T0576724	Solex 32 PDSIT-2 (Left)	24	x132.5	150	50	—	.5	—	—	1.2	.5	7.0	.35-.55	.60-.65
		Solex 32 PDSIT-3 (Right)	24	x130	120	50	—	.5	—	—	1.2	.5	7.0	.35-.55	.60-.65
Type 3 Dual Carbu-retors—Auto-matic	1,600 cc From No. T0690001	Solex 32 PDSIT-2 (Left)	24	x130	155	—	135	—	—	—	1.2	.5	7.0	.3-.45	.7
		Solex 32 PDSIT-3 (Right)	24	x127.5	120	—	135	—	—	—	1.2	.5	7.0	.3-.45	.7
	1,600 cc From No. T0463930	Solex 32 PDSIT-2 (Left)	24	130	155	50	—	.5 (9 mm)	—	—	1.2	.5	7.0	.25-.4	.60-.65
		Solex 32 PDSIT-3 (Right)	24	127.5	120	50	—	.5 (9 mm)	—	—	1.2	.5	7.0	.25-.4	.60-.65
	1,600 cc From No. T069000	Solex 32 PDSIT-2 (Left)	24	130	155	—	135	—	—	—	1.2	.5	7.0	.23-.4②	.9
		Solex 32 PDSIT-3 (Right)	24	127.5	120	—	135	—	—	—	1.2	.5	7.0	.23-.4②	.9

FUSES

Model	Circuit	Amp
1,300 Type 1 (6 Volt)	Horn, flashers, stoplight, wipers	16
	High-beam warning light, left high-beam	8
	Right high-beam	8
	Left low-beam	8
	Right low-beam	8
	Left parking light, left taillight	8
	Right parking light, right taillight license plate light	8
	Headlight dimmer, radio, interior light	16
1,500 Type 1 (12 Volt)	Turn signals, horn, Stoplights brake warning light, Automatic Stickshift and rear window defroster switch current	8
	Wipers	8
	High-beam warning light, left high-beam	8
	Right high-beam	8
	Left low-beam	8
	Right low-beam	8
	Left parking light, left taillight	8
	License plate light, right parking light, right taillight	8
	Interior light, emergency blinkers	8
	Spare fuse	—
	Rear window defroster main current (under rear seat, left side)	8
	Back-up lights (right side of engine fan housing)	8
	Automatic Stickshift control valve (left side of engine fan housing)	8
1,500 Type 2 (6 Volt)	Left low-beam	8
	Right low-beam	8
	Left high-beam, high-beam warning light	8
	Right high-beam	8
	Left taillight	8
	Right taillight, license plate light, parking lights	8
	Stoplights, turn indicators	16
	Horn, interior lights, wipers, headlight dimmer	16
1,600 Type 3 (6 Volt)	Right parking light, left parking light left taillight, luggage compartment light	8
	Right taillight, license plate light	8
	Left low-beam	8
	Right low-beam	8
	Left high-beam, high-beam warning light	8
	Right high-beam	8
	Spare fuse	—
	Emergency blinkers, interior light, horn, clock, radio	16
	Stoplights, turn signals	8
	Wipers, fuel gauge, warning lights	16

LIGHT BULBS

Model	Usage	U.S. Replacement Bulbs	VW Part No.	Wattage
36 hp 1,200 Type 1 (6 Volt) January, 1954—August 1955	Headlights	—	—	35/35
	Parking lights	—	—	1.5
	Stoplights	—	—	15
	Taillights	—	—	5
	License plate light	—	—	5
	Interior light	—	—	10
	All warning lights	—	—	1.2
	Instrument lighting	—	—	1.2
	Turn signals	—	—	3
36 hp 1,200 Type 1 (6 Volt) from August, 1955	Headlights	—	—	35/35
	Parking lights	—	—	2
	Stoplights	—	—	20
	Taillights	—	—	5
	License plate light (tubular bulb)	—	—	5
	Interior light	—	—	10
	Semaphore type	—	—	3
	Turn signals (tubular bulbs)	—	—	1.2
	All warning lights	—	—	1.2
	Instrument lighting	—	—	1.2
36 hp 1,200 Type 1 (6 Volt) Karmann Ghia, from August, 1955	Headlights	—	—	35/35
	Parking lights	—	—	3
	Taillights	—	—	5
	Rear stop/turn signal	—	—	15
	License plate lights	—	—	5
	Interior light	—	—	5
	Front turn signals	—	—	15
42 hp 1,200 and 1,300 Type 1 6 (Volt) Sedan and Convertible	Headlights	—	N177051	45/40
	Parking lights	—	N177171	4
	Stoplight/taillight	—	N177371	18/5
	Turn signals	—	N177311	18
	License plate light	—	N177191	10 ①
	Interior light	—	N177231	10
	Warning and instrument lights	—	N177221	1.2
42 hp 1,200 and 1,300 Type 1 (6 Volt) Karmann Ghia	Headlights	—	—	45/40
	Parking lights	—	—	4
	Taillights	—	—	5
	Stoplights	—	—	18
	Turn signals	—	—	18
	License plate lights	—	—	5
	Interior light	—	—	10
	Warning, instrument lights, clock	—	—	1.2
1,300 Type 1 (12 Volt)	Headlights	6012	11194126A	45/40
	License plate light	—	—	10
	Interior light	—	—	10
	Instrument and warning lights	—	—	2
	Parking lights	—	—	4
	Turn signals	—	—	18
	Stoplight/taillight	—	—	18/5
1,500 and 1,600 Type 1 (12 Volt) Sedan and Convertible	Headlights	6012	111941261A	—
	Parking/turn signal, taillight/stoplight	1034	N177382	—
	Rear turn signal	1073	N177322	—
	License plate light	89	N177192	—
	Backup lights	1073	N177332	—
	Instrument and warning lights	—	N177222	—
	Sedan interior light	—	N177232	—
	Convertible interior light	—	N177252	—

LIGHT BULBS

Model	Usage	U.S. Replacement Bulbs	VW Part No.	Wattage
	Warning lights for emergency flasher, brake, rear window defroster	—	N177512	—
1,500 Type 2 (6 Volt)	Headlights	—	N177051	45/40
	Parking lights	—	N177171	4
	Turn signals	—	N177311	18
	Taillights/stoplights	—	N177371	5/18
	License plate light	—	N177191	10
	Warning lights, instrument lights	—	N177221	1.2
	Dome lights	—	N177251	5
	Clock	—	N177221	1.2
1,600 Type 3 (6 Volt)	Headlights	6006, Type 2	N177051	—
	Front parking/turn signal	1154	N177171	5/18
	Rear turn signal, stoplight	1129	N177311	18
	Taillight	81	N177181	5
	License plate light	81	N177191	10
	Warning, instrument lights	—	N177221	1.2
	Interior and luggage compartment lights	—	N177231	10

① 1,200 uses 5 watt bulb after August, 1965.

FUSES

Model	Circuit	Amps
1600 Type 1 (12 volt)	Left parking and side marker lights, left tail lights	8
	Parking and side marker lights (right side), right tail light	8
	Low beam (left side)	8
	Low beam (right side)	8
	High beam (left side)	8
	High beam (right side), high beam indicator light	8
	License plate light	8
	Emergency flasher system	8
	Interior light	16
	Windshield wipers, rear window defroster, fresh air fan	16
	Horn, stop lights, transmission control valve and Automatic Stick Shift warning light	8
	Fuel gauge, turn signals, warning lights for brake and oil pressure, turn signals and generator	8
1700 Type 2 (12 volt)	Chart is the same as above except that the license plate light fuse is an accessory outlet. It holds an 8 amp fuse.	
1600 Type 3 (12 volt)	Right tail light, license plate light, parking and side marker lights; luggage compartment light	8
	Left tail light	8
	Left low beam	8
	Right low beam	8
	Left high beam; high beam indicator light	8
	Right high beam	8
	Electric fuel pump	8
	Emergency flasher; interior light Buzzer	16
	Windshield wipers; fresh air fan; rear window defogger	16
	Stop lights; turn signals; horn; brake warning light; back-up lights	8
	Accessories	8
1600 Type 4 (Ghia)	Parking and side marker lights; right tail light license plate lights	8
	Left tail light	8
	Left low beam	8
	Right low beam	8
	Left high beam; high beam indicator light	8
	Right high beam	8
	Accessories	8
	Emergency flasher	8
	Buzzer alarm; interior light	16
	Windshield wipers; rear window defogger	16
	Horn; stop lights, control valve	8
	Warning lights for turn signals, oil pressure and generator, turn signals, fuel gauge and brake warning light	8
1700 Type 4 (12 volt)	Left/right parking lights, left tail light, left rear side marker light	8
	Right tail light, right rear side marker light, license plate light, selector lever console light (Automatic)	8
	Left low beam	8
	Right low beam	8
	Left high beam	8
	Right high beam, high beam indicator light	8
	Fuel pump	8
	Interior light, emergency flasher, buzzer	8
	Cigarette lighter, heater switch	16
	Windshield wipers, fresh air fan, heater, rear window defogger	16
	Turn signals, back-up lights, warning lamps, oil pressure and fuel gauge	8
	Horn, brake warning light, stop lights	8

CAPACITIES AND PRESSURES

Model	Crankcase Refill After Draining (pts)	TRANSMISSION REFILL AFTER DRAINING (pts)				Final Drive (pts)	Air Cleaner (pts)⑧	Fuel Tank (gals)	Normal Fuel Pressure (psi)
		Standard	Auto Stick Shift	Fully Auto	Reduction Gears				
Type 1	5.3	6.3	6.3①	—	—	②	.5③	10.5⑨	⑩
Type 2	5.3	7.4	—	—	.5 each	②	.63④	15.8	⑩
Type 3	5.3	6.3	—	6.3-8.4⑥	—	2.1⑦	.85⑤	10.5	⑩
Type 4	7.4	—	—	6.3⑥	—	2.1	.9	13.2	3-5 max @ 4000 rpm

— Not applicable to this vehicle
① The total capacity of the Automatic Stickshift torque converter circuit is 7.6 pts ATF. The refill capacity is somewhat less.
② In unit with transmission
③ 1,300 cc Karmann Ghia—.63 pt, 1,500 cc Karmann Ghia—.96 pt, 1,500 cc sedan and convertible—.85 pt
④ 1,200 cc—.44 pt, Late 1,500 and 1,600 cc—.95 pt
⑤ Single-carburetor engine; 44 pts fuel injected engine .53 pt
⑥ Total capacity—12.6 pts ATF
⑦ Only with automatic transmission; otherwise, note ② applies.
⑧ Since so many different air cleaners have been used in production, it is best to rely on the full mark on the air cleaner body. If there is no such mark, these figures may be used.
⑨ Super Beetle—11.1 gals
⑩

Pump Marking	Pressure @ rpm
Unmarked (36 hp & earlier)	1.3-1.8 @ 1,000-3,000
Unmarked	2.5 @ 3,000-3,400
VW 2	5.0 @ 3,800
VW 3	3.5 @ 3,400-3,800
VW 4	3.5 @ 3,800
VW 6	5.0 @ 3,800
VW 7	3.5 @ 3,800
VW 8	3.5 @ 3,800

CYLINDER HEAD BOLT TIGHTENING SEQUENCE

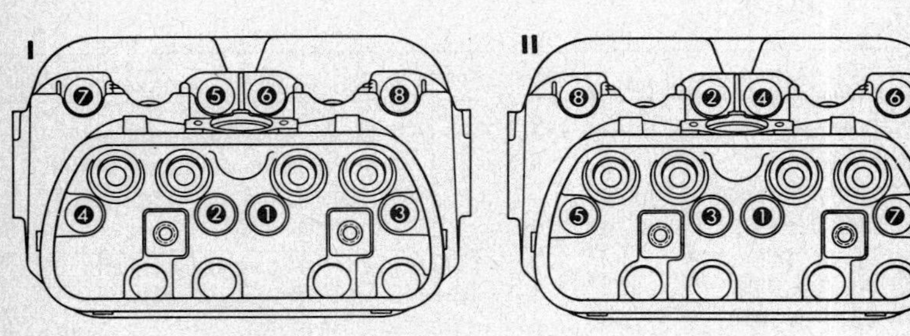

The cylinder head nuts should initially be tightened to 7 ft. lbs. in order I, then tightened to the recommended torque in order II.

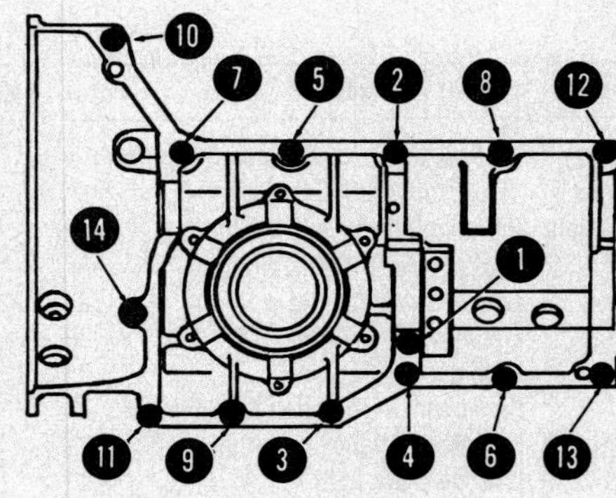

Split-type trans-axle.

Introduction

In 1932, Ferdinand Porsche produced prototypes for the NSU company of Germany. These led to the design of the Volkswagen. The prototypes had a rear, air-cooled engine, torsion-bar suspension, and the spare tire mounted at an angle in the front luggage compartment. In 1936, Porsche produced three Volkswagen prototypes, one of which was a 995 cc, horizontally opposed, four-cylinder automobile. In 1945 Volkswagen production began and 1,785 beetles were built. The Volkswagen convertible was introduced in 1949, the year when only two Volkswagens were sold in the entire U.S.A. The year 1950 marked the beginning of the sunroof models and the transporter series. The Volkswagen Karmann Ghia was introduced in 1956, and is still of the same basic styling format. The "big" Volkswagen, the 1500 Squareback, was introduced in Europe in 1961, and sold in the U.S.A. in 1966 as a member of the new type 3 series (Fastback and Squareback). The Type 4 was introduced to the U.S.A. with the 1971 model line.

Vehicle and Engine Serial Number Identification

Volkswagen Types

Volkswagen models are differentiated by type. Type 1 is the beetle and Karmann Ghia. Type 2 is the transporter, or bus and truck, series. Type 3 is the Fastback and Squareback. Type 4 is the 411 sedan and wagon. The current model numbers are as follow:

Model No. (LHD)	*Description*
111	VW 1300A sedan, 1971 1600 sedan
115	VW 1300A sedan with folding sunroof
113	VW 1500 sedan, 1971 1600 Super Beetle
117	VW 1500 sedan with steel sunroof
141	VW 1500 Karmann Ghia Convertible
143	VW 1500 Karmann Ghia Coupe
151	VW 1500 Convertible (4 seater)
211–215	Delivery Van
221–225	Micro Bus
231–237	Kombi
241	Deluxe Micro Bus (9 seater)
251	Deluxe Micro Bus (7 seater)
261–267	Pickup
271–273	Ambulance
281–285	Micro Bus (7 seater)
311	Fastback sedan (1600TL)
313	Fastback sedan with steel sunroof
315	1600A sedan
317	1600A sedan with steel sunroof
343	1600L Karmann Ghia Coupe
345	1600L Karmann Ghia Coupe with steel sunroof
361	1600L Squareback sedan
363	1600L Squareback sedan with steel sunroof
365	1600A Squareback sedan
367	1600A Squareback sedan with steel sunroof
411	411 Four door sedan
411	411 Three door sedan (wagon)

BASIC BODY TYPES

411 4-Door Sedan, Type 4

411 3-Door Sedan, Type 4

Micro Bus, Type 2

Sedan (Beetle), Type 1

Convertible, Type 1

Fastback sedan, Type 3

Karmann Ghia, Type 1

Squareback Sedan, Type 3

Chassis Number

The chassis number is on the frame tunnel under the back seat in the Types 1 and 3. In the Type 2, the chassis number is on the right engine cover plate in the engine compartment.

Beginning with the 1965 model year, a nine-digit serial number system was instituted. In this system, the first two numbers are the first two digits of the car's model number and the third digit stands for the car's model year—"5" stands for 1965, "8" stands for 1968, etc. A tenth digit was added when production passed one million.

Identification Plate

The identification plate carries the vehicle serial number and paint, body, and assembly codes. It is behind the spare tire in the luggage compartment on Type 1 models, and on the right side of the overhead air duct in early Type 2 vehicles. The Type 3 identification plate is next to the hood latch, in front of the spare tire in the luggage compartment. Starting 1970, all models have an identification plate on top of the driver's side of the instrument panel. This plate may be seen through the windshield.

Engine Number

On type 1 and 2 vehicles, which have the upright engine fan housing, the engine number is on the crankcase flange for the generator support. The number can readily be seen by looking through the center of the fan belt. On type 3 and 4 engines, which have the fan on the end of the crankshaft, the number is along the crankcase joint between the oil cooler and the air cleaner. The engine can be identified by the letter preceding the serial number. Refer to the Engine Identification Chart.

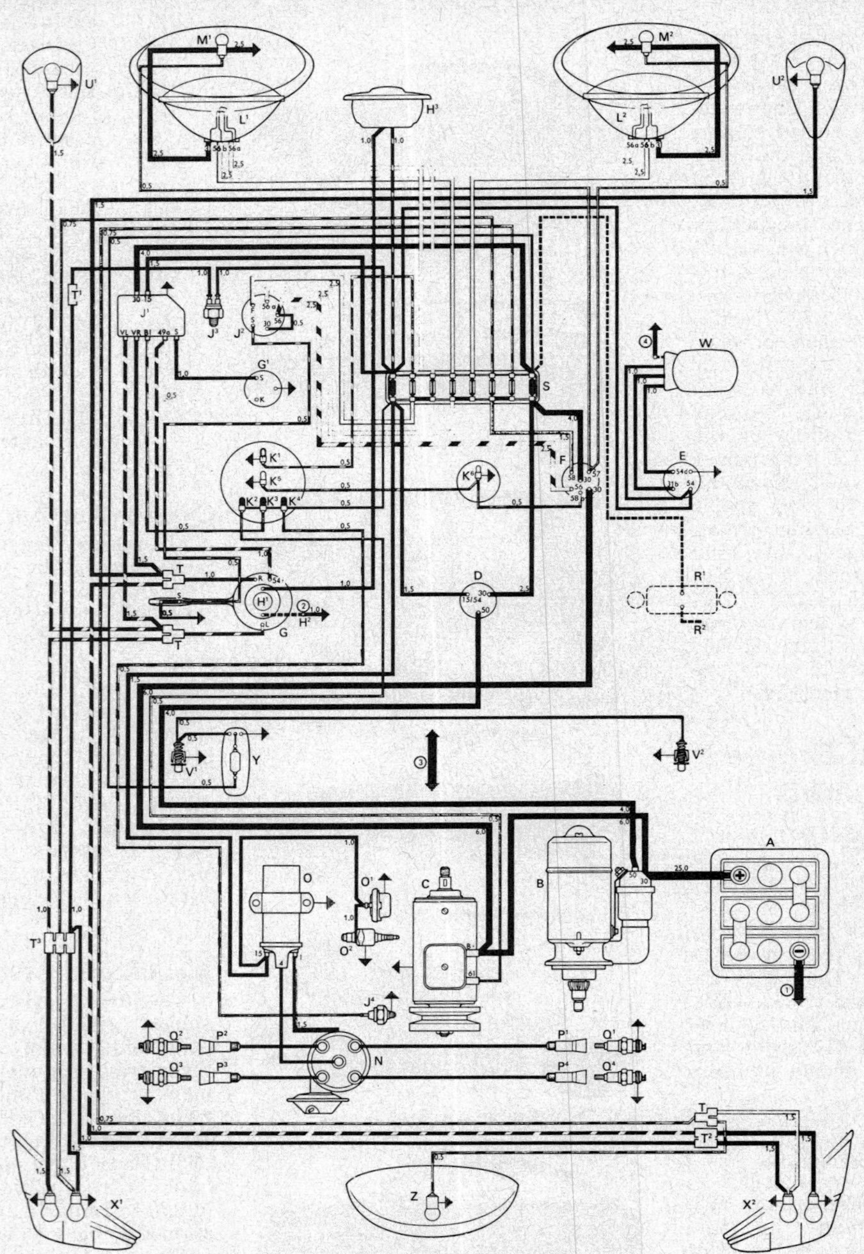

Wiring diagram, VW 1300 (from August, 1965). © Volkswagen

- A Battery
- B Starter
- C Generator
- D Ignition/starter switch
- E Windshield wiper switch
- F Lighting switch
- G Turn signal switch with dimmer switch
- G^1 Emergency light switch
- H^1 Horn half ring
- H^2 Steering column connection
- H^3 Horn
- J^1 Flasher and emergency light relay
- J^2 Dimming relay
- J^3 Brake light switch
- J^4 Oil pressure switch
- K^1 High beam warning light
- K^2 Generator warning light
- K^3 Turn signal warning light
- K^4 Oil pressure warning light
- K^5 Speedometer light
- K^6 Fuel gauge light
- L^1 Sealed-beam unit, left
- L^2 Sealed-beam unit, right
- M^1 Parking light, left
- M^2 Parking light, right
- N Distributor
- O Ignition coil
- O^1 Automatic choke
- O^2 Electromagnetic pilot jet
- P^1 Spark plug connector, No. 1 cylinder
- P^2 Spark plug connector, No. 2 cylinder
- P^3 Spark plug connector, No. 3 cylinder
- P^4 Spark plug connector, No. 4 cylinder
- Q^1 Spark plug for No. 1 cylinder
- Q^2 Spark plug for No. 2 cylinder
- Q^3 Spark plug for No. 3 cylinder
- Q^4 Spark plug for No. 4 cylinder
- R^1 Radio
- R^2 Aerial connection
- S Fuse box
  white fuses: 8 Ampere
  red fuses: 16 Ampere
- T Cable adaptor
- T^1 Cable connector, single
- T^2 Cable connector, double
- T^3 Cable connector, triple
- U^1 Turn signal, left
- U^2 Turn signal, right
- V^1 Door switch, left
- V^2 Door switch, right
- W Windshield wiper motor
- X^1 Brake, turn signal and tail lights, left
- X^2 Brake, turn signal and tail lights, right
- Y Interior light
- Z License plate light
- ① Battery to frame ground strap
- ② Horn ring to steering coupling ground connection
- ③ Transmission to frame ground strap
- ④ Wiper motor to body ground strap

Black dotted line = Service installation

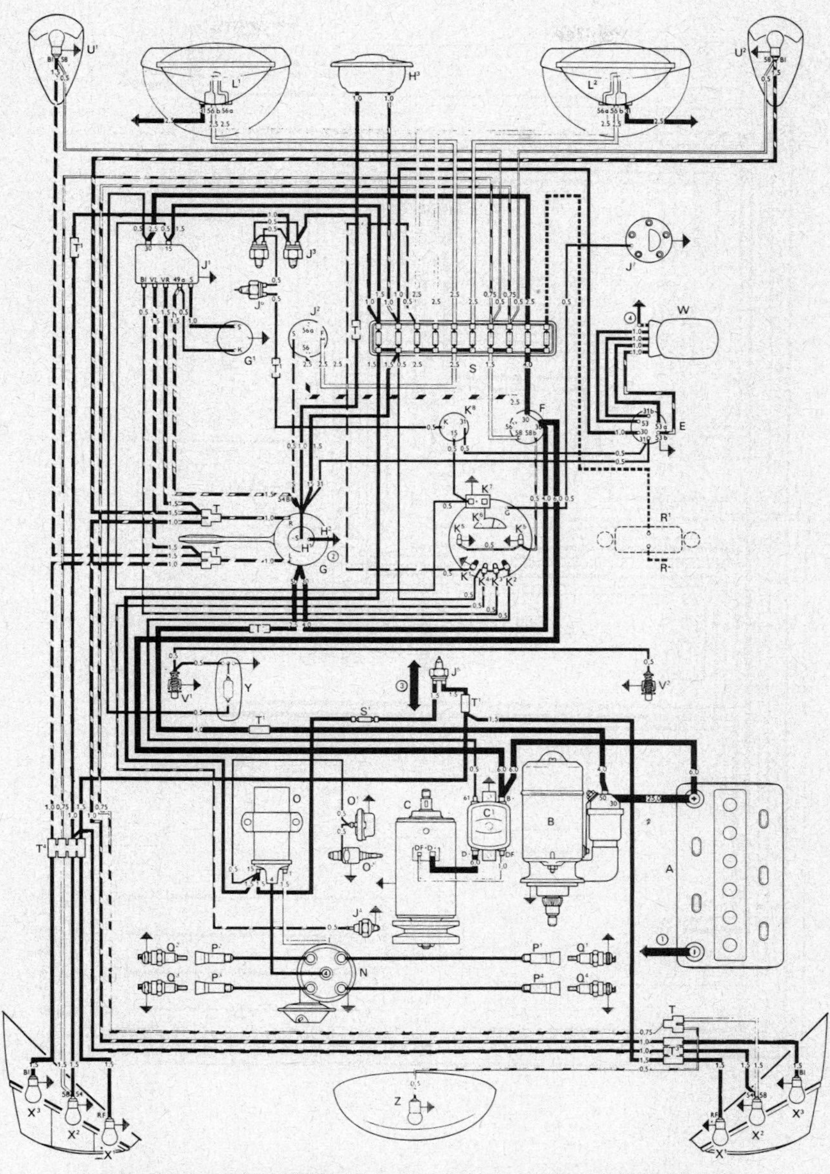

Wiring diagram, VW 1500 sedan and convertible (1968). © Volkswagen

A	Battery
B	Starter
C	Generator
C¹	Regulator
E	Windshield wiper switch
F	Lighting switch
G	Turn signal switch with automatic canceling, hand dimmer button and ignition/starter switch
G¹	Emergency light switch
H¹	Horn half ring
H²	Steering column connection
H³	Horn
J¹	Turning signal and emergency light relay
J²	Dimmer relay
J³	Brake light switch (2 X)
J⁴	Oil pressure switch
J⁵	Back-up light switch
J⁶	Warning switch for brake system
J⁷	Fuel gauge sender unit
K¹	High beam warning light
K²	Generator warning light
K³	Turn signal warning light
K⁴	Oil pressure warning light
K⁵	Speedometer light
K⁶	Fuel gauge light
K⁷	Resistance for fuel gauge
K⁸	Brake warning lamp with test button
L¹	Sealed-beam insert, left
L²	Sealed-beam insert, right
N	Distributor
O	Ignition coil
O¹	Automatic choke
O²	Electromagnetic pilot jet
P¹	Spark plug connector, No. 1 cylinder
P²	Spark plug connector, No. 2 cylinder
P³	Spark plug connector, No. 3 cylinder
P⁴	Spark plug connector, No. 4 cylinder
Q¹	Spark plug for No. 1 cylinder
Q²	Spark plug for No. 2 cylinder
Q³	Spark plug for No. 3 cylinder
Q⁴	Spark plug for No. 4 cylinder
R¹	Radio
R²	Aerial connection
S	Fuse box
T	Cable adapter
T¹	Cable connector, single
T²	Cable connector for horn under front luggage compartment lining
T³	Cable connector, triple
U¹	Front turn signal and parking light, left
U²	Front turn signal and parking light, right
V¹	Door contact switch, left
V²	Door contact switch, right
W	Windshield wiper motor
X¹	Back-up lights
X²	Brake and tail lights
X³	Turn signal lights
Y	Interior light
Z	License plate light
①	Battery to frame ground strap
②	Horn ring to steering coupling ground connection
③	Transmission to frame ground strap
④	Wiper motor to body ground strap

Black dotted line = Optional extras or service installation.

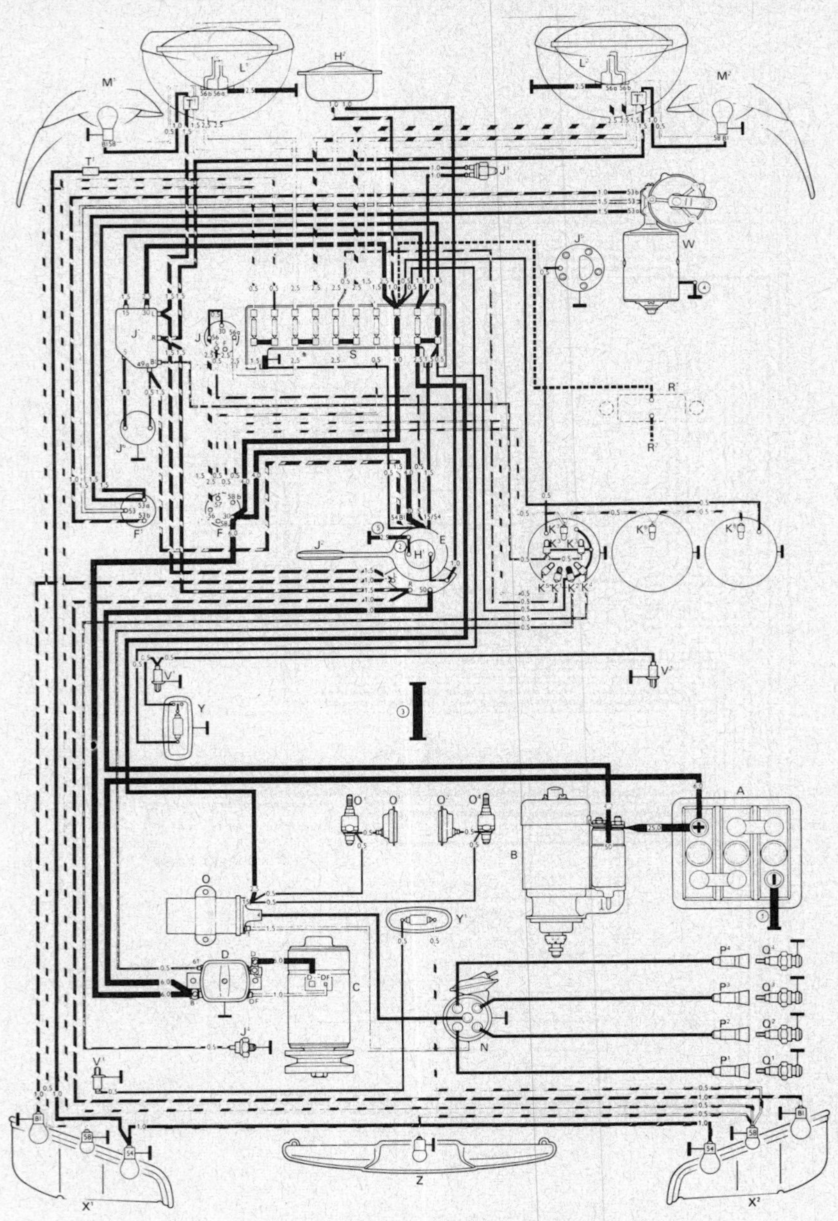

Wiring diagram, VW 1600 (from August, 1965). © Volkswagen

- A Battery
- B Starter
- C Generator
- D Regulator
- E Turn signal switch with ignition starter lock
- F Lighting switch
- F^1 Windshield wiper switch
- H^1 Horn half ring
- H^2 Horn
- J Hand dimmer relay
- J^1 Flasher and emergency light relay
- J^2 Headlamp flasher button
- J^3 Brake light switch
- J^4 Oil pressure switch
- J^5 Fuel gauge sender unit
- J^6 Emergency light switch
- K^1 High beam warning light
- K^2 Generator warning light
- K^3 Turn signal warning light
- K^4 Oil pressure warning light
- K^5 Parking light warning light
- K^6 Speedometer light
- K^7 Fuel gauge light
- K^8 Clock light
- L^1 Headlamp, left
- L^2 Headlamp, right
- M^1 Parking light and turn signal light, left
- M^2 Parking light and turn signal light, right
- N Distributor
- O Ignition coil
- O^1 Automatic choke, left
- O^2 Automatic choke, right
- O^3 Electromagnetic pilot jet, left
- O^4 Electromagnetic pilot jet, right
- P^1 Spark plug connector, No. 1 cylinder
- P^2 Spark plug connector, No. 2 cylinder
- P^3 Spark plug connector, No. 3 cylinder
- P^4 Spark plug connector, No. 4 cylinder
- Q^1 Spark plug for No. 1 cylinder
- Q^2 Spark plug for No. 2 cylinder
- Q^3 Spark plug for No. 3 cylinder
- Q^4 Spark plug for No. 4 cylinder
- R^1 Radio
- R^2 Aerial connection
- S Fuse box—10 fuses
- T^1 Cable connector, single
- T^2 Cable connector, double
- V^1 Door switch, left
- V^2 Door switch, right
- V^3 Luggage compartment light switch
- W Windshield wiper motor
- X^1 Tail light, left
- X^2 Tail light, right
- Y Interior light
- Y^1 Luggage compartment light
- Z License plate light
- ① Battery to frame ground strap
- ② Horn half ring steering coupling ground connection
- ③ Transmission to frame ground connection
- ④ Windshield wiper motor to body ground strap
- ⑤ Front axle to frame ground strap

Black dotted lines = Service installation
1.5; 0.5 etc.: Cable cross section

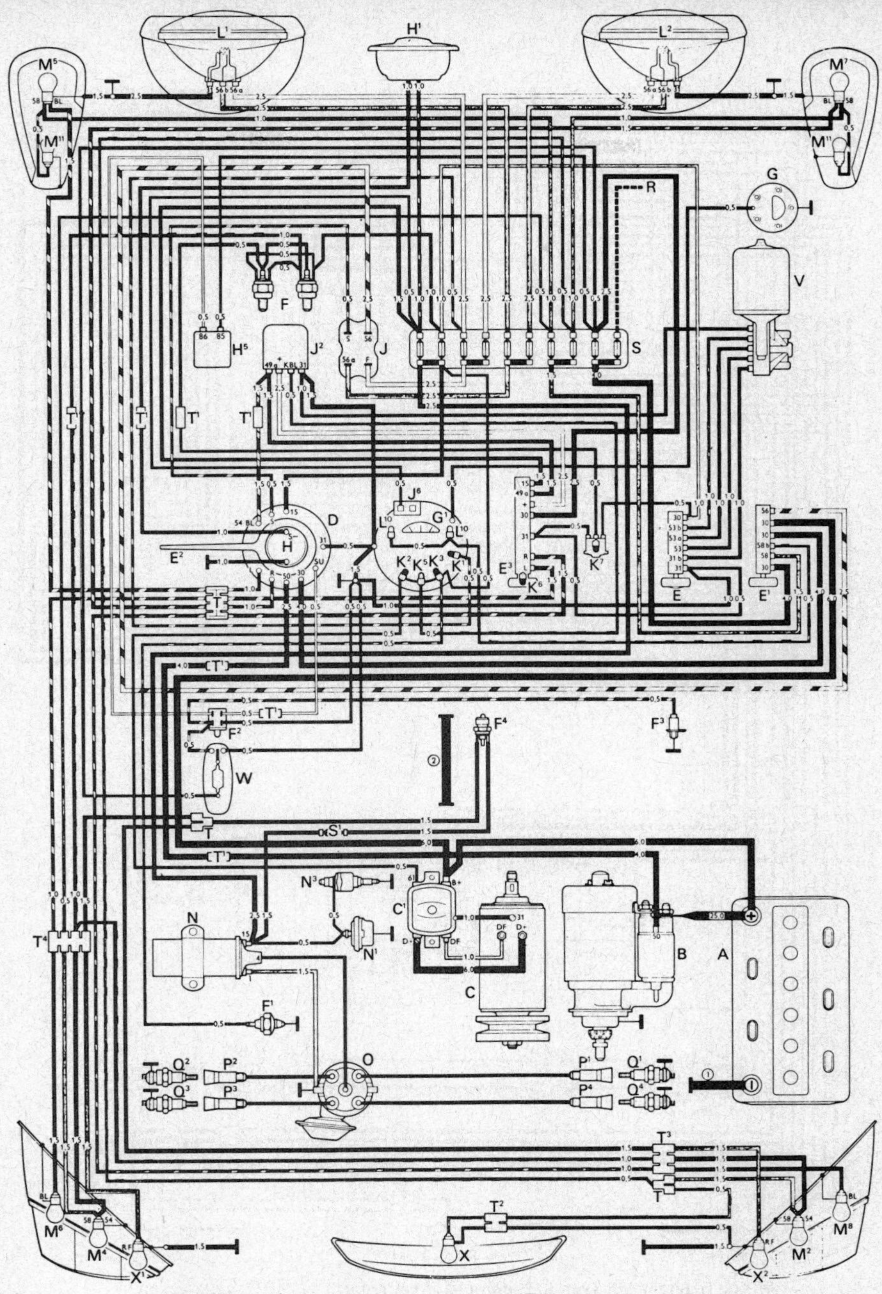

Wiring diagram, VW Type 1 (from August 1969). © Volkswagen

A Battery
B Starter
C Generator
C^1 Regulator
D Ignition/starter switch
E Windshield wiper switch
E^1 Light switch
E^2 Turn signal and headlight dimmer switch
E^3 Emergency flasher switch
F Brake light switch with warning switch
F^1 Oil pressure switch
F^2 Door contact switch, left, with contact for buzzer H 5
F^3 Door contact switch, right
F^4 Back-up light switch
G Fuel gauge sending unit
G^1 Fuel gauge
H Horn button
H^1 Horn
H^5 Ignition key warning buzzer
J Dimmer relay
J^2 Emergency flasher relay
J^6 Vibrator for fuel gauge
K^1 High beam warning light
K^2 Generator charging warning light
K^3 Oil pressure warning light
K^5 Turn signal warning light
K^6 Emergency flasher warning light
K^7 Dual circuit brake system warning light
L^1 Sealed beam unit, left headlight
L^2 Sealed beam unit, right headlight
L^{10} Instrument panel light
M^2 Tail and brake light, right
M^4 Tail and brake light, left
M^5 Turn signal and parking light, front, left
M^6 Turn signal, rear, left
M^7 Turn signal and parking light, front, right
M^8 Turn signal, rear, right
M^{11} Side marker light, front
N Ignition coil
N^1 Automatic choke
N^3 Electro-magnetic pilot jet
O Ignition distributor
P^1 Spark plug connector, No. 1 cylinder
P^2 Spark plug connector, No. 2 cylinder
P^3 Spark plug connector, No. 3 cylinder
P^4 Spark plug connector, No. 4 cylinder
Q^1 Spark plug, No. 1 cylinder
Q^2 Spark plug, No. 2 cylinder
Q^3 Spark plug, No. 3 cylinder
Q^4 Spark plug, No. 4 cylinder
R Radio connection
S Fuse box
S^1 Back-up light fuse
T Cable adapter
T^1 Cable connector, single
T^2 Cable connector, double
T^3 Cable connector, triple
T^4 Cable connector (four connections)
V Windshield wiper motor
W Interior light
X License plate light
X^1 Back-up light, left
X^2 Back-up light, right
① Battery to frame ground strap
② Transmission to frame ground strap

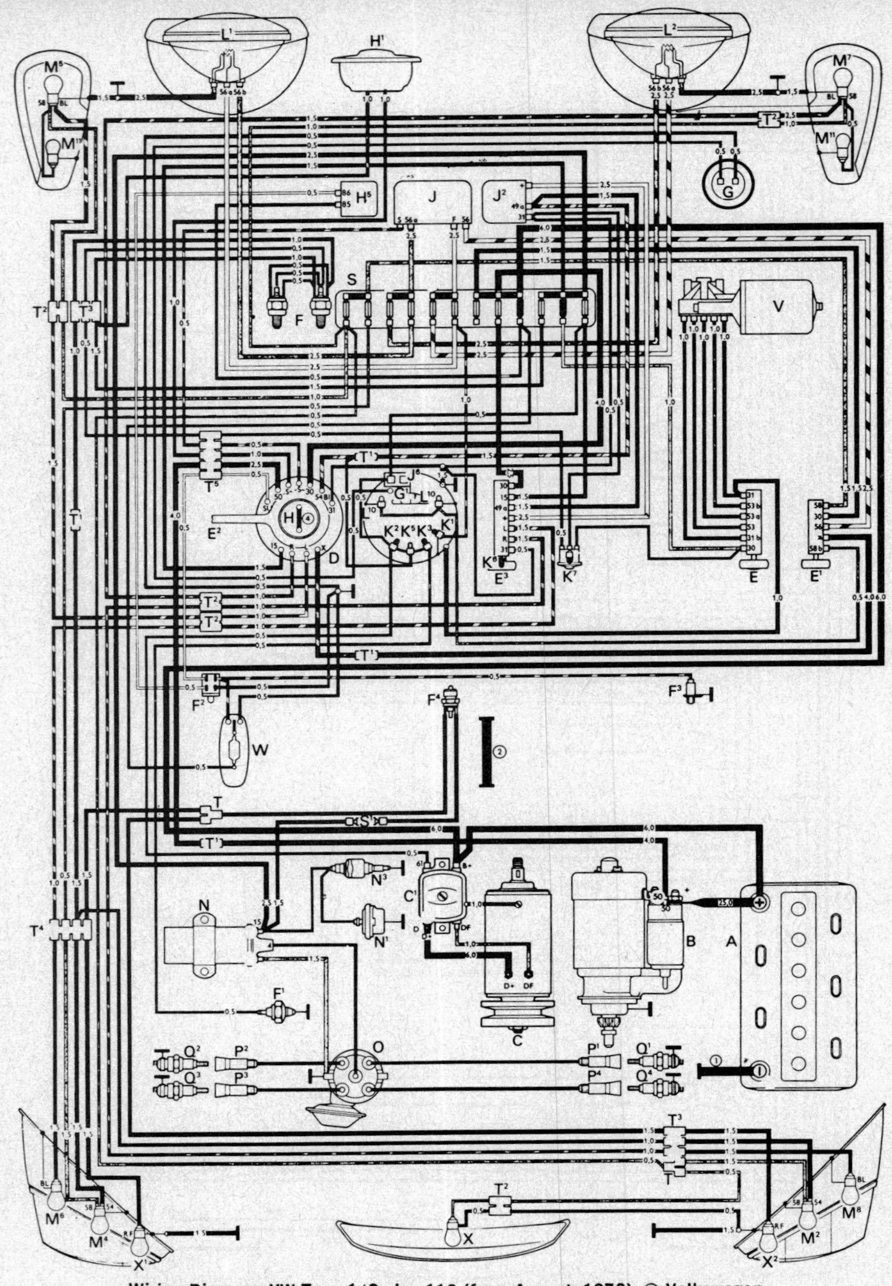

Wiring Diagram, VW Type 1/Sedan 113 (from August, 1970). © Volkswagen

A Battery
B Starter
C Generator
C^1 Regulator
D Ignition/starter switch
E Windshield wiper switch
E^1 Light switch
E^2 Turn signal and headlight dimmer switch
E^3 Emergency flasher switch
F Brake light switch
F^1 Oil pressure switch
F^2 Door contact and buzzer alarm switch, left
F^3 Door contact switch, right
F^4 Back-up light switch
G Fuel gauge sending unit
G^1 Fuel gauge
H Horn button
H^1 Horn
H^5 Ignition key warning buzzer
J Dimmer relay
J^2 Emergency flasher relay
J^6 Fuel gauge vibrator
K^1 High beam warning light
K^2 Generator charging warning light
K^3 Oil pressure warning light
K^5 Turn signal warning light
K^6 Emergency flasher warning light
K^7 Dual circuit brake warning light
L^1 Sealed-Beam unit, left headlight
L^2 Sealed-Beam unit, right headlight
L^{10} Instrument panel light
M^1 Parking light, left
M^2 Tail/brake light, right
M^4 Tail/brake light, left
M^5 Turn signal and parking light front left
M^6 Turn signal, rear, left
M^7 Turn signal and parking light front right
M^8 Turn signal, rear, right
M^{11} Side marker light, front
N Ignition coil
N^1 Automatic choke
N^3 Electromagnetic pilot jet
O Distributor
P^1 Spark plug connector, No. 1 cylinder
P^2 Spark plug connector, No. 2 cylinder
P^3 Spark plug connector, No. 3 cylinder
P^4 Spark plug connector, No. 4 cylinder
Q^1 Spark plug, No. 1 cylinder
Q^2 Spark plug, No. 2 cylinder
Q^3 Sparg plug, No. 3 cylinder
Q^4 Spark plug, No. 4 cylinder
S Fuse box
S^1 Back-up light in-line fuse
T Cable adapter
T^1 Cable connector, single
T^2 Cable connector, double
T^3 Cable connector, triple
T^4 Cable connector (four connections)
T^5 Cable connector (five connections)
V Windshield wiper motor
W Interior light
X License plate light
X^1 Back-up light, left
X^2 Back-up light, right
① Ground strap from battery to frame
② Ground strap from transmission to frame
④ Ground cable from front axle to frame

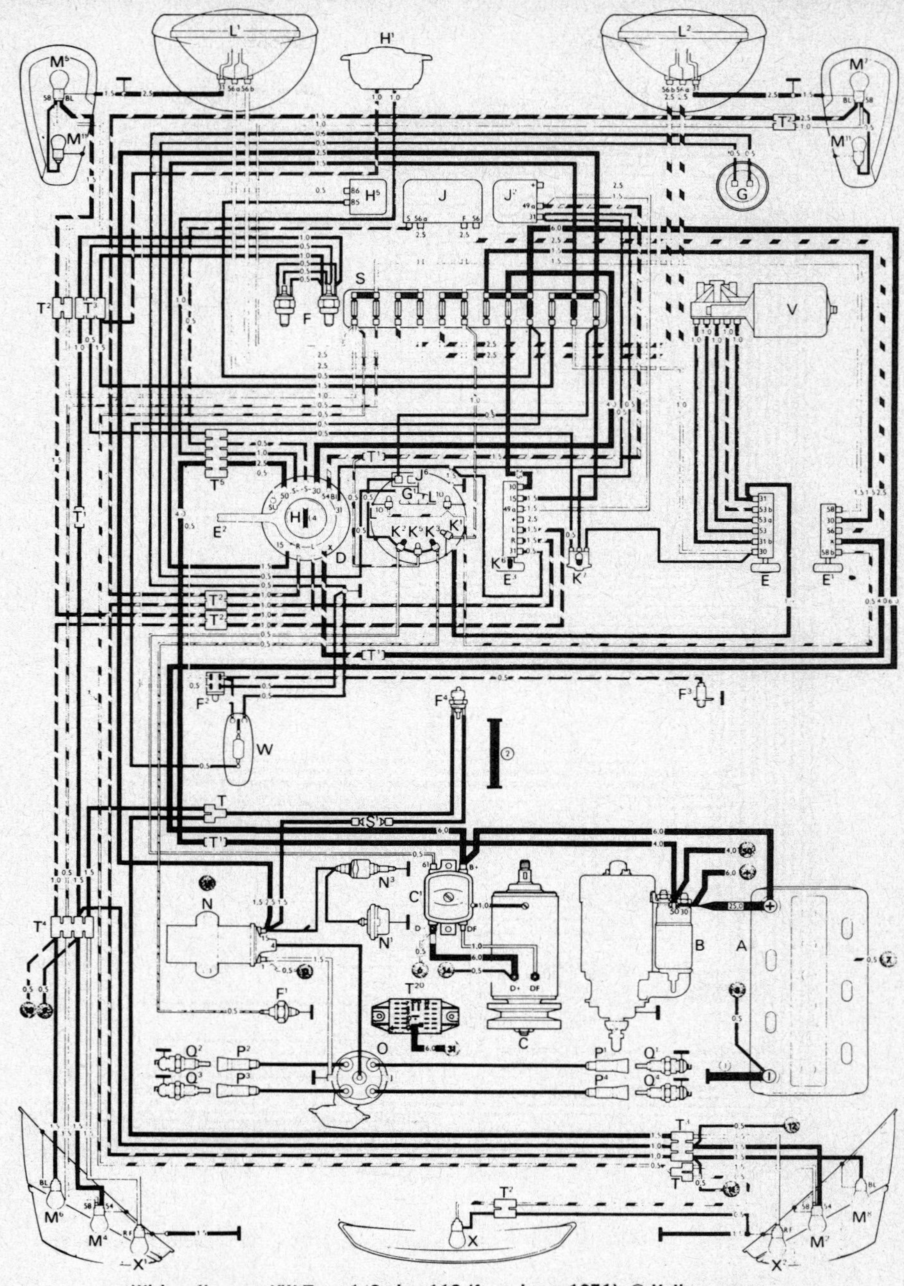

Wiring diagram, VW Type 1/Sedan 113 (from June, 1971). © Volkswagen

A Battery
B Starter
C Generator
C^1 Regulator
D Ignition/starter switch
E Windshield wiper switch
E^1 Light switch
E^2 Turn signal and headlight dimmer switch
E^3 Emergency flasher switch
F Brake light switch
F^1 Oil pressure switch
F^2 Door contact and buzzer alarm switch, left
F^3 Door contact switch, right
F^4 Back-up light switch
G Fuel gauge sending unit
G^1 Fuel gauge
H Horn button
H^1 Horn
H^5 Ignition key warning buzzer
J Dimmer relay
J^2 Emergency flasher relay
J^6 Fuel gauge vibrator
K^1 High beam warning light
K^2 Generator charging warning light
K^3 Oil pressure warning light
K^5 Turn signal warning light
K^6 Emergency flasher warning light
K^7 Dual circuit brake warning light
L^1 Sealed-Beam unit, left headlight
L^2 Sealed-Beam unit, right headlight
L^{10} Instrument panel light
M^1 Parking light, left
M^2 Tail/brake light, right
M^4 Tail/brake light, left
M^5 Turn signal and parking light front left
M^6 Turn signal, rear, left
M^7 Turn signal and parking light front right
M^8 Turn signal, rear, right
M^{11} Side marker, light, front
N Ignition coil
N^1 Automatic choke
N^3 Electromagnetic pilot jet
O Distributor
P^1 Spark plug connector, No. 1 cylinder
P^2 Spark plug connector, No. 2 cylinder
P^3 Spark plug connector, No. 3 cylinder
P^4 Spark plug connector, No. 4 cylinder
Q^1 Spark plug, No. 1 cylinder
Q^2 Spark plug, No. 2 cylinder
Q^3 Spark plug, No. 3 cylinder
Q^4 Spark plug, No. 4 cylinder
S Fuse box
S^1 Back-up light in-line fuse
T Cable adapter
T^1 Cable connector, single
T^2 Cable connector, double
T^3 Cable connector, triple
T^4 Cable connector (four connections)
T^5 Cable connector (five connections)
T^{20} Test network, central plug
V Windshield wiper motor
W Interior light
X License plate light
X^1 Back-up light, left
X^2 Back-up light, right
① Ground strap from battery to frame
② Ground strap from transmission to frame
④ Ground cable from front axle to frame

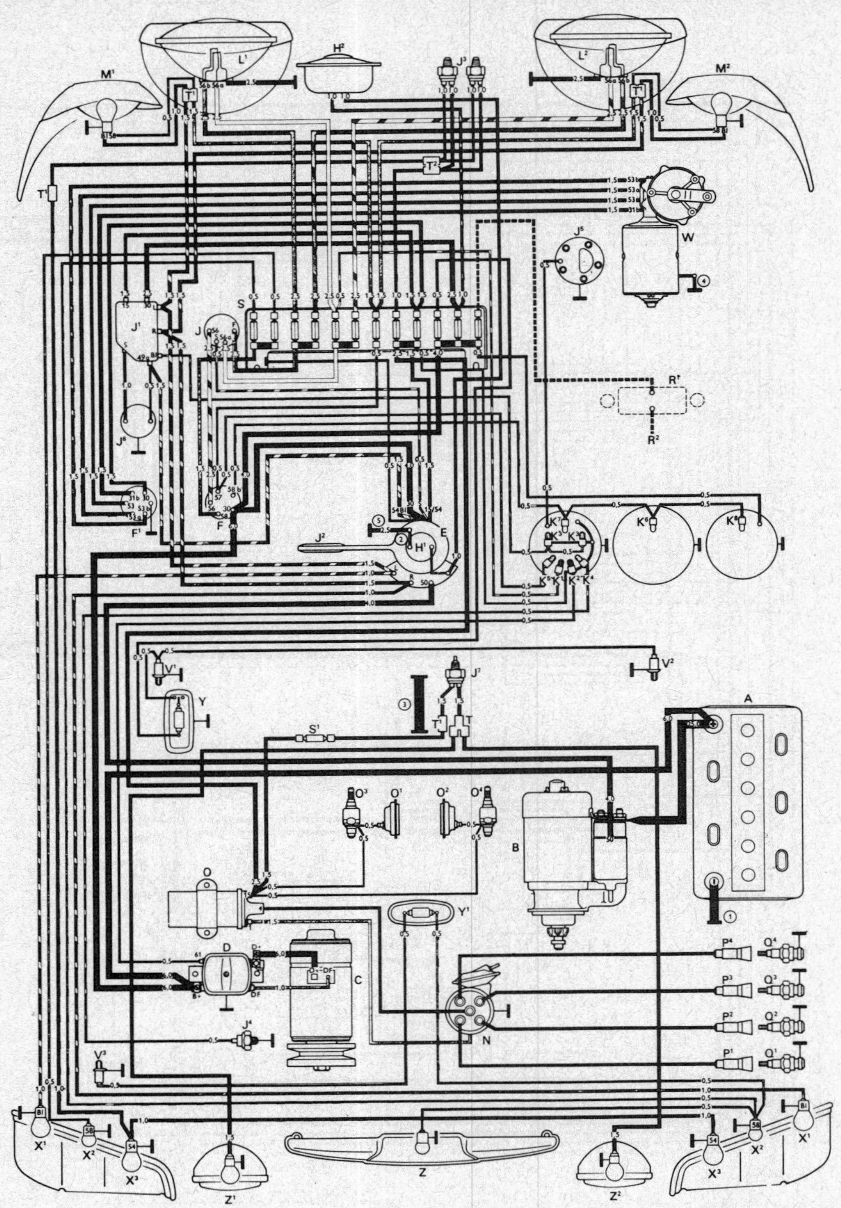

Wiring diagram, VW Type 3, 1600 (from August, 1966)—US version. © Volkswagen

A Battery
B Starter
C Generator
D Regulator
E Turn signal switch with ignition/starter lock
F Light switch
F^1 Windshield wiper switch
H^1 Horn half ring
H^2 Horn
J Hand dimmer relay
J^1 Turn signal/emergency flasher
J^2 Hand dimmer switch
J^3 Brake light switch
J^4 Oil pressure switch
J^5 Fuel gauge sender unit
J^6 Emergency flasher switch
J^7 Back-up light switch
K^1 High beam warning light
K^2 Generator charging warning light
K^3 Turn signal warning lights
K^4 Oil pressure warning light
K^5 Parking light warning light
K^6 Speedometer light
K^7 Fuel gauge light
K^8 Clock light
L^1 Sealed beam unit, left
L^2 Sealed beam unit, right
M^1 Parking light and turn signal light, left
M^2 Parking light and turn signal light, right
N Distributor
O Ignition coil
O^1 Automatic choke, left
O^2 Automatic choke, right
O^3 Electromagnetic pilot, jet, left
O^4 Electromagnetic pilot jet, right
P^1 Spark plug connector, No. 1 cylinder
P^2 Spark plug connector, No. 2 cylinder
P^3 Spark plug connector, No. 3 cylinder
P^4 Spark plug connector, No. 4 cylinder
Q^1 Spark plug, No. 1 cylinder
Q^2 Spark plug, No. 2 cylinder
Q^3 Spark plug, No. 3 cylinder
Q^4 Spark plug, No. 4 cylinder
R Radio
R^2 Aerial connection
S Fuse box
S^1 Back-up light fuse
T^1 Cable connector, single
T^2 Cable connector, double
V^1 Door contact switch, left
V^2 Door contact switch, right
V^3 Luggage compartment light switch
W Windshield wiper motor
X^1 Turn signal lights
X^2 Tail lights
X^3 Brake lights
Y Interior light
Y^1 Luggage compartment light
Z License plate light
Z^1 Back-up light, left
Z^2 Back-up light, right
① Battery to frame ground strap
② Horn half ring to steering coupling ground cable
③ Transmission to frame ground strap
④ Windshield wiper motor to body ground strap
⑤ Front axle to frame ground cable

Black dotted lines = optional extras
1.5; 0.5 etc.: cable cross section

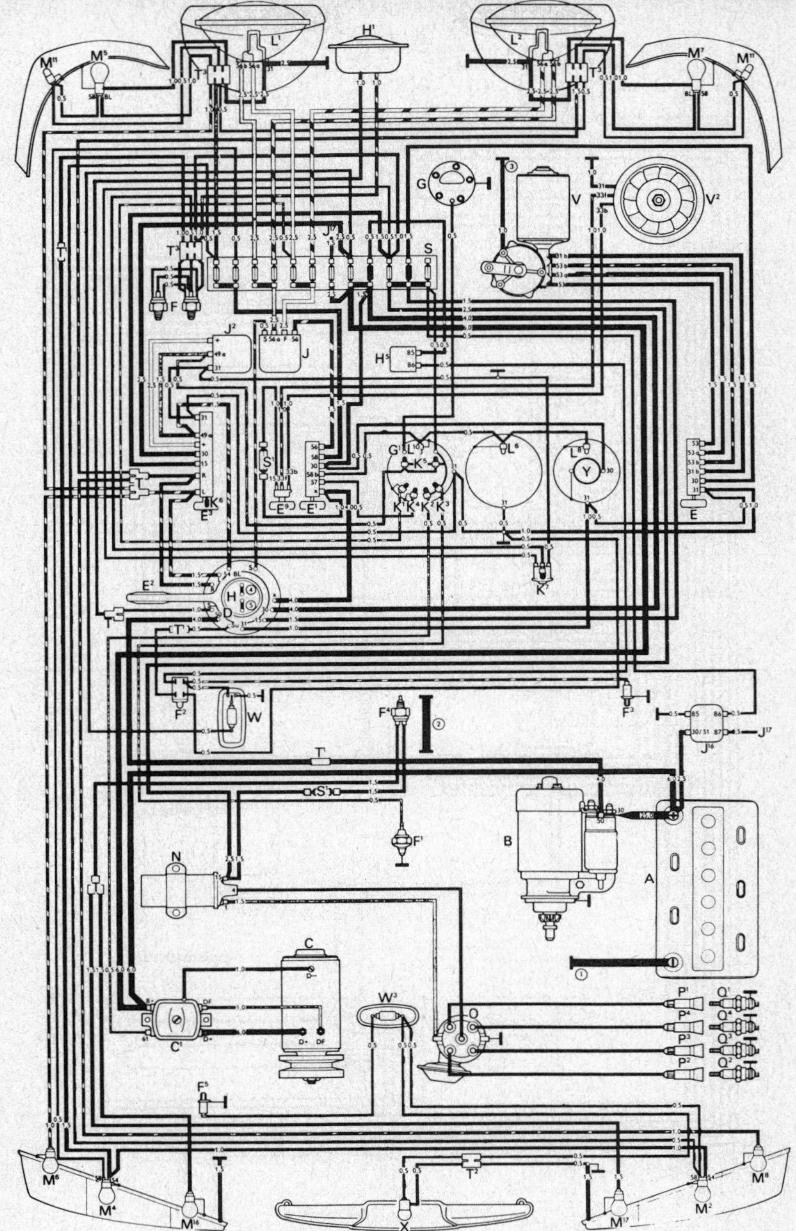

Wiring diagram, VW Type 3 (from August, 1970). © Volkswagen

A	Battery
B	Starter
C	Generator
C¹	Regulator
D	Ignition/starter switch
E	Windshield wiper switch
E¹	Light switch
E²	Turn signal and headlight dimmer switch
E³	Emergency flasher switch
E⁹	Fresh air fan motor switch
F	Brake light switch
F¹	Oil pressure switch
F²	Door contact and buzzer alarm switch, left
F³	Door contact switch, right
F⁴	Back-up light switch
F⁵	Luggage compartment light switch
G	Fuel tank sending unit
G¹	Fuel gauge
H	Horn button
H¹	Horn
H⁵	Ignition key warning buzzer
J	Dimmer relay
J²	Emergency flasher relay
J¹⁶	Power supply relay for fuel injection
J¹⁷	Connection to fuel pump relay
K¹	High beam warning light
K²	Generator charging warning light
K³	Oil pressure warning light
K⁴	Parking light warning light
K⁵	Turn signal warning light
K⁶	Emergency flasher warning light
K⁷	Dual brake circuit warning light
L¹	Sealed-Beam unit left headlight
L²	Sealed-Beam unit right headlight
L⁶	Speedometer light
L⁸	Clock light
L¹⁰	Instrument panel light
M²	Tail/brake light, right
M⁴	Tail/brake light, left
M⁵	Turn signal and parking light/front, left
M⁶	Turn signal, rear, left
M⁷	Turn signal and parking light, front, right
M⁸	Turn signal, rear, right
M¹¹	Side marker light, front
M¹⁶	Back-up light, left
M¹⁷	Back-up light, right
N	Ignition coil
O	Distributor
P¹	Spark plug connector, No. 1 cylinder
P²	Spark plug connector, No. 2 cylinder
P³	Spark plug connector, No. 3 cylinder
P⁴	Spark plug connector, No. 4 cylinder
Q¹	Spark plug, No. 1 cylinder
Q²	Spark plug, No. 2 cylinder
Q³	Spark plug, No. 3 cylinder
Q⁴	Spark plug, No. 4 cylinder
S	Fuse box
S¹	In-line fuse for back-up lights and fresh air fan motor
T	Cable adapter
T¹	Cable connector, single
T²	Cable connector, double
T³	Cable connector, triple
V	Windshield wiper motor
V²	Fresh air motor front
W	Interior light
W³	Luggage compartment light
X	License plate light
Y	Clock
①	Ground strap from battery to frame
②	Ground strap from transmission to frame
④	Ground cable from horn to steering coupling
⑤	Ground cable from front axle to frame

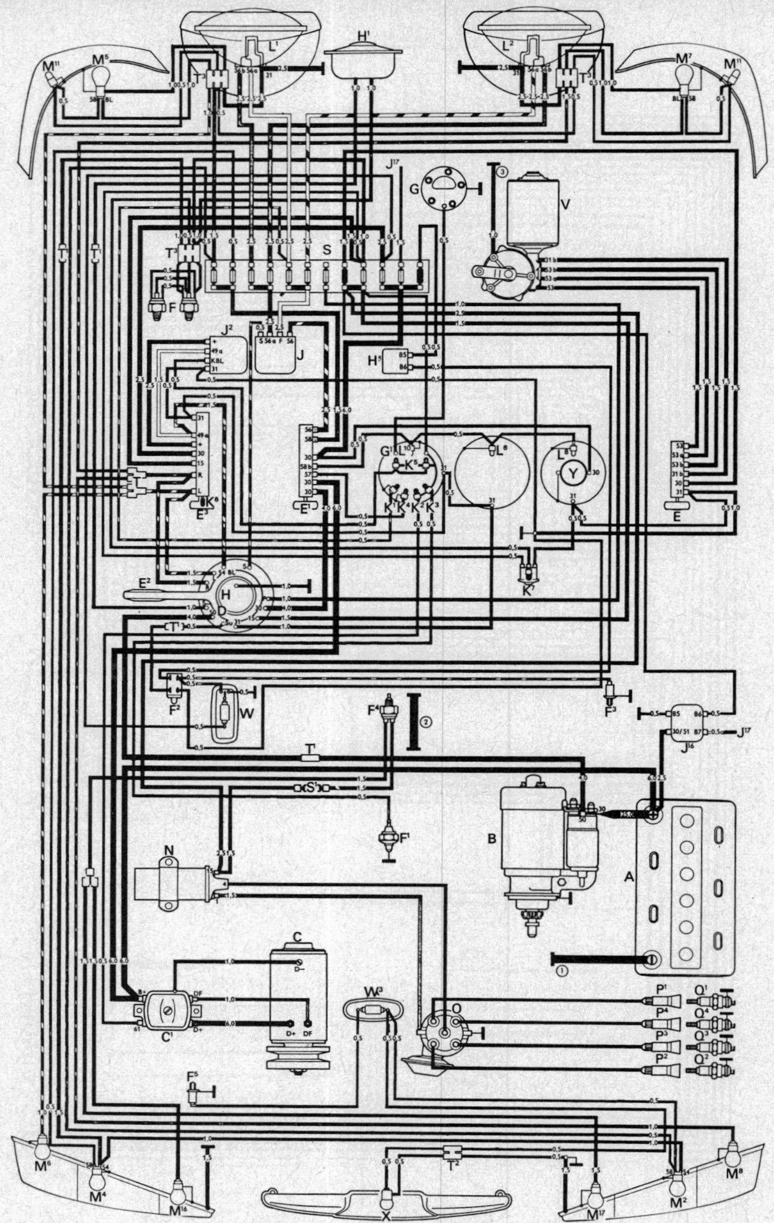

Wiring diagram, VW Type 3 (from August, 1969). © Volkswagen

A	Battery
B	Starter
C	Generator
C^1	Regulator
D	Ignition/starter switch
E	Windshield wiper switch
E^1	Light switch
E^2	Turn signal and head light dimmer switch
E^3	Emergency flasher switch
F	Brake light switch
F^1	Oil pressure switch
F^2	Door contact switch, left, with contact for buzzer
F^3	Door contact switch, right
F^4	Back-up light switch
F^5	Luggage compartment light switch
G	Fuel gauge sending unit
G^1	Fuel gauge
H	Horn button
H^1	Horn
H^5	Ignition key warning buzzer
J	Dimmer relay
J^2	Emergency flasher relay
J^{16}	Power supply relay for fuel injection system
J^{17}	To fuel pump relay
K^1	High beam warning light
K^2	Generator charging warning light
K^3	Oil pressure warning light
K^4	Parking light warning light
K^5	Turn signal warning lights
K^6	Hazard warning light
K^7	Dual circuit brake system warning light
L^1	Sealed beam unit, left
L^2	Sealed beam unit, right
L^6	Speedometer light
L^8	Clock light
L^{10}	Instrument panel light
M^2	Tail and brake light, right
M^4	Tail and brake light, left
M^5	Turn signal and parking light, front, left
M^6	Turn signal and parking light, front, right
M^7	Turn signal, rear, left
M^8	Turn signal, rear, right
M^{11}	Side marker light, front
M^{16}	Back-up light, left
M^{17}	Back-up light, right
N	Ignition coil
O	Distributor
P^1	Spark plug connector, No. 1 cylinder
P^2	Spark plug connector, No. 2 cylinder
P^3	Spark plug connector, No. 3 cylinder
P^4	Spark plug connector, No. 4 cylinder
Q^1	Spark plug, No. 1 cylinder
Q^2	Spark plug, No. 2 cylinder
Q^3	Spark plug, No. 3 cylinder
Q^4	Spark plug, No. 4 cylinder
S	Fuse box
S^1	Back-up light in-line fuse
T	Cable adapter
T^1	Cable connector, single
T^2	Cable connector, double
T^3	Cable connector, triple
V	Windshield wiper motor
W	Interior light
W^3	Luggage compartment light
X	License plate light
①	Battery to frame ground strap
②	Transmission to frame ground strap
③	Windshield wiper motor to body ground strap

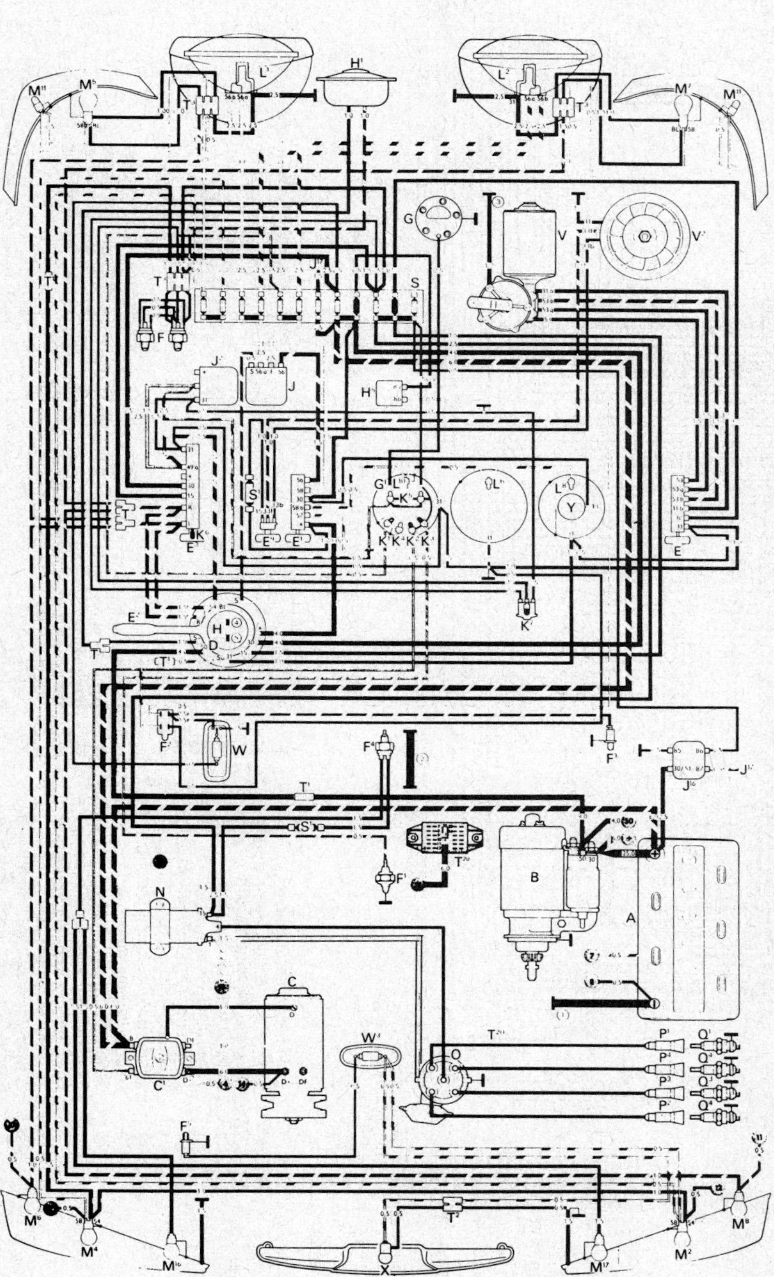

Wiring diagram, VW Type 3 (from May 1971). © Volkswagen

- A Battery
- B Starter
- C Generator
- C^1 Regulator
- D Ignition/starter switch
- E Windshield wiper switch
- E^1 Light switch
- E^2 Turn signal and headlight dimmer switch
- E^3 Emergency flasher switch
- E^9 Fresh air fan motor switch
- F Brake light switch
- F^1 Oil pressure switch
- F^2 Door contact and buzzzer alarm switch, left
- F^3 Door contact switch, right
- F^4 Back-up light switch
- F^5 Luggage compartment light switch
- G Fuel gauge sending unit
- G^1 Fuel gauge
- H Horn button
- H^1 Horn
- H^5 Ignition key warning buzzer
- J Dimmer relay
- J^2 Emergency flasher relay
- J^{16} Power supply relay for fuel injection
- J^{17} Connection to fuel pump relay
- K^1 High beam warning light
- K^2 Generator charging warning light
- K^3 Oil pressure warning light
- K^4 Parking light warning light
- K^5 Turn signal warning light
- K^6 Emergency flasher warning light
- K^7 Dual brake circuit warning light
- L^1 Sealed-Beam unit left headlight
- L^2 Sealed-Beam unit right headlight
- L^6 Speedometer light
- L^8 Clock light
- L^{10} Instrument panel light
- M^2 Tail/brake light, right
- M^4 Tail/brake light, left
- M^5 Turn signal and parking light, front, left
- M^6 Turn signal, rear, left
- M^7 Turn signal and parking light, front, right
- M^8 Turn signal, rear, right
- M^{11} Side marker light, front
- M^{16} Back-up light, left
- M^{17} Back-up light, right
- N Ignition coil
- O Distributor
- P^1 Spark plug connector, No. 1 cylinder
- P^2 Spark plug connector, No. 2 cylinder
- P^3 Spark plug connector, No. 3 cylinder
- P^4 Spark plug connector, No. 4 cylinder
- Q^1 Spark plug, No. 1 cylinder
- Q^2 Spark plug, No. 2 cylinder
- Q^3 Spark plug, No. 3 cylinder
- Q^4 Spark plug, No. 4 cylinder
- S Fuse box
- S^1 In-line fuse for back-up lights and fresh air fan motor
- T Cable adapter
- T^1 Cable connector, single
- T^2 Cable connector, double
- T^3 Cable connector, triple
- T^{20} Test network, central plug
- V Windshield wiper motor
- V^2 Fresh air motor front
- W Interior light
- W^3 Luggage compartment light
- X License plate light
- Y Clock
- ① Ground strap from battery to frame
- ② Ground strap from transmission to frame
- ④ Ground cable from horn to steering coupling
- ⑤ Ground cable from front axle to frame

Test network

The orange colored spots are the connections in the test network which are wired to the central plug. The numbers in the spots correspond to the terminals in the central plug.

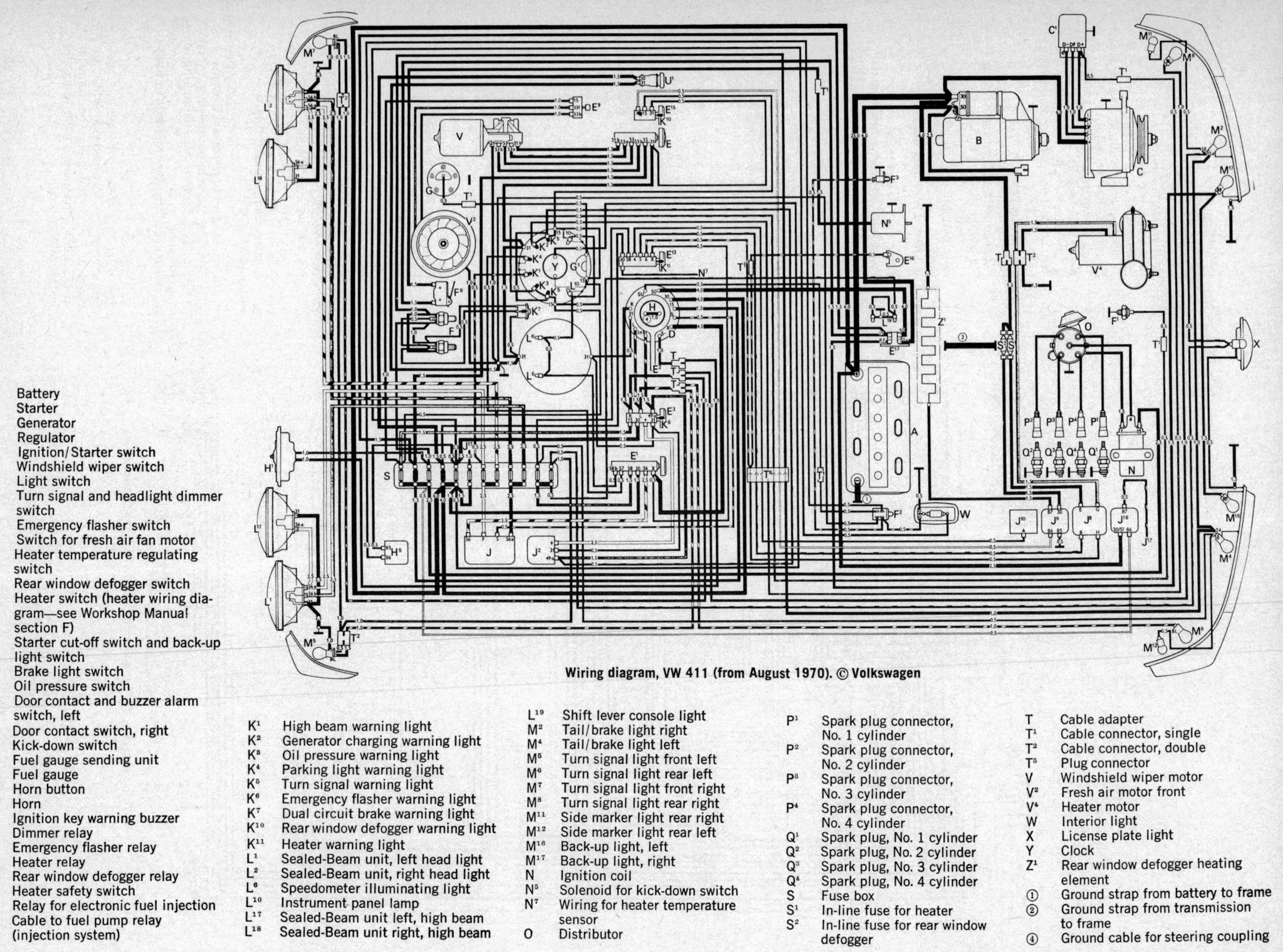

Wiring diagram, VW 411 (from August 1970). © Volkswagen

A	Battery
B	Starter
C	Generator
C^1	Regulator
D	Ignition/Starter switch
E	Windshield wiper switch
E^1	Light switch
E^2	Turn signal and headlight dimmer switch
E^3	Emergency flasher switch
E^9	Switch for fresh air fan motor
E^{13}	Heater temperature regulating switch
E^{15}	Rear window defogger switch
E^{16}	Heater switch (heater wiring diagram—see Workshop Manual section F)
E^{17}	Starter cut-off switch and back-up light switch
F	Brake light switch
F^1	Oil pressure switch
F^2	Door contact and buzzer alarm switch, left
F^3	Door contact switch, right
F^5	Kick-down switch
G	Fuel gauge sending unit
G^1	Fuel gauge
H	Horn button
H^1	Horn
H^5	Ignition key warning buzzer
J	Dimmer relay
J^2	Emergency flasher relay
J^8	Heater relay
J^9	Rear window defogger relay
J^{10}	Heater safety switch
J^{16}	Relay for electronic fuel injection
J^{17}	Cable to fuel pump relay (injection system)
K^1	High beam warning light
K^2	Generator charging warning light
K^3	Oil pressure warning light
K^4	Parking light warning light
K^5	Turn signal warning light
K^6	Emergency flasher warning light
K^7	Dual circuit brake warning light
K^{10}	Rear window defogger warning light
K^{11}	Heater warning light
L^1	Sealed-Beam unit, left head light
L^2	Sealed-Beam unit, right head light
L^6	Speedometer illuminating light
L^{10}	Instrument panel lamp
L^{17}	Sealed-Beam unit left, high beam
L^{18}	Sealed-Beam unit right, high beam
L^{19}	Shift lever console light
M^2	Tail/brake light right
M^4	Tail/brake light left
M^5	Turn signal light front left
M^6	Turn signal light rear left
M^7	Turn signal light front right
M^8	Turn signal light rear right
M^{11}	Side marker light rear right
M^{12}	Side marker light rear left
M^{16}	Back-up light, left
M^{17}	Back-up light, right
N	Ignition coil
N^5	Solenoid for kick-down switch
N^7	Wiring for heater temperature sensor
O	Distributor
P^1	Spark plug connector, No. 1 cylinder
P^2	Spark plug connector, No. 2 cylinder
P^3	Spark plug connector, No. 3 cylinder
P^4	Spark plug connector, No. 4 cylinder
Q^1	Spark plug, No. 1 cylinder
Q^2	Spark plug, No. 2 cylinder
Q^3	Spark plug, No. 3 cylinder
Q^4	Spark plug, No. 4 cylinder
S	Fuse box
S^1	In-line fuse for heater
S^2	In-line fuse for rear window defogger
T	Cable adapter
T^1	Cable connector, single
T^2	Cable connector, double
T^5	Plug connector
V	Windshield wiper motor
V^2	Fresh air motor front
V^4	Heater motor
W	Interior light
X	License plate light
Y	Clock
Z^1	Rear window defogger heating element
①	Ground strap from battery to frame
②	Ground strap from transmission to frame
④	Ground cable for steering coupling

Engine Electrical

Distributor

Distributor R & R

Take off the vacuum hose at the distributor. Disconnect cable one at the ignition coil and remove the distributor cap. Mark the relationship between the distributor body and the engine case. Unscrew the distributor retaining screw on the crankcase and lift out the distributor.

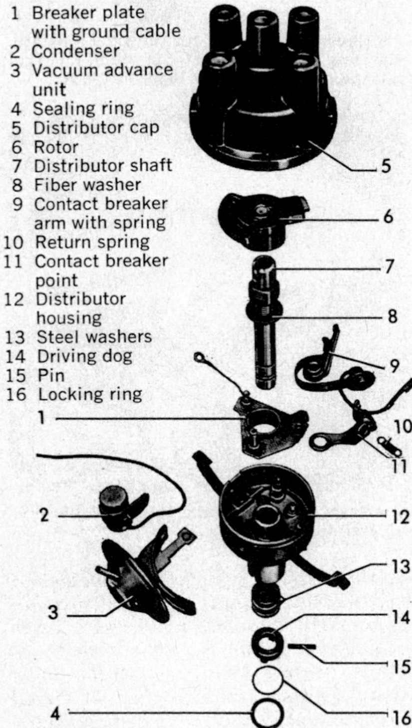

1 Breaker plate with ground cable
2 Condenser
3 Vacuum advance unit
4 Sealing ring
5 Distributor cap
6 Rotor
7 Distributor shaft
8 Fiber washer
9 Contact breaker arm with spring
10 Return spring
11 Contact breaker point
12 Distributor housing
13 Steel washers
14 Driving dog
15 Pin
16 Locking ring

Exploded view, typical VW distributor.

NOTE: Before removing the distributor, it is best to turn the engine until the rotor points to number one cylinder lead; i.e., toward the notch in the distributor housing. In this way one can be sure of having the rotor pointing in the proper direction when the distributor is reinstalled.

Installation is in the reverse sequence. Align the marks made before removal. When the distributor is reinstalled in the engine, the timing must then be adjusted.

Contact Point Adjustment

The breaker points are the heart of the Volkswagen ignition system and must be given their share of attention. All Volkswagens ever made require a breaker point gap of .016 in. (COLD) and a dwell angle of 50 degrees (50°). In adjusting the contact points, the following steps are taken:

1. Remove the distributor cap and rotor.
2. Turn the engine by hand until the fiber block on the movable breaker point rests on a high point of the cam lobe.
3. With a screwdriver, loosen the locking screw of the stationary breaker point.
4. Manipulate the stationary point plate so that the clearance between the points is .016 in.
5. Tighten the locking screw of the stationary point.
6. Recheck gap and correct if it has changed from step (4) due to the tightening of the locking screw.

When replacing points, the same steps as above are followed, except that in between steps three and four, the old points are taken out and the new points inserted. Points should be replaced when they have been badly burned or have been in use so long that correct adjustment is no longer possible.

If necessary, multipurpose grease should be applied to the breaker arm fiber block whenever the points are inspected. Use enough to do the job but avoid excess grease that could come into contact with the breaker points and cause misfiring of the ignition system.

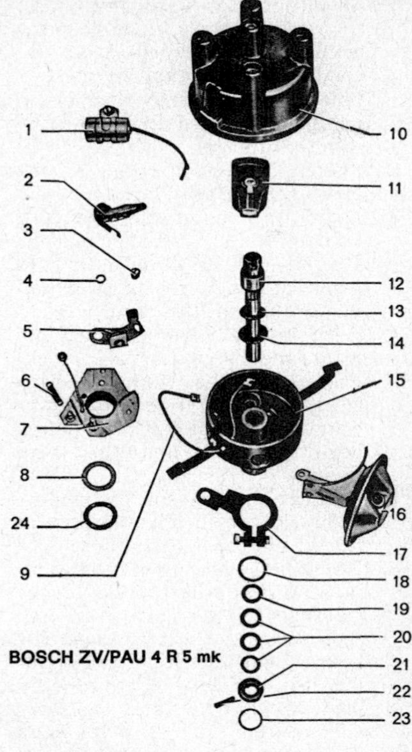

1 Condenser
2 Contact breaker arm
3 Securing screw with flat and spring washers
4 Insulating washer
5 Contact breaker point
6 Return spring
7 Breaker plate with ground cable
8 Plastic washer
9 Low-tension cable
10 Distributor cap
11 Rotor
12 Distributor shaft
13 Steel washer
14 Fiber washer
15 Distributor housing
16 Vacuum advance
17 Clip
18 Sealing ring
19 Fiber washer
20 Shim
21 Driving dog
22 Pin
23 Locking spring
24 Shim

Exploded view, typical Bosch distributor.

1 Spring for breaker arm
2 Breaker arm
3 Distributor with cam
4 Connection for contact
5 Breaker plate
6 Vacuum unit
7 Condenser
8 Insulator
9 Securing screw
10 Pins on breaker plate
11 Breaker point
12 Eccentrics for return springs
13 Return springs
14 Pull rod

Details of typical distributor.

Ignition Timing

It is only after adjusting the breaker points properly that the ignition timing should be adjusted. It is most important that the ignition timing adjustment be carried out only when the engine is dead cold, because rising engine temperature causes the setting to become different.

If, in exceptional cases, it is necessary to adjust the timing with a warm engine, not exceeding 122°F, the timing should be advanced about 2.5° beyond the normal setting. The timing must then be rechecked at the first opportunity with the engine cold.

VW engines have had several different arrangements of crankshaft pulley timing marks. On early Type 1 engines, the pulley bore two timing marks, 7.5° before top dead center and 10° before top dead center, reading clockwise. Later, with the introduction of emission controls, a 0° top dead center mark was added. The

Right mark is 10° BTDC, one on left is 7.5° BTDC on early Type 1 and 2 engines. See text for details of markings on other engines.

A 6 or 12 volt static test lamp is used in setting the ignition timing of all pre-1968 VW engines. One lead of the test lamp is connected to terminal 1 of the coil, the other to ground.

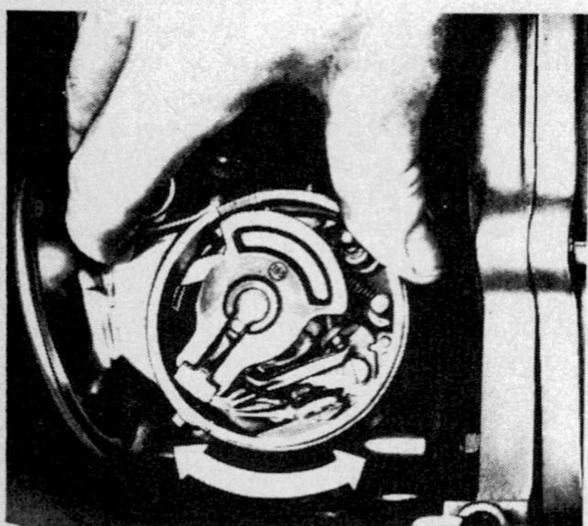

Turning the distributor body clockwise retards the ignition timing; turning counterclockwise advances the timing.

7.5° and 10° marks were subsequently removed, leaving only the 0° mark. Current engines have only a 5° after top dead center mark. Type 2 engines are generally the same as Type 1 models. Early Type 3 engines have marks at 7.5° and 10° before top dead center; later engines have marks at 7.5°, 10°, and 12.5° before top dead center. Fuel-injected Type 3 engines have marks corresponding to 0°, 7.5°, 10°, and 12.5° before top dead center.

Timing Procedure

1. Turn the engine by hand until the appropriate mark on the crankshaft pulley is lined up with the crankcase dividing line. (On Type 3 models, the mark is to be lined up with the timing setting surface, or pointer, on the fan housing. At the same time the appropriate mark is opposite the dividing line, the rotor must be pointing to the lead wire of cylinder number one (the cylinder toward the front of the car on the passenger [right] side). Number one position is indicated by a mark on the rim of the distributor. See the illustration showing cylinder numbering. If the rotor is not pointed toward number one cylinder, the crankshaft must be turned one more revolution clockwise until it is. On recent models, number three cylinder is retarded about 4° compared with number one cylinder and only number one cylinder is to be used in setting the ignition timing.
2. Loosen the clamp screw at the base of the distributor.
3. Attach the lead of a test lamp (6 volt for 1966 and earlier models, 12 volt for 1967 and later) to terminal one of the ignition coil and ground the test lamp.
4. With the ignition switched on, rotate the distributor body clockwise until the contact points close, and then rotate it slowly counterclockwise until the points begin to open and the lamp lights.
5. Without moving the distributor body, tighten the clamp screw at the base of the distributor.
6. Recheck the adjustment by turning the crankshaft pulley counterclockwise one-half turn, and then turning clockwise until the mark is within 1 in. of the dividing line. At this point, proceed more slowly by tapping the right side of the fan belt with your hand. Such tapping will cause the fan belt to move in either moderate or very small jumps, depending on the strength of the tap. Slight taps toward the end of the check will ensure the finest pssible check on the accuracy of the adjustment. If, upon rechecking, the lamp lights before the mark gets to the dividing line, the timing will have to be retarded slightly by loosening the clamp screw and rotating the distributor body in the clockwise direction. Rotating the distributor clockwise retards the timing, while rotation in the counterclockwise direction advances the timing.

NOTE: Adjustment of ignition timing on 1967 and earlier engines must always be done with a test lamp. A stroboscopic timing light should not be used, as it will alter the engine setting range. It is, however, recommended that exhaust emission controlled engines 1968 and later and Type 3 and 4 fuel-injected engines be timed with a stroboscopic light. These engines should be timed at idle speed, with the distributor vacuum line disconnected and the engine at normal operating temperature.

A stroboscopic timing light must be used to set the ignition timing of all 1968 and later exhaust emission controlled VW engines.

Distributor used with fuel-injected engines. The two screws pointed out hold the fuel injection trigger contact plate in place.

A removal tool is required to extract the distributor driveshaft.

Distributor Trigger Contact R & R

The distributor on fuel-injected engines has two breaker plates. The first is the normal breaker point plate for the ignition system. The second plate, mounted in the base of the distributor head, carries two similar breaker assemblies which regulate fuel injection. There is no adjustment provided for the injection trigger contact breakers. To replace the trigger contacts:

1. Remove the distributor cap. Pull out the triple plug and disconnect the flat plug at terminal one of the coil. Loosen the clamp and remove the distributor after noting the rotor position and marking the relationship between the engine block and the distributor body.
2. Remove the two contact plate holding screws.
3. Pull out the plate holder.

4. Reverse the procedure to install the new plate holder. If ignition timing is correct, the injection timing will also be correct.

Distributor Driveshaft R & R

To remove the distributor driveshaft, loosen the distributor clamp bolt, turn the engine so that the rotor is pointing to number one cylinder (the notch on the distributor housing), and lift out the distributor. Remove fuel pump and intermediate flange, gaskets, and fuel pump push rod. Remove the distance spring on the distributor driveshaft. Be sure that number one cylinder is at its firing point, and withdraw the driveshaft via a removal tool by pulling with the extractor and turning the driveshaft to the left at the same time.

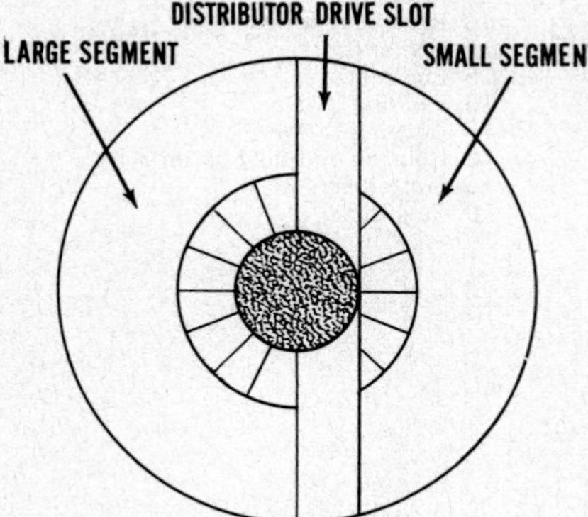

Detail of top of distributor driveshaft, showing offset slot referred to in text.

Installing the distributor driveshaft in Type 1 and 2 engines.

Installing the distributor driveshaft in Type 3 engines. With No. 1 cylinder at its firing point, the slot of the driveshaft must form an angle of approximately 60°, with the smaller segment toward the oil cooler. See the text for details on other engines.

Remove the washer(s) under the driveshaft, being careful not to drop a washer into the crankcase. When the engine is installed, a magnet is handy for removing these washers.

When installing, the reverse of the previous procedure applies. The fuel-pump push rod drive eccentric and the pinion teeth should be checked for wear. If the teeth are badly worn, the teeth on the crankshaft should also be examined. Check the washer under the driveshaft for wear and replace it if necessary. Position number one cylinder at its firing point and insert the distributor driveshaft.

The slot in the top of the distributor driveshaft is offset, dividing the top of the driveshaft into two unequal segments. The driveshaft is installed as follows:

Insert the distance spring, install the distributor, set the ignition timing, and install the fuel pump.

NOTE: When the engine has been completely disassembled, it is necessary that the oil pump, the fan housing, the fan, and the crankshaft pulley be installed before the distributor driveshaft is inserted.)

Generator

Different types of generators have been used throughout the years and models. Refer to the "Generator and Regulator Electrical Equipment Specifications" chart for details.

The generator warning light in the speedometer housing connects to the voltage regulator by means of terminals in the ignition switch. The warning lamp lights as soon as the ignition is turned on, and goes out when the voltage of the generator approaches that of the battery. The warning lamp simply gives a "yes-no" answer to the question of whether the generator is charging or not. As such, it is potentially useful in detecting broken fan belts, because when a fan belt is broken, the generator is no longer being turned and will not charge. In a Type 1 or 2, a broken belt means that the entire car is out of commission, but with the Type 3, the fan is mounted directly on the crankshaft and the car can be driven until the battery runs out of electricity.

The generator is equipped with ball bearings that are packed with special high melting-point grease. Lubrication of the generator is not necessary under normal conditions. However, if the unit has been disassembled and/or overhauled, it is then necessary to provide new lubricant for the bearings. Under no circumstances should ordinary grease be used, for it will not hold up under operating conditions.

Testing Generator No-Load Voltage

In testing the no-load voltage of the generator, the cable from terminal B+(51) at the regulator must first be disconnected. The positive lead of the voltmeter to be used should be attached to terminal B+(51) of the regulator and the negative lead of the meter grounded. With the engine running, the speed should be increased gradually until the reading of the voltmeter peaks out. If the regulator is functioning properly, the peaking point of the no-load voltage should be approximately 7.4–8.1 volts (V) for the 6 volt system and 13.6–14.4 for the 12 volt system. When the engine is turned off, the needle of the voltmeter should drop from 6 V (12 V) to zero just before the engine stops.

Testing Generator Without Regulator

The generator can be given a very quick check without the regulator. It is most important that the duration of the test be very brief (only a few seconds) in order that the generator field windings will not be overloaded during the test.

Disconnect the D+ and DF leads from the generator. Connect terminal DF of the generator to the D—terminal. Connect the positive terminal of the voltmeter to terminal D+ and the negative terminal to the generator ground. For 6 V systems, approximately 6 V should be generated at 1500 rpm and about 15 at 3000 rpm. For 12 V systems, 12 V should be generated at 1500 rpm and 36 V at 3000 rpm. A circuit diagram for this test is included in this section.

Regulator R & R

On pre-1967 models, the regulator is located on top of the generator. Take off the connections from terminals B+ (51) and 61 at the regulator. Remove the screws that hold the reg-

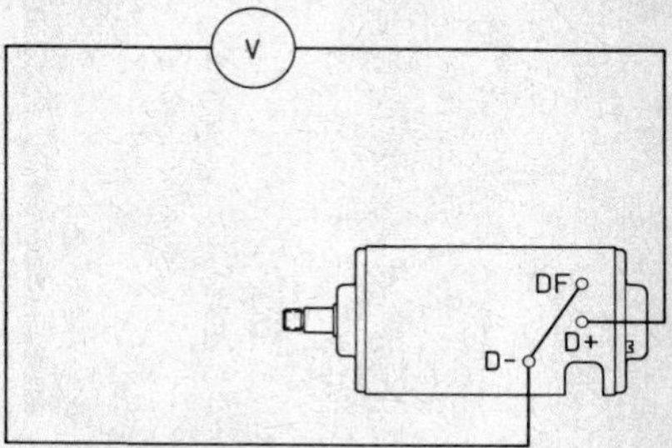

Circuit diagram for making quick check of generator without regulator. Test must not take longer than a few seconds or generator will be damaged.

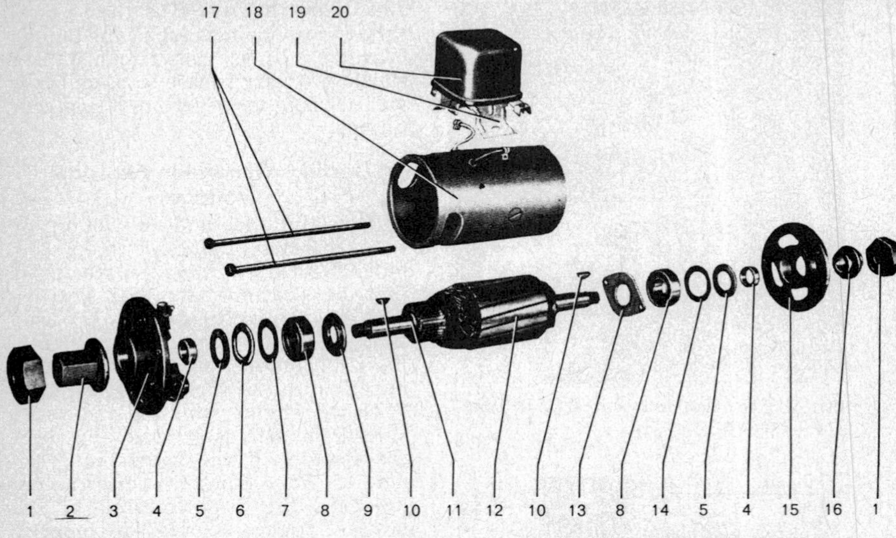

1 Nut
2 Pulley hub
3 Brush holder end plate
4 Spacer ring
5 Felt washer
6 Retainer
7 Thrust ring
8 Ball bearing
9 Washer
10 Key
11 Spacer
12 Armature
13 Bearing retainer
14 Thrust ring
15 End plate
16 Fan hub
17 Housing screws
18 Housing and field assembly
19 Slotted screw
20 Regulator

Exploded view, VW generator.

1 Nut
2 End plate
3 Retaining plate
4 Screw
5 Woodruff key
6 Armature
7 Pole housing
8 Housing screw
9 End plate with brush holders
10 Screw
11 Spacer
12 Washer
13 Bearing
14 Washer
15 Washer
16 Circlip
17 Spring ring

Exploded view, Bosch generator.

ulator onto the generator and remove the regulator from its position on the generator. Disconnect the electrical cables from the bottom of the regulator. These are marked + (D+) and F (DF).

Removing voltage regulator, early Type 1 vehicles.

Installation of the regulator is the reverse of the preceding, but it should be noted that the thicker cable (coming from the positive brush of the generator) must be attached at the regulator bottom to terminal + (D+). The thin cable coming from the generator field windings should be attached to the F (DF) terminal at the bottom of the regulator. If the replacement of the regulator does not correct a deficiency in the charging system, chances are that the generator itself is defective.

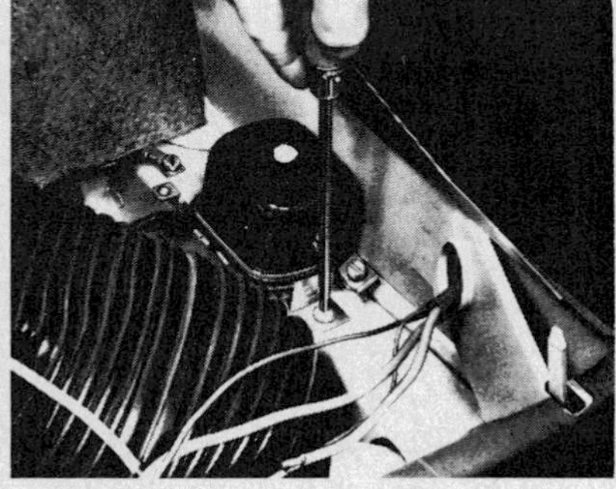

Removing voltage regulator, Type 3 and late Type 1 vehicles.

Checking Generator Brushes

The generator brushes should be examined periodically for wear. If they are worn to the point where they no longer extend from their holders, they should be replaced.

Alternator R & R Type 4

NOTE: The factory procedure recommends removing the engine to remove the alternator, however, it is possible to reach the alternator by first removing the right heater box which will provide access to the alternator.

1. Remove the engine. Disconnect the battery.
2. Remove the dipstick and the rear engine cover plate.
3. Remove the fan belt.
4. Remove the lower alternator bolt and the alternator cover plate.
5. Disconnect the wiring harness.
6. Remove the allen-head screws holding the fan, then remove the fan.
7. Remove the rubber elbow from the fan housing that provides alternator cooling.
8. Remove the alternator adjusting bracket.
9. Remove the alternator.
10. Reverse the above steps to install.

Regulator Type 4

The regulator is located near the air cleaner, mounted either on the air cleaner or on the firewall. Make careful note of the wiring.

Generator R & R

Disconnect the ground strap of the battery and disconnect the leads from the regulator. Remove the air cleaner and the carburetor and take off the fan belt. Remove the retaining strap from the generator. Remove the cooling air thermostat. Remove hot air hoses from the fan housing, take out the fan housing screws, and lift off the housing. After removing the fan housing screws, the generator can be lifted off along with the fan.

Installation is the reverse of the preceding. Except on Type 3, where the generator must be installed so that the mark on the housing is in line with the notch on the clamping strap.

Battery, Starter

Battery

The electrical system of the Volkswagen is of the negative-ground type, the negative terminal of the battery being grounded. In most VW models, the battery is located under the right-hand side of the rear seat. In the Karmann Ghia and Transporter models, it is in the engine compartment.

The 6V electrical system was standard on all Volkswagens through the 1966 models. Beginning with the 1967 models (August 1966), the change was made to the 12 V system.

Starter

The starter is flange-mounted on the right-hand side of the transmission housing. Attached to the starter motor housing is a solenoid which engages the pinion and connects the starting motor to the battery when the ignition key is turned on. When the engine starts and the key is released from the start position, the solenoid circuit is opened and the pinion is returned to its original position by the return spring. If for any reason the starter is not switched off immediately after the engine starts, a pinion free-wheeling device stops the armature from being driven so that the starter will not be damaged.

Starter R & R

Disconnect the ground strap of the battery and remove the cable from terminal 30 and the lead from terminal 50 of the solenoid. After removal of the two retaining screws, the starter can be taken out. One of the starter attaching bolts is located in the engine compartment.

Prior to installation, the outboard bushing should be lubricated with special lithium grease, and sealing compound should be applied to the mating surfaces between the starter and the transmission. After putting the long screw into the hole in the flange, locate the starter on the transmission housing. Be sure that the cables are tightly connected to the terminals and that the contact points between the cables and terminals are clean.

Solenoid R & R

Unscrew the hexagon nut and remove the connector strip. Take out the two retaining screws on the mounting bracket and withdraw the solenoid after it has been unhooked from its actuating lever. When replacing a defective solenoid with a new one, care should be taken to see that the distance "a" in the accompanying diagram is 19+ or —.1 mm when the magnet is drawn in. The actuating rod can be adjusted after loosening the locknut.

Installation of the solenoid is the reverse of the preceding. Be certain that the rubber seal on the starter mounting bracket is properly seated. A small strip of VW Sealing Compound D 14 should be placed on the

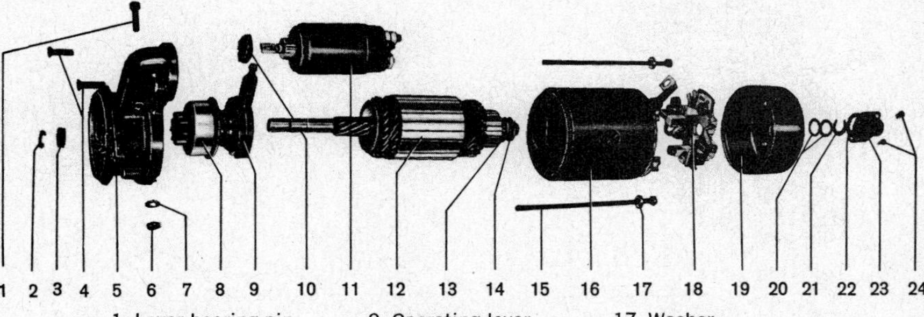

1 Lever bearing pin
2 Circlip
3 Stop-ring
4 Securing screws
5 Mounting bracket
6 Nut
7 Spring washer
8 Pinion
9 Operating lever
10 Rubber seal
11 Solenoid
12 Armature
13 Steel washer
14 Synthetic washer
15 Housing screw
16 Pole housing
17 Washer
18 Brush holder
19 End plate
20 Shims
21 Lockwasher
22 Sealing ring
23 End cap
24 Screws

Exploded view of typical Bosch starter.

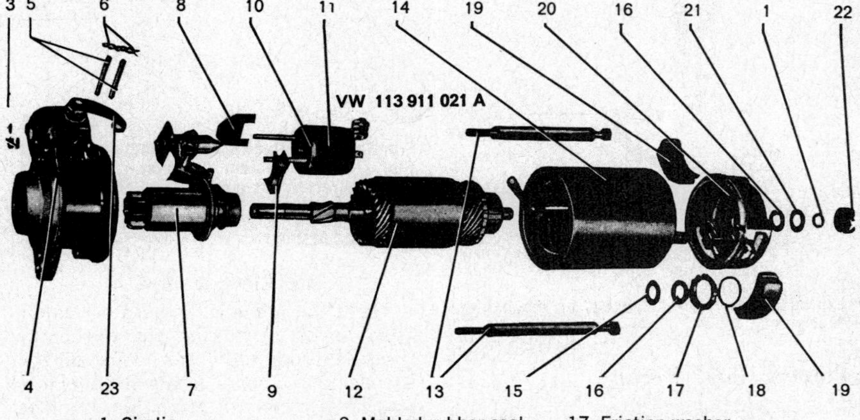

1 Circlip
2 Cup washer
3 Nuts and lockwashers
4 Intermediate bracket
5 Pivot pins
6 Spring clips
7 Drive pinion with linkage and solenoid core
8 Insulating plate
9 Molded rubber seal
10 Insulating disc
11 Solenoid housing
12 Armature
13 Housing screws
14 Housing and field assembly
15 Steel washer
16 Bronze washer
17 Friction washer
18 Thrust ring
19 Brush inspection cover
20 Commutator end plate
21 Steel washer
22 Cap
23 Connecting strip

Exploded view of typical VW starter.

outside of the switch. In order to facilitate engagement of the actuating rod, the pinion should be pulled out as far as possible when the solenoid is inserted.

The solenoid may be withdrawn after removal of the two screws securing it to the starter motor intermediate bracket.

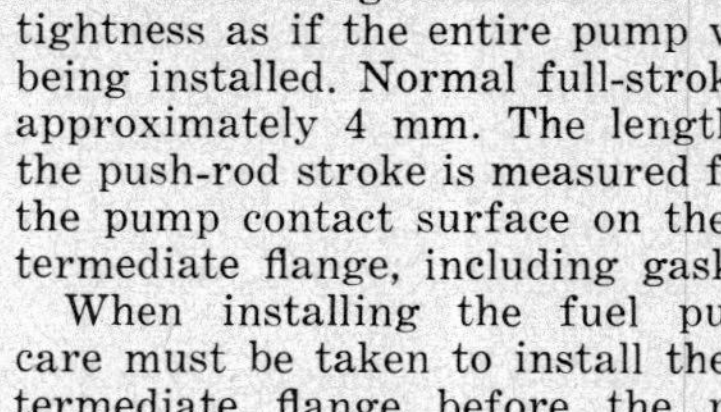

When installing a new solenoid, distance "a" should be 19 ± .1 mm with the magnet drawn in.

Fuel System

The Fuel Pump

The Volkswagen fuel pump, except on fuel-injected engines, is mechanical, and of the diaphragm type, being push-rod operated from a cam on the distributor drive gear.

Other than cleaning the filter of the pump at regular intervals, no other maintenance is necessary. The push rod and pump rocker arm are lubricated by the lubricant in the lower part of the pump. The fuel pump filter on recent Volkswagen models is removed by unscrewing the hexagonal head plug from the side of the fuel pump assembly.

Mechanical Fuel Pump R & R

The fuel pump is removed by taking off the fuel line, disconnecting the hose from the pump, and removing the retaining nuts from the mounting studs. After the pump has been removed, the intermediate flange, push rod, and gaskets can be removed. Be careful in handling the push rod, as it could be inconvenient to have to fish it out of the crankcase.

Once removed, the stroke of the fuel pump is adjusted by insertion or removal of the proper number of flange gaskets. Adjustment is checked after installing the intermediate flange with two gaskets and push rod, and nuts are tightened to the same tightness as if the entire pump were being installed. Normal full-stroke is approximately 4 mm. The length of the push-rod stroke is measured from the pump contact surface on the intermediate flange, including gaskets.

When installing the fuel pump, care must be taken to install the intermediate flange before the push rod, otherwise the rod may fall through into the crankcase. Before installing the fuel pump, the lower chamber should be filled with universal grease. Tighten nuts to mounting studs, taking care not to overtighten. (Nuts should be retightened when the engine has reached operating temperature.) Connect the fuel line and hose, and check for correct seating of the fuel line rubber grommet in the panel of the engine compartment.

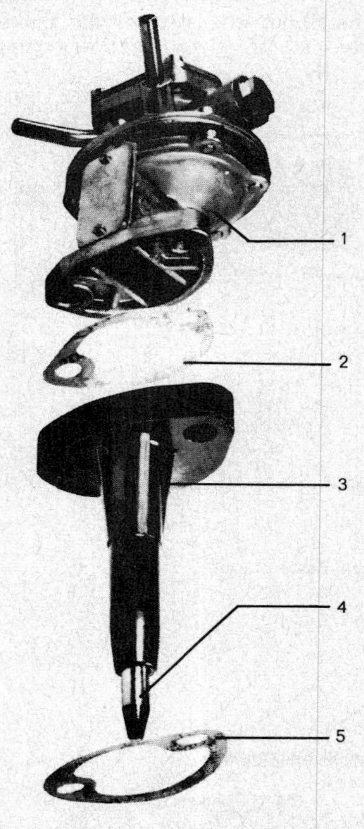

1 Fuel pump
2 Gasket
3 Plastic intermediate flange
4 Push rod
5 Gasket

Exploded view, lower portion of mechanical fuel pump.

Electric Fuel Pump

Electric Fuel Pump R & R

The electric fuel pump is mounted at the front of the chassis. There are three fuel lines: suction, pressure, and return.

To remove the pump:

1. Pinch-clamp the fuel lines shut to prevent leakage.
2. Unplug the electrical cable plug.
3. Cut off the original hose clamps Pull off the hoses and catch the fuel which drains out.
4. Raise the pressure hose to prevent draining the fuel loop line.
5. Unbolt and remove the pump.

To replace the pump:

1. Connect the three fuel hoses. Install screw type hose clamps at all three connections.
2. Bolt the pump to the mounting supports.
3. Remove the pinch clamps from the hoses.
4. Install the cable plug. The brown, negative ground wire must be to the bottom and the half circular cavity toward the right. Install the protective plug cap.

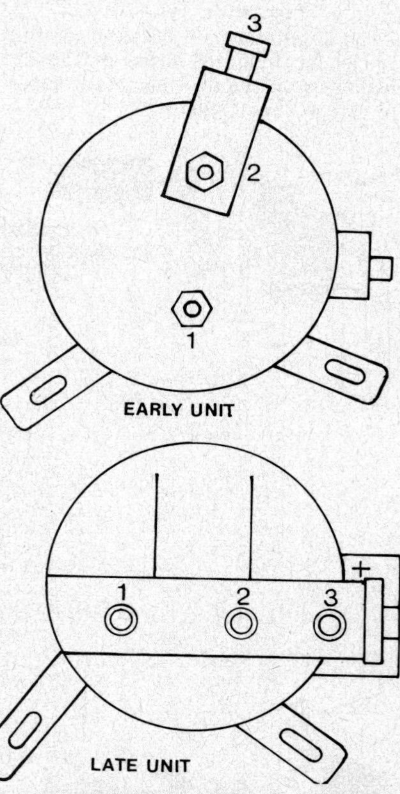

Front view of electric fuel pumps used with fuel injection system. Suction (1), pressure (2), and return (3) connections are shown.

Air Cleaner

Air Cleaner R & R

On Type 1 models, the air cleaner is removed by taking the preheater pipe(s) from the intake tube of the air cleaner, disconnecting the thermostatic flap control wire, pulling the crankcase breather hose from the cleaner, and loosening the clamp screw that holds the cleaner onto the carburetor throat. After the air cleaner has been removed, the top part can be separated from the lower part by removing the clips that hold the halves together.

When the cleaner has been taken

The dual-carburetor, Type 3 engine's air cleaner is fastened down at three points. The center wingnut should always be loosened first and tightened last to avoid disturbing the linkage adjustment.

apart, the dirty oil should be poured out and the lower part cleaned. The upper part does not generally require cleaning. The bottom part of the air cleaner should then be filled to the mark with new engine oil of the same viscosity as that used in the engine. If there is no mark, refill with the quantity of oil specified in the "Capacities and Pressures" chart.

Removal of the air cleaner in the Type 3, dual-carburetor engine is slightly more complex, but accomplished in much the same manner. The right-hand connecting rod must be removed from between the rotating lever and the carburetor, the cables removed from the automatic choke and electromagnetic pilot jet, the crankcase ventilation hose taken off the air cleaner, and the three wing nuts unscrewed. The center wing nut is removed before removing the air cleaner; those at each of the carburetors remain in place. After the center wing nut is removed, the air cleaner can be lifted from its position and the upper and lower parts separated.

When installing the air cleaner of the Type 3 engine, care should be taken to see that the oil is up to the mark, that the rubber sealing ring on each carburetor is secure, that the water drain hole is free in the lower part of the air cleaner, and that the marks are lined up when the upper and lower halves are put back together. If the marks do not line up exactly, the intake pipe will point in the wrong direction and be either difficult or impossible to connect to the intake extension. When tightning the wing nuts of the air cleaner, it is very important that the outer wing nuts are tightened down first. There is an expansion-contraction joint between the left outer wing nut and the center wing nut which makes these not quite so critical. However, there is no such joint between the center and right-hand wing nuts. Subsequently, if the center nut is tightened first, and then the right-hand nut, the result could be a slight movement on the part of the right-hand carburetor, thus causing an alteration in a very sensitive adjustment. Tighten down the center wing nut only after the two outer wing nuts have been fully tightened.

To remove the air cleaner from fuel injected engines:

1. Detach crankcase and auxiliary air regulator hoses.
2. Loosen the hose clamps at either end of the air cleaner. Pull off the rubber hoses.
3. Remove the wingnut and air cleaner.

To clean, refill, and replace the air cleaner on fuel-injected engines:

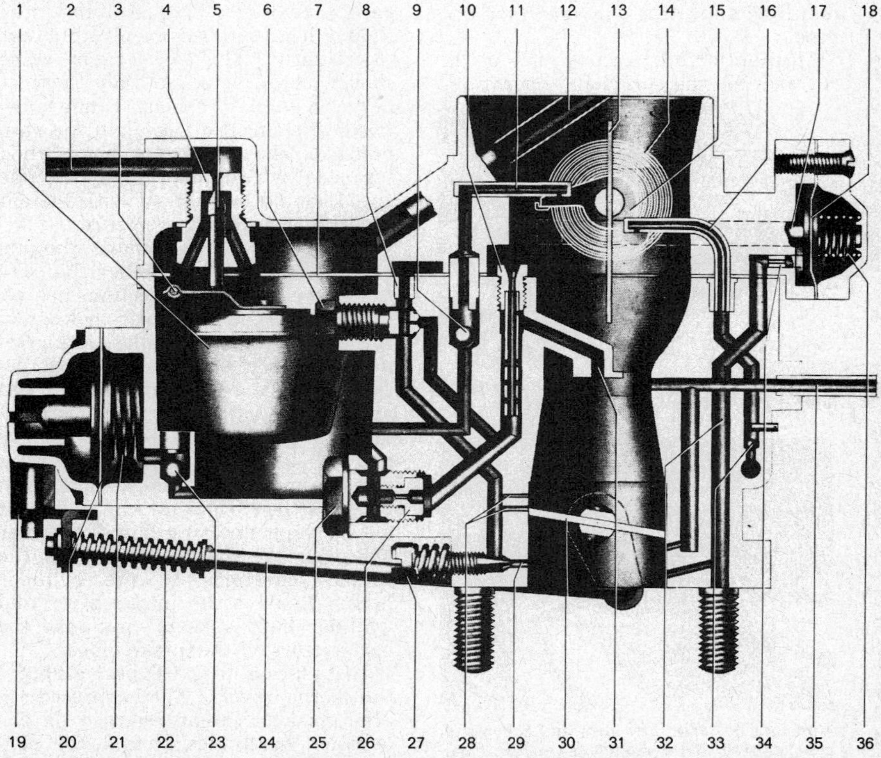

1 Float
2 Fuel line
3 Float lever
4 Float needle valve
5 Float needle
6 Pilot jet
7 Gasket
8 Pilot air drilling
9 Ball check valve in power fuel system
10 Air correction jet with emulsion tube
11 Power fuel tube
12 Float bowl vent tube
13 Choke valve
14 Bimetal spring
15 Operating lever
16 Accelerator pump discharge tube
17 Diaphragm rod
18 Vacuum diaphragm
19 Pump lever
20 Pump diaphragm
21 Spring
22 Push rod spring
23 Ball check valve for accelerator pump
24 Pump connector rod
25 Main jet carrier
26 Main jet
27 Volume control screw
28 Bypass port
29 Idle port
30 Throttle valve
31 Discharge arm
32 Vacuum drilling
33 Ball check valve in accelerator pump drilling
34 Jet in vacuum drilling
35 Vacuum connection
36 Diaphragm spring

Solex 28 PICT-1 carburetor used on 1,200 cc engines.

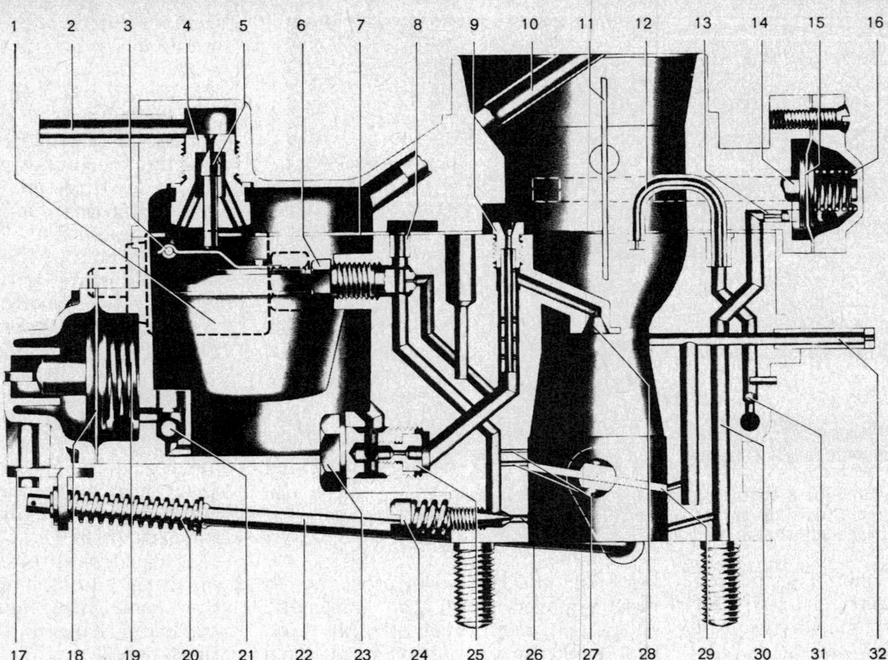

1 Float
2 Fuel line
3 Float lever
4 Float needle valve
5 Float needle
6 Electromagnetic pilot jet
7 Gasket
8 Pilot air drilling
9 Air correction jet with emulsion tube
10 Float bowl vent tube
11 Choke valve
12 Accelerator pump discharge tube
13 Jet in vacuum drilling
14 Diaphragm rod
15 Vacuum diaphragm
16 Spring for vacuum diaphragm
17 Pump lever
18 Pump diaphragm
19 Pump spring
20 Spring
21 Ball check valve for accelerator pump
22 Pull rod for accelerator pump
23 Main jet carrier
24 Volume control screw
25 Main jet
26 Idle port
27 Bypass port
28 Discharge arm
29 Throttle valve
30 Vacuum drilling
31 Ball check valve in accelerator pump drilling
32 Vacuum connection

The carburetors on the Karmann Ghia models are fitted with a power fuel system.

Solex 30 PICT-1 carburetor used on 1,300 and 1,500 cc engines.

1. Release the three clips. Remove the top section.
2. Clean the filter assembly out and refill it with SAE 30 oil to the red mark. SAE 10 may be used in arctic climates.
3. Be sure that the red arrows on the top and bottom sections are aligned when reassembling.
4. Reconnect the hoses, and tighten the clamps and wingnut.

Carburetor

Carburetor R & R

On the Type 1, remove the preheat hose from the air cleaner intake pipe. Disconnect the thermostatic flap control wire. Disconnect the crankcase breather hose from the air cleaner intake. Loosen the air cleaner holding clamp and remove the air cleaner. Disconnect the fuel and vacuum hoses from the carburetor. Disconnect the wires from the automatic choke and the electromagnetic pilot jet. Disconnect the throttle cable at the carburetor and take off the spring, pin, and spring retaining plate. Take off the two carburetor retaining nuts and remove the carburetor from the intake manifold. The throttle positioner may be removed in unit with the carburetor. It would, at this point, be a good idea to stuff part of a clean rag into the intake manifold hole in order to ensure that dirt and other foreign matter will not find its way into the manifold and cause damage to the engine.

Installation of the carburetor is the reverse of the previous operation.

Main jet can be removed after unscrewing plug 1. 2 is idle mixture control screw.

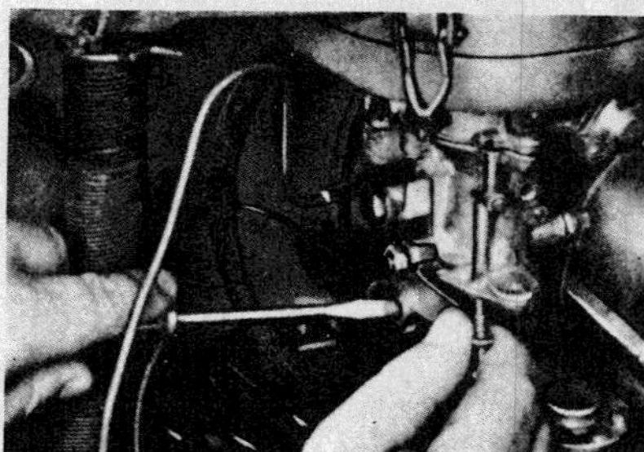

With throttle valve fully open and accelerator pedal floored, there should be a slight clearance (about 1 mm) between the throttle lever and the stop on the carburetor body.

When installing the carburetor, it is advisable that a new intake manifold gasket be used. The retaining nuts should be tightened evenly, but not too tightly. The accelerator cable should be adjusted so that there is very little play (about 1 mm) between the throttle lever and the stop point on the carburetor body when the pedal is fully depressed. The idle speed should be checked with the engine at operating temperature.

On the Type 3, remove the air cleaner as described earlier. Be sure that the electrical connections are removed from the automatic chokes and the electromagnetic pilot jets. Remove the connecting rods from between the center lever and the left- and right-hand carburetors. Disconnect the carburetor return springs and pull off the spark plug connecting caps. Remove the balance tube from between the carburetors by pulling it out of the connecting hoses on either side. Remove the nuts that hold the intake manifolds to the cylinder heads. Remove the intake pipes and cylinder head gaskets, and take the carburetors off the intake pipes.

Installation of the Type 3 carburetor is the reverse of the preceding. New gaskets should be used on the cylinder head intake, and the carburetor gaskets should be inspected for damage and replaced if necessary.

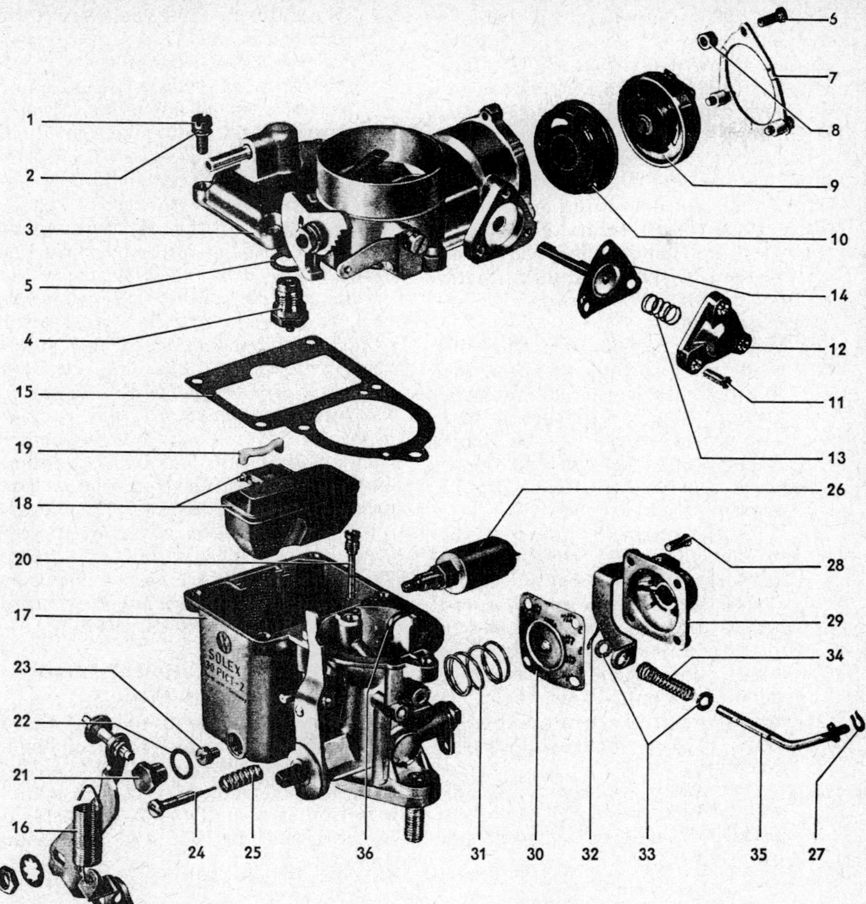

1 Screw for carburetor upper part
2 Spring washer
3 Carburetor upper part
4 Float needle valve 1.5mm diameter
5 Washer 15 x 12 x 1 mm for float needle valve
6 Screw for retaining ring
7 Retaining ring for cap
8 Spacer for retaining ring
9 Choke unit with spring and heater element
10 Plastic cap
11 Fillister head screw
12 Cover for vacuum diaphragm
13 Diaphragm spring
14 Vacuum diaphragm
15 Gasket
16 Return spring for accelerator cable
17 Carburetor lower part
17 Float and pin
19 Bracket for float pin
20 Air correction jet
21 Plug for main jet
22 Plug seal
23 Main jet
24 Volume control screw (designation 1, 2, and 3)
25 Spring
26 Pilot jet cut-off valve "A"
27 Circlip
28 Fillister head screw
29 Cover for pump
30 Pump diaphragm
31 Spring for diaphragm
32 Cotter pin 1.5 x 15 mm
33 Washer 4.2 mm
34 Spring for connecting rod
35 Connecting rod
36 Injector tube for accelerator pump

Solex 30 PICT-2 carburetor used on 1968-69, 1,500 cc engines with throttle positioner.

Checking Electromagnetic Pilot Jet

If the engine is equipped with an electromagnetic pilot jet in the carburetor, and still shows a tendency to "run-on" after being shut off, chances are that the electromagnetic jet is defective. Operation can be checked by turning on the ignition and touching the slip-on connector against the terminal of the jet. If the jet is operating properly, a clicking sound will be heard each time the connector touches the terminal. When the current is off, the needle of this jet moves so as to block off the fuel supply, so when the connector is removed while the engine is running, it should stop the engine.

On 1971 Type 1 and 2 engines, with the Solex 34 PICT-3 carburetor, the pilot jet cut-off valve has been replaced by an idle bypass mixture cutoff valve. The new unit performs the same function.

Choke housing cover alignment, Type 1 single carburetor shown.

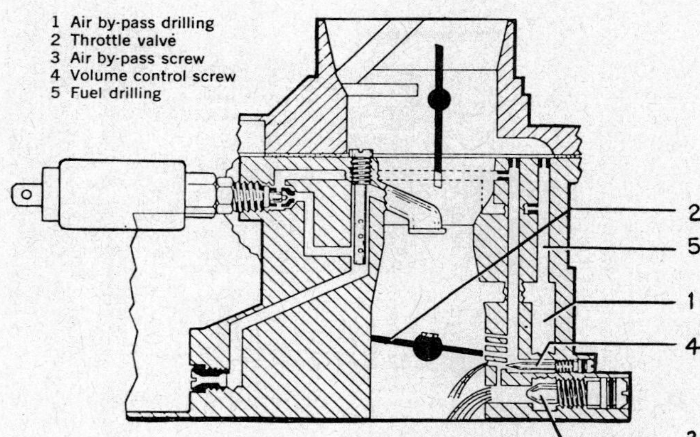

Solex 30 PICT-3 carburetor used on 1970 1,600 cc Type 1 and 2 engines. Idling speed adjustments are made with the air bypass screw.

Carburetor Adjustment

As a part of a routine tune-up it is necessary only to adjust the idling speed and mixture screws on the carburetors of most single carburetor Volkswagens. On 1970 and later Type 1 and 2 engines, the volume control screw is factory set and the throttle valve remains closed during idling. Idling speed adjustments are made with the air bypass screw. On the 30

Idle speed adjustment, pre-1970 Type 1 and 2.

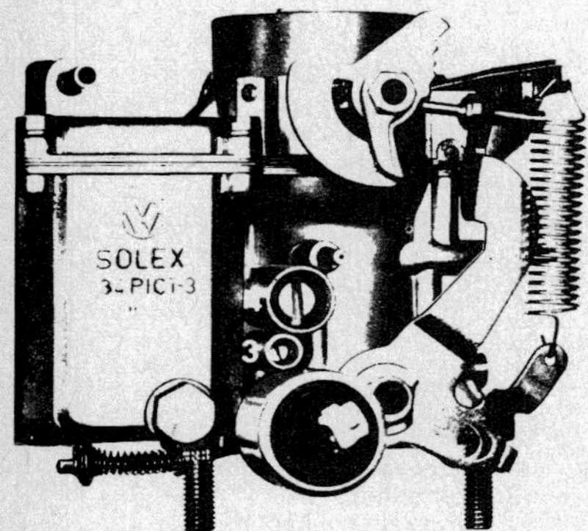

Adjustment screws on Solex 34 PICT-3 carburetor, 1971 Type 1 and 2. 3 is the volume screw. 4 is the air bypass screw.

PICT-3 carburetor (1970), the air bypass screw is below the volume control screw. On the 34 PICT-3 carburetor (1971), the air bypass screw is above the volume control screw. Before adjustment is begun, the engine should be at normal operating temperature and the idle adjusting screw must not be resting on the fast idle cam of the automatic choke. The following steps should be followed in setting the idle speed and mixture adjustments on single-carburetor Volkswagen engines:

1. With the engine warm and running, turn the idling speed adjusting screw in or out until the proper idling speed is attained. The correct speed can be found in the "Tune-Up Specifications" chart and on the sticker on the engine.
2. With the engine running at the proper idle speed, turn the idle mixture control screw slowly clockwise until the engine speed begins to drop, then turn slowly in the counterclockwise direction until the engine is running smoothly again. Now turn the mixture control screw another 1/4 turn in the counterclockwise direction.
3. If necessary, readjust the idle speed. With the clutch pedal depressed, the engine should continue to run after the accelerator has been quickly depressed and released. If the engine stalls, either the mixture adjustment or the idle speed adjustment is incorrect and should be remedied.

NOTE: The setting of the slow-speed (idle) mixture will have a great influence on the performance and economy of the Volkswagen at speeds as great as 50 or 60 miles per hour. If the mixture is too rich, the result will be excess fuel consumption, stalling when the accelerator pedal is suddenly released, and possible "running on" when the ignition switch is turned off. If the mixture is too lean (too much air, not enough gasoline), the result will be better fuel consumption, but exhaust valves may suffer burning or warping. The previously given method for adjusting the slow-speed adjustment will give the proper mixture setting. Turning the mixture screw clockwise will lean the mixture, while turning counterclockwise will enrich it.

Carburetor Adjustment—Dual Carburetor Models

On certain Type 3 models, there are two carburetors—one for each bank of two cylinders. While the current models are equipped with a fuel injection system, Type 3 vehicles sold in the U.S.A. in 1966 and 1967 have

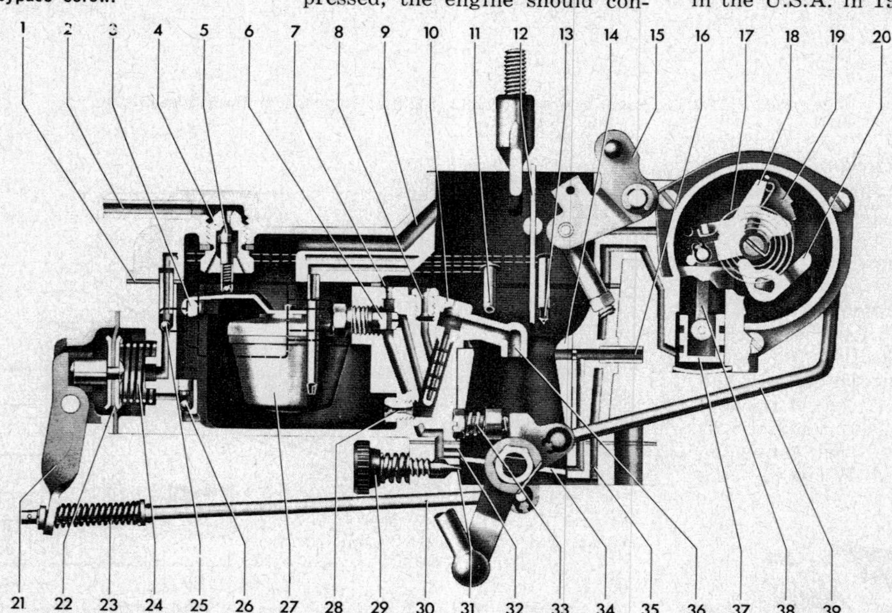

1 Gasket
2 Fuel pipe
3 Float pin
4 Float needle valve
5 Float needle
6 Pilot jet
7 Pilot air bleed drilling
8 Air correction jet
9 Vent passage for float chamber
10 Emulsion tube with ventilation jet
11 Power fuel pipe
12 Choke valve
13 Injector tube accelerator pump
14 Venturi
15 Relay lever
16 Vacuum connection
17 Bimetal coil
18 Intermediate lever
19 Fast idle cam
20 Stop lever
21 Pump lever
22 Pump diaphragm
23 Connecting rod spring
24 Diaphragm spring
25 Ball pressure valve
26 Ball suction valve
27 Float
28 Main jet
29 Volume control screw
30 Connecting rod
31 Idling mixture port
32 Bypass port
33 Idle adjustment screw
34 Throttle valve
35 Vacuum drilling
36 Discharge arm
37 Vacuum piston
38 Piston rod
39 Operating rod

Solex 32 PDSIT-2 carburetor used on dual-carburetor Type 3 engine. The 32 PDSIT-2 is the left carburetor, and has a double vacuum drilling for the distributor advance mechanism.

1 Accelerator cable
2 Connecting rod, right
3 Connecting rod, left
4 Carburetor pull rod with return spring

Dual carburetor linkage.

dual carburetors and require slightly more sophistication in the tune-up operation. Adjusting the carburetors on the dual-carb models requires the use of a special instrument to measure air flow. A commonly used product is that known as the Uni-Syn, available for under $10 from most mail-order auto accessory sources. This device measures the vacuum created by carburetor suction by means of a red piston which rides up and down inside a graded glass tube. The higher the vacuum, the higher the piston is raised.

Besides the synchronizing device mentioned above, a small frozen-juice can will also be required in order that the device will fit on the air horns of the carburetors. Because of the screws that stick straight up from the air horn for the purpose of holding the air cleaner, the small can (open on both ends) is needed. By mounting it on top of the can, the test device will clear the screws without losing vacuum. Before attempting adjustment, the engine must be at operating temperature.

Adjustment Steps

1. Remove the right-hand connecting rod of the carburetor linkage system. This is the rod which connects the center bellcrank with the right-hand carburetor throttle.
2. Remove the air cleaner. It is held on by two wing nuts on each carburetor and one wing nut in the center. The connections to the air intake and to the crankcase ventilation system must also be removed.
3. With the engine running, adjust the idle speed adjusting screw of each carburetor until the correct idling speed is attained. Each carburetor should then be drawing the same amount of air. When the test device is moved from one carburetor to the other, the height of the red piston should not change more than 1 in., preferably less.
4. In adjusting the volume control screw of each carburetor, slowly turn the screw clockwise until the engine speed begins to drop, then turn counterclockwise until the engine runs smoothly once again, then a further $\frac{1}{4}$ of a turn in the counterclockwise direction.
5. Recheck the idle speed adjustment, and if necessary increase or decrease the idle speed of each carburetor so that the correct speed is maintained and the test device shows the same reading when it is moved from one carburetor to the other without moving the disc on the device.
6. Recheck the adjustment on the mixture control screws. On the 1600 models, there is a raised portion on the outside perimeter of each screw. This will enable one to feel the position of the screw when he cannot see it. The correct position for the mixture control screw will be approximately $1\frac{1}{2}$ turns from the screwed-in position. When turning the screw fully in the closed position, care should be taken not to apply too much torque, for the seat or needle of the screw could be damaged in this way.
7. After the mixture adjustment has been rechecked, the idle speed and balance should also be checked again and corrected if necessary.
8. In checking the balance of the carburetors at an increased speed, it is necessary to install once again the right-hand connecting rod which was removed in step (1). By means of a suitable object (e.g., a tool box) wedged against the accelerator pedal, the engine speed should be maintained at approximately 1,200–1,500 rpm in order to check the higher speed balance of the two carburetors.
9. Apply the test device to the left-hand carburetor and adjust the disc until the red piston rides in the center of the range. Now move the device over to the right-hand carburetor and, without moving the disc, compare the height of the piston here with the height achieved at the left carburetor. If the height of the piston is higher on the right side, the length of the right-hand connecting rod must be increased slightly. If the height of the piston is lower on the right side, the length of the right-hand connecting rod will have to be decreased. Changing the length of the right-hand connecting rod is accomplished by loosening the nuts on both ends and twisting the rod while leaving the ends stationary. The opposite ends have threads which tighten in opposite directions. The length of the right control rod must be adjusted until there is little or no difference between the readings of the test device when it is moved from one carburetor to the other.
10. After low-speed and high-speed balance has been checked, the connecting rods should be lubricated at their ends with lithium grease and the carburetor's moving parts lubricated with a light oil.
11. Reinstall the oil bath air cleaner, being careful to tighten the two outer wing nuts first, and then the center wing nut. If the center wing nut is tightened first, it is possible that the adjustment of the right-hand carburetor will be altered when the air cleaner is fastened tightly to the screw protruding from its air horn. Replace the crankcase ventilation hose and air intake connections. In order to install the air cleaner it will be necessary to remove the right-hand carburetor connecting rod temporarily. Take care not to bend this rod.

Accelerator Cable R & R, Type 1

The Volkswagen accelerator cable runs from the accelerator pedal to the carburetor by means of the central tunnel, the fan housing and the throttle valve lever. Guide tubes are used in both the central frame tunnel and the fan housing, while a plastic hose is present between the tunnel and the front engine cover plate.

To remove the accelerator cable, disconnect the cable from the throttle lever pin, raise the rear of the car,

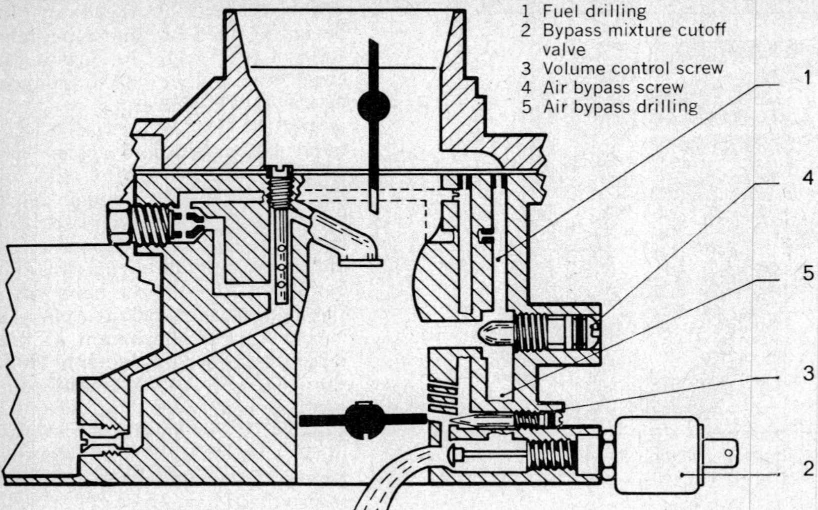

Solex 34 PICT-3 carburetor used on 1971 1,600 cc Type 1 and 2 engines. The volume control screw is factory set. Idling speed adjustments are made with the air bypass screw.

and pull the cable through from the front of the car after disconnecting the rod from the accelerator pedal.

Installation is the reverse of the removal. Grease the cable well before inserting from the front of the car. Be sure that the rear rubber boot and hose are properly seated, so that water will not enter the guide tubes. In order to avoid excessive strain of the throttle cable and assembly, there should be about 1 mm (.04 in.) clearance between the throttle stop and the carburetor body when the throttle is in the wide-open position. For this reason, it is advisable that the cable be tightened down at the carburetor end only when the accelerator pedal is at the fully floored position.

Fuel Injection System

The Bosch electronic fuel injection system is used on all Type 3 and 4 vehicles, beginning with 1968 models. Fuel pressure in the system is maintained at a constant 28 psi by an electric pump and a pressure regulator. Excess fuel bled off by the pressure regulator is routed back to the tank. Opening of the injector valves is timed by a pair of breaker trigger contacts in the base of the ignition distributor. The injector valves open in pairs; cylinders No. 1 and 4, and 2 and 3. The duration of the injector opening, and thus the volume of fuel injected, is regulated by the famous black box, or electronic computer. This unit takes into account inputs from sensors which measure engine temperature, air temperature, engine vacuum, air density, and throttle opening.

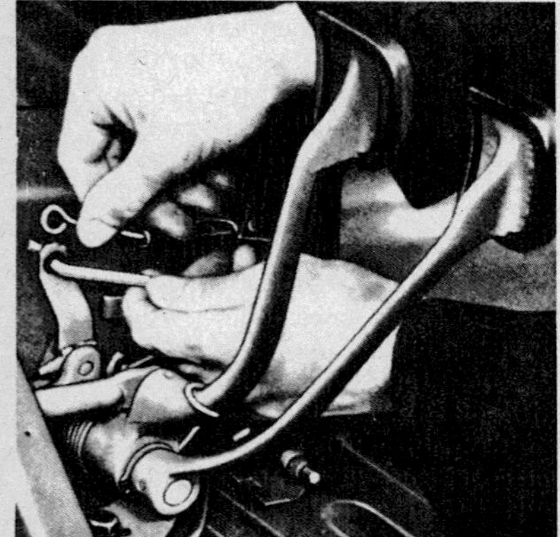

Accelerator cable is removed from the front of the car and is attached as shown.

Testing and troubleshooting of the fuel injection system requires special Bosch electronic testing apparatus. For this reason, these operations are best left to qualified personnel at an authorized dealer's shop. Removal and replacement of components, and adjustments that can be made without special equipment are covered in this section.

Idle Speed Adjustment

The only tune-up adjustment possible on the Bosch electronic fuel injection system is that for idle speed. The adjusting screw is located on the left side of the intake air distributor. Early models have a knurled screw with a lockspring; current models have a locknut on the adjusting screw. After adjusting the idle speed to specifications, make sure that the throttle valve is completely closed at idle.

Throttle Valve Switch Adjustment

The throttle valve switch is mounted to a base plate with graduated markings secured to the intake air distributor inlet. An alignment mark is located on the air distributor housing. The switch is affixed by two mounting screws and an electrical plug. To adjust the switch:

1. Remove the air cleaner for access.
2. Close the throttle valve completely.
3. Loosen the base plate mounting screws. Slowly rotate the switch and plate assembly counterclockwise until a click is heard.
4. Continue rotating the switch and plate assembly counterclockwise one more graduation. (Each graduation indicates 2°.)
5. Tighten the base plate mounting screws.
6. The throttle valve switch should come into operation when throttle has moved 4° from the closed position. Unhook the throttle return spring and check to see that the throttle is not binding.
7. Replace the throttle spring and air cleaner.

Pressure Regulator Adjustment

The pressure regulator is located on the front engine cover plate beneath the right side of the intake manifold. It is fitted with an adjusting nut and a locknut. There is a T-fitting for a pressure gauge in the fuel loop line between the takeoff points for the right side injector units. This fitting is normally plugged with a stopscrew.

NOTE: Before making any adjustment, be absolutely certain that the pressure gauge being used is accurate.

Adjusting idle speed on fuel-injected engine. Turn screw toward a to increase speed. Turn the locknut toward c to tighten.

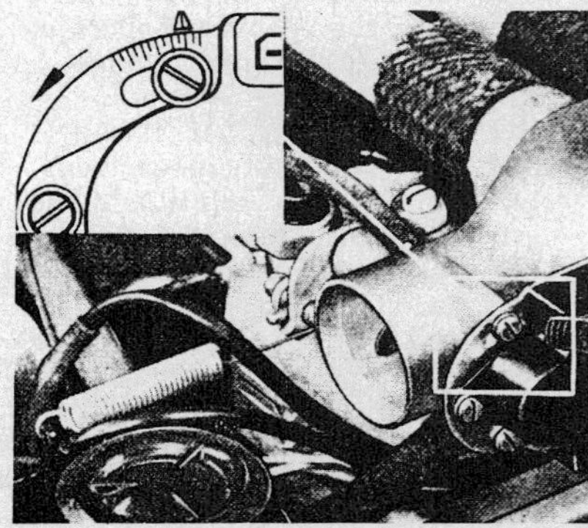

Throttle valve switch details. Each graduation indicates 2°.

To adjust the pressure regulator:

1. Remove the air cleaner for access.
2. Attach the pressure gauge securely to the T-fitting.
3. Start the engine and allow it to idle. Make sure that the idle speed is correct. Adjustment of idling speed is explained in chapter two.
4. If the pressure reading is not 28 psi (2 atmospheres), loosen the locknut and regulate the pressure with the adjusting nut.
5. Tighten the locknut. Check to see that the pressure is still correct.
6. Stop the engine. Disconnect the pressure gauge and plug the T-fitting with a stopscrew. Replace the air cleaner.

Pressure regulator, located under the right side of the intake manifold. A is the locknut; B is the adjusting nut.

Injector R & R

To remove the injectors on either side of the engine.

1. Remove both cable plugs.
2. Unscrew both retainer plate nuts.
3. Pull out both injectors with the retainer plate, centering bushings, base plate, and stud sleeves. Be sure to remove the inner bushings from the intake manifold base.
4. Loosen the hose clamps and pull out the injectors. Be careful not to damage the needles.
5. Reverse the procedure to replace the injectors. Use lockwashers under the retaining nuts. Torque them to 4.3 ft lbs. Install the cable plug with the gray protective cap toward the rear of the car, and the plug with the black cap at the front.

Fuel Filter R & R

The fuel filter is in the pump suction line, either near to, or mounted on, the fuel pump. It should be replaced every 6,000 miles. To replace the filter:

1. Pinch-clamp the fuel lines shut on either side of the filter.
2. Remove the pin holding the filter bracket to the pump. Remove the filter.
3. Install the new filter, making sure that the arrow points to the pump. Replace the bracket and pin.
4. Install screw type hose clamps on the fuel lines.

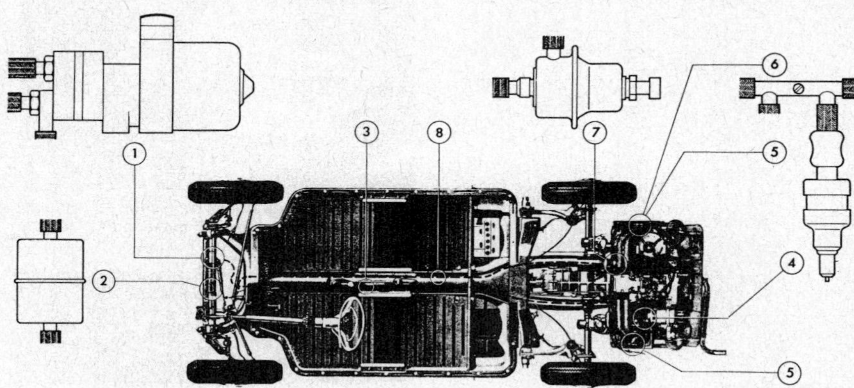

Fuel system of the fuel-injected engine: (1) electric fuel pump, (2) filter, (3) pressure line, (4) ring main, (5) electromagnetic fuel injectors, (6) distributor pipes, (7) pressure regulator, and (8) return line.

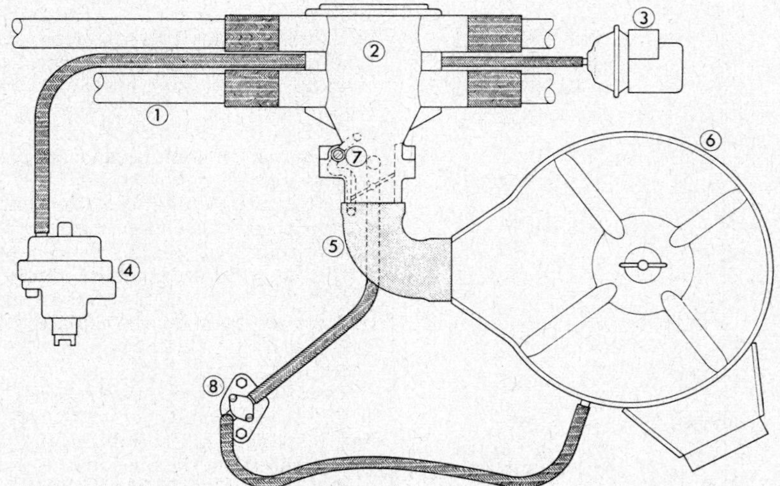

Air system of the fuel-injected engine: (1) intake pipes, (2) intake air distributor, (3) pressure switch, (4) pressure sensor, (5) idle air circuit, (6) air cleaner, (7) idling air screw, (8) auxiliary air regulator.

Exhaust System

Exhaust Pipe, Muffler, and Tail Pipe

R & R, Muffler

To remove the muffler from all Volkswagen models, first remove the clamps from the muffler and heat exchangers. (Early 1963 and earlier models do not have exchangers.) Remove the clips connecting the warm air channels. Loosen the clamps on the tail pipe(s) and remove the tail pipe(s). Remove the nuts from the muffler flange and the preheater adaptor pipe. Remove the four screws from the manifold preheater pipe and take off the muffler, including the gaskets. Check the muffler to be installed and the exhaust pipes for leaks or damage. If necessary, exhaust pipes can be reused. However, in practice, it is often difficult to remove tailpipes from an old muffler without damaging them extensively. This generally occurs with old mufflers that have become rusty, and in such cases it is advisable to install new tailpipes. Type 1 tailpipes should protrude about 7.5 in. on pre-1968 models; 8.3 in. on later models. New gaskets should be used in installing the muffler.

R & R, Heat Exchangers

To remove the heat exchangers, remove the exhaust pipe clamps, the clamps between the heat exchanger and the exhaust pipe, and the rear engine cover plate (Type 1 and 2). Remove the nuts on the cylinder head and the warm air pipe connecting clips. The heat exchanger can now be removed. Check the outer shell and exhaust pipes for damage and leakage. If the heat exchangers leak, there could be a possibility of poisonous gases entering the heating system. Sealing surfaces must be clean and smooth, and flanges that are distorted or bent through excessive tightening should be straightened or machined. Use new gaskets and ensure that all connections are gastight. Heat exchangers must be attached at the cylinder heads with self-locking, 8 mm hexagon nuts. It is not permissible for any other types of nuts to be used, even with lockwashers.

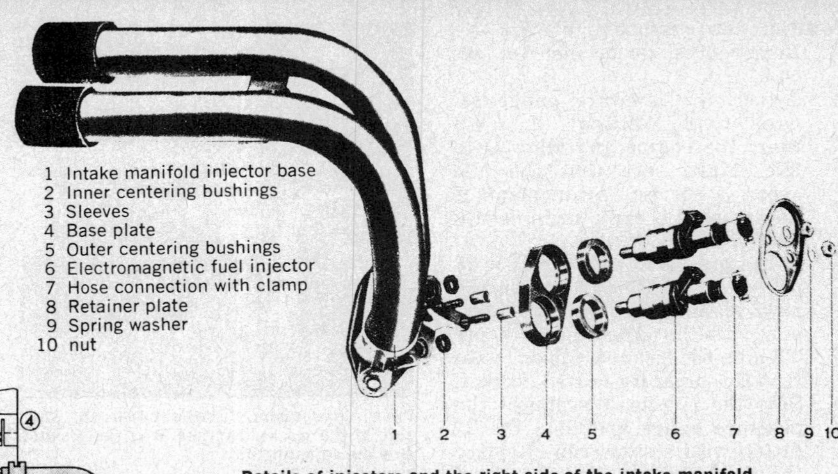

Details of injectors and the right side of the intake manifold.

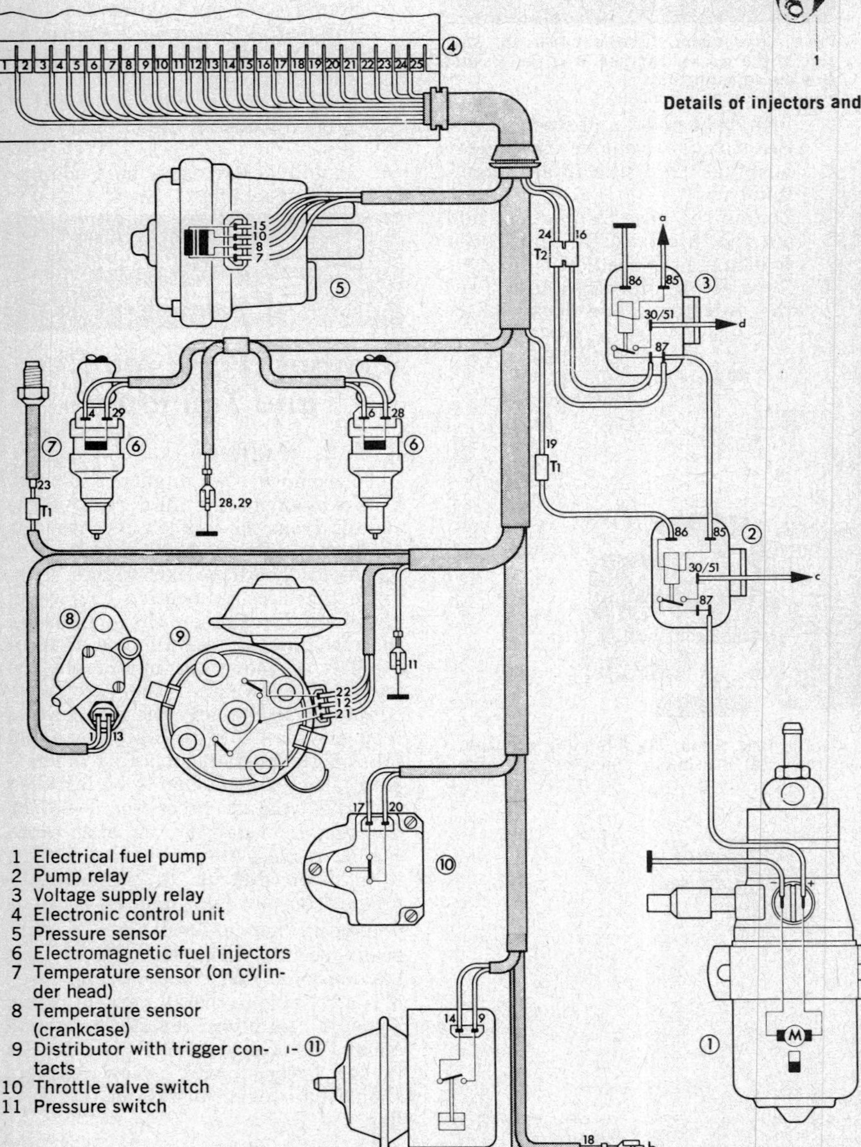

Control system and components of fuel injection system.

Fuel filter, which must be replaced periodically. The arrow shown must point to the pump.

Cooling System

R & R, Fan Housing

Removal of the Type 1 and 2 fan housing is as follows: Remove the two heater hoses and generator strap. Pull out the lead wire of the ignition coil. Remove the distributor cap and take off the spark plug connectors. Remove the retaining screws on both sides of the fan housing. Remove the outer half of the generator pulley and remove the fan belt. Remove the thermostat securing screw and take out the thermostat. Remove the lower part of the carburetor preheater duct. The fan housing can now be removed with the generator. After removal, check the fan housing for damage and for loose air-deflector plates. Accumulated dirt should be removed at this time.

Installation is in the reverse sequence, and involves installation of fan housing flap assemblies and the insertion of the thermostat actuating rod in the cylinder head and lower fan housing. It is necessary that the fan housing fit properly on the cylinder cover plates so that loss of cool-

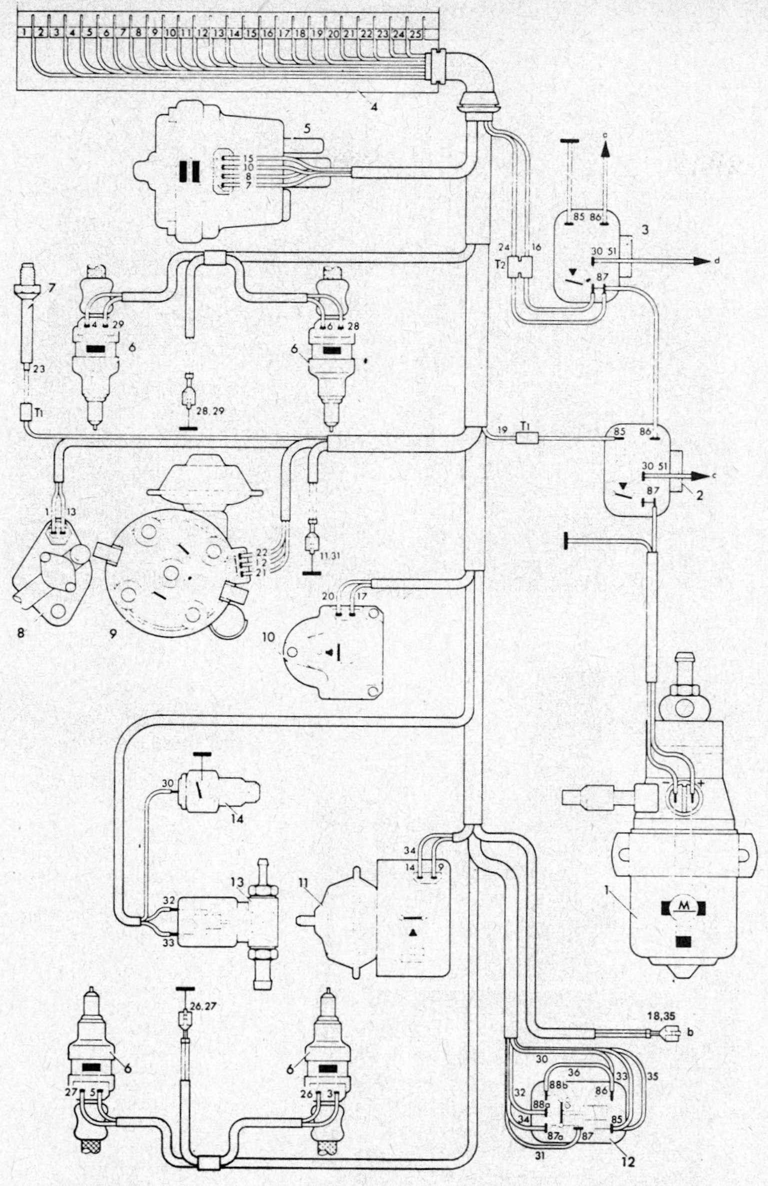

1 Electric fuel pump
2 Pump relay (relay 1)
3 Voltage supply relay (relay 2)
4 Electronic control unit
5 Pressure sensor
6 Elec magnetic fuel injectors
7 Temp sensor (cyl head)
8 Temp sensor (crank-case)
9 Ign distr with trigger contacts
10 Throttle valve switch
11 Pressure switch (no longer used)
12 Relay (cold starting jet)
13 Elec magnetic cut-off (cold starting jet)
14 Thermo switch (cold starting)
a Wire to ign switch (terminal 15)
b Wire to starter solenoid (term. 50)
c Wire to terminal 30
d Wire to pos battery terminal

Control system and components of fuel injection system with cold starting device.

ing air will be avoided. In order to achieve proper fit, the cover plates may have to be bent slightly.

The removal of the fan housing of the Type 3 is accomplished in a slightly different manner due to the different layout of the cooling system of this engine. Remove the crankshaft pulley, the rear fan housing half, and the fan. Unhook the linkage and spring at the right-hand air control flap. Remove the attaching screws of the front half of the fan housing. Prior to installation, the front half of the fan housing should be checked for damage.

In installing the fan housing, first install the front half of the fan housing, ensuring correct sealing with the cylinder cover plates. Replace and tighten the two lower mounting screws slightly. Turn the two halves of the fan housing to the left until the left crankcase half is contacted by the front lug. Tighten the two lower mounting screws fully. Loosen the nuts at the breather support until it can be moved. Insert and tighten the mounting screws of the upper fan housing half. Tighten the breather support nuts fully. Connect the linkage and spring to the right-hand air control flap. Install the fan and the rear half of the fan housing.

R & R, Fan

The cooling fan of the Type 1 and 2 models is removed as follows: using a T-wrench, remove the four retaining screws on the fan cover. Remove the generator and fan. While holding the fan to keep it from rotating, unscrew the fan retaining nut and take off the fan, spacer washers, and hub.

Installation of the fan is as follows: place the hub on the generator shaft, making sure that the woodruff key is securely positioned. Insert the spacer washers. (Note: the distance between the fan and the fan cover should be 1.5–1.8 mm (.06–.07 in.). Place the fan into position and tighten its retaining nut with a torque wrench and socket to 40–47 ft lbs. Check the distance from the fan to the cover. Correct spacing is achieved by inserting the proper number of spacer washers between the hub and the thrust washer. When only one washer is used, the other two should be positioned between the lockwasher and the fan. Insert the generator in the fan housing and tighten the retaining screws on the fan housing cover. (With 1967 and more recent models, be sure that the cooling air intake slot is at the bottom when the retaining plate is screwed onto the fan housing.)

On the Type 3, fan removal begins with the removal of the crankshaft pulley, coil, and the rear half of the fan housing. The fan can then be removed.

On installation of the fan, check the condition of the oil return thread on the fan hub, and install rear half of fan housing, coil and crankshaft pulley.

R & R Fan and Fan Housing Type 4

1. Remove the engine. Remove the fan belt.
2. Remove the allen head screws (3) and remove the belt pulley and fan as an assembly.

NOTE: It is not necessary to remove the alternator to remove the fan housing.

3. Remove the spacer, alternator cover plate, and alternator if necessary.
4. Disconnect the cooling air regulating cable at the shaft.
5. Remove the nuts (4) and remove both halves of the fan housing at the same time.
6. Installation is the reverse of the removal procedure.

Engine

The Volkswagen engine's flat four (i.e., pancake) design has proven itself in automotive, industrial, and aerial applications as one of the most rugged and reliable made in the world today. The four-cycle, overhead valve engine has two pairs of cylinders horizontally opposed; it is attached to the transmission case by four bolts, and is easily removed for service.

The engine in the Type 3 (Fastback and Squareback) series is similar to the "Beetle" engine, the main exception being the location of the cooling fan on the crankshaft rather than on the generator shaft. With the Type 3 engine, there is no chance of cooling fan failure due to fan belt breakage, because there is no fan belt. If the generator belt should fail, the driver could drive some distance in daylight before running out of electricity for the ignition. In addition, the Type 3 engine is slightly different in the location of the oil cooler and, of course, in the layout of the cooling ductwork.

Fan Belt

Adjusting Fan Belt Tension

If belt tension is too great, the result will be a shortening of the life of the generator bearings due to unnecessary stress. If the belt is too loose, the result will be a loss of cooling efficiency in Beetles and a loss of generating power in both the small and large Volkswagens. The following steps should be followed in adjusting the fan belt tension on all Volkswagens, regardless of year:

1. Remove the holding nut from the generator pulley shaft. In Type 3 models, the pulley must be held from turning by using a suitable wrench. In the smaller Volkswagens the pulley is held by a screwdriver wedged between the notch in the generator pulley and the upper generator housing bolt.
2. Remove the outer half of the generator pulley and adjust the fan belt tension by fitting the proper number of spacer washers between the halves of the pulley. Each washer added or removed changes the play in the belt about 1/4 in.
3. If the fan belt is too loose, one or more spacer washers will have to be removed from between the pulley halves. Any spacers not used are installed on the outside of the outer pulley half. If the belt is too tight, one or more washers will have to be added between the pulley halves.
4. When correct adjustment has been achieved, the belt will deflect approximately .6 in. (15 mm) when pressed by thumb pressure at its midpoint.
5. Tighten the pulley nut.

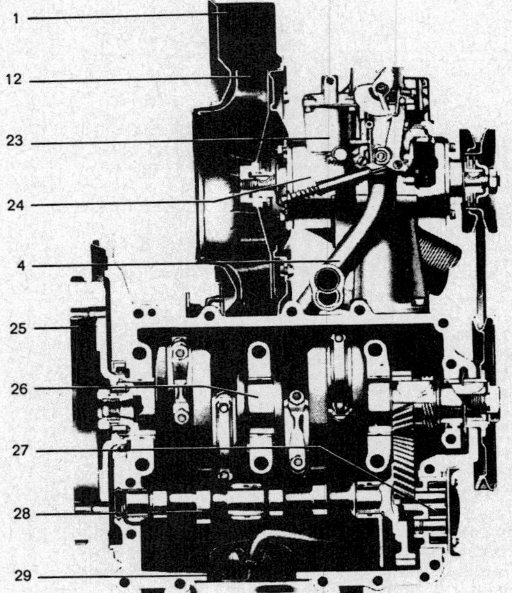

1 Fan housing
2 Ignition coil
3 Oil cooler
4 Intake manifold
5 Fuel pump
6 Ignition distributor
7 Oil pressure switch
8 Valve
9 Cylinder
10 Piston
11 Oil pressure relief valve
12 Fan
13 Oil filter and breather
14 Preheating pipe
15 Connecting rod
16 Spark plug
17 Cylinder head
18 Thermostat
19 Rocker arm
20 Push rod
21 Heat exchanger
22 Cam follower
23 Carburetor
24 Generator
25 Flywheel
26 Crankshaft
27 Oil pump
28 Camshaft
29 Oil strainer

Type 1 and 2 engine.

If the belt has stretched to the extent that correct adjustment can no longer be achieved by removing spacers from between the pulley halves, the belt should be replaced. Also, if a belt has frayed edges or cracks, it should be replaced. Fan belts should be kept free from grease and oil.

It is recommended that a new belt be inspected regularly during the first several hundred miles of use, since new belts have a tendency to stretch slightly.

Exhaust Emission Control

Throttle Regulator Adjustment

The exhaust emission control device used on type 1 and 2 vehicles, 1968–72, is the throttle valve regulator. This device holds the throttle open slightly on deceleration to prevent an excessively rich mixture.

On 1970–72 models, the throttle regulator consists of two parts, connected by a hose. The operating part is mounted at the carburetor, and the control part is located on the left sidewall of the engine compartment. The The 1968–69 unit is one piece, mounted at the carburetor.

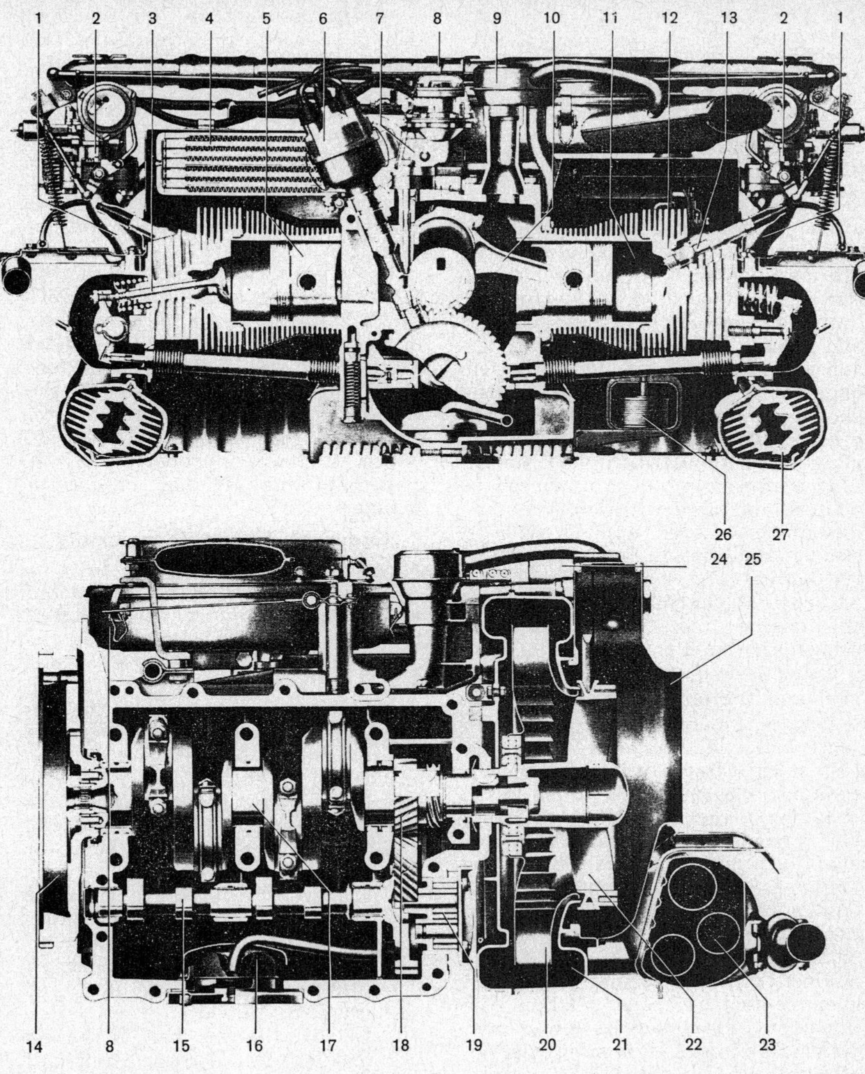

1 Intake pipe
2 Carburetor
3 Valve
4 Oil cooler
5 Piston
6 Distributor
7 Fuel pump
8 Air cleaner
9 Crankcase breather
10 Connecting rod
11 Cylinder
12 Cylinder head
13 Spark plug
14 Flywheel
15 Camshaft
16 Oil strainer
17 Crankshaft
18 Camshaft drive gears
19 Oil pump
20 Fan
21 Fan housing
22 Crankshaft pulley
23 Muffler
24 Coil
25 Cooling air intake housing
26 Thermostat
27 Heat exchanger

Dual carburetor Type 3 engine.

1. The engine must be at operating temperature, with the automatic choke fully open.
2. Start the engine. Turn the regulator adjusting screw clockwise until the control rod just starts to move the throttle valve lever. The stop collar on the control rod will be against the regulator body. Engine speed should be 1,700–1,800 rpm.
3. If speed is too high, shorten the control rod.
4. After adjustment, tighten the locknuts on the control rod.
5. Turn the regulator adjusting screw counterclockwise until an idle speed of 850 rpm is obtained.
6. Increase the engine speed to 3,000 rpm, then release the throttle valve lever. The engine should take 3–4 seconds to return to idle.

Incorrect throttle regulator adjustment may cause erratic idle, excessively high idle speed, and backfiring on deceleration.

Engine Assembly

Engine Removal

NOTE: On Type 4 cars the engine and transmission must be removed as an assembly. The procedure for removing the engine and transmission assembly is found in the transmission removal procedures.

The Volkswagen engine is mounted on the transmission, which in turn is attached to the frame. In the Beetle models, there are four attaching points—two bolts and two studs while on the Type 3 there is an extra mounting point at the rear of the engine. Type 3 vehicles with automatic transmission have front and rear engine and transmission mounts. At the front, the gearbox is supported by the rear tubular crossmember; at the rear, a crossmember is bolted to the crankcase and mounted to the body at either end. When removing the engine from the car, it is recommended that the rear of the car be about three feet off the ground. The engine is removed by bringing it out from underneath the car. However, before raising the car, the following steps should be followed:

1. Disconnect the ground strap from the battery, and cables from the generator (and, in Beetle models, regulator).
2. Remove the air cleaner from the engine, and the rear engine cover plate on Beetle models. Remove the throttle positioner. In Type 2 Volkswagens, with 1600cc engines, remove the rear crossmember.
3. Rotate the distributor of Beetle models so that this part will be able to clear the rear cover plate. *(NOTE: on 1967 and later models, the rear cover plate need not be removed, since the redesigned rear deck and compartment allow sufficient room for engine withdrawal from the car.)*
4. Disconnect the throttle cable from the carburetor(s), and remove the electrical connections to the automatic choke, coil, electromagnetic cut-off jet, and the oil pressure sending unit.
5. Disconnect the fuel hose at the front engine cover plate and seal it to prevent leakage.
6. On Type 3 models, remove the oil dipstick and the rubber boot between the oil filler and body.
7. Remove the cooling air intake bellows on Type 3 models after loosening the clip that secures the unit.
8. Remove the warm air hose on the Type 3 models.
9. After disconnecting the appropriate electrical and control cables, remove the rear engine support (Type 3) and raise the car off the ground.
10. After removing the flexible air hoses between the engine and heat exchangers, disconnect the heater flap cables, unscrew the two lower engine mounting nuts, and slide a jack under the engine. Be sure that it is suitable for supporting the weight of the engine without placing undue

strain on the components. (On Type 2 with 1600cc engine, remove the two bolts from the rubber engine mounts by the muffler.

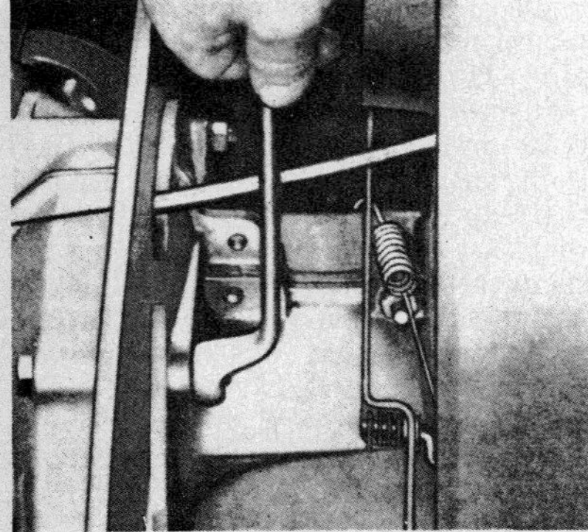

Removing upper engine mounting bolts, Type 1.

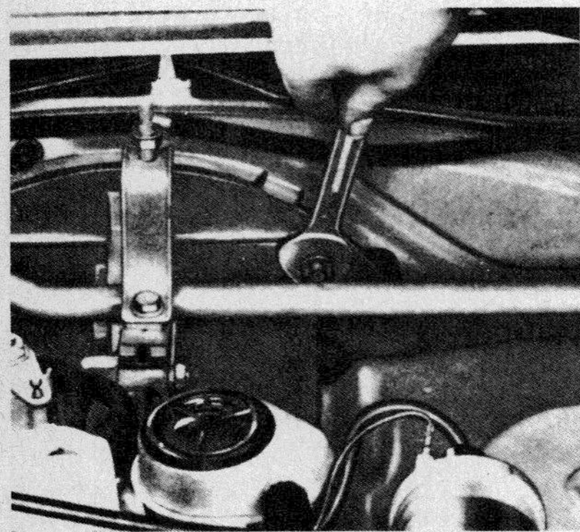

Removing upper engine mounting bolts, Type 3.

On Type 1 Automatic Stickshift models, disconnect the control valve cable and manifold vacuum hoses. Disconnect the ATF suction line and plug it with a 16 X 1.5 mm cap. On Type 3 fully automatic models, disconnect the vacuum hose and kick-down cable. On either model, remove the four 8 mm bolts from the converter drive plate through the holes in the transmission case. After removing the engine, hold the torque converter in place on the transmission with a strap. On fuel-injected Type 3 models, the fuel pressure and return lines must be clamped off and disconnected, and the injection unit wiring disconnected.

11. Raise the jack until it just contacts the engine, and have an assistant hold the bolts of the two upper engine mounts so that you will be able to unscrew the nuts.
12. When the engine mounts are disconnected and there are no remaining cables or controls linking the engine with the car, move the engine backward slightly so that the release plate will be able to clear the main driveshaft.
13. Lower the engine very slowly and be sure that the clutch release plate does not contact the main driveshaft of the transmission.

Engine Installation

Engine installation is the reverse of the preceding operation, although it is important that some special precautions be taken. Before replacing the engine, the clutch plate must be centered, the clutch release bearing and release plate checked for wear, and a number of components greased or cleaned. The starter shaft bush should be lubricated with lithium grease, the needle bearing in the gland nut supplied with one gram of universal grease, the main driveshaft splines lubricated with molybdenum-disulphide powder applied with a clean cloth or brush. Before installing the engine, care must also be taken to ensure that the mating surfaces of the engine and transmission are cleaned thoroughly.

The engine is then lifted into position and the engine rotated via the generator pulley so that the clutch plate hub will engage the transmission shaft splines. In pushing the engine home, care must be taken to see that the gland nut needle bearing, clutch release bearing and main driveshaft are not damaged. After the engine is in position, put the lower engine mounting bolts through the holes in the flange of the transmission case and press the engine against the flange so that proper and even contact is made. Tighten the upper nuts first, then the lower ones. After this initial tightening, tighten all nuts evenly in this same sequence.

On the Type 3 reinstallation, synthetic washers are used to raise the engine about 2–3 mm when the rear engine mounting is attached and tightened. Use only enough washers in the rear mount so that the engine is lifted no more than 3 mm when the mounting is tightened down. Care should be used when installing the rear intake housing bellows of the Type 3 engine, for this unit can be easily damaged through careless handling. Reconnect the cables and controls. Attach the thick lead to terminal D+ of the generator. Adjust the accelerator cable with the engine at full throttle and set the ignition timing.

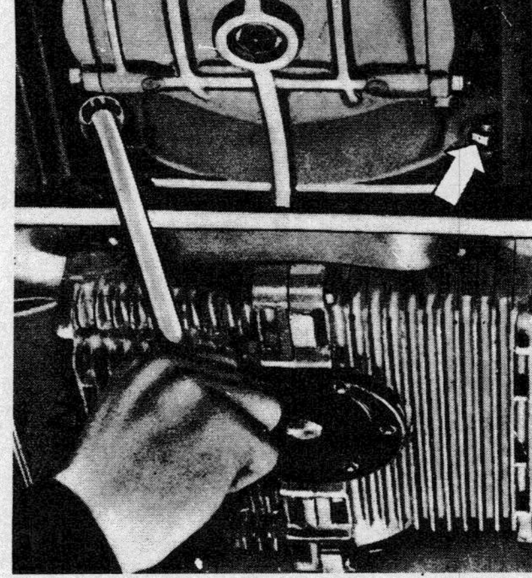

Removing lower engine mounting nuts, Type 1.

To avoid interference with the function of the automatic stickshift clutch, take care to route the connecting hoses so that they are not kinked or jammed when installing the engine. This applies particularly to the small-diameter pipe from the control valve to the carburetor venturi, which will work properly only if routed in the original production manner.

Order of Engine Disassembly Operations

The disassembly of the Type 3 and type 4 engine is different from that of the other VW engines mainly in the removal of the engine cover plates and cooling ductwork. In tearing down a Volkswagen engine, the following is the recommended sequence of operations:

1. Drain the engine oil.
2. Remove the hoses between the engine and the heat exchangers.
3. Remove the front engine cover plate.
4. Remove the muffler and intake manifold, including the carburetor(s).
5. Remove the fan belt, cooling air intake housing, generator, and crankshaft pulley.
6. Remove the rear half of the fan housing, fan, and the front half of the fan housing.
7. Remove the distributor and fuel pump, and take out the distributor drive pinion.
8. Remove the cooling air ductwork from the cylinder area.
9. Remove the oil cooler.
10. Remove the rocker arm shaft and cylinder heads.
11. Remove the cylinders and pistons.
12. Remove the clutch assembly and flywheel.
13. Remove the oil pump and oil strainer.
14. Disassemble the crankcase and remove the camshaft, crankshaft, and connecting rods.

Assembly, generally speaking, is the reverse of the foregoing procedure.

NOTE: The torque, capacity, tune-up, and clearance figures given in the text apply, generally, to the most common engines. However, since there are so many variations in production, it is always best to consult the applicable chart for the figure in question.

Cylinder Heads

R & R

In order to remove the cylinder head of either pair of cylinders, it is first necessary that the rocker arm assembly be removed. The cylinder head is held in place by eight studs. Since the cylinder head also holds the cylinders in place in the VW engine, if it is not desired that the cylinders be removed, they should be held in place with an appropriate holding clamp. After the rocker arm cover, the rocker arm retaining nuts and rocker arm assembly have been removed, the cylinder head nuts can be removed and the cylinder head lifted off.

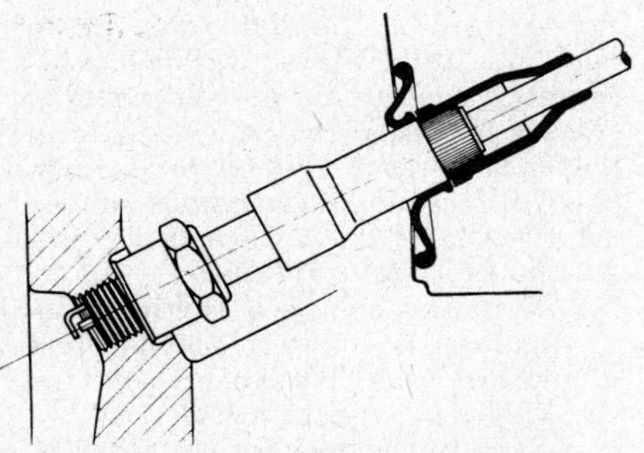

The rubber spark plug seals should fit snugly against the cooling ducts so that cooling air does not escape.

Push rod tube length (distance a) is 190-191 mm for 1,300, 1,500, and 1,600 cc engines, and 180.5-181.5mm for the 40 hp 1,200 cc engines. No measurement is given for earlier engines.

When reinstalling the cylinder head, several points must be remembered. The cylinder head should be checked for cracks both in the combustion chamber and in the intake and exhaust ports. Cracked cylinder heads should be replaced. Spark plug threads should be checked at this time for tightness. If the threads are stripped, they can be corrected by means of Heli-coil threaded inserts. On 1963 and later engines, no gasket is necessary between the cylinder head and the cylinders. However, on earlier models, which do not have a fresh air heating system, a gasket should be fitted. New seals should be used on the push rod tube ends, and should be checked for proper seating.

The push rod tubes should be turned so that the seam faces upward. In order to ensure perfect sealing, used tubes should be stretched to the correct length of 190–191mm before they are installed. (Note: in the 40 hp engine, the correct length is 180.5–181.5 mm On the 40 hp engine, the sealing ring between the outer shoulder of the cylinder and the cylinder head should be renewed, placing the slotted side of the ring toward the cylinder head. On the 50 hp engine of 1966 and subsequent engines, no sealing ring is needed.)

After inserting the cylinder head nut washers, the cylinder head nuts should be tightened slightly, and then to a torque of 7 ft lbs before fully tightening them to a torque of 23 ft lbs (27 ft lbs in 1959 and earlier models). The sequence of tightening shown in the tightening sequence diagram should be followed. (Note the different sequences for the initial and final tightening procedures.)

Cylinders

R & R

Before removing the cylinders, the cylinder head, valve push rods, push rod tubes, and deflector plate below the cylinders must be taken out. The cylinders may then be pulled off. Match-mark the cylinders for reassembly.

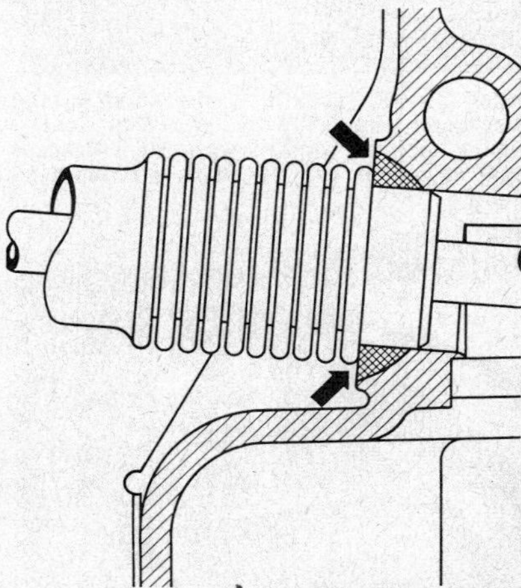

The oil seals at the ends of the push rod tubes must be properly seated to prevent leakage.

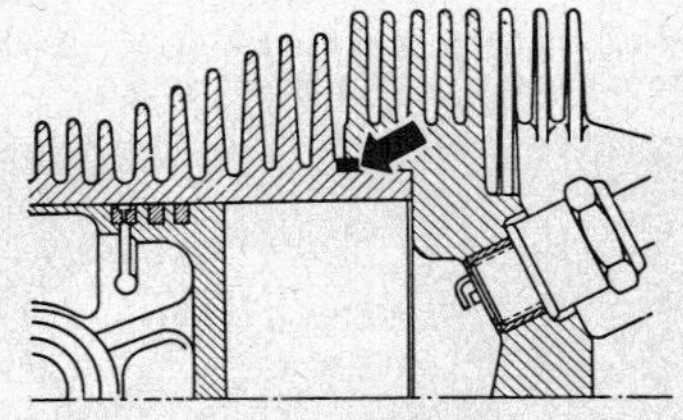

On pre-1963 engines a cylinder head gasket is used. The slotted side of the gasket must be toward the cylinder head.

Reinstall the cylinders as follows:

Cylinders should be checked for wear, and if necessary replaced with another matched cylinder and piston assembly of the same size. Also check the cylinder seating surface on the crankcase, cylinder shoulder, and gasket, for cleanliness. Foreign matter here could cause leaks due to distortion of the mating parts. When reinstalling the cylinders, a new gasket should be used between each cylinder and the crankcase.

The piston rings and piston pin should be liberally oiled (a MoS_2 based lubricant is suitable). Compress the rings with a compression tool. Be sure that ring gaps are adequate and staggered on the piston with the oil ring inserted into the cylinder so that its gap is positioned UP when the pistons are in their horizontal position in the engine.

Lubricate the cylinder wall and slide the cylinder over the piston. Crankcase studs should not contact the cylinder cooling fins. Install the deflector plates under the cylinders, bending slightly if necessary to make them seat tightly on the cylinder head studs.

Install the push rod tubes and push rods, ensuring that the tubes are inserted with the seam facing upward and are of the proper length.

Valve Train

Adjusting Valve Clearance

If valve clearances in the Volkswagen engine are too small, the valves can be seriously damaged by warping or burning, and compression will eventually suffer from the lack of proper valve sealing. On the other hand, if the valve clearance is too great, the result will be rough run-

The deflector plates under the cylinders must be tight against the cylinder studs to prevent rattles.

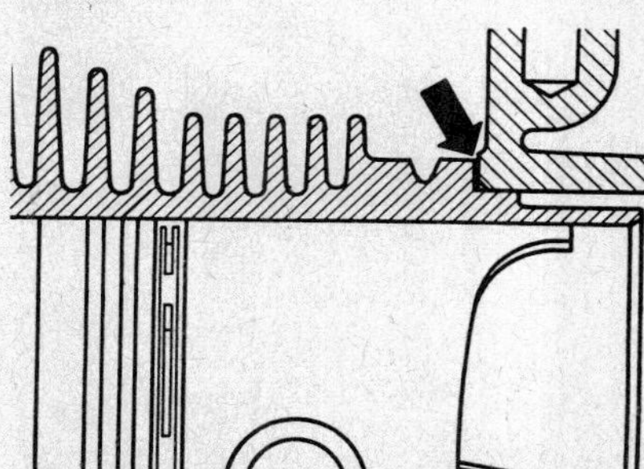

Foreign matter between the cylinder and the crankcase could cause distortion of the cylinder. The gasket indicated should not be reused.

ning, loss of power, and excessive wear of the valve train components.

Before the valves can be adjusted in any Volkswagen, the engine must be cold, preferably after sitting overnight. Volkswagen valve clearances vary somewhat between models of different years. To determine the correct setting, refer to both the "Tune-Up Specifications" chart and the engine sticker.

Preference is to be given to the valve clearance specified on the engine fan housing sticker, if one is present. On models built after late 1964, such a sticker will be on the fan housing. Such stickers will also be present on all factory rebuilt engines, regardless of horsepower output, and the clearances specified should be followed closely.

Steps in Adjustment

1. Remove the distributor cap and turn the engine until the rotor points to the notch in the distributor rim and the crankshaft pulley timing mark is aligned with the crankcase split or pointer. No. 1 cylinder is now at top dead center of its compression stroke. See the illustration showing cylinder numbering.
2. Remove the rocker arm cover of cylinders no. 1 and 2.
3. With the proper feeler gauge, check the clearance between the adjusting screw and the valve stem of both valves for no. 1 cylinder. If the feeler gauge slides in snugly without being forced, the clearance is correct.
4. If the clearance is incorrect, the lock-nut must be loosened and the adjusting screw turned until the proper clearance is attained. After tightening the locknut, it is advisable to recheck the clearance, because it is possible to alter the adjustment when tightening the locknut.
5. Turn the engine one-half revolution in the counterclockwise direction. This will turn the distributor rotor 90° in the counterclockwise direction so that it will now point to the lead wire for cylinder no. 2. No. 2 cylinder is now at top dead center.
6. Repeat the adjustment process for cylinder no. 2.
7. Replace valve rocker arm cover on cylinders no. 1 and 2, using a new gasket and cleaning off the seating surfaces to guard against leakage.
8. Remove the valve rocker arm cover on cylinders no. 3 and 4.
9. Turn the engine another one-half turn in the counterclockwise direction so that the distributor rotor now points to the lead wire of cylinder no. 3. No. 3 cylinder is now at top dead center.
10. Adjust the clearances on cylinder no. 3.

NOTE: On pre-1971 Type 1 and 2 engines, no. 3 cylinder runs hotter than the other three cylinders because its cooling air flow is partially blocked by the oil cooler. To counter a tendency for this cylinder to burn exhaust valves, some mechanics set the no. 3 exhaust valve clearance .001–.002 in. wider than specified.

11. Turn the engine a further one-half turn counterclockwise and adjust the clearances of the valves in cylinder no. 4.
12. Replace the rocker arm cover of cylinders no. 3 and 4, cleaning the sealing surfaces and using a new gasket.
13. Replace the distributor cap. Replace the belt housing cover in Type 3 models.

When sliding the cylinder over the piston, the crankcase studs must not be allowed to contact the cylinder cooling fins.

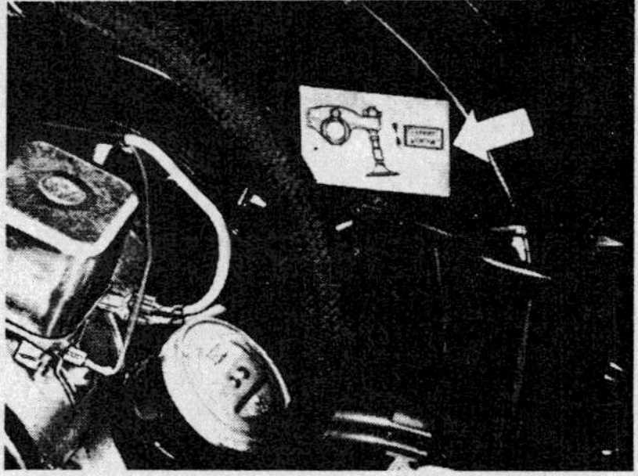

Most late model engines have the correct valve clearance indicated on a sticker on the fan housing.

When the rotor points to the notch in the distributor rim and the crankshaft pulley timing mark is aligned with the crankcase split or pointer, cylinder no. 1 is at top dead center.

Turning the adjusting screw while checking valve clearance with a feeler gauge.

If the engine is turned backward one-half revolution from the firing point for no. 1 cylinder, the distributor rotor will turn backward one quarter turn to the firing point for no. 2 cylinder. Proceeding backward in this manner, the valves can be adjusted in 1-2-3-4 order.

R & R, Rocker Arm Mechanism

Before the valve rocker assembly can be reached, it is necessary to undo the clip that retains the cover plate. Remove the rocker arm retaining nuts, the rocker arm shaft and the rocker arms. Remove the stud seals.

Before installing the rocker arm mechanism, be sure that the parts are as clean as possible, including the inside of the cover plate. Install the stud seals and the rocker shaft, making sure that the chamfered edges of the supports are pointing outward and the slots, upward. Tighten the retaining nuts to a torque of 14–18 ft lbs. The only type of retaining nuts which should be used are 8 mm nuts of the 8 G grade. These nuts are distinguishable by their copper color. Ball ends of the push rods must be centered in the sockets of the rocker arms. In addition, to help valves rotate during operation, the rocker arm adjusting screws should contact the tip of the valve slightly off center. It should be neither in the center nor all the way to one side, but exactly in the middle of the two extremes. After adjusting valves to their proper clearance, reinstall the cover plate with a new gasket. Be sure that the proper cover plate gasket is used. There are two types of gaskets, early and late. the late type is straight across the top edge, while the early type has a tab in the center of the top edge. After the engine has been run for a brief period, check the cover plates for oil leakage.

Disassembly and Assembly of Rocker Arm Mechanism

Remove the spring clips from the rocker arm shaft. Remove the washers, rocker arms, and bearing supports. Before installation, check the rocker arm shaft for wear, and the seats and ball sockets of the rocker arm adjusting screws. Loosen the adjusting screws before installing the rocker arms. Otherwise, installation is the reverse of the disassembly procedure.

R & R, Valves

In order to remove the valves, the cylinder head must first be taken off. With the cylinder head removed, compress the valve springs with a special tool and remove valve keys, valve spring caps, valve springs, and oil deflector rings. Remove the valves from cylinder head after removing any burrs that may be present near the seating surface of the keys on the valve stem. While the valve springs are out, they should be tested. Proper valve spring pressures are given in the "Engine Rebuilding Specifications" chart for "valves." Valve keys should be checked prior to installation, and new and worn keys ground at the joining faces until it is still possible to turn the valve when the key halves are pressed together. Valve stems should be checked for run-out and valve guides for wear. Valves should be checked for leaks and for wear. Because exhaust valves generally do heavy-duty work in the air-cooled engine of the Volkswagen, it is good practice to replace them since their cost is not great and the engine is already apart. If the stems of the valves are hammered in, the valves can still be used again after valve caps have been installed. Polish rough valve stems carefully with emery cloth. After coating the valve stems with a moly paste, insert them into their guides and fit oil deflector rings. Install valve springs with the close-wound coils facing the cylinder head. Used valves must be refaced before being reinstalled. Damaged seats must also be reconditioned.

Crankcase

Disassembly and Assembly of the Crankcase

With the cylinders, pistons, and cylinder heads removed, the crankcase is split as follows:

1. Remove the oil strainer, oil pressure switch, and crankcase nuts. Remove the flywheel and oil pump.
2. Keep the cam followers of the right crankcase half in position by using the retaining springs.
3. Use a rubber hammer to break the seal between the crankcase halves. Never insert sharp tools, wedges, etc., between the crankcase halves; this will surely lead to serious leakage of lubricant.

Use of a valve spring compressor to remove valves.

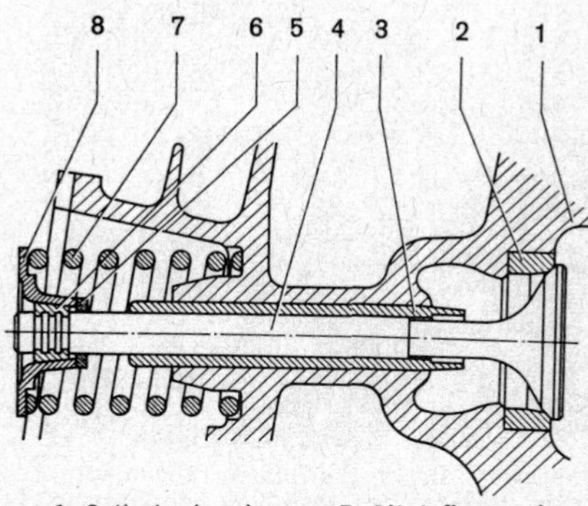

Details of a typical valve.

4. After the seal between the mating surfaces has been broken, remove the right-hand crankcase half, the crankshaft oil seal and camshaft end plug, and lift out the camshaft and the crankshaft.
5. Remove the cam followers, bearing shells, and oil-pressure relief valve.

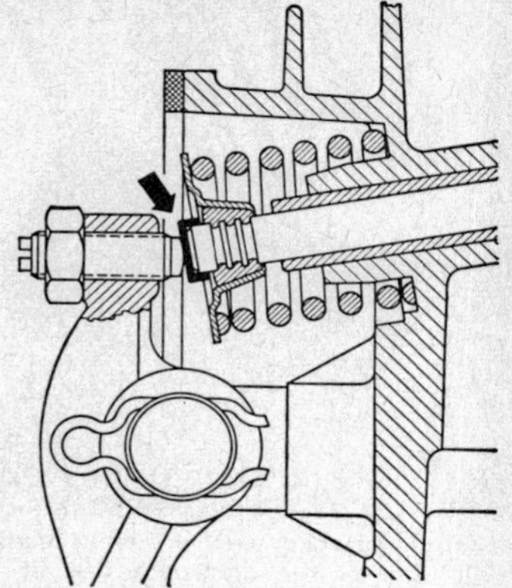

Valves with a damaged stem can be reused after fitting a cap.

Assembly is generally the reverse of the foregoing procedure, but includes the following:

1. Before reassembling the crankcase, check it for damage and cracks after cleaning thoroughly. Mating and sealing surfaces should be cleaned especially well. A solvent should be used to remove traces of the old sealant from the mating surfaces.
2. Flush and blow out all ducts and oil passages.
3. Check the oil suction pipe for leaks.
4. Check the studs for tightness. If tapped holes are worn, correction involves the installation of Helicoil inserts.
5. Insert the cam followers after checking both the followers and their bores in the crankcase.
6. Install the crankshaft bearing dowel pins and bearing shells for crankshaft and camshaft.
7. Install the crankshaft and camshaft after bearings have been well lubricated. (When installing the crankshaft, note the position of the timing marks on the timing gears.)
8. Install the camshaft end plug, using sealing compound.
9. Install the thrust washers and crankshaft oil seal. The oil seal must rest squarely on the bottom of its recess in the crankcase.
10. Check and install the oil pressure switch.
11. Spread a thin film of sealing compound on the crankcase joining faces. Use care so that no sealing compound enters the oil passages of the crankshaft or the camshaft bearings.
12. Keep the cam followers of the right crankcase half in place by using retaining springs.
13. Join the crankcase halves and evenly torque the fasteners to the torque specified in the "Engine Torque Specifications" chart.

Exploded view, rocker arm mechanism.

After being loosened with a rubber mallet, the right half of the crankcase can be removed. Prying tools should never be used to separate the crankcase halves.

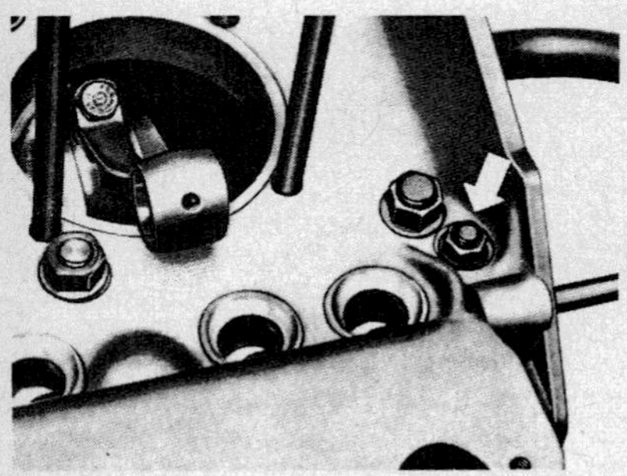

The 8 mm nut pointed out must be tightened fully before the 12 mm nuts are tightened.

NOTE: First tighten the 8 mm nut which is beside the 12 mm stud of the no. 1 crankshaft bearing. Only then should the 12 mm nuts be tightened fully.)

14. Turn the crankshaft to check for ease of movement, and check the endplay of the crankshaft. The crankshaft end-play is measured with the engine assembled and the flywheel installed.

Camshaft and Timing Gears

R & R. Camshaft

Removal of the camshaft requires splitting of the crankcase. The camshaft and camshaft bearing shells are then easily removed. Before reinstalling the camshaft, it should be checked for wear of the bearing faces and bearing points. In addition, the riveted joint between the camshaft timing gear and the camshaft should be examined for security. If there is slight damage to the camshaft, it may be smoothed with a silicon carbide oilstone. A 100–120 grit stone is first used to smooth the damaged area, and then a 280–320 stone may be used for final polishing. The camshaft should be checked for run-out, which should not exceed .0008 in. The timing gear should be checked for correct tooth contact and for wear, and the edges of the camshaft bearing bores lightly chamfered to avoid seizure. If the camshaft shells removed are either worn or damaged, new shells should be fitted. The camshaft bearing shells should be installed with the tabs engaging the notches in the crankcase. Before installing the camshaft, the bearing journals and cams should be generously coated with oil. When the camshaft is installed, care should be taken to ensure that the timing gear tooth marked "O" is located between the two teeth of the crankshaft timing gear marked by a center punch. The end-play at the thrust bearing (bearing no. 3) is .06–.11 mm (.002–.004 in.) and the wear limit is .14 mm (.006 in.).

Camshaft bearings. Note the thrust flange on bearing no. 3, in the foreground.

The arrow shows the proper alignment of timing marks when installing the camshaft and crankshaft.

Crankshaft

R & R, Crankshaft Pulley

On the Type 1 and 2, the crankshaft pulley can be removed while the engine is still in the car. However, in this instance it is necessary for the rear cover plate of the engine to be removed. Remove the cover plate after taking out the screws in the cover plate below the crankshaft pulley. Remove the fan belt and the crankshaft pulley securing screw. Using a puller tool, remove the crankshaft pulley. The crankshaft pulley should be checked for proper seating and for proper belt contact surface. The oil return thread should be cleaned and lubricated with a molybdenum-disulphide based oil. The crankshaft pulley should be installed in the reverse sequence, and should have no run-out.

On the Type 3, the crankshaft pulley can be removed only when the engine is out of the car and the muffler, generator, and cooling air intake housing are removed. After these parts have been removed, take out the plastic cap on the pulley. This can be done easily with a screwdriver. Remove the crankshaft pulley retaining bolt and remove the pulley.

Installation is the reverse of the preceding but the following should be noted: when installing, use a new paper gasket between the fan and the crankshaft pulley. If shims are used, do not forget them. No more than two shims may be used. When inserting the pulley, make sure that the pin engages the hole in the fan. The crankshaft pulley retaining bolt should be tightened to a torque of 94–108 ft lbs. Ensure that the clearance between the generator belt and the intake housing is at least 4 mm and that the belt is parallel to the housing. Check the seal on the cooling air intake housing and if damaged, cement a new seal into place. On the Type 4, the pulley is removed with the fan.

Crankshaft End-Play

With the engine installed, the crankshaft end-play can be read with a dial indicator mounted at the pulley side of the engine. End-play should be as specified with an upper wear limit of .15 mm (.006 in.). When the engine is not installed, crankshaft end-play can be measured at the flywheel end with an indicator mounted on the flywheel. Desirable end-play is obtained by adding or subtracting shims at the outer end of the main bearing. Shims for this purpose are available in various thicknesses. Never use more than one gasket.

R & R, Flywheel

The flywheel is attached to the crankshaft with a gland nut, and is located by four dowels. Some models have a paper gasket between the flywheel and the crankshaft; others have a metal gasket. Beginning with the 1967 model year, a metal sealing gasket is no longer present between the flywheel and crankshaft. An oil seal is recessed in the crankcase casting at no. 1 main bearing. A needle bearing, which supports the main driveshaft, is located in the gland nut. Prior to removing the flywheel, it is necessary to remove the clutch pressure plate and the clutch driven plate. Loosen the gland nut and remove it, using a 36 mm special wrench and flywheel retainer. Remove the gland nut and withdraw the flywheel.

Installation is the reverse of the above procedure, plus the following: check the flywheel teeth for wear and

With the engine assembled and the flywheel installed, crankshaft end-play should be .06-.12 mm (.003-.005 in.) with a wear limit of .15 mm (.006 in.).

damage. Check the dowel holes in the flywheel and crankshaft, and renew the dowels if necessary. Adjust the crankshaft end-play and check the needle bearing in the gland for wear.

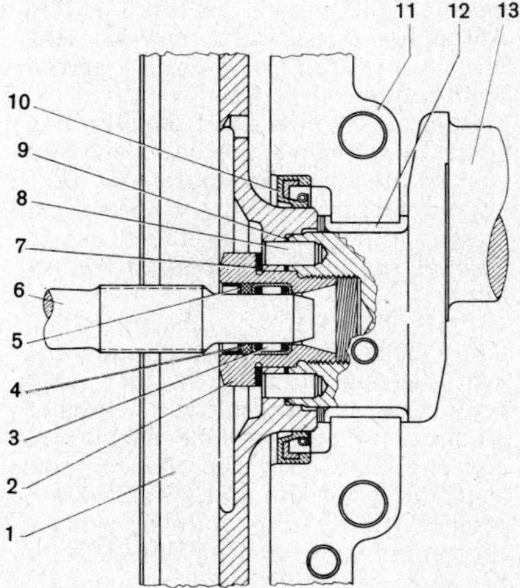

1 Flywheel
2 Gland nut
3 Needle bearing
4 Felt ring
5 Retaining ring
6 Main driveshaft
7 Lockwasher
8 Dowel pin
9 Paper or metal gasket
10 Oil seal
11 Crankcase
12 Crankshaft bearing
13 Crankshaft

Cross-sectional view of flywheel and crankshaft end.

Lubricate the needle bearing with about 10 grams of universal grease. Insert the flywheel gasket, if one is used in the engine. (Note: to minimize engine imbalance, the crankshaft, flywheel, and clutch are marked at their heaviest points. Upon assembly, be sure that the marks on these units are offset by 120°. If but two of these parts are marked, the marks should be offset by 180°. Tighten flywheel gland nut to 217 ft lbs and check flywheel run-out, which should be a maximum of .3 mm (.012 in.).

R & R, Crankshaft Oil Seal (engine assembled)

Oil losses at the flywheel could well be the result of a leaky crankshaft oil seal. This seal is removed after removing the flywheel. After the flywheel is removed, inspect the surface on the flywheel joining flange where the oil seal makes contact. Remove the old oil seal by prying it out of its counterbore. Before installing a new crankshaft oil seal, clean the crankcase oil seal recess and coat it thinly with sealing compound. The sharp edges should be slightly chamfered so that the outer edge of the seal is not damaged. Using VW tool 204b, press in the new seal, being sure that it rests squarely on the bottom of its recess. Remove the tool and reinstall the flywheel after coating the oil seal contact surface with oil.

The flywheel gland nut is torqued to 30 mkg (217 ft lbs).

R & R, Crankshaft and Connecting Rods

Removal of the crankshaft requires splitting of the crankcase halves and the withdrawal of the camshaft. When installing the crankshaft, check to see that the crankcase does not have sharp edges at the points of junction. If foreign matter has become lodged in the main bearings, it will be necessary to remove it with a scraper, taking care not to remove material from the bearing shell itself. Check the dowel pins for tightness. Place one half of no. 2 crankshaft bearing in the crankcase. Slide on crankshaft bearing no. 1 so that the dowel pin hole is toward the flywheel. Install the crankshaft, making sure that the dowel pins are correctly seated in the crankshaft bearings. When installing the camshaft, note the marks on the timing gears.

A special tool is needed to install the crankshaft oil seal.

After the crankshaft has been removed and clamped into position, remove the connecting rod clamping bolts and the connecting rods and caps. Inspect the piston pin bushing. With a new bushing, the correct clearance is indicated by a light finger push-fit of the pin at room temperature. Check and, if necessary, correct connecting rod alignment. Reinsert the connecting rod bearing shells after all parts have been thoroughly cleaned and assemble the connecting rods on the crankshaft. The identification numbers stamped on the connecting rods and bearing caps must both be on one side.

NOTE: New connecting rod screws should always be used and the wax removed from the screws before they are installed.

Tighten the connecting rod bolts to the specified torque. A slight pretension between the bearing halves, which is likely to occur when tightening connecting rod bolts, can be eliminated by light hammer taps. The connecting rods, lubricated with engine oil prior to assembly, must slide on the crankpin by their own weight. The connecting rod bushings must not be scraped, reamed or filed during assembly. Using a peening chisel, secure the connecting rod bolts in place.

Engine Lubrication

R & R, Oil Strainer

All Volkswagen models are equipped with the same type of oil strainer, a view of which is shown in the accompanying diagram. The oil strainer can be easily removed simply by removing the restraining nuts, washers, oil strainer plate, strainer and gaskets. Once taken out, the strainer must be thoroughly cleaned and all traces of old gaskets removed prior to fitting new ones. The suction pipe should be checked for tightness

Note that the marks on the connecting rods are pointing upward, while the rods are pointing toward their respective cylinders.

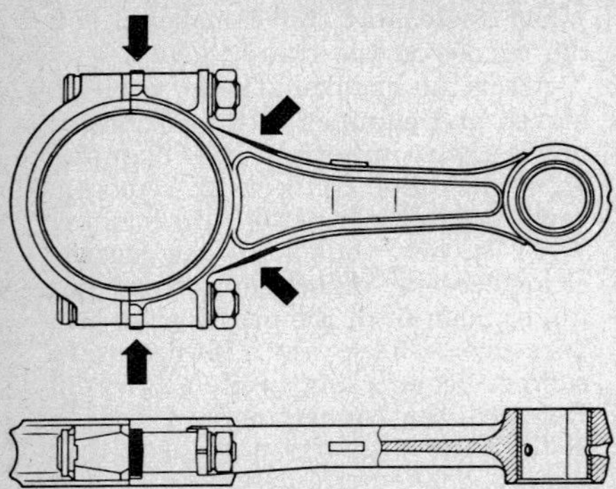

Maximum allowable weight difference between connecting rods in one engine is 10 grams. Metal may be removed from the portions of the connecting rod indicated.

Measuring the axial (side) play of the connecting rods with a feeler gauge.

and proper position. When the strainer is installed, be sure that the suction pipe is correctly seated in the strainer. If necessary, the strainer may be bent slightly. The measurement from the strainer flange to the tip of the suction pipe should be 10 mm, plus or minus 1 mm. The measurement from the flange to the bottom of the strainer should be 6 mm plus or minus 1 mm. The cap nuts at the bottom of the strainer should not be overtightened, for the bottom plate may become distorted and lead to leakage of engine lubricant. If it is desired, the strainer can be equipped with a permanent magnet designed to retain metal particles that are circulating in the oil. This magnet is held in place by means of a spring clip, and should be removed and cleaned whenever the strainer is removed for the same purpose. Magnetic drain plugs are also available. Type 4 engines have an oil filter that is a replaceable cartridge.

R & R, Oil Cooler

The Volkswagen oil cooler is mounted on the crankcase and is positioned in the path of the cooling air. The oil cooler in the Type 1 can be removed with the engine in the car, but it is first necessary that the fan housing be removed. The oil cooler can be removed after the three oil cooler retaining nuts have been taken off. The gaskets should be removed along with the oil cooler and replaced with new ones when the cooler is installed. Before installation, the oil cooler should be checked for leaks at a pressure of 85 psi. If the cooler is found to leak, the oil pressure relief valve should also be checked. The studs and bracket on the cooler should be checked for tightness. See that the hollow ribs of the oil cooler do not touch one another. Clean the contact surfaces on the crankcase, install new gaskets, and attach the oil cooler. Tighten the retaining nuts. On the

1 Gasket
2 Oil strainer
3 Gasket
4 Cover plate
5 Cap nut with washer
6 Plug with washer

Crankcase oil strainer components. The strainer must be cleaned at each oil change, and new gaskets must be used.

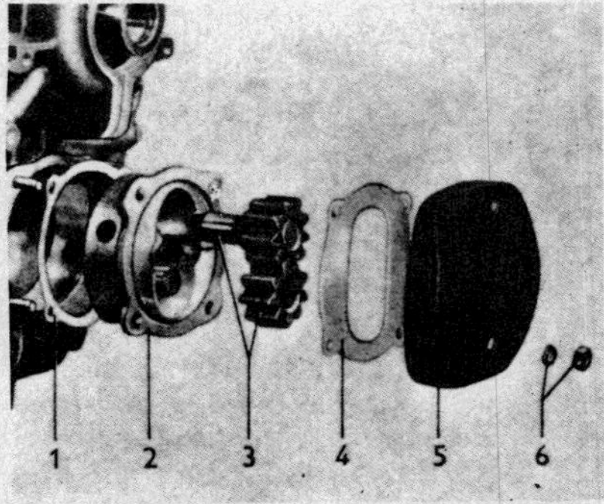

1 Gasket
2 Oil pump body
3 Gears
4 Gasket
5 Oil pump cover
6 Nut and spring washer

Oil pump components, Type 1.

Types 3 and 4, be sure that a spacer ring is present between the crankcase and the cooler at each securing screw. If these rings are omitted, the seals may be squeezed too tightly, resulting in a stoppage of oil flow and consequent damage to the engine. The Type 3 oil cooler is similar in design to that of the Type 1 and 2, except that it lies horizontally cross-wise in the path of the air, while that of the other models is in a vertical position.

Beginning 1971, the Type 1 and 2 oil cooler is mounted farther forward on an intermediate flange and has its own cooling air supply through the fan housing. This prevents the oil cooler from blocking off the cooling air to no. 3 cylinder and causing that cylinder to run hot.

R & R, Oil Pump

An exploded view of the Volkswagen oil pump is given in the accompanying illustration. In the Type 3, the oil pump can be taken out only after the engine is removed from the car and the air intake housing, the belt pulley fan housing, and the fan are dismantled. On the Types 1 and 2, the pump can be removed with the engine in the car, but it is first necessary to remove the cover plate, the crankshaft pulley, and the cover plate under the pulley. Removal from all model Volkswagens is similar. On Automatic Stickshift models, the torque converter oil pump is driven by the engine oil pump.

Remove the nuts from the oil pump cover and remove the cover and its gasket. Remove the gears and take out the pump body with a special extractor. Care should be taken not to damage the inside of the pump housing.

Prior to assembly, check the oil pump body for wear, especially the gear seating surface. If the pump body is worn, the result will be loss of oil pressure and possible damage to the engine. Check the driven gear shaft for tightness and, if necessary, peen it tightly into place or replace the pump housing. The dimension *a* in the accompanying diagram should be .5–1.0 mm (.02–.04 in.) The

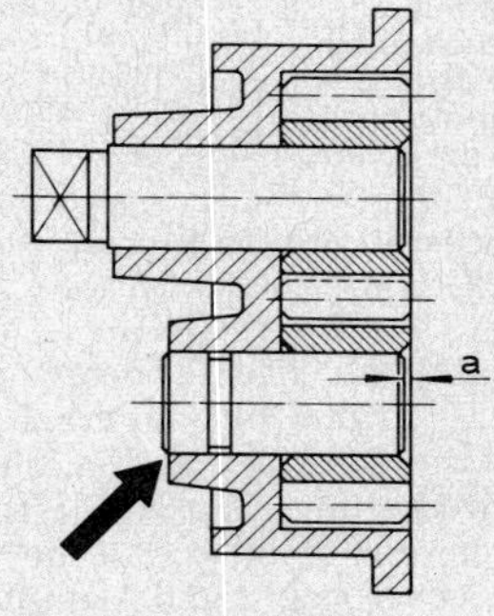

Arrow shows driven shaft of gear type oil pump. Dimension a should be .02-.04 in.

gears should be checked for wear, backlash, and end-play. Backlash may be from .03–.08 mm (.0012–.0031 in.) and the maximum end-play, without gasket, .1 mm (.004 in.). The end-play can be checked using a T-square and a feeler gauge. Check the mating surfaces of the pump body and crankcase for damage and clean them. Install the pump body with gasket, but without sealing com-

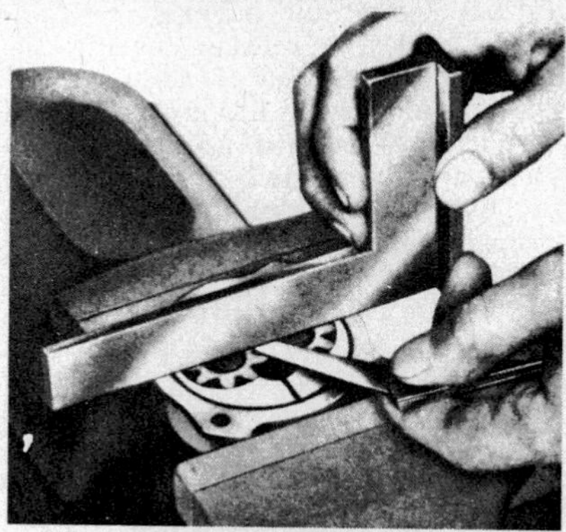

Maximum end-play of the oil pump gears, measured without a gasket, should be .1 mm.

pound. Insert the oil pump pilot instead of the oil pump driveshaft into the pump body. Turn the camshaft by 360°. (One complete turn of the camshaft requires two complete turns of the crankshaft.) This will ensure the centering of the pump body opposite the slot in the camshaft. Mark the pump body so that the correct fit of the oil pump can be checked after the cover has been installed. Remove the oil pump pilot and install the gears. Check the cover for wear—worn covers should be either machined or replaced. Before installing the cover, new gaskets should be fitted and secured with sealing compound. Install the cover and tighten the nuts without disturbing the position of the pump housing.

R & R Oil Pressure Relief Valve

When the oil is cold and thick, and oil pressure is very high, the pressure relief valve plunger is in its lowest position and oil flows directly to the lubrication points; some of it back to the crankcase. When the oil warms and thins, the oil pressure drops, the plunger covers the bypass port and oil flows to the lubrication points both directly and via the oil cooler. After the oil has warmed to normal operating temperature and is thin, oil pressure is low, the plunger of the relief valve is in its highest position, and the oil goes to the lubrication points only after it has passed through the oil cooler.

1 Plunger 3 Gasket
2 Spring 4 Plug

Components of oil pressure relief valve.

The oil pressure relief valve should be checked whenever there is any disturbance in oil circulation, and especially when the oil cooler is found to be leaky. If the plunger should stick at its highest point when the oil is thick, there is danger of the oil cooler leaking from excess pressure. If, on the other hand, the plunger sticks in the bottom of its travel, the oil will tend to flow directly back to the sump and lubrication will be lacking when the engine is warm.

The oil pressure relief valve is removed by unscrewing the end plug and removing the gasket ring, spring, and plunger. If the plunger is stuck, it can be removed by screwing a 10 mm tap into it. Prior to installation, check the plunger and the bore in the crankcase for signs of seizure. If necessary, the plunger should be renewed. The spring should be checked to make sure that it conforms to the following specifications:

Condition	*Length*	*Load in lbs*
Unloaded	2.44–2.52 in.	0
Loaded	.93 in.	17.1 lbs

When installing the relief valve, care should be taken to ensure that the upper end of the spring does not scratch the wall of the bore. The gasket should be removed and the end plug tightened securely.

There are two types of oil pressure relief valve plungers available. The first is the plain type normally found in Type 1 and 2 engines. The second type is longer and has an annular groove. This is used in some Type 3 engines. It has been found that if the grooved plunger is substituted for the plain plunger, the result will be more oil flow through the cooler and a drop in oil temperature of about 15°F. This, as all other engine modifications, is discouraged by the VW factory.

1970 and later Type 1 and 2 engines have two oil pressure relief valves. The second valve is located at the flywheel side of the oil sump and is identical to the first.

Pistons and Connecting Rods

Pistons R & R

Following the removal of the cylinder head and the cylinder, the pistons should be marked with a number (cylinder number) and an arrow (pointing to clutch side of engine) if they are to be reinstalled in the engine. The pistons are removed as follows:

Using piston circlip pliers, remove the circlips used to retain the piston wrist pin. Heat the piston to 80°C (176°F), remove the piston pin and take the piston off the end of the connecting rod. Heating the pistons to

Oil pressure relief valve plungers; the grooved type gives increased oil cooling.

remove the piston pin is accomplished by boiling a rag in water and wrapping the hot rag around the piston. If it is necessary to remove the piston rings, use piston ring pliers in order to avoid damage.

Install the piston as follows: First, clean the piston and the ring grooves, taking care to see that the ring grooves are not scratched or otherwise damaged. The piston should then be checked for wear and, if necessary, replaced by one of corresponding size and weight. Weight between pistons must not be greater than 10 grams. If the running clearance between the piston and cylinder is .2 mm (.008 in.) or more, the piston and cylinder should be replaced by a set of the same size grading. If, however, the cylinder of a worn or damaged piston shows no signs of wear, it is permissible to install a new piston of appropriate size. See the accompanying diagram for piston markings.

After making a decision concerning the piston to be used, select piston rings of the correct size. After the ring has been inserted in the cylinder and pushed down about .2 in. by the piston, check the gap with a feeler gauge. After using a piston ring tool to install the rings, check the side clearance of the rings in their grooves with a feeler gauge.

Ring side clearance and end-gap should be as specified in the "Engine Rebuilding Specifications" chart for pistons, cylinders, and rings.

Because the compression rings are slightly tapered, they should be installed with the marking "Top" or "Oben" toward the top of the piston.

The pistons should be marked in this manner before removal.

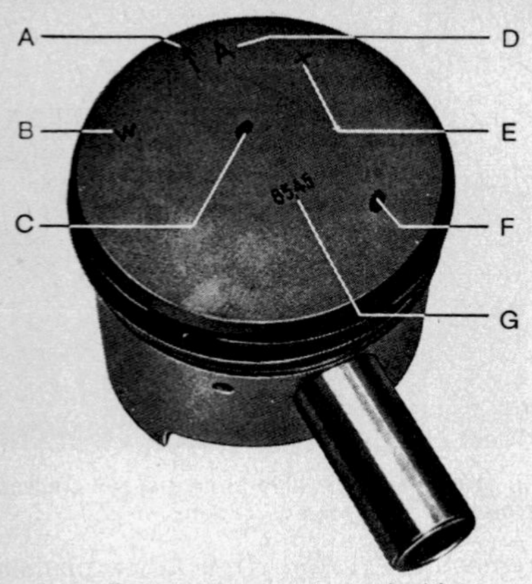

A. Arrow (indented or stamped on) which must point toward the flywheel when piston is installed.
B. Details of piston pin bore size indented or stamped on (s = black, w = white).
C. Paint spot indicating matching size (blue, pink, green).
D. The letter near the arrow corresponds to the index of the part number of the piston concerned. It serves as an identification mark.
E. Details of weight grading (+ or —) indented or stamped on.
F. Paint spot indicating weight grading (brown = — weight, grey = + weight).
G. Details of piston size in mm.

An explanation of the markings on new pistons.

Measuring ring end-gap.

Measuring ring side clearance.

Insert the piston pin circlip which faces toward the flywheel. Because piston pin holes are offset, make sure that the arrow (or word "vorn") points toward the flywheel. This offset is to help accommodate thrust loads which amplify and lead to objectionable piston slap.

Check and fit the piston pin. The pin may be found to be a light finger-push fit in the piston, even when the piston is cold. This condition is normal, even to the extent of the pin sliding out of the piston under its own weight. Clearance between the piston pin and the connecting rod bushing should be as specified in the "Engine Rebuilding Specifications" chart. If the clearance is near the wear limit, renew the piston pin and the rod bushing. It is not advisable to install an oversize pin in this case. In all cases where the pin is not a light finger-push fit in the cold piston, heat the piston in oil to about 176°F. Insert the second circlip and make sure that the circlips fit perfectly in their grooves. A good barometer in deciding whether or not a new cylinder and piston should be installed is oil consumption. If the engine uses more than one quart of oil each 600 miles, it is quite likely that the engine is in need of reconditioning.

Clutch

Clutch R & R

Manual Transmission

To remove the clutch, first remove the engine; then remove the clutch-to-flywheel attaching bolts by gradually and alternately backing the bolts out of the flywheel; finally take off the clutch cover and lift out the clutch driven plate.

Installation of the clutch is the reverse of the preceding. Before installing, inspect and resurface the pressure plate if it is worn in excess of .008 in. The friction surface should be polished. Inspect the driven plate and renew it if there is any doubt as to its reliability. Examine the release plate, release levers, and springs for damage. Check the release bearing for damage and replace if necessary. If the release bearing has a plastic ring, it must be roughed up with emery cloth and lubricated sparingly with molybdenum disulphide paste. This prevents an annoying whistling sound which sometimes comes from the release bearing. Inspect the bearing points of the clutch operating shaft for wear. Lubricate the needle bearing in the flywheel gland nut with approximately 10 grams of universal grease. Reinstall the driven (lined) plate, using a pilot mandrel to ensure correct centering alignment. Evenly and alternately tighten the clutch-to-flywheel bolts. Check for proper distance and parallelism between the clutch cover contact face at flywheel and the clutch release plate with a clutch adjustment gauge. Adjust free-play at the clutch pedal to .4–.8 in.

Clearance between cylinder and piston should not exceed .20 mm (.008 in.). Clearance is determined by measuring both piston and cylinder. The cylinder diameter is measured 10-15 mm below the upper edge.

Automatic Stickshift

To remove the clutch, the engine and then the transmission must first be removed. Proceed as follows:

1. Pull off the torque converter. Seal off the hub opening.
2. Mount the transmission in a repair stand or on a suitable bench.
3. Loosen the clamp screw and pull off the clutch operating lever. Remove the transmission cover. Remove the hex nuts between the clutch housing and the transmission case (two inside the differential housing).
4. The oil need not be drained if the clutch is removed with the cover opening up and the gearshift housing breather blocked.
5. Pull the transmission off the clutch housing studs.
6. Turn the clutch lever shaft to disengage the release bearing.
7. Remove both lower engine mounting bolts.
8. Loosen the clutch retaining bolts gradually and alternately to prevent distortion. Remove the bolts, diaphragm clutch, clutch plate, and release bearing.
9. Do not wash the release bearing. Wipe dry only.

To replace the clutch:

10. Check the clutch plate, pressure plate, and release bearing for wear and damage. Check the clutch carrier plate, needle bearing, and seat for wear. Replace all parts as necessary.
11. If the clutch is wet with ATF, replace the clutch carrier plate seal and clutch. If the clutch is wet with transmission oil, replace the transmission case seal and clutch.
12. Coat the release bearing guide on the transmission case neck and both lugs on the release bearing with lithium grease containing a

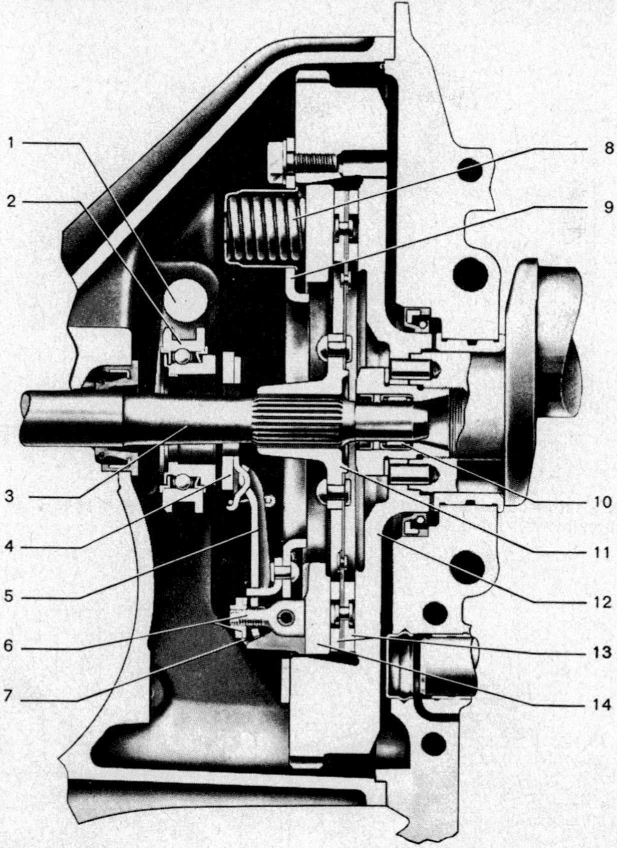

1 Operating shaft
2 Release bearing
3 Main driveshaft
4 Release plate
5 Release lever
6 Bolt and special nut
7 Release lever spring
8 Thrust spring
9 Cover
10 Needle bearing for gland nut
11 Driven plate
12 Flywheel
13 Lining
14 Pressure plate

Cross-sectional view of clutch assembly.

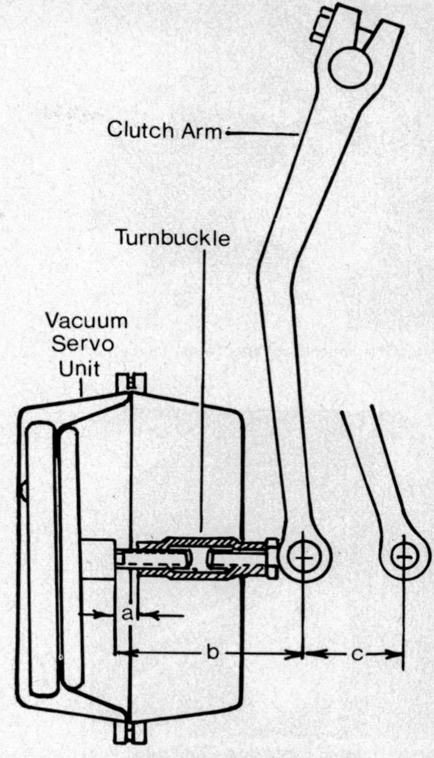

Adjustment dimensions required after installing new clutch in Automatic Stickshift unit. a should be .335 in., b should be 3.03 in., and c should be 1.6 in.

molybdenum disulphide additive. Insert the bearing into the clutch.

13. Apply lithium grease to the carrier plate needle bearing. Install the clutch plate and clutch, centering the plate with an old main driveshaft or a suitable dummy shaft.
14. Tighten the clutch retaining bolts evenly and alternately. Make sure that the release bearing is correctly located in the diaphragm spring.
15. Insert the lower engine mounting bolts from the front. Replace the sealing rings if necessary. Some units have aluminum sealing rings and cap nuts.
16. Push the transmission onto the converter housing studs. Insert the clutch lever shaft behind the release bearing lugs. Push the release bearing onto the transmission case neck. Tighten the hex bolts holding the clutch housing to the transmission case.
17. Install the clutch operating lever.

To adjust a new clutch:

18. The clutch operating lever should contact the clutch housing. Tighten the lever clamp screw slightly.
19. Refer to the adjustment illustration. Adjust dimension a to .335 in., b to 3.03 in., and c to 1.6 in. Tighten the clutch lever clamp screw fully.
20. Push the torque converter onto the support tube. Insert it into the turbine shaft by turning.
21. Check clutch play after installing the transmission and engine.

Clutch pedal free-play should be 10-20 mm (.4-.8 mm.).

R & R, Clutch Cable

Manual Transmission

The clutch cable runs from the pedal to the release bearing, which in turn presses against the release plate and moves it axially. To remove the cable, first remove the left rear wheel. Disconnect the cable from its operating lever on the transmission. Pull the rubber boot from the guide tube and cable. Disconnect the brake master cylinder push rod and unbolt the pedal assembly. Unhook the cable from the pedal cluster and pull it forward through the hole from which the pedal cluster was removed. To gain access to the cable end, on Type 1 cars remove the pedal cluster, on Type 2 cars, remove the cover under the pedal cluster, on Type 3, a frame head cover is located under the pedal cluster under the car.

Installation is the reverse of the above. The cable should be lubricated thoroughly with universal grease. While the pedal assembly is out of the frame tunnel, it is a good idea to lubricate this part well also. The cable

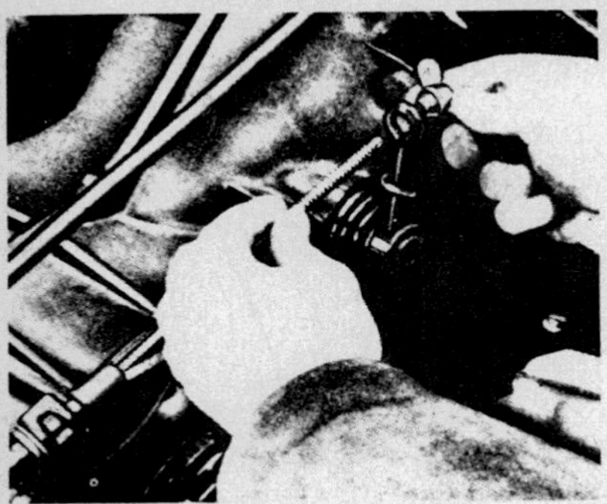

Disconnecting clutch cable from operating lever.

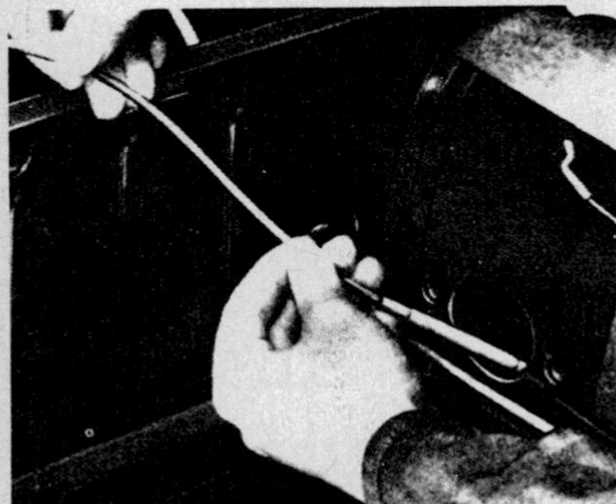

Inserting clutch cable into guide tube.

guide should be bent slightly by inserting a suitable number of washers between the transmission case bracket and the end of the cable guide (A). (See illustration.) Adjust pedal free-play.

Clutch Adjustment—Manual Transmission

The Volkswagen clutch is a dry, singleplate unit fitted to the flywheel. Earlier models had a carbon throw-out bearing, while the later models are equipped with the ball bearing type. With the carbon type bearing, wear on the bearing was significant when the clutch pedal was depressed for any length of time, although in normal and proper use the carbon bearings generally lasted for the life of the clutch lining. Neither the carbon bearing nor the ball type bearing requires periodic maintenance.

Routine clutch maintenance is limited to adjusting the free-play present at the clutch pedal. As the clutch lining wears, clearance between the release bearing and release plate is reduced until these parts touch. Such a condition can lead to damage or excessive wear, as well as clutch slipping and burning of the lining. The proper clutch pedal free-play is 10–20 mm (.4–.8 in.) measured at the pedal.

Adjustment is carried out at the rear of the car, at the cable end of the clutch. First loosen the locking nut and then the adjusting nut. On 1966 and subsequent models, a single wing

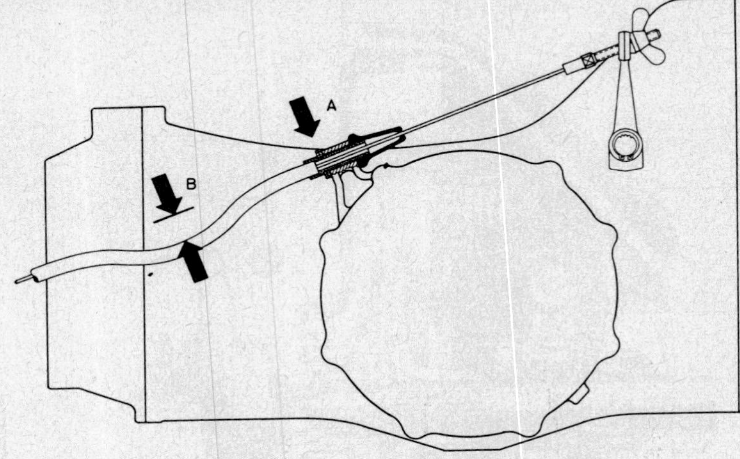

Smooth clutch action requires a slight sag in the cable. Dimension B should be 1.0-1.7 in. Adjustment is made by washers at point A.

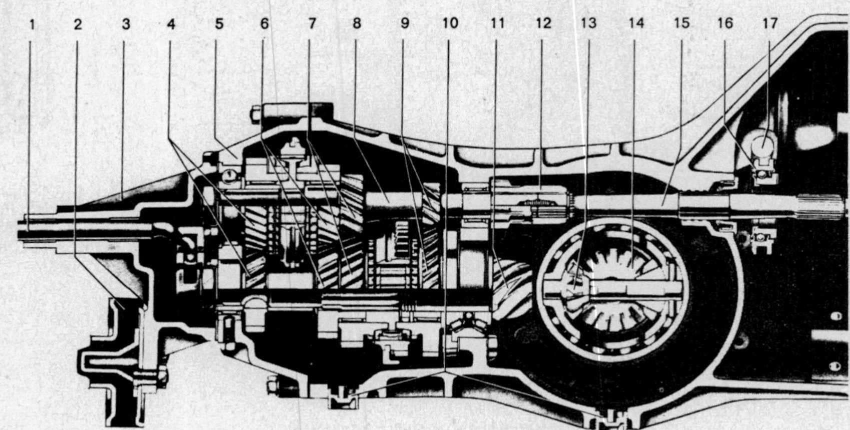

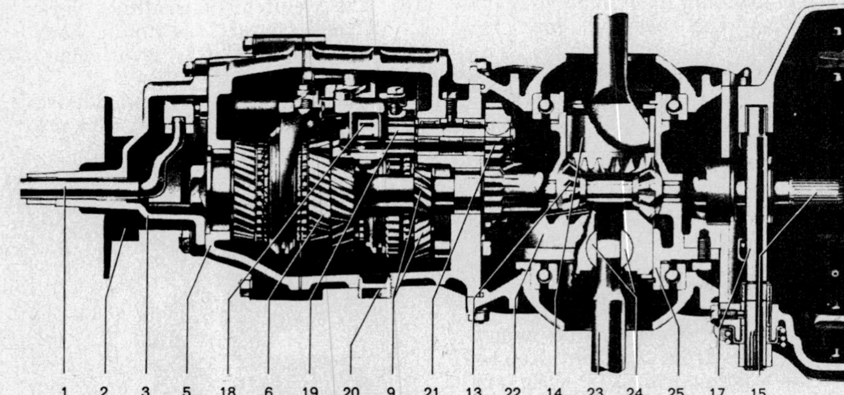

1 Transmission shift lever
2 Bonded rubber mounting
3 Gearshift housing
4 4th speed
5 Gear carrier
6 3rd speed
7 2nd speed
8 Main driveshaft, front
9 1st speed
10 Oil drain plugs
11 Drive pinion
12 Reverse gear
13 Differential pinion
14 Differential side gear
15 Main driveshaft, rear
16 Clutch release bearing
17 Clutch operating shaft
18 Reverse sliding gear
19 Reverse shaft
20 Oil filler plug
21 Reverse drive gear
22 Ring gear
23 Rear axle shaft
24 Fulcrum plate
25 Differential housing

Cross-sectional view of one-piece transaxle with four-speed transmission.

nut serves both purposes. The adjusting nut is turned until the proper amount of free-play is evident at the pedal. The locknut, if present, is tightened, after which the pedal should be depressed several times and the free-play rechecked. After the clutch is adjusted, the thread on the cable end should be greased.

Clutch Adjustment—Automatic Stickshift

Checking Clutch Play

A minimum clutch play is required to prevent slippage and excessive wear. The adjustment is made on the linkage between the clutch arm and the vacuum servo unit. To check the clutch play:

1. Pull off the servo vacuum hose.
2. Measure the clearance between the upper edge of the servo unit mounting bracket and the lower edge of the adjusting turnbuckle. If the clearance is .16 in. or more, the clutch needs adjustment.
3. Replace the vacuum hose.

Adjusting Clutch Play

To adjust the clutch:

1. Pull off the servo vacuum hose. Loosen the turnbuckle locknut slightly. Turn the turnbuckle 5–5½ turns away from the locknut. There should now be .25 in. clearance between the locknut and the turnbuckle.
2. Tighten the locknut against the turnbuckle.
3. Replace the vacuum hose.
4. The clutch adjustment is correct when there is no slippage and reverse can be engaged silently. If the clutch arm contacts the clutch housing, there is no more adjustment possible and the clutch plate must be replaced.

Adjusting Speed of Engagement

The clutch should normally take a full second to engage after shifting down from 2 to 1, at 44 mph without accelerating. Engagement speed may be adjusted to suit personal preference, within certain limits. Excessively fast clutch action may, however, cause transmission damage, while excessively slow action may cause overheating and rapid lining wear. Speed of clutch engagement is adjusted at the reducing valve, to the left of the ignition coil. The adjusting screw is on top of the unit, under a cap. In the normal position, the adjusting screw has two threads protruding from the unit.

To adjust the speed of clutch engagement:

1. Remove the reducing valve cap.
2. To slow engagement, turn the adjusting screw ¼–½ turn clockwise. To speed engagement, turn screw ¼–½ turn counterclockwise.
3. Replace the cap.
4. Test operation by shifting from 2 to 1 at 44 mph without depressing the accelerator.

Trans-Axle

Recent transmission cases are of one-piece, die-cast construction. Transmissions of 1960 and earlier models (36 hp with a non-synchromesh first gear) are of a split type construction. With the 40 hp engine introduced on the 1961 models, all transmissions have been of the one-piece type. In the case of the split type cases, both halves must be replaced at the same time, since they are cast and machined in pairs.

The transmission has four speeds forward and one reverse, with various ratios.

Transmission work of any kind requires removal of the engine.

Transaxle R & R

Manual Transmission With Swing Axles

1. With the engine removed from the car, remove the rear wheels and disconnect the brake lines at the rear wheels and plug the lines.
2. Disconnect the parking brake cables from the push bar at the frame and withdraw the cables from their conduit tubes.
3. Remove the bolts at the rear axle shaft bearing.
4. Disconnect the clutch release cable from the operating shaft lever and pull it from its guide plate.
5. From the access hole under the rear seat, disconnect the shift rod in back of the coupling.
6. Remove the nuts from the mounting studs at the front of the transmission.
7. Remove the lower shock absorber mounting bolts and mark the position of the rear torsion bar radius arm in relation to the rear axle bearing housing by using a chisel.
8. Disconnect the wires from the starter motor.
9. Disconnect the ground strap from the frame and remove the nuts from the auxiliary spring rods (1966 Squareback and 1967–68 Beetles).
10. Place a suitable jack under the unit, and remove the two bolts at the transmission attachments with a 27 mm wrench.
11. Withdraw the transaxle toward the rear of the car. Be sure that the main driveshaft is not damaged or bent when the unit is placed on the ground.

Installation of the transaxle unit is accomplished by reversing the above procedure. The two bolts at the transmission carrier should be greased before being tightened. When a new rear axle is being installed, it is advisable that the retaining nuts of the transmission cradle be tightened fully only after the front mounting has been securely tightened. This tightening sequence is necessary to prevent distortion and premature wear of the rubber mountings.

When the shift rod coupling is reinstalled, the point of the coupling screw should be correctly engaged in the recess. The screw should be secured with a piece of wire. After replacing the ground strap, install the rear axle tubes in their correct positions. The mounting bolts on the spring plate should be tightened to a torque of about 80 ft lbs. Tighten the lower mounting bolts of the shock absorbers securely. Install the engine and adjust the clutch pedal free-play to .4–.8 in. and tighten the rear axle shaft nuts to 217 ft lbs. If the cotter pin cannot be aligned, turn further until it can be inserted. Bleed the brakes and adjust the hand brakes. Note: when a new axle, frame, spring plate, or front transmission mounting is installed, the rear wheels must be realigned. A special optical alignment gauge is necessary for this purpose. An accurate setting is not possible otherwise.

Manual Transmission with Double-Jointed Axles

This procedure is similar to that for vehicles with swing axles; however, the rear wheels and brakes need not be removed or disconnected. The driveshafts should be unbolted at both ends and removed. If the vehicle is not to be moved, the driveshafts may be unbolted at the inner ends only and wired to the body. It is a good idea to cover the axle joints with plastic bags to keep out dirt.

Automatic Stickshift

All Automatic Stickshift models have double-jointed axles. After removing the engine:

1. Detach the gearshift rod coupling.
2. Remove or disconnect and support the driveshafts.
3. Disconnect the ATF hoses from the transmission. Seal the openings. Disconnect the temperature switch, neutral safety switch, and back-up light switch.
4. Pull off the vacuum servo hose.
5. Disconnect the starter cables. (Battery ground strap was disconnected during engine removal.)
6. Remove the front transaxle mounting nuts.
7. Loosen the rear transaxle mounting bolts. Support the unit and remove the bolts.
8. Remove the transaxle.

To replace the transaxle:

9. Raise the transaxle into place. Tighten the nuts for the front mounting. Insert the rear mounting bolts loosely.
10. Replace the vacuum servo hose.
11. Connect the ATF hoses, using new washers.
12. Connect the temperature switch and starter cables.
13. Install the driveshafts, using new lockwashers. Turn the convex sides of the washers toward the screw heads.
14. Align the transaxle and tighten the mounting bolts, being careful that the axle joints cannot rub on the frame fork.
15. Insert the shift rod coupling, tighten the screw, and secure it with wire.
16. After installing engine, bleed the ATF lines if return flow has not started after 2–3 minutes.

R & R, Gearshift Lever—Standard Transmission

The gearshift lever can be removed after the front floor mat has been lifted and the screws removed that attach the gearshift lever ball housing to the central frame tunnel. After the two retaining screws have been removed, the gearshift lever, ball housing, rubber boot, and spring are removed as a unit. The spring will have to be turned in order to clear the pin. Remove the stop plate and clean all components and check them for wear.

Installation of the gearshift lever is the reverse of the preceding. Replace any worn parts. Be sure that the locating pin is a firm fit, but not overly tight. The spring in the steel ball should be checked for tension and replaced if necessary. When installing the stop plate, be sure that the turned-up ramp is on the right-hand side. Lubricate all parts generously with universal grease. After installation is completed, operate the various gears in order to check ease of movement.

VW Automatic Stickshift

Since 1968, Volkswagen has offered an automatic clutch control three-speed transmission. This unit is called the Automatic Stickshift.

It consists of a three-speed gearbox connected to the engine through a hydrodynamic torque converter. Between the converter and gearbox is a vacuum-operated clutch, which automatically separates the power flow from the torque converter while in the process of changing gear ratios.

The converter functions as a conventional clutch for starting and stopping. The shift clutch serves only for engaging and changing the speed ranges. It is very lightly loaded in terms of friction.

There is an independent oil supply for the converter provided by an engine-driven pump and a reservoir. The converter oil pump, driven off the engine oil pump, draws fluid from the reservoir and drives it around a circuit leading through the converter and back to the reservoir.

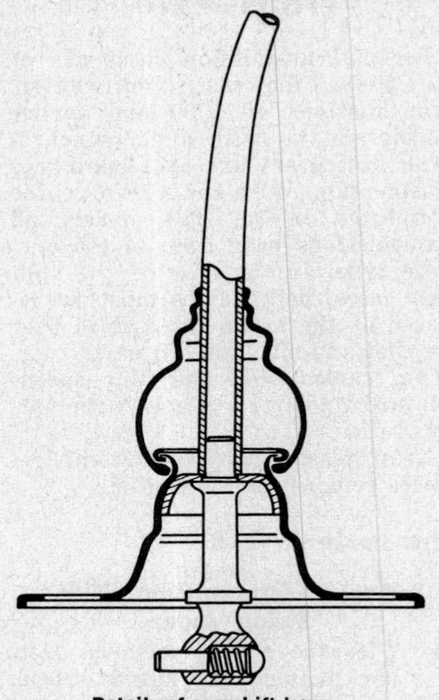

Details of gearshift lever.

This circuit also furnishes cooling for the converter fluid.

Operation

The control valve is activated by a very light touch to the top of the shift selector knob which, in turn, is connected to an electromagnet. It has two functions.

At the beginning of the selection process, it has to conduct the vacuum promptly from the intake manifold to the clutch servo, so that the shift clutch disengages at once, and thus interrupts the power flow between converter and transmission. At the end of the selection process, it must, according to driving conditions, automatically ensure shift clutch engagement at the proper speed. It may neither slip nor engage too harshly. The control valve can be adjusted for this purpose.

Clutch engagement takes place, quickly or slowly, according to engine loading. The clutch will engage suddenly, for example, at full throttle, and can transform the full drive movement into acceleration of the car. This can also be effected slowly and gently if the braking force of the engine is to be used on overrun. In the part-load range, too, the duration of clutch reengagement depends on the throttle opening, and thus the depression in the carburetor venturi. This results in smooth, pleasant driving under all conditions.

Vanes on the outside of the converter housing aid in cooling. In the case of abnormal prolonged loading, however (lugging a trailer over mountain roads in second or third speed), converter heat may exceed maximum permissible temperature. This condition will cause a red warning light to function in the speedometer.

There is also a starter locking switch. This, combined with a bridging switch, is operated by the inner transmission shift lever. It performs two functions:

1. With a speed range engaged, the electrical connection to the starter is interrupted. The en-

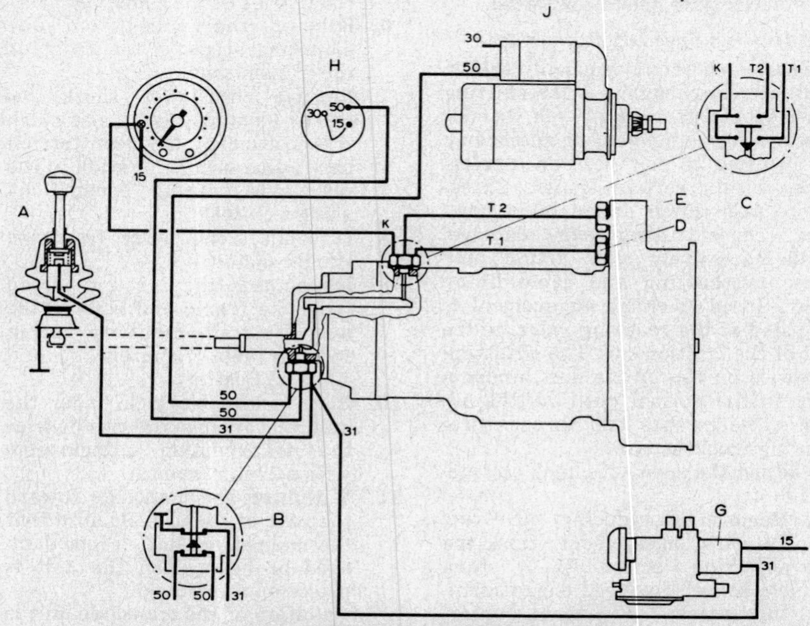

Automatic Stickshift electrical circuit.

gine, therefore, can only be started in neutral.

2. The contacts in the selector lever are not closed in the neutral position. Instead, the bridging switch transmits a voltage to the electromagnets of the control valve. This ensures that the separator clutch is also disengaged in the neutral shifter position.

Fully Automatic Transmission

The fully automatic transmission, consisting of an automatically shifted, three-speed planetary transmission and a torque converter, was introduced in 1969.

The torque converter is a conventional three-element design. The three elements are an impeller (driving member), a stator (reaction member), and the turbine (driven member). Maximum torque multiplication, with the vehicle starting from rest, is two and one-half to one. Maximum converter efficiency is about 96 percent.

The automatic transmission is a planetary unit with three forward speeds which engage automatically depending on engine loading and road speed. The converter, planetary unit, and control system are incorporated together with the final drive in a single housing. The final drive is located between the converter and the planetary gearbox.

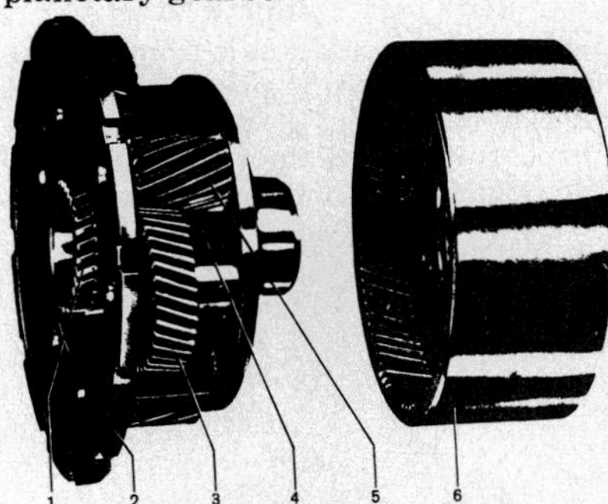

1 Small sungear
2 Planet carrier
3 Large sungear
4 Large sungear
5 Small planet gear
6 Ring gear

Automatic transmission planetary gear unit.

The transmission control system includes a gear type oil pump, a centrifugal governor which regulates shift points, a throttle modulator valve which evaluates engine loading according to intake manifold pressure, and numerous other regulating components assembled in the transmission valve body.

Transmission ranges are Park, Reverse, Neutral, Drive (3), Second (2), and First (1).

Transmission R & R

NOTE: The engine and transmission must be removed as an assembly.

Removal

1. Remove the battery ground cable.
2. On the sedan, remove the cooling air intake duct with the heating fan and hoses. Remove the cooling air intake connection and bellows, then detach the hoses to the air cleaner.
3. On the station wagons, remove the warm air hoses and air cleaner. Remove the boot between the dipstick tube and the body and the boot between the oil filler neck and the body. Disconnect the cooling air bellows at the body.
4. Disconnect the wires at the regulator and the alternator wires at the snap-connector located by the regulator. Disconnect the auxiliary air regulator and the oil pressure switch at the snap-connectors located by the distributor.
5. Disconnect the fuel injection wiring. There are 12 connections and are listed as follows;
   a. Fuel injector cyl 2, 2 pole—protective gray cap
   b. Fuel injector cyl 1, 2 pole—protective black cap
   c. Starter, 1 pole—white
   d. Throttle valve switch, 4 pole
   e. Distributor, 3 pole
   f. Thermo switch, 1 pole—white
   g. Cold start valve, 3 pole
   h. Temperature sensor crankcase, 2 pole
   i. Ground connection, 3 pole—white wires
   j. Temperature sensor for the cyl head, 1 pole
   k. Fuel injector cyl 3, 2 pole—protective black cap
   l. Fuel injector cyl 4, 2 pole—protective gray cap
6. Disconnect the accelerator cable.
7. Disconnect the right fuel return line.
8. Raise the car.
9. Disconnect the warm air hoses from the heat exchangers.
10. Disconnect the starter wires and push the engine wiring harness through the engine cover plate.
11. Disconnect the fuel supply line and plug it.
12. Remove the heater booster exhaust pipe.
13. Remove the rear axles and cover the ends to protect them from dirt.
14. Remove the selector cable by unscrewing the cable sleeve.
15. Remove the wire from the kickdown switch.
16. Remove the bolts from the rubber transmission mountings, taking careful note of the position, number, and thickness of the spacers that are present. These spacers must be reinstalled exactly as they were removed. Do not detach the transmission carrier from the body.
17. Support the engine and transmission assembly in such a way that it may be lowered and moved rearward at the same time.
18. Remove the engine carrier bolts and the engine/transmission assembly from the car.
19. Match-mark the flywheel and the torque converter and remove the three attaching bolts.
20. Remove the engine-to-transmission bolts and separate the engine and transmission. Care must be taken when separating the engine and transmission as the torque converter will easily slip off the input shaft if the transmission is tilted downward.

Installation

1. Install and tighten the engine-to-transmission bolts.
2. Align the converter-to-flywheel match marks and install the bolts.
3. Make sure the rubber buffer is in place and the two securing studs do not project more than 0.7 in. from the transmission case.
4. Tie a cord to the slot in the engine compartment seal. This will make positioning the seal easier.
5. Lift the assembly far enough to allow the accelerator cable to be pushed through the front engine cover.
6. Continue lifting the assembly into place. Slide the rubber

1 Impeller with housing
2 Stator
3 Turbine
4 Housing cover
5 Drive plate

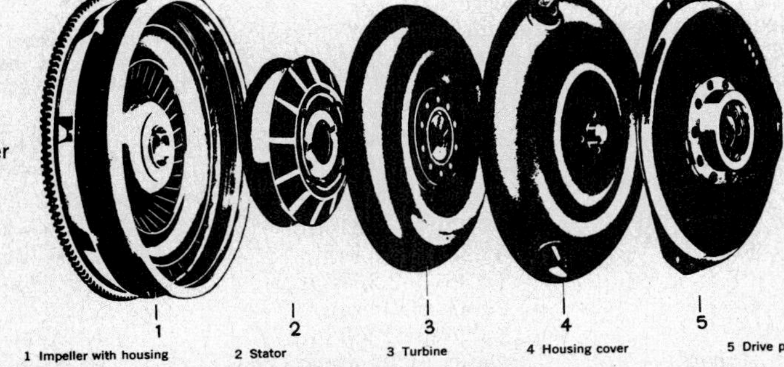

Automatic transmission torque converter.

buffer into the locating tube in the rear axle carrier.

7. Insert the engine carrier bolts and raise the engine until the bolts are at the top of their elongated slots. Tighten the bolts.

NOTE: A set of three gauges must be obtained to check the alignment of the rubber buffer in its locating tube. The dimensions are given in the illustration as is the measuring technique. The rubber buffer is centered horizontally when the 11 mm gauge can be inserted on both sides. The buffer is located vertically when the 10 mm gauge can be inserted on the bottom side and the 12 mm gauge can be inserted on the top side.

8. Install the rubber transmission mount bolts with spacers of the correct thickness. The purpose of the spacers is to center the rubber buffer vertically in its support tube. The buffer is not supposed to carry any weight, it absorbs torsional forces only.
9. To locate the buffer horizontally in its locating tube, the engine carrier must be vertical and parallel to the fan housing. It is adjusted by moving the engine carrier bolts in elongated slots. Further travel may be obtained by moving the brackets attached to the body. It may be necessary to adjust the two rear suspension wishbones with the center of the transmission after the rubber buffer is horizontally centered.
10. Adjust the selector lever cable.
11. Connect the wire to the kick-down switch.
12. Install the rear axles. Make sure the lockwashers are placed with the convex side out.
13. Reconnect the fuel hoses and heat exchanger hoses. Install the pipe for the heater booster.
14. Lower the car and pull the engine compartment seal into place with the cord.
15. Reconnect the fuel injection and engine wiring. Push the starter wires through the engine cover plate and connect the wires to the starter.
16. Install the intake duct with the fan and hoses, also the cooling air intake.

Selector Cable Adjustment

1. Place the gearshift lever in Park.

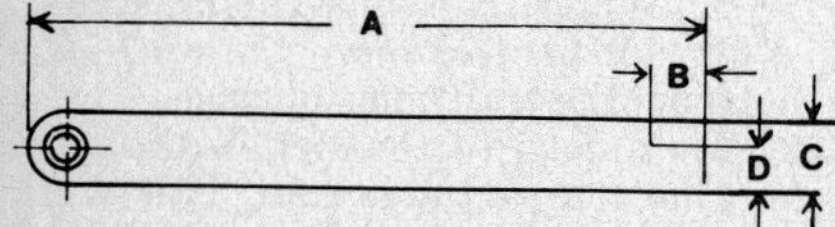

A = 150 mm (5.905 in.)
B = 12 mm (.472 in.)
C = 15 mm (.590 in.)
D = 10, 11, 12 mm (.393, .433, .472 in.)
4 mm (.157 in.) thick strip

Alignment gauges.

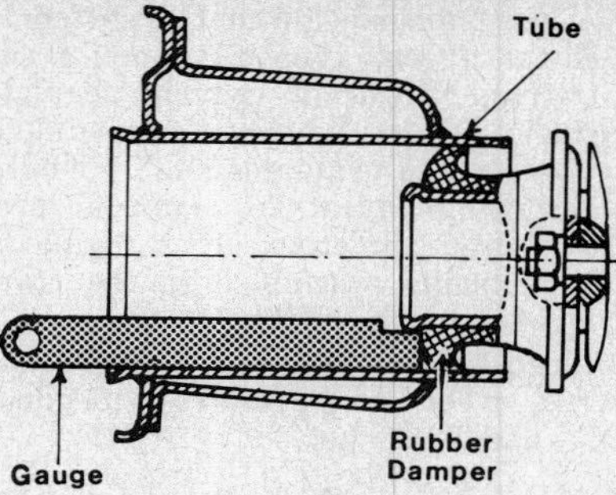

Rubber buffer in locating tube

2. Press the lever on the transmission as far rearward as possible so that the manual valve is against its stop in the valve body.
3. With the transmission lever in this position, tighten the clamp.
4. Check the shift pattern. The brakes must be firmly applied when the pattern is checked.

Drive Axle

Swing Axles

Rear Axle Tube and Shaft R & R

The rear axle tube and shaft can be removed while the transmission is still in the car.

1. Remove the brake drums, bearing cover, back plate, and rear wheel bearing.
2. Remove the nuts of the axle tube retainer and remove the axle tube and retainer.
3. Take off the gasket and plastic packing.
4. Remove the differential side gear lockring, the differential side gear thrust washer, and the axle shaft.
5. After removing the differential side gear and fulcrum plates from the differential housing, knock the dowel pin from the bearing ange.
6. Remove the rear axle dust sleeve.
7. Press the axle tube out of its bearing flange.

Installation is mainly the reverse of the preceding. The rear axle boot should be checked for wear and replaced if necessary. The tube retainer and its seat should be cleaned thoroughly. The clearance between the flat end of the rear axle shaft and the inner diameter of the side gear should be .03-.1 mm (.0012-.004 in.). The axles and gears are coded according to color, and fall into four tolerance groups: yellow, blue, pink, and green. Only parts in the same size group should be mated.

The maximum allowable run-out for the rear axle is .05 mm (.002 in.) This measurement is taken at the seat of the ball bearing. Axles that are slightly bent can be straightened cold. A feeler gauge is used to measure the side clearance between the flat ends of the axle and the fulcrum plates. This clearance should be .035-.244 mm (.0014-.0096 in.). Excessive clearance can be taken care of by installing oversize fulcrum plates which have a groove on the face.

Install the differential side gear, axle, and thrust washer in the differential housing and insert a lockring. Install the retainer gasket and the axle tube with retainer. There should be no end-play between the axle tube and the axle tube retainer. This is accomplished by choosing a gasket of suitable thickness. The axle tube retainer nuts should be tightened to a torque of 14 ft lbs. Over- or under-tightening should be avoided, for this will lead either to rapid wear or to leaks. Axle boots should not be tightened before the car is on the ground, axle intact. Otherwise, the boots may become twisted and damaged.

Rear Axle Boot R & R

The original rear axle boots (dust sleeves) are of a one-piece design and must be cut open in order to be removed for replacement. A split type axle boot is available for replacement

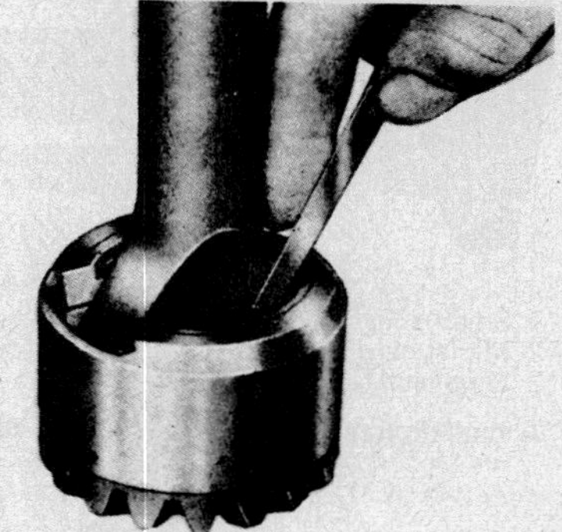

Checking clearance between rear axle shaft and fulcrum plates and between fulcrum plates and differential side gear.

Paint Mark	*Inner Diameter Side Gear*	*Outer Diameter Axle Shaft*
Yellow	59.93–59.97 mm (2.3200–2.3610 in.)	59.87–59.90 mm (2.357–2.3582 in.)
Blue	59.98–60.00 mm (2.3610–2.3622 in.)	59.91–59.94 mm (2.3583–2.3598 in.)
Pink	60.01–60.04 mm (2.3626–2.3638 in.)	59.95–59.97 mm (2.3602–2.3610 in.)
Green	60.05–60.07 mm (2.3642–2.3650 in.)	59.98–60.00 mm (2.3614–2.3622 in.)

which can be installed and then tightened down. To remove the axle boot, take off the retaining clip at each end, and cut off the damaged boot. Clean both the axle tube and the axle tube retainer thoroughly so that the new boot will fit securely.

Upon installation, put a light coating of sealing compound on the join-

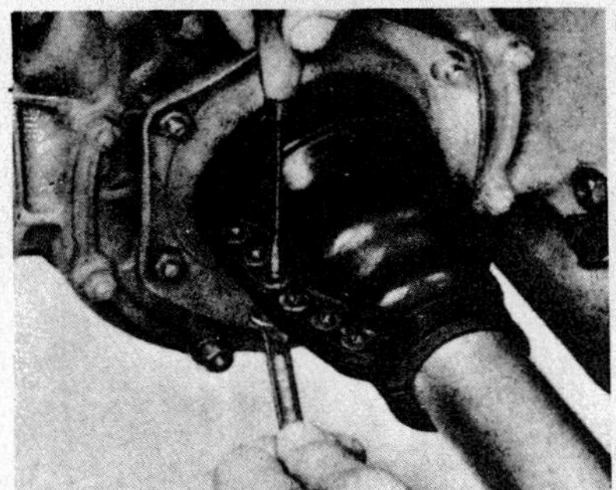

Installation of boot for rear swing axle. The seam must be horizontal, as shown.

ing faces of the boot and ensure that the smaller diameter of the boot is equal to 89 mm. When positioning the new boot, keep the joining faces in a horizontal plane and on the rear of the axle. Tighten the joining screws and the retaining clips (do not overtighten) only after the rear axle is in a loaded condition, and be sure that the boot is not twisted.

Constant Velocity U-Joints and Axle R & R

1. Remove the bolts securing the joints at each end of the shaft, tilt the shaft down, and remove the shaft.
2. Loosen the clamps securing the rubber boot to the axle and slide the boot back on the axle.
3. Drive the stamped steel cover off the joint with a drift.

NOTE: After the cover is removed, do not tilt the ball hub as the balls will fall out of the hub.

4. Remove the circlip from the end of the axle and press the axle out of the joint.
5. Reverse the above steps to install. The position of the dished washer is dependent on the type of transmission. On automatic transmissions it is placed between the ball hub and the circlip. On manual transmission it is placed between the ball hub and the shoulder on the shaft. Be sure to pack the joint with grease.

Disassembly of Constant Velocity U-Joint

1. Remove the ball hub and ball bearing cage from the outer hub.
2. Remove the balls from the cage.
3. Align two grooves in the ball hub and remove the bearing cage from the ball hub.
4. Assembly is the reverse of the disassembly procedure. The chamfer on the splined inside diameter of the ball hub faces the shoulder on the driveshaft.

Suspension

Trailing Arm Front Suspension

The trailing arm type front suspension of the Volkswagen has taken two basically different forms over the years. Models prior to 1966 used link (king) pins to connect the front wheel spindles to the suspension trailing arms. All Volkswagens since the 1966 model year employ ball joints in the front end along with the transverse torsion bars which had always been used.

Strut Front Suspension

The Type 4 and the Type 1 Super Beetle use a strut front suspension. Each wheel is suspended independently on a shock absorber strut surrounded by a coil spring. The strut is located at the bottom by a track control arm and a ball joint, and at the top by a ball bearing which is rubber-mounted to the body.

Greasing Front Wheel Bearings

Beginning with the 1966 models, tapered roller bearings were used in the front wheels of all model Volkswagens. Previously, all models were equipped with ball bearings in the front wheels. The front wheel bearings should be cleaned and repacked with grease at intervals of 30,000 miles. In servicing the front wheel bearings, the following procedures should be followed:

Ball Bearing Equipped Models

NOTE: It is always a good idea to use new plastic seals and locking plates. When working on the left front wheel, take note that this wheel drives the speedometer cable. After

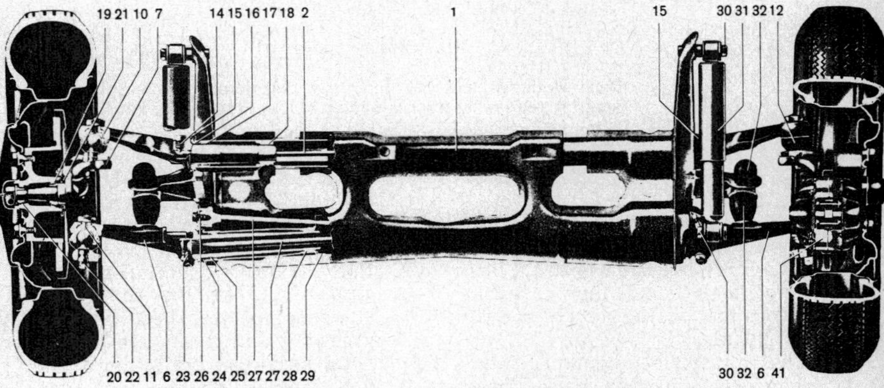

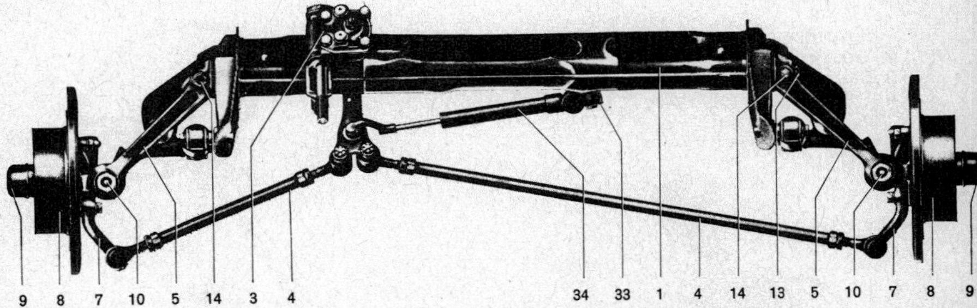

2 1 35 36 37 38 39 40 7

1 Front axle beam
2 Stabilizer
3 Steering gear
4 Tie rods
5 Torsion arm, upper
6 Torsion arm, lower
7 Steering arm
8 Brake disc
9 Grease cap
10 Upper ball joint
11 Lower ball joint
12 Dust seal
13 Adjust screw for upper torsion arm axial play
14 Grub screw
15 Seal, upper
16 Thrust ring
17 Needle bearing, upper
18 Plastic sleeve with metal bush
19 Front wheel bearing, inner
20 Front wheel bearing, outer
21 Seal
22 Eccentric for camber adjustment
23 Grub screw
24 Seal, lower
25 Needle bearing, lower
26 Retaining bolt
27 Torsion bars
28 Plastic sleeve with metal bush, lower
29 Reinforcement plate
30 Shock absorber mounting bolt
31 Shock absorber
32 Rubber stop
33 Steering damper mounting bolt
34 Steering damper
35 Steering gear mounting clamp
36 Steering drop arm
37 Clamping screw
38 Steering knuckle
39 Steering arm mounting bolt
40 Brake back plate
41 Caliper

Cross-sectional view of ball joint front suspension currently in use.

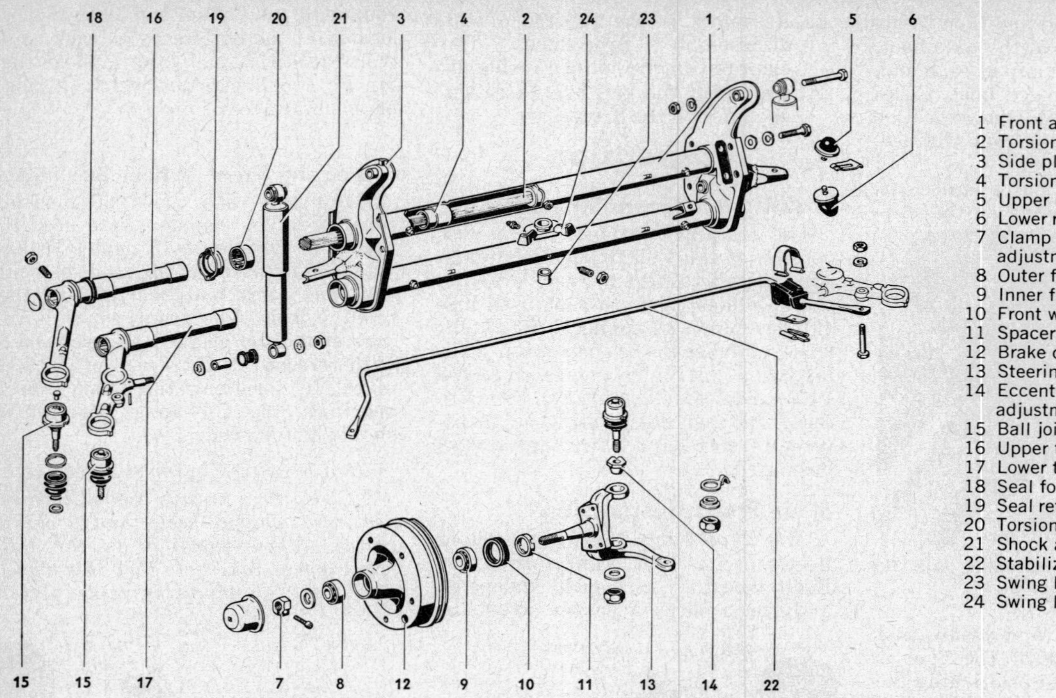

Cross-sectional view of transporter ball joint front suspension currently in use. Note steering gear swing lever in middle of lower torsion bar housing.

removing the cotter pin and the driving end of the cable, proceed normally.

1. Jack up the side of the car; remove the hub cap from the wheel; remove the wheel.
2. Remove the small dust cap that covers the locking nuts at the tip of the axle.
3. Unscrew the hexagonal locknut, remove the locking plate, inner hexagonal nut, and the thrust washer. Nuts on the left axle have left-hand threads; those on the right have right-hand threads.
4. Pull the brake drum off the axle stub, while at the same time being careful to keep the inner raceway and the cage of the outer bearing from falling in the dirt. If brake drum resists being removed, it may be necessary to back off the brake adjustment slightly and also bolt the wheel back onto the brake drum so as to have more leverage in pulling on the drum.

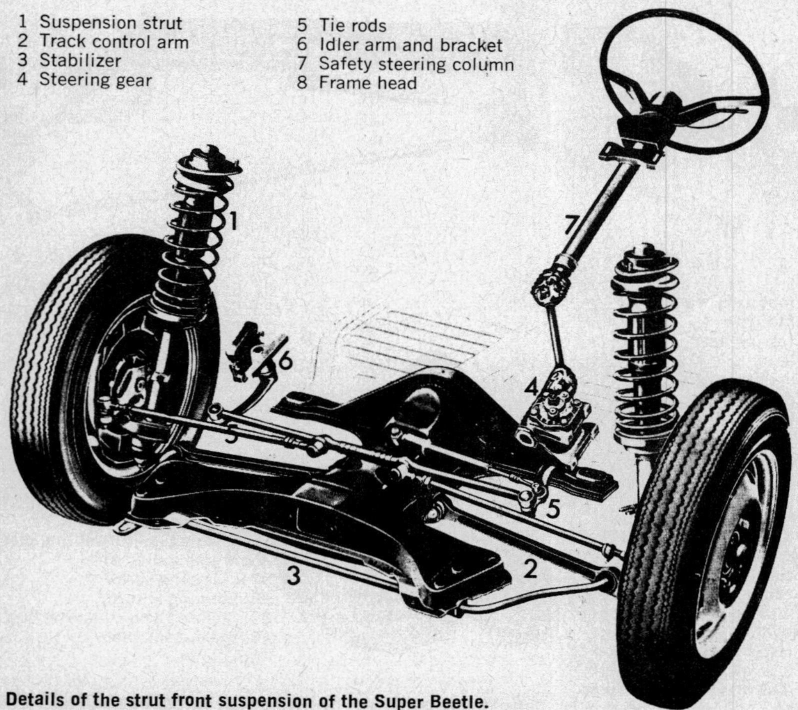

Details of the strut front suspension of the Super Beetle.

5. Remove the plastic grease seal from the hub and take out the cage of the inner bearing.
6. Leaving the inner raceway in place on the axle, and the outer raceway in place in the hub, clean all components in solvent and clean the inside of the brake drum, being careful to keep any grease or oil from touching the interior surface of the drum. Caution should also be exercised in order that the brake shoes themselves will remain free of grease.
7. Repack the inner bearing cage with grease and place it within the hub. Now the plastic seal can be reinstalled by tapping it in lightly until it achieves a flush position. A flat piece of wood placed atop the seal may prove helpful in this operation.
8. The inner raceway on the axle should now be greased and the wheel replaced. After repacking the outer bearing cage, this part can now be inserted in the hub. Bearing installation is completed with the installation of the inner race, thrust washer, and hexagonal nut.
9. Tighten the hexagonal nut until the thrust washer can just be moved sideways with a screwdriver. Replace the locking plate

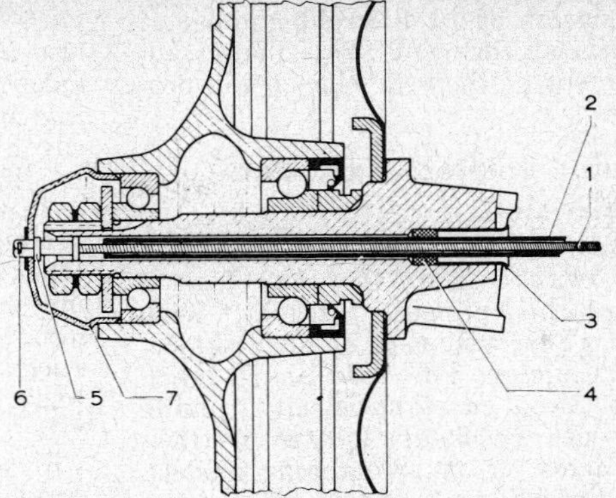

Cross-sectional view of left front wheel bearing. The right side is the same, but does not have the speedometer drive assembly.

(renew if unusable) and the locknut. The locking plate tabs should be bent over, and the hexagonal nut tightened down.

Roller Bearing Equipped Models

Roller bearing equipped models include the Type 3 and the Type 1 Karmann Ghia and Beetle models of 1966 and later.

On Beetle models, equipped with drum brakes, the procedure is much the same as that listed for ball bearing equipped models except that the final adjustment will be more exacting. Adjustment requires that the following procedure be followed:

1. Loosen the clamp nut screw.
2. Tighten the clamp nut to a torque of 11 ft lbs, while at the same time turning the wheel.
3. Loosen the clamp nut until the axial play of the wheel is .03–.12 mm (.001–.005 in.).
4. Tighten the clamp nut screw to 7 ft lbs and recheck axial play.
5. Install the hub cap.

The following directions apply to Type 3 and 1971 and later Type 2 models, and the 1500 and 1600 Karmann Ghia, supplied with disc brakes:

1. After removing the front wheel and disc cap, bend up the lockplates on the caliper securing screws and remove both the screws and the caliper assembly.
2. Secure the caliper to the brake hose bracket by means of a piece of wire or rope. The caliper should not be allowed to hang by the brake hose.
3. Loosen the socket head screw of the clamp nut. Unscrew the clamp nut.
4. Remove the wheel bearing thrust washer.
5. Remove the disc.
6. The parts removed should be cleaned thoroughly in a cleaning solvent solution.
7. Lubricate the bearings with a lithium grease of the proper type, pressing grease into the cages and fill the grease cavity of the disc. Grease should not be put into the disc cap.
8. Press in the outer race of the inner bearing.
9. Fit the inner race and cage, and insert the grease seal. When fitting the grease seal, drive it in by tapping lightly with a rubber hammer; avoid tilting the seal.
10. Press in the outer race of the outer bearing.
11. Install the thrust washer and make sure that it is not tilted.
12. Adjust the bearings so that axial play is .03–.12 mm (.001–.005 in.). The adjustment process is as described in the preceding section on adjusting front wheel bearings on Beetle models equipped with roller bearings.

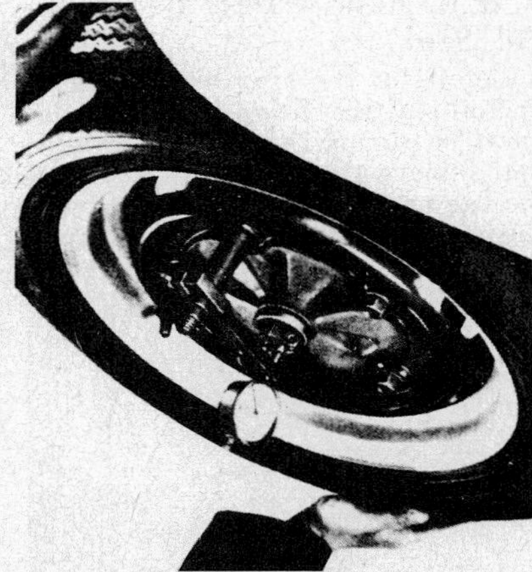

Checking axial (side) play of front wheel bearings with a dial indicator.

Loosening wheel nut pinch bolt at left front wheel. The pinch bolt should be torqued to 7 ft lbs on reinstallation.

Torsion Bar R & R

1. Remove wheels and both steering knuckles, complete with brake drums and backing plates. Attach the assemblies to the axle with wire.
2. Remove the shock absorber. Remove the torsion arms on one side.
3. On Type 2 disconnect the front gearshift rod at coupling.
4. Loosen the setscrew locknuts and remove the screws.
5. Remove the torsion bars.

To install:

1. Coat the torsion bars with lithium grease.
2. Tape the end of the torsion bar leaves. Insert the torsion bars, noting the positions of the countersinks for the set screws.
3. Install the remaining parts and lubricate the torsion arm bearings with general purpose grease.

Link Pin R & R

1. Raise the front end.
2. Remove the front wheels, drums, and backing plates. Disconnect the speedometer cable and the outer tie rod.
3. Remove the torsion arm pinch bolts.
4. Remove the torsion arm link and stub axle by driving out both link pins.
5. Examine all parts carefully and replace them as necessary.

To install:

1. Measure the offset of the torsion arm eye faces. By using .5 mm shims, set the offset to 7 mm.

NOTE: There must always be eight shims and one retainer with a dust excluder fitted to one torsion arm link pin.

2. Install the link pins and shims with universal grease.
3. Replace the remaining parts.
4. Adjust the torsion arm pins, front wheel bearings, and front end alignment, then bleed and adjust the brakes.

Ball Joint R & R

1. Remove the wheel and brake drum. Disconnect the stabilizer bar and speedometer cables.
2. Remove the torsion arms.
3. Press out the ball joints. Check ball joint free-play (.3–2 mm is allowable) and dust seals.

To install:

1. Ball joints and torsion arms are available in standard and oversizes. Press a new joint into the torsion arm, making sure that the notches on the ball joint

align with the projection on the torsion arm.

2. Check the camber and toe-in after reassembly.

Stabilizer Bar R & R

1. Remove the clamp retaining clip.
2. Bend up the clamps and remove the plates.
3. Remove the nut from the securing bolt on lower torsion arm.
4. Remove the stabilizer bar, check for damaged parts, and replace as necessary.
5. Reverse the procedure to install. Torque the securing nut on the lower torsion arm to the figure specified in the "Torque Specifications" chart.

Swing Axle Rear Suspension

The rear wheels of the Volkswagen are independently sprung by means of torsion bars. The inside ends of the torsion bars are anchored to a body crossmember via a splined tube which is welded to the frame. The torsion bar at each side of the rear suspension has a different number of splines at each end. This makes adjustment of the rear suspension possible.

Double-Jointed Axle Rear Suspension

This rear suspension system was first introduced on the 1968 Type 2 and on the Automatic Stickshift Type 1. It is currently used on all Volkswagen vehicles. The axle shafts each have two, constant-velocity joints. The rear wheels are located by trailing arms as on swing axle models, and by diagonal control arms from the rear crossmember.

R & R, Rear Wheel Bearing, Oil Seal

Details of the rear wheel bearing and oil seal are shown in an exploded view. To remove the oil seal and bearing, remove the rear axle nut, raise the car and take off the brake drum. Remove the retaining screws from the cover and take off the cover along with the oil seal. Remove the brake line, and take off the back plate, outer spacer, the gasket between the bearing and the spacer, the washer, and cover gasket. Remove the rear wheel bearing and inner spacer.

Installation is the reverse of the preceding but, in addition, certain other steps should be taken. The bearing should be examined and replaced if necessary. Replace the two sealing rings. If the oil seal is damaged or uneven, it should also be replaced. When installing a new oil seal, coat it with oil and press it into the bearing cover. The outer spacer should be examined for wear, replaced if scored or cracked, and lightly coated with oil when installed. Clean the oil hole in the cover and replace the cover. The splines in the brake drum hub should be inspected and the brake drum replaced if the splines show signs of excessive wear. Tighten the rear axle shaft nut to 217 ft lbs, using a new cotter pin and turning the nut slightly tighter if necessary to line up the holes for the cotter pin.

Check the level of lubricant in the transmission and top up if necessary. The oil should be at a level even with the lower edge of the filler hole. Bleed and adjust the brakes.

Swing axle rear suspension. This is a type 3 vehicle with a transverse reinforcing torsion bar.

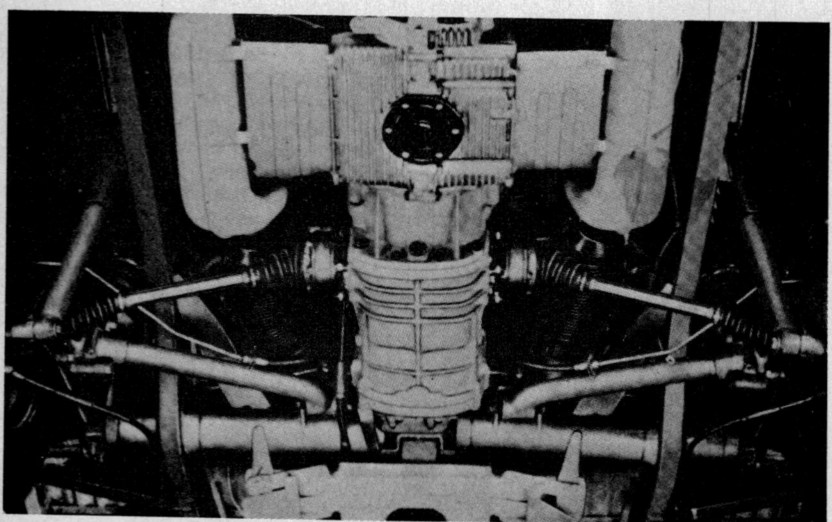

Double-jointed axle rear suspension. The model shown is a Type 2.

Steering

General

Type 1 and 3 steering is of the roller type. The Type 2 uses worm and peg steering. All models since

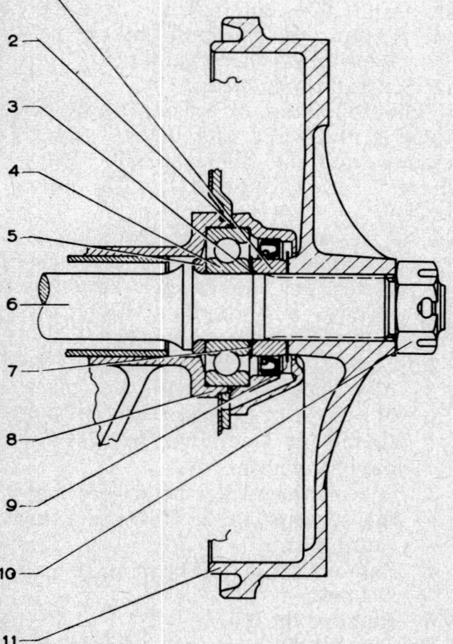

Cross-sectional view of rear wheel bearing.

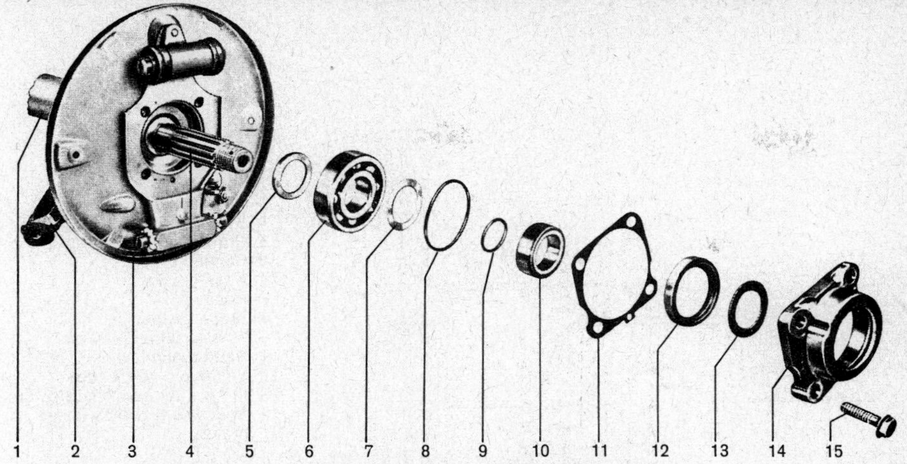

Exploded view of rear wheel bearing assembly.

The correct torque for the rear wheel nut is 217 ft. lbs.

1968 have collapsible or break-away steering column arrangements for crash protection.

The worm in the steering case is adjustable, and is engaged by a roller shaft with a needle-bearing-mounted roller. The roller shaft is held by bronze bushings in the housing and housing cover, while the worm spindle is mounted in ball bearings. The spindle and the roller shaft are both adjustable, the former by a washer fitted under the upper bearing, and the latter by a screw in the housing cover.

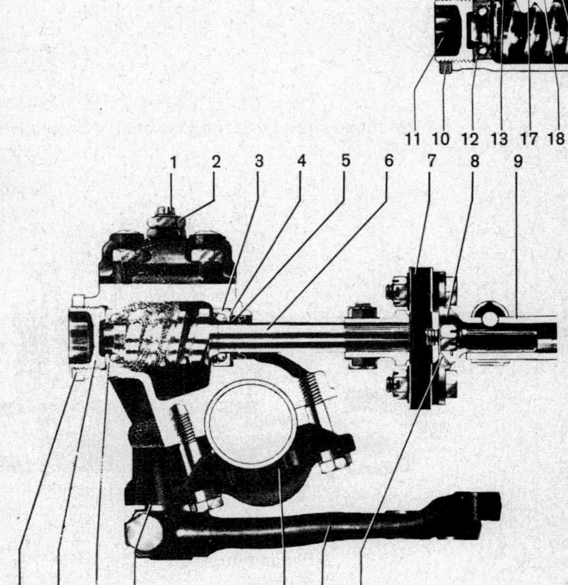

Cross-sectional view of roller type steering gear.

Steering and Front-End Geometry

The critical geometrical angles in the front end of the Volkswagen vary significantly from model to model and even change somewhat from early models to later models. Refer to the "Chassis and Wheel Alignment Chart" for the correct figures for each model.

Brakes

The Hydraulic Brake System

Since 1950, all Volkswagens imported to the U.S. have been equipped with hydraulic brakes. The brakes of the Squareback and Fastback sedans are of the disc/drum type, with discs on the front and conventional drums at the rear. The 1500 Karmann Ghia is also provided with discs at the front, while the Beetle models are, at this writing, still equipped with drums front and rear. The Type 2 models were equipped with front discs starting in 1971.

The VW handbrake is mechanically actuated and operates on the rear wheels via a cable running to the rear.

Master Cylinder

Steps applying to the early single-cylinder type are not covered here; only steps that apply to the dual type are used.

Fluid Reservoir

A dual-section reservoir is used so that loss of fluid in one portion will not cause failure of the entire system.

Push Rod

To obtain proper master cylinder action, the push rod must be set to obtain pedal free movement of 0.02–0.28 in.

If a new rod is to be used, it must be an exact predetermined length. That is, from end of ball to center of pin hole—5.433 ± .019 in. Push rod length is set at the factory.

Master Cylinder Repair

1. Remove the boot.
2. Remove the stop screw.
3. Remove the spring stop-ring.
4. Remove the internal parts.
5. Remove the residual pressure valves and light switches.

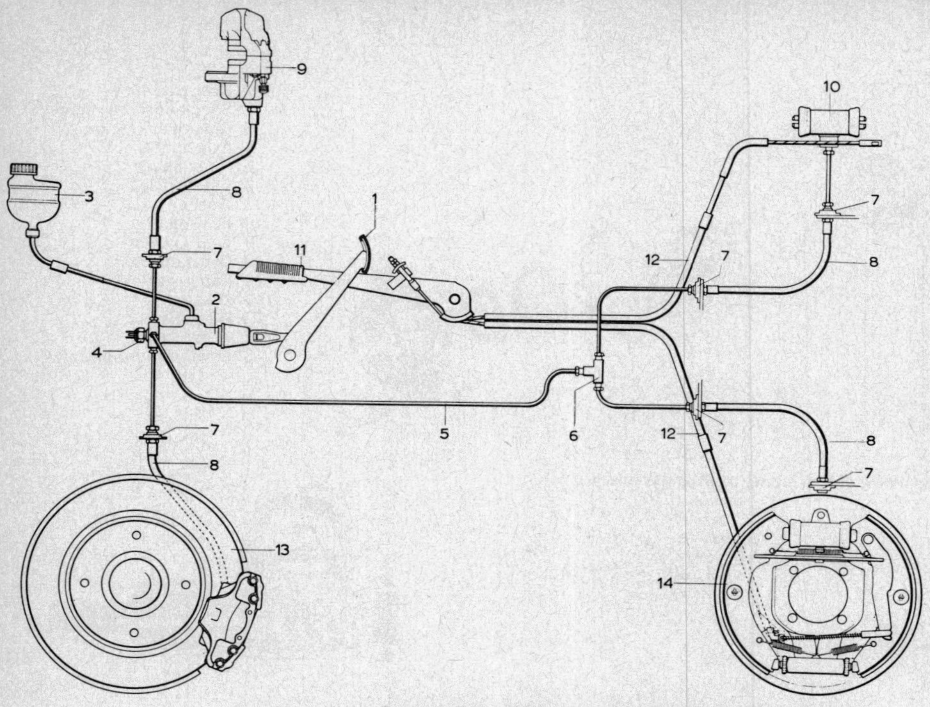

Typical single circuit disc/drum hydraulic brake system.

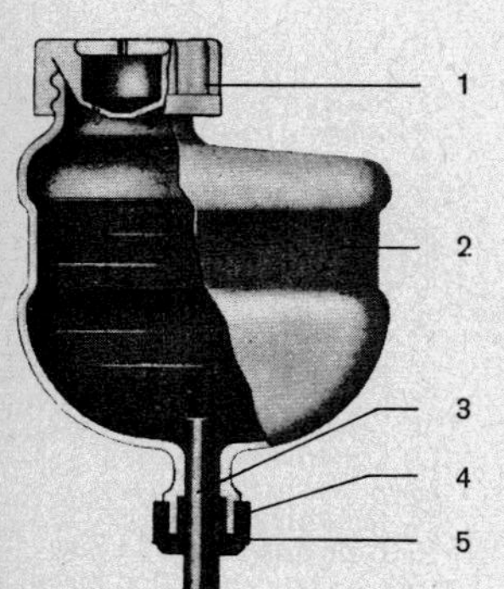

Cross-sectional view, single-circuit master cylinder and reservoir.

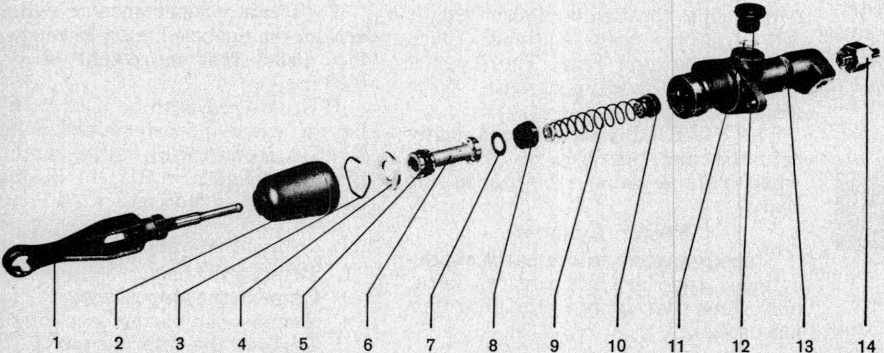

Exploded view, single-circuit master cylinder.

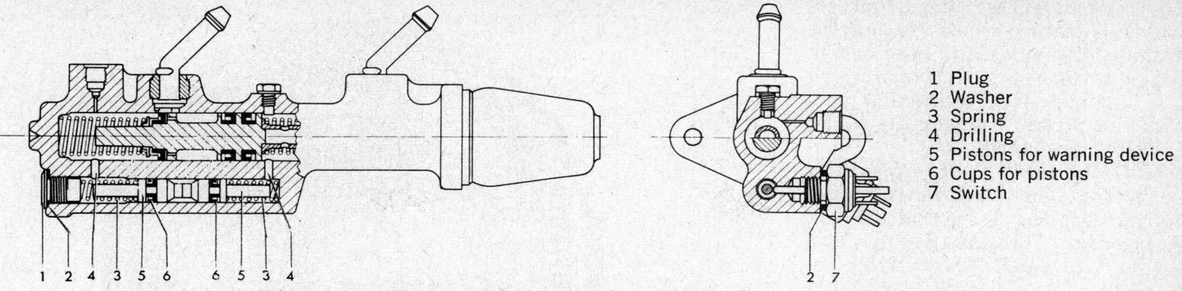

Cross-sectional view of dual-circuit brake master cylinder. Each half of the system serves two brakes. A warning light tells when either half has failed.

6. Replace in the reverse sequence of removal. All parts must be cleaned in methylated spirits or brake fluid. No burrs or corrosive conditions should be overlooked.
7. The residual pressure valves and the brake light switches should be installed and tightened to 11–14 ft lbs.
8. Install the protective cap with the breather hole downward.

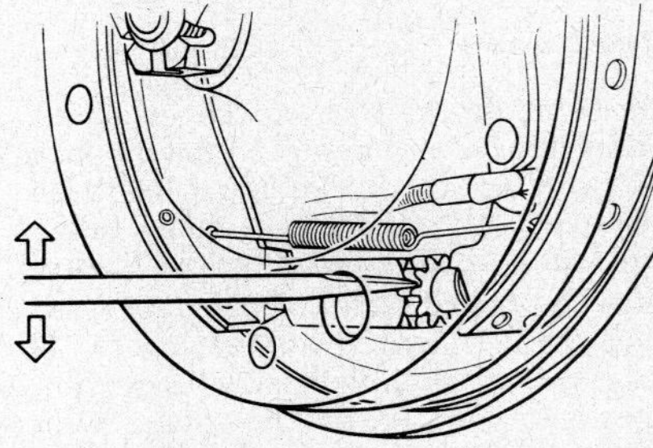
Drum brake adjustment. Later models have two adjusting holes in the backing plate.

Drum Brakes—Adjustment

The only equipment needed to adjust the drum brakes of the Volkswagen is a screwdriver. Pre-1966 Volkswagens have an adjuster hole in the outside of the brake drum for the purpose of adjustment. Models of 1966 and later have adjustment holes in the back plate.

Before adjusting the brakes, press the pedal down several times to centralize the shoes in the drums. Turn the wheel so that an adjusting nut is visible through the adjustment hole. Using the screwdriver, turn the adjustment nut until a slight drag is felt when the wheel is rotated by hand. At this point, back off the adjusting nut until the wheel turns freely. (About three or four teeth of the adjusting nut will pass the adjustment hole.) Move on to the other adjusting nut of the wheel. The adjustment nuts on each wheel turn in opposite directions, so whichever direction of rotation was needed to tighten one shoe will loosen the adjustment of the other shoe. The handbrake is adjusted by means of adjusting nuts at the rear of the control lever inside the car. However, when the rear brakes are adjusted, the handbrake is automatically adjusted also. If this is not enough to hold the rear wheels at four notches, the handbrake should be adjusted by means of the adjusting nuts. When the brake lever is applied by two notches, both rear wheels should resist turning by an equal amount of force. If for some reason, it was necessary to use the handbrake to stop in an emergency, it could be dangerous if both rear wheels did not lock equally.

Parking Brake Adjustment

Unless adjustments are of major proportions, or parts replacement needed, the parking brake may be adjusted inside the vehicle.

1. Raise both rear wheels.
2. Slide off the rubber ring, then fold back the parking brake lever rubber boot until the cable adjusting nuts are accessible.
3. Back off the locknuts, then tighten the adjusting nuts to a point where the rear wheels will still turn freely when the handbrake is off.
4. Pull the handlever up two notches, then check to make sure that both rear wheels have the same value of brake hold. Application to the fourth notch should lock the wheels to hand-turning.
5. Secure the locknuts and reposition the handlever rubber boot.

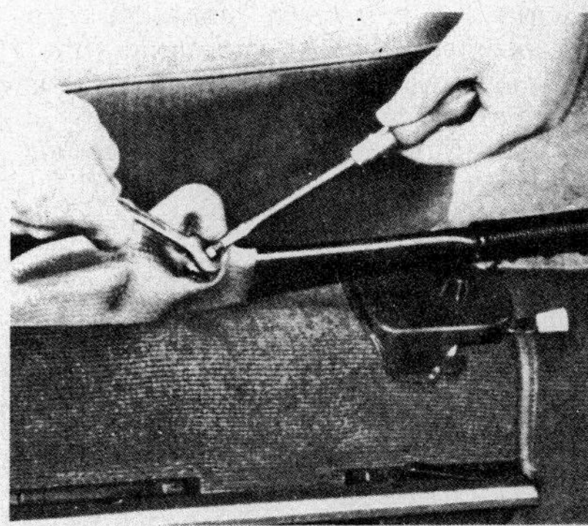
Parking brake adjustment. Each side should be adjusted equally.

Parking Brake Repair

On parking brake levers of this type, the ratchet sometimes disengages itself, making the brake inoperative. The reason for this is that the rear wheel brakes gradually wear down, thus requiring more travel in the parking brake mechanism to tighten them. Eventually, a point is reached where the ratchet can no longer cope with the increasing travel and the unit comes apart. To repair,

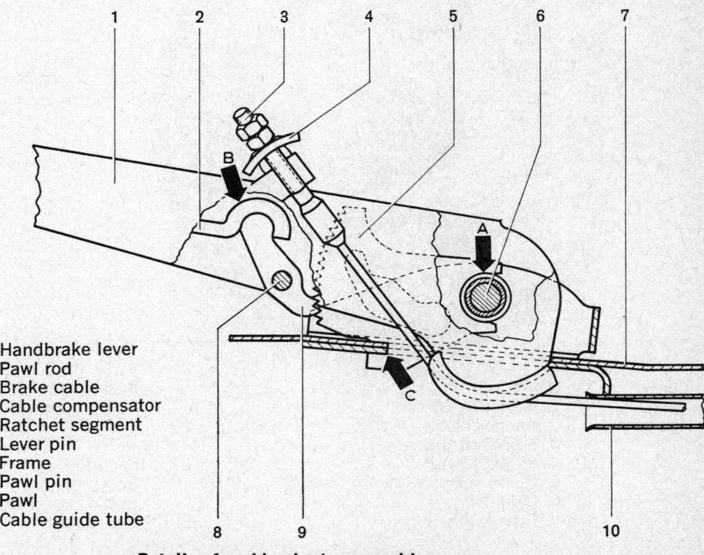

Details of parking brake assembly.

follow the numbered steps, but remember, a lasting repair can only be accomplished by adjusting the system back to normal operating tolerance.

1. Completely remove the four nuts which secure and lock the cables to the mechanism.
2. Lift the lever to its uppermost position and examine the pawl rod, checking to see that it is not physically broken. Slowly drop the rod to about the halfway position.
3. Pull the pawl rod off the pawl (see illustration) and reposition the pawl so it contacts the ratchet (B). At the same time, push down on the pawl rod so that it hooks over the pawl.
4. Slowly lower the lever to the full down position, then carefully check for proper operation by pushing the button and slowly pulling up on the lever a short distance. The ratchet mechanism should make a clicking sound, indicating that the pawl rod is successfully hooked over the pawl.
5. If the lever comes free, the operation must be repeated. A study of the illustration will help greatly, as it indicates the correct positioning of the components.
6. When the operation of the parking brake lever is satisfactory, place two of the nuts on the cable ends and adjust them.

Drum Brakes

The amount of brake lining remaining can be checked by looking through the holes provided in the drums.

1 Cylinder
2 Brake shoe with lining
3 Upper return spring
4 Spring with cup and pin
5 Lower return spring
6 Adjusting screw
7 Back plate
8 Connecting link
9 Lever
10 Brake cable
11 Adjusting nut
12 Anchor block

Rear drum brake of Type 3 vehicle.

Shoe Replacement—Drum Brakes (Front)

Remove the front wheel and grease cap. Remove the cotter pin from the speedometer drive cable (left wheel) before removing the grease cap. Remove the brake drum, the shoe retainer spring assemblies, and the front shoe return springs. Take one brake shoe out of the slot of the adjuster, and remove both shoes from the back plate. When the brake drum has been removed and the brake shoes taken out, care should be taken to ensure that the brake pedal is not depressed through accident or carelessness. If this occurs, the result will be an unchecked expansion of the wheel cylinder and its parts, and a loss of brake fluid.

Before installing new brake shoes,

Front wheel brake

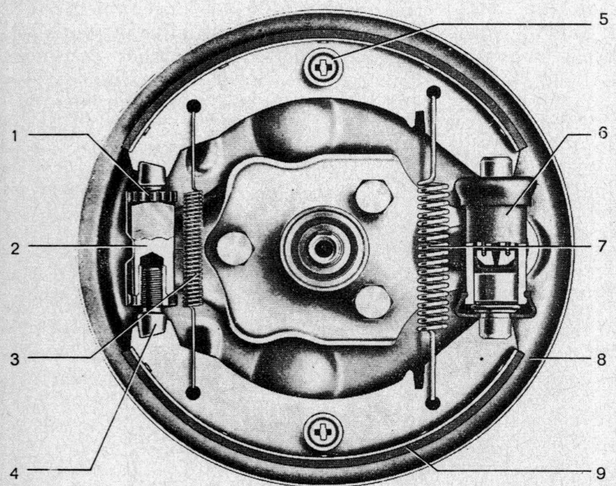

Rear wheel brake

FRONT
1 Adjusting screw
2 Anchor block
3 Front return spring
4 Adjusting nut
5 Guide spring with cup and pin
6 Cylinder
7 Rear return spring
8 Back plate
9 Brake shoe with lining

REAR
1 Cylinder
2 Brake shoe with lining
3 Upper return spring
4 Spring with cup and pin
5 Lower return spring
6 Adjusting screw
7 Back plate
8 Connecting link
9 Lever
10 Brake cable
11 Adjusting nut
12 Anchor block

Front and rear drum brakes, Type 1.

be sure that both front wheels are using the same type of lining. Any difference in lining type, or the use of a lining of the wrong width, can lead only to uneven braking at best, and to a dangerous accident at worst. Care should also be taken to install the shoes correctly. The stronger return spring and the slots in the brake shoes should be at the wheel cylinder side of the assembly. The adjuster slots should be positioned as shown in the accompanying illustration. The brake shoe return springs should be hooked in from the front so that there is no chance of interference with shoe operation. The two brake shoe retainers should also be replaced at this time. The slotted retainer cup should be inspected for wear and replaced if necessary. If the slot has become too large or shows evidence of possible weakness, it should be replaced. Once the brake shoes are installed and retained, they should be centered. Before replacing the brake drum, inspect the oil seal. Adjust the front wheel bearings and adjust and bleed the brakes. Road-test the car and check braking action.

Shoe Replacement—Drum Brakes (Rear)

Remove the wheel and brake drum. (On the Type 3, the drum can be removed after the two drum retaining bolts have been taken out. This eliminates the need to remove the axle shaft nuts in order to remove the drum.) Remove the brake shoe retainers and unhook the lower return spring. (There are two lower return springs on the rear brakes of the Type 3.) Remove the upper return spring, handbrake cable, and the brake shoe with the lever. The lever is held onto the rear brake shoe by a circlip.

Installation of the rear brake shoes is in the opposite sequence. Be sure to install the proper linings on each of the rear wheels. Install the front brake shoe and attach its retaining assembly. The front brake shoe of the Type 3 should be positioned as shown in the accompanying picture. Install the rear brake shoe with the handbrake lever, connecting link, and the upper return spring and clip. Fasten the retainer assembly to the rear brake shoe and attach the handbrake cable end to the lever on the rear shoe. Be sure to position the adjuster slots properly. Install the lower return spring(s), adjust the brakes, and bleed the brake system. If the axle nut was removed to allow removal of the brake drum, tighten it to 217 ft lbs.

Disc Brakes

The principal components of the disc brakes are the disc, friction pad, caliper, and splash shield.

R & R Friction Pads

Replacement of the friction pads is easily done. After raising the front of the car, remove the wheel. Use a punch to drive out the upper retaining pin. Remove the friction pad expander spring and drive out the lower retaining pin.

Push the pistons away from the disc. Before carrying out this part of the operation, however, it is a good idea to remove some fluid from the brake fluid reservoir so that it does not overflow. Clean the calipers with alcohol. Sharp-edged tools and mineral-based solvents should not be used. The retaining plates are removed for the purpose of cleaning, and should

Disconnecting parking brake cable from operating lever.

be replaced if damaged or corroded. When replacing the retaining plate, be sure that it is installed so that the center part is firmly pressed into the center of the piston, and is below the piston cutaway. The piston should be

1 Splash shield 2 Brake disc
3 Brake caliper

Basic components of disc brake.

at an angle of 20°.

The brake pads may now be inserted. Care should be taken to ensure free movement in the caliper housing. Insert the lower retaining pin, using a punch of a larger diameter than the pin itself. Install a new friction pad expanding spring. Insert the upper retaining pin, while at the same time pressing down on the expander spring. While the vehicle is stationary, depress the brake pedal several times to enable the brake pads to settle into their correct positions. The level of brake fluid in the reservoir should be checked and

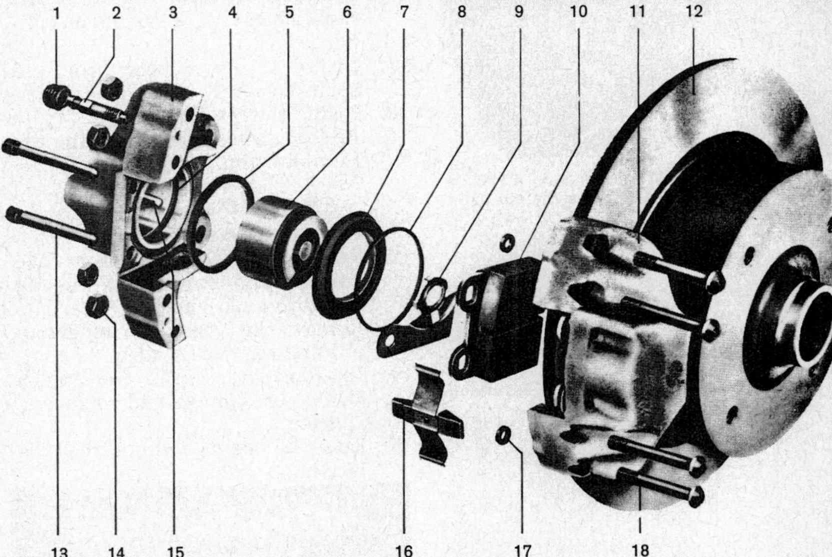

1 Bleeder valve dust cap
2 Bleeder valve
3 Brake caliper inner housing
4 Groove for rubber seal
5 Rubber seal
6 Brake caliper piston
7 Rubber boot
8 Spring ring
9 Piston retaining plate
10 Friction pad
11 Brake caliper outer housing
12 Brake disc
13 Friction pad retaining pin
14 Nut
15 Cylindrical pin (pressed in)
16 Spreader spring
17 Fluid channel O-ring
18 Caliper housing securing bolts

Exploded view of Type 3 disc brake.

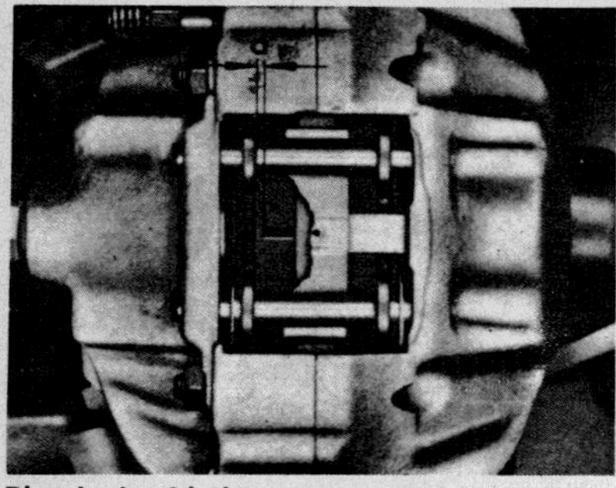

Disc brake friction pads should be checked for wear every 6,000 miles. When the pad thickness, a, is 2 mm or less, the pads must be replaced.

These special pliers are useful in pushing the pistons back into the cylinders.

Insertion or removal of friction pads. A special hook is often needed to remove the old pads.

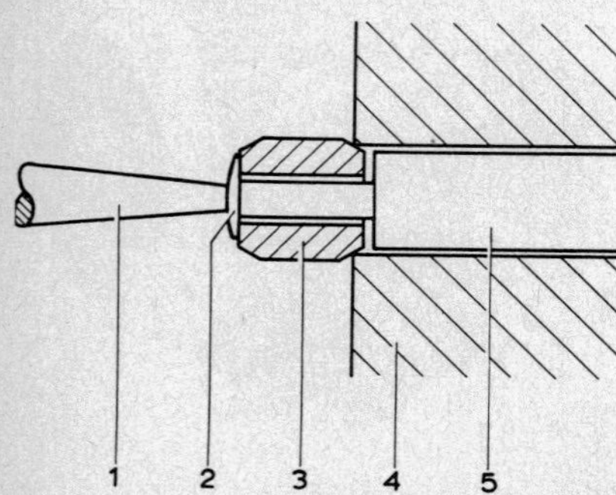

1 Punch (too small)
2 Endangered retaining pin shoulder
3 Split clamping bush
4 Housing
5 Retaining pin

The punch shown is too small to safely drive in the friction pad retaining pin. If the pin is driven in with this size punch, the pin head may shear off and allow the pin to fall out.

the car taken on a test run.

Brake Caliper R & R

1. Remove the front wheel.
2. Remove the brake hose, cap, and bleeder valve dust cap.
3. Bend back the mounting bolt lockplate.
4. Remove the caliper attaching bolts.
5. Remove the caliper.
6. In reinstalling, clean all mating surfaces and steering knuckle.
7. Install the mounting bolts and torque to 43 ft lbs. The bolts and locking plates should be renewed.
8. Bleed the brake system. Be sure to replace the dust caps on the bleeder valves.
9. Road-test.

Brake Caliper Repair

1. Remove the friction pads.
2. Remove the caliper.
3. Mount the caliper in a vise using vise clamps.
4. Remove the piston retaining plates.
5. With a screwdriver, pry out the rubber boot spring ring. Do not damage the boot.
6. With a plastic rod, remove the boot.
7. Remove one piston with air pressure, holding the second piston with retaining pliers.
8. Remove the rubber seal with a plastic rod.
9. To reassemble, first clean with methylated spirits or brake fluid.
10. Replace any parts showing wear, corrosion, or physical damage. A damaged cylinder requires the replacement of a complete caliper.
11. Install a new rubber boot and spring ring.
12. Install the retaining plate.
13. Follow above procedures for the second piston.

Brake Disc R & R

1. Remove the wheel.
2. Remove the caliper from the knuckle and hang it on the tie rod with a wire hook.
3. Remove the wheel bearing clamp nut and remove the disc.
4. In replacing, check the splash shield for damage and replace if needed.
5. Reinstall the disc and adjust the bearing.

Windshield Wipers

Windshield Wiper Motor R & R, Type 1

1. Disconnect the battery ground cable.
2. Loosen the clamp screws and remove the wiper arms.
3. Remove both wiper bearing hex nuts and washers. Take off the outer bearing seals.
4. Remove the back of the instrument panel from the luggage compartment.
5. Disconnect the cable from the wiper motor.
6. Remove the glove compartment box.
7. Remove the screw securing the wiper frame to the body.
8. Remove the frame and motor, with the linkage.

When replacing the motor and linkage:

1. The pressed lug on the wiper frame must engage the groove in the wiper bearing. Make sure that the wiper spindles are vertical to the windshield.
2. Check the linkage bushings for wear.
3. The hollow side of the links must face toward the frame, with the angled end of the driving link toward the right bearing.
4. The inner bearing seal should be placed so that the shoulder of the rubber molding faces the wiper arm.

Windshield Wiper Motor R & R, Type 2

1. Disconnect the ground wire from the battery.
2. Remove both wiper arms.
3. Remove the bearing cover and nut.
4. Remove the heater branch connections under the instrument panel.
5. Disconnect the wiper motor wiring harness.
6. Remove the wiper motor securing screws and remove the motor.
7. Reverse the above steps to install.

Windshield Wiper Motor R & R, Type 3

1. Disconnect the battery.
2. Remove the ashtray and glove compartment.
3. Remove the fresh air controls.
4. Remove the cover for the heater and water drainage hoses.
5. Disconnect the motor wiring.
6. Remove the wiper arms.
7. Remove the bearing covers and nuts, washers, and outer bearing seals.
8. Remove the wiper motor securing screw and remove the motor.
9. Reverse the above steps to install.

VOLVO

Index

INTRODUCTION

Since Volvo imported its first cars to this country in 1956, the company has enjoyed a reputation for building safe, reliable, durable and economical cars. Volvo is currently manufacturing three distinctly different series of cars. The 140 series, first produced in 1967, is a four cylinder, medium priced compact offered in a two-door sedan (142), four-door sedan (144), and station wagon (145) body styles. The 164, first produced in 1969, is a six cylinder, upper-medium priced luxury rendition of the 144, sharing the same sheet metal and mechanical components with the 144 from the firewall back. The 1800 series, first imported to the U.S. in 1964, is a four cylinder, medium priced sports model offered through 1972 in a two-door coupe version (P1800, 1800S, 1800E), and since 1972 in a two-door sportswagon version (1800ES).

1973 140 series—144 shown

MODEL IDENTIFICATION

1967-70 140 series—144 shown

1969-72 164

1971-72 140 series—144 shown

1973 164

1970-72 1800E—1967-69 1800S similar

1972-73 1800ES

SERIAL NUMBER IDENTIFICATION

In all correspondence with the dealer or when ordering spare parts, the vehicle type designation, chassis number, and, if applicable, the engine, transmission, and rear axle (final drive) numbers should be quoted for proper identification.

Serial number identification—1972 144 shown.

Vehicle Type Designation and Chassis Number

Type designation (142, 164, 1800, etc.) and chassis number appear at several locations on every Volvo. On all 140 series and 164 model Volvos, they are stamped into the sheet metal of the right front door pillar. On all 1800 models, they are stamped into the sheet metal on the right side of the engine compartment. The type designation and the chassis number also appear on a metal plate (1) riveted to the engine side of the firewall. For 1972–73, they appear on the V.I.N. plate (3) located at the foot of the left door post.

Chassis Number Chart

Year	Model	Starting Chassis No.
1967	142	1
	144	1
	1800S	21000
1968	142	1500
	144	37100
	145	1
	1800S	25500
1969	142	52900
	144	89900
	145	9200
	164	1
	1800S	28300
1970	142	112400
	144	138700
	145	30900
	164	12200
	1800E	30001
1971	142	178960
	144	194140
	145	61600
	164	32400
	1800E	32800
1972	142	249930
	144	263070
	145	103380
	164	52790
	1800E	37550
	1800ES	1
1973	142	323400
	144	340100
	145	153730
	164	74450
	1800ES	3070

Engine, Transmission, and Final Drive Identification

The engine type designation, part number, and serial number are given on the left side of the block (4). The last figures of the part number are stamped on a tab and are followed by the serial number stamped on the block.

The transmission type designation, serial number, and part number appear on a metal plate (5) riveted to the underside of the transmission.

The final drive reduction ratio, part number, and serial number are found on a metal plate (6) riveted to the left-hand side of the differential.

Engine Identification Chart

Type Number	Engine Type	Horse-power (SAE gross)	Vehicle Type
496836	B 18 B	115	142S, 144S
496838	B 18 B	115	142S, 144S, with BW 35
496842	B 18 B	115	1800S
496864	B 18 B	115	1800S
496865	B 18 B	115	142S, 144S, 145S
496867	B 18 B	115	142S, 144S, 145S, with BW 35
496912	B 20 B	118	142S, 144S, 145S
496913	B 20 B	118	142S, 144S, 145S, with BW 35
496922	B 20 B	118	1800S
496929	B 20 B	118	142S, 144S, 145S
496930	B 20 B	118	142S, 144S, 145S, with BW 35
496940	B 20 E	130	1800E
496941	B 20 E	130	1800E with BW 35
496943	B 20 E	130	142E
496945	B 20 E	130	142E with BW 35
498282	B 20 F	125	1800E, 1800ES
498283	B 20 F	125	1800E, 1800ES, with BW 35
498284	B 20 F	125	142E, 144E, 145E
498285	B 20 F	125	142E, 144E, 145E, with BW 35
496953	B 30 A	145	164
496954	B 30 A	145	164 with BW 35
498100	B 30 F	160	164E
498101	B 30 F	160	164E with BW 35

GENERAL ENGINE SPECIFICATIONS

Year		Engine Displacement Cu in. (cc)	Carburetor Type	Horsepower @ rpm (gross)	Torque @ rpm (ft lbs) (gross)	Bore x Stroke (in.)	Compression Ratio	Oil Pressure @ rpm (psi)
1967-68	B 18 B	109 (1780)	2 sidedraft SU HS6	115 @ 6000	112 @ 4000	3.313 x 3.150	10.0:1	36-85 @ 2000
1969-70	B 20 B	122 (1990)	2 sidedraft Zenith-Stromberg 175 CD 2SE	118 @ 5800	123 @ 3500	3.5000 x 3.150	9.3:1	36-85 @ 2000
1971-72	B 20 B	122 (1990)	2 sidedraft SU HIF 6	118 @ 5800	123 @ 3500	3.5004 x 3.150	9.3:1	36-85 @ 2000
1970-71	B 20 E	122 (1990)	Bosch electronic fuel injection	130 @ 6000	130 @ 3500	3.5008 x 3.150	10.5:1	36-85 @ 2000
1972-73	B 20 F	122 (1990)	Bosch electronic fuel injection	125 @ 6000	123 @ 3500	3.5008 x 3.150	8.7:1	36-85 @ 2000
1970-72	B 30 A	183 (2978)	2 sidedraft Zenith-Stromberg 175 CD 2SE	145 @ 5500	163 @ 3000	3.500 x 3.150 ①	9.3:1	36-85 @ 2000
1972-73	B 30 F	183 (2978)	Bosch electronic fuel injection	160 @ 5800	167 @ 2500	3.501 x 3.150	8.7:1	36-85 @ 2000

① 1972 B 30 A engine has 3.501 bore

TUNE-UP SPECIFICATIONS

When analyzing compression test results, look for uniformity among cylinders, rather than specific pressures.

Year	Engine Displace. (Cu. in)	Spark Plugs Type	Spark Plugs Gap (in.)	Distributor Point Dwell (deg)	Distributor Point Gap (in.)	Ignition Timing (deg) MT	Ignition Timing (deg) AT	Intake Valve Opens (deg)	Fuel Pump Pressure (psi)	Idle Speed (rpm) MT	Idle Speed (rpm) AT	Valve Clearance (in.) In	Valve Clearance (in.) Ex
1967	B 18 B 109	Bosch W225T1	0.030	59-65	0.016-0.020	17-19B	17-19B	TDC	1.56-3.55	800 800	700 700	0.020-0.022	0.020-0.022
1968	B 18 B 109	Bosch W200T35	0.030	59-65	0.016-0.020	3-5B ①	3-5B ①	TDC	1.56-3.55	800 800	700 700	0.020-0.022	0.020-0.022
1969-72	B 20 B 122	Bosch W200T35 ②	0.030	59-65	③	10B	10B	TDC	1.56-3.55	800 800	700 700	0.020-0.022	0.020-0.022
	B 30 A 183	④	0.030	37-43	0.010 min.	10B	10B	TDC	2.10-3.50	800 800	700 700	0.020-0.022	0.020-0.022
1970-71	B 20 E 122	Bosch W225T35 ⑤	0.030	59-65	0.016-0.020	10B	10B	5.5B	28	900	800	0.016-0.018	0.016-0.018
1972-73	B 20 F 122	⑥	0.030	59-65	0.014 min.	10B	10B	5.5B	28	900	800	0.016-0.018	0.016-0.018
1972-73	B 30 F 183	Bosch W200T35	0.030	37-43	0.010 min.	10B	10B	TDC	28	900	800	0.020-0.022	0.020-0.022

① @ 850 rpm
② Severe service—W225T35
③ 1969-71—0.016-0.020 in.
1972 —0.014 min. in.
④ 1969 —W175T35
1970-72—W200T35
⑤ Severe service—W240T1
⑥ W225T35—Severe service
W200T35—Normal service

Firing Orders

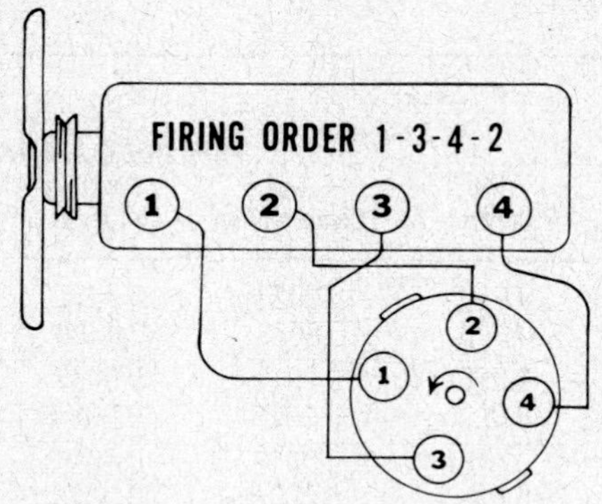

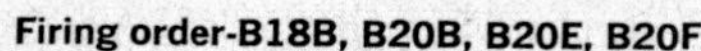
Firing order-B18B, B20B, B20E, B20F

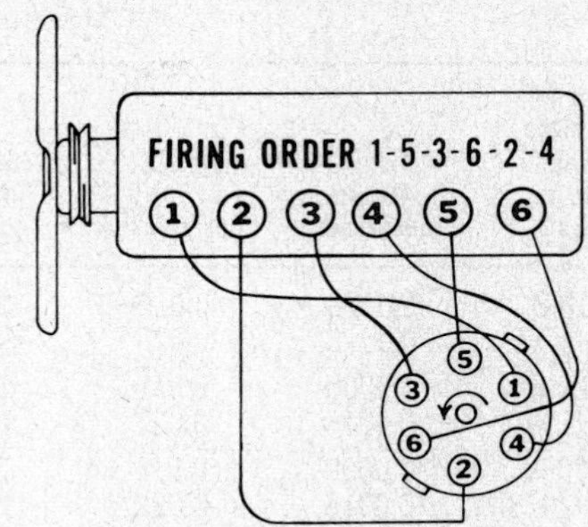

Firing order—B30A, B30F

VALVE SPECIFICATIONS

Year	Engine and Displacement Cu. in. (cc)	Seat Angle (deg)	Face Angle (deg)	Seat Width (in.)	Spring Test Pressure (lbs @ in.)	Spring Installed Height (in.)	Stem to Guide Clearance (in.) Intake	Stem to Guide Clearance (in.) Exhaust	Stem Diameter (in.) Intake	Stem Diameter (in.) Exhaust
1967-68	B 18 B 109 (1780)	44.5	45	0.055	181.5 @ 1.18	1.81	0.0010-0.0022	0.0026-0.0037	0.3419-0.3425	0.3403-0.3409
1969-72	B 20 B 109 (1780)									
1970-71	B 20 E 122 (1990)	44.5	45	0.08	181.5 @ 1.18	1.81	0.0012-0.0026	0.0024-0.0038	0.3132-0.3138	0.3120-0.3126
1972-73	B 20 F 122 (1990)									
1969-72	B 30 A 183 (2978)	44.5	45	0.08	145.0 @ 1.20	1.77	0.0012-0.0026	0.0024-0.0038	0.3132-0.3138	0.3120-0.3126
1972-73	B 30 F 183 (2978)	44.5	45	0.08	181.5 @ 1.18	1.81	0.0012-0.0026	0.0024-0.0038	0.3132-0.3138	0.3120-0.3126

TORQUE SPECIFICATIONS

All readings in ft lbs

Year	Engine	Cyl. Head Bolts	Rod Bearing Bolts	Main Bearing Bolts	Crank-shaft Pulley Bolt	Flywheel-To-Crank-shaft Bolts	Manifold Bolts Intake	Manifold Bolts Exhaust	Cam-shaft Nut	Spark Plug	Oil Pan	Alter-nator Bolt (½ in.)	Gen. Bolt (⅜ in.)
1967-73	All	65①	38-42	87-94	50-58	36-40	13-16	13-16	94-108	25-29 ②	6-8	50-60	25-29

① Torque head bolts in three stages; first, torque in sequence to 29 ft lbs, then to 58 ft lbs, and finally after driving the car for 10 minutes, torque to the final figure of 65 ft lbs.
② W175T1—27-33 ft lbs

Torque Sequences

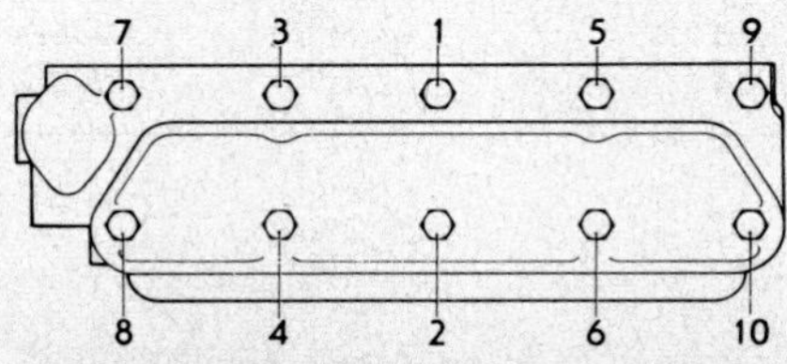

Cylinder head bolt tightening sequence—B18, B20.

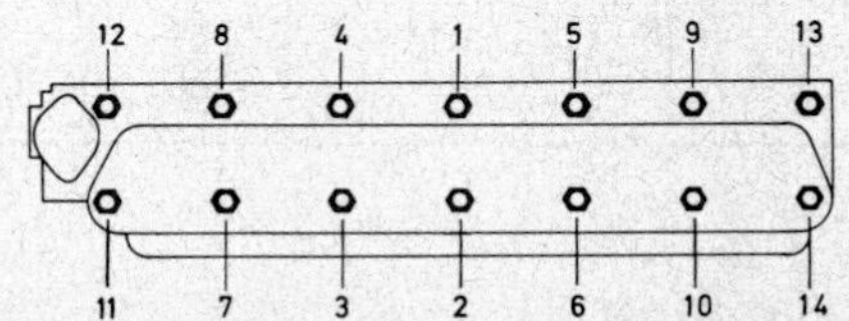

Cylinder head bolt tightening sequence—B30.

PISTON AND RING SPECIFICATIONS

All measurements in inches

Year	Engine Displacement Cu. In. (cc)	Piston Clearance	Ring Gap: Top Compression	Ring Gap: Bottom Compression	Ring Gap: Oil Control	Ring Side Clearance: Top Compression	Ring Side Clearance: Bottom Compression	Ring Side Clearance: Oil Control
1967-68	B 18 B 109 (1780)	0.0008-0.0016	0.010-0.020	0.010-0.020	0.010-0.020	0.0021-0.0032	0.0017-0.0028	0.0017-0.0028
1969-70	B 20 B 122 (1990)	0.0008-0.0016	0.016-0.022	0.016-0.022	0.016-0.022	0.0017-0.0028	0.0017-0.0028	0.0017-0.0028
	B 30 A 183 (2978)	0.0008-0.0016	0.016-0.022	0.016-0.022	0.016-0.022	0.0017-0.0028	0.0017-0.0028	0.0017-0.0028
1971	B 20 B 122 (1990)	0.0014-0.0022	0.016-0.022	0.016-0.022	0.016-0.022	0.0017-0.0028	0.0017-0.0028	0.0017-0.0028
1971	B 20 E 122 (1990)	0.0016-0.0024	0.016-0.022	0.016-0.022	0.016-0.022	0.0017-0.0028	0.0017-0.0028	0.0017-0.0028
	B 30 A 183 (2978)	0.0016-0.0024	0.016-0.022	0.016-0.022	0.016-0.022	0.0017-0.0028	0.0017-0.0028	0.0017-0.0028
1972	B 20 B 122 (1990)	0.0014-0.0020	0.016-0.022	0.016-0.022	0.016-0.022	0.0016-0.0028	0.0016-0.0028	0.0016-0.0028
1972-73	B 20 F 122 (1990)	0.0016-0.0024	0.016-0.022	0.016-0.022	0.016-0.022	0.0016-0.0028	0.0016-0.0028	0.0016-0.0028
1972	B 30 A 183 (2978)	0.0016-0.0024	0.016-0.022	0.016-0.022	0.016-0.022	0.0016-0.0028	0.0016-0.0028	0.0016-0.0028
1972-73	B 30 F 183 (2978)	0.0016-0.0024	0.016-0.022	0.016-0.022	0.016-0.022	0.0016-0.0032	0.0016-0.0028	0.0016-0.0028

CRANKSHAFT AND CONNECTING ROD SPECIFICATIONS

All measurements are given in inches

Year	Engine Displacement Cu. in. (cc)	Crankshaft: Main Brg Journal Dia	Crankshaft: Main Brg Oil Clearance	Crankshaft: Shaft End-Play	Crankshaft: Thrust on No.	Connecting Rod: Journal Diameter	Connecting Rod: Oil Clearance	Connecting Rod: Side Clearance
1967-68	B 18 109 (1780)	2.4977-2.4982	0.0015-0.0035	0.0007-0.0042	5	2.1295-2.1300	0.0015-0.0032	0.006-0.014
1969	B 20 122 (1990)	2.4977-2.4982	0.0010-0.0030	0.0007-0.0042	5	2.1295-2.1300	0.0015-0.0032	0.006-0.014
1970-71	B 20 122 (1990)	2.4981-2.4986	0.0011-0.0031	0.0018-0.0054	5	2.1299-2.1304	0.0012-0.0028	0.006-0.014
1972-73	B 20 122 (1990)	2.4981-2.4986	0.0011-0.0033	0.0018-0.0054	5	2.1299-2.1304	0.0012-0.0028	0.006-0.014
1969	B 30 183 (2978)	2.4977-2.4982	0.0015-0.0035	0.0018-0.0054	7	2.1295-2.1300	0.0016-0.0032	0.006-0.014
1970-71	B 30 183 (2978)	2.4981-2.4986	0.0011-0.0031	0.0018-0.0054	7	2.1299-2.1304	0.0012-0.0028	0.006-0.014
1972-73	B 30 122 (1990)	2.4981-2.4986	0.0011-0.0033	0.0018-0.0054	7	2.1299-2.1304	0.0012-0.0028	0.006-0.014

CAPACITIES

Year	Model	Engine Displacement Cu in. (cc)	Engine Crankcase (qt) With Filter	Engine Crankcase (qt) Without Filter	Transmission (pts) Manual 4 spd*	Transmission (pts) Automatic	Drive Axle (pt)	Gasoline Tank (gal)	Cooling System (qt)
1967-68	142, 144, 145	109 (1790)	4.0	3.4	1.6 (3.4)	13.1	2.7	15.3	9.0
	1800	109 (1790)	4.0	3.4	(3.4)	—	2.7	12.0	9.0
1969-70	142, 144, 145	122 (1990)	4.0	3.4	1.6 (3.4)	13.1	2.7	15.3	9.0
	164	183 (2978)	6.3	5.5	1.3 (3.0)	17.3	3.4	15.3	13.0
	1800	122 (1990)	4.0	3.4	(3.4)	—	2.7	12.0	9.0
1971	142, 144, 145	122 (1990)	4.0	3.4	1.6 (3.4)	13.1	2.7	15.3	10.5
	164	183 (2978)	6.3	5.5	1.3 (3.0)	17.3	3.4	15.3	13.0
	1800	122 (1990)	4.0	3.4	(3.4)	13.3	2.7	12.0	9.0
1972-73	142, 144, 145	122 (1990)	4.0	3.4	1.6 (3.4)	13.5	2.7	15.3	10.5
	164	183 (2978)	6.3	5.5	1.3 (3.0)	17.7	3.4	15.3	13.0
	1800	122 (1990)	4.0	3.4	(3.4)	13.5	2.7	12.0	9.0

* Figures in parentheses are for overdrive transmission

BRAKE SPECIFICATIONS

All measurements are given in inches

Year	Model	Master Cylinder Bore	Wheel Cylinder or Caliper Piston Bore Front Disc	Wheel Cylinder or Caliper Piston Bore Rear Disc	Wheel Cylinder or Caliper Piston Bore Rear Drum	Brake Disc or Drum Diameter Front Disc	Brake Disc or Drum Diameter Rear Drum	Brake Disc or Drum Diameter Rear Drum	New Pad or Lining Thickness
1967-68	140 series	0.882	1.422	1.422	—	10.7	11.6	—	0.394
	1800S	0.875	①	—	0.750	10.6	—	9.0	0.188 (0.421 disc)
1969	140 series	0.882	1.422	1.422②	—	10.7	11.6	—	0.394
	164	0.950	1.422	1.422	—	10.7	11.6	—	0.394
	1800S	0.875	①	—	0.750	10.6	—	9.0	0.188 (0.421 disc)
1970	140 series	0.882	1.422	1.500	—	10.7	11.6	—	0.394
	164	0.950	1.422	1.500	—	10.7	11.6	—	0.394
	1800E	0.882	1.422	1.422	—	10.6	11.6	—	0.394
1971	140 series	0.882	③	④	—	10.7	11.6	—	0.394
	164	0.950	1.422	1.500	—	10.7	11.6	—	0.394
	1800E	0.882	1.422	1.422	—	10.6	11.6	—	0.394
1972	140 series	0.882	③	④	—	10.7	11.6	—	0.394
	164	0.950	1.500	1.700	—	10.7	11.6	—	0.394
	1800	0.882	1.422	1.422	—	10.6	11.6	—	0.394
1973	140 series	0.882	③	④	—	10.7	11.6	—	0.394
	164	⑤	1.500	1.700	—	10.7	11.6	—	0.394
	1800ES								

① Inner cylinders—2.125 in. Outer cylinders—1.500 in.
② 145—1.5 in.
③ Girling—1.6 Ate—1.5
④ Girling—1.8 Ate—1.7
⑤ Up to chassis no. 79020—0.950
Starting from chassis no. 79021—0.875

WHEEL ALIGNMENT

Year	Model	Caster Range (deg)	Camber Range (deg)	Toe-in (in.)	Steering Axis Inclination (at 0° camber)	WHEEL PIVOT RATIO (deg) Inner Wheel	Outer Wheel
1967-71	140 series 164	0-1P	0-1/2P	0-0.16	7.5	20	21.5-23.5
1967-71	1800 series	0-1P	0-1/2P	0-0.16	8.0	20	21.5-23.5
1972	140 series 164	0-1P	0-1/2P	0.080-0.20	7.5	20	21.5-23.5
1972-73	1800 series	①	0-1/2P	0-0.12	8.0	20	21.5-23.5
1973	140 series 164	1 1/2P-2P	0-1/2P	0.08-0.20	7.5	20	21.5-23.5

P Positive N Negative
① 0-1P—165HR15 Tires
2P-2 1/2P—185/70HR15 Tires

BATTERY AND STARTER SPECIFICATIONS

		BATTERY			STARTERS						
					Lock Test			No-Load Test			
Year	Engine	Amp. Hour Cap.	Volts	Term. Grnd.	Amps	Volts	Torque (ft lbs)	Amps	Volts	RPM	Brush Spring Tension (lbs)
1967-73	All Models	60	12	Neg	300-350	6	—	40-50	12	6900-8100	2.53-2.86

ALTERNATOR AND REGULATOR SPECIFICATIONS

		ALTERNATOR			REGULATOR	
Year	Vehicle Model	Part No. and Manufacturer	Output (amps.)	Min. Brush Length (in.)	Part No. and Manufacturer	Volts @ Alternator rpm (cold)
1968	140, 1800	Bosch G 14V 30A 25-027	30	—	BoschVA 14V 30A	13.5-14.5 (unloaded)
1969 1968-70	164 140	S.E.V. Motorola 14V 26641	35	0.20	S.E.V. Motorola 14V 33525	13.1-14.4 @ 4000
1969-71	140, 1800	Bosch K1 14V 35A20	35	0.31	Bosch AD 14V	14.0-15.0 @ 4000
1970-72 1972	164 140, 1800	S.E.V. Motorola 14V 34833	55	0.20	S.E.V. Motorola 14V 33544	13.1-14.4 @ 4000
1971 1971-72	1800 140	S.E.V. Motorola 14V 71270202	35	0.20	S.E.V. Motorola 14V 33525	13.1-14.4 @ 4000
1972	1800	Bosch K1 14V 55A20	55	0.53	Bosch AD 14V	13.9-14.8 @ 4000

D. C. GENERATOR AND REGULATOR SPECIFICATIONS

		GENERATOR				REGULATOR				
						Cut-out Relay				
Year	Vehicle Model	Part Number	Brush Spring Pressure (lbs.)	Field Resistance (ohms)	Max. Output (amps)	Part Number	Cuts in at (volts)	Reverse Current at amps	Max. Current (amps)	Voltage Regulator Setting (volts
1967-68	140, 1800	Bosch LJ/ GG240/12/ 2400/AR7	1.0-1.3	4.8 ± 0.5	30	Bosch RS/ VA240/12/12	12.4-13.1	2.0-7.5	45 cold 30 warm	14.1-14.8 idling 13.0-14.0 loaded

WIRING DIAGRAMS

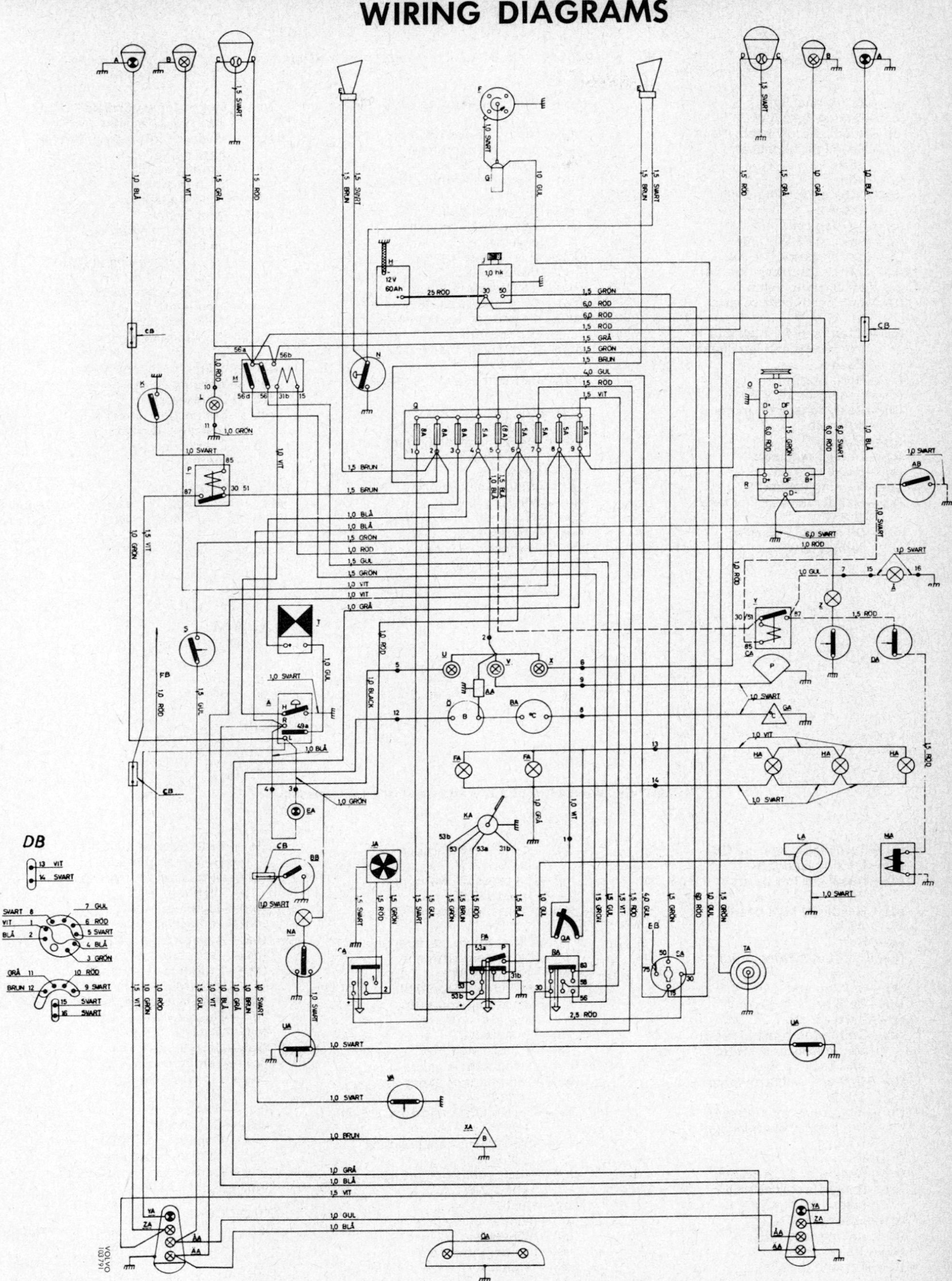

1967-68 142, 144, with B18B and manual transmission

1967-68 142, 144, with B18B and manual transmission

(a)—Turn signal light
(b)—Parking light 5 W
(c)—Headlight low beam 40 W
(d)—Headlight high beam 45 W
(e)—Horn
(f)—Distributor firing order 1-3-4-2
(g)—Ignition coil
(h)—Battery 12 V 60 Ah
(j)—Starter motor, 1.0 h.p.
(k)—Switch (on transmission) for back-up lights
(l)—High beam control lamp 1.2 W
(m)—Step relay for high and low beams and headlight flasher
(n)—Horn ring
(o)—Generator 12 V 30 A
(p)—Relay for starter motor solenoid
(q)—Fusebox
(r)—Voltage regulator
(s)—Brake contact
(t)—Warning flasher
(u)—Handbrake warning lamp 1.2 W
(v)—Oil pressure warning lamp 1.2 W
(x)—Charging warning lamp 1.2 W
(y)—Relay for overdrive
(z)—Glove compartment lighting 2 W
(a)—Overdrive warning lamp 1.2 W
(a)—Switch for headlight signalling and turn signals
(o)—Fuel gauge
(aa)—Voltage stabilizer
(ba)—Temperature gauge
(ca)—Oil pressure warning unit
(da)—Switch (on transmission) for overdrive
(ea)—Turn signal indicators 1.2 W
(fa)—Instrument panel lighting 2 × 3 W
(ga)—Temperature gauge sender
(ha)—Heater control lighting 3 × 1.2 W
(ja)—Heater
(ka)—Windshield wipers
(la)—Windshield washer
(ma)—Solenoid for overdrive
(na)—Interior lamp 10 W
(oa)—Switch for heater
(pa)—Switch for windshield wipers and washer
(qa)—Rheostat for instr. panel lighting
(ra)—Lighting switch
(sa)—Ignition switch
(ta)—Cigarette lighter
(ua)—Door switch
(va)—Switch for handbrake control
(xa)—Fuel level sending unit
(ya)—Flasher light 32 CP
(za)—Back-up lights 15 W
(aa)—Stop lights 25 W
(aa)—Tail lights 5 W
(oa)—License plate light 2 × 5 W
(ab)—Switch for overdrive
(bb)—Warning valve
(cb)—Connector
(db)—Connection unit for instrument cluster
(eb)—Connection for radio (75)
(fb)—Spare cable

COLOR CODE

Bla	=	Blue	Gul	=	Yellow
Brun	=	Brown	Rod	=	Red
Gra	=	Grey	Svart	=	Black
Gron	=	Green	Vit	=	White

1967-68 142, 144, with B18B and automatic transmission

(a)—Turn signal light 32 CP
(b)—Parking light 5 W
(c)—Headlight low beam 40 W
(d)—Headlight high beam 45 W
(e)—Horn
(f)—Distributor firing order 1-3-4-2
(g)—Ignition coil
(h)—Battery 12 V 60 Ah
(j)—Starter motor, 1.0 h.p.
(k)—Switch (on transmission) for neutral start switch and back-up lights
(l)—High beam control lamp 1.2 W
(m)—Step relay for high and low beams and headlight flasher
(n)—Horn ring
(o)—Generator 12 V 30 A
(p)—Relay for starter motor solenoid
(q)—Fusebox
(r)—Voltage regulator
(s)—Brake contact
(t)—Warning flasher
(u)—Handbrake warning lamp 1.2 W
(v)—Oil pressure warning lamp 1.2 W
(x)—Charging warning lamp 1.2 W
(y)—Oil pressure warning unit
(z)—Glove compartment lighting 2 W
(a)—Switch for headlight signalling and turn signals
(a)—Fuel gauge
(o)—Voltage stabilizer
(aa)—Temperature gauge
(ba)—Temperature gauge sender
(ca)—Turn signal indicators 1.2 W
(da)—Instrument panel lighting 2 × 3 W
(ea)—Heater control lighting 3 × 1.2 W
(fa)—Heater
(ga)—Windshield wipers
(ha)—Windshield washer
(ja)—Interior lamp 10 W
(ka)—Switch for heater
(la)—Switch for windshield wipers and washer
(ma)—Rheostat for instr. panel lighting
(na)—Lighting switch
(oa)—Ignition switch
(pa)—Cigarette lighter
(qa)—Door switch
(ra)—Switch for handbrake control
(sa)—Fuel level sending unit
(ta)—Flasher light 32 CP
(ua)—Back-up lights 15 W
(va)—Stop lights 25 W
(xa)—Tail lights 5 W
(ya)—License plate light 2 × 5 W
(za)—Warning valve
(aa)—Connector
(aa)—Connection unit for instrument cluster
(oa)—Connection for radio (75)
(ab)—Spare cable

COLOR CODE

Bla	=	Blue	Gul	=	Yellow
Brun	=	Brown	Rod	=	Red
Gra	=	Grey	Svart	=	Black
Gron	=	Green	Vit	=	White

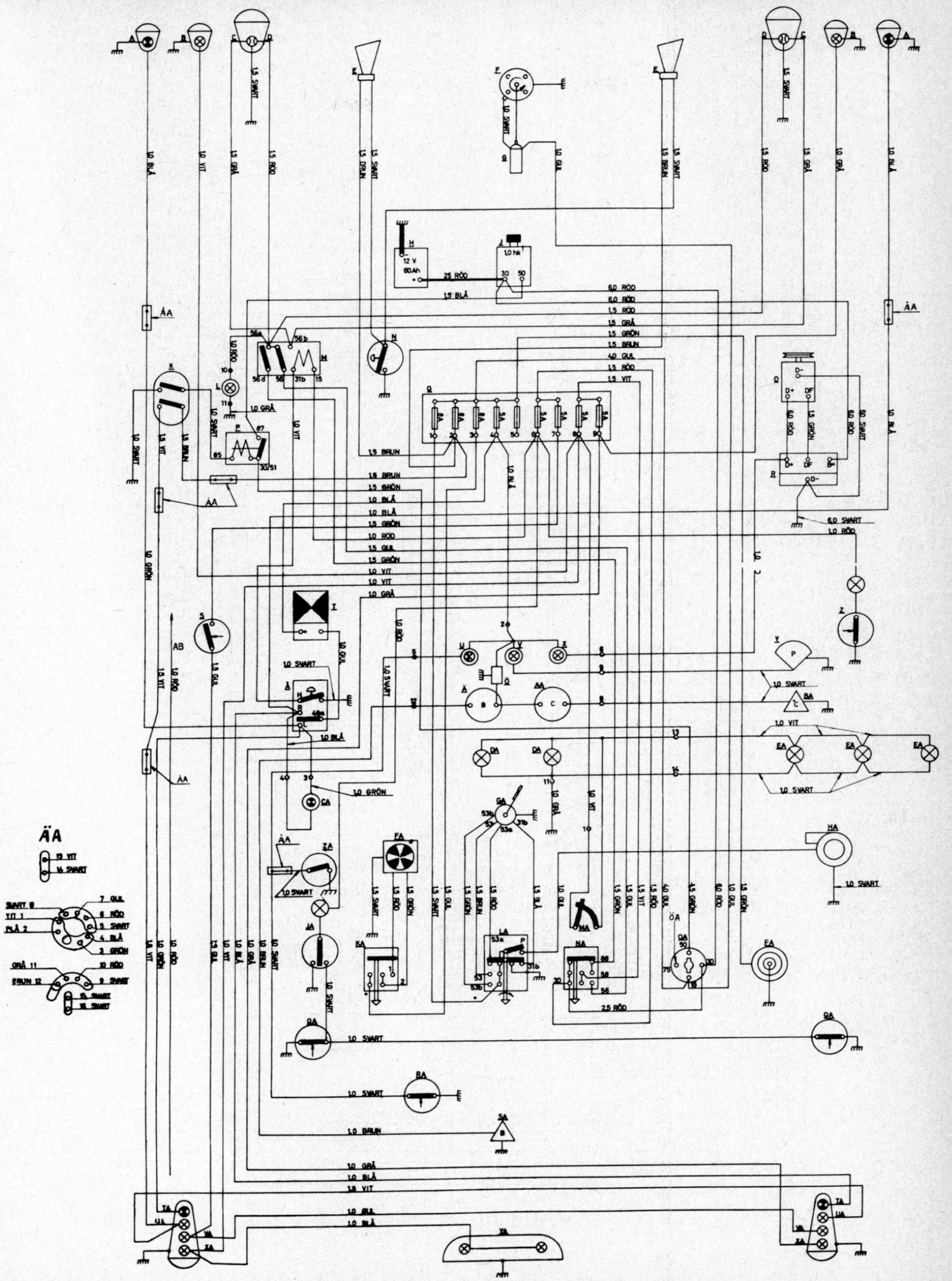

1967-68 142, 144, with B18B and automatic transmission

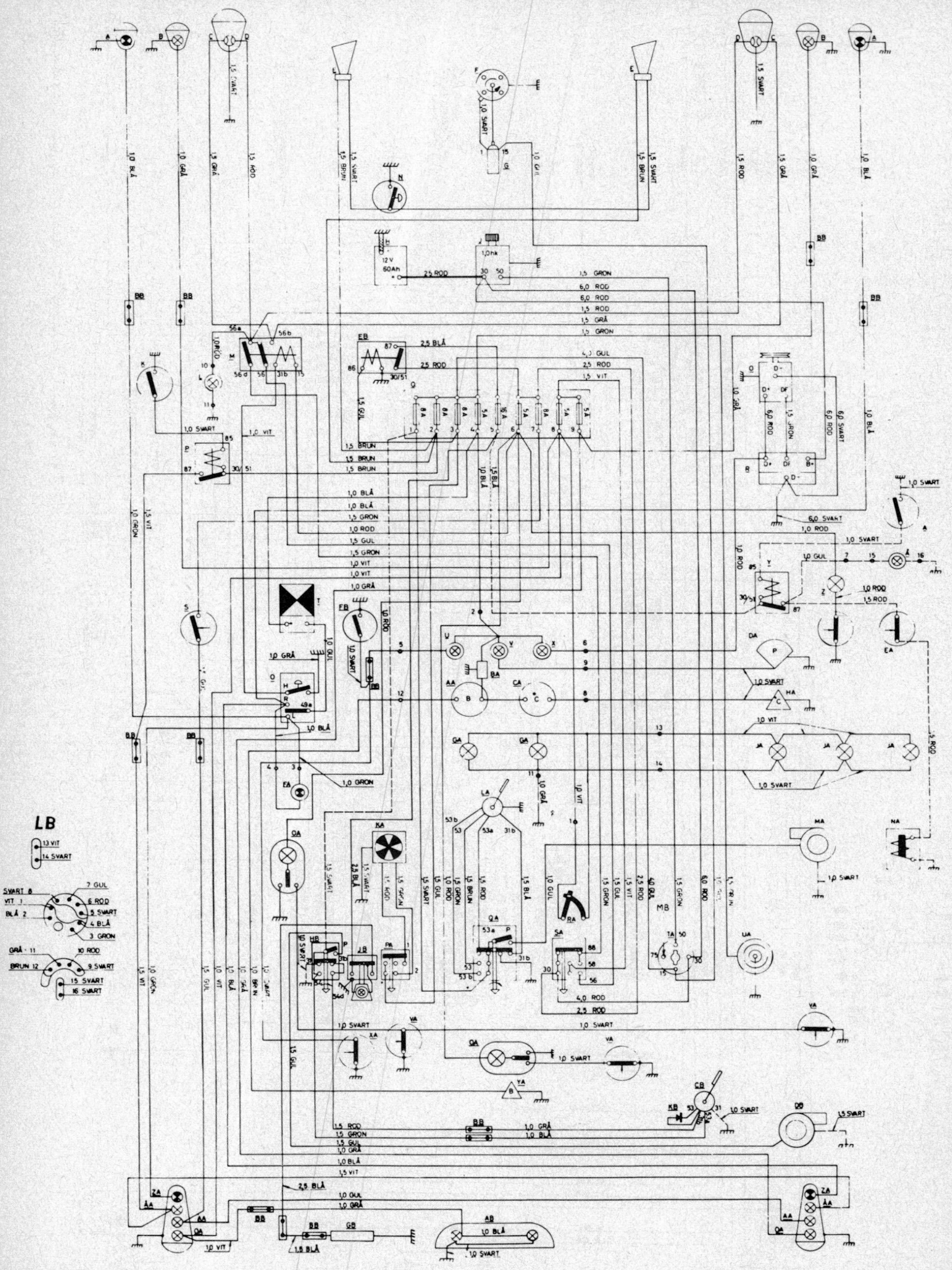

1968 145, with B18B and manual transmission

1968 145, with B18B and manual transmission

(a)—Turn signal light 32 CP
(b)—Parking light 5 W
(c)—Headlight low beam 40 W
(d)—Headlight high beam 45 W
(e)—Horn
(f)—Distributor firing order 1-3-4-2
(g)—Ignition coil
(h)—Battery 12 V 60 Ah
(j)—Starter motor, 1.0 h.p.
(k)—Switch (on transmission) for back-up lights
(l)—Control lamp for high beam 1.2 W
(m)—Step relay for high and low beams and headlight flasher
(n)—Horn ring
(o)—Generator 12 V 30 A
(p)—Relay for back-up lights
(q)—Fusebox
(r)—Voltage regulator
(s)—Brake contact
(t)—Warning flasher
(u)—Handbrake warning lamp 1.2 W
(v)—Oil pressure warning lamp 1.2 W
(x)—Warning charging lamp 1.2 W
(y)—Relay for overdrive
(z)—Glove compartment lighting 2 W
(a)—Overdrive control lamp 1.2 W
(a)—Overdrive switch
(o)—Switch for headlight signalling and turn signals
(aa)—Fuel gauge
(ba)—Voltage stabilizer
(ca)—Temperature gauge
(da)—Oil pressure warning unit
(ea)—Switch (on transmission) for overdrive
(fa)—Turn signal indicators 1.2 W
(ga)—Instr. panel lighting 2 × 3 W
(ha)—Temperature sending unit
(ja)—Heater control lighting 3 × 1.2 W
(ka)—Heater
(la)—Windshield wipers
(ma)—Windshield washer
(na)—Solenoid for overdrive
(oa)—Interior lamp 10 W
(pa)—Switch for heater
(qa)—Switch for windshield wipers and washer
(ra)—Rheostat for instr. panel lighting
(sa)—Lighting switch
(ta)—Ignition switch
(ua)—Cigarette lighter
(va)—Door switch
(xa)—Switch for handbrake control
(ya)—Fuel level sending unit
(za)—Flasher light 32 CP
(aa)—Back-up lights 15 W
(aa)—Stop lights 25 W
(oa)—Rear lights 5 W
(ab)—License plate light 2 × 5 W
(bb)—Connector
(*cb)—Tailgate window wiper
(*db)—Tailgate window washer
(eb)—Relay for heated tailgate window
(fb)—Warning switch
(gb)—Heated tailgate window
(*hb)—Switch for tailgate window wiper
(jb)—Switch for heated tailgate window with control lamp 2 W
(*kb)—Diode
(lb)—Connection unit for instrument cluster
(mb)—Connection for radio (75)
*marker parts are accessories

COLOR CODE

Bla	=	Blue	Gul	=	Yellow
Brun	=	Brown	Rod	=	Red
Gra	=	Grey	Svart	=	Black
Gron	=	Green	Vit	=	White

1967-68 1800S

1. Flasher and parking light, left
2. Headlight, left
3. Horn
4. High-tone horn
5. Headlight, right
6. Flasher and parking light, right
7. Relay for headlight signalling
8. Distributor firing order 1, 3, 4, 2
9. Generator 12 V 30 A
10. Voltage regulator
11. Switch for backup light
12. Switch on transmission for overdrive
13. Solenoid
14. Foot dimmer switch
15. Horn button
16. Ignition coil
17. Starter motor
18. Battery
19. Relay for overdrive
20. Turn signal switch
21. Flasher mechanism for turn signal
22. Warning light for overdrive
23. Overdrive lever switch on steering column
24. Fuse
25. Tachometer
26. Fuel gauge
27. Clock
28. Brake light switch
29. Windshield washer
30. Windshield wipers
31. 3 Warning lights
32. Charging
33. Turn signal
34. High beam
35. Instrument lighting
36. Heater
37. Instrument lighting
38. Switch
39. Switch for windshield wipers and washer
40. Light switch
41. Ignition switch
42. Switch for heater
43. Cigar lighter
44. Map-reading light
45. Door switch
46. Switch for interior light
47. Interior light
48. Switch for interior light
49. Interior light
50. Switch for interior light
51. Door switch
52. Rear light, left
53. Fuel level pickup
54. License plate lighting
55. Rear light, right

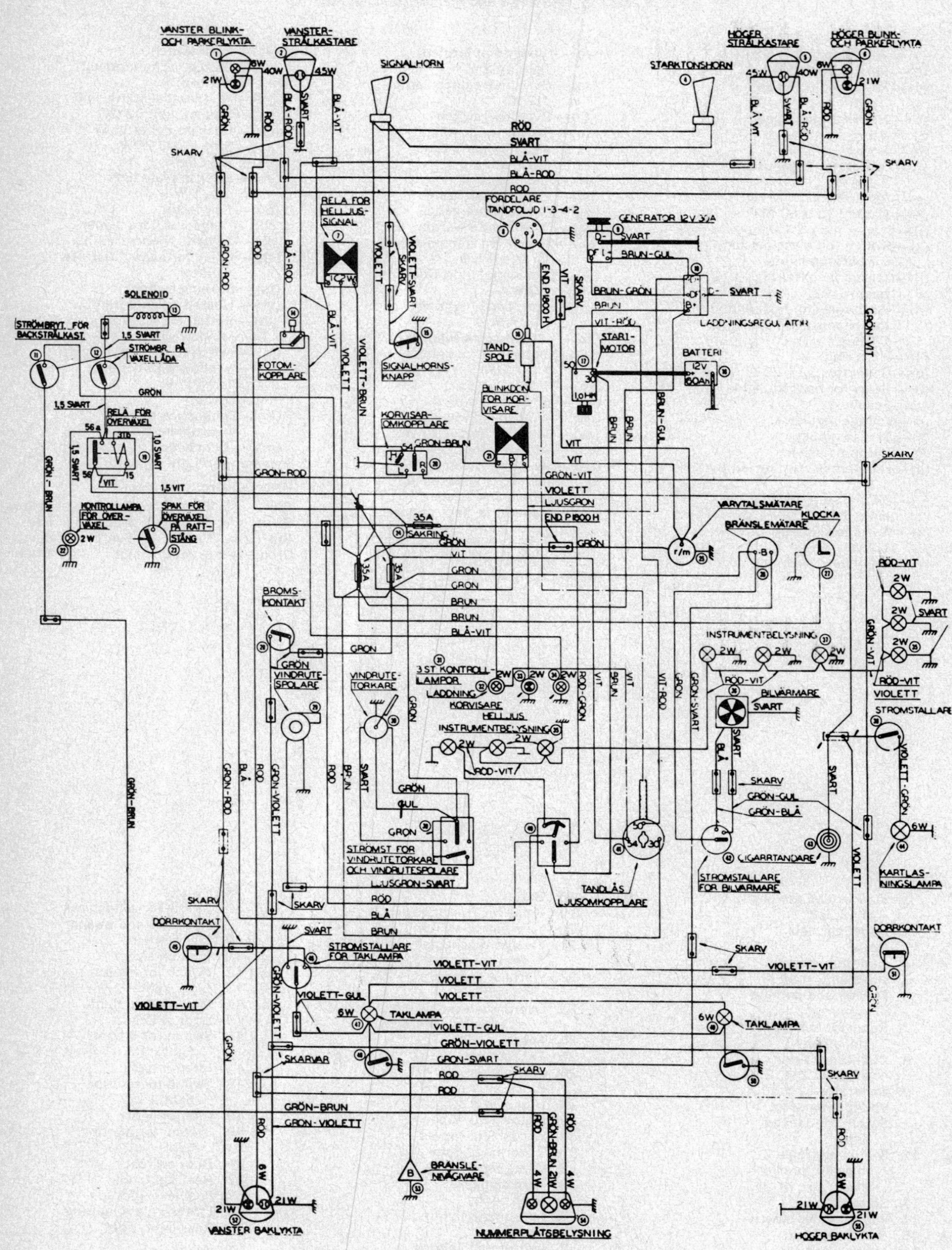

1967-68 1800S

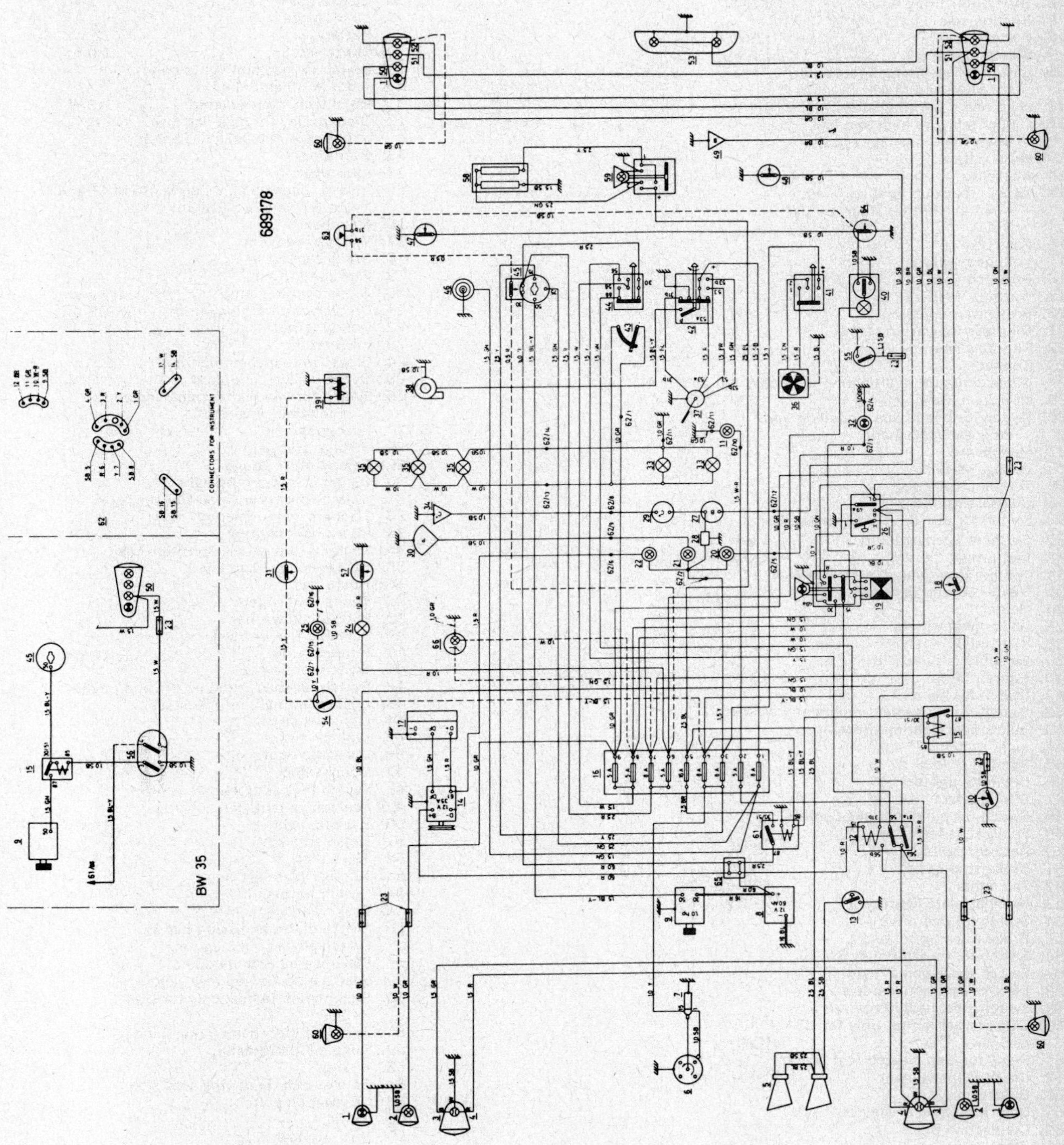

1969-71 142, 144, with B20B

1969-71 142, 144, with B20B

1.	Dir. ind. flashers	32 CP
2.	Parking lights	5 W
3.	Headlight low beam	40 W
4.	Headlight high beam	45 W
5.	Horn	
6.	Distributor firing order	1-3-4-2
7.	Ignition coil	
8.	Battery	12 V 60 Ah
9.	Starter motor	1.0 hp
10.	Switch for reversing lights only for M 40 and M 41	
11.	High beam warning lamp	1.2 W
12.	Dipper relay for high and low beams and headlight flasher	
13.	Horn ring	
14.	Alternator	
15.	Relay f. back-up light on M 40, M 41 and starter Relay on BW 35	
16.	Fuse box	
17.	Voltage regulator	
18.	Brake contact	
19.	Warning flashers	
20.	Brake warning lamp	1.2 W
21.	Oil pressure warning lamp	1.2 W
22.	Charging warning lamp	1.2 W
23.	Connector	
24.	Glove compartment lighting	2 W
25.	Overdrive warning lamp	1.2 W
26.	Switch for headlights signalling and emergency flashers	
27.	Fuel gauge	
28.	Voltage stabilizer	
29.	Temperature gauge	
30.	Oil pressure lamp	
31.	Switch for overdrive on transmission	
32.	Flashers warning lamp	1.2 W
33.	Instrument lighting	2×1.2 W
34.	Temperature gauge, sensitive head	
35.	Heater control lighting	3×1.2 W
36.	Heater	
37.	Windshield wipers	
38.	Windshield washer	
39.	Solenoid f. overdrive	
40.	Interior lamp	10 W
41.	Switch for heater	
42.	Switch for windshield wipers and washer	
43.	Instrument lighting rheostat	
44.	Light switch	
45.	Ignition switch	
46.	Cigarette lighter	
47.	Door contact	
48.	Switch for parking brake control	
49.	Fuel gauge tank unit	
50.	Back-up lights	15 W
51.	Brake stoplights	25 W
52.	Tail lights	5 W
53.	Number plate lighting	2×5 W
54.	Switch for overdrive	
55.	Brake warning contact	
56.	Switch on transmission BW 35	
57.	Switch glove comp. lighting	
58.	Elec. heated rear window	
59.	Switch elec. heated rear window	
60.	Side marker lamps, only for USA 5 W	5 W
61.	Relay for elec. heated rear window	
62.	Conn. at instrument	
63.	Buzzer	
64.	Door switch on driving seat side	
65.	Connection plate	
66.	Clock	

Color code:

SB	Black
W	White
Y	Yellow
GN	Green
GR	Grey
BL	Blue
R	Red
BR	Brown
W-R	White-Red
BL-Y	Blue-Yellow

1969-71 145, with B20B

1.	Dir. ind. flashers	32 CP
2.	Parking light	5 W
3.	Headlight low beam	40 W
4.	Headlight high beam	45 W
5.	Horn	
6.	Distributor firing order	1-3-4-2
7.	Ignition coil	
8.	Battery	12 V 60 Ah
9.	Starter motor	1.0 hp
10.	Switch for back-up lights only for M 40 and M 41	
11.	High beam control lamp	1.2 W
12.	Dipper relay for high and low beams and headlight flasher	
13.	Horn ring	
14.	Alternator	
15.	Relay f. back-up lights on M 40, M 41 and starter Relay on BW 35	
16.	Fuse box	
17.	Voltage regulator	
18.	Brake contact	
19.	Warning flashers	
20.	Brake warning lamp	1.2 W
21.	Oil pressure warning lamp	1.2 W
22.	Charging warning lamp	1.2 W
23.	Connector	
24.	Glove compartment lighting	2 W
25.	Overdrive warning lamp	1.2 W
26.	Switch for headlights signalling and emergency flashers	
27.	Fuel gauge	
28.	Voltage stabilizer	
29.	Temperature gauge	
30.	Oil pressure warning light	
31.	Switch for overdrive on transmission	
32.	Flashers warning lamp	1.2 W
33.	Instrument lighting	2x1.2 W
34.	Temperature gauge, sensitive head	
35.	Heater control lighting	3x1.2 W
36.	Heater	
37.	Windshield wipers	
38.	Windshield washer	
39.	Solenoid f. overdrive	
40.	Interior lamp	10 W
41.	Switch for heater	
42.	Switch for windshield wipers and washer	
43.	Instrument lighting rheostat	
44.	Light switch	
45.	Ignition switch	
46.	Cigarette lighter	
47.	Door switch	
48.	Switch for parking brake control	
49.	Fuel gauge tank unit	
50.	Back-up lights	15 W
51.	Brake stoplights	25 W
52.	Tail lights	5 W
53.	Number plate lighting	2x5 W
54.	Switch for overdrive	
55.	Brake warning contact	
56.	Switch on transmission BW 35	
57.	Switch glove comp. lighting	
58.	Elec. heated rear window	
59.	Switch elec. heated rear window	
60.	Side marker lamps, only for USA 5 W	5 W
61.	Relay for elec. heated rear window	
62.	Conn. at instrument	
63.	Buzzer	
64.	Door switch on driving seat side	
65.	Connection plate	
66.	Clock	
67.	Rear window wiper	
68.	Rear window washer	
69.	Diode	
70.	Switch f. rear window wiper	

Color code:

SB	Black
W	White
Y	Yellow
GN	Green
GR	Grey
BL	Blue
R	Red
BR	Brown
W-R	White-Red
BL-Y	Blue-Yellow

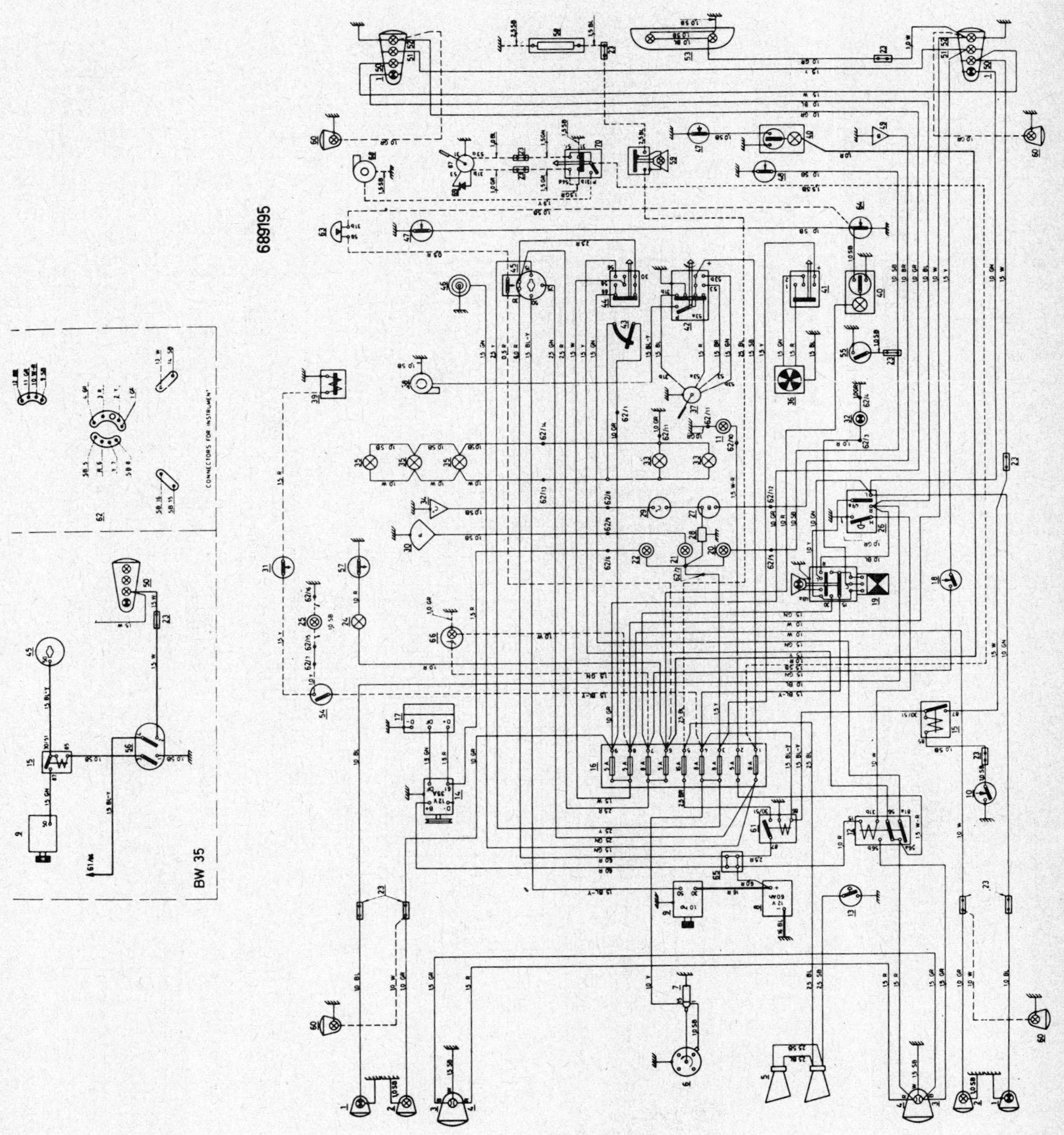

1969-71 145, with B20B

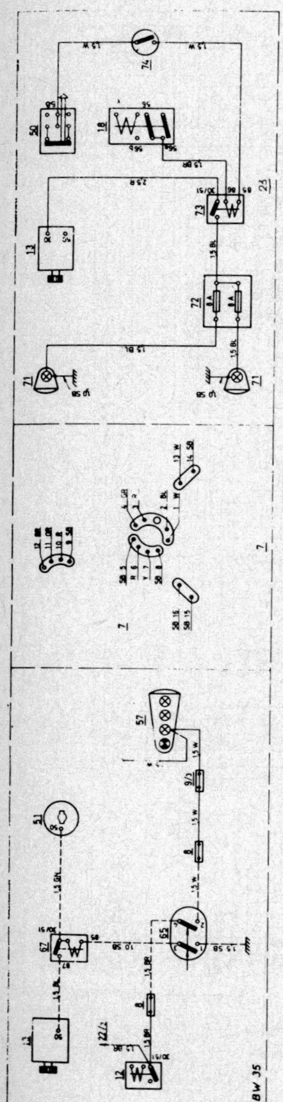

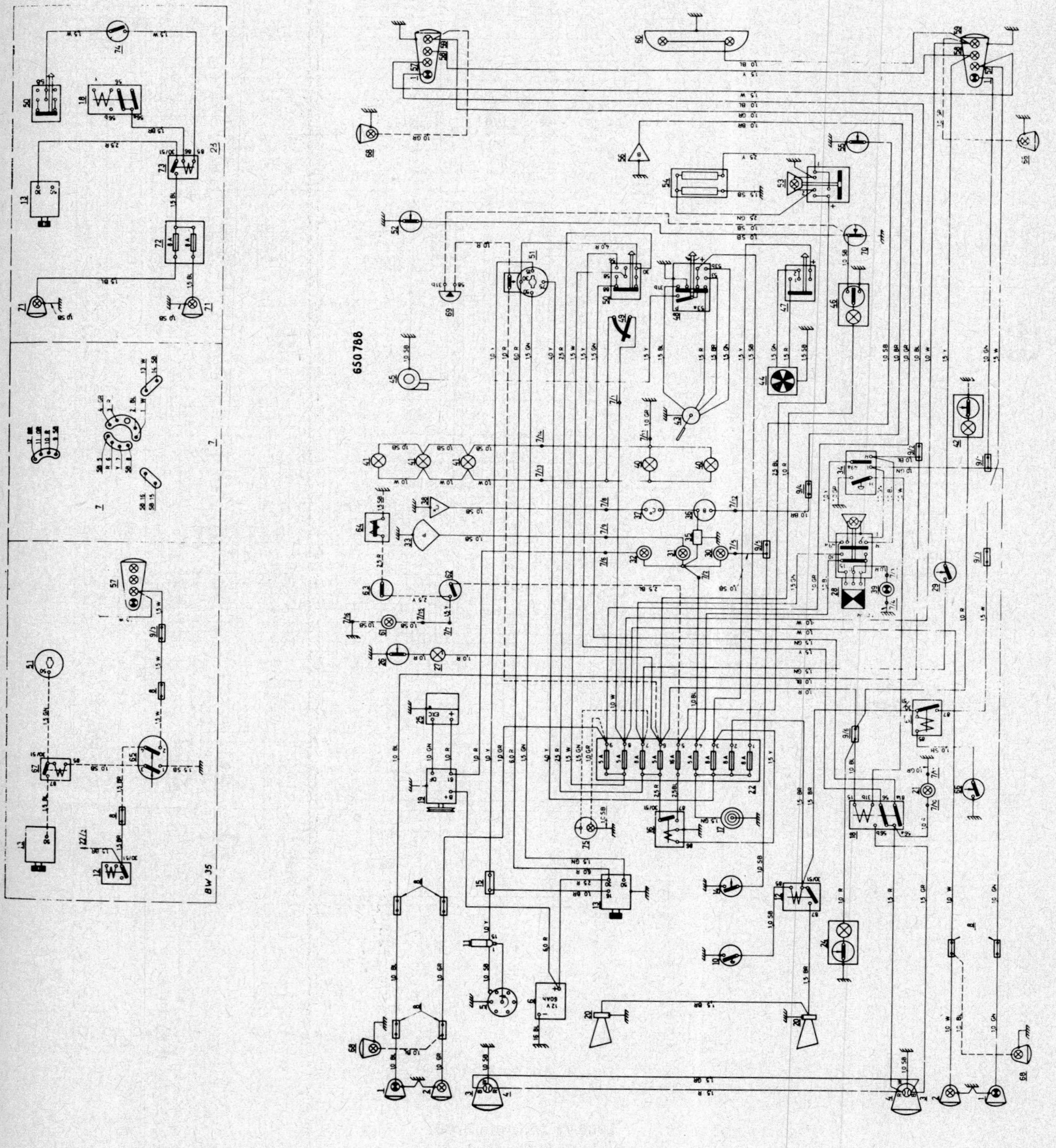

1969-71 164, with B30A

1969-71 164, with B30A

1.	Dir. ind. flashers	32 cp
2.	Parking lights	5 W
3.	Headlight low beam	40 W
4.	Headlight high beam	45 W
5.	Distributor firing order	1-5-3-6-2-4
6.	Battery	12 V 60 Ah
7.	Conn. at instrument	
8.	Junction	
9.	Part of 6-pole connector	
10.	Horn ring	
11.	Ignition coil	
12.	Relay for horn	
13.	Starter motor	10 h.p.
14.	Brake warning valve contact	
15.	Resistor	
16.	Relay for heated rear window	
17.	Cigarette lighter	
18.	Dipped relay for high and low beams and headlight flasher	
19.	Alternator	12 V 55 A
20.	Horn	
21.	High beam control lamp	1.2 W
22.	Fusebox	
23.	Wiring of foglights	
24.	Engine comp. lighting	18 W
25.	Voltage regulator	
26.	Switch glove comp. lighting	
27.	Glove compartment lighting	2 W
28.	Emergency warning flashers	
29.	Brake contact	
30.	Brake warning lamp	1.2 W
31.	Oil pressure warning lamp	1.2 W
32.	Charging warning lamp	1.2 W
33.	Oil pressure warning lamp	
34.	Switch for headlight signalling and turn ind.	
35.	Voltage stabilizer	
36.	Fuel gauge	
37.	Temperature gauge	
38.	Temperature gauge sensitive head	
39.	Emergency flashers warning lamp	1.2 W
40.	Instrument lighting	2x3 W
41.	Heater control lighting	3x1.2 W
42.	Luggage comp. light	18 W
43.	Windshield wipers	
44.	Heater	
45.	Windshield washers	
46.	Interior light	10 W
47.	Switch for heater	
48.	Switch for windshield wipers and washer	
49.	Instrument lighting rheostat	
50.	Light switch	
51.	Ignition switch	
52.	Door contact	
53.	Switch f. elec. heated rear window	
54.	Elec. heated rear window	
55.	Switch for parking brake control	
56.	Fuel gauge tank unit	
57.	Back-up lights	15 W
58.	Brake stoplights	25 W
59.	Rear lights	5 W
60.	Number plate lighting	2x5 W
61.	Overdrive warning lamp	1.2 W
62.	Switch for overdrive	
63.	Switch f. overdr. on transmission	
64.	Solenoid f. overdrive	
65.	Switch on transmission BW 35	
66.	Switch for back-up lights only for M 400 and M 410	
67.	Relay for back-up on M 400, M 410 and starter relay on BW 35	
68.	Side marker lamps	5 W
69.	Buzzer, ignition key	
70.	Door contact on driving seat side	
71.	Foglights	
72.	Fusebox for foglights	
73.	Relay for foglights	
74.	Switch for foglights	
75.	Clock	

Color code:

SB	Black
W	White
Y	Yellow
GN	Green
GR	Gray
BL	Blue
R	Red
BR	Brown

1970-71 1800 E

1. Directional indicators 23 CP
2. Parking lights, 4 CP
3. Low beam headlights 40 W
4. High beam headlights 45 W
5. Horn
6. Distributor (firing order 1-3-4-2)
7. Ignition coil
8. Battery, 12 V 60 Ah
9. Starter motor, 1 h.p.
10. Switch for back-up light
11. Warning lamp for high beam, 3 W
12. Step relay for high beam and low beam headlights
13. Horn control
14. Alternator, 35 A
15. Switch, courtesy lighting
16. Fusebox
17. Voltage regulator
18. Brake switch
19. Emergency warning flashers
20. Warning lamp for brakes, 2 W
21. Warning lamp for oil pressure, 2 W
22. Warning lamp for battery charging, 3 W
23. Connector
24. Connector (only right-hand drive)
25. Warning lamp for overdrive, 2 W
26. Switch for directional indicators and flashers
27. Fuel gauge
28. Voltage stabilizer
29. Temperature gauge
30. Oil pressure pickup
31. Overdrive switch on transmission
32. Warning lamp for directional indicators
33. Instrument lighting
34. Temperature pickup
35. Lighting for heating controls
36. Heater
37. Windshield wipers
38. Windshield washer
39. Control solenoid for overdrive, on transmission
40. Courtesy lighting, 2 x 5 W
41. Switch for heater
42. Switch for windshield wipers and washer
43. Rheostat for instrument lighting
44. Lighting switch
45. Ignition
46. Cigarette lighter
47. Door switch
48. Switch for parking brake control
49. Fuel level pickup
50. Rear lights
51. Stop lights, 32 CP
52. Back-up lights, 4 CP
53. License plate lighting, 2x4 CP
54. Switch for overdrive
55. Brake warning switch
56. Map-reading lamp
57. Switch for map-reading lamp
58. Electrically heated rear window, 150/40 W
59. Switch for electrically heated rear window
60. Side marker lights (only U.S.A.), 5 W
61. Relay for electrically heated rear window
62. Spark plugs
63. Warning buzzer (only U.S.A.)
64. Door switch on driver's side
65. Horn relay
66. Oil temperature gauge
67. Oil temperature sender
68. Oil pressure gauge
69. Lock
70. Control unit for fuel injection
71. Main relay for fuel injection
72. Relay for fuel pump
73. Relay for cold start valve
74. Pressure sensor
75. Throttle switch
76. Cold start valve
77. Temperature sensor 1 (induction air)
78. Temperature sensor II (coolant)
79. Triggering contacts
80. Fuel pump
81. Injectors
82. Tachometer
83. Speedometer
84. Relay for rear lights
85. Switch for autom, transmission BW 35
86. Quadrant lighting (only BW 35)

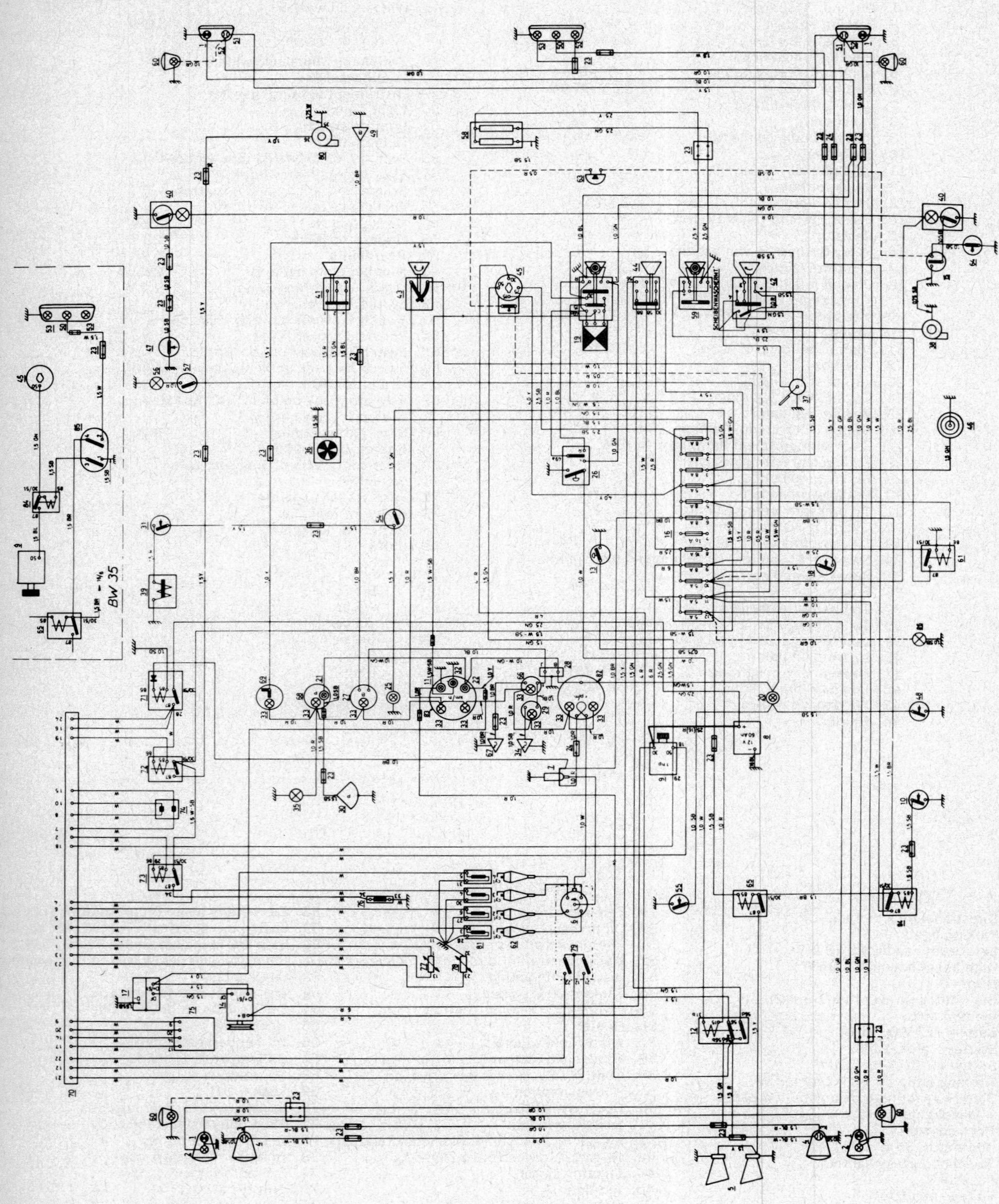

1970-71 1800 E

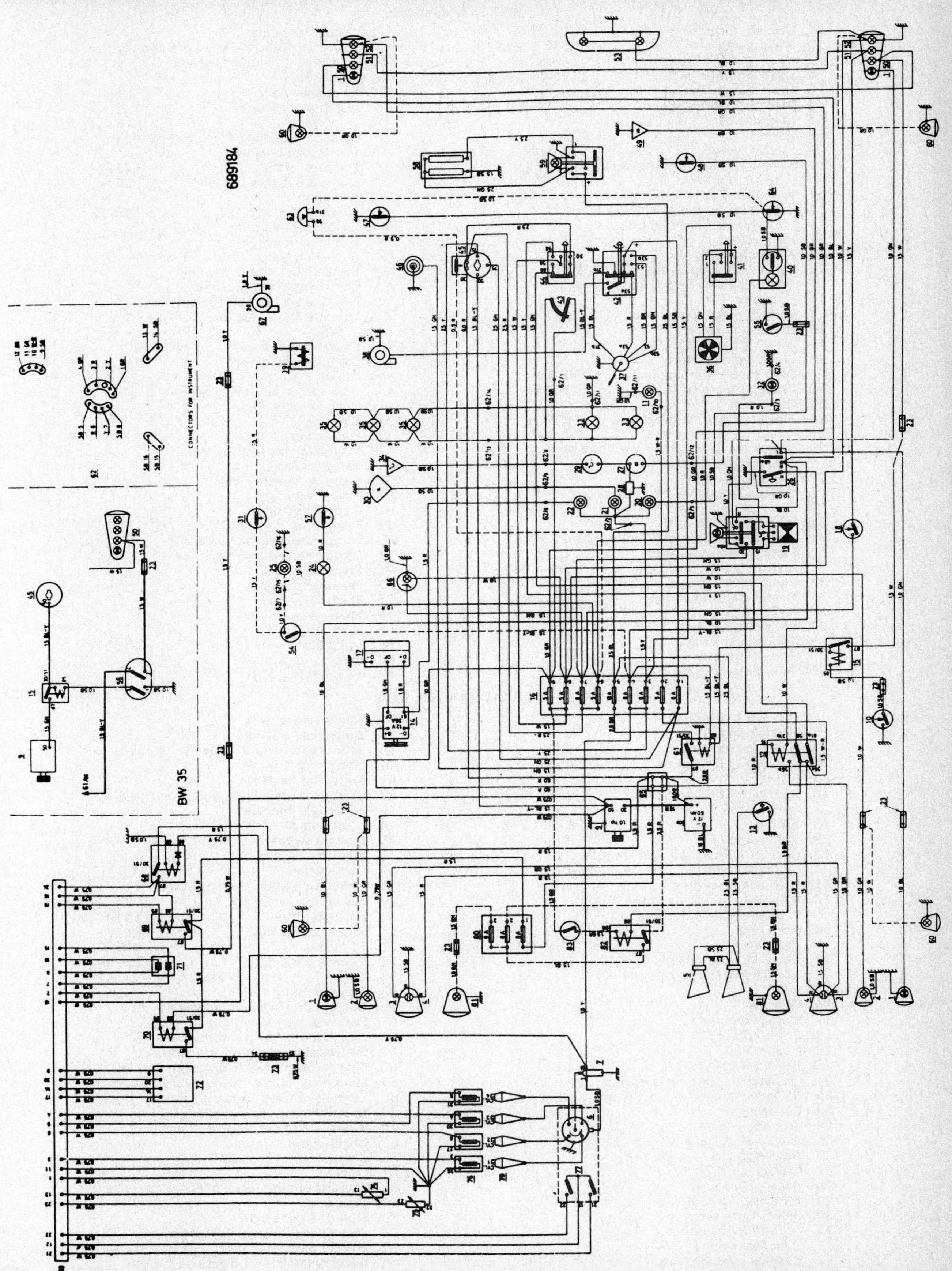

1971 142, with B20E

1971 142, with B20E

1. Dir. ind. flashers 32 CP
2. Parking lights 5 W
3. Headlight low beam 40 W
4. Headlight high beam 45 W
5. Horn
6. Distributor firing order 1-3-4-2
7. Ignition coil
8. Battery 12 V 60 Ah
9. Starter motor 1.0 hp
10. Switch for back-up lights only M 40 and M 41
11. High beam warning lamp 1.2 W
12. Dipper relay for high and low beams and headlight flasher
13. Horn ring
14. Alternator
15. Relay f. back-up lights on M 40, M 41 and Starter Relay on BW 35
16. Fuse box
17. Voltage regulator
18. Brake contact
19. Warning flashers
20. Brake warning lamp 1.2 W
21. Oil pressure warning lamp 1.2 W
22. Charging warning lamp 1.2 W
23. Connector
24. Glove compartment lighting 2 W
25. Overdrive warning lamp 1.2 W
26. Switch for headlights signalling and emergency flashers
27. Fuel gauge
28. Voltage regulator
29. Temperature gauge
30. Oil pressure tell-tale
31. Switch for overdrive on transmission
32. Flashers warning lamp 1.2 W
33. Instrument lighting 2x1.2 W
34. Temperature gauge, sensitive head
35. Heater control lighting 3x1.2 W
36. Heater
37. Windshield wipers
38. Windshield washer
39. Solenoid f. overdrive
40. Interior lamp 10 W
41. Switch for heater
42. Switch for windshield wipers and washer
43. Instrument lighting rheostat
44. Light switch
45. Ignition switch
46. Cigarette lighter
47. Door switch
48. Switch for parking brake control
49. Fuel gauge tank unit
50. Back-up lights 15 W
51. Brake stoplights 25 W
52. Tail lights 5 W
53. Number plate lighting 2x5 W
54. Switch for overdrive
55. Brake warning contact
56. Switch on transmission BW 35
57. Switch glove comp. lighting
58. Elec. heated rear window
59. Switch elec. heated rear window
60. Side marker lamps, only for USA 5 W 5 W
61. Relay for elec. heated rear window
62. Conn. at instrument
63. Buzzer
64. Door switch on driving seat side
65. Connection plate
66. Clock
67. Fuel pump
68. Main relay for fuel injection
69. Relay for fuel pump
70. Relay for starting valve
71. Pressure sensor
72. Flap valve contact
73. Start valve
74. Temperature sensor, intake air
75. Temperature sensor, coolant
76. Injection valves
77. Release contact
78. Electronic unit
79. Spark plugs
80. Fuse box
81. Foglights 2x55 W
82. Relay f. foglights
83. Switch f. foglights

1972 142, 144, with B20B

1. Dir. ind. flashers 32 CP
2. Parking lights 5 W
3. Headlight low beams 40 W
4. Headlight high beams 45 W
5. Horn
6. Distributor firing order 1-3-4-2
7. Ignition coil
8. Battery 12 V 60 Ah
9. Starter motor 1.0 hp
10. Contact for back-up light (M40 and M41 only)
11. High beam warning lamp 1.2 W
12. Step relay for high and low beams and headlight flashers
13. Horn ring
14. Alternator 12 V 35A
15. Relay for back-up light on M40, M41 and starter relay on BW 35
16. Fusebox
17. Voltage regulator
18. Brake contact
19. Flasher unit
20. Brake warning lamp 1.2 W
21. Oil pressure warning lamp 1.2 W
22. Battery charging warning lamp 1.2 W
23. Connector
24. Glove box light 2 W
25. Overdrive warning lamp M41 1.2 W
26. Warning buzzer, ignition key
27. Fuel gauge
28. Voltage stabilizer
29. Temperature gauge
30. Oil pressure sender
31. Contact for overdrive on M41 transmission
32. Flashers warning lamp 1.2 W
33. Instrument lighting 2x3 W
34. Temperature gauge sensor
35. Heater control light 3x1.2 W
36. Heater
37. Windshield wipers
38. Windshield washers
39. Solenoid for overdrive on M41 transmission
40. Interior light 10 W
41. Switch for heater
42. Switch for windshield wipers and washers
43. Panel light rheostat
44. Light switch
45. Ignition switch
46. Cigarette lighter
47. Door switch
48. Switch for parking brake control
49. Fuel gauge tank unit
50. Back-up lights 15 W
51. Brake stoplights 25 W
52. Tail lights 5 W
53. License plate light 2x5 W
54. Switch for overdrive M41
55. Brake warning switch
56. Contact on transmission BW 35
57. Switch glove locker light
58. Elec. heated rear window
59. Switch, elec. heated rear window
60. Side marker lights (USA only) 5 W
61. Main relay, starter switch
62. Terminal at instrument
63. Switch for dir. ind. and headlight flashers
64. Switch for hazard warning flasher
65. Choke warning lamp
66. Choke control contact
67. Clock
68. Warning buzzer, headlights
69. Connector
70. Shift positions light
71. Switch, seat buckle, passenger
72. Switch, passenger seat
73. Warning lamp, seat belts
74. Buzzer, seat belts
75. Relay, seat belts
76. Contact, M40, M41 transmission
77. Switch, seat buckle, driver

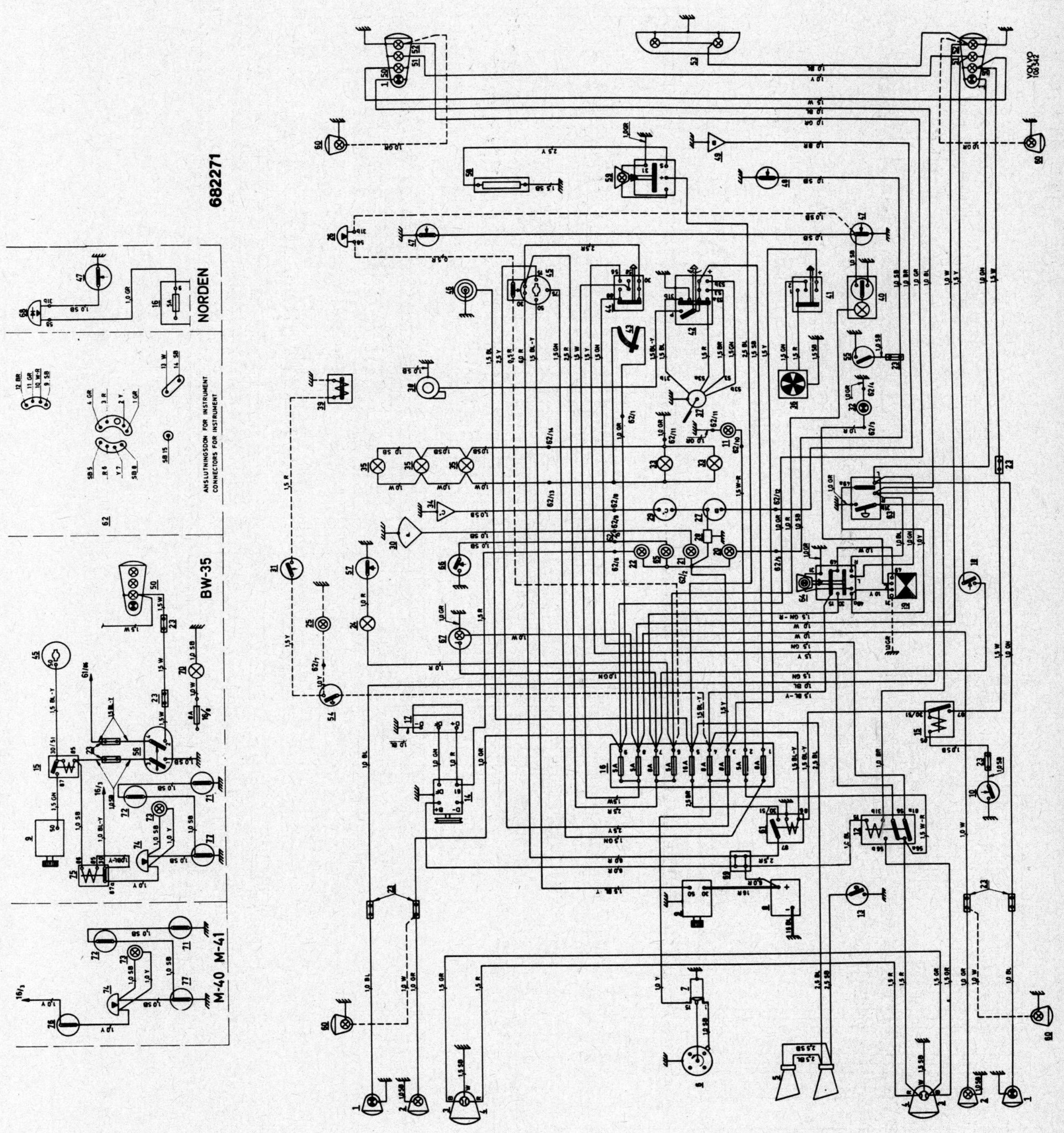

1972 142, 144, with B20B

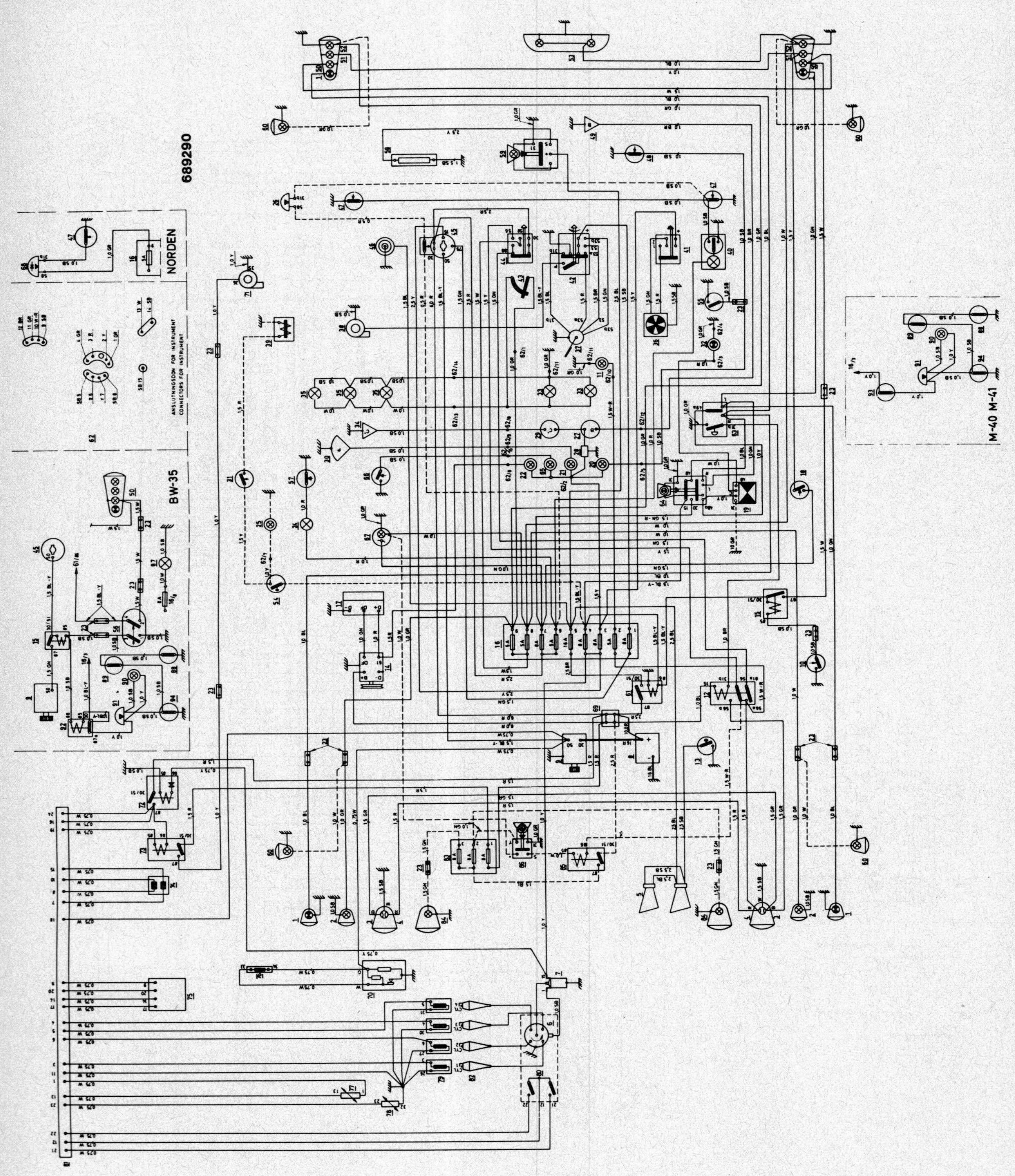

1972 142, 144, with B20F

1972 142, 144, with B20F

1. Dir. ind. flashers 32 CP
2. Parking lights 5 W
3. Headlight low beams 40 W
4. Headlight high beams 45 W
5. Horn
6. Distributor firing order 1-3-4-2
7. Ignition coil
8. Battery 12 V 60 Ah
9. Starter motor 1.0 hp
10. Contact for back-up light (M40 and M41 only)
11. High beam warning lamp 1.2 W
12. Step relay for high and low beams and headlight flashers
13. Horn ring
14. Alternator 12 V 5 A
15. Relay for back-up light on M40, M41 and starter relay on BW 35
16. Fusebox
17. Voltage regulator
18. Brake switch
19. Flasher unit
20. Brake warning lamp 1.2 W
21. Oil pressure warning lamp 1.2 W
22. Battery charging warning lamp 1.2 W
23. Connector
24. Glove box light 2 W
25. Overdrive warning lamp M41 1.2 W
26. Warning buzzer, ignition key
27. Fuel gauge
28. Voltage stabilizer
29. Temperature gauge
30. Oil pressure
31. Switch for overdrive on M41 transmission
32. Headlight flashers warning lamp 1.2 W
33. Instrument lighting 2x3 W
34. Temperature gauge sensor
35. Heater controls light 3 x1.2 W
36. Heater
37. Windshield wipers
38. Windshield washers
39. Solenoid for overdrive on M41 transmission
40. Interior light 10 W
41. Switch for heater
42. Switch for windshield wipers and washers
43. Instrument panel light rheostat
44. Light switch
45. Ignition switch
46. Cigarette lighter
47. Door switch
48. Switch for parking brake control
49. Fuel gauge tank unit
50. Back-up light 15 W
51. Brake stoplights 25 W
52. Tail lights 5 W
53. License plate light 2x5 W
54. Switch for overdrive M41
55. Brake warning switch
56. Contact on transmission BW 35
57. Switch glove box light
58. Elec. heated rear window
59. Switch, elec. heated rear window
60. Side marker lights (USA only) 5 W
61. Main relay, starter switch, rear window
62. Terminal at instrument panel
63. Switch for dir. ind. and headlight flashers
64. Switch for hazard warning flashers
65. Choke warning lamp
66. Choke control contact
67. Clock
68. Warning buzzer, headlights
69. Connector
70. Thermal timer contact
71. Fuel pump
72. Main relay for fuel injection
73. Relay for fuel pump
74. Pressure sensor
75. Throttle valve switch
76. Start valve
77. Temperature sensor, intake air
78. Temperature sensor, coolant
79. Injection valves
80. Triggering contacts
81. Electronic control unit
82. Spark plugs
83. Fusebox
84. Foglights 2x55 W
85. Relay for foglights
86. Switch for foglights
87. Shift positions light, aut. trans.
88. Switch, seat buckle, passenger
89. Switch, passenger seat
90. Seat belts warning lamp
91. Warning buzzer, seat belts
92. Relay, seat belts
93. Switch, M40, 41 transmission
94. Switch, seat buckle, driver

Color code:

SB	Black
W	White
Y	Yellow
GN	Green
GR	Grey
BL	Blue
R	Red
BR	Brown
BL-Y	Blue-yellow
W-R	White-red
GN-R	Green-red

1972 145, with B20B

1. Dir. ind. flashers 32 CP
2. Parking lights 5 W
3. Headlight low beams 40 W
4. Headlight high beams 45 W
5. Horn
6. Distributor firing order 1-3-4-2
7. Ignition coil
8. Battery 12 V 60 Ah
9. Starter motor 1.0 hp
10. Contact for back-up light (M40 and M41 only)
11. High beam warning lamp 1.2 W
12. Step relay for high and low beams and headlight flashers
13. Horn ring
14. Alternator 129 V 55A
15. Relay for back-up light on M40, M41 and starter relay on BW 35
16. Fusebox
17. Voltage regulator
18. Brake contact
19. Flasher unit
20. Brake warning lamp 1.2 W
21. Oil pressure warning lamp 1.2 W
22. Battery charging warning lamp 1.2 W
23. Connector
24. Glove box light 2 W
25. Overdrive warning lamp M41 1.2 W
26. Switch for dir. ind. and headlights flashers
27. Fuel gauge
28. Voltage stabilizer
29. Temperature gauge
30. Oil pressure sender
31. Contact for overdrive on M41 transmission
32. Flashers warning lamp 1.2 W
33. Instrument lighting 2x3 W
34. Temperature gauge sensor
35. Heater control light 3x1.2 W
36. Heater
37. Windshield wipers
38. Windshield washers
39. Solenoid for overdrive on M41 transmission
40. Interior light 10 W
41. Switch for heater
42. Switch for windshield wipers and washers
43. Panel light rheostat
44. Light switch
45. Ignition switch
46. Cigarette lighter
47. Door switch
48. Switch for parking brake control
49. Fuel gauge tank unit
50. Back-up lights 32 CP
51. Brake stoplights 32 CP
52. Tail lights 5 W
53. License plate light 2x5 W
54. Switch for overdrive M41
55. Brake warning switch
56. Contact on transmission BW 35
57. Switch glove box light
58. Elec. heated rear window
59. Switch, elec. heated rear window
60. Side marker lights (USA only) 5 W
61. Main relay, starter switch rear window
62. Terminal at instrument
63. Warning buzzer, ignition key
64. Door switch on driver's side
65. Connector
66. Clock
67. Tailgate window wiper
68. Tailgate window washer
69. Warning buzzer, headlights
70. Switch for tailgate window wiper
71. Switch for hazard warning flasher
72. Shift positions light
73. Choke warning lamp
74. Choke control contact
75. Diode
76. Switch, seat buckle, passenger
77. Switch, passenger seat
78. Warning lamp, seat belts
79. Buzzer, seat belts
80. Relay, seat belts
81. Contact, M40-41 transmission
82. Switch, seat buckle, driver

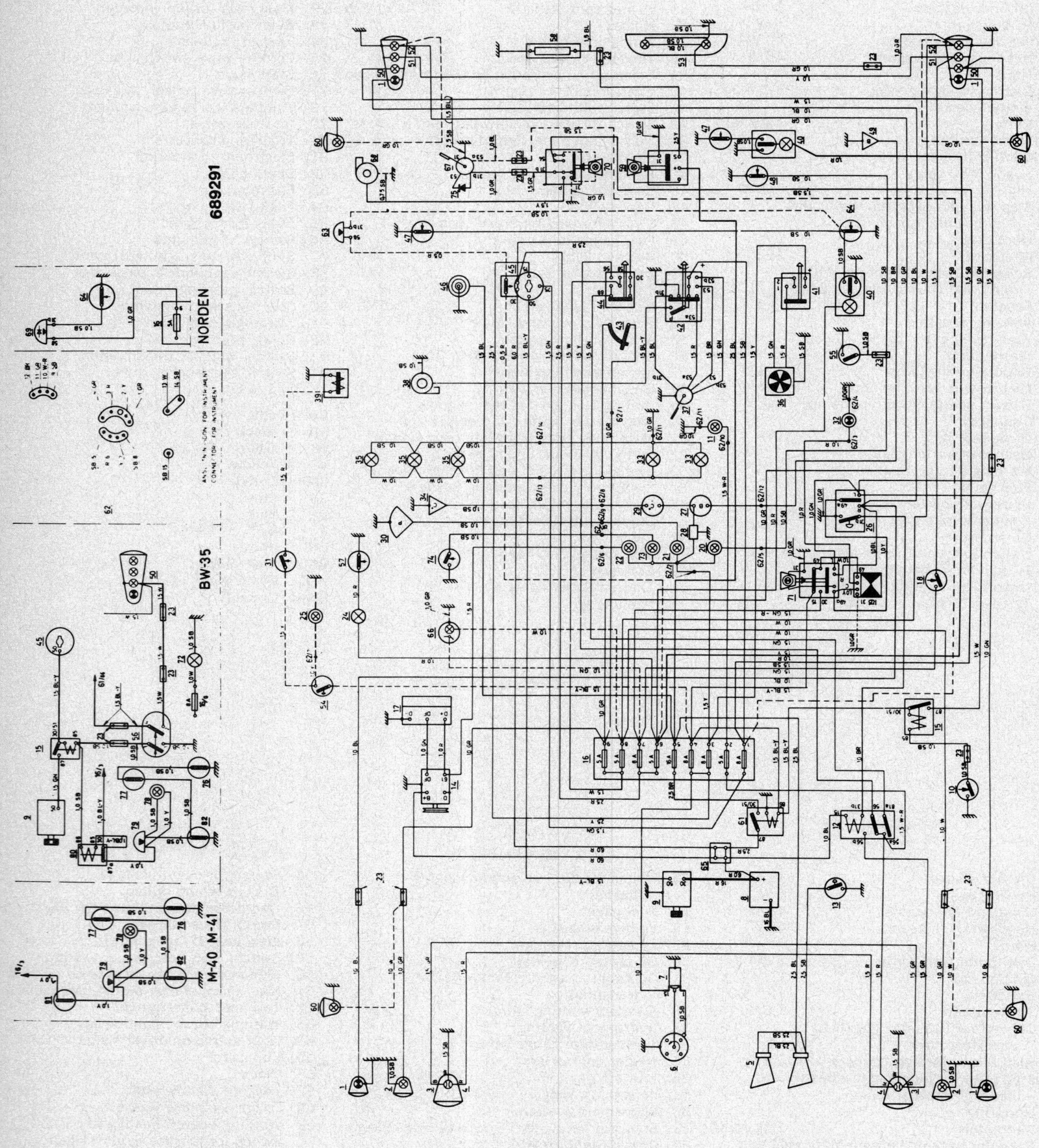

1972 145, with B20B

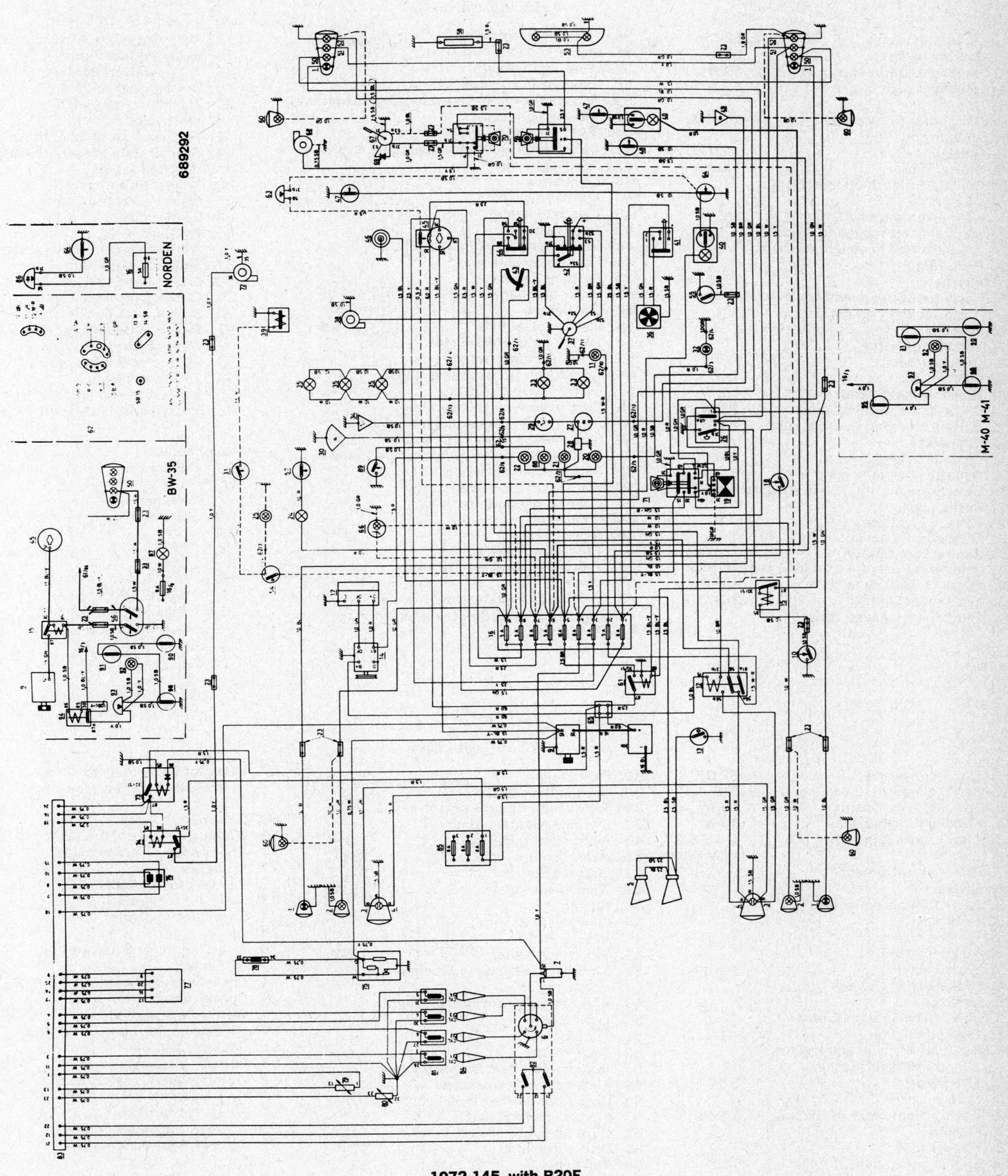

1972 145, with B20F

1972 145, with B20F

1. Dir. ind. flashers 32 CP
2. Parking lights 5 W
3. Headlight low beams 40 W
4. Headlight high beams 45 W
5. Horn
6. Distributor firing order 1-3-4-2
7. Ignition coil
8. Battery 12 V 60 Ah
9. Starter motor 1.0 hp
10. Contact for back-up light (M40 and M41 only)
11. High beam warning lamp 1.2 W
12. Step relay for main and dipped beams and headlight flashers
13. Horn ring
14. Alternator 12 V 55A
15. Relay for back-up light on M40, M41 and starter relay on BW 35
16. Fusebox
17. Voltage regulator
18. Brake contact
19. Flasher unit
20. Brake warning lamp 1.2 W
21. Oil pressure warning lamp 1.2 W
22. Battery charging warning lamp 1.2 W
23. Connector
24. Glove box light 2 W
25. Overdrive warning lamp M41 1.2 W
26. Switch for dir. ind. and headlights flashers
27. Fuel gauge
28. Voltage stabilizer
29. Temperature gauge
30. Oil pressure sender
31. Contact for overdrive on M41 transmission
32. Flashers warning lamp 1.2 W
33. Instrument lighting 2x3 W
34. Temperature gauge sensor
35. Heater control light 3x1.2 W
36. Heater
37. Windshield wipers
38. Windshield washers
39. Solenoid for overdrive on M41 transmission
40. Interior light 10 W
41. Switch for heater
42. Switch for windshield wipers and washers
43. Panel light rheostat
44. Light switch
45. Ignition switch
46. Cigarette lighter
47. Door switch
48. Switch for parking brake control
49. Fuel gauge tank unit
50. Back-up lights 32 CP
51. Brake stoplights 32 CP
52. Tail lights 5 W
53. License plate light 2x5 W
54. Switch for overdrive M41
55. Brake warning switch
56. Contact on transmission BW 35
57. Switch glove box light
58. Elec. heated tailgate window
59. Switch, elec. heated tailgate window
60. Side marker lights (USA only) 5 W
61. Main relay, starter switch tailgate window
62. Terminal at instrument
63. Warning buzzer, ignition key
64. Door switch on driver's side
65. Connector
66. Clock
67. Tailgate window wiper
68. Tailgate window washer
69. Diode
70. Switch for tailgate window wiper
71. Switch for hazard warning flasher
72. Fuel pump
73. Main relay for fuel injection
74. Relay for fuel pump
75. Thermal timer contact
76. Pressure sensor
77. Throttle valve switch
78. Start valve
79. Temperature sensor, intake air
80. Temperature sensor, coolant
81. Injection valve
82. Triggering contacts
83. Electronic control unit
84. Spark plugs
85. Fusebox
86. Warning buzzer, headlights
87. Shift positions light
88. Choke warning lamp
89. Choke control contact
90. Switch, seat buckle, passenger
91. Switch, passenger seat
92. Warning lamp, seat belts
93. Buzzer, seat belts
94. Relay, seat belts
95. Contact transmission M40-41
96. Switch, seat buckle, driver

Color code:

SB	Black
W	White
Y	Yellow
GN	Green
GR	Grey
BL	Blue
R	Red
BR	Brown
W-R	White-red
BL-Y	Blue-yellow
GN-R	Green-red

1972 164, with B30A

1. Dir. ind. flashers 32 CP
2. Parking lights 5W
3. Headlight low beams 40 W
4. Headlight high beams 45 W
5. Distributor firing order 1-5-3-6-2-4
6. Battery 12 V 60 Ah
7. Conn. at instrument
8. Connector
9. Part of 6-pole conn. unit
10. Horn ring
11. Ignition coil
12. Relay for horn
13. Starter motor 1.0 hp
14. Brake warning switch
15. Resistor
16. Main relay, ignition switch
17. Cigarette lighter
18. Dip relay for high and low beams and headlight flasher
19. Alternator 12 V 55 A
20. Horn
21. Warning lamp for high beams 1.2 W
22. Fusebox
23. Flasher unit
24. Engine comp. light 18 W
25. Voltage regulator
26. Contact, glove compartment light
27. Glove compartment light 2 W
29. Brake contact
30. Brake warning lamp
31. Oil pressure warning lamp 1.2 W
32. Battery charging warning lamp 1.2 W
33. Oil pressure switch 1.2 W
34. Switch for dir. ind. and headlight flashers
35. Voltage stabilizer
36. Fuel gauge
37. Temperature gauge
38. Temperature gauge sensor
39. Flashers, warning lamp
40. Instrument panel light 1.2 W
41. Heater control light 2x3 W
42. Luggage comp. light 3x1.2 W
43. Windshield wipers 18 W
44. Heater
45. Windshield washer
46. Interior lamp
47. Switch for heater 10 W
48. Switch for windshield wipers and washer
49. Rheostat, instrument panel light
50. Light switch
51. Ignition switch
52. Door switch
53. Switch, elec. heated rear window
54. Elec. heated rear window
55. Switch for parking brake control
56. Fuel gauge tank unit
57. Back-up lights
58. Brake stoplights 32 CP
59. Tail lights 32 CP
60. License plate light 5 W
61. Overdrive warning lamp 2x5 W
62. Switch for overdrive 1.2 W
63. Switch, overdrive on transmission
64. Solenoid for overdrive
65. Contact on transmission BW 35
66. Contact for back-up lights (M400 and M 410 only)
67. Relay for back-up lights on M400, M410 and starter relay on BW 35
68. Side marker lights
69. Warning buzzer, ignition key 5 W
70. Door switch on driving side
71. Foglights
72. Fusebox for foglights
73. Relay for foglights
74. Switch for foglights
75. Clock
76. Switch for emergency warning flashers
77. Choke warning lamp
78. Choke contact
79. Warning buzzer, lights
80. Shift positions, light, aut. trans.
81. Contact, seat buckle, passenger
82. Contact, passenger seat
83. Warning buzzer, safety belts
84. Warning lamp, safety belts
85. Relay, safety belts
86. Contact, transmission M 41
87. Contact, seat buckle, driver

Color code

GN-R	Green-red
SB	Black
W	White
Y	Yellow
GN	Green
GR	Grey
BL	Blue
R	Red
BR	Brown
BL-Y	Blue-yellow
W-R	White-red

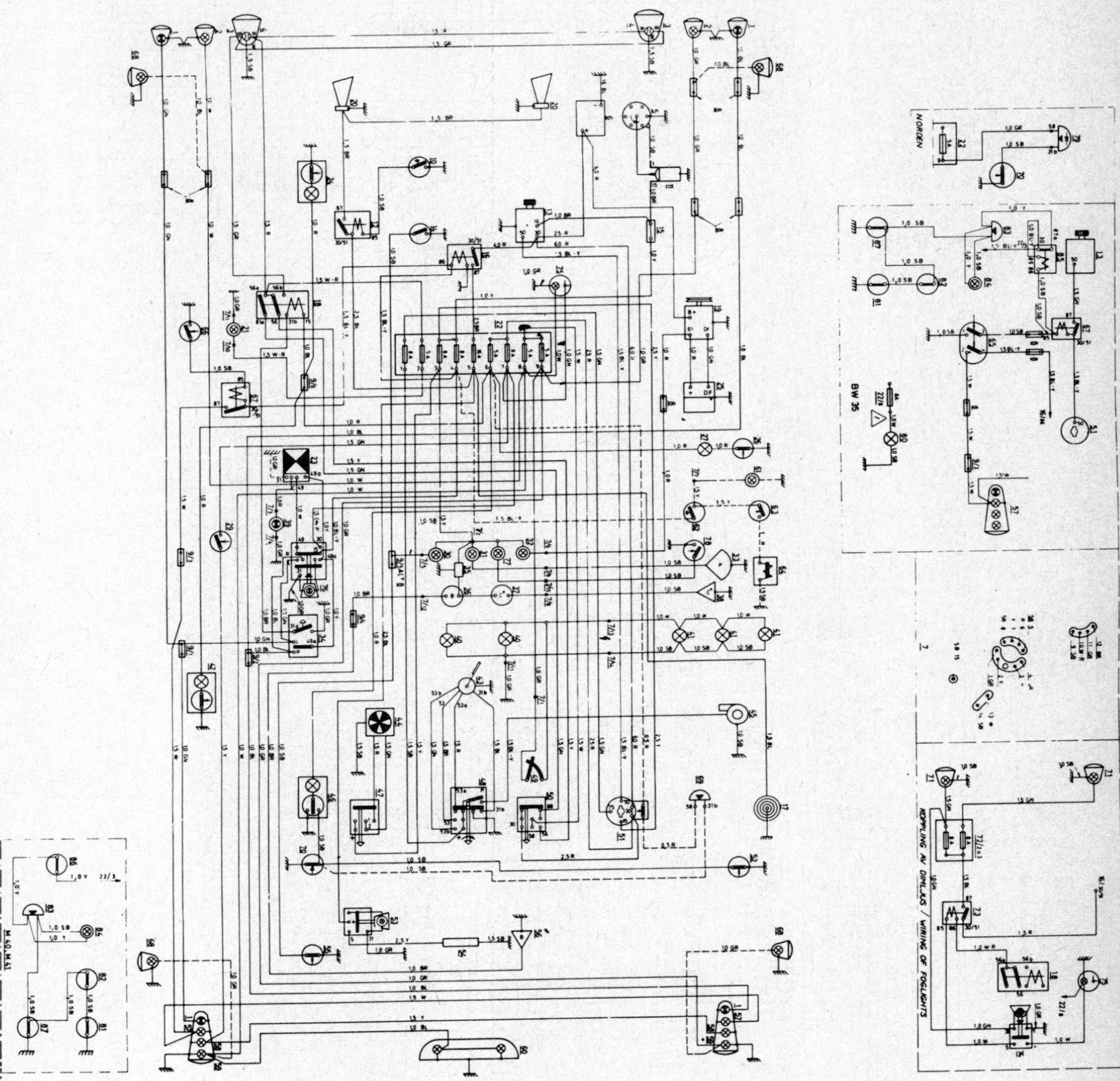

1972 164, with B30A

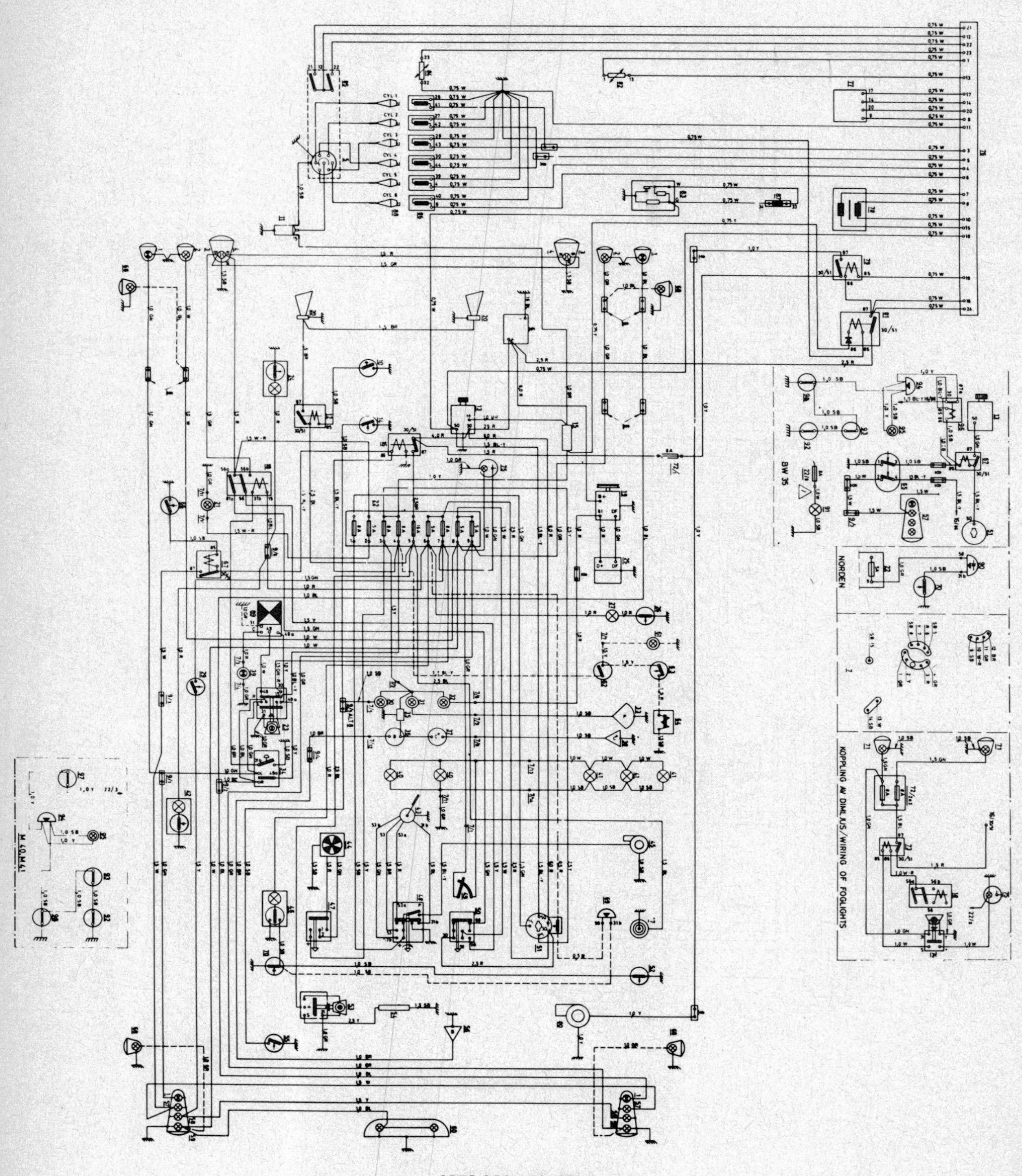

1972 164, with B30F

1972 164, with B30F

1.	Dir. ind. flashers	32 CP
2.	Parking lights	5 W
3.	Headlight low beams	40 W
4.	Headlight high beams	45 W
5.	Distributor firing order	1-5-3-6-2-4
6.	Battery	12 V 60 Ah
7.	Conn. at instrument	
8.	Connector	
9.	Part of 6-pole conn. unit	
10.	Horn ring	
11.	Ignition coil	
12.	Relay for horn	
13.	Starter motor	1.0 hp
14.	Brake warning contact	
15.	Resistor	
16.	Main relay, ignition switch	
17.	Cigarette lighter	
18.	Dipped relay for high and low beams and headlight flashers	
19.	Alternator	12 V 55 A
20.	Horn	
21.	High beams warning lamp	1.2 W
22.	Fusebox	
23.	Switch, emergency warning flashers	
24.	Engine comp. light	18 W
25.	Voltage regulator	
26.	Switch, glove box light	
27.	Glove light	2 W
29.	Brake contact	
30.	Brake warning lamp	1.2 W
31.	Oil pressure warning lamp	1.2 W
32.	Battery charging warning lamp	1.2 W
33.	Oil pressure sensor	
34.	Switch for dir. ind. and headlight flashers	
35.	Voltage stabilizer	
36.	Fuel gauge	
37.	Temperature gauge	
38.	Temperature gauge sensor	
39.	Flashers warning lamp	1.2 W
40.	Instrument panel light	2x3 W
41.	Heater control light	3x1.2 W
42.	Luggage comp. light	18 W
43.	Windshield wipers	
44.	Heater	
45.	Windshield washer	
46.	Interior light	10 W
47.	Switch for heater	
48.	Switch for windshield wipers and washer	
49.	Instrument panel light rheostat	
50.	Light switch	
51.	Ignition switch	
52.	Door contact	
53.	Switch, elec. heated rear window	
54.	Elec. heated rear window	
55.	Contact for parking brake warning lamp	
56.	Fuel gauge tank unit	
57.	Back-up lights	32 CP
58.	Brake stoplights	32 CP
59.	Tail lights	5 W
60.	License plate light	2x5 W
61.	Overdrive warning lamp	1.2 W
62.	Switch for overdrive	
63.	Switch for overdrive on transmission	
64.	Solenoid for overdrive	
65.	Contact on aut. trans. BW 35	
66.	Contact for reversing lights (M400 and M410 only)	
67.	Relay for reversing lights on M400, M410 and starter relay on BW 35	
68.	Side marker lights	5 W
69.	Warning buzzer, ignition key	
70.	Door contact on driving seat side	
71.	Foglights	
72.	Fusebox	
73.	Relay for foglights	
74.	Switch for foglights	
75.	Clock	
76.	Electronic control unit	
77.	Throttle valve switch	
78.	Pressure sensor	
79.	Relay for fuel pump	
80.	Fuel pump	
81.	Main relay for fuel injection	
82.	Temperature sensor, intake air	
83.	Thermal timer contact	
84.	Temperature sensor, coolant	
85.	Triggering contacts	
86.	Injection valves	
87.	Cold start valve	
88.	Spark plugs	
89.	Flasher unit	
90.	Warning buzzer, lights	
91.	Shift positions light	
92.	Contact, seat buckle, passenger	
93.	Contact, passenger seat	
94.	Warning buzzer, safety belts	
95.	Warning lamp, safety belts	
96.	Relay, safety belts	
97.	Contact, transmission M 41	
98.	Contact, seat buckle, driver	

SB	Black
W	White
Y	Yellow
GN	Green
GR	Gray
BL	Blue
R	Red
BR	Brown
BL-Y	Blue-yellow
R-W	Red-white

1972 1800E

1.	Dir. ind. flashers	32 CP
2.	Parking lights	4 CP
3.	Headlight low beams	40 W
4.	Headlight high beams	45 W
5.	Horn	
6.	Distributor firing order	1-3-4-2
7.	Ignition coil	
8.	Battery	12 V 60 Ah
9.	Starter motor	1.0 hp
10.	Contact for back-up light M41	
11.	High beams warning lamp	
12.	Dipper relay for high and low beams and headlight flashers	
13.	Horn ring	
14.	Alternator	35 A
15.	Contact seat belt	
16.	Fusebox	
17.	Voltage regulator	
18.	Brake contact	
19.	Flasher unit	
20.	Switch for emergency warning flashers	
21.	Battery charging warning lamp	3 W
22.	Oil pressure warning lamp	2 W
23.	Connector	
24.	Connector (R-H drive only)	
25.	Overdrive warning lamp M41	1.2 W
26.	Switch for dir. ind. and headlight flashers	
27.	Fuel gauge	
28.	Voltage stabilizer	
29.	Temperature gauge	
30.	Oil pressure sender	
31.	Contact for overdrive on transmission M41	
32.	Flashers warning lamp	3 W
33.	Instrument panel light	
34.	Coolant temperature sensor	
35.	Heater control light	3 W
36.	Heater	
37.	Windshield wipers	
38.	Windscreen washer	
39.	Solenoid for overdrive on transmission M41	
40.	Interior lamp	10 W
41.	Switch for heater	
42.	Switch for windshield wipers and washer	
43.	Instrument panel light rheostat	
44.	Light switch	
45.	Starter switch	
46.	Cigarette lighter	
47.	Door switch	
48.	Switch for parking brake control	
49.	Fuel gauge tank unit	
50.	Back-up lights	32 CP
51.	Rear lights	4 CP
52.	Brake stoplights	32 CP
53.	License plate light	2x4 CP
54.	Switch for overdrive M41	
55.	Brake warning contact	
56.	Map light	
57.	Switch for map light	
58.	Elec. heated rear window	
59.	Switch, elec. heated rear window	
60.	Side marker lights (USA only)	5 W
61.	Relay for elec. heated rear window	
62.	Spark plugs	
63.	Warning buzzer	
64.	Contact on transmission BW 35	
65.	Horn relay	
66.	Oil temperature gauge	
67.	Oil temperature sensor	
68.	Oil pressure gauge	
69.	Clock	
70.	Electronic unit	
71.	Main relay for fuel injection	
72.	Relay for fuel pump	
73.	Thermal timer contact	
74.	Pressure sensor	
75.	Throttle valve switch	
76.	Start valve	
77.	Temperature sensor, intake air	
78.	Temperature sensor, coolant	
79.	Triggering contacts	
80.	Fuel pump	
81.	Injection valves	
82.	Tachometer	
83.	Speedometer	
84.	Brake warning lamp	2 W
85.	Seat belts light	1.2 W
86.	Seat belt warning lamp	1.2 W
87.	Relay for back-up lights starter relay on BW 35	
88.	Shift positions light (BW 35 only)	1.2 W
89.	Radio	
90.	Speaker	
91.	Dimmer switch for overdrive warning lamp M41	
92.	Warning buzzer light	
93.	Contact, seat buckle, passenger	
94.	Contact, passenger seat	
95.	Warning buzzer, safety belts	
96.	Relay, safety belts	
97.	Contact, transmission M41	
98.	Contact, seat buckle, driver	

Color code:

SB	Black
W	White
Y	Yellow
GN	Green
GR	Gray
BL	Blue
R	Red
BR	Brown
W-SB	White-black
W-GN	White-green
BL-R	Blue-red
BL-W	Blue-white
BL-Y	Blue-yellow
GN-R	Green-red

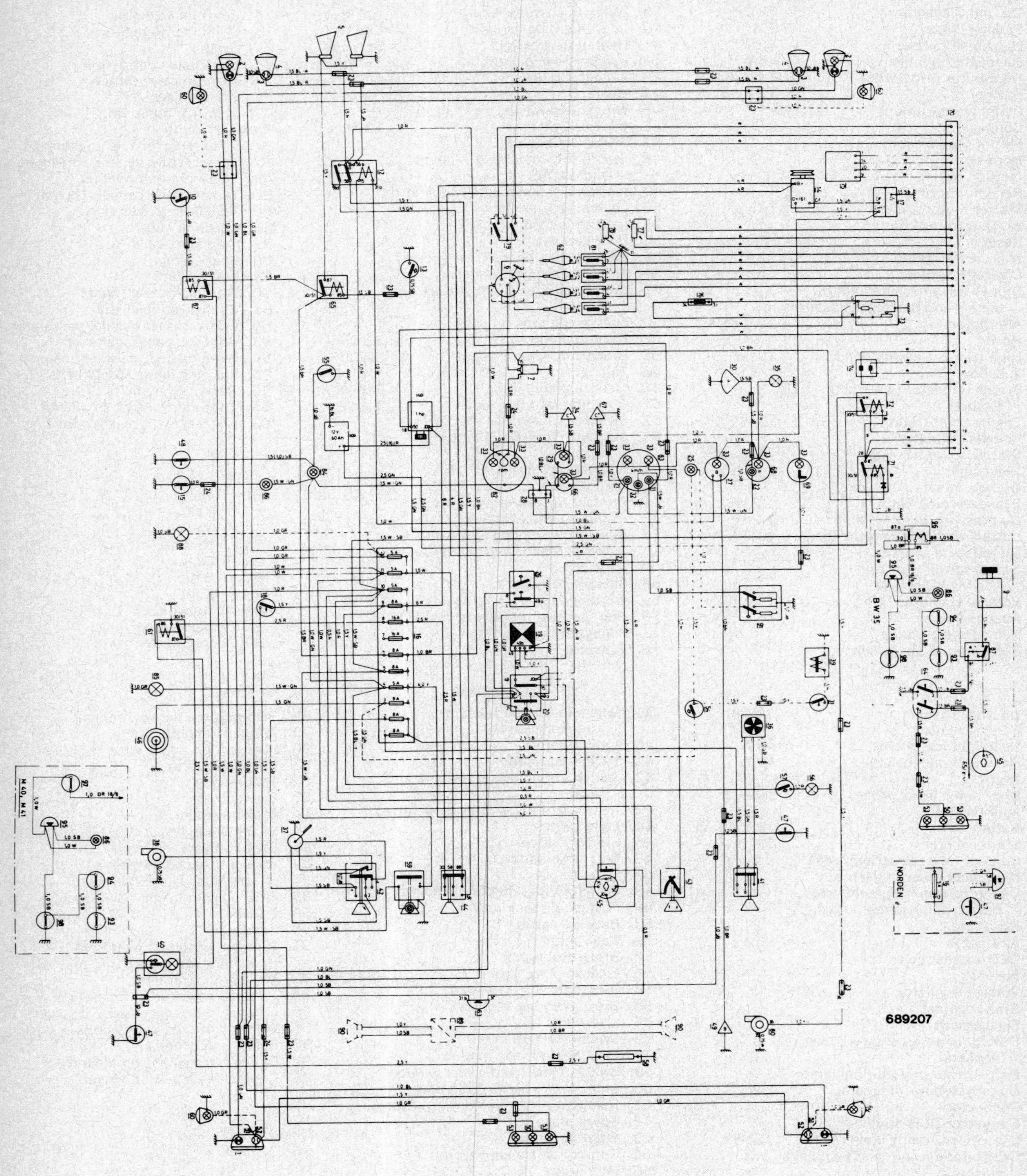

1972 1800E

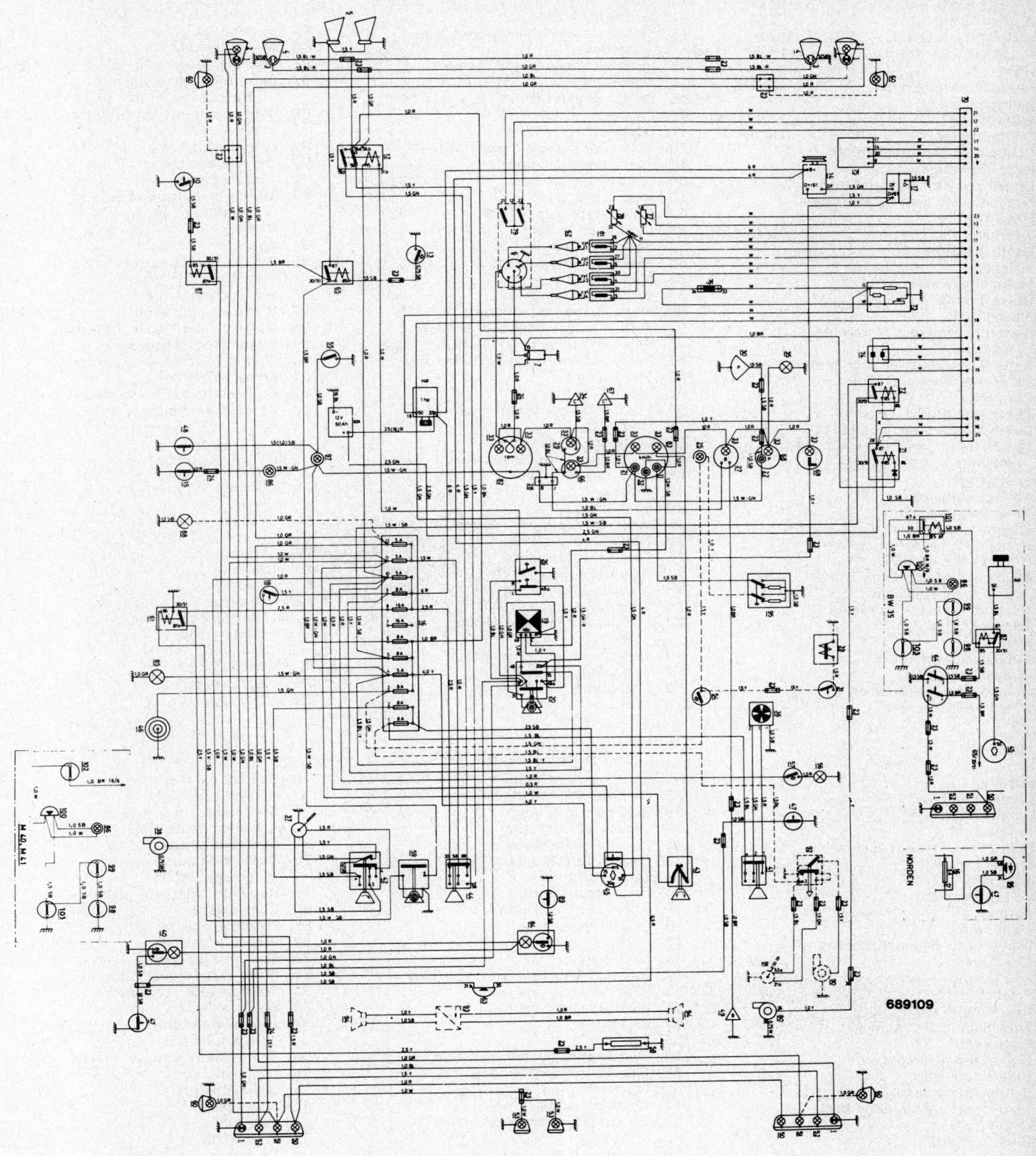

1972 1800ES

1972 1800ES

1. Dir. ind. flashers 32 CP
2. Parking lights 4 CP
3. Headlight low beams 40 W
4. Headlight high beams 45 W
5. Horn
6. Distributor firing order 1-3-4-2
7. Ignition coil
8. Battery 12 V 60 Ah
9. Starter motor 1.0 hp
10. Contact for back-up light M41
11. High beams warning lamp
12. Dipper relay for high and low beams and headlight flashers
13. Horn ring
14. Alternator 35 A
15. Contact seat belt
16. Fusebox
17. Voltage regulator
18. Brake contact
19. Flasher unit
20. Switch for emergency warning flashers
21. Battery charging warning lamp 3 W
22. Oil pressure warning lamp 2 W
23. Connector
24. Connector (R-H drive only)
25. Overdrive warning lamp M41 1.2 W
26. Switch for dir. ind. and headlight flashers
27. Fuel gauge
28. Voltage stabilizer
29. Temperature gauge
30. Oil pressure sender
31. Contact for overdrive on transmission M41
32. Flashers warning lamp 3 W
33. Instrument panel light
34. Coolant temperature sensor
35. Heater control light 3 W
36. Heater
37. Windshield wipers
38. Windshield washer
39. Solenoid for overdrive on transmission M41
40. Interior lamp 10 W
41. Switch for heater
42. Switch for windshield wipers and washer
43. Instrument panel light rheostat
44. Light switch
45. Starter switch
46. Cigarette lighter
47. Door switch
48. Switch for parking brake control
49. Fuel gauge tank-unit
50. Back-up lights 32 CP
51. Rear lights 4 CP
52. Brake stoplights 32 CP
53. License plate light 2x4 CP
54. Switch for overdrive M41
55. Brake warning contact
56. Map light
57. Switch for map light
58. Elec. heated rear window
59. Switch, elec. heated rear window
60. Side marker lights (USA only) 5 W
61. Relay for elec. heated rear window
62. Spark plugs
63. Warning buzzer
64. Contact on transmission BW 35
65. Horn relay
66. Oil temperature gauge
67. Oil temperature sensor
68. Oil pressure gauge
69. Clock
70. Electronic unit
71. Main relay for fuel injection
72. Relay for fuel pump
73. Thermal timer contact
74. Pressure sensor
75. Throttle valve switch
76. Start valve
77. Temperature sensor, intake air
78. Temperature sensor, coolant
79. Triggering contacts
80. Fuel pump
81. Injection valves
82. Tachometer
83. Speedometer
84. Interior light, rear 10 W
85. Seat belts light 2 W
86. Seat belt warning lamp 1.2 W
87. Relay for back-up lights starter relay on BW 35
88. Shift positions light (BW 35 only) 1.2 W
89. Door switch, rear
90. Tailgate washer
91. Tailgate wiper
92. Switch for tailgate wiper and and washer
93. Radio
94. Speaker
95. Dimmer switch for overdrive warning lamp M41
96. Warning buzzer light
97. Brake warning lamp 1.2 W
98. Contact, seat buckle, passenger
99. Contact, passenger seat
100. Warning buzzer, safety belts
101. Relay, safety belts
102. Contact, transmission M41
103. Contact, seat buckle, driver

Color code:

SB	Black
W	White
Y	Yellow
GN	Green
GR	Grey
BL	Blue
R	Red
BR	Brown
W-SB	White-black
W-GN	White-green
BL-R	Blue-red
BL-W	Blue-white
BL-Y	Blue-yellow
GN-R	Green-red

1973 142, 144, with B20F

1. Battery 12 V 60 Ah
2. Connection box
3. Ignition switch
4. Ignition coil
5. Distributor, firing sequence 1-3-4-2
6. Starter motor
7. Alternator
8. Voltage regulator
9. Fusebox
10. Light switch
11. Dip relay for high and low beams
12. Headlights 45 W
13. Low beams 40 W
14. Position light 5 W
15. Rear light 5 W
16. Side marking lights 5 W
17. Plate light 2x5 W
18. Brake stop light contact
19. Brake stop lights 32 cp
20. Connection at instrument
21. Contact on transmission M 40, M 41
22. Back-up lights 32 cp
23. Flasher unit
24. Dir. ind. switch
25. Switch, emergency warning flashers
26. Flasher lights 32 cp
27. Part of 6-pole connection block
28. Tachometer
29. Temperature gauge
30. Fuel gauge
31. Voltage stabilizer
32. Flasher light warning lamp 1.2 W
33. Diode
34. Warning lamp for high beams 1.2 W
35. Warning lamp for battery charging 1.2 W
36. Parking brake warning lamp 1.2 W
37. Choke warning lamp 1.2 W
38. Oil pressure warning lamp 1.2 W
39. Brake warning lamp 1.2 W
40. Vacant warning lamp
41. Parking brake contact
42. Choke control contact
43. Temperature sensor
44. Oil pressure sensor
45. Brake warning contact
46. Brake level sender
47. Horn
48. Horn ring
49. Switch, windshield wipers/washer
50. Windshield wipers
51. Windshield washer
52. Switch, fan
53. Fan
54. Switch, elec. heated rear window
55. Elec. heated rear window
56. Clock
57. Cigarette lighter
58. Rheostat for instrument panel lighting
59. Instrument panel lighting 3x2 W
60. Lighting for controls 3x1.2 W
61. Shift positions light, aut. trans. 1.2 W
62. Glove box contact
63. Glove box lamp
64. Interior lamp
65. Door switch on left side
66. Door switch on right side
67. Reminder buzzer for ignition key
68. Joint
69. Connection at instrument
70. Passenger seat contact
71. Reminder buzzer for seat belt
72. Seat belt warning lamp 1.2 W
73. Contact for seat belt
74. Switch for overdrive M 41
75. Contact for overdrive on transmission M 41
76. Solenoid for overdrive on transmission M 41
77. Overdrive warning lamp 1.2 W
78. Contact on automatic transmission BW 35
79. Reminder buzzer for lights
80. Control unit
81. Throttle valve switch
82. Pressure sensor
83. Relay for fuel pump
84. Main relay for fuel injection
85. Thermal timer contact
86. Start valve
87. Temperature sensor, intake air
88. Temperature sensor, coolant
89. Injection valves
90. Cut-in contact
91. Spark plug
92. Fusebox
93. Fuel pump
94. Connection at instrument
95. Connection at instrument

Color code

SB	Black
Y	Yellow
Bl	Blue
Bl-Y	Blue-Yellow
Bl-R	Blue-Red
Gn-R	Green-Red
R	Red
Gn	Green
W-R	White-Red
W	White
Br	Brown
Gr	Grey

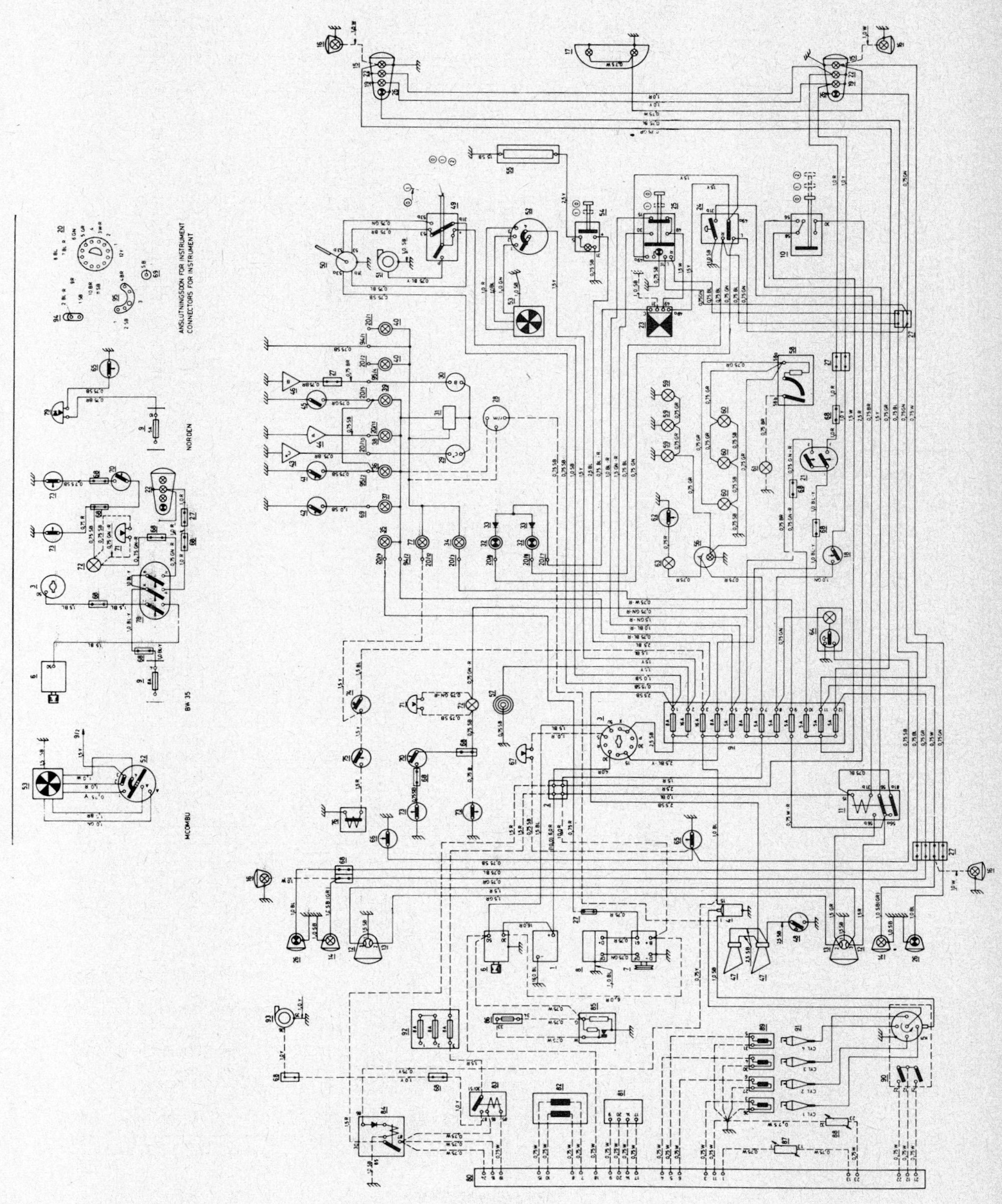

1973 142, 144, with B20F

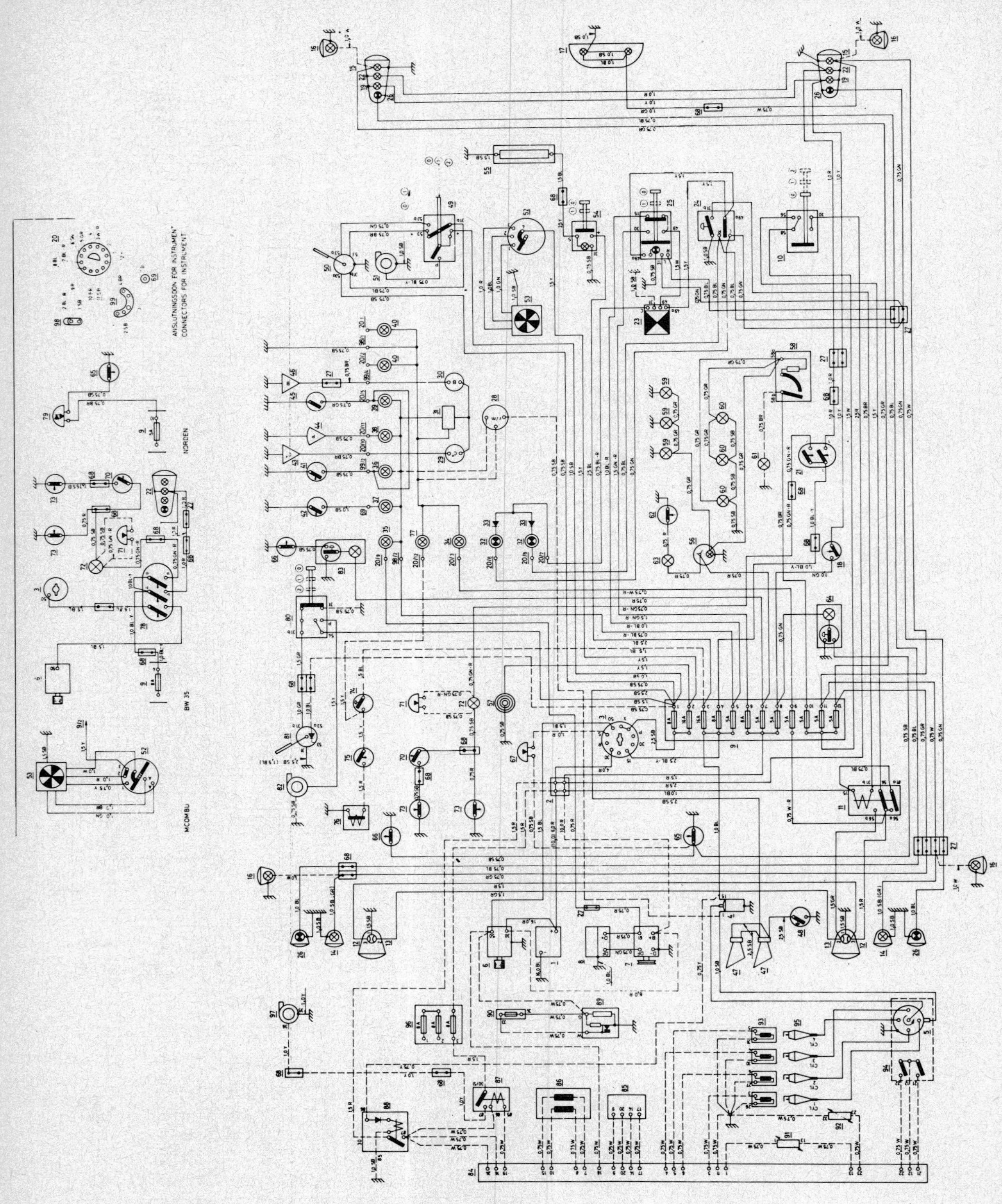

1973 145, with B20F

1973 145, with B20F

1.	Battery	12 V 60 Ah
2.	Connection box	
3.	Ignition switch	
4.	Ignition coil	
5.	Distributor, firing sequence	1-3-4-2
6.	Starter motor	
7.	Alternator	
8.	Voltage regulator	
9.	Fusebox	
10.	Light switch	
11.	Dip relay for high and low beams	
12.	Headlights	45 W
13.	Low beams	40 W
14.	Position light	5 W
15.	Rear lights	5 W
16.	Side marking lights	5 W
17.	Plate light	2x5 W
18.	Brake stop light contact	
19.	Brake stop lights	32 cp
20.	Connection at instrument	
21.	Contact on transmission M 40, M 41	
22.	Back-up lights	32 cp
23.	Flasher unit	
24.	Dir. ind. switch	
25.	Switch, emergency warning flashers	
26.	Flasher lights	32 cp
27.	Part of 6-pole connection block	
28.	Tachometer	
29.	Temperature gauge	
30.	Fuel gauge	
31.	Voltage stabilizer	
32.	Flasher light warning lamp	1.2 W
33.	Diode	
34.	Warning lamp for high beams	1.2 W
35.	Warning lamp for battery charging	1.2 W
36.	Parking brake warning lamp	1.2 W
37.	Choke warning lamp	1.2 W
38.	Oil pressure warning lamp	1.2 W
39.	Brake warning lamp	1.2 W
40.	Vacant warning lamp	
41.	Parking brake contact	
42.	Choke control contact	
43.	Temperature sensor	
44.	Oil pressure sensor	
45.	Brake warning contact	
46.	Brake level sender	
47.	Horn	
48.	Horn ring	
49.	Switch, windshield wipers/washer	
50.	Windshield wipers	
51.	Windshield washer	
52.	Switch, fan	
53.	Fan	
54.	Switch, elec. heated rear window	
55.	Elec. heated rear window	
56.	Cook	
57.	Cigarette lighter	
58.	Rheostat for instrument panel lighting	
59.	Instrument panel lighting	3x2 W
60.	Lighting for control panel	3x1.2 W
61.	Shift positions light, aut. trans.	1.2 W
62.	Glove box contact	
63.	Glove box lamp	
64.	Interior lamp	
65.	Door switch on left side	
66.	Door switch on right side	
67.	Reminder buzzer for ignition key	
68.	Joint	
69.	Connection at instrument	
70.	Passenger seat contact	
71.	Reminder buzzer for seat belt	
72.	Seat belt warning lamp	1.2 W
73.	Contact for seat belt	
74.	Switch for overdrive M 41	
75.	Contact for overdrive on transmission M 41	
76.	Solenoid for overdrive on transmission M 41	
77.	Overdrive warning lamp	1.2 W
78.	Contact on automatic transmission BW 35	
79.	Reminder buzzer for lights	
80.	Switch for elec. heated tailgate window	
81.	Tailgate window wiper	
82.	Tailgate window washer	
83.	Rear roof light	10 W
84.	Control unit	
85.	Throttle valve switch	
86.	Pressure sensor	
87.	Relay for fuel pump	
88.	Main relay for fuel injection	
89.	Thermal timer contact	
90.	Start valve	
91.	Temperature sensor, intake air	
92.	Temperature sensor, coolant	
93.	Injection valves	
94.	Trip contact	
95.	Spark plug	
96.	Fusebox	
97.	Fuel pump	
98.	Connection at instrument	
99.	Connection at instrument	

Color code

SB	Black
Y	Yellow
Bl	Blue
Bl-Y	Blue-Yellow
Bl-R	Blue-Red
Gn-R	Green-Red
R	Red
Gn	Green
W-R	White-Red
W	White
Br	Brown
Gr	Grey

1973 164, with B30F

1. Battery
2. Connection box
3. Ignition switch
4. Ignition coil
5. Distributor, firing sequence
6. Starter motor
7. Alternator
8. Voltage regulator
9. Fusebox
10. Light switch
11. Dip relay for high and low beams
12. Headlights
13. Low beams
14. Position light
15. Rear lights
16. Side marking lights
17. Plate light
18. Brake stop light contact
19. Brake stop lights
20. Relay for horn
21. Contact on transmission M 40, M 41
22. Back-up lights
23. Flasher unit
24. Dir. ind. switch
25. Switch, emergency warning flashers
26. Flasher lights
27. Part of 6-pole connection block
28. Tachometer
29. Temperature gauge
30. Fuel gauge
31. Voltage stabilizer
32. Flasher light warning lamp
33. Diode
34. Warning lamp for high beams
35. Warning lamp for battery charging
36. Parking brake warning lamp
37. Choke warning lamp
38. Oil pressure warning lamp
39. Brake warning lamp
40. Vacant warning lamp
41. Parking brake contact
42. Choke control contact
43. Temperature sensor
44. Oil pressure sensor
45. Brake warning contact
46. Fuel level sender
47. Horn
48. Horn ring
49. Switch, windshield wiper/washer
50. Windshield wipers
51. Windshield washer
52. Switch, fan
53. Fan
54. Switch, elec. heated rear window
55. Elec. heated rear window
56. Clock
57. Cigarette lighter
58. Rheostat for instrument panel lighting
59. Instrument panel lighting
60. Lighting for controls
61. Shift positions light, aut. trans.
62. Glove box contact
63. Glove box lamp
64. Interior lamp
65. Door switch on left side
66. Door switch on right side
67. Warning buzzer for ignition key
68. Joint
69. Engine comp. lighting
70. Passenger seat contact
71. Warning reminder for seat belt
72. Seat belt warning lamp
73. Contact for seat belt
74. Switch for overdrive M 41
75. Contact for overdrive on transmission M 41
76. Solenoid for overdrive on transmission M 41
77. Overdrive warning lamp
78. Contact on automatic transmission BW 35
79. Warning buzzer for light
80. Fog light
81. Fusebox
82. Fog light relay
83. Fog light switch
84. Injection control unit
85. Throttle valve switch
86. Pressure sensor
87. Relay for fuel pump
88. Main relay for fuel injection
89. Thermal timer contact
90. Cold start valve
91. Temperature sensor, intake air
92. Temperature sensor, coolant
93. Injectors
94. Triggering contacts
95. Spark plug
96. Luggage comp. light
97. Fuel pump
98. Connection at instrument
99. Connection at instrument
100. Connection at instrument
101. Connection at instrument
102. Switch for compressor
103. Thermostat
104. Solenoid on compressore
105. Solenoid valve
106. Resistor

Color code

SB	Black
Y	Yellow
Bl	Blue
Bl-Y	Blue-Yellow
Bl-R	Blue-Red
Gn-R	Green-Red
R	Red
Gn	Green
W-R	White-Red
W	White
Br	Brown
Gr	Grey

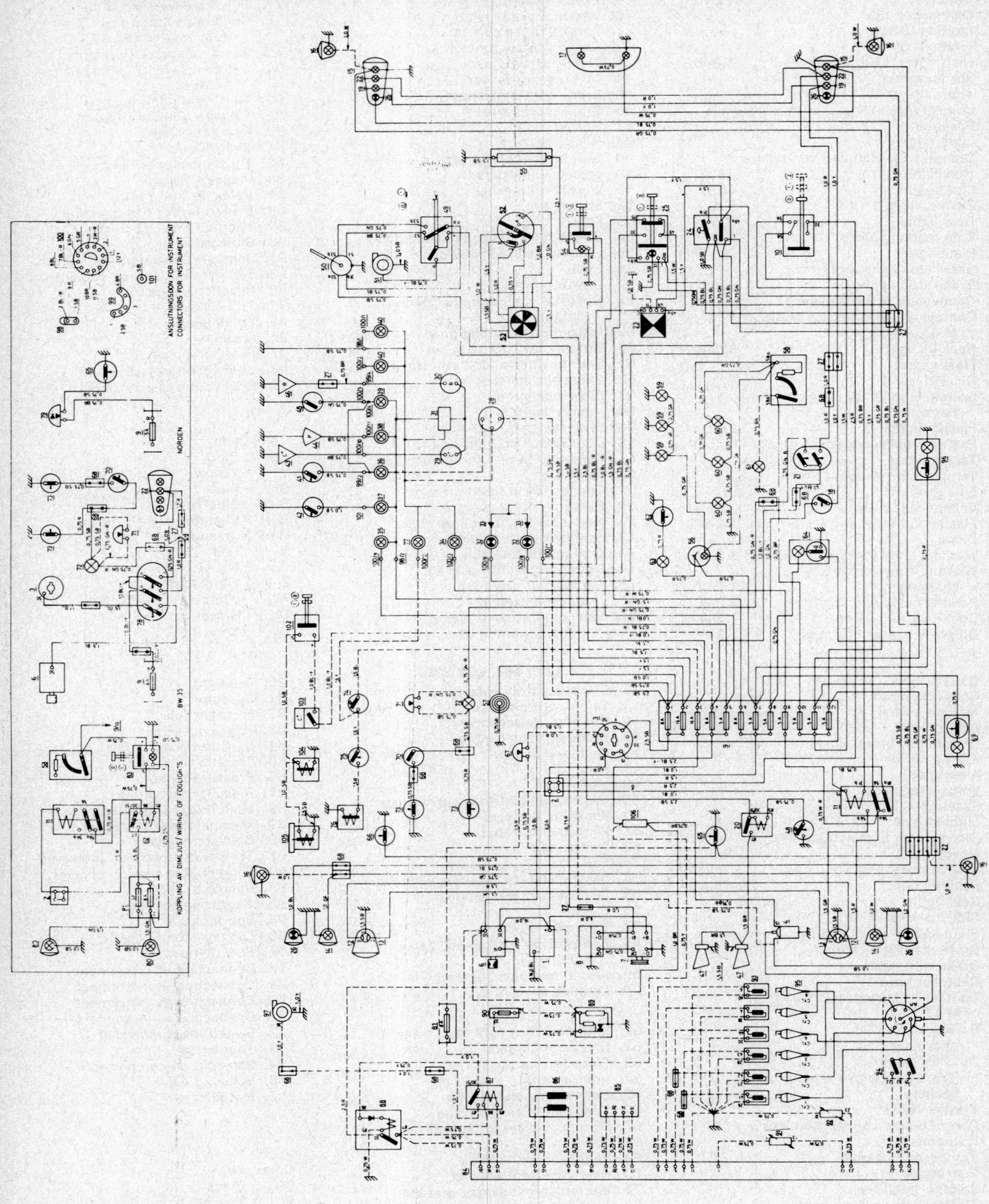

1973 164, with B30F

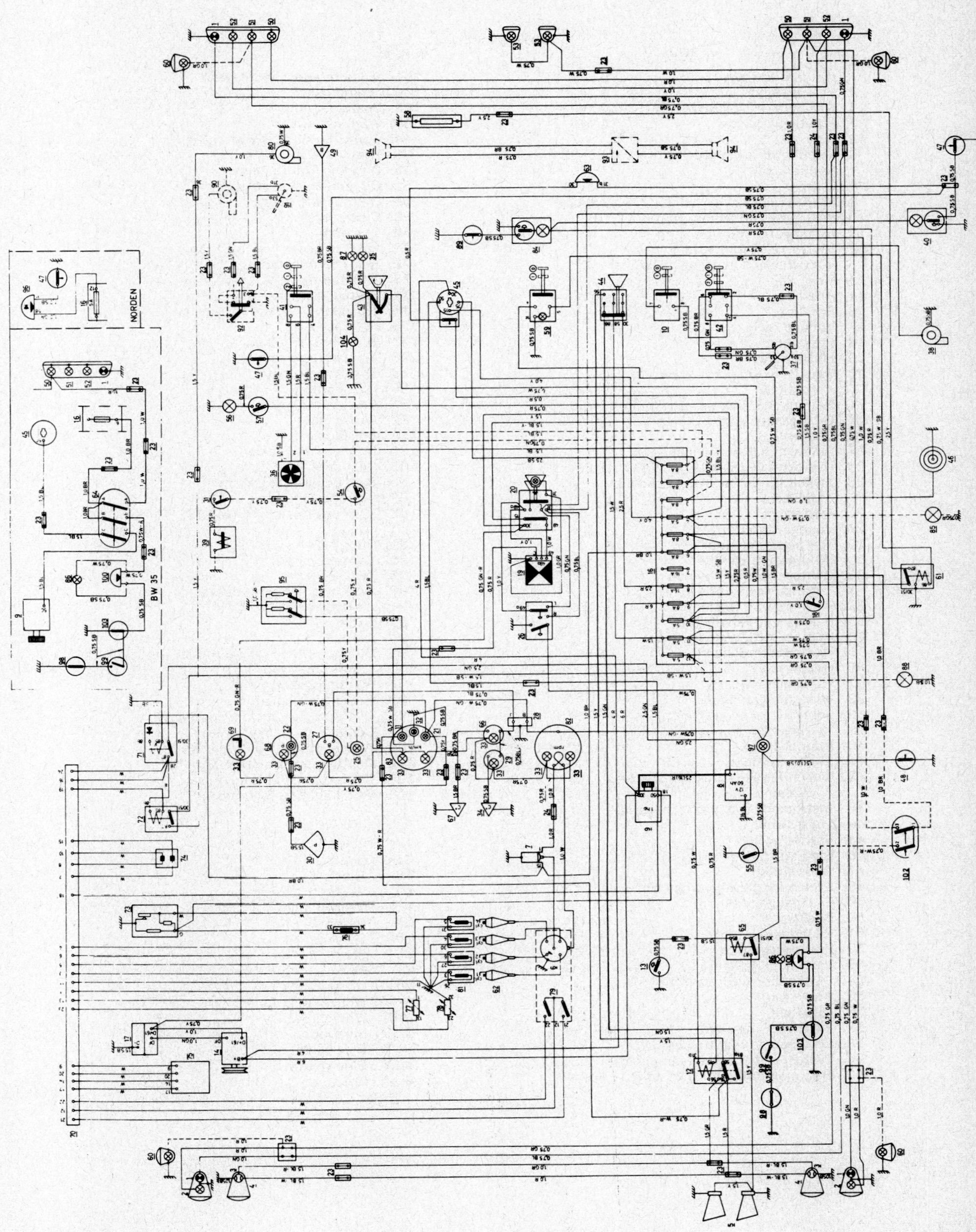

1973 1800ES

1973 1800ES

1. Dir. ind. flashers 32 CP
2. Parking lights 4 CP
3. Headlight low beams 40 W
4. Headlight beams 45 W
5. Horn
6. Distributor firing order 1-3-4-2
7. Ignition coil
8. Battery 12 V 60 Ah
9. Starter motor 1.0 hp
10. Switch for windshield washer
11. High beams warning lamp
12. Dipper relay for high and low beams and headlight flashers
13. Horn ring
14. Alternator 35 A
16. Fusebox
17. Voltage regulator
18. Brake contact
19. Flasher unit
20. Switch for emergency warning flashers
21. Battery charging warning lamp 3 W
22. Oil pressure warning lamp 2 W
23. Connector
24. Connector (R-H drive only)
25. Overdrive warning lamp M 41 1.2 W
26. Switch for dir. ind. and headlight flashers
27. Fuel gauge
28. Voltage stablizer
29. Temperature gauge
30. Oil pressure sender
31. Contact for overdrive on transmission M 41
32. Flashers warning lamp 3 W
33. Instrument panel light
34. Coolant temperature sensor
35. Heater control light 3 W
36. Heater
37. Windshield wipers
38. Windshield washer
39. Solenoid for overdrive on transmission M 41
40. Interior lamp 10 W
41. Switch for heater
42. Switch for windshield wipers and washer
43. Instrument panel light rheostat
44. Light switch
45. Starter switch
46. Cigarette lighter
47. Door switch
48. Switch for parking brake control
49. Fuel gauge tank unit
50. Back-up 32 CP
51. Rear lights 4 CP
52. Brake stoplights 32 CP
53. License plate light 2x4 CP
54. Switch for overdrive M 41
55. Brake warning contact
56. Map light
57. Switch for map light
58. Elec. heated rear window
59. Switch, elec. heated rear window
60. Side marker lights (USA only) 5 W
61. Relay for elec. heated rear window
62. Spark plugs
63. Warning buzzer
64. Contact on transmission BW 35
65. Horn relay
66. Oil temperature gauge
67. Oil temperature sensor
68. Oil pressure gauge
69. Clock
70. Electronic unit
71. Main relay for fuel injection
72. Relay for fuel pump
73. Thermal timer contact
74. Pressure sensor
75. Throttle valve switch
76. Start valve
77. Temperature sensor I
78. Temperature sensor II
79. Triggering contact
80. Fuel pump
81. Injection valves
82. Tachometer
83. Speedometer
84. Interior light, rear 10 W
85. Seat belts light 2 W
86. Seat belt warning lamp 1.2 W
87. Lighting for switch
88. Shift positions light (BW 35 only) 1.2 W
89. Door switch, rear
90. Tailgate washer
91. Tailgate wiper
92. Switch for tailgate wiper and washer
93. Radio
94. Speaker
95. Dimmer switch for overdrive warning lamp M 41
96. Warning buzzer light
97. Brake warning lamp 1.2 W
98. Contact, seat buckle, passenger
99. Contact, passenger seat
100. Warning buzzer, safety belts
102. Contact, transmission M 41
103. Contact, seat buckle, driver
104. Decal lighting (only USA)

Color code

SB	Black
W	White
Y	Yellow
GN	Green
GR	Grey
BL	Blue
R	Red
BR	Brown
W-SB	White-black
W-GN	White-green
BL-R	Blue-red
BL-W	Blue-white
BL-Y	Blue-yellow
GN-R	Green-red

TUNE-UP PROCEDURES

CAUTION: *When working with a running engine, make sure that there is proper ventilation. Also make sure that the transmission is in neutral, and the parking brake is firmly applied. Always keep hands, clothing, and tools well clear of the radiator fan.*

Spark Plug Removal and Installation

Every six months or 6,000 miles, the spark plugs should be removed for inspection. At this time they should be cleaned and regapped. At 12-month or 12,000-mile intervals, the plugs should be replaced.

Prior to removal, number each spark plug wire with a piece of masking tape bearing the cylinder number. Remove each spark plug wire by grasping its rubber boot on the end and twisting slightly to free the wire from the plug. Using a 13/16 in. spark plug socket, turn the plugs counterclockwise to remove them. Do not allow any foreign matter to enter the cylinders through the spark plug holes.

Consult the spark plug inspection chart in step 4.6 of the "Troubleshooting" section when in doubt about plug condition. If the spark plugs are to be reused, check the porcelain insulator for cracks and the electrodes for excessive wear. Replace the entire set if one plug is damaged. Clean the reusable plugs with a stiff wire brush, or have them cleaned in a plug sandblasting machine (found in many service stations). Uneven wear of the center or ground electrode may be corrected by leveling off the unevenly worn section with a file.

The gap must be checked with a feeler gauge before installing the plug in the engine. With the ground electrode positioned parallel to the center electrode, a 0.030 in. wire gauge must pass through the opening with a slight drag. If the air gap between the two electrodes is not correct, the ground electrode must be bent to bring it to specifications.

After the plugs are gapped correctly, they may be inserted into their holes and hand-tightened. Be careful not to cross-thread the plugs. Torque the plugs to the proper specification with a 13/16 in. socket and a torque wrench. Install each spark plug wire on its respective plug, making sure that each spark plug end is making good metal-to-metal contact in its wire socket.

Breaker Points and Condenser Removal and Installation

Volvo recommends that the breaker points be inspected and adjusted every six months on 6,000 miles. If, upon inspection, the points prove to be faulty, they must be replaced with the condenser as a unit.

CAUTION: *Make sure the ignition is off.*

Remove the distributor cap and rotor from the top of the distributor, taking note of their placement. On fuel-injected six cylinder models, remove the breaker point protective cover. Place a screwdriver against the breaker points and examine the condition of the contacts. Replace the points if the contacts are blackened, pitted, or worn excessively, if the breaker arm has lost its tension, or if the fiber rubbing block on the breaker has become worn or loose. Contact points that have become slightly burned (light gray) may be cleaned with a point file.

To replace the points and condenser, disconnect the electrical leads for both at the primary connection. Remove the lockscrew for the contact breakers and lift them straight up. Loosen the condenser bracket retaining screw and slide out the condenser. While the points are out, lubricate the breaker cam with a very light coating of silicone-based grease. Clean the distributor base plate with alcohol to free it of any oil film that might impede completion of the ground circuit. Also clean the contact point surfaces with the solvent. Install the new points and new condenser and tighten their retaining screws. Connect the electrical leads for both at the primary connection. Make sure that the point contacts are aligned horizontally and vertically. If the points are not aligned properly, bend the stationary arm to suit.

The breaker points must be correctly gapped before proceeding any further. Turn the engine until the rubbing block on the point assembly is resting on the high point of a breaker cam lobe. Loosen the point hold-down screw slightly and insert a feeler gauge of the proper thickness between the point contacts. Fine adjustment is made by inserting a screwdriver into the adjusting recess and turning the screwdriver until the proper size feeler gauge passes between the point contacts with a slight drag. Without disturbing the setting, tighten the breaker point retaining screw.

If a dwell meter is available, proceed to "Dwell Angle Setting." A dwell meter is considered a more accurate means of measuring point gap. If the meter is not available, except on fuel-injected six cylinder models, proceed to replace the rotor in top of the distributor shaft, making sure that the tab inside the rotor aligns with the slot on the distributor. Before replacing the rotor on fuel-injected six cylinder models, install the breaker point protection cover. Place the distributor cap on top of the distributor and snap the cap clasps into the slots on the cap. Make sure that all the spark plug wires fit snugly into the cap. Proceed to "Ignition Timing Adjustment."

Recess for adjusting contact points

Dwell Angle Setting

The dwell angle is the number of degrees of distributor cam rotation through which the breaker points remain fully closed (conducting electricity). Increasing the point gap decreases dwell, while decreasing the point gap increases dwell.

Using a dwell meter of known accuracy, connect the red lead (positive) wire of the meter to the distributor primary wire connection on the positive (+) side of the coil, and the black ground (negative) wire of the meter to a good ground on the engine (e.g. thermostat housing nut).

The dwell angle may be checked either with the distributor cap and rotor installed and the engine running, or with the cap and rotor removed and the engine cranking at starter speed. The meter gives a constant reading with the engine running. With the engine cranking ,the reading will fluctuate between zero degrees dwell and the maximum figure for that angle. While cranking, the maximum figure is the correct one for that setting. Never attempt to change dwell angle while the ignition is on. Touching the point contacts or primary wire connection with a metal screwdriver may result in a 12 Volt shock.

To change the dwell angle, loosen the point retaining screw slightly and make the approximate correction. Tighten the retaining screw and test the dwell with the engine cranking. If the dwell appears to be correct, install the breaker point protective cover (if so equipped), the rotor and distributor cap and test the dwell with the engine running. Take the engine through its entire rpm range and observe the dwell meter. The dwell should remain within specifications at all times. Great fluctuation of dwell at different engine speeds indicates worn distributor parts.

Following the dwell angle adjustment, the ignition timing must be checked. A 1° increase in dwell results in the ignition timing being retarded 2° and vice versa.

Ignition Timing Adjustment

Volvo recommends that the ignition timing be checked every six months or 6,000 miles. The timing adjustment should always follow a breaker point gap and/or dwell angle adjustment, and be made with the engine at operating temperature.

Clean the crankshaft damper and pointer on the water pump housing with a solvent-soaked rag so that the marks can be seen. Connect a stroboscopic timing light to the no. 1 cylinder spark plug and to the battery, according to the manufacturer's instructions. Scribe a mark on the crankshaft damper and on the marker with chalk or luminescent (day-glo) paint to highlight the correct timing setting. On carbureted models, disconnect the vacuum advance line from the intake manifold at the distributor and plug it with a pencil, golf tee, or some other suitably small object. On fuel-injected models, disconnect and plug the above-mentioned vacuum line and also disconnect the hose between the air cleaner and the inlet duct at the duct. On all 1973 models equipped with exhaust gas recirculation, disconnect and plug the vacuum hose at the EGR valve.

Ignition timing marks

Attach a tachometer to the engine and set the idle speed to specifications. With the engine running, aim the timing light at the pointer and the marks on the damper. If the marks made with the chalk or paint coincide when the timing light flashes, the engine is timed correctly. If the marks do not coincide, stop the engine, loosen the distributor attaching bolt, and start the engine again. While observing the timing light flashes on the markers, grasp the distributor vacuum regulator—not the distributor cap—and rotate the distributor until the marks do coincide. Stop the engine and tighten the distributor attaching bolt, taking care not to disturb the setting. As a final check, start the engine once more to make sure that the timing marks align.

Reconnect all disconnected hoses and remove the timing light and tachometer from the engine.

Valve Lash Adjustment

The recommended maintenance interval for valve clearance adjustment is 12 months or 12,000 miles. Valve clearance should be checked at every tune-up or whenever excessive valve train noise is noticed. The clearance may be checked with the engine hot or cold.

Remove the valve cover and crank the engine until number one cylinder is at Top Dead Center (TDC). TDC is the point at which both intake and exhaust valves are fully closed and the piston is on its compression stroke. To find TDC, crank the engine, preferably with a remote starter switch, until the pushrods for both valves on the subject cylinder stop falling. Stop cranking the engine. At this point, it will be easier to find TDC by turning the engine over manually. To accomplish this, remove all of the spark plugs so the compression and resistance to cranking are diminished, and remove the distributor cap so the position of the rotor may be observed. To crank the engine manually, position a socket or closed-end wrench—with a long handle for greater leverage—on the crankshaft damper bolt and turn the crankshaft in the required direction. **CAUTION:** *Do not attempt to crank the engine by grasping the viscous drive fan as damage to the fan may result. At TDC, the piston for the subject cylinder should be at its highest point of travel. Make a visual check or insert a screwdriver through the spark plug hole to make sure that the piston is no longer traveling upward. As an additional check, the distributor rotor should be pointed to the spark plug wire for the subject cylinder at TDC.*

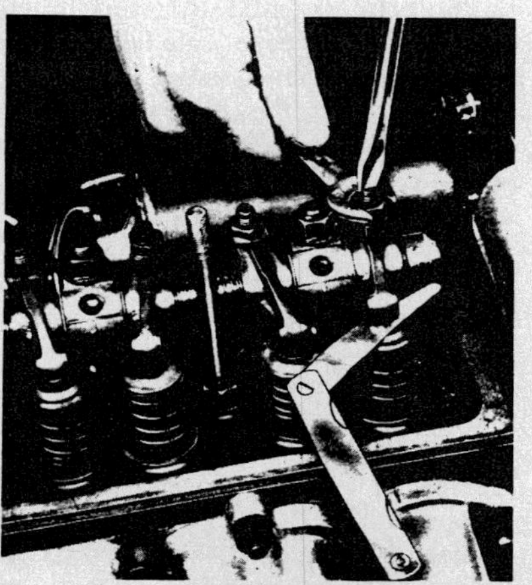

Adjusting valve clearance

Number one cylinder is at TDC when the 0 degree mark on the crankshaft damper aligns with the pointer on the water pump housing. On four-cylinder models, with number one cylinder at TDC, valves (counting from the front) 1, 2, 3, and 5 may be adjusted. On six-cylinder models, with number one cylinder at TDC, valves 1, 2, 3, 6, 7, and 10 may be adjusted.

Insert a step-type (go and no-go) feeler gauge of the specified thickness between the rocker arm and the valve stem. Adjust each rocker arm so that the thinner gauge slides in easily but the thicker gauge cannot be inserted. Adjustment is accomplished by loosening the locknut and turning the adjusting screw and then, without disturbing the adjustment, retightening the locknut.

The remainder of the valves may be adjusted in the following manner. On four-cylinder models, with no. 4 cylinder at TDC, valves (counting from the front) 4, 6, 7, and 8 may be adjusted. On six-cylinder models, with no. 6 cylinder at TDC, valves 4, 5, 8, 9, 11, and 12 may be adjusted.

Make sure that the feeler gauge of the minimum thickness may pass between the rocker arm and the valve stem easily. Excessive clearance may cause greater valve train noise but insufficient clearance may burn a valve. When in doubt, be generous with the clearance adjustment to avoid costly valve work.

After adjusting the valves, replace the valve cover with a new gasket, if needed, and install the spark plugs and distributor cap if they were removed. Start the engine. Listen for excessive valve train noise and check for oil leaks.

Carburetor Adjustments

NOTE: *Consult local law enforcement agency for regulations regarding adjustment of emission control equipment on 1968 and later model cars.*

Idle Speed and Mixture

SU HS6

1.Check the oil level in the damping cylinders. After unscrewing the black cap on top of each carburetor, lift out the damping pistons. The oil level in each carburetor should be at the top of the center spindle (piston bore) with the piston removed. Top up as necessary with Type "A" automatic transmission fluid.

2. Run the engine until it has reached full operating temperature. Remove the air cleaner(s).

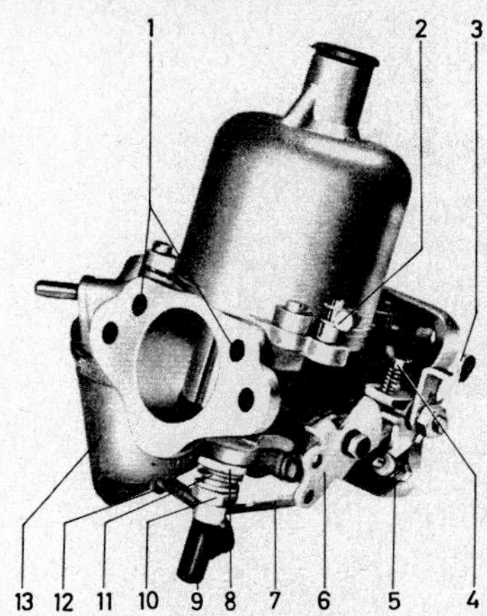

SU HS6 carburetor—right side

1. Ventilation holes
2. Attachment for choke control
3. Lever
4. Idling screw
5. Screw for fast idle
6. Lever
7. Link for jet
8. Locknut
9. Jet
10. Adjusting nut
11. Spring
12. Fuel line
13. Floatchamber

SU HS6 carburetor—left side

1. Suction chamber
2. Screw for damper piston
3. Lifting pin
4. Floatchamber cover
5. Ventilation hole
6. Fuel line
7. Lever
8. Throttle flap
9. Connecting flange

3. Adjust the fuel jets to their basic setting by screwing the fuel/air mixture adjusting nuts, at the bottom of both carburetors, to their upper positions. Then screw both mixture adjusting nuts down one and one-half turns each.

4. Turn the idle adjusting screws on both carburetors equally and adjust the idling speed of the engine to specifications. Using a length of rubber hose, make sure that the intake sounds of both carburetors sound the same.

5. Adjust the fuel jets, one at a time, until the highest idle speed is obtained. When adjusting, first turn the adjusting nut slowly downward (richer mixture) until the engine begins to run roughly, and then turn the adjusting nut slightly upward (leaner mixture) until the engine runs smoothly.

6. Re-adjust the idling speed to specifications by turning the idle adjusting screws on both carburetors equally.

7. As a final check of the fuel/air mixture in both carburetors, lift the air valve (piston) of one of the carburetors ⅛ in. by using the pin next to the air intake. If the engine falters and stalls when the piston is lifted, the mixture in the other carburetor is probably too lean. If the engine speed increases, the mixture in the other carburetor is too rich. Repeat the checking procedure by lifting the pin and piston for the other carburetor. When the pin and piston are lifted ⅛ in., a properly adjusted carburetor will drop the engine idle speed approximately 100–150 rpm.

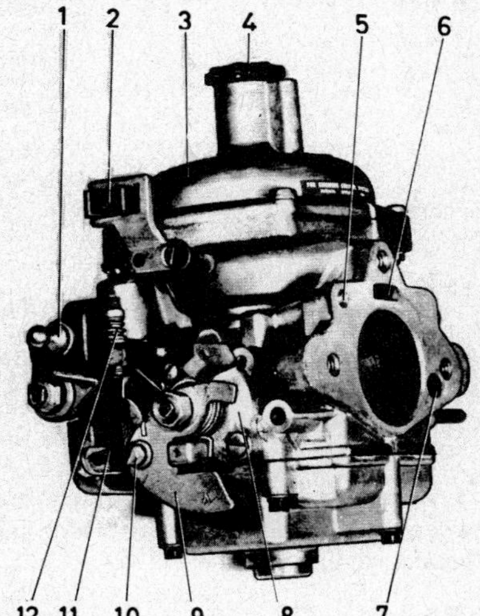

Zenith-Stromberg 175 CD2 SE carburetor—left side

1. Lever for throttle control
2. Clamp for choke wire
3. Suction chamber
4. Hydraulic damper
5. Vent drilling from floatchamber
6. Drilling for air supply under diaphragm
7. Drilling for air supply to temp. compensator and idle trimming screw
8. Cold start device
9. Cam disc for fast idle
10. Connection for choke control
11. Fast idle stop screw
12. Throttle stop screw

Stromberg 175 CD 2SE

1. Check the oil level in the damper cylinders. If the oil is not ¼ in. from the top of the spindle, top us as necessary with Type "A" automatic transmission fluid.

2. Run the engine until it has reached full operating temperature. A good way to check this is to feel the upper radiator hose. When the engine reaches operating temperature, the thermostat opens, filling the upper radiator hose with 180° coolant.

3. Adjust the idling speed of the engine to the specifications on the tune-up chart by turning the throttle stopscrews. Turn the screws on both carburetors equally. Check to make sure that both carburetors have the same air valve lift by visually comparing the distance between the carburetor housing bridge and the air valve.

4. Adjust the idle mixture of the engine with the idle trimming screws until the highest engine speed is attained. The basic setting is two turns counterclockwise from lock. Again, turn the screws on both carburetors equally.

5. Adjust the idling speed of the engine to specifications with the throttle stopscrews.

6. Remove the plastic caps over the mixture adjusting screws. Turn both adjusting screws equally until maximum

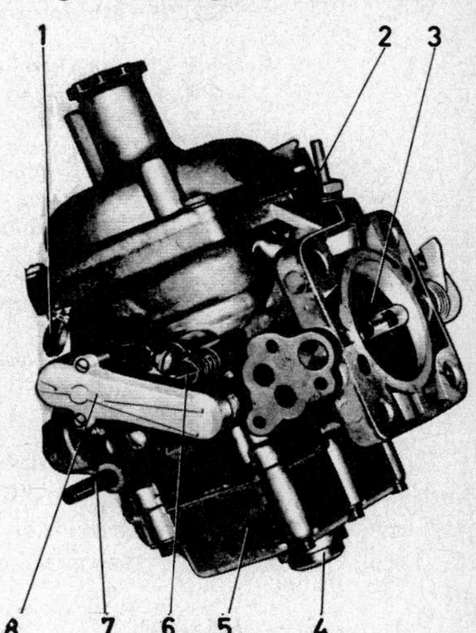

Zenith-Stromberg 175 CD2 SE carburetor—right side

1. Sealed plug
2. Connection for vacuum hose to distributor
3. Primary throttle
4. Floatchamber plug
5. Floatchamber
6. Idle trimming screw
7. Connection for fuel hose
8. Temperature compensator

rpm is achieved. Turn both adjusting screws equally in the opposite direction until the engine just starts to falter. Remember that, in this case, the proper setting is not when maximum rpm is reached but when the engine just starts to falter. As a further check, unscrew the adjusting screws ¼–½ of a turn. The speed should then drop a further 20–40 rpm. Turn back the screws equally to the point where the engine just starts to falter and install the plastic caps over the screws.

7. Adjust the idling speed of the en-

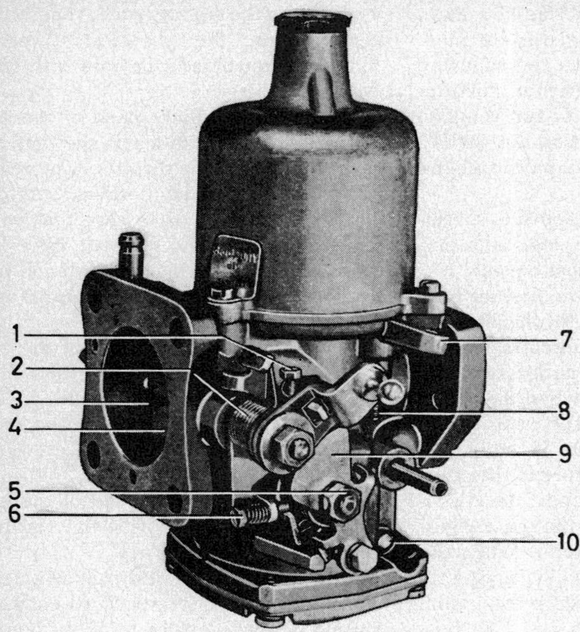

SU HIF carburetor-front, left side

1. Throttle stop screw
2. Return spring
3. Throttle
4. Overrev valve
5. Cold-start device
6. Fast-idle stop screw
7. Attachment for choke control
8. Lift pin
9. Cam disc for fast idle
10. Screw head for float shaft

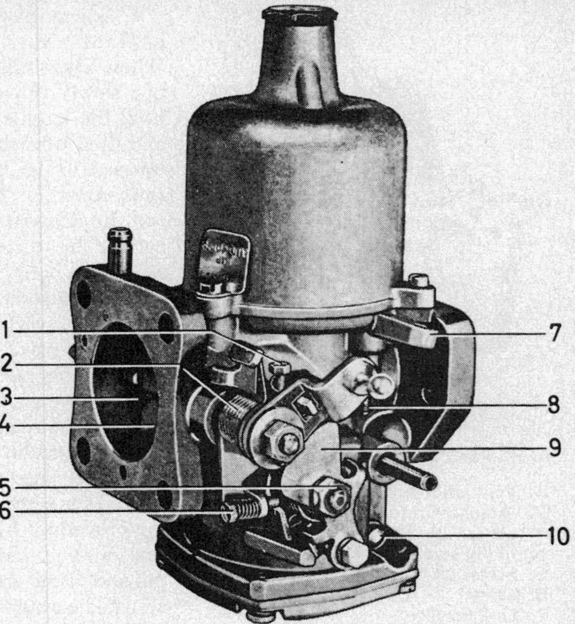

SU HIF carburetor-front, right side

1. Hydraulic damper
2. Suction chamber
3. Drillings for air supply under air valve
4. Vent hole from floatchamber
5. Connection for fuel line
6. Jet adjusting screw
7. Floatchamber cover
8. Connection (positive) for hose to venting filter
9. Plug for outlet for speed compensator (air condition)
10. Boss for guard
11. Hot start valve adjusting screw
12. Hot start valve
13. Outlet from floatchamber (connection for hose to venting filter)

gine to specifications with the throttle stopscrews.

SU HIF 6

1. Check the oil level in the damper cylinders. If the oil is not ¼ in. from the top of the spindle, top up as necessary with Type "A" automatic transmission fluid.

2. Remove the air cleaner.

3. Adjust the fuel jets to their basic setting by lifting the air valve and turning the adjusting screw until the upper edge of the fuel jet is level with the bridge. The jet is then lowered two and one-half turns clockwise. This basic jet setting is correct for a carburetor temperature of approximately 70° F. Turning the adjusting screw a quarter turn in either direction compensates for a temperature difference of approximately 70° F. Turn the adjusting screw less than the two and one-half turns for temperatures above 70° F, and more than two and one-half turns for lower temperatures.

4. Run the engine until it has reached full operating temperature. The upper radiator hose should be very warm at this point.

5. Adjust the idling speed of the engine to the specifications on the tune-up chart by turning the throttle stop screws. Turn the screws on both carburetors equally. Check to make sure that both carburetors have the same air valve lift by visually comparing the distance between the carburetor housing bridge and the air valve.

Bosch Electronic Fuel Injection Adjustments

Idle Speed and Mixture

The idle mixture adjustment or CO value may be set only with the use of a CO meter. This adjustment is made by attaching a CO meter to the exhaust pipe of a vehicle with a warm (176° F) engine, and turning the adjusting screw of the Bosch control unit (beneath the passenger seat) until the correct CO value is obtained. The correct value is 1–1.5 percent for cars with manual transmissions and 0.5–1.0 percent for cars with automatic transmissions. Because this operation requires highly technical skills and expensive equipment, it is best referred to a Volvo or Bosch agency. In other words, don't mess with the control unit.

The idle speed adjustment may, on the other hand, be set with a tachometer and an average amount of expertise. The check should be made with the engine idling at operating temperature (176°F). On 140 and 1800 series Volvos, remove the air cleaner-to-inlet duct hose. Check to see that the auxiliary air regulator is closed properly by removing the inlet

Idle speed adjusting screw—B20E, B20F

Idle speed adjusting screw—B30F

duct-to-regulator hose and covering the opening with your hand. If the idle speed differs greatly, the engine is not fully warm or the regulator is faulty. Fit the hose again and adjust the idle speed to specifications with the idle adjusting screw. The idle adjusting screw is located on the inlet duct below the air cleaner hose opening on four-cylinder models, and inline in the auxiliary air pipe on six-cylinder models (see illustrations). On 140 and 1800 series Volvos, install the air cleaner hose.

ENGINE ELECTRICAL

All Volvos with B 18, B 20 and B 30 engines are equipped with a 12 V, negative ground electrical system which consists of a battery, generator or alternator and voltage regulator, starter motor, ignition system, lighting system, accessories, and signaling and instrumentation components.

All Volvos bearing the suffix "E" also employ the Bosch electronic fuel injection system. This is an assembly of sensitive electronic parts including an electric fuel pump, a highly sophisticated control unit, and various electronic engine sensors. Because of the complexity of this fuel injection system, the Volvos using it require special precautions when fast-charging the battery, jump starting, arc welding, or oven baking (after painting). Consult the Fuel Systems and Emission Control System section for details.

Distributor

The distributor performs two functions within the ignition system: its breaker points time (with changing engine speed) the collapse of the magnetic field in the ignition coil, converting primary voltage (12 V) to secondary (high) voltage; and its rotor and cap then distribute the high voltage spark to the correct spark plug. In order to prevent arcing between the points, and subsequent burning when they are open (not making contact), a distributor condenser is arranged in parallel with the breaker point circuit.

All Volvos have Bosch distributors located on the left side of the engine which are driven by the camshaft. A centrifugal governor beneath the breaker plate regulates advance, according to engine speed. A vacuum regulator outside the distributor controls advance in relation to engine load. All six-cylinder models have a dual-diaphragm vacuum regulator. The regulator retards the basic ignition timing adjustment during engine idling. On some early production B 20 B models with automatic transmissions, a plastic holder (vacuum delay valve) is fitted inline between the carbu-

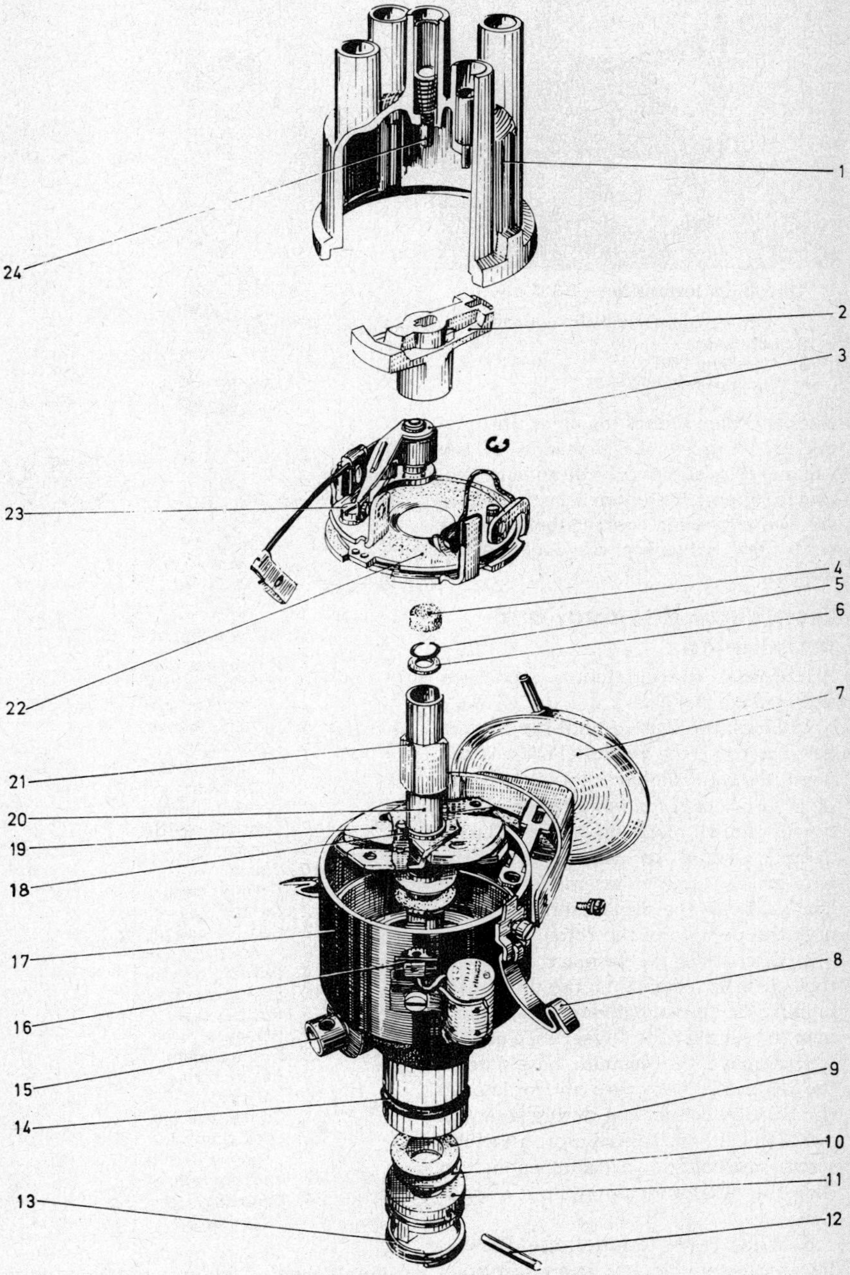

Distributor assembly—B20B

1. Distributor cap
2. Distributor arm
3. Contact breaker
4. Lubricating felt
5. Circlip
6. Washer
7. Vacuum regulator
8. Cap clasp
9. Fiber washer
10. Steel washer
11. Driving collar
12. Lock pin
13. Resilient ring
14. Rubber seal
15. Lubricator
16. Primary connection
17. Distributor housing
18. Centrifugal governor spring
19. Centrifugal weight
20. Breaker camshaft
21. Breaker cam
22. Breaker plate
23. Lock screw for breaker contacts
24. Rod brush (carbon)

Distributor installation—B30A shown

1. Primary connection with condenser
2. Lubricator
3. Attaching bolt
4. Vacuum regulator

retor and the vacuum regulator. Its function is to delay the resetting of the vacuum regulator to the idle advance setting for approximately six seconds. There are two triggering contacts beneath the centrifugal governor on fuel-injected models.

Distributor Removal and Installation

1. Unsnap the distributor cap clasps and remove the cap.

2. Crank the engine until no. 1 cylinder is at Top Dead Center (TDC). At this point, the rotor should point to the spark plug wire socket for no. 1 cylinder, and the 0° timing mark on the crankshaft damper should be aligned with the pointer. For ease of assembly, scribe a chalkmark on the distributor housing to note the position of the rotor.

3. Disconnect the primary lead from the coil at its terminal on the distributor housing. On fuel-injected models, disconnect the plug for the triggering contacts.

4. Remove the vacuum hose(s) from the regulator. Take care not to damage the bakelite connection during removal.

5. Slacken the distributor attaching screw and hold-down clamp enough to slide the distributor up and out of position.

6. When ready to install the distributor, if the engine has been disturbed (cranked), find TDC for no. 1 cylinder as outlined under "Valve Lash Adjustment". If the engine has not been disturbed, install the distributor with the rotor pointing to the no. 1 cylinder spark plug wire socket, or the chalkmark made prior to removal. To approximate ignition timing, position the vacuum regulator to the rear of the distributor (firewall side). If the distributor is installed incorrectly, the rotor will be 180° (of distributor rotation) out of place; incorrectly pointing at no. 4 spark plug wire on four-cylinder engines and incorrectly pointing at no. 6 spark plug wire on six-cylinder engines. Do not tighten the distributor attaching screw at this time.

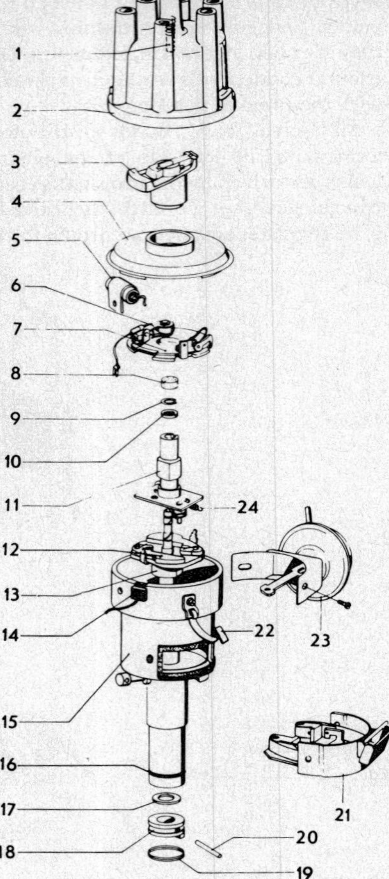

Distributor assembly—B30F

1. Rod brush (carbon)
2. Distributor cap
3. Distributor arm
4. Protective cover
5. Condenser
6. Ignition contact breaker
7. Breaker plate
8. Lubricating felt
9. Circlip
10. Washer
11. Breaker cam
12. Centrifugal weight
13. Cam for triggering contacts
14. Primary terminal
15. Distributor body
16. Rubber seal
17. Washers
18. Driving collar
19. Resilient ring
20. Lock pin
21. Contact device
22. Lock clamp for distr. cap
23. Vacuum regulator
24. Centrifugal governor spring

7. Connect the primary lead to its terminal on the distributor housing. On fuel-injected models, connect the plug for the triggering contacts.

8. Connect the vacuum hose(s) to the bakelite connection(s) on the vacuum regulator.

9. If the distributor was disassembled, or if the contact point setting was disturbed, proceed to set the point gap and/or dwell angle.

10. Install the distributor cap and secure the clasps. Proceed to set the ignition timing. Tighten the distributor attaching screw.

Generator

A Bosch direct current generator was used on 1967 models. This 30 amp unit is a two brush, two pole, shunt wound, conventional design. In 1968, the D. C. generator was replaced by an A. C. alternator. Removal and installation procedures for both are the same.

Alternator

The alternator converts the mechanical energy which is supplied by the drive belt into electrical energy by electromagnetic induction. When the ignition switch is turned on, current flows from the battery, through the charging system light or ammeter, to the voltage regulator, and finally to the alternator. When the engine is started, the drive belt turns the rotating field (rotor) in the stationary windings (stator), inducing alternating current. This alternating current is converted into usable direct current by the diode rectifier. Most of this current is used to charge the battery and power the electrical components of the vehicle. A small part is returned to the field windings of the alternator enabling it to increase its output. When the current in the field windings reaches a predetermined control voltage, the voltage regulator grounds the circuit, preventing any further increase. The cycle is continued so that the voltage remains constant.

Volvo has used six different alternators in its 1968–73 models. Three Motorola (two 35 and one 55 amp) and three Bosch (one 30, one 35 and one 55 amp) units have been utilized. Removal and replacement procedures are the same for all.

Alternator Precautions

Several precautions must be observed when performing work on alternator equipment.

1. If the battery is removed for any reason, make sure that it is reconnected with the correct polarity. Reversing the battery connections may result in damage to the one-way rectifiers.

2. Never operate the alternator with the main circuit broken. Make sure that the battery, alternator, and regulator leads are not disconnected while the engine is running.

3. Never attempt to polarize an alternator.

4. When charging a battery that is installed in the vehicle, disconnect the negative battery cable.

5. When utilizing a booster battery as a starting aid, always connect it in parallel; negative to negative, and positive to positive.

6. When arc welding is to be performed on any part of the vehicle, disconnect the negative battery cable, disconnect the alternator leads, and unplug the voltage regulator.

Drive Belt Adjustment

Accessory drive belt tension is checked every six months or 6,000 miles. Loose belts can cause poor engine cooling and diminish alternator (generator) output. A belt that is too tight places a severe strain on the water pump and alternator (generator) bearings.

Alternator (generator) drive belt tension is correct when the deflection made with light finger pressure on the belt at a point midway between the water pump and alternator is about ½ in. Any belt that is glazed, frayed, or stretched so that it cannot be tightened sufficiently must be replaced.

Incorrect belt tension is corrected by moving the driven accessory (alternator or generator) away from or toward the driving pulley. Loosen the mounting and adjusting bolts on the respective accessory and tighten them, once the belt tension is correct. Never position a metal pry bar on the rear end of the alternator housing; they can be deformed easily.

Alternator (Generator) Removal and Installation

1. Disconnect the negative battery cable.

2. Disconnect the electrical leads to the alternator (generator).

3. Remove the adjusting arm-to-alternator (generator) bolt and the adjusting arm-to-engine bolt.

4. Remove the alternator (generator)-

Bosch alternator terminals

1. DF To field winding
2. 61/D + From magnetizing rectifier
3. B + To battery

to-engine mounting bolt.

5. Remove the fan belt and lift the alternator (generator) forward and out.

6. Reverse the above procedure to install, taking care to properly tension the fan (drive) belt.

D.C. Voltage Regulator

The regulator is mounted on the right hand wheel well on both 140 series and 1800 series cars. Its function is to automatically control the charging voltage and the current supplied by the generator to the battery.

Since voltage produced by the generator is in direct proportion to the product of armature speed and exciting current in the magnetic field, a constant voltage output can be easily maintained by making compensating adjustments to the field current. Armature speed is based on engine rpm and is therefore not independently controllable. The regulator maintains a constant voltage output by interrupting the field current.

The Bosch D.C. regulator used on the Volvo has a semi-conductor component, (variometer) having a variable resistance under different voltage loads, ranging from high resistance at low voltages to

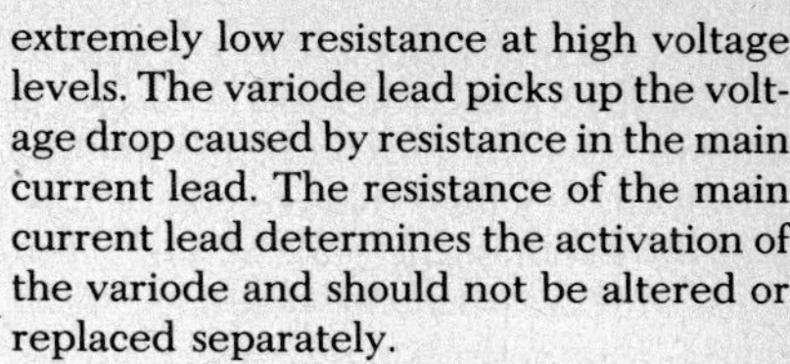

extremely low resistance at high voltage levels. The variode lead picks up the voltage drop caused by resistance in the main current lead. The resistance of the main current lead determines the activation of the variode and should not be altered or replaced separately.

D.C. Voltage Adjustment

Cut-In Voltage Adjustment

D.C. cut-in voltage adjustment

Connect a 0-20v D.C. voltmeter between the regulator terminal D+ and ground. Start the engine and increase its speed gradually, noting the reading of the voltmeter. The reading should first increase to about 12.1–12.8v then fall back to 0.1 or 0.2v when the cut-in relay is actuated, after which it should remain constant. Adjustment is carried out by decreasing the pressure of the spring on the cut-in relay. If it is too low, the adjustment is made by increasing the pressure on the spring.

Cut-out Current Adjustment

Connect a 0–50A ammeter in series with the battery (B+) connection to the regulator. Increase the engine speed to obtain a reading. Then, reduce the speed gradually to idle, watching the ammeter reading go down to zero and slightly into the discharge scale, when it should jump up suddenly to zero. At this point, the reverse current relay has cut-out. If the

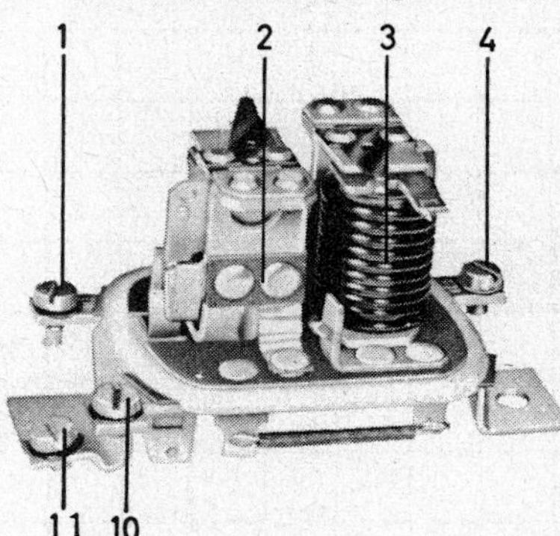

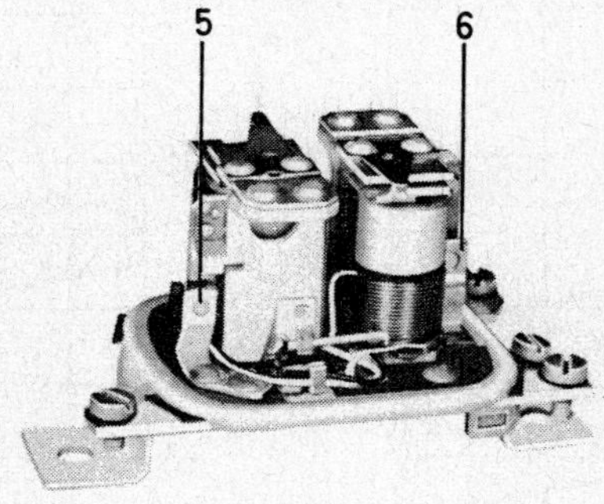

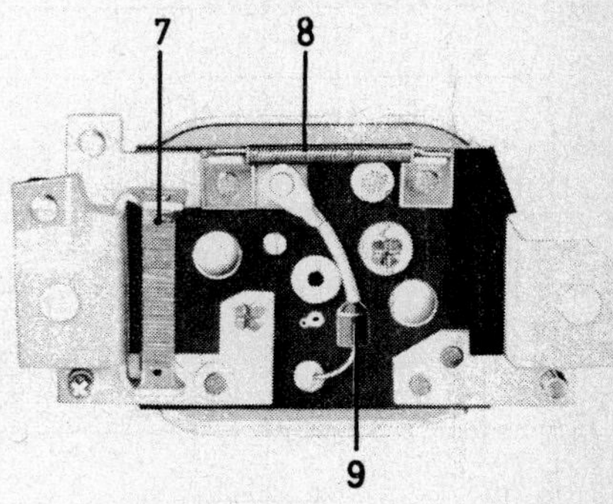

D.C. Voltage regulator

1. Terminal, DF
2. Voltage control
3. Cut-in relay
4. Terminal, B +
5. Cut-in contact
6. Control contact
7. Resistor wR
8. Variode resistor
9. Variode
10. Terminal D +, 61
11. Earth lead

reverse current (into discharge scale) is less than two amps, the reverse current is too low, and the tension of the contact spring on the cut-in relay should be lowered by bending the yoke of the cut-in contact. If the discharge reading is more than 7.5 amps, the bending of the contact spring must be increased until the cut-out current is within specifications.

Fine adjustment of D.C. voltage control

Voltage Control Adjustment

Remove the wire from the B+ connection on the regulator. Connect a voltmeter between the B terminal on the regulator and ground. Accelerate the engine gradually to increase the generator output. Watch the voltmeter reading increase and note at which point it stops increasing. This voltage should be 13.9–14.9v for warm, unloaded engines. The engine must reach operating temperature before making any adjustments. Adjustment is made by bending the spring support to change spring pressure on the voltage control relay. Increasing spring pressure increases the voltage at which control takes place, and decreasing the pressure lowers the control voltage.

A.C. Voltage Regulator

The voltage regulator, as previously mentioned, controls the amount of current fed to the field windings of the alternator. When the control voltage value is reached, the regulator forces the current to pass through a resistance. If the voltage rises further, the circuit is grounded by the regulator, thereby lowering the voltage to a safe level. Temperature compensation is accomplished by a bimetal spring which adjusts the spring tension in the regulator to receive less voltage at higher operating temperatures, and more voltage at lower temperatures.

Volvo uses Bosch and Motorola A.C. voltage regulators. The regulator and alternator (generator) are a matched pair. On 1968–70 140 series Volvos, the regulator is located to the right of the radiator. On all other Volvos, except the 1800 series, the regulator is located on the right wheel well in the engine compartment. The regulators on Volvo 1800s are located on the left wheel well in the engine compartment.

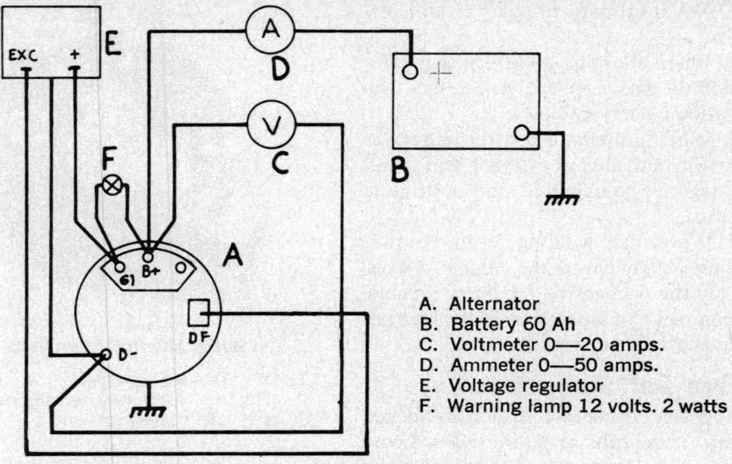

Wiring diagram for testing Motorola regulator.

Voltage Regulator Removal and Installation (D.C. and A.C.)

1. Disconnect the negative battery cable.

2. Disconnect the leads or plug socket from the old regulator taking note of their (its) location.

3. Remove the hold-down screws from the old regulator and install the new one.

4. Connect the leads or plug socket and reconnect the negative battery cable.

AC Voltage Adjustment

Motorola Regulator

If the Motorola A.C. regulator is found to be defective, it must be replaced. No adjustments can be made on this unit.

The following test may be performed on the Motorola regulator to see if it is functioning properly. An ammeter, tachometer, and voltmeter are required.

1. Connect the alternator and regulator as shown in the illustration.

2. Run the engine at 2500 rpm (5000 alternator rpm) for 15 seconds. With no load on the alternator, and the regulator ambient temperature at 77°F, the reading on the voltmeter should be 13.1–14.4 V. For regulator ambient temperatures other than 77°F, consult the voltage-temperature diagram for cold regulator.

3. Load the alternator with 10–15 amps (high-beam headlights) while the

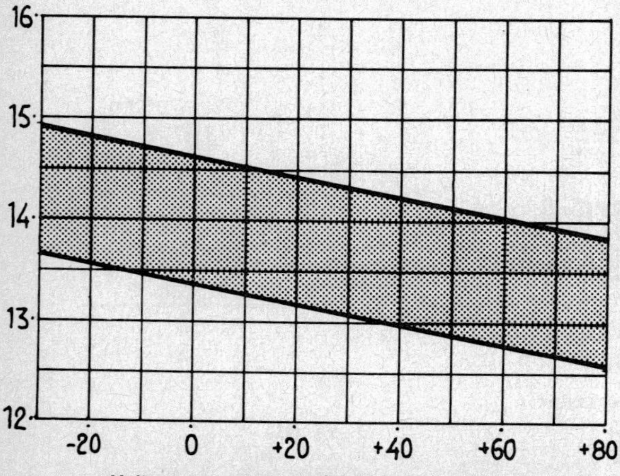

Voltage-temperature diagram for cold regulator—Motorola.

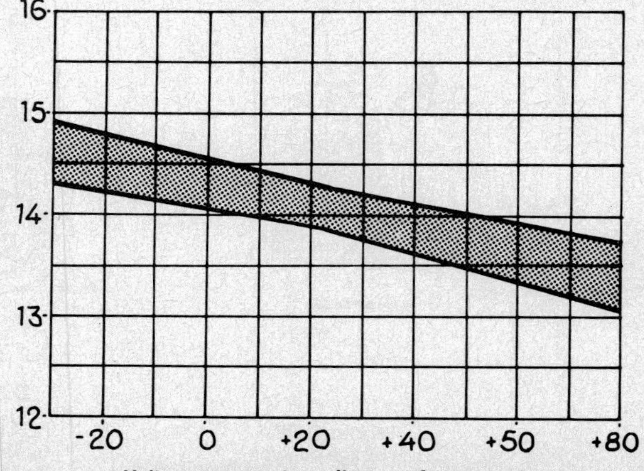

Voltage-temperature diagram for warm regulator—Motorola.

engine is running at 2500 rpm. The voltmeter reading should again be 13.-1–14.4 V. Replace the regulator if it does not fall within these limits.

4. For a more accurate indication of the regulator's performance, drive the vehicle for about 45 minutes at a minimum speed of 30 mph. The regulator will be at the correct working temperature immediately after this drive.

5. With the engine running at 2500 rpm, and the regulator ambient temperature at 77°F, the voltmeter reading should be 13.85–14.25 V. For regulator ambient temperatures other than 77°F, consult the Voltage-temperature diagram for warm regulator.

Bosch A.C. Regulator (35, 55 amp)

The Bosch A.C. regulator is fully adjustable. To determine which adjustments are necessary—if any—perform the following test. (An ammeter, 12 V control lamp, tachometer, and voltmeter are required for this test.)

NOTE: *Where the numerical values differ for the 35 amp voltage regulator and the 55 amp unit, the figures for the 55 amp regulator will be given in parentheses.*

1. Connect the alternator and regulator as shown in the illustration.

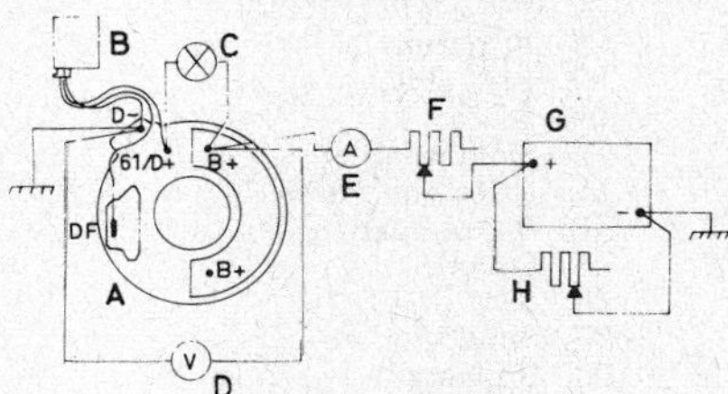

Wiring diagram for testing Bosch A.C. regulator.

A. Alternator
B. Voltage lamp 12 volts
C. Control lamp 12 volts, 2 watts
D. Voltmeter 0-20 volts
F. Regulator resistance
G. Battery 60 amperehours
H. Load resistance
E. Ammeter 0-50 amps

NOTE: *the first reading must be taken within 30 seconds of beginning of test.*

2. While running the engine at 2000 rpm, load the alternator with 28–30 amps (44–46 for 55 amp alternator).

3. Rapidly lower the engine to idle speed or 500 rpm, and then return it to 2000 rpm. With a load of 28–30 amps (44–46 for 55 amp alternator), the voltmeter reading should be 14.0–15.0 V (13.-9–14.8 V for 55 amp alternator). The regulator should be regulated on the left (lower) contact.

4. Reduce the alternator load to 3–8 amps. The voltmeter reading should not decrease more than 0.3 (0.4 for 55 amp. alternator) V. The regulator should be regulated on the right (upper) contact.

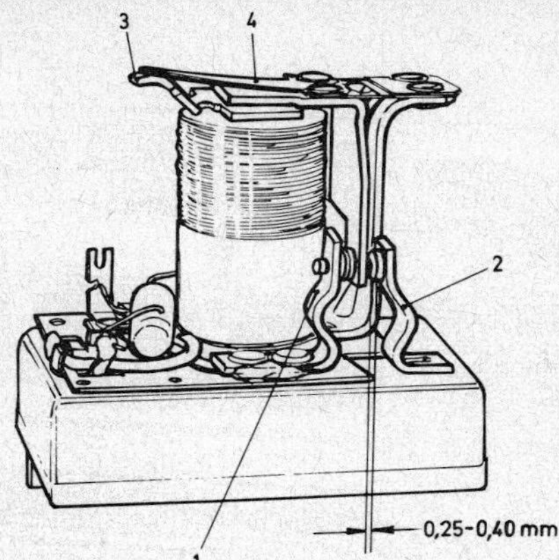

Bosch A.C. voltage adjustments

1. Regulator contact for lower control range (lower contact)
2. Regulator contact for upper control range (upper contact)
3. Spring tensioner
4. Spring upper section: Steel spring Lower section: Bimetal spring

5. Adjustment is made by bending the stop bracket for the bimetal spring. Bending the stop bracket down lowers the regulating voltage; bending it up raises the voltage. If the voltmeter reading for the low amp alternator load decreased more than 0.3 (0.4 for 55 amp alternator) V, compared to the reading for the high amp alternator load, adjust the regulator by bending the holder for the left (lower) contract and simultaneously adjust the gap between the right (upper) contact and the movable contact. The gap should be adjusted to 0.010–0.-015 in. (0.25–0.40 mm). If the holder is bent toward the right (upper) contact, the regulating voltage under high amp alternator load will be lowered.

To avoid faulty adjustments due to residual magnetism in the regulator core, it may be necessary to rapidly lower the engine rpm to idle after each adjustment, and then raise it to 2000 rpm to take a new reading.

NOTE: *Warm regulators may be cooled to ambient temperature by directing a stream of compressed air on them. Final readings should be made with the regulator at ambient temperature.*

Starter

The starter motor on all Volvos is located on the flywheel housing at the left-hand side of the engine. It is a four-pole series-wound unit to which an outboard solenoid is mounted. When the ignition is turned to the starting position, the solenoid armature is drawn in, engaging the starter pinion with the flywheel. When the starter pinion and flywheel are fully engaged, the solenoid armature closes the main contacts for the starter, causing the starter to crank the engine. When the engine starts, the increased speed of the flywheel causes the gear to overrun the starter clutch and rotor. The gear continues in full mesh until the ignition is switched from the "start" to the "on" position, interrupting the starter current. The shift lever spring then returns the gear to its neutral position.

Starter Removal and Installation

1. Disconnect the negative battery cable at the battery.
2. Disconnect the leads from the starter motor.
3. Remove the bolts retaining the starter motor to the flywheel housing and lift it off.
4. Position the starter motor to the flywheel housing and install the retaining bolts finger-tight. Torque the bolts to approximately 25 ft lbs, and apply locking compound to the threads.
5. Connect the starter motor leads and the negative battery cable.

Starter Drive Replacement

In order to remove the starter pinion drive, it is necessary to disassemble the starter. The procedure for disassembling the starter is as follows.

1. Remove the starter from the car as outlined in "Starter Removal and Installation."
2. Unscrew the two screws and remove the small cover from the front end of the starter shaft.
3. Unsnap the lockwasher and remove the adjusting washers from the front end of the shaft.
4. Unscrew the two screws retaining the commutator bearing shield and remove the shield.
5. Lift up the brushes and retainers and remove the brush bridge from the rotor shaft. The negative brushes are removed with the bridge while the positive brushes remain in the field winding. Do not remove the steel washer and the fiber washer at this time.
6. Unscrew the nut retaining the field terminal connection to the control solenoid.
7. Unscrew the two solenoid-to-starter housing retaining screws and remove the solenoid.
8. Remove the drive end shield and rotor from the stator.
9. Remove the rubber and metal sealing washers from the housing.
10. Unscrew the nut and remove the screw on which the engaging arm pivots.
11. Remove the rotor, with the pinion and engaging arm attached, from the drive end shield.
12. Push back the stop washer and

Starter motor assembly

1. Shift lever
2. Pivot pin
3. Plunger
4. Steel washer
5. Rubber washer
6. Winding
7. Contact plate
8. Terminal for battery lead
9. Terminal lead to field
10. Screw
11. Rubber gasket
12. Shims
13. Lock washer
14. Bushing
15. Commutator end frame
16. Adjusting washers
17. Brush holder
18. Brush
19. Bush spring
20. Commutator
21. Armature
22. Pole shoe
23. Stator
24. Field winding
25. Drive end frame
26. Roller bearing
27. Pinion
28. Stop ring
29. Snap ring
30. Bushing

remove the snap-ring from the rotor shaft.

13. Remove the stop washer and pull off the starter pinion with a gear puller.

While the starter is disassembled, a few quick checks may be performed. Check the rotor shaft, commutator, and windings. If the rotor shaft is bent or worn, it must be replaced. Maximum rotor shaft radial throw is 0.003 in. If the commutator is scored or worn unevenly, it should be turned. Minimum commutator diameter is 1.3 in. Check the end shield, which houses the brushes, for excessive wear. Maximum bearing clearance is 0.005 in.

14. Lubricate the starter as shown in the illustration.

15. Press the starter pinion onto the rotor shaft. Install the stop washer and secure it with a new snap-ring.

16. Position the engaging arm on the pinion. Install the rotor into the drive end frame.

17. Install the screw and nut for the engaging arm pivot.

18. Install the rubber and metal sealing washers into the drive end housing.

19. Install the stator onto the rotor and drive end shield.

20. Position the solenoid so that the eyelet on the end of the solenoid plunger fits onto the engaging arm (shift lever). Tighten the solenoid retaining screws.

21. Place the metal and fiber washers on the rotor shaft.

22. Install the brush bridge on the rotor shaft and replace the brushes.

23. Fit the commutator bearing shield into position and install the retaining screws.

24. Install the adjusting washers and snap a new lockwasher into position on the end of the shaft. Make sure that the rotor axial clearance does not exceed 0.12 in. If necessary, adjust the clearance with washers, maintaining a minimum clearance of 0.002 in.

25. Replace the small cover over the front end of the shaft and install the two retaining screws.

Starter motor lubrication

Use Bosch lubricant (or equivalent) in accordance with the following directions:

1.	Ft 2 V 3.	Place a thin layer of grease on the insulation washers, the shaft end, the adjusting washers and lock washer.
2.	Ol 1 V 13.	Place the bush in oil for 1 hour before fitting.
3.	Ft 2 V 3.	Apply plenty of grease in the rotor thread and the engaging lever groove.
4.	Ft 2 V 3.	Place a thin layer of grease on the armature shaft.
5.	Ol 1 V 13.	Place the bushes in oil for 1 hour before fitting.
6.	Ft 2 V 3.	Lubricate the engaging lever joints and the iron core of the solenoid with a thin layer of grease.

26. Install the starter in the car as outlined in "Starter Removal and Installation."

Solenoid Replacement

Before replacing the solenoid when the starter will not crank, see if the battery has sufficient charge. If the no-crank condition persists when the battery is known to be good, connect a jumper wire between the positive terminal of the battery and the contact screw for the solenoid lead. If the solenoid engages the starter pinion, the starter switch or leads are at fault. If the starter still does not crank, replace the solenoid. To remove the solenoid, remove the starter from the car. The solenoid may be removed from the starter while installed in the car, but then aligning the solenoid plunger eyelet with the engaging arm during installation can be difficult. The procedure for replacement of the solenoid is as follows.

1. Remove the starter from the car as outlined in "Starter Removal and Installation."
2. Unscrew the two solenoid-to-starter housing retaining screws and remove the solenoid.
3. As a final test, wipe the solenoid clean and press in the armature. Test its operation by connecting it to a battery. If the solenoid still does not function, replace it with a new unit.
4. Position the new solenoid so that the eyelet on the end of the plunger fits into the engaging arm. Tighten the retaining screws.
5. Replace the starter in the car as outlined in "Starter Removal and Installation."

ENGINE MECHANICAL

All post-1966 Volvos are equipped with either the B 18, B 20 or B 30 engine. All of these engines have evolved from those seemingly indestructible cast-iron, water-cooled, pushrod, inline fours of yesteryear. The B 18, introduced in 1962, is a 1.8 liter (1780 cc) four cylinder unit. The B 20, introduced in 1968, is a two liter (1990 cc) four-cylinder powerplant. The B 30, introduced in 1969, is a three liter (2978 cc) six-cylinder powerplant. The six-cylinder B 30 is, in effect, a stretched four-cylinder B 20. All of these engines share the same basic design.

The B 18 engine has been manufactured in three variations; the B 18 A, B 18 B, and the B 18 D. The low compression (8.7:1) B 18 A engine was equipped with a single downdraft Zenith 36 VN carburetor and rated at 75 hp in early production. Later production B 18 A's were equipped with a single sidedraft Zenith-Stromberg 175 CD2 S carburetor and rated at 85 hp. Neither version was regularly imported into this country. The high compression (10.0:1) B 18 B and low compression (8.7:1) B 18 D engines were imported into this country through 1968 with dual sidedraft SU HS6 carburetors. The B 18 B was used exclusively in the 1800 until 1967 when it was also installed in the 140 series.

The B 20 engine has been manufactured in four variations; the B 20 A, B 20 B, B 20 E, and the B 20 F. The B 20 B, with its 9.3:1 compression ratio and dual sidedraft carburetors (Stromberg 175 CD2 SE in 1969–70 and SU HIF in 1971–72), is standard equipment in the 140 series Volvos of 1969–72 vintage. The B 20 E, with its high-compression head (10.5:1) and Bosch electronic fuel injection, has been standard equipment in all 1970–71 1800E series, and optional in the 1971 142S (known as the 142E). Due to the decision to convert to low-lead fuels in this country, which makes high-compression engines unfeasible, the B 20 F engine was introduced in 1972. This engine incorporates the the Bosch electronic fuel injection with the low-compression head (8.7:1). The B 20 F was optional on 1972 140 series models, and is standard on all 1972–73 1800 series, and all 1973 140 series models.

The B 30 engine has been manufactured in three variations; the B 30 A, B 30 E, and the B 30 F. The B 30 A has a 9.3:1 compression ratio and is equipped with dual sidedraft Stromberg 175 CD2 SE carburetors. This engine is standard equipment on all 1969–72 164 models. The B 20 E, with its high-compression (10:1) head and Bosch electronic fuel injection, has not been imported into this country since 1971 due to its reliance on high-octane, leaded fuel. The B 30 F is the same engine with a lower compression ratio (8.7:1) and is optional on 1972 164 models, and standard for 1973.

Engine Removal

All Volvo engines and transmissions are removed as a unit. In most cases, a good chain hoist will suffice. Do not attempt to lift the engine with the chain wrapped around either the oil filter or the distributor. Lifting eyes may be fabricated from heavy gauge steel or angle iron.

1. Scribe the outline of the hinges on the hood and remove the hood.
2. Drain the oil from the crankcase. Open the drain plug on the right-hand side of the engine block, disconnect the lower radiator hose at the radiator, and drain the cooling system. On Volvos with automatic transmissions, disconnect and plug the transmission oil cooler lines.
3. Remove the expansion tank, radiator cover plate, upper radiator hose, radiator, and fan shroud, if so equipped.
4. Remove the positive lead from the battery.
5. Remove the electric cables for the starter, the coil high-tension wire, the distributor lead, alternator wires, water and oil temperature sensors, and the lead for the oil pressure sensor, if so equipped.
6. Remove the vacuum hoses for the distributor advance, and the power brake booster, if so equipped. Remove the positive crankcase ventilation (PCV) hoses, and the oil pressure gauge hose at the pipe connection, if so equipped.
7. On carburetted models, remove the air cleaner, air intake hoses, and preheating plate. Also disconnect and plug the inlet hose to the fuel pump, disconnect the choke linkage, and remove the throttle control shaft from the pedal shaft, intermediate shaft, and bracket.
8. On fuel-injected models, remove the air cleaner and intake hoses; pressure sensor hose from the inlet duct; the plug contacts for the temperature sensor, cold start valve, throttle valve switch, fuel injectors, and distributor impulse. In addition, remove the ground wire from the inlet duct, the throttle cable bracket from the inlet duct, the throttle cable from the throttle valve switch, the cold start valve fuel hose from the distribution pipe, the fuel return line from the pressure regulator, and the fuel inlet line from the distribution pipe. Remove the injectors by turning the lockrings counterclockwise and lifting them out of their bayonet fittings. The injectors should then be fitted with protective covers and plugs to prevent dirt from entering.
9. Disconnect the heater pipes from all models. Remove the exhaust pipe flange nuts and disconnect the exhaust pipe from the manifold. On models equipped with power steering, remove the steering pump bolts and place the pump and reservoir to one side.
10. On Volvos with manual transmissions, place the gearshift in neutral and remove the shifter lever. On Volvos with automatic transmissions, disconnect the control rod from the selector lever, and the ground cable from the start inhibitor switch.
11. Disconnect the wires for the backup lights and overdrive, if so equipped. Remove the speedometer drive cable from the transmission. Remove the clamp for the exhaust manifold and the clamp for the automatic transmission filler tube, if so equipped.
12. Jack up the vehicle and place two jackstands under the front jack attachments and two more in front of the rear jack attachments.
13. Place a hydraulic jack under the transmission. On manual transmission cars, remove the return spring from the throw-out fork, and disconnect the clutch cable.

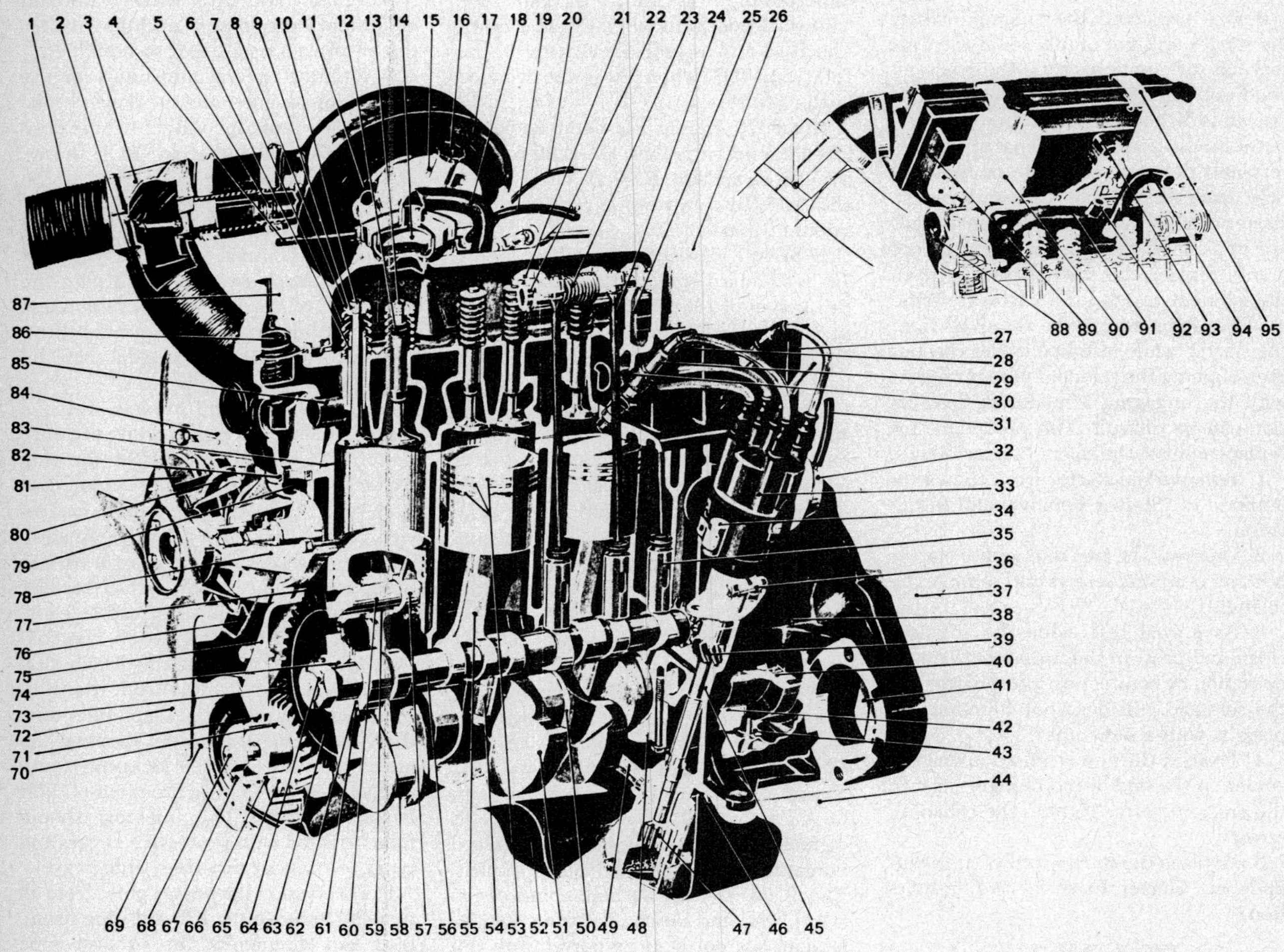

B20A engine—B18B similar (B20B supplement in upper right corner).

1. Cold air hose
2. Hot air hose
3. Flap, constant air temperature device
4. Fuel line
5. Thermostat
6. Valve tappet
7. Valve spring
8. Washer
9. Valve collet
10. Exhaust valve
11. Connection for crankcase hose
12. Valve tappet seal
13. Intake valve
14. Oil filler cap
15. Carburetor
16. Damping device
17. Air cleaner
18. Hose for crankcase gases
19. Vacuum hose for distributor
20. Choke wire
21. Rocker arm
22. Rocker arm shaft
23. Spring
24. Push rod
25. Bearing bracket
26. Rocker arm casing
27. Rubber seal
28. Rubber terminal
29. Rubber seal
30. Cylinder head
31. Vacuum hose
32. Vacuum governor
33. Distributor
34. Condenser
35. Valve tappet
36. Retainer
37. Flywheel casing
38. Gear wheel
40. Pilot bearing
41. Flywheel
42. Flange bearing shell
44. Reinforcing bracket
45. Bushing
46. Seal
47. Oil pump
48. Main bearing cap
49. Delivery pipe
50. Main bearing shell
51. Crankshaft
52. Sump
53. Piston rings
54. Connecting rod cap
55. Connecting rod
56. Camshaft
57. Piston
58. Bushing
59. Big-end bearing shell
60. Wrist pin
61. Washer
62. Spacing ring
63. Camshaft gear
64. Nut
65. Crankshaft gear
66. Hub
67. Washer
68. Bolt
69. Pulley
70. Key
71. Seal
72. Fan
73. Oil nozzle
74. Key
75. Timing gear cover
76. Coolant inlet
77. Gasket
78. Water pump
79. Gasket
80. Pulley
81. Alternator
82. Sealing ring
83. Cylinder head gasket
84. Tensioner
85. Water distributing pipe
86. Thermostat
87. Coolant outlet
88. Guard for throttle spindle
89. Air cleaner
90. Carburetor
91. Manifold
92. Connection for servo brake hose
93. Connection for crankcase hose
94. Hose for crankcase gases
95. Clamp

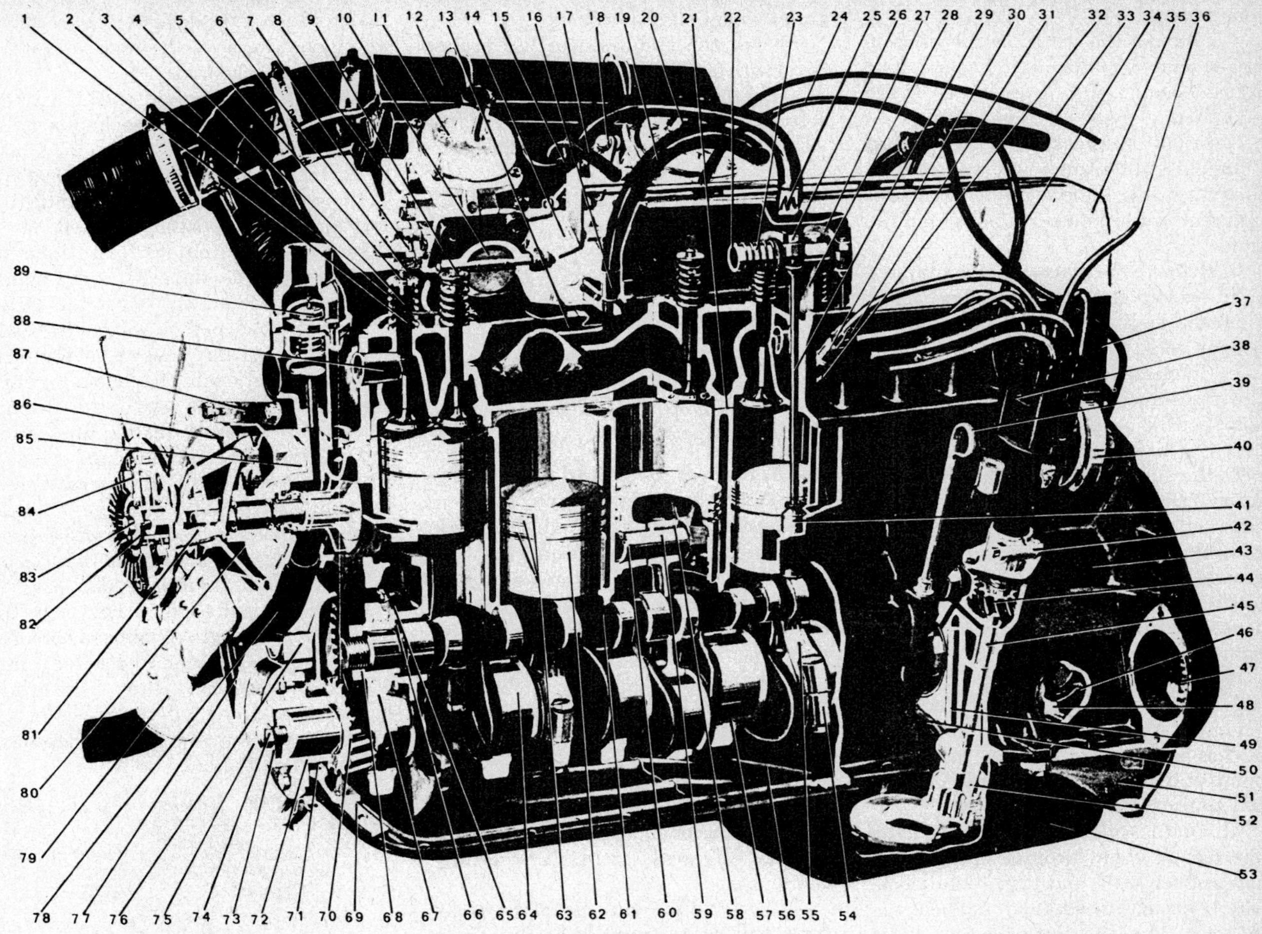

B30A engine

1. Valve guide
2. Valve spring
3. Air preheating flap
4. Valve guide seal
5. Valve collet
6. Intake valve
7. By-pass valve
8. Temperature compensator
9. Exhaust valve
10. Secondary throttle
11. Front carburetor
12. Air cleaner
13. Manifold pipe
14. Bracket
15. Hose for fresh air supply
16. Nipple
17. Fuel hose
18. Carburetor control
19. Hose for crankcase gases
20. Rear carburetor
21. Cylinder head gasket
22. Rocker arm shaft
23. Spring
24. Vacuum hose for ignition distributor
25. Flame protector
26. Adjusting device
27. Rocker arm
28. Bearing bracket
29. Push rod
30. Cable terminal
31. Rubber seal
32. Rubber seal
33. Choke wire
34. Vacuum hose for negative vacuum adjustment
35. Rocker arm casing
36. Ignition cable to ignition coil
37. Cylinder head
38. Distributor
39. Oil dipstick
40. Vacuum governor
41. Valve tappet
42. Retainer
43. Cylinder block
44. Gear wheel
45. Bushing
46. Rubber lip seal
47. Flywheel
48. Sealing flange
49. Main bearing bolt
50. Delivery pipe
51. Cover plate
52. Oil pump
53. Sump
54. Cap
55. Connecting rod
56. Splash plate
57. Main bearing
58. Bushing
59. Wrist pin
60. Circlip
61. Camshaft
62. Piston
63. Piston rings
64. Crankshaft
65. Thrust washer
66. Spacer ring
67. Camshaft gear
68. Nut
69. Seal
70. Crankshaft gear
71. Rubber lip seal
72. Polygon hub
73. Washer
74. Pulley
76. Flywheel damper
77. Fan belt
78. Coolant pipe
79. Fan blade
80. Pulley
81. Flange
82. Washer
83. Center bolt
84. Fan coupling
85. Water pump
86. Alternator
87. Tensioner
88. Water distribution pipe
89. Thermostat

14. Separate the transmission (or overdrive) from the front universal joint by unbolting the flange. Unbolt the rear crossmember.

15. Disconnect the negative ground cable from the engine.

16. Remove the rear crossmember and rear engine mounts. Remove the lower nuts for the front engine mounts.

17. Install the lifting eyes and lifting crossbar. The lifting eyes are attached by ⅜ x 1¾ x 1 in. bolts. Lift out the engine and set it on an engine stand or rack. The engine is removed by raising its front and lowering its back while pulling forward until it clears the front crossmember, then leveling it and raising the complete unit.

Engine Installation

1. Install the lifting apparatus on the engine. Make sure that the jackstands are located beneath the front jack attachments and in front of the rear jack attachments. Place the hydraulic jack beneath the transmission tunnel.

2. Carefully lower the engine into the engine compartment. Place the hydraulic jack under the transmission and guide the unit into place. Be careful not to damage the oil filter, or oil pressure sending unit against the exhaust pipe. Be careful not to damage the distributor against the steering column.

3. Tighten the nuts for the front en-

gine mounts.

4. Connect the wires for the back-up lights, start inhibitor switch (automatic transmission), and overdrive, if so equipped.

5. Install the brackets for the exhaust manifold and the automatic transmission filler tube. Install the rear engine mounts and rear crossmember, then tighten the nuts.

6. Remove the hydraulic jack from the transmission and the lifting apparatus from the engine. Connect the negative ground cable to the engine.

7. Connect the front universal joint to the transmission (or overdrive) flange. Connect the speedometer drive cable.

8. On manual transmission cars, connect the clutch cable and install the return spring. Adjust clutch free-play. On automatic transmission cars, connect the control rod to the selector lever, and the ground cable to the start inhibitor switch.

9. Connect the exhaust pipe to the exhaust manifold with new gaskets and tighten the nuts.

10. Remove the jackstands from the jack attachments and lower the vehicle.

11. Connect the heater pipes. On models with power steering, install the pump and reservoir to the engine block and adjust the drive belt tension.

12. On fuel-injected models, place the injectors in their bayonet fittings with new rubber seals, and turn them clockwise to install. In addition, connect the fuel inlet line and the cold start valve hose to the distribution pipe, and the return line from the pressure regulator. Install the ground wire and the throttle cable bracket to the inlet duct, and connect the throttle cable. Connect the plug contacts for the temperature sensor, cold start valve, throttle valve switch, fuel injectors, and distributor impulse. Install the pressure sensor vacuum hose, air cleaner, and intake hoses.

13. On carbureted models, connect the fuel pump inlet hose, choke linkage, and throttle linkage. Install the preheating plate, intake hoses, and air cleaner.

14. On all models, connect the positive crankcase ventilation hoses, and the distributor vacuum advance hose. Connect the vacuum hose for the power brake booster, and the oil pressure gauge hose at the pipe connection, if so equipped.

15. Install the electric cables for the starter, the coil high-tension wire, the distributor lead, alternator wires, water and oil temperature sensors, and the lead for the oil pressure sensor, if so equipped.

16. Connect the positive lead to the battery.

17. Install the radiator and fan shroud, if so equipped, and the radiator cover plate. Install the expansion tank, the upper and lower radiator hoses, and, on automatic transmission cars, the transmission oil cooler lines.

18. Fill the crankcase to the proper level with oil. Fill the cooling system with a 50 percent ethylene glycol, 50 percent water solution.

19. Install the hood. Install the gearshift lever.

20. Start the engine and check for leaks.

Cylinder Head

Cylinder Head Removal and Installation

NOTE: *To prevent warpage of the head, removal should be attempted only on a cold engine.*

B 18 B, B 20 B and B 30 A

1. Drain the cooling system by opening the drain plug on the right-hand side of the engine and disconnecting the lower radiator hose at the radiator.

2. Disconnect the choke control cables at the carburetors. Remove the positive crankcase ventilation hoses from the air cleaner and intake manifold. Remove the vacuum hoses for the distributor advance and the power brake booster, if so equipped.

3. Remove the throttle control shaft from the pedal shaft, link rods, and bracket. (Disconnect the downshift linkage on cars with automatic transmissions.)

4. Remove the air cleaner(s), inlet hose, and heat control valve hose from the engine.

5. Remove the upper radiator hose. Remove the heater hose clamp from the head.

6. Remove and plug the fuel line at the carburetors.

7. Label the spark plug wires and disconnect them from the plugs. Disconnect the coolant temperature sensor.

8. Remove the exhuast manifold preheating plate. Remove the nuts and disconnect the exhaust pipe from the exhaust manifold.

9. Unbolt the alternator (generator) adjusting arm from the head.

10. Remove the valve cover. Remove the rocker shaft and arm assembly as a unit and draw out the push rods, keeping them in order.

11. Loosen the head bolts gradually, in the same order as their tightening sequence. Remove the head bolts, noting their locations, and lift off the head. Do not attempt to pry off the head. The head may be tapped lightly with a rubber mallet to break the gasket seal. If any residual water in the cooling passages of the head falls into the combustion chambers during removal, remove it immediately and coat the cylinder walls with oil.

12. On B 20 and B 30 engines, remove the integrally cast Intake and exhaust manifold from the cylinder head. On B 18 engines, remove the separate intake and exhaust manifolds.

13. Remove the old head gasket, flange gasket, and rubber sealing rings for the water pump.

14. Inspect the condition of the valves in the combustion chambers, and the intake and exhaust ports in the head. Small deposits may be removed with rotating brushes. If large deposits are present, however, proceed to "Cylinder Head Reconditioning" in the "Engine Rebuilding" section of this chapter. Make sure that no foreign matter has fallen into the cylinders or onto the tops of the pistons. Thoroughly clean the mating surfaces of the cylinder head and block and remove any traces of the old head gasket. Check the mating surfaces for warpage. There is an oil feed hole for the rocker arm assembly on the tappet side, in the middle of the head. (See illustration.) Make sure it is clean. A clogged oil feed hole may be opened with a length of thin gauge metal wire and some kerosine to dissolve some of the deposits. Clean the top of the cylinder head and the oil return holes to remove any gum or foreign deposits. Clean and oil the head bolts.

Oil feed hole in cylinder head

15. On B 20 and B 30 engines, install the combination intake and exhaust manifold on the head with new gaskets. On B 18 engines, install the separate intake and exhaust manifolds with new gaskets.

16. Install new sealing rings for the water pump.

17. Use a pair of guide studs for proper alignment of the cylinder head, head gasket, and block. Guide studs can be easily made by cutting the heads off a pair of spare head bolts. The tops of the bolts are then filed to a tapered edge and slotted so that they may be installed and removed with a screwdriver. The guide studs should be installed in the cylinder block; one in the front right-hand head bolt hole, and the other in the rear left-hand head bolt hole.

18. Fit a new head gasket on the cylinder block with the lettering "TOP" (wide edge) facing up. Slide the gasket down over the two guide studs.

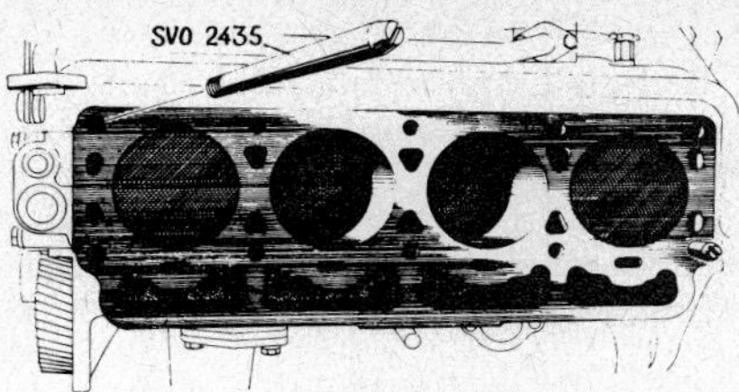

Guide stud installation

19. Carefully lower the cylinder head over the guide studs onto the block. Install, but do not tighten, two head bolts at opposite ends to secure the gasket, and remove the guide studs. Install the remaining head bolts finger-tight. Torque the head bolts in proper sequence first to 29 ft lbs, and then to 58 ft lbs.

20. Roll the pushrods on a level surface to inspect them for straightness. Replace any bent pushrods. Install the pushrods in their original positions and install the rocker shaft and arm assembly. Torque the bolts to approximately 20 ft lbs.

21. Adjust the valve clearnace to a *preliminary* setting of 0.018–0.020 for the B 30 A, and 0.022–0.024 for the B 20 B. Use the procedure outlined under "Valve Lash Adjustment". Install the valve cover with a new gasket.

22. Install the alternator adjusting arm and adjust the drive (fan) belt tension.

23. Install the following: exhaust manifold preheating plate, exhaust pipe and flange nuts (with new gaskets), spark plug wires, coolant temperature sensor, heater hose clamp, upper and lower radiator hoses, fuel line, air cleaner, inlet hose, heat control valve hose, choke and throttle linkage (downshift linkage on cars with automatic transmissions), vacuum hoses for the distributor and power brake (if so equipped), and the positive crankcase ventilation hoses.

24. Close the drain plug and fill the cooling system with a 50 percent antifreeze, 50 percent water solution.

25. Run the engine for 10 minutes so that it reaches operating temperature. Stop the engine.

26. Remove the valve cover and torque the head bolts in proper sequence to the final figure of 65 ft lbs. Adjust the valve clearance to the final setting of 0.-020–0.022. Install the valve cover.

B 20 E, B 20 F, and B 30 F

NOTE: *To prevent warpage of the head, removal should only be attempted on a cold engine.*

The procedure for removal and installation of the cylinder head for the previously mentioned fuel-injected engines differs from the carbureted engines only in the type of fuel system equipment that must be moved to gain access to the head.

1. Drain the cooling system by opening the drain plug on the right-hand side of the engine and disconnecting the lower radiator hose at the radiator.

2. Disconnect the positive battery cable from the engine.

3. On the B 30 F engine, remove the air cleaner.

4. Remove the following hoses from the inlet duct, pressure sensor, power brake (if so equipped), distributor advance, and crankcase ventilation.

5. Remove the electrical contacts for the throttle valve switch, cold start valve, thermal timer, temperature sensor, and injectors.

6. Remove the ground cable from the inlet duct and remove the cable harness.

7. Disconnect the sensor for the coolant temperature gauge. Remove the spark plug wires from the plugs.

8. On the B 20 E and B 20 F engines, remove the inlet hose.

9. Disconnect the throttle control cable from the throttle valve and inlet duct.

10. Remove and pinch shut the fuel hoses from the distributing pipe.

11. Remove the upper radiator hose, the heater control valve hose, and the clamp for the heater pipe.

12. Unbolt the alternator adjusting arm from the head.

13. Remove the bolts for the inlet duct stay. Remove the inlet duct-to-cylinder head retaining nuts and disconnect the inlet duct.

14. If any cleaning or machine work is to be performed on the cylinder head, remove the fuel injectors beforehand. Turn the lockrings on the injectors counterclockwise and lift out the injectors and distributing pipe as a unit. Remove the injector holders from the head.

15. Remove the exhaust manifold-to-exhaust pipe flange nuts and disconnect the pipe.

16. Refer to steps 10 and 11 under "Cylinder Head Removal and Installation" for the B 18 B, B 20 B and B 30 A.

17. Remove the exhaust manifold from the head.

18. Refer to steps 13 and 14 under "Cylinder Head Removal and Installation" for the B 18 B, B 20 B and B 30 A.

19. Install the exhaust manifold on the head with a new gasket.

20. Refer to steps 16–20 under "Cylinder Head Removal and Installation" for the B 18 B, B 20 B and B 30 A engines.

21. Adjust the valve clearance to a *preliminary* setting of 0.018–0.020 for the B 20 E and B 20 F, and 0.022–0.024 for the B 30 F. Use the procedure outlined under "Valve Lash Adjustment". Install the valve cover with a new gasket.

22. If the injectors were removed, install the holders with new sealing rings. Install the injectors and distributing pipe as a unit.

23. Install the alternator adjusting arm and adjust the drive (fan) belt tension.

24. Install the inlet duct with a new gasket. Install the inlet duct retaining nuts and the bolts for the inlet duct stay. On B 20 engines, install the inlet hose.

25. Install the following: upper and lower radiator hoses, heater hose, heater hose clamp, exhaust pipe flange nuts, fuel line, throttle linkage, temperature gauge sensor, ground cable to inlet duct, cable harness, electrical contacts for the throttle valve switch, cold start valve, thermal timer, temperature sensor and injectors, pressure sensor hose, power brake hose, distributor advance line, crankcase ventilation hoses, and the positive battery cable.

26. On the B 30 F engine, install the air cleaner.

27. Close the drain plug and fill the cooling system with a 50 percent antifreeze, 50 percent water solution.

28. Run the engine for 10 minutes so that it reaches operating temperature and then stop it.

29. Remove the valve cover and torque the head bolts in proper sequence to the final figure of 65 ft lbs. Adjust the valve clearance to the final setting of 0.-016–0.018 for the B 20 E and B 20 F, and 0.020–0.022 for the B 30 F as outlined under "Valve Lash Adjustment". Install the valve cover.

Cylinder Head Overhaul

Refer to "Cylinder Head Reconditioning" in the "Engine Rebuilding" section.

Rocker Shafts

Removal and Installation

1. Remove the four retaining screws and the valve cover and gasket.

2. Remove the rocker shaft-to-cylinder head bolts and lift out the shaft and rocker arms as a unit.

3. Lift out the pushrods, keeping them in order, and check them for straightness by rolling them on a flat surface. Replace any bent pushrods.

4. Inspect the rocker shaft and arms. If the shaft and rockers are coated with baked-on sludge, oil may not be reaching them. Clean out the oil feed holes in the rocker shaft with 0.020 in. wire (piano wire). If the clearance between the rocker arms and shaft exceeds 0.004 in., the rocker arm needs to be rebushed. The rocker arm bushings are press fitted, and are removed with a drift. When pressing in a new bushing, make sure that the oil hole in the bushing aligns with the hole in the arm.

5. Position the pushrods on their respective lifters. Install the the rocker shaft and arm assembly on the head, and install the retaining bolts. Step-tighten the bolts, moving front to rear, until a torque of approximately 20 ft lbs is reached.

6. Check to see that valve lash has remained within specifications. Adjust valve lash, if necessary.

7. Install the valve cover and gasket,

and snugly tighten the valve cover retaining screws.

Intake and Exhaust Manifolds

On all 1969–72 carbureted Volvos, the intake and exhaust manifolds are cast integrally. A preheating chamber is located within the combination manifold. The chamber's function is to transfer the heat from the exhaust ports to the fuel-air mixture in the intake manifold for improved cold-weather operation.

On all fuel-injected Volvos, as well as all 1967–68 B 18 B carbureted models, the intake manifold (inlet duct) and exhaust manifold are separate units. The inlet duct is constructed of a light aluminum alloy, while the exhaust manifold is cast iron.

Removal and Installation

1. Remove the exhaust manifold preheating plate 1968-72 carbureted models only. Remove the nuts and disconnect the exhaust pipe from the exhaust manifold.

2. Remove the air cleaner(s). Disconnect the throttle, choke, and downshift linkage, if so equipped. Disconnect the positive crankcase ventilation hoses, and the vacuum hoses for the distributor advance, and power brake, if so equipped.

3. Remove the nuts and slide the combination intake and exhaust manifold off the studs. Remove and discard the old manifold gasket.

4. To install, reverse the above procedure. Remember to use a new manifold gasket and exhaust pipe flange gasket in assembly. Torque the manifold retaining nuts to 13–16 ft lbs.

Inlet Duct Removal and Installation

1. On B 30 F engines, remove the air cleaner. On B 20 E and B 20 F engines, remove the inlet duct-to-air cleaner hose at the inlet duct.

2. Disconnect the positive battery cable (fuel-injection models only).

3. Disconnect the throttle and downshift linkage. Remove from the inlet duct, the positive crankcase ventilation, distributor advance, pressure sensor (fuel-injection models only) and power brake hoses.

4. On fuel-injected models, disconnect the contact for the throttle valve switch, and remove the ground cable for the inlet duct.

5. Remove the bolts for the inlet duct stay. Remove the inlet duct-to-cylinder head retaining nuts and slide the inlet duct off the studs. Discard the old gasket.

6. To install, reverse the above procedure. Use a new inlet duct gasket. Torque the nuts to 13–16 ft lbs.

Timing Gear Cover

Removal and Installation

B 18, B 20

1. Loosen the fan (drive) belt. Remove the fan and water pump pulley. Disconnect the stabilizer attachment from the frame.

2. Remove the crankshaft pulley and bolt.

3. Remove the retaining bolts and the timing gear cover. Loosen a few oil pan bolts, being carefull not to damage the pan gasket.

4. Remove the circlip, washer, and felt ring from the cover. Replace any gasket in questionable condition. Make sure that the oil drain hole is open and clean.

5. Place the cover in position and install the retaining bolts finger-tight.

6. Center the cover with a sleeve. Turn the sleeve while tightening and adjust the position of the cover so that that the sleeve may be easily rotated without jamming.

7. Install a new felt ring, washer, and circlip. Push them into their positions with the engaging sleeve. Check to make sure that the circlip has seated in its groove.

8. Tighten the cover bolts. Install the pulleys and fan. Tension the accessory drive belts. Tighten the stabilizer attachment firmly to the frame.

Timing Gear Cover Oil Seal Replacement

B 18, B 20

1. Remove the fan belt. Loosen the stabilizer attachment at the frame.

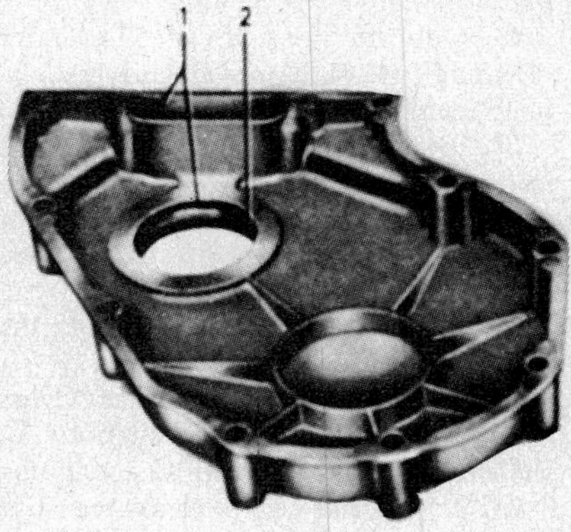

Timing gear cover—B18, B20

1. Drain holes 2. Sealing ring

2. Remove the crankshaft pulley and bolt.

3. Remove the circlip for the washer retaining the felt ring. Check to make sure that the cover is correctly installed by inserting a 0.004 in. feeler gauge between the casing and the crankshaft hub. If the feeler gauge jams at any point, the cover must be centered.

4. Install a new felt ring. Place the washer in position and install the circlip in its groove.

5. Install the crankshaft pulley and fan. Tension the fan (drive) belt. Tighten the stabilizer attachment at the frame.

B 30

1. Drain the cooling system by opening the engine drain plug and disconnecting the lower radiator hose. On automatic transmission cars, disconnect and plug the transmission oil cooler lines at the radiator. Remove the radiator, fan shroud, and grille.

2. Remove the fan (drive) belt. Remove the bolts for the pulley and crankshaft damper.

3. Remove the center bolt and pull off the hub by hand or, if necessary, with a puller.

4. Remove the oil seal. Lubricate the sealing lip on the new seal and install the seal with a drift. The seal may be installed in one of three positions, depending on the amount of wear on the hub. With a new hub, the seal will be installed in its outer position (position 1). With a wear mark on the hub, install the seal in position 2. With two wear marks on the hub, install the seal in position 3. With three wear marks on the hub, you either have a very old engine or you have gone through more than a normal share of oil seals, and it's time to think about replacing that old hub with a new one.

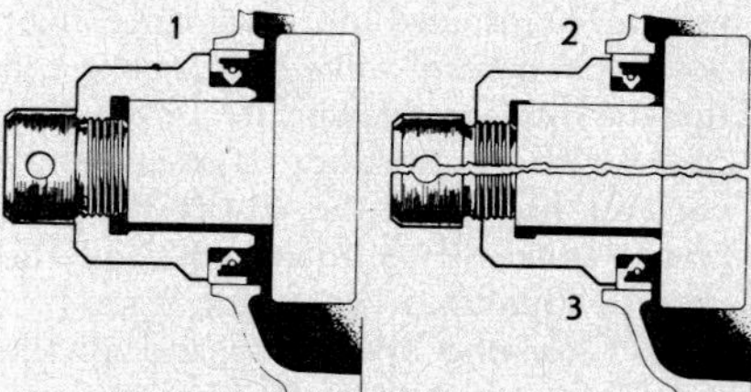

Center spindle position—B30

5. Grease the sliding surfaces of the hub and install the hub. Note the center punch marks on the crankshaft end and hub. Install the center bolt and torque it to 50–57 ft lbs.

6. Install the crankshaft damper and pulley.

7. Install and properly tension the fan (drive) belt. Install the radiator, fan shroud, and grille. Install the lower radiator hose, close the drain plug, and fill the cooling system. On cars with automatic transmissions, connect the transmission oil cooler lines at the radiator.

Camshaft

Timing Gear and Camshaft Replacement

1. Disconnect the lower radiator hose, open the engine drain plug, and drain the cooling system. On cars with automatic

transmissions, disconnect and plug the transmission oil cooler lines at the radiator. Remove the fan shroud (if so equipped) and the radiator.

2. Remove the fan and the pulley on the water pump. Remove the crankshaft bolt and remove the pulley using a puller.

3. Remove the timing gear cover. Loosen a few oil pan bolts, being careful not to damage the pan gasket.

4. Measure the tooth flank clearance. Maximum permissible gear backlash is 0.005 in. Check to make sure that the end-play of the camshaft does not exceed 0.002 in. Camshaft end-play is determined by the shim behind the camshaft timing gear.

5. Try to align the marks on the timing gears dot to dot (or line to dot) prior to removing the gears. If this is not possible, note the correct relative position of the timing gear marks. Remove the hub from the crankshaft with a puller. Remove the crankshaft gear and the camshaft gear with a puller. Remove the oil jet, blow it clean, and reposition it. Oil fed through this jet lubricates the timing gears.

6. If the camshaft is being replaced, it is necessary to remove the distributor (noting its position), fuel pump, valve cover, rocker shaft and arm assembly, pushrods, cylinder head, valve lifters, and the thrust flange. The camshaft may then be pulled out the front.

Timing gear alignment—B18, B20 shown—B30 similar.

1. Oil nozzle 2. Markings

7. Reverse the above procedure to install. Replace the camshaft if the lobes exhibit excessive or uneven wear. Install the crankshaft and camshaft timing gears, making sure that they align in the correct relative positions. Do not push the camshaft backward, or the seal washer on the rear end may be forced out. Recheck the tooth flank clearance and the camshaft end-play.

8. When installing the timing case cover, make sure that the drain holes are open. Center the cover with a sleeve.

9. Install the pulleys and fan. Install the fan (drive) belt and adjust the tension. Refit the radiator hose, close the drain plug, and fill the cooling system.

Pistons and Connecting Rods

Removal

This procedure is more easily accomplished with the engine removed from the vehicle and placed in an engine stand.

1. Remove the cylinder head. Remove any ridge and/or carbon deposits from the upper end of the cylinder bores with a ridge reamer.

2. Remove the oil pan. Check connecting rods and pistons for identification numbers and, if necessary, number them.

3. Remove the connecting rod cap nuts and caps from the crankshaft. Push the rods away from the crankshaft and install the bearing shells, caps, and nuts on the rods to avoid possible interchange of parts.

4. Push the piston and rod assemblies up and out of the cylinders. Remove the rings.

Piston and Connecting Rod Inspection

1. Inspect the cylinder walls for scoring, roughness, or ridges formed from excessive wear. With an accurate cylinder gauge or inside micrometer, check for cylinder taper and out-of-round at the top, middle, and bottom of the bore, both parallel and at right angles to the center line of the engine. Wear is indicated by the difference between the highest and lowest readings. The cylinder is in need of reboring when wear reaches 0.010 in., or if scoring is evident. Hone or rebore the cylinder for fitting of smallest possible oversized piston and rings. Clearance between the piston and cylinder wall, with the rings removed, should be 0.0008–0.0016 in.

2. Measure the outside diameter of the pistons with a micrometer at right angles to the wrist pin hole approximately 0.098 in. from the bottom of the piston.

3. Check the piston ring gap by pressing the rings, one after another, into the bore and inserting a feeler gauge into the gap. The gap should be 0.016–0.022 in. The gap may be widened by filing the ring ends with a thin, flat file. Remember that when you are checking ring gap in a worn cylinder, the rings should be positioned at the bottom of the bore where the diameter is the smallest.

4. Clean the ring grooves on the sides of the pistons. With the rings installed in their respective grooves, measure the side clearance at several points around the piston, and check the reading against the specifications. Inspect the ring grooves for wear, especially the upper edge of the chromed top compression ring.

5. If the wrist pin hole in the piston exhibits excessive wear, an oversized wrist pin should be installed in the connecting rod. Ream out the hole to the oversized wrist pin specification. This is correct when the wrist pin can be pushed through the hole with light resistance.

6. Inspect the connecting rods for straightness. Check the bushings for excessive wear. When installing a new bushing, make sure that the oil holes align with the holes in the connecting rod. Ream the bushing to the correct fit. When the wrist pin slides through the hole with light thumb pressure, but without noticeable looseness, the bushing is fitted correctly.

Installation

1. Lightly coat the pistons, rings, wrist pins, and cylinder walls with light engine oil.

2. Install the wrist pin and fit the circlip into position.

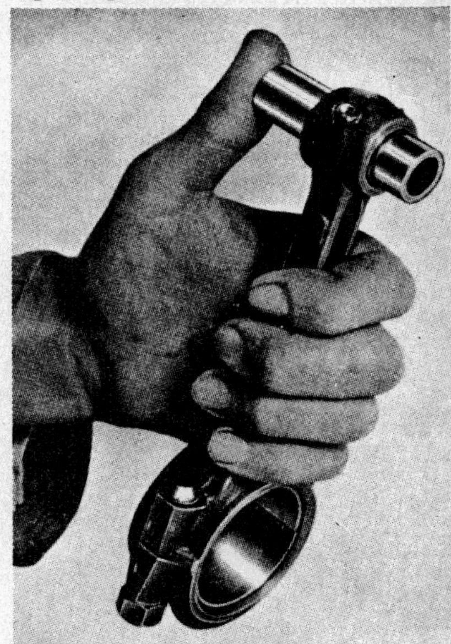

Wrist pin fit

3. Use a piston ring expander tool to install the rings on the piston. Position the rings so that their gaps do not come directly under one another, or directly opposite one another. Remember that the top compression ring is chromed and its upper side is marked "TOP."

4. Prior to installation, make sure that the pistons will be positioned in the cylinders with the slot facing forward, and that the numbers on the side of the connecting rods will be facing away from the camshaft side. Install each piston in its respective bore from the top, using a piston installation ring as shown. A hard wood hammer handle may be used to lightly tap the piston into position. Guide the rod bearings into place on the crankshaft journal.

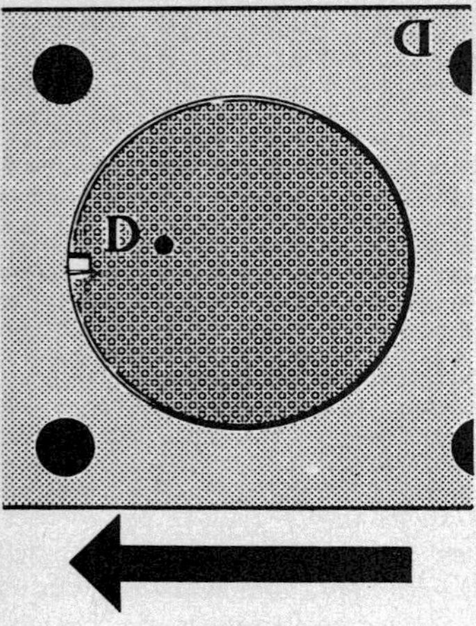

Piston marking

5. Install the lower half of the bearing and cap. Torque the bolts to 38–42 ft lbs. Check the clearances against specifications.

6. Install the oil pan with a new gasket.

7. Install the cylinder head as outlined in "Cylinder Head Removal and Installation."

ENGINE LUBRICATION

All Volvos use a forced-feed lubricating system. Oil pressure is provided by a camshaft-driven pump fitted beneath the crankshaft in the oil pan. The pump forces oil past the relief valve on the pump, through the oil filter and oil cooler, if so equipped, through the oil passages to the various lubricating points. Therefore, all oil reaching the lubricating points has first passed through the oil filter.

Oil Pan

Removal and Installation

The oil pan may be removed from the engine while the engine is still in the chassis.

1. Place supports on the frame side members as shown. Insert a lifting hook into the lifting plate bolted to the front of the engine. Using the lifting apparatus, raise the engine until there is no weight on the front engine mounts. Remove the oil dipstick.

2. Jack up the vehicle and place jackstands under the front jacking points. Drain the crankcase oil.

3. Remove the lower nuts for the engine mounts. On 140 series models, remove the steering rods from the pitman arm and relay arm with a puller.

4. Place a hydraulic floor jack beneath the front axle member. Remove the rear bolts of the front axle member and replace them with two longer auxiliary bolts (UNC ½-13X114). Remove the front bolts for the front axle member and lower the hydraulic jack, allowing the axle member to hang on the auxiliary bolts.

5. Remove the plug for the oil temperature gauge, if so equipped, and the reinforcing bracket at the flywheel.

6. Unscrew the oil pan bolts and lower the pan. Remove the old gasket and clean the surfaces of the cylinder block and oil pan. Remove any sludge or foreign matter that has accumulated at the bottom of the pan.

7. Using a new gasket, position the pan to the cylinder block and install the oil pan bolts. Torque the bolts to 6–8 ft lbs.

8. Install the plug for the oil temperature gauge, if so equipped. Position the reinforcing bracket to the cylinder block and flywheel casing and install the bolts finger-tight. Snugly tighten the bolts for the flywheel casing and then those for the cylinder block.

9. Raise the hydraulic jack, raising the front axle member, and tighten the front bolts. Remove the auxiliary bolts and install the original rear bolts of the front axle member.

10. Install the lower nuts for the front engine mounts. On 140 series models, connect the steering rods at the pitman arm and relay arm, and fit the nuts.

11. Remove the jackstands and hydraulic jack. Lower the vehicle. Remove the lifting apparatus.

12. Insert the dipstick. Fill the crankcase with the proper amount and grade of oil.

13. Start the engine and check for leaks.

Rear Main Oil Seal Replacement

1. Dowel pin
2. Core plug
3. Sealing flange
4. Circlip
5. Pilot bearing
6. Sealing ring
7. Crankshaft
8. Plug
9. Dowel pin

Rear end of engine

1. Remove the transmission, clutch (if so equipped), and flywheel from the engine. Remove the two oil pan bolts from the bottom of the sealing flange, and loosen two more on each side so that the pressure on the sealing flange is reduced.

2. Remove the sealing flange retaining bolts and pull off the sealing flange and

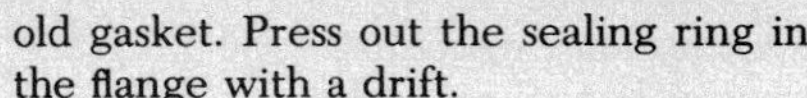

old gasket. Press out the sealing ring in the flange with a drift.

3. Make sure that the sealing surfaces of the flange are clean. Also make sure that the oil drain hole is not blocked by the oil pan gasket.

4. Oil the sealing ring. Install the sealing ring, sealing flange, and new gasket to the block, but do not tighten the bolts.

5. Center the flange with special SVO tool 2439 (for B 18 and B 20), or 2817 (for B 30). Rotate the sleeve while tightening the flange bolts. Adjust the position of the flange if the sleeve jams. After tightening, the sleeve should rotate easily if the flange is properly positioned. Make sure that the sealing flange is seated against the underside of the block.

6. Install a new felt ring and replace the washer and circlip. Install the scaling ring into its groove with the centering sleeve.

7. Install and tighten the oil pan bolts. Install the flywheel, clutch (if so equipped), and transmission.

Oil Pump

Replacement

The oil pump must be removed with the engine removed from the car.

1. Crank the engine to TDC at no. 1 cylinder. Remove the distributor.

2. Drain the crankcase and remove the oil pan. Remove the oil pump retaining bolts.

3. Disconnect the oil pump from the delivery tube by unscrewing the connecting flange. Be careful not to discard the rubber sealing rings from the sealing flange.

4. Unscrew the connecting flange and remove the delivery tube from the block.

5. To install, fit the delivery tube with sealing rings to the oil pump, and then to the block. If the tube does not seat properly in the block, it may be tapped lightly with a soft mallet. Tightly screw the connecting flanges.

6. With no. 1 cylinder at TDC, install the oil pump drive and distributor. Make

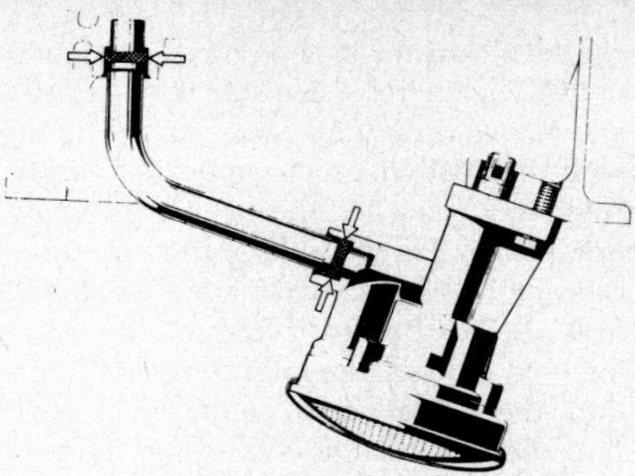
Oil pump delivery pipe sealing rings

sure that the shaft goes down into its groove in the pump shaft. Tighten the oil pump retaining bolts.

7. Install the oil pan with a new gasket and fill the crankcase.

Oil Pump Clearance

After removing the oil pump from the engine, place the pump body in a vise. Remove the four bolts which retain the pick-up screen housing to the pump body, exposing the oil pump gears, relief valve, ball and spring. To measure the tooth flank clearance, insert a proper size feeler gauge between the engaging teeth of the oil pump gears. Proper tooth flank clearance is 0.006–0.014 in. If the clearance is not within specifications, the pump must be replaced. To measure the oil pump gear end-float, place a straightedge ruler over top of the two pump gears so that it lies flat on the pump housing at both ends, and insert a proper size feeler gauge between the top of the pump gear and the straightedge. Proper gear end float is 0.0008–0.0040 in. If all clearances are within specifications, reassemble the oil pump taking care to install the relief valve, ball, and spring in their original locations.

Oil pump assembly

1. Pump body
2. Spring for relief valve
3. Gear
4. Valve ball
5. Hole for oil pipe

Measuring oil pump tooth flank clearance

Oil Cooler

Replacement

1. Remove the plug in the oil cooler and drain the coolant.
2. Disconnect the coolant connection at the oil cooler. Remove the oil filter.
3. Unscrew the oil cooler nipple nut and remove the cooler. Remove and discard the rubber sealing ring at the cylinder block connection.
4. Install a new O-ring into the groove in the oil cooler and apply a thin layer of oil-resistant (up to 280°F) adhesive, such as Pliobond® 20, to the groove. Postion the cooler and new rubber sealing ring to the block and tighten the nipple nut to 23–25 ft lbs. Make sure that the cooler is flush against the block.
5. Install the oil filter and connect the coolant pipe. Install the cooler plug.
6. Replace the coolant, and, if necessary, the engine oil. Run the engine and check for leaks.

ENGINE COOLING

All Volvos are equipped with a sealed cooling system. Radiator overflow and trapped air in the system are conveyed to the expansion tank where they are stored. Therefore, loss of coolant is prevented, reducing the chances of corrosion forming in the system or of the antifreeze being diluted. The air cushion developed in the expansion tank forces the coolant back into the radiator until it is full, ensuring that the radiator is always topped up.

The fan, on 1969 and later model Volvos, is of the viscous type, with a slip coupling that limits the maximum fan speed to approximately 3500 rpm. This arrangement reduces fan noise and lowers the load on the engine at high engine rpm, but provides a good cooling air current at low rpm where it is needed.

The water pump is belt-driven by the engine pulleys and provides coolant circulation in direct proportion to engine speed. When the engine is cold, the thermostat is closed, directing the coolant through the engine passages and to the car heater. At approximately 190°F, the thermostat is open, allowing the coolant to flow through the radiator.

Radiator

Removal and Installation

1. Remove the radiator and expansion tank caps, disconnect the lower radiator hose, and drain the cooling system.
2. Remove the expansion tank and hose, and drain the coolant. Remove the upper radiator hose. On cars with automatic transmissions, disconnect and plug the transmission oil cooler lines at the radiator.
3. Remove the retaining bolts for the radiator and fan shroud, if so equipped, and lift out the radiator.
4. To install, place the radiator and fan shroud in position and install the retaining bolts.
5. On automatic transmission cars, connect the oil cooler lines.
6. Install the lower and upper radiator hoses.
7. Install the expansion tank with its hose. Make sure that the overflow hose is clear of the fan and is free of any sharp bends.
8. Fill the cooling system with a 50 percent ethylene glycol, 50 percent water solution. Replace the caps.
9. Start the engine and check for leaks. After the engine has reached operating temperature make sure that the coolant level in the expansion tank is between the maximum and minimum marks.

Water Pump

Removal and Installation

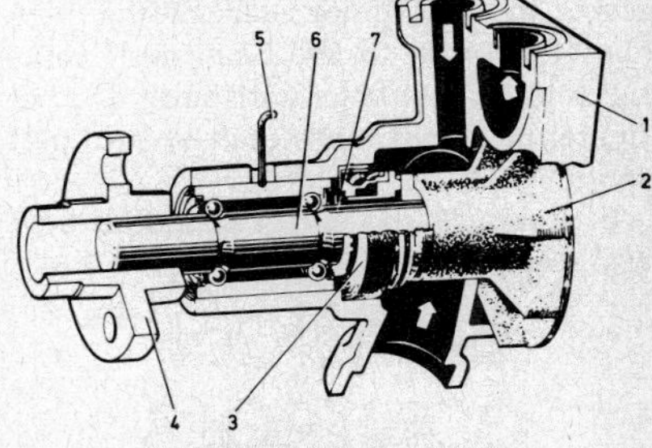

Water pump assembly

1. Housing
2. Impeller
3. Seal ring
4. Flange
5. Lock spring
6. Shaft with ball bearings (integral unit)
7. Wear ring

1. Drain the cooling system and remove the radiator as previously described.
2. Loosen the fan belt by slackening the alternator (generator) adjusting bolt. Remove the fan.

3. Remove the housing bolts from the water pump. Carefully remove the aluminum housing from the engine along with all the old gasket material.

4. Pull the water pump assembly from the block and remove the sealing rings.

5. To install, position the water pump assembly to the block, making sure that the sealing rings on the upper side of the pump are seated fully. Press the pump upward against the cylinder head extension to seat the rings.

6. Install the housing and new gasket. Hand-tighten the housing bolts until snug. Do not tighten the bolts more than ½ turn further to avoid cracking the housing or breaking the bolts.

7. Install the fan and adjust the fan (drive) belt tension.

8. Install the radiator as previously described. Fill the cooling system.

9. Start the engine and check for leaks.

Thermostat

Removal and Installation

1. Disconnect the lower radiator hose and drain the cooling system.

2. Remove the two bolts securing the thermostat housing to the cylinder head and carefully lift the housing free.

3. Remove all old gasket material from the mating surfaces and remove the thermostat.

4. Test the operation of the thermostat by immersing it in a container of heated water. Two types of thermostats are used on 1967–73 Volvos. Type one is a 170° unit which bears a 170 marking. It begins to open at 168–172°F and is fully open at 194°F. Type two is a 180° unit which bears an 85° marking (85° Centigrade). It begins to open at 177–181°F and is fully open at 195°F. Replace any thermostat that does not open at the correct temperatures.

5. Place the thermostat, with a new gasket, in the cylinder head. Fit the thermostat housing to the head and hand-tighten the two bolts until snug. Do not tighten the bolts more than ¼ turn past snug.

6. Connect the lower radiator hose and replace the coolant.

EMISSION CONTROLS

Volvos have been equipped with positive crankcase ventilation (PCV) systems to control crankcase vapors since the early 1960s. The present system is a closed one; it is sealed to the atmosphere. A metal filter located inline between the fresh air source and the crankcase prevents engine backfire from reaching the crankcase and oil from being drawn into the induction system.

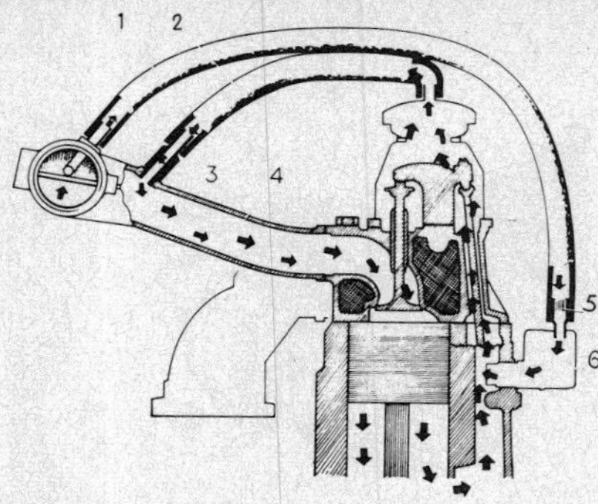

Positive crankcase ventilation system—B20E, B20F system shown

1. Hose for fresh air supply
2. Hose for crankcase gases
3. Nipple
4. Inlet duct
5. Flame guard
6. Oil trap

All post-1969 model Volvos have been equipped with an evaporative control system to prevent unburnt fuel vapors in the fuel tank and, in carbureted models, the float chambers, from escaping into the atmosphere. An expansion tank above the fuel tank provides for thermal expansion of fuel vapors in warm weather. Those vapors which do not condense and return to the fuel tank are displaced and drawn into an activated charcoal canister in the engine compartment. The charcoal canister then absorbs and stores these fuel tank vapors, along with the float chamber vapors (on carbureted models) when the engine is shut off or is idling. Throttling the engine causes the vapors to be drawn out of the canister into the carburetor venturi (on fuel-injected models, the inlet duct) and then into the combustion chambers where they are burned. On carbureted models, the float chamber vapors are diverted from the canister to the air cleaner upon acceleration. As a result of these fumes being vented to the air cleaner, an overly rich fuel mixture may develop, leading to starting difficulties—especially in warm weather. A hot start valve is located in-line between the float chamber and the air cleaner which returns the vapors to the charcoal canister until the engine can handle the extra-rich mixture.

Various measures have been taken since 1968 to limit exhaust emissions of hydrocarbons, carbon monoxide, and more recently, oxides of nitrogen. Basic modifications include a distributor which retards the timing from its basic setting during idle, and the installation of a "hotter" 190° F thermostat in the cooling system. Fuel injection, which is inherently

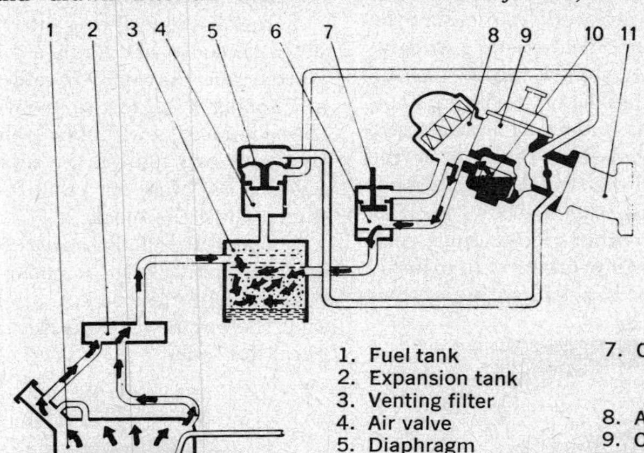

1. Fuel tank
2. Expansion tank
3. Venting filter
4. Air valve
5. Diaphragm
6. Valve (hot start valve)
7. Control rod (connected to throttle)
8. Air cleaner
9. Carburetor
10. Floatchamber
11. Intake manifold

Fuel evaporative control system at idle

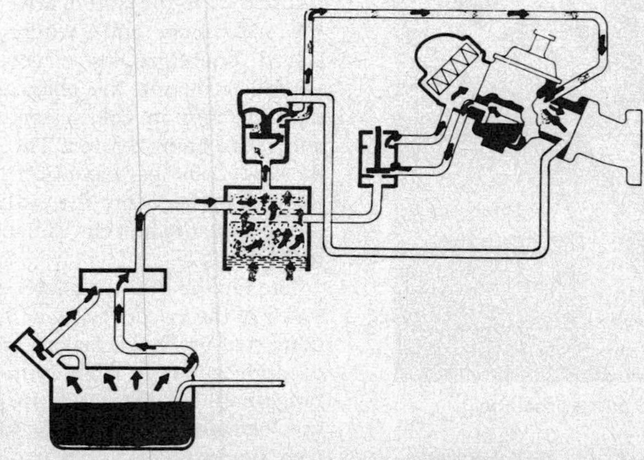

Fuel evaporative control system at throttling

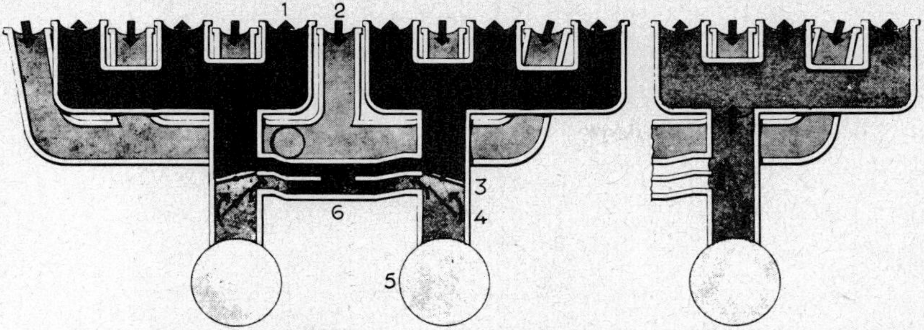

Pre-heating chamber—light load (left), heavy load (right)

1. Intake manifold
2. Exhaust manifold
3. Secondary throttle
4. Primary throttle
5. Carburetor
6. Preheating chamber

cleaner due to its precise regulation of the air-fuel mixture under varying rpm, engine load, and ambient temperature conditions, has been available since 1970. Carbureted engines have incorporated many modifications including such pollutant control devices as a temperature-regulated fuel jet, an air-fuel mixture preheating chamber, and a throttle bypass or overrev valve, and measures to improve the operation and driveability of emission-controlled engines such as a cold-start device, a constant intake air temperature device, and, as previously mentioned, a hot-start valve.

The temperature-regulated fuel mixture is accomplished differently on the Zenith-Stromberg 175 CD2 SE carburetor than on the SU HIF carburetor. On the Stromberg carburetor, a temperature-sensitive bimetal spring in the temperature compensator actuates an air valve that varies the air supplied the venturi area to maintain the air-fuel ratio constant, despite changing fuel temperature. On the SU HIF carburetor, a temperature-sensitive bimetal spring raises or lowers the adjustable jet to maintain the proper air-fuel ratio at changing fuel temperatures.

On 1969 and later models, the throttle bypass or overrev valve serves to direct a regulated flow of fuel and air around the closed carburetor throttle, during engine deceleration (braking) from high speeds, and into the combustion chambers. This eliminates the over-rich surge condition that occurs when the throttle is finally opened after a period of engine braking.

The cold-start device on the rear carburetor is designed to improve the starting capabilities of a "lean" emissions engine during cold weather by providing extra fuel for starting and warm-up.

On 1968 and later models, the constant intake air temperature device also aids in cold weather warm-up by providing exhaust manifold heat to the hose for the intake air. A thermostatically controlled flap regulates the mixture of intake air and exhaust heated air to an approximate temperature of 90°F.

Exhaust gas recirculation valve installed—B20F shown, B30F similar.

In order to control emissions of NO_x, all 1973 140 series, 164 E and 1800ES models with automatic transmission are equipped with an exhaust gas recirculation system. The system consists of a metering valve, a tubular pipe running from the exhaust manifold to the valve, another tubular pipe running from the valve to the inlet duct, and a vacuum hose running from the valve's diaphragm to the inlet duct in front of the air regulator shutter. The valve permits a regulated amount of exhaust gasses to enter the inlet duct and mix with the incoming intake air when the throttle is partly open. Every 12 months or 12,000 miles, the system must be disassembled and cleaned. Every 24 months or 24,000 miles, the valve must be replaced with a new one.

Component Testing and Adjustment

Temperature Compensator

Zenith-Stromberg 175 CD2 SE Carburetor

If the idle speed drops off sharply during extended periods of idling, especially during warm weather, the temperature compensator may be in need of adjustment or replacement.

1. Remove the one screw retaining the plastic cover to the compensator and remove the cover.
2. With the ambient temperature at or above 85°F, the valve should be able to be pressed inward with light finger pressure and then return to its position without jamming. If the valve jams and is stiff in operation, the temperature compensator should be replaced as a unit. See "Temperature Compensator Replacement."
3. If properly adjusted, the valve will begin to open at 70–77°F, and be fully open at 85°F. If not properly adjusted, the valve may be adjusted while the temperature compensator is still on the carburetor by slackening one of the cross-slotted screws for the bimental spring, and centering the valve so that it opens and closes at the proper temperatures. If necessary, the temperature compensator may be removed and isolated at 70–77°F, then adjusted with the nut for the bimetal spring so that the valve is loose in its seat at this temperature.
4. Replace the cover and retaining screw on the compensator and check its operation during idling.

Bypass Valve

Zenith-Stromberg 175 CD2 SE Carburetor

If the engine does not return to idle speed soon after the throttle is released, and the throttle control linkage is properly adjusted, the bypass valve may be in need of adjustment or replacement.

1. If the engine still refuses to lower its rpm to idle speed when the throttle is released, turn the bypass adjusting screw on the front carburetor to the left, and manually lower the idle.
2. Run the engine briefly up to approximately 2000 rpm, then release the throttle. If the engine returns to idle speed, turn the screw ½ turn further to the left. If the engine does not return to idle, replace the bypass valve as a unit. See "Bypass Valve Replacement."
3. Remove the air cleaner. While peering into the carburetor bores, observe the air valves. Briefly race the engine and then release the throttle. The air valve of the front carburetor should normally go down to the bridge slower than the air valve of the rear carburetor. Turn the bypass adjusting screw to the right until the above-mentioned normal function is obtained. If the valve cannot be adjusted so that the front air valve goes down to the bridge slower than the rear air valve, the bypass valve must be replaced as a unit. See "Bypass Valve Replacement."

Hot-Start Valve

Zenith-Stromberg 175 CD2 SE Carburetor

When the throttle control is in the idling position, adjust the valve control of the hot-start valve so that the valve is against the carburetor lever with the valve piston in the upper position.

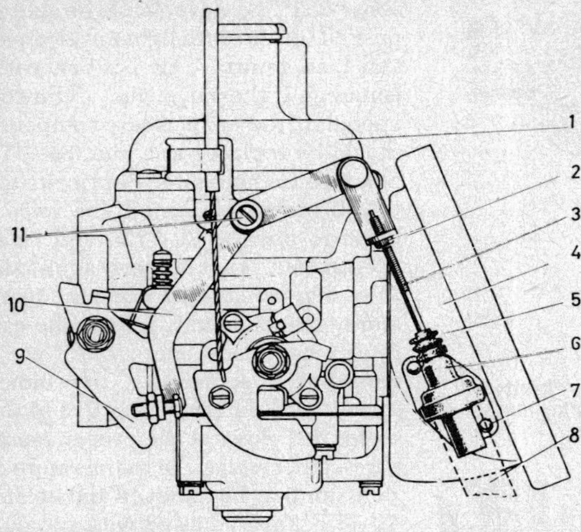

Hot start valve installation—Stromberg 175 CD2 SE carburetor.

1. Rubber seal
2. Rubber seal
3. Valve
4. Bi-metal spring
5. Cover
6. Screws for temperature compensator
7. Screw for cover
8. Cross slotted screw
9. Adjusting nut
10. Housing
11. Marking

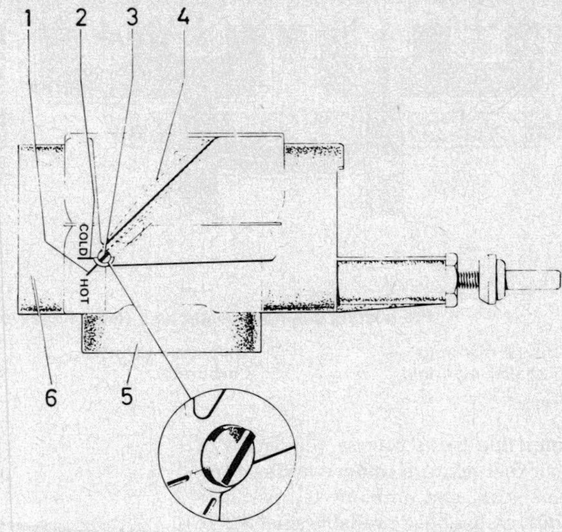

Checking constant air temperature flap function.

1. HOT—open for warm air
2. COLD—open for cold air
3. Tab
4. Flap
5. Hot air intake
6. Cold air intake

Coat the contact surfaces on the valve and carburetor with high-temperature white grease such as Molykote®.

Test the operation of the hot-start valve by determining that the engine returns to idle speed after several brief periods of racing the engine.

SU HIF Carburetor

To adjust the hot-start valve, press the control rods down to the bottom position and measure the distance (A) between the rod and the adjusting screw. Adjust the distance to a maximum of 0.04 in.

Test the operation of the control rods—making sure that they do not jam.

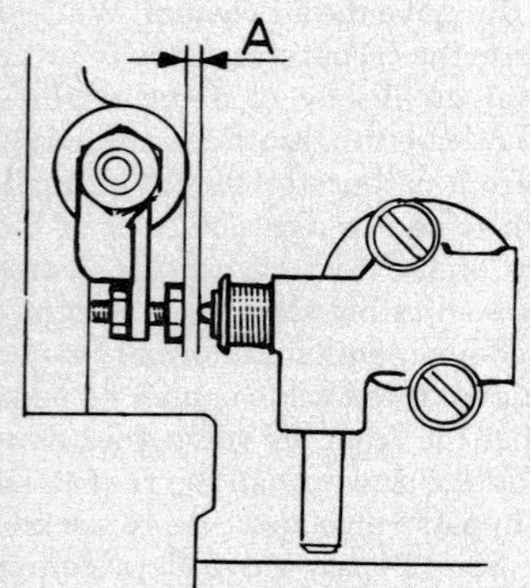

Hot start valve adjustment—SU HS6 carburetor.

Constant (Intake) Air Temperature Device

If the flap for the constant air temperature device sticks in one position, engine operation will suffer. Normally, the flap is closed to cold air (intake hose) at an ambient temperature of 70–77° F, and closed to hot air (exhaust manifold heated) at 95–105° F.

1. The operation of the flap may be checked with the flap housing installed in position. When the small tab on the flap housing points toward the mark closest the exhaust heat hose, the flap is open for cold (unheated) air. When the tab points to the mark nearest the cold air intake, the flap is open for warm (exhaust heated) air. If the tab indicates that the flap is opening and closing the air sources at the right temperatures, you may rest your soul. If not, check the operation of the flap control thermostat.

2. Disconnect the flap housing from the air intake hoses. Immerse the thermostat in lukewarm water. At a water temperature of 70–77° F, the thermostat should be in its upper (toward the flap housing) position. At 95–105° F, the thermostat should be in its lower position (away from the flap housing). If correct operation cannot be obtained, replace the thermostat and flap housing as a unit.

3. Replace the flap housing and thermostat assembly, making sure that the thermostat is centered in the middle of the air flow. Secure the hose clamp screw on top of the flap.

Component Replacement

Temperature Compensator

Zenith-Stromberg 175 CD2 SE Carburetor

1. Remove the retaining screws (6) and lift off the compensator.

2. Discard the old rubber seals (1, 2) and replace them with new ones.

3. Position the compensator to the side of the carburetor and install the retaining screws.

4. Check the operation of the compensator during idle as outlined in "Temperature Compensator Testing and Adjustment."

Bypass Valve

Zenith-Stromberg 175 CD2 SE Carburetor

1. Remove the three retaining screws and lift off the bypass valve.

2. Discard the old bypass valve-to-carburetor housing gasket.

3. Position a new gasket and bypass valve to the carburetor, making sure that the orifices and mating surfaces of the valve and gasket align, then install the three retaining screws.

4. Check the operation of the bypass valve as outlined in "Bypass Valve Testing and Adjustment."

Hot-Start Valve

Zenith-Stromberg 175 CD2 SE Carburetor

The hot-start valve on the Stromberg carburetor is riveted to the air cleaner. If cleaning is to be performed on the valve, it must be accomplished with the valve in place on the air cleaner.

SU HIF Carburetor

1. Remove the two retaining screws and lift off the valve.

2. Discard the old gasket and clean the channels in the carburetor with a low-pressure air line.

3. Position the valve and new gasket to the carburetor, making sure that the gasket is aligned properly, then install the two retaining screws.

4. Adjust the position of the control rod and test the operation of the valve as outlined in "Hot-Start Valve Testing and Adjustment."

Constant Air Temperature Device Flap Housing

1. Loosen the hose clamps, and disconnect the flap housing and thermostat assembly from the hoses for the intake air,

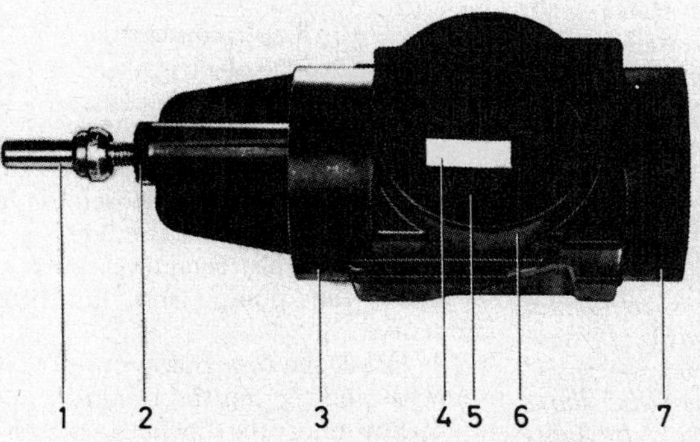

Constant air temperature flap

exhaust heated air, and intake manifold.

2. Install the new flap housing assembly in position and reconnect the three hoses. Make sure that the thermostat is centered in the middle of the intake air flow. Secure the hose clamp screw on top of the flap.

3. Check the operation of the new flap housing as outlined in "Constant Air Temperature Device Testing and Adjustment."

Cold-Start Device Seals

SU HIF Carburetor

1. Pry off the lockwasher (12) for the cold-start device and unscrew the channel disc nut (13).

2. Disconnect the return spring (10) and remove the channel disc and spring.

3. Remove the two retaining screws (9) and the spring retainer (8).

4. Lift the cold-start device away from the carburetor. Press the spindle (3) out of the cold-start device housing (5). Remove the gasket (7), the rubber ring (4), and rubber seal (6) from the spindle, and discard them. Clean all metal parts in kerosine, and clean the fuel channels with an air line.

5. Install a new rubber ring and seal on the housing and oil them with light (10W) engine oil. Install the spindle into the housing.

6. Position the housing assembly, with a new gasket, to the carburetor, fit the spring retainer, and install the retaining screws.

7. Position the return spring in its retainer so that the spring's short end fits into the retainer slot.

8. Hook the channel disc onto the spring's longer end and install the disc on the spindle. Install the channel disc retaining nut and snap on the lockwasher.

1. Circlip
2. Washer
3. Spindle
4. Rubber ring
5. House
6. Rubber seal for spindle
7. Gasket
8. Spring retainer
9. Screws for cold start device
10. Return spring
11. Fast idle screw
12. Tab washer
13. Nut

Cold start device disassembled—SU HIF carburetor.

Component Service

Positive Crankcase Ventilation System

The only service required for the PCV system is the cleaning of the hoses, nipples, and metal filter every two years or 24,000 miles.

Fuel Evaporative Control System

The only items requiring service in the evaporative control system are the foam plastic filter in the bottom of the charcoal canister and the hot-start valve. The canister filter is replaced every two years or 24,000 miles. The hot-start valve is serviced when hard starting in warm weather occurs. Adjust the control rods and lubricate the contact surfaces as outlined in "Hot-Start Valve Testing and Adjustment." On models equipped with SU carburetors, the valve may be removed and the passages cleaned of all impurities with compressed air.

FUEL SYSTEM

Fuel Pump

Volvo has used three different mechanical and two different electrical fuel pumps on its 1967–73 models. The mechanical units are used with carbureted engines, and the electrical units with fuel-injection. The procedure for replacing the three mechanical types is the same and the procedure for replacing the two electrical types is the same.

Mechanical Type

The Pierburg PV 3025 fuel pump used on the 164, and the Pierburg APG and AC YD fuel pump used on the 140 series and 1800S models are all camshaft-driven diaphragm types. The fuel pump is located on the left (driver's) side of the engine block.

Testing and Adjustment

No adjustments may be made to the fuel pump. Before removing the old fuel pump, the following test may be made while the pump is still installed on the engine.

CAUTION: *To avoid accidental ignition of fuel during the test, first remove the coil high-tension wire from the distributor and the coil.*

1. If a fuel pressure gauge is available, connect the gauge to the engine and operate the engine until the pressure stops rising. Stop the engine and take the reading. If the reading is within the specifications given in the "Tune-Up Specifications" chart, the malfunction is not in the fuel pump. Also check the pres-

sure drop after the engine is stopped. A large pressure drop below the minimum specification indicates leaky valves. If the pump proves to be satisfactory, check the tank and inlet line.

2. If a fuel pressure gauge is not available, disconnect the fuel line at the pump outlet, place a vessel beneath the pump outlet, and crank the engine. A good pump will force the fuel out of the outlet in steady spurts. A worn diaphragm spring may not provide proper pumping action.

3. As a further test, disconnect and plug the fuel line from the tank at the pump, and hold your thumb over the pump inlet. If the pump is functioning properly, a suction should be felt on your thumb. No suction indicates that the pump diaphragm is leaking, or that the diaphragm linkage is worn.

4. Check the crankcase for gasoline. A ruptured diaphragm may leak fuel into the engine.

Replacement

1. Disconnect and plug the inlet and outlet lines to the fuel pump.
2. Remove the two fuel pump retaining bolts and carefully pull the pump and old gasket away from the block.
3. Discard the old gasket and position a new one on the pump.
4. Mount the fuel pump and gasket to the engine block, being careful to insert the pump lever (rocker arm) in the engine block, aligning it correctly above the camshaft.
5. While holding the pump securely against the block, install the two fuel pump retaining bolts, and tighten them securely.
6. Unplug and reconnect the fuel lines to the pump.
7. Start the engine and check for fuel leaks. Also check for oil leaks where the pump attaches to the block.

Electric Type

Volvo has used electric fuel pumps on all of its fuel-injected models. On pre-1972 models, a Bosch unit with a 2.5 ampere current consumption and a 13 gallon per hour capacity is used. Post-1971 models use another Bosch unit with a 5 ampere current consumption and a 26 gallon per hour capacity. For purposes of desciption, testing, and replacement, the two units may be grouped together. The electric pump and pumping motor are completely enclosed in the fuel pump housing.

NOTE: *Volvo states that a no-start condition may occasionally occur when the car has not been started for an extended period of time. This may be due to the fuel pump sticking in one position because of foreign matter entering the pump, or corrosion forming on the rotor shaft or commutator and brushes.*

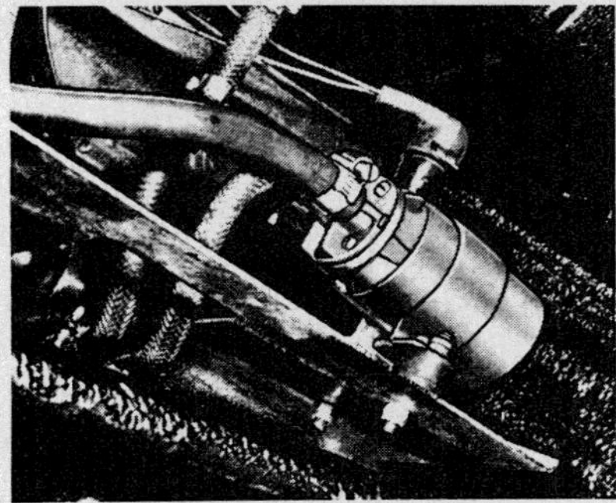

Electric fuel pump installed—1970-71 1800E installation shown.

It is, therefore, very important to replace the inline fuel filter at its regular intervals on pre-1972 fuel-injected models, and clean the fuel tank pick-up screen every 12 months or 12,000 miles on post-1971 fuel-injected models to prevent corrosion causing water condensation and foreign matter from entering the pump. As an additional corrosion prevention measure, add an alcohol solution or "dry gas" to the fuel, especially in winter months. If, however, the pump does become "stuck" in one position for any of the above reasons, it may be "unstuck" by lighty rapping on the pump casing with a length of hardwood such as a hammer handle, while the ignition is switched on.

Testing and Adjustment

No adjustments may be made to the fuel pump. If the pump is not functioning properly, it must be discarded and replaced. To check the function of the fuel pump, the pump should be connected to a pressure gauge. Be careful not to switch the electrical leads. If the pump fails to pump its normal capacity, or if it cannot pump that capacity at its specified rate of current consumption, it must be replaced. Because of the highly technical nature of this operation, it is best to have this task delegated to your local Volvo or Bosch agency.

Replacement

1. Remove the electrical lead from the pump as well as the template to which the pump is mounted.
2. Clean around the hose connections. Pinch shut the fuel lines, loosen the hose clamps, and disconnect the lines.
3. Loosen the retaining nuts and remove the pump from its rubber mounts.
4. Install the new pump on its rubber mounts and tighten the retaining nuts.
5. Reconnect the fuel lines, tighten the hose clamps, and remove the pinchers.
6. Mount the template beneath the car and connect the electrical lead.
7. Start the engine and check for leaks.

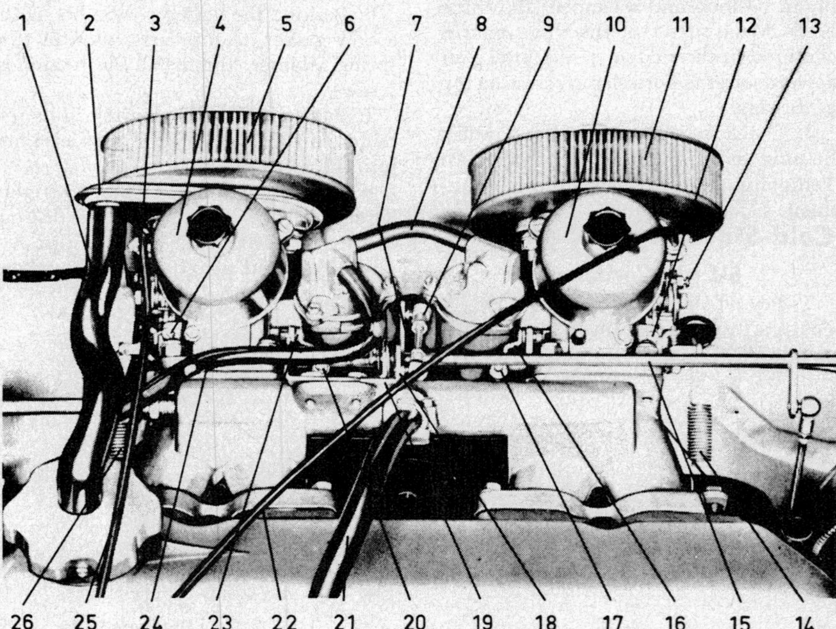

Twin horizontal SU HS6 carburetor installation—B18B shown

1. Rubber hose for crankcase ventilation
2. Intermediate piece for crankcase ventilation
3. Clamping screw for choke control
4. Front carburetor
5. Front air cleaner
6. Idle adjusting screw
7. Lever
18. Lever
19. Stop
20. Locking screw
21. Rubber hose for crankcase ventilation
22. Choke control
23. Lever on intermediate shaft
24. Fuel hose
25. Choke control
26. Return spring
8. Fuel hose
9. Link
10. Rear carburetor
11. Rear air cleaner
12. Idle adjusting screw
13. Clamping screw for choke control
14. Return spring
15. Control shaft
16. Lever on intermediate shaft
17. Locking screw

Twin horizontal Stromberg 175 CD2 SE carburetor installation—B30A shown

1. Cold air hose
2. Constant temperature device flap
3. Warm air hose
4. Temperature compensator
5. Front carburetor
6. Clasp for air cleaner cover
7. Air cleaner
8. Fuel hoses
9. Temperature compensator
10. Rear carburetor
11. Hot start valve
12. Hose between hot start valve and venting filter
13. Hose for fuel fumes to carburetors
14. Venting filter
15. Air valve
16. Vacuum hose for vacuum for air valve and distributor
17. Hose between fuel tank and venting filter
18. Vacuum hose for distributor (negative vacuum setting)
19. Vacuum hose for brake booster
20. Choke wire
21. Secondary throttle
22. Throttle stop screw
23. Air hose for crankcase gases
24. Hose for crankcase gases
25. Idle trimming screw
26. Throttle control
27. Bracket
28. Throttle stop screw
29. Manifold with preheating chamber
30. Vacuum connection
31. Idle trimming screw
32. Throttle by-pass valve

Twin horizontal SU HIF carburetor installation—B20B shown

1. Cold air hose
2. Constant temperature device flap
3. Warm air hose
4. Guard for throttle spindle
5. Hot start valve
6. Front carburetor
7. Clamp for air cleaner cover
8. Air cleaner
9. Fuel hose
10. Choke wires
11. Hydraulic damper
12. Rear carburetor
13. Vacuum hose for distributor (Negative vacuum setting)
14. Hot start valve
15. Idle trimming screw
16. Manifold
17. Throttle control
18. Fresh-air intake for crankcase
19. Hose for crankcase gases
20. Hose for brake booster
21. Idle trimming screw
22. Fuel hose
23. Hoses connected to start valves
24. Hose to fuel tank
25. Vacuum hose (joined to "negative connection" on carburetor)
26. Hose for fuel fumes

Carburetors

Three different types of carburetors have been used on 1967–72 Volvos. A pair of sidedraft SU HS6 units were used on 1967–68 models. A pair of sidedraft Stromberg 175 CD2 SE units were used on 1969–70 140 series models, and on 1970–72 164 models. A pair of sidedraft SU HIF units were used on 1971–72 140 series models.

Removal and Installation

1. On the Stromberg carburetor, disconnect the hot-start valve control. On 1968 and later models, separate the air cleaner halves and remove the inner half from the carburetors. On 1967 models, remove the four nuts and bolts and remove both air cleaners.
2. Disconnect the throttle linkage by removing the link rod ball joints from the carburetors. Disconnect the choke cable, taking note of its proper location.
3. Disconnect and plug the fuel lines at the float chambers. Remove the vacuum hose for the distributor. On the SU HIF carburetor, disconnect the hot-start valve hose.
4. Remove the four (each) nuts retaining the carburetors to the intake manifold. Remove the carburetors, gaskets, and protection plate.
5. Position the protection plate, new gaskets, and carburetors on the intake manifold studs. Install the carburetor retaining nuts and tighten them evenly until they are snug against the manifold.
6. Connect the vacuum hose, fuel hoses, choke, and throttle linkage. On the SU HIF carburetor, connect the hot-start valve hose.
7. On 1968 and later models, install the inner half of the air cleaner to the carburetors. Adjust the idle speed and mixture of the carburetors as outlined in the "Tune-Up" section.
8. Fit the air cleaner halves together and, on the Stromberg carburetor, connect the hot-start valve control.

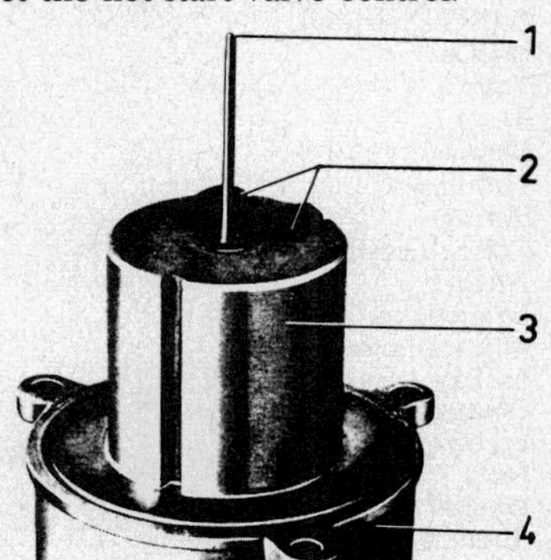

Fit of air valve (suction piston)

1. Metering needle
2. Rubber or cork plugs
3. Air valve
4. Suction chamber

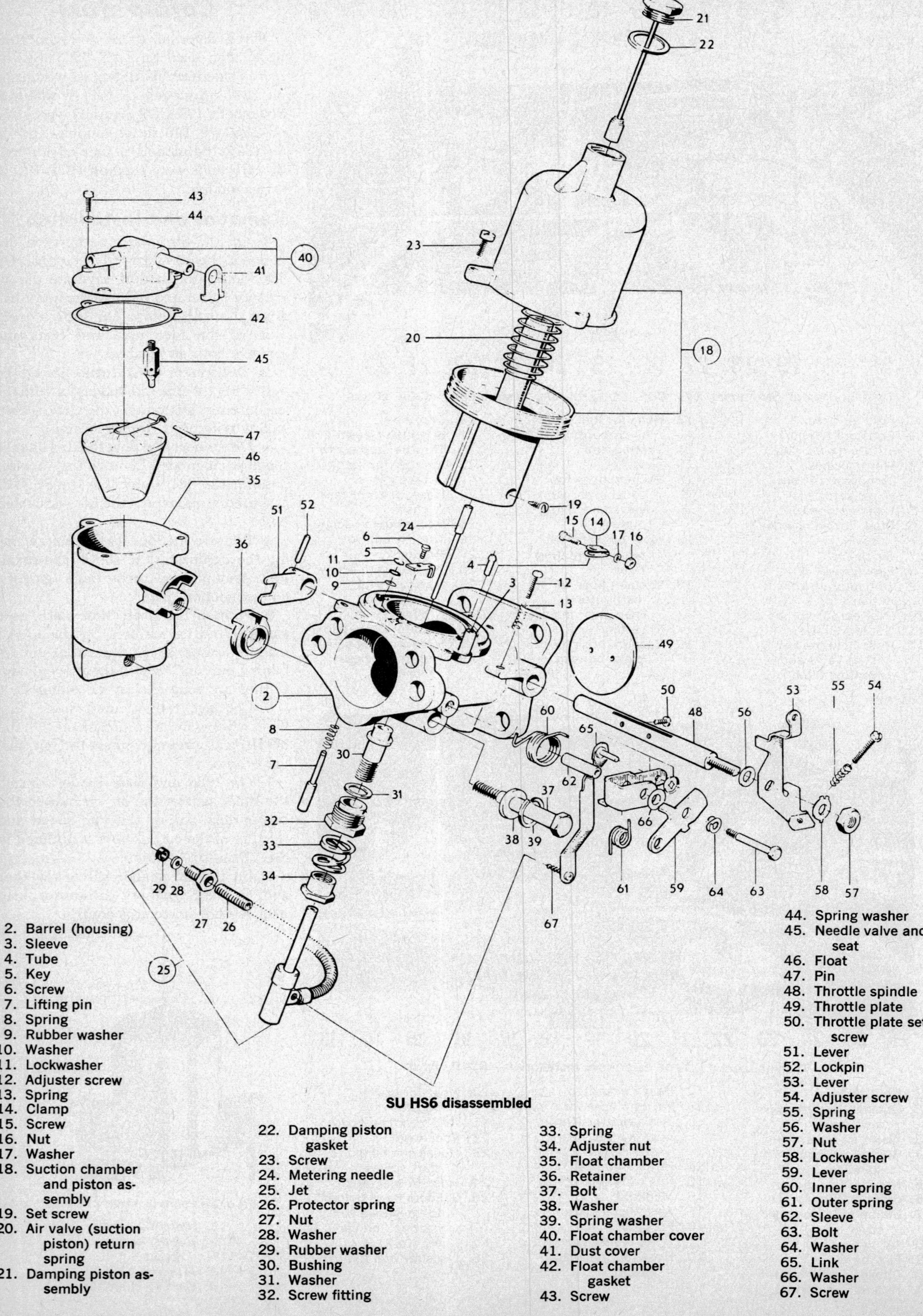

SU HS6 disassembled

2. Barrel (housing)
3. Sleeve
4. Tube
5. Key
6. Screw
7. Lifting pin
8. Spring
9. Rubber washer
10. Washer
11. Lockwasher
12. Adjuster screw
13. Spring
14. Clamp
15. Screw
16. Nut
17. Washer
18. Suction chamber and piston assembly
19. Set screw
20. Air valve (suction piston) return spring
21. Damping piston assembly
22. Damping piston gasket
23. Screw
24. Metering needle
25. Jet
26. Protector spring
27. Nut
28. Washer
29. Rubber washer
30. Bushing
31. Washer
32. Screw fitting
33. Spring
34. Adjuster nut
35. Float chamber
36. Retainer
37. Bolt
38. Washer
39. Spring washer
40. Float chamber cover
41. Dust cover
42. Float chamber gasket
43. Screw
44. Spring washer
45. Needle valve and seat
46. Float
47. Pin
48. Throttle spindle
49. Throttle plate
50. Throttle plate set screw
51. Lever
52. Lockpin
53. Lever
54. Adjuster screw
55. Spring
56. Washer
57. Nut
58. Lockwasher
59. Lever
60. Inner spring
61. Outer spring
62. Sleeve
63. Bolt
64. Washer
65. Link
66. Washer
67. Screw

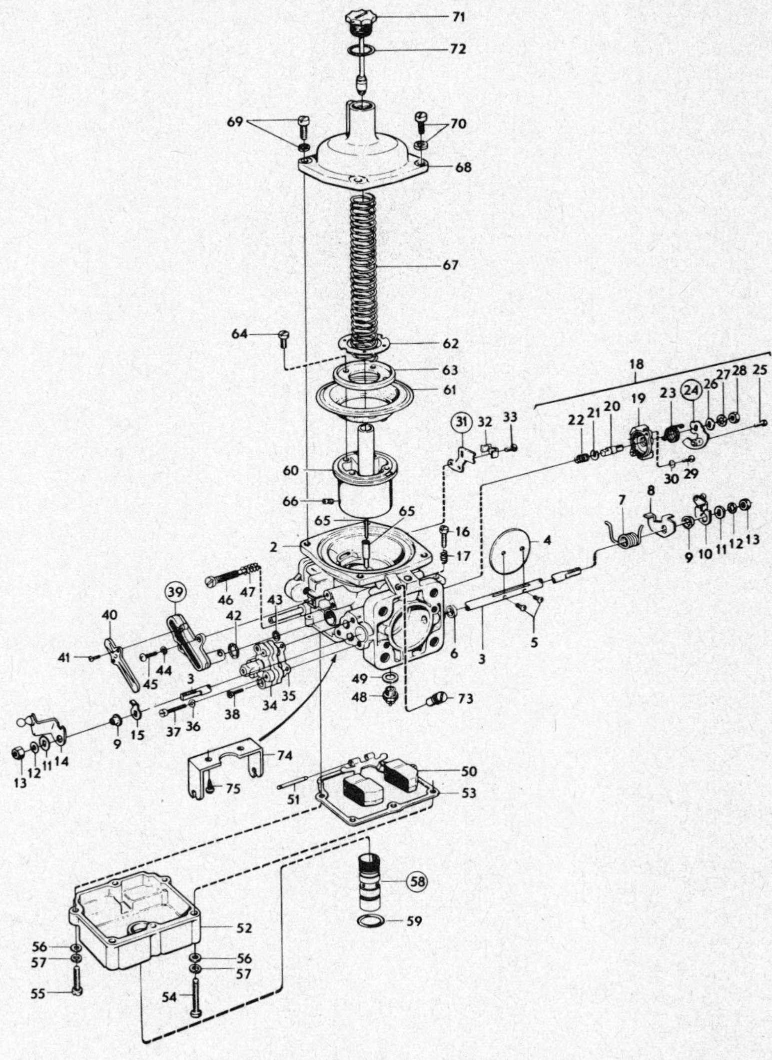

Stromberg 175 CD2 SE disassembled

2. Body
3. Throttle plate spindle
4. Throttle plate
5. Throttle plate set screws
6. Seal
7. Return spring
8. Lever
9. Bushing
10. Lever
11. Spacing masher
12. Lockwasher
13. Nut
14. Lever
15. Lever
16. Adjuster screw
17. Spring
18. Cold start device assembly
19. Cold start device housing
20. Shaft
21. Circlip
22. Spring
23. Return spring
24. Fast idle choke lever
25. Choke cable attaching screw
26. Spacing washer
27. Lockwasher
28. Nut
29. Screw
30. Lockwasher
31. Choke cable support
32. Choke cable retaining clip
33. Screw
34. By-pass valve assembly (front carb only)
35. Gasket
36. Lockwasher
37. Screw
38. Screw
39. Temperature compensator housing
40. Temperature compensator cover
41. Screw
42. Rubber seal
43. Rubber seal
44. Lockwasher
45. Screw
46. Idle trimming screw
47. Spring
48. Needle valve with seat
49. Gasket
50. Float
51. Float hinge pin
52. Floatchamber cover
53. Gasket
54. Screw
55. Screw
56. Washer
57. Lockwasher
58. Floatchamber plug
59. Gasket
60. Air valve
61. Diaphragm
62. Washer
63. Washer
64. Screw
65. Metering needle
66. Metering needle retaining set screw
67. Air valve return spring
68. Suction chamber cover
69. Screw and washer
70. Screw and washer
71. Damping piston assembly
72. Damping piston gasket
73. Plug for air conditioner speed compensator

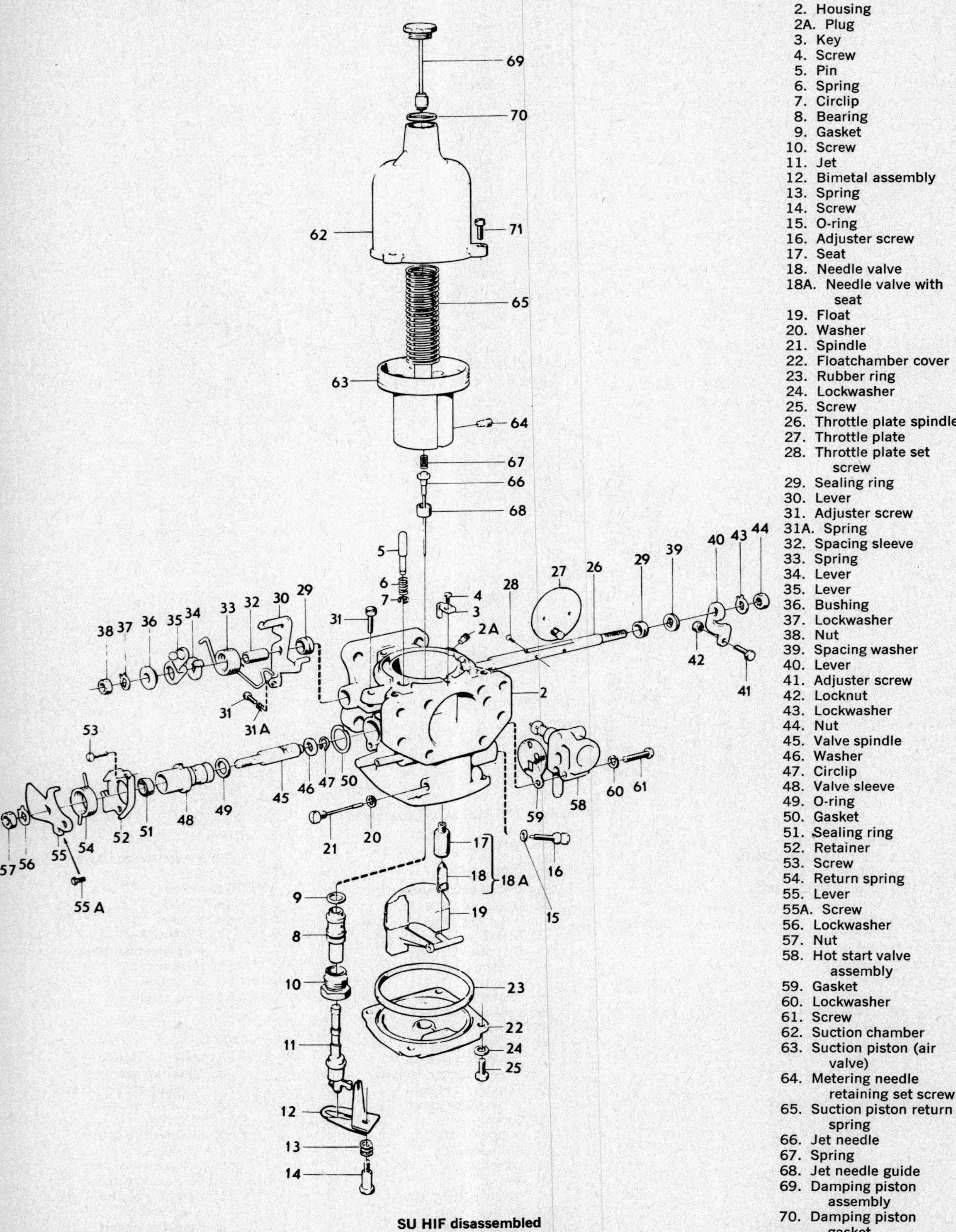

SU HIF disassembled

Carburetor Overhaul

Carburetors are relatively complex units. Proper performance depends upon the cleanliness and proper adjustment of all internal and external components. In addition to the usual adjustments performed at the regular tune-up intervals, it eventually becomes necessary to remove, disassemble, clean, and overhaul the entire carburetor(s), in order to restore its original performance. To overhaul a carburetor, first purchase the proper rebuilding kit. Read the instructions and study the exploded view of the carburetor thoroughly prior to the actual removal and disassembly.

After reading the detailed carburetor rebuilding instructions, the following general procedure may be used. Remove the carburetor and place it on a clean work table. Disassemble the carburetor by removing the screws securing the upper and lower sections together. Remove the damping piston, air valve, spring, metering needle, fuel jet (SU only), and float assembly, and soak all metal parts in carburetor cleaning solvent. Scrape all old gasket material from the mating surfaces. After the metal parts have been soaked to remove all gum, varnish, and dirt, rinse them off with a clean, uncontaminated, solvent solution. Blow out all passages with compressed air and allow them to air dry. Do not use drills or wire to clean the passages. Check the throttle shaft and choke disc for excessive wear. Inspect the float hinge pins for distortion. All nonmetal parts that are not being replaced should be wiped clean with a lint-free cloth. After all of the parts have been sufficiently cleaned or replaced, assemble the carburetor using new gaskets and seals, and, on Zenith-Stromberg carburetors, a new air valve diaphragm. If any of the replacement seals in the SU carburetor are cork, they must first be soaked in penetrating oil for a minimum of a half hour to avoid splitting during installation. Assemble the float chamber and adjust the float height. Assemble the air valve, spring, and metering needle with setscrew into the upper housing. Join the upper and lower housing together, taking care to properly align the metering needle and fuel jet. When the jet and needle are installed correctly, the air valve should drop to the bridge with a distinctive click. Any binding of these two parts will result in poor carburetor performance. Install the damping piston. Install the carburetor on its manifold with a new gasket. Adjust the choke and throttle linkage, and the idle speed and mixture.

Centering the Fuel Jet

SU HS6

Place the carburetor on its side with the intake manifold flange facing down.

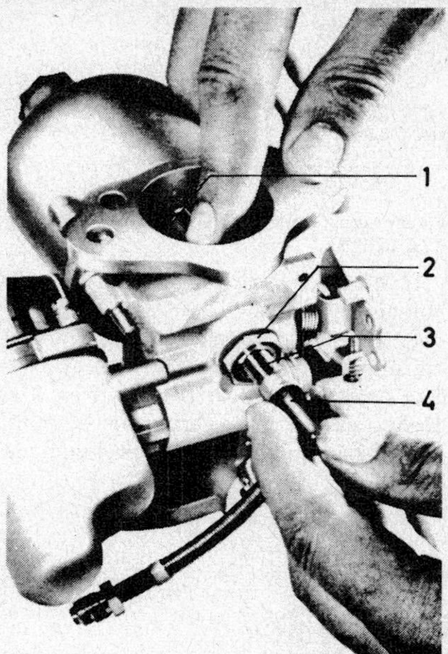

Centering the fuel jet—SU HS6 carburetor

1. Lower section of air valve
2. Locknut
3. Jet sleeve
4. Jet

Screw in the jet adjusting nut until the top of the jet is raised above the bridge. Loosen the locknut and press the air valve (suction piston) against the bridge, move it back and forth a few times, and then tighten the locknut. Make sure that the jet is centered correctly and not binding by lifting the air valve about ¼ in. and then releasing it. If the jet is centered correctly, the air valve will drop to the bridge with a distinctive click. After centering the jet, adjust the idle speed and mixture.

Throttle Linkage Adjustment

SU HS6

1. Position a 0.02 in. feeler gauge at point "A" between the lever and its abutment. Screw out the fast idle and idle screws so that the throttle flap is fully closed.

2. Loosen the locknuts on the intermediate shaft. Press the outer ends of the levers on the intermediate shaft carefully downward so that the pins just touch the lower tooth on the throttle flap spindle levers, taking care not to disturb the throttle flap itself. Tighten the locknuts, making sure that the end float of the shaft is equal in both directions, and that there is a small axial clearance between the levers on the intermediate shaft and the throttle flap spindle levers.

3. Remove the feeler gauge. Make sure that both throttle flaps are actuated simultaneously and equally.

4. Screw in the idle screws so that they just touch the throttle levers when the throttles are closed. Then screw the idle screws in a further ½ turn. If the setting of the fuel jet was disturbed, readjust it according to the procedure for setting idle speed and mixture in the "Tune-Up" section.

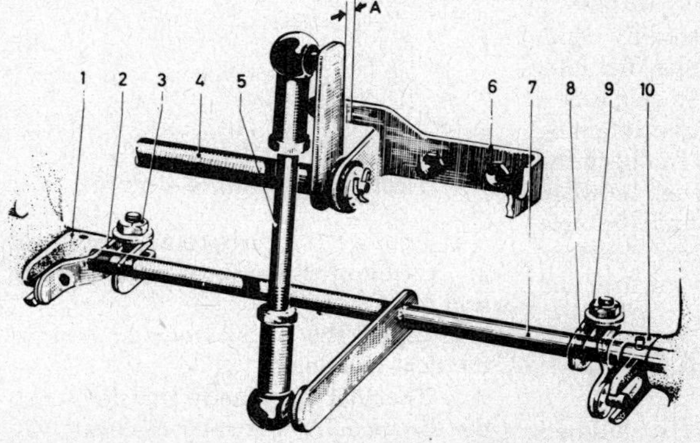

A—clearance between abutment and lever
1. Lever on throttle flap spindle
2. Lever on intermediary shaft
3. Lock nut
4. Control shaft
5. Link
6. Bracket
7. Intermediary shaft
8. Lever on intermediary shaft
9. Lock nut
10. Lever on throttle flap spindle

Throttle linkage—SU HS6 carburetors

Zenith-Stromberg 175 CD2 SE, SU HIF

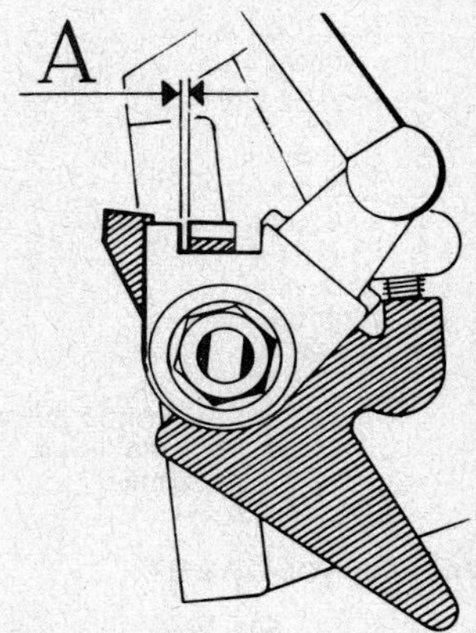

Throttle linkage adjustment—Stromberg 175 CD2 SE.

On each carburetor, the link rods should maintain a 0.004 in. clearance "A" between the lever and the throttle spindle flange when the throttle control is against its stop on the intake manifold bracket. To adjust this clearance, remove the link rod ball socket from the carburetor lever ball stud, and turn the socket on the threaded link rod until the adjustment is correct.

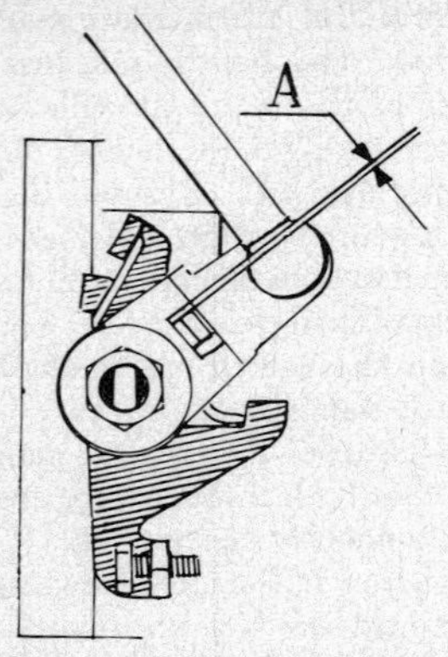

Throttle linkage adjustment—SU HIF

Float level adjustment—Zenith-Stromberg 175 CD2 SE.

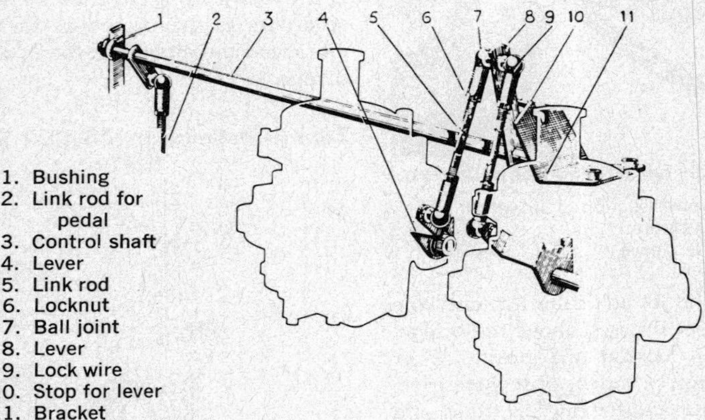

1. Bushing
2. Link rod for pedal
3. Control shaft
4. Lever
5. Link rod
6. Locknut
7. Ball joint
8. Lever
9. Lock wire
10. Stop for lever
11. Bracket

Throttle linkage—Stromberg 175 CD2 SE installation shown, SU HIF installation similar.

Float Adjustment

SU HS6

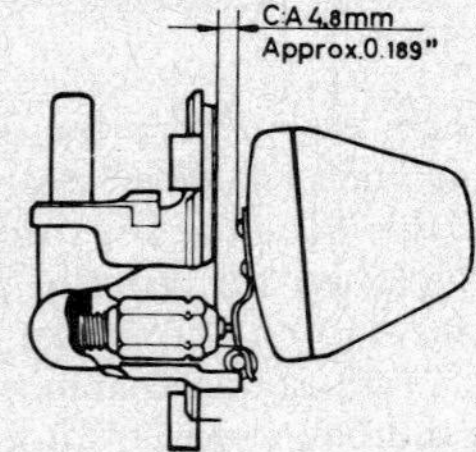

Float level adjustment—SU HS6

Although these carburetors are relatively insensitive to float level variations, the float level may be adjusted by bending the float arm between the fuel inlet needle valve and the float. To gain access to the float, remove the three retaining screws and the float cover. To check the float level, insert a feeler gauge between the float arm lower rivet and the float bowl base. The float is properly adjusted when the distance between the float and the base is 0.189 in.

Zenith-Stromberg 175 CD2 SE Carburetor

1. Remove the carburetor as outlined in "Carburetor Removal and Installation."

2. Invert the carburetor and remove the float chamber.

3. The float is correctly adjusted when the high point of the float is ⅝ in., and the low point of the float is ½ in. from the sealing surface of the carburetor housing.

4. To adjust the float level, bend the tang at the float chamber inlet valve. Do not bend the arm between the float and the pin.

5. When the proper adjustment has been made, install the float chamber to the housing with a new gasket.

6. Install the carburetor on the intake manifold as outlined in "Carburetor Removal and Installation."

SU HIF Carburetor

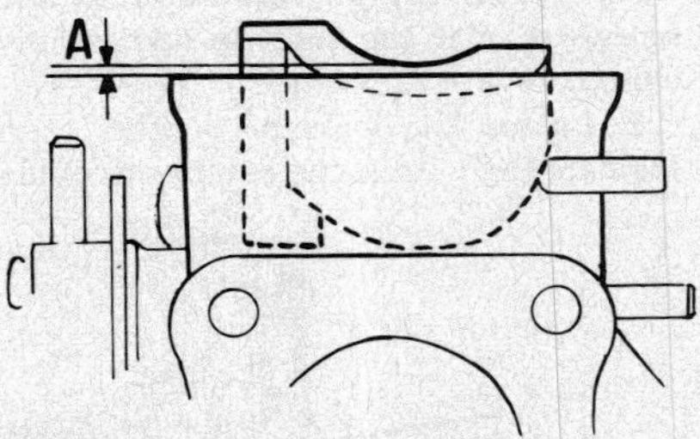

Float level adjustment—SU HIF

1. Remove the carburetor as outlined in "Carburetor Removal and Installation."

2. Invert the carburetor and remove the float chamber.

3. The float is correctly adjusted when the distance "A" between the float "valley" and the housing flange is approximately 0.02–0.06 in.

4. The float is adjusted by bending the metal tab at the float chamber inlet valve.

5. When the correct adjustment has been made, install the float chamber to the housing with a new gasket.

6. Install the carburetor as outlined in "Carburetor Removal and Installation."

Fast Idle Adjustment

SU HS6

Pull out the choke control 0.6 in. from the dash. Loosen the locking screw for the choke control cable. Lift the choke control lever enough to allow the jet to start to go down. Adjust the fast idle screw so that it just touches the fast idle cam on the lever when the jet starts to go down. Tighten the control cable locking screw. Check that both carburetors are operated to the same extent by pulling the choke control cable 0.813 in. and observing the jets as they go down. Adjust the setting if the jets do not go down equally.

Zenith-Stromberg 175 CD2 SE Carburetor

Pull out the choke control one inch from the dash. If the choke is adjusted correctly, the mark on the rapid idle cam (see illustration) should be opposite the centerline of the fast idle screw. Adjust the fast idle with the fast idle screws to 1100–1300 rpm on both carburetors.

SU HIF Carburetor

Pull out the choke control 0.8 in. from the dash. Adjust the fast idle with the fast idle screws to 1100–1600 rpm on both carburetors.

Damping Piston Replacement

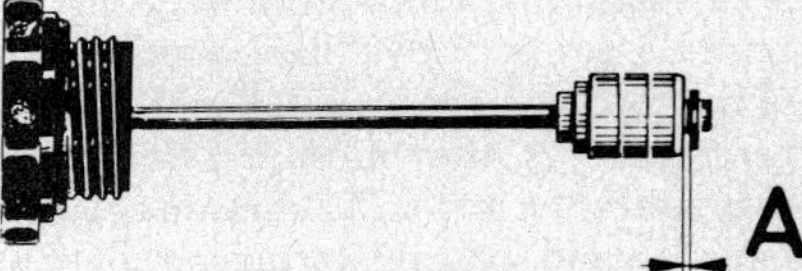

Damping piston clearance

If the engine stumbles upon acceleration, and the damping cylinders are filled to their proper level with oil, the problem may be with the damping pistons themselves. Unscrew the black knobs on top of the carburetors and remove the damping pistons. If the axial clearance "A" between the bottom of the piston and the retaining clip is not 0.04–0.07 in., the damping piston must be replaced as a unit.

Fuel Injection

Volvo has made Bosch electronic fuel injection available since 1970, when it was standard equipment on the 1800 series. The system was optional on the 140 series in 1971, and on the 164 in 1972.

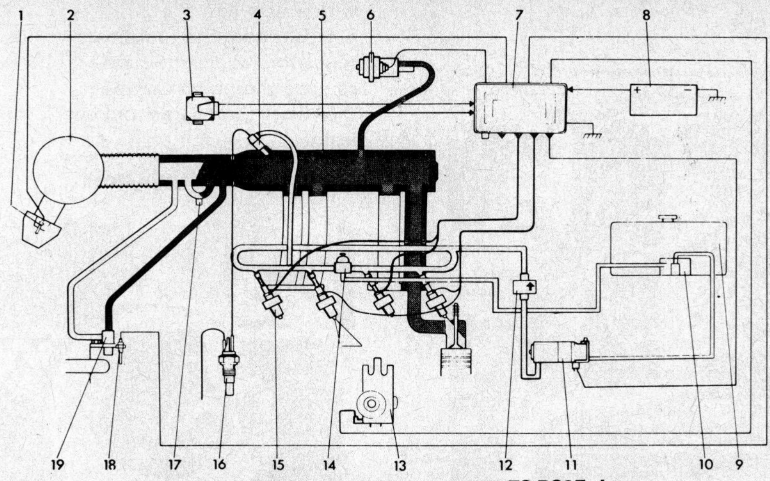

Fuel injection principle of operation—1972- 73 B20F shown.

1. Temperature sensor for induction air
2. Air cleaner
3. Throttle valve switch
4. Cold start valve
5. Inlet duct
6. Pressure sensor
7. Control unit (electronic)
8. Battery
9. Fuel tank
10. Fuel filter, suction side
11. Fuel pump
12. Fuel filter, discharge side
13. Triggering contacts in distributor
14. Pressure regulator
15. Injectors
16. Thermal timer contact
17. Idling adjusting screw
18. Temperature sensor for coolant
19. Auxiliary air regulator

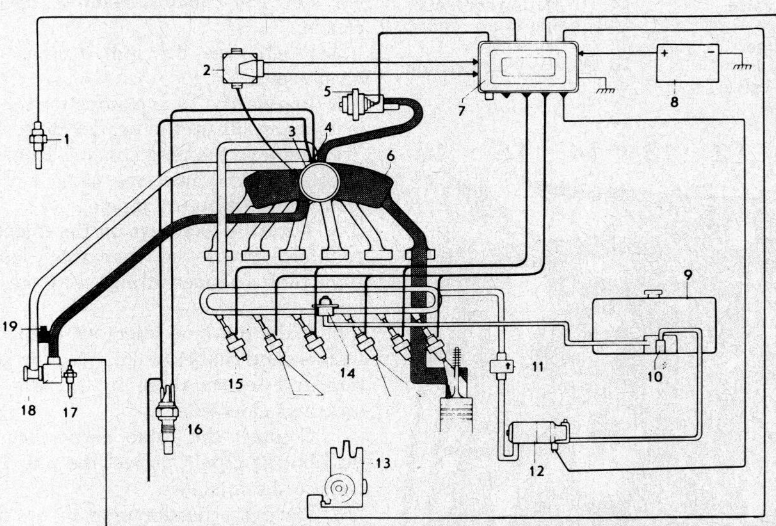

Fuel injection principle of operation—1972-73 B30F shown

1. Temperature sensor for induction air
2. Throttle valve switch
3. Throttle housing
4. Cold start valve
5. Pressure sensor
6. Inlet duct
7. Control unit (electronic)
8. Battery
9. Fuel tank
10. Fuel filter, suction side
11. Fuel filter, discharge side
12. Fuel pump
13. Triggering contacts in distributor
14. Pressure regulator
15. Injectors
16. Thermal timer contact
17. Temperature sensor for coolant
18. Auxiliary air regulator
19. Idling adjusting screw

For 1973, all Volvos imported into the U.S. will be equipped with the system.

The complete system contains the following componets: electronic control unit (brain), electric fuel pump, fuel filter, fuel pressure regulator, fuel injectors, cold-start valve, inlet duct (for intake air), throttle valve switch, auxiliary air regulator, intake air temperature sensor, coolant temperature sensor, intake air pressure sensor, and the triggering contacts in the ignition distributor.

Fuel Injection System Precautions

Due to the highly sensitive nature of the Bosch electronic fuel injection system, the following special precautions must be strictly adhered to in order to avoid damage to the system.

1. Do not operate the engine with the battery disconnected.
2. Do not utilize a high-speed battery charger as a starting aid.
3. When using a high-speed battery charger to charge the battery while it is installed in the vehicle, at least one battery cable must be disconnected.
4. Do not allow the control unit to be subjected to temperatures exceeding 185° F, such as when the vehicle is being baked after painting. If there is a risk of the temperature exceeding 185° F, the control unit must be removed.
5. The engine must not be started when the ambient temperature exceeds 158° F, or damage to the control unit will result.
6. The ignition must be in the off position when disconnecting or connecting the control unit.
7. When working on the fuel system, take care not to allow dirt to enter the system. Small dust particles may jam fuel injectors.

Component Replacement

The fuel injection system is repaired simply by replacing the defective component. There are adjustments that can be made to the pressure regulator, throttle valve, throttle valve switch, throttle stop-screw, and the fuel mixture. To make resistance checks, use an ohmmeter, and for continuity checks, a 12 V test light. If the control unit is defective, return it to a qualified repair agency and install a new unit.

Control Unit

1. On 1800 series models, disconnect the defroster hose, remove the control unit bracket retaining screws, and lower the unit to the floor. On 140 series and 164 models, move the passenger's front seat all the way back, unscrew the bolt securing the seat's front, move the seat forward while folding the seat bottom to the rear, remove the control unit retaining screws, and draw out the unit.
2. Remove the screw for the cap holding the cable harness to the unit. Pull out the plastic cover strip.
3. Construct a puller out of 5/64 in. welding wire (see illustration) to disconnect the main plug contact. Insert the puller in the rear of the control unit and pull out the plug carefully.

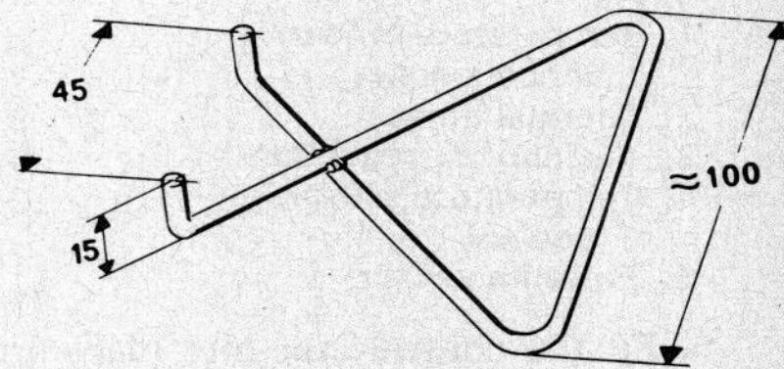

Puller for control unit plug contact

4. Press the plug contact firmly into the new or reconditioned control unit. Fit the plastic cover strip, retaining cap, and screw.

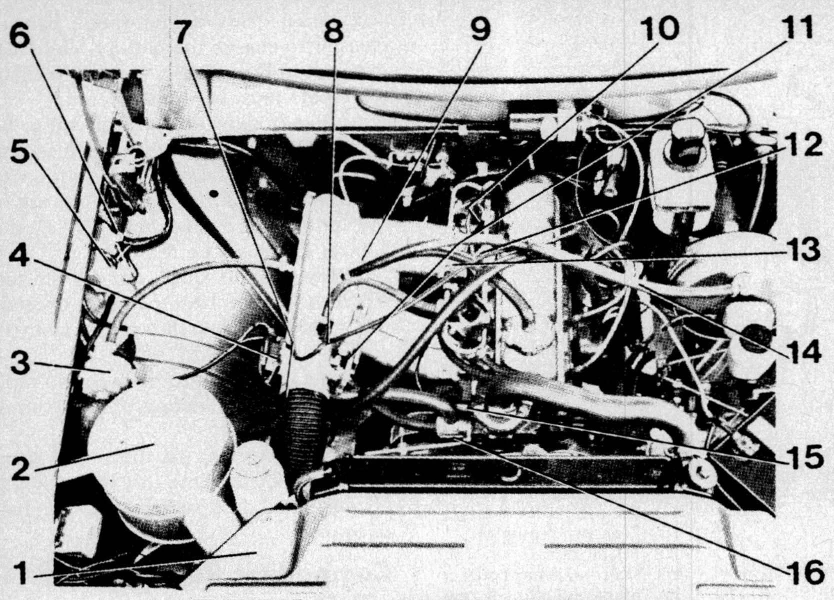

Fuel injection system installation—1972-73 B20F shown, 1970-71 B20E similar

1. Temperature sensor (induction air)
2. Air cleaner
3. Pressure sensor
4. Throttle switch
5. Pump relay
6. Main relay
7. Screw for adjusting idling (not visible)
8. Cold start valve
9. Inlet duct
10. Thermal timer
11. Stop screw for throttle valve
12. Injector
13. Pressure regulator
14. Triggering contacts
15. Temperature sensor (coolant)
16. Auxiliary air regulator

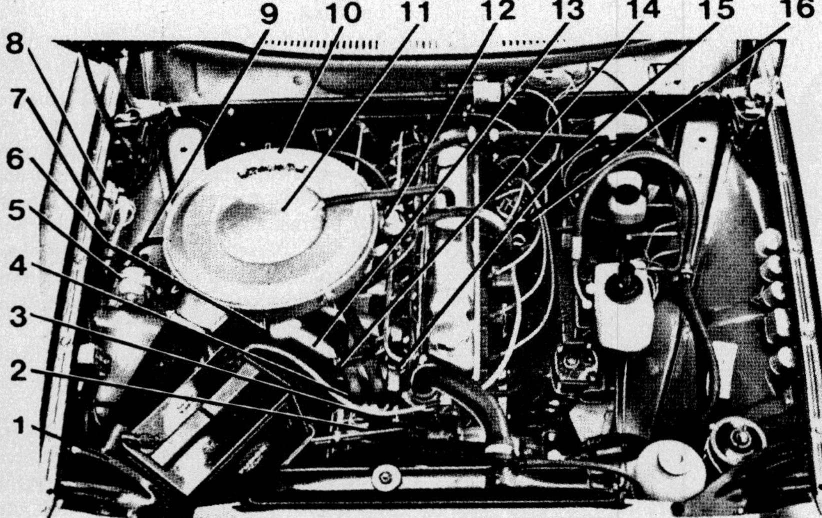

Fuel injection system installation—1972-73 B30F shown

1. Temperature sensor, induction air
2. Thermal timer
3. Auxiliary air regulator
4. Temperature sensor, coolant
5. Pressure sensor
6. Throttle switch
7. Pump relay
8. Main relay
9. Cold start valve
10. Stop screw for throttle valve
11. Air cleaner
12. Pressure regulator
13. Inlet duct
14. Screw for adjusting idling
15. Injector
16. Triggering contacts

5. Fit the control unit into place and install its retaining screws. On 1800 series models, connect the defroster hose. On 140 series and 164 models, secure the seat front.

Pressure Regulator

If the pressure regulator cannot be adjusted to 28 psi with its adjusting nut, it must be replaced.

1. Place pinch clamps on the three fuel hoses connected to the regulator.

2. Loosen the hose clamps and remove the hoses.

3. On 1970–71 models, remove the regulator from its bracket and replace it with a new one.

4. Connect the fuel hoses to the new regulator, tighten the hose clamps, and remove the pinch clamps.

5. Start the engine and check for fuel leaks.

Fuel Injectors

Removing injector

1. On 164 models, remove the air cleaner.

2. Pinch shut the fuel hose to the header pipe.

3. Loosen the hose clamps for the injectors and lift up the header pipe.

4. Remove the plug contacts from the injectors. Disconnect the cable harness from the distributing pipe.

5. Turn the lockrings on the injectors counterclockwise so that they loosen from their bayonet fittings. Lift out the injectors.

6. Place the new injectors, with new washers and rubber sealing rings, in position and secure them by turning the lockrings clockwise.

7. Connect the cable harness at the distributing pipe. Connect the plug contacts to the injectors.

8. Place the header pipe in position,

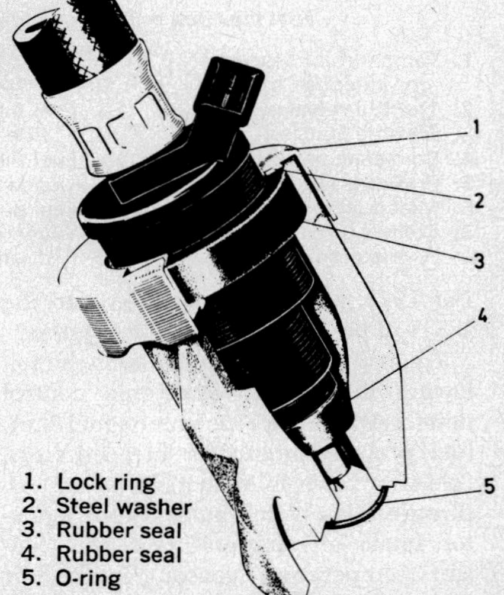

1. Lock ring
2. Steel washer
3. Rubber seal
4. Rubber seal
5. O-ring

Injector with holder

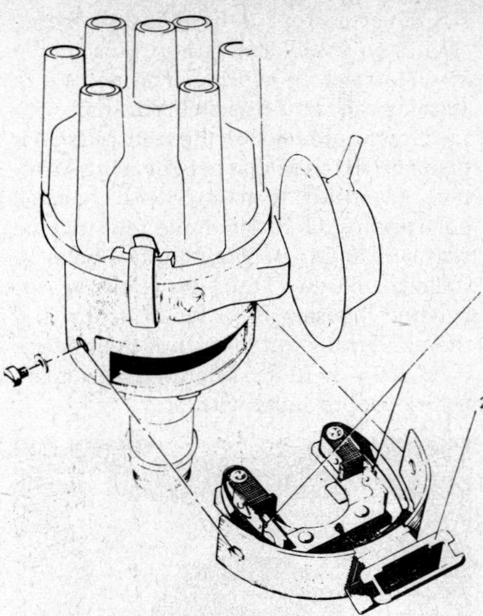

Distributor with control device—B30F shown, B20E and B20F similar

1. Triggering contacts
2. Electrical connection

and tighten the hose clamps. Remove the pinch clamps.

9. On 164 models, install the air cleaner.

Cold-Start Valve

1. On 164 models, remove the air cleaner.
2. Pinch shut the fuel line to the valve.
3. Remove the plug contact and the fuel hose from the valve.
4. Remove the two retaining screws and the cold-start valve from the inlet duct.
5. Place the new cold-start valve in position with packing and install the retaining screws.
6. Connect the plug contact and fuel hose to the valve. Remove the pinch clamp.
7. On 164 models, install the air cleaner.

Thermal Timer

1. Drain the cooling system.
2. Disconnect the plug contacts and unscrew the thermal timer from the cylinder head.
3. Install a new timer and connect the plug contacts.
4. Refill the cooling system.

Throttle Valve Switch

1. Disconnect the plug contact from the switch. Remove the two retaining screws and pull the switch straight out of the inlet duct.
2. Fit the new switch to the inlet duct and install the retaining screws. Connect the plug contact.
3. Adjust the switch as outlined in "Throttle Valve Switch Adjustment."

Auxiliary Air Regulator

1. Drain the cooling system.
2. Remove the plug contact from the temperature sensor and disconnect the air hoses from the regulator.
3. Remove the two retaining bolts and draw out the regulator.
4. Using a new sealing ring, position the new regulator to the cylinder head and install the retaining bolts.
5. Connect the plug contact and the two air hoses.
6. Refill the cooling system.

Intake Air Temperature Sensor

1. On 164 models, remove the right drip protection, and the air hose from the right side.
2. Disconnect the four-way plug contact from the sensor.
3. Unscrew the old sensor and install a new one, taking care not to overtighten it.
4. Plug in the four-way contact for the sensor.
5. On 164 models, install the right air hose and drip protection.

Coolant Temperature Sensor

1. Drain a portion of the cooling system so that the coolant level in the radiator and engine is below the temperature sensor.
2. Disconnect the plug contact from the sensor.
3. Unscrew the old sensor and install a new one with a new sealing ring.
4. Connect the plug contact.
5. Top up the cooling system.

Pressure Sensor

1. Disconnect the four-way plug contact and the air hose from the sensor.
2. Remove the three screws retaining the sensor to the right wheel housing.
3. Transfer the attaching bracket to the new pressure sensor.
4. Position the new sensor to the wheel well and install the retaining screws.
5. Connect the plug contact and the air hose to the sensor.

Triggering Contacts

1. Remove the distributor as outlined under "Distributor Removal and Installation."
2. Remove the two screws securing the triggering contacts holder to the distributor and then pull out the holder.
3. Lubricate the fiber pieces of the contact breaker lever on the new holder with Bosch Ft 1V4 or similar silicone cam lobe grease.
4. Check to see that the rubber ring is not damaged. Replace if necessary.
5. Install the new holder in the distributor and tighten the retaining screws.
6. Install the distributor as outlined in "Distributor Removal and Installation."

Component Testing and Adjustment

Control Unit

The idle mixture may be adjusted with the slotted knob on the control unit. This operation is best performed with the use of a CO meter. Refer to the "Fuel Injection System Idle Mixture Adjustment" for details.

The control unit may be tested only with the help of sophisticated test equipment available, again, only at the dealer level.

Pressure Regulator

The regulator may be adjusted with its adjusting nut. Pinch and disconnect the flexible fuel hose between the pressure regulator and the header pipe and insert a tee fitting and pressure gauge. Tighten the fuel connections and start the engine. Slacken the locknut and adjust the pressure to 28 psi. If the regulator cannot be adjusted properly, it must be replaced. Remove the tee fitting and gauge, and connect the fuel hoses.

Throttle Valve

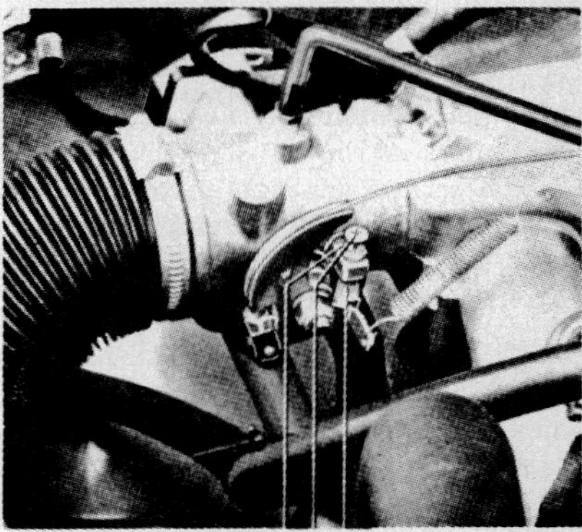

Throttle valve adjustment—B20E, B20F

1. Locknut
2. Stop screw
3. Stop on throttle valve spindle

Throttle valve adjustment—B30F

1. Stop screw
2. Locknut
3. Stop on valve spindle

The throttle valve may be adjusted with its stopscrew near the mouth of the inlet duct. Release the stopscrew locknut for the throttle valve switch, and back off the screw several turns so that it does not lie against the throttle valve spindle stop. Make sure that the valve is completely closed. Screw in the stopscrew so that it contacts the spindle stop. At this point, turn the stopscrew ¼–1/3 additional turn and tighten the locknut. Check to see that the switch does not jam in the closed position. Proceed to adjust the throttle valve switch as follows.

NOTE: *The stopscrew must not be used for idle adjustment.*

Throttle Valve Switch

The throttle valve switch may be adjusted with an ohmmeter. Connect the ohmmeter to the control unit (contacts 14 and 17 for four-cylinder, and contacts 9 and 14 for six-cylinder). Loosen the screws slightly so that the switch may be rotated. Scribe a mark at the upper switch screw on the inlet duct if one is not there already. Close the throttle valve by turning the switch clockwise as far as it will go. Then, observing the ohmmeter, carefully turn the switch counterclockwise until the ohmmeter registers 0 (zero). At this point, the switch is turned a further 1° counterclockwise (½ graduation mark at upper screw), and both switch screws are tightened. Check to make sure that the ohmmeter reading rises to infinity when the throttle valve opens approximately 1°.

Auxiliary Air Regulator

To check the operation of the auxiliary air regulator, start the engine and allow it to reach operating temperature (176° F). Make a note of the idle speed and then disconnect the hose between the inlet duct and the regulator. While covering the hose opening with your hand, check to see that the idle speed does not drop significantly over the first reading. A drop in idle speed indicates a leak in the regulator, requiring its replacement.

MANUAL TRANSMISSION

Manual transmissions installed in 1967–73 Volvos are the M40, M41, M400, and the M410. All are fully synchronized four speed transmissions, with all forward gears in constant mesh. The M41 and M410 units are equipped with Laycock-de-Normanville overdrive units, and except for the overdrive engaging switch and push plate, are identical to their M40 and M400 counterparts. The heavy-duty, top cover, Volvo manufactured M40 is installed as standard equipment on 140 series models. The similar M41 overdrive transmission is optional on 140 series models, and standard equipment on most 1800E, 1800S, and all 1800ES models. The extra heavy-duty, top cover, ZF manufactured M400 is standard equipment on 164 models. The similar M410 overdrive transmission is optional on the 164, and was installed on some early 1970 1800E models.

Removal and Installation

The transmission or the transmission-overdrive assembly may be removed with the engine installed in the vehicle.

140 series

1. If an engine lifting (support) apparatus, such as SVO 2727, is available, install it in the engine compartment. If using an SVO 2727, secure the lifting hook around the exhaust pipe. The purpose of supporting the rear of the engine here is to prevent damage to the viscous fan, radiator, or front engine mounts by limiting the downward travel of the rear of the engine when the transmission support crossmember is removed. If no lifting apparatus is available, place a jack with a protective wooden block beneath the engine oil pan. Do not place the jack under the flywheel (clutch) housing.
2. Lift up the rubber boot, unscrew the protective cover, and remove the gear shift lever from the transmission.
3. Jack up the vehicle sufficiently to allow removal of the transmission. Maintain the car at a level attitude and place jackstands beneath the jack points for support. Remove the lower drain plug from the transmission and drain the oil.
4. Slowly loosen the nuts for the transmission support crossmember. Make sure that the supporting apparatus or the jack prevent the rear of the engine from lowering. Remove the crossmember. Disconnect the front universal joint from the transmission (or overdrive) output shaft flange. Disconnect the speedometer cable. Disconnect the rear engine mount and the exhaust pipe bracket.
5. Allow the rear of the engine to drop 0.8 in. Disconnect the back-up light wires, and the wires for the overdrive, if so equipped.
6. Remove the four bolts which retain the transmission to the flywheel (clutch) housing. It may be necessary to use a universal joint on the wrench to gain access to the two upper bolts. Before removing the transmission, keep in mind that it is quite heavy, and a hydraulic floor jack may offer some support and maneuverability as the box is being removed. To remove the transmission, pull it straight out to the rear.
7. While the transmission is removed, it is a good time to inspect the condition of the clutch and the throwout bearing. Replace the throwout bearing if it is scored or if it has been emitting metal-to-metal noises.
8. Reverse steps 1–6 to install, being careful to install two guide pins in the flywheel (clutch) housing. This will aid in aligning the transmission input shaft with the clutch spline when the transmission is being fitted to the flywheel housing. After two transmission-to-flywheel housing bolts are installed, the guide pins may be removed and the remaining two bolts installed. Torque the transmission-to-flywheel housing bolts to 45 ft. lbs, and the universal joint-to-output shaft flange bolts to 25–30 ft. lbs. Fill the transmission to the proper level with oil.

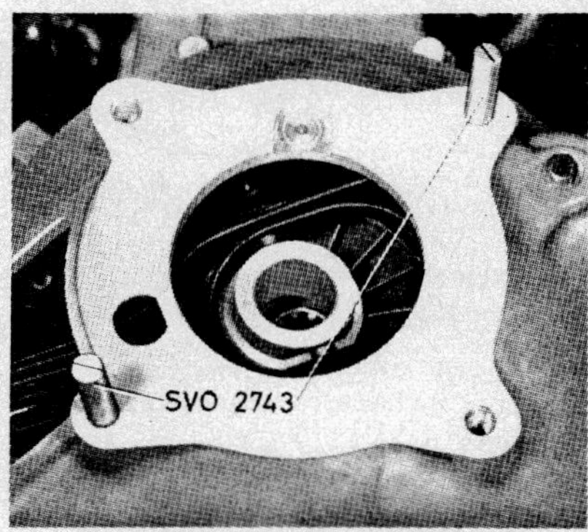

Transmission guide pins installed

164

1. Follow steps 1–3 under "Transmission Removal and Installation" for the 140 series.
2. Remove the upper radiator bolts and the exhaust manifold flange nuts. Disconnect the negative battery cable, the throttle shaft and clutch cable from the flywheel (clutch) housing.
3. Slowly loosen the nuts for the transmission support crossmember. Making sure that the rear of the engine remains supported, remove the crossmember. Disconnect the exhaust pipe bracket and the speedometer cable. Disconnect the front universal joint from the transmission (or overdrive) output shaft flange.
4. Lower the rear of the engine approximately 1.8 in. Disconnect the back-up light wires and the wires for the overdrive, if so equipped.
5. Place a hydraulic floor jack beneath the transmission. Remove the bolts which retain the transmission and flywheel (clutch) housing assembly to the engine. Leave the starter connected but position it to one side. Remove the transmission by pulling it straight to the rear.
6. Prior to assembly, inspect the condition of the clutch and throwout bearing. Replace the bearing if it is scored or noisy in operation.
7. Reverse steps 1–5 to install. Torque the flywheel (clutch) housing-to-engine bolts to 45 ft. lbs, and the universal joint-to-output shaft flange bolts to 25–30 ft. lbs. Fill the transmission to the proper level with oil.

1800 series (M41)

1. Remove the storage console from the transmission tunnel. Lift up the boot, unscrew the protective cover and remove the gear shift lever.

2. Disconnect the negative battery cable. Remove the radiator attaching bolts.

3. Jack up the vehicle sufficiently to allow removal of the transmission. Install jackstands. Remove the lower drain plug and drain the transmission oil.

4. Remove the bolts which retain the driveshaft to the flanges, and remove the attaching bolts for the support bearings. Pull the driveshaft approximately 0.4 in. to the rear.

5. Place a jack, with a protective wooden block, beneath the oil pan of the engine.

6. Disconnect the exhaust pipe bracket and the speedometer. Remove the rear engine mount. Slowly loosen the nuts for the transmission support crossmember making sure that the jack supports the rear of the engine.

7. Lower the engine approximately 0.8 in. Disconnect the electric cables from the transmission.

8. Remove the four bolts which secure the transmission to the flywheel (clutch) housing. It may be necessary to use a universal joint to gain access to the two upper bolts. Support the weight of the transmission with another jack and pull the unit straight out to the rear.

9. Inspect the condition of the clutch and throwout bearing. Replace the bearing if it is scored or has been noisy in operation.

10. Reverse steps 1–8 to install, making sure to install two guide pins in the flywheel (clutch) housing to aid in aligning the transmission input shaft with the clutch spline when the transmission is being fitted to the flywheel housing. After two transmission–to–flywheel housing bolts are installed, the guide pins may be removed and the remaining two bolts installed. Torque the bolts to 45 ft. lbs. Fill the transmission to the proper level with oil.

1800 series (M410)

1. Disconnect the upper and lower radiator hoses and drain the cooling system. Disconnect the heater hoses and the air intake hose. Pull up the rubber boot, unscrew the protective cover and remove the gear shift lever.

2. Raise the vehicle sufficiently to remove the transmission, and install jackstands. Disconnect the driveshaft, exhaust pipe bracket, clutch cable, the electrical wires for the back-up lights and the overdrive.

3. Place a hydraulic floor jack beneath the transmission, and remove the transmission support crossmember.

4. Place a protective wooden block between the rear of the engine and the firewall. Lower the jack and the rear of the engine until the engine contacts the wooden block.

5. Remove the bolts which secure the flywheel (clutch) housing to the engine. Leave the starter connected but position it to one side. Remove the transmission by pulling it straight to the rear.

6. Prior to installation, inspect the condition of the clutch and throwout bearing. Replace the bearing if it is scored or has been noisy in operation.

7. Reverse steps 1–5 to install. Torque the flywheel (clutch) housing–to–engine bolts to 45 ft. lbs. Fill the transmission to the proper level with oil.

Overhaul

M40, M41

The following procedure applies to units without overdrive. If the transmission has overdrive, first remove the overdrive.

Disassembly

1. Place the transmission in a support fixture.

2. Unscrew the bolts for the transmission cover. Lift off the cover. Remove the springs and interlock balls for the selector rails.

3. Remove the cover over the selector rails. Unscrew the selector fork bolts.

4. Slide the selector fork backward to 1st speed position. Drive out the pin slightly (it must not foul 1st gear). Then move the selector fork forward sufficiently to allow the pin to pass in front of the gear. Drive out the pin.

5. Slide out the selector rails. When doing this, hold the selector forks so that they do not jam on the rails. Remove the selector forks.

6. Unscrew the bolts for the rear cover. Turn the cover so that it does not lock the shafts for the idler and reverse gears (early production only. On late production, there is no locking tab). Drive out the shaft for the idler gear. The shaft must be driven out backward. Let the idler gear fall into the bottom of the transmission.

7. Pull out the mainshaft.

8. Remove the cover over the input shaft. Pry out the oil seal from the cover with a screwdriver.

9. Drive out the input shaft. If necessary, remove the circlip and press the ball bearing off the shaft.

10. Take out the idler gear. Pull out the shaft for the reverse gear. Take out the reverse gear and other parts.

11a. Transmission with overdrive (M41): Remove the circlip and press off the rotor for the overdrive oil pump. Remove the circlip for the mainshaft rear bearing. Slide the engaging sleeve for 1st and 2nd forward. Place the shaft in a press and support under 1st gear. Press out the shaft.

11b. Transmissions without overdrive: Unscrew the yoke (flange) nut. Slide the engaging sleeve for 1st and 2nd forward. Place the shaft in a press and support under 1st gear. Press out the shaft with a drift.

12. Remove the synchronizing cone, thrust washer, engaging sleeves, engaging springs and snap rings from the shaft.

13. Remove the circlip on the front end of the shaft. Pull off the synchronizing hub and 3rd gear with a puller. Remove the thrust washer.

14. Remove the circlip and then the thrust washer, 2nd gear, synchronizing cone and spring.

15. Remove the oil seal from the rear cover and take out the speedometer gear. If necessary, remove the circlip and press out the ball bearing.

Inspection

Check the gears, particularly for cracks or chips on the tooth surfaces. Damaged or worn gears must be replaced. Check the synchronizing cones and all the other synchronizing components. Damaged or worn parts must be replaced. Check the ball bearings, particularly for scoring or cracks on the races or balls.

Assembly

1. Press the ball bearing into the rear cover. Install the circlip. There are different sizes of circlips, so select one which fits snugly into the groove.

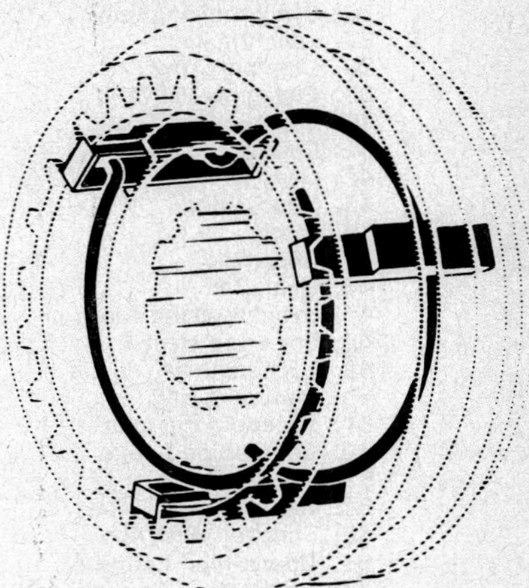

Assembling synchronizer

2. Transmission without overdrive: Place the speedometer gear on the bearing in the rear cover. Press in the oil seal with a drift.

3. Install the parts for the 1st and 2nd gear synchronizer on the mainshaft. Install the snap rings.

4a. Transmission without overdrive: Install the synchronizing cone, 1st gear, and thrust washer. Place the rear cover on the shaft. Ensure that the speedometer gear is positioned correctly. Install the yoke (flange). Use a sleeve which fits into the recess in the yoke (flange), press on the cover and yoke (flange). Install the

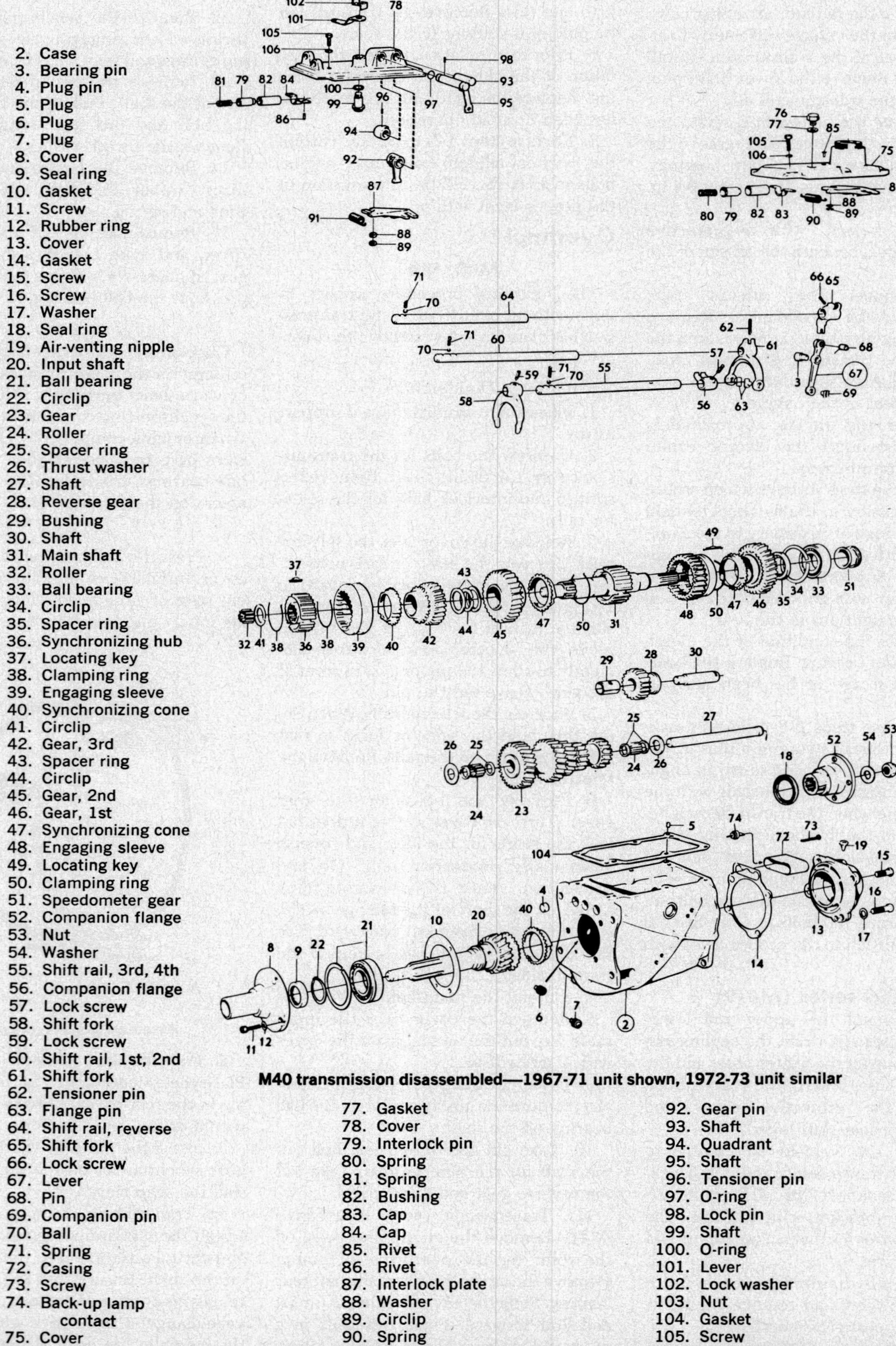

M40 transmission disassembled—1967-71 unit shown, 1972-73 unit similar

2. Case
3. Bearing pin
4. Plug pin
5. Plug
6. Plug
7. Plug
8. Cover
9. Seal ring
10. Gasket
11. Screw
12. Rubber ring
13. Cover
14. Gasket
15. Screw
16. Screw
17. Washer
18. Seal ring
19. Air-venting nipple
20. Input shaft
21. Ball bearing
22. Circlip
23. Gear
24. Roller
25. Spacer ring
26. Thrust washer
27. Shaft
28. Reverse gear
29. Bushing
30. Shaft
31. Main shaft
32. Roller
33. Ball bearing
34. Circlip
35. Spacer ring
36. Synchronizing hub
37. Locating key
38. Clamping ring
39. Engaging sleeve
40. Synchronizing cone
41. Circlip
42. Gear, 3rd
43. Spacer ring
44. Circlip
45. Gear, 2nd
46. Gear, 1st
47. Synchronizing cone
48. Engaging sleeve
49. Locating key
50. Clamping ring
51. Speedometer gear
52. Companion flange
53. Nut
54. Washer
55. Shift rail, 3rd, 4th
56. Companion flange
57. Lock screw
58. Shift fork
59. Lock screw
60. Shift rail, 1st, 2nd
61. Shift fork
62. Tensioner pin
63. Flange pin
64. Shift rail, reverse
65. Shift fork
66. Lock screw
67. Lever
68. Pin
69. Companion pin
70. Ball
71. Spring
72. Casing
73. Screw
74. Back-up lamp contact
75. Cover
76. Plug
77. Gasket
78. Cover
79. Interlock pin
80. Spring
81. Spring
82. Bushing
83. Cap
84. Cap
85. Rivet
86. Rivet
87. Interlock plate
88. Washer
89. Circlip
90. Spring
91. Spring
92. Gear pin
93. Shaft
94. Quadrant
95. Shaft
96. Tensioner pin
97. O-ring
98. Lock pin
99. Shaft
100. O-ring
101. Lever
102. Lock washer
103. Nut
104. Gasket
105. Screw
106. Spring washer

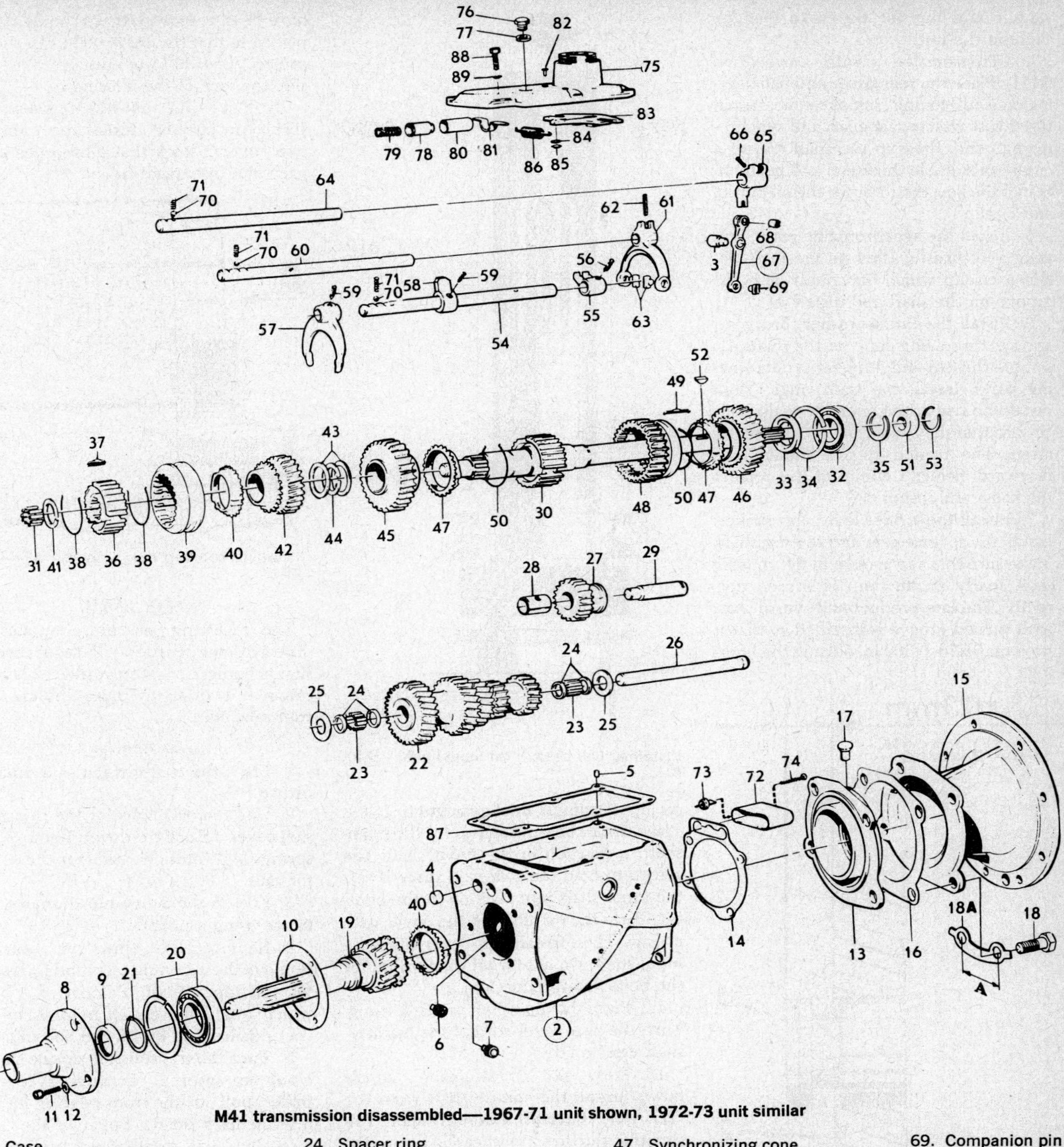

M41 transmission disassembled—1967-71 unit shown, 1972-73 unit similar

2. Case
3. Bearing pin
4. Plug
5. Pin
6. Plug
7. Plug
8. Cover
9. Seal ring
10. Gasket
11. Screw
12. Rubber ring
13. Cover
14. Gasket
15. Spacer flange
16. Gasket
17. Air-venting nipple
18. Screw

18A. Lock washer

19. Input shaft
20. Ball bearing
21. Circlip
22. Gear
23. Roller
24. Spacer ring
25. Thrust washer
26. Countershaft
27. Reverse gear
28. Bushing
29. Shaft
30. Main shaft
31. Roller
32. Ball bearing
33. Spacer ring
34. Circlip
35. Circlip
36. Synchronizing hub
37. Locating key
38. Clamping ring
39. Engaging sleeve
40. Synchronizing hub
41. Circlip
42. Gear, 3rd
43. Spacer ring
44. Circlip
45. Gear, 2nd
46. Gear
47. Synchronizing cone
48. Engaging sleeve
49. Locating key
50. Clamping ring
51. Cam
52. Key
53. Circlip
54. Shift rail, 3rd, 4th
55. Companion flange
56. Lock screw
57. Shift fork, 3rd, 4th
58. Companion flange
59. Lock screw
60. Shift rail, 1st, 2nd
61. Shift fork, 1st, 2nd
62. Tensioner pin
63. Companion pin
64. Shift rail, reverse
65. Shift fork
66. Lock screw
67. Lever
68. Pin
69. Companion pin
70. Ball
71. Spring
72. Casing
73. Back-up lamp contact
74. Screw
75. Cover
76. Plug
77. Gasket
78. Interlock pin
79. Spring
80. Bushing
81. Cap
82. Rivet
83. Interlock plate
84. Washer
85. Circlip
86. Spring
87. Gasket
88. Screw
89. Spring washer

washer and nut for the yoke (flange). Tighten the nut.

4b. Transmission with overdrive (M41): Place the rear cover and ball bearing on a cushioning ring or sleeve. Install the thrust washer, 1st gear, and synchronizing cone. Press in the shaft. Select a circlip of suitable thickness and install it. Install the key, the rotor for the oil pump, and circlip.

5. Install the synchronizing cone, 2nd gear, and thrust washer on the shaft. Select a circlip which fits snugly into the groove on the shaft and install it.

6. Install the thrust washer, 3rd gear, and synchronizing cone on the shaft. Assemble the 3rd and 4th gear synchronizing parts. Install the snap rings. Then install the synchronizer on the mainshaft. Ensure that the synchronizer is correctly fitted. The turned groove should face rearward. Select a circlip of the correct thickness and install it.

7. Install the striker lever and striker. Install the reverse gear and reverse shaft. Make sure that the groove in the reverse shaft (early production) is turned correctly. The late production reverse shaft with turned groove is installed so that it projects 0.276–0.300 in. outside the housing.

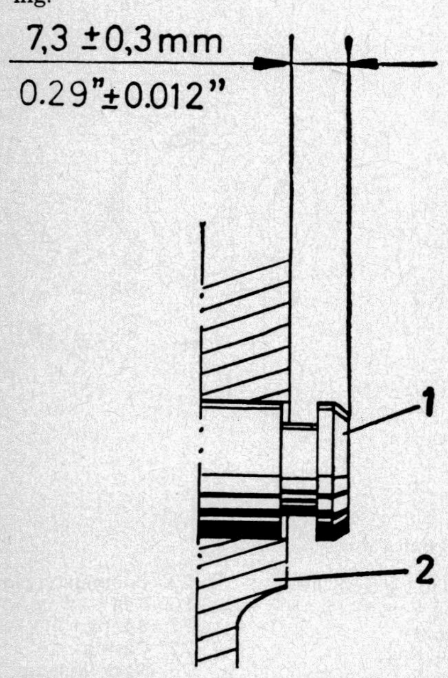

Installing reverse shaft—M40, M41

1. Reverse shaft
2. Transmission case

8. Place a dummy shaft in the idler gear. Put in spacer washers and needles (24 in each bearing). Use grease to hold the needles and washers in position.

9. Attach the washers to the housing with grease and guide them into position, with the centering plugs. Lay the idler gear in the bottom of the housing.

10. Press the bearing onto the input shaft with the help of a drift. Select a circlip of suitable thickness and install it. Place the 14 bearing rollers for the mainshaft in position in the input shaft. Use grease to hold the rollers in place. Press the input shaft into position in the housing. Press the oil seal into the cover with a drift. Then install the cover over the input shaft. Do not forget the O-rings for the bolts (late production).

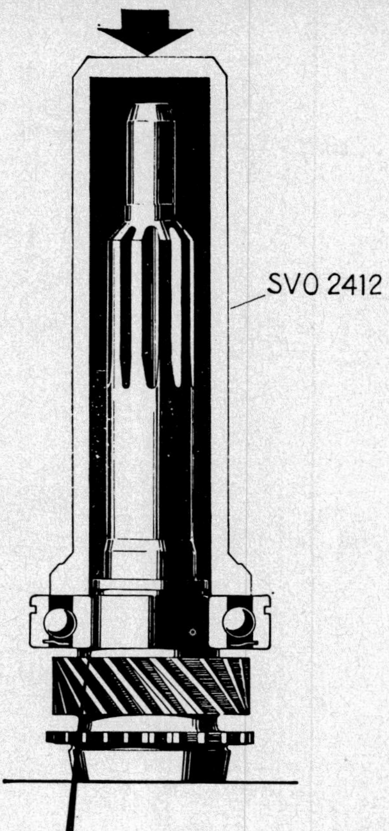

Installing ball bearing on input shaft—M40, M41.

11. Place the mainshaft in the housing. Turn the rear cover so that the countershaft can be fitted.

12. Turn the transmission upside down. Install the countershaft from the rear. Hold it against a dummy shaft. Ensure that the thrust washers do not loosen and fall down.

13a. Transmissions without overdrive: Turn the rear cover correctly so that it locks the reverse shaft (early production). Install the bolts for the cover.

13b. Transmission with overdrive: Turn the rear cover correctly so that it locks the reverse shaft (early production). Make sure that the rotor for the overdrive oil pump is turned. Install the overdrive. Use new locking washers for the intermediate flange.

14. Install the selector rails and forks. Move the selector fork to the rear position when fitting the pin. Use a new pin. Fit the cover over the selector rails. If the end caps at the front end of the housing have been removed, these should be replaced so that the center end cap should project about (0.16 in.) distance "A" outside the face of the housing.

15. Place the interlock balls and springs in position. Install the transmission cover. Check that all the gears engage and disengage freely.

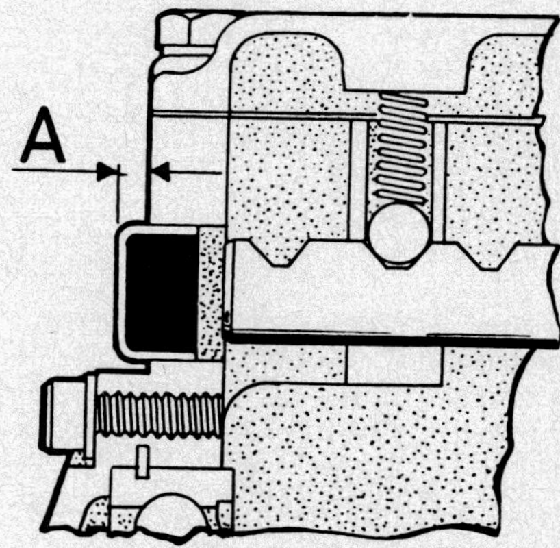

Installing end cap over selector rail—M40, M41.

M400, M410

The following procedure applies to units without overdrive. If the transmission is equipped with overdrive (M410), remove it prior to disassembling the transmission.

Disassembly

1. Place the transmission in a support fixture.

2. Unscrew the bolts for the transmission cover. Lift off the cover. Remove the springs and interlock balls for the selector rails.

3. Loosen the flange nut. Remove the flange using a puller.

4. Remove the throwout bearing. Remove the retaining bolts and the cover for the input shaft. Remove the bolts which retain the clutch housing to the transmission and lift off the housing.

5. Turn the transmission upside down. Using an internal, expanding bearing puller, pull out the front bearing for the intermediate shaft. Remove the rear cover, and pull out the rear bearing for the intermediate shaft.

6. Return the transmission to its normal position, taking care not to damage the teeth of the intermediate shaft as the shaft drops to the bottom of the transmission.

7. Remove the bolts for the selector forks. Push the selector rails backward and drive out the tensioning pin in the flange of the selector rails. Push out the selector rails, taking care not to jam them onto the selector forks. Remove the forks.

8. Remove the speedometer gear. Remove the rear bearing for the mainshaft on the M400 transmission with internal, expanding puller SVO 2828. If the bearing remains lodged in the case, push

the mainshaft forward until the drive and synchronizers are positioned against the intermediate shaft drive. For the overdrive (M410) transmission, remove the bolt in SVO 2828 and install puller SVO 2832 in place of the bolt. Using both tools in conjunction, pull out the rear mainshaft bearing.

9. Pull out the input shaft and remove the synchronizing ring. Remove the thrust washer from the rear of the mainshaft. Push the 1st and 2nd speed engaging sleeve rearward. Lift out the mainshaft.

10. Pull out the reversing shaft and remove the reverse gear. Remove the front and rear cover oil seals with a drift.

11. If a lifting tool was used to remove the mainshaft from the case, remove it. Remove the 1st speed gear wheel, the needle bearing and the synchronizing cone.

12. Remove the engaging sleeves and the flanges for the synchronizers. Remove the synchronizing hub circlips.

13. Place the mainshaft in a press and support it under the 1st speed synchronizing hub. Press off the 2nd speed gear wheel and the 1st and 2nd speed synchronizing hub.

14. Invert the mainshaft and press off the 3rd speed gear wheel and the 4th speed synchronizing hub.

Inspection

After dismantling the mainshaft, clean all parts in an alcohol-based solvent and allow to air dry. Check the gear wheels for cracked teeth or scoring. Inspect the synchronizing cones and hubs for galling or scoring. Check all ball bearings for cracks or scoring on the bearing races or on the balls themselves. Replace all damaged or worn parts.

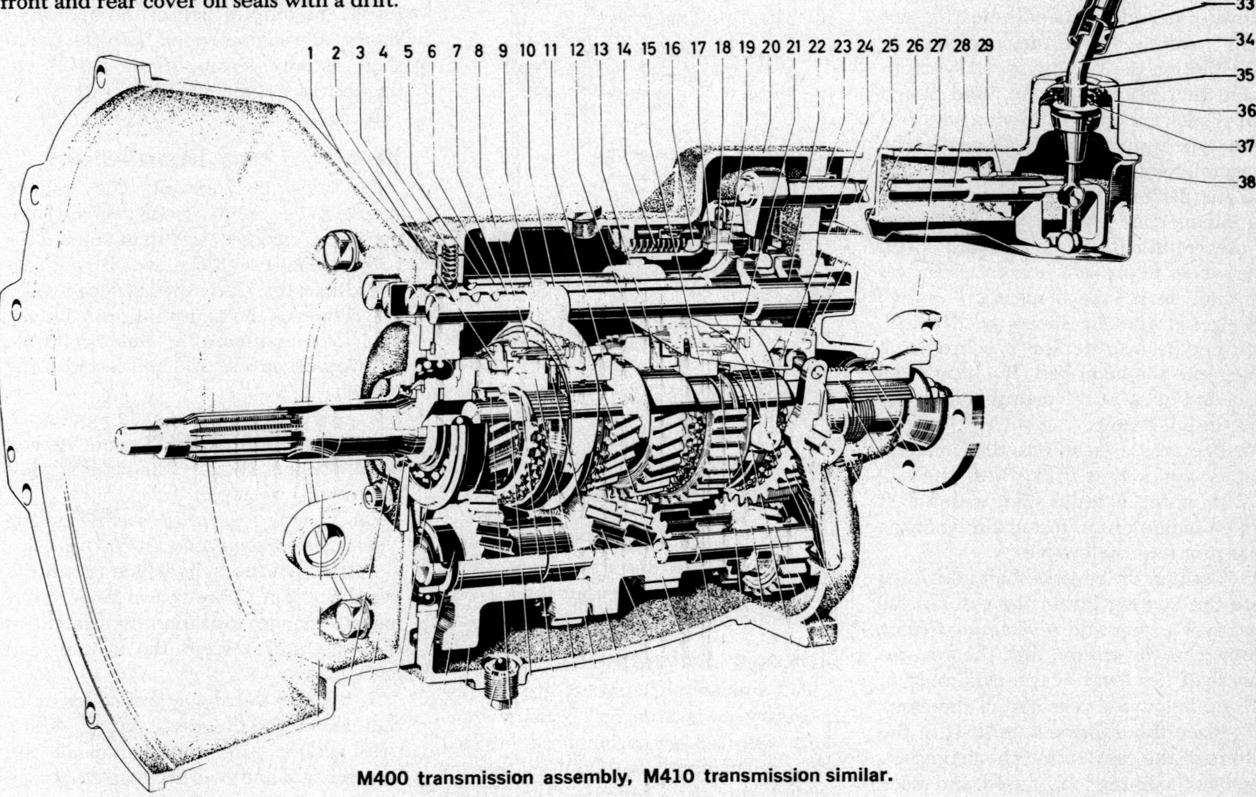

M400 transmission assembly, M410 transmission similar.

1. Clutch housing
2. Engaging ring
3. Interlock ball
4. Spring
5. Selector rail, reverse gear
6. Selector rail for 1st and 2nd gears
7. Selector rail for 3rd and 4th gears
8. Insert
9. Spring
10. Selector fork
11. Gear wheel, 3rd speed
12. Gear wheel, 2nd speed
13. Needle bearing
14. Spring
15. Synchronizing hub, 1st—2nd gears
16. Interlock ball
17. Sliding plate
18. Gate
19. Selector fork, 1st and 2nd gears
20. Case cover
21. Synchronizing cone
22. Gate
23. Bushing
24. Thrust washer
25. Ball bearing
26. Friction ring
27. Flange
28. Shaft
29. Bushing
30. Gear lever knob
31. Gear lever, upper section
32. Rubber bushing
33. Rubber bushing
34. Gear lever, lower section
35. Washer
36. Cover
37. Spring
38. Protective casing

Assembly

1. Assemble the 1st/2nd and 3rd/4th speed synchronizers, taking care to fit the snap-rings according to the illustration. Position the snap-ring in the hub for the 3rd/4th speed synchronizers.

2. Position the 3rd/4th speed synchronizer, synchronizing cone, 3rd speed gear wheel and needle bearing on top of a ring type support, and after making sure that the synchronizing flange locates correctly into the synchronizing cone grooves, and that the snap-ring fits properly on the 3rd speed gear wheel, press the mainshaft into the synchronizing hub. While pressing in the mainshaft, rotate the 3rd speed gear wheel to make sure that it and the needle bearing are fitted correctly. Install the snap-ring.

3. Position the 1st/2nd speed synchronizer, synchronizing cone, 2nd speed gear wheel, and needle bearing on top of a ring type support, making sure that the engaging sleeve gear ring comes forward and the flanges fit correctly in the synchronizing cone grooves. While pressing in the mainshaft, rotate the 2nd speed gear wheel to prevent it from seizing on the shaft. Install the snap-ring.

4. Install the 1st speed gear wheel, with needle bearing and synchronizing cone, onto the mainshaft. If a lifting tool is needed to lower the mainshaft into the case, install it now.

5. Press the oil seals into the front and rear covers with a drift. Press the ball bearing onto the input shaft with a drift and cushioning ring. Install a snug fitting snap-ring into the groove.

6. Position the reverse shaft gear lever onto the bearing pin in the case. Install the reverse gear and reverse gear shaft, taking care to ensure that the reverse gear shaft lies level or is a maximum of 0.08 in. below the rear end of the case.

7. Place the intermediate shaft in the bottom of the case. Install the mainshaft. Remove the lifting tool, if used, and place the thrust washer on the mainshaft.

8. Press the rear ball bearing onto the mainshaft. If the bearing does not seat correctly in the case, the spindle on SVO tool 2831 can be screwed out and a flat iron piece placed between this and the front end of the case, then the bearing pressed in.

9. Fit the needle bearing into the input shaft. Install the loose synchronizing cone in the synchronizer for the 3rd/4th speeds, taking care to insert the flanges in the grooves. Push the input shaft into the case and onto the mainshaft pin.

10. Turn the transmission upside down. Press on the front and rear bearings for the intermediate shaft. Install the clutch housing with a new gasket.

11. Install the selector forks, flanges, and selector rails. Make sure that the flange for the reverse gear fits correctly in the gear lever. Install the bolts and new tensioning pins.

12. Position the transmission with the rear end facing upward. Drive the intermediate shaft forward until its front bearing contacts the clutch housing. Install shims for the intermediate shaft bearing so that they lie flush or within a maximum of 0.002 in. (distance "A") of the rear end.

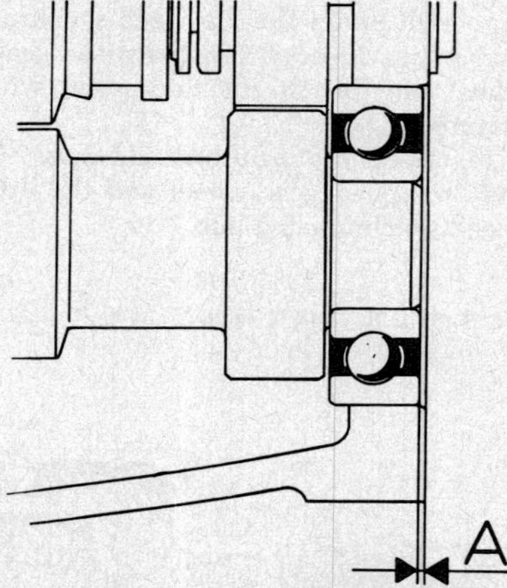

Clearance for intermediate shaft—M400, M410.

13. Install the speedometer gear. Install the rear cover with a new gasket, taking care to compress the gasket. Make sure that the intermediate shaft has 0.-008–0.010 in. clearance.

14. Press on the rear flange. Install the washer and nut and torque to 80–110 ft lbs.

15. Position the interlock balls and springs and install the case cover with a new gasket. Install the input shaft cover. Install the throwout bearing.

Linkage Adjustment

Shift linkage adjustments are neither necessary nor possible on Volvo transmissions. The linkage is mounted inboard and is permanently bathed in oil thus insulated from the elements. On 1970–71 140 series, the shift lever mounts directly in the top of the transmission. This configuration, although providing for more direct shifting action by elimination of the levers and rods of conventional transmissions, required the use of a long wand-like shift lever with long throws required to change gears. This situation is remedied on 1972 and later 140 series cars, as well as all 164 and 1800 series cars, with the implementation of an inboard mounted, intermediate shifter rod. This rod allows the use of a much shorter, sportier shift lever and provides shorter throws between gears.

Overdrive

The overdrive unit for the M41 and M410 transmissions is a planetary gear type and is mounted on the rear of the transmission. When the overdrive is in the direct drive position (overdrive switched off) and the car is driven forward, power from the transmission mainshaft is transmitted through the freewheel rollers and uni-directional clutch to the overdrive output shaft. When the car is backing up or during periods of engine braking, torque is transmitted through the clutch sliding member which is held by spring pressure against the tapered portion of the output shaft. When the overdrive is actuated, the clutch sliding member is pressed by hydraulic pressure against the brake disc (ring), which locks the sun wheel. As a result, the output shaft of the overdrive rotates at a higher speed than the mainshaft thereby accomplishing a 20% reduction in engine speed in relation to vehicle speed.

Removal and Installation

To facilitate removal, the vehicle should first be driven in 4th gear with the overdrive engaged, and then coasted for a few seconds with the overdrive disengaged and the clutch pedal depressed.

1. Remove the transmission from the vehicle as outlined in the applicable "Transmission Removal and Installation" section.

2. Disconnect the solenoid cables.

3. If the overdrive unit has not already been drained, remove the six bolts and the overdrive oil pan.

CAUTION: *Be careful to avoid spilling hot transmission fluid on the skin.*

4. Remove the bolts which retain the overdrive unit to the transmission intermediate flange. Pull the unit straight to the rear until it clears the transmission mainshaft.

5. Reverse the above procedure to install. Install the overdrive oil pan with a new gasket. After installation of the transmission and overdrive assembly, fill the transmission (which automatically fills the overdrive) to the proper level with the correct lubricant. Check the lubricant level in the transmission after driving 6–9 miles.

CLUTCH

All 1967 and later model Volvos are equipped with Borg and Beck or Fichtel and Sachs diaphragm spring clutches. The 140 and 1800 series use an 8 ½ in. disc, while the carbureted 164 uses a 9 in. disc, and the fuel-injected 164 uses a 9 ½ in. disc.

Removal and Installation

M40, M41

1. Remove the transmission as outlined in the applicable "Transmission Re-

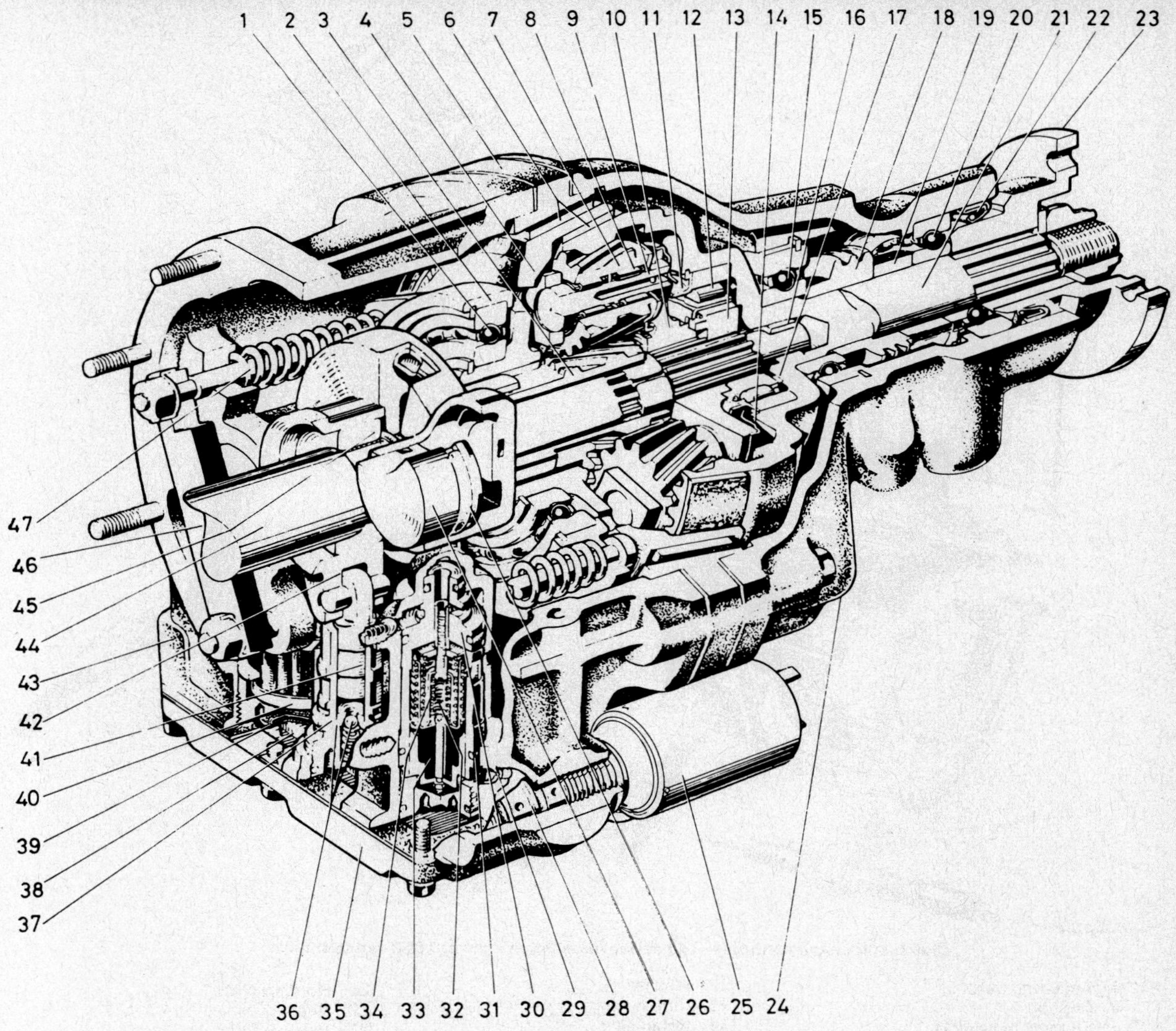

Overdrive assembly

1. Output shaft support bearing
2. Thrust bearing retainer
3. Sunwheel
4. Clutch sliding member
5. Brake ring
6. Clutch member outer lining
7. Planet gear
8. Needle bearing
9. Shaft
10. Planet carrier
11. Oil thrower
12. Uni-directional clutch rollers
13. Uni-directional clutch
14. Oil trap
15. Ball bearing
16. Bushing
17. Thrust washer
18. Speedometer driving gear
19. Spacer
20. Ball bearing
21. Output shaft
22. Oil seal
23. Coupling flange
24. Rear casing
25. Solenoid
26. Piston seal
27. Piston
28. Operating valve
29. Orifice nozzle
30. Cylinder top
31. Cylinder
32. Spring
33. Large piston
34. Small piston
35. Base plate
36. Check valve for oil pump
37. Pump cylinder
38. Magnet
39. Pre-filter
40. Fine filter
41. Pump plunger
42. Connecting rod
43. Front casing
44. Input shaft (transmission mainshaft)
45. Eccentric
46. Bridge piece
47. Spring

moval and Installation" procedure.

2. Remove the upper bolt for the starter motor.

3. Remove the throwout bearing. Disconnect the clutch cable at the release lever (fork), and slacken the cable sleeve at its bracket.

4. Remove the bolts which retain the flywheel (clutch) housing to the engine, and lift off the housing.

5. Remove the bolt for the release fork ball joint, and remove the ball and release fork.

6. Scribe alignment marks on the clutch and flywheel. In order to prevent warpage, slowly loosen the bolts which retain the clutch to the flywheel diagonally in rotation. Remove the bolts and lift off the clutch and pressure plate.

7. Inspect the clutch assembly as outlined under "Clutch Inspection."

8. When ready to install, wash the clutch facings, pressure plate and flywheel with solvent to remove any traces of oil, and wipe them clean with a cloth.

9. Position the clutch assembly (the longest side of the hub facing backward) to the flywheel and align the bolt holes. Insert a pilot shaft (centering mandrel),

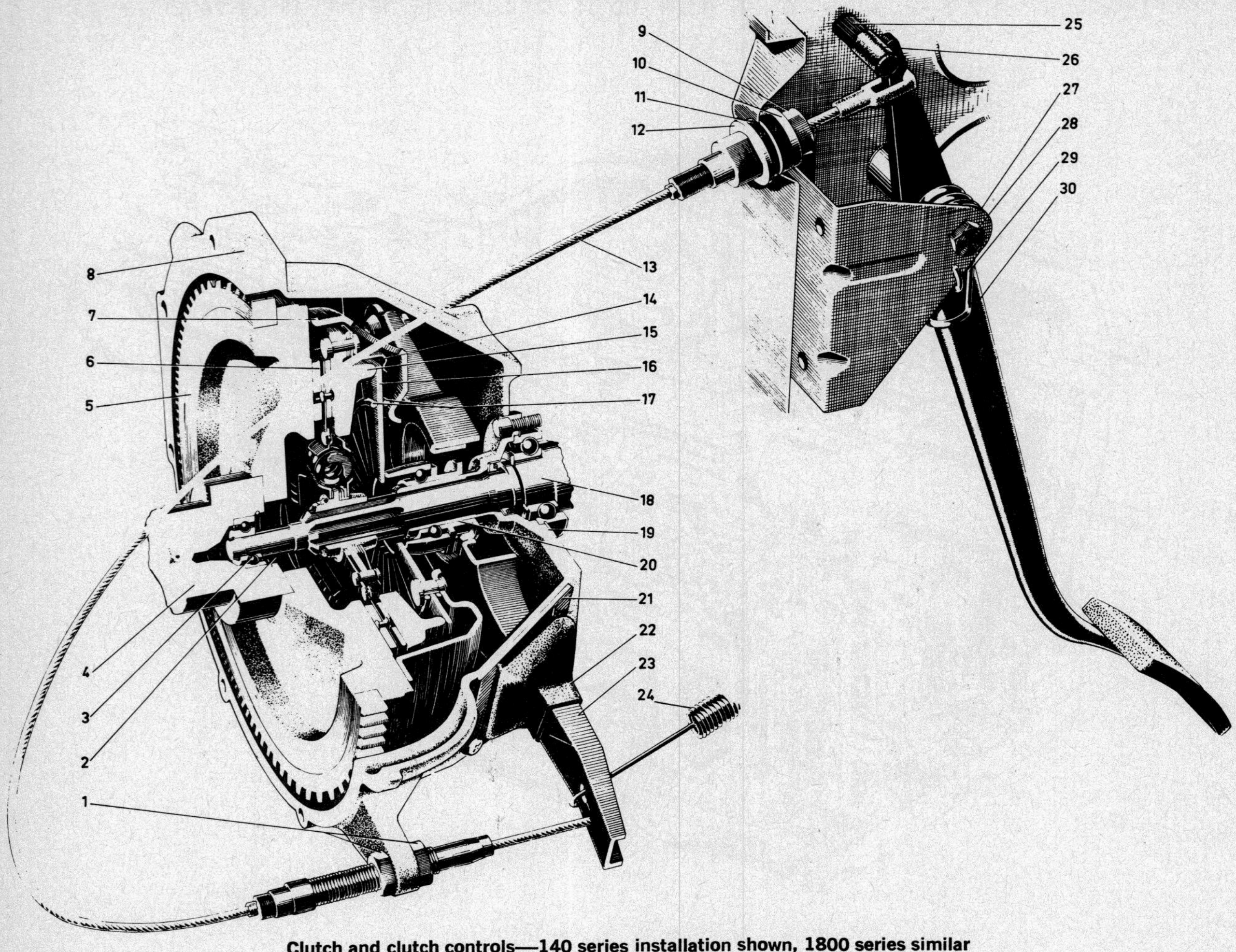

Clutch and clutch controls—140 series installation shown, 1800 series similar

1. Adjusting nuts
2. Circlip
3. Support bearing in crankshaft
4. Crankshaft
5. Flywheel
6. Clutch plate
7. Clutch cover
8. Flywheel housing
9. Nut
10. Washer
11. Rubber bushing
12. Washer
13. Clutch wire
14. Retainer
15. Pressure plate
16. Thrust spring
17. Support rings
18. Clutch plate shaft (input shaft transmission)
19. Cover, transmission
20. Throw-out bearing
21. Holding plate
22. Dust cover
23. Release fork
24. Return spring
25. Pedal stop
26. Rubber sleeve
27. Bracket
28. Screw for pedal shaft
29. Return spring
30. Clutch pedal

or an input shaft from an old transmission of the same type, through the clutch assembly and flywheel so that the flywheel pilot bearing is centered.

10. Install the six bolts which retain the clutch assembly to the flywheel and tighten them diagonally in rotation, a few turns at a time. After all of the bolts are tightened, remove the pilot shaft (centering mandrel).

11. Install the ball and release fork in the flywheel housing.

12. Place the upper starter bolt in the housing. Position the housing to the engine and first install the four upper bolts (7/16 in.), then the lower starter bolt, and finally the two lower bolts (3/8 in.).

13. Insert the cable sleeve in its bracket and install the rear nut. Connect the cable at the release lever (fork), and install the throwout bearing.

14. Install the nut for the upper starter motor bolt.

15. Install the transmission as outlined in the applicable "Transmission Removal and Installation" section.

16. Adjust the clutch pedal free travel.

M400, M410

1. Remove the transmission as outlined in the applicable "Transmission Removal and Installation" section.

2. Scribe alignment marks on the clutch and flywheel. In order to prevent warpage, slowly loosen the bolts which retain the clutch assembly to the flywheel diagonally in rotation. Remove the bolts and lift off the clutch and pressure plate.

3. Inspect the clutch assembly as outlined under "Clutch Inspection."

4. When ready to install, wash the clutch facings, pressure plate and flywheel with solvent to remove any traces of oil, and wipe them clean with a cloth.

5. Position the clutch assembly (the longest side of the hub facing backward) to the flywheel and align the bolt holes. Insert a pilot shaft (centering mandrel), or an input shaft from an old transmission of the same type, through the clutch assembly and flywheel so that the flywheel pilot bearing is centered.

6. Install the six bolts which retain the clutch assembly to the flywheel, and tighten them diagonally in rotation, a few turns at a time. After all of the bolts are

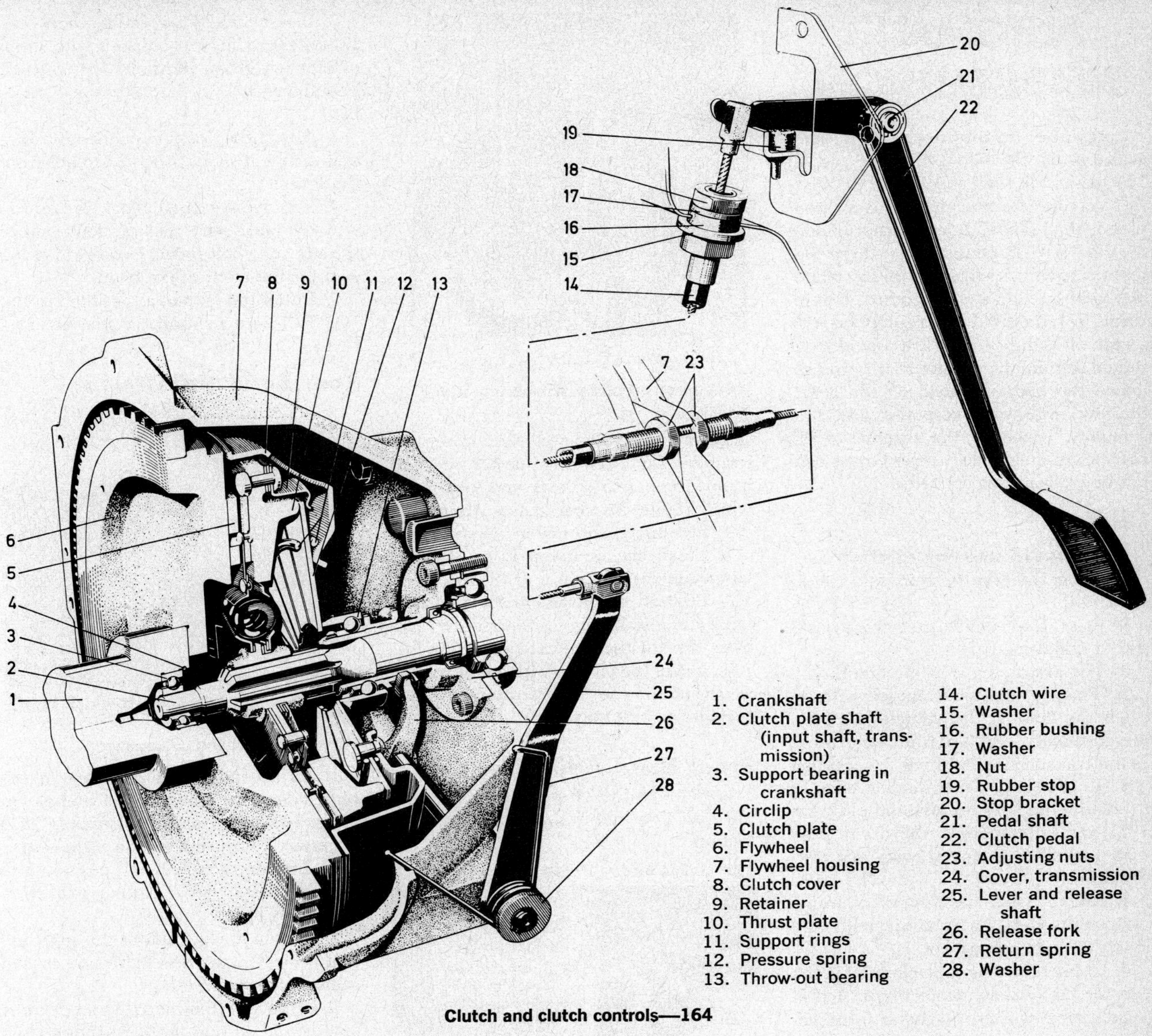

Clutch and clutch controls—164

1. Crankshaft
2. Clutch plate shaft (input shaft, transmission)
3. Support bearing in crankshaft
4. Circlip
5. Clutch plate
6. Flywheel
7. Flywheel housing
8. Clutch cover
9. Retainer
10. Thrust plate
11. Support rings
12. Pressure spring
13. Throw-out bearing
14. Clutch wire
15. Washer
16. Rubber bushing
17. Washer
18. Nut
19. Rubber stop
20. Stop bracket
21. Pedal shaft
22. Clutch pedal
23. Adjusting nuts
24. Cover, transmission
25. Lever and release shaft
26. Release fork
27. Return spring
28. Washer

tightened, remove the pilot shaft (centering mandrel).

7. Install the transmission as outlined in the applicable "Transmission Removal and Installation" section.

Clutch Inspection

Check the pressure plate for heat damage, cracks, scoring, or other damage to the friction surface. Check the curvature of the pressure plate with a 9 ½ in. steel ruler. Place the ruler diagonally over the pressure plate friction surface and measure the distance between the straight edge of the ruler and the inner diameter of the pressure plate. This measurement must not be greater than 0.0012 in. In addition, there must be no clearance between the straight edge of the ruler and the outer diameter of the pressure plate. This check should be made at several points. Replace the clutch as a unit if it proves faulty.

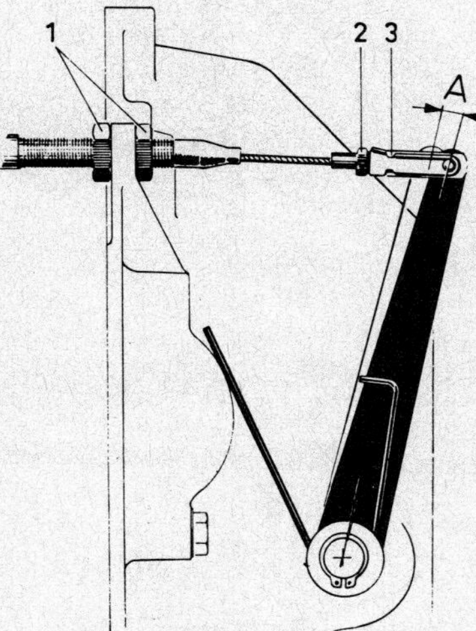

Clutch free play adjustment—164

1. Adjusting nuts
2. Locknut
3. Fork

Check the throwout bearing by rotating it several times while applying finger pressure, so that the ball bearings roll against the inside of the races. If the bearing does not turn easily or if it binds at any point, replace it as a unit. Also make sure that the bearing slides easily on the guide sleeve from the transmission.

Clutch Pedal Play Adjustment

1. Loosen the locknut for the fork on the clutch cable.

2. Make the necessary adjustment and tighten the locknut. The free play (A) should be 0.12 in. for 140 series models, 0.12–0.16 for 1800 series, and 0.16–0.20 for the 164.

3. If this adjustment is insufficient, or if a new cable is installed, the sleeve attachment to the flywheel housing should be adjusted with the adjusting nuts.

AUTOMATIC TRANSMISSION

Automatic transmissions have been available on 1967–73 140 series and all 164 models, as well as 1971–73 1800 series Volvos. The transmission is a three-speed, dual-range, Borg-Warner model 35. The BW 35 consists of a three element torque converter coupling, planetary gear set, and a valve control system. Until 1971, the BW 35 was equipped with a rear oil pump. In 1972 it was discontinued. Elimination of the rear pump reduced the hydraulic load on the gears, thereby improving response and fuel economy. However, the absence of the rear pump means that these Volvos cannot be push or tow started.

Oil Pan

Removal and Installation

1. Place the transmission selector in Park.
2. Raise the vehicle and place jackstands underneath.
3. The drain plug is located on the oil pan. Place a container underneath to catch the fluid. If the vehicle has been driven for any length of time, be careful, as the transmission fluid will be scalding hot. On 1970 and earlier models, use a ¼ in. allen wrench to remove the plug. On 1971 and later models, the drain plug, with gasket, is removed with a screwdriver.
4. After the fluid has stopped draining, remove the 15 oil pan retaining bolts, and lower the pan and gasket.
5. Inspect the magnetic element in the pan for metal shavings or chips. A preponderance of these particles foreshadows a future trip to your dealer. Also remove any sludge or gum from the bottom of the pan. Clean the mating surfaces of the transmission case and oil pan.
6. Position the pan (with a new gasket) to the case and install the 15 retaining bolts. Step torque the bolts diagonally in rotation to 8–13 ft. lbs. Coat the threads of the drain plug with Loctite®. Install the plug (1971 and later models use a new plug gasket) and torque to 8–10 ft. lbs.
7. Remove the jackstands and lower the vehicle. Refer to the capacities chart in Chapter 1 and fill the transmission to the proper level (between the MAX and MIN marks for a cold transmission) with type "F" automatic transmission fluid.

Oil Pump Strainer Service

1. Remove the oil pan as outlined in the "Oil Pan Removal and Installation" section.
2. Remove the four screws which retain the front oil pump wire-mesh strainer to the valve body, and lower the strainer. On 1971 and earlier models, remove the two screws and two bolts which retain the rear pump strainer to the valve body, and lower the strainer.
3. Clean the strainers in an alcohol based solvent solution.
4. Position the strainers to the valve body and install the retaining screws and bolts. Torque the screws to 1.7–2.5 ft. lbs.
5. Install the oil pan with a new gasket as outlined in the "Oil Pan Removal and Installation" section.

Location of oil pump strainer(s)—1967-71 shown.

Front Band Adjustment

1. Remove the oil pan as outlined in the "Oil Pan Removal and Installation" section.

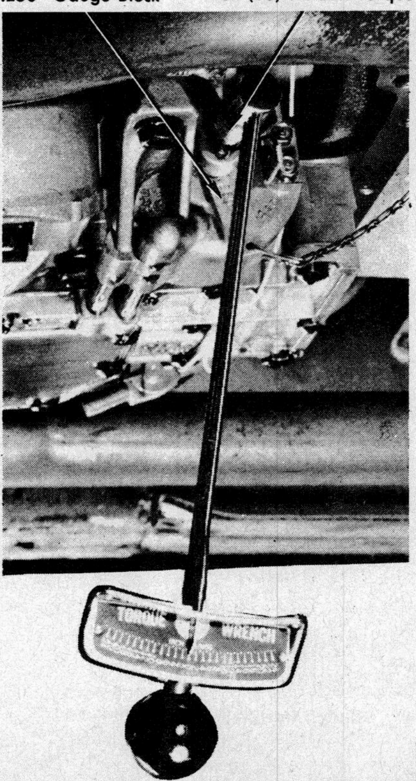

Front band adjustment

2. Insert a 0.25 in. gauge block between the adjusting bolt and the servo cylinder. Tighten the bolt with an inch pound torque wrench to a torque of 10 in. lbs.
3. Adjust the position of the adjusting bolt spring. It should be 1–2 threads from the lever.
4. Remove the gauge block and torque wrench. Make sure that the long end of the adjusting bolt spring is inserted in the cam for the front brake band.
5. Install the oil pan as outlined in the "Oil Pan Removal and Installation" section.

Rear Band Adjustment

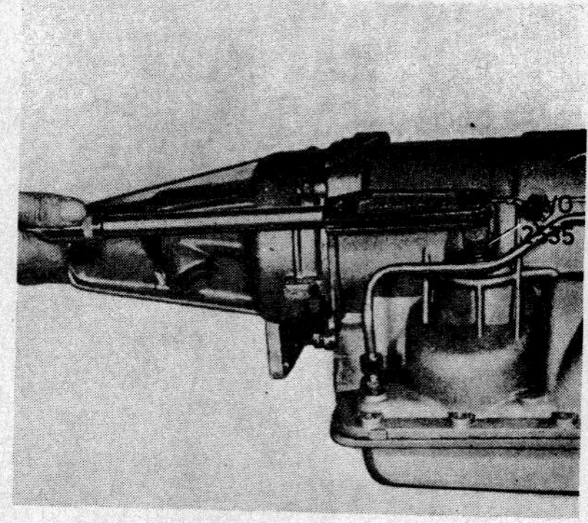

Rear band adjustment

1. An access hole is provided in the right side of the transmission tunnel. On some 140 series and 164 models, it is necessary to disconnect the right heater duct. Lift up the carpet and position it to one side. Remove the rubber plug from the access hole.
2. Loosen the locknut for the adjusting screw located on the right side of the transmission case.
3. Using a 5/16 in. square socket and a foot pound torque wrench, tighten the adjusting screw to a torque of 10 ft. lbs; then back off the adjusting screw one complete turn.
4. Without disturbing the adjustment, tighten the locknut.
5. Install the rubber plug, fit the carpet, and install the heater duct, if removed.

Neutral Start Switch Adjustment

The neutral start switches on 1967–72 Volvos are adjustable. If a switch on a 1973 or later model Volvo is not operating correctly it must be replaced complete with a new spacing washer, as it is not adjustable. The switch serves a dual function: first, it prevents the engine from being started while the gear selector is in any position other than Neutral or Park, and second, it closes the circuit that actuates the back-up lights when the selector is placed in Reverse. The following procedure is used to adjust the switch.

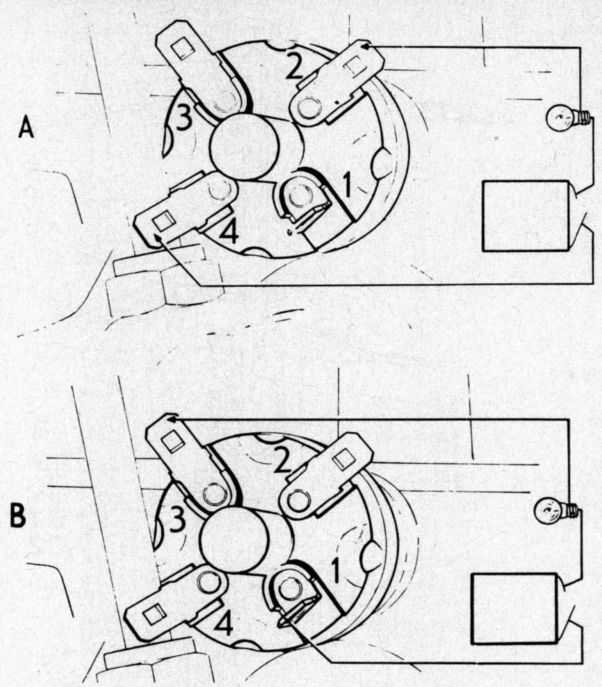

Neutral start switch adjustment—1967-71

(a)—Bulb connected to back-up light contacts
(b)—Bulb connected to starter inhibitor contacts

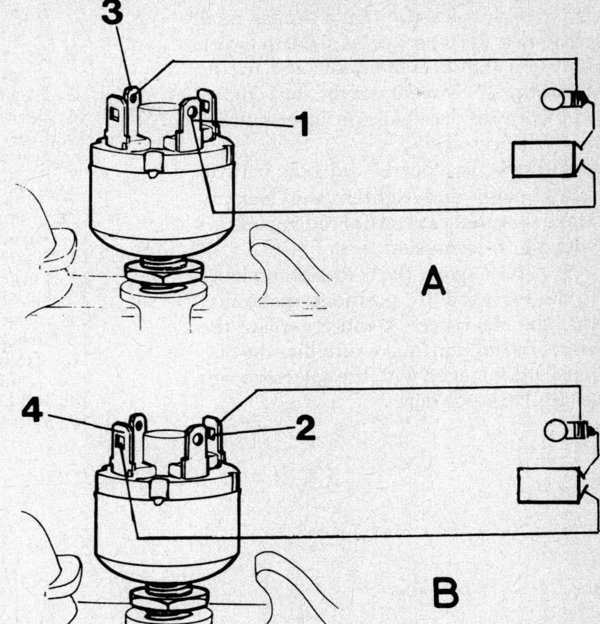

Neutral start switch adjustment—1972

(a)—Bulb connected to starter inhibitor contacts
(b)—Bulb connected to back-up light contacts

1. Check the adjustment of the gear selector as outlined under "Selector Linkage Adjustment." Place the gear selector in Drive. Firmly apply the parking brake.

2. On 1972 140 series and 164 models, remove the control lever from the transmission.

3. Loosen the locknut for the switch. Taking note of their positions, disconnect the electrical leads. Unscrew the switch until it is held on by just a few threads.

4a. On 1967–71 models, first connect a 12 volt test light to the back-up light terminals (2 and 4), and screw in the switch until the test light goes out. Disconnect the light and mark this position on the switch and transmission with a pencil. Then connect the test light to the start inhibitor terminals (1 and 3), and screw out the switch until the light goes on. Disconnect the light and also mark this position. The proper adjustment is midway between these two marks.

4b. On 1972 models, first connect a 12 volt test light to the start inhibitor terminals (1 and 3), and screw in the switch until the test light goes out. Disconnect the light and mark this position on the switch and transmission with a pencil. Then connect the test light to the back-up light terminals (2 and 4), and screw out the switch until the light goes on. Disconnect the light and also mark this position. The proper adjustment is midway between these two marks.

5. When the proper adjustment is achieved, tighten the locknut, taking care not to disturb the adjustment. Connect the four electrical leads.

6. On 1972 140 series and 164 models, install the control lever on the transmission.

7. Block the wheels so that the car cannot move either forward or backward. Make sure that the engine can only be started with the gear selector in Neutral or Park. Make sure that the back-up lights operate when the selector is placed in Reverse.

Gear Selector Linkage Adjustment

140 series, 164

1967–71

1. Disconnect the pull rod from the selector shaft lever. Place the selector lever in Neutral.

2. Place the lever on the transmission in the central position. Adjust the length of the pull rod so that, on 140 series models, the ball socket can easily be snapped onto the lever ball, and so that, on 164 models, the pin can easily be pushed through the yoke and lever. When the pull rod is adjusted correctly, the distance to the link in the Neutral position should be equal to the distance to the link in the Drive position.

3. Make sure that the gear indicator points correctly on the scale (quadrant). Adjustments are made to the cable sleeve at the indicator.

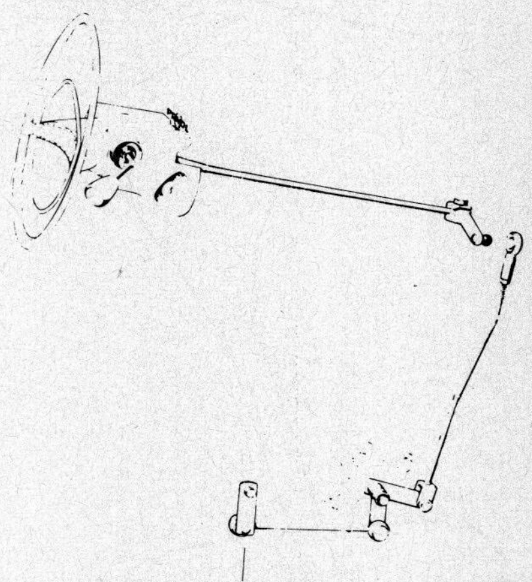

Gear selector linkage adjustment—1967-70 140 series, 1969-70 164.

4. Make sure that the output shaft is locked with the control lever in the Park position.

5. Connect the pull rod to the selector shaft lever.

1972–73

1. Disconnect the shift rod from the transmission lever. Place both the transmission lever and the gear selector lever in the "2" position.

2. Adjust the length of the shift control rod so that a small clearance (distance B) of 0.04 in. is obtained between the gear selector lever inhibitor and the inhibitor plate, when the shift control rod is connected to the transmission lever.

3. Position the gear selector lever in Drive and make sure that a similar small clearance (distance A) of 0.04 in. exists between the lever inhibitor and the inhibitor plate. Disconnect the shift control rod from the transmission lever and adjust, if necessary.

4. Lock the control rod bolt with its safety clasp and tighten the locknut. Make sure that the control rod lug follows with the transmission lever.

5. After moving the transmission lever to the Park and "1" positions, make sure that the clearances A and B remain the same. In addition, make sure that the output shaft is locked with the selector lever in the Park position.

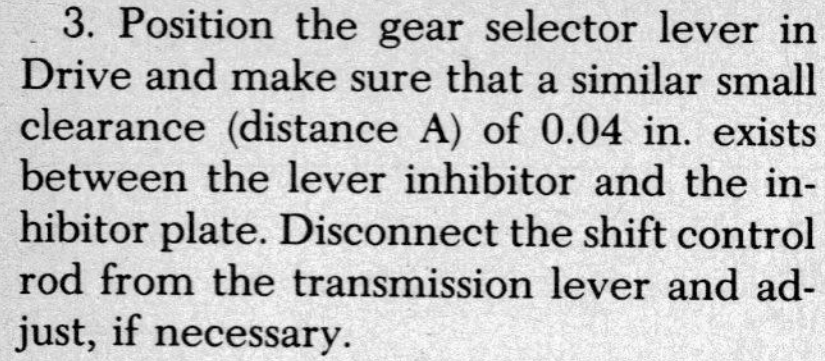

1. Selector lever knob, upper section
2. Selector lever knob, lower section
3. Washer
4. Spring
5. Push rod
6. Selector lever
7. Shift positions cover
8. Shift positions lamp
9. Inhibitor plate
10. Housing
11. Shaft
12. Lever
13. Control rod
14. Lever
15. Bracket
16. Cable, shift positions lamp
17. Inhibitor
18. Button

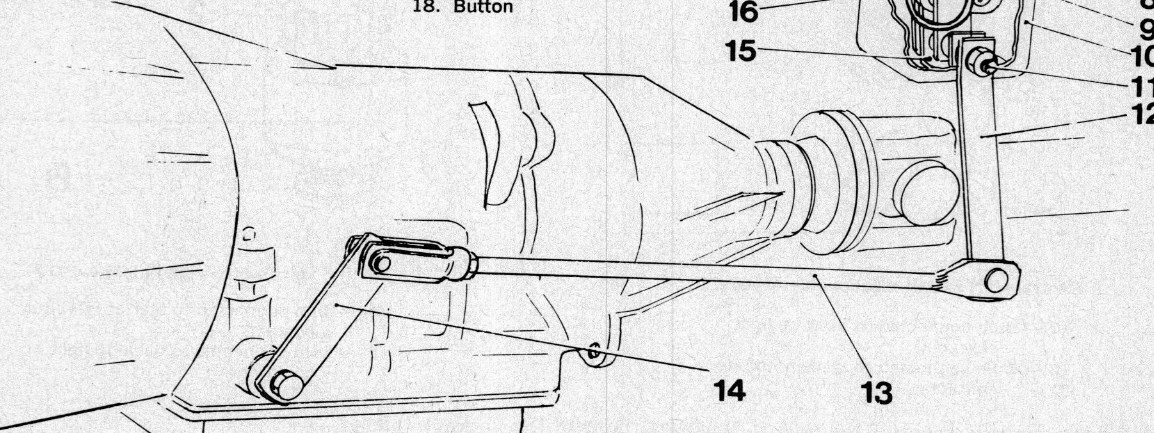

Gear selector linkage assembly—1972-73 140 series, 164

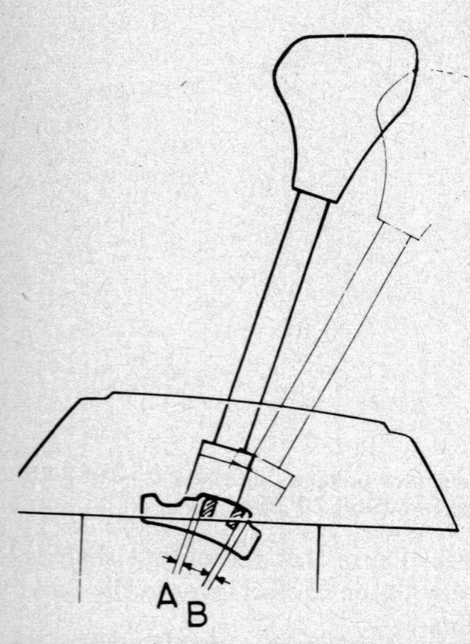

Gear selector linkage adjustment—1972-73 140 series, 164.

1800 series

1971–73

1. Check to make sure that the transmission lever and the lever at the linkage bracket are parallel. If necessary, adjust the length of the lower control rod.

2. Disconnect the upper control rod from the intermediate lever (5). Place the gear selector in Neutral. Also set the transmission lever to its third (Neutral) position. Adjust the length of the upper

1. Selector lever
2. Quadrant lighting
3. Lever
4. Control rod, upper
5. Lever arm with shaft
6. Bracket
7. Lever
8. Control rod, lower
9. Lever
10. Shaft
11. Lock pin
12. Bearing housing
13. Spring
14. Rubber bellows
15. Gating
16. Casing

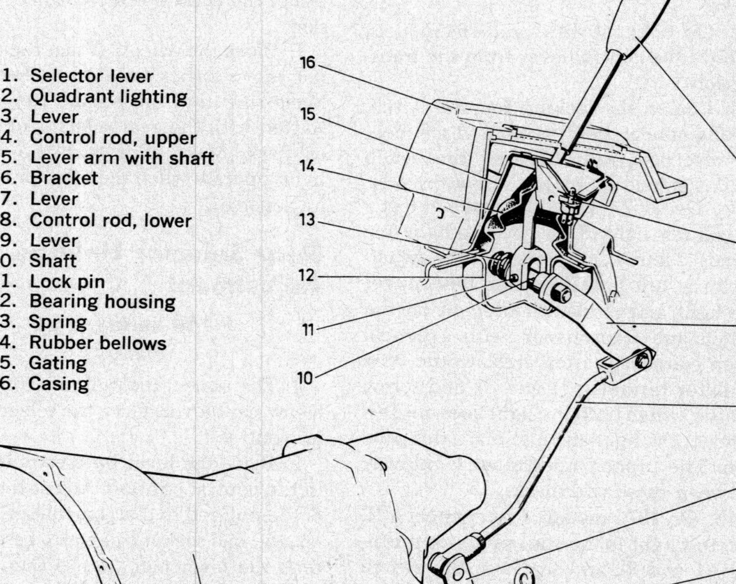

Gear selector linkage assembly—1971-73 1800 series

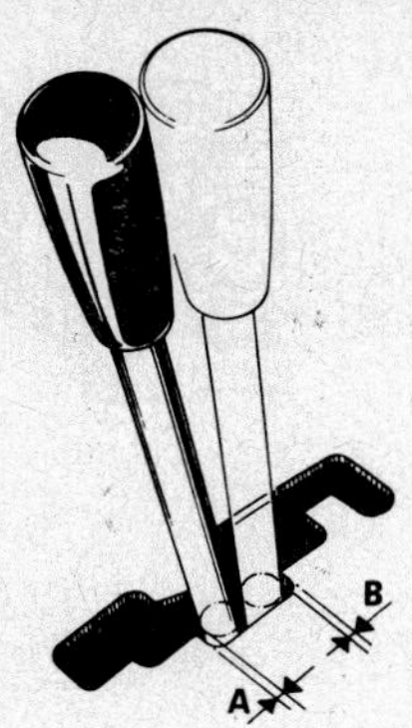

Gear selector linkage adjustment—1971-73 1800 series.

control rod so that the ball socket aligns with the ball stud. Connect the control rod to the lever.

3. If the upper control rod adjustment is correct, the distances to the inhibitor plate in Neutral and Drive (A and B) should be equal.

4. Make sure that the output shaft is locked with the selector lever in the Park position.

Throttle Cable Adjustment

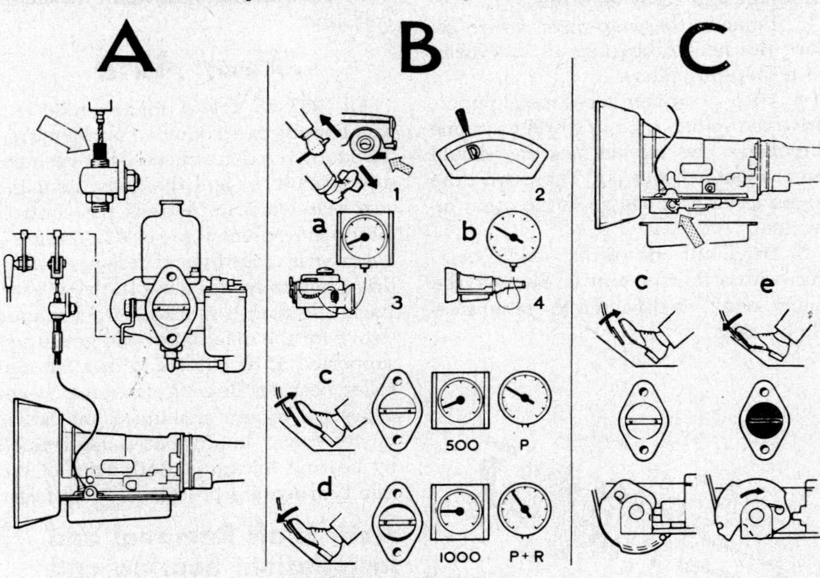

Throttle cable adjustment

(a)—Adjusting cable stop
(b)—Adjusting with tachometer and manometer
1. Chock the wheels and apply the brakes
2. Select position "D"
3. Connect a tachometer (a)
4. Connect a pressure gauge (b)
(c)—Measure pressure (P) at 500 r.p.m
(d)—Measure pressure (P+R) at 1000 r.p.m.
(r)—Should be (15—20 lb/sq in.)
(c)—Adjust the cam in transmission
(c)—Accelerator pedal in idling position
(e)—Accelerator pedal fully depressed

A correct adjustment of the throttle cable is imperative for the proper shifting operation of the transmission. Connect a tachometer to the engine and an oil pressure gauge (manometer) to the rear of the transmission (as shown) for this adjustment.

Procedure A

1. Warm up the engine and check the idle speed against specifications in the "Tune-Up Chart." Make sure that the throttle cable and cable housing (outer cable) are attached correctly.

2. On dual-carbureted engines, the threaded sleeve is then screwed to within 1/32 in. of the crimped stop on the cable.

3. Check the adjustment by making sure (with the accelerator pedal fully depressed), first, that the carburetor lever is at the full open stop position, and second, that the line pressure reading at converter stall speed is a minimum of 160 psi.

Procedure B

If the cable stop has been damaged, the adjustment disturbed, or if the transmission is not functioning properly, the throttle cable must be adjusted as follows.

1. Firmly apply the parking brake and place blocks in front and in back of the wheels.

2. Place the gear selector in Drive. Note the line pressure readings at 700 rpm and 1200 rpm. The line pressure increase between the two readings should be a minimum of 15 psi and a maximum of 20 psi for B 20 engines, and 25–30 psi for B 30 engines. The effective length of the outer cable (cable housing) must be increased if the pressure increase is lower than 15 psi (or 25 psi) and decreased if the pressure rise is greater than 20 psi (or 30 psi). The length of the outer cable is determined by the adjuster.

Procedure C

If the cable itself has been damaged and is in need of replacement, the transmission oil pan must be removed first. Refer to "Oil Pan Removal and Installation." Adjust the new cable as follows.

NOTE: *Do not lubricate the new cable as it is pre-lubricated.*

1. With the oil pan removed, observe the position of the throttle cable cam in the transmission, in relation to the accelerator pedal position.

2. With the accelerator fully released and the carburetor lever at the idle stop, the heel of the cam must contact the full diameter of the downshift valve, taking up all of the slack in the inner throttle cable.

3. With the accelerator fully depressed and the carburetor lever at the full open stop, the constant radius area of the cam must be the point of contact with the downshift valve.

4. Make sure that the outer cable (cable housing) is correctly positioned in its adjuster.

DRIVE AXLES

Driveshaft and U-Joints

The driveshaft is a two-piece, tubular unit, connected by an intermediate universal joint. The rear end of the front section of the driveshaft forms a splined sleeve. A splined shaft forming one of the yokes for the intermediate U-joint fits into this sleeve. The front section is supported by a ball bearing contained in an insulated rubber housing which is attached to the bottom of the driveshaft tunnel. The front section is connected to the transmission flange, and the rear section is connected to the differential housing flange by universal joints. Each joint consists of a spider with four ground trunnions carried in the flange yokes by needle bearings.

Driveshaft and Universal Joint Removal and Installation

1. Jack up the vehicle and install safety stands.

2. Mark the relative positions of the driveshaft yokes and transmission and differential housing flanges for purposes of assembly. Remove the nuts and bolts which retain the front and rear driveshaft sections to the transmission and differential housing flanges, respectively. Remove the support bearing housing from the driveshaft tunnel, and lower the

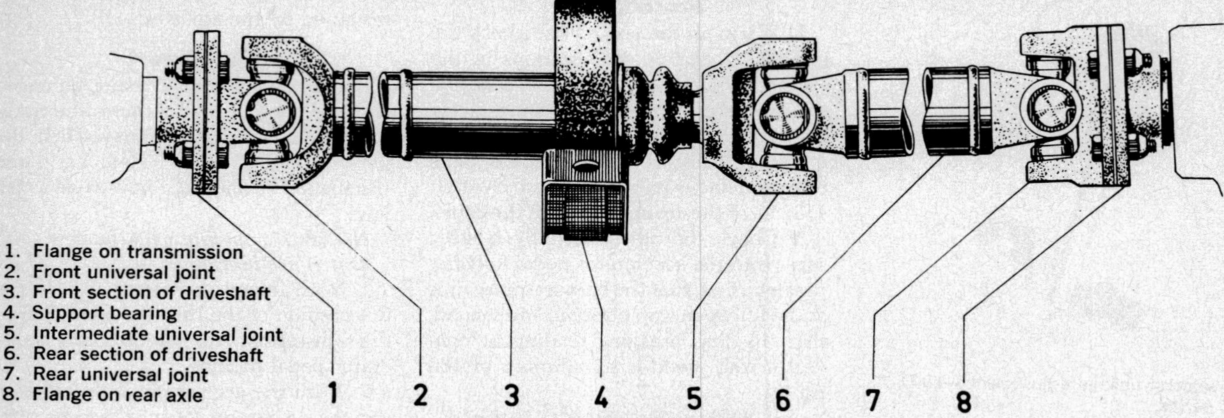

Driveshaft with support bearing

driveshaft and universal joint assembly as a unit.

3. Pry up the lock washer and remove the support bearing retaining nut. Pull off the rear section of the driveshaft with the intermediate universal joint and splined shaft of the front section. The support bearing may now be pressed off the driveshaft.

4. Remove the support from its housing.

5. For removal of the universal joints from the driveshaft, consult "Universal Joint Overhaul."

6. Inspect the driveshaft sections for straightness. Using a dial indicator, or rolling the shafts along a flat surface, make sure that the driveshaft out-of-round does not exceed 0.010 in. Do not attempt to straighten a damaged shaft. Any shaft exceeding 0.010 in. out-of-round will cause substantial vibration, and must be replaced. Also, inspect the support bearing by pressing the races against each other by hand, and turning them in opposite directions. If the bearing binds at any point, it must be discarded and replaced.

7. Install the support bearing into its housing.

8. Press the support bearing and housing onto the front driveshaft section. Push the splined shaft of the front section, with the intermediate universal joint and rear driveshaft section, into the splined sleeve of the front section. Install the retaining nut and lock washer for the support bearing.

9. Taking note of the alignment marks made prior to removal, position the driveshaft and universal joint assembly to its flange connections and install but do not tighten its retaining nuts and bolts. Position the support bearing housing to the driveshaft tunnel and install the retaining nut. Tighten the nuts which retain the driveshaft sections to the transmission and differential housing flanges to a torque of 25–30 ft. lbs.

10. Remove the safety stands and lower the vehicle. Road test the car and check for driveline vibrations.

Universal Joint Overhaul

1. Remove the driveshaft and universal joint assembly as outlined in "Driveshaft and Universal Joint Assembly Removal and Installation."

2. Place the driveshaft section in a vise so that the joint being removed comes as close as possible to the vise jaws. Do not tighten the vise any more than is necessary as the driveshaft is of tubular construction, and easily deformed.

3. Remove the snap-rings, which secure the needle bearings in the yokes, with snap-ring pliers.

4. With a hammer and a metal punch, drive the spider as far as it will go in one direction. The needle bearing should come about half-way out. Then, drive the spider as far as it will go in the other direction.

5. Drive out one of the needle bearings with a thinner punch. Remove the spider, and then drive out the other needle bearing.

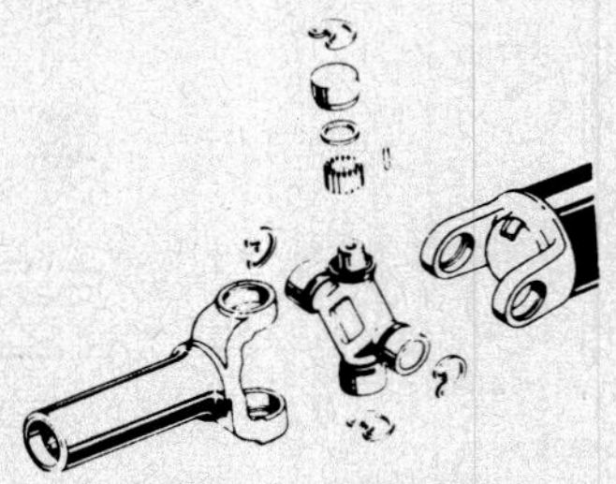
Universal joint disassembled

6. Clean the spider and needle bearings completely. Check the frictional surfaces for wear. Replace any worn or broken parts. If the old needle bearings and spider are to be reused, fill them with molybdenum disulphide chassis grease, and make sure that the rubber seals are not damaged. If new needle bearings are used, fill them half-way with the grease.

7. To install, position the spider in the yoke and push the spider in one direction as far as it will go, so that the needle bearing can be fitted onto the spider trunnion. Then, using a drift of a slightly smaller diameter than the needle bearing sleeve, press the needle bearing in until the bearing sleeve and snap-ring can be fitted.

8. Install the other needle bearing, bearing sleeve, and snap-ring as outlined in step 7.

9. Remove the driveshaft section from the vise and repeat steps 2–8 for the other universal joints.

10. Install the driveshaft and universal joint assembly as outlined under "Driveshaft and Universal Joint Removal and Installation."

Rear Axle

All 1967–73 Volvos utilize a solid rear axle housing carried in two support arms. Two torque rods, connected between the axle shaft tubes and the body, limit the rear axle wind-up. A track bar controls lateral movement of the axle housing. Final drive is of the hypoid design, with the drive pinion lying below the ring gear. Each axle shaft is indexed into a splined sleeve for the differential side gears, and supported at its outer end in a tapered roller bearing. Bearing clearance is not adjustable by use of shims as on earlier model Volvos, but instead is determined by bearing thickness. Both sides of the axle bearings are protected by oil seals.

Axle Shaft Removal and Installation, Bearing and Oil Seal Replacement

1967–73 140 Series, 1969–73 164, 1970–73 1800 Series

1. Raise the vehicle and install safety stands.

2. Remove the applicable wheel and tire assembly.

3. Place a wooden block beneath the brake pedal, plug the master cylinder reservoir vent hole, and remove and plug the brake line from the caliper. Be careful not to allow any brake fluid to spill onto the disc or pads. Remove the two bolts which retain brake caliper to the axle housing, and lift off the caliper. Lift off the brake disc.

4. Remove the thrust washer bolts through the holes in the axle shaft flange.

Using a slide hammer, remove the axle shaft, bearing and oil seal assembly.

5. Using an arbor press, remove the axle shaft bearing and its locking ring from the axle shaft. Remove and discard the old oil seal.

6. Fill the space between the lips of the new oil seal with wheel bearing grease. Position the new seal on the axle shaft. Using an arbor press, install the bearing with a new locking ring, onto the axle shaft.

7. Thoroughly pack the bearing with wheel bearing grease. Install the axle shaft into the housing, rotating it so that it indexes with the differential. Install the bolts for the thrust washer and tighten to 36 ft. lbs.

8. Install the brake disc. Position the brake caliper to its retainer on the axle housing and install the two retaining bolts. Torque the caliper retaining bolts to 45–50 ft. lbs.

9. Unplug the brake line and connect it to the caliper. Bleed the caliper of all air trapped in the system. Follow the instructions under "Bleeding" in Chapter 9.

10. Position the wheel and tire assembly on its lugs and hand-tighten the lug nuts. Remove the jackstands and lower the vehicle. Torque the lug nuts to 70–100 ft. lbs.

1800S

1967–69

1. Remove the wheel and pull off the hub. Remove the brake backing plate after placing a wooden block under the brake pedal and loosening the brake line from the backing plate.

2. Pull out the axle shaft. Check and, if necessary, replace the oil seal.

3. Press off the bearing. Install the new bearing with the help of a sleeve.

4. Pack the bearing with multi-purpose grease. After installation, the entire space between the oil seals should be filled with grease. Install the axle shaft in the drive pinion carrier. Drive in the bearing outer ring with a sleeve.

5a. Replacement of right-side bearing: Install the brake backing plate and retainer with the felt seal. Pull the bearing outer ring out toward the brake backing plate. Install a dial indicator on the axle shaft. Set the indicator pointer facing the brake backing plate and measure the step play. Play should be 0.0019–0.0059 in. If the play is incorrect, remove the brake drum on the left-hand side and also the brake backing plate. Then adjust the play according to steps 5b–10 below. If the play is correct proceed with steps 7–10.

5b. Replacement of bearing on left-hand side: Pull the bearing outer ring toward the plate.

6. Install a dial indicator on the axle shaft. Aim the indicator pointer at the plate, move in the shaft and zero the indicator. Pull the driveshaft outward and read the end play. To adjust the play, install suitable shims.

7. Install the brake backing plate together with the shims (left side) and the retainer with the felt seal.

8. Install the brake line, hub, brake drum, and wheel.

9. Bleed and adjust the brakes.

10. Check the oil level.

Rear Axle Housing Removal

1800 Series

1. Block the front wheels. Unscrew the rear wheel nuts and the nuts on the axle shafts. Jack up the rear. Place blocks under the body in front of the rear wheels.

2. Disconnect the rear section of the driveshaft from the flange (yoke) on the pinion and disconnect the brake lines from the master cylinder to the rear axle.

3. Loosen the track bar, shock absorber and shock absorber straps from the rear axle. Disconnect the handbrake cables and the adjuster.

4. Unscrew the nuts for the support arms. Lower the rear axle and remove the springs. Loosen the bolts for the torque rod and remove the rear axle.

140 Series, 164

1. Block the front wheels. Unscrew the rear wheel nuts. Jack up the rear of the vehicle. Place blocks in front of the rear jack attachments and lower the jack slightly. Remove the rear wheels.

2. Unscrew the upper bolts for the shock absorbers. Disconnect the handbrake cables from the lever arms and brackets on the brake backing plates.

3. Disconnect the driveshaft from the flange (yoke) on the pinion. Remove the brake line union from the differential carrier.

4. Loosen the front attaching bolt for the support arms about 1 turn. Remove the rear screws for the torque rods. Disconnect the track rod from the bracket on the differential carrier. Remove the lower attaching bolts for the springs.

5. Lower the jack until the support arms release from the springs. Remove the bolts which secure the differential carrier to the support arms. Lower the jack and pull the rear axle forward.

Differential Overhaul

Disassembly

1. Place the rear axle with the pinion pointing down. Remove the brake lines.

2a. 1967–69 1800S: Remove the brake backing plates from the differential carrier. Do not lose the shims. Pull out the axle shafts with a slide hammer.

2b. 140 Series 1970–73 1800, 164: Unscrew the bolts for the brake backing plates and retainers. The bolts are loosened through the holes in the axle shaft flanges. Pull out the axle shafts with a slide hammer.

3. Remove the inspection cover.

4. If the unit is being overhauled because of noise, the backlash and the gear tooth pattern should be checked before disassembly. Clean the teeth to avoid a misleading tooth pattern.

5. Check the alignment markings on the cap and carrier. If there are no alignment marks, or if they are difficult to see, mark one side with a punch. Remove the cap.

6. Expand the pinion carrier with a special tool. Pull out the differential carrier with ring gear. A special tool is available for this purpose.

7. Turn the assembly and allow the oil to run out. Remove the nuts for the flange. Pull the flange off with a puller. Press out the pinion.

8. Drive out the front pinion bearing, the washer, and oil seal.

9. If necessary, drive out the rear bearing outer ring.

10. Clean the gasket surface. Remove all burrs with a file.

11. If necessary, pull off the rear bearing from the pinion with a puller. Slide the puller down over the rollers and press down the lock ring. Then tighten the puller until the rollers are flush against the edge of the inner race. Tap the lock ring with a hammer.

12. Loosen the ring gear bolts and remove the ring gear.

13. Drive out the lock pin, and the shaft for the differential gears. Remove the thrust block, the differential gears, and the thrust washers.

14. Remove the differential carrier bearings with a puller. Do not lose the shims.

Inspection

Clean all the parts thoroughly. Check all the bearing races and bearings. All damaged bearings and bearing races must be replaced. Check both the pinion drive and ring gear carefully for damage to the teeth. Tooth damage is caused by incorrect break-in, wrong oil, insufficient tooth flank clearance, or faulty tooth contact.

The differential gears should also be examined for tooth damage. They should be placed in the differential carrier together with the shaft and thrust washers. Play should then be checked. If the play exceeds 0.0024 in. install thicker washers. These are available in 0.78 mm., 0.86 mm., and 0.94 mm. sizes. Also check to see whether the cylindrical part of the flange which goes into the oil seal is worn or scratched. If it is, replace the flange and the oil seal.

The pinion nut has a locking slit. In time this slit loses its effectiveness. For

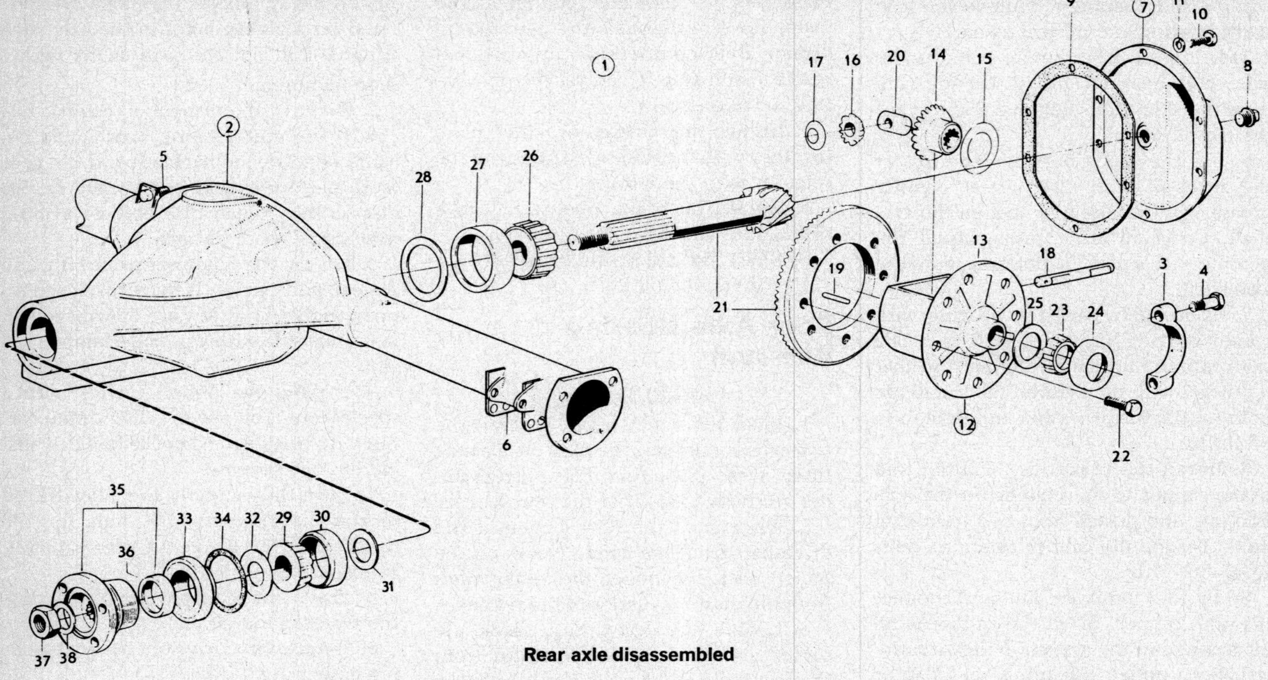

Rear axle disassembled

2. Rear axle housing
3. Bearing cap
4. Bolt
5. Anchorage point (track bar)
6. Anchorage point (support arm)
7. Inspection cover
8. Plug
9. Gasket
10. Bolt
11. Washer
12. Differential
13. Differential housing
14. Differential side pinion
15. Thrust washer
16. Differential side gear
17. Thrust washer
18. Pivot pin
19. Lock pin
20. Spacer sleeve
21. Ring and pinion
22. Bolt
23. Roller bearing cone
24. Roller bearing cup
25. Shim
26. Roller bearing cone
27. Roller bearing cup
28. Shim
29. Roller bearing cone
30. Roller bearing cup
31. Shim
32. Oil deflector
33. Oil seal
34. Gasket
35. Flange
36. Mud slinger
37. Nut
38. Washer

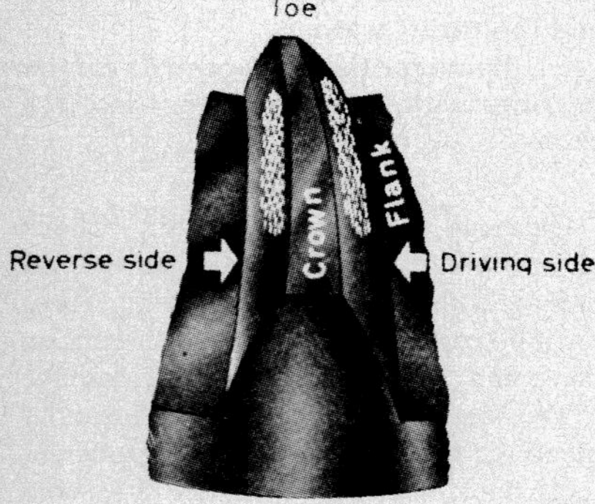

Correct tooth contact

this reason, the nut should be replaced if it has been removed more than once. The washer under the nut should also be replaced if it is deformed.

Check the oil seals and replace them if they are damaged or worn.

Check for cracks in the rear axle casing. Make sure that the brackets for the support arms and track rod are intact.

Assembly

Great cleanliness should be observed when assembling and adjusting the differential. Dirt in a tapered roller bearing can result in inaccurate measurement. When measuring the bearing clearance or preloading, the bearing should be oiled and rotated several turns loaded.

1. Place the differential side gears and the thrust washers in the differential carrier. Then roll in the differential pinions simultaneously with the dished thrust washers.
2. Insert the thrust block and drive in the shaft.
3. Check the differential unit. If the gear play has not been measured, check it as described under "Inspection." If oversize washers are installed, check by turning the gears one turn. The turning torque should not exceed 7.23 ft.lbs. The tool for making this check can be easily made from a shortened axle shaft adapted to a suitable torque wrench. After checking the replacement of the thrust washers, install the lock pin.
4. Install the ring gear. Make sure that the contact surfaces are clean and without burrs. Tighten the bolts to 45–65 ft lbs.

NOTE: *Always use new bolts for gears in which the bolts are locked only by thread friction and the contact surface of the screw head.*

Pinion Installation

1. Polish the marking surface on the pinion with very fine emery cloth. Place the pinion in the casing so that the screw on the adjusting ring faces the larger part of the casing.
2. The pinion should have a certain nominal measurement to the center line of the ring gear. Due to manufacturing tolerances, there are deviations from the nominal measurement. This is indicated on the pinion.

On differentials made by Volvo, the surface is generally ground down 0.012 in. so that the deviation is always indicated by plus tolerance in hundredths of a millimeter. The plus sign is not indicated. On other units, the deviation is indicated in thousandths of an inch and with a plus or minus sign. If there is a plus sign in front of the figure, the nominal measurement is to be increased and, in the case of a minus sign, the nominal measurement is to be decreased.

To check the pinion location, use a dial indicator, an indicator retainer (SVO 2284), and a measuring tool (SVO 2393), which consists of two parts: a pinion gauge and an adjuster fixture. Place the pinion gauge on the ground end surface of the pinion and place the adjuster fixture in the differential bearing recesses. Place the indicator retainer on the drive pinion carrier and zero the indicator against the adjuster fixture. Then move the indicator retainer so that the indicator is against the pinion gauge. Read the indicator.

On a Volvo unit on which the pinion is, for example, marked 33, the pinion gauge should be 0.013 in. (0.33mm) under the adjuster fixture. On other units, if the pinion is marked 0, the adjuster fixture and pinion gauge should be at the same height; if the pinion is marked −, the pinion gauge should be higher than the adjuster fixture; and if it is marked +, the pinion gauge should be lower than the adjuster fixture. The setting is adjusted by turning the cam on the pinion until the gauge dial shows the correct figure, then locking in the adjusting ring with the lock screw. Remove the measuring tool and pinion.

3. Place the rear pinion bearing complete with the outer ring in a measuring fixture (SVO 2600). Install the plate, spring and nut. The flat side of the nut should face upward. The plate (and the bearing) should be turned forward and backward several times so that the rollers take up the correct position. Place the adjusting ring in the measuring fixture. Use an indicator retainer (SVO 2284) and a dial indicator. Place the measuring point of the gauge against the adjusting ring and set the gauge to zero. Then place the point of the gauge against the outer ring of the bearing. The gauge now shows the required size for the shims. Measure the thickness of the shims with a micrometer. It is not always possible to obtain shims with exactly the correct thickness. However, they may not be more than 0.0012 in. thicker than the measured value but may be up to 0.0020 in. thinner.

4. Press the rear bearing on the pinion with a sleeve. The washer under the rear bearing inner ring on a new Volvo unit should not be installed after overhaul. Install the measured shims and press in both the outer rings of the bearings.

5. Install the pinion in the carrier and mount three 0.30 in. thick shims and the front pinion bearing. Tighten the pinion. If a nut remover is used when installing the pinion, the pinion must be pressed forward so that it does not strike against the bearing positions.

6. Install the pinion gauge and indicator retainer. Move the pinion down while turning it forward and backward at the same time. Set the indicator gauge to zero. Then press the pinion upward while turning it backward and forward at the same time. Read the play.

7. Remove the pinion. Remove a sufficient number of shims corresponding to the measured play plus 0.0028 in. Reinstall the pinion.

8. Then check the pinion bearings with a torque gauge. The torque gauge should show a torque of 5–10 in.lbs. for used bearings and 10–20 in.lbs. for new bearings when the pinion rotates. On new units, turning torque may be higher due to another installation method.

Check the location of the pinion with a dial indicator, an indicator retainer (SVO 2284), and a measuring tool (SVO 2393).

Differential Installation

1. Oil the adjusting rings internally and install them on the differential carrier. The ring with the oxidized adjusting ring is placed on the ring gear side. Also oil the bearing seal in the carrier. The differential carrier and adjusting rings are placed in the carrier. Use the dial indicator and adjust the ring so that the correct tooth flank clearance, 0.0060 in. is obtained. The tooth flank clearance may vary between 0.0040 in. (model 30: 0.-0052 in.) and 0.0080 in., but should be kept as near 0.0060 in. as possible. Tighten the lock bolts in the adjusting rings.

2. Coat several teeth with marking blue at three points on the ring gear. By this means a check can be kept on possible ring gear warping. Pull the pinion 10–12 turns in both directions and check the tooth pattern. When the tooth contact is correct, the contact pattern should be vertical in the middle of the tooth but somewhat nearer to the toe than to the heel. The contact pattern on the reverse side and driving side should lie opposite each other. If the contact pattern is incorrect, the location of the pinion must be adjusted before assembly continues. If the contact pattern lies too far toward the heel on the driving side and too far toward the toe on the reverse side, the pinion should be moved inward. If the contact pattern lies too far toward the toe on the driving side and too far toward the heel on the reverse side, the pinion should be moved outward. Note that the contact pattern will lie somewhat nearer the toe when the adjusting rings are installed than when the bearings are installed.

3. When correct tooth flank clearance and contact pattern are obtained, remove the differential and adjusting ring. Place the center washer on the measuring fixture. Place a bearing in the measuring fixture and fit the plate, spring and nut. The nut should be fitted with the flat side facing downward. Turn the plate forward and backward several times. Install the dial indicator gauge and retainer. Set the gauge to zero against the adjusting ring and then place the pointer facing the bearing. Read the gauge. With a micrometer, measure the shims. The total shim thickness should correspond to the indicator reading plus 0.0028 in. Repeat with the other bearing. Keep a careful check on which side the bearing and shim are to be fitted.

4. Install the shims on the differential carrier and press on the bearings. Use a drift. When installing the second bearing, use a drift as a cushioning ring to avoid damage to the first bearing.

5. Expand the pinion carrier with a special tool. Install the differential and outer rings. Remove the tool. Install the bearing caps and tighten the bolts to 35–50 ft lbs.

6. Check the tooth flank clearance and contact pattern.

7. Install the oil slinger and the oil seal. The oil seal should be fitted with a drift. Press on the flange. Install the washer and nut. Tighten the nut to a torque of 200–220 ft lbs.

8. Install the inspection cover and gasket.

9. Install the axle shafts as outlined in the applicable "Axle Shaft Removal and Installation" procedure.

Rear Axle Housing Installation

1800 Series

1. Place the rear axle on a jack. Lift up the axle and install the torque rods. Slide the support arms into the retainers on the body and install the rubber blocks, washers, and nuts. The nuts should be tightened only a couple of turns to begin with.

2. Install the springs, retainers, and rubber blocks. Install bolts. Lift up the rear axle with the jack. Tighten the nuts for the support arms. Install the shock absorbers, shock absorber straps, and track rod.

3. Connect the universal joint at the flange, the brake hose, and the handbrake cables. Bleed the brake system and adjust the handbrake. Fill with oil. Use only hypoid oil.

4. Install the wheels and nuts. Lower the car and tighten the wheel nuts to 70–100 ft lbs.

140 Series, 164

1. Place the rear axle on a garage jack. Move the axle in under the car and install the bolts for the support arms and torque rods.

2. Raise the jack until the track rod attachment on the shaft is at the level with the attachment on the body. Install the track rod.

3. Install the attaching bolts for the springs. Tighten the nuts for the torque rods and support arms.

4. Install the bracket, union, and brake hoses. Connect the universal joint to the flange.

5. Install the upper bolts for the shock absorbers. Install the handbrake cable in

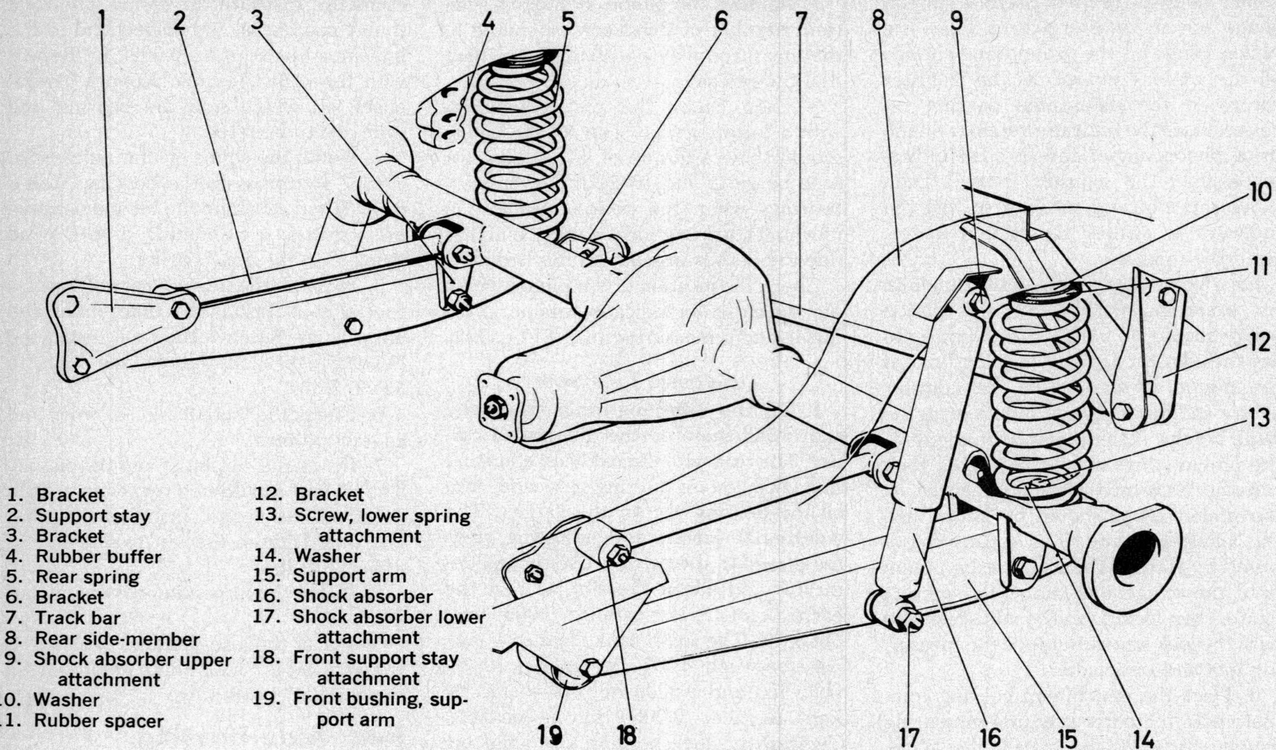

Rear suspension assembly—140 series, 164.

the brackets and at the levers. Adjust the handbrake and bleed the brake system. Fill with oil.

6. Install the wheels and nuts. Lower the car. Tighten the wheel nuts to 70–100 ft lbs. Fill with oil. Use only hypoid oil.

REAR SUSPENSION

All Volvos use a coil spring rear suspension. The solid rear axle is suspended from the rigid frame member by a pair of support arms and damped by a pair of double-acting telescopic shock absorbers. A pair of torque rods control rear axle wind-up and a track rod limits the lateral movement of the rear axle in relation to the car.

Springs

Removal and Installation

140 series, 164

1. Remove the hub cap and loosen the lug nuts a few turns. Jack up the car and place jack stands in front of the rear jacking points. Remove the wheel and tire assembly.

2. Place a hydraulic jack beneath the rear axle housing and raise the housing sufficiently to compress the spring. Loosen the nuts for the upper and lower spring attachments.

CAUTION: *Due to the fact that the spring is compressed under several hundred pounds of pressure, when it is freed from its lower attachment, it will attempt to suddenly return to its extended position. It is therefore imperative that the axle housing be lowered with extreme care until the spring is fully extended. As an added safety measure, a chain may be attached to the lower spring coil and secured to the axle housing.*

3. Disconnect the shock absorber at its upper attachment. Carefully lower the jack and axle housing until the spring is fully extended. Remove the spring.

4. To install, position the retaining bolt and inner washer, for the upper attachment, inside the spring and then, while holding the outer washer and rubber spacer to the upper body attachment, install the spring and inner washer to the upper attachment (sandwiching the rub-

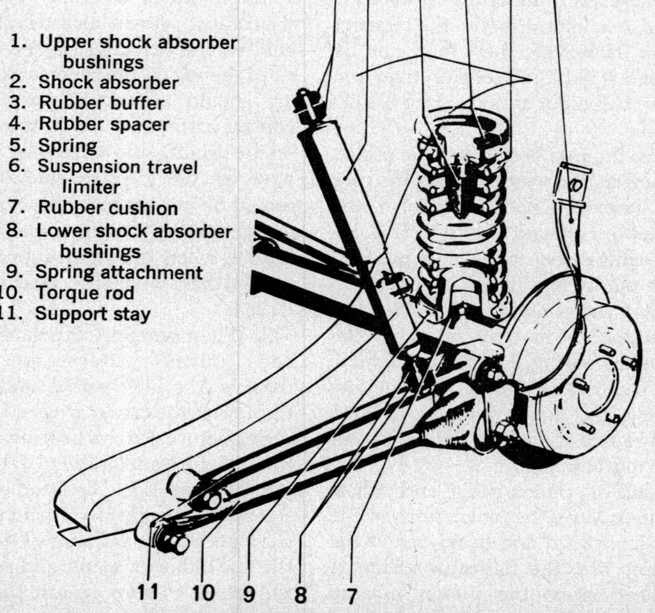

Rear suspension assembly—1800 series

ber spacer), and tighten the retaining bolt.

5. Raise the jack and secure the bottom of the spring to its lower attachment with the washer and retaining bolt.

6. Connect the shock absorber to its upper attachment. Install the wheel and tire assembly.

7. Remove the jack stands and lower the car. Tighten the lug nuts to 70–100 ft lbs and install the hub cap.

1800 series

1. Remove the hub cap and loosen the lug nuts a few turns. Place blocks in front of the front wheels. Jack up the rear of the car and place jack stands in front of the rear jacking points.

2. Remove the wheel and tire assembly and release the parking brake.

3. Place a hydraulic jack beneath the rear axle housing and raise the jack and axle housing sufficiently to off-load the suspension downward travel limiter (shock absorber band).

4. Disconnect the shock absorber at its lower attachment. Also disconnect the suspension travel limiter (shock absorber band) at its upper attachment.

CAUTION: *Do not attempt to remove the spring until it is fully extended. As an added safety measure, a chain may be attached to the lower spring coil and secured to the axle housing.*

5. Carefully lower the jack and axle housing until the spring is fully extended. Remove the spring and rubber spacer.

6. To install, fit the rubber spacer to the top of the spring and position the spring into its upper attachment. Secure the bottom of the spring into its lower attachment, making sure that the rubber cushion on the axle housing is positioned correctly.

7. Raise the jack sufficiently so that the shock absorber may be connected to its lower attachment. Connect the suspension travel limiter to its upper attachment.

8. Install the wheel and tire assembly. Remove the jack stands and lower the car. Tighten the lug nuts to 70–100 ft lbs, and install the hub cap.

Shock Absorbers

Removal and Installation

140 series, 164

1. Remove the hub cap and loosen the lug nuts a few turns. Place blocks in front of the front wheels. Jack up the rear of the car and place jack stands in front of the rear jacking points. Remove the wheel and tire assembly.

2. Remove the nuts and bolts which retain the shock absorber to its upper and lower attachments and remove the shock absorber. Make sure that the spacing sleeve, inside the axle support arm for the lower attachment, is not misplaced.

3. The damping effect of the shock absorber may be tested by securing the lower attachment in a vise and extending and compressing it. A properly operating shock absorber should offer approximately three times as much resistance to extending the unit as compressing it. Replace the shock absorber if it does not function as above, or if its fixed rubber bushings are damaged.

4. To install, position the shock absorber to its upper and lower attachments. Make sure that the spacing sleeve is installed inside the axle support arm and is aligned with the lower attachment bolt hole. Install the retaining nuts and bolts.

5. Install the wheel and tire assembly. Remove the jack stands and lower the car. Tighten the lug nuts to 70–100 ft lbs, and install the hub cap.

1800 series

1. Fold the rear seat back forward. On 1800E and 1800S models, remove the upholstery for the shelf under the rear window, and on 1800ES models, fold back the carpet for the bed, which will reveal the shock absorber upper attaching points.

2. Remove the upper nut, washers, and outer rubber bushing from the top of the shock absorber.

3. Remove the lower nut, washers, and outer rubber bushing from the bottom of the shock absorber.

4. Compress and remove the shock absorber.

5. Test the damping action of the shock absorber. Extending the unit should offer about three times as much resistance as compressing the unit. If the shock absorber is operating properly and is being reinstalled, be sure to use new rubber bushings.

6. Install inner washers and new rubber bushings, if removed, on the unit. Compress the shock absorber and position it to its upper and lower attachments.

7. Install the outer nuts, washers, and new rubber bushings first to the top and then to the bottom, of the shock absorber.

8. Replace the package shelf upholstery or the bed carpet to its original position.

FRONT SUSPENSION

All Volvos use a coil spring independ-

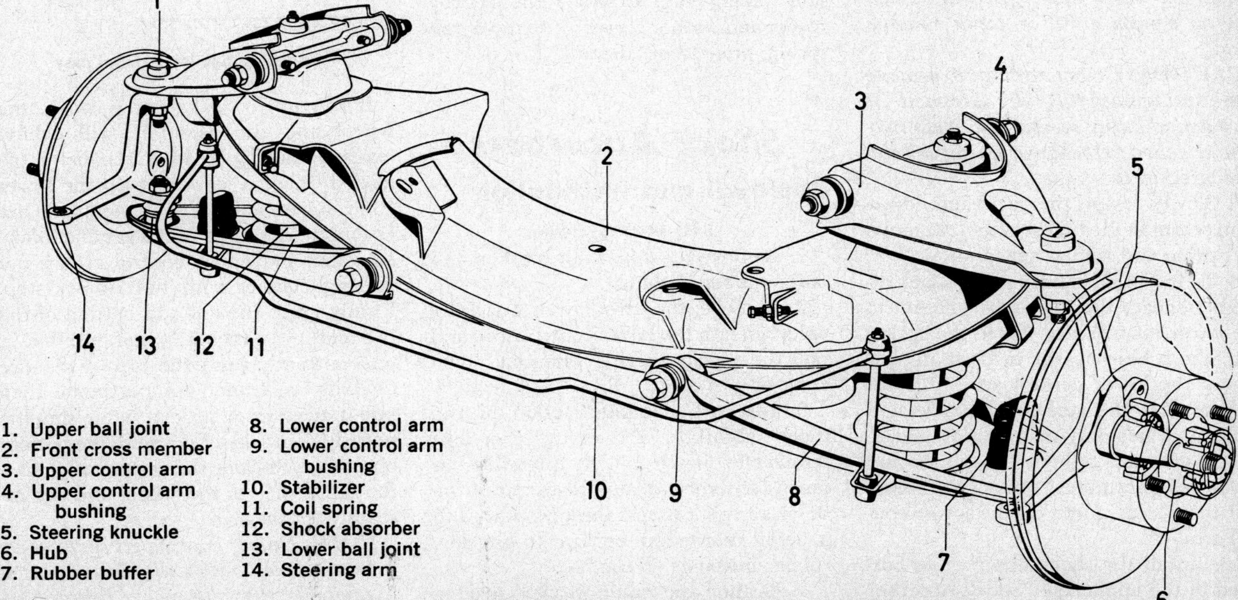

Front suspension assembly—140 series, 164 shown, 1800 series similar

ent front suspension. A pair of upper and lower control arms are bolted to each side of the rigid front frame member. The coil springs and telescopic double-acting shock absorbers are bolted to the lower control arms at the bottom and seat in the crossmember at the top. A pair of steering knuckles are carried in ball joints between the upper and lower control arms. A stabilizer bar is attached to the lower control arms and to the body.

Springs

Removal and Installation

140 series, 164

1. Remove the hub cap and loosen the lug nuts a few turns.
2. Firmly apply the parking brake and place blocks in back of the rear wheels. Jack up the front of the car and place jackstands in back of the front jacking points. Remove the wheel and tire assembly.
3. Remove the shock absorber as outlined in the applicable "Shock Absorber Removal and Installation" procedure.
4. Remove the cotter pin and ball nut and disconnect the steering rod from the steering knuckle. Loosen the clamp for the flexible brake hoses. Remove the stabilizer attachment from the lower control arm.
5. Place a jack under the lower control arm. Raise the jack to unload the lower control arm. Remove the cotter pins and loosen the nuts for the upper and lower ball joints; then rap with a hammer until they loosen from the spindle. Remove the nuts and lower the jack slightly.
6. Remove the steering knuckle with the front brake caliper and disc still connected to the brake lines. In order not to stretch the brake lines, place the brake unit on a milk crate or other suitable stand.

CAUTION: *Do not attempt to remove the spring until it is fully extended. As an added safety measure, a chain may be attached to the lower spring coil and secured to the frame.*

7. Slowly lower the jack and lower control arm to the fullest extent. Remove the spring and rubber spacer.
8. To install the spring place a jack directly beneath the spring attachment to the lower control arm. Place the spring with the rubber spacer in position, and lift up the lower control arm with the jack so that the steering knuckle and brake unit assembly may be installed.
9. Install and tighten the upper and lower ball joint nuts. Connect the stabilizer to its attachment on the lower control arm.
10. Install the shock absorber as outlined in the applicable "Shock Absorber Removal and Installation" section.
11. With the wheels pointing straight ahead, and the lower control arm unloaded, connect the steering rod to the steering knuckle and install the ball nut and cotter pin.
12. Clamp the brake hoses to the stabilizer bolt.
13. Install the wheel and tire assembly. Remove the jackstands and lower the car. Tighten the lug nuts to 70–100 ft lbs, and install the hub cap.

1800 series

1. Remove the hub cap and loosen the lug nuts a few turns.
2. Firmly apply the parking brake and place blocks in back of the rear wheels.
3. Jack up the front of the car and place jackstands beneath the front crossmember. Remove the wheel and tire assembly.
4. Remove the shock absorber as outlined in the applicable "Shock Absorber Removal and Installation" procedure.
5. Position a jack directly beneath the lower spring attachment on the lower control arm, and raise the jack until the upper control arm rubber buffer is lifted.
6. Disconnect the stabilizer from the lower control arm. Remove the cotter pin and ball nut from the lower ball joint.

CAUTION: *Do not attempt to remove the spring until it is fully extended. As an added safety measure, a chain may be attached to the lower spring coil and secured to the frame.*

7. Slowly lower the jack and lower control arm. If the lower ball joint does not release when the jack is lowered, it must be pressed out with a press tool such as SVO 2281. When the lower control arm is lowered sufficiently, carefully remove the spring, rubber spacer and washer assembly.
8. Reverse the above procedure to install, taking care to place the rubber spacer and washer correctly on top of the spring, prior to installation.

Shock Absorbers

Removal and Installation

140 series, 164

1. Remove the upper nut, washer, and outer rubber bushing.
2. Remove the two lower attaching bolts beneath the lower control arm, and pull the shock absorber assembly down and out.
3. Test the damping action of the shock absorber. Extending the unit should offer approximately three times as much resistance as compressing it. If the shock absorber is operating properly and is being reinstalled, be sure to use new rubber bushings on top.
4. Position the inner washer, spacing sleeve, and inner rubber bushing on top of the shock absorber.
5. Position the shock to its upper and lower attachments, and install the lower attaching bolts.
6. Install the outer rubber bushing, washer, and the upper nut on top of the unit. Tighten the upper nut until it makes firm contact with the spacing sleeve.

1800 series

1. Remove the upper nut, washer, and outer rubber bushing from the top of the shock absorber.
2. Remove the lower nut, washer, and outer rubber bushing from beneath the shock absorber.
3. Remove the two lower attaching bolts from beneath the lower control arm, and pull the shock absorber assembly down and out.
4. Test the damping action of the shock absorber. Extending the unit should offer approximately three times as much resistance as compressing it. If the shock absorber is operating properly and is being reinstalled, be sure to use new rubber bushings.
5. Reverse steps 1–3 to install.

Upper Ball Joint

Inspection

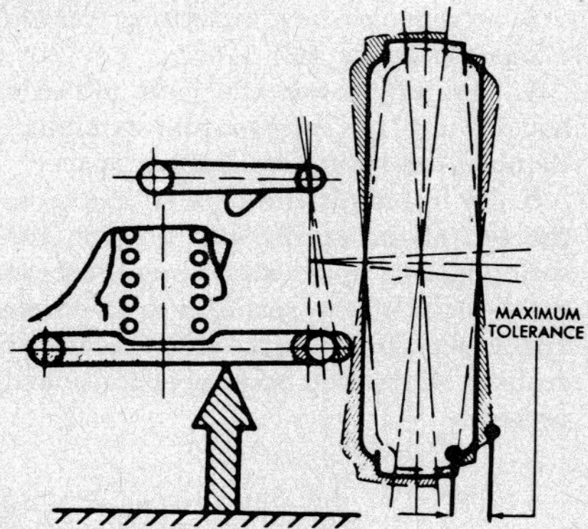

Checking ball joint radial play

If the upper ball joint is worn, the wheel and tire assembly will exhibit excessive radial play when the joint is off-loaded. Place a jack beneath the lower control arm, and lift the wheel and tire assembly until clear of the ground. Make sure that the upper control arm is not making contact with the rubber stop. Firmly grasp the top and bottom of the tire and try to rock it in and out; that is, intermittently push the top of the tire towards the engine compartment, then pull it away from the car, while simultaneously doing the opposite to the bottom of the tire. Replace the upper ball joint if the radial play of the wheel and tire assembly is excessive.

NOTE: *Do not confuse possible wheel bearing play with ball joint play. It is advisable that the wheel bearing adjustment procedure in Chapter nine be* *followed prior to replacing the ball joint.*

Removal and Installation

140 series, 164

1. Remove the hub cap and loosen the lug nuts a few turns.

2. Jack up the front of the vehicle and place safety stands beneath the front jacking points. Remove the wheel and tire assembly.

3. Loosen, but do not remove the nut for the upper ball joint. With a hammer, rap around the ball joint stud on the steering knuckle until it loosens. Remove the nut, and safety wire the upper end of the steering knuckle to the stabilizer bar to avoid straining the flexible brake hoses.

4. Loosen the nuts for the upper control arm shaft ½ turn. Lift up the control arm slightly and press out the old ball joint with a press tool and a sleeve.

4. Make sure that the rubber cover of the new ball joint is filled with multipurpose grease. Bend the pin end over the slot, and make sure that the grease forces its way out, then fill as necessary.

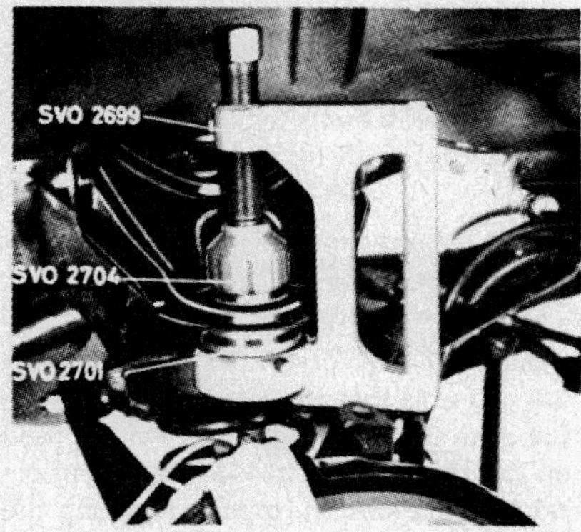

Installing upper ball joint—140 series, 164

5. Press the ball joint into the upper control arm using the press tool, a sleeve, and a drift. It is imperative that the ball joint be aligned so that the slot (A) comes in line with the longitudinal shaft of the control arm, either internally or externally, as the pin has maximum movement along this line.

6. Lower the upper control arm to its operating position, and tighten the shaft nuts. to 40–45 ft lbs. Remove the safety wire; place the steering knuckle in position; install and tighten the ball nut to 60–70 ft lbs. If the pin rotates during tightening, clamp it firmly with a screw vise.

7. Install the wheel and tire assembly. Remove the safety stands and lower the vehicle. Tighten the lug nuts to 70–100 ft lbs, and install the hub cap.

1800 series

1. Remove the hub cap and loosen the lug nuts a few turns.

2. Jack up the front of the vehicle and place safety stands beneath the lower

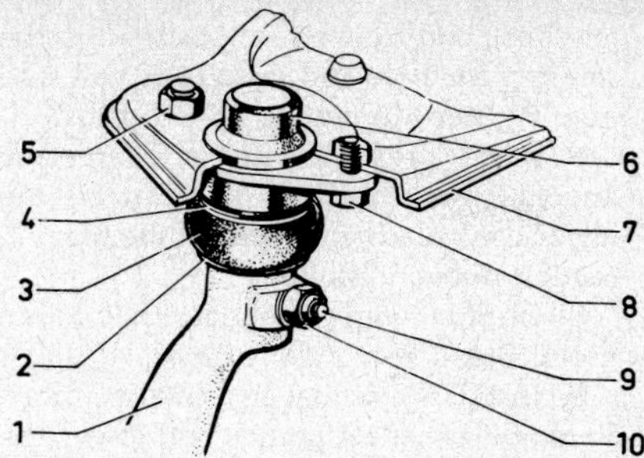

Upper ball joint attachment—1800 series

1. Spindle
2. Circlip
3. Rubber cover
4. Circlip
5. Nut
6. Upper ball joint
7. Upper wishbone
8. Bolt
9. Clamp bolt
10. Nut

control arms. Remove the wheel and tire assembly.

3. Remove the two nuts (5) and bolts (8) which retain the ball joint to the upper control arm. Lift the upper control arm up and out of the way.

4. Remove the clamping nut (10) and bolt (9) which secure the ball joint to the steering knuckle. Remove the upper ball joint, sealing washers, and rubber cover assembly.

5. Make sure that the rubber cover of the new ball joint is filled with multipurpose (universal) grease. If the old ball joint is being reused, make sure that the rubber cover is not damaged, and fill it with grease.

6. After making sure that the sleeve and sealing washers (circlips) are positioned properly, place the ball joint assembly on the steering knuckle and install the clamping nut and bolt.

7. Lower the upper control arm into position over the ball joint and install the attaching nuts and bolts.

8. Install the wheel and tire assembly. Remove the safety stands and lower the vehicle. Tighten the lug nuts to 70–100 ft lbs, and install the hub cap.

Lower Ball Joint

Inspection

If the lower ball joint is worn, a measurement (A) taken from the ball stud to the cover of the ball joint will exceed the maximum allowable length for the ball joint when it is normally loaded. The check is made with the vehicle standing on the ground, wheels pointing straight ahead. Two types of lower ball joints have been used on late model Volvos; one utilizing a pressure spring, and the other not. The maximum allowable length for the spring type ball joint is 4.5 in. for the 140 series and 164, and 4.4 in. for the 1800 series. The maximum allowable length for the non-spring type ball joint is 3.91 in. for the 140 series and 164, and 3.76 in. for the 1800 series.

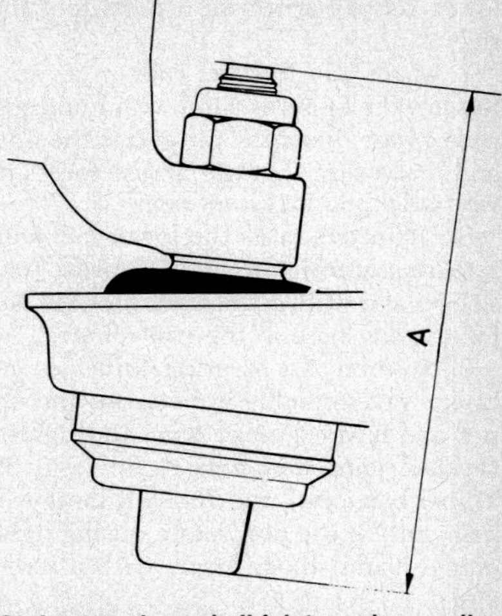

Spring type lower ball joint maximum allowable length.

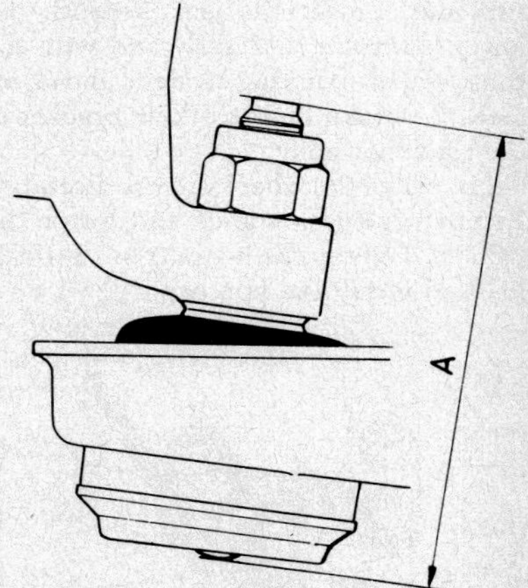

Non-spring type lower ball joint maximum allowable length.

Removal and Installation

140 series, 164

1. Remove the hub cap and loosen the lug nuts a few turns.

2. Jack up the front of the vehicle and place jack stands beneath the front jacking points. Remove the whẽel and tire assembly.

3. Remove the cotter pin and ball stud nut, and press the steering rod ball stud from the steering knuckle. Remove the brake lines from their bracket at the stabilizer bolt.

4. Remove the cotter pins and loosen but do not remove the nuts for both the upper and lower ball joints. Rap with a hammer until the ball joints loosen from the spindle. Place a jack beneath the lower control arm and raise it to off-load the control arm. Remove the ball joint nuts.

5. Remove the steering knuckle with the front brake unit still connected to the brake lines. In order not to stretch the brake lines, place the brake unit on a milk crate or other suitable stand.

6. Press the lower ball joint out of the

lower control arm with a press tool and sleeve.

7. Make sure that the rubber cover of the new ball joint is filled with multipurpose grease. Bend the pin end to the side, and make sure that the grease forces its way out, then fill as necessary.

8. To install, press the lower ball joint into its control arm with a press tool, sleeve, and drift. Make sure that the ball joint is not loose in the control arm.

9. Position the steering knuckle and brake unit assembly in between the upper and lower control arms and tighten the ball joint stud nuts to 60–70 ft lbs (upper ball joint), and 75–90 ft lbs (lower ball joint). If the pins rotate during tightening, clamp them firmly with a screw vise.

10. Install the steering rod ball stud into the steering knuckle and tighten the stud nut. Lower the jack beneath the lower control arm slightly and with the front wheels pointing straight ahead, attach the brake lines to their bracket at the stabilizer bolt.

11. Install the wheel and tire assembly. Remove the jack stands and lower the vehicle. Tighten the lug nuts to 70–100 ft lbs, and install the hub cap.

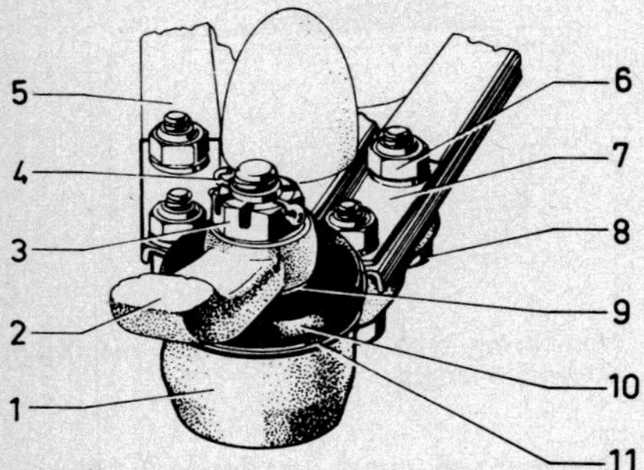

Lower ball joint attachment—1800 series

1. Lower ball joint
2. Spindle
3. Castle nut
4. Cotter pin
5. Lower wishbone
6. Nut
7. Bracket
8. Bolt
9. Circlip
10. Rubber cover
11. Circlip

1800 series

1. Remove the hub cap and loosen the lug nuts a few turns.

2. Jack up the front of the car and place safety stands beneath the lower control arms. Remove the wheel and tire assembly.

3. Remove the four nuts (6) and bolts (8) which retain the ball joint to the lower control arm. Remove the cotter pin and ball stud nut which secure the steering knuckle to the ball joint.

4. Disconnect and plug the brake hoses at their retainer. Remove the ball joint from the steering knuckle by lightly rapping its attachment with a hammer.

5. Make sure that the rubber cover of the new ball joint is filled with multipurpose (universal) grease.

6. Place the ball joint, sealing washers (circlips), and sleeve into position on the steering knuckle and install the ball stud nut. Tighten the nut to 35–40 ft lbs.

7. Place the ball joint and steering knuckle assembly into position on the lower control arm and install the four retaining nuts and bolts.

8. Unplug and connect the brake hoses. Bleed the brake caliper.

9. Install the wheel and tire assembly. Remove the safety stands and lower the vehicle. Tighten the lug nuts to 70–100 ft lbs, and install the hub cap.

Wheel Alignment

Caster and Camber Adjustment

The procedures for adjusting caster and camber are grouped together here as they may be performed at the same time on all Volvos. Both adjustments are made by inserting shims between the upper control arm shaft and the sheet metal of the shock absorber tower. Loosen the bolts which retain the control arm shaft to the shock tower and insert the shims. Before each adjustment is completed, the bolts must be tightened or an erroneous measurement will be obtained. A special SVO tool (no. 2713) is available from dealers for loosening or tightening the control arm shaft bolts on the 140 series and 164 models, because gaining access to these bolts is difficult.

Caster is adjusted by either removing a shim at one of the bolts, adding a shim at the other bolt, or by transferring half of the required shim thickness from one bolt to another. Caster is adjusted to the positive side, for example, by inserting shims at the rear bolt or removing shims at the front bolt.

Camber is adjusted by either removing or adding shims of equal thickness at both bolts. Camber is increased toward the positive by removing shims, and decreased toward the negative by adding shims.

Shims are available in sizes of 0.15, 0.5, 1.0, 3.0, and 6.0 mm (0.006, 0.020, 0.039, 0.12, and 0.24 in.). Remember to torque the control arm shaft bolts to 40–50 ft lbs after making the adjustment.

Toe-In Adjustment

Toe-in may be adjusted after performing the caster and camber adjustments. With a wheel spreader, measure the distance (X) between the rear of the right and left front tires, at spindle (hub) height, and then measure the distance (Y) between the front of the right and left front tires, also at spindle (hub) height. Subtract the front distance (Y) from the rear distance (X), and compare that to the specifications table. X—Y=toe-in. If the adjustment is not correct, loosen the locknuts on both sides of the tie rod, and rotate the tie rod itself. Toe-in is increased by turning the tie rod in the normal forward rotation of the wheels, and reduced by turning it in the opposite direction. After the final adjustment is made, torque the locknuts to 55–65 ft lbs, being careful not to disturb the adjustment.

STEERING

All 1967–73 Volvos use divided steering columns that protect the dirver during front end collisions. The system used on the 140 series utilizes a flange connection that breaks on impact, allowing the lower portion to travel backward but keeping the upper portion stable. The 164 uses a telescoping column and a

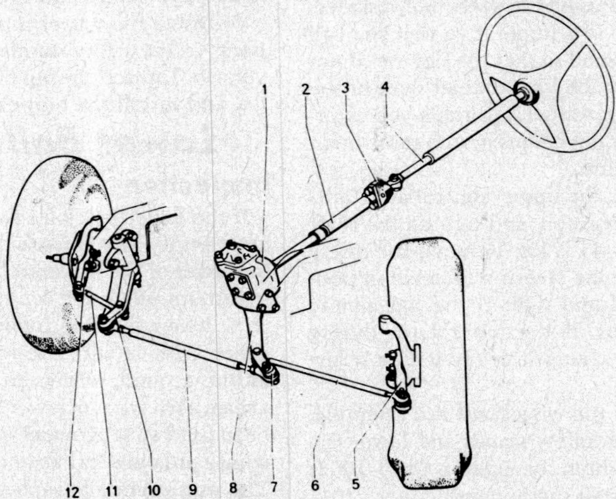

Steering linkage assembly—1800 series shown—140 series, 164 similar.

1. Steering box
2. Safety device
3. Rubber flange
4. Steering column
5. Left stering arm
6. Left steering rod
7. Ball joint
8. Pitman arm
9. Tie rod
10. Relay arm
11. Right steering rod
12. Right steering arm

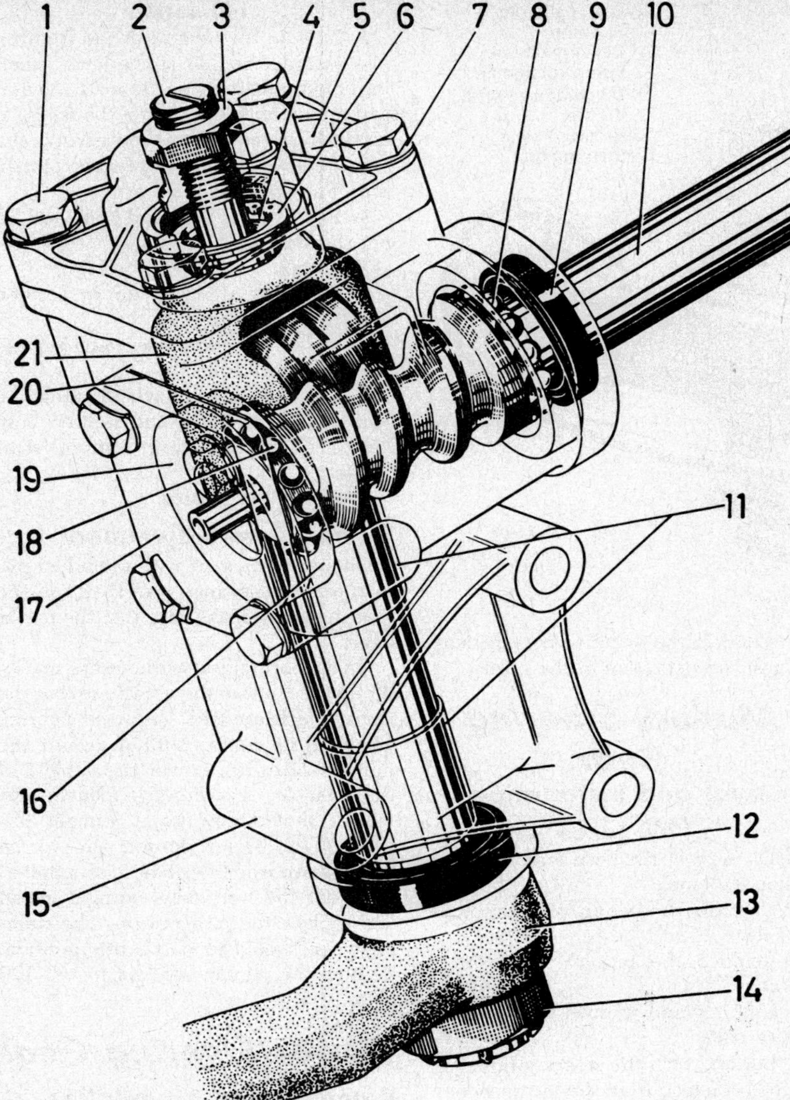

Manual steering gear assembly

1. Bolt
2. Adjusting screw
3. Locknut
4. Pitman arm shaft bushing
5. Cover
6. Lock ring
7. Tab washer
8. Upper steering cam bearing
9. Oil seal, steering column
10. Steering cam
11. Pitman arm shaft bushing
12. Pitman arm shaft seal
13. Pitman arm
14. Nut
15. Housing
16. Lower bearing cap
17. Steering column cover
18. Lower cam bearing
19. Washer
20. Shims
21. Pitman arm shaft with roller

breakaway flange at the steering box. The 1800 series utilizes the telescoping column. All 1973 models are collapsible column types.

The manual steering gear used on the 140 series, and 1800 series models is the Gemmer worm and roller type. The power steering gear used on the 164 series, and some late production 1973 automatic transmission equipped 145 models, is the ZF worm and roller type.

Steering Wheel

Removal and Installation

NOTE: *the use of a knock-off type steering wheel puller, or the use of a hammer may damage the collapsible column.*

140 series, 164

1967–71

1. Disconnect the negative battery cable.
2. Remove the retaining screw from the upper half of the molded turn signal switch housing, and the three retaining screws from the lower half. Remove both halves from the column.
3. Remove the two screws which retain the horn ring to the steering wheel. Turn and lift up the horn ring and disconnect the plug contact.
4. Remove the steering wheel nut.
5. With the front wheels pointing straight ahead, and the steering wheel centered, install a steering wheel puller, such as SVO 2711, and pull off the steering wheel.
6. To install, make sure that the front wheels are pointing straight ahead, then place the centered steering wheel on the column and install the nut. Tighten the steering wheel nut to 25–30 ft lbs.
7. Connect the horn plug contact and install the horn ring.
8. First install the lower and then the upper turn signal housing halves and their retaining screws.
9. Connect the negative battery cable and check the operation of the horn.

1972

1. Disconnect the negative battery cable.
2. Remove the retaining screw for the upper half of the molded turn signal switch housing and lift off the housing.
3. Pry up and remove the impact protection badge from the horn ring. Disconnect the plug contact for the horn and remove the four retaining screws for the horn ring. Lift off the horn ring, noting the positions of the various springs and washers.
4. Remove the steering wheel nut.
5. With the front wheels pointing straight ahead, and the steering wheel centered, install a steering wheel puller, such as SVO 2972, and pull off the steering wheel.
6. Remove the turn signal switch flange.
7. To install, make sure that the front wheels are pointing straight ahead, then position the turn signal switch flange into the column and place the centered steering wheel on the column. Install the steering wheel nut and tighten to 20–30 ft lbs.
8. Making sure that the springs and washers are positioned correctly, install the horn ring on the steering wheel and tighten the four retaining screws. Connect the horn plug contact.
9. Install the upper turn signal housing halve.
10. Connect the negative battery cable and test the operation of the horn.

1973

1. Disconnect the negative battery cable.
2. Remove the retaining screws for the upper half of the molded turn signal housing and lift off the housing.
3. Pry off the steering wheel impact pad.
4. Disconnect the horn plug contact.
5. Remove the steering wheel nut.
6. With the front wheels pointing straight ahead, and the steering wheel

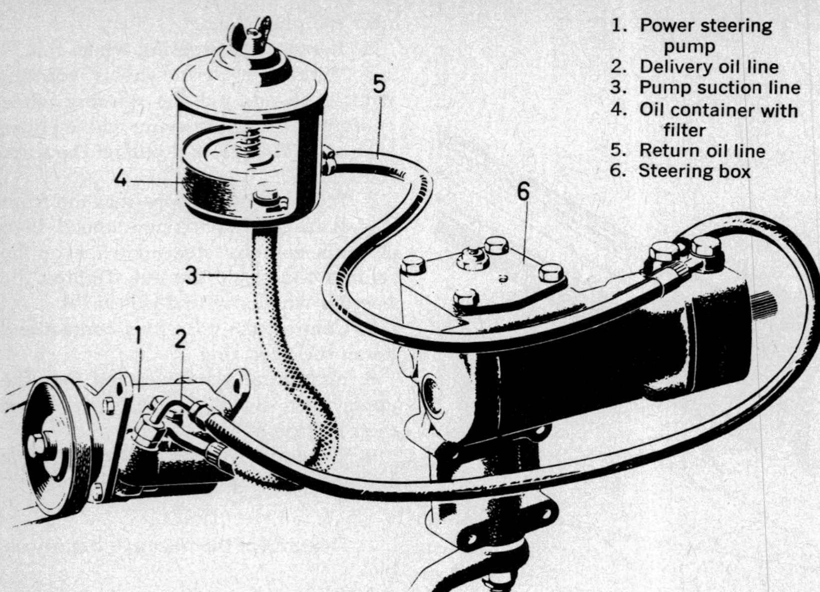

Power steering system

centered, install a steering wheel puller, such as SVO 5003, and pull off the steering wheel.

7. To install, make sure that the front wheels are pointing straight ahead, then place the centered steering wheel on the column with the plug contact to the left. Install the nut and tighten to 20–30 ft lbs.

8. Connect the horn plug contact and install the impact pad.

9. Install the upper turn signal housing half.

10. Connect the negative battery cable and test the operation of the horn.

1800 series

1967–73

1. Disconnect the negative battery cable.
2. Pry off the steering wheel impact pad (late production) or horn button (early production).
3. Disconnect the horn plug contact. Remove the three retaining screws and lift off the horn ring, (if so equipped) noting the placement of the springs and washers.
4. Bend back the locking washer and remove the steering wheel nut. Mark the relative positions of the steering wheel to the column. Slacken the horn wire.
5. Install a steering wheel puller and pull off the wheel.
6. To install, place the steering wheel on the column so that the alignment marks made prior to removal line up. Install the nut and tighten to 20–30 ft lbs.
7. Connect the horn plug contact, and install the horn ring, springs, and washers with the three retaining screws (if so equipped).
8. Snap on the impact pad (late production) or horn button (early production).
9. Connect the negative battery cable and test the operation of the horn.

Manual Steering Gear

Removal and Installation

1800 Series

1. Disconnect the horn lead from the connecting block.
2. Unscrew the two nuts and remove the bolts.
3. Remove the pitman arm with a puller.
4. Unscrew and remove the three attaching bolts.
5. Lift and turn the steering box. Pull out the horn lead from the lower section of the steering column and steering box. Lift off the steering box, being careful when moving to clamp past the brake line.

To replace:

1. Place the steering box in position. Be careful when moving the clamp past the brake line. Install the attaching bolts. On P1800, insert the horn lead through the lower section of the steering column with the help of a piece of wire. Place the steering box in position and install the attaching bolts, washers, and nuts loosely.
2. Assemble the clamp to the coupling disc. Do not forget the ground lead.
3. Adjust the position of the steering box so that the upper and lower sections of the steering column form a straight line. Tighten the attaching bolts.
4. Install the pitman arm so that the alignment mark on the pitman arm shaft aligns with the mark on the pitman arm. Tighten the nut to 100–120 ft lbs.
5. Make sure that the steering wheel spokes are horizontal when the wheels are straight.

140 Series

1. Jack up the vehicle at the front.
2. Loosen the bolt at the lower steering column shaft flange. Remove the nuts and move the lower part of the flange as far down as possible on the steering cam.
3. Remove the lock nut for the pitman arm. Pull off the pitman arm.
4. Remove the nuts and bolts and lift out the steering box.

To install:

1. Place the steering box in position and tighten the bolts.
2. Install the pitman arm and tighten the nut to 135 ft lbs.
3. Move the steering wheel so that the wheels point straight and tighten both halves of the steering column shaft flange.
4. Lower the vehicle.

Pitman Arm Adjustment

On a steering gear with a marked pitman arm and pitman arm shaft (on the steering gear), make sure that the marks align.

On a steering gear without the marks, lift up the front of the vehicle so that the front wheels are free. Turn the steering wheel to its center position (count the number of turns). Lower the vehicle. If the vehicle is correctly loaded, the wheels should now point straight forward. If the wheels do not, remove the pitman arm from the shaft with a puller. Then set the left wheel straight ahead and replace the pitman arm. The steering wheel should be in its center position. Tighten the pitman arm nut to 100–120 ft lbs.

Power Steering Gear

Removal and Installation

164

1. Jack up the front end.
2. Drain the system.
3. Remove the lock nut for the pitman arm. Pull the pitman arm off.
4. Disconnect the lines from the steering box after the connections have been cleaned. Loosen the clamp bolt.
5. Remove the attaching bolts and pull the steering box forward.

To replace:

1. Place the steering box in the center position. A slight increase in resistance should then be felt, the position of the pitman arm shaft lands should be as marked and the alignment marks on the control spindle and housing should coincide.
2. Check to make sure that the steering wheel is straight.
3. Install the steering box spindle in the flange of the lower steering column section. Install and tighten the attaching bolts. Tighten the clamp bolt. Connect the lines. The longer delivery line should

run in a curve and be clamped.

4. Point the front wheels straight and install the pitman arm. Tighten the nut to 125–141 ft lbs.

5. Fill and bleed the system.

Power Steering Pump

Removal and Installation

1. Remove all dirt and grease from around the suction line connections and from around the delivery line on the pump housing.

2. Using a container to catch any power steering fluid that might run out, disconnect the oil lines, and plug them to prevent dirt from entering the system.

3. Remove the tensioning bolt and the attaching bolts.

4. Clear the pump free of the fan belt and lift it out.

5. If a new pump is to be used, the old brackets, fittings, and pulley must be transferred from the old unit. The pulley may be removed with a puller, and pressed on the pump shaft with a press tool. Under no circumstances should the pulley be hammered on, as this will damage the pump bearings.

6. To install, place the pump in position and loosely fit the attaching bolts. Connect the oil lines to the pump with new seals.

7. Place the fan belt onto the pulley and adjust the fan belt tension as outlined in Chapter one.

8. Tighten the tensioning bolt and the attaching bolts.

9. Fill the reservoir with Type "A" automatic transmission fluid and bleed the system as outlined under "Power Steering System Bleeding".

Power Steering System Bleeding

1. Fill the reservoir up to the edge with Automatic Transmission Fluid Type "A". Raise the front wheels off the ground, and install safety stands. Place the transmission in neutral and apply the parking brake.

2. Keeping a can of ATF Type "A" within easy reach, start the engine and fill the reservoir as the level drops.

3. When the reservoir level has stopped dropping, slowly turn the steering wheel from lock to lock several times. Fill the reservoir if necessary.

4. Locate the bleeder screw on the power steering gear. Open the bleeder screw ½–1 turn, and close it when oil starts flowing out.

5. Continue to turn the steering wheel slowly until the fluid in the reservoir is free of air bubbles.

6. Stop the engine and observe the oil level in the reservoir. If the oil level rises more than ¼ in. past the level mark, air still remains in the system. Continue bleeding until the level rise is correct.

7. Remove the safety stands and lower the car.

Steering and Tie Rod Service

Bent or otherwise damaged steering rods and tie rods must be replaced, never straightened. All components of the steering linkage, including the pitman arm and idler arm, are connected by means of ball joints. Ball joints cannot be disassembled or adjusted, so they must also be replaced when damaged.

The ball joints of the steering rods are made in unit with the rods, therefore the entire rod assembly must be replaced when their ball joints become unserviceable. Maximum permissible axial (vertical) play is .120 in. After removing the cotter pins and ball stud nuts at the rod's connections, press the ball joint out of its connecting socket.

The ball joints of the tie rod may be replaced individually. After the ball joint is disconnected, the lock nut on the tie rod is loosened and the clamp bolt released. The ball joint is then screwed out of the tie rod, taking note of the number of turns. The new ball joint is screwed in the same number of turns, and the clamp bolt and lock nut tightened. The ball joint is locked to the rod with 55–65 ft lbs. of torque. The new ball joint is pressed into its connection and the ball stud nut tightened to 23–27 ft lbs.

After reconditioning of the rods and joints, the wheel alignment must be adjusted.

BRAKE SYSTEMS

All 140 Series and 164 models, as well as post-1969 1800 Series Volvos are equipped with a four wheel power-assisted disc brake system. 1967–69 1800 Series models are equipped with a disc front and a drum rear set-up. The four wheel disc system utilizes a pair of four-piston, fixed calipers at the rear. The 1967–69 1800 uses a pair of three-piston calipers at the front and a pair of duo-servo self-adjusting brakes at the rear. The calipers are either Girling or ATE manufacture, so when ordering disc pads or caliper rebuilding kits, you must identify which you have. The discs are one-piece castings. Since 1972, 164 models have been equipped with internally vented discs.

Whenever adding to or replacing brake fluid, it is imperative that the fluid be of SAE 70 R3 (SAE J 1703) quality or better. Fluid meeting DOT 3 or DOT 4 specifications is also acceptable. Using inferior brake fluids may result in premature failure of the hydraulic components, or in braking effect. Fluids not meeting specifications may not withstand the great temperatures generated by the disc pad clamping action or may deteriorate chemically allowing water and, later, air to form in the system. Avoid mixing brake fluids from different manufacturers and never reuse old brake fluid.

Drum Brake Adjustment

1. Jack up the car and place supports under the rear axle. Release the handbrake.

2. Remove the rubber seal. Turn the wheel in its normal direction of rotation while bringing the brake shoes into contact with the drum. Use an adjusting tool to turn the adjuster screw. When the wheel can just be turned by using one hand, stop tightening the screw. Then back off the adjuster screw 1–2 notches. Install the rubber seal.

3. Repeat the adjustment procedure on the other brake. Remove the supports and lower the car.

Disc Brake Adjustment

Disc brakes require no adjustment. They should, however, be checked frequently for wear. Consult the specifica-

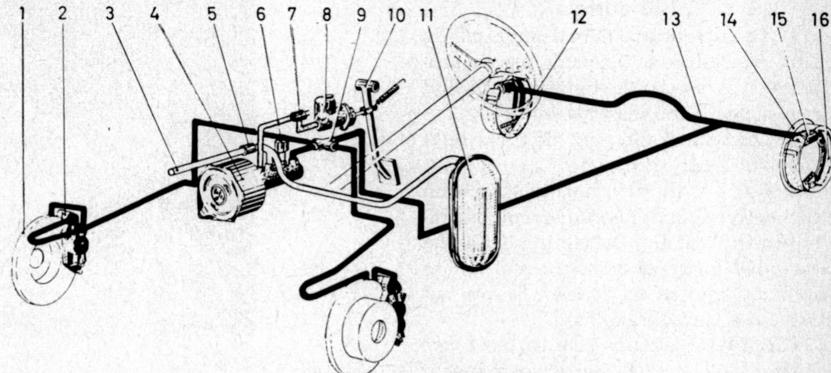

Hydraulic system—1967-69 1800 series

1. Brake disc
2. Front wheel brake unit
3. Vacuum line from engine
4. Vacuum booster cylinder
5. Check valve
6. Air filter
7. Brake contact
8. Master cylinder
9. Branch union
10. Brake pedal
11. Vacuum tank
12. Adjusting device
13. Brake line
14. Brake drum
15. Wheel unit cylinder
16. Brake shoe

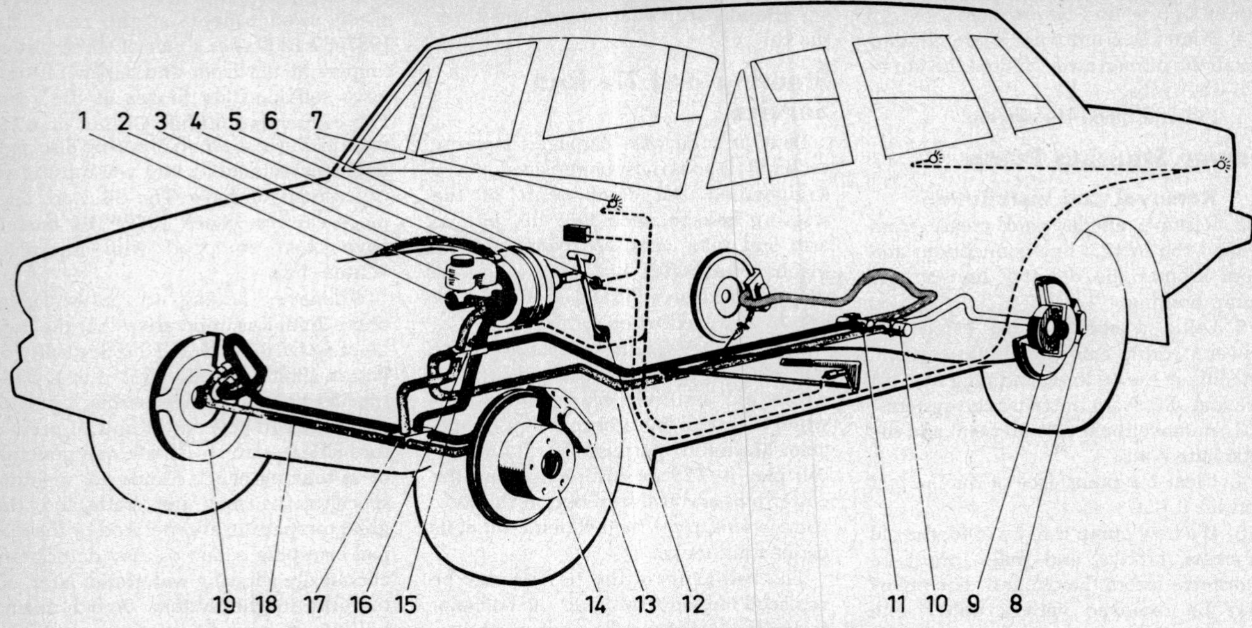

Hydraulic system—1967-73 140 series, 1969-73 164, 1970-73 1800 series

1. Tandem master cylinder
2. Brake fluid container
3. Vacuum line
4. Check valve
5. Vacuum booster
6. Brake switch
7. Warning lamp
8. Rear brake caliper
9. Brake disc with drum
10. Brake valve, secondary circuit
11. Brake valve, primary circuit
12. Brake pedal
13. Front brake caliper
14. Brake disc
15. Warning switch
16. Warning valve
17. 6-branch union, (double 3-branch union)
18. Brake pipe
19. Cover plate

tions table for new pad thickness. Pads should never be allowed to wear down to less than 0.125 in., or disc damage may occur.

HYDRAULIC SYSTEM

Master Cylinder

Removal and Installation

140 series

1. To prevent brake fluid from spilling onto and damaging the paint, place a protective cover over the fender apron, and rags beneath the master cylinder.

2. Disconnect and plug the brake lines from the master cylinder.

3. Remove the two nuts which retain the master cylinder and reservoir assembly to the vacuum booster, and lift the assembly forward, being careful not to spill any fluid on the fender. Empty out and discard the brake fluid.

CAUTION: *Do not depress the brake pedal while the master cylinder is removed.*

4. In order for the master cylinder to function properly when installed to the vacuum booster, the adjusting nut for the thrust rod of the booster must not prevent the primary piston of the master cylinder from returning to its resting position. A clearance (C) of 0.020–0.059 in. on 1970 models, and 0.004–0.04 in. on 1971 and later models, is required between the thrust rod and primary piston with the master cylinder installed. The clearance may be adjusted by rotating the adjusting nut for the booster thrust rod in the required direction. To deter-

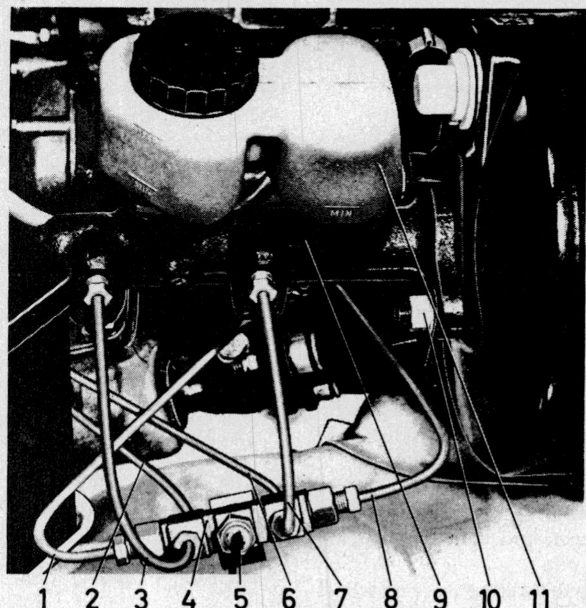

Master cylinder installation—140 series shown, 164 similar.

1. To left brake valve
2. To 6-branch union, lower
3. From secondary circuit (master cylinder)
4. Warning valve
5. Warning switch
6. To 6-branch union, upper
7. From primary circuit (master cylinder)
8. To right brake valve
9. Master cylinder
10. Attaching nut
11. Reservoir

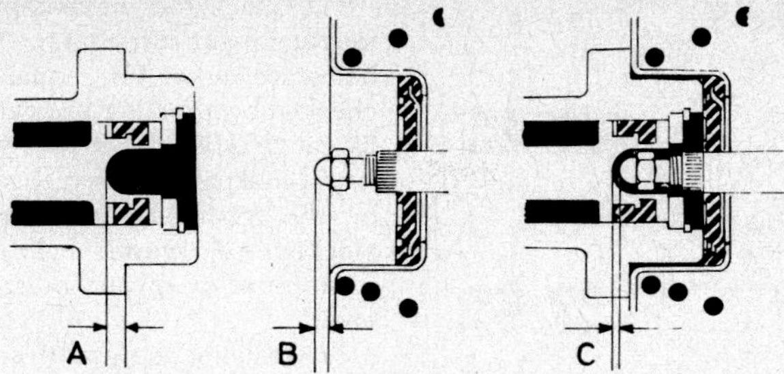

Adjusting thrust rod

mine what the clearance (C) will be when the master cylinder and booster are connected, first measure the distance (A) between the face of the attaching flange and the center of the primary piston on the master cylinder, then measure the distance (B) that the thrust rod protrudes from the fixed surface of the booster (making sure that the thrust rod is depressed fully with a partial vacuum existing in the booster). When measurement (B) is subtracted from measurement (A), clearance (C) should be obtained. If not, adjust the length of the thrust rod by turning the adjusting screw to suit. After the final adjustment is obtained, apply a few drops of locking compound, such as Loctite®, to the adjusting nut.

5. Position the master cylinder and reservoir assembly onto the studs for the booster, and install the washers and nuts. Tighten the nuts to 17 ft lbs.

6. Remove the plugs and connect the brake lines.

7. Bleed the entire brake system, as outlined in this chapter.

164, 1800 series

1. Follow steps 1–3 under "Master Cylinder Removal and Installation" for the 140 series.

CAUTION: *Do not depress the brake pedal while the master cylinder is removed.*

2. To install, place a new sealing ring onto the sealing flange of the master cylinder. Position the master cylinder and reservoir assembly onto the booster studs, and install the washers and nuts. Tighten the nuts to 8.7–10.8 ft lbs.

3. Remove the plugs and loosely connect the brake lines. Have a friend depress the brake pedal to remove air from the cylinder. Tighten the nuts for the lines when brake fluid (free of air bubbles) is forced out.

4. Bleed the entire brake system, as outlined in this chapter.

Master Cylinder Overhaul

140 series

1. Remove the master cylinder from the booster as outlined in the applicable "Master Cylinder Removal and Installation" section.

2. Firmly fasten the flange of the master cylinder in a vise.

3. Position both hands beneath the reservoir and pull it free of its rubber seals. Remove the filler cap and strainer from the reservoir, as well as the rubber seals and nuts (if so equipped) from the cylinder.

4. Remove the stop screw. Using a pair of snap-ring pliers, remove the snap-ring from the primary piston and shake out the piston. If the secondary piston remains lodged in the bore, it may be forced out by blowing air into the stoplight switch hole.

5. Remove both the seals from the secondary piston, taking care not to damage or score the surfaces of the plunger. The old primary piston should be discarded and replaced.

6. Clean all reusable metal parts in clean brake fluid or methylated alcohol. The parts may be allowed to thoroughly air dry, or compressed air may be used. At any rate, all alcohol must be removed from the parts, as alcohol lowers the boiling temperature of brake fluid. If the inside of the cylinder is scored or scratched, the cylinder must be replaced. Minor pitting or corrosion may be removed by honing. Remember to flush the cylinder clean after honing, and make sure that the passages are clear.

Check the piston for damage and proper clearance in the bore. The cylinder diameter may not exceed 0.881 in., while the piston diameter may not be less than 0.870 in.

7. Install new seals on the secondary piston, making sure that they are positioned in the proper direction.

8. Coat the cylinder bore with brake fluid and dip the secondary piston and seals in brake fluid prior to installation. Slide the spring, spring plate, and washer onto the secondary piston and install the assembly in the bore, taking care not to damage the seals. Dip the new primary piston and seal assembly in brake fluid. Press the primary piston assembly into the bore and install a new washer and snap-ring.

9. Make sure that the hole for the stop screw is clear and install the new stop screw and sealing washer. Torque the screw to 9.5 ft lbs on 1970–71 models, and 7–9 ft lbs on 1972 and later models.

10. Check the movement of the pistons and make sure that the flow-through holes are clear. The equalizing hole is checked by inserting a 25 gauge soft copper wire through it and making sure that it is not blocked by the secondary piston seal. If it is blocked, then the master cylinder is incorrectly assembled, and you must take it through the numbers once more.

11. Install the nuts (if so equipped), new rubber seals, and washers onto the master cylinder at the reservoir connections. After making sure that the venting hole in the cap is open, install the cleaned strainer and cap. Press the reservoir into the master cylinder by hand. If the stoplight switch was removed, reinstall it.

12. Install the master cylinder as outlined in the applicable "Master Cylinder Removal and Installation" section.

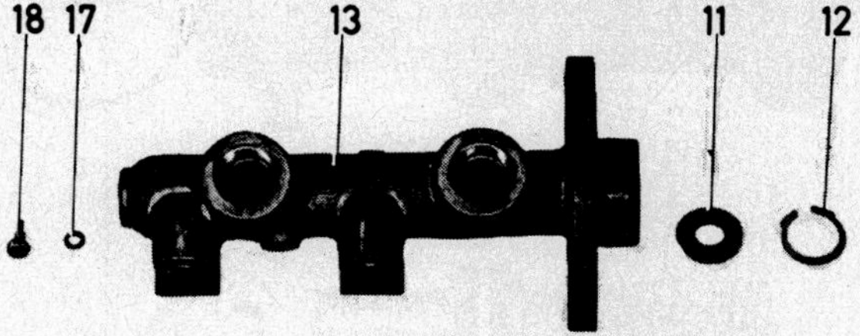

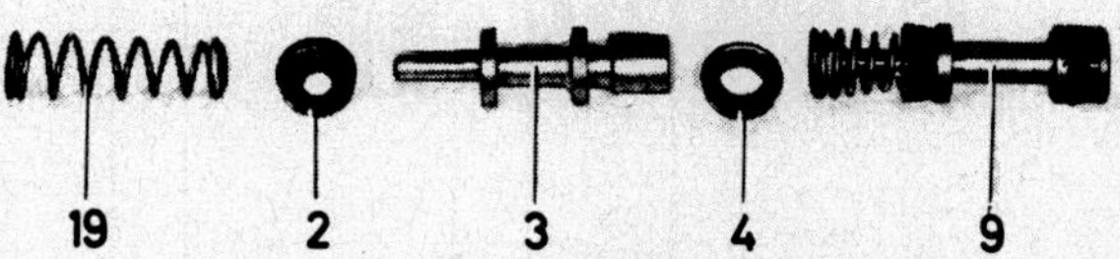

Master cylinder disassembled (with type 1 secondary piston)—140 series.

2. Piston seal
3. Secondary piston
4. Piston seal
9. Primary piston (assembled)
11. Thrust washer
12. Circlip
13. Cylinder housing
17. Sealing washer
18. Stop screw
19. Return spring

1. Spring
2. Spring plate
3. Back-up ring
4. Piston seal
5. Washer
6. Piston
7. Piston seal
8. Piston seal

Type 2 secondary piston—140 series

164, 1800 series

1. Remove the master cylinder from the booster as outlined in the applicable "Master Cylinder Removal and Installation" section.

2. Follow steps 2–4 under "Master Cylinder Overhaul" for the 140 series.

3. Discard both the primary and secondary pistons.

4. Clean all reusable metal parts in clean brake fluid or methylated alcohol. The parts must be thoroughly dried with filtered, water-free compressed air, or air dried. All cleaning alcohol must be removed from the parts, as it lowers the boiling temperature of brake fluid. If the inside of the cylinder is scored or scratched, the cylinder must be replaced. Minor pitting and corrosion may be removed by honing. Remember to flush the cylinder clean after honing, and make sure that the passages are clear.

Check the cylinder bore for excessive wear. On 1800 series models, the bore must not exceed 0.881 in., and on 164 models, no more than 0.942 in.

5. Make sure that new rubber seals, a new brass washer and back-up ring are installed on the new secondary piston. Make sure that the rubber seals are pointing in the right direction.

6. Coat the cylinder bore with brake fluid and dip the secondary piston and seals in brake fluid prior to installation. Install the secondary piston and spring in the bore, taking care not to damage the rubber seals.

7. Make sure that the new rubber seals, metal washers, plastic washer, back-up ring, sleeve, and spring are installed on the new primary piston. Make sure that the seals are facing in the right direction.

8. On 1800 models, compress the primary piston spring and tighten the screw for the sleeve until it bottoms. Torque the screw to 1.5–2.2 ft lbs.

9. Dip the primary piston assembly in brake fluid and install it in the bore, taking care not to damage the rubber seals. While holding the piston in the bore, install the snap-ring.

10. Check that the hole for the stop screw is clear, and install the new stop screw and sealing washer. Torque the screw to 3.5–5.7 ft lbs on all 164 models and 1972 and later 1800 series models, and 7–8.5 ft lbs on 1971 and earlier 1800 series models.

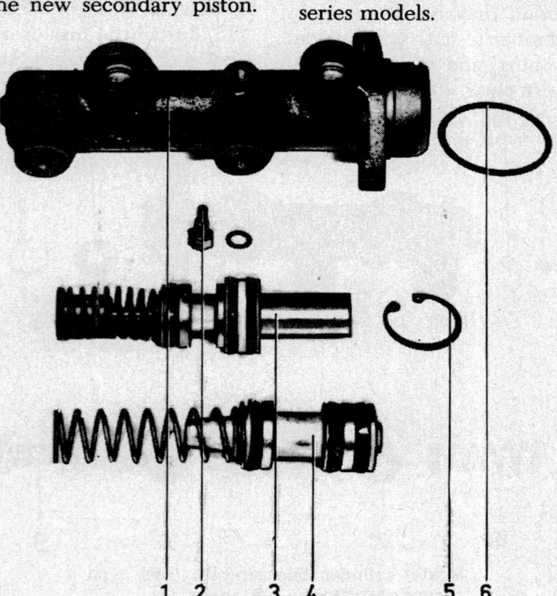

Master cylinder disassembled—164, 1800 series.

1. Cylinder housing
2. Stop screw
3. Primary piston
4. Secondary piston
5. Circlip
6. Sealing ring

11. Check the movement of the pistons and make sure that the flow-through holes are clear. The equalizing hole is checked by inserting a 25 gauge (1800) or 22 gauge (164) soft copper wire through it and making sure that it is not blocked by the secondary piston seal. If it is blocked, the master cylinder will not function properly and must be reassembled.

12. Install the nuts (if so equipped), new rubber seals and washers onto the master cylinder at the reservoir connections. After making sure that the venting hole in the cap is open, install the cleaned strainer and cap. Press the reservoir into the master cylinder by hand. If the stoplight switch was removed, reinstall it.

13. Install the master cylinder as outlined in the applicable "Master Cylinder Removal and Installation" section.

Brake System Warning Valve

The brake system warning valve is located near the master cylinder in the engine compartment. The valve is centered by hydraulic pressure from the primary circuit on one side and the secondary circuit on the other. When a hydraulic imbalance exists, such as a leak in one of the calipers, the valve will move off-center toward the system with the leak and, therefore, the lowest pressure. When the valve moves off-center, it closes a circuit to a warning light on the dashboard, warning the driver of the imbalance. Sometimes, the valve will actuate the warning light when one of the systems is bled during normal maintenance. When this happens, the valve has to be reset.

Valve Resetting

1. Disconnect the plug contact and screw out the warning switch so that the pistons inside the valve may return to their normal position.

2. Repair and bleed the faulty hydraulic circuit.

3. Screw in the warning switch and tighten it to a torque of 10–14 ft lbs. Connect the plug contact.

Valve Replacement

1. Placing a rag beneath the valve to catch the brake fluid, loosen the pipe connections, and disconnect the six brake lines. Disconnect the electrical plug contact, and lift out the valve.

2. Connect the new warning valve in the reverse order of removal, and connect the plug contact.

3. Bleed the entire brake system.

Brake System Proportioning Valves

Each of the brake circuits has a proportioning (relief) valve located inline between the rear wheels. The purpose of these valves is to ensure that brake pressure on all four wheels compensates for the change in weight distribution under varied braking conditions. The harder the brakes are applied, the more weight there is on the front wheels. The valves regulate the hydraulic pressure to the rear wheels so that under hard braking conditions, they receive a smaller percentage of the total braking effort. This prevents premature rear wheel lock-up when the brakes are applied in emergency situations.

Valve Replacement

Sophisticated pressure testing equipment is required to troubleshoot the dual hydraulic system in order to determine if the proportioning valve(s) are in need of replacement. However, if the car is demonstrating signs of rear wheel lock-up under moderate to heavy braking pressure, and other variables such as tire pressure, tread depth, etc. have been ruled out, the valve(s) may be at fault. Rebuilding kits are available from the dealer for the valves in 1972 and earlier model Volvos. However, the valves installed in 1973 and later models are not rebuildable, and must be replaced as a unit.

1. Unscrew, disconnect and plug the brake pipe from the master cylinder, at the valve connection.
2. Slacken the connection for the flexible brake hose to the rear wheel a *maximum* of ¼ turn.
3. Remove the bolt(s) which retain the valve to the underbody, and unscrew the valve from the rear brake hose.
4. To install the valve, place a new seal on it, and screw the valve onto the rear brake hose and hand tighten. Secure the valve to the underbody with the retaining bolt(s).
5. Connect the brake pipe and tighten both connections, making sure that there is no tension on the flexible rear hose.
6. Bleed the brake system.

Bleeding Hydraulic System

Whenever a spongy brake pedal indicates that there is air in the system, or when any part of the hydraulic system has been removed for service, the system must be bled. In addition, if the level in the master cylinder reservoir is allowed to go below the minimum mark for too long a period of time, air may enter the system, necessitating bleeding.

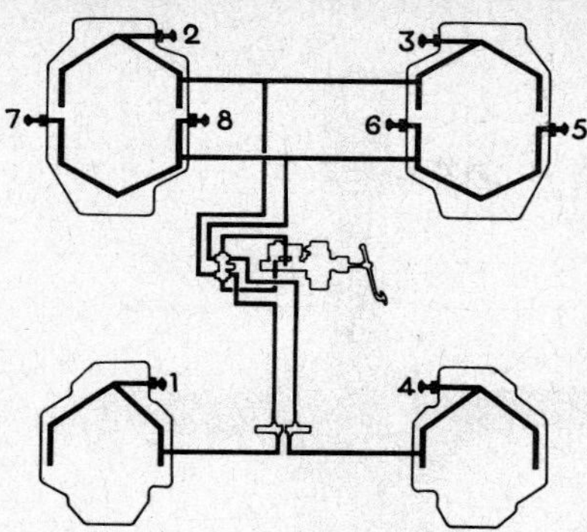

Bleeding sequence—140 series, 164, with Girling brakes.

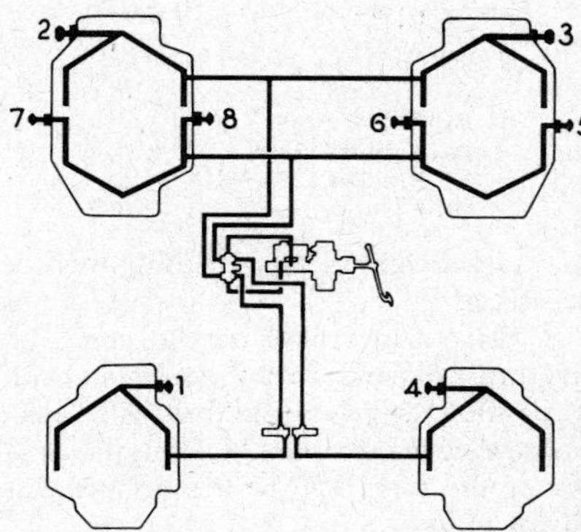

Bleeding sequence—140 series, 164, with ATE brakes.

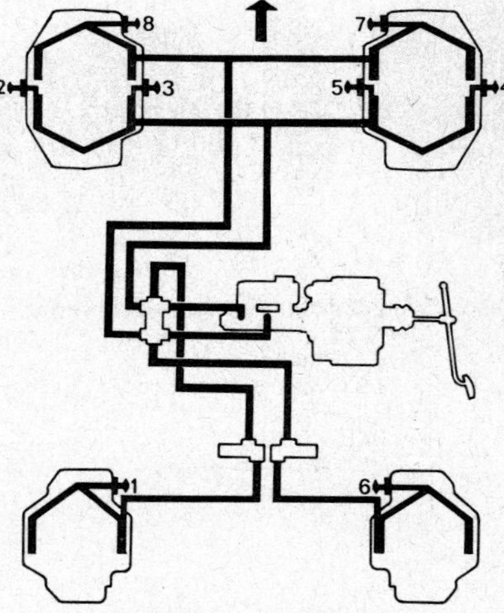

Bleeding sequence—1800 series

If only one brake caliper or wheel cylinder is removed for servicing, it is usually only necessary to bleed that unit. If, however, the master cylinder, warning valve, or any of the main brake lines are removed, the entire system must be bled.

Be careful not to spill any brake fluid onto the brake disc or pads or drum and linings and, of course, the paintwork. When bleeding the entire system, the rear of the car should be raised higher than the front. Only use brake fluid bearing the designation SAE 1703 (SAE 70 R3), DOT 3, or DOT 4. Never reuse old brake fluid.

1. Check to make sure that there are no mats or other materials obstructing the travel of the brake pedal. During bleeding, the full pedal travel should be 6 in. for the 140 series, and 5.5 in. for the 164 and 1800 series (providing that both circuits are bled simultaneously)
2. Disconnect the plug contact, and unscrew the electric switch from the warning valve.
3. Clean the cap and the top of the master cylinder reservoir, and make sure that the vent hole in the cap is open. Fill the reservoir to the maximum mark, if necessary. Never allow the level to dip below the minimum mark during bleeding, as this will allow air into the system.
4. If only one brake caliper or wheel cylinder was removed, it will usually suffice to bleed only that wheel. Otherwise, prepare to bleed the entire system according to the numbered sequence in the bleeding diagrams. For 1967–69 1800, bleed the wheel units in order of their decreasing distance from the master cylinder.

Bleeding front wheel caliper—rear caliper similar.

5. Remove the protective cap for the bleeder screw, and fit a 5/16 in. ring spanner wrench on the nipple. Install a tight fitting plastic hose onto the nipple, and insert the other end of the hose into a glass bottle containing clean brake fluid. The hose must hang down below the surface of the fluid, or air will be sucked into the system when the brake pedal is released. Open the bleeder screw a maximum of ½ turn. Slowly depress the brake pedal until it bottoms, pause a second or two, and then quickly release the pedal. This should be repeated until the fluid flowing into the bottle is completely free of air bubbles. Then have a friend press the pedal to the bottom and hold it there while you tighten the bleeder screw to 3–4.5 ft lbs. Install the protective cap.
6. If the entire system is to be bled, follow the above procedure for the re-

maining nipples. Generally, it is sufficient to bleed each circuit once. However, if the pedal continues to feel spongy, repeat the bleeding sequence. Remember to keep the master cylinder reservoir level above the minimum mark.

7. Fill the reservoir with the specified brake fluid to the maximum mark.

8. Screw the electric switch into the warning valve and connect the plug contact. Tighten the switch to 10–14 ft lbs. Make sure that the warning light is actuated only when the parking brake is applied.

Stoplight Switch Adjustment

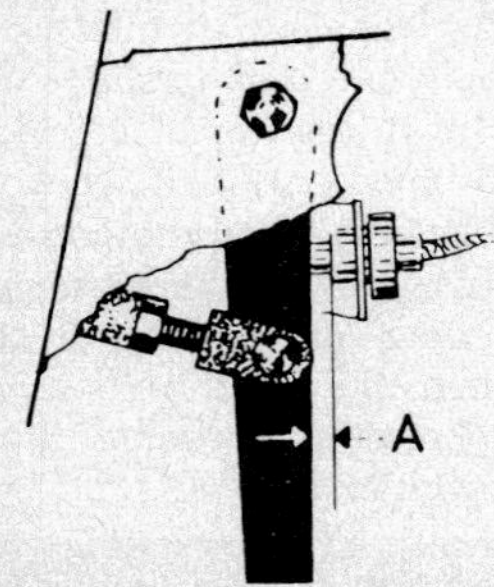

Stoplight switch adjustment

With the brake pedal in the released position, the distance (A) between the brass hub of the switch and the pedal lever should be 0.08–0.24 in. To adjust, loosen the attaching screws for the switch bracket and move the switch in the required direction.

Power Booster System

Vacuum Booster Removal and Installation

140 series

1. Remove the master cylinder as outlined in the applicable "Master Cylinder Removal and Installation" section.

2. Loosen the fork from the pedal by removing the cotter pin and bolt.

3. Disconnect the vacuum hose at the check valve. Remove the ignition coil and position it to one side.

4. Remove the nuts which retain the booster mounting bracket onto the firewall and remove the support bracket.

5. Lift off the booster and place it on a bench. Loosen the locknut (2) and screw off the fork. Remove the rubber cover (4) and the mounting bracket (5). Unscrew the thrust rod (3) from the rear thrust rod of the booster.

6. Apply locking compound, such as Loctite® type B, to the booster thrust rod. Then screw in the thrust rod (3) that runs inside of the bracket, as far as possible onto the booster thrust rod.

7. Position the brackets on the booster,

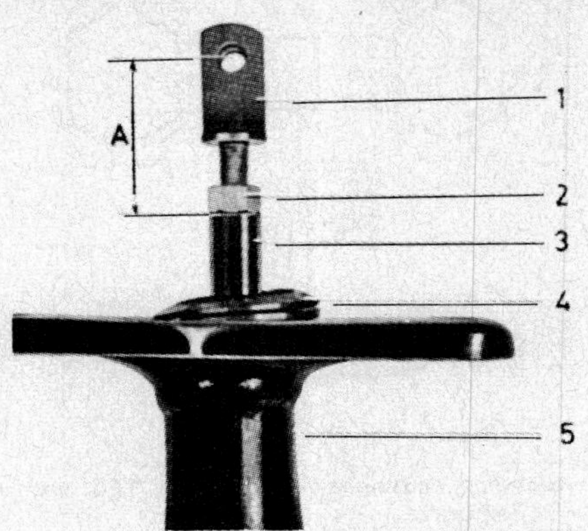

Removing thrust rod—140 series

1. Fork
2. Locknut
3. Thrust rod
4. Rubber cover
5. Bracket
6. A=approx. 45 mm (1.8")

but do not tighten the attaching nuts at this time.

8. Place a new filter on the sleeve of the thrust rod and place the rubber cover in position. Screw in the fork with locknut so that the distance (A) from the center of the fork hole to the end of the thrust rod is 1.8 in.

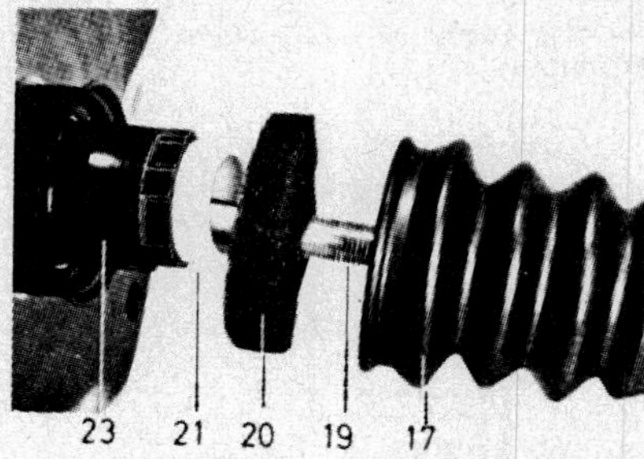

Replacing booster air filter—140 series

17. Rubber cover
19. Ingoing thrust rod
20. Filter
21. Plastic
23. Valve housing

9. Place the booster with brackets in the vehicle and install, but do not tighten the attaching nuts. After all of the nuts are loosely fitted, tighten them.

10. Install the ignition coil, and connect the vacuum hose to the check valve.

11. Connect the fork to the brake pedal and install the cotter pin.

12. Install the master cylinder as outlined in the applicable "Master Cylinder Removal and Installation" section.

164

1. Remove the master cylinder as outlined in the applicable "Master Cylinder Removal and Installation" section.

2. Disconnect the vacuum hose at the booster.

3. Disconnect the link arm from the brake pedal. Remove the bracket with the clutch pedal stop from the firewall.

4. Remove the four nuts which retain the booster to the firewall.

5. Pull the booster forward, and from the engine compartment, disconnect the fork from the link arm. Lift out the unit.

6. Lift the rubber cover and pry up the protective washer from the booster. Lift out the old damper and filter, and replace them with new ones, making sure that they are installed with their slots positioned 180° opposite each other. Install the protective washer and rubber cover, making sure that the rubber cover is pressed down properly at the inner edge of the washer.

7. Place the booster in the engine compartment, and connect the fork to the link arm. Push in the booster so that the attaching bolts are positioned.

8. Secure the booster to the firewall with the lock washers and nuts.

9. Install the clutch pedal bracket on the inside of the firewall, and connect the link arm to the brake pedal.

10. Connect the vacuum hose to the booster, with the connection facing downward.

11. Install the master cylinder as outlined in the applicable "Master Cylinder Removal and Installation" section.

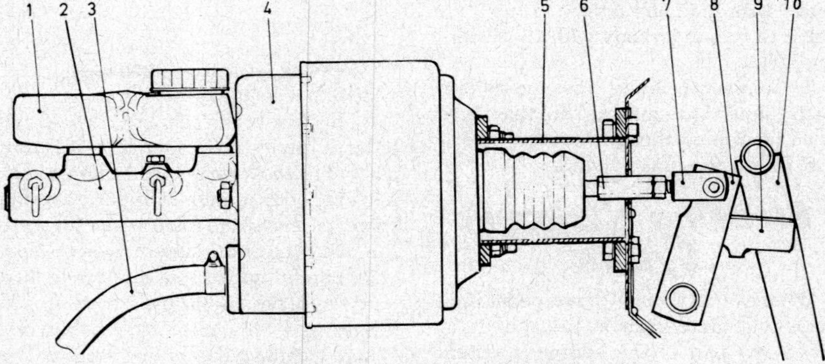

Power booster installed—1800 series

1. Brake fluid container
2. Master cylinder
3. Vacuum hose
4. Vacuum booster
5. Bracket
6. Thrust rod
7. Yoke
8. Double lever
9. Thrust link
10. Brake pedal

1800 series

1. Remove the master cylinder as outlined in the applicable "Master Cylinder Removal and Installation" section.
2. Disconnect the vacuum hose from the booster.
3. Disconnect the support clamp and remove the nuts which attach the booster to the firewall.
4. Unscrew the locknut on the thrust rod and unscrew the yoke.
5. Pull forward and lift out the booster.
6. Lift the rubber cover and pry up the washer from the booster. Lift out the old damper and filter, and install new ones, making sure that they are installed with their slots positioned 180° opposite each other. Install the washer and rubber cover, making sure that the cover is correctly positioned onto the washer and booster.
7. Position the booster in the engine compartment and screw the yoke to the bottom of the thrust rod. Tighten the locknut. Install the lock washers and nuts which secure the booster to the firewall and to the support clamp.
8. Connect the vacuum hose to the booster.
9. Install the master cylinder as outlined in the applicable "Master Cylinder Removal and Installation" section.

Vacuum Booster Filter Replacement

Under normal driving conditions, the filter in the vacuum booster should be replaced every three years. The booster must be removed to replace the filter. Consult the applicable "Vacuum Booster Removal and Installation" section for the procedure.

DISC BRAKES

Brake Pads

Removal and Installation

Girling Brakes

1. Remove the hub caps and loosen the lug nuts a few turns.
2. Raise the vehicle and place jackstands beneath the rear axle and the front jack attachments. Remove the wheel and tire assemblies.
3. Remove the hairpin-shaped locking clips, one lock pin then the other, together with the damping springs for the brake pads. Pull out the pads. Discard them if they are worn down to a lining thickness of ⅛ in. or less. If they are reusable, mark them for ease of assembly.
4. Carefully clean out the pad cavity. Replace any damaged dust covers. If any dirt has contaminated the cylinders, the caliper must be removed for overhaul. Inspect the brake disc as described under "Brake Discs—Inspection and Replacement".
5. Carefully depress the pistons in their cylinders so that the new pads will fit. This may be done with a screwdriver, but extra care must be exercised not to damage the rubber piston seals, the pistons, or the new pads themselves. A piston depressing tool (SVO 2809) is available from the dealer that accomplishes the job without danger to the caliper components. Remember that when the pistons are depressed in their bores, brake fluid is displaced causing the level in the master cylinder to rise, and perhaps, overflow.
6. Install the new pads and secure them with first one lock pin, then the other pin with the damping springs. Install new locking clips on the lock pins. Make sure that the pads are able to move and that the linings do not project outside of the brake disc.
7. Depress the brake pedal several times and make sure that the movement feels normal. Bleeding is not usually necessary after pad replacement.
8. Clean the contact surfaces of the wheel and hub. Install the wheel and tire assemblies. Remove the jackstands and lower the vehicle. Tighten the lug nuts to 70–100 ft lbs, and install the hub cap.

NOTE: *If at all possible, braking should be moderate for the first 25 miles or so until the new pads seat correctly. Avoid panic stops in the beginning, unless necessary.*

Ate Brakes

1. Remove the hub caps and loosen the lug nuts a few turns.
2. Raise the vehicle and place jack stands beneath the rear axle and the front jack attachments.
3. Using a 9/64 in. drift, tap out the upper guide pin for the pads and remove and discard the tensioning spring. Tap out the lower pin. Pull out the pads. Discard them if they are worn down to a

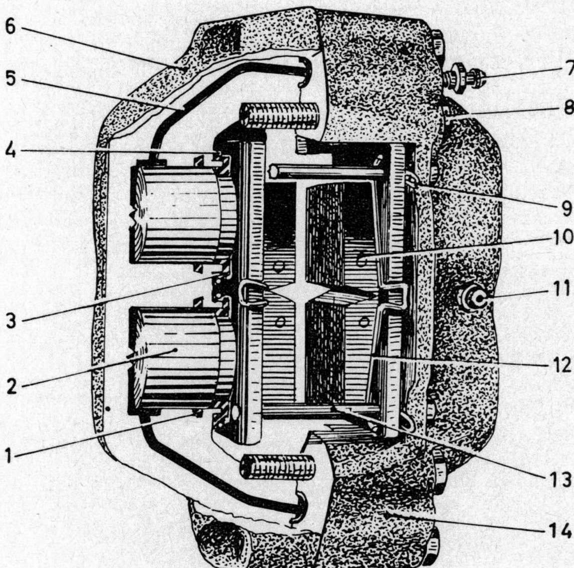

Girling front caliper assembly

1. Sealing ring
2. Piston
3. Rubber dust cover
4. Retaining ring
5. Channel
6. Outer half
7. Upper bleeder nipple
8. Bolt
9. Retaining clip
10. Brake pad
11. Lower bleeder nipple
12. Damping spring
13. Retaining pin
14. Inner half

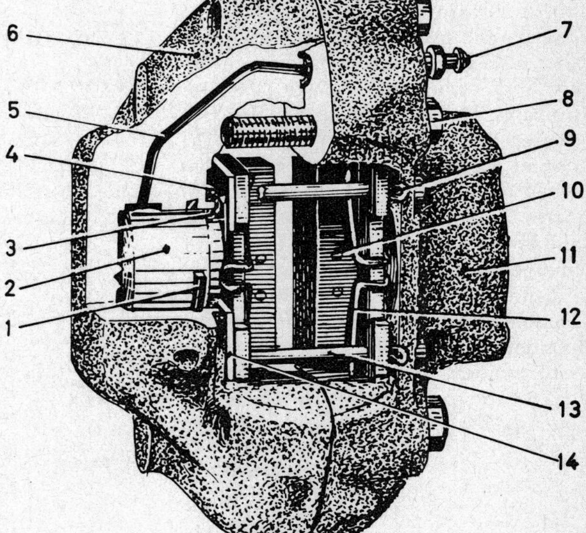

Girling rear caliper assembly

1. Sealing ring
2. Piston
3. Rubber dust cover
4. Retaining ring
5. Channel
6. Outer half
7. Bleeder nipple
8. Bolt
9. Retaining clip
10. Brake pad
11. Inner half
12. Damping spring
13. Retaining pin
14. Washer

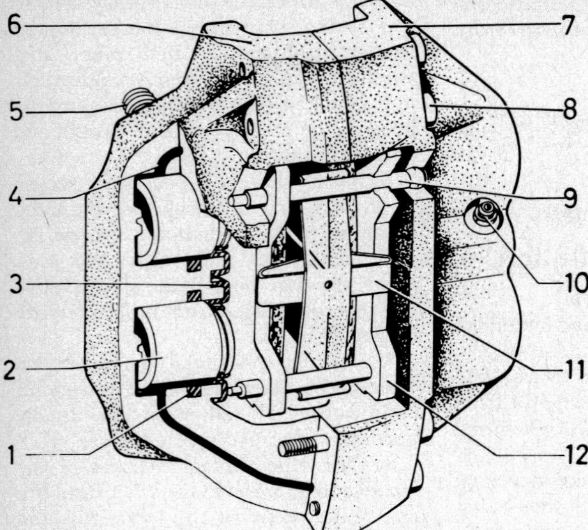

ATE front caliper assembly

1. Sealing ring
2. Piston
3. Rubber dust cover
4. Channel
5. Upper bleeder nipple
6. Outer half
7. Inner half
8. Bolt
9. Guide pin
10. Inner bleeder nipple
11. Damping spring
12. Brake pad

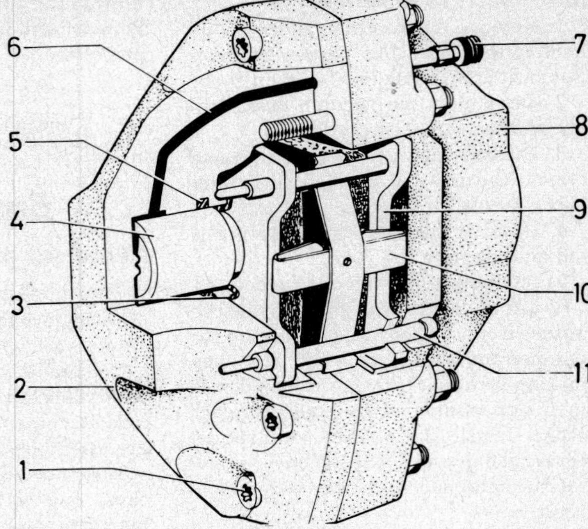

ATE rear caliper assembly

1. Bolt
2. Outer half
3. Rubber dust cover
4. Piston
5. Sealing ring
6. Channel
7. Bleeder nipple
8. Inner half
9. Brake pad
10. Damping spring
11. Guide pin

lining thickness of ⅛ in. or less. If they are reusable, mark them for ease of assembly.

4. Carefully clean out the pad cavities. Replace any damaged dust covers. If any dirt has contaminated the cylinders, the caliper must be removed for overhaul. Inspect the brake disc as described under "Brake Discs—Inspection and Replacement".

5. Carefully depress the pistons in their cylinders so that the new pads will fit. This may be done with a screwdriver, but extra care must be exercised not to damage the rubber piston seals, the pistons, or the new pads themselves. A piston depressing tool (SVO 2809) is available from the dealer that accomplishes the job without danger to the caliper components. Remember that when the pistons are depressed in their bores, brake fluid is displaced, causing the level in the master cylinder to rise, and perhaps, overflow.

6. Install the new pads. Using only a hammer, tap one of the guide pins into position. Place a new tensioning spring into position, and while pushing it in against the pads, tap the other guide pin into position. Make sure that the pads can move.

7. Depress the brake pedal several times and make sure that the movement feels normal. Bleeding is not normally necessary after pad replacement.

8. Clean the contact surfaces of the wheel and hub. Install the wheel and tire assemblies. Remove the jackstands and lower the vehicle. Tighten the lug nuts to 70–100 ft lbs, and install the hub cap.

NOTE: *If at all possible, avoid hard or lengthy braking for the first 25 miles or so, until the new pads seat correctly.*

Front Brake Caliper

Removal and Installation

1. Remove the hub cap and loosen the lug nuts a few turns. Block the reservoir cap vent hole to reduce leakage of brake fluid when the lines are disconnected. Firmly apply the parking brake.

2. Raise the front end and place jackstands beneath the front jack attachments. Remove the wheel and tire assembly.

3. On 140 series and 164 models, remove the brake hose retaining clip from the stabilizer bar, and disconnect the lower hose and secondary circuit brake pipe from their inboard connection underneath the car. Disconnect the upper hose from the caliper. Plug all brake connections to prevent leakage.

4. On 1800 series models, disconnect both brake lines at the caliper and plug them.

5. Remove the two caliper attaching bolts and lift the unit off the retainer.

6. To install, first check the mating surfaces of the caliper and its retainer to make sure that they are clean and not

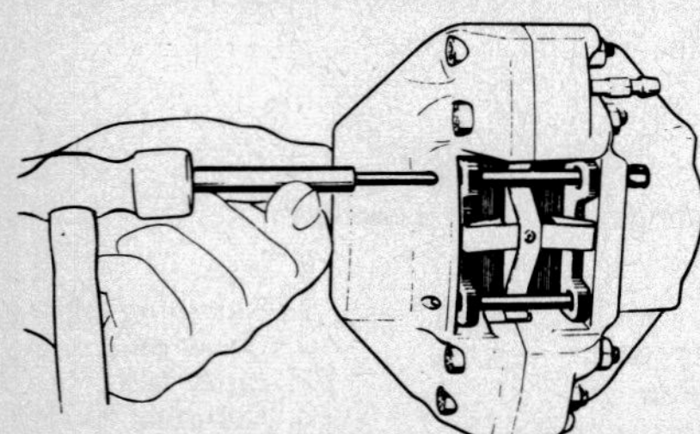

Removing guide pin—ATE brakes

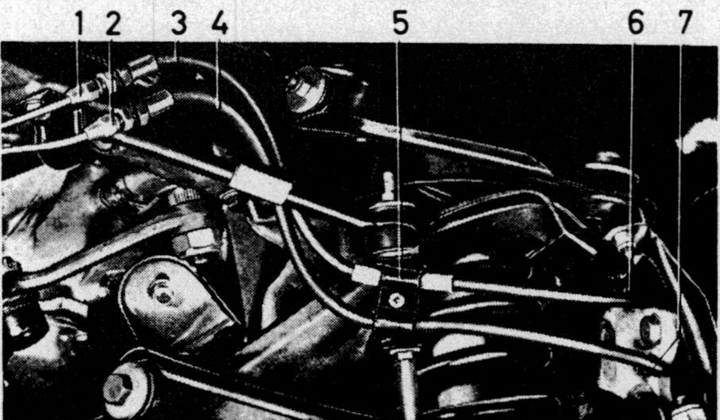

Front brake hose connections—140 series,164.

1. Connection for the primary circuit
2. Connection for the secondary circuit
3. Upper brake hose
4. Lower brake hose
5. Clip
6. Connection for lower wheel unit cylinder
7. Connection for upper wheel unit cylinder

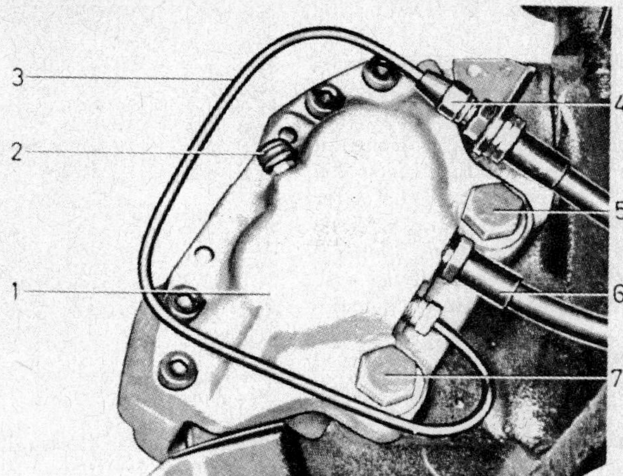

Front caliper installed—ATE shown, Girling similar.

1. Front wheel brake caliper
2. Lower bleeder nipple
3. Upper bleeder nipple
4. Connection for lower wheel unit cylinder
5. Attaching bolt
6. Connection for upper wheel unit cylinder
7. Attaching bolt

damaged. Coat the threads of the attaching bolts with a locking compound such as Loctite. Position the caliper to its retainer over the disc and install the two attaching bolts. Tighten the bolts to 65–70 ft lbs. Make sure that the caliper is parallel to the disc, and that the disc can rotate freely in the brake pads.

7. On 140 series and 164 models, connect the lower brake hose and the secondary circuit brake pipe to their inboard connection and install the brake hose retaining clip to the stabilizer bar. Connect the upper brake hose to the caliper.

8. On 1800 series models, connect both brake lines to the caliper.

9. Unplug the reservoir cap vent hole. Install the wheel and tire assembly. Remove the jackstands and lower the car. Tighten the lug nuts to 70–100 ft lbs and install the hub cap.

10. Bleed the brake system as outlined under "Bleeding Hydraulic System".

Rear Brake Caliper

Removal and Installation

1. Remove the hub cap and loosen the lug nuts a few turns. Block the reservoir cap vent hole to reduce leakage of brake fluid when the line is disconnected.

2. Place blocks in front of the front wheels. Raise the rear of the car and place jackstands beneath the rear axle. Remove the wheel and tire assembly. Release the parking brake.

3. Disconnect the brake line from the caliper and plug it to prevent leakage.

4. Remove the two caliper attaching bolts and lift the unit off the retainer.

5. To install, first check the mating surfaces of the caliper and its retainer to make sure that they are clean and not damaged. Coat the threads of the attaching bolts with locking compound, such as Loctite type AV. Position the caliper to its retainer and install the two attaching bolts. Tighten the bolts to 45–50 ft lbs. Make sure that the caliper is parallel to the disc, and that the disc can rotate freely in the brake pads.

6. Connect the brake line to the caliper. Unplug the reservoir cap hole.

7. Install the wheel and tire assembly. Remove the jackstands and lower the car. Tighten the lug nuts to 70–100 ft lbs, and install the hub cap.

8. Bleed the applicable rear brake caliper as outlined under "Bleeding Hydraulic System".

Caliper Overhaul

The following procedure applies to front calipers and rear calipers of both Girling and Ate design.

1. Remove the brake caliper from the car as outlined in the applicable "Caliper Removal and Installation" section.

2. Remove the brake pads as outlined in step 3 of the applicable "Brake Pad Removal and Installation" section.

3. Remove the retaining rings and the rubber dust covers. Place a wooden block (1) between the pistons. Using compressed air applied through the brake line connection, force the pistons toward the wooden block. Remove the pistons from their bores, taking care not to burr or scratch them.

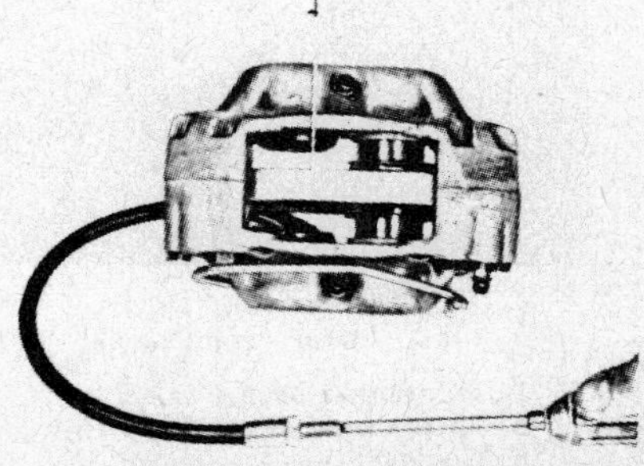

Removing pistons with compressed air

4. Remove the sealing rings with a blunt plastic tool. Be careful not to damage the edges of the grooves. Screw out the bleeder nipple(s), and on front calipers, remove the external connecting pipe.

NOTE: *It is not necessary to separate the caliper halves. Assembling the halves would require special pressure testing equipment.*

5. Clean all reusable metal parts in clean brake fluid or methylated alcohol. Dry all parts with compressed air or allow to air dry. Make sure that all of the passages are clear. All alcohol must be removed from the parts as alcohol lowers the boiling temperature of brake fluid. If any of the cylinders are scored or scratched, the entire housing must be replaced. Minor scratching may be removed from the pistons by fine polishing. Replace any piston that is damaged or worn.

6. Coat the mating surfaces of the pistons and cylinders with brake fluid.

7. Install new sealing rings in the cylinders.

8. On Girling brakes and Ate front brakes, press the pistons into their bores with the large diameter end facing inward. Make sure that the pistons are installed straight and are not scratched in the process.

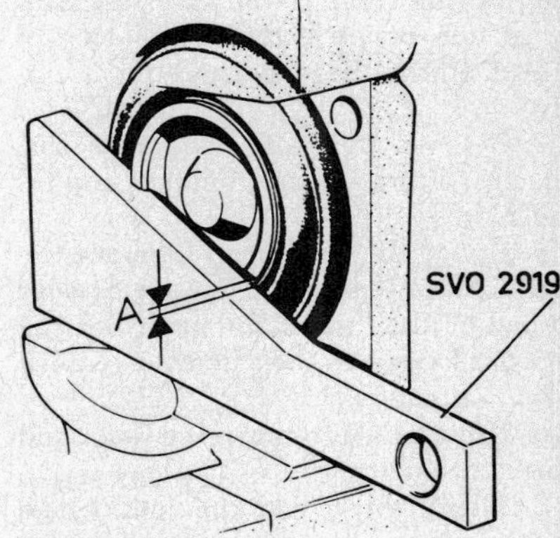

Checking location of rear caliper pistons—ATE brakes.

9. On Ate rear brakes, check to make sure that the pistons are in the proper positions to prevent brake squeal. The piston recess should incline 20° in relation to the lower guide area on the caliper. Check the location of the piston with template SVO 2919. When the template is placed against the one recess, the distance (A) to the other recess may be no greater than 0.039 in. If the location of the piston needs adjusting, press SVO 2918 against the piston and force out the

shoes by screwing in the handle. Turn the piston in the required direction, release the tool, and re-measure with the template. Repeat this operation for the other piston.

10. Place the new rubber dust covers on the pistons and housing. Install the new retaining rings.

11. Install the brake pads as outlined in step 6 of the applicable "Brake Pad Removal and Installation" section.

12. Screw in the bleeder nipple(s).

13. Install the caliper as outlined in the applicable "Caliper Removal and Installation" section.

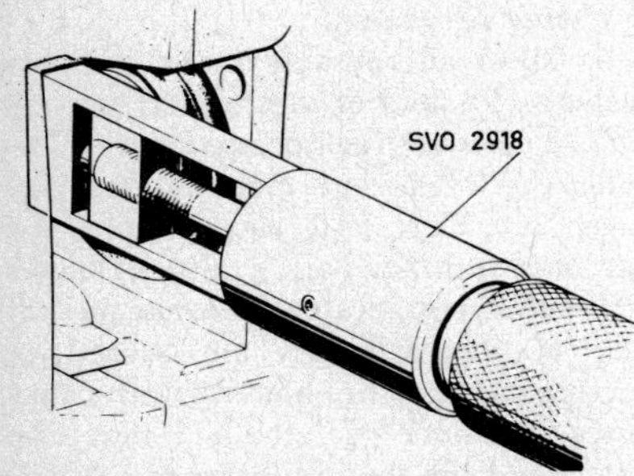

Adjusting location of rear caliper pistons—ATE brakes.

Front Wheel Bearings

Replacement and Adjustment

1. Remove the hub cap, and loosen the lug nuts a few turns.

2. Firmly apply the parking brake. Jack up the front of the car and place jackstands beneath the lower control arms. Remove the wheel and tire assembly.

3. Remove the front caliper as outlined in "Front Caliper Removal and Installation".

4. Pry off the grease cap. Remove the cotter pin and castle nut. Use a hub puller to pull off the hub. If the inner bearing remains lodged on the stub axle, remove it with a puller.

5. Using a drift, remove the inner and outer bearing rings.

6. Thoroughly clean the hub, brake disc, and grease cap.

7. Press in the new inner and outer bearing rings with a drift.

8. Press grease into both bearings with a bearing packer. If one is not available, pack the bearings with as much wheel bearing grease as possible by hand. Also coat the outsides of the bearings and the outer rings pressed into the hub. Fill the recess in the hub with grease up to the smallest diameter on the outer ring for the outer bearing. Place the inner bearing in position in the hub and press its seal in with a drift. The felt ring should be thoroughly coated with light engine oil.

9. Place the hub onto the stub axle. Install the outer bearing, washer, and castle nut.

10. Adjust the front wheel bearings by tightening the castle nut to 50 ft lbs to seat the bearings. Then, back off the nut 1/3 of a turn counterclockwise. If the nut slot does not align with the hole in the stub axle, loosen the nut until the cotter pin may be installed. Make sure that the wheel spins freely without any side play.

11. Fill the grease cap halfway with wheel bearing grease, and install it on the hub.

12. Install the front caliper as outlined in "Front Caliper Removal and Installation".

13. Install the wheel and tire assembly. Remove the jackstands and lower the car. Tighten the lug nuts to 70–100 ft lbs, and install the hub cap.

Brake Discs

Inspection and Replacement

Remove the hub cap, loosen the lug nuts, raise the car, and remove the wheel and tire assembly. The friction surface on

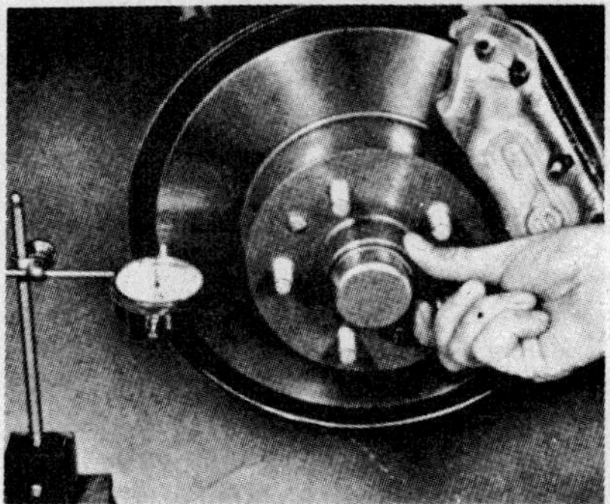

Checking brake disc lateral run-out—front disc shown.

both sides of the disc should be examined for surface deviations such as scoring or corrosion. Minor radial scratches and small rust spots may be removed by turning or fine polishing the disc. The lateral run-out of the disc must not exceed 0.004 in. for the front, and 0.006 in. for the rear, measured at the outer edge of the disc. Do not mistake a faulty wheel bearing adjustment, or an improperly mounted disc for lateral runout. Actual disc thick-

Rear drum brake unit—1967-69 1800 series.

1. Front brake shoe
2. Lock washer
3. Guide pin
4. Link
5. Spring clip
6. Wheel cylinder
7. Upper return spring
8. Rear brake shoe
9. Lever
10. Return spring for lever
11. Adjusting device
12. Lower return spring

ness, which varies from model to model (see specifications), should not vary more than 0.0012 in. when taken at several points on the same disc. If the disc is worn at any point to less than the minimum permissible thickness (see specifications), it must be replaced.

When removing the disc, either to have it machined or replaced, the brake line must be disconnected from the caliper and plugged, the two bolts attaching the caliper to its retainer removed, and the caliper lifted off. The disc is then removed by unscrewing its two philips head retaining screws and rapping on the inside of the disc with a plastic hammer or rubber mallet. Machining should be performed in unit with the hub, and should be equal on both sides. After machining, recheck the disc thickness and compare it to the minimum permissible thickness value on the specifications chart. To install the disc, reverse the removal procedure, taking care to bleed the brake caliper.

REAR DRUM BRAKES

Drum and Lining Removal and Installation

1. Remove the hub cap and cotter pin in the axle shaft. Loosen the castle nut and wheel nuts slightly. Jack up the car and place blocks under the rear axle. Remove the wheel.
2. Release the handbrake. Pull off the hub. The friction surface and out of round of the brake drums should be checked. The out of round must not exceed 0.006 in. If the friction surface is concave, scored or cracked, the drum should be replaced. Minor rust spots can, however, be polished off or ground away.
3. Place a clamp over the wheel cylinder so that the plungers cannot be pressed out. Remove the upper return spring with brake spring pliers. Pull down the front shoe into the groove in the brake backing plate, hold against the guide pin on the other side of the backing plate, and turn and then remove the locking washer. Lift out the shoe.
4. Remove the rear shoe and disconnect it from the handbrake cable. Unhook the return spring and if necessary the handbrake link.
5. Turn in the adjusting screw slightly. Remove the adjusting plunger.
6. Turn back the adjusting screw and install the adjusting plungers after cleaning and coating them with heat-resistant grease. Make sure that the plungers move easily.
7. Install the lever on the rear brake shoe. Hook on the handbrake cable and return springs. Place the shoe in position and install the guide pin and locking clip. Make sure that the head of the guide pin enters the countersink of the clip.
8. Place the handbrake link in position, ensuring that it is turned correctly. Hook on the lower return spring and install the front brake shoe with brake spring pliers. Install the spring clip.
9. Make sure that the springs and locking washers are in position and that the linings are free from burrs, grease, and dirt.
10. Make sure that the key fits in the axle shaft and replace the hub with brake drum. Put on the washer and tighten the castle nut. If the wheel cylinder has been removed, bleed the system. Put on the wheel after cleaning the contact surfaces between the wheel and hub.

Adjust the brakes. Lower the car and tighten the wheel nuts. Tighten alternately a little at a time until all are tightened to 70–100 ft lbs. Tighten the castle nut and lock it with a cotter pin. Replace the hub cap.

Wheel Cylinder

Removal and Installation

1. Remove the hub and brake drum assembly.
2. Move the brake shoes to one side so far that the push rods are clear from the shoes.
3. Disconnect and plug the brake line and remove the wheel cylinder attaching bolts.
4. Remove the wheel cylinder by moving it forward. Make sure that no brake fluid gets on to the brake linings.

To replace:

1. Put the wheel cylinder in place on the brake backing plate and install the attaching bolts. Connect the brake line. Move the brake shoes into position.
2. Fill the master cylinder with new brake fluid. Bleed the brake system until all air bubbles are exhausted from the fluid. Only the brake lines that were opened to remove the wheel cylinder need be bled.

Overhaul

Remove the clip, force off the rubber cover, and remove the seals and the spring. Wash all the parts in clean brake fluid.

Examine the internal cylinder carefully. There must be no scars, scratches, or rust patches on the polished surface. Damage of this type can usually be repaired by honing the cylinder. Clean the cylinder thoroughly after honing. The bleeding nipple should be removed while this is done.

The clearance between the piston and the cylinder must not exceed 0.010 in. This can be determined by measuring the piston diameter with a micrometer and the cylinder with an indicator. If the clearance exceeds 0.010 in. try a new piston. If this does not help, the cylinder must be replaced.

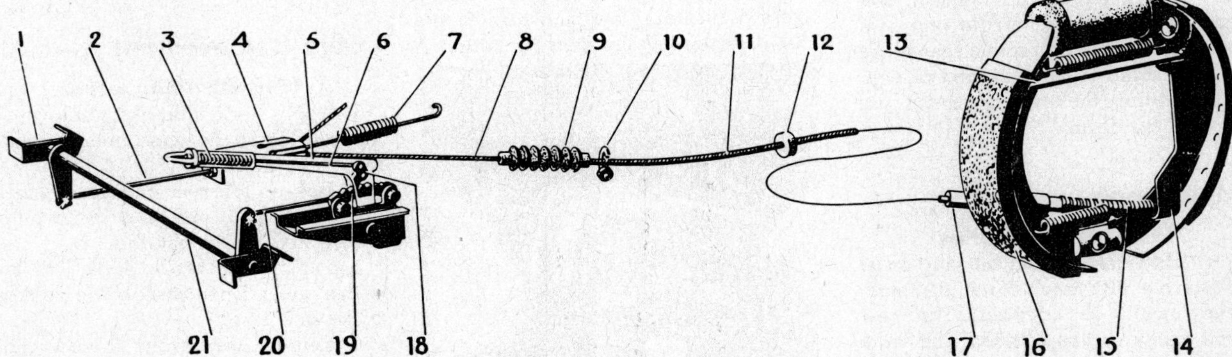

Parking brake assembly—1967-69 1800 series.

1. Support attachment
2. Pull rod
3. Spring
4. Clevis (early production)
5. Handbrake lever
6. Push rod
7. Return spring
8. Handbrake cable
9. Rubber cover
10. Attachment for outer casing
11. Outer casing
12. Bushing
13. Link
14. Lever
15. Return springs
16. Brake shoe
17. Sleeve
18. Pawl
19. Ratchet segment
20. Pull rod
21. Shaft

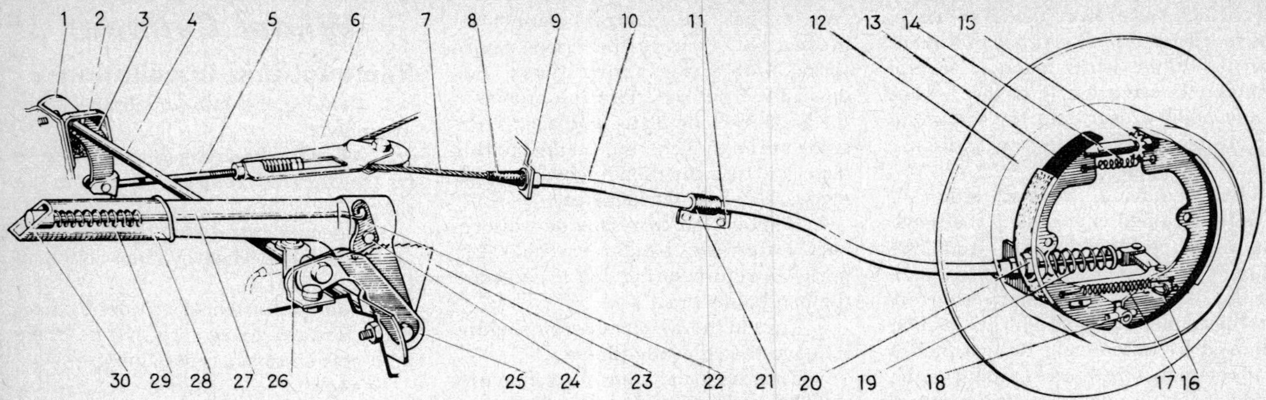

Parking brake assembly—1967-73 140 series, 1969-73 164, 1970-73 1800 series.

1. Inside support attachment
2. Rubber cover
3. Lever
4. Shaft
5. Pull rod
6. Block
7. Rubber cover
9. Front attachment
10. Cable sleeve
11. Attachment
12. Brake drum
13. Brake shoe (secondary shoe)
14. Return spring
15. Adjusting device
16. Lever
17. Movable rod
18. Anchor bolt
19. Return spring
20. Rear attachment
21. Rubber cable guide
22. Pawl
23. Ratchet segment
24. Rivet
25. Outside support attachment
26. Warning valve switch
27. Push rod
28. Parking brake lever
29. Spring
30. Push button

The clearance can also be checked by using a feeler gauge. The clearance obtained by measuring in this way should not exceed 0.006 in.

The seals and the rubber casing should be replaced by new units. Replace worn and damaged parts.

Assemble the parts in the reverse order of disassembly. Dip the piston and seals in brake fluid first.

PARKING BRAKE

The parking brake is mechanically actuated by a cable which is connected, by means of a pull rod and linkage, to a lever mounted on the floor to the left of the driver's seat. On disc brake equipped models, the brake consists of two miniature duo-servo drum brakes, one mounted at each end of the rear axle housing inside the hub of the rear brake discs. On drum brake equipped models, the cable brings the brake shoes into contact with the drum.

Adjustment

1967–69 1800 Series

The handbrake should be fully on at the fourth or fifth notch. If not, the handbrake should be adjusted. The rear brakes should first be adjusted. The handbrake is adjusted by moving the clevis on the pull rod. Tighten the nuts after adjusting.

140 Series, 164, 1970–73 1800 Series

The parking brake should be fully engaged when the lever is pulled up to the third or fourth notch. If it does not, adjust as follows.

1. Apply the parking brake. Remove the rear hub caps and loosen the lug nuts a few turns.
2. Place blocks in front of the front wheels. Jack up the rear end and place jackstands beneath the rear axle. Remove the wheel and tire assemblies. Release the parking brake.
3. Make sure that the brake pads are not stuck to their discs. Disconnect the cable from the lever.
4. Rotate the disc until the adjusting screw hole aligns with the serrations on the adjusting screw. Insert a screwdriver, and adjust the shoes by moving the handle of the screwdriver upward. When the disc cannot be rotated easily, stop adjusting the shoes. Turn the adjusting screw back 4 or 5 serrations. Make sure that the shoes do not drag by hand turning the disc in its normal direction of rotation. A slight drag is permissible. However, if there is a heavy drag, back off the adjusting screw 2 or 3 serrations more. Connect the cable to the lever.

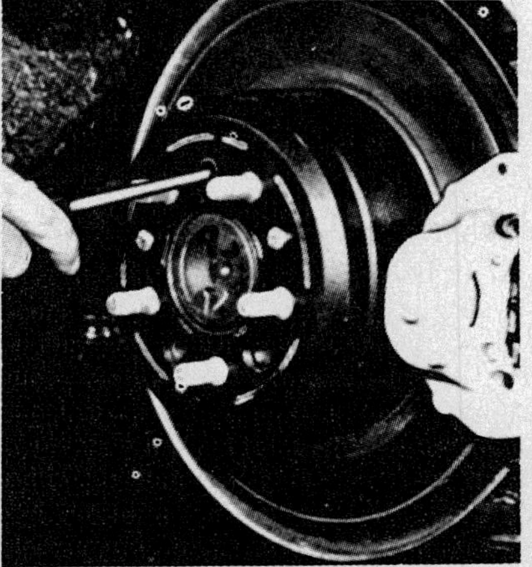

Adjusting parking brake (vehicles equipped with rear disc brakes).

5. Repeat the adjusting procedure for the other wheel.
6. Apply the parking brake lever and make sure that the parking brake is fully engaged with the lever at the third or fourth notch. If not, tighten the cable. This is accomplished by loosening the locknuts and screwing in the block on the pull rod. After adjusting, tighten the locknuts. Make sure that there is approximately the same braking effect on both rear wheels.
7. Install the wheel and tire assemblies. Remove the jackstands and lower the car. Tighten the lug nuts to 70–100 ft lbs and install the hub caps.

Cable Replacement

1967–69 1800 Series

1. Apply the handbrake, remove the hub cap, loosen the wheel nuts and castle nut.
2. Jack up the rear end, place blocks under the rear axle and remove the wheel. Release the handbrake.
3. Pull off the brake drum and hub with a puller. Unhook the cable from the brake shoe lever.
4. Remove the screws for the cable casing attachment on the brake backing plate. Remove the cable casing front attachment and rubber support sleeve. Unhook the cable from the clevis and pull out the cable.

To replace:

1. Install the rubber support sleeve on the cable casing. Insert the cable into the

brake backing plate and hook it onto the lever.

2. Hook the cable onto the clevis.

3. Tighten the bolts in the brake backing plate. Install the cable casing front attachment and make sure that the clamp enters the groove on the sleeve. If necessary, loosen the adjusting nuts. Install the rubber support sleeve in its bracket.

4. Install the hub with brake drum and wheel.

5. Adjust the handbrake. Lower the car and tighten the wheel nuts to 70–100 ft lbs. Tighten and lock the castle nut. Install the hub cap.

140 Series, 164, 1970–73 1800 Series

1. Apply the parking brake. Remove the hub caps for the rear wheels and loosen the lug nuts a few turns.

2. Place blocks in front of the front wheels. Jack up the rear end and place jackstands beneath the rear axle. Remove the wheel and tire assembly. Release the parking brake.

3. Remove the bolt and the wheel from the pulley.

4. Remove the rubber cover for the front attachment of the cable sleeve and nut, as well as the attachment for the rubber suspension ring on the frame. Remove the cable from the other side of the attachment in the same manner.

5. Hold the return spring in position. Pry up the lock and remove the lock pin so that the cable releases from the lever.

6. Remove the return spring with washers. Loosen the nut for the rear attachment of the cable sleeve. Lift the cable forward, after loosening both sides of the attachments, and remove it.

6. To install, first adjust the rear brake shoes of the parking brake as outlined in steps 3, 4, and 5 under "Parking Brake Adjustment".

7. Install new rubber cable guides for the cable suspension. Place the cable in position in the rear attachment and tighten the nut. Install the washers and return spring. Oil the lock pin and install it, together with the cable, on the lever. Install the attachment and rubber cable guide on the frame.

8. Install the cable in the same manner on the side of the vehicle.

9. Place the cable sleeve in position in the front attachments and install the rubber covers.

10. Lubricate and install the pulley on the pull rod. Adjust the pulley so that the parking brake is fully engaged with the lever at the third or fourth notch.

11. Install the wheel and tire assemblies. Remove the jackstands and lower the vehicle. Tighten the lug nut to 70–100 ft lbs and install the hub caps.

CHASSIS ELECTRICAL

Heater

Heater Unit Removal and Installation

140 series, 164

1967–72

1. Remove the lower radiator hose, open the engine drain plug, and drain the cooling system. Disconnect the negative battery cable.

2. Remove the control valve hoses.

3. Remove the heater control panel below the dashboard by removing the two retaining screws. Tilt the top of the panel back so that it loosens from the dashboard clips and clears the hood release.

4. Remove the transmission tunnel mat, defroster hoses, heater control cables, and fan switch wires.

5. Remove the two screws which retain the fuse box to the heater.

6. Remove the control valve, being careful not to damage the copper capillary tube. Loosen the upper hose to the heater.

7. Plug the heater outlets to avoid spilling coolant upon removal. Loosen the heater unit ground cables, remove the four retaining screws, loosen the drain hose, and lift out the heater unit and control valve from their brackets.

8. Reverse the above procedure to install.

1973 Standard Heating System

1. Remove the lower radiator hose, open the engine drain plug, and drain the cooling system. Disconnect the negative battery cable.

2. Remove the center panel and the left-hand defroster hose.

3. Lift up the driveshaft tunnel mat, disconnect the front and rear attaching screws of the rear seat heater ducts, and then remove the ducts from the heater.

4. Disconnect the heater control valve and air-mix cables from their shutters.

5. Disconnect and plug the pressure hose at the heater. Also plug the heater pipes to prevent residual coolant from spilling onto the carpet.

6. Remove the attaching screws which secure the left-hand upper bracket to the dashboard and the left-hand lower bracket to the transmission tunnel.

7. Remove the glovebox by unscrewing the four attaching screws, removing the glovebox door stop, and disconnecting the wires from the glovebox courtesy light.

8. Disconnect the defroster and floor heating cables from their levers.

9. Disconnect the fan motor wires at the switch contact plate.

10. Remove the attaching screws which secure the right-hand upper bracket to the dashboard and the right-hand lower bracket to the transmission tunnel.

11. Remove the right-hand defroster hose. Disconnect the hose between the heater and the dashboard circular vents. Lift the heater unit to the right, and then out of the vehicle.

12. Reverse the above procedure to install, taking care to ensure that the air vent rubber seal is properly located, and that the fan motor ground cable is attached to the upper right-hand bracket attaching screw.

1973 Combination Heater-Air Conditioner System

1. Remove the lower radiator hose, open the engine drain plug, and drain the cooling system. Disconnect the negative battery cable.

2. Remove the heater hoses from the heater pipes at the engine side of the firewall. Plug the heater pipes.

3. Remove the evaporator hose brackets from their body mounts and disconnect the dryer from its bracket. Position the dryer as close to the firewall as the evaporator hose permits.

4. Remove the instrument cluster by removing the steering column molded casings, removing the bracket retaining screw and lowering it toward the steering column, removing the four instrument cluster retaining screws, disconnecting the speedometer cable, tilting the speedometer out of its snap fitting, moving the cluster forward and disconnecting the electrical plug contacts, then lifting the cluster out of the vehicle.

5. Remove the air hose between the central unit and the left inner air vent. Remove the hose from the vacuum motor for the left defroster nozzle.

6. Remove the left-side panel from the central unit.

7. Lift up the driveshaft tunnel mat and disconnect the rear seat heater duct from the central unit.

8. Remove the heater pipes from the passenger side of the firewall.

9. Remove the upper and lower attaching screws for the left support leg. Remove the attaching screws which secure the upper bracket to the dashboard and the lower bracket to the transmission tunnel.

NOTE: *If the upper bracket screw holes are slotted, the screws need only be slackened a few turns.*

10. Remove the right-side panel from the central unit.

11. Remove the glovebox by unscrewing the four attaching screws, removing

the glovebox door stop, and disconnecting the glovebox courtesy light wires.

12. Remove the right defroster nozzle, and also the air hose between the central unit and the right inner air vent.

13. Lift up the driveshaft tunnel mat and disconnect the rear seat heater duct from the central unit.

14. Remove the upper and lower attaching screws for the right support leg. Remove the lower attaching screws for the control panel.

15. Disconnect the fan motor wires and the ground wires from the control panel.

16. Disconnect the yellow lead cable from its plug contact.

17. Separate the halves of the vacuum hose connector and disconnect the vacuum tank hose at the connector.

18. Position the control panel as far back on the transmission tunnel as the cables permit.

19. Remove the screws which attach the upper brackets to the firewall and the lower brackets to the transmission tunnel.

20. Remove the thermostat clamp from the central unit, and the two evaporator cover retaining clamps.

21. Without disconnecting any of the refrigerant lines, remove the evaporator from the central unit, placing it on the right-hand side of the firewall.

22. Remove the molded dashboard padding from beneath the glovebox.

23. Remove the retaining clamps for the right outer vent duct, and remove the duct. Pry off the locking retainer for the turbine (blower), and remove the turbine. Remove the clamps which retain the blower housing (inner end) to the central unit and remove the housing.

24. Remove the passenger's front seat cushion and lift the central unit forward and onto the floor of the vehicle. Be careful not to place undue stress on the connected refrigerant lines.

25. Reverse the above procedure to install, taking care to ensure that the evaporator pipes and thermostat capillary are enclosed in sealing compound, that the drainage tubes are inserted in their respective transmission tunnel holes, and that the ground cables are connected.

1800 series

1967–73

1. Disconnect the lower radiator hose, open the engine drain plug, and drain the cooling system. Disconnect the negative battery cable.

2. Disconnect the heater hoses from the heater core pipe and the control valve pipe. Disconnect the fan motor wires.

3. Disconnect the fresh air intake from the heater.

4. On 1970–71 models, remove the pressure regulator bracket retaining screws and allow the pressure regulator to hang free while still connected to the hoses.

5. Remove the four heater-to-firewall attaching nuts.

6. Remove the defroster hoses. Disconnect the heater control valve and the control cables.

7. Lift out the heater and control valve as a unit.

8. Reverse the above procedure to install.

Blower Motor Removal and Installation

140 series, 164

1967–72

1. Remove the heater unit as outlined in "Heater Unit Removal and Installation."

2. Remove the four rubber bushings on the sides of the heater unit.

3. Scribe marks on both sides of the fan housing to facilitate assembly. Remove the spring clips and separate the housing halves.

4. Mark the mounting plate's relative position to the fan housing. Straighten the tabs and separate the mounting plate from the housing.

5. Remove the retaining screws and separate the fan motor from the mounting plate.

6. Reverse the above procedure to install, being careful to apply soft sealer to the housing halves.

1973 Standard Heating System

1. Remove the heater unit as outlined in "Heater Unit Removal and Installation."

2. Place the unit on its side with the control valve facing upward. Remove the spring clips and separate the housing halves.

3. Lift out the old fan motor and replace it with a new unit, making sure that the support leg without the "foot" points to the output for the defroster channel.

4. Assemble the heater housing halves with new spring clips, and seal the joint without clips with soft sealing compound.

5. Install the heater unit as outlined in "Heater Unit Removal and Installation."

1973 Combination Heater-Air Conditioner System

In order to remove the blower motor, both the right and left turbines (blower wheels) must first be removed. The heater unit does not have to be removed.

1. Disconnect the negative battery cable.

2. Lift the carpet and remove the central unit side panels.

3. Remove the retaining screws for the control panel and move the panel as far back on the transmission tunnel as the electrical cables will permit.

4. Remove the attaching screws for the rear seat heater ducts and disconnect the ducts from the central unit.

5. Remove the instrument cluster as outlined in "Instrument Cluster Removal and Installation."

6. Remove the glovebox by unscrewing the four attaching screws, removing the glovebox door stop, and disconnecting the wires from the glovebox courtesy light. Remove the molded dashboard padding from beneath the glovebox.

7. Disconnect the vacuum hoses to the left and right defroster nozzle vacuum motors, then remove the nozzles and the left and right air ducts.

8. Remove the air hoses between the left and right inside air vents.

9. Remove the clamps on the central unit outer ends, and remove the ends.

10. Pry off the locking retainer for the turbines (blower wheels), and remove both left and right turbines.

11. Position the heater control valve capillary tube to one side.

12. Remove the left inner end (blower housing) from the central unit.

13. Unscrew the three retaining screws and remove the fan motor retainer.

14. Disconnect the plug contact from the fan motor control panel. Release the tabs of the electric cables from the plug contact, and, removing the rubber grommet, pull the electrical cables down through the central unit right opening.

15. Remove the fan motor from the left opening.

16. Reverse the above procedure to install.

1800 series

1967–73

NOTE: *The fan motor and fan are replaced as a unit.*

1. Remove the valve cover and place a rag over the rocker arm assembly.

2. On 1970–71 models, remove the pressure regulator bracket from the heater and allow it to hang freely.

3. Disconnect the fan motor wires at the fan terminals.

4. Remove the six retaining screws and remove the fan motor from the heater assembly.

5. Reverse the above procedure to install.

Heater Core Removal and Installation

140 series, 164

1967–72

1. Remove the heater unit as outlined in "Heater Unit Removal and Installation."

2. Remove the four rubber bushings on the sides of the heater unit.

3. Scribe marks on both sides of the fan housing to facilitate assembly. Remove the spring clips and separate the housing halves.

4. Separate the heater core from the housing half, taking care not to damage the sensitive body for the control valve.

5. Reverse the above procedure to install, being careful to apply soft sealer to the housing halves.

1973 Standard Heating System

1. Remove the heater unit as outlined in "Heater Unit Removal and Installation."

2. Place the unit on its side with the control valve facing upward. Remove the spring clips and separate the housing halves.

3. Disconnect the capillary tube from the heater core and then lift out the core.

4. Reverse the above procedure to install, being careful to transfer the foam plastic packing to the new heater core, and to install the fragile capillary tube carefully on the core.

1973 Combination Heater-Air Conditioner System

1. Remove the combination heater-air conditioner unit as outlined under "Heater Unit Removal and Installation."

2. Remove the left outer end of the central unit. Remove the locking retainer and the turbine (blower wheel).

3. Remove the two retaining screws for the left transmission tunnel bracket.

4. Remove the lockring for the left intake shutter shaft.

5. Remove the three retaining screws and lift off the inner end.

6. Remove the three retaining screws for the fan motor retainer.

7. Disconnect the heater hoses at the heater core.

8. Remove the clamps which retain the central unit halves together, lift off the left half, and remove the heater core.

9. Reverse the above procedure to install, taking care to transfer the foam plastic packing to the new heater core.

1800 series

1967–73

1. Remove the heater unit as outlined in "Heater Unit Removal and Installation."

2. Remove the fan motor as outlined in "Blower Motor Removal and Installation."

3. Remove the screws securing the heater housing halves together and then separate the halves.

4. Remove the heater core from the housing.

5. Install the new or reconditioned core in the housing. Check the operation of the shutters for binding or looseness.

6. Install the thermostat capillary tube on the core.

7. Apply new soft sealing compound to the housing halves prior to assembly.

8. Reverse the above procedure to install.

Radio

Radio Removal and Installation

1. Disconnect the negative battery cable.

2. Remove the radio control knobs by pulling them straight out. Remove the control shaft retaining nuts.

3. Disconnect the speaker wires, the power lead (either at the fuse box or the in-line fuse connection), and the antenna cable from its jack on the radio.

4. Remove the hardware which attaches the radio to its mounting (support) bracket(s), and slide it back and down from the dash.

5. Reverse the above procedure to install.

Windshield Wipers

Motor Removal and Installation

140 series, 164

1967–72

1. Disconnect the negative battery cable.

2. Remove the wiper arm and blade assemblies.

3. Remove the molded panel from under the dash.

4. Remove the heater switch.

5. Remove the instrument cluster as outlined in "Instrument Cluster Removal and Installation."

6. Remove the intermediate defroster nozzle and disconnect the hoses.

7. Remove the retaining bolts and lower the wiper motor.

8. Reverse the above procedure to install.

1973

1. Disconnect the negative battery cable.

2. Disconnect the drive link from the wiper motor lever by unsnapping the locking tab.

3. Disconnect the plug contact from the motor.

4. Remove the three attaching screws and lower the motor out from under the dash.

5. Reverse the above procedure to install, taking care to transfer the rubber seal, rubber damper, and spacer sleeves to the new motor.

Linkage Removal and Installation

140 series, 164 1967–72

1. Remove the wiper motor as outlined in "Wiper Motor Removal and Installation."

2. Disconnect the heater control cable.

3. Remove the fuse box from its bracket and allow it to hang free.

4. Disconnect the ground cables.

5. On carbureted versions, remove the choke control.

6. Release the attaching screws for the wiper frame and lower the frame.

7. Reverse the above procedure to install.

140 series, 164 1973

Drive Link

1. On vehicles equipped with a combination heater-air conditioner unit, remove the glovebox and the right defroster nozzle.

2. Remove the right-hand side panel and the defroster hoses.

3. Remove the locking tab for the wiper motor lever connection, loosen the nut for the cable stretcher, and remove the drive link.

4. Reverse the above procedure to install, carefully placing the cable around the wiper arm drive segment with the cable nipple inserted in the segment recess.

Parallel Drive Link

1. On vehicles equipped with a combination heater-air conditioner unit, remove the glovebox and the right defroster nozzle.

2. Remove the right-hand side panel and the defroster hoses.

3. Remove the drive link by releasing the locking tab for the wiper motor lever connection and loosening the cable stretcher.

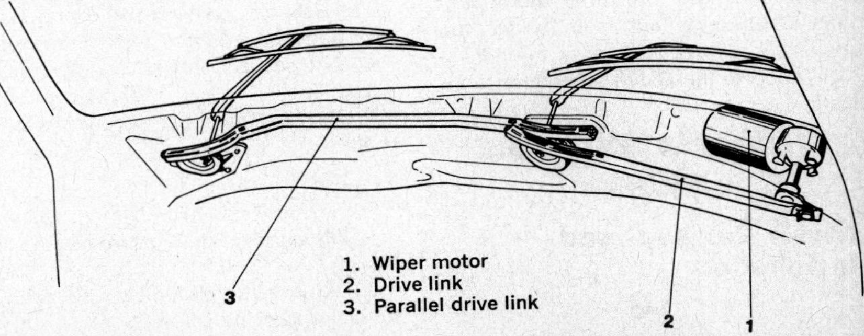

Windshield wiper unit—1973 140 series, 164.

4. Remove each cable stretcher nut and disconnect both ends of the cable from their wiper arm drive segments.

5. Lift forward and remove the parallel drive link.

6. Reverse the above procedure to install, taking care to place each cable end around its respective wiper drive arm segments with the cable nipple inserted in the segment recess.

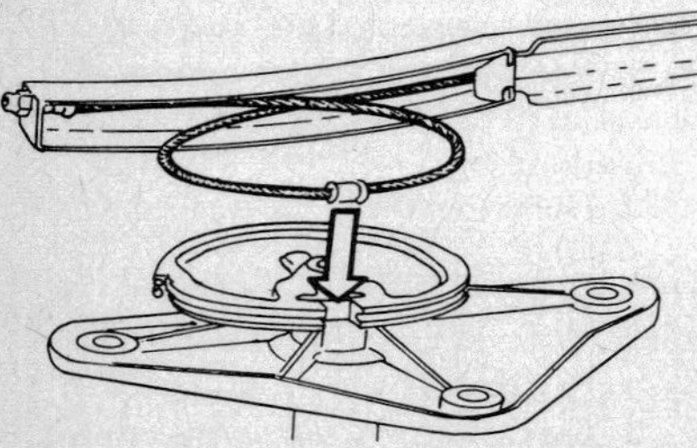

Installing cable for drive link and parallel drive link, left hand side—1973 140 series, 164.

Cable

1. Remove the drive link and parallel drive link as outlined in "Drive Link Removal and Installation" and "Parallel Drive Link Removal and Installation."

2. Pry up and remove the cable retaining lockwasher. Remove the old cable.

3. Position the new cable on its wiper arm drive segments and secure it with a new retaining lockwasher.

4. Install the cable stretcher in the drive link. The tensioning nut should not be tightened until the drive link and parallel drive link are installed.

5. Install the drive link and parallel drive link.

Windshield Wiper Unit (complete) Removal and Installation

1800 series

1967–73

1. Disconnect the negative battery cable.

2. Remove the wiper arm and blade assemblies. Unscrew the wiper arm shaft retaining nuts, and then lift off the washers and rubber seals.

3. Disconnect the electrical wires at the wiper motor.

4. Remove the two wiper motor retaining bolts and lower the motor and linkage assembly out from under the dash.

5. Reverse the above procedure to install.

Tailgate Window Wiper

Motor Removal and Installation

145

1. Disconnect the negative battery cable.

2. Remove the upholstered finish panel on the inside of the tailgate.

3. Remove the screws which retain the reinforcing bracket beneath the wiper motor.

4. Disconnect the wiper link arm. Bend the reinforcing bracket to one side and lower the wiper motor until it is clear of the bracket.

5. Disconnect the electrical wires from the motor and remove the motor.

6. Reverse the above procedure to install.

Instruments

Instrument Cluster Removal and Installation

A voltage stabilizer feeds a 10 V current to both the temperature gauges and the fuel gauge. Electrical malfunctions in these gauges must be checked with an ohmmeter, not a 12 V test light. If malfunctions occur simultaneously in all three of the gauges that are fed by the stabilizer, the stabilizer itself is probably malfunctioning. When replacing the voltage stabilizer, the new unit must fit in the same position as the old one. If the stabilizer is not located correctly in the dash, the voltage output may be altered.

140 series, 164

1967–72

1. Disconnect the negative battery cable.

2. Remove the two screws which retain the control panel.

3. Remove the two retaining screws and lower the molded panel beneath the dashboard.

4. Pull the upper section of the cluster outward so it loosens from its retaining clips. Loosen the panel from the hood release mechanism.

5. Move the control panel—with the short side first—through the dashboard opening.

6. Disconnect the heater controls and the speedometer cable. Remove the flange nuts for the instrumentation.

7. Rotate the instrument cluster slightly, so that the electrical connections may be removed from the reverse side.

8. Lift out the cluster from the dashboard.

9. Reverse the above procedure to install.

1973

1. Disconnect the negative battery cable.

2. Remove the molded plastic casings from the steering column.

3. Remove the bracket retaining screw and lower the bracket toward the steering column.

4. Remove the cluster attaching screws.

5. Disconnect the speedometer cable.

6. Tilt the cluster out of its snap fitting and disconnect the plug contact. On vehicles equipped with a tachometer, disconnect the tachometer sending wire.

7. Lift the cluster out of the dashboard.

8. Reverse the above procedure to install.

1800 series

1967–73

The 1800 series Volvos are equipped with a tachometer, coolant temperature gauge, oil temperature gauge, speedometer (with odometer, tripmeter, and warning lamps), fuel gauge, oil pressure gauge, and clock. Each of these instruments must be removed separately. When replacing an instrument, first disconnect the negative battery cable, then disconnect the electrical connections on the instrument's reverse side. Remove the retaining nuts and attaching bracket, and pull the instrument straight out.

Fuses

All electrical equipment is protected from overloading, by fuses. Each fuse has a rating that will allow it to transmit a predetermined amount of resistance before its filament melts, thereby stopping the excessive current flow. If a fuse blows repeatedly, the trouble is probably in the electrical component that the fuse protects. Never replace a fuse with another of a higher ampere rating. Sometimes, a fuse will blow when all of the electrical equipment protected by the fuse is operating, especially under severe weather conditions. For this reason, it is wise to carry a few spare fuses of each type in the car. Consult the fuse chart for ampere ratings.

On 1967–71 140 series and 164 models, the fuse box is located behind a snap-out panel in the dashboard above the transmission tunnel. On 1972 140 series and 164 models, the fuse box is located behind the control panel for the clock, rear defroster, and emergency flashers, over the transmission tunnel. To tilt-down the control panel and gain access to the fuse box, remove the two retaining screws at the upper corners of the panel.

On 1973 140 series and 164 models, the fuse box is located beneath a protective cover, below the dashboard, in front of the driver's door.

On all 1800 series models, the fuse box is located under the dashboard, to the left of the driver.

On fuel-injected models, an additional fuse box is located in the engine compartment on the left wheel well. It houses a single fuse protecting the electrical fuel pump.

Engine Tune-Up

Engine tune-up is a procedure performed to restore engine performance, deteriorated due to normal wear and loss of adjustment. The three major areas considered in a routine tune-up are compression, ignition, and carburetion, although valve adjustment may be included.

A tune-up is performed in three steps: *analysis*, in which it is determined whether normal wear is responsible for performance loss, and which parts require replacement or service; *parts replacement or service*; and *adjustment*, in which engine adjustments are returned to original specifications. Since the advent of emission control equipment, precision adjustment has become increasingly critical, in order to maintain pollutant emission levels.

Analysis

The procedures below are used to indicate where adjustments, parts service or replacement are necessary within the realm of a normal tune-up. If, following these tests, all systems appear to be functioning properly, proceed to the Troubleshooting Section for further diagnosis.

—Remove all spark plugs, noting the cylinder in which they were installed. Remove the air cleaner, and position the throttle and choke in the full open position. Disconnect the coil high tension lead from the coil and the distributor cap. Insert a compression gauge into the spark plug port of each cylinder, in succession, and crank the engine with the starter to obtain the highest possible reading. Record the readings, and compare the highest to the lowest on the compression pressure limit chart. If the difference exceeds the limits on the chart, or if all readings are excessively low, proceed to a wet compression check (see Troubleshooting Section).

Maxi. Press. Lbs. Sq. In.	*Min. Press. Lbs. Sq. In.*	*Max. Press. Lbs. Sq. In.*	*Min. Press. Lbs. Sq. In.*
134	101	188	141
136	102	190	142
138	104	192	144
140	105	194	145
142	107	196	147
146	110	198	148
148	111	200	150
150	113	202	151
152	114	204	153
154	115	206	154
156	117	208	156
158	118	210	157
160	120	212	158
162	121	214	160
164	123	216	162
166	124	218	163
168	126	220	165
170	127	222	166
172	129	224	168
174	131	226	169
176	132	228	171
178	133	230	172
180	135	232	174
182	136	234	175
184	138	236	177
186	140	238	178

Compression pressure limits
© Buick Div. G.M. Corp.)

—Evaluate the spark plugs according to the spark plug chart in the Troubleshooting Section, and proceed as indicated in the chart.

—Remove the distributor cap, and inspect it inside and out for cracks and/or carbon tracks, and inside for excessive wear or burning of the rotor contacts. If any of these faults are evident, the cap must be replaced.

—Check the breaker points for burning, pitting or wear, and the contact heel resting on the distributor cam for excessive wear. If defects are noted, replace the entire breaker point set.

—Remove and inspect the rotor. If the contacts are burned or worn, or if the rotor is excessively loose on the distributor shaft (where applicable), the rotor must be replaced.

—Inspect the spark plug leads and the coil high tension lead for cracks or brittleness. If any of the wires appear defective, the entire set should be replaced.

—Check the air filter to ensure that it is functioning properly.

Parts Replacement and Service

The determination of whether to replace or service parts is at the mechanic's discretion; however, it is suggested that any parts in questionable condition be replaced rather than reused.

—Clean and regap, or replace, the spark plugs as needed. Lightly coat the threads with engine oil and install the plugs. CAUTION: *Do not over-torque taper-seat spark plugs, or plugs being installed in aluminum cylinder heads.*

SPARK PLUG TORQUE

Thread size	*Cast-Iron Heads*	*Aluminum Heads*
10 mm.	14	11
14 mm.	30	27
18 mm.	34*	32
7/8 in.—18	37	35

* 17 ft. lbs. for tapered plugs using no gaskets.

—If the distributor cap is to be reused, clean the inside with a dry rag, and remove corrosion from the rotor contact points with fine emery cloth. Remove the spark plug wires one by one, and clean the wire ends and the inside of the towers. If the boots are loose, they should be replaced.

If the cap is to be replaced, transfer the wires one by one, cleaning the wire ends and replacing the boots if necessary.

—If the original points are to remain in service, clean them lightly with emery cloth, lubricate the contact heel with grease specifically designed for this purpose. Rotate the crankshaft until the heel rests on a high point of the distributor cam, and adjust the point gap to specifications.

When replacing the points, remove the original points and condenser, and wipe out the inside of the distributor housing with a clean, dry rag. Lightly lubricate the contact heel and pivot point, and install the points and condenser. Rotate the crankshaft until the heel rests on a high point of the distributor cam, and adjust the point gap to specifications. NOTE: *Always replace the condenser when changing the points.*

—If the rotor is to be reused, clean the contacts with solvent. Do not alter the spring tension of the rotor center contact. Install the rotor and the distributor cap.

—Replace the coil high tension lead and/or the spark plug leads as necessary.

—Clean the carburetor using a spray solvent (e.g., Gumout Spray). Remove the varnish from the throttle bores, and clean the linkage. Disconnect and plug the fuel line, and run the engine until it runs out of fuel. Partially fill the float chamber with solvent, and reconnect the fuel line. In extreme cases, the jets can be pressure flushed by inserting a rubber plug into the float vent, running the spray nozzle through it, and spraying the solvent until it squirts out of the venturi fuel dump.

—Clean and tighten all wiring connections in the primary electrical circuit.

Additional Services

The following services *should* be performed in conjunction with a routine tune-up to ensure efficient performance.

—Inspect the battery and fill to the proper level with distilled water. Remove the cable clamps, clean clamps and posts thoroughly, coat the posts lightly with petroleum jelly, reinstall and tighten.

—Inspect all belts, replace and/or adjust as necessary.

—Test the PCV valve (if so equipped), and clean or replace as indicated. Clean all crankcase ventilation hoses, or replace if cracked or hardened.

—Adjust the valves (if necessary) to manufacturer's specifications.

Adjustments

—Connect a dwell-tachometer between the distributor primary lead and ground. Remove the distributor cap and rotor (unless equipped with Delco externally adjustable distributor). With the ignition off, crank the engine with a remote starter switch and measure the point dwell angle. Adjust the dwell angle to specifications. NOTE: *Increasing the gap decreases the dwell angle and vice-versa.* Install the rotor and distributor cap.

—Connect a timing light according to the manufacturer's specifications. Identify the proper timing marks with chalk or paint. NOTE: *Luminescent (day-glo) paint is excellent for this purpose.* Start the engine, and run it until it reaches operating temperature. Disconnect and plug any distributor vacuum lines, and adjust idle to the speed required to adjust timing, according to specifications. Loosen the distributor clamp and adjust timing to specifications by rotating the distributor in the engine. NOTE: *To advance timing, rotate distributor opposite normal direction of rotor rotation, and vice-versa.*

—Synchronize the throttles and mixture of multiple carburetors (if so equipped) according to procedures given in the individual car sections.

—Adjust the idle speed, mixture, and idle quality, as specified in the car sections. Final idle adjustments should be made with the air cleaner installed. CAUTION: *Due to strict emission control requirements on 1969 and later models, special test equipment (CO meter, SUN Tester) may be necessary to properly adjust idle mixture to specifications.*

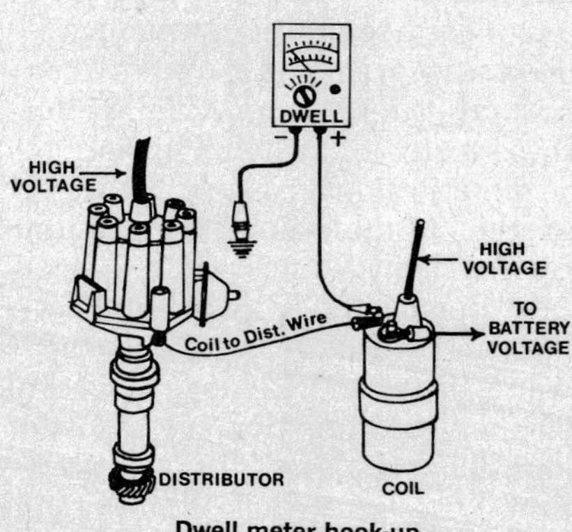

Dwell meter hook-up

Trouble-shooting

The following section is designed to aid in the rapid diagnosis of engine problems. The systematic format is used to diagnose problems ranging from engine starting difficulties to the need for engine overhaul. It is assumed that the user is equipped with basic hand tools and test equipment (tach-dwell meter, timing light, voltmeter, and ohmmeter).

Troubleshooting is divided into two sections. The first, *General Diagnosis*, is used to locate the problem area. In the second, *Specific Diagnosis*, the problem is systematically evaluated.

General Diagnosis

PROBLEM: Symptom	*Begin diagnosis at Section Two, Number ———*
Engine won't start:	
Starter doesn't turn	1.1, 2.1
Starter turns, engine doesn't	2.1
Starter turns engine very slowly	1.1, 2.4
Starter turns engine normally	3.1, 4.1
Starter turns engine very quickly	6.1
Engine fires intermittently	4.1
Engine fires consistently	5.1, 6.1
Engine runs poorly:	
Hard starting	3.1, 4.1, 5.1, 8.1
Rough idle	4.1, 5.1, 8.1
Stalling	3.1, 4.1, 5.1, 8.1
Engine dies at high speeds	4.1, 5.1
Hesitation (on acceleration from standing stop)	5.1, 8.1
Poor pickup	4.1, 5.1, 8.1
Lack of power	3.1, 4.1, 5.1, 8.1
Backfire through the carburetor	4.1, 8.1, 9.1
Backfire through the exhaust	4.1, 8.1, 9.1
Blue exhaust gases	6.1, 7.1
Black exhaust gases	5.1
Running on (after the ignition is shut off)	3.1, 8.1
Susceptible to moisture	4.1
Engine misfires under load	4.1, 7.1, 8.4, 9.1
Engine misfires at speed	4.1, 8.4
Engine misfires at idle	3.1, 4.1, 5.1, 7.1, 8.4

PROBLEM: Symptom	*Probable Cause*
Engine noises: ①	
Metallic grind while starting	Starter drive not engaging completely
Constant grind or rumble	*Starter drive not releasing, worn main bearings
Constant knock	Worn connecting rod bearings
Knock under load	Fuel octane too low, worn connecting rod bearings
Double knock	Loose piston pin
Metallic tap	*Collapsed or sticky valve lifter, excessive valve clearance, excessive end play in a rotating shaft
Scrape	*Fan belt contacting a stationary surface
Tick while starting	S.U. electric fuel pump (normal), starter brushes
Constant tick	*Generator brushes, shreaded fan belt
Squeal	*Improperly tensioned fan belt
Hiss or roar	*Steam escaping through a leak in the cooling system or the radiator overflow vent
Whistle	*Vacuum leak
Wheeze	Loose or cracked spark plug

①—It is extremely difficult to evaluate vehicle noises. While the above are general definitions of engine noises, those starred (*) should be considered as possibly originating elsewhere in the car. To aid diagnosis, the following list considers other potential sources of these sounds.

Metallic grind:
: Throwout bearing; transmission gears, bearings, or synchronizers; differential bearings, gears; something metallic in contact with brake drum or disc.

Metallic tap:
: U-joints; fan-to-radiator (or shroud) contact.

Scrape:
: Brake shoe or pad dragging; tire to body contact; suspension contacting undercarriage or exhaust; something non-metallic contacting brake shoe or drum.

Tick:
: Transmission gears; differential gears; lack of radio suppression; resonant vibration of body panels; windshield wiper motor or transmission; heater motor and blower.

Squeal:
: Brake shoe or pad not fully releasing; tires (excessive wear, uneven wear, improper inflation); front or rear wheel alignment (most commonly due to improper toe-in).

Hiss or whistle:
: Wind leaks (body or window); heater motor and blower fan.

Roar:
: Wheel bearings; wind leaks (body and window).

Specific Diagnosis

This section is arranged so that following each test, instructions are given to proceed to another, until a problem is diagnosed.

INDEX

Group		Topic
1	*	Battery
2	*	Cranking system
3	*	Primary electrical system
4	*	Secondary electrical system
5	*	Fuel system
6	*	Engine compression
7	**	Engine vacuum
8	**	Secondary electrical system
9	**	Valve train
10	**	Exhaust system
11	**	Cooling system
12	**	Engine lubrication

*—The engine need not be running.
**—The engine must be running.

SAMPLE SECTION

Test and Procedure	*Results and Indications*	*Proceed to*
4.1—Check for spark: Hold each spark plug wire approximately 1/4″ from ground with gloves or a heavy, dry rag. Crank the engine and observe the spark.	→ If no spark is evident: →	4.2
	→ If spark is good in some cases: →	4.3
	→ If spark is good in all cases: →	4.6

DIAGNOSIS

Test and Procedure	Results and Indications	Proceed to
1.1—Inspect the battery visually for case condition (corrosion, cracks) and water level.	If case is cracked, replace battery:	1.4
	If the case is intact, remove corrosion with a solution of baking soda and water (CAUTION: *do not get the solution into the battery*), and fill with water:	1.2
1.2—Check the battery cable connections: Insert a screwdriver between the battery post and the cable clamp. Turn the headlights on high beam, and observe them as the screwdriver is gently twisted to ensure good metal to metal contact.	If the lights brighten, remove and clean the clamp and post; coat the post with petroleum jelly, install and tighten the clamp:	1.4
	If no improvement is noted:	1.3

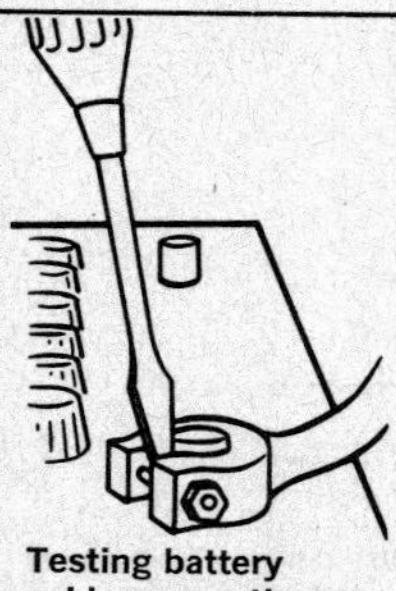

Testing battery cable connections using a screwdriver

Test and Procedure	Results and Indications	Proceed to
1.3—Test the state of charge of the battery using an individual cell tester or hydrometer.	If indicated, charge the battery. NOTE: *If no obvious reason exists for the low state of charge (i.e., battery age, prolonged storage), the charging system should be tested:*	1.4

Spec. Grav. Reading	*Charged Condition*
1.260-1.280	Fully Charged
1.230-1.250	Three Quarter Charged
1.200-1.220	One Half Charged
1.170-1.190	One Quarter Charged
1.140-1.160	Just About Flat
1.110-1.130	All The Way Down

State of battery charge

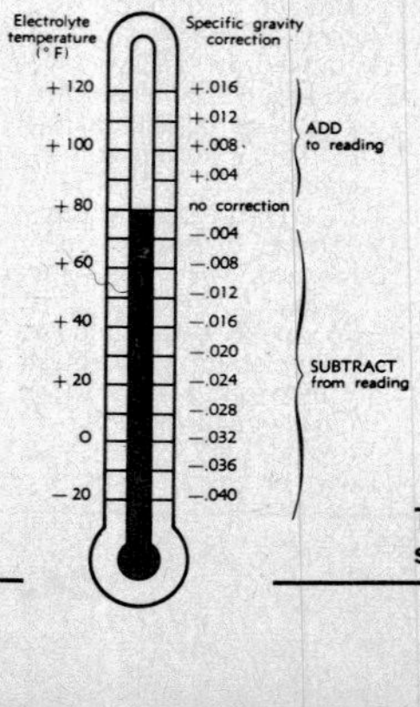

Electrolyte temperature (°F)	Specific gravity correction
+120	+.016
	+.012
+100	+.008
	+.004
+80	no correction
	−.004
+60	−.008
	−.012
+40	−.016
	−.020
+20	−.024
	−.028
0	−.032
	−.036
−20	−.040

ADD to reading (+.016 to +.004); SUBTRACT from reading (−.004 to −.040)

The effect of temperature on the specific gravity of battery electrolyte

Test and Procedure	*Results and Indications*	*Proceed to*
1.4—Visually inspect battery cables for cracking, bad connection to ground, or bad connection to starter.	If necessary, tighten connections or replace the cables:	2.1

Tests in Group 2 are performed with coil high tension lead disconnected to prevent accidental starting.

Test and Procedure	*Results and Indications*	*Proceed to*
2.1—Test the starter motor and solenoid: Connect a jumper from the battery post of the solenoid (or relay) to the ignition switch post of the solenoid (or relay).	If starter turns the engine normally:	2.2
	If the starter buzzes, or turns the engine very slowly:	2.4
	If no response, replace the solenoid (or relay).	3.1
	If the starter turns, but the engine doesn't, ensure that the flywheel ring gear is intact. If the gear is undamaged, replace the starter drive.	3.1
2.2—Determine whether ignition override switches are functioning properly (clutch start switch, neutral safety switch), by connecting a jumper across the switch(es), and turning the ignition switch to "start".	If starter operates, adjust or replace switch:	3.1
	If the starter doesn't operate:	2.3
2.3—Check the ignition switch "start" position: Connect a 12V test lamp between the starter post of the solenoid (or relay) and ground. Turn the ignition switch to the "start" position, and jiggle the key.	If the lamp doesn't light when the switch is turned, check the ignition switch for loose connections, cracked insulation, or broken wires. Repair or replace as necessary:	3.1
	If the lamp flickers when the key is jiggled, replace the ignition switch.	3.3

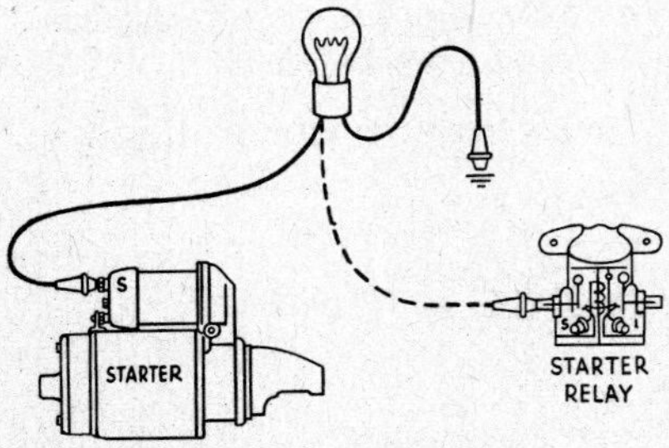

Checking the ignition switch "start" position

Test and Procedure	*Results and Indications*	*Proceed to*
2.4—Remove and bench test the starter, according to specifications in the car section.	If the starter does not meet specifications, repair or replace as needed:	3.1
	If the starter is operating properly:	2.5
2.5—Determine whether the engine can turn freely: Remove the spark plugs, and check for water in the cylinders. Check for water on the dipstick, or oil in the radiator. Attempt to turn the engine using an 18″ flex drive and socket on the crankshaft pulley nut or bolt.	If the engine will turn freely only with the spark plugs out, and hydrostatic lock (water in the cylinders) is ruled out, check valve timing:	9.2
	If engine will not turn freely, and it is known that the clutch and transmission are free, the engine must be disassembled for further evaluation:	Next Chapter

Tests and Procedures	*Results and Indications*	*Proceed to*
3.1—Check the "on" position: Connect a jumper wire between the distributor side of the coil and ground, and a 12V test lamp between the switch side of the coil and ground. Remove the high tension lead from the coil. Turn the ignition switch on and jiggle the key.	If the lamp lights:	3.2
	If the lamp flickers when the key is jiggled, replace the ignition switch:	3.3
	If the lamp doesn't light, check for loose or open connections. If none are found, remove the ignition switch and check for continuity. If the switch is faulty, replace it:	3.3
Checking the ignition switch "on" position		
3.2—Check the ballast resistor or resistance wire for an open circuit, using an ohmmeter.	Replace the resistor or the resistance wire if the resistance is zero.	3.3
3.3—Visually inspect the breaker points for burning, pitting, or excessive wear. Gray coloring of the point contact surfaces is normal. Rotate the crankshaft until the contact heel rests on a high point of the distributor cam, and adjust the point gap to specifications.	If the breaker points are intact, clean the contact surfaces with fine emery cloth, and adjust the point gap to specifications. If pitted or worn, replace the points and condenser, and adjust the gap to specifications: NOTE: *Always lubricate the distributor cam according to manufacturer's recommendations when servicing the breaker points.*	3.4
3.4—Connect a dwell meter between the distributor primary lead and ground. Crank the engine and observe the point dwell angle.	If necessary, adjust the point dwell angle: NOTE: *Increasing the point gap decreases the dwell angle, and vice-versa.*	3.6
	If dwell meter shows little or no reading:	3.5
	Dwell angle	
3.5—Check the condenser for short: Connect an ohmmeter across the condenser body and the pigtail lead.	If any reading other than infinite resistance is noted, replace the condenser:	3.6
Checking the condenser for short		

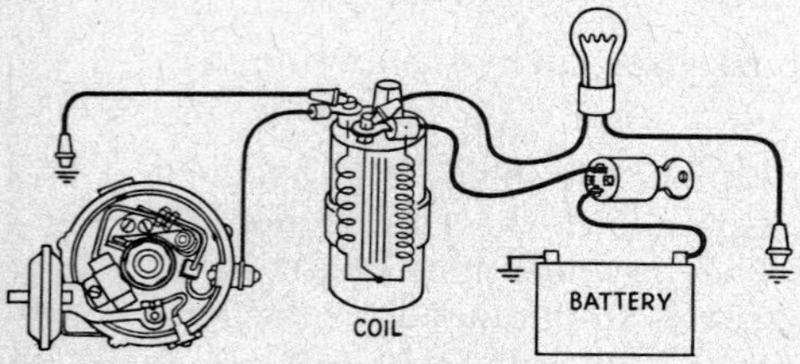

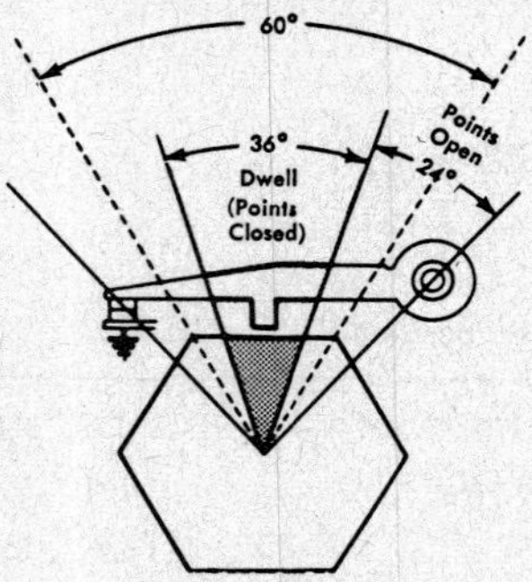

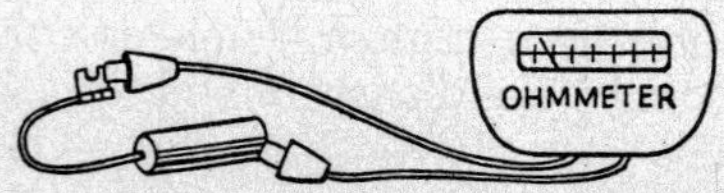

Test and Procedure	*Results and Indications*	*Proceed to*
3.6—Test the coil primary resistance: Connect an ohmmeter across the coil primary terminals, and read the resistance on the low scale. Note whether an external ballast resistor or resistance wire is utilized.	Coils utilizing ballast resistors or resistance wires should have approximately 1.0Ω resistance; coils with internal resistors should have approximately 4.0Ω resistance. If values far from the above are noted, replace the coil:	4.1
Testing the coil primary resistance		
4.1—Check for spark: Hold each spark plug wire approximately ¼″ from ground with gloves or a heavy, dry rag. Crank the engine, and observe the spark.	If no spark is evident:	4.2
	If spark is good in some cylinders:	4.3
	If spark is good in all cylinders:	4.6
4.2—Check for spark at the coil high tension lead: Remove the coil high tension lead from the distributor and position it approximately ¼″ from ground. Crank the engine and observe spark. CAUTION: *This test should not be performed on cars equipped with transistorized ignition.*	If the spark is good and consistent:	4.3
	If the spark is good but intermittent, test the primary electrical system starting at 3.3:	3.3
	If the spark is weak or non-existent, replace the coil high tension lead, clean and tighten all connections and retest. If no improvement is noted:	4.4
4.3—Visually inspect the distributor cap and rotor for burned or corroded contacts, cracks, carbon tracks, or moisture. Also check the fit of the rotor on the distributor shaft (where applicable).	If moisture is present, dry thoroughly, and retest per 4.1:	4.1
	If burned or excessively corroded contacts, cracks, or carbon tracks are noted, replace the defective part(s) and retest per 4.1:	4.1
	If the rotor and cap appear intact, or are only slightly corroded, clean the contacts thoroughly (including the cap towers and spark plug wire ends) and retest per 4.1:	
	If the spark is good in all cases:	4.6
	If the spark is poor in all cases:	4.5
4.4—Check the coil secondary resistance: Connect an ohmmeter across the distributor side of the coil and the coil tower. Read the resistance on the high scale of the ohmmeter.	The resistance of a satisfactory coil should be between 4KΩ and 10KΩ. If the resistance is considerably higher (i.e., 40KΩ) replace the coil, and retest per 4.1: NOTE: *This does not apply to high performance coils.*	4.1
Testing the coil secondary resistance		

Test and Procedure	*Results and Indications*	*Proceed to*
4.5—Visually inspect the spark plug wires for cracking or brittleness. Ensure that no two wires are positioned so as to cause induction firing (adjacent and parallel). Remove each wire, one by one, and check resistance with an ohmmeter.	Replace any cracked or brittle wires. If any of the wires are defective, replace the entire set. Replace any wires with excessive resistance (over 8000Ω per foot for suppression wire), and separate any wires that might cause induction firing.	4.6
4.6—Remove the spark plugs, noting the cylinders from which they were removed, and evaluate according to the chart below.	See below.	See below.

Condition	*Cause*	*Remedy*	*Proceed to*
 Electrodes eroded, light brown deposits.	Normal wear. Normal wear is indicated by approximately .001″ wear per 1000 miles.	Clean and regap the spark plug if wear is not excessive: Replace the spark plug if excessively worn:	4.7
 Carbon fouling (black, dry, fluffy deposits).	If present on one or two plugs:		
	Faulty high tension lead(s).	Test the high tension leads:	4.5
	Burnt or sticking valve(s).	Check the valve train: (Clean and regap the plugs in either case.)	9.1
	If present on most or all plugs: Overly rich fuel mixture, due to restricted air filter, improper carburetor adjustment, improper choke or heat riser adjustment or operation.	Check the fuel system:	5.1
 Oil fouling (wet black deposits)	Worn engine components. NOTE: *Oil fouling may occur in new or recently rebuilt engines until broken in.*	Check engine vacuum and compression:	6.1
		Replace with new spark plug	
 Lead fouling (gray, black, tan, or yellow deposits, which appear glazed or cinder-like).	Combustion by-products.	Clean and regap the plugs: (Use plugs of a different heat range if the problem recurs.)	4.7

Condition	Cause	Remedy	Proceed to
Gap bridging (deposits lodged between the electrodes).	Incomplete combustion, or transfer of deposits from the combustion chamber.	Replace the spark plugs:	4.7
Overheating (burnt electrodes, and extremely white insulator with small black spots).	Ignition timing advanced too far.	Adjust timing to specifications:	8.2
	Overly lean fuel mixture.	Check the fuel system:	5.1
	Spark plugs not seated properly.	Clean spark plug seat and install a new gasket washer: (Replace the spark plugs in all cases.)	4.7
Fused spot deposits on the insulator.	Combustion chamber blow-by.	Clean and regap the spark plugs:	4.7
Pre-ignition (melted or severely burned electrodes, blistered or cracked insulators, or metallic deposits on the insulator).	Incorrect spark plug heat range.	Replace with plugs of the proper heat range:	4.7
	Ignition timing advanced too far.	Adjust timing to specifications:	8.2
	Spark plugs not being cooled efficiently.	Clean the spark plug seat, and check the cooling system:	11.1
	Fuel mixture too lean.	Check the fuel system:	5.1
	Poor compression.	Check compression:	6.1
	Fuel grade too low.	Use higher octane fuel:	4.7

Test and Procedure	Results and Indications	Proceed to
4.7—Determine the static ignition timing: Using the flywheel or crankshaft pulley timing marks as a guide, locate top dead center on the *compression* stroke of the No. 1 cylinder. Remove the distributor cap.	Adjust the distributor so that the rotor points toward the No. 1 tower in the distributor cap, and the points are just opening:	4.8
4.8—Check coil polarity: Connect a voltmeter negative lead to the coil high tension lead, and the positive lead to ground (NOTE: *reverse the hook-up for positive ground cars*). Crank the engine momentarily.	If the voltmeter reads up-scale, the polarity is correct:	5.1
	If the voltmeter reads down-scale, reverse the coil polarity (switch the primary leads):	5.1

Checking coil polarity

Test and Procedure	Results and Indications	Proceed to
5.1—Determine that the air filter is functioning efficiently: Hold paper elements up to a strong light, and attempt to see light through the filter.	Clean permanent air filters in gasoline (or manufacturer's recommendation), and allow to dry. Replace paper elements through which light cannot be seen:	5.2
5.2—Determine whether a flooding condition exists: Flooding is identified by a strong gasoline odor, and excessive gasoline present in the throttle bore(s) of the carburetor.	If flooding is not evident:	5.3
	If flooding is evident, permit the gasoline to dry for a few moments and restart.	
	If flooding doesn't recur:	5.6
	If flooding is persistant:	5.5
5.3—Check that fuel is reaching the carburetor: Detach the fuel line at the carburetor inlet. Hold the end of the line in a cup (not styrofoam), and crank the engine.	If fuel flows smoothly:	5.6
	If fuel doesn't flow (NOTE: *Make sure that there is fuel in the tank*), or flows erratically:	5.4
5.4—Test the fuel pump: Disconnect all fuel lines from the fuel pump. Hold a finger over the input fitting, crank the engine (with electric pump, turn the ignition or pump on), and feel for suction.	If suction is evident, blow out the fuel line to the tank with low pressure compressed air until bubbling is heard from the fuel filler neck. Also blow out the carburetor fuel line (both ends disconnected):	5.6
	If no suction is evident, replace or repair the fuel pump:	5.6
	NOTE: *Repeated oil fouling of the spark plugs, or a no-start condition, could be the result of a ruptured vacuum booster pump diaphragm, through which oil or gasoline is being drawn into the intake manifold (where applicable).*	
5.5—Check the needle and seat: Tap the carburetor in the area of the needle and seat.	If flooding stops, a gasoline additive (e.g., Gumout) will often cure the problem:	5.6
	If flooding continues, check the fuel pump for excessive pressure at the carburetor (according to specifications). If the pressure is normal, the needle and seat must be removed and checked, and/or the float level adjusted:	5.6
5.6—Test the accelerator pump by looking into the throttle bores while operating the throttle.	If the accelerator pump appears to be operating normally:	5.7
	If the accelerator pump is not operating, the pump must be reconditioned. Where possible, service the pump with the carburetor(s) installed on the engine. If necessary, remove the carburetor. Prior to removal:	5.7
5.7—Determine whether the carburetor main fuel system is functioning: Spray a commercial starting fluid into the carburetor while attempting to start the engine.	If the engine starts, runs for a few seconds, and dies:	5.8
	If the engine doesn't start:	6.1

Test and Procedures	*Results and Indications*	*Proceed to*
5.8—Uncommon fuel system malfunctions: See below:	If the problem is solved:	6.1
	If the problem remains, remove and recondition the carburetor.	

Condition	*Indication*	*Test*	*Usual Weather Conditions*	*Remedy*
Vapor lock	Car will not restart shortly after running.	Cool the components of the fuel system until the engine starts.	Hot to very hot	Ensure that the exhaust manifold heat control valve is operating. Check with the vehicle manufacturer for the recommended solution to vapor lock on the model in question.
Carburetor icing	Car will not idle, stalls at low speeds.	Visually inspect the throttle plate area of the throttle bores for frost.	High humidity, 32-40° F.	Ensure that the exhaust manifold heat control valve is operating, and that the intake manifold heat riser is not blocked.
Water in the fuel	Engine sputters and stalls; may not start.	Pump a small amount of fuel into a glass jar. Allow to stand, and inspect for droplets or a layer of water.	High humidity, extreme temperature changes.	For droplets, use one or two cans of commercial gas dryer (Dry Gas) For a layer of water, the tank must be drained, and the fuel lines blown out with compressed air.

Test and Procedure	*Results and Indications*	*Proceed to*
6.1—Test engine compression: Remove all spark plugs. Insert a compression gauge into a spark plug port, crank the engine to obtain the maximum reading, and record.	If compression is within limits on all cylinders:	7.1
	If gauge reading is extremely low on all cylinders:	6.2
	If gauge reading is low on one or two cylinders: (If gauge readings are identical and low on two or more adjacent cylinders, the head gasket must be replaced.)	6.2

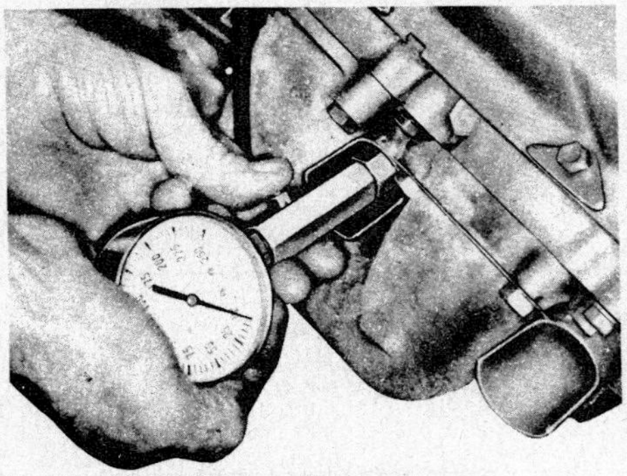

Testing compression
(© Chevrolet Div. G.M. Corp.)

Maxi. Press. Lbs. Sq. In.	*Min. Press. Lbs. Sq. In.*	*Maxi. Press. Lbs. Sq. In.*	*Min. Press. Lbs. Sq. In.*	*Max. Press. Lbs. Sq. In.*	*Min. Press. Lbs. Sq. In.*	*Max. Press. Lbs. Sq. In.*	*Min. Press. Lbs. Sq. In.*
134	101	162	121	188	141	214	160
136	102	164	123	190	142	216	162
138	104	166	124	192	144	218	163
140	105	168	126	194	145	220	165
142	107	170	127	196	147	222	166
146	110	172	129	198	148	224	168
148	111	174	131	200	150	226	169
150	113	176	132	202	151	228	171
152	114	178	133	204	153	230	172
154	115	180	135	206	154	232	174
156	117	182	136	208	156	234	175
158	118	184	138	210	157	236	177
160	120	186	140	212	158	238	178

Compression pressure limits
(© Buick Div. G.M. Corp.)

Test and Procedure	*Results and Indications*	*Proceed to*
6.2—Test engine compression (wet): Squirt approximately 30 cc. of engine oil into each cylinder, and retest per 6.1.	If the readings improve, worn or cracked rings or broken pistons are indicated:	Next Chapter
	If the readings do not improve, burned or excessively carboned valves or a jumped timing chain are indicated: NOTE: *A jumped timing chain is often indicated by difficult cranking.*	7.1
7.1—Perform a vacuum check of the engine: Attach a vacuum gauge to the intake manifold beyond the throttle plate. Start the engine, and observe the action of the needle over the range of engine speeds.	See below.	See below

Reading	*Indications*	*Proceed to*
 Steady, from 17-22 in. Hg.	Normal.	8.1
 Low and steady.	Late ignition or valve timing, or low compression:	6.1
 Very low	Vacuum leak:	7.2
 Needle fluctuates as engine speed increases.	Ignition miss, blown cylinder head gasket, leaking valve or weak valve spring:	6.1, 8.3
 Gradual drop in reading at idle.	Excessive back pressure in the exhaust system:	10.1
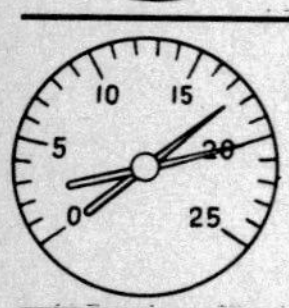 Intermittent fluctuation at idle.	Ignition miss, sticking valve:	8.3, 9.1
 Drifting needle.	Improper idle mixture adjustment, carburetors not synchronized (where applicable), or minor intake leak. Synchronize the carburetors, adjust the idle, and retest. If the condition persists:	7.2
 High and steady.	Early ignition timing:	8.2

Test and Procedure	*Results and Indications*	*Proceed to*
7.2—Attach a vacuum gauge per 7.1, and test for an intake manifold leak. Squirt a small amount of oil around the intake manifold gaskets, carburetor gaskets, plugs and fittings. Observe the action of the vacuum gauge.	If the reading improves, replace the indicated gasket, or seal the indicated fitting or plug:	8.1
	If the reading remains low:	7.3
7.3—Test all vacuum hoses and accessories for leaks as described in 7.2. Also check the carburetor body (dashpots, automatic choke mechanism, throttle shafts) for leaks in the same manner.	If the reading improves, service or replace the offending part(s):	8.1
	If the reading remains low:	6.1
8.1—Check the point dwell angle: Connect a dwell meter between the distributor primary wire and ground. Start the engine, and observe the dwell angle from idle to 3000 rpm.	If necessary, adjust the dwell angle. NOTE: *Increasing the point gap reduces the dwell angle and vice-versa.* If the dwell angle moves outside specifications as engine speed increases, the distributor should be removed and checked for cam accuracy, shaft endplay and concentricity, bushing wear, and adequate point arm tension (NOTE: *Most of these items may be checked with the distributor installed in the engine, using an oscilloscope*):	8.2
8.2—Connect a timing light (per manufacturer's recommendation) and check the dynamic ignition timing. Disconnect and plug the vacuum hose(s) to the distributor if specified, start the engine, and observe the timing marks at the specified engine speed.	If the timing is not correct, adjust to specifications by rotating the distributor in the engine: (Advance timing by rotating distributor opposite normal direction of rotor rotation, retard timing by rotating distributor in same direction as rotor rotation.)	8.3
8.3—Check the operation of the distributor advance mechanism(s): To test the mechanical advance, disconnect all but the mechanical advance, and observe the timing marks with a timing light as the engine speed is increased from idle. If the mark moves smoothly, without hesitation, it may be assumed that the mechanical advance is functioning properly. To test vacuum advance and/or retard systems, alternately crimp and release the vacuum line, and observe the timing mark for movement. If movement is noted, the system is operating.	If the systems are functioning:	8.4
	If the systems are not functioning, remove the distributor, and test on a distributor tester:	8.4
8.4—Locate an ignition miss: With the engine running, remove each spark plug wire, one by one, until one is found that doesn't cause the engine to roughen and slow down.	When the missing cylinder is identified:	4.1

Test and Procedure	*Results and Indications*	*Proceed to*
9.1—Evaluate the valve train: Remove the valve cover, and ensure that the valves are adjusted to specifications. A mechanic's stethoscope may be used to aid in the diagnosis of the valve train. By pushing the probe on or near push rods or rockers, valve noise often can be isolated. A timing light also may be used to diagnose valve problems. Connect the light according to manufacturer's recommendations, and start the engine. Vary the firing moment of the light by increasing the engine speed (and therefore the ignition advance), and moving the trigger from cylinder to cylinder. Observe the movement of each valve.	See below	See below

Observation	*Probable Cause*	*Remedy*	*Proceed to*
Metallic tap heard through the stethoscope.	Sticking hydraulic lifter or excessive valve clearance.	Adjust valve. If tap persists, remove and replace the lifter:	10.1
Metallic tap through the stethoscope, able to push the rocker arm (lifter side) down by hand.	Collapsed valve lifter.	Remove and replace the lifter:	10.1
Erratic, irregular motion of the valve stem.*	Sticking valve, burned valve.	Recondition the valve and/or valve guide:	Next Chapter
Eccentric motion of the pushrod at the rocker arm.*	Bent pushrod.	Replace the pushrod:	10.1
Valve retainer bounces as the valve closes.*	Weak valve spring or damper.	Remove and test the spring and damper. Replace if necessary:	10.1

*—When observed with a timing light.

Test and Procedure	*Results and Indications*	*Proceed to*
9.2—Check the valve timing: Locate top dead center of the No. 1 piston, and install a degree wheel or tape on the crankshaft pulley or damper with zero corresponding to an index mark on the engine. Rotate the crankshaft in its direction of rotation, and observe the opening of the No. 1 cylinder intake valve. The opening should correspond with the correct mark on the degree wheel according to specifications.	If the timing is not correct, the timing cover must be removed for further investigation:	

Test and Procedure	Results and Indications	Proceed to
10.1—Determine whether the exhaust manifold heat control valve is operating: Operate the valve by hand to determine whether it is free to move. If the valve is free, run the engine to operating temperature and observe the action of the valve, to ensure that it is opening.	If the valve sticks, spray it with a suitable solvent, open and close the valve to free it, and retest.	
	If the valve functions properly:	10.2
	If the valve does not free, or does not operate, replace the valve:	10.2
10.2—Ensure that there are no exhaust restrictions: Visually inspect the exhaust system for kinks, dents, or crushing. Also note that gasses are flowing freely from the tailpipe at all engine speeds, indicating no restriction in the muffler or resonator.	Replace any damaged portion of the system:	11.1
11.1—Visually inspect the fan belt for glazing, cracks, and fraying, and replace if necessary. Tighten the belt so that the longest span has approximately ½″ play at its midpoint under thumb pressure.	Replace or tighten the fan belt as necessary:	11.2

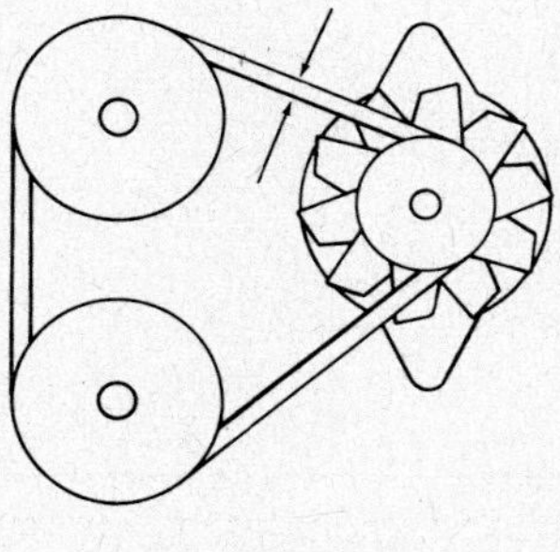

Checking the fan belt tension
(© Outboard Marine Corp.)

Test and Procedure	Results and Indications	Proceed to
11.2—Check the fluid level of the cooling system.	If full or slightly low, fill as necessary:	11.5
	If extremely low:	11.3
11.3—Visually inspect the external portions of the cooling system (radiator, radiator hoses, thermostat elbow, water pump seals, heater hoses, etc.) for leaks. If none are found, pressurize the cooling system to 14-15 psi.	If cooling system holds the pressure:	11.5
	If cooling system loses pressure rapidly, reinspect external parts of the system for leaks under pressure. If none are found, check dipstick for coolant in crankcase. If no coolant is present, but pressure loss continues:	11.4
	If coolant is evident in crankcase, remove cylinder head(s), and check gasket(s). If gaskets are intact, block and cylinder head(s) should be checked for cracks or holes.	
	If the gasket(s) is blown, replace, and purge the crankcase of coolant:	12.6
	NOTE: *Occasionally, due to atmospheric and driving conditions, condensation of water can occur in the crankcase. This causes the oil to appear milky white. To remedy, run the engine until hot, and change the oil and oil filter.*	

Test and Procedure	*Results and Indication*	*Proceed to*
11.4—Check for combustion leaks into the cooling system: Pressurize the cooling system as above. Start the engine, and observe the pressure gauge. If the needle fluctuates, remove each spark plug wire, one by one, noting which cylinder(s) reduce or eliminate the fluctuation. **Radiator pressure tester** (© American Motors Corp.)	Cylinders which reduce or eliminate the fluctuation, when the spark plug wire is removed, are leaking into the cooling system. Replace the head gasket on the affected cylinder bank(s).	
11.5—Check the radiator pressure cap: Attach a radiator pressure tester to the radiator cap (wet the seal prior to installation). Quickly pump up the pressure, noting the point at which the cap releases. **Testing the radiator pressure cap** (© American Motors Corp.)	If the cap releases within ± 1 psi of the specified rating, it is operating properly:	11.6
	If the cap releases at more than ± 1 psi of the specified rating, it should be replaced:	11.6
11.6—Test the thermostat: Start the engine cold, remove the radiator cap, and insert a thermometer into the radiator. Allow the engine to idle. After a short while, there will be a sudden, rapid increase in coolant temperature. The temperature at which this sharp rise stops is the thermostat opening temperature.	If the thermostat opens at or about the specified temperature:	11.7
	If the temperature doesn't increase: (If the temperature increases slowly and gradually, replace the thermostat.)	11.7
11.7—Check the water pump: Remove the thermostat elbow and the thermostat, disconnect the coil high tension lead (to prevent starting), and crank the engine momentarily.	If coolant flows, replace the thermostat and retest per 11.6:	11.6
	If coolant doesn't flow, reverse flush the cooling system to alleviate any blockage that might exist. If system is not blocked, and coolant will not flow, recondition the water pump.	—
12.1—Check the oil pressure gauge or warning light: If the gauge shows low pressure, or the light is on, for no obvious reason, remove the oil pressure sender. Install an accurate oil pressure gauge and run the engine momentarily.	If oil pressure builds normally, run engine for a few moments to determine that it is functioning normally, and replace the sender.	—
	If the pressure remains low:	12.2
	If the pressure surges:	12.3
	If the oil pressure is zero:	12.3

Test and Procedure	*Results and Indications*	*Proceed to*
12.2—Visually inspect the oil: If the oil is watery or very thin, milky, or foamy, replace the oil and oil filter.	If the oil is normal:	12.3
	If after replacing oil the pressure remains low:	12.3
	If after replacing oil the pressure becomes normal:	—
12.3—Inspect the oil pressure relief valve and spring, to ensure that it is not sticking or stuck. Remove and thoroughly clean the valve, spring, and the valve body. Oil pressure relief valve (© British Leyland Motors)	If the oil pressure improves:	—
	If no improvement is noted:	12.4
12.4—Check to ensure that the oil pump is not cavitating (sucking air instead of oil): See that the crankcase is neither over nor underfull, and that the pickup in the sump is in the proper position and free from sludge.	Fill or drain the crankcase to the proper capacity, and clean the pickup screen in solvent if necessary. If no improvement is noted:	12.5
12.5—Inspect the oil pump drive and the oil pump:	If the pump drive or the oil pump appear to be defective, service as necessary and retest per 12.1:	12.1
	If the pump drive and pump appear to be operating normally, the engine should be disassembled to determine where blockage exists:	Next Chapter
12.6—Purge the engine of ethylene glycol coolant: Completely drain the crankcase and the oil filter. Obtain a commercial butyl cellosolve base solvent, designated for this purpose, and follow the instructions precisely. Following this, install a new oil filter and refill the crankcase with the proper weight oil. The next oil and filter change should follow shortly thereafter (1000 miles).		

Engine Rebuilding

This section describes, in detail, the procedures involved in rebuilding a typical engine. The procedures specifically refer to an inline engine, however, they are basically identical to those used in rebuilding engines of nearly all design and configurations. Procedures for servicing atypical engines (i.e., horizontally opposed) are described in the appropriate section, although in most cases, cylinder head reconditioning procedures described in this chapter will apply.

The section is divided into two sections. The first, Cylinder Head Reconditioning, assumes that the cylinder head is removed from the engine, all manifolds are removed, and the cylinder head is on a workbench. The camshaft should be removed from overhead cam cylinder heads. The second section, Cylinder Block Reconditioning, covers the block, pistons, connecting rods and crankshaft. It is assumed that the engine is mounted on a work stand, and the cylinder head and all accessories are removed.

Procedures are identified as follows:

Unmarked—Basic procedures that must be performed in order to successfully complete the rebuilding process.

Starred (*)—Procedures that should be performed to ensure maximum performance and engine life.

Double starred (**)—Procedures that may be performed to increase engine performance and reliability. These procedures are usually reserved for extremely heavy-duty or competition usage.

In many cases, a choice of methods is also provided. Methods are identified in the same manner as procedures. The choice of method for a procedure is at the discretion of the user.

The tools required for the basic rebuilding procedure should, with minor exceptions, be those

TORQUE (ft. lbs.)*

U.S.

Bolt Diameter (inches)	Bolt Grade (SAE) 1 and 2	5	6	8	Wrench Size (inches) Bolt	Nut
1/4	5	7	10	10.5	3/8	7/16
5/16	9	14	19	22	1/2	9/16
3/8	15	25	34	37	9/16	5/8
7/16	24	40	55	60	5/8	3/4
1/2	37	60	85	92	3/4	13/16
9/16	53	88	120	132	7/8	7/8
5/8	74	120	167	180	15/16	1
3/4	120	200	280	296	1-1/8	1-1/8
7/8	190	302	440	473	1-5/16	1-5/16
1	282	466	660	714	1-1/2	1-1/2

Metric

Bolt Diameter (mm)	Bolt Grade 5D	8G	10K	12K	Wrench Size (mm) Bolt and Nut
6	5	6	8	10	10
8	10	16	22	27	14
10	19	31	40	49	17
12	34	54	70	86	19
14	55	89	117	137	22
16	83	132	175	208	24
18	111	182	236	283	27
22	182	284	394	464	32
24	261	419	570	689	36

*—Torque values are for lightly oiled bolts. CAUTION: Bolts threaded into aluminum require much less torque.

General Torque Specifications

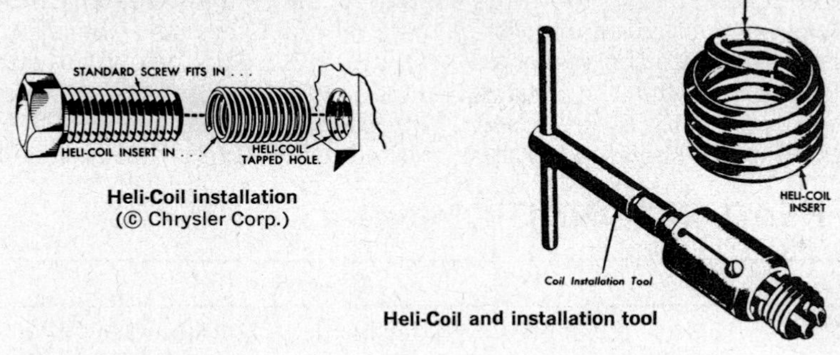

Heli-Coil installation
(© Chrysler Corp.)

Heli-Coil and installation tool

Heli-Coil Insert			*Drill*	*Tap*	*Insert. Tool*	*Extracting Tool*
Thread Size	*Part No.*	*Insert Length (In.)*	*Size*	*Part No.*	*Part No.*	*Part No.*
1/2 -20	1185-4	3/8	17/64(.266)	4 CPB	528-4N	1227-6
5/16-18	1185-5	15/32	Q(.332)	5 CPB	528-5N	1227-6
3/8 -16	1185-6	9/16	X(.397)	6 CPB	528-6N	1227-6
7/16-14	1185-7	21/32	29/64(.453)	7 CPB	528-7N	1227-16
1/2 -13	1185-8	3/4	33/64(.516)	8 CPB	528-8N	1227-16

Heli-Coil Specifications

included in a mechanic's tool kit. An accurate torque wrench, and a dial indicator (reading in thousandths) mounted on a universal base should be available. Bolts and nuts with no torque specification should be tightened according to size (see chart). Special tools, where required, all are readily available from the major tool suppliers (i.e., Craftsman, Snap-On, K-D). The services of a competent automotive machine shop must also be readily available.

When assembling the engine, any parts that will be in frictional contact must be pre-lubricated, to provide protection on initial start-up. Vortex Pre-Lube, STP, or any product specifically formulated for this purpose may be used. NOTE: *Do not use engine oil.* Where semi-permanent (locked but removable) installation of bolts or nuts is desired, threads should be cleaned and coated with Loctite. Studs may be permanently installed using Loctite Stud and Bearing Mount.

Aluminum has become increasingly popular for use in engines, due to its low weight and excellent heat transfer characteristics. The following precautions must be observed when handling aluminum engine parts:

—Never hot-tank aluminum parts.

—Remove all aluminum parts (identification tags, etc.) from engine parts before hot-tanking (otherwise they will be removed during the process).

—Always coat threads lightly with engine oil or anti-seize compounds before installation, to prevent seizure.

—Never over-torque bolts or spark plugs in aluminum threads. Should stripping occur, threads can be restored according to the following procedure, using Heli-Coil thread inserts:

Tap drill the hole with the stripped threads to the specified size (see chart). Using the specified tap (NOTE: *Heli-Coil tap sizes refer to the size thread being replaced, rather than the actual tap size*), tap the hole for the Heli-Coil. Place the insert on the proper installation tool (see chart). Apply pressure on the insert while winding it clockwise into the hole, until the top of the insert is one turn below the surface. Remove the installation tool, and break the installation tang from the bottom of the insert by moving it up and down. If the Heli-Coil must be removed, tap the removal tool firmly into the hole, so that it engages the top thread, and turn the tool counter-clockwise to extract the insert.

Snapped bolts or studs may be removed, using a stud extractor (unthreaded) or Vise-Grip pliers (threaded). Penetrating oil (e.g., Liquid Wrench) will often aid in breaking frozen threads. In cases where the stud or bolt is flush with, or below the surface, proceed as follows:

Drill a hole in the broken stud or bolt, approximately ½ its diameter. Select a screw extractor (e.g., Easy-Out) of the proper size, and tap it into the stud or bolt. Turn the extractor counterclockwise to remove the stud or bolt.

Magnaflux and Zyglo are inspection techniques used to locate material flaws, such as stress cracks. Magnafluxing coats the part with fine magnetic particles, and subjects the part to a magnetic field. Cracks cause breaks in the magnetic field, which are outlined by the particles. Since Magnaflux is a magnetic process, it is applicable only to ferrous materials. The Zyglo process coats the material with a fluorescent dye penetrant, and then subjects it to blacklight inspection, under which cracks glow bright-

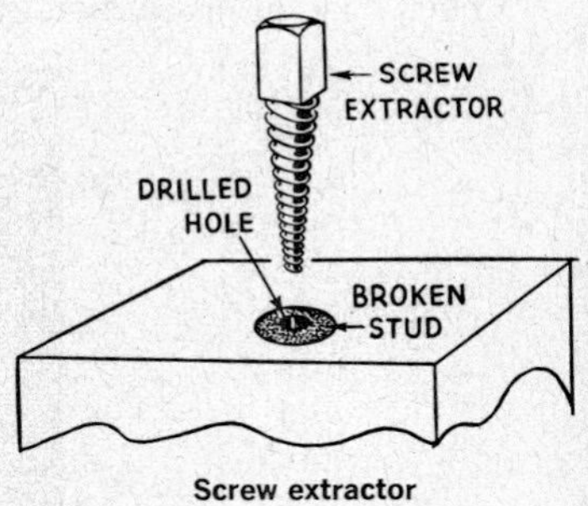

Screw extractor

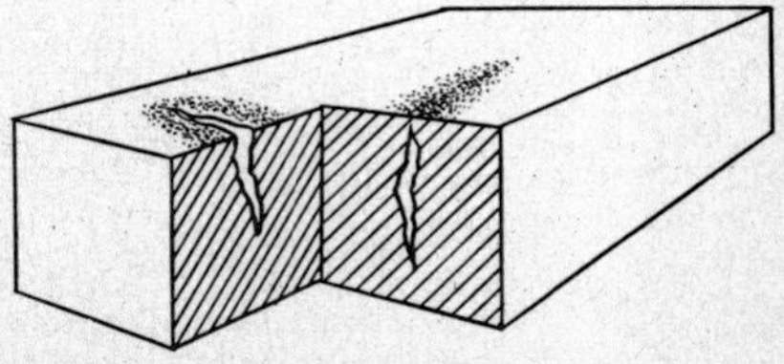
Magnaflux indication of cracks

ly. Parts made of any material may be tested using Zyglo. While Magnaflux and Zyglo are excellent for general inspection, and locating hidden defects, specific checks of suspected cracks may be made at lower cost and more readily using spot check dye. The dye is sprayed onto the suspected area, wiped off, and the area is then sprayed with a developer. Cracks then will show up brightly. Spot check dyes will only indicate surface cracks; therefore, structural cracks below the surface may escape detection. When questionable, the part should be tested using Magnaflux or Zyglo.

CYLINDER HEAD RECONDITIONING

Procedure	*Method*
Identify the valves: 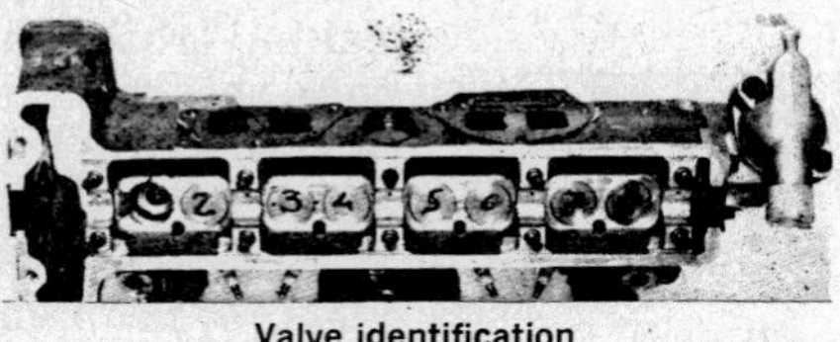 **Valve identification** (© SAAB)	Invert the cylinder head, and number the valve faces front to rear, using a permanent felt-tip marker.
Remove the rocker arms:	Remove the rocker arms with shaft(s) or balls and nuts. Wire the sets of rockers, balls and nuts together, and identify according to the corresponding valve.
Remove the valves and springs:	Using an appropriate valve spring compressor (depending on the configuration of the cylinder head), compress the valve springs. Lift out the keepers with needlenose pliers, release the compressor, and remove the valve, spring, and spring retainer.
Check the valve stem-to-guide clearance:  **Checking the valve stem-to-guide clearance** (© American Motors Corp.)	Clean the valve stem with lacquer thinner or a similar solvent to remove all gum and varnish. Clean the valve guides using solvent and an expanding wire-type valve guide cleaner. Mount a dial indicator so that the stem is at 90° to the valve stem, as close to the valve guide as possible. Move the valve off its seat, and measure the valve guide-to-stem clearance by moving the stem back and forth to actuate the dial indicator. Measure the valve stems using a micrometer, and compare to specifications, to determine whether stem or guide wear is responsible for excessive clearance.
De-carbon the cylinder head and valves: 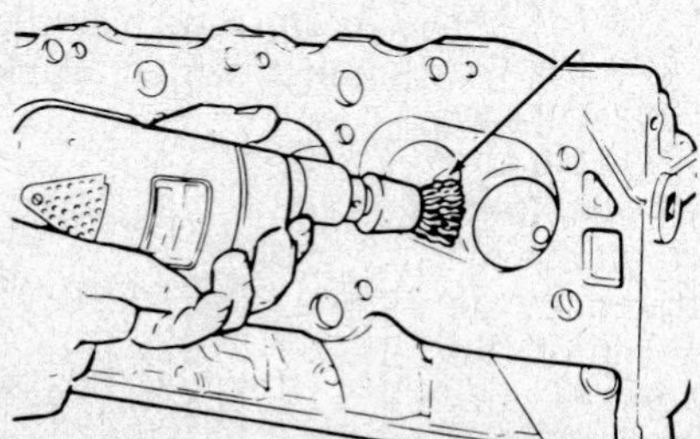 **Removing carbon from the cylinder head** (© Outboard Marine Corp.)	Chip carbon away from the valve heads, combustion chambers, and ports, using a chisel made of hardwood. Remove the remaining deposits with a stiff wire brush. NOTE: *Ensure that the deposits are actually removed, rather than burnished.*

Procedure	*Method*
Hot-tank the cylinder head:	Have the cylinder head hot-tanked to remove grease, corrosion, and scale from the water passages. NOTE: *In the case of overhead cam cylinder heads, consult the operator to determine whether the camshaft bearings will be damaged by the caustic solution.*
Degrease the remaining cylinder head parts:	Using solvent (i.e., Gunk), clean the rockers, rocker shaft(s) (where applicable), rocker balls and nuts, springs, spring retainers, and keepers. Do not remove the protective coating from the springs.
Check the cylinder head for warpage: 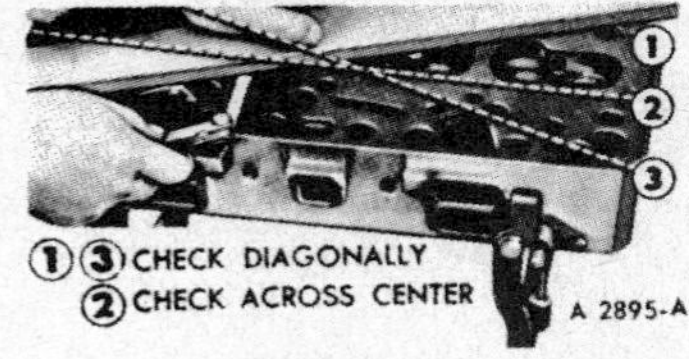 Checking the cylinder head for warpage (© Ford Motor Co.)	Place a straight-edge across the gasket surface of the cylinder head. Using feeler gauges, determine the clearance at the center of the straight-edge. Measure across both diagonals, along the longitudinal centerline, and across the cylinder head at several points. If warpage exceeds .003″ in a 6″ span, or .006″ over the total length, the cylinder head must be resurfaced. NOTE: *If warpage exceeds the manufacturers maximum tolerance for material removal, the cylinder head must be replaced.* When milling the cylinder heads of V-type engines, the intake manifold mounting position is altered, and must be corrected by milling the manifold flange a proportionate amount.
** Porting and gasket matching:  Marking the cylinder head for gasket matching (© Petersen Publishing Co.)  Port configuration before and after gasket matching (© Petersen Publishing Co.)	** Coat the manifold flanges of the cylinder head with Prussian blue dye. Glue intake and exhaust gaskets to the cylinder head in their installed position using rubber cement and scribe the outline of the ports on the manifold flanges. Remove the gaskets. Using a small cutter in a hand-held power tool (i.e., Dremel Moto-Tool), gradually taper the walls of the port out to the scribed outline of the gasket. Further enlargement of the ports should include the removal of sharp edges and radiusing of sharp corners. Do not alter the valve guides. NOTE: *The most efficient port configuration is determined only by extensive testing. Therefore, it is best to consult someone experienced with the head in question to determine the optimum alterations.*

Procedure	Method
** Polish the ports:	** Using a grinding stone with the above mentioned tool, polish the walls of the intake and exhaust ports, and combustion chamber. Use progressively finer stones until all surface imperfections are removed. NOTE: *Through testing, it has been determined that a smooth surface is more effective than a mirror polished surface in intake ports, and vice-versa in exhaust ports.*

Relieved and polished ports
(© Petersen Publishing Co.)

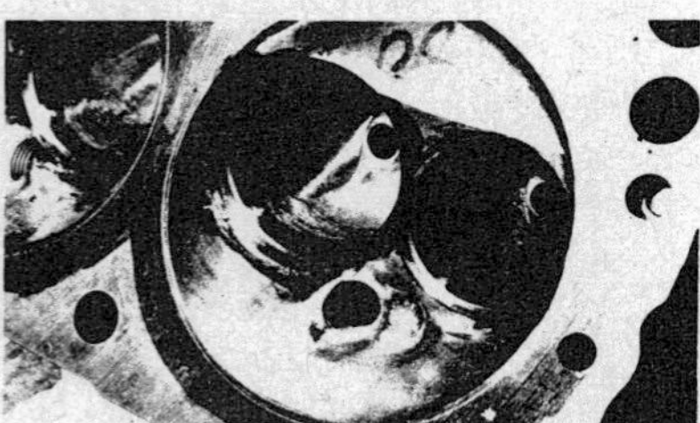

Polished combustion chamber
(© Petersen Publishing Co.)

Procedure	Method
* Knurling the valve guides:	* Valve guides which are not excessively worn or distorted may, in some cases, be knurled rather than replaced. Knurling is a process in which metal is displaced and raised, thereby reducing clearance. Knurling also provides excellent oil control. The possibility of knurling rather than replacing valve guides should be discussed with a machinist.

Cut-away view of a knurled valve guide
(© Petersen Publishing Co.)

Procedure	Method
Replacing the valve guides: NOTE: *Valve guides should only be replaced if damaged or if an oversize valve stem is not available.*	Depending on the type of cylinder head, valve guides may be pressed, hammered, or shrunk in. In cases where the guides are shrunk into the head, replacement should be left to an equipped machine shop. In other cases, the guides are replaced as follows: Press or tap the valve guides out of the head using a stepped drift (see illustration). Determine the height above the boss that the guide must extend, and obtain a stack of washers, their I.D. similar to the guide's O.D., of that height. Place the stack of washers on the guide, and insert the guide into the boss. NOTE: *Valve guides are often tapered or beveled for installation.* Using the stepped installation tool (see illustration), press or tap the guides into position. Ream the guides according to the size of the valve stem.

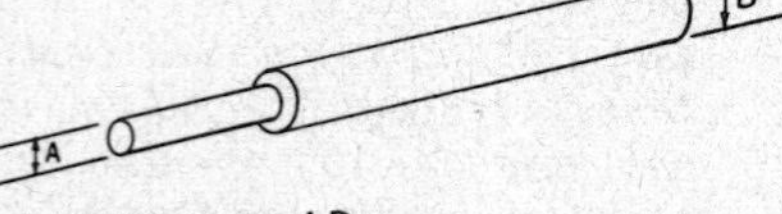

Valve guide removal tool

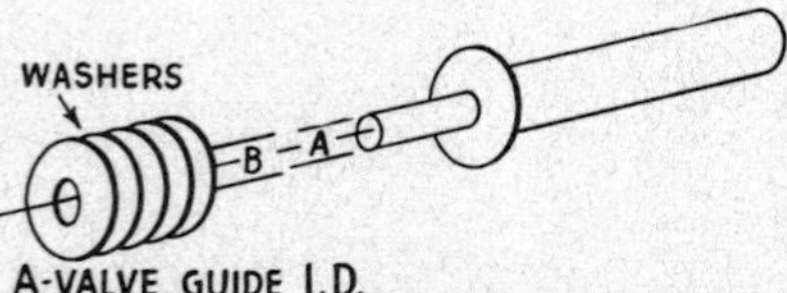

Valve guide installation tool (with washers used during installation)

Procedure	*Method*
Replacing valve seat inserts:	Replacement of valve seat inserts which are worn beyond resurfacing or broken, if feasible, must be done by a machine shop.

Resurfacing (grinding) the valve face:

Grinding a valve
(© Subaru)

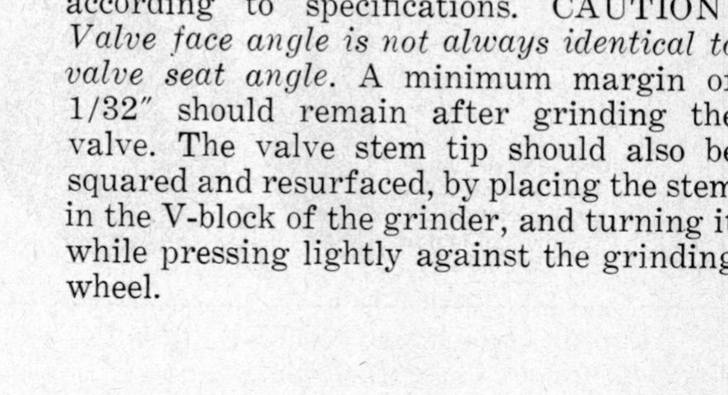

Using a valve grinder, resurface the valves according to specifications. CAUTION: *Valve face angle is not always identical to valve seat angle.* A minimum margin of 1/32" should remain after grinding the valve. The valve stem tip should also be squared and resurfaced, by placing the stem in the V-block of the grinder, and turning it while pressing lightly against the grinding wheel.

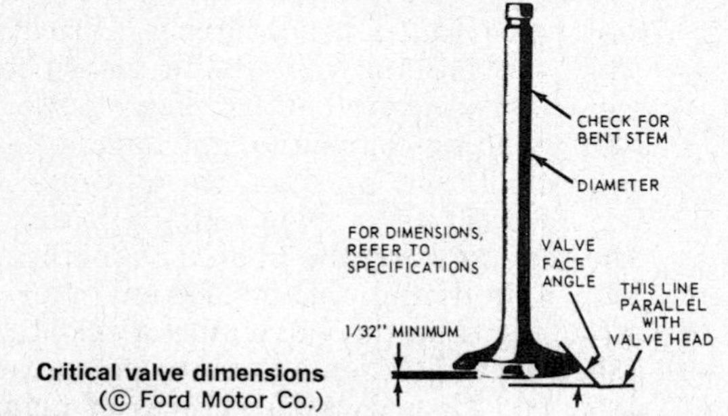

Critical valve dimensions
(© Ford Motor Co.)

Resurfacing the valve seats using reamers:

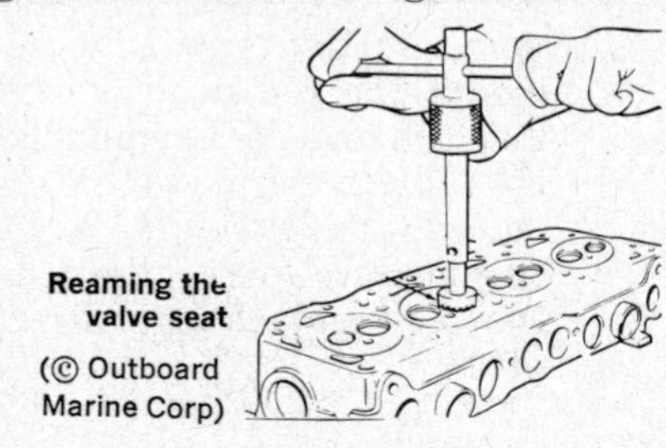

Reaming the valve seat
(© Outboard Marine Corp)

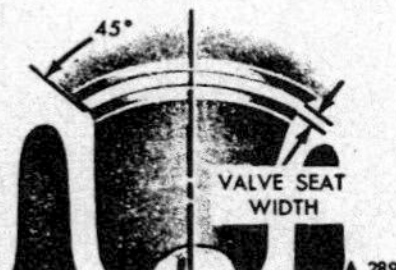

Valve seat width and centering
(© Ford Motor Co.)

Select a reamer of the correct seat angle, slightly larger than the diameter of the valve seat, and assemble it with a pilot of the correct size. Install the pilot into the valve guide, and using steady pressure, turn the reamer clockwise. CAUTION: *Do not turn the reamer counter-clockwise.* Remove only as much material as necessary to clean the seat. Check the concentricity of the seat (see below). If the dye method is not used, coat the valve face with Prussian blue dye, install and rotate it on the valve seat. Using the dye marked area as a centering guide, center and narrow the valve seat to specifications with correction cutters. NOTE: *When no specifications are available, minimum seat width for exhaust valves should be 5/64", intake valves 1/16".* After making correction cuts, check the position of the valve seat on the valve face using Prussian blue dye.

* Resurfacing the valve seats using a grinder:

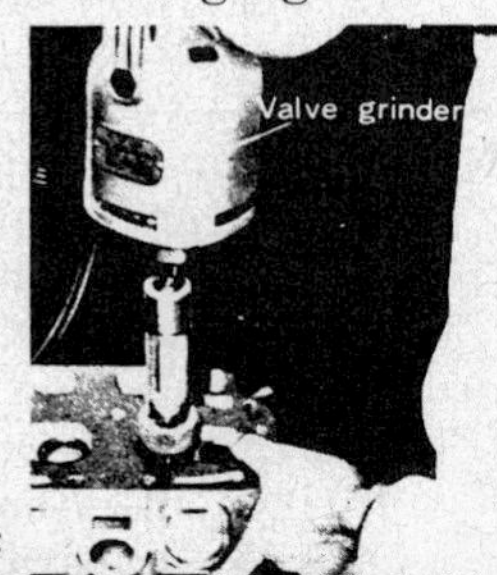

Grinding a valve seat
(© Subaru)

Select a pilot of the correct size, and a coarse stone of the correct seat angle. Lubricate the pilot if necessary, and install the tool in the valve guide. Move the stone on and off the seat at approximately two cycles per second, until all flaws are removed from the seat. Install a fine stone, and finish the seat. Center and narrow the seat using correction stones, as described above.

Procedure	*Method*
Checking the valve seat concentricity: 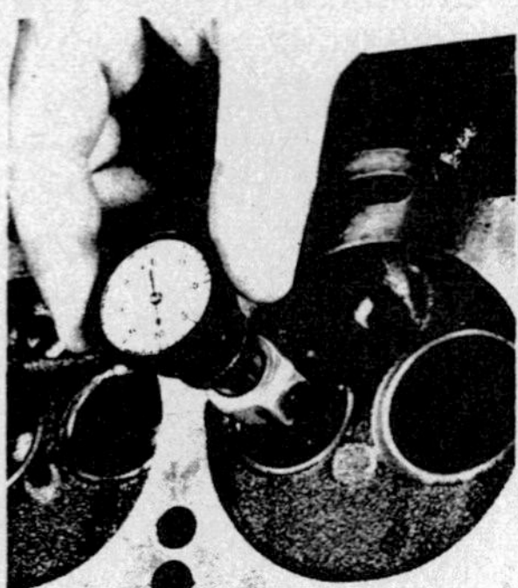 Checking the valve seat concentricity using a dial gauge (© American Motors Corp.)	Coat the valve face with Prussian blue dye, install the valve, and rotate it on the valve seat. If the entire seat becomes coated, and the valve is known to be concentric, the seat is concentric.
	* Install the dial gauge pilot into the guide, and rest the arm on the valve seat. Zero the gauge, and rotate the arm around the seat. Run-out should not exceed .002″.
* Lapping the valves: NOTE: *Valve lapping is done to ensure efficient sealing of resurfaced valves and seats. Valve lapping alone is not recommended for use as a resurfacing procedure.* 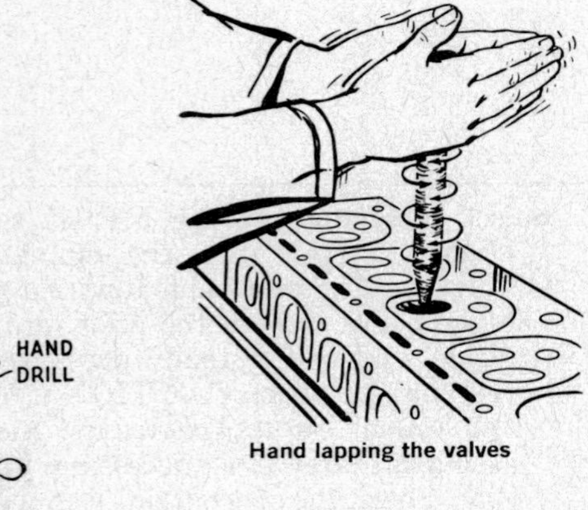 Hand lapping the valves Home made mechanical valve lapping tool	* Invert the cylinder head, lightly lubricate the valve stems, and install the valves in the head as numbered. Coat valve seats with fine grinding compound, and attach the lapping tool suction cup to a valve head (NOTE: *Moisten the suction cup*). Rotate the tool between the palms, changing position and lifting the tool often to prevent grooving. Lap the valve until a smooth, polished seat is evident. Remove the valve and tool, and rinse away all traces of grinding compound.
	** Fasten a suction cup to a piece of drill rod, and mount the rod in a hand drill. Proceed as above, using the hand drill as a lapping tool. CAUTION: *Due to the higher speeds involved when using the hand drill, care must be exercised to avoid grooving the seat.* Lift the tool and change direction of rotation often.
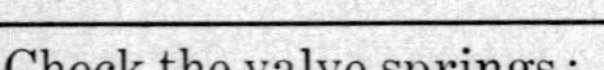 Check the valve springs: 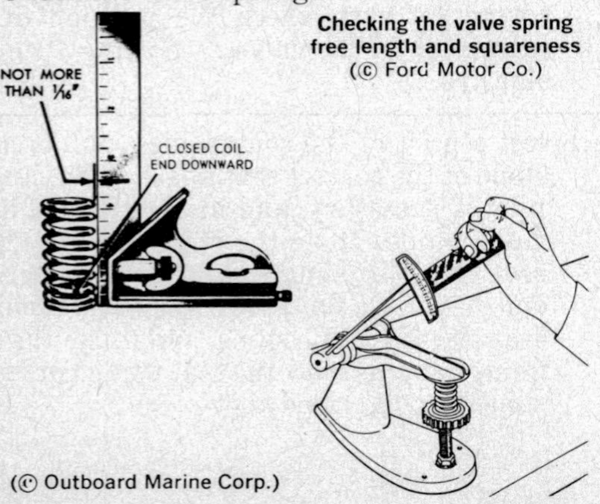 Checking the valve spring free length and squareness (© Ford Motor Co.) (© Outboard Marine Corp.)	Place the spring on a flat surface next to a square. Measure the height of the spring, and rotate it against the edge of the square to measure distortion. If spring height varies (by comparison) by more than 1/16″ or if distortion exceeds 1/16″, replace the spring.
	** In addition to evaluating the spring as above, test the spring pressure at the installed and compressed (installed height minus valve lift) height using a valve spring tester. Springs used on small displacement engines (up to 3 liters) should be ± 1 lb. of all other springs in either position. A tolerance of ± 5 lbs. is permissible on larger engines.

Procedure	*Method*
* Install valve stem seals: 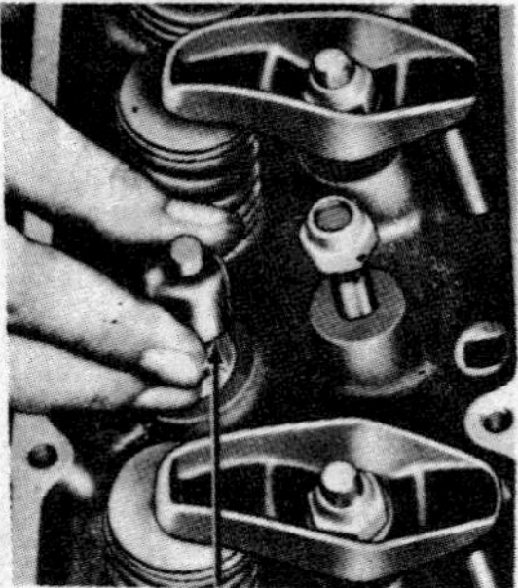 Valve stem seal installation (© Ford Motor Co.)	* Due to the pressure differential that exists at the ends of the intake valve guides (atmospheric pressure above, manifold vacuum below), oil is drawn through the valve guides into the intake port. This has been alleviated somewhat since the addition of positive crankcase ventilation, which lowers the pressure above the guides. Several types of valve stem seals are available to reduce blow-by. Certain seals simply slip over the stem and guide boss, while others require that the boss be machined. Recently, Teflon guide seals have become popular. Consult a parts supplier or machinist concerning availability and suggested usages. NOTE: *When installing seals, ensure that a small amount of oil is able to pass the seal to lubricate the valve guides; otherwise, excessive wear may result.*
Install the valves:	Lubricate the valve stems, and install the valves in the cylinder head as numbered. Lubricate and position the seals (if used, see above) and the valve springs. Install the spring retainers, compress the springs, and insert the keys using needlenose pliers or a tool designed for this purpose. NOTE: *Retain the keys with wheel bearing grease during installation.*
Checking valve spring installed height: 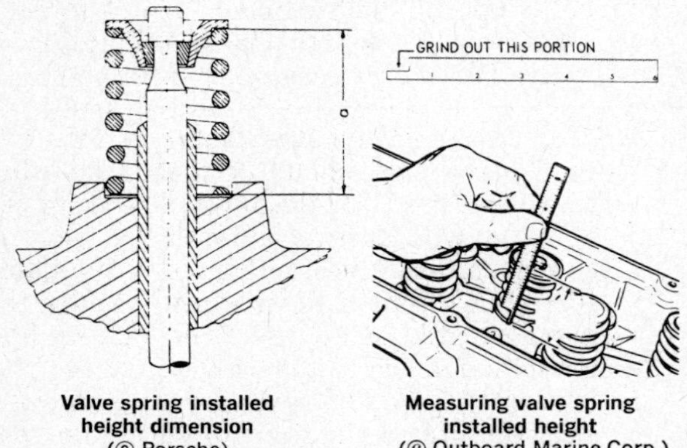 Valve spring installed height dimension (© Porsche) Measuring valve spring installed height (© Outboard Marine Corp.)	Measure the distance between the spring pad and the lower edge of the spring retainer, and compare to specifications. If the installed height is incorrect, add shim washers between the spring pad and the spring. CAUTION: *Use only washers designed for this purpose.*
** CC'ing the combustion chambers:	** Invert the cylinder head and place a bead of sealer around a combustion chamber. Install an apparatus designed for this purpose (burette mounted on a clear plate; see illustration) over the combustion chamber, and fill with the specified fluid to an even mark on the burette. Record the burette reading, and fill the combustion chamber with fluid. (NOTE: *A hole drilled in the plate will permit air to escape*). Subtract the burette reading, with the combustion chamber filled, from the previous reading, to determine combustion chamber volume in cc's. Duplicate this procedure in all combustion

Procedure | *Method*

CC'ing the combustion chamber (© Petersen Publishing Co.)

chambers on the cylinder head, and compare the readings. The volume of all combustion chambers should be made equal to that of the largest. Combustion chamber volume may be increased in two ways. When only a small change is required (usually), a small cutter or coarse stone may be used to remove material from the combustion chamber. NOTE: *Check volume frequently.* Remove material over a wide area, so as not to change the configuration of the combustion chamber. When a larger change is required, the valve seat may be sunk (lowered into the head). NOTE: *When altering valve seat, remember to compensate for the change in spring installed height.*

Inspect the rocker arms, balls, studs, and nuts (where applicable):

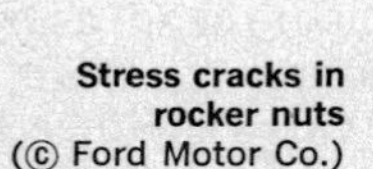

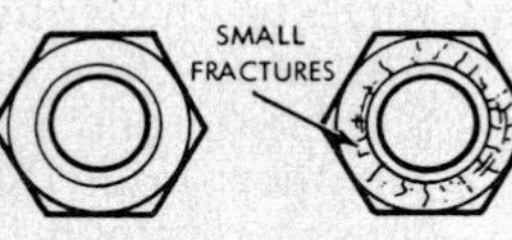

Stress cracks in rocker nuts (© Ford Motor Co.)

Visually inspect the rocker arms, balls, studs, and nuts for cracks, galling, burning, scoring, or wear. If all parts are intact, liberally lubricate the rocker arms and balls, and install them on the cylinder head. If wear is noted on a rocker arm at the point of valve contact, grind it smooth and square, removing as little material as possible. Replace the rocker arm if excessively worn. If a rocker stud shows signs of wear, it must be replaced (see below). If a rocker nut shows stress cracks, replace it. If an exhaust ball is galled or burned, substitute the intake ball from the same cylinder (if it is intact), and install a new intake ball. NOTE: *Avoid using new rocker balls on exhaust valves.*

Replacing rocker studs:

Reaming the stud bore for oversize rocker studs (© Buick Div. G.M. Corp.)

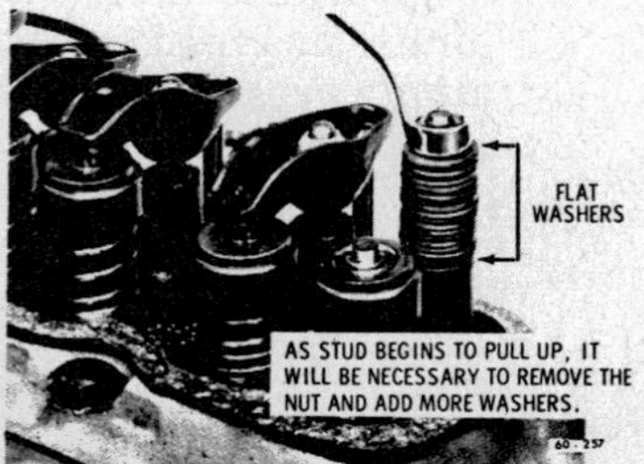

Extracting a pressed in rocker stud (© Buick Div. G.M. Corp.)

In order to remove a threaded stud, lock two nuts on the stud, and unscrew the stud using the lower nut. Coat the lower threads of the new stud with Loctite, and install.

Two alternative methods are available for replacing pressed in studs. Remove the damaged stud using a stack of washers and a nut (see illustration). In the first, the boss is reamed .005-.006″ oversize, and an oversize stud pressed in. Control the stud extension over the boss using washers, in the same manner as valve guides. Before installing the stud, coat it with white lead and grease. To retain the stud more positively, drill a hole through the stud and boss, and install a roll pin. In the second method, the boss is tapped, and a threaded stud installed. Retain the stud using Loctite Stud and Bearing Mount.

Procedure	*Method*

Inspect the rocker shaft(s) and rocker arms (where applicable):

Disassembled rocker shaft parts arranged for inspection
(© American Motors Corp.)

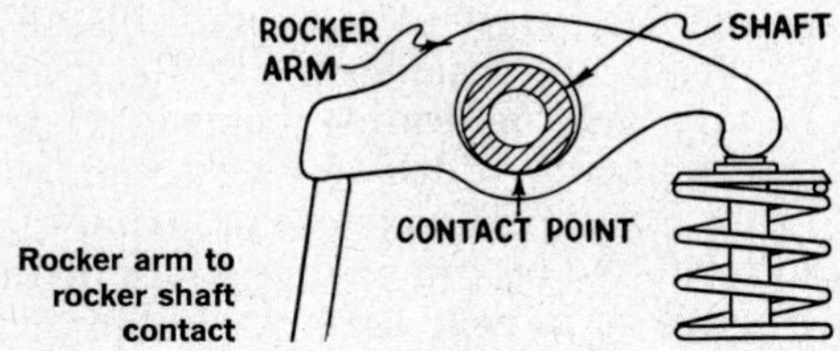

Rocker arm to rocker shaft contact

Remove rocker arms, springs and washers from rocker shaft. NOTE: *Lay out parts in the order they are removed.* Inspect rocker arms for pitting or wear on the valve contact point, or excessive bushing wear. Bushings need only be replaced if wear is excessive, because the rocker arm normally contacts the shaft at one point only. Grind the valve contact point of rocker arm smooth if necessary, removing as little material as possible. If excessive material must be removed to smooth and square the arm, it should be replaced. Clean out all oil holes and passages in rocker shaft. If shaft is grooved or worn, replace it. Lubricate and assemble the rocker shaft.

Inspect the camshaft bushings and the camshaft (overhead cam engines):

See next section.

Inspect the pushrods:

Remove the pushrods, and, if hollow, clean out the oil passages using fine wire. Roll each pushrod over a piece of clean glass. If a distinct clicking sound is heard as the pushrod rolls, the rod is bent, and must be replaced.

* The length of all pushrods must be equal. Measure the length of the pushrods, compare to specifications, and replace as necessary.

Inspect the valve lifters:

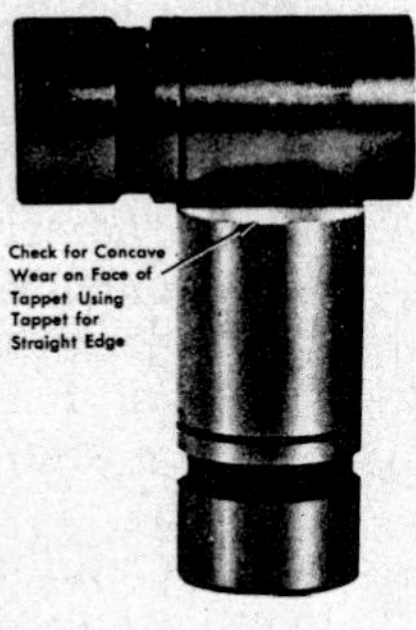

Checking the lifter face
(© American Motors Corp.)

Remove lifters from their bores, and remove gum and varnish, using solvent. Clean walls of lifter bores. Check lifters for concave wear as illustrated. If face is worn concave, replace lifter, and carefully inspect the camshaft. Lightly lubricate lifter and insert it into its bore. If play is excessive, an oversize lifter must be installed (where possible). Consult a machinist concerning feasibility. If play is satisfactory, remove, lubricate, and reinstall the lifter.

---

* Testing hydraulic lifter leak down:

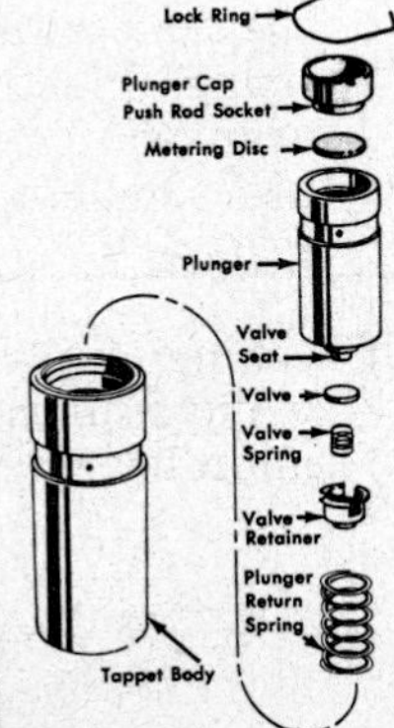

Exploded view of a typical hydraulic lifter
(© American Motors Corp.)

Submerge lifter in a container of kerosene. Chuck a used pushrod or its equivalent into a drill press. Position container of kerosene so pushrod acts on the lifter plunger. Pump lifter with the drill press, until resistance increases. Pump several more times to bleed any air out of lifter. Apply very firm, constant pressure to the lifter, and observe rate at which fluid bleeds out of lifter. If the fluid bleeds very quickly (less than 15 seconds), lifter is defective. If the time exceeds 60 seconds, lifter is sticking. In either case, recondition or replace lifter. If lifter is operating properly (leak down time 15-60 seconds), lubricate and install it.

CYLINDER BLOCK RECONDITIONING

Procedure	*Method*

Checking the main bearing clearance:

Plastigage installed on main bearing journal
(© Chevrolet Div. G.M. Corp.)

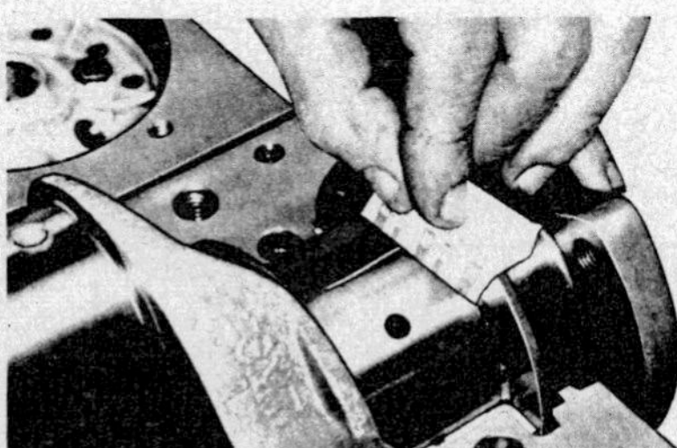

Measuring Plastigage to determine main bearing clearance
(© Chevrolet Div. G.M. Corp.)

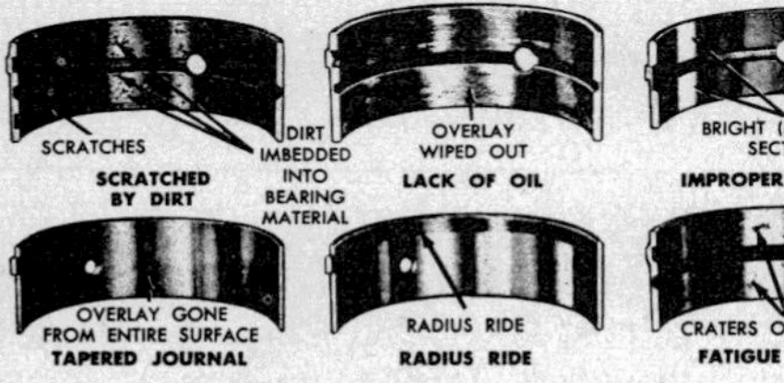

Causes of bearing failure
(© Ford Motor Co.)

Invert engine, and remove cap from the bearing to be checked. Using a clean, dry rag, thoroughly clean all oil from crankshaft journal and bearing insert. NOTE: *Plastigage is soluble in oil; therefore, oil on the journal or bearing could result in erroneous readings.* Place a piece of Plastigage along the full length of journal, reinstall cap, and torque to specifications. Remove bearing cap, and determine bearing clearance by comparing width of Plastigage to the scale on Plastigage envelope. Journal taper is determined by comparing width of the Plastigage strip near its ends. Rotate crankshaft 90° and retest, to determine journal eccentricity. NOTE: *Do not rotate crankshaft with Plastigage installed.* If bearing insert and journal appear intact, and are within tolerances, no further main bearing service is required. If bearing or journal appear defective, cause of failure should be determined before replacement.

* Remove crankshaft from block (see below). Measure the main bearing journals at each end twice (90° apart) using a micrometer, to determine diameter, journal taper and eccentricity. If journals are within tolerances, reinstall bearing caps at their specified torque. Using a telescope gauge and micrometer, measure bearing I.D. parallel to piston axis and at 30° on each side of piston axis. Subtract journal O.D. from bearing I.D. to determine oil clearance. If crankshaft journals appear defective, or do not meet tolerances, there is no need to measure bearings; for the crankshaft will require grinding and/or undersize bearings will be required. If bearing appears defective, cause for failure should be determined prior to replacement.

Checking the connecting rod bearing clearance:

Plastigage installed on connecting rod bearing journal
(© Chevrolet Div. G.M. Corp.)

Connecting rod bearing clearance is checked in the same manner as main bearing clearance, using Plastigage. Before removing the crankshaft, connecting rod side clearance also should be measured and recorded.

* Checking connecting rod bearing clearance, using a micrometer, is identical to checking main bearing clearance. If no other service

Procedure	*Method*
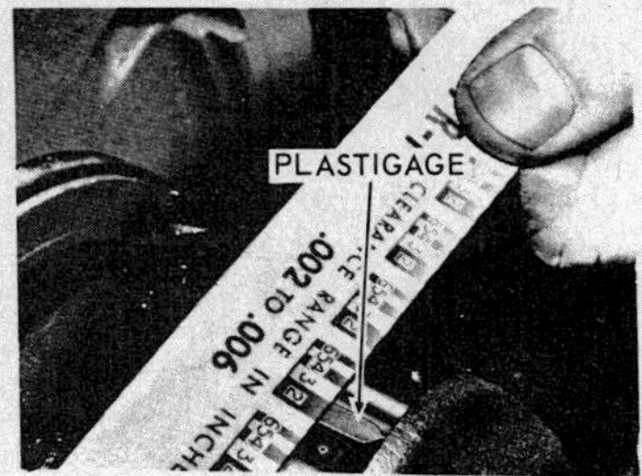 **Measuring Plastigage to determine connecting rod bearing clearance** (© Outboard Marine Corp.)	is required, the piston and rod assemblies need not be removed.
Removing the crankshaft:  **Connecting rod matching marks** (© Ford Motor Co.)	Using a punch, mark the corresponding main bearing caps and saddles according to position (i.e., one punch on the front main cap and saddle, two on the second, three on the third, etc.). Using number stamps, identify the corresponding connecting rods and caps, according to cylinder (if no numbers are present). Remove the main and connecting rod caps, and place sleeves of plastic tubing over the connecting rod bolts, to protect the journals as the crankshaft is removed. Lift the crankshaft out of the block.
Remove the ridge from the top of the cylinder: 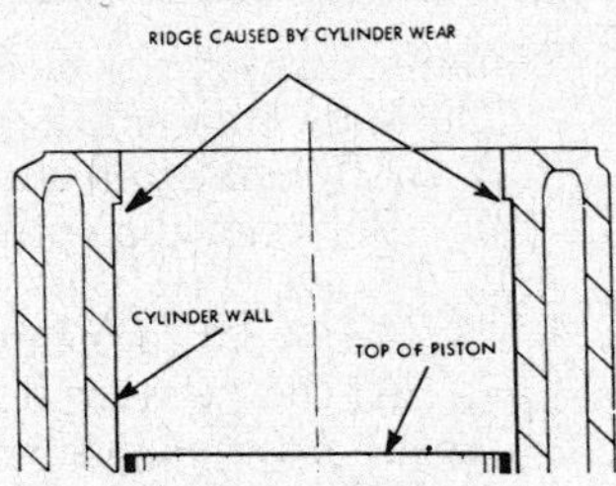 **Cylinder bore ridge** (© Pontiac Div. G.M. Corp.)	In order to facilitate removal of the piston and connecting rod, the ridge at the top of the cylinder (unworn area; see illustration) must be removed. Place the piston at the bottom of the bore, and cover it with a rag. Cut the ridge away using a ridge reamer, exercising extreme care to avoid cutting too deeply. Remove the rag, and remove cuttings that remain on the piston. CAUTION: *If the ridge is not removed, and new rings are installed, damage to rings will result.*
Removing the piston and connecting rod:  **Removing the piston** (© SAAB)	Invert the engine, and push the pistons and connecting rods out of the cylinders. If necessary, tap the connecting rod boss with a wooden hammer handle, to force the piston out. CAUTION: *Do not attempt to force the piston past the cylinder ridge* (see above).

Procedure	*Method*
Service the crankshaft:	Ensure that all oil holes and passages in the crankshaft are open and free of sludge. If necessary, have the crankshaft ground to the largest possible undersize.
	** Have the crankshaft Magnafluxed, to locate stress cracks. Consult a machinist concerning additional service procedures, such as surface hardening (e.g., nitriding, Tuftriding) to improve wear characteristics, cross drilling and chamfering the oil holes to improve lubrication, and balancing.
Removing freeze plugs:	Drill a hole in the center of the freeze plugs, and pry them out using a screwdriver or drift.
Remove the oil gallery plugs:	Threaded plugs should be removed using an appropriate (usually square) wrench. To remove soft, pressed in plugs, drill a hole in the plug, and thread in a sheet metal screw. Pull the plug out by the screw using pliers.
Hot-tank the block:	Have the block hot-tanked to remove grease, corrosion, and scale from the water jackets. NOTE: *Consult the operator to determine whether the camshaft bearings will be damaged during the hot-tank process.*
Check the block for cracks:	Visually inspect the block for cracks or chips. The most common locations are as follows: Adjacent to freeze plugs. Between the cylinders and water jackets. Adjacent to the main bearing saddles. At the extreme bottom of the cylinders. Check only suspected cracks using spot check dye (see introduction). If a crack is located, consult a machinist concerning possible repairs.
	** Magnaflux the block to locate hidden cracks. If cracks are located, consult a machinist about feasibility of repair.
Install the oil gallery plugs and freeze plugs:	Coat freeze plugs with sealer and tap into position using a piece of pipe, slightly smaller than the plug, as a driver. To ensure retention, stake the edges of the plugs. Coat threaded oil gallery plugs with sealer and install. Drive replacement soft plugs into block using a large drift as a driver.
	* Rather than reinstalling lead plugs, drill and tap the holes, and install threaded plugs.

Procedure	*Method*
Check the bore diameter and surface:	Visually inspect the cylinder bores for roughness, scoring, or scuffing. If evident, the cylinder bore must be bored or honed oversize to eliminate imperfections, and the smallest possible oversize piston used. The new pistons should be given to the machinist with the block, so that the cylinders can be bored or honed exactly to the piston size (plus clearance). If no flaws are evident, measure the bore diameter using a telescope gauge and micrometer, or dial gauge, parallel and perpendicular to the engine centerline, at the top (below the ridge) and bottom of the bore. Subtract the bottom measurements from the top to determine taper, and the parallel to the centerline measurements from the perpendicular measurements to determine eccentricity. If the measurements are not within specifications, the cylinder must be bored or honed, and an oversize piston installed. If the measurements are within specifications the cylinder may be used as is, with only finish honing (see below). NOTE: *Prior to submitting the block for boring, perform the following operation(s).*

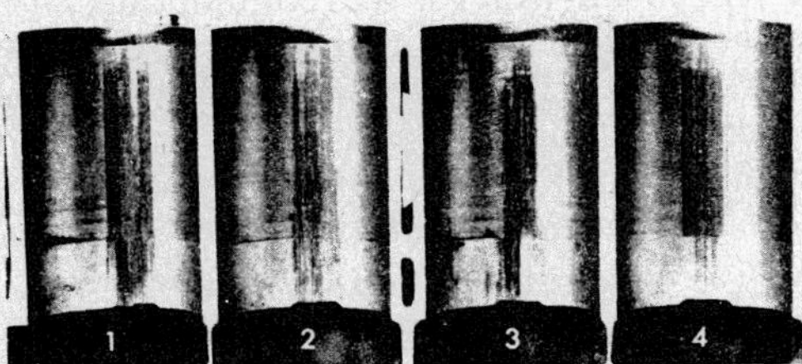

1, 2, 3 Piston skirt seizure resulted in this pattern. Engine must be rebored

4. Piston skirt and oil ring seizure caused this damage. Engine must be rebored

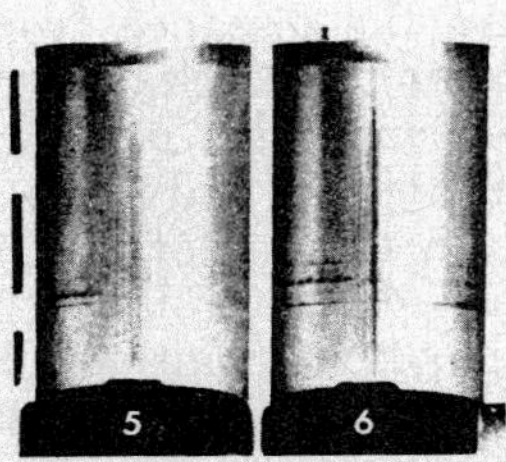

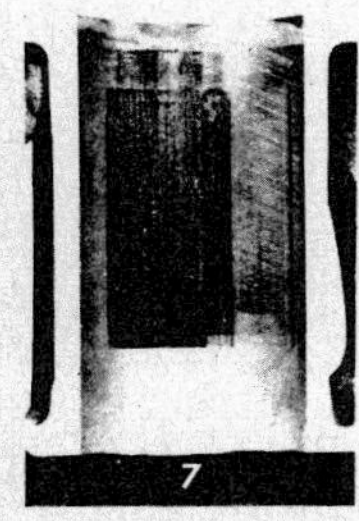

5, 6 Score marks caused by a split piston skirt. Damage is not serious enough to warrant reboring

7. Ring seized longitudinally, causing a score mark 1 3/16" wide, on the land side of the piston groove. The honing pattern is destroyed and the cylinder must be rebored

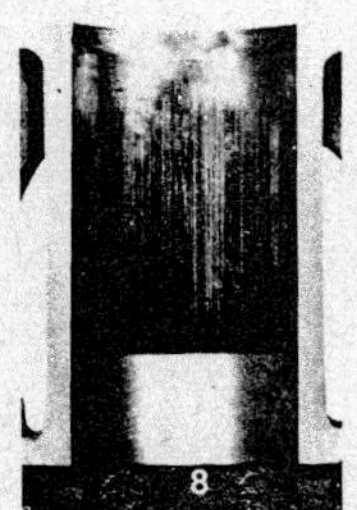

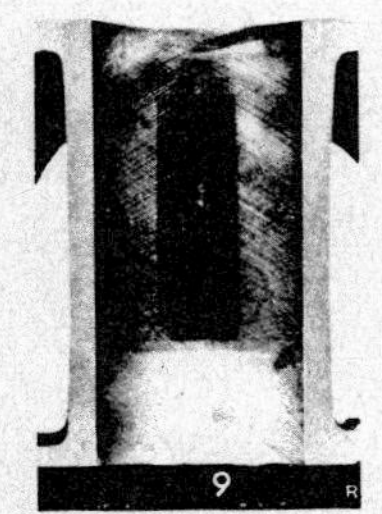

8. Result of oil ring seizure. Engine must be rebored

9. Oil ring seizure here was not serious enough to warrant reboring. The honing marks are still visible

Cylinder wall damage
(© Daimler-Benz A.G.)

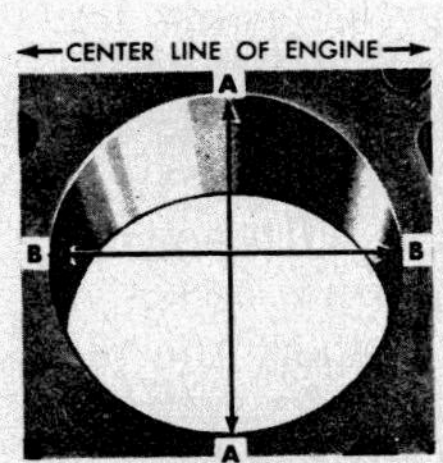

Cylinder bore measuring positions
(© Ford Motor Co.)

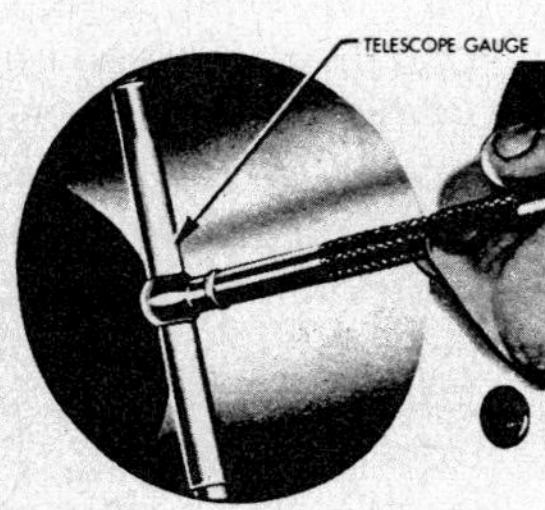

Measuring the cylinder bore with a telescope gauge
(© Buick Div. G.M. Corp.)

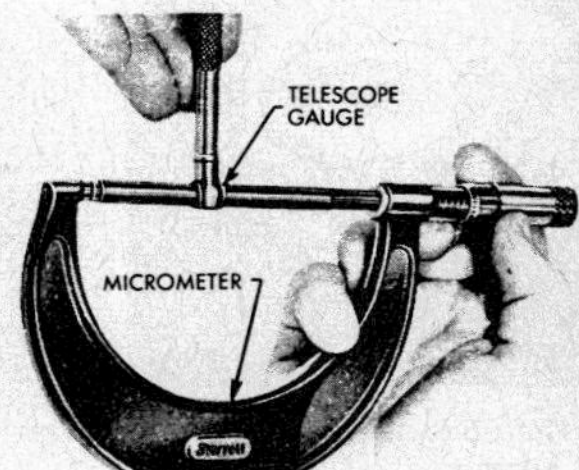

Determining the cylinder bore by measuring the telescope gauge with a micrometer
(© Buick Div. G.M. Corp.)

Measuring the cylinder bore with a dial gauge
(© Chevrolet Div. G.M. Corp.)

Procedure	*Method*
Check the block deck for warpage:	Using a straightedge and feeler gauges, check the block deck for warpage in the same manner that the cylinder head is checked (see Cylinder Head Reconditioning). If warpage exceeds specifications, have the deck resurfaced. NOTE: *In certain cases a specification for total material removal (Cylinder head and block deck) is provided. This specification must not be exceeded.*
* Check the deck height:	The deck height is the distance from the crankshaft centerline to the block deck. To measure, invert the engine, and install the crankshaft, retaining it with the center main cap. Measure the distance from the crankshaft journal to the block deck, parallel to the cylinder centerline. Measure the diameter of the end (front and rear) main journals, parallel to the centerline of the cylinders, divide the diameter in half, and subtract it from the previous measurement. The results of the front and rear measurements should be identical. If the difference exceeds .005″, the deck height should be corrected. NOTE: *Block deck height and warpage should be corrected concurrently.*
Check the cylinder block bearing alignment:  Checking main bearing saddle alignment (© Petersen Publishing Co.)	Remove the upper bearing inserts. Place a straightedge in the bearing saddles along the centerline of the crankshaft. If clearance exists between the straightedge and the center saddle, the block must be alignbored.
Clean and inspect the pistons and connecting rods: 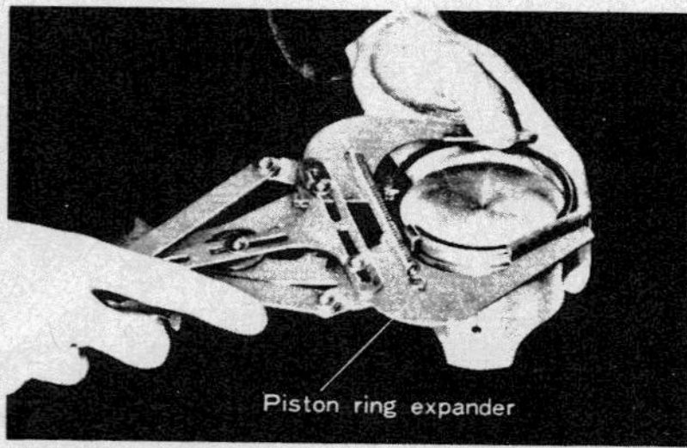 Removing the piston rings (© Subaru)	Using a ring expander, remove the rings from the piston. Remove the retaining rings (if so equipped) and remove piston pin. NOTE: *If the piston pin must be pressed out, determine the proper method and use the proper tools; otherwise the piston will distort.* Clean the ring grooves using an appropriate tool, exercising care to avoid cutting too deeply. Thoroughly clean all carbon and varnish from the piston with solvent. CAUTION: *Do not use a wire brush or caustic solvent on pistons.* Inspect the pistons for scuffing, scoring, cracks, pitting, or excessive ring groove wear. If wear is evident, the piston must be replaced. Check the connecting rod length by measuring the rod from the inside of the large end to the inside of the small end using calipers (see

Procedure	Method

Cleaning the piston ring grooves
(© Ford Motor Co.)

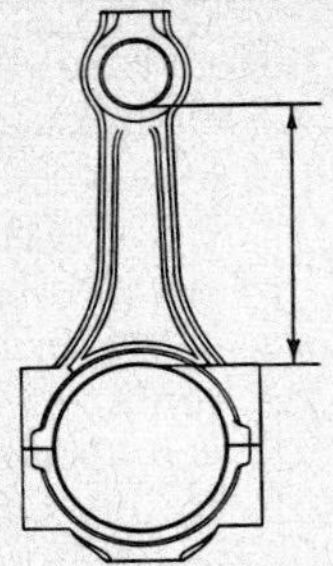
Connecting rod length checking dimension

illustration). All connecting rods should be equal length. Replace any rod that differs from the others in the engine.

* Have the connecting rod alignment checked in an alignment fixture by a machinist. Replace any twisted or bent rods.

* Magnaflux the connecting rods to locate stress cracks. If cracks are found, replace the connecting rod.

Fit the pistons to the cylinders:

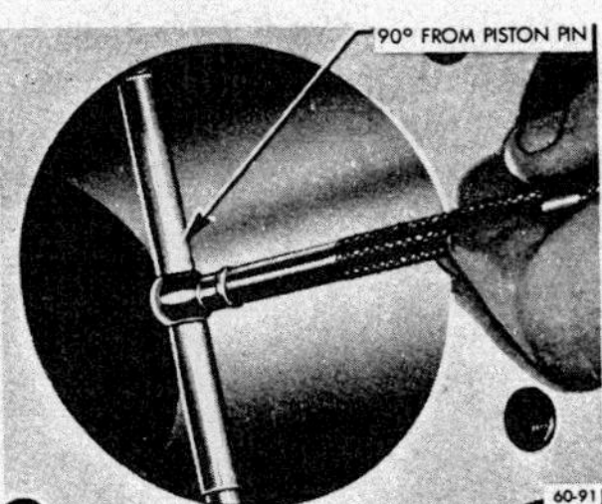

Measuring the cylinder with a telescope gauge for piston fitting
(© Buick Div. G.M. Corp.)

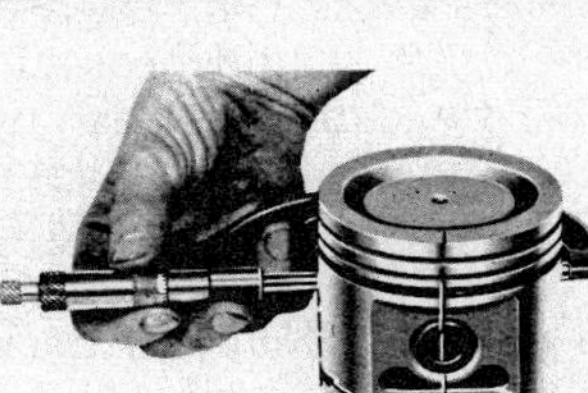

Measuring the piston for fitting
(© Buick Div. G.M. Corp.)

Using a telescope gauge and micrometer, or a dial gauge, measure the cylinder bore diameter perpendicular to the piston pin, 2½″ below the deck. Measure the piston perpendicular to its pin on the skirt. The difference between the two measurements is the piston clearance. If the clearance is within specifications or slightly below (after boring or honing), finish honing is all that is required. If the clearance is excessive, try to obtain a slightly larger piston to bring clearance within specifications. Where this is not possible, obtain the first oversize piston, and hone (or if necessary, bore) the cylinder to size.

Assemble the pistons and connecting rods:

Installing piston pin lock rings
(© Nissan Motor Co., Ltd.)

Inspect piston pin, connecting rod small end bushing, and piston bore for galling, scoring, or excessive wear. If evident, replace defective part(s). Measure the I.D. of the piston boss and connecting rod small end, and the O.D. of the piston pin. If within specifications, assemble piston pin and rod. CAUTION: *If piston pin must be pressed in, determine the proper method and use the proper tools; otherwise the piston will distort.* Install the lock rings; ensure that they seat properly. If the parts are not within specifications, determine the service method for the type of engine. In some cases, piston and pin are serviced as an assembly when either is defective. Others specify reaming the piston and connecting rods for an oversize pin. If the connecting rod bushing is worn, it may in many cases be replaced. Reaming the piston and replacing the rod bushing are machine shop operations.

Procedure	*Method*
Clean and inspect the camshaft: 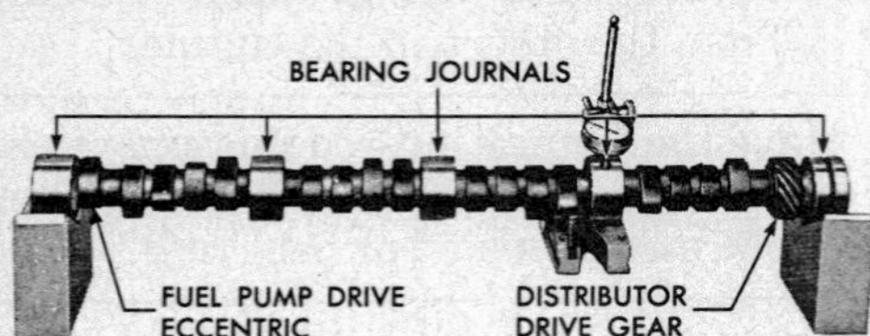 **Checking the camshaft for straightness** (© Chevrolet Motor Div. G.M. Corp.)	Degrease the camshaft, using solvent, and clean out all oil holes. Visually inspect cam lobes and bearing journals for excessive wear. If a lobe is questionable, check all lobes as indicated below. If a journal or lobe is worn, the camshaft must be reground or replaced. NOTE: *If a journal is worn, there is a good chance that the bushings are worn.* If lobes and journals appear intact, place the front and rear journals in V-blocks, and rest a dial indicator on the center journal. Rotate the camshaft to check straightness. If deviation exceeds .001″, replace the camshaft.
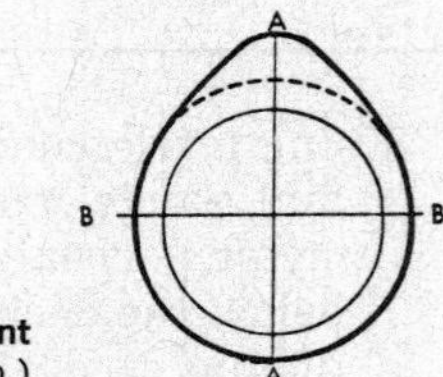 **Camshaft lobe measurement** (© Ford Motor Co.)	* Check the camshaft lobes with a micrometer, by measuring the lobes from the nose to base and again at 90° (see illustration). The lift is determined by subtracting the second measurement from the first. If all exhaust lobes and all intake lobes are not identical, the camshaft must be reground or replaced.
Replace the camshaft bearings: 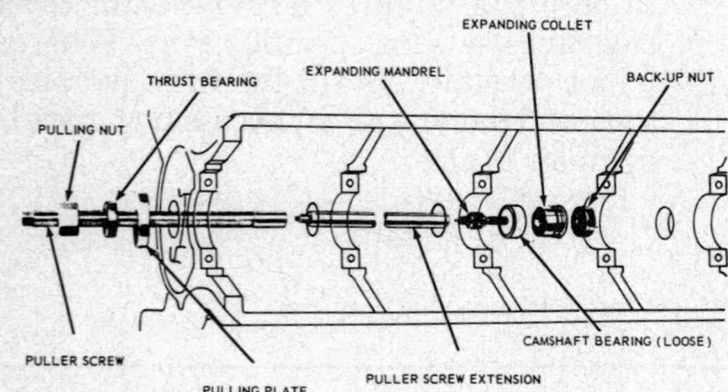 **Camshaft removal and installation tool (typical)** (© Ford Motor Co.)	If excessive wear is indicated, or if the engine is being completely rebuilt, camshaft bearings should be replaced as follows: Drive the camshaft rear plug from the block. Assemble the removal puller with its shoulder on the bearing to be removed. Gradually tighten the puller nut until bearing is removed. Remove remaining bearings, leaving the front and rear for last. To remove front and rear bearings, reverse position of the tool, so as to pull the bearings in toward the center of the block. Leave the tool in this position, pilot the new front and rear bearings on the installer, and pull them into position. Return the tool to its original position and pull remaining bearings into position. NOTE: *Ensure that oil holes align when installing bearings.* Replace camshaft rear plug, and stake it into position to aid retention.
Finish hone the cylinders: 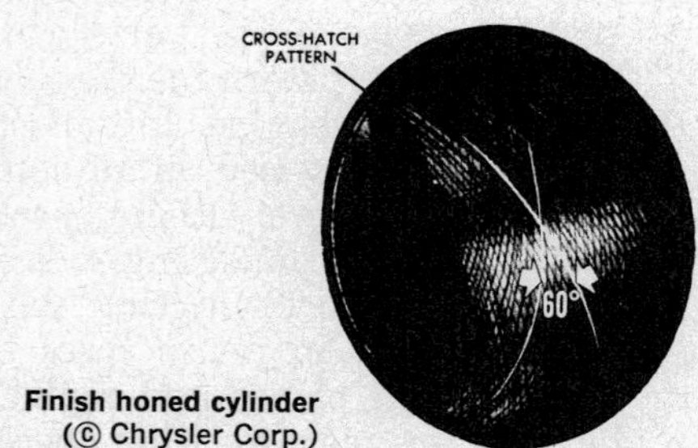 **Finish honed cylinder** (© Chrysler Corp.)	Chuck a flexible drive hone into a power drill, and insert it into the cylinder. Start the hone, and move it up and down in the cylinder at a rate which will produce approximately a 60° cross-hatch pattern (see illustration). NOTE: *Do not extend the hone below the cylinder bore.* After developing the pattern, remove the hone and recheck piston fit. Wash the cylinders with a detergent and water solution to remove abrasive dust, dry, and wipe several times with a rag soaked in engine oil.

Procedure	*Method*
Check piston ring end-gap: 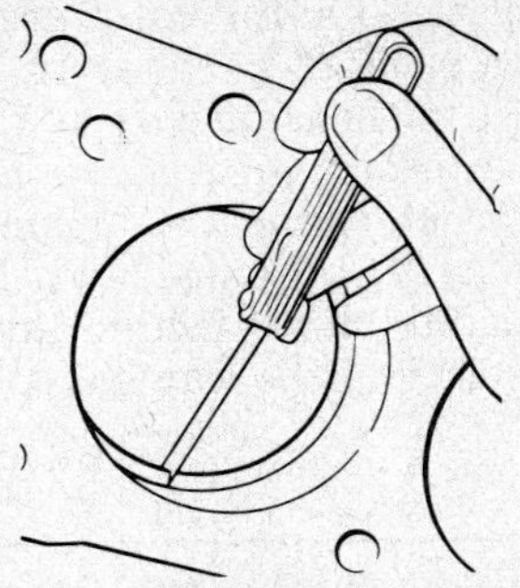 Checking ring end-gap (© Outboard Marine Corp.)	Compress the piston rings to be used in a cylinder, one at a time, into that cylinder, and press them approximately 1″ below the deck with an inverted piston. Using feeler gauges, measure the ring end-gap, and compare to specifications. Pull the ring out of the cylinder and file the ends with a fine file to obtain proper clearance. CAUTION: *If inadequate ring end-gap is utilized, ring breakage will result.*
Install the piston rings: 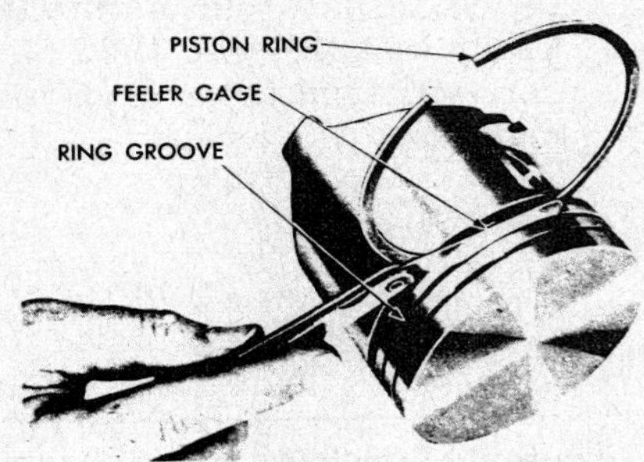 Checking ring side clearance (© Chrysler Corp.) 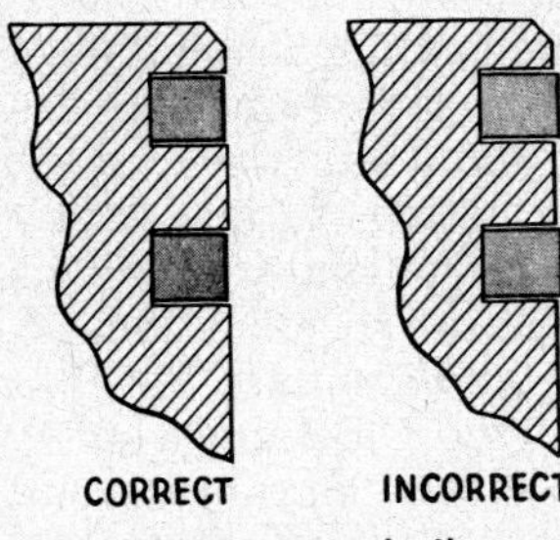 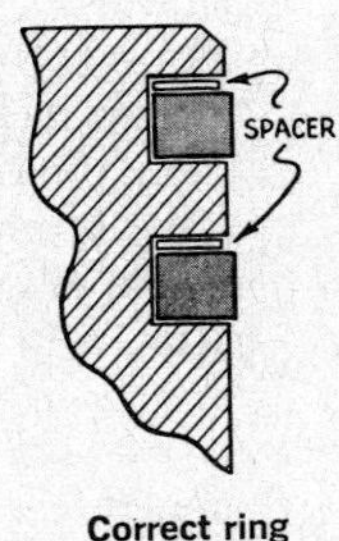 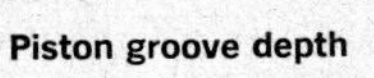 CORRECT INCORRECT Piston groove depth Correct ring spacer installation	Inspect the ring grooves in the piston for excessive wear or taper. If necessary, recut the groove(s) for use with an overwidth ring or a standard ring and spacer. If the groove is worn uniformly, overwidth rings, or standard rings and spacers may be installed without recutting. Roll the outside of the ring around the groove to check for burrs or deposits. If any are found, remove with a fine file. Hold the ring in the groove, and measure side clearance. If necessary, correct as indicated above. NOTE: *Always install any additional spacers above the piston ring.* The ring groove must be deep enough to allow the ring to seat below the lands (see illustration). In many cases, a "go-no-go" depth gauge will be provided with the piston rings. Shallow grooves may be corrected by recutting, while deep grooves require some type of filler or expander behind the piston. Consult the piston ring supplier concerning the suggested method. Install the rings on the piston, lowest ring first, using a ring expander. NOTE: *Position the ring markings as specified by the manufacturer (see car section).*
Install the camshaft:	Liberally lubricate the camshaft lobes and journals, and slide the camshaft into the block. CAUTION: *Exercise extreme care to avoid damaging the bearings when inserting the camshaft.* Install and tighten the camshaft thrust plate retaining bolts.
Check camshaft end-play: 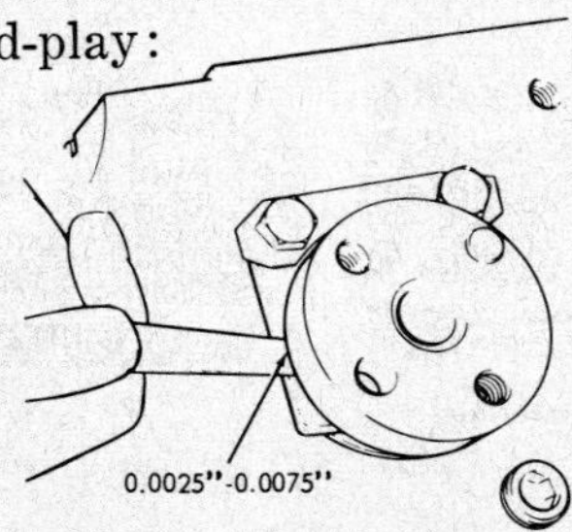 Checking camshaft end-play with a feeler gauge (© Outboard Marine Corp.)	Using feeler gauges, determine whether the clearance between the camshaft boss (or gear) and backing plate is within specifications. Install shims behind the thrust plate, or reposition the camshaft gear and retest end-play.

Procedure	*Method*
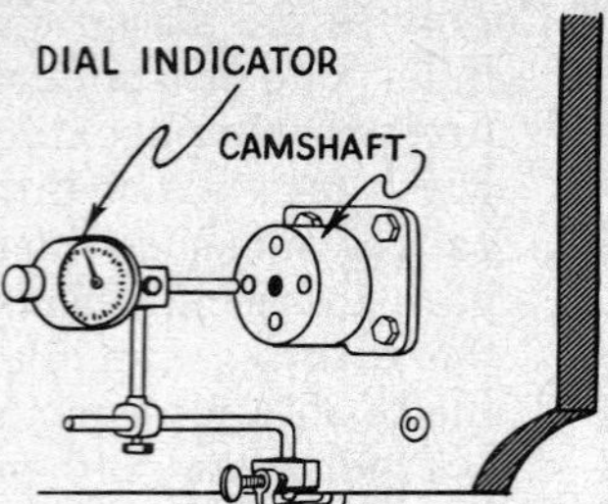 Checking camshaft end-play with a dial indicator	* Mount a dial indicator stand so that the stem of the dial indicator rests on the nose of the camshaft, parallel to the camshaft axis. Push the camshaft as far in as possible and zero the gauge. Move the camshaft outward to determine the amount of camshaft end-play. If the end-play is not within tolerance, install shims behind the thrust plate, or reposition the camshaft gear and retest.
Install the rear main seal (where applicable): 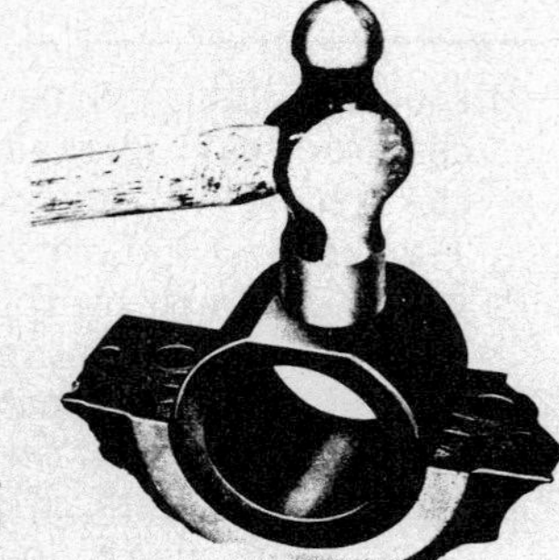 Seating the rear main seal (© Buick Div. G.M. Corp.)	Position the block with the bearing saddles facing upward. Lay the rear main seal in its groove and press it lightly into its seat. Place a piece of pipe the same diameter as the crankshaft journal into the saddle, and firmly seat the seal. Hold the pipe in position, and trim the ends of the seal flush if required.
Install the crankshaft: 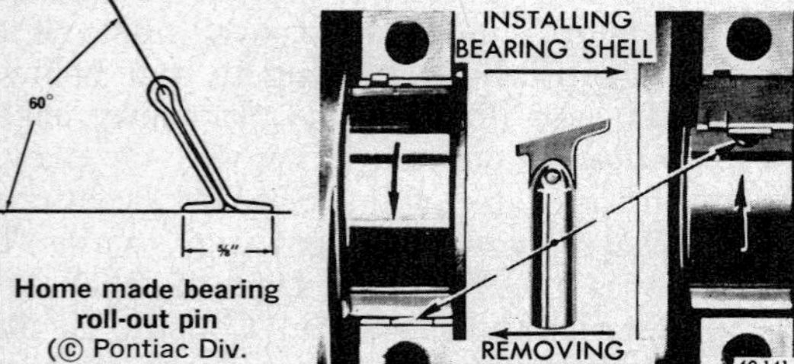 Home made bearing roll-out pin (© Pontiac Div. G.M. Corp.) Removal and installation of upper bearing insert using a roll-out pin (© Buick Div. G.M. Corp.)	Thoroughly clean the main bearing saddles and caps. Place the upper halves of the bearing inserts on the saddles and press into position. NOTE: *Ensure that the oil holes align.* Press the corresponding bearing inserts into the main bearing caps. Lubricate the upper main bearings, and lay the crankshaft in position. Place a strip of Plastigage on each of the crankshaft journals, install the main caps, and torque to specifications. Remove the main caps, and compare the Plastigage to the scale on the Plastigage envelope. If clearances are within tolerances, remove the Plastigage, turn the crankshaft 90°, wipe off all oil and retest. If all clearances are correct, remove all Plastigage, thoroughly

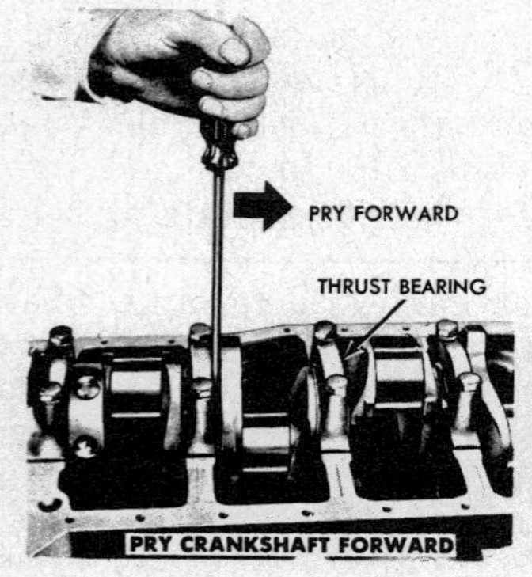

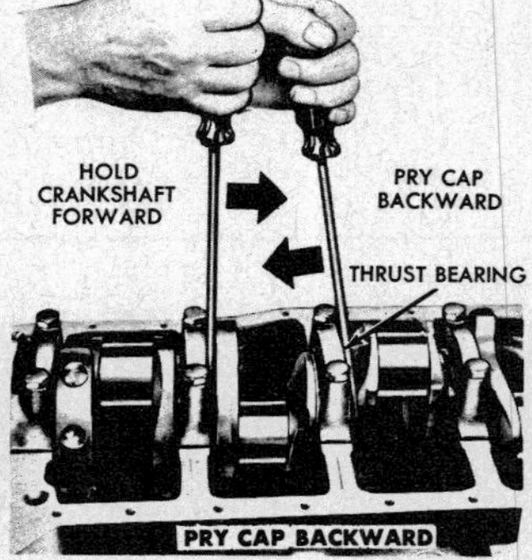

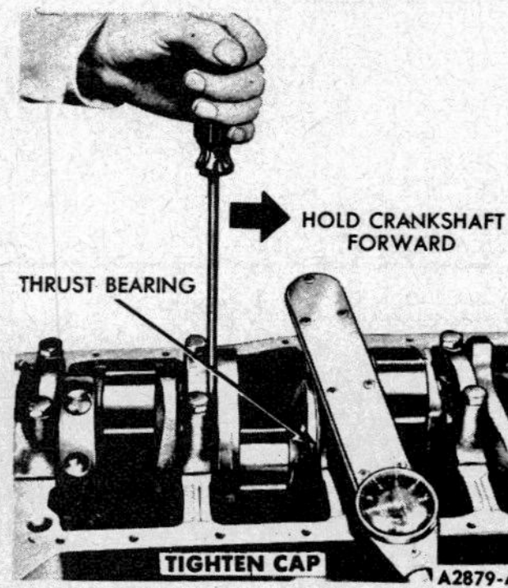

Aligning the thrust bearing
(© Ford Motor Co.)

Procedure	Method
	lubricate the main caps and bearing journals, and install the main caps. If clearances are not within tolerance, the upper bearing inserts may be removed, without removing the crankshaft, using a bearing roll out pin (see illustration). Roll in a bearing that will provide proper clearance, and retest. Torque all main caps, excluding the thrust bearing cap, to specifications. Tighten the thrust bearing cap finger tight. To properly align the thrust bearing, pry the crankshaft the extent of its axial travel several times, the last movement held toward the front of the engine, and torque the thrust bearing cap to specifications. Determine the crankshaft end-play (see below), and bring within tolerance with thrust washers.
Measure crankshaft end-play:  **Checking crankshaft end-play with a dial indicator** (© Ford Motor Co.) 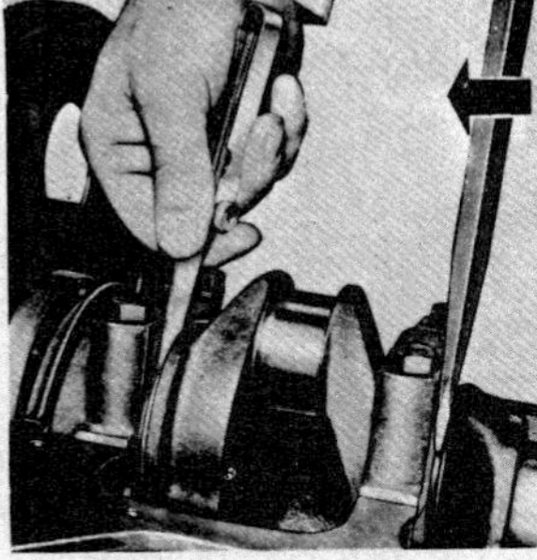 **Checking crankshaft end-play with a feeler gauge** (© Outboard Marine Corp.)	Mount a dial indicator stand on the front of the block, with the dial indicator stem resting on the nose of the crankshaft, parallel to the crankshaft axis. Pry the crankshaft the extent of its travel rearward, and zero the indicator. Pry the crankshaft forward and record crankshaft end-play. NOTE: *Crankshaft end-play also may be measured at the thrust bearing, using feeler gauges* (see illustration).
Install the pistons:	Press the upper connecting rod bearing halves into the connecting rods, and the lower halves into the connecting rod caps. Position the piston ring gaps according to specifications (see car section), and lubricate the pistons. Install a ring compresser on a piston, and press two long (8″) pieces of plastic tubing over the rod bolts. Using the plastic tubes as a guide, press the pistons into the bores and onto the crankshaft with a wooden hammer handle. After seating the rod on the crankshaft journal, remove the tubes and install the cap finger tight. Install the remaining pistons in the same man-

Procedure	*Method*
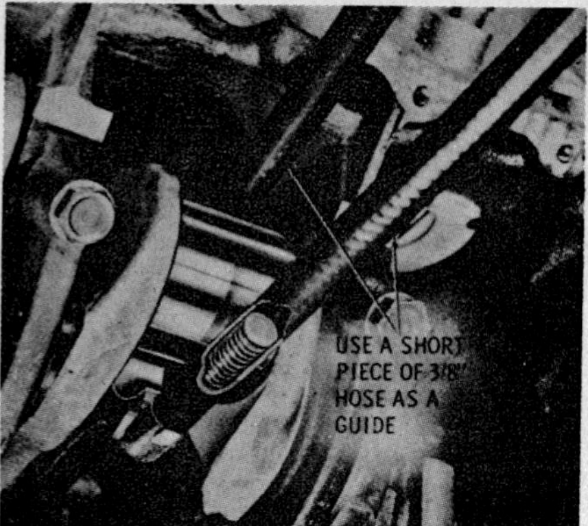 Tubing used as guide when installing a piston (© Oldsmobile Div. G.M. Corp.) 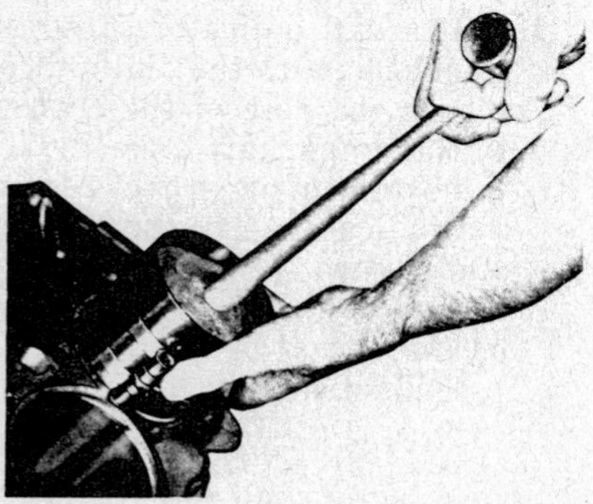 Installing a piston (© Chevrolet Div. G.M. Corp.)	ner. Invert the engine and check the bearing clearance at two points (90° apart) on each journal with Plastigage. NOTE: *Do not turn the crankshaft with Plastigage installed.* If clearance is within tolerances, remove *all* Plastigage, thoroughly lubricate the journals, and torque the rod caps to specifications. If clearance is not within specifications, install different thickness bearing inserts and recheck. CAUTION: *Never shim or file the connecting rods or caps.* Always install plastic tube sleeves over the rod bolts when the caps are not installed, to protect the crankshaft journals.
Check connecting rod side clearance: 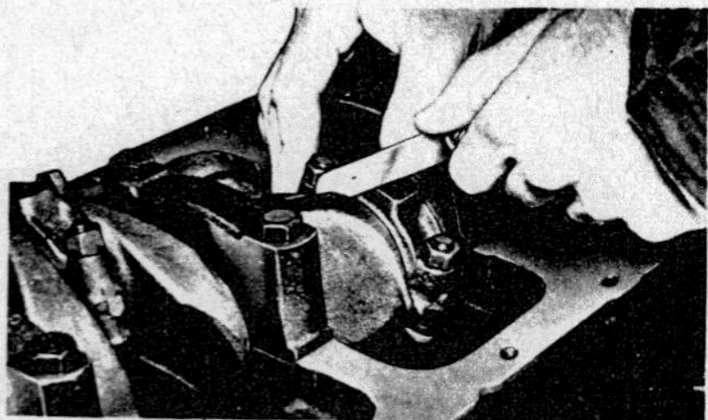 Checking connecting rod side clearance (© Chevrolet Div. G.M. Corp.)	Determine the clearance between the sides of the connecting rods and the crankshaft, using feeler gauges. If clearance is below the minimum tolerance, the rod may be machined to provide adequate clearance. If clearance is excessive, substitute an unworn rod, and recheck. If clearance is still outside specifications, the crankshaft must be welded and reground, or replaced.
Inspect the timing chain:	Visually inspect the timing chain for broken or loose links, and replace the chain if any are found. If the chain will flex sideways, it must be replaced. Install the timing chain as specified. NOTE: *If the original timing chain is to be reused, install it in its original position.*

Procedure	*Method*
Check timing gear backlash and runout:	Mount a dial indicator with its stem resting on a tooth of the camshaft gear (as illustrated). Rotate the gear until all slack is removed, and zero the indicator. Rotate the gear in the opposite direction until slack is removed, and record gear backlash. Mount the indicator with its stem resting on the edge of the camshaft gear, parallel to the axis of the camshaft. Zero the indicator, and turn the camshaft gear one full turn, recording the runout. If either backlash or runout exceed specifications, replace the worn gear(s).

Checking camshaft gear backlash
(© Chevrolet Div. G.M. Corp.)

Checking camshaft gear runout
(© Chevrolet Div. G.M. Corp.)

Completing the Rebuilding Process

Following the above procedures, complete the rebuilding process as follows:

Fill the oil pump with oil, to prevent cavitating (sucking air) on initial engine start up. Install the oil pump and the pickup tube on the engine. Coat the oil pan gasket as necessary, and install the gasket and the oil pan. Mount the flywheel and the crankshaft vibrational damper or pulley on the crankshaft. NOTE: *Always use new bolts when installing the flywheel.* Inspect the clutch shaft pilot bushing in the crankshaft. If the bushing is excessively worn, remove it with an expanding puller and a slide hammer, and tap a new bushing into place.

Position the engine, cylinder head side up. Lubricate the lifters, and install them into their bores. Install the cylinder head, and torque it as specified in the car section. Insert the pushrods (where applicable), and install the rocker shaft(s) (if so equipped) or position the rocker arms on the pushrods. If solid lifters are utilized, adjust the valves to the "cold" specifications.

Mount the intake and exhaust manifolds, the carburetor(s), the distributor and spark plugs. Adjust the point gap and the static ignition timing. Mount all accessories and install the engine in the car. Fill the radiator with coolant, and the crankcase with high quality engine oil.

Break-in Procedure

Start the engine, and allow it to run at low speed for a few minutes, while checking for leaks. Stop the engine, check the oil level, and fill as necessary. Restart the engine, and fill the cooling system to capacity. Check the point dwell angle and adjust the ignition timing and the valves. Run the engine at low to medium speed (800-2500 rpm) for approximately ½ hour, and retorque the cylinder head bolts. Road test the car, and check again for leaks.

Follow the manufacturer's recommended engine break-in procedure and maintenance schedule for new engines.

The Wankel Engine

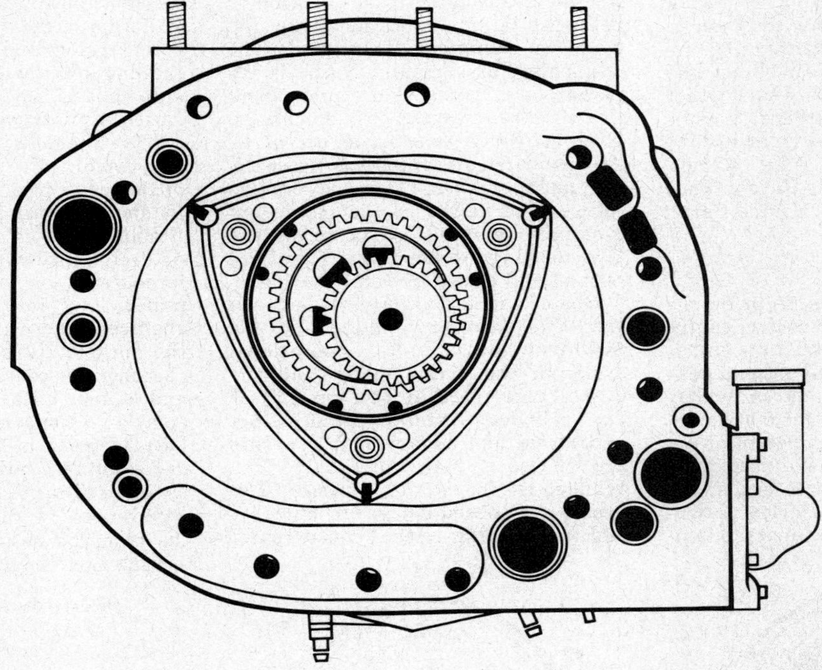

By JAN P. NORBYE

Mr. Norbye is the author of the definitive work entitled *The Wankel Engine*, 1971, Chilton Book Co., 519 pages, $15.00. (This book can be purchased from your bookstore or from Chilton Book Co., Chilton Way, Radnor, Pennsylvania 19089.

The Wankel Engine

The Wankel engine is a rotary internal-combustion engine working on the four-stroke cycle. It differs from the conventional piston engine in having purely rotary motion, without pistons that move up and down. It runs on the same kind of gasoline; the charge is fired by spark plugs; and the exhaust fumes have similar composition. The Wankel engine has many advantages over the conventional piston engines and 22 automobile manufacturers have signed license agreements for the rights to build it.

The leading producers of Wankel engines are Mazda in Japan, with an output of about 25,000 Wankel-powered cars a month, and NSU in Germany, with an output of 85,000 Wankel-powered cars a year. General Motors is reportedly planning the introduction of its first Wankel-powered car in the 1974 model year. Other licensees are Mercedes-Benz, Toyota, Datsun, Comotor (jointly owned by NSU and Citroën), Alfa Romeo, Fichtel & Sachs, Rolls-Royce, Ford of Germany, Outboard Marine Corp., and Curtiss-Wright.

Applications

The Wankel engine is primarily considered as an automotive engine for passenger car installation, but it is also suitable for many other applications. It can be made in widely different sizes, from 3 to 1,000 horsepower. A partial list of potential applications includes marine uses, light aircraft, motorcycles, scooters, snowmobiles, all-terrain vehicles, lawnmowers, golf carts, stationary pumping sets, generator sets, industrial utility vehicles, construction machinery, agricultural equipment, and military vehicles.

How the Wankel Engine Works

The cylinders are replaced by chambers, and the pistons are replaced by rotors. The chambers are not circular in section, but have a curved circumference that is identified as an *epitrochoid*. An epitrochoid is the curve described by a given point on a circle as the circle rolls around the periphery of another circle of twice the radius of the generating circle.

The rotor is three-cornered, with curved sides. All three corners are in permanent contact with the epitrochoidal surface as the rotor moves around the chamber. This motion is both orbital and rotational, as the rotor is mounted off center. The crankshaft of a piston engine is replaced by a rotor shaft, and crank throws are replaced by eccentrics. Each rotor is carried on an eccentric. Any number of rotors is possible, but most engines have one or two rotors. The valves of the piston engine are replaced by ports in the Wankel engine housing. They are opened and closed by rotor motion.

One of the key differences between the Wankel rotary engine and the piston engine is in the operational cycle. In the piston engine, all the events take place at the top end of the cylinder (intake, compression, expansion, and exhaust). The events are spaced out in time only. The Wankel engine is the opposite. The events are spaced out geographically, and are taking place concurrently and continuously around the epitrochoidal surface.

The intake phase takes place in the area following the intake port, and overlaps with the area used for compression. Expansion takes place in the area opposite the ports, and the exhaust phase takes place in the area preceding the exhaust port, overlapping with the latter part of the expansion phase. All three rotor faces are engaged in one of the four phases at all times.

In other words, one rotor gives three working spaces, all of which are permanently in action. As one rotor apex sweeps past the intake port, it ends the intake phase in the leading space, and starts it in the trailing space. The third space is then engaged in its expansion phase. As rotor motion continues, the leading space will approach the point of maximum compression and ignition, while the trailing space will enter the compression phase as the following apex closes it off from the intake port.

The trochoidal shape of the chamber, combined with the orbital motion of the rotor, produces large variations in displacement in the three spaces. Displacement is at its minimum on one rotor face when its opposite apex is centered on the minor axis. The minor axis is the line across the chamber where it is narrowest, and the major axis is the line across the chamber where it is widest. The major and minor axes intersect perpendicularly in the center of the chamber. Displacement is at its maximum on one rotor face when its opposite apex is centered on the major axis. These differences in displacement produce the pumping action required for operation as an engine.

How the Wankel engine works

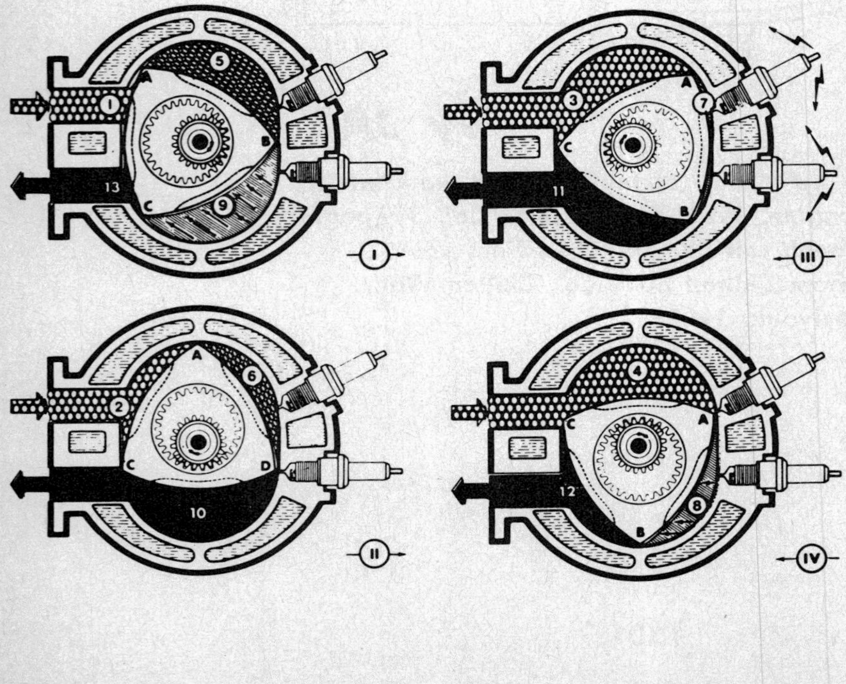

Here's how the Wankel engine works: As the triangular rotor goes through its mixed sliding/turning motions, a fuel air mixture is drawn in (1, 2, 3, 4) and then compressed (5, 6) before being ignited by the spark plugs. The high-pressure gases created by combustion drive the rotor around (7, 8, 9) and after doing their work are swept out the exhaust port by the rotor (10, 11, 12, 13). The process is continuous on all the rotor's flanks, with power taken off at the gear hub.

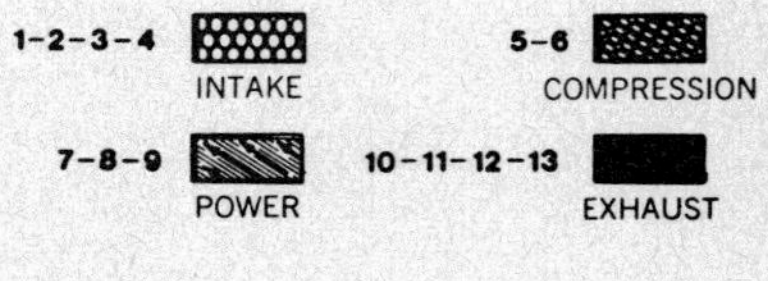

1-2-3-4 INTAKE
5-6 COMPRESSION
7-8-9 POWER
10-11-12-13 EXHAUST

How does rotor motion turn the rotor shaft? by exerting pressure on the eccentric. Here is what happens. Gas pressure on the rotor face during the expansion phase produces rotor motion. That means rotation. But the rotor is not free to spin—it is mounted on its eccentric, and has to follow an eccentric path. The rotor transfers the gas pressure to the eccentric. That moves the eccentric, which is part of the rotor shaft, and as the eccentric moves, it causes the shaft to rotate.

The relationship between the eccentric and the position of the rotor apices is quite intricate. Each apex is always in contact with the epitrochoidal surface, and to avoid jamming the rotor at some point, its position relative to the eccentric's position must be closely controlled.

This phasing is controlled by a stationary reaction gear that meshes with an internal ring gear in the rotor. It is important to note that this gearing has nothing to do with power flow or torque transmission. It is simply a phasing gear to assure smooth rotation of the eccentric and its rotor.

The stationary reaction gear is carried by a sleeve fixed to the end cover. The gear ratio is 3:2. If the reaction gear has 36 teeth, the rotor ring gear must have 54 teeth. A corresponding 3:1 ratio exists between the rotor and the rotor shaft (eccentric bearing). When the rotor makes one revolution, the shaft makes three revolutions.

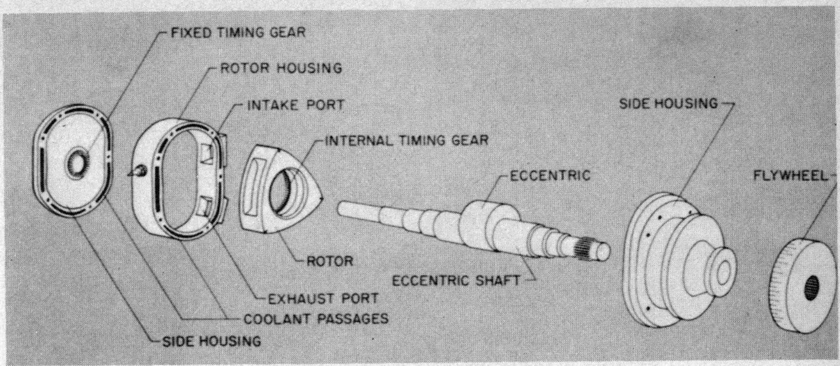

The main parts in the Wankel engine

When the rotor advances 30°, the eccentric advances 90°. For each time a rotor apex passes the intake port, the main shaft starts another complete revolution. There is a power impulse for each 1/3 turn of each rotor. That gives one expansion (or power) phase for each main shaft revolution.

In passenger car Wankel engines, the housing is water-cooled and the rotor is oil-cooled. The coolant passages in most engines run axially, and the passages are dimensioned to provide the most cooling in the area around the spark plugs(s).

The oil supply can be carried in the sump or in a separate reservoir. It is fed in through the rotor shaft, circulates inside the rotor, and returns to the reservoir (often via a heat exchanger cooled by water). The same oil that cools the rotor also lubricates the eccentric bearing.

It is not exactly true that the rotor touches the epitrochoidal surface. The rotor comes close, but is never in direct contact with the surface or the end covers. To seal the spaces for gas leaks, there is a complex seal system. Its duties are similar to those of piston rings in conventional engines.

A radial slot in each apex has a seal strip that rubs against the chamber surface. It is spring-loaded, and designed to make use of gas pressure to increase its sealing effectiveness. The rotor flanks have a seal grid intersecting with the trunnions that provide the mounting base for the apex seals. In order to fulfill their sealing duties, the seals must be lubricated. This oil is, of course,

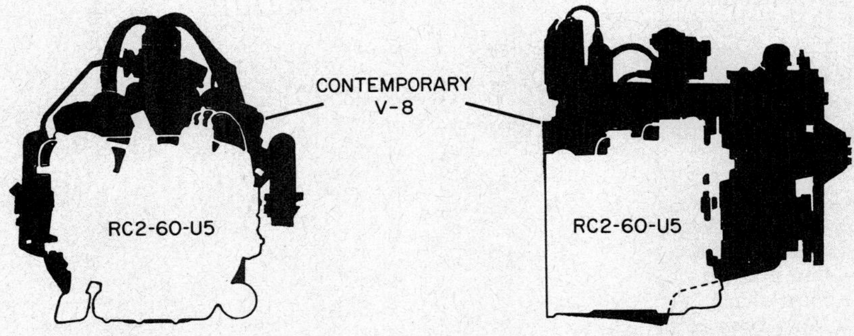

	RC2-60-U5	CONTEMPORARY V-8
HORSEPOWER / RPM	185/5000	195/4800
WEIGHT - LBS	237	607
L x W x H - IN	18.0 x 22.1 x 21.5	29.5 x 28 x 31.5
VOLUME - CU. FT.	5	15
NUMBER OF PARTS	633	1029
NUMBER OF MOVING PARTS IN POWER SECTION AND DRIVE LINE	154	388

Comparison between Wankel engine and contemporary V-8 engine

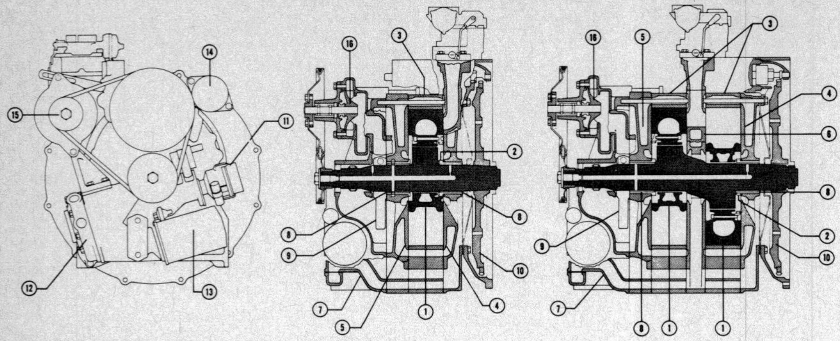

Elevation of Curtiss Wright single and twin rotor power units

1 Rotor
2 Stationary gear
3 Rotor housing
4 Side housing—drive side
5 Side housing—anti-drive side
6 Intermediate housing
7 Accessory housing
8 Main bearing
9 Balance weight
10 Flywheel cum balance weight
11 Ignition contact maker
12 Oil pumps
13 Oil filter
14 Starter
15 Generator
16 Water pump

burned. The amounts needed are minute, and oil consumption is on a par with modern V-8 engines. The lube oil for the seals can be mixed with the gasoline (for instance in the carburetor float bowl) or injected separately by a metering pump.

There are two types of intake ports: peripheral ports, and side ports. Examples of both are illustrated. Side ports produce a gas flow that tends to give higher low-range torque, while peripheral ports produce a gas flow that tends to give higher peak power. All Wankel engines have peripheral exhaust ports.

In the air-cooled Fichtel & Sachs and Outboard Marine engines, the rotor is also air-cooled. The incoming charge is led through the rotor, and thereby undergoes a preheating process. This type of engine is not considered suitable for automotive purposes.

Advantages of the Wankel Engine

Since the Wankel engine has no reciprocating parts, it is practically free of vibration. In a single-rotor engine, balance is maintained by counterweight on the rotor shaft, 180° opposite the eccentric. In a twin-rotor engine, the eccentrics are spaced 180° and automatically cancel any imbalance.

The Wankel engine has far fewer parts than a piston engine of comparable power output, and especially fewer moving parts (see the comparison chart).

The Wankel engine is smaller and lighter than a piston engine of comparable power output. It has less than half the space requirement, and the weight saving is about 50 percent. That doubles the power-to-weight ratio of a piston engine.

The Wankel engine has higher volumetric efficiency. An engine's efficiency depends on how much air it can consume in a given time, and the Wankel engine breathes much better than the piston engine. That is because it fills the chamber with a fresh combustion charge during 270° of rotor shaft rotation, against only 180° of crankshaft rotation in a piston engine.

The Wankel engine has smoother torque output, which means smoother running, because it delivers power during two-thirds of the combustion phase, against only one-quarter of the expansion stroke in a piston engine.

Due to the absence of reciprocating motion, the Wankel engine has a higher limit on rotational speeds. That offers a further potential increase in power-to-weight ratio.

The Wankel engine is uncritical of gasoline antiknock properties. It can digest fuels of wide octane rating variations. Mazda has made tests with 68 octane gasoline under wide-open-throttle conditions, without causing abnormal combustion, and without any loss in power or economy. The Wankel engine does not require lead or other additives.

The Wankel engine is also uncritical of lube oil quality. There are no blow-by gases entering the oil system. Foaming or cavitation is not a problem. Sludge caused by dirt does not form. Raw fuel is not present in the oil system. As a result, oil contamination is not a serious problem.

The Wankel engine's compactness facilitates installation and makes for improved space utilization in the car. It offers greater design freedom and better opportunities to develop new vehicle concepts. The simplicity of the engine promises lower cost. Many parts are eliminated (the entire valve

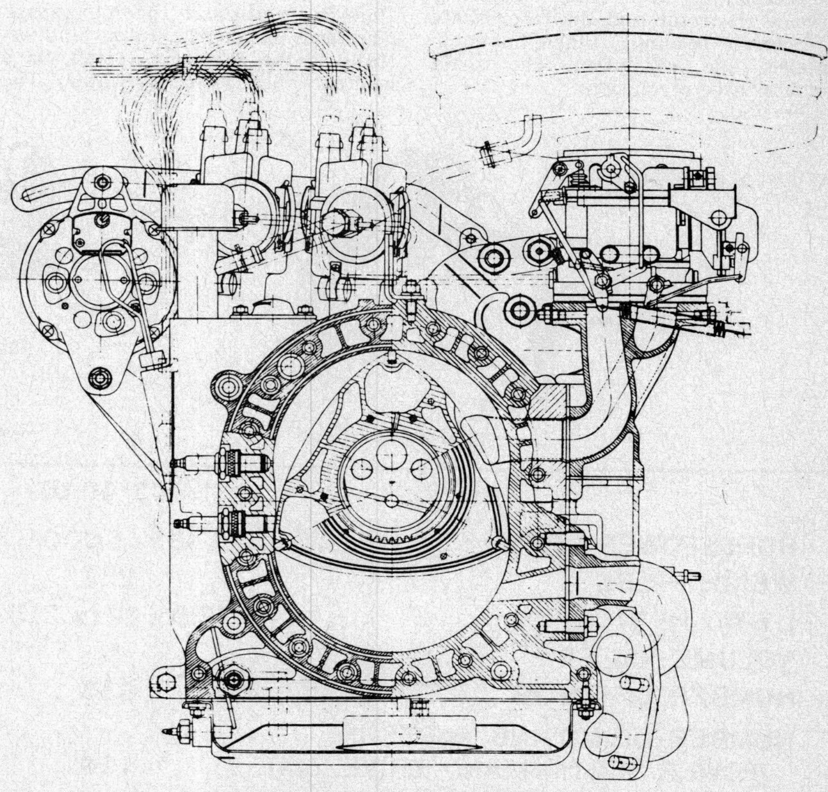

Cross section of Mazda 0813 engine

Cutaway view of the Mazda RX2 and RX3 engine

Interior view of Mazda rotary engine. Note dual rotor chambers where cylinders and pistons would normally be located (at center of cutaway). The unique Mazda rotary engine offers superior high-speed performance, better throttle response and about twice the horsepower per pound of a conventional piston engine. It also operates on unleaded, low octane gasoline and is virtually vibration free.

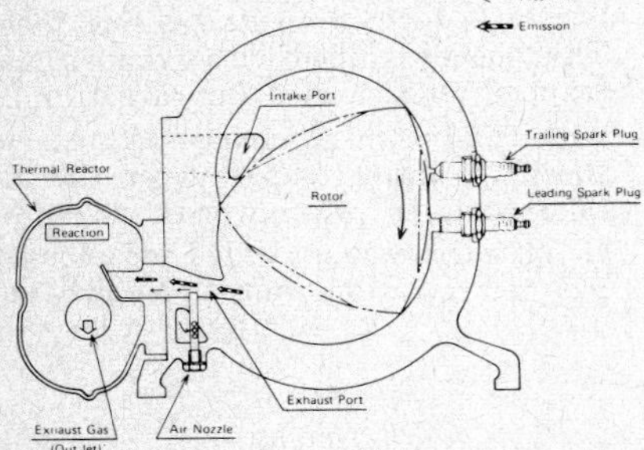

Mazda rotary engine with thermal reactor and additional air injection

train, for instance.) The design also lends itself well to automated manufacture and assembly.

Wankel Engine Emissions

Since it is an internal-combustion engine with spark ignition, it emits the same types of pollutants as the conventional piston engine. Three types of pollutants are now limited by federal standards: carbon monoxide, hydrocarbons, and oxides of nitrogen.

The same types of emission control devices that work on piston engines can be used on the Wankel. That includes such basic modifications as retarded ignition timing and leaner air-fuel mixtures. It also includes exhaust gas recirculation and thermal reactors (a type of afterburner). The Wankel engine does not require a catalytic converter (as now considered necessary for piston engines) to meet the 1975 standards.

Most of the reasons for the Wankel engine's advantages in the emission

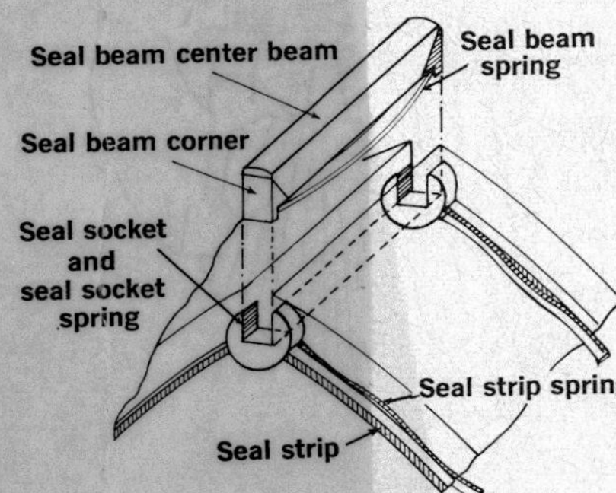

Apex seal configuration developed by Mercedes-Benz

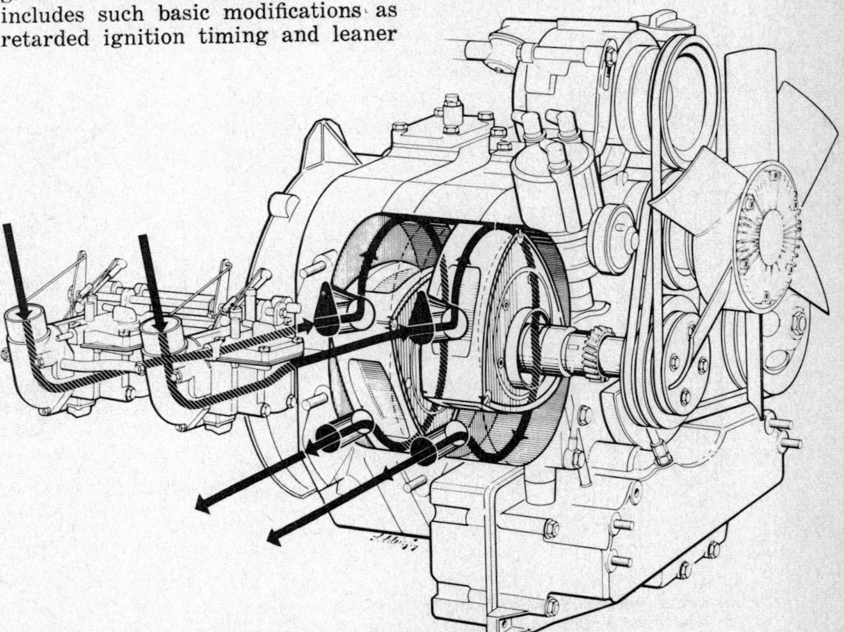

Gas flow in the NSU Ro 80 engine

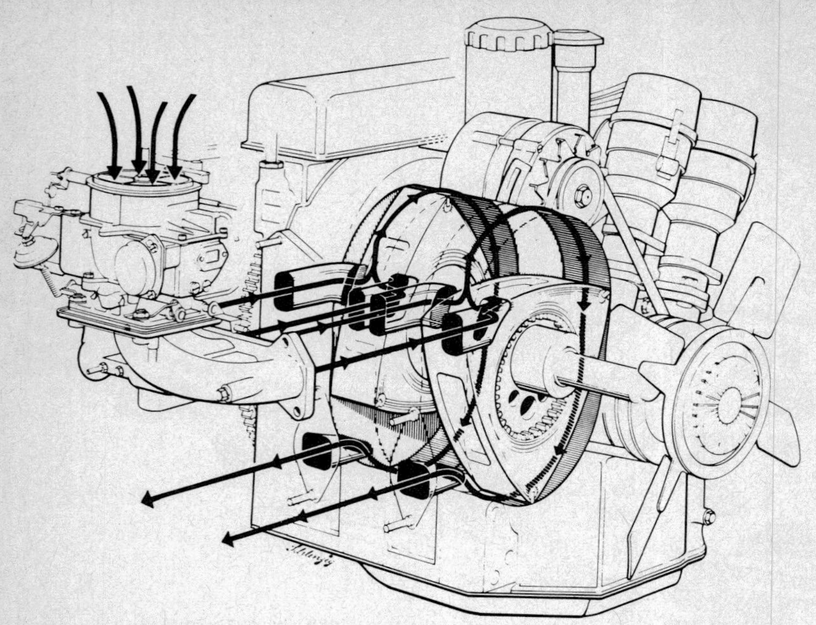

Gas flow in the NSU/Wankel-system rotary piston engine produced by the Japanese manufacturer Toyo Kogyo

control area are to be found in the combustion process. As one rotor face goes through the compression and expansion phases, the combustion chamber is transported along the epitrochoidal surface, and is constantly changing its shape. The combustion process takes up more time than in a piston engine with equal flame front velocity. As a result, the burning rate of the air-fuel mixture is slower in the Wankel engine, and peak combustion temperature is lower.

Average (as opposed to *peak*) combustion temperature is higher in the Wankel engine. That translates into higher exhaust gas temperature, which normally would be considered as an energy loss, but is turned into an advantage from the point of view of emission control.

Higher exhaust gas temperature means higher efficiency in the thermal reactor. The same thermal reactor would be more efficient when mounted on a Wankel engine than when installed on a piston engine, because exhaust gas heat assures better burning. Additional air injection is needed to assure ignition, but the system again is more efficient than is possible in piston engines.

Additional air does a better job the closer to the combustion chamber it can be injected. In the piston engine, that's right behind the exhaust valve. In the Wankel engine, it can be injected anywhere, including the combustion chamber itself (through the end cover) and the port area.

Oxides of nitrogen emissions are controlled by a system of exhaust gas recirculation in piston engines as well as the Wankel engine. But on the piston engine, it means additional valves, pipes, and hoses. The Wankel engine has automatic exhaust gas recirculation. The exact amount of exhaust gas to be recirculated is controlled by port location and design.

When the rotor apex slides across the exhaust port, a small triangular pocket is formed on its trailing face. This pocket is filled with exhaust gas, trapped, and carried forward to mix with the incoming charge as soon as the apex starts to pass over the intake port. In other words, no additional hardware is needed for exhaust gas recirculation in the Wankel engine.

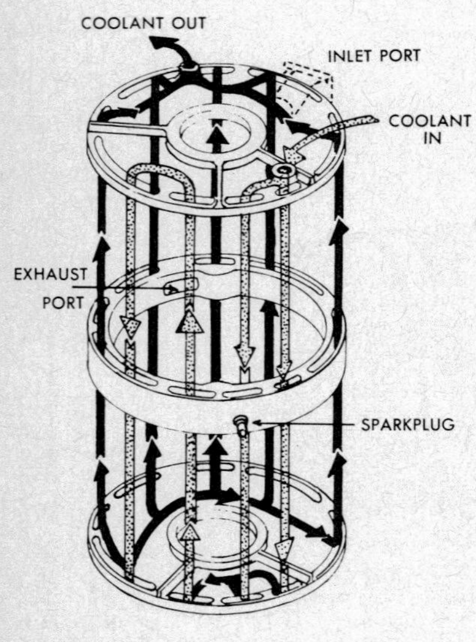

Cooling system for rotary engine housing as developed by Curtiss Wright

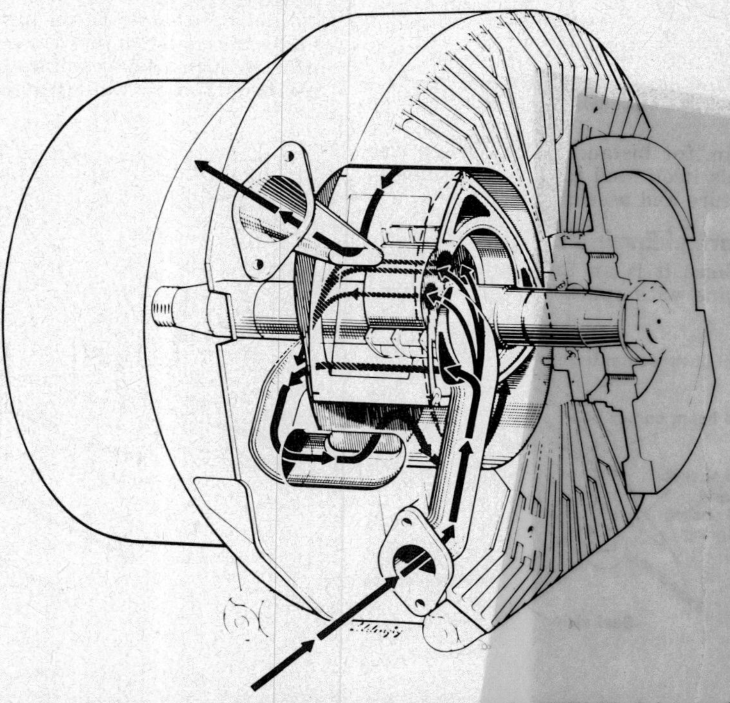

Gas flow in the air-cooled Fichtel & Sachs rotary piston engine (NSU/Wankel system)

Appendix

General Conversion Table

Multiply by	*To convert*	*To*	
2.54	Inches	Centimeters	.3937
30.48	Feet	Centimeters	.0328
.914	Yards	Meters	1.094
1.609	Miles	Kilometers	.621
.645	Square inches	Square cm.	.155
.836	Square yards	Square meters	1.196
16.39	Cubic inches	Cubic cm.	.061
28.3	Cubic feet	Liters	.0353
.4536	Pounds	Kilograms	2.2045
4.546	Gallons	Liters	.22
.068	Lbs./sq. in. (psi)	Atmospheres	14.7
.138	Foot pounds	Kg. m.	7.23
1.014	H.P. (DIN)	H.P. (SAE)	.9861
——	To obtain	From	Multiply by

Note: 1 cm. equals 10 mm.; 1 mm. equals .0394″.

Conversion—Common Fractions to Decimals and Millimeters

Inches			Inches			Inches		
Common Fractions	*Decimal Fractions*	*Millimeters (approx.)*	*Common Fractions*	*Decimal Fractions*	*Millimeters (approx.)*	*Common Fractions*	*Decimal Fractions*	*Millimeters (approx.)*
1/128	.008	0.20	11/32	.344	8.73	43/64	.672	17.07
1/64	.016	0.40	23/64	.359	9.13	11/16	.688	17.46
1/32	.031	0.79	3/8	.375	9.53	45/64	.703	17.86
3/64	.047	1.19	25/64	.391	9.92	23/32	.719	18.26
1/16	.063	1.59	13/32	.406	10.32	47/64	.734	18.65
5/64	.078	1.98	27/64	.422	10.72	3/4	.750	19.05
3/32	.094	2.38	7/16	.438	11.11	49/64	.766	19.45
7/64	.109	2.78	29/64	.453	11.51	25/32	.781	19.84
1/8	.125	3.18	15/32	.469	11.91	51/64	.797	20.24
9/64	.141	3.57	31/64	.484	12.30	13/16	.813	20.64
5/32	.156	3.97	1/2	.500	12.70	53/64	.828	21.03
11/64	.172	4.37	33/64	.516	13.10	27/32	.844	21.43
3/16	.188	4.76	17/32	.531	13.49	55/64	.859	21.83
13/64	.203	5.16	35/64	.547	13.89	7/8	.875	22.23
7/32	.219	5.56	9/16	.563	14.29	57/64	.891	22.62
15/64	.234	5.95	37/64	.578	14.68	29/32	.906	23.02
1/4	.250	6.35	19/32	.594	15.08	59/64	.922	23.42
17/64	.266	6.75	39/64	.609	15.48	15/16	.938	23.81
9/32	.281	7.14	5/8	.625	15.88	61/64	.953	24.21
19/64	.297	7.54	41/64	.641	16.27	31/32	.969	24.61
5/16	.313	7.94	21/32	.656	16.67	63/64	.984	25.00
21/64	.328	8.33						

Conversion—Millimeters to Decimal Inches

mm	inches	mm	inches	mm	inches	mm	inches	mm	inches
1	.039 370	31	1.220 470	61	2.401 570	91	3.582 670	210	8.267 700
2	.078 740	32	1.259 840	62	2.440 940	92	3.622 040	220	8.661 400
3	.118 110	33	1.299 210	63	2.480 310	93	3.661 410	230	9.055 100
4	.157 480	34	1.338 580	64	2.519 680	94	3.700 780	240	9.448 800
5	.196 850	35	1.377 949	65	2.559 050	95	3.740 150	250	9.842 500
6	.236 220	36	1.417 319	66	2.598 420	96	3.779 520	260	10.236 200
7	.275 590	37	1.456 689	67	2.637 790	97	3.818 890	270	10.629 900
8	.314 960	38	1.496 050	68	2.677 160	98	3.858 260	280	11.032 600
9	.354 330	39	1.535 430	69	2.716 530	99	3.897 630	290	11.417 300
10	.393 700	40	1.574 800	70	2.755 900	100	3.937 000	300	11.811 000
11	.433 070	41	1.614 170	71	2.795 270	105	4.133 848	310	12.204 700
12	.472 440	42	1.653 540	72	2.834 640	110	4.330 700	320	12.598 400
13	.511 810	43	1.692 910	73	2.874 010	115	4.527 550	330	12.992 100
14	.551 180	44	1.732 280	74	2.913 380	120	4.724 400	340	13.385 800
15	.590 550	45	1.771 650	75	2.952 750	125	4.921 250	350	13.779 500
16	.629 920	46	1.811 020	76	2.992 120	130	5.118 100	360	14.173 200
17	.669 290	47	1.850 390	77	3.031 490	135	5.314 950	370	14.566 900
18	.708 660	48	1.889 760	78	3.070 860	140	5.511 800	380	14.960 600
19	.748 030	49	1.929 130	79	3.110 230	145	5.708 650	390	15.354 300
20	.787 400	50	1.968 500	80	3.149 600	150	5.905 500	400	15.748 000
21	.826 770	51	2.007 870	81	3.188 970	155	6.102 350	500	19.685 000
22	.866 140	52	2.047 240	82	3.228 340	160	6.299 200	600	23.622 000
23	.905 510	53	2.086 610	83	3.267 710	165	6.496 050	700	27.559 000
24	.944 880	54	2.125 980	84	3.307 080	170	6.692 900	800	31.496 000
25	.984 250	55	2.165 350	85	3.346 450	175	6.889 750	900	35.433 000
26	1.023 620	56	2.204 720	86	3.385 820	180	7.086 600	1000	39.370 000
27	1.062 990	57	2.244 090	87	3.425 190	185	7.283 450	2000	78.740 000
28	1.102 360	58	2.283 460	88	3.464 560	190	7.480 300	3000	118.110 000
29	1.141 730	59	2.322 830	89	3.503 903	195	7.677 150	4000	157.480 000
30	1.181 100	60	2.362 200	90	3.543 300	200	7.874 000	5000	196.850 000

To change decimal millimeters to decimal inches, position the decimal point where desired on either side of the millimeter measurement shown and reset the inches decimal by the same number of digits in the same direction. For example, to convert .001 mm into decimal inches, reset the decimal behind the 1 mm (shown on the chart) to .001; change the decimal inch equivalent (.039″ shown) to .00039″).

Tap Drill Sizes

National Fine or S.A.E.

Screw & Tap Size	Threads Per Inch	Use Drill Number
No. 5	44	37
No. 6	40	33
No. 8	36	29
No. 10	32	21
No. 12	28	15
1/4	28	3
5/16	24	1
3/8	24	Q
7/16	20	W
1/2	20	29/64
9/16	18	33/64
5/8	18	37/64
3/4	16	11/16
7/8	14	13/16
1 1/8	12	1 3/64
1 1/4	12	1 11/64
1 1/2	12	1 27/64

National Coarse or U.S.S.

Screw & Tap Size	Threads Per Inch	Use Drill Number
No. 5	40	39
No. 6	32	36
No. 8	32	29
No. 10	24	25
No. 12	24	17
1/4	20	8
5/16	18	F
3/8	16	5/16
7/16	14	U
1/2	13	27/64
9/16	12	31/64
5/8	11	17/32
3/4	10	21/32
7/8	9	49/64
1	8	7/8
1 1/8	7	63/64
1 1/4	7	1 7/64
1 1/2	6	1 11/32

Decimal Equivalent Size of the Number Drills

Drill No.	Decimal Equivalent	Drill No.	Decimal Equivalent	Drill No.	Decimal Equivalent
80	.0135	53	.0595	26	.1470
79	.0145	52	.0635	25	.1495
78	.0160	51	.0670	24	.1520
77	.0180	50	.0700	23	.1540
76	.0200	49	.0730	22	.1570
75	.0210	48	.0760	21	.1590
74	.0225	47	.0785	20	.1610
73	.0240	46	.0810	19	.1660
72	.0250	45	.0820	18	.1695
71	.0260	44	.0860	17	.1730
70	.0280	43	.0890	16	.1770
69	.0292	42	.0935	15	.1800
68	.0310	41	.0960	14	.1820
67	.0320	40	.0980	13	.1850
66	.0330	39	.0995	12	.1890
65	.0350	38	.1015	11	.1910
64	.0360	37	.1040	10	.1935
63	.0370	36	.1065	9	.1960
62	.0380	35	.1100	8	.1990
61	.0390	34	.1110	7	.2010
60	.0400	33	.1130	6	.2040
59	.0410	32	.1160	5	.2055
58	.0420	31	.1200	4	.2090
57	.0430	30	.1285	3	.2130
56	.0465	29	.1360	2	.2210
55	.0520	28	.1405	1	.2280
54	.0550	27	.1440		

Decimal Equivalent Size of the Letter Drills

Letter Drill	Decimal Equivalent	Letter Drill	Decimal Equivalent	Letter Drill	Decimal Equivalent
A	.234	J	.277	S	.348
B	.238	K	.281	T	.358
C	.242	L	.290	U	.368
D	.246	M	.295	V	.377
E	.250	N	.302	W	.386
F	.257	O	.316	X	.397
G	.261	P	.323	Y	.404
H	.266	Q	.332	Z	.413
I	.272	R	.339		

ANTI-FREEZE INFORMATION

Freezing and Boiling Points of Solutions According to Percentage of Alcohol or Ethylene Glycol

Freezing Point of Solution	Alcohol Volume %	Alcohol Solution Boils at	Ethylene Glycol Volume %	Ethylene Glycol Solution Boils at
20°F.	12	196°F.	16	216°F.
10°F.	20	189°F.	25	218°F.
0°F.	27	184°F.	33	220°F.
–10°F.	32	181°F.	39	222°F.
–20°F.	38	178°F.	44	224°F.
–30°F.	42	176°F.	48	225°F.

Note: above boiling points are at sea level. For every 1,000 feet of altitude, boiling points are approximately 2°F. lower than those shown. For every pound of pressure exerted by the pressure cap, the boiling points are approximately 3°F. higher than those shown.

To Increase the Freezing Protection of Anti-Freeze Solutions Already Installed

Cooling System Capacity Quarts	Number of Quarts of **ALCOHOL** Anti-Freeze Required to Increase Protection													
	From +20°F. to					From +10°F. to					From 0°F. to			
	0°	−10°	−20°	−30°	−40°	0°	−10°	−20°	−30°	−40°	−10°	−20°	−30°	−40°
10	2	2 3/4	3 1/2	4	4 1/2	1	2	2 1/3	3 1/4	3 3/4	1	1 3/4	2 1/2	3
12	2 1/2	3 1/4	4	4 3/4	5 1/4	1 1/4	2 1/4	3	3 3/4	4 1/2	1 1/4	2	2 3/4	3 1/2
14	3	4	4 3/4	5 1/2	6	1 1/2	2 1/2	3 1/2	4 1/2	5	1 1/4	2 1/2	3 1/4	4
16	3 1/4	4 1/2	5 1/2	6 1/4	7	1 3/4	3	4	5	5 3/4	1 1/2	2 3/4	3 3/4	4 3/4
18	3 3/4	5	6	7	7 3/4	2	3 1/4	4 1/2	5 3/4	6 1/2	1 3/4	3	4 1/4	5 1/4
20	4	5 1/2	6 3/4	7 3/4	8 3/4	2	3 1/4	5	6 1/4	7 1/4	1 3/4	3 1/2	4 3/4	5 3/4
22	4 1/2	6	7 1/2	8 1/2	9 1/2	2 1/4	4	5 1/2	6 3/4	8	2	3 3/4	5 1/4	6 1/2
24	5	6 3/4	8	9 1/4	10 1/2	2 1/2	4 1/2	6	7 1/2	8 3/4	2 1/4	4	5 1/2	7
26	5 1/4	7 1/4	8 3/4	10	11 1/4	2 3/4	4 3/4	6 1/2	8	9 1/2	2 1/2	4 1/2	6	7 1/2
28	5 3/4	7 3/4	9 1/2	11	12	3	5 1/4	7	8 3/4	10 1/4	2 1/2	4 3/4	6 1/2	8
30	6	8 1/4	10	11 3/4	13	3	5 1/2	7 1/2	9 1/4	10 3/4	2 3/4	5	7	8 3/4

Test radiator solution with proper tester. Determine from the table the number of quarts of solution to be drawn off from a full cooling system and replace with concentrated anti-freeze, to give the desired increased protection. For example, to increase protection of a 22-quart cooling system containing Alcohol anti-freeze, from +10°F. to −20°F. will require the replacement of 5 1/2 quarts of solution with concentrated anti-freeze.

Cooling System Capacity Quarts	Number of Quarts of **ETHYLENE GLYCOL** Anti-Freeze Required to Increase Protection													
	From +20°F. to					From +10°F. to					From 0°F. to			
	0°	−10°	−20°	−30°	−40°	0°	−10°	−20°	−30°	−40°	−10°	−20°	−30°	−40°
10	1 3/4	2 1/4	3	3 1/2	3 3/4	3/4	1 1/2	2 1/4	2 3/4	3 1/4	3/4	1 1/2	2	2 1/2
12	2	2 3/4	3 1/2	4	4 1/2	1	1 3/4	2 1/2	3 1/4	3 3/4	1	1 3/4	2 1/2	3 1/4
14	2 1/4	3 1/4	4	4 3/4	5 1/2	1 1/4	2	3	3 3/4	4 1/2	1	2	3	3 1/2
16	2 1/2	3 1/2	4 1/2	5 1/4	6	1 1/4	2 1/2	3 1/2	4 1/4	5 1/4	1 1/4	2 1/4	3 1/4	4
18	3	4	5	6	7	1 1/2	2 3/4	4	5	5 3/4	1 1/2	2 1/2	3 3/4	4 3/4
20	3 1/4	4 1/2	5 3/4	6 3/4	7 1/2	1 3/4	3	4 1/4	5 1/2	6 1/2	1 1/2	2 3/4	4 1/4	5 1/4
22	3 1/2	5	6 1/4	7 1/4	8 1/4	1 3/4	3 1/4	4 3/4	6	7 1/4	1 3/4	3 1/4	4 1/2	5 1/2
24	4	5 1/2	7	8	9	2	3 1/2	5	6 1/2	7 1/2	1 3/4	3 1/2	5	6
26	4 1/4	6	7 1/2	8 3/4	10	2	4	5 1/2	7	8 1/4	2	3 3/4	5 1/2	6 3/4
28	4 1/2	6 1/4	8	9 1/2	10 1/2	2 1/4	4 1/4	6	7 1/2	9	2	4	5 3/4	7 1/4
30	5	6 3/4	8 1/2	10	11 1/2	2 1/2	4 1/2	6 1/2	8	9 1/2	2 1/4	4 1/4	6 1/4	7 3/4

Test radiator solution with proper hydrometer. Determine from the table the number of quarts of solution to be drawn off from a full cooling system and replace with undiluted anti-freeze, to give the desired increased protection. For example, to increase protection of a 22-quart cooling system containing Ethylene Glycol (permanent type) anti-freeze, from +20°F. to −20°F. will require the replacement of 6 1/4 quarts of solution with undiluted anti-freeze.

ANTI-FREEZE CHART

Temperatures Shown in Degrees Fahrenheit
+32 is Freezing

Cooling System Capacity Quarts	Quarts of **ALCOHOL** Needed for Protection to Temperatures Shown Below												
	1	2	3	4	5	6	7	8	9	10	11	12	13
10	+23°	+11°	− 5°	−27°									
11	+25	+13	0	−18	−40°								
12		+15	+ 3	−12	−31								
13		+17	+ 7	− 7	−23								
14		+19	+ 9	− 3	−17	−34°							
15		+20	+11	+ 1	−12	−27							
16		+21	+13	+ 3	− 8	−21	−36°						
17		+22	+16	+ 6	− 4	−16	−29						
18		+23	+17	+ 8	− 1	−12	−25	−38°					
19		+24	+17	+ 9	+ 2	− 8	−21	−32					
20			+18	+11	+ 4	− 5	−16	−27	−39°				
21			+19	+12	+ 5	− 3	−12	−22	−34				
22			+20	+14	+ 7	0	− 9	−18	−29	−40°			
23			+21	+15	+ 8	+ 2	− 7	−15	−25	−36°			
24			+21	+16	+10	+ 4	− 4	−12	−21	−31			
25			+22	+17	+11	+ 6	− 2	− 9	−18	−27	−37°		
26			+22	+17	+12	+ 7	+ 1	− 7	−14	−23	−32		
27			+23	+18	+13	+ 8	+ 3	− 5	−12	−20	−28	−39°	
28			+23	+19	+14	+ 9	+ 4	− 3	− 9	−17	−25	−34	
29			+24	+19	+15	+10	+ 6	− 1	− 7	−15	−22	−30	−39°
30			+24	+20	+16	+11	+ 7	+ 1	− 5	−12	−19	−27	−35

+ Figures are above Zero, but below Freezing.

− Figures are below Zero. Also below Freezing.

Cooling System Capacity Quarts	Quarts of **ETHYLENE GLYCOL** Needed for Protection to Temperatures Shown Below													
	1	2	3	4	5	6	7	8	9	10	11	12	13	14
10	+24°	+16°	+ 4°	−12°	−34°	−62°								
11	+25	+18	+ 8	− 6	−23	−47								
12	+26	+19	+10	0	−15	−34	−57°							
13	+27	+21	+13	+ 3	− 9	−25	−45							
14			+15	+ 6	− 5	−18	−34							
15			+16	+ 8	0	−12	−26							
16			+17	+10	+ 2	− 8	−19	−34	−52°					
17			+18	+12	+ 5	− 4	−14	−27	−42					
18			+19	+14	+ 7	0	−10	−21	−34	−50°				
19			+20	+15	+ 9	+ 2	− 7	−16	−28	−42				
20				+16	+10	+ 4	− 3	−12	−22	−34	−48°			
21				+17	+12	+ 6	0	− 9	−17	−28	−41			
22				+18	+13	+ 8	+ 2	− 6	−14	−23	−34	−47°		
23				+19	+14	+ 9	+ 4	− 3	−10	−19	−29	−40		
24				+19	+15	+10	+ 5	0	− 8	−15	−23	−34	−46°	
25				+20	+16	+12	+ 7	+ 1	− 5	−12	−20	−29	−40	−50°
26					+17	+13	+ 8	+ 3	− 3	− 9	−16	−25	−34	−44
27					+18	+14	+ 9	+ 5	− 1	− 7	−13	−21	−29	−39
28					+18	+15	+10	+ 6	+ 1	− 5	−11	−18	−25	−34
29					+19	+16	+12	+ 7	+ 2	− 3	− 8	−15	−22	−29
30					+20	+17	+13	+ 8	+ 4	− 1	− 6	−12	−18	−25

For capacities over 30 quarts divide true capacity by 3. Find quarts Anti-Freeze for the ⅓ and multiply by 3 for quarts to add.

For capacities under 10 quarts multiply true capacity by 3. Find quarts Anti-Freeze for the tripled volume and divide by 3 for quarts to add.